PRENTICE HALL

Powerful presentation with breakthrough curriculum options.

Science

The quality choice for today's classrooms

A new approach to motivation and content, this program has been designed to actively involve every student.

Lively presentation. More manageable content. Interactive learning. Renowned authors Ken Miller and Joe Levine have created a brand new science program called **Biology: The Living Science ©1998.** What's more, this program offers breakthrough instructional "pathways" to help manage curriculum for diverse student needs.

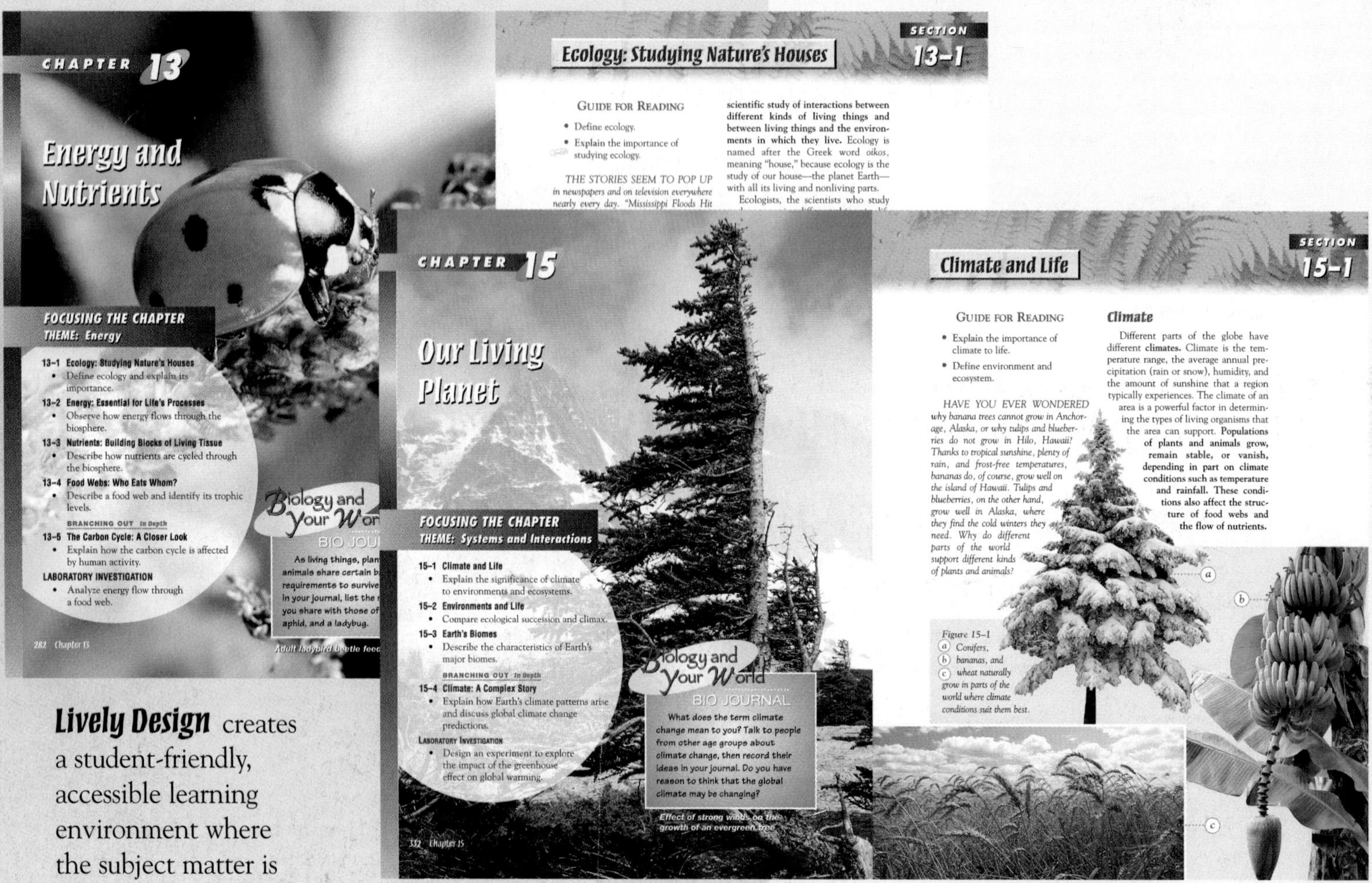

Lively Design creates a student-friendly, accessible learning environment where the subject matter is serious but the learning is fun!

Biology and Your World
BIO JOURNAL

Bio Journal serves to connect subject matter directly to students' own experiences, while also giving them a chance to record their thoughts and observations.

MINI LAB Classifying

Life in Your Neighborhood

Mini Labs offer point-of-use, hands-on experiences that help make students' learning more exciting and relevant—all with a minimum of preparation.

Problem Solving

INTERPRETING DIAGRAMS

Flowering Plants

Problem Solving allows students to explore a range of real-life situations and encourages them to apply critical thinking to arrive at meaningful solutions.

Integrated at point-of-use activities

Laboratory Investigations

Laboratory Investigations make learning an active, student-oriented adventure. "Design an Experiment" requires students to adapt their skills to scientific inquiry as they create and implement their own experimental setups.

INTEGRATING
CAREERS
EARTH SCIENCE
HEALTH
TECHNOLOGY AND SOCIETY
LANGUAGE ARTS
CHEMISTRY
MATH
PHYSICS
SOCIAL STUDIES
BIOLOGY AND SOCIETY

Integration Features are designed to give students an understanding of how biology works within an interdisciplinary context.

Career Track relates biology to actual occupations in order to help students put topics they are studying into real-world context.

CAREER TRACK

As you explore the topics in this unit, you will discover many different types of careers associated with biology. Here are a few of these careers:

- Biologist
- Respiratory Therapist
- Cytotechnologist
- Biological Technician
- Histologic Technician

Applications to students' lives

Biology AND YOU Connections

The Mississippi River Floods—How Can Wetlands Help?

Connections present important issues in biology that students face today and will continue to face in the future. They also feature new discoveries and explain how those discoveries actually relate to students' lives.

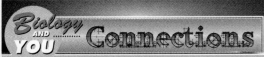

The first biology program flexible enough to help you achieve success in every classroom.

Biology: The Living Science ©1998 is the first biology program that actually gives teachers the option of choosing materials for exactly what they teach.

The first four units cover all the basic biology concepts, including characteristics of living things, cell biology, genetics, evolution and natural selection, biodiversity, and ecology. Unit 5 provides a comprehensive overview of all the phyla from bacteria to humans.

If a teacher wants to explore further, Units 6, 7, and 8 provide a more detailed exploration and discussion of bacteria, plants, animals, and the human body.

COVER AS MANY TOPICS AS YOU WANT

IN-DEPTH OPTIONS

UNITS 1–5: CORE COURSE
(Meets National Science Education Standards)

- **The World of Life,** *including cell biology*
- **Genetics**
- **Evolution**
- **Ecology**
- **Life on Earth: An Overview**

BRANCHING OUT

This breakthrough feature provides additional content at the section level to be used at the teacher's discretion to expand the scope of the students' learning experience.

UNIT 6
FROM BACTERIA TO PLANTS

From microorganisms through structure, function, and diversity of green plants.

BRANCHING OUT

Includes:
Bacteria in Our World, Protists and Fungal Diseases, Algae in Our World, What's in a Fruit?, Plant Propagation

ENGAGE, EXPLORE, TEACH, ASSESS

4-Step Lesson Plan provides teachers with the most innovative teaching strategies, including helpful hints for implementing the text's visual resources.

Wrap-around Teacher's Edition Features

The Teacher's Edition is designed to help you manage information and implement teaching strategies to stimulate diverse student interests. Features include:

- Managing Classroom Diversity
- Tech Prep
- Ecology Notes
- Discovery Learning Activity
- Historical Perspective
- Additional Activities

TEACHER SUPPORT

MINI LAB

Skills Trace

- Focus
- Practice
- Assess

Skills Trace starts in a MiniLab, continues in the Section Review, and concludes at the end of Chapter Assessment.

Technology

BioVue
Mini Doc: Adopt-a-Reef
Videodisc Side 4

Go to Chapter 15

CD-ROM
The Wetlands

Technology is integrated at point-of-use throughout the program to develop key concepts in a very visual, relevant context.

Meeting the Standards

Sections 13–1 through 13–5 cover four of the five content standards under **The Interdependence of Organisms** and three of the six content standards under **Matter, Energy, and Organization in Living Systems** as described on pages 186–187 of The National Science Education Standards.

Featured in comprehensive Chapter Planning Guide.

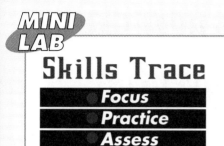

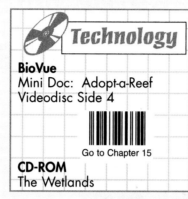

UNIT 7
ANIMALS

Covers all the major phlya, including fish, amphibians, reptiles, birds, and mammals.

UNIT 8
THE HUMAN BODY

A detailed exploration of all the major human body systems.

BRANCHING OUT

Includes:
The Importance of Arthropods, The World of Fishes, Evolution of Birds, The Influence of Humans, Insect and Primate Societies

BRANCHING OUT

Includes:
Physiology in Action, Nerve Impulses and Drugs, The Biology of Exercise, The Hazards of Smoking, A Cure for Ulcers?, Cancer

PROGRAM PURCHASE OPTIONS

- ***Single Volume (Units 1–8)***
- ***Core Course (Units 1–5)***
- ***Unit 6: From Bacteria to Plants***
- ***Unit 7: Animals***
- ***Unit 8: The Human Body***

All books in hardcover

This expanded selection of resources helps you better manage your classes and makes learning an adventure.

BIOLOGY: THE LIVING SCIENCE COMPLETE PROGRAM COMPONENTS

Student Edition
Teacher's Edition
Teaching Resources
Laboratory Manual
Laboratory Manual, Annotated Teacher's Edition
BioLog
BioLog, Annotated Teacher's Edition
Transparencies
Technology Components:
- —BioVue Videodiscs
- —The Digital Frog CD-ROM
- —CyberEd 12-CD-ROM Series
- —The Mayo Clinic CD-ROM:
  - The Total Heart
  - Family Health
- —Computer Test Bank (MAC/WIN) with Dial-a-Test

EXCLUSIVE

BioVue

New technology so inspiring it could only have been created by Oscar- and Emmy-winning directors.

Now capture every student's imagination with this motivating and groundbreaking new program.

- vibrant and relevant
- nationwide biology teacher input
- fully integrated to **Biology: The Living Science**
- can be used with any quality high school biology program

EXCLUSIVE

BioLog

A revolutionary way to monitor and bring together all aspects of the course.

The **BioLog** serves as a study aid, an activity book, and a portfolio—a collection and record of a student's work, progress, and achievement.

- Inquiry Activities
- Integrating the Media
- Involving the Community
- Biology and Art
- chapter assessment materials

Interested in customized program options? Contact your local Prentice Hall sales representative.

PRENTICE HALL

BIOLOGY

The Living Science

PRENTICE HALL
Simon & Schuster Education Group
A VIACOM COMPANY

PRENTICE HALL INTERACTIVE

TEACHER'S EDITION

PRENTICE HALL

BIOLOGY

The Living Science

Kenneth R. Miller, Ph.D.
Professor of Biology
Brown University
Providence, Rhode Island

Joseph Levine, Ph.D.
Science Writer and Producer
Adjunct Assistant Professor of Biology
Boston College
Boston, Massachusetts

PRENTICE HALL
Upper Saddle River, New Jersey
Needham, Massachusetts

TEACHER'S EDITION

PRENTICE HALL

BIOLOGY

The Living Science

Components

- Student Edition
- Teacher's Edition
- Laboratory Manual and Annotated Teacher's Edition
- Teaching Resources
- BioLog and Annotated Teacher's Edition
- Transparency Box With Teacher's Guide
- Computer Test Bank
- BioVue and BioVue Plus CD-ROMs
- Resource Pro

Editorial Development: Editorial Alliance
Columbus, Ohio

ISBN 0-13-426032-5

3 4 5 6 7 8 9 10   01 00 99 98

PRENTICE HALL
Simon & Schuster Education Group
A VIACOM COMPANY

Contents of Teacher's Edition

Science Safety Guidelines

SCIENCE SAFETY CLASSROOM DO'S AND DON'TS

It is essential that students follow safety guidelines whenever performing an investigation or activity. Make sure your students read the Science Safety Rules in Appendix C of their textbooks (pages 926–927). You may also want to read the following do's and don'ts to your class.

Do

1. Wear protective goggles when working with chemicals, burners, or any substance that might get into your eyes. Many materials in a lab can cause injury to the eyes and even blindness.
2. Learn what to do in case of specific accidents such as getting acid in your eyes or on your skin. (Rinse acids on your body with lots of water.)
3. Before starting any Laboratory Investigation or other experiment, make a list of the things that could go wrong that might hurt you. Then make a list of what you should do if the accident occurs.
4. Make sure you have a fire extinguisher nearby to put out a fire.
5. Work with a friend, when you can, under the supervision of a science teacher or adult who understands lab safety rules.
6. Work in a well-ventilated area.
7. Learn how to use first aid to treat burns, cuts, and bruises quickly. Seek help if you are injured.
8. Carefully read directions for an experiment two or more times. Follow the directions exactly as they are written.

Don't

1. Do not mix chemicals "for the fun of it." You might produce an explosive reaction that could seriously injure you.
2. Do not taste, touch, or smell any chemical in the laboratory unless instructed by your teacher to do so.
3. Do not heat any chemical unless you are instructed to do so. A chemical that is harmless when cool can be dangerous when heated.
4. Do not heat a liquid in a closed container. The expanding gases produced may blow the container apart, injuring you.
5. Do not perform an experiment in which you must connect wires to house current. You could electrocute yourself. (Use dry cells instead.)
6. Do not tilt a test tube toward yourself or anyone else (or hold it upright) when you are heating its contents. (Always tilt the tube away from yourself and others.)
7. Do not perform any experiment unless you have written instructions (in a text or from your teacher).

FIELD TRIP SAFETY

Field trips are an exciting part of the year in biology and provide students with the opportunity to have firsthand evidence and experiences outside the classroom. The following tips will help you plan and execute a successful field trip.

1. **Site Selection:** It is up to you to select an appropriate field trip site for your students, depending upon your locale. To aid you in making the necessary arrangements, we suggest that you make a school file of available sites in your area. The file should contain specific instructions concerning whom to contact at the site, directions or a map to the site, fees (if any), the hours the site is open to the public, and availability of meal facilities and restrooms.

   It is suggested that you visit the site prior to the field trip to inspect the facilities. While you are there, locate and inventory work-study areas. Make a list of specific equipment your students will need and note the site restrictions and danger spots. Also note facilities for the handicapped if any of your students have physical limitations.

Science Safety Guidelines

2. Planning the Trip: Be sure that the field trip is justified in view of the school's educational program and your individual lesson objectives. Request written permission for the trip from school personnel and keep this written permission on file. After obtaining permission, send a written statement of your destination, departure and arrival times, mode of transportation, and necessary expenditures to each student's parent or guardian.

Meanwhile, provide time in class for advance research on the site. Correlate the projected field trip with your lessons and text material. Tell your students the why, where, and when of the field trip. Be sure to inform them of any special equipment or clothing they will need—special shoes, shorts, hand lenses, notebooks, and so on.

3. The Actual Field Trip: Make a head count of your students at each boarding and departure and periodically during the trip. Each adult should receive a list of the students he or she is to supervise and should remain with that group throughout the entire trip. While you are on the way to the site, discuss the investigation with your students. When you arrive at the site, keep the group together unless you have planned otherwise.

Make certain the students understand the purpose of the field trip. Have them make sketches, drawings, plans, or maps or take notes. Do not allow students to remove anything from its natural setting unless carefully selected items are taken for observation and returned to their natural habitats.

Most importantly, be enthusiastic but don't rush. Don't try to crowd too much into one field trip. Keep in contact with the individuals in the group and be alert and prepared for the "teachable moment."

4. Follow-up Activities: A good field trip provides a base experience for other class activities. While you are returning to the school, have students exchange ideas and discuss their experiences and observations at the site. Encourage students to ask questions and propose future activities related to the field trip. Schedule individual or group reports and have the students evaluate the trip. The vehicle for evaluation can be developed as a class activity.

Later, you may want to have your students prepare exhibits or displays using their sketches, maps, photographs, or other materials from the trip. Have them use the library to investigate questions arising from the trip. A number of library investigations can usually be proposed after a successful field trip. Remember, the learning value of a field trip depends largely on you and the type of follow-up activities you provide or encourage.

NABT Guidelines for the Use of Live Animals

The National Association of Biology Teachers (NABT) has developed the following set of guidelines to be used when working with live animals.

Living things are the subject of biology, and their direct study is an appropriate and necessary part of biology teaching. Textbook instruction alone cannot provide students with a basic understanding of life and life processes. We further recognize the importance of research to understanding life processes and providing information on health, disease, medical care, and agriculture.

The abuse of any living organism for experimentation or any other purpose is intolerable in any segment of society. Because biology deals specifically with living things, professional biological educators must be especially cognizant of their responsibility to prevent inhumane treatment to living organisms in the name of science and research. This responsibility should extend beyond the confines of the teacher's classroom to the rest of the school and community.

The National Association of Biology Teachers, in speaking to the dilemma of providing a sound biological education, while addressing the problem of humane experimentation, presents the following guidelines on the use of live animals.

A. Biological experimentation should lead to and be consistent with a respect for life and all living things. Humane treatment and care of animals should be an integral part of any lesson that includes living animals.

B. All aspects of exercises and/or experiments dealing with living things must be within the comprehension and capabilities of the students involved. It is recognized that these parameters are necessarily vague, but it is expected that competent teachers of biology can recognize these limitations.

C. Lower orders of life such as bacteria, fungi, protozoans, and invertebrates can reveal much basic biological information and are preferable as subjects for invasive studies wherever and whenever possible.

D. Vertebrate animals may be used as experimental organisms in the following situations:
1. Observations of normal living patterns of wild animals in the free living state or in zoological parks, gardens, or aquaria
2. Observations of normal living patterns of pets, fish, or domestic animals
3. Observations of biological phenomena, i.e., including ovulation in frogs through hormone injections that do not cause discomfort or adverse effects to the animals

E. Animals should be properly cared for as described in the following guidelines:
1. Appropriate quarters for the animals being used should be provided in a place free from undue stresses. If housed in the classroom itself, animals should not be constantly subjected to disturbances that might be caused by students in the classroom or other upsetting activities.
2. All animals used in teaching or research programs must receive proper care. Quarters should provide for sanitation, protection from the elements, and have sufficient space for normal behavioral and postural requirements of the species. Quarters shall be easily cleaned, ventilated, and lighted. Proper temperature regulation shall be provided.
3. Proper food and clean drinking water for those animals requiring water shall be available at all times in suitable containers.
4. Animals' care shall be supervised by a science teacher experienced in proper animal care.
5. If euthanasia is necessary, animals shall be sacrificed in an approved, humane manner by an adult experienced in the use of such procedures. Laboratory animals should not be released in the environment if they were not originally a part of the native fauna. The introduction of nonnative species which may become feral must be avoided.

NABT Guidelines for the Use of Live Animals

6. The procurement and use of wild or domestic animals must comply with existing local, state, or federal rules regarding same.

F. Animal studies should be carried out under the provisions of the following guidelines:
1. All animal studies should be carried out under the direct supervision of a competent science teacher. It is the responsibility of that teacher to ensure that the student has the necessary comprehension for the study being done.
2. Students should not be allowed to take animals home to carry out experimental studies. These studies should be done in a suitable area in the school.
3. Students doing projects with vertebrate animals should adhere to the following:
a. No experimental procedures should be attempted that would subject vertebrate animals to pain or distinct discomfort, or interfere with their health in any way. Pithing of live frogs should be carried out by a teacher experienced in such procedures and should not be a part of the general class activity.
b. Students should not perform surgery on living vertebrate animals except under the direct supervision of a qualified biomedical scientist.
4. Experimental procedures should not involve the use of microorganisms pathogenic to humans or other animals, ionizing radiation, carcinogens, drugs, or chemicals at toxic levels, drugs known to produce adverse or teratogenic effects, pain-causing drugs, alcohol in any form, electric shock, exercise until exhaustion, or other distressing stimuli.
5. Behavioral studies should use only positive reinforcement in training studies.
6. Egg embryos subjected to experimental manipulation must be destroyed humanely at least two days prior to hatching. Normal egg embryos allowed to hatch must be treated humanely within these guidelines.
7. The administration of anesthetics should be carried out by a qualified science teacher competent in such procedures. (The legal ramifications of student use of anesthetics are complex and such use should be avoided.)

G. The use of living animals for science fair projects and displays shall be in accordance with these guidelines. In addition, no living vertebrate animals shall be used in displays for science fair exhibitions.

H. It is recognized that an exceptionally talented student may wish to conduct original research in the biological or medical sciences. In those cases where the research value of a specific project is obvious by its potential contribution to science, but its execution would be otherwise prohibited by the guidelines governing the selection of an appropriate experimental animal or procedure, exceptions can be obtained if
1. the project is approved by and carried out under the direct supervision of a qualified biomedical scientist or a designated adult supervisor in the field of the investigation and
2. the project is carried out in an appropriate research facility and
3. the project is carried out with the utmost regard for the humane care and treatment of the animals involved in the project and
4. a research plan is developed and approved by the qualified biomedical scientists prior to the start of any research.

List of Suppliers of Laboratory Materials

Carolina Biological Supply Company
2700 York Road
Burlington, NC 27215

Central Scientific Company
3300 Cenco Parkway
Franklin Park, IL 60131

Connecticut Valley Biological Supply Company, Inc.
P.O. Box 326
82 Valley Road
Southampton, MA 01073

Fisher Scientific Company
Educational Materials Division
485 South Frontage Road
Burr Ridge, IL 60521

Flinn Scientific, Inc.
P.O. Box 219
770 North Raddant Street
Batavia, IL 60510

Frey Scientific Company
P.O. Box 8101
100 Paragon Parkway
Mansfield, OH 44901-8101

Lab-Aids, Inc.
17 Colt Court
Ronkonkoma, NY 11779

Nasco
901 Janesville Avenue
Fort Atkinson, WI 53538

Parco Scientific Company
P.O. Box 189
316 Youngstown-Kingsville Road
Vienna, OH 44473

Sargent-Welch Scientific Company
911 Commerce Court
Buffalo Grove, IL 60089-2362

Science Kit and Boreal Labs
777 East Park Drive
Tonawanda, NY 14150

Ward's Natural Science Establishment, Inc.
P.O. Box 92912
5100 West Henrietta Road
Rochester, NY 14692-9012

List of Materials for Laboratory Investigations

Item	Quantity per Group	Chapter
Acetic acid, dilute	25 mL per class	23, 33
Aceto-orcein stain	1 dropper bottle per class	5
Adrenaline solution, 0.01%	25 mL per class	34
Agar, sterile nutrient plate	1	11
	6	40
Alcohol solution	10 mL	8
American chameleon, live	1	31
Bacteria culture	1 culture per class	11
Baking soda solution	10 mL	8
Balance	1	1, 16, 32
triple-beam	1	37
Beaker		
25-mL	4	14
50-mL	2	22, 38
	8	2
1000-mL	1	8
Blotting paper squares, 1 cm^2	4	36
Bottle, plastic		
8-oz.	4	20
2-L	2	15, 16
Brine shrimp	6	27
Bunsen burner	1	37
Burette	1	38
Carborundum powder	1 small bottle per class	22
Cardboard	1 large piece	15
Carnoy's fixative	30 mL per class	5
Carrot, whole	1	26
Celery stalk	1	18
Cellophane sheets, in 2 colors	2 sheets of each color	30
Chlamydomonas culture	1 culture per class	24
Cloth, porous	1 large piece per class	16
Compass, drawing	1	29
Compost materials	See investigation.	16
Container		
clear plastic	1	18
large plastic	3	30
storage	1	28
Cotton balls	3 bags per class	37
Cotton swabs		
nonsterile	1	36
	2	22
sterile	1	11
Coverslip	1	3, 5, 13, 23, 26
	3	27
	4	24
Culture dish	3	27

List of Materials for Laboratory Investigations

Item	Quantity per Group	Chapter
Daphnia culture	1 culture per class	34
Dibasic potassium phosphate solution	1 small bottle per class	22
Dilute acid solution	25 mL per class	27
Dishwashing detergent, liquid	5 mL	8
Disinfectants, household, 2 different types	1 container of each	40
Dissecting needle	1	24, 25, 26
Dissecting tray	1	35
Distilled water	50 mL	2
	100 mL	8
	1 L per class	26
Earthworm, live	1	28
Filter paper disks	1	37
	5	2
antibiotic	4	11
Food coloring, blue	1 bottle per class	18
Food samples	See investigation.	29
Forceps	1	2, 5, 11, 26, 33
Fruit drinks, various kinds	See investigation.	38
Fruit fly larvae	1 culture per class	29
Funnel	1	38
Garlic bulbs with roots	4 per class	5
Glass stirring rod	1	8, 38
Gloves, latex	1 pair per student	35
Glucose	10 g per class	4
Graduated cylinders		
10-mL	1	8
100-mL	1	32
Hand lens	1	25, 26, 28
Heat source (See investigation.)	1	31
Hot plate	1	8
Hydra culture	1 culture per class	19, 27
Hydrochloric acid-ethyl alcohol solution (See investigation.)	30 mL per class	5
Hydrogen peroxide	50 mL per class	40
Hydrogen peroxide solution, 1%	75 mL	2
Ice	1 container	8
	10 cubes	15
Index cards, white	1	33
	2	7, 22
	1 package	17
Indicator (See investigation.)	1 dropper bottle per class	21
Indophenol solution	30 mL	38
Ink pad	1	7
Iodine solution	1 dropper bottle	3, 36
Knife	1	16

List of Materials for Laboratory Investigations

Item	Quantity per Group	Chapter
Lab table cover, paper or cloth	1	10
Lactose	10 g per class	4
Lamp	1	28
Lettuce	1 leaf	26
Light bulb, 100-watt	1	15
Light source (See investigation.)	1	31
Live organism	1	1
Liver	1 small piece	33
Magnifying glass	1	1, 7
Mammal skull	1	32
Markers, colored	1 box	13, 16, 17
Matches	1 book	37
Mealworm (or other small live insects)	See investigation.	31
Meat tenderizer	3 g	8
Medicine dropper	1	3, 5, 19, 21, 23, 24, 26, 27, 28
	2	34
sterile	1	40
Meterstick	1	17
Methyl cellulose	1 dropper bottle	22
Metric ruler	1	1, 6, 11, 18, 29, 36, 40
Microscope, compound light	1	3, 5, 14, 16, 18, 19, 23, 24, 26, 27, 34, 39
Molasses	10 mL per class	4
Molasses solution	40 mL	14
Mortar and pestle	1	22
Onion	1 per class	3
Orange juice, 100%, refrigerated	50 mL	38
Paper		
adding machine	5 meters	17
colored	5 sheets	31
brown, green, yellow, gray, black, white, blue, purple, violet, red	4 sheets of each color per 4 students	10
construction: red and blue	1 sheet of each	20
drawing	1 sheet	29
graph	1 sheet	14
	2 sheets	15
notebook	2 sheets	13
white, unlined	1 sheet	6
large	2 sheets	13
white and dark	1 sheet of each	1
Paper towels	1 large roll per class	2, 3, 5, 9, 28
Paramecium culture	1 culture per class	23
Pea, soaked	1	25
Pea pod (or string bean or lima bean pod)	1	25
Pencil	1	6, 13
colored	1 box	31
glass-marking	1	2, 4, 9, 11, 14, 22, 33
graphite	1	29

List of Materials for Laboratory Investigations

Item	Quantity per Group	Chapter
Penlight (or flashlight)	1	1, 23
Petri dish, bottoms only	1	19, 26, 33
	2	9
Petroleum jelly	1 jar per class	27
Photographs and artwork of different life forms	See investigation.	17
Pipe cleaner	1	6
Pipettes	2	14
disposable plastic	5	4
large	1	21
Planaria culture	1 culture per class	19, 27, 33
Plastic cup, 200-mL	1	8
Plastic wrap, clear	1 roll per class	15
Pond water	10 mL	33
Potato extract solution	50 mL	2
Pot with soil	10	9
Prepared slides		
cheek cells, human	1	3
ovary, human, x.s.	1	39
sperm, human, x.s.	1	39
testis, human, x.s.	1	39
Probe	1	19, 27, 35
Radish seedlings	5	26
Rice, uncooked	1 bag	32
Rocks	See investigation.	31
Rubber bands		
large	1	15
small	1	16
Salt, table	1 container per class	33
Salt solution, 0.5%	25 mL per class	23
Sand or gravel	3 bags per class	31
Scalpel	1	3, 5, 18, 20, 25, 26, 35
Scissors	1	15, 20
Screen terrarium lid	1	31
Seeds, irradiated and nonirradiated, from same organism	20	9
Sheep brain	1	35
Slides		
depression	1	23, 34
	3	27
microscope	1	3, 5, 14, 16, 26
	4	24
Sod (or other plants)	1 large bag per class	15
Soil, potting	1 bag per class	15
Spatula	1	22
Spirogyra culture	1 culture per class	24
Sponge, 4 cm^2	1	31
Stereomicroscope	1	27
Stock solutions in large test tubes	See investigation.	21
Sucrose	10 g per class	4

List of Materials for Laboratory Investigations

Item	Quantity per Group	Chapter
Tadpole food	See investigation.	30
Tadpoles of same species and age	12	30
Tape		
clear mailing	1 roll per class	20
medical adhesive	1 roll per class	36
transparent	1 roll per class	11, 13, 15, 17, 30, 40
Terrarium, 20-gallon	1	31
Test-tube holder	1	37
Test-tube rack	1	37
Test tubes	1	21
	3	37
large	5	4
with cork or stopper	1	33
Thermometer, Celsius	1	4, 8
outdoor	2	15
Tobacco plants, young, in pots with soil	2	22
Tobacco samples	1	22
cigarette, pipe, and cigar	2 g of each	37
Tongs	1	8
Toothpick	4	27
Tray	1	28
Tree branches, dried small	5	31
Tweezers	1	3
Ulva culture	1 culture per class	24
Volvox culture	1 culture per class	24
Watch (or clock)	1	31
with second-hand timer	1	4
Watch glass (or Petri dish cover)	2	5
Water, pond or dechlorinated tap	10 L	30
Weight (See investigation.)	1	4
Wheat germ, raw	1.5 g	8
Yarn, red and blue	1 large ball of each color	20
Yeast	3 packages per class	4
Yeast culture, colored	1 culture per class	23
Yeast solution	4 mL	14

Materials Inventory

Equipment
Balance
  triple-beam
Bottles, plastic
  8-oz.
  2-L
Bunsen burner
Burette
Compass, drawing
Containers
Coverslip
Culture dish
Dissecting needle
Dissecting tray
Forceps
Funnel
Gloves, latex
Hand lens
Heat source (See investigation.)
Hot plate
Knife
Lamp
Light source (See investigation.)
Medicine dropper
  sterile
Meterstick
Metric ruler
Microscope, compound light
Mortar and pestle
Penlight
Probe
Scalpel
Scissors
Screen terrarium lid
Spatula
Stereomicroscope
Terrarium
Test-tube holder
Test-tube rack
Tongs
Tray
Tweezers
Watch
Weight (See investigation.)

Glassware
Beaker
  25-mL
  50-mL
  1000-mL
Graduated cylinder
  10-mL
  100-mL
Magnifying glass
Petri dish
Pipettes
Slides
  depression
  microscope
Stirring rod
Test tubes
  large
  regular
  with cork or stopper
Thermometer, Celsius
  outdoor
Watch glass

Living Organisms
American chameleon
Bacteria culture
Brine shrimp
Chalmydomonas culture
Daphnia culture
Earthworm
Fruit fly larvae
Hydra culture
Mealworm
Paramecium culture
Planaria culture
Radish seedlings
Random live organism (See investigation.)
Spirogyra culture
Tadpoles
Tobacco plants
Ulva culture
Volvox culture
Yeast culture

Prepared Slides
Cheek cells, human
Ovary, human, x.s.
Sperm, human, x.s.
Testis, human, x.s.

Preserved Specimens
Mammal skull
Sheep brain

Other Biological Supplies
Agar, sterile nutrient plate
Dechlorinated tap water
Pond water

Materials Inventory

Chemical Supplies

Acetic acid, dilute
Aceto-orcein stain
Adrenaline solution, 0.01%
Alcohol solution
Baking soda solution
Carborundum powder
Carnoy's fixative
Dibasic potassium phosphate solution
Dilute acid solution
Glucose
Hydrochloric acid-ethyl alcohol solution
Hydrogen peroxide
Hydrogen peroxide solution, 1%
Indicator (See investigation.)
Indophenol solution
Iodine solution
Lactose
Methyl cellulose
Molasses solution
Potato extract solution
Salt solution, 0.5%
Stock solutions (See investigation.)
Sucrose
Yeast solution

Consumables

Blotting paper squares
Cardboard
Carrot, whole
Celery stalk
Cellophane sheets
Cloth, porous
Compost materials (See investigation.)
Cotton balls
Cotton swabs
  nonsterile
  sterile
Dishwashing detergent, liquid
Disinfectants, household
Distilled water
Filter paper disks
  antibiotic
Food coloring, blue
Food samples (See investigation.)
Fruit drinks (See investigation.)
Garlic bulbs with roots
Ice
Index cards
Ink pad
Lab table cover
Lettuce
Light bulb, 100-watt
Liver
Markers
Matches
Meat tenderizer
Molasses
Onion
Orange juice
Paper
  adding machine
  colored
  construction: red and blue
  drawing
  graph
  notebook
  white, unlined
  white and dark
Paper towels
Pea pod
Peas
Pencil
  colored
  glass-marking
  graphite
Petroleum jelly
Photographs and artwork of life forms (See investigation.)
Pipe cleaner
Pipettes, disposable plastic
Plastic cup, 200-mL
Plastic wrap
Pot with soil
Rice, uncooked
Rocks
Rubber bands
Salt, table
Sand or gravel
Seeds, irradiated and nonirradiated
Sod
Soil, potting
Sponge, 4 cm^2
Tadpole food
Tape
  clear mailing
  medical adhesive
  transparent
Tobacco
Toothpick
Tree branches
Wheat germ
Yarn
Yeast

PRENTICE HALL

BIOLOGY
The Living Science

Kenneth R. Miller, Ph.D.
Professor of Biology
Brown University
Providence, Rhode Island

Joseph Levine, Ph.D.
Science Writer and Producer
Adjunct Assistant Professor of Biology
Boston College
Boston, Massachusetts

PRENTICE HALL
Upper Saddle River, New Jersey
Needham, Massachusetts

PRENTICE HALL

BIOLOGY

The Living Science

Components

Student Edition
Teacher's Edition
Laboratory Manual and Annotated Teacher's Edition
Teaching Resources
BioLog and Annotated Teacher's Edition
Transparency Box with Teacher's Guide
Computer Test Bank
BioVue and BioVue Plus CD-ROMs

The photograph on the cover shows female lions hunting at night on the African savanna—a brief glimpse into the amazing diversity of life on our planet.

Credits begin on page 971.

ISBN 0-13-415563-7

3 4 5 6 7 8 9 10   01 00 99 98

PRENTICE HALL
Simon & Schuster Education Group
A VIACOM COMPANY

Staff Credits for Prentice Hall *Biology: The Living Science*

Advertising and Promotion: Judy Goldstein, Carol Leslie, Rip Odell
Business Office: Emily Heins
Design: Laura Jane Bird, Kerri Folb, Kathryn Foot, AnnMarie Roselli, Gerry Schrenk
Manufacturing and Inventory Planning: Katherine Clarke, Rhett Conklin
Market Research: Eileen Friend, Gail Stark
Media Resources: Martha Conway, Libby Forsyth, Vickie Menanteaux, Maureen Raymond, Emily Rose, Melissa Shustyk
National Science Consultants: Charles Balko, Patricia Cominsky, Jeannie Dennard, Kathleen French, Brenda Underwood
Pre-Press Production: Carol Barbara, Kathryn Dix, Paula Massenaro
Production: Christina Burghard, Elizabeth O'Brien, Marilyn Stearns, Elizabeth Torjussen
Science Department
- **Director:** Julie Levin Alexander
- **Editorial:** Laura Baselice, Joseph Berman, Christine Caputo, Maureen Grassi, Rekha Sheorey, Lorraine Smith-Phelan
- **Marketing:** Arthur Germano, Andrew Socha, Kathleen Ventura, Jane Walker Neff, Victoria Willows
- **Technology Development:** Matthew Hart

Electronic Services: Greg Myers, Cleasta Wilburn

Acknowledgments

Teacher Advisory Panel

Leslie Ferry Bettencourt
Lincoln High School
Lincoln, Rhode Island

Jean T. (Caye) Boone
Hume-Fogg Academic High School
Nashville, Tennessee

David A. Dowell
Carmel High School
Carmel, Indiana

Deborah H. Fabrizio
Seminole High School
Seminole, Florida

Yvonne Favaro
Fort Lee High School
Fort Lee, New Jersey

Steve Ferguson
Lee's Summit High School
Lee's Summit, Missouri

Patricia Anne Johnson
Ridgewood High School
Ridgewood, New Jersey

Mamie Lew
George W. Brackenridge High School
San Antonio, Texas

Ned C. Owings
Florence School District One
Florence, South Carolina

Kathey A. Roberts
Lakeside High School
Hot Springs, Arkansas

College Reviewers

Brian Alters, Ph.D.
Harvard University
Cambridge, Massachusetts

Lauren Brown, Ph.D.
Illinois State University
Normal, Illinois

Maura Flannery, Ph.D.
St. John's University
Jamaica, New York

Ann Lumsden, Ph.D.
Florida State University
Tallahassee, Florida

Gerry Madrazo, Ph.D.
University of North Carolina
Chapel Hill, North Carolina

Cynthia Moore, Ph.D.
Washington University
St. Louis, Missouri

Laurence D. Mueller, Ph.D.
University of California
Irvine, California

Carl Thurman, Ph.D.
University of Northern Iowa
Cedar Falls, Iowa

High School Reviewers

Louise Ables
A & M Consolidated High School
College Station, Texas

Bernard Adkins
Wayne High School
Wayne, West Virginia

Tony Beasley
Science Consultant
Nashville, Tennessee

Victor Choy
John Oliver Secondary School
Vancouver, British Columbia, Canada

Gary Davis
Albuquerque Academy
Albuquerque, New Mexico

Barbara Foots
Houston Independent School District
Houston, Texas

Elaine Frank
Durant High School
Plant City, Florida

Truman Holtzclaw
Sacramento High School
Sacramento, California

Michael Horn
Centennial High School
Boise, Idaho

Jerry Lasnik
Agoura High School
Agoura, California

Marva Moore
Hamilton Southeast High School
Fishers, Indiana

Michael O'Hare
New Trier High School
Winnetka, Illinois

Susan Plati
Brookline High School
Brookline, Massachusetts

James Pulley
Science Consultant
Independence, Missouri

Eddie Rodriguez
Math Science Academy
San Antonio, Texas

Beverly St. John
Milton High School
Milton, Florida

John Young, Ph.D.
Council Rock School District
Newtown, Pennsylvania

Student Reviewers

Emma Greig
Home School
Rochester, Michigan

Rebecca Irizarry
Columbia High School
Maplewood, New Jersey

Laura Stearns
Park Ridge High School
Park Ridge, New Jersey

Adam D. Stuble
Green River High School
Green River, Wyoming

Keri Ann Wolfe
Clarkstown Senior High School South
West Nyack, New York

Elizabeth Ashley Wolgemuth
Santa Margarita Catholic High School
Rancho Santa Margarita, California

Laboratory Teacher's Panel

Judith Dayner
Northern Highlands Regional High School
Allendale, New Jersey

Paul Fimbel
Northern Valley Regional High School
Old Tappan, New Jersey

Deidre Galvin
Ridgewood High School
Ridgewood, New Jersey

Patricia Anne Johnson
Ridgewood High School
Ridgewood, New Jersey

Carole Linkiewicz
Academic High School
Jersey City, New Jersey

Joan Picarelli
Leonia High School
Leonia, New Jersey

Robert Richard
Hillsborough High School
Belle Mead, New Jersey

Tom Russo
Weehawken High School
Weehawken, New Jersey

Sandy Shortt
Ridgewood High School
Ridgewood, New Jersey

Contributing Writers

Sandra Alters, Ph.D.
Salem State College
Salem, Massachusetts

John C. Kay
Iolani School
Honolulu, Hawaii

LaMoine Motz, Ph.D.
Oakland Schools
Waterford, Michigan

Sue Whitsett
L. P. Goodrich High School
Fond du Lac, Wisconsin

Ronnee Yashon, Ph.D.
Tufts University
Medford, Massachusetts

Reading Consultant

Laurence J. Swinburne, President
Swinburne Readability Laboratory

CONTENTS

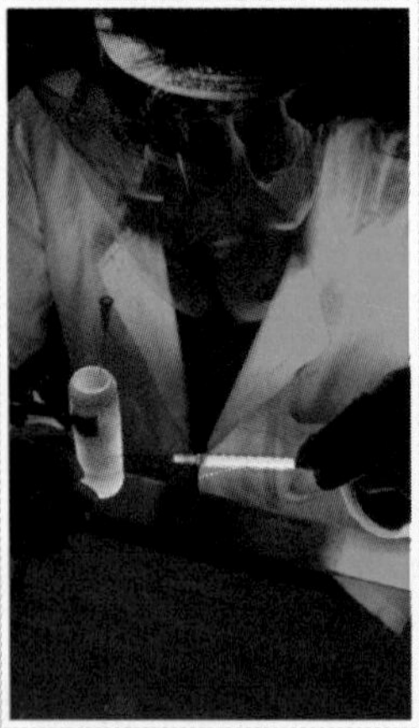

CHAPTER 3 CELL STRUCTURE AND FUNCTION 48

CHAPTER 4 ENERGY AND THE CELL 74

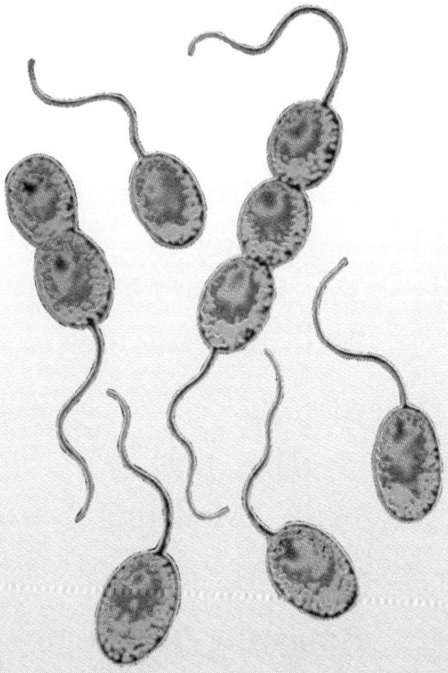

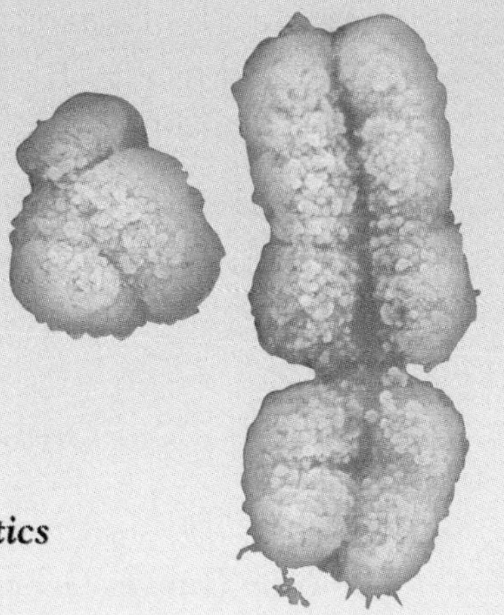

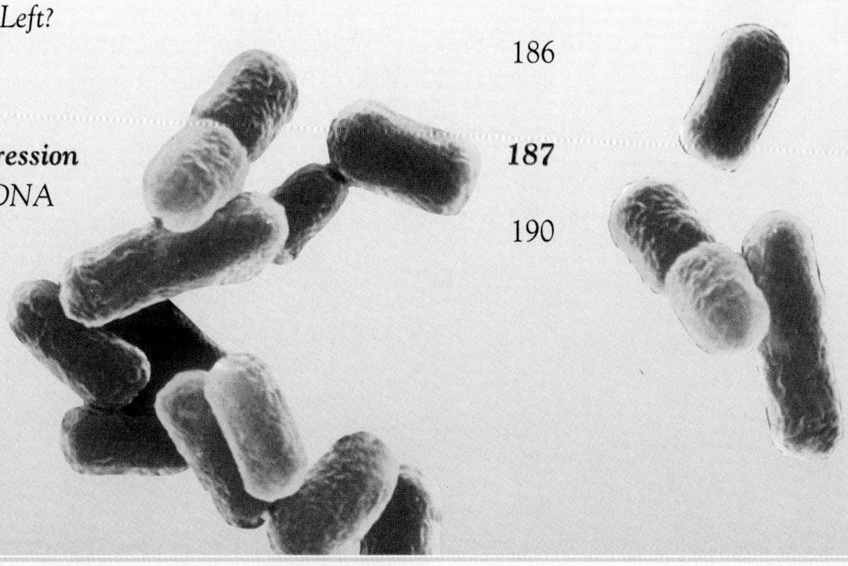

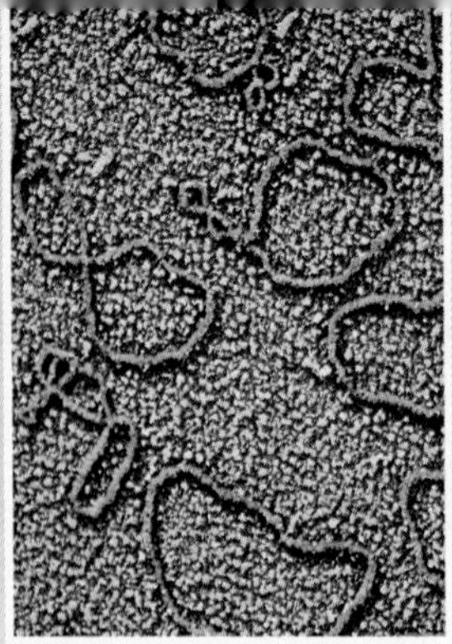

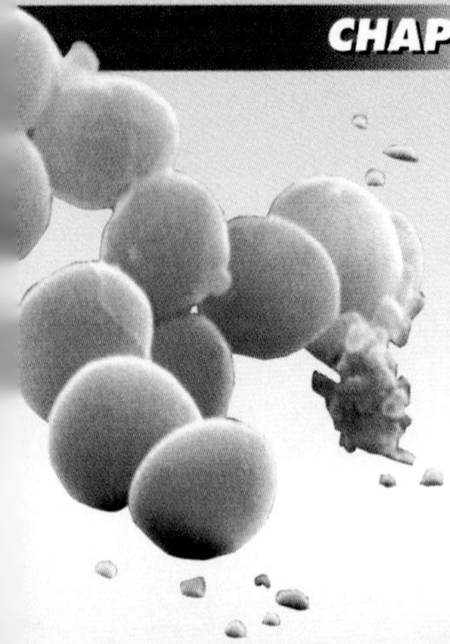

UNIT 4 Ecology 280

UNIT 5 Life on Earth: An Overview 384

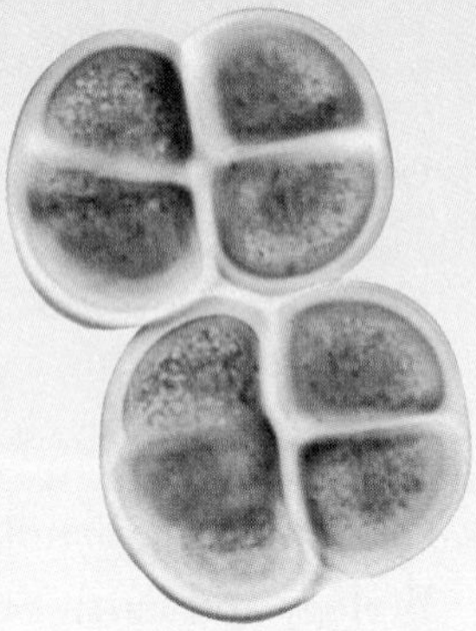

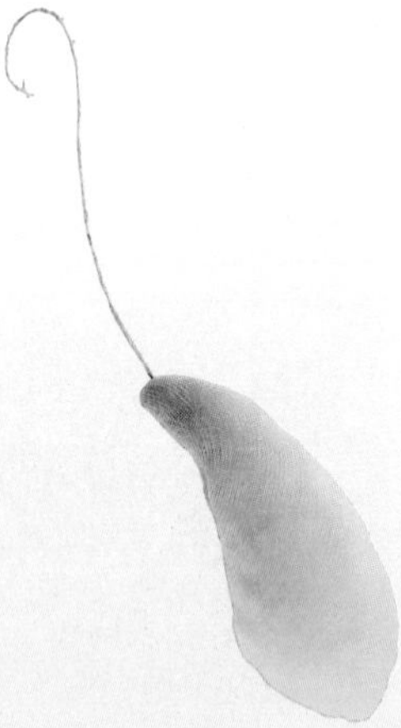

UNIT 6 From Bacteria to Plants 512

UNIT 7 Animals 626

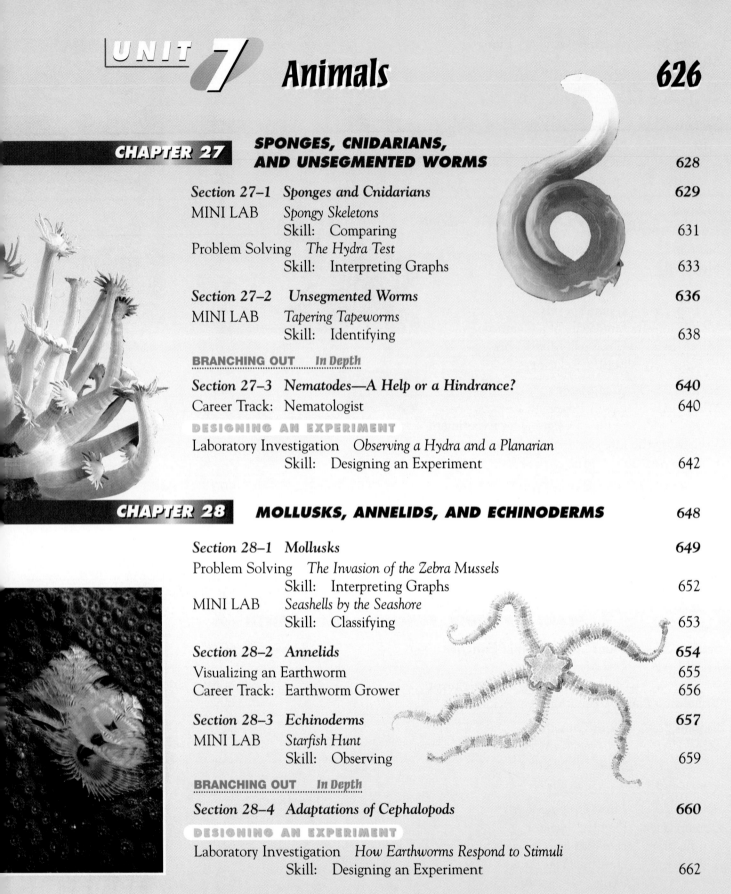

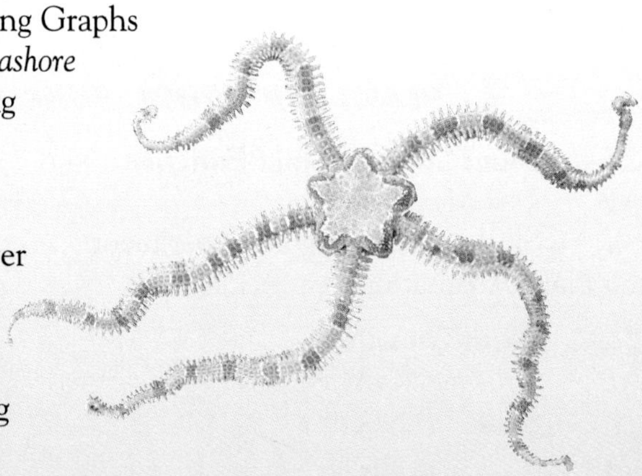

CHAPTER 29 ARTHROPODS 668

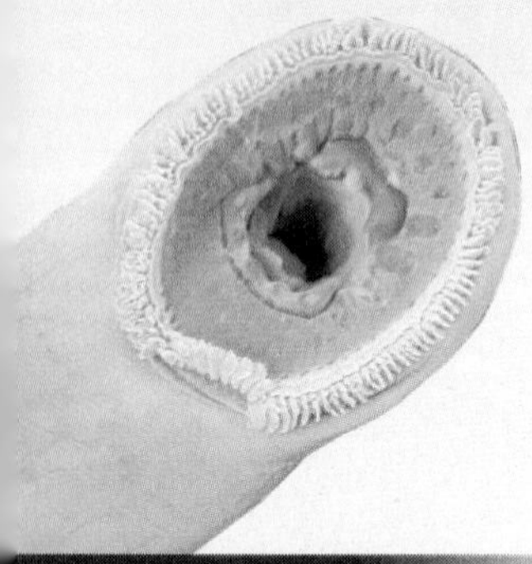

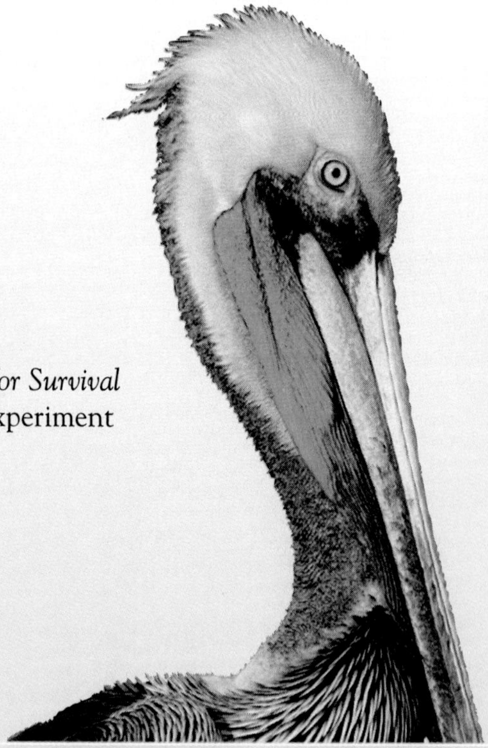

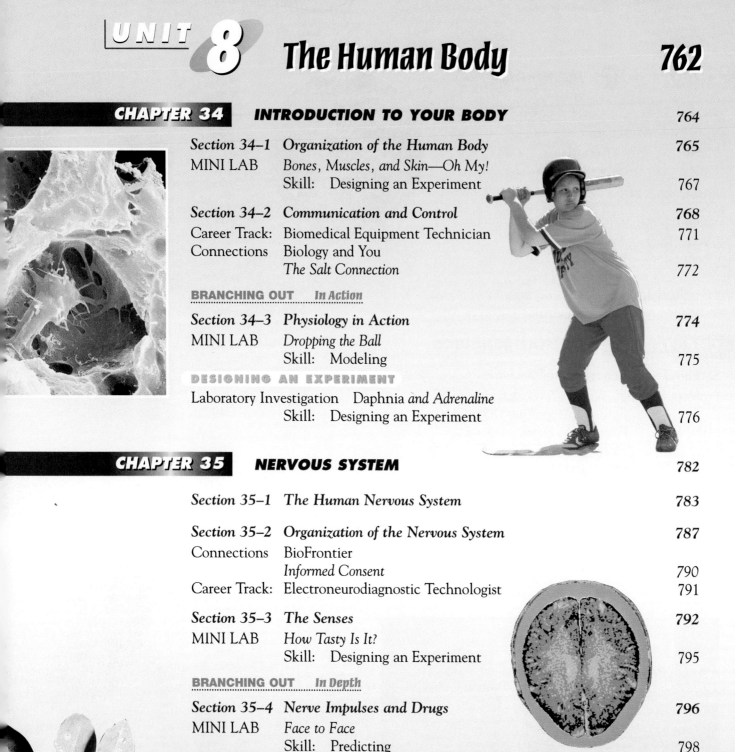

UNIT 8 The Human Body 762

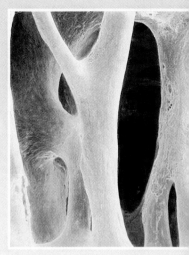

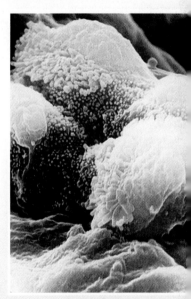

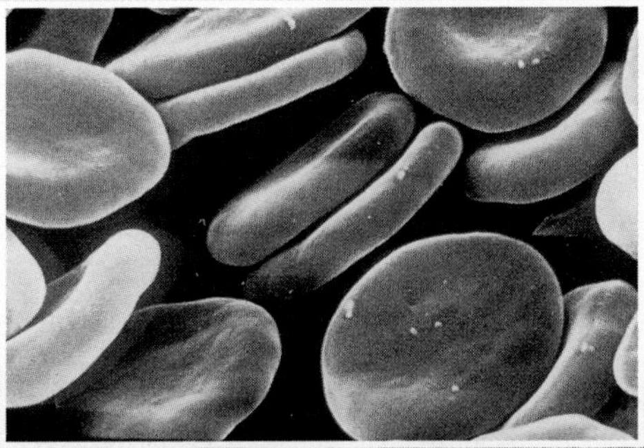

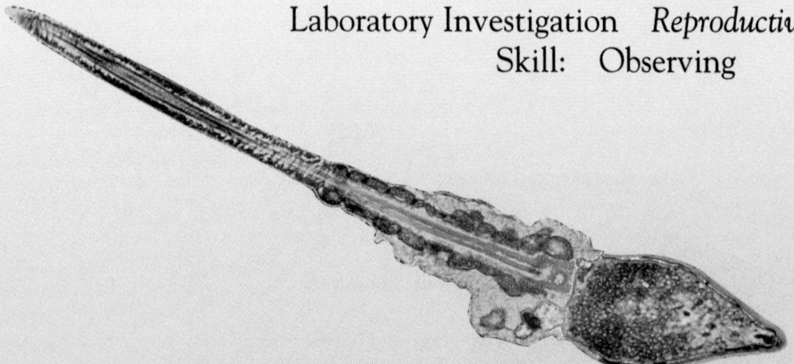

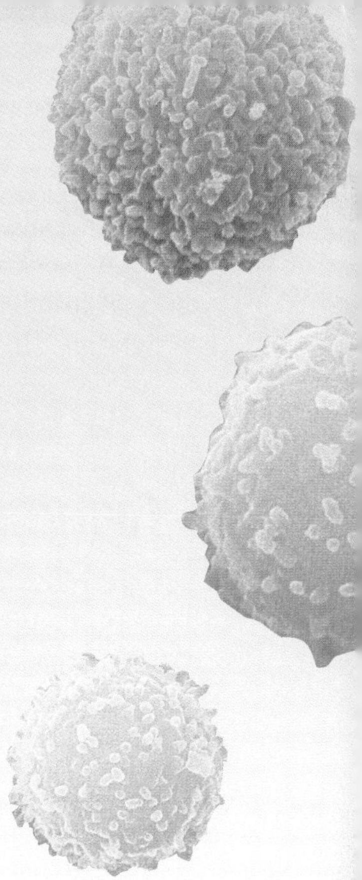

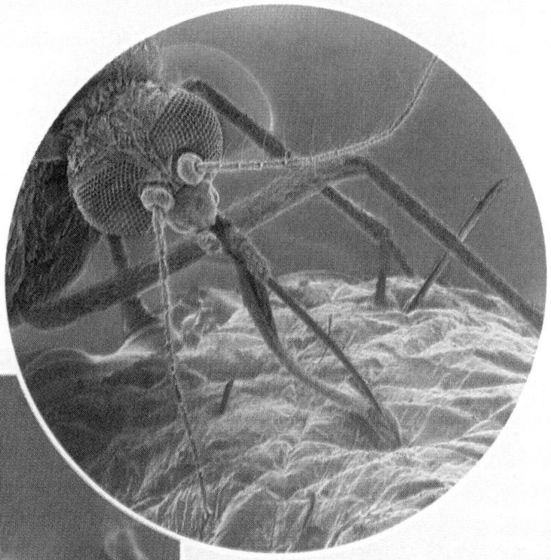

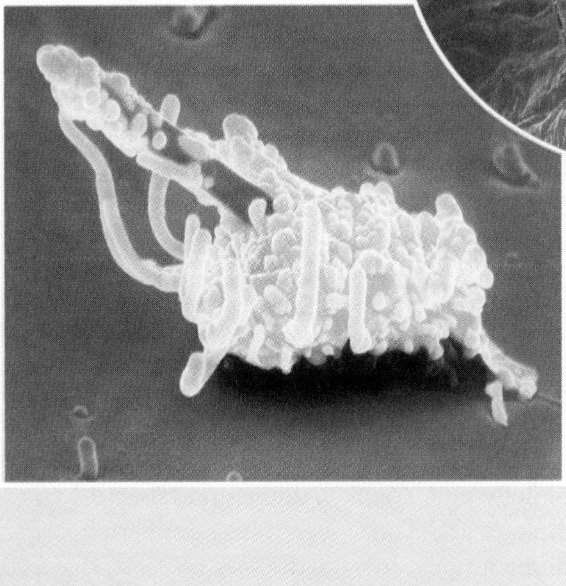

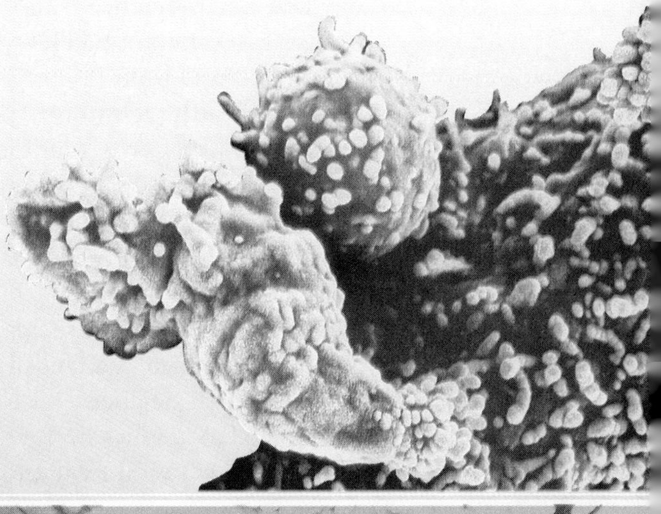

Reference Section

Features

Career Track

Connections

Laboratory Investigations

Mini Labs

Mini Labs continued

Problem Solving

Visualizing . . .

WELCOME TO BIOLOGY!

YOU MAY HAVE HEARD PEOPLE SAY: "The future of our planet lies in the hands of our children." That might not mean much to you right now, but eventually the reins of power in our society, including the right to vote, will be passed to you and to your generation. As new discoveries in science and technology occur at an incredible pace, virtually every choice you make will require an understanding of science. Whether you become a scientist or an educated citizen in another career, the quality of your life, as well as the life of generations to come, will depend on how wisely you make those choices.

We wrote this book to inform, and maybe even to inspire, you about the living science of biology. We are all part of a great web of life that covers this planet, and your future depends on the survival and success of that life. The discoveries of science have greatly improved your quality of life over that of your parents and grandparents. But biology is still wide open to new discoveries that can make our world an even better place for you and your children.

The words, photographs, and illustrations in this book have been selected to help you master the basic concepts of biology in an intriguing and enjoyable manner. Many features, some of which are highlighted on these pages, have been included to help you learn and develop skills that can be used as you study biology, as well as other disciplines. We invite you to read the story of biology, to wonder and question, and to appreciate the beauty of this truly fascinating science.

The **Chapter Opener** helps you to focus on the themes and concepts that will be presented in the forthcoming pages. The **chapter-opener photograph** was selected as an interesting representation of the main ideas of the chapter.

Focusing the Chapter can be a very helpful organizational tool to use as you begin your study. All the major divisions, or sections, of the chapter are listed to help you familiarize yourself with the content of the chapter. The **theme** of the chapter helps you to make connections among the concepts presented.

You may be surprised to discover that you are already familiar with many of the concepts in the chapter. By using the **BioJournal,** you can determine what you already know and start thinking about what you would like to know.

Every section begins with a **Guide for Reading,** which highlights several of the more important ideas presented. As you read the section, you will also see **key terms** and **key ideas** presented in boldface type. This should alert you that these are important and may, indeed, be items that you will be tested on later.

Use the **visuals** and **captions** to help clarify the concepts. They have been carefully selected to visually enhance the content, as well as to relate the topic to real-world situations. Notice that the letters in the caption match the letters that identify the pictures.

In most of the chapters, you will find a feature called **Visualizing. . . .** This example shows **Visualizing Aquatic Biomes.** A lot of information is conveyed through pictures and illustrations, so you should pay close attention to these pages to ensure a complete understanding of the big ideas being presented.

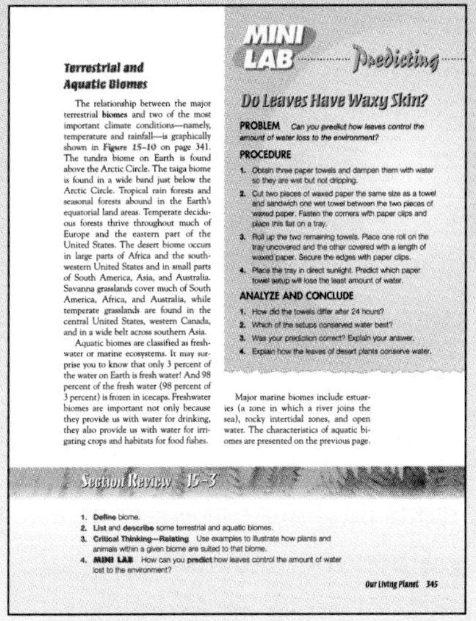

No study of biology would be complete without some kind of hands-on experience. The **Mini Labs,** as well as the **Laboratory Investigations** (not pictured), give you that opportunity—often by using materials as simple as those found in your own kitchen! They also give you the opportunity to exercise your creative thought processes as you put on a scientific hat and **design your own experiments.**

The way to an A is in large part your responsibility. By evaluating yourself and your study habits, you can discover how much you know and where you need more review. To help you assess your own progress, **Checkpoint** questions (not pictured) are integrated throughout the content. The **Section Review** questions are also designed to help you do this.

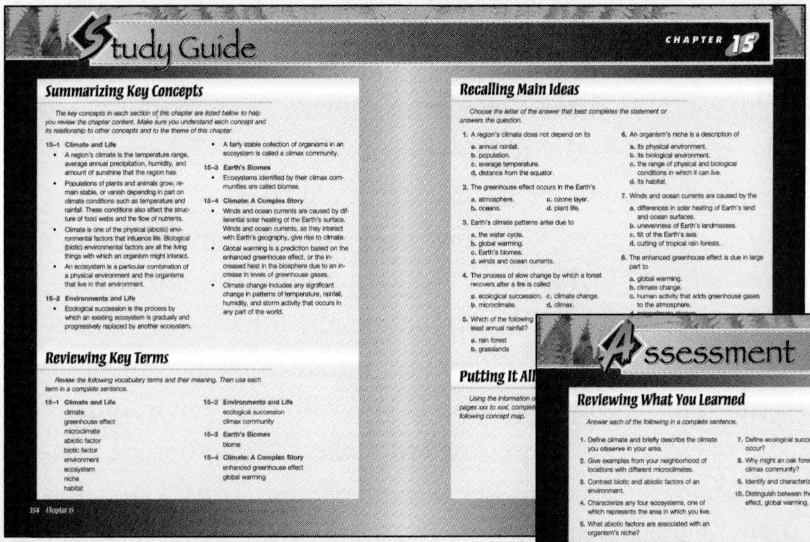

The **Study Guide** includes a list of important ideas that you should have mastered by the time you complete each section, as well as key vocabulary terms. To use this information effectively, check yourself by answering the **Recalling Main Ideas** questions and by completing the concept map under **Putting It All Together.**

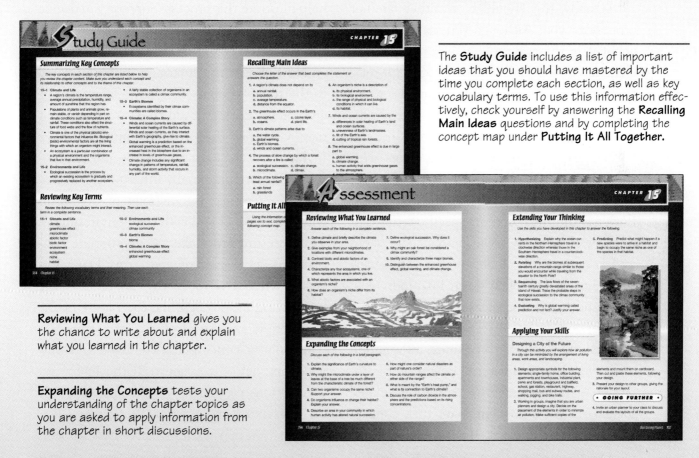

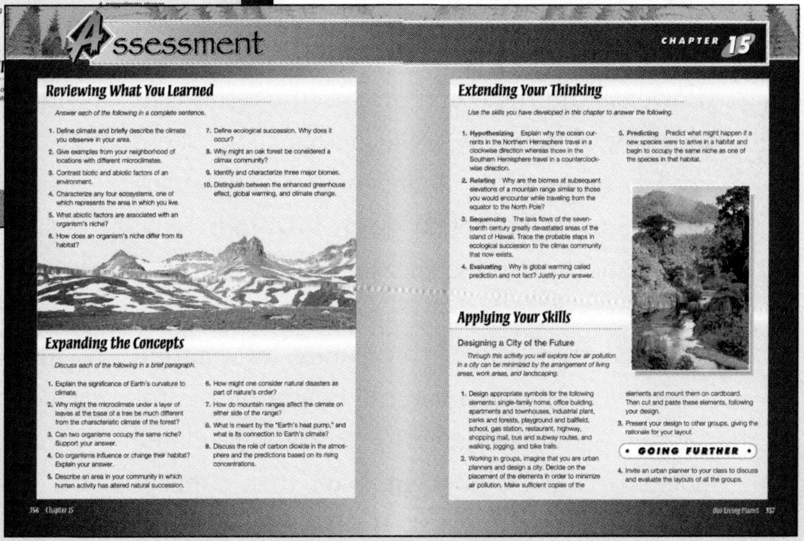

Reviewing What You Learned gives you the chance to write about and explain what you learned in the chapter.

Expanding the Concepts tests your understanding of the chapter topics as you are asked to apply information from the chapter in short discussions.

Extending Your Thinking challenges your knowledge and skills as you solve the creative problems and the case studies and apply your knowledge to new situations.

Applying Your Skills allows you to put your skills to the test as you complete challenging tasks involving one or more skills.

CONCEPT MAPPING

THROUGHOUT YOUR STUDY OF science, you will learn a variety of terms, facts, and concepts. Each new topic you encounter will provide its own collection of words and ideas—which, at times, you may think seems endless. But each of the ideas within a particular topic is related in some way to the others. No concept in science is isolated. Thus, it will help you to understand the topic if you see the whole picture; that is, the interconnectedness of all the individual terms and ideas. This is a much more effective and satisfying way of learning than memorizing separate facts.

Actually, this should be a rather familiar process for you. Although you may not think about it in this way, you analyze many of the elements in your daily life by looking for relationships or connections. For example, when you look at a collection of flowers, you may divide them into groups: roses, carnations, and daisies. You may then associate colors with these flowers: red, pink, and white. The general topic is flowers. The subtopic is types of flowers. And the colors are specific terms that describe flowers. A topic makes more sense and is more easily understood if you understand how it is broken down into individual ideas and how these ideas are related to one another and to the entire topic.

It is often helpful to organize information visually so that you can see how it all fits together. One technique for describing related ideas is called a **concept map.** In a concept map, an idea is represented by a word or phrase enclosed in a box. There are several ideas in any concept map. A connection between two ideas is made with a line. A word or two that describes the connection is written on or near the line. The general topic is located at the top of the map. That topic is then broken down into subtopics, or more specific ideas, by branching lines. The most specific topics are located at the bottom of the map.

To construct a concept map, first identify the important ideas or key terms in the chapter or section. Do not try to include too much information. Use your judgment as to what is really important. Write the general topic at the top of your map. Let's use an example to help illustrate this process. Suppose you decide that the key term is Biology. Write and enclose this word in a box at the top of your map.

Now choose the subtopics that are related to the topic—Botany, Zoology, Genetics, Microbiology, Ecology. Add these words to your map. Continue this procedure until you have included all the important ideas and terms—study of plants, animals, inheritance, microscopic organisms, interactions of organisms with one another and with their environment. Then use lines to make the appropriate connections between ideas and terms. Don't forget to write a word or two on or near the connecting line to describe the nature of the connection.

Do not be concerned if you have to redraw your map before you show all the important connections clearly. If, for example, you rely on observation and experimentation as well as analysis, you may want to place these subjects next to each other so that the lines do not overlap.

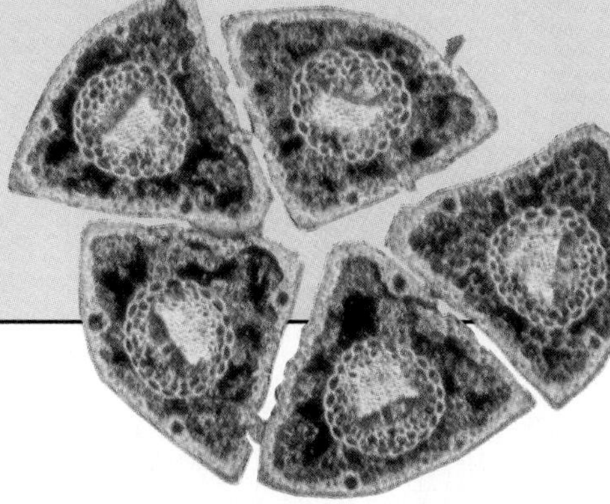

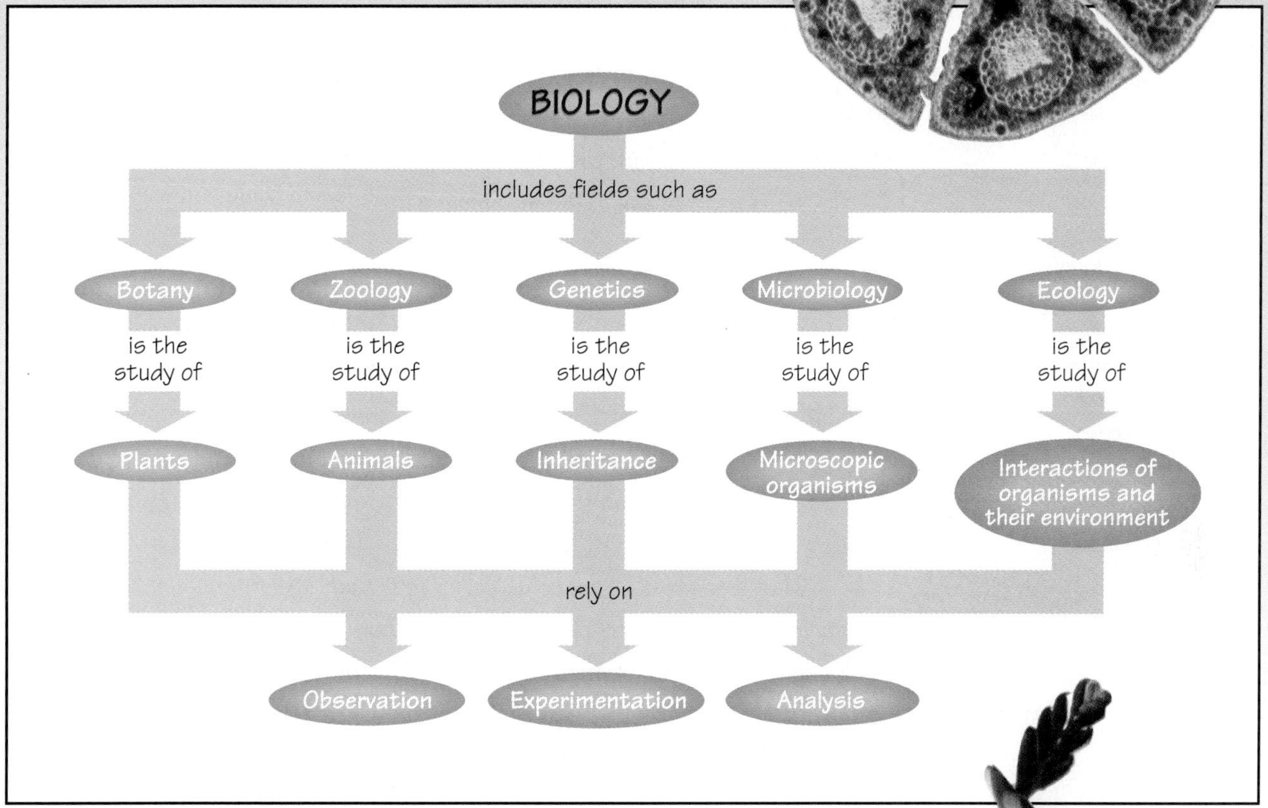

One more thing you should know about concept mapping: Concepts can be correctly mapped in many different ways. In fact, it is unlikely that any two people will draw identical concept maps for a complex topic. Thus, there is no one correct concept map for any topic. Even though your concept map may not match those of your classmates, it will be correct as long as it shows the most important concepts and the clear relationships among them. Your concept map will also be correct if it has meaning to you and if it helps you understand the material you are reading. A concept map should be so clear that if some of the terms are erased, the missing terms could easily be filled in by following the logic of the concept map.

TO THE STUDENT

WHEN I WAS 9 OR 10, I WANTED TO BE AN *explorer. I imagined myself hiking through wild country, a hunting knife strapped to my ankle, fearlessly stepping into adventures at every turn. Growing up in suburban New Jersey, my friends and I "invented" a wilderness around the creek in a little woods at the end of our street. Almost every day we pretended to discover the place for the first time. On cool days we blazed new trails in the imaginary forest and on hot days we built dams and canals in the clay bed of the creek.*

Four or five years later, when I walked into Mr. Zong's ninth-grade biology class in Rahway Junior High, I had become way too grown up to play at the creek anymore. Like most of the boys in my class, I was more interested in acting cool and learning how to do the latest dance—they called it "the twist"!

Our teacher had filled his classroom with specimens—stuffed animals, mounted bugs, pressed flowers, bones, leaves, cocoons. Everywhere you looked there was something new, something unknown, something mysterious. I began to get interested. Then one day, he asked for a volunteer. On my way to school the next morning I made a trip to the old creek. All grown up, the woods now seemed small and ordinary. I filled a jar of creek water to bring to school.

In lab that day we put a drop of the water under the microscope, and I could hardly believe my eyes. The water was teeming with life! After my last class that day, Mr. Zong let me spend another session at the microscope, and this time he helped me identify the tiny critters. We found rotifers and ciliates and a half dozen different kinds of algae. There were things that even he couldn't name for sure.

When I walked home from school that day my view of the creek had changed—and so had my view of the world. For the first time, I understood that the neighborhood I thought I knew was filled with hidden secrets, and I wanted to learn every one of them. To me, that's what biology still is like—a chance, every day, to understand a little more about the mystery of being alive.

With all my heart, I hope that this textbook, every now and then, will give you a little bit of the same feeling I had when I looked at that water under the microscope for the very first time. Life is the single most amazing thing about this remarkable little planet. I hope you will enjoy reading this textbook, but I also hope it will encourage you to study the living things outside your classroom. Who knows? Depending on what you find in that drop of water, you just might grow up to be an explorer, after all!

Ken Miller

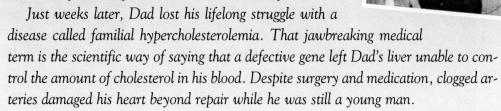

"AH, THOSE WONDERFUL ZOO SMELLS!"

That was my reaction as a child whenever I walked into the elephant house at the Bronx Zoo. The grand old building was well-stocked with awesome animals, but it didn't have much fresh air. While my parents held their noses, I took deep breaths, enjoying the "organic" odors. My father reminded me of this a year ago, when he and I took my two-year-old son to the zoo. We had a great time. I was glad that the elephant house now has better ventilation, because my little boy thinks zoos can be "stinky."

Just weeks later, Dad lost his lifelong struggle with a disease called familial hypercholesterolemia. That jawbreaking medical term is the scientific way of saying that a defective gene left Dad's liver unable to control the amount of cholesterol in his blood. Despite surgery and medication, clogged arteries damaged his heart beyond repair while he was still a young man.

Why do I tell you this? Because finishing this textbook has made me stop to think about how biology has affected me and what it will mean to my son—and to you—in the future. As you'll learn, my brother Daniel and I each had a 50-percent chance of inheriting that bad cholesterol gene from Dad. Unfortunately, we both got it. Happily, we were diagnosed in early childhood and received treatments that Dad never had as a boy. In time, Daniel joined a biomedical team to battle heart disease with his own research. Their findings prolonged Dad's life, offered more years to many other patients, and we hope will keep us around for a while longer, too. Meanwhile, researchers elsewhere are studying a host of other disease-causing genes, including some that may affect you or your family.

But biological links between past and future involve more than genes. Why? Because some human genes enable us to learn and to teach. My father—by encouraging his sons to think for themselves, to ask questions, and to search for answers—planted seeds that grew into a lifelong love of learning. By wandering with us through zoos, in and out of museums, and along hiking trails till his legs ached, he gave us our love of nature. Whenever I take my son to the zoo, read him a book about animals, or write a book myself, I remember that love and respect for life aren't passed from generation to generation by chromosomes.

That's why my part of this textbook has a dual dedication. It is dedicated to you, in the hope that it will help to open your eyes to the joy of a science that can better all our lives, as it helps humanity survive into the future that belongs to my son and to you. And it is dedicated to the best father and grandfather anyone could have—the man who laid the foundation for everything worthwhile that I will ever do.

Joe Levine

UNIT 1

The World of Life

Introducing the Unit

. . . In Words

Albert Einstein (1879–1955) is one of the most important scientists of the twentieth century, and perhaps of all time. Although he is best known for his theory of relativity, he also made many other contributions to science, especially in the field of physics.

Einstein had a strong belief that the universe is one of law and order, and most of his scientific work dealt with trying to understand universal order. This quotation reveals his belief in an ordered world by saying that though the world seems very complex, there is a logic to it that we humans can understand.

- **Would you agree that the world seems incomprehensible? Explain your answer.** (Most students will probably agree.)
- **How can studying science help make the world more comprehensible?** (By studying science, one can gain knowledge about how the world is made up and how it works.)

. . . In Pictures

The common zebra, *Equus burchelli*, is a member of the horse family that lives in herds in deserts and grasslands of eastern and southern Africa. Zebras are herbivores that primarily eat grass. This striking photograph emphasizes the interdependence of organisms. After students have examined the photograph, ask the following questions.

- **What living things do you see in this photograph?** (Zebras and grass.)

UNIT 1

The World of Life

CHAPTERS

“The most incomprehensible thing about the world is that it is comprehensible.”

— Albert Einstein

TEACHER SUPPORT

Unit Discovery Learning Activity

THE LITTLEST BITS OF LIFE

This activity introduces students to cells. In the activity, students observe a variety of types of cells and then make inferences about how cells are alike.

1. Set up six learning stations, each with a microscope. Position one of the following slides on each microscope.

- wet mount of pond water with protozoans
- prepared slide of paramecium
- wet mount of *Spirogyra*
- prepared slide of stem cross section
- prepared slide of human muscle cells
- prepared slide of bacteria

CAREER TRACK

As you explore the topics in this unit, you will discover many different types of careers associated with biology. Here are a few of these careers:

- Biologist
- Respiratory Therapist
- Cytotechnologist
- Biological Technician
- Histologic Technician

Zebras grazing in Africa

2. If necessary, review microscope procedures. Then have students visit each station and observe all slides. Students should make a sketch and take notes about what they observe at each station.
3. After students have visited each station, they should review their sketches and notes and look for common characteristics of all the cells. You may wish to have students work in pairs.
4. Ask students to develop a list of what they think are common characteristics of cells.
5. Discuss students' lists in class, and develop a class list that will be reviewed and revised after students have studied Chapter 3, Cell Structure and Function.

By observing the slides and making inferences about cells, students will be introduced to concepts related to **scale and structure**, one of the themes developed in this unit.

- **How does this photograph illustrate the interdependence of organisms?** (The zebras depend on the grass for food. The grass benefits from nutrients in the zebras' waste products.)
- **What do the zebras obtain when they eat the grass?** (They obtain energy and nutrients from the grass when it is digested.)
- **Why do living things need energy?** (They need energy to grow and to carry on all vital functions of life.)

Point out that in this unit students will learn about the importance of energy to life.

CAREER TRACK

Throughout this unit, you will find a broad range of biology-related careers that vary in educational and training requirements. You may wish to have your students find out more about the following careers:

- Biologist, p. 11
- Respiratory Therapist, p. 38
- Cytotechnologist, p. 50
- Biological Technician, p. 85
- Histologic Technician, p. 113

Technology

BioVue
Life Down Under: Researching a Coral Reef
Videodisc Side 1

Go to Chapter 2

Ancillary Support

The resource below can be used to support your teaching strategy for these two pages.

BL Integrating the Media
Unit Discovery Learning Activity

Chapter 1 The Science of Biology

Content Management	Student Edition Activities
■ Section 1–1 The Characteristics of Life, pp. 3–10 Questions About Life Organisms Coral Biology at Different Levels	**MINI LAB:** Are They Alive?, p. 7 **Laboratory Investigation:** Looking Closely at Living Things, pp. 20–21
■ Section 1–2 The Scientific Method and Biology, pp. 11–15 The Scientific Method Science and Truth Biology and You	**MINI LAB:** The Mystery Box, p. 12
◆ BRANCHING OUT • In Action Section 1–3 The Scientific Method and Yellow Fever, pp. 16–19 The Fight Against Yellow Fever Reed's Experiment	**MINI LAB:** A Moldy Question, p. 17

■ These sections cover all the necessary content and concepts for a basic course in biology.
◆ This section covers content and concepts that are either applications or extensions of the basic material.

Integration Strategies

SE Careers, p. 7
Earth Science, p. 10
Social Studies, p. 16
Social Studies p. 19

BL Investigating Careers Involving the Community
Science Through Art

Tech Prep

Teaching strategies appropriate for students who are in technical/vocational programs or who are considering post-secondary technical education can be found on the following **TE** pages: 11 and 16.

Assessment Strategies

SE Chapter Review, pp. 22–25
TR Section Reviews
Chapter Test
Performance-Based Assessment
BL Investigating Further
Chapter Review
Practice Test
CTB Chapter 1 Test

Meeting the Standards

Section 1–1 covers one of the six content standards under **The Cell** and Sections 1–1 and 1–3 cover one of the five content standards under **The Interdependence of Organisms** as described on pages 184 and 186, respectively, of The National Science Education Standards.

Chapter Planning Guide

Teacher's Edition Activities	Other Activities	Media and Technology
Chapter Discovery Learning Activity, p. 2 **Inquiry Activity:** What Makes a Living Thing Alive?, p. 4 **Investigate:** Research, p. 6 **Investigate:** Cooperative Learning, p. 8	**LM** Observing the Characteristics of Living Things, #1 Identifying Life on Earth, #2 **TR** **Apply:** Acorns to Oak Trees **BL** **Inquiry Activity:** A Question of Science	**BioVue Mini Doc:** Just What Is Life Anyway?, Videodisc Side 1 **BioVue Plus CD-ROMs:** Life Down Under: Researching a Coral Reef **CD-ROM:** Biology: The Study of Life
Inquiry Activity: A Method of Investigation, p. 11	**TR** **Writing in Biology:** Connecting to Your Environment **Enrich:** The Dawn of Modern Science **BL** **Inquiry Activity:** Science Sleuth	**BioVue Mini Doc:** The Scientific Method, Videodisc Side 1 **BioVue Plus CD-ROMs:** The Scientific Method **TB** The Compound Microscope, #1
Inquiry Activity: Testing a Hypothesis, p. 16 **Investigate:** Research, p. 18	**TR** **Explore:** Follow the Bouncing Ball **BL** **Inquiry Activity:** Sink or Swim	

KEY: **SE** Student Edition **TE** Teacher's Edition **LM** Laboratory Manual **TR** Teaching Resources **BL** BioLog **TB** Transparency Box **CTB** Computer Test Bank

Materials List

TE Chapter Discovery Learning Activity, p. 2 (20 minutes); pictures of natural environments.
TE Inquiry Activity: What Makes a Living Thing Alive?, p. 4 (20 minutes); watch or clock with second hand, a living animal such as a fish or insect.
SE MINI LAB: Are They Alive?, p. 7 (20 minutes); various substances students might not immediately recognize as being living or nonliving, hand lenses.
SE MINI LAB: The Mystery Box, p. 12 (20 minutes); closed boxes with various partition arrangements, marbles.
SE MINI LAB: A Moldy Question, p. 17 (1 week); slices of bread, various plates and containers.

CHAPTER 1

The Science of Biology

Introducing the Chapter

. . . In Pictures

A flock of cedar waxwings—crested, brownish birds found in open woodlands throughout much of the United States—inhabits the branches of a mountain ash tree. The organisms shown in this photograph represent the living things on Earth and their interactions that are the object of biologists' studies. Several of the characteristics of living things that students will learn about in this chapter are apparent in this photograph.

• **What characteristics do birds and trees have in common that make them both living things?** (Accept all reasonable responses, including that they both grow and develop and reproduce.)

• **In what ways might biologists study these living things?** (Students might suggest various levels of study, from the cellular to the interaction of the organisms.)

Teaching Strategy

In the first two sections of this chapter, students will learn about the characteristics of living things and about the method scientists use to investigate biological questions. Use the BRANCHING OUT section at the end of the chapter as a case study of the scientific method in action.

CHAPTER 1

The Science of Biology

FOCUSING THE CHAPTER
THEME: Scale and Structure

1–1 The Characteristics of Life
- Identify the characteristics of life.

1–2 The Scientific Method and Biology
- Explain the procedures of the scientific method.

BRANCHING OUT *In Action*

1–3 The Scientific Method and Yellow Fever
- Give an example of how the scientific method is applied.

LABORATORY INVESTIGATION
- Observe a living thing and identify its characteristics.

Biology and Your World

BIO JOURNAL

In your journal, describe the living things you see in the photographs on this page and the next page. How are these living things alike? How are they different?

Cedar waxwings on a mountain ash

2 Chapter 1

BIO JOURNAL

The Bio Journal topic can be used to stimulate classroom discussion about life on Earth and about the characteristics of living things. Ask students to consider the great variety of living things and the characteristics that make each one alive. Instruct students to keep their entries in their portfolios.

TEACHER SUPPORT — Chapter Discovery Learning Activity

Display several pictures of natural environments that show a variety of organisms, including various plants and animals. These pictures might be of a rain forest or a lagoon, both of which are environments that contain a diversity of life. After students have completed the Bio Journal activity, ask them to choose one of the pictures to examine closely. Then have each student compile a list of 20 questions a biologist might ask about the organisms in the picture. Explain that these questions could concern anything from the atomic level to the global level.

The Characteristics of Life

Guide for Reading

- **Identify** five characteristics of living things.
- **Describe** the different levels of questions that biologists ask.

MINI LAB

- **Predict** whether a sample is living or nonliving.

WE LIVE IN A REMARKABLE place, and we live in remarkable times. Our home, the Earth, is unlike any other planet that orbits the sun. The Earth is the only planet with great oceans of liquid water. It is the only planet surrounded by an atmosphere that is rich in oxygen. And it has something else that may not exist on any other planet: The Earth has life.

No matter where you live—city, farm, small town, or suburb—life is all around you. In fact, it is almost impossible to think of a single place on Earth that is not a home to living things. Life is found in golden grasslands, scorching deserts, deep oceans, and even the frozen wastes of the Antarctic.

It's often easy to think that life is the most ordinary thing in the world. However, life is far from simple or ordinary. As you study the living things of the world, you will come to appreciate their special qualities all the more.

Questions About Life

Why do many trees and other plants sprout leaves in spring and lose them in autumn? How does a bird learn to fly and to build a nest? Why are there so many kinds of insects, and why are they so different from one another?

If every now and then you have asked a question about something you have seen in the world of living things, you have taken the first step toward understanding that world. What steps should you take next? The curiosity that makes you human really leaves you with only one choice—to try to answer the questions you ask.

Figure 1–1 The Earth is home to an enormous number of living things—from (a) fishes in the oceans to (b) penguins in Antarctica to (c) hippopotamuses in Africa.

SECTION 1–1

The Characteristics of Life

Performance Objectives

- Discuss the characteristics of living things.
- Explain the levels on which biologists study living things.

Mini Lab Skill: Predicting
Laboratory Investigation Skill: Observing

1 ENGAGE

Ideas Through Images

Have students examine Figure 1–1, read the caption, and answer the following questions.

- **What characteristics do hippopotamuses, penguins, and fishes have in common?** (Students may mention that all three are animals, are made up of cells, move about through the environment, eat to gain energy, and reproduce. Accept all logical responses.)
- **What other types of living things are found on Earth?** (Students may mention plants, various protists, bacteria, algae, fungi.)
- **What characteristics do those organisms have in common with the animals shown in Figure 1–1?** (Most students should mention cellular structure, reproduction, and an interaction between organism and environment.)

TEACHER SUPPORT

Managing Classroom Diversity

LEP STUDENTS
Make sure students understand the hierarchy implied in the sequence of sections that address questions biologists ask: chemical, molecular, cellular, organism, population, global. Have students use a dictionary to clarify the meaning of those terms. Ask students to make a drawing that could represent relationships among the terms, such as a series of larger and larger circles.

GIFTED STUDENTS
Ask students to investigate the work of the type of biologist who generally addresses questions at each level, beginning with a biochemist asking questions on a chemical level.

Technology

BioVue
Mini Doc: Just What Is Life, Anyway?
Videodisc Side 1

Go to Chapter 15

2 EXPLORE

Inquiry Activity

Comparing

What Makes a Living Thing Alive?

Allow students to examine two objects: a watch or clock with a working second hand and an active living animal such as a fish or an insect. Ask them to compare the two, noting similarities and differences. Have students write a paragraph explaining what makes one object alive and the other object not.

3 TEACH

Laboratory Investigation

The Laboratory Investigation, Looking Closely at Living Things, on pages 20–21 is appropriate to use at this point in the chapter.

Ideas Through Images

Have students examine Figure 1–2, read the caption, and answer the following questions.

- **What characteristics of life do these organisms exhibit?** (Although these are still photographs, students may say that the mite and the sequoia tree contain cells, respond to their environment, and grow.)
- **How are these two living things similar? How are they different?** (They are similar because they are living things. They are different in that the mite is an animal and the tree is a plant. They also differ in size and shape.)

Biology as a Science

For most of human history, the laws and forces of nature were great mysteries. In the last few centuries, however, much of that has changed. Thanks to human curiosity and intelligence, we have developed a remarkable process of thinking and learning about the world around us. This process is called **science.** As you know, there are many fields of science, each of which tries to explain one aspect of our world. **Biology,** the science of life, is the subject of this textbook.

What Is Life?

Is something "alive" simply because it can move? The answer is not so simple! Cars move, but you would not consider a car to be alive. And plants are not as mobile as animals, yet plants are alive. So just what are the characteristics of life?

The answer to this question is not an easy one—even for the experts. Especially because of viruses and certain other things found in nature, biologists find it very difficult to draw an exact line between living and nonliving things. However, we can list five basic characteristics that are common to all living things. **Living things are made of cells, grow and develop, obtain and use energy, respond to their environment, and are able to reproduce.** These characteristics are described in detail in the illustrations on the next page.

You may be able to think of a few other characteristics that describe living things. In fact, you may even be able to think of nonliving things that have some of the characteristics of life just listed. For example, how many of these characteristics does a copying machine have?

☑ *Checkpoint* What are five characteristics of living things? 1

Organisms

An individual living thing is called an **organism.** You are an organism, as is each animal and plant. Many organisms, such as redwood trees, are so big you just can't miss seeing them. However, we are also surrounded by billions of organisms that are so small their existence wasn't even suspected until microscopes were invented less than 400 years ago.

As you study one type of organism after another in your biology course, try to see how each one meets the five characteristics of life that we just presented. Let's take a close look at one interesting organism to better understand these characteristics.

☑ *Checkpoint* What is an organism? 2

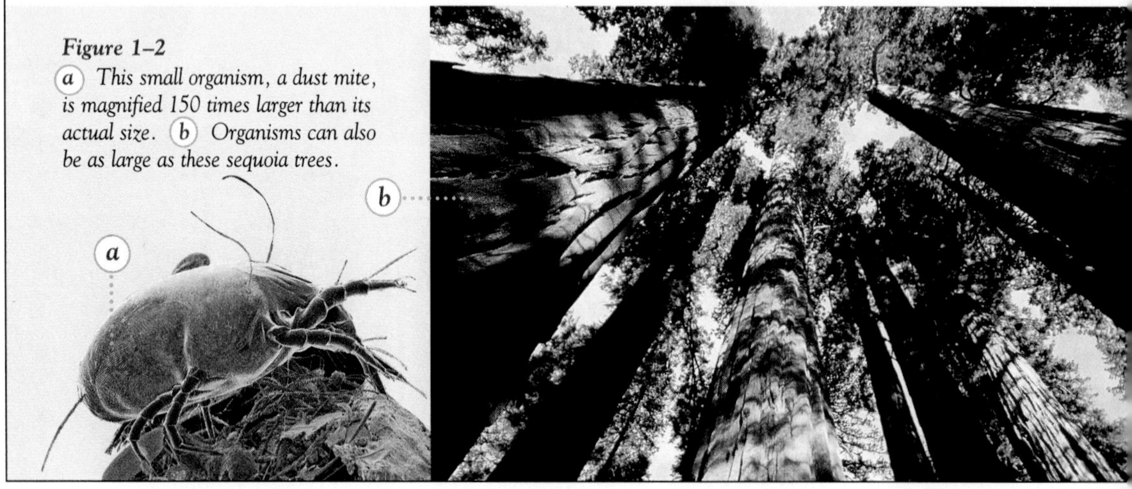

Figure 1–2
(a) This small organism, a dust mite, is magnified 150 times larger than its actual size. (b) Organisms can also be as large as these sequoia trees.

TEACHER SUPPORT

Historical Perspective

Although the word biology was not used until the early nineteenth century, the science of life has a history of thousands of years. Alcmaeon, a Greek physician born in about 535 BC, is the first known to have studied the human body in a scientific way. He discovered the optic nerve, and he speculated that the brain was the center of intellectual activity. Aristotle, a Greek born in 384 BC, was a meticulous observer of living things, and he classified over 500 animal species in a strict hierarchy. He even proposed a theory of progressive change among animals—an early suggestion of evolution.

Visualizing the Characteristics of Living Things

How do living things differ from nonliving things? In some cases, answering this question is not so easy! However, we can list five basic characteristics of all living things.

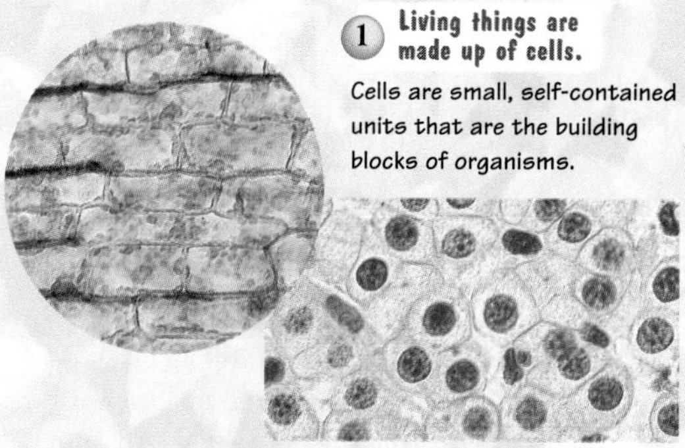

1 Living things are made up of cells.
Cells are small, self-contained units that are the building blocks of organisms.

2 Living things obtain and use energy.
Most plants obtain energy directly from the sun, whereas most animals get energy from chemical compounds in their food.

5 Living things can reproduce.
Living things produce new living things of the same type. Although a living thing does not need to reproduce in order to survive, life would quickly die out without reproduction.

3 Living things respond to their environment.
Anything in an organism's environment that causes it to react is called a stimulus. Organisms typically react in ways that keep their bodies suitable for life—a process called homeostasis.

4 Living things grow and develop.
An organism grows and develops by absorbing raw materials and processing them into new tissues and structures.

Visualizing the Characteristics of Living Things

These five characteristics are broad enough to include the great diversity of life on Earth, from the 2700 known bacterial species to the more than 1.5 million named animal species. Because viruses don't fully exhibit any of these characteristics, they are not usually considered living things.

Use the Visualizing feature to begin a discussion about how a variety of plants and animals exhibit the five characteristics of living things. Ask students how an oak tree, for example, obtains and uses energy. Through the discussion, emphasize these points.

- Responding to the environment includes an organism's reacting to a stimulus such as light but it also includes a population's adapting to a changing environment.
- Obtaining and using energy includes the intake of nutrients, the processing of those nutrients within cells, and the elimination of wastes.

Checkpoints

1. Living things are made of cells, grow and develop, obtain and use energy, respond to their environment, and are able to reproduce.
2. An organism is any individual living thing.

TEACHER SUPPORT

Facts and Figures

The largest animal alive is the blue whale, which can be as long as 30 meters and weigh as much as 130 metric tons—the equivalent of 30 elephants. The largest living thing, shown in Figure 1–2, is the giant sequoia, which can reach heights of well over 100 meters. The smallest living thing is a type of bacteria known as *Mycoplasma*, which can be almost as small as 1000 nanometers in length. Viruses can be 100 times smaller, but they are not considered living things. The smallest protozoans are about 1000 nanometers, or 1 micron, in length.

Ancillary Support

The resources below can be used to support your teaching strategy for these two pages.

LM Observing the Characteristics of Living Things, #1
TR Apply: Acorns to Oak Trees

Ideas Through Images

Have students examine Figures 1–3 and 1–4, read the captions, and answer the following questions.

- **How would you describe the coral animals shown in the photographs?** (Students might suggest that the corals look like branches of a plant or a textured mound. Make sure students understand that individual coral animals are shown in Figure 1–4. They live in colonies and form the hard, plantlike or moundlike structures that they live in.)
- **Since you know that corals are living things, what characteristics must they have?** (They must be made up of cells, obtain and use energy, reproduce, respond to their environment, and grow and develop.)

Investigate

Research Ask a group of students to investigate the ecology of coral reefs, including their development and location in the world's oceans, the variety of organisms associated with coral reefs, and the threat to such ecosystems from ocean pollution. Students could prepare a report or construct a collage or model of a coral reef.

Correcting Misconceptions

Many students may have the misconception that a characteristic of all animals is the ability to move around. Point out that corals, like some other marine invertebrates, remain stationary and depend on ocean currents to bring nutrients to them.

Figure 1–3
Corals are found in shallow ocean waters—as here off the coast of Florida. Coral is alive because it exhibits the five characteristics of living things.

Coral

The Florida Keys are a chain of small islands that reach into the waters of the Caribbean Sea off the southern coast of Florida. The waters around the islands are warm and inviting, and many visitors enjoy swimming in the shallow areas near the shoreline. It is in these warm, shallow waters that divers encounter a stunning sight—great branches and colorful mounds that look like underwater forests from a fantasy world.

What are these branches and mounds? They are small organisms called coral, and they inhabit warm, shallow waters in oceans around the world. Corals form great clusters called coral reefs. In fact, some coral reefs are so large that they form whole islands.

Why Coral Is Alive

How do we know that coral is alive? First, look very closely at the surface of a coral, as shown in ***Figure 1–4.*** In this photograph, you can see tiny tentacles waving in the passing currents. What makes up these tentacles? Through a high-powered microscope, you could see that they are made up of individual units called cells—an important characteristic of living things.

Next, as anyone who lives near a coral reef will tell you, a coral reef grows from year to year as its branches and mounds become larger. Corals also obtain and use energy, and they respond to

Figure 1–4
If you could magnify this photograph of orange clump coral, you would discover that it is made of cells—evidence that orange clump coral is alive.

TEACHER SUPPORT

Background Information

Reef-building corals have a mutualistic relationship with a type of green algae, zooxanthella, which lives within the coral tissue. The algae help in the process that results in the formation of the calcium-carbonate (lime) skeleton that creates the reef. Conditions conducive to reef building include warm, shallow waters where a constant flow of water carries food to the waiting coral tentacles. The optimum water temperature is about 27°C; the maximum depth is about 150 m. There are about 700 coral reefs known in the world. About 600 of those are found in a region bounded by Indonesia, Malaysia, the Philippines, and southern Japan.

their environment. A coral's tentacles react to the presence of food particles in the passing water by capturing them. Then the coral uses the energy from the food to move and maintain its body.

The last characteristic on our list—the ability to reproduce—is also true of corals. From all these observations, then, we can state without a doubt that coral is alive.

☑ *Checkpoint* Why is coral alive? ❶

A Living Colony

Coral is not just a single organism but exists as a colony of thousands of individual organisms. Some of these coral organisms produce an intricate supporting skeleton of calcium carbonate, a material also found in bones. Throughout its life, coral builds up larger and larger amounts of calcium carbonate. When it dies, a new coral grows directly on the remains. In this way, the coral colony gets larger and larger over time.

Biology at Different Levels

Deciding whether something is alive is only the first step in trying to understand it. As a biologist, you must also decide where to begin to ask questions. Living things can be studied on many levels, and a biologist will ask different types of questions, depending on the size and scale of what is being studied. Let's take a look at the different levels of questions that might be asked about coral.

Questions at the Chemical Level

What are the chemical compounds that make up the coral and its skeleton? What other chemical compounds are found in a coral's body? Questions like these are asked in the field of biochemistry, an important branch of biology. A biochemist might seek to learn how the coral animals obtain calcium from sea water or how they process calcium into calcium carbonate. ●

Questions at the Molecular Level

Every organism contains a variety of molecules, which are fundamental units of matter. Like other animals, a coral contains specialized molecules that regulate its growth and development, that help it to break down food and to eliminate waste, and that give shape and texture to its body.

MINI LAB ······ **Predicting** ······

Are They Alive?

PROBLEM *How can you predict whether something is living or nonliving?*

PROCEDURE

1. Obtain a set of five unidentified samples from your teacher.
2. Carefully inspect each sample—both with the unaided eye and with a magnifying glass. You may also touch the samples. **CAUTION:** *Do not taste them.* Record your observations.
3. For each sample, predict whether the sample is composed of living or nonliving things. Give reasons for each prediction.

ANALYZE AND CONCLUDE

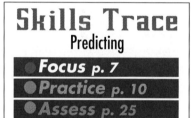

1. From your results, is it possible to determine whether each sample is living or nonliving? Explain.
2. What further questions do you have about each sample? What answers would you expect if the sample was alive? If it was not alive?
3. Ask your teacher to identify the samples. How accurate were your predictions? Which characteristic of living things proved most helpful in classifying your samples?

INTEGRATING CAREERS

Visit the library to discover more about biochemists and their work.

MINI LAB **Predicting**

Teacher Notes

- For time required and materials needed, see page 2b.
- Ask students what are some characteristics of living things.

Answers to Analyze and Conclude

1. Students may not be able to conclusively determine whether their samples met some of the characteristics of life, including cell composition and the ability to reproduce. For many samples, students may be able to formulate only a reasonable guess as to whether the sample is alive.
2. Accept all logical responses.
3. Accept all logical responses.

Skills Trace
Predicting
- Focus p. 7
- Practice p. 10
- Assess p. 25

INTEGRATING CAREERS

Biochemists conduct research, analyses, syntheses, and experimentation on substances. They analyze organic and inorganic compounds to determine chemical and physical properties. All biochemists have a bachelor's degree, with a major in biology or biochemistry; most go on to earn an advanced degree as they specialize in the field.

☑ **Checkpoint**

❶ Coral is alive because it satisfies the five characteristics of living things.

TEACHER SUPPORT

Ecology Note

Among marine environments, coral reefs have the greatest diversity of living things (and are second in diversity only to tropical rain forests among all environments). As many as 3000 species can be found living together on a southeast Asian reef; about 1000 species might be found on a single Caribbean reef. In addition to the corals and their associated algae, the reefs are home to a great variety of other algae as well as fishes, crustaceans, sponges, sea urchins, and many other invertebrates. Mollusks, including giant clams and octopuses, are even more abundant than fish. In addition, the ocean water around a coral reef is rich in phytoplankton because the reef structure helps concentrate necessary nutrients.

Ancillary Support

The resource below can be used to support your teaching strategy for these two pages.

LM Identifying Life on Earth, #2

Ideas Through Images

Have students examine Figure 1–6, read the caption, and answer the following questions.

- **In what way does a coral goby depend on the coral animals of a coral reef?** (The fish depends on the corals for food and protection.)
- **If the population of corals declined for some reason, what would probably happen to the population of this type of fish?** (Its population would be likely to decline as well.)

Discussion

Ask students which level of question is the most important for an understanding of living things. After several students have expressed opinions, guide them to the concept that no level is more important than any other, and that a full knowledge of life on Earth demands that questions on every level be asked and explored.

Investigate

Cooperative Learning To help students understand that scientists are not the only ones who can conduct scientific investigations, have students get into groups and play a game of 20 questions in which they think of familiar plants and animals. Have one student in each group think of a certain living organism. Then have the members of the group ask 20 yes-or-no questions to find out what the organism is.

Figure 1–5
The size of chemical compounds and molecules such as calcium carbonate ($CaCO_3$) and DNA is measured in tiny units called nanometers. The period at the end of this sentence is about 500,000 nanometers in diameter.

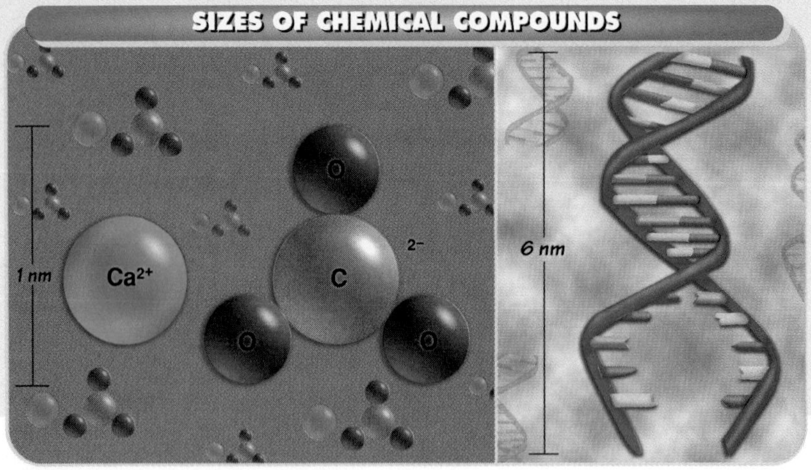

What are these molecules? How are they made? How do they work? A molecular biologist asks questions such as these.

Questions at the Cellular Level

How are coral cells organized, and how do they interact? Like all organisms with many cells, coral grows when cells divide to produce new cells. How does this process take place? Why are new cells sometimes different from their parents? Cell biologists specialize in studying questions at the cellular level.

Questions at the Organism Level

What controls the rate at which coral reproduces? How does one type of coral differ from another? Did coral exist hundreds of millions of years ago? Most species of coral contain single-celled green organisms called algae. What are algae doing in coral?

Many types of biologists would be interested in questions at this level. Paleontologists, who study ancient life, might wonder how coral has changed over time. Ecologists, who study the relationships among different types of organisms, would be interested in the relationship between coral and algae.

Questions at the Population Level

When thousands of coral animals form a coral reef, they begin to interact with their environment in interesting and important ways. Coral reefs provide homes for hundreds of other organisms, including sponges, seaweeds, and an enormous variety of fishes.

How do coral reefs affect these and other marine organisms? When the population of one kind of animal rises, is the population of another kind of animal affected? Ecologists and population biologists study questions such as these.

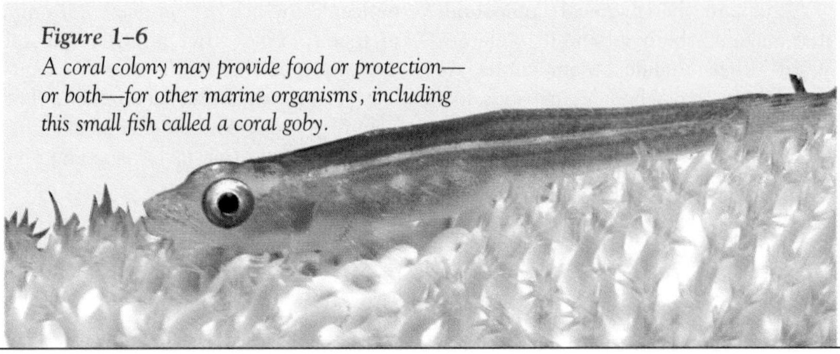

Figure 1–6
A coral colony may provide food or protection—or both—for other marine organisms, including this small fish called a coral goby.

TEACHER SUPPORT

Ecology Note

Coral reefs provide a variety of habitats for some 5000 different types of fish worldwide, from the waves on the crest of the reef to the calm water of the lagoon that forms on the opposite side of the reef from the open sea. The coral goby, which can be less than 1 centimeter in length, is one of the smallest of known fish. The goby, as well as other types of small fish, finds protection in the coral's tentacles from larger predator fish, including sharks and barracudas. Relationships within the reef environment can be even more complex. For example, the coral reef provides a home for sea urchins, which are spiny echinoderms. Little shrimpfish are often found swimming head down among the sea urchins' spines, and in that way they are protected from larger predator fish.

Biology and Earth Science Connections

As Lifeless as a Grain of Sand?

Spread on the sunscreen and break out the blankets and the beach balls—it's time for a day at the beach! On a hot summer afternoon, a clean, sandy beach is a great place to relax and have fun. It's also a good place to ask questions. Where does beach sand come from? Why does beach sand come in different colors and textures? What keeps many beaches clean and attractive? As you will see, there's more to beaches than meets the eye!

Beach Sand

In many cases, beach sand comes from the silt and other materials that rivers carry with them to an ocean or large lake. But sand comes from other places as well. White sand comes from the remnants of countless numbers of marine organisms. Black sand, which can be found on islands in the Pacific Ocean, was originally lava flows from volcanoes.

Yet whatever its origin, beach sand acquires its texture and consistency from the waves that repeatedly pound and weather it. Given enough time, waves will grind even the rockiest coastline into stretches of finely ground particles.

Biology at the Beach

Certainly, an earth scientist can find much to investigate in the sand at the beach. But is the sand also of interest to a biologist? You may be surprised to learn that the answer is yes.

A handful of sand may contain as many as 10,000 creatures living on the surfaces of the grains! These creatures include tiny worms, mites, miniature shellfish, and even organisms so strange and unique that biologists have had to place them in their own phylum (a special category) of the animal kingdom. Biologists are discovering dozens of new creatures in beach sand every year.

What do these creatures do? The same things that animals do everywhere: They search for food, fight battles with predators, and reproduce their own kind—only on what you might consider to be a very small scale!

Any Dangers?

Does the presence of so many strange, tiny creatures mean that you should stay away from the beach? No, not at all. In fact, the cleanest and most attractive beaches seem to have the greatest numbers of these tiny animals. They cruise the surfaces of sand grains, scouring for algae and bacteria and removing organic wastes. You may not realize they are there, but their secret kingdom is the key to the glistening beaches that you enjoy.

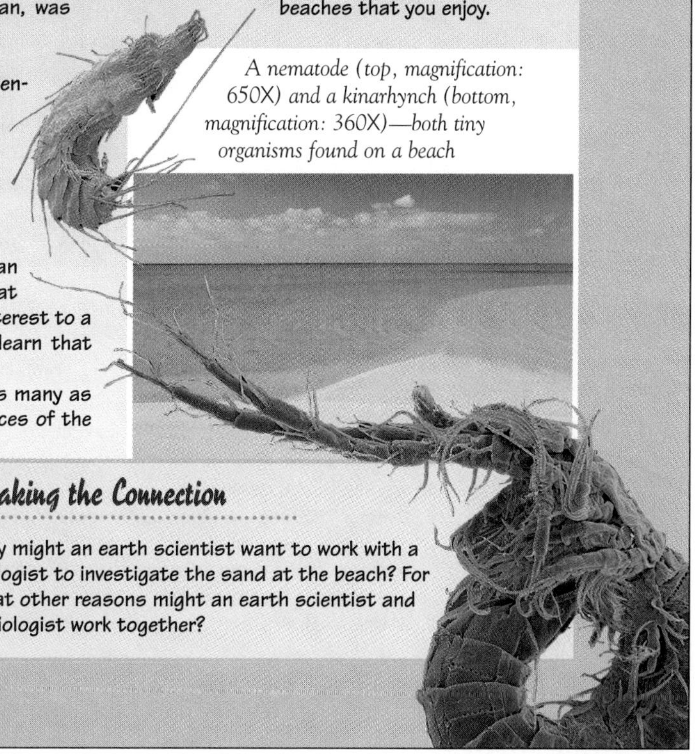

A nematode (top, magnification: 650X) and a kinarhynch (bottom, magnification: 360X)—both tiny organisms found on a beach

Making the Connection

Why might an earth scientist want to work with a biologist to investigate the sand at the beach? For what other reasons might an earth scientist and a biologist work together?

Connections

The creatures that live in this beach environment are known as meiofauna, or "lesser animals," because of their size. They were first discovered in the 1920s, and biologists have been finding more kinds of meiofauna ever since.

Meiofauna exist in many different shapes, but most have these characteristics in common: (1) a shape that lets them squeeze through the holes in the sand grain, (2) some sort of gripping mechanism (including suction toes and special adhesive organs) to keep them from being washed out into the sea, (3) shells or scales for protection, and (4) a transparent body.

Answer to Making the Connection

Working together, an earth scientist and a biologist might investigate how a beach affects the organisms that live on it or how organisms affect the beach. They might also work together to determine the effects of climate and other types of soil on living things.

Teacher Support: Background Information

A beach consists of sediment deposited by ocean waves along the wave-cut bench of the shoreline. The beach composition depends on the source of the sediment, such as eroded material from coastal mountains or the material carried into the sea by nearby rivers. Where there are no mountains or other rocky features nearby—such as in Florida—the beach sediment, or sand, consists mostly of shell fragments and the remains of microscopic protists, especially foraminifera. The sizes of the sand particles depend both on the origin of the material and the age of the beach; the older the beach, the smaller the grains of sand.

Ancillary Support

The resource below can be used to support your teaching strategy for these two pages.

BL Inquiry Activity: A Question of Science

Section 1–1 (continued)

INTEGRATING EARTH SCIENCE

A tremendous variety of organisms is found in the ocean, from the microscopic to the largest animal in the world (the blue whale). Other forms of life on Earth depend on the health of these organisms, especially the phytoplankton, whose photosynthesis affects the composition of Earth's atmosphere.

4 ASSESS

Quick Check

Ask students to write one question for each of the levels discussed on pages 7–10. Have them write these questions about the organisms described in the Connections feature on page 9.

Section Review 1-1

1. Living things are made of cells, grow and develop, obtain and use energy, respond to their environment, and are able to reproduce.
2. Biologists ask questions at the chemical, molecular, organism, population, and global levels.
3. Coral is alive because it has the five characteristics of living things.
4. Yes, attending this conference could help a biochemist's research. While biochemists are principally interested in life at the chemical level, all levels of biology are interconnected. Chemical changes in frogs and toads could conceivably be caused by pollution, the damaged ozone layer, or other global events.
5. Living things should exhibit each of the characteristics of life. For some living things, however, not all the characteristics are readily apparent. For example, a seed may take a long time to respond to its environment, and it will respond only under precise conditions.

Skills Trace

Predicting

- Focus p. 7
- Practice p. 10
- Assess p. 25

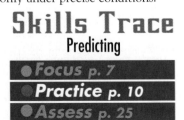

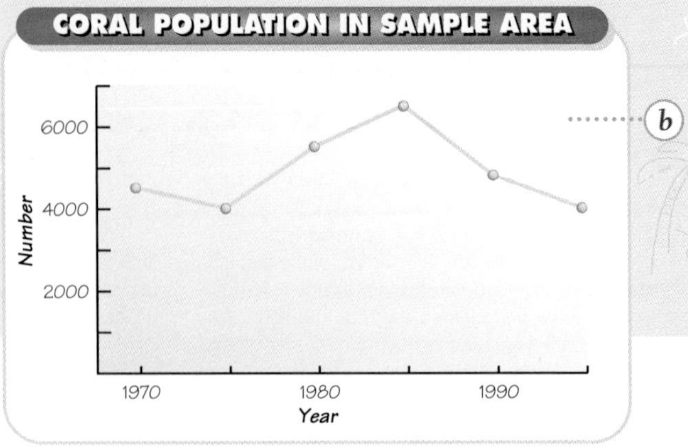

Figure 1–7
(a) *Although you cannot see any individual coral organisms in this photograph of southern Florida, the organisms are there nevertheless. Coral, like every other organism, can be studied at the global level.* (b) *A population biologist might study how the numbers of coral organisms change over time.*

INTEGRATING EARTH SCIENCE

What types of organisms are found in oceans? Why is the health of these organisms important?

Questions at the Global Level

Many biologists take a worldwide view of biology, asking questions about organisms and their environment on a global scale. Is coral a global concern? Indeed, it is.

In fact, a coral reef is the largest and most spectacular structure on the whole planet that living things assemble. The Great Barrier Reef, which is found along the coast of northern Australia, is more than 2000 kilometers long and more than 100 kilometers wide in some areas. Because coral is affected by a delicate balance of temperature, minerals, and chemicals in ocean water, it may serve as an indicator of the overall health of Earth's oceans—home to so much life on our planet. ●

Asking questions on so many levels makes biology a very broad subject. A single living thing—a coral, for example, or a fish or a human—can interest any number of different biologists asking all sorts of different questions. Taken together, the results of their efforts provide us with as complete a view as possible of life on Earth.

Section Review 1–1

1. **Identify** the five characteristics of living things.
2. **Describe** the different levels of organization at which biologists ask questions.
3. Is coral alive? **Explain** your answer.
4. **Critical Thinking—Making Judgments** You are a biochemist studying chemicals in frogs and toads. You just received an invitation to a conference on pollution, the damaged ozone layer, and other global concerns. Could attending this conference help your research? Explain your answer.
5. **MINI LAB** How can you **predict** whether something is living or nonliving?

Learning Modality

Auditory Learning Ask students to choose a natural area in their region with which they are fairly familiar. Then ask a variety of questions a biologist might address when studying that area. Have students evaluate each question according to the different levels of questions discussed in the section.

The Scientific Method and Biology

GUIDE FOR READING

- **Define** the scientific method.
- **Describe** the steps of the scientific method.
- **Compare** a hypothesis and a theory.

MINI LAB

- **Formulate a hypothesis** based on observations.

HUMANS ARE ALWAYS ASKING questions about the world around them. But once we pose a question, the next step is to decide on how to go about answering it. Although this may sound difficult, it is something that people do automatically every day.

People often answer their questions about life by thinking about their everyday experiences. However, science demands that questions be answered by the use of a precise method. In this section, you'll discover just what that method is.

The Scientific Method

The precise method used by scientists is called the **scientific method,** and it separates science from other ways of studying and learning. **The scientific method is a system of asking questions, developing explanations, and testing those explanations against the reality of the natural world.**

Other fields—such as art, music, history, and philosophy—all have a great deal to tell us about the world. But although each is important and deserving of careful study, none of them uses the scientific method, which means that none of them is a field of science.

Figure 1–8
The scientific method has been applied to answer all sorts of different questions—and to solve a huge variety of problems. (a) *In 1928, Scottish biologist Alexander Fleming used the scientific method to discover penicillin, the first drug to fight infections effectively.*
(b) CAREER TRACK *This biologist is measuring an unusually large flower on the island of Borneo.*

TEACHER SUPPORT

Managing Classroom Diversity

LEP STUDENTS
Students may have difficulty understanding the concept of a scientific theory. Make sure they understand how the term theory differs from the way it is often used in common speech. Ask them to look up the word in a dictionary, and then discuss the different ways it is used.

TECH PREP STUDENTS
Point out that students who plan careers in biotechnology will often be participating in the third step of the scientific method—that of experimentation. A lab technician, for instance, might check blood or tissue samples in order to support a medical hypothesis.

SECTION 1–2

The Scientific Method and Biology

Performance Objectives

- Explain the scientific method and identify its steps.
- Recognize the difference between a hypothesis and a theory.

Mini Lab Skill: Hypothesizing

1 ENGAGE

Inquiry Activity

Experimenting

A Method of Investigation

Have students consider the question of how deep in the ocean a coral reef can develop. Biologists do not find coral reefs on the deep ocean floor. In fact, a depth of 150 meters is about the greatest depth at which a reef will develop because of the lack of sunlight at greater depths. Ask students to develop a method they could use to test whether 150 meters is the limit. Have them write a series of steps a scientist could follow to check the validity of that statement.

Technology

BioVue
Mini Doc: The Scientific Method
Videodisc Side 1

Go to Chapter 10

Ancillary Support

The resource below can be used to support your teaching strategy for these two pages.

TB The Compound Microscope, #1

2 EXPLORE

MINI LAB Hypothesizing

Teacher Notes

• For time required and materials needed, see page 2b.
• Number the boxes and make a sketch of the partition arrangement for each box.

Answers to Analyze and Conclude

1. The contents of the mystery box can only be inferred from indirect evidence. Regardless of the evidence supporting a hypothesis, it must be tested in a controlled experiment to be considered valid.
2. Students might suggest constructing their own model of the box and its partitions, using their hypothesis as a guide.

Skills Trace
Hypothesizing
- Focus p. 12
- Practice p. 15
- Assess p. 25

3 TEACH

Discussion

Begin a class discussion about the steps in the scientific method. Through the discussion, emphasize the following points.
• Scientific investigations always begin with observations of the natural world. From those observations, hypotheses are proposed.
• Hypotheses often are proven untrue, and that is part of the purpose of experimentation.

MINI LAB .... Hypothesizing ....

The Mystery Box

PROBLEM *What is inside the mystery box? **Formulate a hypothesis.***

PROCEDURE

1. Obtain a mystery box from your instructor. The box contains a unique arrangement of partitions and one or more marbles.
2. Tilt, turn, and tap the box to move the marbles inside. The sounds and sensations provide clues to the arrangement of partitions inside the box.
3. On a sheet of paper, sketch your hypothesis of how the partitions are arranged inside the mystery box.

ANALYZE AND CONCLUDE

1. How certain can you be of your hypothesis? Explain your answer.
2. Without opening the mystery box, what further tests might you perform to verify your hypothesis?

The Steps of the Scientific Method

The biologist Claude Villée once described the scientific method as "organized common sense," and that's a good description. No matter how complex science may seem, at its heart is an organized system of asking and answering questions.

In practice, scientists apply the scientific method in a number of different ways. However, a formal version of the scientific method can be described as a series of steps:

- First, state a specific problem or question based on observations of the natural world. Sometimes the most important questions become clear only after you have learned a great deal of information about the problem you are investigating.
- With that problem in mind, propose a **hypothesis.** A hypothesis is a possible explanation, a preliminary conclusion, or even a guess at the solution to your problem.
- Next, test the hypothesis. Sometimes the test involves gathering more observations to see if they are consistent with the hypothesis. In other cases, it is possible to set up a controlled test, or **experiment,** to check the hypothesis. The best hypotheses allow scientists to make clear predictions about the results of experiments.
- Finally, analyze the experimental results and draw conclusions. Sometimes the results are so clear-cut that you can say the hypothesis is either correct or incorrect. Other times the results suggest new hypotheses that, in turn, require new experiments.

When you are sure of your results, there is another step that you may need to take. This final step is to repeat the experiment to make sure that your results are reliable. Experiments are often complicated, and careful scientists want to make sure that their results hold true whenever the experiment is performed. If your experiment gives different results on repeated trials, then you should try to find out what is influencing your results.

☑ ***Checkpoint*** What is the scientific method? (1)

In the Garden

Is the scientific method a complex technique that only scientists can use? In fact, people use the scientific method every day. No special training is required—just a bit of common sense.

For example, suppose you grow tomatoes in a small garden. Each spring you plant 20 seedlings, and by autumn you have usually harvested 50 to 60 tomatoes. But last spring, following your

TEACHER SUPPORT

Historical Perspective

Galileo Galilei (1564–1642) is generally considered to have established the modern scientific method, as demonstrated in his famous investigation of falling bodies at the Leaning Tower of Pisa, Italy. According to legend, he simultaneously dropped from the tower two cannon balls—one 10 times heavier than the other. When he observed that they struck the ground at the same time, he concluded that all objects fall at the same rate regardless of weight. His emphasis on experimentation as the way to prove the validity of ideas was part of the broader movement of free thought and skepticism that was characteristic of the European Renaissance.

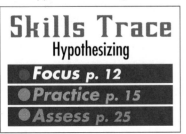

neighbor's advice, you mixed 5 kilograms of fertilizer into the soil. Instead of the usual crop, your 20 plants produced more than 100 tomatoes—a great yield!

You may be tempted to believe that you have proven that the fertilizer increased your tomato crop. But did it really? What other factors might have influenced your results?

Last year's weather might have been very good for tomatoes. Could the weather have been partly responsible? You also remember that you used a different type of tomato seed. Could the seed type have caused your success? Maybe your garden had fewer insects last year. Suddenly, things don't seem so simple. In fact, many factors could explain the good harvest.

Figure 1–9
The growth of tomatoes is influenced by many factors, including sunlight, soil, temperature, and rainfall. Performing a controlled experiment is the best way to test the effects of any factor.

A Logical Experiment

The best way to find out what caused your results is to use the scientific method. Start with a hypothesis: Using fertilizer increases the tomato crop. Then design a logical experiment to test the hypothesis.

This year, divide your garden into two sections, planting 12 seedlings grown from the same seed supply in each section. Each section of the garden should receive the same amount of rainfall and sunlight, be subjected to the same insects and other pests, and contain similar soil. However, add fertilizer to one section and not to the other.

By managing the garden this way, you make the two sets of plants as similar as possible—except for the presence of fertilizer. These two sections provide an accurate, scientific test for your hypothesis.

The Results

What will happen? The result might be as shown in ***Figure 1–10*** on the next page—the fertilized plot produces nearly 50 percent more tomatoes than the unfertilized plot. This result is much more meaningful than your observation from the year before because this time you have carried out a controlled, logical experiment.

What role did the section of unfertilized plants serve in this experiment? These plants were treated just like the plants in the other section except for the use of fertilizer. Therefore, you can reasonably conclude that the fertilizer was responsible for any differences between the two sections.

Control and Variable

The group of unfertilized plants is called the **control** group. The control group provided a benchmark that allowed you to measure the fertilizer's effect. The fertilizer is called the **variable** of the experiment. A variable is the factor that differs among the test groups.

Ideas Through Images

Have students examine Figure 1–9, read the caption, and answer the following questions.

- **What factors might affect the growth of tomatoes in a garden?** (Factors include sunlight, soil, temperature, and rainfall.)
- **What factor is being investigated in the experiment described in the text?** (The factor investigated is the presence of fertilizer.)
- **What is that factor called in the experiment described?** (The variable.)

Discussion

Initiate a class discussion about why a control group is necessary in establishing the validity of a scientific hypothesis. Through the discussion, emphasize the following points: (1) Through a controlled experiment, scientists can compare two situations that are identical except in one crucial way. (2) If there is a difference in results, the control group establishes that the variable caused the difference. If there is no difference in results, then the variable is not the factor scientists thought it might be.

Checkpoint

1 The scientific method is a system of asking questions, developing explanations, and testing those explanations in the natural world.

TEACHER SUPPORT

Ecology Note

A basic principle of ecology is the interrelatedness of all things. Any experiment in the field, such as one involving factors affecting the growth of tomatoes, must acknowledge the possibility that something not considered in the design of the experiment has affected the outcome. For that reason, biologists like to perform experiments in the laboratory, where a variable can be isolated and conditions can be strictly controlled. In practice, controlling all variables that can affect an outcome is extremely difficult and sometimes next to impossible.

Ancillary Support

The resource below can be used to support your teaching strategy for these two pages.

TR Writing in Biology: Connecting to Your Environment
Enrich: The Dawn of Modern Science

Ideas Through Images

Have students examine Figure 1–10, read the caption, and answer the following questions.

- **What was the purpose of the experiment on tomato growth?** (To find out whether the use of fertilizer made a difference in the growth of tomatoes.)
- **Which was the control group, and what was the variable in this experiment?** (The control group was the unfertilized plants; the variable was the fertilizer.)
- **What can you conclude about the hypothesis by examining the results, as shown in the bar graph?** (Students should conclude that the results support the hypothesis as correct.)

Correcting Misconceptions

Ask students to give their theories about why people voted the way they did in a recent election. Then point out that such theories are simply opinions and not close observation and controlled experiments. Ask them to contrast that meaning of the word theory with the meaning as used in a scientific context.

Discussion

Emphasize to students that the function of a control setup is to eliminate the possibility of many variables. Stress that the control setup tries to duplicate the experimental setup in every one except one—the variable being tested. Explain that in the experiment in the text, the factor that is not duplicated in the control setup is the presence of the fertilizer.

Figure 1–10 *(a) The only difference between these two plots of a tomato garden is the presence of fertilizer. (b) At the end of the growing season, the fertilized plot produced far more tomatoes than the unfertilized plot.*

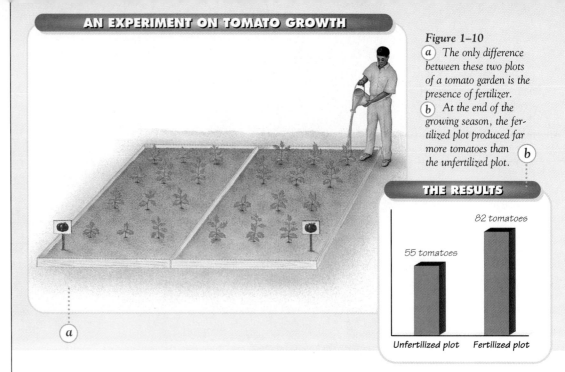

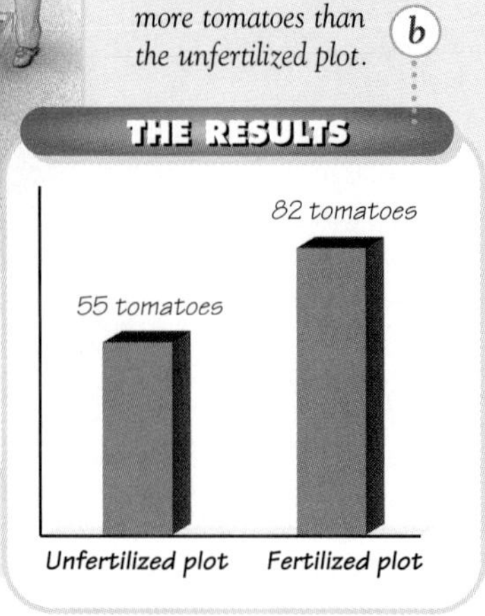

Every scientific experiment has a variable that is measured against a control.

Does this experiment on tomato plants seem almost too simple? Remember that the scientific method is nothing more than organized common sense—and a controlled experiment.

Checkpoint What is a control group? A variable? 1

Science and Truth

Although the scientific method is a powerful way to learn about the world around us, one of the most important lessons to be learned about scientific knowledge is how changeable it can be. Many "scientific facts" of the past are now known to be incorrect.

A Human Activity

For example, years ago high school and college students were taught that genetic information is carried only in a molecule called DNA. Scientists now know that this is not quite true. Another molecule, called RNA, carries genetic information in certain viruses.

It is also worth noting that scientists, like other people, are influenced by their own prejudices, beliefs, and intuitions. They sometimes close their minds to results that "don't make sense," and they often jump to conclusions that the facts may not actually support. After all, science is a human activity, and it is as likely to go wrong as anything else that people do.

This does not mean, however, that you should disregard scientific results. The fact that science is open to new ideas and the constant testing of old ones should give us confidence that science eventually will arrive at the correct answers for the important questions that we put to it. Indeed, what makes science special is the demand that scientific conclusions be constantly tested against the reality of the natural world.

Theories

When repeated experiments consistently confirm a hypothesis, the scientific

TEACHER SUPPORT

Background Information

In common speech, the word theory is often used to mean an unproven assumption, in contrast to a fact, something that actually exists. In scientific usage, a theory is an overarching generalization that explains, and is supported by, a broad range of observation and experimentation. Thus, the germ theory of disease is not just a theory, but an established principle of modern science. This confusion about the meaning of the term is often heard in debates about the theory of evolution, with those opposing the teaching of that theory attacking it on the basis that it is unproven, or "just a theory." In fact, the opposite is closer to the truth. There is so much evidence for evolution that it has become an established principle, or a scientific theory.

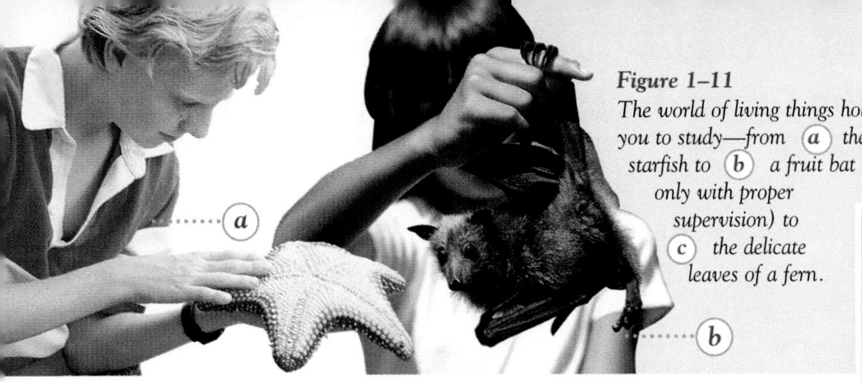

Figure 1–11
The world of living things holds all sorts of wonders for you to study—from (a) the spiny underbelly of a starfish to (b) a fruit bat (which you should handle only with proper supervision) to (c) the delicate leaves of a fern.

community may come to accept the hypothesis as valid. In this book, the authors have tried to rely on generally accepted hypotheses and to point out those issues over which the scientific community disagrees.

In many cases, however, a series of closely related hypotheses have been confirmed so many times that they can properly be described as a **theory.** A theory is a logical explanation that explains a broad range of observations. The theory that certain diseases are caused by germs is one such example.

Are theories always true? No theory is ever beyond dispute. Therefore, it would be a serious mistake to believe that science ever produces absolute truth. Nonetheless, in science, theories represent solid, logical explanations of the natural world—explanations that have stood up under repeated analysis. Put another way, a theory is the best explanation that the process of science has produced to date.

Biology and You

Both authors of this textbook have a simple message to tell you about biology. Biology is, as far as we're concerned, the most interesting subject in the world!

No matter where you live and no matter what your school is like, you are surrounded by living organisms. Each organism has its own story to tell, and each is fascinating in its own right. Don't think for a second that you need a license or a degree to call yourself a biologist. All you need is an interest in living things. You will find plenty of them to investigate.

Throughout your biology course, take the time to observe the living things that share the world with you—the birds that feed in your yard, the insects that hover near lights on a summer night, the trees that line the streets of your town or city. You will come to understand and appreciate biology even more.

Section Review 1–2

1. **Define** the scientific method.
2. **Describe** the steps of the scientific method.
3. How do a hypothesis and a theory **compare**?
4. **Critical Thinking—Applying Concepts** Your friend argues that there are no facts in science—only theories that could be proved false. Do you agree or disagree with this argument? Explain your answer.
5. **MINI LAB** After you **formulate a hypothesis,** how can you prove or disprove the hypothesis?

4 ASSESS

Quick Check

Have students work in small groups to consider this question: Does the amount of sleep a student gets affect how well the student does in school? Ask each group to propose how the scientific method could be used to find an answer.

Section Review 1–2

1. The scientific method is a system of asking questions, developing explanations, and testing those explanations.

2. State a problem or question based on observations; propose a hypothesis; test the hypothesis with a controlled experiment; analyze the results.

3. A hypothesis is a preliminary explanation that could be proven correct or incorrect, whereas a theory represents the best explanation that the process of science has produced.

4. Science does not produce absolute truths. Instead, scientists observe the natural world, perform controlled experiments, and develop theories. Theories are often revised as further observations are made and more knowledge is acquired.

5. The best way to prove or disprove a hypothesis is with a controlled experiment.

Checkpoint

1 A control group is a test group that provides a benchmark to measure the effects of the variable. A variable is a factor that differs among the test groups.

Skills Trace

Hypothesizing

- Focus p. 12
- Practice p. 15
- Assess p. 25

Learning Modality

Visual Learning Ask students to make a flow chart that includes a description of each of the steps of the scientific method.

Ancillary Support

The resource below can be used to support your teaching strategy for these two pages.

BL Inquiry Activity: Science Sleuth

SECTION 1–3

The Scientific Method and Yellow Fever

Performance Objectives

• Explain how testing is used in a scientific investigation.
• Describe Walter Reed's classic experiment.

Mini Lab Skill: Experimenting

1 ENGAGE

Inquiry Activity

Designing an Experiment

Testing a Hypothesis

Ask students what experiment they could use to find out how a disease is being spread. Suppose one hypothesis is that a deadly disease is being spread through the water supply in the area. Have students describe a controlled experiment that could be used to test this hypothesis. Ask them to explain in their descriptions what the variable in the experiment would be.

INTEGRATING SOCIAL STUDIES

The immediate cause of the Spanish-American War was the sinking of the U.S. battleship *Maine* in Havana's harbor, allegedly by the Spanish colonial power. A deeper cause was a clash between Spain's old empire and the spreading empire of the United States.

The Scientific Method and Yellow Fever

GUIDE FOR READING

- **Explain** the role of testing in science.
- **Describe** Walter Reed's experiment on yellow fever.

MINI LAB

- **Design an experiment** to test the effects of water and sunlight on the growth of bread mold.

INTEGRATING SOCIAL STUDIES

Why did the United States and Spain fight the Spanish-American War?

AS YOU HAVE READ, GENUINE science requires much more than observation. Scientists must develop explanations for their observations, then use the scientific method to test those explanations.

Why has science become so important in our lives? In part, because the scientific method has proved to be effective in solving one problem after another.

The Fight Against Yellow Fever

During the Spanish-American War of the late 1800s, United States soldiers fighting in Cuba faced an especially deadly problem—an enemy far more terrifying than the Spanish soldiers they were defeating on the battlefields. This enemy was yellow fever, a disease well known in tropical Central and South America. Before the smoke of battle had cleared, United States troops were suffering from fever and nausea, vomiting black liquid, and their skin had turned a ghastly shade of yellow, which gave the disease its name. ●

Checkpoint What is yellow fever? 1

Walter Reed

When United States military leaders realized that yellow fever was causing more deaths than enemy bullets, they appealed to their government in Washington, DC. Help came in the form of a

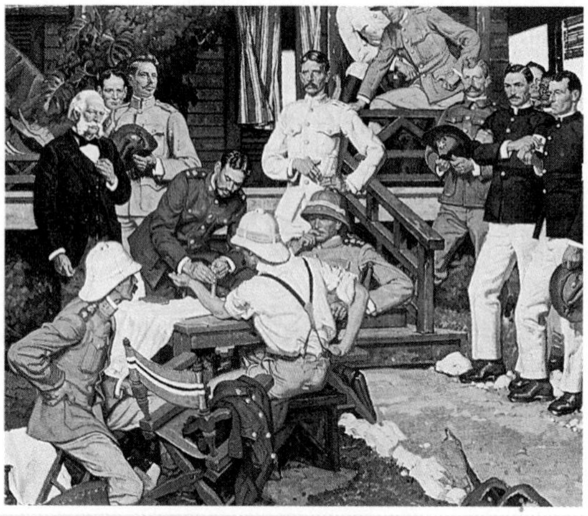

Figure 1–12
(a) The fight against yellow fever was led by Dr. Walter Reed. (b) Because so many soldiers were dying from yellow fever, several soldiers volunteered to take part in the experiments of Reed (left center) and Findlay (far left).

TEACHER SUPPORT

Managing Classroom Diversity

TECH PREP STUDENTS

Point out to students who are planning careers in health care or food services that each infectious disease has a specific way of spreading. Walter Reed's classic experiment both emphasized that concept and proved that the common wisdom—in this case, that yellow fever was spread by poor sanitation—was misleading to those fighting the disease. Have students investigate how a specific disease, such as AIDS or influenza, is spread.

commission headed by an army research doctor named Walter Reed.

Reed's first step was to analyze the old ways of fighting yellow fever. Because the disease moved from one section of a town to another, most people believed that yellow fever must be spread from person to person. To fight the disease, they isolated the sick, boiled their bedsheets and clothes, and sterilized their plates, cups, and forks.

These precautions would make good sense if yellow fever was transmitted by personal contact. Reed quickly discovered, however, that none of these measures stopped the spread of the disease.

Findlay's Hypothesis

Reed's commission listened to many physicians, including a Cuban doctor named Carlos Findlay. Findlay hypothesized that the disease was spread by mosquitoes, of which Cuba had more than its share.

Most people believed that better sanitation was the key to controlling yellow fever, and they did not believe Findlay's hypothesis. But Reed believed that there was not enough evidence to draw any logical conclusions. **To test Findlay's hypotheses, Reed decided he needed to conduct a controlled experiment.**

It was thought at the time that yellow fever affected people but did not affect animals. So Reed performed his experiment on brave but frightened groups of human volunteers.

☑ *Checkpoint* What was the goal of Reed's experiment? ❷

Reed's Experiment

Reed's commission assembled two groups of volunteers for a terrifying experiment. One group spent 20 nerve-wracking days wearing the filthy clothing of yellow fever patients, sleeping on their bedsheets, and eating from plates they had used. During this time, however, they lived behind screens that protected them from being bitten by mosquitoes.

The other group of volunteers used only fresh clothing, slept in clean beds, and remained totally isolated from yellow fever patients. These volunteers, however, were not protected by mosquito netting and so were bitten by mosquitoes. Unwilling to let soldiers take a risk that they would not take themselves, three doctors on the commission joined this group. (Reed also wanted to take part, but his associates refused his request to do so.)

MINI LAB .... Experimenting ......

A Moldy Question

PROBLEM *Why does bread turn moldy?* ***Design an experiment*** *to help answer this question.*

PROCEDURE

1. Mold will grow on bread that is exposed to air at room temperature. Design an experiment to test the effects of water and sunlight on the growth of bread mold. You may use up to four slices of bread and any materials available in your classroom.
2. Under your teacher's supervision, perform the experiment you designed.

ANALYZE AND CONCLUDE

1. What were the variables in your experiment? What were the controls?
2. Could factors other than water and sunlight have influenced the results? Explain.
3. What conclusions can you draw from this experiment? Explain your answer.

2 EXPLORE

MINI LAB Experimenting

Teacher Notes

• For time required and materials needed, see p. 2b.

• Provide sunny places and darkened places for students to put their slices of bread. They should be away from the classroom area so that students with allergies are not affected.

Answers to Analyze and Conclude

1. The variables should be water and sunlight. The controls will depend on the design. A control for an experiment on the effect of sunlight, for instance, might be a slice of bread placed away from direct sunlight but not in total darkness.
2. Students' responses should take into consideration other factors in the environment, such as temperature, exposure to air, or the quality of the bread.
3. Students should find that bread mold grows best in a damp, dark environment.

Skills Trace
Experimenting

Focus p. 17
Practice p. 19
Assess p. 25

☑ Checkpoints

❶ A potentially fatal disease, causing fever, nausea, and vomiting. It turns the skin yellow.

❷ To show whether contact with mosquitoes or people caused yellow fever.

TEACHER SUPPORT Background Information

Yellow fever is a tropical viral disease carried by the mosquito *Aedes aegypti*. The mosquito picks up the virus by biting a person sick with the disease and then passes the virus on when it bites another person. Three to six days later, symptoms appear, including fever, headache, nausea, and vomiting. Over the next three or four days, the disease can worsen, causing damage to the kidneys, spleen, liver, and heart. Jaundice, or yellowish skin, is a common symptom caused by liver failure. Yellow fever is endemic to Central and South America, as well as Africa. There is a vaccine, but it can have fatal side effects. Destroying the reservoir of the disease agent—in this case, eliminating the mosquito population of an area—remains an effective way to prevent epidemics of the disease.

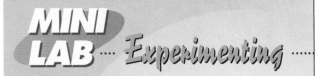

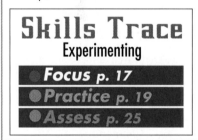

3 TEACH

Ideas Through Images

Have students examine Figure 1–13, read the caption, and answer the following questions.

- **What was the purpose of having the group of volunteers who lived in filthy clothing and bedding?** (The purpose of that group was to establish a control group to provide a benchmark for measuring the effectiveness of preventing mosquito bites.)
- **What was the variable in Reed's experiment?** (The variable was the access that mosquitoes had to each of the two groups.)
- **What did the results of the experiment prove?** (The results proved that mosquitoes carry the disease.)

Investigate

Research Have students research the lives of Carlos Findlay, Walter Reed, Jesse Lazear, and Max Theiler and their contributions to science.

INTEGRATING SOCIAL STUDIES

Controlling yellow fever was essential to the building of the canal. The French suspended their attempt to build a canal across Panama in part because of the toll that yellow fever took on workers. Before Americans began their building effort, they worked at eradicating the disease-carrying mosquitoes. Building the Panama Canal enabled the countries of Central America to open up a trade route between the Atlantic and Pacific oceans.

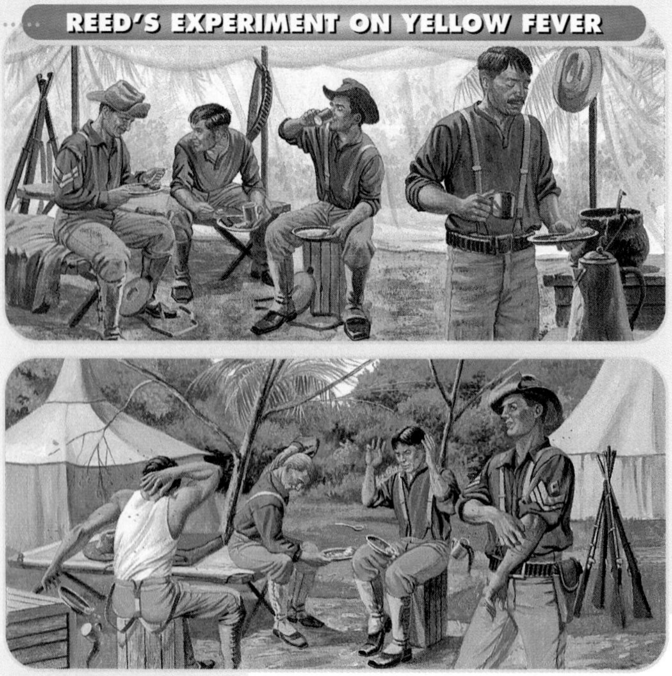

Figure 1–13
(a) In Reed's experiment, one group of volunteers lived in the filthy clothing and bedding of yellow fever patients, and they were kept isolated from mosquitoes. The second group lived in clean clothing and surroundings but were not protected from being bitten by mosquitoes. (b) Only those who were bitten by mosquitoes developed yellow fever. As a result, Reed concluded that mosquitoes transmitted this disease.

The Results

What happened? Not a single volunteer in the first group developed yellow fever. But many of the volunteers in the second group—including the three doctors—became sick with yellow fever. One of the doctors, Jesse Lazear, died from the disease.

The results of the experiment were very clear. Yellow fever was not spread by poor sanitation, person-to-person contact, or food. Instead, yellow fever was spread by mosquitoes. As a result, the United States government declared war on the mosquito. And within 90 days, the city of Havana, Cuba, was free of yellow fever.

Today, Jesse Lazear is remembered as a hero, and Findlay and Reed are recognized as the people who led the way to conquering a terrible disease. In addition, the work of these scientists had effects well beyond the fields of science and medicine.

TEACHER SUPPORT

Historical Perspective

Walter Reed worked on the spread of yellow fever without knowing for sure what infectious agent caused the disease. His contribution was to identify mosquitoes as the carriers of the disease, but it was unrealistic to think that yellow fever could be prevented by destroying all mosquitoes. Not until the late 1920s did scientists prove that a virus was the cause. In 1930 Max Theiler, a South African–born scientist working at Harvard Medical School, discovered that the virus could also infect mice. Working with mice and monkeys, he then developed a vaccine for the disease. To test that vaccine, Theiler vaccinated himself and then exposed himself to the yellow fever virus. For this work, he was awarded the 1951 Nobel Prize in medicine and physiology.

Figure 1–14
(a) *Like Cuba, the country of Panama was once plagued by yellow fever. But when the disease was under control, the United States government decided to build the Panama Canal.* (b) *This photograph shows* Aëdes aegypti, *the mosquito that transmits yellow fever.*

For example, yellow fever had been a common disease in the Central American country of Panama. Once the disease was under control, people in the United States began seriously to consider building the Panama Canal.

Beyond Yellow Fever

As you know, the application of the scientific method in fighting disease did not stop with the conquest of yellow fever. In the decades since Reed's work, biology has changed from a science that only studies the world around us to one that makes changes in that world.

As a result, we live at one of the most remarkable times in human history. Biology will influence life in the twenty-first century—the century in which you will spend most of your life—to an extent never approached before. These are exciting times to be alive, and they are especially exciting times to study the science of biology.

INTEGRATING SOCIAL STUDIES

Why was controlling yellow fever important in building the Panama Canal? How did the Panama Canal affect the countries of Central America?

Section Review 1–3

1. **Explain** the role of testing in science.
2. **Describe** how Dr. Walter Reed demonstrated that mosquitoes transmitted yellow fever.
3. **MINI LAB** How might water and sunlight influence the growth of bread mold? **Design an experiment** to test your hypothesis.
4. **BRANCHING OUT ACTIVITY** Suppose that both you and your neighbor have bird feeders, but more birds eat from your neighbor's feeder. Why might the neighbor's feeder be a more popular place than yours? **Formulate a hypothesis** to answer this question, and **design an experiment** to test it.

Learning Modality

Visual Learning Have students make a diagram of how the yellow fever virus is spread from one person to another.

4 ASSESS

Quick Check

Ask students to compose a letter Walter Reed might have written to the President of the United States, explaining how he had proved that yellow fever was transmitted by mosquitoes.

Section Review 1–3

1. Scientists determine the validity of their explanations by testing them against the reality of the natural world.

2. Reed performed a controlled experiment on two test groups. One group was kept isolated from mosquitoes; a second group was allowed to be bitten by mosquitoes. Because only the members of the second group contracted yellow fever, the experiment showed that mosquitoes transmitted yellow fever.

3. Factors that might influence bread mold include temperature and exposure to air. The experiments should use at least two test groups: a control group and a group that measures the effect of a variable.

Skills Trace
Experimenting

- Focus p. 17
- Practice p. 19
- Assess p. 25

4. The neighbor's bird feeder could be more popular because of the type of birdseed, for example. Students' experiments should test the effect of only one variable, and they should use a control group.

Ancillary Support

The resources below can be used to support your teaching strategy for these two pages.

TR Explore: Follow the Bouncing Ball
BL Inquiry Activity: Sink or Swim

CHAPTER 1

Laboratory Investigation

Looking Closely at Living Things

Before the Lab

1. In the two or three days before the lab, collect a variety of living things for students to observe, including various small plants, fish in aquaria, small reptiles, various insects, worms, and small mammals, such as mice or hamsters. Gather enough types of organisms for students to work individually or in pairs. Make sure that the various animals are in jars or cages that allow close observation but protect both the animals and the students from harm.
2. Provide magnifying glasses for each student, as well as a sufficient number of flashlights or penlights, sheets of dark paper, and measuring tools, including meter sticks and balances.

Pre-Lab Discussion

Have students read the entire procedure for this investigation. Then ask students the following questions.

What is the purpose of this investigation? (To discover the characteristics shared by all living things.)

What characteristics do you think you will be able to observe in the living things you examine? (Students' answers will vary. Most will mention movement or response to the environment, especially in animals.)

CHAPTER 1

Laboratory Investigation

Looking Closely at Living Things

As you know, living things come in a variety of sizes, forms, shapes, and colors. Yet, all living things share certain characteristics. You can discover some of these characteristics by carefully observing a living thing.

Problem

What are the characteristics of life? **Observe** a living organism to discover possible answers.

Materials (per group)

a live organism
magnifying glass
metric ruler
laboratory balance
penlight or flashlight
white and dark paper

Procedure

1. **Obtain a live organism from your teacher. Be sure to follow any special precautions that your teacher gives you for handling the organism.**
2. **Observe the organism for 5 minutes, using your senses of sight, smell, and hearing. Record your observations in a data table similar to the one shown.**
3. **On a sheet of paper, sketch the organism. Indicate its color, shape, and size, as well as any other characteristics that you observe. Label any parts that you can identify.**
4. **Observe the organism through the magnifying glass. Sketch any interesting features that you see.**
5. **Use a metric ruler to measure the length, width, and height of the organism. In addition, measure any noticeable projections on the organism. Record all measurements.**
6. **If the organism can be placed on a balance, find and record the organism's mass.**

Safety Tips

Caution students not to handle any of the animals unless you have given them permission to handle a specific organism. This will protect both the students and the organisms from harm.

7. Use a penlight or flashlight to shine a beam of light on the organism, and observe its response. Record your observations.

8. Use a sheet of dark paper to shade the organism from the light, and observe its response. Record your observations.

Observations

Share your observations with your classmates, who studied different organisms. How are the organisms different? How are they similar?

Analysis and Conclusions

1. Which characteristics of life did you observe in the organism you studied?
2. For the characteristics of life that you did not observe in the organism, discuss whether or not you believe the organism has them. Use your observations as evidence for your answer.
3. Are you convinced that the organism you studied is alive? Explain your answer.
4. Among the organisms your class studied, was there a common color, shape, mass, or other physical characteristic? Discuss the significance of your answer.

DATA TABLE

Organism's name	
Color	
Shape	
Measurements	
Mass	
Response to light	

More to Explore

Design an experiment to show how your organism is affected by temperature or some other factor. Be sure your experiment does not harm your organism.

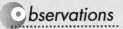

Skills Development

Students will use these skills while completing the laboratory investigation: observing, measuring, comparing, and drawing conclusions.

Teaching Strategies

1. Point out that the characteristics of living things cannot always be observed in every organism at all times. A biologist could observe growth and development, for example, only through examination over a period of time.
2. Advise students to record each observation in the data table immediately rather than waiting until several observations are made.

Answers to
Observations

Students' answers will vary depending on what organisms they compare. Accept any reasonable responses.

Answers to
Analysis and Conclusions

1. Students who observe animals will most likely observe some sort of response to the environment. Students who observe plants may not observe any of the five characteristics of life.
2. Students should discuss all of the characteristics presented in the visual essay on page 5. For example, a student might discuss size or shape of the organism as evidence of growth and development.
3. Students should state their conclusions in terms of the observations they made of the organism and the five characteristics of living things.
4. No color, shape, mass, or other physical characteristic is common to all organisms. Students should infer that living things have a great variety of physical characteristics.

More to Explore

Each student's design should incorporate one factor, such as light or temperature, as a variable, and also include some sort of control for comparison.

CHAPTER 1

Study Guide

Review Strategy

Have students form small groups of three or four. If possible, match at-risk or LEP students with gifted students who are proficient in English. Then ask students to reexamine the questions they recorded in the Chapter Discovery Learning Activity and classify them according to the types of questions discussed on pages 7–10. After they have classified the questions originally written, ask them to look at the pictures again and propose new questions that would address any level of question not originally addressed.

Study Guide

Summarizing Key Concepts

The key concepts in each section of this chapter are listed below to help you review the chapter content. Make sure you understand each concept and its relationship to other concepts and to the theme of this chapter.

1–1 The Characteristics of Life

- Science is a process of thinking and learning about the world around us. Biology is the science of life.
- Living things are made of cells, grow and develop, obtain and use energy, respond to their environment, and are able to reproduce.
- Biologists may ask questions at many different levels of organization—from the chemical level to the global level.

1–2 The Scientific Method and Biology

- The scientific method is a system of asking questions, developing explanations, and testing those explanations against the reality of the natural world.
- The steps of the scientific method include stating a problem, proposing a hypothesis for the problem, testing the hypothesis in an experiment, and analyzing the results and drawing conclusions.
- A scientific experiment uses one or more control groups and one variable. A variable is the factor that differs among the test groups. A control group provides a benchmark to measure the variable's effects.
- A scientific theory comes from a series of hypotheses that have been confirmed many times. Theories represent scientists' best explanations of the natural world.

1–3 The Scientific Method and Yellow Fever

- To obtain evidence for or against Findlay's hypothesis, Walter Reed realized he had to conduct a controlled experiment.
- From the results of their experiment, Reed and his associates demonstrated that yellow fever was transmitted by mosquitoes, not personal contact.

Reviewing Key Terms

Review the following vocabulary terms and their meaning. Then use each term in a complete sentence.

1–1 The Characteristics of Life

science
biology
organism

1–2 The Scientific Method and Biology

scientific method
hypothesis
experiment
control
variable
theory

Inquiry-Based Strategy

Several students have become ill after eating in the school cafeteria. Have students research how a public-health official might investigate such a problem. Then ask them to answer the following question: How could the scientific method be used to answer the question of what made the students ill? Most students will formulate a hypothesis about the cafeteria food and design an experiment that tests that hypothesis.

Recalling Main Ideas

Choose the letter of the answer that best completes the statement or answers the question.

1. Biology is the study of
   a. living things. **c.** matter.
   b. growth. **d.** reproduction.

2. Not every organism is able to
   a. grow and develop.
   b. obtain energy.
   c. move independently.
   d. respond to its environment.

3. Biologists study life at
   a. the chemical level only.
   b. the cellular level only.
   c. the global level only.
   d. many different levels.

4. The factor that differs among the test groups of an experiment is called a
   a. theory. **c.** control.
   b. variable. **d.** hypothesis.

5. Artists and historians are not scientists because they do not rely on
   a. observations.
   b. careful study.
   c. provable facts.
   d. the scientific method.

6. In Walter Reed's experiment on yellow fever, both test groups were subjected to
   a. unsanitary living conditions.
   b. mosquito bites.
   c. contact with yellow fever patients.
   d. a strict set of living conditions.

7. A hypothesis can be described as a(an)
   a. controlled experiment.
   b. possible explanation.
   c. answerable question.
   d. proven theory.

Putting It All Together

Using the information on pages xxx to xxxi, complete the following concept map.

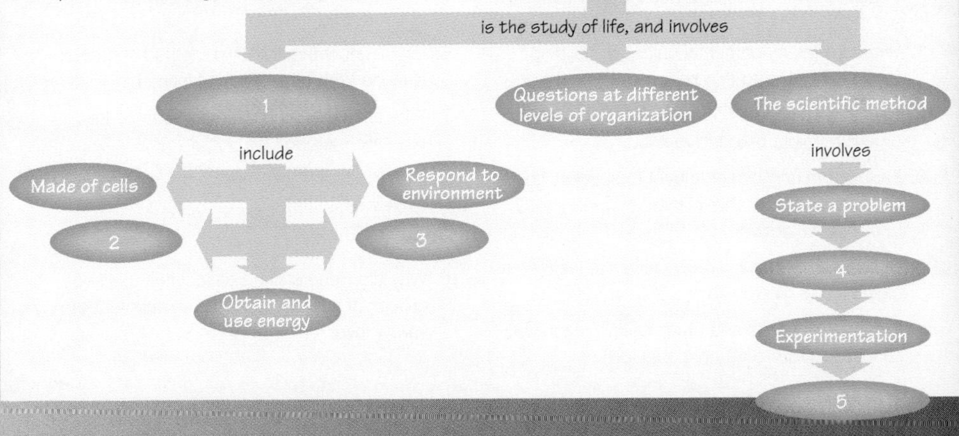

Recalling Main Ideas

1. a
2. c
3. d
4. b
5. d
6. d
7. b

Putting It All Together

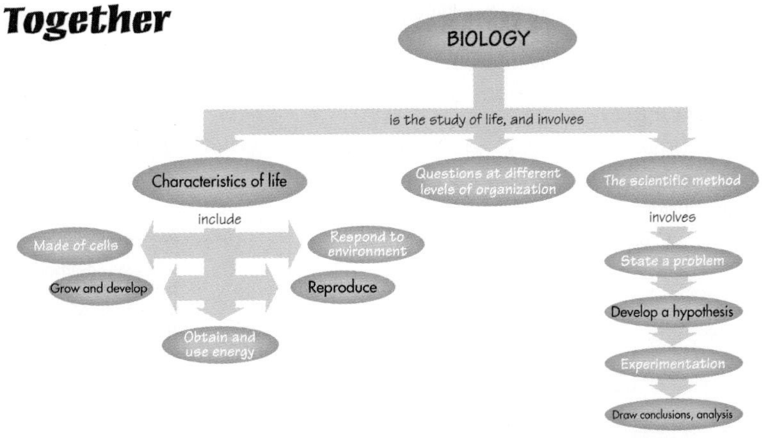

Assessment

Reviewing What You Learned

1. Accept all reasonable questions about the nature of living things.
2. Biology is the study of living things.
3. Living things are made of cells, grow and develop, obtain and use energy, respond to their environment, and are able to reproduce.
4. An organism is any individual living thing.
5. Organisms obtain energy from energy-containing molecules—such as glucose—or from sunlight.
6. Corals are made of cells, they grow and develop over time, their tentacles capture food passing by them in the current, they use food for energy, and they reproduce.
7. Ecology is the branch of biology concerned with the relationships among organisms.
8. The scientific method is a system of asking questions, developing explanations, and testing those explanations against the reality of the natural world.
9. A hypothesis is a possible explanation, a preliminary conclusion, or a guess at the solution to a problem. The role of a hypothesis in the scientific method is to serve as an explanation that can be tested through experimentation.
10. A biologist might observe the height of a tree, the way a paramecium takes in food, or the cellular structure of a plant or animal. Accept all reasonable responses.
11. A controlled experiment uses at least two test groups. The test groups differ by a factor called the variable.

Assessment (continued)

Expanding the Concepts

1. Cells are the building blocks of all living things.
2. Students' answers may vary. For example: The smell of food might cause an animal to salivate, touching an animal might cause it to jump away, shining light on a plant might cause the plant to grow toward the light.
3. Accept all reasonable responses for which students have given valid support.
4. Students should describe four of these levels: chemical, or the chemical composition of organisms; molecular, or the molecules that are involved in an organism's life processes; cellular, or the structure and function of cells in organisms; organism, or the individual living things; population, or the populations of organisms; and global, or the interaction of organisms and their environments.
5. The well-being of coral and other marine organisms may serve as an indicator of the overall health of the oceans, as well as life on Earth.
6. The scientific method demands that scientists test their ideas against the reality of the natural world. Other disciplines do not require such tests.
7. Experiments allow scientists to test the validity of their hypotheses, or proposed solutions to scientific problems.
8. If the results of an experiment are valid, they should hold true on repeated trials. If they do not, the results most likely depend on a factor that the experimenter has not considered.
9. A scientific theory is a logical explanation that explains a broad range of observations.
10. By using two groups, Reed and his associates were able to determine whether yellow fever developed from personal contact or contact with mosquitoes.

Assessment

Reviewing What You Learned

Answer each of the following in a complete sentence.

1. Give three examples of questions about living things.
2. What is biology?
3. List five major characteristics of life.
4. What is an organism?
5. From which sources do organisms obtain energy?
6. How do corals exhibit the characteristics of life?
7. Which field of biology is concerned with the relationships among organisms?
8. Describe the scientific method.
9. What is a hypothesis? Describe the role of the hypothesis in the scientific method.
10. Give an example of an observation a biologist might make.
11. What is a controlled experiment?

Expanding the Concepts

Discuss each of the following in a brief paragraph.

1. What are the fundamental units—or building blocks—of all living things?
2. Give three examples of a stimulus and how an organism might respond to it.
3. Earth is the only planet known to support life. Do you think that other planets support life? Explain your answer.
4. Describe four of the different levels at which biology may be studied.
5. Explain why corals and other marine organisms should be studied at the global level.
6. Explain how the scientific method separates science from other fields of learning.
7. Why are experiments fundamental to the scientific method?
8. Why is reliability an important factor in scientific experimentation?
9. What is a scientific theory?
10. Why did Reed and his associates use two groups of volunteers in their experiment on yellow fever?

Extending Your Thinking

1. Earth's organisms range from around 1 micrometer in diameter—the size of a small bacterium—to over 30 meters long—the length of an adult blue whale. Factors that limit an organism's size include the amount of food it can take in and the power it can generate.

2. The experiment might include four test groups—one for each soil mixture. The factors other than soil should be as constant as possible among the four test groups.

Skills Trace
Experimenting

- Focus p. 17
- Practice p. 19
- Assess p. 25

Extending Your Thinking

Use the skills you have developed in this chapter to answer the following.

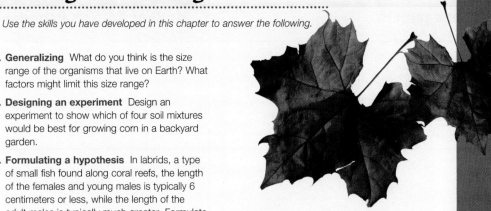

1. **Generalizing** What do you think is the size range of the organisms that live on Earth? What factors might limit this size range?
2. **Designing an experiment** Design an experiment to show which of four soil mixtures would be best for growing corn in a backyard garden.
3. **Formulating a hypothesis** In labrids, a type of small fish found along coral reefs, the length of the females and young males is typically 6 centimeters or less, while the length of the adult males is typically much greater. Formulate a hypothesis based on this evidence.
4. **Evaluating** A crystal of calcium carbonate can grow over time. Does this mean that the crystal is alive? Explain your answer.
5. **Applying** Suppose that a bed of unusual fossils has been discovered at a construction site. Which type of biologists should be invited to study the site? Explain your answer.
6. **Applying** People often develop and test hypotheses as part of their daily lives. What hypotheses have you recently developed or tested?
7. **Predicting** You have been asked to observe a maple tree over the course of one year. Based on your knowledge of the characteristics of life, predict some of the observations that you will make.

Applying Your Skills

Where's the Jelly?

Every scientific experiment needs a logical procedure—a series of steps that are clear to follow and that serve the experiment's purpose. But as you will discover, writing and following even the simplest procedures are not so easy!

1. Write a procedure for making a peanut butter and cracker sandwich from the materials your teacher provides.
2. Exchange procedures with one of your classmates.
3. Follow your classmate's procedure exactly as it is written.

• GOING FURTHER •

4. Evaluate your classmate's procedure. Share the evaluation with your classmate.
5. Did your classmate accurately interpret and follow the procedure you had written? Could you improve the procedure in any way?

3. Accept all reasonable responses. One hypothesis is that when male labrids reach a certain age, they synthesize a chemical that increases their length.

Skills Trace
Hypothesizing
- Focus p. 12
- Practice p. 15
- Assess p. 25

4. The crystal is not necessarily alive. The crystal is not likely to show other characteristics of life, such as cellular construction and the ability to reproduce.
5. A paleontologist—a biologist who studies the life of the past—should certainly be invited to the site. However, many other biologists might contribute to the study of the site. For example, a biochemist might identify unusual compounds in the fossils, or an ecologist might explain how bacteria decomposed the fossils over time.
6. Students may have developed and tested hypotheses concerning a pet's favorite type of food, the best way to remove a stain from a piece of clothing, or the best way to kill insects or other pests. Accept all reasonable responses.

7. Leaves should sprout in the spring and change color and fall in the autumn. Branches and seeds should grow in the summer.

Skills Trace
Predicting
- Focus p. 7
- Practice p. 10
- Assess p. 25

Applying Your Skills

Preparation

1. For this activity, you will need to supply boxes of crackers, a jar of peanut butter, plastic knives for each student, and paper napkins.
2. Check for food allergies among the students. If students are allergic to these foods, caution them to refrain from eating the sandwiches.

Suggestions

3. Emphasize to students that the written procedure must include every step necessary to make the sandwiches, with nothing implied.
4. Advise students that they should follow the procedures exactly; if there is no instruction to open the jar of peanut butter, for example, then the jar should not be opened.

Scoring Rubric

4 Response is thorough, accurate, and creative; shows an in-depth understanding of science skills, procedures, and concepts.

3 Response is complete, mostly accurate, and original; shows a satisfactory understanding of science skills, procedures, and concepts.

2 Response is mostly complete but includes some inaccuracies; shows an adequate understanding of science skills, procedures, and concepts.

1 Response is only partially complete and has many inaccuracies; shows an incomplete understanding of science skills, procedures, and concepts.

0 Response is mostly incomplete and/or inaccurate; shows a lack of understanding of science skills, procedures, and concepts.

Chapter 2 The Chemistry of Life

Content Management	Student Edition Activities
■ Section 2–1 Introduction to Chemistry, pp. 27–32 Atoms and Compounds Water	
■ Section 2–2 The Compounds of Life, pp. 33–36 Carbon—A Special Element Macromolecules	MINI LAB: The Starch Test, p. 34
■ Section 2–3 Chemical Reactions and Enzymes, pp. 37–39 Chemical Reactions Enzymes	Laboratory Investigation: Three, Two, One . . . BLASTOFF!, pp. 42–43
◆ BRANCHING OUT • In Depth Section 2–4 Mirror-Image Molecules, pp. 40–41 Two Types of Tryptophan A Mirror-Image Puzzle	MINI LAB: Mirror, Mirror, p. 41

■ These sections cover all the necessary content and concepts for a basic course in biology.
◆ This section covers content and concepts that are either applications or extensions of the basic material.

Integration Strategies

SE Language Arts, p. 34

Assessment Strategies

SE Chapter Review, pp. 44–47
TR Section Reviews
Chapter Test
BL Chapter Review
Practice Test
CTB Chapter 2 Test

Tech Prep

Teaching strategy appropriate for students who are in technical/vocational programs or who are considering post-secondary technical education can be found on the following **TE** page: 34.

Meeting the Standards

Sections 2–1 through 2–4 cover two of the six content standards under **The Cell** and one of the six content standards under **Matter, Energy, and Organization in Living Systems** as described on pages 184 and 186 of The National Science Education Standards.

Chapter Planning Guide

Teacher's Edition Activities	Other Activities	Media and Technology
Chapter Discovery Learning Activity, p. 26 **Investigate:** Research, p. 28	**LM** Constructing Molecular Models, #3 **TR** **Explore:** Atomic Modeling **BL** **Inquiry Activity:** Atomic Art	BioVue Animation: Bonding, Videodisc Side 1 Looking for Solutions, Videodisc Side 1 BioVue Plus CD-ROMs: Bonding and Looking for Solutions
	LM Identifying Organic Compounds, #4 **TR** **Writing in Biology:** Stocking Up on the Right Stuff **Enrich:** Paper Proteins **BL** **Inquiry Activity:** Look What You're Eating!	CD-ROM: Biochemistry: The Chemistry of Living Things **TB** Peptide Bond Formation, #2
Inquiry Activity: A Mouthful of Reaction, p. 37 **Investigate:** Long-Term Project, p. 38 **Activity:** Enzyme Action!, p. 39	**TR** **Enrich:** The Case of the Missing Enzyme **BL** **Inquiry Activity:** Gas Reaction	CD-ROM: Enzymes
Activity: Smelling Right and Smelling Left, p. 40	**TR** **Apply:** Molecules in Stereo **BL** **Inquiry Activity:** Mirror, Mirror	

KEY: **SE** Student Edition **TE** Teacher's Edition **LM** Laboratory Manual **TR** Teaching Resources **BL** BioLog **TB** Transparency Box **CTB** Computer Test Bank

Materials List

TE Chapter Discovery Learning Activity, p. 26 (15 20 minutes); small beakers, large beakers or pitchers, teaspoons, small plates or saucers, water, salt.

SE MINI LAB: The Starch Test, p. 34 (30 minutes); Lugol's solution, droppers, test tubes, soda crackers, potato, white bread, oatmeal, granulated sugar.

TE Inquiry Activity: A Mouthful of Reaction, p. 37 (15–20 minutes); Lugol's solution, droppers, test tubes, soda crackers, artificial saliva.

TE Activity: Enzyme Action!, p. 39 (20 minutes); toothpicks, watches or clock with second hand.

SE MINI LAB: Mirror, Mirror, p. 41 (20–30 minutes); white construction paper, colored pencils, rulers, scissors, tape.

TE Activity: Smelling Right and Smelling Left, p. 41 (10 minutes); caraway seeds, spearmint gum.

CHAPTER 2

The Chemistry of Life

Introducing the Chapter

. . . In Pictures

The visual provides a close-up view of a biochemist at work in her laboratory. Have students examine the photograph and answer the following questions.

- **What is biochemistry?** (Biochemistry is the study of the chemistry of living things.)
- **What do biochemists do?** (Biochemists investigate the chemical processes that occur in living things.)

This photograph sets the theme for this chapter, which introduces students to the basics of biochemistry.

Teaching Strategy

In the first three sections of this chapter, students learn about basic concepts in biochemistry, including chemical compounds and bonds, chemical reactions, and the organic compounds found in living things. Use the BRANCHING OUT section at the end of the chapter to provide an in-depth look at some special chemical compounds. This will give students an indication of the complexity of biochemistry.

BIO JOURNAL

The Bio Journal topic can be used to stimulate classroom discussion. Ask students to discuss what they know about the chemical processes in living things. Guide the discussion to such processes as photosynthesis and respiration, which most students should have some knowledge about. After this discussion, have students generate a list of questions that a biochemist might investigate. Instruct students to keep their entries in their portfolios.

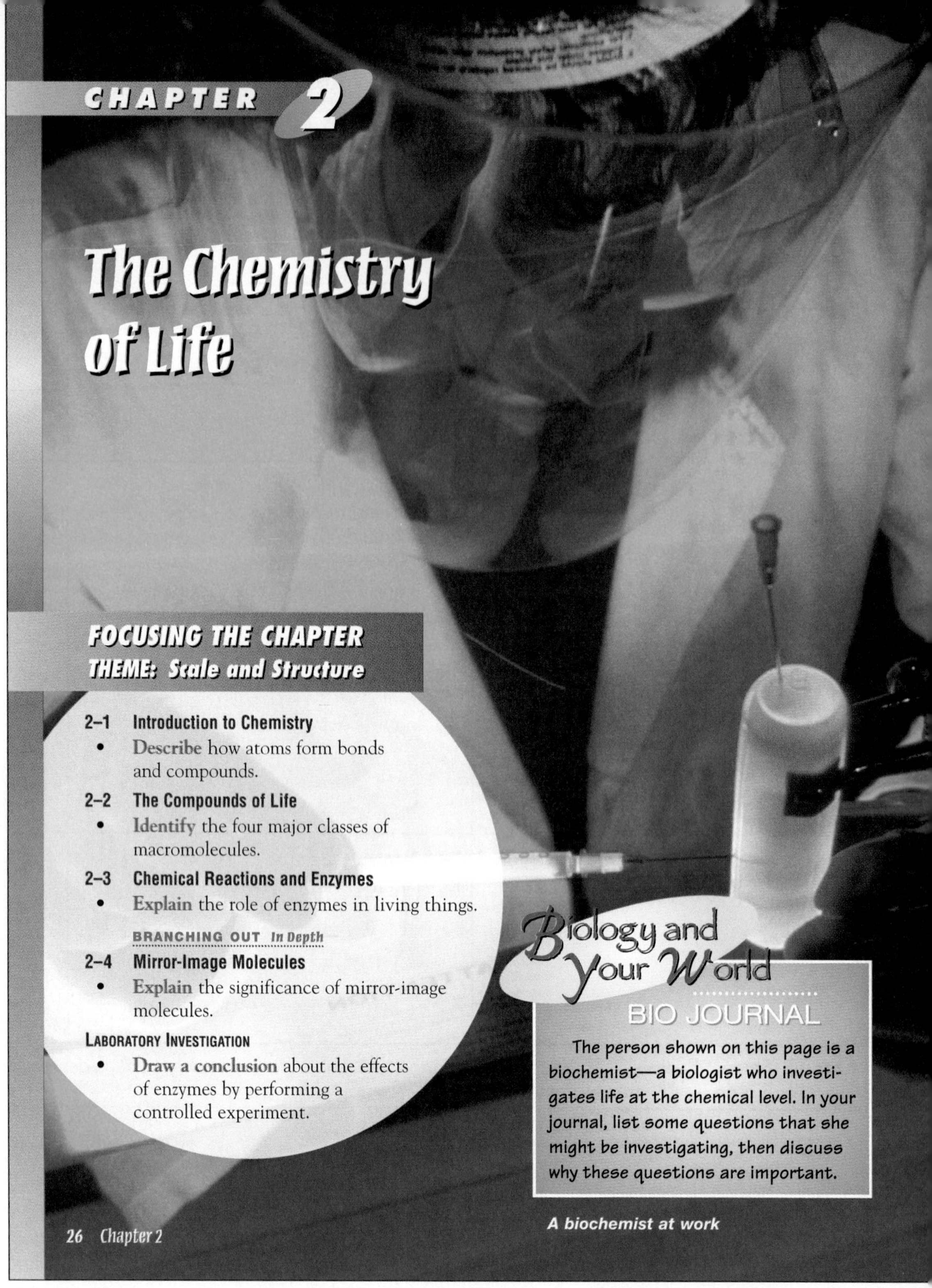

CHAPTER 2

The Chemistry of Life

FOCUSING THE CHAPTER THEME: Scale and Structure

2–1 Introduction to Chemistry
- **Describe** how atoms form bonds and compounds.

2–2 The Compounds of Life
- **Identify** the four major classes of macromolecules.

2–3 Chemical Reactions and Enzymes
- **Explain** the role of enzymes in living things.

BRANCHING OUT *In Depth*

2–4 Mirror-Image Molecules
- **Explain** the significance of mirror-image molecules.

LABORATORY INVESTIGATION
- **Draw a conclusion** about the effects of enzymes by performing a controlled experiment.

Biology and Your World

BIO JOURNAL

The person shown on this page is a biochemist—a biologist who investigates life at the chemical level. In your journal, list some questions that she might be investigating, then discuss why these questions are important.

A biochemist at work

TEACHER SUPPORT

Chapter Discovery Learning Activity

A PROPERTY OF WATER

Provide each pair of students with a clear glass or beaker, a plate or saucer, a pitcher or large beaker, a teaspoon, a box of salt, and a supply of water. Ask them whether they think matter has any empty space within it. Then ask students to follow these steps.

- Fill the pitcher or large beaker with water.
- Place the glass or smaller beaker on the plate or saucer and fill it to the brim with water. Students should stop adding water when the glass or beaker just begins to overflow. They should be able to see the water bulging over the rim of the glass.
- Add salt to the glass of water, teaspoon by teaspoon. Record how many teaspoons of salt the water can hold before it overflows the glass.

Ask students to speculate about how the water could hold the salt without overflowing.

Introduction to Chemistry

GUIDE FOR READING

- **Explain** how atoms of elements differ.
- **Compare** the different bonds that atoms form.
- **Describe** the properties of the H^{+} ion and the OH^{-} ion

WHY ARE LIVING THINGS SO different from nonliving things? One way to examine this question is at the chemical and molecular levels. As you will discover, the arrangement of chemical elements in living things is far more complex than anything found in the nonliving world.

Atoms and Compounds

A chemical element is a substance that cannot be broken down into any other substance. And the smallest unit of a chemical element is a particle called the **atom.**

Atoms are extremely small—so small, in fact, that 100 million atoms placed side by side would measure only about 1 centimeter, or about the width of your pinky finger. Yet despite their tiny size, atoms are made of subatomic particles, which are even smaller.

Parts of the Atom

In the center of every atom is a compact core called a nucleus. Although the nucleus takes up only a small fraction of an atom's volume, it accounts for almost all—99.9 percent—of an atom's mass.

The nucleus contains two types of subatomic particles—the **proton** and the **neutron.** A proton carries a positive charge while a neutron carries no charge, and both particles have approximately the same mass. Strong forces bind these two kinds of particles together in the nucleus.

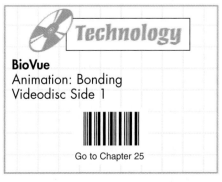

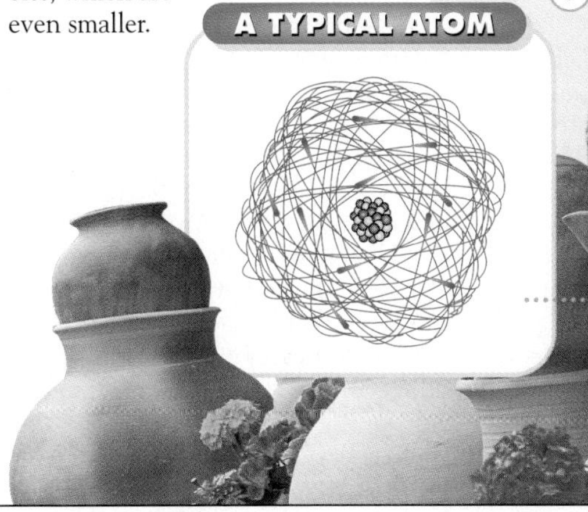

Figure 2–1 (a) Vendors at this open-air market in Central America sell a wide variety of goods—including vegetables, blankets, and (b) handmade pottery. (c) Even the most diverse substances, however, are made of the same type of fundamental unit—the atom.

SECTION 2–1

Introduction to Chemistry

Performance Objectives

- Explain how the atoms of different elements vary.
- Describe the different chemical bonds and how they form.
- Compare the properties of the H^{+} ion and the OH^{-} ion.

1 ENGAGE

Ideas Through Images

Have students examine the model of an atom in Figure 2–1, read the caption, and answer the following questions.

- **What does the caption tell you about the atom?** (The atom is a fundamental unit of matter.)
- **What does it mean to be a "fundamental unit"?** (Accept any reasonable response. Students might suggest that a fundamental unit is the smallest piece of a type of matter that retains the properties of that type.)
- **How would you describe the typical atom shown?** (The typical atom has a central core of particles surrounded by other smaller particles that seem to be in orbit around the core.)

TEACHER SUPPORT

Historical Perspective

The person who named the atom was Democritus (470–380 BC), an early Greek philosopher. The word atom is derived from a Greek word meaning indivisible. Democritus theorized that all matter consisted of atoms, tiny particles that were eternal, unchangeable, and indestructible. He believed that there were different kinds of atoms, which accounted for the various properties of the different kinds of matter.

The ideas of Democritus remained pure speculation for more than 2000 years. In the early nineteenth century, John Dalton, an English chemist, developed a modern atomic theory. In 1897, English physicist J. J. Thomson discovered what came to be known as electrons, the first indication that there were particles smaller than the atom. Ernest Rutherford and Niels Bohr were later scientists who contributed to atomic theory.

Technology

BioVue
Animation: Bonding
Videodisc Side 1

Go to Chapter 25

2 EXPLORE

Investigate

Research Ask students to investigate the atomic model of matter, including the scientists who contributed significantly to an understanding of the atom. Such scientists include John Dalton, J. J. Thomson, Ernest Rutherford, and Niels Bohr. Ask students to write a paragraph about the achievements of each of these scientists. Also have them make drawings of any representations of the atom that they find in their research.

3 TEACH

Ideas Through Images

Have students examine Figure 2–2, read the caption, and answer the following questions.

- **How do the electron arrangements compare in the three atoms shown?** (Each atom has 2 electrons at the first level, the second and third atoms also have 8 electrons at the second level, and the third atom has 8 additional electrons at the third level.

- **Why are these three atoms particularly stable?** (The outer energy level of each atom contains the maximum number of electrons.)

Discussion

Show students a Periodic Table of Elements or a table of elements that includes the name, symbol, and atomic number of all the elements. Help students review these concepts. Then discuss why atoms of different elements form compounds. Point out that the answer to why compounds form lies in an understanding of the electron arrangements of atoms.

Figure 2–2
An atom's electrons are arranged in distinct energy levels. The electrons in helium, neon, and argon each fill the energy levels, which makes these atoms especially stable.

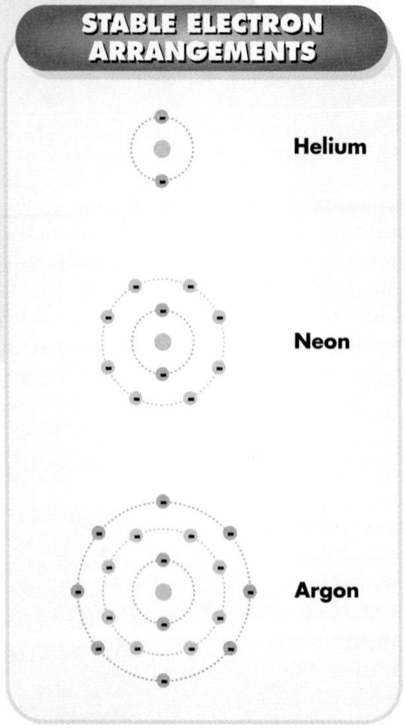

Atoms also contain a third type of subatomic particle, which is known as the **electron.** Electrons move around the nucleus in clouds of pathways called orbitals. An electron carries a negative charge, and its mass is about 1/2000 the mass of a proton or neutron.

Because opposite charges attract, the strong positive charges in the nucleus help to hold electrons in their orbitals. And because atoms have equal numbers of protons and electrons, they are electrically neutral, carrying no overall charge.

Why are atoms of one element, such as oxygen, different from the atoms of another element, such as gold? **The key difference between the atoms of different elements is the number of protons and electrons they contain.** An oxygen atom, for example, has 8 protons in its nucleus and 8 electrons surrounding the nucleus. A gold atom, by contrast, has 79 protons and 79 electrons.

Bonds and Compounds

There are 92 different chemical elements found in nature, and another 20 have been artificially produced in research laboratories. But if these 112 elements were the only substances found in nature, the world would be a very dull place.

Fortunately for us, the atoms of most elements link up with each other in different arrangements and combinations. The links between atoms are called chemical bonds. And a substance that is formed by the bonding of atoms in definite proportions is called a **chemical compound.** Water, salt, sugar, and ammonia are examples of common chemical compounds.

Why do atoms form bonds? The answer lies with the arrangement of their electrons. Among the atoms with fewer than 20 electrons, the most stable electron arrangements are found in helium (with 2 electrons), neon (with 10 electrons), and argon (with 18 electrons).

For the other small atoms—including atoms of hydrogen, carbon, nitrogen, and oxygen—electrons are shared or transferred, as though the atoms were trying to obtain the electron arrangement of helium, neon, or argon. As you will discover, shared and transferred electrons serve to bond atoms together.

Ionic Bonds

Consider the sodium atom and the chlorine atom shown in ***Figure 2–3.*** When these atoms approach each other, both become more stable when one electron transfers from the sodium atom to the chlorine atom. As a result, both atoms become **ions.** An ion is an atom that has gained or lost one or more of its electrons, thus acquring a net electrical charge.

Because opposite charges attract each other, the positively charged sodium

TEACHER SUPPORT

Background Information

The ions in an ionic compound are arranged in a crystal lattice, a three-dimensional structure in which the positive and negative ions are held together by the attraction between their opposite charges. The crystal lattice of sodium chloride, for example, is a cube in which the positive sodium ions and negative chloride ions attract each other.

Covalent bonds link atoms together into molecules. Other forces, known as intermolecular forces, hold the molecules together when the substance is in a solid or liquid state. One of the strongest of such forces is the hydrogen bond, which holds water molecules together. This bond is an attraction between the slightly positive hydrogen atoms of one water molecule and the slightly negative oxygen atom of another water molecule. The hydrogen bonds of water account for many of its special properties.

ion (Na^+) attracts the negatively charged chloride ion (Cl^-). **The strong attraction between oppositely charged ions is called an ionic bond.** Strong **ionic bonds** link ions in simple compounds, like sodium chloride, and they help to hold together different parts of much larger chemical compounds.

Covalent Bonds

A **covalent bond** is another type of bond. **In a covalent bond, electrons are shared between two atoms.** For example, consider the two oxygen atoms in ***Figure 2–3.*** Individually, each oxygen atom is surrounded by 8 electrons—not an especially stable arrangement. But when each atom shares 2 electrons with the other atom, both acquire a stable arrangement of 10 electrons.

The more electrons in the covalent bond, the more strongly the two atoms are joined. A covalent bond can be formed from 2 electrons (called a single bond), 4 electrons (a double bond), or 6 electrons (a triple bond).

Because shared electrons help both atoms to be stable, a covalent bond usually does not break easily. Therefore, a group of atoms united by covalent bonds typically acts as a single unit, called a **molecule.** A molecule may contain as few as 2 atoms or it may contain atoms in the thousands or millions. DNA, the molecule of genetic inheritance, is a molecule made of millions of atoms. Sucrose, or ordinary table sugar, contains only 45 atoms. And one of the most important molecules in nature—the water molecule—contains only 3 atoms.

☑ ***Checkpoint*** How do ionic and covalent bonds differ? (1)

Chemical Formulas

Most chemical compounds can be described by a kind of shorthand notation known as a chemical formula. A chemical formula indicates the elements that form the compound and the proportions in which they combine. Sodium chloride, for example, has the chemical formula NaCl. This formula indicates that sodium chloride contains one sodium ion (Na^+) for every chloride ion (Cl^-).

For compounds composed of molecules, a chemical formula also indicates the numbers of each atom in the molecule. For example, the formula for glucose, $C_6H_{12}O_6$, indicates that a molecule of glucose contains 6 carbon atoms, 12 hydrogen atoms, and 6 oxygen atoms.

Water

Liquid water is found inside every living cell—as well as outside most cells. Even the cells of organisms that live on dry land are bathed in a liquid that contains water.

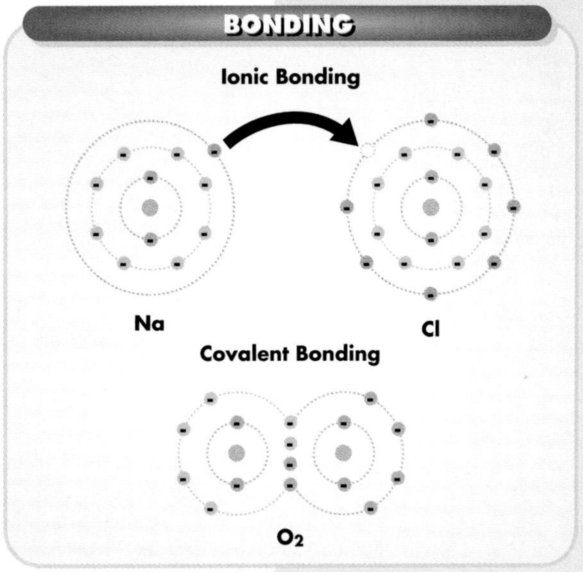

Figure 2–3
A sodium atom (Na) readily loses an electron to a chlorine atom (Cl), changing both atoms into ions and creating an ionic bond between them. In a molecule of oxygen (O_2), 2 oxygen atoms share 4 electrons, creating a covalent bond.

Ideas Through Images

Have students examine Figure 2–3, read the caption, and answer the following questions.

- **What does the arrow designate in the diagram that represents ionic bonding?** (A transfer of an electron from a sodium atom to a chlorine atom.)
- **What links the 2 oxygen atoms together in the illustration of covalent bonding?** (The 2 oxygen atoms share 4 electrons, giving both oxygen atoms a stable arrangement of 10 electrons.)

Correcting Misconceptions

Students may have difficulty in distinguishing between an atom and a molecule. Point out that an atom is the smallest particle of an element, whereas a molecule is the smallest particle of a covalent compound. A molecule consists of one or more atoms from each of the elements that make up the compound.

☑ Checkpoint

(1) In an ionic bond, electrons are transferred from one atom to another. In a covalent bond, electrons are shared between two atoms.

Technology

BioVue
Animation: Looking for Solutions
Videodisc Side 1

Go to Chapter 30

TEACHER SUPPORT — Managing Classroom Diversity

AT-RISK STUDENTS

Some students may not be familiar with reading and understanding chemical formulas. Provide students with a list of chemical elements and their symbols and then have them write the number of the different kinds of atoms in the following formulas of organic compounds.

- Acetylene C_2H_2
- Aniline $C_6H_5NH_2$
- Benzene C_6H_6
- Camphor $C_{10}H_{16}O$
- Chloroform $CHCl_3$
- Lactic acid C_2H_5OCOOH
- Menthol $C_{10}H_{19}OH$
- Naphthalene $C_{10}H_8$
- Oxalic acid $H_2C_2O_4$
- Stearic acid $C_{17}H_{35}COOH$
- Tannin $C_{14}H_{10}O_9$
- Toluene $C_6H_5CH_3$

Ancillary Support

The resources below can be used to support your teaching strategy for these two pages.

TR Explore: Atomic Modeling
BL Inquiry Activity: Atomic Art

Ideas Through Images

Have students examine Figures 2–4 and 2–5, read the captions, and answer the following questions.

- **What force links individual water molecules together?** (One end of the water molecule has a slight positive charge and the other end has a slight negative charge. Opposite ends of different molecules attract each other and link the molecules together.)
- **Describe how sodium chloride dissolves in water.** (The positive sodium ions are attracted to the slight negative charge of water's oxygen atoms. The negative chlorine ions are attracted to the positive hydrogen atoms. The result is that the sodium chloride dissolves in water.)
- **What happens when cooking oil is added to water?** (Cooking oil does not dissolve in water because cooking oil is a nonpolar compound. For this reason, water and cooking oil stay separate from each other.)

Discussion

Initiate a class discussion about the difference between acids and bases. Through this discussion, emphasize the following points.

- Compounds that produce H^+ ions when they are dissolved in water are called acids. Examples are hydrochloric acid, sulfuric acid, and ascorbic acid (vitamin C).
- Compounds that produce OH^- ions when they are dissolved in water are called bases. Examples are sodium hydroxide and ammonia.
- The pH scale is a measure of the strength of an acidic or basic solution.

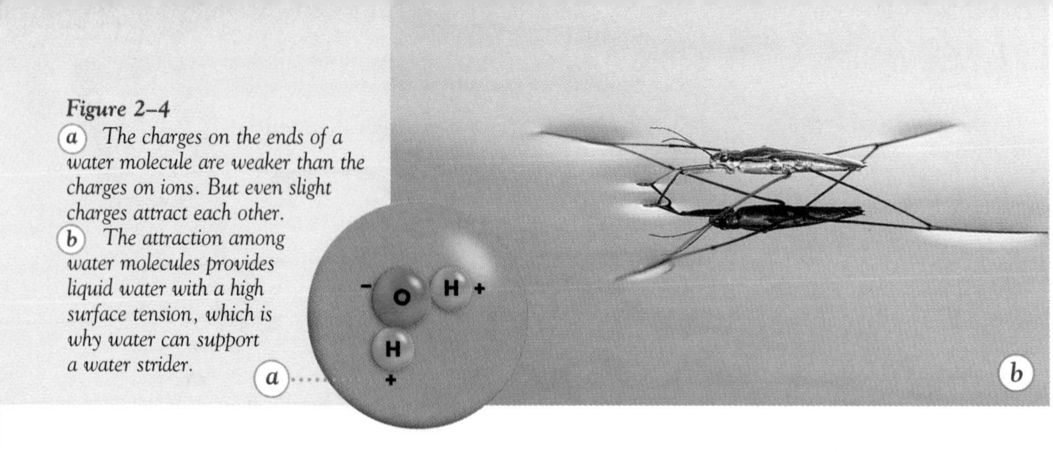

Figure 2–4
ⓐ *The charges on the ends of a water molecule are weaker than the charges on ions. But even slight charges attract each other.*
ⓑ *The attraction among water molecules provides liquid water with a high surface tension, which is why water can support a water strider.*

The Water Molecule

As shown in ***Figure 2–4,*** the 3 atoms in the water molecule form an angle of approximately 105°. In addition, the oxygen nucleus attracts electrons so strongly that the electrons spend much more time near it than they do near the hydrogen nuclei. As a result, the oxygen atom acquires a slight negative charge and the 2 hydrogen atoms acquire slight positive charges.

Because of this charge separation, water is a polar molecule. A polar molecule has one end with a slight positive charge and another end with a slight negative charge. Molecules without positive and negative ends are called nonpolar.

Solutions

When water dissolves a substance, the liquid that results is known as a **solution.** Many compounds in cells are in solution, which is one reason why water is so vital to life.

As a general rule, water is good at dissolving polar and ionic compounds. ***Figure 2–5*** shows how water dissolves sodium chloride (NaCl).

H^+ and OH^- Ions

Another important property of water is its ability to dissociate into ions of its own. A water molecule will occasionally dissociate to produce hydrogen ions (H^+) and hydroxide ions (OH^-):

$$H_2O \rightarrow H^+ + OH^-$$

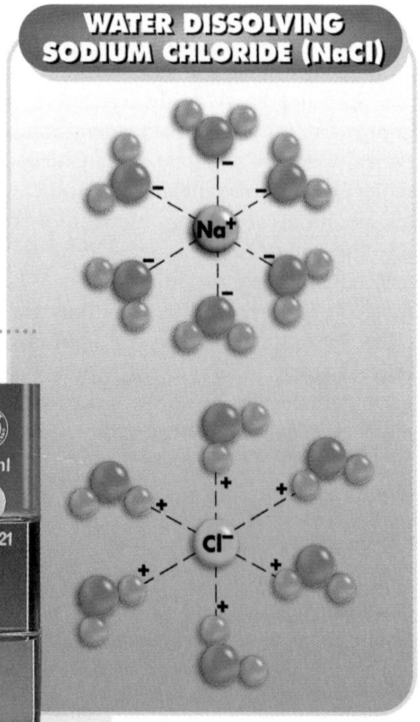

Figure 2–5
ⓐ *Sodium chloride (NaCl) dissolves in water because the negative ends of water molecules cluster around the Na^+ ions, while the positive ends cluster around the Cl^- ions.* ⓑ *Water does not dissolve nonpolar compounds, such as cooking oil, which is why the cooking oil rests apart from the water in this separating funnel.*

TEACHER SUPPORT

Ecology Note

All life on Earth is water based. The typical animal is composed of 70 percent water; the typical plant, 90 percent. Some organisms also depend on certain properties of water in their environment. For example, the water strider can walk on water because of its surface tension, which results from the cohesion of water molecules at its surface.

Other properties of water are important to living things. Water is the only substance that exists as a solid, a liquid, and a gas in Earth's normal range of temperatures. In addition, water, unlike almost every other substance, is less dense as a solid than it is as a liquid. Thus, ice floats on water rather than sinking to the bottom of a river or lake.

Bio Frontier Connections

Acid Rain

Over the past 25 years, many trees in the American Northeast have come to look like those shown in the photograph. What is causing this damage? Some scientists suspect that the culprit is acid rain. Although rainwater is almost always acidic, some rainwater there has been found to be nearly as acidic as soda water.

Recent studies suggest that acid rain may wash away important substances from the soil, depriving large trees of nutrients they need to survive. Acid rain also kills fishes and other aquatic life. However, carefully controlled studies have shown that acid rain alone does not affect the growth of many types of trees—including pine, oak, and poplar.

The Causes of Acid Rain

What causes acid rain? One important cause is the burning of coal. Coal is composed principally of carbon, but it also contains small amounts of sulfur. When coal is burned, the sulfur reacts with oxygen to form sulfur dioxide (SO_2). Sulfur dioxide reacts with water in the atmosphere to form sulfuric acid (H_2SO_4), producing acid rain.

The Clean Air Act

To prevent acid rain, would it help to reduce the sulfur dioxide released into the atmosphere? In 1990, the United States government enacted a law to do just that. This law, called the Clean Air Act, required coal-burning power plants to reduce their sulfur dioxide emissions by 50 percent in 1995 and to cut them even more by the year 2000.

Has the Clean Air Act reduced acid rain, and will it do so in the years ahead? The question is not easy to answer. From 1972 to 1990, total SO_2 emissions decreased by about 30 percent, but the average acid content of rainwater in the eastern United States changed little. The Clean Air Act also forces reductions in particles released into the air. Many of these particles are alkaline, or basic, and thus help to lower the acidity of rainfall.

Acid rain destroyed these fir trees in North Carolina.

Changing Times for Coal Miners

Whether or not it has environmental effects, the Clean Air Act has had an economic impact. For many years, coal mines provided thousands of jobs in the eastern United States. But because the coal in much of this region is especially high in sulfur content, many mines are closing. Workers are without jobs and without the skills to get new jobs. However, some coal-production jobs have shifted to western regions of the United States, where the coal has less sulfur content.

Making the Connection

If a law to reduce acid rain led to a loss in your family's income, would you support the law? Should the government compensate or relocate the coal miners who lost their jobs? What do you think?

Connections

Acid rain is more properly called acid precipitation because it includes acid snow, fog, and even dew. As ponds and other aquatic ecosystems become more acidic, the process that often suffers most is reproduction because eggs, sperm, and developing young cannot adapt to the changing pH. In forest ecosystems, the acid rain not only damages trees directly; it also removes nutrients from the soil. Trees grow more slowly and fall prey to attacks by insects and fungal diseases.

Prevailing winds carry pollutants from coal-burning power plants in the eastern Midwest to areas in the northeastern United States. Restrictions on the amount of pollution these plants can produce have already meant a loss of coal-mining jobs in Ohio, West Virginia, and elsewhere, as companies have switched to lower-sulfur coal from the West.

Answers to Making the Connection

Accept any thoughtful responses to the questions. Some students will suggest that a loss of income or jobs would be a necessary short-term price to pay for a long-term benefit to the environment. Other students may suggest that such a price would be too high.

Teacher Support: Facts and Figures

Although pure water has a neutral pH, all rain is slightly acidic. As raindrops form and fall to the ground, the water reacts with CO_2 in the atmosphere, forming carbonic acid. Thus, unpolluted rainwater may have a pH as low as 5.6. But air pollutants, most notably SO_2 from the burning of fossil fuels, lower the pH even further. The rain that normally falls in the eastern United States, for example, has a pH of 4.5—with some areas averaging as low as 4.0. Researchers measuring the moisture in Los Angeles fogs have found pH values as low as 2.0. Since one pH unit represents a tenfold difference in value, acid rain may be a hundred and even a thousand times more acidic than normal rain.

Ancillary Support

The resource below can be used to support your teaching strategy for these two pages.

LM Constructing Molecular Models, #3

4 ASSESS

Quick Check

Have students compare and contrast acids and bases in a concept map. Suggest that they include a definition of each, the ions associated with each, the pH range of each, and examples of each, taken from the text and from Figure 2–6.

Section Review 2-1

1. The key difference between the atoms of different elements is the number of protons and electrons they contain.
2. In an ionic bond, atoms become ions as they transfer electrons, and the attraction of oppositely charged ions links them into compounds. In a covalent bond, atoms are bonded as they share electrons.
3. The H^+ ion and the OH^- ion are two of the most reactive ions in nature.
4. If water were added to the mixture of crystals, the sodium chloride would dissolve in the liquid while the silica would not. A filter could then be used to separate the silica crystals from the liquid solution.

Learning Modality

Tactile Learning Ask students to make gumdrop-and-toothpick models of the two types of bonding. Students may also use small styrofoam balls and dowels. Have them work from the illustrations in Figure 2–3. Based on Figure 2–5 and their knowledge of chemistry, have students make a model of a water molecule.

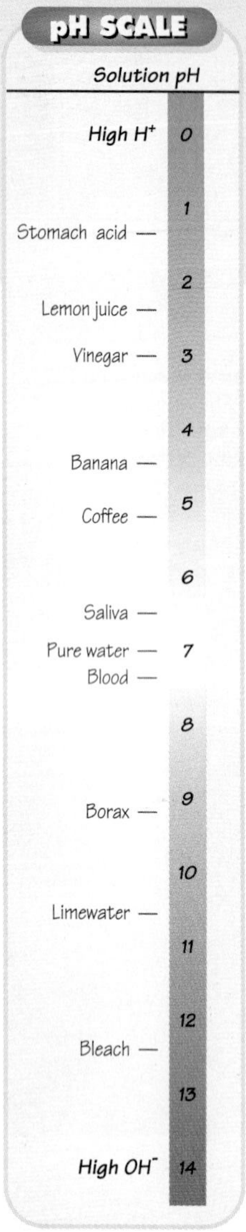

Figure 2–6
The pH scale indicates the concentrations of H^+ ions and OH^- ions in a solution. The two ions are at equal concentrations at pH 7.

The H^+ ion and the OH^- ion are two of the most reactive ions in nature. As shown in ***Figure 2–6,*** the higher the concentration of H^+ or OH^- ions, the more reactive the solution.

Acids and Bases

What is the source of extra H^+ ions or OH^- ions in a solution? Certain compounds dissociate in water to produce these ions. A compound that produces H^+ ions is called an **acid.** One acid that is produced in your own stomach is hydrochloric acid (HCl). Hydrochloric acid dissociates in water to produce H^+ ions and Cl^- ions:

$$HCl \rightarrow H^+ + Cl^-$$

A compound that produces OH^- ions is called a **base.** One example is sodium hydroxide (NaOH), which dissociates to produce Na^+ ions and OH^- ions:

$$NaOH \rightarrow Na^+ + OH^-$$

However, many bases do not themselves contain OH^- ions. Instead, they produce OH^- ions by accepting an H^+ ion from a water molecule. One base that reacts with water in this way is ammonia (NH_3):

$$NH_3 + H_2O \rightarrow NH_4^+ + OH^-$$

In living things, compounds that are related to ammonia are especially important bases.

Checkpoint What is an acid? A base? 1

pH

To indicate the strength of an acidic or a basic solution, scientists use the **pH scale.** As illustrated in ***Figure 2–6,*** the pH of a solution decreases with acidity. Therefore, a pH of 1 or 2 indicates a very acidic solution, and a pH of 12 or 13 indicates a very basic solution. Pure water contains equal amounts of H^+ ions and OH^- ions, and it has a pH of 7.

Biologists are often interested in the pH of solutions in living organisms. In your stomach, for example, the solution of hydrochloric acid (HCl) has a pH of approximately 2. This solution is far more acidic than human cells can tolerate. Normally, the stomach is lined with a material that protects its cells from the acid. But when that lining breaks down, the result is a painful condition called an ulcer.

Section Review 2-1

1. **Explain** how the atoms of elements differ.
2. **Compare** the different bonds that atoms form.
3. **Describe** the properties of the H^+ ion and the OH^- ion.
4. **Critical Thinking—Applying Concepts** Silica is a hard, glassy material that does not dissolve in water. Suppose silica crystals are accidentally mixed with sodium chloride. Describe how the mixture could be separated.

TEACHER SUPPORT

Facts and Figures

The letters pH stand for the power of the Hydrogen ion. The pH scale actually is a measurement of the concentration of hydronium ions (H_3O^+). Each unit of the scale represents a tenfold difference; therefore, a solution with a pH of 5 is ten times more acidic than a solution with a pH of 6. The following are the pH values of common substances.

- soft drinks 2.5–3.5
- orange 3.0–4.0
- tomato 4.0–4.4
- rainwater 5.6
- cow's milk 6.3–6.6
- human milk 6.6–7.6
- drinking water 6.5–8.0
- fresh eggs 7.6–8.0
- sea water 7.8–8.3
- household ammonia 10.5–11.9

The Compounds of Life

SECTION 2–2

Guide for Reading

- **Describe** the special properties of carbon.
- **Identify** the four major classes of macromolecules.

MINI LAB

- **Observe** how different foods react with Lugol's solution.

HOW DO THE COMPOUNDS OF life differ from the compounds of the nonliving world? The answer begins with the element carbon. Indeed, science-fiction writers often use the phrase "carbon-based life forms" to describe the living things of Earth. As you will discover, this description is quite accurate!

Carbon—A Special Element

As illustrated in *Figure 2–7,* a carbon atom has 6 electrons. In order to gain a stable arrangement of 10 electrons, a carbon atom typically forms 4 covalent bonds. And because the carbon atom is relatively small, the bonds it forms are significantly short and strong. As a result, carbon is able to form long, stable chains of atoms.

The bonds in the carbon chains can be single, double, or triple covalent bonds, and the chains can even close upon themselves to form rings and loops. In addition, a carbon chain can include or be attached to atoms of other elements, including nitrogen, oxygen, and phosphorus. **Although a few other elements form chains, none matches carbon in forming chains of different shapes, sizes, and complexity.**

With some exceptions, compounds that contain at least 2 carbon atoms are called **organic compounds.** All the other compounds are called **inorganic compounds.** As you will discover, living things make and use a tremendous number and

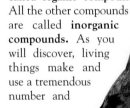

Figure 2–7 (a) *A tropical rain forest is home to an incredible diversity of organisms—from leafy green palms and red heliconia flowers to* (b) *a colorful keel-billed toucan.* (c) *At the molecular level, life in the rain forest—and every place else on Earth—depends on carbon. Carbon is the principal element in all of the large molecules that organisms make and use.*

TEACHER SUPPORT

Facts and Figures

Carbon is one of the most widely distributed of all the elements. More than 90 percent of all known compounds contain carbon—more than 2 million compounds. It exists in a pure state in three crystalline forms, including diamond, graphite, and fullerenes (spheres of carbon atoms that were first discovered in 1985). Carbon also exists in noncrystalline form as charcoal, coke, and lampblack.

The chemistry of carbon is called organic chemistry because scientists once thought that carbon compounds could be produced only by living organisms. That notion was disproved in 1828, when German chemist Friedrich Wöhler synthesized the organic compound urea in his laboratory.

Section 2–2

The Compounds of Life

Performance Objectives

- Discuss the special properties of carbon.
- Describe the four major classes of macromolecules.

Mini Lab Skill: Observing

1 ENGAGE

Ideas Through Images

Have students examine Figure 2–7, read the caption, and answer the following questions.

- **Why is carbon an important element in the study of living things?** (Carbon is the principal element in all the large molecules that organisms make and use.)
- **What does the illustration of the carbon atom show about how many electrons it needs to gain a stable arrangement?** (A carbon atom has only 4 electrons in its outer energy level, and thus it needs 4 more to fill that level.)
- **Therefore, how many covalent bonds do you think carbon would typically form?** (Students should conclude that carbon would typically form 4 covalent bonds.)
- **How many atoms of oxygen are needed to join with one carbon atom to form carbon dioxide?** (2 atoms.)

Checkpoint

1 An acid is a compound that produces H^+ ions. A base is a compound that produces OH^- ions.

2 EXPLORE

MINI LAB Observing

Teacher Notes
- For time required and materials needed, see page 26b.
- Prepare an adequate number of slices of peeled potato and small pieces of white bread before class.
- Caution students not to taste any of the foods, before or after the addition of Lugol's solution.

Answers to Analyze and Conclude
1. As indicated by the dark blue color, the foods containing starch include the soda cracker, potato, white bread, and oatmeal. The granulated sugar does not contain starch.
2. In a dark-colored food, the color change caused by the drops of Lugol's solution might not be observable.

Skills Trace
Observing
- Focus p. 34
- Practice p. 36
- Assess p. 47

INTEGRATING LANGUAGE ARTS

A virtually limitless number of combinations can be made from the 26 letters of the alphabet. Some languages, such as Chinese, do not use letters to build words; rather, each word has its own symbol.

MINI LAB .... Observing ....

The Starch Test

PROBLEM *Which foods contain starch? **Observe** the results of adding Lugol's solution to different foods.*

PROCEDURE

1. Place pieces of a soda cracker into a test tube.
2. Add 5 drops of Lugol's solution to the test tube. Lugol's solution is a test for starch. If the solution turns dark blue or black, starch is present. Record your observations.
3. Repeat the procedure using small amounts of peeled potato, white bread, oatmeal, and granulated sugar.

ANALYZE AND CONCLUDE

1. Of the foods you tested, which contain starch? Which do not contain starch?
2. Why might this procedure not indicate starch in a dark-colored food, such as a graham cracker?

variety of organic compounds. And they do so with a speed, accuracy, and efficiency that is far greater than any chemical process in the nonliving world.

Macromolecules

Most complex organic molecules are **polymers,** meaning "many units." Polymers are large molecules assembled from small, individual molecules. The small molecules are called **monomers,** meaning "single units". You can think of monomers as the individual letters and other characters of the English language. When these characters join together, they can form a nearly infinite variety of words, sentences, or paragraphs—the polymers.

INTEGRATING LANGUAGE ARTS
Why can a huge variety of English words and sentences be created from only 26 letters? Do all languages use letters to build words?

Many organic polymers are so large that they are known as **macromolecules,** meaning "giant molecules." **The four major classes of macromolecules are carbohydrates, lipids, proteins, and nucleic acids.** Let's take a closer look at each of these four classes.

Carbohydrates

Sugars and starches are members of the class of compounds called **carbohydrates.** Carbohydrates are made of carbon, hydrogen, and oxygen. They generally contain 2 hydrogen atoms for each oxygen atom, the same ratio found in water.

The smallest carbohydrates are the simple sugars. The simple sugars include galactose (found in milk), fructose (found in fruits), and glucose (found in the cells of every organism). Each of these simple sugars has the chemical formula $C_6H_{12}O_6$. However, they are different because each has a slightly different arrangement of its atoms.

Sugars are easy for cells both to make and to break down. They serve as a convenient way for cells to store chemical energy, and their breakdown provides cells with energy for all sorts of activities, including cell movement.

While organisms use simple sugars individually, they can also assemble them into polymers. For this reason, a simple sugar is also called a monosaccharide, meaning "single sugar." Two simple sugars joined together form a disaccharide. Ordinary table sugar, or sucrose, is one example of a disaccharide.

A polysaccharide consists of a large number of monosaccharides joined together. You can think of polysaccharides as warehouses for simple sugars. Plants store excess sugar in the form of a polysaccharide, called starch. Animals store excess sugar by making a slightly different polysaccharide, called glycogen.

☑ **Checkpoint** How do organisms use polysaccharides? 1

TEACHER SUPPORT

Managing Classroom Diversity

TECH PREP STUDENTS
Students who plan careers in food service, health care, and home economics will need to know which foods are high in protein, carbohydrates, and fats. Ask these students to research what dietary professionals recommend about the daily consumption of these classes of macromolecules in foods.

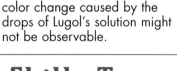

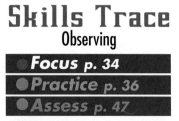

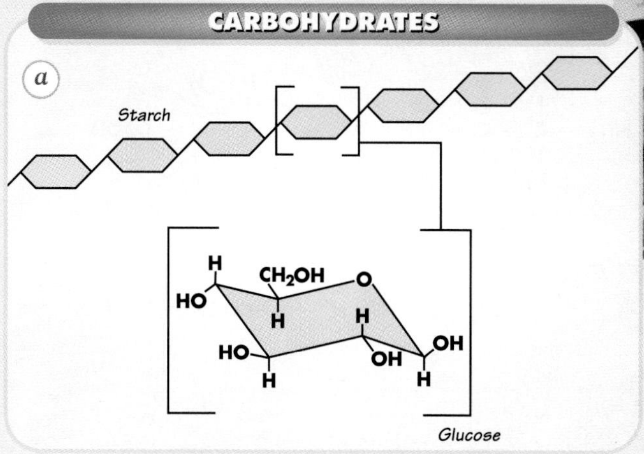

Figure 2–8
(a) Glucose is the monomer for starch, a common polysaccharide. In this drawing, each hexagon represents a glucose monomer. (b) Starch is found in many foods, including pasta.

Lipids

Another class of macromolecules made from carbon, oxygen, and hydrogen atoms is known as the **lipids.** Lipids are waxy, fatty, or oily compounds. Like carbohydrates, lipids can be used to store and release energy. But lipids have other uses as well.

Many lipids are formed by combining smaller compounds such as fatty acids and glycerol. Fatty acids are long chains of carbon and hydrogen acids that have an acidic carboxyl group (–COOH) attached to one end. Glycerol is a 3-carbon alcohol that contains three hydroxyl groups (–OH). Other lipids are based on a series of carbon rings, such as a compound called cholesterol.

☑ **Checkpoint** What are lipids? ②

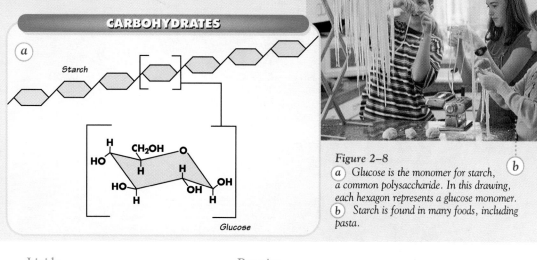

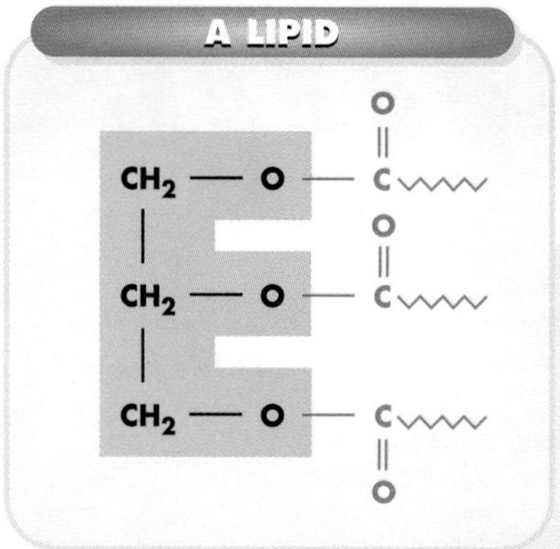

Proteins

An especially important class of organic compounds is the **proteins.** Proteins are polymers of molecules called **amino acids.** There are 20 common amino acids, but each one has a central carbon bonded to an amino group ($-NH_2$), a carboxyl group (–COOH), a hydrogen atom, and a fourth group abbreviated by the letter R. The R group is what makes the amino acids different from each other. In glycine, the R group is a hydrogen atom. In alanine, the R group is a methyl group ($-CH_3$).

Two amino acids can be joined together in a reaction between the amino group ($-NH_2$) of one amino acid and the carboxyl group (–COOH) of the other amino acid. The bond that forms from this reaction is called a peptide bond. For this reason, a chain of amino acids is often called a polypeptide. A complete protein contains one or more polypeptides, and it may contain a few other chemical groups.

Figure 2–9
A glycerol molecule can combine with three fatty acids to form a lipid. The fatty acid portion of the lipid contains long tails of carbon and hydrogen atoms, represented here as zigzag lines.

3 TEACH

Ideas Through Images

Have students examine Figure 2–8, read the caption, and answer the following questions.

- **What does each hexagon in the illustration represent?** (A glucose monomer.)
- **What is the chemical formula for glucose?** ($C_6H_{12}O_6$.)

Discussion

Initiate a discussion about the four major classes of macromolecules. Through this discussion, emphasize the following points.

- All four classes are organic compounds and thus contain carbon chains.
- Carbohydrates include sugars and starches.
- Lipids are waxy, fatty, or oily compounds.
- Proteins are polymers of molecules called amino acids. A chain of amino acids is called a polypeptide.
- Nucleic acids, which include DNA and RNA, are the molecules of inheritance.

☑ Checkpoints

① Organisms store excess sugar in the form of polysaccharides.

② Lipids are waxy, fatty, or oily compounds used to store and release energy.

TEACHER SUPPORT

Historical Perspective

Animal fat was once commonly used by American pioneers to make soap. A large amount of the fat was boiled in a vat of water, which broke the fat apart into its component parts, glycerol and fatty acids. Then powdered lye (sodium hydroxide or potassium hydroxide) was added to the vat. The acid parts of the fatty acids quickly reacted with these strong bases, forming organic salts that contained sodium or potassium bound to the carboxyl ends of the fatty acids. These compounds could dissolve well in water (because they were strongly charged at the carboxyl end) and could also bind strongly to fats and oils (because of the long hydrocarbon chain of the fatty acids). These properties made this old-fashioned soap ideal for dissolving oil and grease.

Ancillary Support

The resources below can be used to support your teaching strategy for these two pages.

LM Identifying Organic Compounds, #4
TR Writing in Biology: Stocking Up on the Right Stuff
Enrich: Paper Proteins
BL Inquiry Activity: Look What You're Eating!

Ideas Through Images

Have students examine Figure 2–11, read the caption, and answer the following questions.

- **What is DNA?** (DNA is one type of nucleic acid.)
- **DNA is found in the form of a double helix. How would you describe that shape?** (A double helix consists of two strands of molecules twisted around each other.)

4 ASSESS

Quick Check

Have students make a table to organize information about the four major classes of macromolecules. The table should contain definitions, chemical formulas, and examples of each.

Section Review 2-2

1. Carbon is able to form long, stable chains of atoms of different shapes, sizes, and complexity that can include or be attached to atoms of different elements.
2. The four major classes are carbohydrates, lipids, proteins, and nucleic acids.
3. Such a cell could no longer produce carbohydrates, which are simple sugars or combinations of simple sugars.
4. With the addition of Lugol's solution, the soda cracker turned a dark blue, indicating the presence of starch in the cracker.

Skills Trace
Observing

- Focus p. 34
- Practice p. 36
- Assess p. 47

Figure 2–10
(a) The amino acids in proteins are joined by peptide bonds, which form between –COOH groups and –NH_2 groups. (b) Proteins are made linearly—one peptide bond after another. However, they bend and fold to form complex, three-dimensional structures.

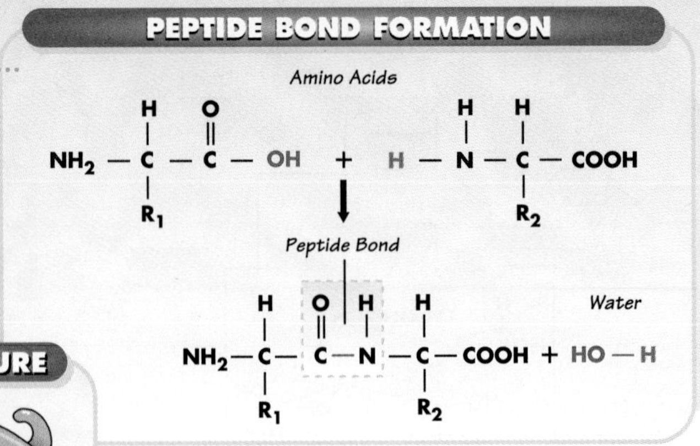

$$NH_2-\underset{R_1}{\overset{H}{C}}-\overset{O}{\overset{\|}{C}}-OH + H-\overset{H}{N}-\underset{R_2}{\overset{H}{C}}-COOH \rightarrow NH_2-\underset{R_1}{\overset{H}{C}}-\overset{O}{\overset{\|}{C}}-\overset{H}{N}-\underset{R_2}{\overset{H}{C}}-COOH + HO-H$$

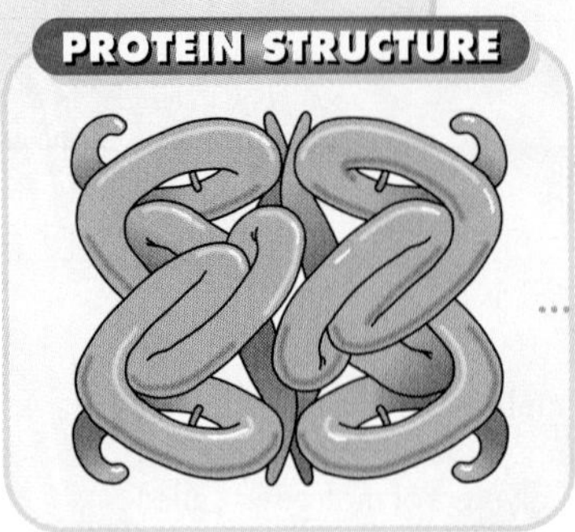

Proteins are the principal components of a number of different structures, including feathers, skin, and muscles. They also help chemical reactions to proceed, pump small molecules in and out of cells, and they can even produce motion.

☑ **Checkpoint** What are the monomers of proteins? 1

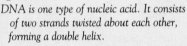

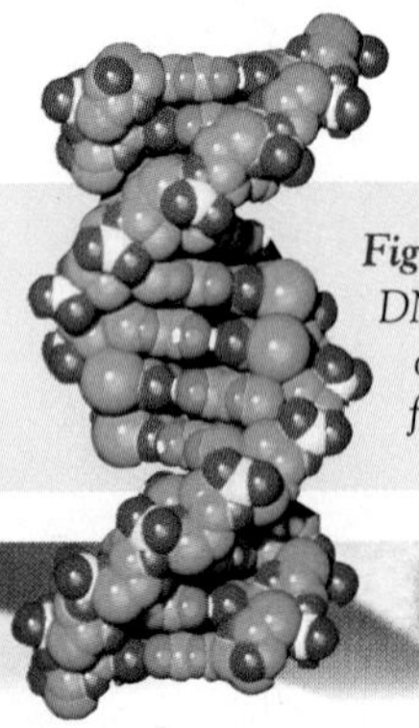

Figure 2–11
DNA is one type of nucleic acid. It consists of two strands twisted about each other, forming a double helix.

Nucleic Acids

The information-carrying molecules of the cell are the **nucleic acids.** The nucleic acids also are the molecules of inheritance—the molecules that parents pass on to their offspring.

There are two principal kinds of nucleic acids: DNA (deoxyribonucleic acid) and RNA (ribonucleic acid). As the beginnings of their names indicate, DNA contains the sugar deoxyribose and RNA contains the sugar ribose.

Nucleic acids are assembled from monomers called nucleotides. Each nucleotide contains three parts: a phosphate group, an organic compound known as a nitrogenous base, and a 5-carbon sugar—either ribose or deoxyribose. DNA and RNA each contain four different kinds of nucleotides. The arrangement of these nucleotides determines the information that the nucleic acid contains.

Section Review 2-2

1. **Describe** the special properties of carbon.
2. **Identify** the four major classes of macromolecules.
3. **Critical Thinking—Interpreting Data** Suppose that a cell lost its supply of simple sugars and its ability to make its own simple sugars. Which macromolecules could the cell no longer produce? Explain your answer.
4. **MINI LAB** When you added Lugol's solution to the soda cracker, what did you **observe?** What does your observation indicate about the soda cracker?

Learning Modality

Visual Learning To reinforce students' understanding of polypeptides, ask them to make a sketch of the peptide bond formation shown in Figure 2–10.

Chemical Reactions and Enzymes

SECTION 2–3

GUIDE FOR READING

- **Describe** the function of enzymes.

INDIVIDUALLY, DRY CHOCOLATE cake mix, raw eggs, and vegetable oil are not especially tasty or good to eat. But if you were to mix them together, then bake the mixture in the oven, the result—a chocolate cake—would be delicious!

Of course, a living thing is not an oven, and the materials inside it are far more organized and specialized than the materials in cake batter. But in some respects, the processes involved in baking a cake are quite similar to processes that take place in living things.

Chemical Reactions

When you bake a cake, you are controlling a series of **chemical reactions.** A chemical reaction is a process that changes one set of substances into a new set of substances. In this example, the cake mix, eggs, and oil react with each other to produce a chocolate cake—a substance with far different properties from its individual ingredients.

Reactions in Living Things

Do chemical reactions take place in living organisms? Yes, absolutely! Every day, you take in the ingredients of food, water, and oxygen. You use these raw materials to produce energy, to build new cells, and to assemble important compounds. Your body uses a huge number of chemical reactions in each of these processes—and in many others.

$CO_2 + H_2O$

To better understand the chemical reactions that take place in living things, let's examine one important example. This example involves carbon dioxide (CO_2) and water (H_2O). Carbon dioxide is a waste product of cells. In humans and other animals, the blood transports carbon dioxide from the cells to the lungs, where it is eliminated from the body with every breath.

Figure 2–12 *Flour, eggs, sugar, and other ingredients undergo a chemical reaction to become a new substance—a cake. Living things need to control the chemical reactions inside them, just as a chef needs to control the reactions in cake batter for the cake to come out just right.*

TEACHER SUPPORT

Managing Classroom Diversity

LEP/AT-RISK STUDENTS

Some students may not be familiar with how to read and interpret a chemical equation, which is a way in which symbols and formulas are used to represent a chemical reaction. Help students interpret the chemical equation $CO_2 + H_2O \rightarrow H_2CO_3$, which could be expressed in words as "carbon dioxide plus water produces or yields carbonic acid." Explain that the substances undergoing the reaction—on the left side of the arrow—are called the reactants. The arrow itself represents the process of the reaction and indicates that new and different substances are formed. The substances that are formed by the reaction—on the right side of the arrow—are called the products of the reaction.

SECTION 2–3

Chemical Reactions and Enzymes

Performance Objective

- Explain the role of enzymes in chemical reactions.

Laboratory Investigation Skill: Drawing conclusions

1 ENGAGE

Inquiry Activity

Observing

A Mouthful of Reaction

Ask students whether they think saliva in their mouths has any effect on the food they eat. Provide each student with Lugol's solution and a cracker, a test tube containing water, and a test tube containing artificial saliva. Then have students follow these steps.

- Break the cracker in half. Crumble one half and place it in the test tube with water. Crumble the other half and place it in the test tube with artificial saliva. Add five drops of Lugol's solution to each tube.
- Students should note that the cracker with artificial saliva is much paler than the cracker with water when the Lugol's solution is added. Artificial saliva, like the saliva in the mouth, contains amylase, which catalyzes a reaction that breaks down the starch into sugars.

Checkpoint

1. The monomers of proteins are amino acids.

Ancillary Support

The resources below can be used to support your teaching strategy for these two pages.

TR Enrich: The Case of the Missing Enzyme
BL Inquiry Activity: Gas Reaction
TB Peptide Bond Formation, #2

2 EXPLORE

Investigate

Long-Term Project Ask students to create a table to keep track of important chemical reactions that occur in living things. Such a table might include columns for a name, an equation for the reaction, and a description. The first entry should be the reaction that forms carbonic acid in the blood. As students continue through the chapters, they should keep adding important chemical reactions to this table, such as photosynthesis and cellular respiration.

3 TEACH

Ideas Through Images

Have students examine Figure 2–14, read the caption, and answer the following questions.

- **In what way is an enzyme and a substrate like a lock and key?** (An enzyme is like a lock with a place—the active site—that only one key can fit. The substrate is like that key, as it fits into the enzyme's active site.)
- **What purpose is served by this lock-and-key function?** (By locking the key—or substrate—into just the right place, an enzyme allows a chemical reaction to begin.)

Laboratory Investigation

The Laboratory Investigation, Three, Two, One . . . BLASTOFF! on pages 42–43 is appropriate to use at this point in the chapter.

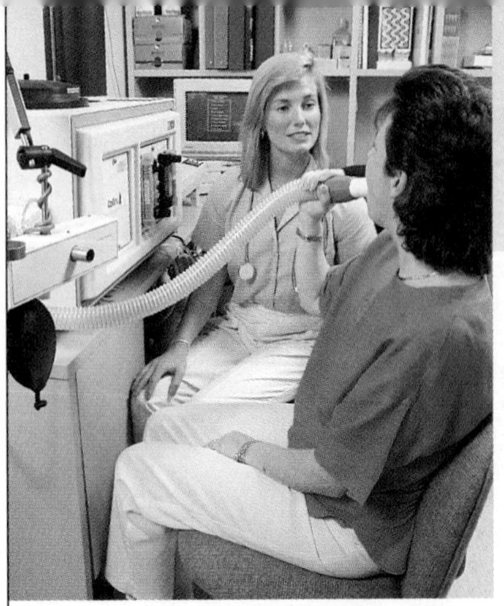

Figure 2–13
CAREER TRACK *A respiratory therapist works with people who have trouble breathing. The machine shown in this photograph analyzes the gases that a person exhales.*

When carbon dioxide enters the blood, it reacts with water to form a compound called carbonic acid (H_2CO_3). This reaction is described by the following equation:

$$CO_2 + H_2O \rightarrow H_2CO_3$$

This reaction is important because carbon dioxide dissolves only minimally in water, while carbonic acid dissolves in water to a much greater extent. By converting carbon dioxide to carbonic acid, the bloodstream is able to accept much more carbon dioxide than it could accept otherwise. Then, when the blood reaches the lungs, carbonic acid is rapidly converted back into carbon dioxide and water, and the carbon dioxide is exhaled from the lungs with every breath.

☑ ***Checkpoint*** Why is the reaction between carbon dioxide and water important? 1

Enzymes

There is one problem with the reaction between carbon dioxide and water, however—it occurs very slowly. It occurs so slowly, in fact, that carbon dioxide would build up in the body faster than the bloodstream could take it away.

How does the body speed up this reaction? The answer is that it produces a molecule that serves as a **catalyst** for the reaction. A catalyst is a substance that speeds up a chemical reaction without itself being used up in the reaction.

In living things, the molecules that serve as catalysts are called **enzymes**—an extremely important group of organic molecules. **Enzymes catalyze almost every important chemical reaction in living things.** By speeding up chemical reactions, enzymes allow living things to carry out a dazzling collection of chemical feats—far more impressive than the reactions chemists create in their laboratories.

How Enzymes Work

Almost all enyzmes are proteins. The enzyme that catalyzes the reaction between carbon dioxide and water is a protein called carbonic anhydrase. In one second, a single molecule of carbonic anhydrase helps to form 600,000 molecules of carbonic acid. Carbonic anhydrase allows the reaction between carbon dioxide and water to occur 10 million times faster than it would occur otherwise.

How do enzymes perform such astounding feats? They do so by reducing the amount of energy it takes for reactions to occur.

Every chemical reaction involves making and breaking chemical bonds. Without an enzyme, the molecules of a reaction would need to collide with each other with enough energy to break existing bonds and form new ones. Enzymes, however, bind the reactions' components individually. This process requires much less energy and, therefore, allows the reaction to run faster.

Active Sites and Substrates

The components of the reaction that bind to the enzyme are called **substrates.** And the region of the enzyme where the substrates bind is called the **active site.**

Some enzymes bind their substrates at the active site in exactly the right orientation for the reaction to occur. Other

TEACHER SUPPORT

Background Information

All enzymes are proteins—at least that's what biologists thought until recently. In 1981, Paula Grabowski and Arthur Zaug, graduate students at the University of Colorado, began investigating a natural process that involved the splicing of RNA molecules. The students assumed an enzyme was in some way responsible, but to their surprise they found that the most active RNA-splicing extracts contained no protein at all. They eventually came to the conclusion that the RNA molecules were being cut and spliced by RNA itself. Therefore, RNA had the ability to catalyze a chemical reaction. Soon other biologists discovered that RNA molecules could catalyze a variety of chemical reactions, so many that the term *ribozyme* was coined to describe an RNA molecule that acts as an enzyme.

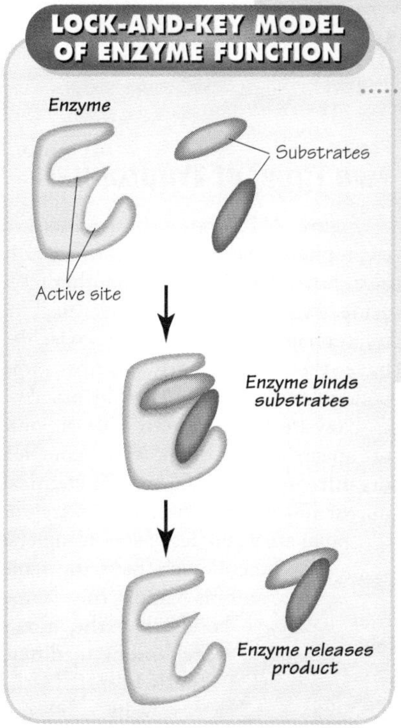

Figure 2–14
(a) An enzyme binds its substrates at the active site, placing them in just the right position for a reaction to occur. (b) An enzyme and its substrates are often compared to a lock and key, because only substrates of the proper shape can fit in the enzyme's active site.

enzymes bend or twist the substrates at the active site, straining or even breaking chemical bonds in order to start the reaction. When the reaction is complete, the reaction's products are released from the active site, the enzyme is free to bind new substrates, and the process can start all over again.

Interestingly, a single enzyme is able to catalyze one and only one chemical reaction. Why is this so? In general, the reason is because the shape of an active site precisely fits the shape of its substrates. In fact, scientists often compare an enzyme and its substrates to a lock and key, as shown in *Figure 2–14*.

☑ **Checkpoint** What is an active site? A substrate? ❷

What Enzymes Do

Enzymes regulate chemical pathways, catalyze the synthesis and breakdown of important compounds, help a cell to store and release energy, and transfer information from one part of a cell to the next. As you will discover in your study of biology, enzymes are involved in digestion, respiration, reproduction, vision, movement, thought, and even in the making of other enzymes. The world of living things could not survive without them!

Section Review 2–3

1. **Describe** the function of enzymes.
2. **Outline** the steps in which an enzyme catalyzes a reaction.
3. **Critical Thinking—Applying Concepts** Changing the temperature or pH changes an enzyme's shape. Describe how changing the temperature or pH would affect the function of carbonic anhydrase.

TEACHER SUPPORT

Activity

ENZYME ACTION!
Divide students into groups, with each successive group having one more student than the group before it. That is, Group 1 has two students, Group 2 has three students, and so on. Have each group count out two hundred wooden toothpicks, and ask one member of each group to act as a timer. Then have all groups begin a "chemical reaction" at the same time—breaking the toothpicks in half. In this activity, the toothpicks represent the substrates and the students represent the enzymes. Students will find that the groups with more members—more enzymes—will complete the reaction faster than groups with fewer members. Have students make a graph of the results, plotting enzyme concentration on the X axis and time of reaction on the Y axis.

4 ASSESS

Quick Check

Ask students to write a story about a "reaction" that fails to occur between two people until a third person plays the role of catalyst.

Section Review 2–3

1. To speed up chemical reactions in living things.
2. The enzyme (a) binds with a substrate at an active site, (b) places the substrate in such a position that the reaction begins, and (c) releases from the substrate once the reaction is complete.
3. If the shape of the enzyme changes due to a change in temperature or pH, then it would not be able to function as a catalyst in the formation of carbonic acid.

Learning Modality

Visual Learning Show students a large padlock and ask them what it represents in a chemical reaction. (An enzyme.) Then place a key in the lock and ask what the key and the keyhole represent. (Substrate and active site.)

☑ Checkpoints

❶ Because the conversion of carbon dioxide to carbonic acid allows the bloodstream to accept much more carbon dioxide than it could accept otherwise.

❷ An active site is the region of an enzyme where a substrate binds. A substrate is a reaction component that binds to an enzyme.

Technology
CD-ROM
Enzymes

Section 2–4

Mirror-Image Molecules

Performance Objective

- Describe and give examples of stereoisomers in living things.

Mini Lab Skill: Modeling

1 ENGAGE

Ideas Through Images

Have students examine Figure 2–15, read the caption, and answer the following question.

- **Why are the fox and its mirror image nonidentical?** (The reflection is oriented in exactly the opposite way.)

2 EXPLORE

MINI LAB Modeling

Teacher Note

- For time required and materials needed, see page 26b.

Answers to Analyze and Conclude

1. Similar in shape and parts. Different in the position of the parts.

2. Structures of the two types of tryptophan are composed of the same parts, but they are oriented differently in space.

Skills Trace
Modeling

- Focus p. 41
- Practice p. 41
- Assess p. 47

2–4 Mirror-Image Molecules

Guide for Reading

- **Explain** how different molecules can have the same atoms and bonds.
- **Give examples** of the types of amino acids and sugars found in nature.

MINI LAB

- **Construct a model** of two mirror-image molecules.

PROTEINS HAVE A COMPLEX, three-dimensional structure, and this structure is very important to their function. The active site of an enzyme, for example, needs to have exactly the right shape to bind its substrates.

As scientists looked closely at the three-dimensional structures of amino acids, sugars, and other organic molecules, they discovered some very surprising facts about them. You will discover some of these surprises in this section.

Two Types of Tryptophan

Figure 2–15 shows the structure of tryptophan, one of the amino acids. It also shows the structure of another molecule, one that is almost identical to tryptophan. In fact, the two molecules have the same atoms and the same bonds, and they look almost identical.

How are they different? They are mirror images of each other! **Many complex organic molecules have nonidentical mirror images.** The two types of tryptophan are examples of **stereoisomers.** Stereoisomers have the same atoms and the same bonds, but the atoms are oriented differently in space.

Why are the two mirror images of tryptophan not the same? To answer this question, think about a pair of mirror-image objects in every-day life—such as a pair of gloves. A pair of gloves consists of a right-handed glove

(a)

TWO MIRROR-IMAGE MOLECULES

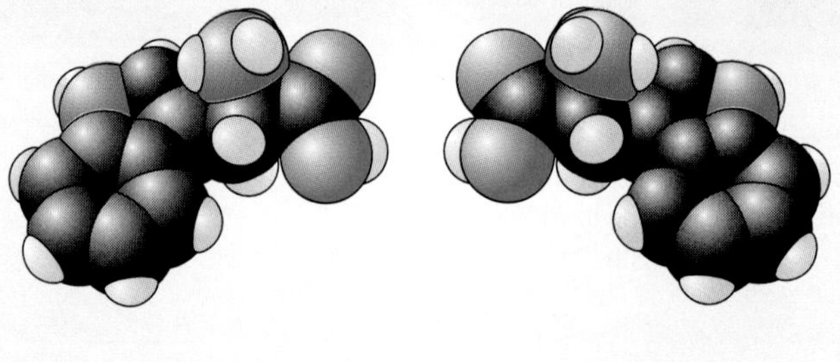

(b)

Figure 2–15 (a) *Like this fox—and many complex three-dimensional objects—some molecules have nonidentical mirror images.* (b) *These computer-generated models represent L-tryptophan and D-tryptophan, two mirror-image molecules.*

TEACHER SUPPORT

Activity

SMELLING RIGHT AND SMELLING LEFT
Carvone is an organic compound that exists in left and right stereoisomers. D-carvone can be isolated from caraway, whereas L-carvone can be isolated from spearmint. Remarkably, these stereoisomers are responsible for the particular smells of caraway and spearmint, which are quite different. Have students smell caraway seeds and spearmint gum, noting the difference caused by the right and left types of carvone. Discuss with students what this implies about the smell receptors in the nose—they are stereoisomers themselves.

and a left-handed glove, and each glove is the mirror image of the other. Despite the fact that a left-handed glove is almost the same as a right-handed one, no matter how you turn or twist the left-handed glove, you cannot make it into a right-handed one.

The two types of tryptophan are related to each other in the same way. In fact, chemists describe them as left-handed and right-handed molecules. One type is called L-tryptophan. The letter L stands for *levo*, the Latin word for left-handed. The other type is called D-tryptophan. The letter D stands for *dextra*, the Latin word for right-handed.

☑ ***Checkpoint*** Why is a pair of gloves like L-tryptophan and D-tryptophan? (1)

A Mirror-Image Puzzle

Surprisingly, with very few exceptions, the amino acids found in living organisms are all of one type—the L type. Like a left-handed glove—one that fits only a left hand—the enzymes in living cells will fit only left-handed amino acids.

Sugars also exist in mirror-image forms. Cells, however, use and produce only right-handed sugars. The 6-carbon sugar D-glucose is one of the most common sugars in the cell. But although L-glucose can be made in the laboratory, it is not used in nature. It's almost as though living organisms decided many hundreds of millions of years ago to use only one type of amino acid and one type of sugar.

MINI LAB ········ *Modeling*

Mirror, Mirror

PROBLEM *How would you* ***construct a model*** *of two mirror-image molecules?*

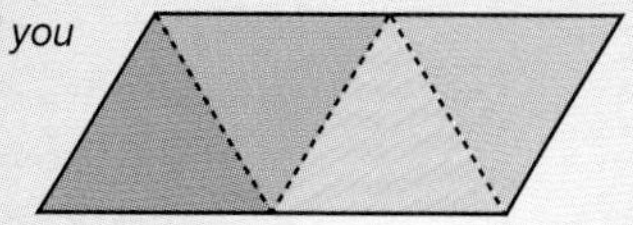

PROCEDURE

1. On a sheet of construction paper, draw the four colored triangles in the arrangement shown. The sides of the triangles should be the same length and be at least 10 cm.
2. Cut the paper along the outer edge of the arrangement.
3. Fold along the borders of the triangles to create a three-dimensional shape called a tetrahedron. Tape together the sides of the tetrahedron.
4. Construct a second tetrahedron by switching the positions of the blue and green triangles in the original arrangement and repeating steps 1 to 3.

ANALYZE AND CONCLUDE

1. Compare the two tetrahedrons you created. How are they similar? Different? Explain your answers.
2. How do the two tetrahedrons relate to the structures of D-tryptophan and L-tryptophan?

Section Review 2-4

1. **Explain** how two molecules can have the same atoms and bonds, yet still be different.
2. **Give examples** of the stereoisomers of amino acids and sugars that are found in living things.
3. **MINI LAB** How would you **construct a model** of mirror-image molecules?
4. **BRANCHING OUT ACTIVITY** **Write** a science-fiction story about a planet where the molecules of life are the mirror images of those on Earth. In your story, explore the problems a visitor from Earth might encounter on this planet.

3 TEACH

Discussion

Initiate a discussion about why an understanding of stereoisomers would be important for a biochemist to have. Emphasize that L-type enzymes predominate in living organisms and that cells use and produce only D-type sugars.

4 ASSESS

Quick Check

Ask students to make a sketch of the type of tryptophan that would most likely be found in living organisms. Students should know to sketch L-tryptophan.

Section Review 2-4

1. Although the atoms and bonds of two molecules may be the same, the atoms are oriented differently in space.
2. The amino acids found in living things are all of the L type. The sugars found in living things are all of the D type.
3. Students should describe making a three-dimensional shape with several colored parts and then switching the position of those parts in the making of a shape that mirrors the first.
4. A typical story might describe the problems faced by a left-handed person in a right-handed world.

☑ Checkpoint

(1) The two types of tryptophan are like gloves in that they are mirror images of each other.

Skills Trace

Modeling

- Focus p. 41
- Practice p. 41
- Assess p. 47

Learning Modality

Kinesthetic Learning Point out to students that their hands are mirror images of each other. Then ask pairs of students to (a) shake hands right to left and (b) right to right. Note that nonidentical mirror images do not work the same.

Ancillary Support

The resources below can be used to support your teaching strategy for these two pages.

TR Apply: Molecules in Stereo
BL Inquiry Activity: Mirror, Mirror

Laboratory Investigation

Three, Two, One . . . BLASTOFF!

Before the Lab

1. At least one day prior to the investigation, gather enough materials for students to work in groups of three or four.
2. Prepare a 1% solution of H_2O_2 by mixing 30 mL of commercial hydrogen peroxide (3% solution) with 60 mL of distilled water. Store in a tightly sealed dark bottle or flask.
3. Prepare potato extract by pureeing two peeled potatoes in 400 mL of distilled water in a blender and filtering the mixture through two layers of cheesecloth placed in a funnel. Each group needs 50 mL.
4. Place the filter paper disks in a clean, dry petri dish.

Pre-Lab Discussion

Have students read the entire procedure for this investigation. Then ask students the following questions.

What is the function of an enzyme? (An enzyme speeds up a chemical reaction in a living thing.)

What is the purpose of this investigation? (To investigate how the concentration of an enzyme affects the rate of a reaction.)

How would you predict the effect of the concentration of an enzyme on the rate of a reaction? (Most students will predict that the higher the concentration of the enzyme, the faster the reaction.)

What is the purpose of doing several trials when performing an experiment? (To make sure that a mistake or an unusual result does not make the findings invalid.)

Laboratory Investigation

Three, Two, One . . . BLASTOFF!

The enzyme catalase speeds up the breakdown of hydrogen peroxide (H_2O_2) into water (H_2O) and oxygen gas (O_2). The reaction is described by the following equation:

$$2\,H_2O_2 \rightarrow 2\,H_2O + O_2$$

Problem

How does the concentration of an enzyme affect the rate of a reaction? Perform a controlled experiment to **draw a conclusion** about the function of enzymes.

Materials (per group)

- potato extract solution
- 1% hydrogen peroxide solution
- 8 50-mL beakers
- distilled water
- filter paper disks
- forceps
- paper towels
- glass-marking pencil

Solution	Potato Extract	Distilled Water
0% Potato extract	0 mL	20 mL
25% Potato extract	5 mL	15 mL
50% Potato extract	10 mL	10 mL
75% Potato extract	15 mL	5 mL
100% Potato extract	20 mL	0 mL

Procedure

1. **Catalase is found in potato extract. Using 5 of the 50-mL beakers, prepare the 5 solutions of potato extract that are described in the table shown. Label each beaker to indicate the percentage of potato extract in the solution.**
2. **Label each of the remaining 3 beakers H_2O_2. Pour 25 mL of the 1% hydrogen peroxide solution into each beaker.**
3. **Using the forceps, dip a filter paper disk into the beaker labeled 0% potato extract. Keep the disk in the solution for 4 seconds, then remove it.**
4. **Place the disk on a paper towel for 4 seconds to remove any excess liquid.**
5. **Using the forceps, transfer the filter paper disk to the bottom of one of the beakers labeled H_2O_2. The enzyme in the potato extract catalyzes the formation of bubbles of oxygen gas, which causes the disk to rise to the surface.**
6. **Release the filter paper disk. Have one person in your group measure how long it takes for the bubbles to carry the disk to the top of the beaker. Record the time in a data table similar to the one shown on the next page.**

Safety Tips

- Remind students to wear safety goggles during the procedure and to handle glassware carefully.
- Caution students to be very careful when working with the hydrogen peroxide solution. Ask them to alert the teacher if there are any major spills.
- Have students wash their hands as soon as they have completed the procedure.

7. Repeat step 6 two more times, using the other two beakers labeled H_2O_2.

8. Repeat steps 3 to 7 for each of the four remaining potato extract solutions.

9. Calculate the average rising time for each of the potato extract solutions. Record this information in your data table.

DATA TABLE

Beaker	Rising Time Trial 1	Rising Time Trial 2	Rising Time Trial 3	Rising Time Average
0% Potato extract				
25% Potato extract				
50% Potato extract				
75% Potato extract				
100% Potato extract				

Observations

Construct a graph that plots the concentration of potato extract (on the X axis) versus the average rising time (on the Y axis).

Analysis and Conclusions

1. Suppose you had dipped a filter paper disk in a 30% potato extract solution. Using the graph, predict how long it would take this disk to rise to the top of a beaker of H_2O_2.
2. How does the concentration of the enzyme affect the rate of the breakdown of hydrogen peroxide? Use the results of this experiment to justify your answer.

More to Explore

Design an experiment to show how the concentration of hydrogen peroxide affects the rate of its breakdown.

Skills Development

Students will use the following skills while completing the laboratory investigation: experimenting, measuring, observing, interpreting, and drawing conclusions.

Teaching Strategies

1. Remind students to label each beaker as they prepare their solutions of potato extract.
2. Demonstrate how to use the forceps to dip the filter paper disk into a beaker, place it on a paper towel, and transfer it to one of the beakers containing hydrogen peroxide.
3. Make sure each group has designated a recorder of data before beginning its trials.

Answers to
Observations

Students' graphs should show the five solutions, from 0% to 100%, along the X axis, and units of time (in seconds) along the Y axis. Using average rising times from their data tables, students should plot a descending line, with the shortest time corresponding to the 100% potato extract.

Answers to
Analysis and Conclusions

1. Students' predictions will vary, depending on the times they recorded in their data tables. Each prediction, though, should fall between the average rising time in the 25% solution and the average rising time in the 50% solution.
2. Students should use the results from their data table to draw the conclusion that the rate of the breakdown of hydrogen peroxide increases with an increase in the concentration of the enzyme.

More to Explore

Most students' designs will be similar to the Laboratory Investigation, with the use of multiple trials and a data table. In this experiment, though, students should vary the amount of hydrogen peroxide that is added to an unvarying amount of distilled water and potato extract.

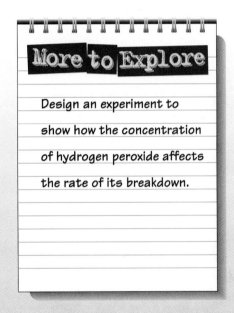

Chapter 2

Study Guide

Review Strategy

Ask students to think about their results in the Chapter Discovery Learning Activity on TE page 26. Have them write a description of what they observed and an explanation of why the salt did not at first cause the water to overflow. Students should augment their written explanations with a sketch of what they think occurred on a molecular level when a teaspoon of salt was added to the water. These sketches should look like the illustration in Figure 2–5 of water dissolving sodium chloride.

Study Guide

Summarizing Key Concepts

The key concepts in each section of this chapter are listed below to help you review the chapter content. Make sure you understand each concept and its relationship to other concepts and to the theme of this chapter.

2–1 Introduction to Chemistry

- The key difference among the atoms of different elements is their number of protons and electrons.
- The links between atoms are called chemical bonds. In ionic bonds, electrons are transferred. In covalent bonds, electrons are shared.
- Water is a polar molecule, which allows water to dissolve ionic substances such as NaCl.
- The pH of a water solution indicates its concentration of H^+ ions and OH^- ions. Acidic solutions have a low pH, and basic solutions have a high pH.

2–2 The Compounds of Life

- Carbon atoms form the backbone of every large molecule found in living organisms. Most carbon compounds are classified as organic compounds.
- A polymer is a large molecule made of repeated units called monomers. Macromolecules are large organic polymers.
- The four major classes of macromolecules are the carbohydrates, lipids, proteins, and nucleic acids.

2–3 Chemical Reactions and Enzymes

- Enzymes catalyze almost every important chemical reaction in living things. Almost all enzymes are proteins.
- Enzymes bind substrates, or the components of a reaction, at a region called the active site.

2–4 Mirror-Image Molecules

- Many complex organic molecules have nonidentical mirror images.
- Stereoisomers have the same atoms and the same bonds, but the atoms are oriented differently in space.

Reviewing Key Terms

Review the following vocabulary terms and their meaning. Then use each term in a complete sentence.

2–1 Introduction to Chemistry

atom, proton, neutron, electron, chemical compound, ion, ionic bond, covalent bond, molecule, solution, acid, base, pH scale

2–2 The Compounds of Life

organic compound, inorganic compound, polymer, monomer, macromolecule, carbohydrate, lipid, protein, amino acid, nucleic acid

2–3 Chemical Reactions and Enzymes

chemical reaction, catalyst, enzyme, substrate, active site

2–4 Mirror-Image Molecules

stereoisomer

Inquiry-Based Strategy

Explain to students that the organisms inhabiting a small lake in the area have been dying at an alarming rate. Some local scientists have suggested that acid rain might be the cause. Have students research how they could find out whether the lake water is more acidic than normal and whether anything could be done on a local level to alleviate the situation. Students should determine what research is necessary to investigate these questions and to develop an appropriate response.

CHAPTER 2

Recalling Main Ideas

Choose the letter of the answer that best completes the statement or answers the question.

1. An atom's nucleus contains protons and
   a. neutrons. **c.** ions.
   b. electrons. **d.** elements.

2. Atoms of different elements always contain different numbers of
   a. neutrons. **c.** ions.
   b. protons. **d.** nuclei.

3. The three atoms in water form a(an)
   a. straight line. **c.** angle of about 105°.
   b. angle of 90°. **d.** ring.

4. Which pH indicates an acidic solution?
   a. 10 **c.** 7
   b. 8 **d.** 5

5. The backbone of large organic molecules is made mostly of
   a. carbon. **c.** nitrogen.
   b. hydrogen. **d.** oxygen.

6. To which class of macromolecules do sugars belong?
   a. carbohydrates **c.** proteins
   b. lipids **d.** nucleic acids

7. Which macromolecules are waxy or oily?
   a. carbohydrates **c.** proteins
   b. lipids **d.** nucleic acids

8. The role of enzymes is to
   a. slow down reactions.
   b. inhibit reactions.
   c. speed up reactions.
   d. store energy.

9. D-glucose and L-glucose are examples of
   a. enzymes. **c.** polysaccharides.
   b. stereoisomers. **d.** amino acids.

Putting It All Together

Using the information on pages xxx to xxxi, complete the following concept map.

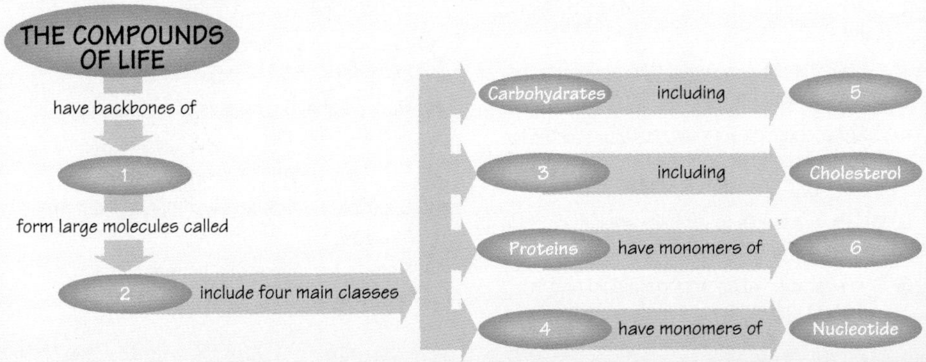

Putting It All Together

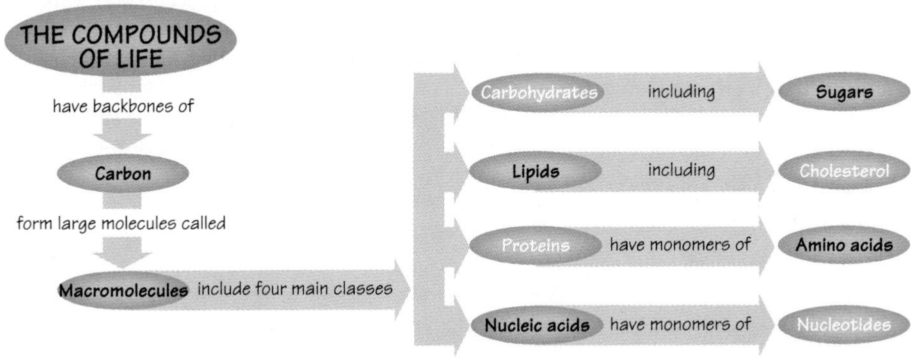

Recalling Main Ideas

1. a
2. b
3. c
4. d
5. a
6. a
7. b
8. c
9. b

Assessment

Reviewing What You Learned

1. An atom is a particle that is the smallest unit of a chemical element.
2. The proton, neutron, and electron.
3. Each water molecule is made of 2 hydrogen atoms and 1 oxygen atom.
4. The oxygen atom has a slight negative charge and the 2 hydrogen atoms have slight positive charges.
5. An atom is neutral, whereas an ion has an electrical charge because it has gained or lost one or more of its electrons.
6. An acid is a compound that produces H^+ ions; a base is a compound that produces OH^- ions.
7. Acidic pH ranges from 1 to 6, neutral pH is 7, and basic pH ranges from 8 to 14.
8. A molecule that contains a chain of at least 2 carbon atoms.
9. A large molecule assembled from small, individual molecules.
10. Types of lipids include fatty acids, glycerol, and cholesterol.
11. Its nucleotides.
12. The blood transports carbon dioxide from the cells to the lungs, where it is eliminated from the body with every breath.
13. The region where it binds its substrates.
14. Examples include L-leucine/D-leucine and L-glucose/D-glucose.

Assessment (continued)

Expanding the Concepts

1. For small atoms, electrons are shared or transferred and serve to bond the atoms together.
2. A single covalent bond is formed from 2 electrons, a double covalent bond from 4 electrons, and a triple covalent bond from 6 electrons.
3. An ionic bond involves the transfer of one or more electrons, whereas a covalent bond involves the sharing of electrons.
4. It could indicate more than one chemical compound if there were a pair of stereoisomers with the same formula.
5. Water is good at dissolving polar or ionic compounds, and sodium chloride is ionic. Water does not dissolve nonpolar compounds, including cooking oil.
6. In humans, hydrochloric acid is produced in the stomach; in many living things, compounds related to ammonia are especially important bases.
7. Because a carbon atom has 6 electrons, it typically forms 4 covalent bonds, and the smallness of the carbon atom results in short and strong bonds. These properties allow carbon to form long chains of atoms.
8. Organisms use sugars as the source of energy for many cell activities. Plants store carbohydrates in a form called starch. Animals store carbohydrates in a form called glycogen.
9. Two amino acids can be joined together in a reaction between the amino group of one amino acid and the carboxyl group of the other amino acid, forming a peptide bond.
10. All four classes are giant molecules that contain chains of carbon atoms. They differ in their structure and their uses in organisms.
11. Catalysts are substances that speed up chemical reactions without being used up in the process. Enzymes are molecules that serve as catalysts in living things.
12. The shape of the active site fits the shape of its substrates very precisely, like a lock and key.

Assessment

Reviewing What You Learned

Answer each of the following in a complete sentence.

1. What is an atom?
2. Identify the three fundamental particles that make up an atom.
3. What does the formula H_2O indicate about water?
4. Why is water a polar molecule?
5. Describe the difference between an atom and an ion.
6. Define the terms acid and base.
7. Give examples of an acidic pH, a neutral pH, and a basic pH.
8. What is an organic molecule?
9. What is a polymer?
10. Identify two different types of lipids.
11. What are the monomers of a nucleic acid?
12. How is carbon dioxide eliminated from the human body?
13. What is the active site of an enzyme?
14. Give an example of a pair of mirror-image molecules.

Expanding the Concepts

Discuss each of the following in a brief paragraph.

1. Describe the way that bonds form between small atoms such as hydrogen, carbon, nitrogen, and oxygen.
2. Compare single, double, and triple covalent bonds.
3. Explain the difference between an ionic bond and a covalent bond.
4. Could a chemical formula, such as $C_5H_{10}O_5$, indicate more than one chemical compound? Explain your answer.
5. Why is water able to dissolve sodium chloride but not cooking oil?
6. Give examples of an important acid and an important base in living things.
7. Why is carbon able to form long chains of atoms?
8. Identify three ways in which organisms use carbohydrates.
9. Describe how amino acids are joined together in a protein.
10. How are the four classes of macromolecules similar? Different?
11. Compare enzymes with other catalysts.
12. Describe the lock-and-key model of enzyme function.
13. Discuss the differences between D- and L- amino acids.

13. Each amino acid exists in a pair of mirror-image forms, the L type and the D type, that have the same atoms and the same bonds but with the atoms oriented differently in space. Almost all of the amino acids in living things are of the L type.

Extending Your Thinking

1. The 2 atoms form a covalent bond because they share electrons to gain a stable arrangement.
2. Students may predict that the polar regions of the lipid molecules will dissolve in the water, while the nonpolar regions will not.
3. Students' drawings should be similar to those of amino acids in Figure 2–10, though with $—COO^-$ in place of $—COOH$ and $—NH_3^+$ in place of $—NH_2$. The amino acid has not acquired a net charge.

Extending Your Thinking

Use the skills you have developed in this chapter to answer the following.

1. **Drawing conclusions** A nitrogen atom contains 7 electrons. Describe the bond between the 2 nitrogen atoms in a molecule of nitrogen gas (N_2).
2. **Predicting** Certain lipid molecules have regions that are polar and regions that are nonpolar. Predict how these lipid molecules would behave in water.
3. **Constructing formulas** At a pH of 7, the –COOH end of an amino acid loses an H^+ ion, while the $-NH_2$ end gains an H^+ ion. Draw the structure of this form of an amino acid and label any charged ends. Has the amino acid acquired a net charge?
4. **Analyzing** A student adds a small amount of the enzyme catalase to a solution of hydrogen peroxide (H_2O_2). The solution produces bubbles of oxygen gas for 10 minutes, then the bubbling stops. Next, the student adds more catalase to the solution. Will more bubbles of oxygen gas be produced? Explain your answer.
5. **Recognizing patterns** Look at the structure of a molecule of acetone. Is acetone found in distinct left- and right-hand versions? Explain.

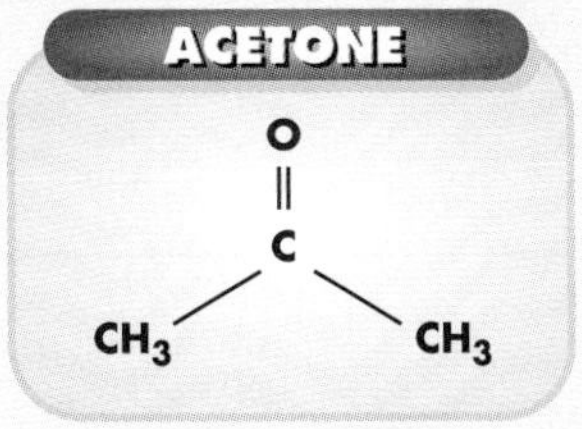

6. **Observing** When you look at a soda cracker with the unaided eye, can you observe the carbohydrates that compose it? Explain why or why not.
7. **Constructing a model** Construct a model of a carbon atom. Label the nucleus, protons, neutrons, and electrons in your model. In what ways is your model accurate? In what ways is it inaccurate?

Applying Your Skills

Read Those Labels!

Carbohydrates, proteins, and lipids are a part of every healthful diet. Just how much of these compounds are in the foods you eat? Perform this activity to find out.

1. Select ten packaged foods that are a part of your diet.
2. For each product, record the serving size and the total grams of carbohydrates, proteins, and lipids (or fats) in each serving. This information is printed on the product's packaging, typically in a table called Nutrition Facts.
3. Which foods provide the most carbohydrates, proteins, and lipids? Which provide the least?

• GOING FURTHER •

4. Bring to class the packaging containing the nutrition facts for your favorite snack. Then construct a table that lists the number of grams of carbohydrates, proteins, and lipids for each snack that you and your classmates brought. Which snack do you suspect is the most healthful? The least healthful? Explain your answers.

4. No, because enzymes are not used up in a reaction. Thus, the bubbling stopped because the components of the reaction had all been used.
5. No, because the atoms in a mirror image would be oriented exactly the same in space.

6. No, because individual molecules are too small to see without powerful instruments.

Skills Trace
Observing
- Focus p. 34
- Practice p. 36
- Assess p. 47

7. The model is accurate in that it shows the correct number of protons, neutrons, and electrons in each carbon atom. It is inaccurate in the relative size and placement of these subatomic particles.

Skills Trace
Modeling
- Focus p. 41
- Practice p. 41
- Assess p. 47

Applying Your Skills

Preparation
1. Bring to class several food packages, including cereal boxes, cracker boxes, milk cartons, and rice boxes.

Suggestions
1. Show students the Nutrition Facts table on several food packages. Point out where the grams of each class of macromolecule are given. Discuss the other information contained on the label.
2. Students can do this activity at home. Ask that they record the information and write down their conclusions. Then have a classroom discussion about the results.

Scoring Rubric
4 Response is thorough, accurate, and creative; shows an in-depth understanding of science skills, procedures, and concepts.

3 Response is complete, mostly accurate, and original; shows a satisfactory understanding of science skills, procedures, and concepts.

2 Response is mostly complete but includes some inaccuracies; shows an adequate understanding of science skills, procedures, and concepts.

1 Response is only partially complete and has many inaccuracies; shows an incomplete understanding of science skills, procedures, and concepts.

0 Response is mostly incomplete and/or inaccurate; shows a lack of understanding of science skills, procedures, and concepts.

Chapter 3 Cell Structure and Function

Content Management	Student Edition Activities
■ Section 3–1 Microscopes and Cells, pp. 49–52 Early Microscopes Modern Microscopes	MINI LAB: Is Seeing Believing?, p. 51
■ Section 3–2 Cell Boundaries, pp. 53–59 Cell Membrane Cell Wall Passive Transport Active Transport	
■ Section 3–3 Inside the Cell, pp. 60–65 Nucleus Cytoplasm	Laboratory Investigation: Inside Plant and Animal Cells, pp. 68–69 MINI LAB: A Colorful Paramecium, p. 64
◆ BRANCHING OUT • In Depth Section 3–4 The Origin of the Eukaryotic Cell, pp. 66–67 The Work of Lynn Margulis Further Evidence	

■ These sections cover all the necessary content and concepts for a basic course in biology.
◆ This section covers content and concepts that are either applications or extensions of the basic material.

Integration Strategies

SE Physics, pp. 49, 51

Assessment Strategies

SE Chapter Review, pp. 70–73
TR Section Reviews
Chapter Test
BL Chapter Review
Practice Test
CTB Chapter 3 Test

Tech Prep

Teaching strategies appropriate for students who are in technical/vocational programs or who are considering post-secondary technical education can be found on the following **TE** page: 53

Meeting the Standards

Sections 3–1 through 3–4 cover five of the six content standards under **The Cell** and one of the five content standards under **Biological Evolution** as described on pages 184–185 of The National Science Education Standards.

Chapter Planning Guide

Teacher's Edition Activities	Other Activities	Media and Technology
Chapter Discovery Learning Activity, p. 48 **Inquiry Activity:** The Parts of a Microscope, p. 49	**LM** Measuring With a Microscope, #5 **TR** **Writing in Biology:** What's in a Name? **Explore:** When Bigger Is Not Better **BL** **Inquiry Activity:** It's So Big!	
Inquiry Activity: An Even Spread, p. 53 **Inquiry Activity:** Passing Through a Membrane, p. 54 **Activity:** A Reversal of Direction, p. 54 **Inquiry Activity:** A Way In but No Way Out, p. 57	**TR** **Explore:** Osmosis: It's in the Bag **BL** **Inquiry Activity:** The Case of the Swollen Grape	**CD-ROM:** The Plasma Membrane & Cellular Transport
Inquiry Activity: What's Inside a Cell?, p. 60 **Investigate:** Cooperative Learning, p. 60	**LM** Comparing Plant and Animal Cells, #6 **TR** **Apply:** Get Out the Map **BL** **Inquiry Activity:** Don't Judge a Cell by Its Membrane	**BioVue Animation:** A Tour of the Animal Cell, Videodisc Side 1 **BioVue Plus CD-ROMs:** A Tour of the Animal Cell **CD-ROM:** Cell Structure and Function **TB** Cell Structure, #3
Investigate: Research, p. 66	**TR** **Enrich:** Guests or Prisoners **BL** **Inquiry Activity:** Cells Within Cells	

KEY: **SE** Student Edition **TE** Teacher's Edition **LM** Laboratory Manual **TR** Teaching Resources **BL** BioLog **TB** Transparency Box **CTB** Computer Test Bank

Materials List

TE Chapter Discovery Learning Activity, p. 48 (20 minutes); photos or drawings of a variety of different kinds of cells.

TE Inquiry Activity: The Parts of a Microscope, p. 49 (20–30 minutes); microscopes.

SE MINI LAB: Is Seeing Believing?, p. 51 (30 minutes); microscopes, prepared slides of printed material.

TE Inquiry Activity: An Even Spread, p. 53 (20 minutes the first day, 10 minutes the next day); water, salt, cups, food coloring, teaspoon, beakers.

TE Inquiry Activity: Passing Through a Membrane, p. 54 (20 minutes the first day, 10 minutes two days later); beaker, balances, pasteurized raw eggs in shells, vinegar.

TE Activity: A Reversal of Direction, p. 54 (10 minutes the first day, 10 minutes the next day); beakers, tablespoon, balance, paper towels, corn syrup or molasses.

TE Inquiry Activity: A Way In but No Way Out, p. 57 (30–40 minutes); beakers, teaspoon, water, cornstarch, tincture of iodine, plastic sandwich bag, twist tie.

SE MINI LAB: A Colorful Paramecium, p. 64 (30 minutes); Paramecium culture, Congo red indicator, yeast, water, slides and coverslips, dropper, microscope, toothpicks.

Chapter 3

Cell Structure and Function

Introducing the Chapter

. . . In Pictures

The visual shows a light microscope's magnification of the epithelial cells that cover the villi in the small intestine. These cells absorb ions and digested food. Have students examine the photograph and answer the following questions.

- **How would you describe the internal structure of cells such as these?** (Most students will know that each of these cells contains a nucleus.)
- **These cells absorb nutrients from the food you eat. How do you think substances are able to get into the cells?** (Students might describe variations on active or passive transport.)

This photograph provides a good introduction to the topics students will learn about in this chapter, including cell structure and movement into and out of cells.

Teaching Strategy

In the first three sections of this chapter, students will learn about instruments used to study cells, cell membranes and walls, and the internal structure of cells. Use the BRANCHING OUT section at the end of the chapter as a way to pique students' interest in the origin of some cell organelles as well as the evolution of life on Earth.

BIO JOURNAL

The Bio Journal topic can be used to stimulate classroom discussion about the structure and function of cells. Ask students to describe functions they think cells must carry out. This will help students to begin thinking about the chapter and also provide some idea of their prior knowledge of cells. Instruct students to keep their entries in their portfolios.

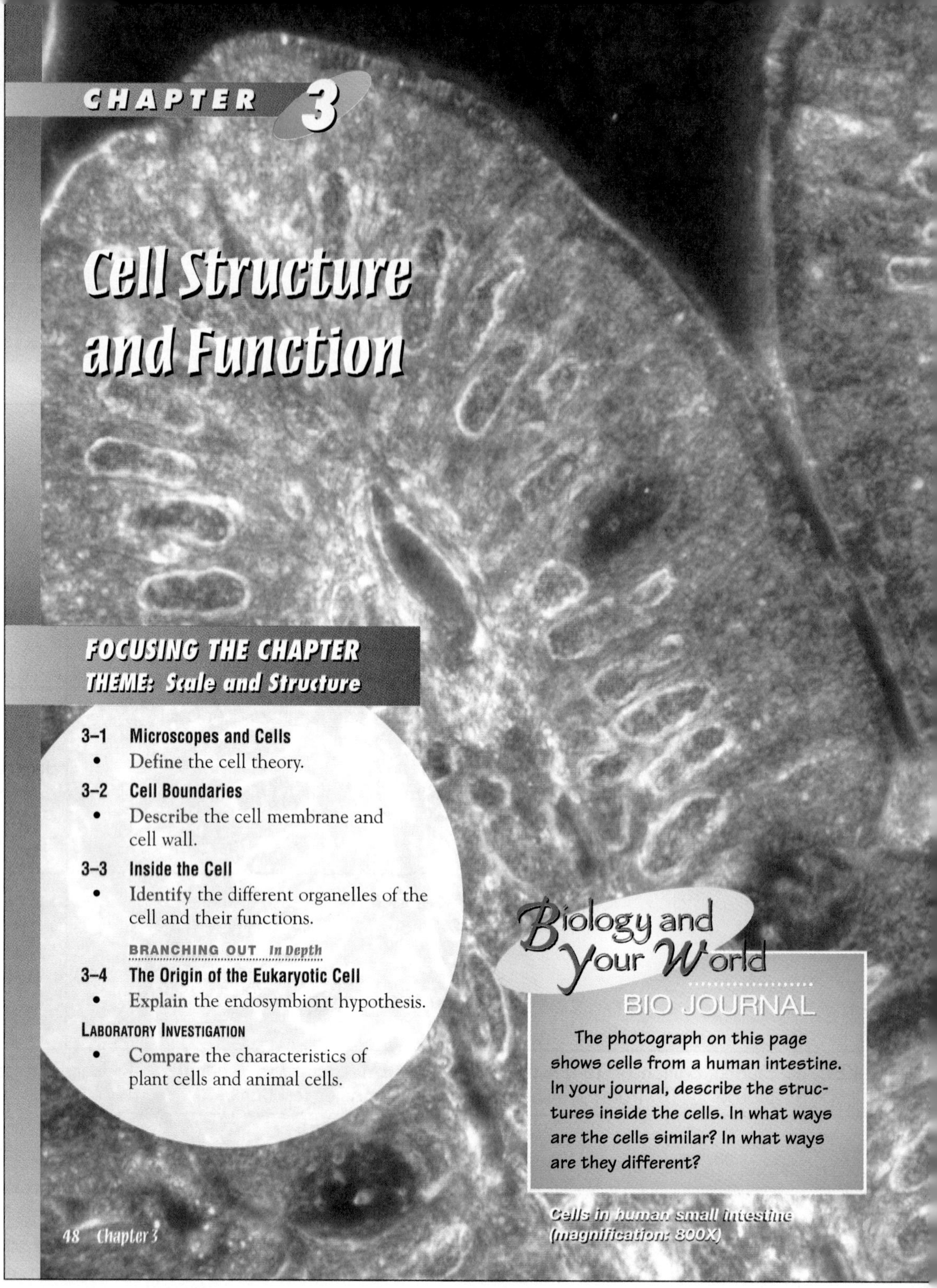

CHAPTER 3

Cell Structure and Function

FOCUSING THE CHAPTER
THEME: *Scale and Structure*

Biology and Your World

BIO JOURNAL

The photograph on this page shows cells from a human intestine. In your journal, describe the structures inside the cells. In what ways are the cells similar? In what ways are they different?

Cells in human small intestine (magnification: 800X)

TEACHER SUPPORT

Chapter Discovery Learning Activity

Display a variety of photographs and drawings of cells taken from old biology texts, magazine articles, and microbiology texts. You also might use a video camera or a microprojector to show slides of a variety of cells, including one-celled organisms as well as cells from various parts of plants and animals. Ask students to make drawings of several cells, labeling any internal structure, such as a nucleus, that they think they recognize. Discuss how cells are the smallest working units of living things. Ask students to try to think of any living thing that is not composed of cells.

Microscopes and Cells

GUIDE FOR READING

- **Define** the cell theory.
- **Identify** the magnification powers of different types of microscopes.

MINI LAB

- **Observe** how the compound microscope changes an image.

THE TYPICAL CELL IS ONLY about 10 micrometers wide—far too small for the unaided eye to see. So how do biologists study cells? Although biologists study cells with a variety of different tools, arguably their most important tool is the microscope. A microscope is an instrument that produces magnified images of tiny structures. Without microscopes, we might never have discovered cells at all!

Early Microscopes

In the 1600s, Dutch businessman Anton van Leeuwenhoek discovered another purpose for the glass lenses he was grinding. By placing several magnifying lenses at the proper distances from each other, Leeuwenhoek created instruments that could produce magnified images of very, very small objects. These instruments were some of the world's first microscopes. One of Leeuwenhoek's microscopes is illustrated in **Figure 3–1.**

INTEGRATING PHYSICS

Why can lenses magnify an image?

Leeuwenhoek's microscopes are, in fact, examples of the most familiar type of microscope, the light microscope. In a light microscope, rays of light are bent through lenses to produce an enlarged image.

Discovery of Cells

Leeuwenhoek used his light microscopes to look at drops of pond water and other liquids. To his amazement, he discovered that many

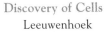

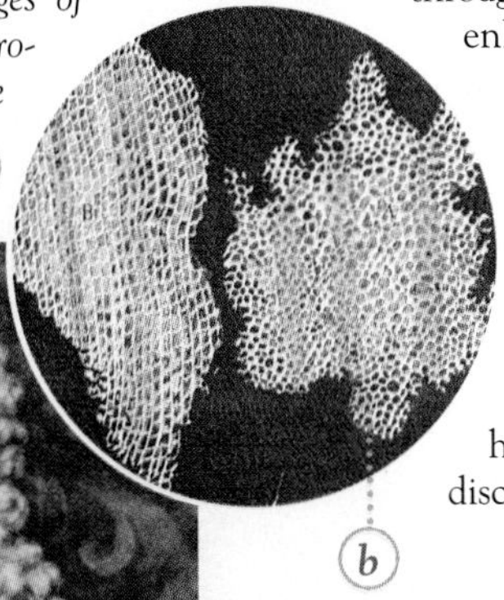

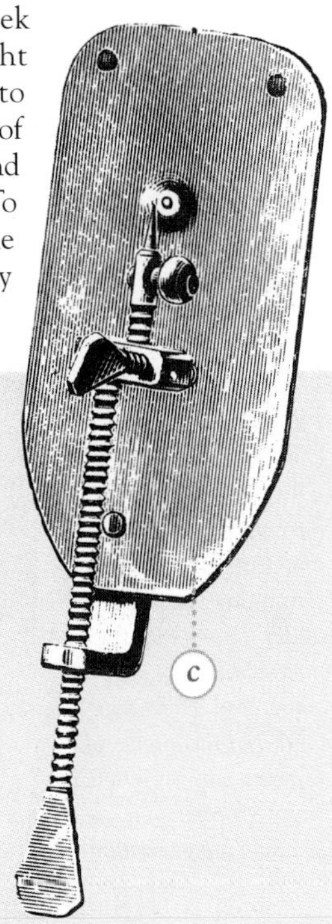

Figure 3–1 (a) *Anton van Leeuwenhoek was the first person to use a microscope to identify living things.* (b) *Robert Hooke used his microscope to study cork, and he made these drawings of his observations. Hooke was looking not at living cork cells but at the cell walls of dead cells.* (c) *Although Leeuwenhoek's microscope may look simple or primitive, it could magnify objects a few hundred times.*

SECTION 3–1

Microscopes and Cells

Performance Objectives

- Explain the cell theory.
- Describe the different types of microscopes and discuss their strengths and limitations.

Mini Lab Skill: Observing

1 ENGAGE

Inquiry Activity

Observing

The Parts of a Microscope

Ask students if they can identify the different parts of a compound light microscope. Provide them with this list of terms: arm, base, clips, coarse adjustment, eyepiece, fine adjustment, mirror, nosepiece, objective lenses (low-power and high-power), stage, and tube. Then allow students to closely examine the microscopes they will be using. Ask them to make a labeled sketch of a microscope, using all of the terms provided.

Have students compare their microscopes to the one shown in Figure 3–1.

- **Where do you think the specimen is placed on Leeuwenhoek's microscope?** (On the pointed tip.)

INTEGRATING PHYSICS

A lens is any transparent material that refracts, or bends, light. A convex lens, the type used in microscopes, causes light to converge, or come together, and in so doing magnifies an image.

TEACHER SUPPORT

Historical Perspective

Anton van Leeuwenhoek had a passion for tiny things. During a lifetime of investigation, he studied the structure of muscle, skin, hair, tooth scrapings, and various small insects. His famous discovery of "animalcules" occurred late in the summer of 1674 when he returned home from boating on a local lake with a sample of the water. That water was cloudy, and most people at the time thought that such cloudiness was caused by a heavy dew. But when Leeuwenhoek used one of the lenses he had mounted as a microscope, he was surprised to see that the water was teeming with tiny organisms, so many that it was cloudy with them. This and other discoveries made him world famous. Perhaps his most remarkable discovery was made in 1676 when he described tiny organisms that are now known to have been bacteria.

2 EXPLORE

MINI LAB Observing

Teacher Notes

- For time required and materials needed, see page 48b.
- Prepare slides prior to class, using small print from newspaper classified ads or stock quotes.

Answers to Analyze and Conclude

1. Students should note that the image they see is both enlarged and inverted.
2. The image moves in the opposite direction from the way the slide is moved. For example, the image appears to move left when the slide is moved right.
3. An advantage is that the object is greatly magnified; a disadvantage is that the field of vision is greatly reduced.

Skills Trace
Observing

- Focus p. 51
- Practice p. 52
- Assess p. 73

3 TEACH

Ideas Through Images

Have students examine the organisms shown in Figures 3–2 and 3–3b, read the captions, and answer the following questions.

- **In what way are these three very different organisms alike?** (They are all composed of cells.)
- **What is the smallest working unit of each of these living things?** (Cells.)
- **What is the origin of each and every cell in all three of these organisms?** (Each cell came from a preexisting cell by cell division.)

Figure 3–2
The cell theory applies to all organisms—from (a) a koala and eucalyptus tree in Australia to (b) a saguaro cactus in Arizona.

of these liquids were filled with tiny living things. He called these tiny things *animalcules*, meaning "little animals."

At about the same time, Robert Hooke, an English physicist, used a microscope to observe flowers, insects, spider webs, and slices of cork. In 1665, Hooke published a book of drawings of his observations. He pointed out that the woody parts of plants contained tiny rectangular chambers, which he called **cells.** Hooke chose this name because the chambers reminded him of the tiny rooms in a monastery, which are also called cells.

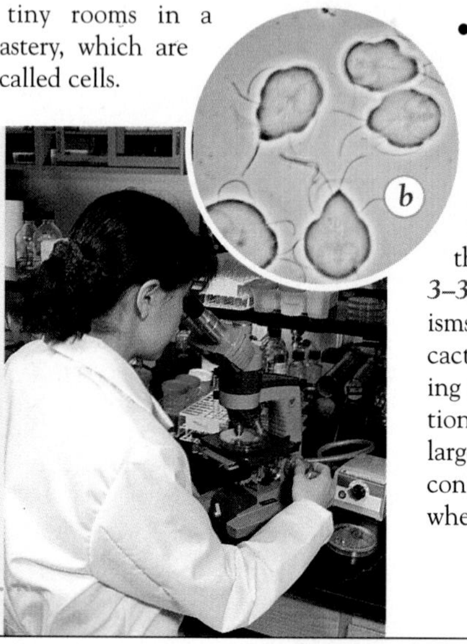

Figure 3–3
CAREER TRACK
(a) Cytotechnologists typically study cells by preparing slides, then examining the slides under a compound microscope. (b) A compound microscope produced this image of Giardia lamblia, *which cause an intestinal disease (magnification: 100X).*

Hooke believed that only plants were made of cells—an idea that scientists did not challenge for nearly 200 years. But in 1839, the German biologist Theodor Schwann found that some animal tissues closely resembled the cellular tissues of plants. As Schwann looked at animal tissues with better microscopes, he gradually came to the conclusion that animals too were made of cells.

The Cell Theory

In the meantime, Robert Brown, a Scottish biologist, had discovered an object near the center of many cells, a structure now called the nucleus. German biologist Matthias Schleiden expanded on Brown's work, suggesting that the cell's nucleus plays a role in cell reproduction. In 1855, German physician Rudolf Virchow further studied cell reproduction. Virchow proposed that animal and plant cells are produced only by the division of cells that already exist.

The discoveries and observations of these scientists make up what is now called the **cell theory.** The cell theory forms a basis for the way biologists study living things. **The cell theory states:**

- **All living things are composed of cells.**
- **Cells are the smallest working units of living things.**
- **All cells come from preexisting cells by cell division.**

The cell theory applies to all organisms. Some organisms, such as the *Giardia lamblia*, shown in **Figure 3–3,** contain only one cell. Other organisms, such as the koala and the saguaro cactus, contain millions of cells—all acting together to help the organism function as a single unit. Yet no matter how large the organism or how many cells it contains, each of its cells was produced when another cell divided in two. It is

TEACHER SUPPORT — Facts and Figures

Here are some facts about light microscopes:

- The first compound microscope was invented in about 1590 by a Dutch spectacle maker named Zacharias Janssen. It measured about 30 cm in length.
- Robert Hooke's compound microscopes also used two lenses, one at each end of a long, dark tube.
- Leeuwenhoek's microscopes used only one lens. His best microscope could magnify an object almost 400 times.
- The magnification of a compound microscope is the product of the magnification of the objective lens and that of the eyepiece. If the objective lens is marked 100X and the eyepiece is marked 12.5X, then the object will be magnified 1250X.
- A compound light microscope is limited to those objects that either are transparent or reflect a great deal of light. Most objects must be sliced into very thin sections to be observed.

interesting to note that, in most cases, an organism begins its life as nothing more than a single cell.

Checkpoint What is the cell theory? ①

Modern Microscopes

It is not surprising that biologists learned more and more about the cell as better and more powerful microscopes were developed. Let's take a look at some of the different kinds of microscopes that biologists use today.

Compound Light Microscope

The most common and familiar type of microscope is the **compound light microscope**—or compound microscope, for short. The word compound indicates that the microscope contains more than one lens. You probably will use this type of microscope in your biology classroom or laboratory.

Most compound microscopes can magnify an image up to 1000 times. This makes the compound microscope useful for studying many kinds of cells and small organisms. In addition, these cells and organisms can sometimes be studied while they are still alive.

Electron Microscope

In the 1920s, German physicists discovered a way to use magnets to focus a beam of electrons, similar to the way a glass lens focuses a beam of light. They used this discovery to build a device with which you are already familiar—the television set. In addition, their work led to the development of the **electron microscope.** An electron microscope uses a beam of electrons instead of light to examine a sample.

An electron microscope can magnify images as much as 1000 times larger than a light microsope can magnify them. For this reason, the electron microscope can show much smaller structures than an ordinary light microscope can reveal.

Checkpoint What is an electron microscope? ②

Types of Electron Microscopes

There are two basic kinds of electron microscopes. A transmission electron microscope (TEM) shines a beam of electrons through a sample, then magnifies the image onto a fluorescent screen. A scanning electron microscope (SEM) uses a thin beam of electrons to scan a sample's surface. The SEM collects the electrons that bounce off the sample, then forms an image on a television screen.

INTEGRATING PHYSICS

How does a television screen change a beam of electrons into a picture?

MINI LAB .... Observing

Is Seeing Believing?

PROBLEM *What affects the image that you observe through a compound microscope?*

PROCEDURE

1. Obtain a slide with a typewritten label. Place the slide on the stage of a compound microscope. Use the stage clips to hold the slide in place.
2. Use the low-power objective to bring the letters on the label into focus. Record the image that you see.
3. While looking through the eyepiece, slowly move the slide in different directions along the stage. Then record your observations.
4. Switch to the high-power objective and record the image that you see.

ANALYZE AND CONCLUDE

1. In what ways did the compound microscope alter the image of the letters?
2. How did moving the slide affect the image?
3. What are the advantages of using the high-power objective? What are the disadvantages?

Discussion

Initiate a discussion on the history of microscopes and the uses of the compound light microscope. Ask students to compare Leeuwenhoek's microscope, shown in Figure 3–1, with a modern compound light microscope. Through this discussion, emphasize these points.

- The compound microscope uses two lenses for greater magnification.
- With the compound light microscope, living organisms can sometimes be studied.

INTEGRATING PHYSICS

A television screen is coated with materials that glow when struck by a beam of electrons. These materials are arranged in clusters of dots or stripes. A beam of electrons sweeps across the screen and creates an image by activating different dots for different shapes and colors.

Checkpoints

① The cell theory states that all living things are composed of cells, that cells are the smallest working units of living things, and that all cells come from preexisting cells by cell division.

② A microscope that uses a beam of electrons instead of light to examine a sample.

TEACHER SUPPORT

Background Information

The first electron microscope was developed in 1932. In both the TEM and the SEM, the lenses are made of electromagnets, which gather and focus the beam of electrons. The beam of electrons is produced by heating a filament. Objects must be extremely thin—less than 0.1 micron—to be examined by a TEM because the electrons produce an image by striking a photographic plate after passing through the object. Objects examined by an SEM need not be thin because the electrons are collected after bouncing off the specimen.

Scanning probe microscopes, developed in the 1980s, are not the only new technology in microscopy. An acoustic microscope sends an ultrasonic wave through an object, and a computer interprets the results. A scanning tunnelling microscope passes an electric current through a specimen. Laser microscopes are in development.

Ancillary Support

The resources below can be used to support your teaching strategy for these two pages.

LM Measuring With a Microscope, #5

TR Writing in Biology: What's in a Name?

Explore: When Bigger Is Not Better

BL Inquiry Activity: It's So Big!

Ideas Through Images

Have students examine Figures 3–4 and 3–5, read the captions, and answer the following questions.

- **What is the difference between the way in which the intestine cells were magnified and the way in which the pollen cells were magnified?** (For the intestine cells, students should describe the way in which a TEM magnifies images. For the pollen cells, students should describe the way in which a SEM magnifies an image.)
- **What process was used to obtain the image of the surface of lipid molecules?** (Using a scanning probe microscope, the surface was traced with a tiny tip known as a probe.)

4 ASSESS

Quick Check

Have students make a concept map that incorporates the three aspects of the cell theory.

Section Review 3-1

1. The cell theory states that all living things are composed of cells, that cells are the smallest working units of living things, and that all cells come from preexisting cells.
2. A compound light microscope magnifies specimens up to 1000 times. An electron microscope magnifies images as much as 1000 times larger than a compound light microscope can magnify them.
3. A light microscope allows the study of live specimens although its magnification is not very high. An electron microscope can view specimens at a very high magnification; however, it cannot be used to study live specimens. A scanning probe microscope provides maximum magnification.
4. Students should describe the discoveries of Leeuwenhoek and Hooke. Most students will suggest that the cell theory would not have been developed without microscopes because individual cells are too small to see with the naked eye.
5. The image is an enlarged and inverted version of the object.

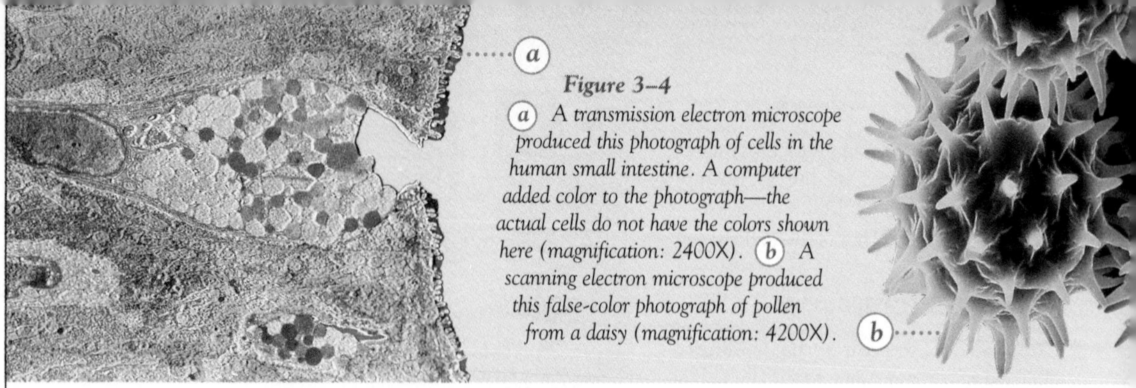

Figure 3–4
(a) A transmission electron microscope produced this photograph of cells in the human small intestine. A computer added color to the photograph—the actual cells do not have the colors shown here (magnification: 2400X). (b) A scanning electron microscope produced this false-color photograph of pollen from a daisy (magnification: 4200X).

electron microscopes can be used to study only nonliving specimens.

In addition, specimens for a TEM generally must be cut into very thin slices so that the electron beam can pass through them. And while the SEM produces realistic, often dramatic pictures of a sample's surface, it does not reveal the internal structure of a sample.

Scanning Probe Microscope

In the 1980s, researchers developed a new class of microscope that does not use lenses of any kind to produce images. Because these microscopes trace the surfaces of a sample with a tiny tip known as a probe, they are called **scanning probe microscopes.**

Scanning probe microscopes have revolutionized the study of surfaces. They have even produced pictures of individual atoms and molecules, as shown in ***Figure 3–5.*** Unlike electron microscopes, scanning probe microscopes do not require that specimens be placed in a vacuum. Researchers are eagerly searching for the best ways to apply these powerful new instruments in biology.

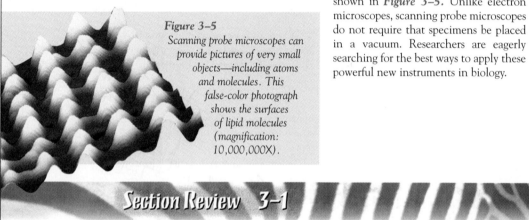

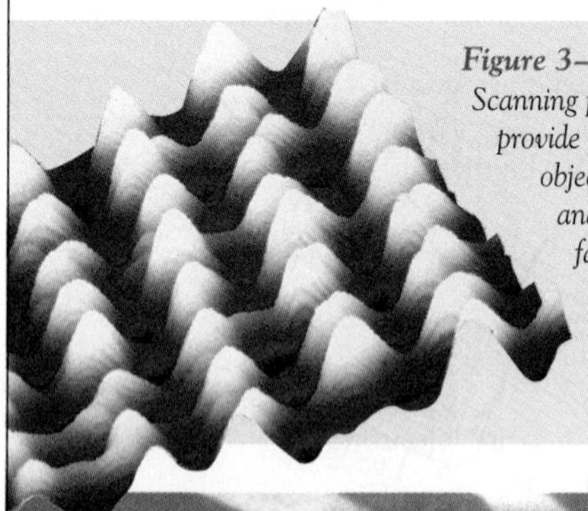

Figure 3–5
Scanning probe microscopes can provide pictures of very small objects—including atoms and molecules. This false-color photograph shows the surfaces of lipid molecules (magnification: 10,000,000X).

Section Review 3-1

1. **Define** the cell theory.
2. **Identify** the magnification powers of the compound light microscope and the electron microscope.
3. How do different kinds of microscopes **compare?**
4. **Critical Thinking—Sequencing** Describe the events that led to the development of the cell theory. If microscopes had not been invented, do you think the cell theory would have been developed? Explain.
5. **MINI LAB** Compare the image you **observe** through a compound microscope with the object on the stage of the microscope.

Skills Trace
Observing

- Focus p. 51
- Practice p. 52
- Assess p. 73

Learning Modality

Auditory Learning Ask various students to describe orally the ways in which the compound light microscope, the TEM, the SEM, and the scanning probe microscope magnify images.

Cell Boundaries

SECTION 3–2

Guide for Reading

- **Discuss** the roles of the cell membrane and cell wall.
- **Describe** passive transport and active transport.

WHEN POWERFUL MICROSCOPES are used to look at cells, do all the cells look alike? The answer is no, they do not. In fact, two cells can differ as much from each other as can two completely different organisms.

However, even the most distinctive cells have some structures in common, as you will see as you read this chapter. Let's begin by looking at the structures that enclose and contain the cell.

Cell Membrane

Every cell has a **cell membrane** along its outer boundary. **The principal role of the cell membrane is to separate and protect the cell from its surroundings.** In this sense, the cell membrane is similar to the walls that surround and protect a house or the walls that divide the individual apartments in an apartment building.

However, a cell could not survive if its cell membrane were an ordinary wall or container. To stay alive, every cell must take in raw materials and eliminate waste products. This means that the cell membrane must allow certain substances to permeate it, or pass through it. For this reason, the cell membrane is described as selectively permeable.

Why does the cell membrane allow some substances to pass through but deny passage to other substances? To answer this question, let's first look at the cell membrane at the molecular level.

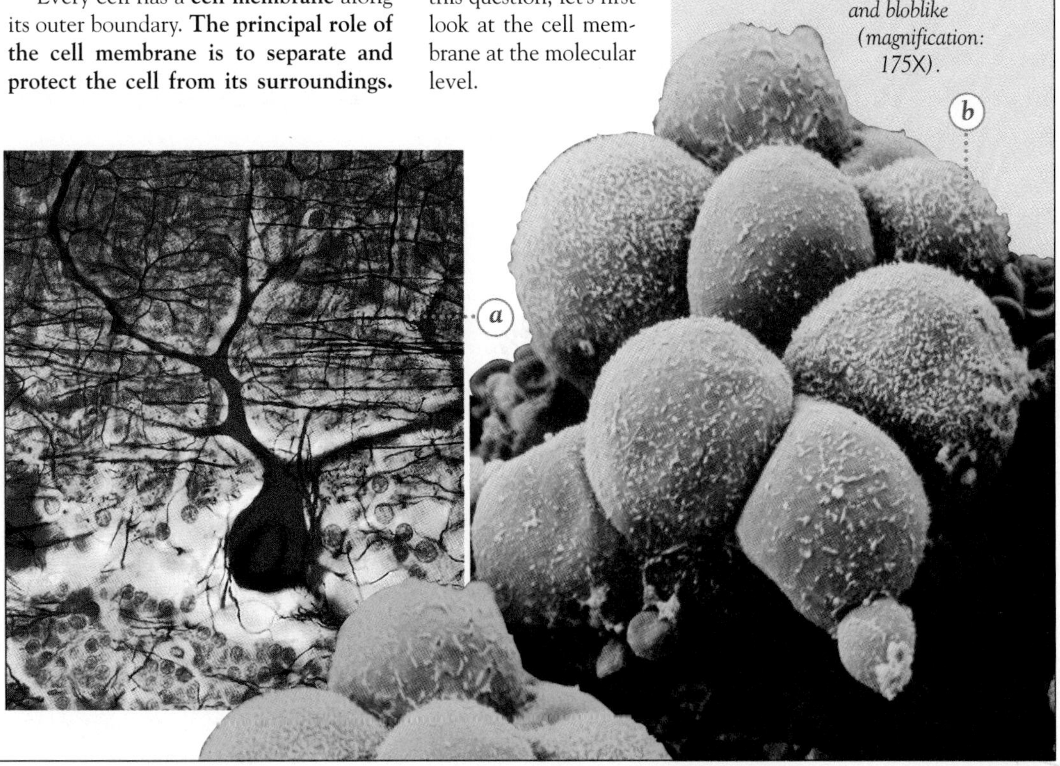

Figure 3–6
Cells in the same organism can be very different from each other. (a) This human nerve cell has long, spindly projections (magnification: 924X). (b) Human fat cells, on the other hand, are round and bloblike (magnification: 175X).

TEACHER SUPPORT

Managing Classroom Diversity

TECH PREP STUDENTS
Students who plan careers in biotechnology and health care will most likely be using microscopes of one type or another. Have these students investigate the technology they will most likely be using. Ask them to write a report on the uses of microscopes in their future fields. They might also want to visit a lab to interview technicians who use microscopic technology.

Section 3–2
Cell Boundaries

Performance Objectives
- Describe the structure of the cell membrane and cell wall and discuss their functions.
- Describe the processes of passive transport and active transport.

1 ENGAGE

Inquiry Activity
Observing
An Even Spread
Have each group of students stir a half teaspoon of salt and a few drops of food coloring into a half cup of water. Next, they should pour half a cup of clear water into a beaker, and then pour the half cup of water with salt and food coloring down the side of the beaker into the clear water. Ask students to write a description of what they see. (The colored saltwater will sink to become a layer at the bottom.) Have them let the beaker stand overnight. The next day, ask students to write a description of any changes they observe. (The color will be uniform throughout the liquid.) Discuss why they think this change occurred.

Ideas Through Images
Have students examine Figure 3–6, read the caption, and answer the following questions.

- **What types of cells are shown in the photographs?** (Human nerve cells and fat cells.)
- **How do they differ from one another?** (The nerve cell has projections, whereas the fat cells are round.)
- **How are they similar?** (Students may say that both are cells, have cell membranes, and contain cytoplasm.)

2 EXPLORE

Inquiry Activity

Comparing

Passing Through a Membrane

Ask students whether they think water is more concentrated inside an egg or in a vinegar solution. Then have them follow these steps.

- Place a pasteurized raw egg in an empty beaker. Then use a balance to find the mass of the egg and beaker. Record that measurement.
- Pour enough vinegar into the beaker to cover the egg. Observe for 2 days.
- After 2 days, carefully pour off the vinegar from the beaker, leaving the egg. Then determine the mass of the egg and beaker. Record that mass and compare it with the original measurement.

Students should find that the mass of the egg has increased. Have students speculate about what caused this increase. Then, after they learn about osmosis, have them rethink their explanations about what occurred. (The vinegar dissolved the shell, leaving the membrane around the egg intact. Then water moved through the membrane by osmosis. The result was that the mass of the egg increased.)

3 TEACH

Ideas Through Images

Have students examine Figures 3–7 and 3–8, read the captions, and answer the following questions.

- **What are the two layers of the lipid bilayer?** (One layer consists of the heads of the phospholipids, and the other layer consists of the tails of the phospholipids.)

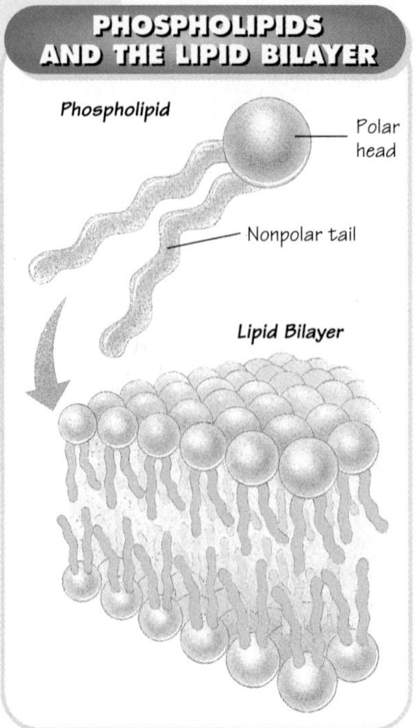

Figure 3–7 *In water, a group of phospholipids forms a structure called a lipid bilayer. The polar heads are found on the outside of the lipid bilayer, and the nonpolar tails are found on the inside.*

Lipid Bilayer

Cell membranes are built around a core of lipid molecules, including ones known as phospholipids. As shown in ***Figure 3–7,*** a phospholipid has a polar end called the head and a nonpolar end called the tail. Recall that polar substances tend to attract water and nonpolar substances tend to avoid water. As a result, a collection of phospholipids in water is typically found in a double-layered pattern.

This pattern is known as the **lipid bilayer.** The polar heads group together on the outside of the lipid bilayer because they are attracted to water. The nonpolar tails group together on the inside of the lipid bilayer because they avoid water. Because water is the main component of all cells, it is perhaps not surprising that all cell membranes contain a lipid bilayer.

The lipid bilayer provides cell membranes with a tough, flexible barrier that effectively protects the cell from many

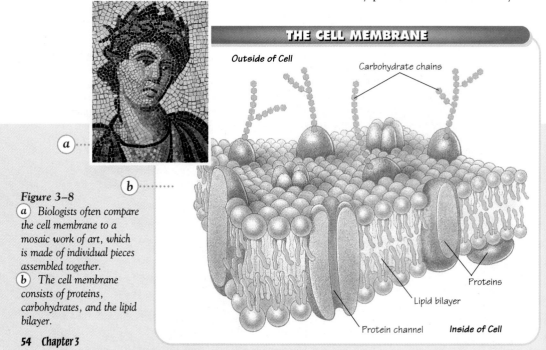

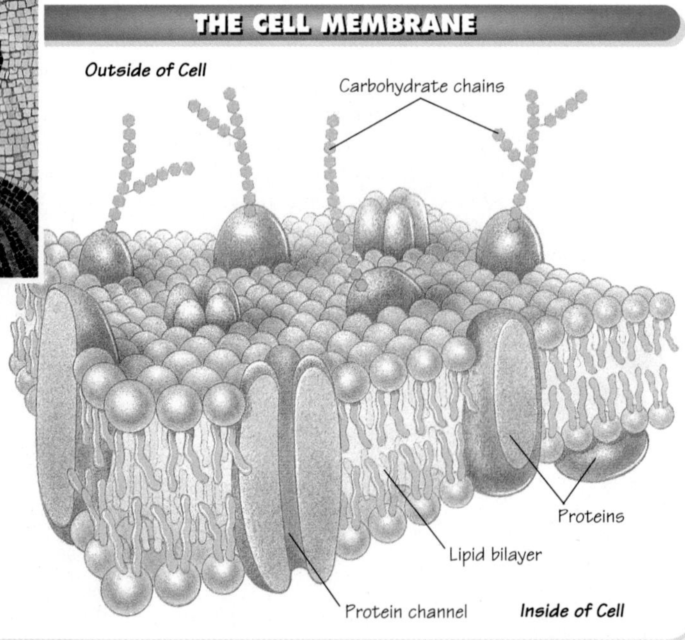

Figure 3–8 *(a) Biologists often compare the cell membrane to a mosaic work of art, which is made of individual pieces assembled together. (b) The cell membrane consists of proteins, carbohydrates, and the lipid bilayer.*

TEACHER SUPPORT

Activity

A REVERSAL OF DIRECTION

Students could use the product of the Explore activity, Passing Through a Membrane, to further investigate osmosis. Have them follow these steps.

- Keep the raw egg—now without a shell and with an increased mass—inside the empty beaker.
- Pour enough corn syrup into the beaker to cover the egg. Allow this to stand overnight.
- Using a tablespoon, remove the egg from the beaker and blot away any excess liquid with a paper towel.
- Place the egg into a clean beaker and determine the mass of the egg and beaker. Compare that mass with the final mass determined in the Explore activity.

Students should find that the mass of the egg has decreased because water moved by osmosis from the egg into the syrup.

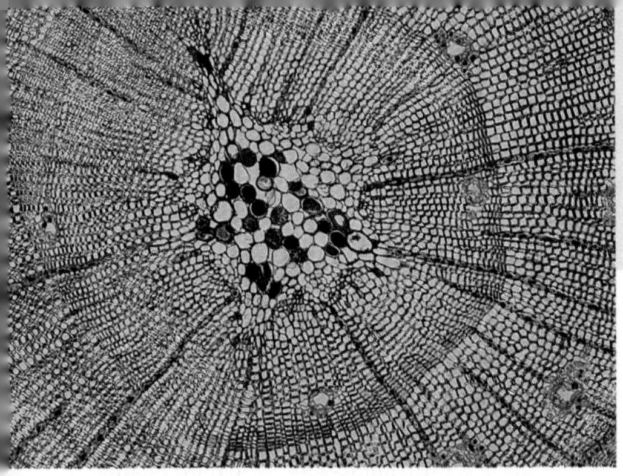

Figure 3–9
Tough, thick cell walls surround the cells in this cross section of a pine stem. Cell walls are found in plants, algae, and some bacteria, but not in animals (magnification: 100X).

substances—although not all of them. In general, substances that dissolve in lipids can easily pass through the cell membrane, but lipid-insoluble substances cannot pass through. You will discover the consequences of this fact as you read on in this section.

☑ **Checkpoint** What is the lipid bilayer? ❶

Other Cell Membrane Components

Lipids aren't the only molecules that make up the cell membrane, however. Most cell membranes have proteins embedded in the lipid bilayer, and many of these proteins have carbohydrates or other types of molecules attached to their outer surfaces.

What roles do these different molecules play? Some proteins form channels and pumps that help to move material across the cell membrane. Other proteins protect the membrane. And many of the carbohydrates act as chemical identification cards, allowing the organism to recognize which cells belong in the organism and which are foreign.

☑ **Checkpoint** What other molecules make up the cell membrane? ❷

Cell Wall

In many organisms—including plants, algae, and bacteria—a **cell wall** is located outside the cell membrane. Animal cells, however, do not have cell walls. This is one of the important differences between plant cells and animal cells.

The cell wall helps to support and protect the cell. Unlike the walls of your house or apartment, however, most cell walls are very porous. They allow water, gases, and other substances to pass through easily.

Most cell walls are made of fibers of carbohydrate and protein. In the cell walls of plants, the principal carbohydrate is cellulose. Cellulose is a tough, flexible compound that gives plant cells much of their strength and rigidity. Cellulose is also the main component of both wood and paper. This means that you are looking at the cell walls of tree trunks as you read this page!

☑ **Checkpoint** What is the cell wall? ❸

Passive Transport

How does the cell transport substances across the cell membrane? In a kind of transport known as **passive transport,** the substances literally transport themselves. **In passive transport, substances cross the cell membrane without the cell expending energy.**

Figure 3–10
Drops of colored dye will spread out gradually in water, moving from regions of high concentration to regions of low concentration. This process is called diffusion.

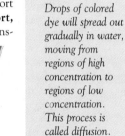

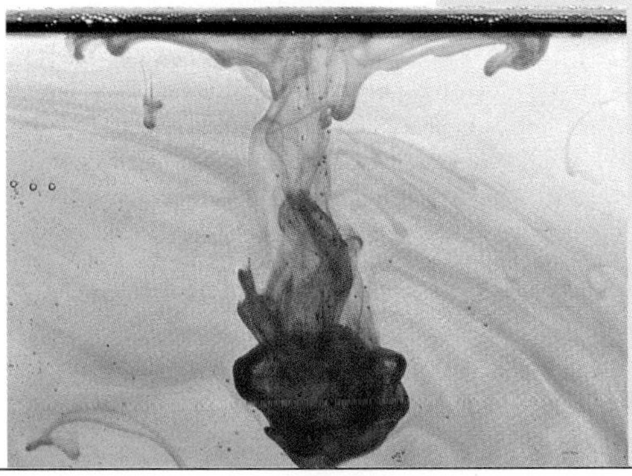

- **Why does this bilayer pattern occur?** (The polar heads of the phospholipids group together because they are attracted to water molecules. The nonpolar tails group together in avoidance of water.)
- **Are phospholipids the only kinds of molecules in cell membranes?** (No. Proteins are embedded in the lipid bilayer, and some proteins have carbohydrates attached to them.)
- **Where are the polar heads of the phospholipids found?** (On the outside of the lipid bilayer.)
- **Where are the nonpolar tails of the phospholipids found?** (On the inside of the lipid bilayer.)

Discussion

Initiate a discussion about organisms that have cell walls. Emphasize that cell walls do not take the place of cell membranes but rather are an added characteristic of some types of cells. Students will readily understand the function of cell walls in plant cells. Point out that other cells, including bacteria, also have cell walls.

☑ Checkpoints

❶ A double-layered pattern of phospholipids found in water, in which the polar heads of the molecules are grouped together on the outside of the bilayer and the nonpolar tails are grouped together on the inside of the bilayer.

❷ Other molecules include proteins and carbohydrates.

❸ A boundary on the outside of the cell membrane made of fibers of carbohydrate and protein.

TEACHER SUPPORT

Managing Classroom Diversity

LEP STUDENTS
Some students may not understand the meaning of the antonyms active and passive. Have these students look the words up in a dictionary and write down the appropriate definitions. Point out that in this instance, the difference involves the use of energy by the cell. The transport is passive only in the sense that the cell does not expend energy, not because nothing is happening to the cell.

Ideas Through Images

Have students examine Figures 3–11, 3–12, and 3–13, read the captions, and answer the following questions.

- **What does it mean for a substance to diffuse across a membrane?** (Molecules of a substance, if not prevented by the membrane, will randomly move from areas of high concentration to areas of low concentration.)
- **Describe a way some substances can cross a membrane even if prevented from crossing by the lipid bilayer.** (Some substances are able to cross through a channel in proteins, a process called facilitated diffusion.)
- **How is osmosis related to diffusion?** (Osmosis is a special case of diffusion, since osmosis is the diffusion of water molecules through a selectively permeable membrane.)
- **Why do blood cells have different volumes in solutions of different concentrations?** (Osmotic pressure causes water either to move out of blood cells or to move into blood cells, depending on the concentration of water in the fluid surrounding the cells.)

Correcting Misconceptions

Some students may think that osmosis could not be a form of passive transport because of the power of osmotic pressure. Point out that the force that causes the movement of water may be quite powerful, and the change in the cell may be dramatic. However, the cell is still passive in the sense that it uses none of its chemical energy to generate the process.

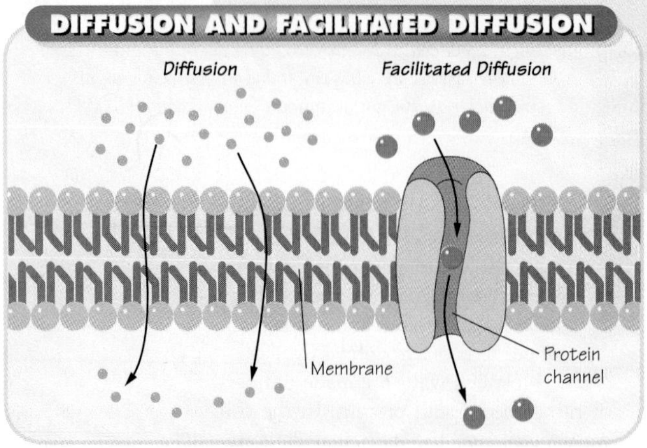

Figure 3–11
Some substances can diffuse directly across the lipid bilayer. Other substances can diffuse only through special protein channels, a process called facilitated diffusion.

Diffusion

Suppose you walk into a crowded room with four of your friends. If each of you is free to go your own way, before long you will spread out into the crowd and lose track of each other.

This process also happens in liquids—only at the molecular level. Because molecules in a liquid do not have fixed positions, a group of molecules that are close together in one instant will generally not be together for very long.

The random movement of molecules causes **diffusion.** Diffusion is the process by which substances spread through a liquid or gas. In diffusion, substances move from regions of high concentration to regions of low concentration. For example, when a drop of dye is added to water, the dye diffuses through the water until it becomes evenly distributed, as shown in ***Figure 3–10*** on page 55.

What happens if a membrane is placed in the solution? In one sense, nothing changes—diffusion still causes substances to move from regions of high concentration to regions of lower concentration. Substances such as alcohol, water, and small lipids easily cross the lipid bilayer, and so they diffuse directly across the cell membrane.

☑ ***Checkpoint*** What is diffusion? 1

Facilitated Diffusion

Many membranes contain protein channels that allow some substances to pass through. The cell membranes of red blood cells, for example, contain a protein channel that allows free passage to one substance and one substance only—glucose. As a result, glucose can diffuse either into or out of the cell through this channel.

Because the diffusion of glucose is facilitated, or helped, by the protein, this process is called facilitated diffusion.

Figure 3–12
This membrane allows water but not sugar to pass through it. Thus, water moves into the sugar solution by the process of osmosis.

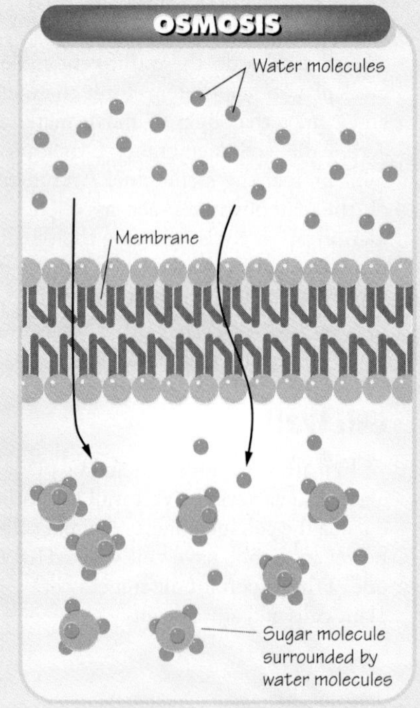

TEACHER SUPPORT — Background Information

Facilitated diffusion depends—just as simple diffusion does—on a difference in concentration. In simple diffusion, that is the only factor in the rate of diffusion. In facilitated diffusion, the rate also depends on the number of specific transport protein molecules in the membrane, because the diffusing molecules can move across the membrane only through the proteins. An example is the diffusion of glucose into cells, which occurs most of the time as facilitated diffusion. No matter how much the cell "needs" the glucose—no matter how great the difference is in concentration inside and outside the cell—the rate at which the glucose can diffuse into the cell has a limit because of the limited number of glucose-transporting protein molecules in the lipid bilayer.

Figure 3–13
Red blood cells have different volumes in solutions of different concentrations. (a) *Water moves into red blood cells by osmosis when the surrounding solution is hypotonic, or less concentrated than the cells.* (b) *Water moves out of red blood cells by osmosis when the surrounding solution is hypertonic, or more concentrated than the cells.* (c) *In an isotonic solution—a solution of equal concentration with the cells—there is no net movement of water across the membranes (magnification of each: 11,500X).*

In facilitated diffusion, substances diffuse across the cell membrane through special channels in proteins. Researchers have discovered hundreds of different channel proteins—each specific for an ion, sugar, salt, or other substance.

Osmosis

As you have read earlier, only substances that dissolve in lipids can pass through the cell membrane. However, water is an important exception to this rule. Water is not lipid soluble, yet it passes through most biological membranes very easily. This fact has important consequences for the cell.

The diffusion of water through a selectively permeable membrane is called **osmosis.** ***Figure 3–12*** shows a membrane that, like the cell membrane, is permeable to water but is not permeable to sugar. On one side of the membrane is a sugar solution, and on the other side is pure water.

As the figure shows, there is a net movement of water into the sugar solution. This occurs because water, like any other substance, diffuses from regions of high concentration to regions of low concentration. In this example, the pure water has a higher concentration of water than the sugar solution does.

Checkpoint What is osmosis? 2

Osmotic Pressure

When water moves by osmosis, it can produce powerful pressure. How powerful? Enough to destroy a cell.

The cytoplasm of a typical cell is filled with salts, sugars, and other dissolved substances. Therefore, if a dilute water solution should come in contact with a cell, water would rapidly enter the cell by osmosis. If uncontrolled, the cell would swell like a balloon and burst.

All cells must deal with osmotic pressure. In general, cells control this powerful force in one of three ways:

- **They use a cell wall.** As you have read, bacteria and plants are surrounded by strong, tough cell walls. This prevents the cell from expanding, thus counteracting the osmotic pressure.
- **They pump out the water.** Many single-celled organisms pump out water as quickly as it enters. These organisms rely on specialized structures such as the contractile vacuole.
- **They bathe cells in blood.** Most large animals prevent their cells from being in direct contact with dilute water—even if the animal drinks water or swims in it. But cells still need water in order to survive. Therefore, these animals bathe their cells in blood or bloodlike liquids. An animal's blood and its cells have nearly the same concentrations of dissolved substances.

Inquiry Activity

Modeling

A Way In but No Way Out

Tell students that iodine is an indicator of starch. Then have them follow these steps to observe a model of osmosis.

- In a beaker, stir in 2 teaspoons (10 mL) of starch in 125 mL of water. Pour about half of that mixture into a sandwich bag and secure it with a tie.
- Fill a second beaker with 250 mL of water, and add 15 drops of iodine.
- Place the sandwich bag of water and starch into the beaker of water and iodine. Note any changes after 30 minutes.
- While waiting, add 8 drops of iodine to the rest of the water-starch mixture in the first beaker, and note any changes that occur.

Students should observe a change in color to blue-black inside the sandwich bag and in the first beaker. But the water outside the bag remains clear because water and iodine molecules could pass through the selectively permeable bag while the starch molecules could not.

Checkpoints

1 The process by which substances spread through a liquid or gas.

2 The diffusion of water through a selectively permeable membrane.

TEACHER SUPPORT

Background Information

Osmosis is easy to observe in cells, yet it was long a mystery as to why water should cross membranes so quickly. Water is a polar molecule, and as such is not lipid soluble and should not be expected to cross a lipid bilayer. Many puzzled physical chemists suggested that biochemists should look for some kind of channels in the membrane. A few years ago such channels were in fact discovered. These channels, which are membrane-spanning proteins, have been named aquaporins. They have been found in scores of cells, and some scientists think that they may be present in nearly all cells. Their discovery is so recent that a detailed analysis of how they work may be years away.

Ancillary Support

The resources below can be used to support your teaching strategy for these two pages.

TR Explore: Osmosis: It's in the Bag

BL Inquiry Activity: The Case of the Swollen Grape

Connections

The effects of penicillin were discovered by the Scottish bacteriologist Alexander Fleming in 1928. His discovery was an accident. Upon entering his lab one day after a long weekend, he noticed a culture of *Staphylococcus* in a dish that had been left uncovered for days. Fleming noticed that specks of mold had fallen on the dish, and the bacteria had died around the mold. After further examination, he found that the bacteria had fallen apart. A substance from that mold, *Penicillium,* was later isolated, and penicillin became the first antibiotic. Its use as a therapeutic agent did not become widespread until the 1940s, when it was hailed as a miracle drug. Since then, many more antibiotics have been developed to fight infectious diseases.

Answers to Making the Connection

Penicillin does not kill human cells, because those cells do not have the cell walls that the bacteria have, and penicillin destroys bacteria by weakening their cell walls. Some students may think a person should take penicillin on a regular basis in order to prevent disease. Other students, though, may recognize that the bacteria could evolve to become resistant to penicillin's effects, which is just what has occurred.

Biology and Health Connections

Death by Osmosis

Have you ever had an earache? How about a strep throat or an infected cut or scrape? Each of these conditions—and many others—is typically caused by bacteria. Bacteria are single-celled prokaryotic organisms. There is an almost countless variety of bacteria, and they can be found almost everywhere on Earth. Many types of bacteria live their entire lives inside the body of a human or other animal yet cause no ill effects. Other bacteria, however, can easily harm an animal once they infect it. And all bacteria can cause serious damage if their numbers grow beyond tolerable limits.

Penicillin—The Bacteria Killer

Until the 1940s, doctors had only mildly effective ways to treat bacterial infections, let alone cure them. All that changed, however, with the discovery of powerful drugs known as antibiotics. The first of these drugs was penicillin. Today, penicillin is still widely used to help kill bacteria and fight infections.

Penicillin works by weakening the bacteria's cell walls. Bacteria form cell walls by binding together special proteins and carbohydrates. In many ways, penicillin looks just like one of these proteins. Thus, when penicillin is present, the bacteria will incorporate it into new cell walls. As a result, the fibers of the cell walls are linked together more loosely than is normal.

Penicillium notatum—*the green mold that produces penicillin*

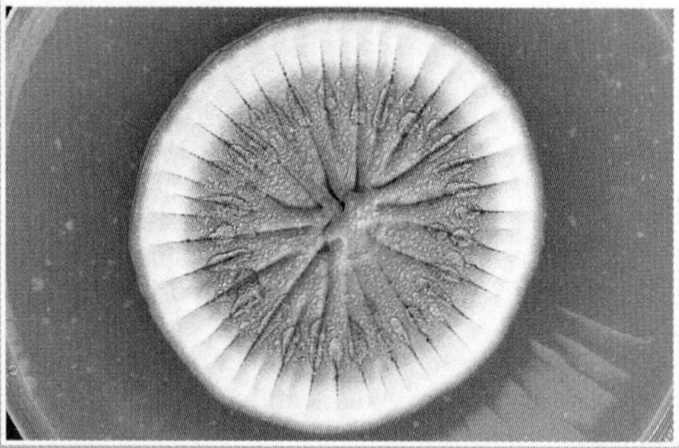

E. coli *bacteria can be killed with penicillin (magnification: 20,000X)*

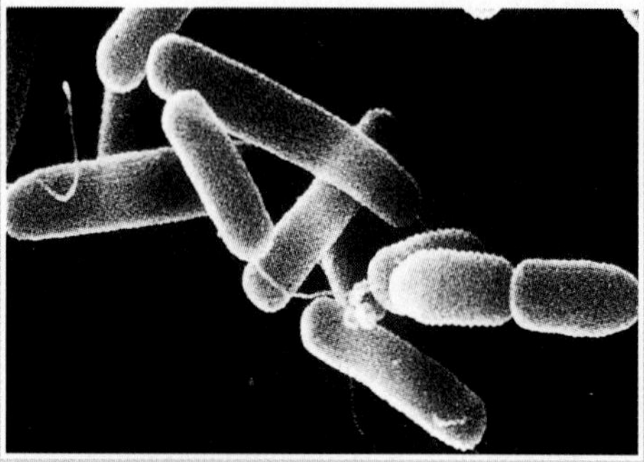

Exploding Bacteria!

Bacteria depend on their cell walls to control osmotic pressure. Because of osmosis, bacteria are constantly subjected to water pressure across their cell membranes, and only tough cell walls keep bacteria from bursting. Because the cell wall is looser and weaker when penicillin is present, the cell wall will stretch, crack, and finally break as water streams across the cell membrane. In a matter of seconds, so much water enters the cell that it literally explodes.

The picture may not be pretty, but it is exactly how penicillin kills bacteria. Death by osmosis!

Making the Connection

Why does penicillin not kill human cells? Do you think a person should take penicillin on a regular basis? Why or why not?

TEACHER SUPPORT

Ecology Note

The development of penicillin and other antibiotics was considered by people around the world as next to miraculous. At first, these medicines seemed to be able to cure anything—even cancer, some thought. Their overuse, however, has brought into question their effectiveness against disease in the future. Because they have been used for all sorts of ailments, in humans as well as domestic animals, the environment, in a sense, is awash in antibiotics. The result has been that many populations of bacteria have developed a resistance to these drugs—some even to antibiotics in general. These bacteria have adapted to their environment in many ways. Some are able to transport the antibiotic back out of the cell. Some are able to chemically modify the antibiotic to make it inactive. Others are able to produce enzymes that destroy the antibiotic.

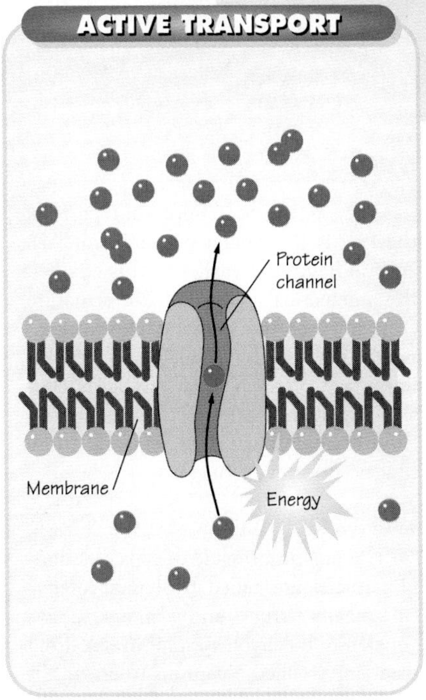

Figure 3–14
In active transport, a cell expends energy to move substances against a concentration difference.

Active Transport

As you have just read, passive transport moves substances from regions of high concentrations to regions of lower concentrations. Can a cell move substances in the opposite direction—from regions of low concentration to higher concentration? The answer is yes. In fact, cells constantly move certain substances against a concentration difference. However, they have to pay a price to do this. That price is energy.

Movement of a substance against a concentration difference is called active transport, and it always requires energy. The process of **active transport** is often compared to a pump. Most animal cells, for example, have membrane proteins that pump sodium ions out of the cell and pump potassium ions into it. Active transport is not limited to small ions or molecules, however. Many cells expend energy to transport large molecules, clumps of food, or even whole cells.

One way in which cells import larger materials is literally to turn part of the cell membrane inside out. This process is called endocytosis, and it is illustrated in ***Figure 3–15.*** When the particles are very large, the process is sometimes called phagocytosis. In another process, called exocytosis, cells use energy to expel material.

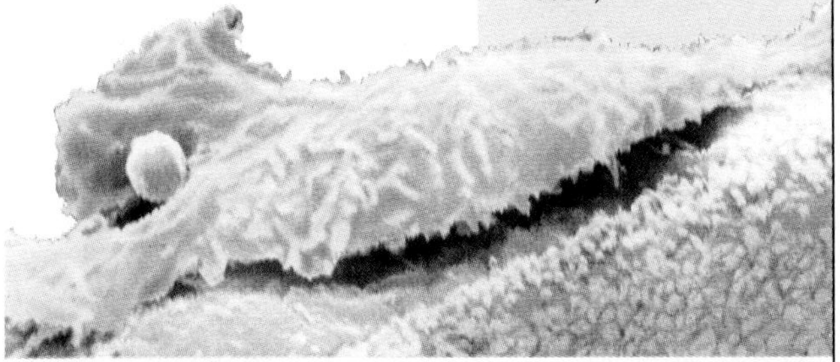

Figure 3–15
In endocytosis, a cell wraps its membrane around a particle, then turns its membrane inside out to take in the particle. In this false-color photograph from a scanning electron microscope, a cell is taking in a small particle by endocytosis (magnification: 6000X).

Section Review 3–2

1. **Discuss** the roles of the cell membrane and the cell wall.
2. **Describe** the processes of passive transport and active transport.
3. **Critical Thinking—Applying Concepts** "Water, water, everywhere; Nor any drop to drink." This quote from *The Rime of the Ancient Mariner* refers to sea water. If you drink sea water, your body actually loses water. Explain why this happens.

4 ASSESS

Quick Check

Ask students to make flow charts that describe these processes discussed in the section: diffusion, facilitated diffusion, osmosis, and active transport.

Section Review 3–2

1. The cell membrane separates and protects the cell from its surroundings. A cell membrane is composed of a lipid bilayer, proteins, and carbohydrates. The cell wall supports and protects the cell. A cell wall is made of fibers of carbohydrate and protein.

2. In passive transport, substances diffuse through the cell membrane without the cell expending any energy. In active transport, the cell uses energy to move substances into and out of a cell against a concentration difference.

3. Water diffuses from regions of high concentration to regions of low concentration. The inside of a cell has a higher concentration of water than sea water. Therefore, water would diffuse out of cells into the sea water.

Learning Modality

Kinesthetic Learning Have students act out the process of diffusion. To begin, group class members at the classroom door. Then tell them to spread out through the classroom in such a way that no two students are closer to each other than to any other students. Discuss how molecules randomly spread out through a liquid or gas.

TEACHER SUPPORT

Background Information

One of the most important examples of active transport is known as the sodium-potassium pump, in which sodium ions are maintained at a lower concentration inside the cell and potassium ions are maintained at a higher concentration inside the cell. The active transport by protein molecules of these ions is central to the production of electrical impulses by nerve cells.

At one time, scientists thought that the protein molecules actually rotated as they transported substances through the cell membrane, picking up their parcels on the outside and dumping them on the inside. Now scientists think that the transported molecules are somehow squeezed through the transport proteins, as the proteins change their configuration to accommodate their riders.

Section 3–3

Inside the Cell

Performance Objectives

- Discuss the composition of the cell nucleus and describe its function.
- Identify the organelles of the cytoplasm and describe the function of each.

Laboratory Investigation Skill: Comparing
Mini Lab Skill: Interpreting

1 ENGAGE

Inquiry Activity

Predicting

What's Inside a Cell?

Ask students what specific functions a one-celled organism would need to carry out in order to live. Then have students work in small groups to make a table of predictions about what structures would likely be found inside a one-celled organism. The table should have two columns: Necessary Function and Structure Needed to Carry Out Function.

2 EXPLORE

Investigate

Cooperative Learning Have students work in groups to make a labeled, two-dimensional drawing of a typical cell. First have groups meet before reading the section to discuss what the inside of a cell might contain. Then ask them to meet again after learning about the structures of a cell to make the labeled drawing.

SECTION 3–3 Inside the Cell

Guide for Reading

- **Describe** the composition and function of the nucleus.
- **List** and **describe** the organelles of the cytoplasm.

MINI LAB

- **Interpret** the changes observed when a paramecium takes in food.

WHAT DOES A FACTORY NEED to operate efficiently? Certainly, it needs the proper machines and workers to assemble the factory's products, to package the products, and to ship them for delivery. The factory also needs a source of energy to power the machines, with mechanics on hand to fix the machines if they break. And the factory needs a main office, or control center, from which all the work can be regulated.

Like a factory, the cell meets its needs by using distinct parts. As you will discover, the parts of the cell function much like the different parts of the factory.

Nucleus

One of the most important parts of the cell is the **nucleus** (plural: nuclei). As you have read earlier in this chapter, the nucleus is a large, dense structure contained in the cells of many organisms. In fact, the nucleus is such an important organelle that biologists classify organisms into two categories—those that do have a nucleus and those that do not have a nucleus.

Prokaryotes and Eukaryotes

The organisms made of cells that contain nuclei are called the **eukaryotes**—*eu-* means "true" and *-karyon* means "nucleus." Eukaryotes range in size from tiny, single-celled organisms to organisms composed of millions of cells, including all large plants and animals. The organisms that do not contain nuclei are called **prokaryotes**—*pro-* means "before." Most prokaryotes are small, single-celled organisms. They include the bacteria and relatives of bacteria.

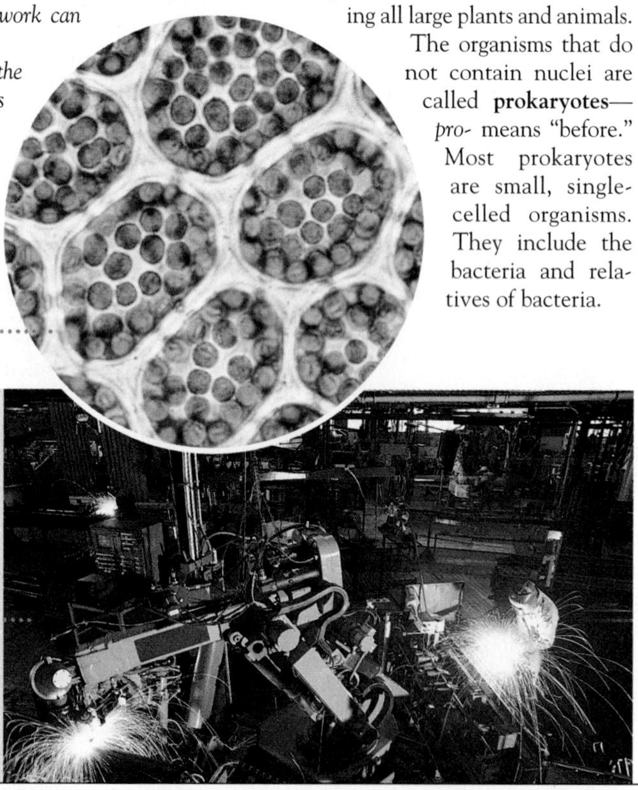

Figure 3–16 (a) This photograph of plant cells reveals only some of the cells' distinct parts (magnification: 500X). (b) Like this factory, a cell uses different parts to accomplish different tasks.

TEACHER SUPPORT — Managing Classroom Diversity

LEP/AT-RISK STUDENTS

Some students may have difficulty with the many new terms in this section. Make sure they keep a list of the different cell structures as they read, along with a description of each structure's function. Check the lists and descriptions to discover any misunderstandings.

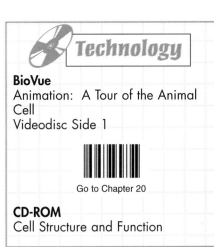

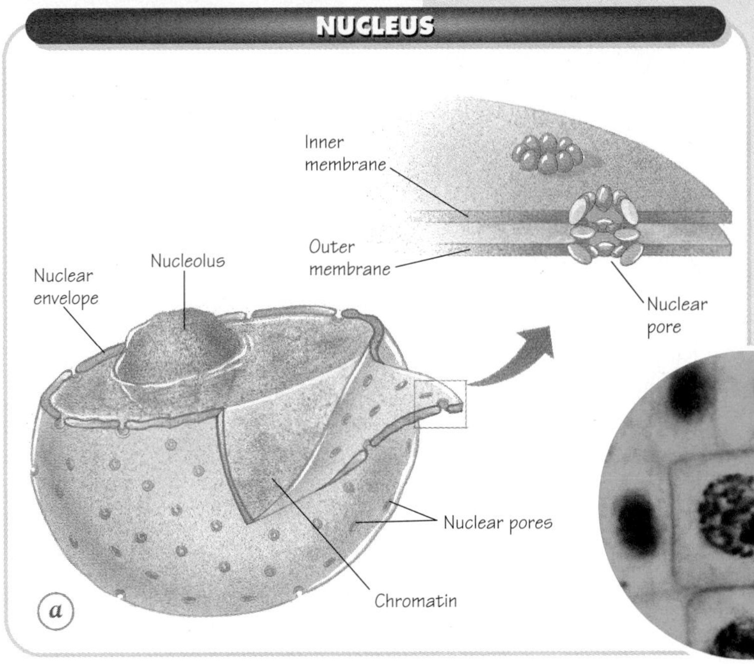

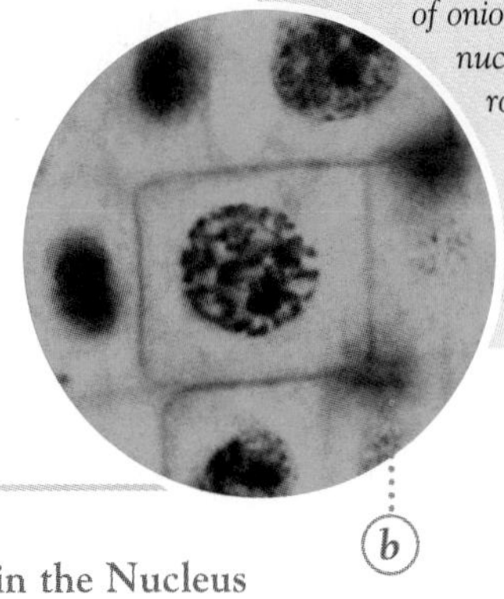

Figure 3–17 (a) *The nucleus stores DNA, which is spread throughout the nucleus in a material called chromatin. When needed, instructions are copied from DNA and sent through the nuclear pores to the rest of the cell.* (b) *In this photograph of onion cells, the nuclei are the round structures in the center of each cell. (magnification: 100X).*

Role of the Nucleus

Why is the nucleus so important? **The nucleus contains nearly all of a cell's DNA.** Recall that DNA is the molecule that contains coded instructions for making proteins and other important molecules. By storing DNA in the nucleus, the cell is better able to control and regulate its use.

The DNA molecules and proteins form a material called chromatin. Chromatin is usually spread throughout the nucleus. But when a cell divides, the chromatin condenses to form larger structures called **chromosomes.** As shown in ***Figure 3–17,*** chromosomes are large enough to be visible under the compound microscope.

If the nucleus were the control center of a factory, then the chromosomes would be the plans or blueprints for the factory. When necessary, instructions from these blueprints are sent out of the control center to the factory floor.

Checkpoint What are chromosomes? ①

Structures in the Nucleus

Most nuclei also contain a small, dense region known as the nucleolus. For many years, the function of the nucleolus was a mystery. But biologists now know that the nucleolus is the site where ribosomes are assembled. You will learn more about ribosomes later in this section.

The nucleus is surrounded by two distinct membranes that together are called the nuclear envelope. The envelope contains many nuclear pores, or tiny holes that allow material to move into and out of the nucleus.

Cytoplasm

The portion of the cell outside the nucleus is known as the **cytoplasm**—*cyto-* means "cell" and *-plasm* means "fluid." At one time, biologists thought that the cytoplasm was a simple fluid, as the name cytoplasm suggests. But as biologists studied cells with the compound microscope and other microscopes, they realized that the cytoplasm is quite complex.

3 TEACH

Ideas Through Images

Have students examine Figure 3–17, read the caption, and answer the following questions.

- **What does the nucleus look like in a magnification of an onion cell?** (It can be seen as a dark, round structure in the center of the cell.)
- **What does the nucleus contain that makes it the control center of the rest of the cell?** (DNA, which has the coded information necessary for the making of proteins and other molecules.)
- **How is the information in the DNA of the nucleus carried out in the rest of the cell?** (Instructions are copied from the DNA in the nucleus and sent through nuclear pores to other parts of the cell.)
- **What material in the nucleus contains DNA?** (Chromatin.)

Checkpoint

① The structures that form when the chromatin in a nucleus condenses as a cell divides.

TEACHER SUPPORT

Historical Perspective

Whatever happened to protoplasm? At one time, practically everyone was taught that the fluid material of the cell was something called protoplasm, a colloid whose wonderful properties accounted for many of the unique abilities of the cell. The term actually meant "first fluid," and it reflected the idea that the composition of a living cell was something so extraordinary that the common laws of chemistry could not explain it. That is an idea whose time has passed; as biologists began to explore the composition of the cell with modern tools, it became increasingly clear that the properties of the cell could be explained in other ways. Instead of protoplasm, we now speak of cytoplasm, or "cell fluid," a term that encompasses all the complexity of the contents of the cell outside of the nucleus.

Technology

BioVue
Animation: A Tour of the Animal Cell
Videodisc Side 1

Go to Chapter 20

CD-ROM
Cell Structure and Function

Ideas Through Images

Have students examine Figure 3–18, read the caption, and answer the following questions.

- **What kinds of cells are these?** (An animal cell and a plant cell.)
- **What parts of these cells does the cytoplasm include?** (Everything inside the cell membrane except the nucleus. All the organelles are part of the cytoplasm.)

As students read through the rest of the section, they should refer back to Figure 3–18 for an illustration of what the various cytoplasmic structures look like.

Discussion

Begin a discussion of ribosomes by referring back to the caption of Figure 3–17, where students learned about instructions being sent from the DNA of the nucleus to the rest of the cell. Point out that ribosomes are on the receiving end of instructions about how to assemble proteins, which are necessary for many structures within a cell. Emphasize that whereas a cell contains only one nucleus, it could contain thousands of the tiny ribosomes.

Laboratory Investigation

The Laboratory Investigation, Inside Plant and Animal Cells, on pages 68–69 is appropriate to use at this point in the chapter.

Discussion

Reemphasize the function of ribosomes. Inform students that the number of ribosomes in a cell is related to how much protein a cell makes because protein synthesis occurs at the ribosomes.

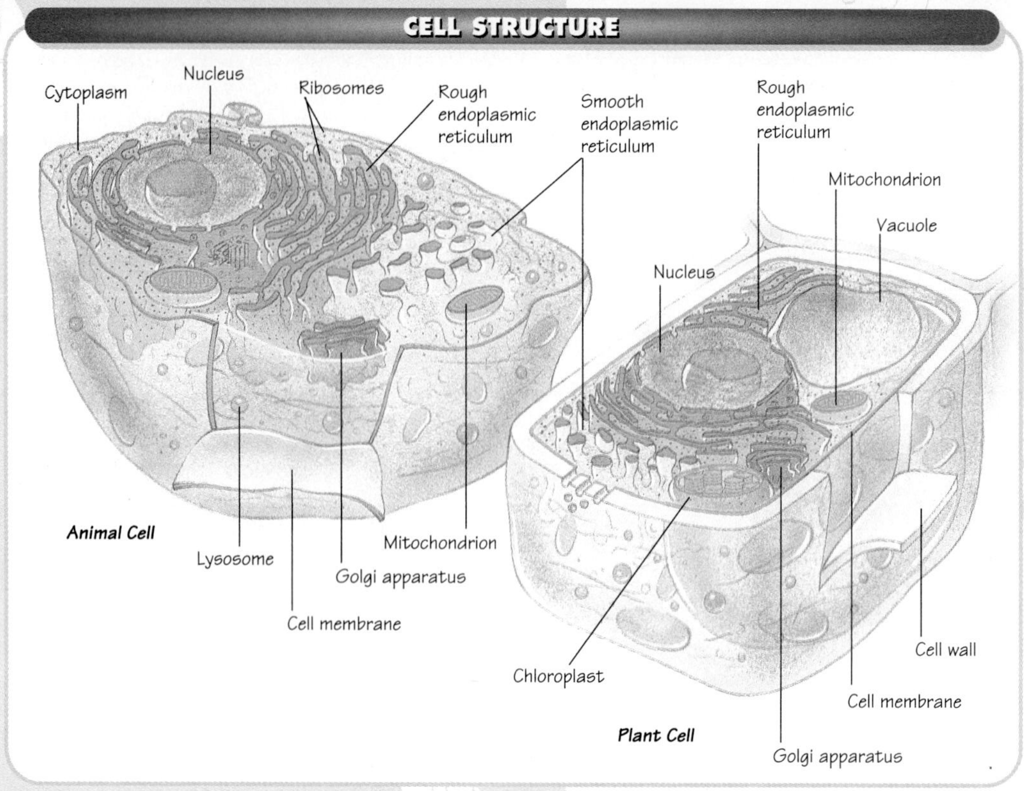

Figure 3–18
Both plant and animal cells contain a variety of organelles. Although some organelles are specific to either plant or animal cells, others—such as the mitochondrion—are found in both types of cells.

Organelles

The cytoplasm contains many individual parts called **organelles.** The word organelle means "little organ." **An organelle is a small structure that performs a specialized function within a cell, just as a machine performs a specialized function in a factory.** Understanding the cell's organelles is the key to understanding the cell as a whole.

Figure 3–18 shows many of the organelles in a typical animal cell and those in a typical plant cell. Let's take a look at each of these organelles.

☑ ***Checkpoint*** What is an organelle? 1

Ribosomes

Most cells contain small structures called **ribosomes.** Ribosomes are tiny particles made of RNA and protein. A ribosome is only 25 nanometers wide, or about 0.25 percent of the width of a typical cell. Some cells have ribosomes in the thousands or tens of thousands.

What purpose do ribosomes serve? Ribosomes are the sites where proteins are assembled. Later on, you will learn more about ribosomes and their role in making proteins. For now, you can picture each ribosome as a small assembler that produces proteins—an assembler that gets its instructions from the nucleus.

☑ ***Checkpoint*** What are ribosomes? 2

Endoplasmic Reticulum and Golgi Apparatus

In many cases, the cell can use a protein immediately after a ribosome has

TEACHER SUPPORT

Background Information

Is a ribosome a true organelle? Other organelles, such as mitochondria and vacuoles, are enclosed by membranes, but ribosomes are tiny structures without membranes. The truth is that biologists do not have an official definition of what does or does not qualify as an organelle. The working definition, though, is that an organelle is a specialized structure that carries out a specific function. By that definition ribosomes qualify.

These protein-synthesizing structures are the most numerous of a cell's organelles. A growing *E. coli* cell contains about 15,000 ribosomes. A eukaryotic cell, normally larger than a prokaryotic cell, often has many times that number. The more proteins a cell must make to carry out its functions, the more ribosomes it has.

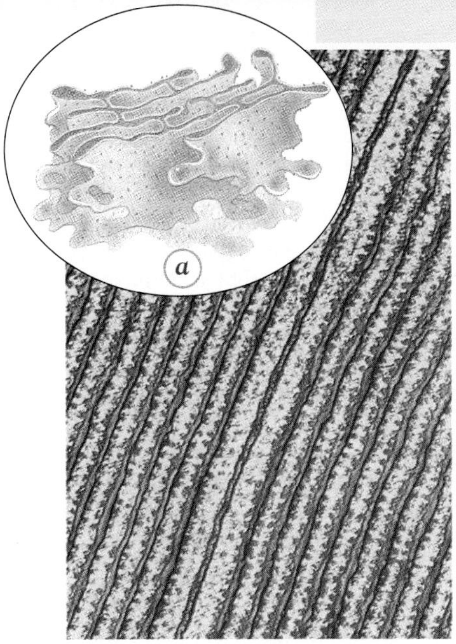

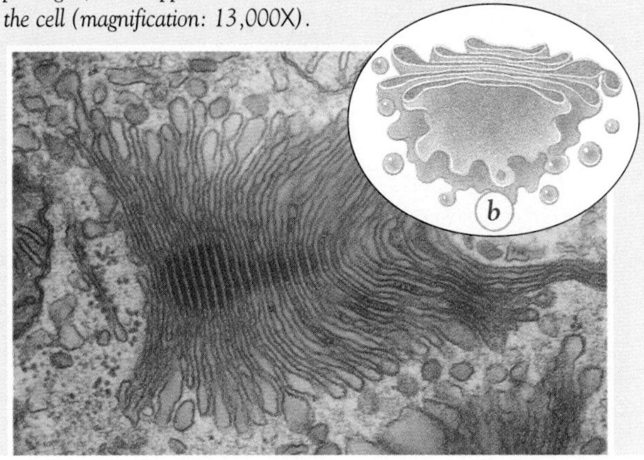

Figure 3–19
(a) The endoplasmic reticulum (ER) shown here is called rough ER because it is studded with ribosomes. Proteins are assembled at ribosomes, then travel through the ER network (magnification: 50,000X). (b) In the Golgi apparatus, proteins are modified, packaged, and shipped to their destinations in the cell (magnification: 13,000X).

assembled it. However, some proteins need further processing. Many proteins need to be delivered to specific locations within the cell, while others need to be packaged for export, or removal from the cell. In addition, some proteins need special components attached to them before they can be used.

Processing and transporting proteins and other macromolecules is the function of the **endoplasmic reticulum**—or ER, for short—and the **Golgi apparatus.** Both the endoplasmic reticulum and the Golgi apparatus are networks of membranes within the cell. The term endoplasmic reticulum means "network inside the cell." The Golgi apparatus is named after Camillo Golgi, the Italian scientist who first identified it.

As illustrated in ***Figure 3–19,*** ribosomes stud the surface of one form of ER, giving it a "rough" appearance. This type of ER is called rough ER. After a protein is assembled at a ribosome in the rough ER, it travels through the ER network into the Golgi apparatus, where special enzymes may attach carbohydrates or lipids. The modified protein then travels out of the Golgi apparatus to locations throughout the cell or outside the cell.

Together, the ER and the Golgi apparatus work like the packaging and shipping divisions of a factory. They modify and add components to proteins, then ship them to their final destinations.

☑ ***Checkpoint*** What is the function of the ER and the Golgi apparatus? (3)

Lysosomes

Every well-organized factory needs a cleanup crew, and the cell is no exception. The workers of the cleanup crew of the cell are the **lysosomes.** Lysosomes are saclike membranes filled with chemicals and enzymes that

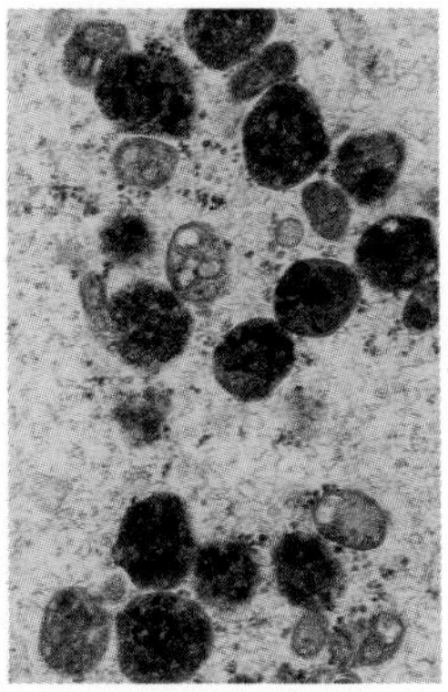

Figure 3–20
The round black structures in this photograph are lysosomes—the cell's cleanup crews. Lysosomes are used to break down nonfunctioning organelles or foreign materials in the cell (magnification: 95,000X).

Ideas Through Images

Have students examine Figure 3–19, read the caption, and answer the following questions.

- **What is the function of the endoplasmic reticulum?** (It transports proteins through its network inside the cell to places where the proteins are needed.)
- **Why are some ER called rough?** (That form of ER is studded with ribosomes, giving it a rough appearance.)
- **What happens to proteins in the Golgi apparatus?** (They are modified or packaged for specific uses at various places inside the cell.)

Discussion

Discuss with students the functions of lysosomes, the cytoskeleton, and vacuoles. Point out that the enzymes in lysosomes and the proteins that make up components of the cytoskeleton would have been assembled by ribosomes on instructions from the DNA. Note for students that vacuoles serve two functions, storage and support.

☑ Checkpoints

(1) A small structure that performs a specialized function within a cell.

(2) Small structures of RNA and protein that serve as sites where proteins are assembled.

(3) To process and transport proteins and other macromolecules in the cell.

TEACHER SUPPORT

Background Information

The endoplasmic reticulum, found in eukaryotic cells, is a network that consists of membranous tubes, flattened sacs, and channels. The two types of ER, rough and smooth, are defined by whether or not they have ribosomes attached. These are not separate structures; in cells where they are both present, the two types are continuous with each other. This ER network has many turns and folds, and therefore it provides a relatively large surface area for chemical reactions to be carried out.

The Golgi apparatus is also composed of membranous sacs, though in a more limited area than the ER. Materials that need to be sent outside the cell are enclosed in tiny vesicles that bud off from the Golgi sacs. These vesicles move to the cell membrane, where the material is released outside the cell.

Ancillary Support

The resources below can be used to support your teaching strategy for these two pages.

BL Inquiry Activity: Don't Judge a Cell by Its Membrane
TB Cell Structure, #3

MINI LAB Interpreting

Teacher Notes

• For time required and materials needed, see page 48b.

• Prepare the yeast solution by adding a pinch of Congo red indicator to a thick suspension of yeast and water, and then bring it to a gentle boil for 5 minutes. Cool before using.

• Transfer some paramecium culture from the stock culture at least a day ahead of time, and then limit the food supply to the transferred culture.

Answers to Analyze and Conclude

1. Students should observe that the organisms immediately move toward the yeast to ingest some.
2. Students should observe that the organisms sweep the yeast through their oral grooves and then form food vacuoles to enclose it. The vacuoles become blue at first, and then eventually turn to red.
3. Students' responses may vary. Some students may rightly infer that the color change to blue occurred because of the presence in the vacuoles of acids used in digestion, acids that are released into the vacuoles from lysosomes. The return to red occurred once digestion was complete.

Skills Trace

Interpreting

Focus p. 64
Practice p. 65
Assess p. 73

MINI LAB ······· Interpreting ····

A Colorful Paramecium

PROBLEM *How does a paramecium take in food? Interpret observations to answer this question.*

PROCEDURE

1. Prepare a slide of a live paramecium. Focus the slide under the low-power objective of a microscope.
2. Obtain a small sample of a yeast suspension. The yeast suspension has been treated with an acid/base indicator that is red above pH 5 and blue below pH 3.
3. Use a toothpick to transfer a small drop of the yeast suspension to the edge of the slide. Observe the paramecium under the microscope for 5 minutes. Record your observations.

ANALYZE AND CONCLUDE

1. Describe how the paramecium reacted to the yeast.
2. What changes did you observe in the paramecium? Which organelles were involved in these changes?
3. Propose an explanation for any color changes that you observed.

can break down almost any substance within the cell.

In some cases, lysosomes will fuse with a damaged organelle and literally break it apart into basic chemical compounds. As a result, the lysosomes both clear away the damaged organelle and recycle its components for other uses in the cell.

Cytoskeleton

Every large factory building needs internal beams for support. On a smaller scale, a cell must cope with stresses and strains that are just as powerful as those on a building. So it is no surprise that the cell has its own support structures.

Eukaryotic cells contain a supporting framework called the **cytoskeleton**—meaning "cell skeleton." The cytoskeleton has many components, including structures called microtubules and microfilaments. Microtubules are hollow tubes of protein about 25 nanometers wide. Microfilaments are also made of protein but are only about 7 nanometers wide. Together, microtubules and microfilaments provide a tough, flexible framework of support for the cell.

A large factory also needs ways to move materials from one end of the factory floor to the other. In the cell, the cytoskeleton takes care of this job, too. Proteins can attach to the cytoskeleton and move organelles along it, just as a locomotive moves on a railroad track.

Cytoskeletal proteins are responsible for other types of cellular movement, too. For example, microtubules make up hairlike structures called cilia and flagella. Cilia and flagella are found on the surfaces of many cells. In some organisms, the beating of cilia or flagella propel the cell from one location to the next.

Vacuoles

Many cells store materials in saclike structures called **vacuoles.** In animal cells, vacuoles may store proteins, fats, or carbohydrates. In plant cells, a large, central vacuole often stores water and dissolved salts.

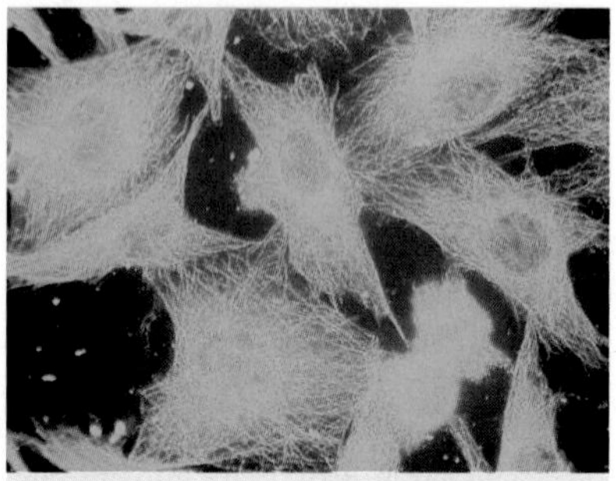

Figure 3–21
The cells in this photograph were specially treated to highlight their cytoskeleton frameworks (magnification: 275X).

TEACHER SUPPORT Background Information

One of the most important cell components packaged and distributed by the Golgi apparatus is material for the membranes of the cell and its organelles. Lysosomes, which are essentially membranous bags, are products of the Golgi apparatuses. These bags enclose enzymes that would destroy the cell if it were not surrounded by membrane.

An example of how lysosomes function in cells can be seen in the way paramecia digest their food. Upon contact with a food organism or some other particle, the paramecium envelops the food in a vacuole. Lysosomes then fuse with the vacuole and release their enzymes. The enzymes quickly digest the contents of the vacuole.

Vacuoles also provide plant cells with support. The pressure inside the vacuoles allows a plant to grow quickly and to support heavy structures such as leaves and flowers.

Mitochondria and Chloroplasts

To complete our picture of the cell as a busy and productive factory, we need one last component—a supply of energy. Without energy, a cell could not produce proteins, move molecules through its cytoplasm, or perform any of the other activities necessary for life.

If the owners of a factory had to produce their own energy, they might choose to produce energy by burning a chemical fuel, such as coal or natural gas. Or they might choose to harvest energy from the sun. In either case, they would need to build a specialized power plant to convert the energy source into a usable form of energy, such as electricity.

Like a factory, the cell can produce its energy from either a chemical fuel or the sun. The organelle that produces energy from a chemical fuel is called the **mitochondrion** (plural: mitochondria). And the organelle that harvests the energy of sunlight is called the **chloroplast.** Mitochondria are found in all sorts of eukaryotic organisms, including most plants and animals. Chloroplasts, however, are found only in plants and certain types of algae.

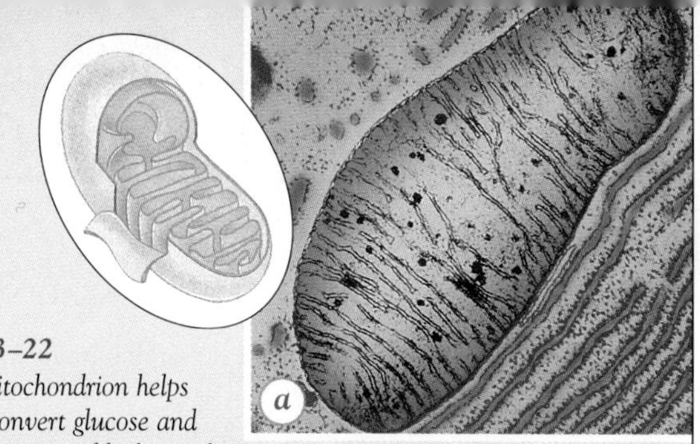

Figure 3–22 (a) *A mitochondrion helps the cell convert glucose and oxygen into a usable form of energy (magnification: 85,000X).* (b) *Chloroplasts, which are found in plant cells but not in animal cells, convert sunlight into chemical energy (magnification: 1850X).*

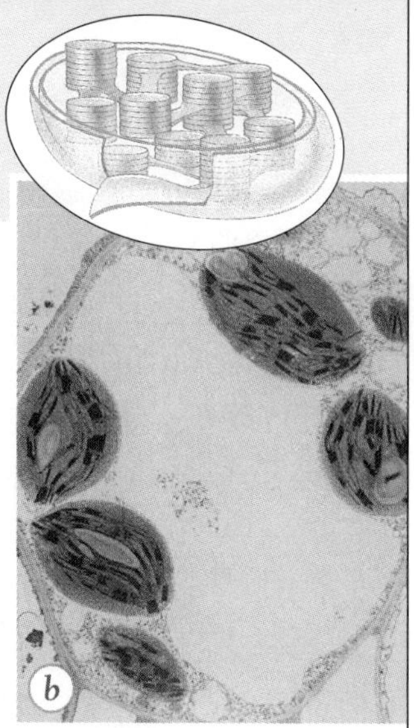

For the mitochondrion, the source of chemical fuel is not coal or natural gas but complex organic molecules, such as glucose or other sugars. And unlike power plants, neither a mitochondrion nor a chloroplast produces electricity. Instead, both organelles produce molecules that serve as small packets of chemical energy. In the next chapter, you will learn much more about these molecules and how they are produced.

☑ **Checkpoint** What is a chloroplast? A mitochondrion? (1)

Section Review 3–3

1. **Describe** the composition and function of the nucleus.
2. **List** and **describe** the organelles of the cytoplasm.
3. **Critical Thinking—Drawing Conclusions** Red blood cells, which do not contain mitochondria, transport oxygen gas through the bloodstream. Based on this information, would you conclude that oxygen crosses red blood cell membranes by active transport or by passive transport? Explain.
4. **MINI LAB** A paramecium produces acid to help digest food. Use this fact to **interpret** the color changes you observed as the paramecium took in dye-stained food.

Discussion

Initiate a discussion of mitochondria and chloroplasts by asking students why cells need energy. Students might respond by mentioning movement, reproduction, active transport, and other cell processes. Point out that the organelles that provide the needed energy are the mitochondria and the chloroplasts. Make sure students understand that though these organelles are related in their functions, only plants and some algae contain chloroplasts.

4 ASSESS

Quick Check

Ask students to make a table that lists all the parts of a typical cell, describes their structures, and explains their functions.

Section Review 3-3

1. Contains DNA molecules and proteins in the form of chromatin; most also contain a nucleolus; is surrounded by the nuclear envelope; and is the control center of the cell.

2. See pages 62 to 65.

3. Mitochondria are the producers of energy in a cell. Because red blood cells contain no mitochondria, they have no energy to use in active transport. Therefore, oxygen must cross the membrane by passive transport.

☑ Checkpoint

(1) An organelle that harvests the energy of sunlight; an organelle that produces energy from a chemical fuel.

4. The paramecium used the acid to digest the yeast in the vacuole, and that acid changed the indicator color to blue. The color changed back to red once the acid had been used in the digestion of the yeast.

Skills Trace

Interpreting

- Focus p. 64
- **Practice p. 65**
- Assess p. 73

Learning Modality

Tactile Learning Have groups of students make three-dimensional cutaway models of a typical cell, using papier-mâché, string, clay, plastic foam, or any other materials found around the home or classroom. Students could use Figure 3–18 for reference. Make sure they label the cell structures in their models.

Ancillary Support

The resources below can be used to support your teaching strategy for these two pages.

LM Comparing Plant and Animal Cells, #6
TR Apply: Get Out the Map

Section 3–4

The Origin of the Eukaryotic Cell

Performance Objective

- Discuss evidence for the endosymbiont hypothesis.

1 ENGAGE

Ideas Through Images

Have students examine Figure 3–24, read the caption, and answer the following questions.

- **What are the different kinds of prokaryotes shown in the drawing on the left?** (The host cell, spirochete bacteria, energy-producing bacteria.)
- **According to the endosymbiont hypothesis, what did those various prokaryotes become?** (The host cell became the primary cell of the primitive eukaryote, the spirochete bacteria became the flagella, and the energy-producing bacteria became the chloroplasts and mitochondria.)

2 EXPLORE

Investigate

Research Have students investigate this hypothesis by finding books and articles in which Margulis discusses her proposal. Ask that they also try to find references in other works about evolution to discover whether Margulis's hypothesis is widely accepted.

SECTION 3–4 BRANCHING OUT In Depth

The Origin of the Eukaryotic Cell

GUIDE FOR READING

- **Define** the endosymbiont hypothesis.

EUKARYOTES HAVE NUCLEI AND prokaryotes do not have nuclei—but that is only the beginning of the differences between them. Eukaryotes also have mitochondria, chloroplasts, and a host of other organelles that prokaryotes do not have.

How did eukaryotes and prokaryotes come to be so different? No one can answer this question for sure. However, one scientist has proposed a very interesting hypothesis.

The Work of Lynn Margulis

Lynn Margulis, a scientist from the University of Massachusetts, focused her attention on two organelles—the mitochondrion and the chloroplast. As Margulis noted, both organelles have several unusual properties. First, they contain their own DNA. While other organelles rely solely on the DNA in the nucleus, mitochondria and chloroplasts use their own DNA to produce many important compounds.

Second, both the mitochondrion and the chloroplast are surrounded by two membranes. Most membrane-bound organelles—including the Golgi apparatus, the ER, and the lysosome—are surrounded by only one membrane.

Third, in many respects the mitochondrion and chloroplast reproduce separately from the rest of the cell. The cell can produce other organelles individually, but mitochondria seem to come only from other mitochondria, and chloroplasts seem to come only from other chloroplasts.

These facts raised several questions in Margulis's mind. Why do mitochondria and chloroplasts have their own DNA? Why do they have a second membrane, while other organelles have only one? And why do they reproduce separately from the rest of the cell?

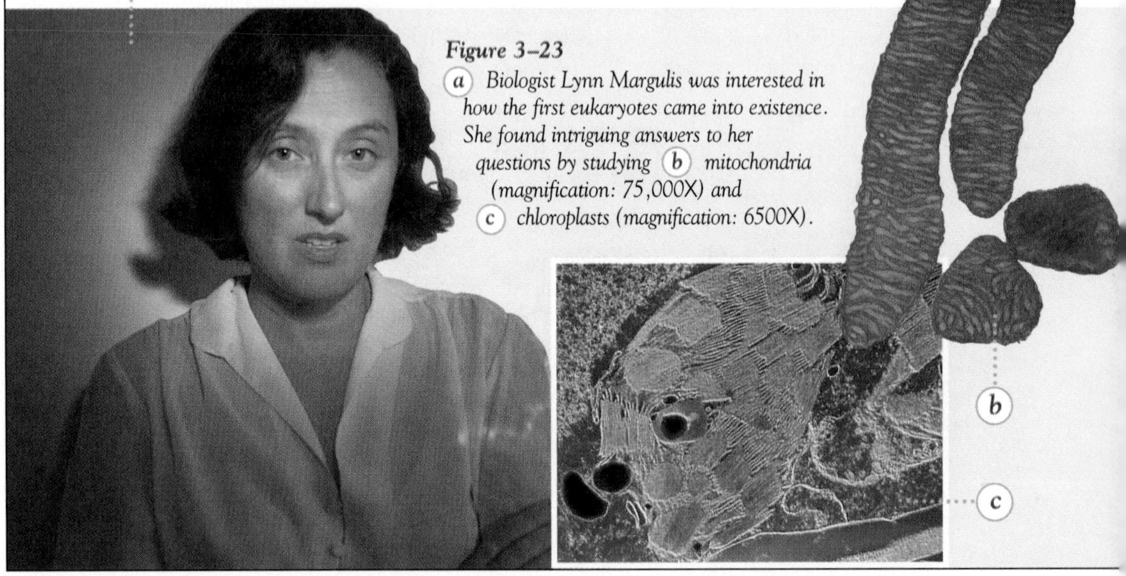

Figure 3–23
(a) Biologist Lynn Margulis was interested in how the first eukaryotes came into existence. She found intriguing answers to her questions by studying (b) mitochondria (magnification: 75,000X) and (c) chloroplasts (magnification: 6500X).

TEACHER SUPPORT

Managing Classroom Diversity

EDUCATIONAL EQUITY

Point out to students that Lynn Margulis is one of the world's most famous life scientists and a distinguished professor of biology at the University of Massachusetts. Have interested students research her accomplishments and review some of her books. In addition to her scholarly work, she has written several books for a general audience, some with her son, Dorion Sagan.

The Endosymbiont Hypothesis

Margulis proposed an interesting hypothesis that answered each of the questions she raised. **Margulis proposed that billions of years ago, eukaryotic cells arose as a combination of different prokaryotic cells.** She called this hypothesis the **endosymbiont hypothesis.** *Endo-* means "inside," and a symbiotic relationship is a close association between two organisms—sometimes of benefit to both organisms. The term endosymbiont highlights the idea that one organism might actually have been living inside the other.

☑ **Checkpoint** What is the endosymbiont hypothesis? ❶

Margulis's Model

According to Margulis, both mitochondria and chloroplasts had ancestors that were free-living organisms. These organisms formed endosymbiotic relationships with larger cells. Over time, the offspring of these organisms lost their independence, becoming organelles in larger cells.

This model answers each of Margulis's questions about chloroplasts and mitochondria. These organelles have their own DNA and reproduce separately because they were once independent organisms. Their inner membranes could be the remnant of the cell membrane of the free-living organism, and the outer membranes could be the cell's membrane surrounding the "foreign" cell.

THE ENDOSYMBIONT HYPOTHESIS

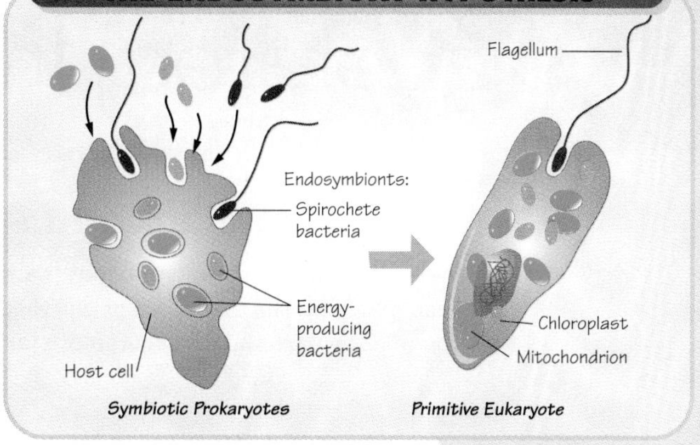

Figure 3–24 *According to the endosymbiont hypothesis, a collection of prokaryotic bacteria joined together billions of years ago. Eventually, they lost their independence and became a primitive eukaryote.*

Further Evidence

There is further evidence for the endosymbiont hypothesis. For example, detailed studies of the DNA molecules in chloroplasts show that they are much more like the DNA of prokaryotes than they are like the DNA found in the nucleus of plants. This result would be expected if chloroplasts were once independent prokaryotic organisms.

Researchers have also discovered that mitochondria and chloroplasts contain their own ribosomes and make many of their own proteins. These ribosomes, however, are smaller and chemically different from those found in the rest of the eukaryotic cell. Instead, they resemble the ribosomes found in prokaryotes.

Section Review 3–4

1. **Define** the endosymbiont hypothesis.
2. **Describe** the evidence in favor of the endosymbiont hypothesis.
3. **BRANCHING OUT ACTIVITY** Think of two organisms—either real or imaginary—that might form an endosymbiotic relationship. In a series of drawings, **describe** the organisms and the endosymbiotic relationship that you propose they form.

3. Students' drawings will vary; however, each series should show a close association between the two organisms that is beneficial to both.

Learning Modality

Auditory Learning Ask each of a series of students to explain orally one piece of evidence that supports the endosymbiont hypothesis.

3 TEACH

Discussion

Discuss the evidence for the endosymbiont hypothesis, including the DNA, the membranes, and the separate reproduction of mitochondria and chloroplasts, as well as the similarity of prokaryotic and chloroplast DNA. Once you are sure of students' understanding of the evidence, ask for their opinions about the probability of this hypothesis being true.

4 ASSESS

Quick Check

Have students make a flow chart that explains how eukaryotic cells might have developed from prokaryotic cells.

Section Review 3–4

1. The endosymbiont hypothesis is the proposal that billions of years ago eukaryotic cells arose as a combination of different prokaryotic cells through symbiotic relationships between cells.
2. Students should mention the DNA, the two membranes, and the separate reproduction of mitochondria and chloroplasts. They should also cite the similarity between prokaryotic and chloroplast DNA.

☑ Checkpoint

❶ The idea that eukaryotic cells arose as a combination of different prokaryotic cells.

Ancillary Support

The resources below can be used to support your teaching strategy for these two pages.

TR Enrich: Guests or Prisoners
BL Inquiry Activity: Cells Within Cells

CHAPTER 3

Laboratory Investigation

Inside Plant and Animal Cells

Before the Lab

1. At least one day prior to the lab, gather enough materials for students to work in teams of two to four.
2. Practice the procedure for staining the piece of onion on the slide so that you can demonstrate it for students.

Pre-Lab Discussion

Have students read the entire procedure for this investigation. Then ask students the following questions.

What is the purpose of this investigation? (To compare the structures of an animal cell and a plant cell.)

Why is the iodine solution used to stain the piece of onion? (To make some cell structures more prominent under the microscope.)

Skills Development

Students will use these skills while completing the laboratory investigation: observing, comparing, and inferring.

Teaching Strategies

1. Demonstrate how students should peel the skin from the inner surface of the onion and then cut a small piece to use on the slide.
2. Show students how to use the dropper and piece of paper towel at the same time in order to draw the iodine solution underneath the coverslip and stain the onion cells.

CHAPTER 3

Laboratory Investigation

Inside Plant and Animal Cells

Ever since the first microscopes were invented, biologists have been studying the structure of all living cells. In this investigation, you will compare the structures of plant cells and animal cells.

Problem

How do the structures of plant cells and animal cells **compare?**

Materials (per group)

scalpel
tweezers
onion
medicine dropper
glass slide
coverslip
iodine solution
paper towel
prepared slide of human cheek cells
microscope

Procedure

1. **Using tweezers, peel the thin, transparent skin from the inner surface of an onion, as shown.**

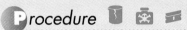

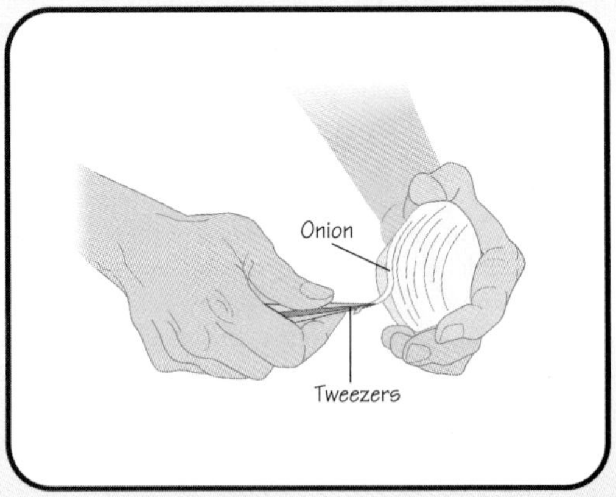

2. **With a scalpel, cut a small piece of the skin from the section that was removed from the onion. CAUTION: *Be careful when using a scalpel or any other sharp instrument.* Place the small piece of onion skin on a clean glass slide.**
3. **Add a drop of water to the piece of onion skin and cover with a coverslip.**

Safety Tips

Caution students to be extremely careful with the scalpel. Advise them to cut the onion in a direction that takes the scalpel blade away from the hand holding the onion. Also, warn students never to walk around the classroom with the scalpel in hand. Make sure students do not get the iodine solution on their hands or clothes because it stains.

4. **Using the medicine dropper, place a drop of iodine solution at one end of the coverslip. Holding a piece of paper towel near the opposite edge, draw the iodine solution underneath the coverslip.**
5. **Examine the onion skin slide under the low-power objective of the microscope. Sketch and label what you observe.**
6. **Repeat step 5 using the high-power objective.**
7. **Repeat steps 5 and 6 using the prepared slide of the human cheek cells.**

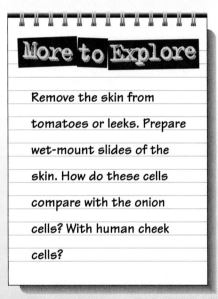

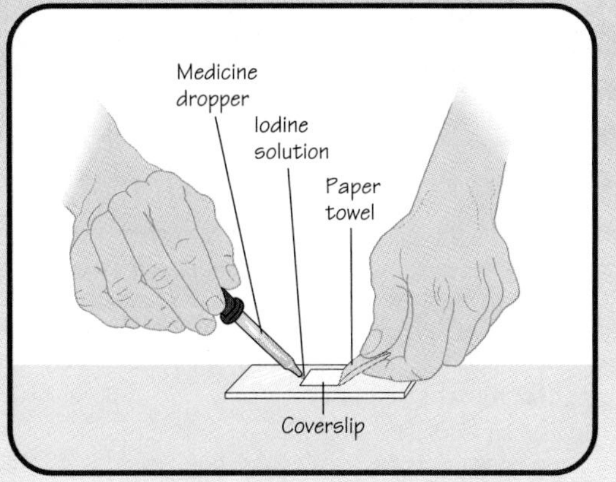

Observations

1. What is the shape of the onion skin cells? The shape of the human cheek cells?
2. Describe the general structures of the onion cells and the cheek cells.

Analysis and Conclusions

1. How are plants and animals similar in structure? How are they different?
2. What was the purpose of adding the iodine solution to the onion cells?
3. In onion plants, the liquid outside the cells is significantly less concentrated than the liquid inside the cells. This concentration difference creates high osmotic pressure. Describe how onion cells respond to osmotic pressure.
4. Of the cell structures presented in this chapter, which did you not see in either the cheek cell or the onion cell? Discuss the reasons why you did not see these structures.
5. Based on your observations, draw and label a generalized structure of a plant cell and an animal cell.

More to Explore

Remove the skin from tomatoes or leeks. Prepare wet-mount slides of the skin. How do these cells compare with the onion cells? With human cheek cells?

Answers to
Observations

1. Onion skin cells are generally rectangular, with some variation in size and shape. Human cheek cells are generally rounded. Some may be folded, while others are flat.
2. An onion cell has a rigid cell wall and a distinct nucleus, both of which stain blue-black with iodine. Students may be able to see vacuoles and darkened spots outside the nucleus. The cheek cells, without cell walls, should not be as uniform in appearance. Students should observe a cell membrane as well as a large darkened spot, the nucleus, within each cell. Other spots may also appear dark.

Answers to
Analysis and Conclusions

1. Plant and animal cells both have cell membranes and nuclei. Plant cells have cell walls, whereas animal cells do not.
2. Adding the stain makes certain cell structures more prominent and thus easier to see.
3. An onion cell uses a cell wall to counteract osmotic pressure, thus preventing a cell from expanding too much.
4. Students' responses may vary, depending on what they saw or how they interpreted what they saw. Students might mention any structures other than the nucleus, the cell membrane, and the cell wall, citing the low power of their microscopes as the reason.
5. Students' drawings should at least include a nucleus and a cell membrane for each type, with a cell wall drawn for the generalized plant cell.

More to Explore

Because tomatoes and leeks contain plant cells, students should observe more similarities with the onion cells than with the cheek cells.

Chapter 3

Study Guide

Review Strategy

Divide the class into two teams and have them quiz each other about the vocabulary and concepts discussed in the chapter. Ask that each team meet first to generate a list of questions. These questions could be weighted from easy to difficult, with points assigned to each question depending on its difficulty. During the game, teams could earn points by answering a series of increasingly harder questions. The winning team—the one with the most points at the end of the game—could be granted some special privilege.

Study Guide

Summarizing Key Concepts

The key concepts in each section of this chapter are listed below to help you review the chapter content. Make sure you understand each concept and its relationship to other concepts and to the theme of this chapter.

3–1 Microscopes and Cells

- Anton van Leeuwenhoek used light microscopes to identify small living things. Robert Hooke was the first person to identify cells.
- The cell theory states that living things are made of cells, that cells are the smallest working units of living things, and that cells arise from the division of other cells.
- The compound light microscope is arguably the most useful tool in biology. Electron microscopes and scanning probe microscopes are especially powerful microscopes.

3–2 Cell Boundaries

- The cell membrane separates and protects the cell from its surroundings.
- The cell membrane contains a double layer of lipids, called the lipid bilayer. The cell membrane also contains proteins, carbohydrates, and other compounds.
- In passive transport, substances move from regions of high concentration to low concentration. In active transport, cells use energy to move substances against a concentration difference.

3–3 Inside the Cell

- The nucleus contains nearly all of a cell's DNA.
- An organelle is a small structure that performs a specialized function within a cell.
- The different organelles include the ribosomes, endoplasmic reticulum, Golgi apparatus, lysosomes, cytoskeleton, vacuoles, mitochondria, and chloroplasts.

3–4 The Origin of the Eukaryotic Cell

- Lynn Margulis proposed the endosymbiont hypothesis, which states that billions of years ago eukaryotic cells arose as a combination of different prokaryotic cells.

Reviewing Key Terms

Review the following vocabulary terms and their meaning. Then use each term in a complete sentence.

3–1 Microscopes and Cells

cell
cell theory
compound light microscope
electron microscope
scanning probe microscope

3–2 Cell Boundaries

cell membrane
lipid bilayer
cell wall
passive transport
diffusion
osmosis
active transport

3–3 Inside the Cell

nucleus
eukaryote
prokaryote
chromosome
cytoplasm
organelle
ribosome
endoplasmic reticulum
Golgi apparatus
lysosome
cytoskeleton
vacuole
mitochondrion
chloroplast

3–4 The Origin of the Eukaryotic Cell

endosymbiont hypothesis

Inquiry-Based Strategy

Explain to students that some human blood cells are able to recognize foreign invaders and destroy them before they do any harm. Challenge students to research which cells do this job and how they accomplish it. Have them try to answer these questions: Which specific blood cells are involved in this process? What cell organelles are used to destroy the invading cells? How is this accomplished without the blood cell itself being destroyed?

Have students write a short report with diagrams to summarize their findings.

Recalling Main Ideas

Choose the letter of the answer that best completes the statement or answers the question.

1. The smallest working units of living things are
   a. nuclei. c. cells.
   b. organelles. d. atoms.

2. Organisms that have cells without nuclei are called
   a. eukaryotes. c. prokaryotes.
   b. animals. d. plants.

3. Which of the following could produce an image of individual atoms?
   a. transmission electron microscope
   b. scanning electron microscope
   c. scanning probe microscope
   d. Van Leeuwenhoek's microscope

4. A lipid bilayer forms the core of the
   a. cytoplasm. c. nucleus.
   b. cell membrane. d. ribosome.

5. Which structure is found in the cells of plants but not in animals?
   a. cell membrane c. mitochondrion
   b. cell wall d. lysosome

6. The nucleus stores almost all of a cell's
   a. ribosomes. c. proteins.
   b. DNA. d. amino acids.

7. Which organelle harvests energy from sunlight?
   a. lysosome c. chloroplast
   b. mitochondrion d. ribosome

8. The principal role of the endoplasmic reticulum and the Golgi apparatus is to
   a. store food. c. produce energy.
   b. move the cell. d. package proteins.

9. According to the endosymbiont hypothesis, early ancestors of mitochondria were
   a. free-living organisms.
   b. ribosomes.
   c. chloroplasts.
   d. nuclei.

Putting It All Together

Using the information on pages xxx to xxxi, complete the following concept map.

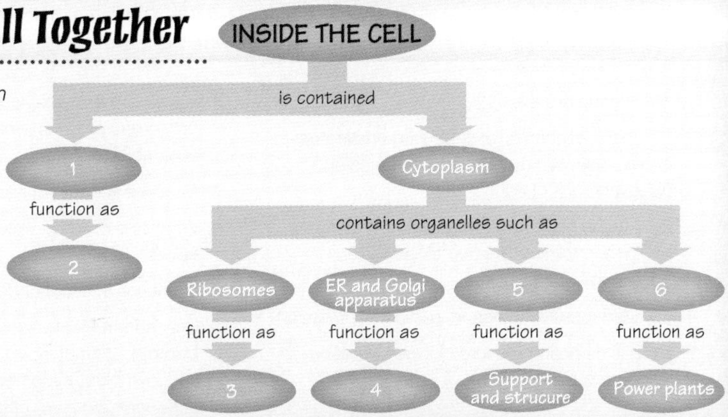

Recalling Main Ideas

1. c
2. c
3. c
4. b
5. b
6. b
7. c
8. d
9. a

Assessment

Reviewing What You Learned

1. Leeuwenhoek created microscopes that could magnify very small organisms, and he discovered many tiny living things.
2. Most can magnify an image up to 1000 times.
3. A TEM is a transmission electron microscope, which uses an electron beam to magnify an image onto a fluorescent screen. An SEM is a scanning electron microscope, which uses a thin beam of electrons to scan a sample's surface.
4. It separates and protects the cell from its surroundings.
5. A cell membrane's phospholipids are arranged in a lipid bilayer, with the polar ends grouped on the outside and the nonpolar ends grouped together on the inside.
6. Students' examples may vary. One example might be the movement of water through a cell membrane from the outside to the inside when the concentration of water on the outside is higher than on the inside of the membrane.
7. The nucleus contains nearly all of a cell's DNA and is the control center for the cell.
8. The lysosomes act as the cell's cleanup crew.
9. The endoplasmic reticulum processes and transports proteins and other macromolecules in the cell.
10. Vacuoles are the organelles that store food for the cell.
11. A cell's microtubules and microfilaments provide a tough, flexible framework of support for the cell.
12. Lynn Margulis first proposed the endosymbiont hypothesis.

Putting It All Together

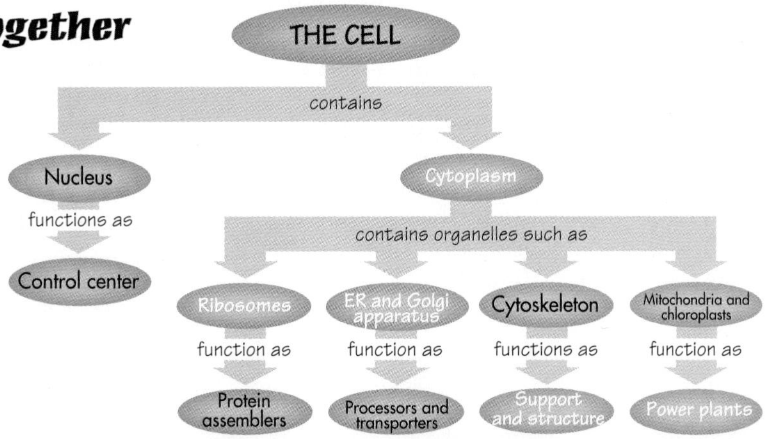

Assessment (continued)

Expanding the Concepts

1. The cell theory states that all living things are composed of cells, that cells are the smallest working units of living things, and that all cells come from preexisting cells by cell division.
2. The advantage of a light microscope is its ability to magnify live organisms; its disadvantage is its relatively low magnification. The advantage of an electron microscope is its high magnification, 1000 times more than a light microscope; its disadvantage is that the object cannot be alive.
3. When phospholipids are in water, they form a lipid bilayer, with the polar region on the outside and the nonpolar region on the inside. This lipid bilayer provides cell membranes with a tough, flexible barrier that protects the cell.
4. Passive transport, the movement of substances across cell membranes from regions of high concentration to regions of lower concentration, does not require the cell to expend energy. Active transport, the movement of substances across cell membranes from regions of low concentration to regions of higher concentration, does require the cell to expend energy.
5. Osmotic pressure is the pressure exerted by the diffusion of water through a cell membrane. Cells respond to it in three ways: They use a cell wall, they pump out the water, or they bathe cells in blood.
6. Proteins are assembled at ribosomes. The endoplasmic reticulum and the Golgi apparatus process proteins after they are assembled.
7. Lysosomes function as the cleanup crew of the cell, breaking down damaged organelles and other substances in the cell.
8. In plant cells, vacuoles store water and dissolved salts and also provide support for heavy structures.
9. Both organelles produce molecules that serve as small packets of chemical energy, both are surrounded by two membranes, and both contain their own DNA. Mitochondria, found in both plants and animals, convert complex organic molecules into a usable form of energy. Chloroplasts, found only in plants and certain kinds of algae, convert sunlight into a usable form of energy.
10. Both organelles contain their own DNA and use it to produce important compounds. Both are surrounded by two membranes. And both reproduce separately from the rest of the cell. These facts led to the endosymbiont hypothesis.

Extending Your Thinking

1. The actual spatial relationship is that the air bubble is above and to the right of the cell.

Skills Trace
Observing
- Focus p. 51
- Practice p. 52
- Assess p. 73

Assessment

Reviewing What You Learned

Answer each of the following in a complete sentence.

1. How did Anton van Leeuwenhoek contribute to the study of biology?
2. How powerful is the compound light microscope?
3. What is a TEM? An SEM?
4. What is the purpose of the cell membrane?
5. How are phospholipids arranged in a cell membrane?
6. Give an example of water moving by osmosis.
7. What is the role of the nucleus?
8. Which organelle acts as the cell's "cleanup crew"?
9. What is the function of the endoplasmic reticulum?
10. Which organelle stores food for the cell?
11. For what purpose do cells use microtubules and microfilaments?
12. Who first proposed the endosymbiont hypothesis?

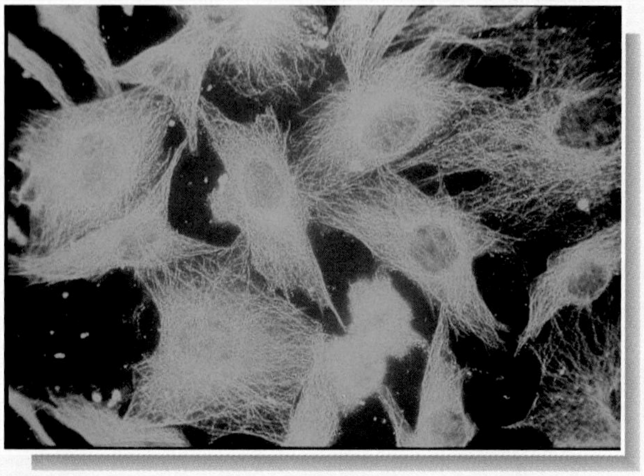

Expanding the Concepts

Discuss each of the following in a brief paragraph.

1. What is the cell theory?
2. Compare a light microscope with an electron microscope. What are the advantages and disadvantages of each?
3. Identify the polar and the nonpolar regions of a phospholipid. Why are these regions significant?
4. Compare passive transport with active transport.
5. What is osmotic pressure? How do cells respond to it?
6. Where are proteins assembled? What organelles process proteins after they are assembled?
7. Describe the role of lysosomes.
8. What two roles do vacuoles serve in plant cells?
9. Compare a mitochondrion with a chloroplast.
10. Describe the facts about mitochondria and chloroplasts that led to the development of the endosymbiont hypothesis.

Extending Your Thinking

Use the skills you have developed in this chapter to answer the following.

1. **Observing** While looking through a compound light microscope, you observe an air bubble below and to the left of the image of a cell. What is the actual spatial relationship between the cell and the air bubble? Explain.
2. **Applying concepts** A beaker contains two salt solutions divided by a membrane. The solution is higher on the left side of the beaker than on the right side. The membrane is permeable to water but not to salt. Which side of the beaker contains the more concentrated salt solution? Explain your answer.
3. **Designing an experiment** Design an experiment to determine the water concentration of a peeled potato. (*Hint:* When placed in a sugar solution, a peeled potato will either gain or lose water through osmosis.)
4. **Interpreting data** The photograph at right was produced by an electron microscope. What structures can you identify? Can you determine whether the photograph shows a plant cell or an animal cell? Explain.
5. **Evaluating evidence** Suppose that researchers discover a way to separate mitochondria from the rest of the cell, then develop the mitochondria into free-living organisms. Would this discovery strengthen, weaken, or have no effect on Margulis's endosymbiont hypothesis? Explain.

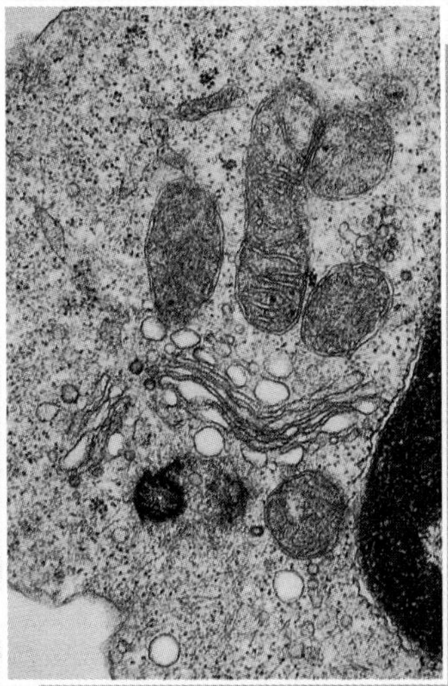

Applying Your Skills

A Model Membrane

A diagram in a textbook can provide a great deal of information, but scientists often use three-dimensional models to better understand complex structures.

1. Using ***Figure 3–8*** on page 54 as a guide, construct a model of the cell membrane. You may use Styrofoam™ balls, toothpicks, construction paper, or any other materials available in your classroom.
2. Label the components of your model.
3. In what ways is your model accurate? In what ways is it inaccurate?

• GOING FURTHER •

4. Research other models of the cell membrane. Use the results of your research to improve the model you constructed.
5. Using your model as a visual aid, present a report to your class on the structure and function of the cell membrane.

2. The solution is still more concentrated on the left side of the membrane than on the right side because the force of osmosis does not completely overcome air pressure.
3. Students' designs may vary. A possible design would use known sugar solutions to test whether the peeled potato would gain or lose water when placed in a sugar solution. That could be determined either by measuring changes in the volume of the solution or changes in mass of the potato.

4. Students should be able to identify a nucleus and vacuoles in the cell shown in the photograph. They should also conclude that the cell is an animal cell, because of its rounded shape and lack of a cell wall.

Skills Trace
Interpreting
- Focus p. 64
- Practice p. 65
- Assess p. 73

5. Such a discovery would strengthen the hypothesis, because in Margulis's model, mitochondria developed from free-living organisms that formed endosymbiotic relationships with larger cells.

Applying Your Skills

Preparation

1. Collect various materials for students to use. In addition to those mentioned in the text, students might use straws, pipe cleaners, cotton balls, tape, rubber bands, paper clips, straight pins, facial tissue, and plastic wrap.
2. A model could be made using all edible materials instead of the materials listed. Such a model might be made using spaghetti, licorice, gumdrops, fruit snacks, sticks of gum, and so on.

Suggestions

1. Direct students to Figure 3–8 for an example of how a cell membrane could be represented in a model.
2. Have students work in cooperative learning groups of three or four.
3. Have students develop a brief plan of what materials they will use where in their models. Review those plans before students actually begin construction.

Scoring Rubric

4 Response is thorough, accurate, and creative; shows an in-depth understanding of science skills, procedures, and concepts.

3 Response is complete, mostly accurate, and original; shows a satisfactory understanding of science skills, procedures, and concepts.

2 Response is mostly complete but includes some inaccuracies; shows an adequate understanding of science skills, procedures, and concepts.

1 Response is only partially complete and has many inaccuracies; shows an incomplete understanding of science skills, procedures, and concepts.

0 Response is mostly incomplete and/or inaccurate; shows a lack of understanding of science skills, procedures, and concepts.

Chapter 4 Energy and the Cell

Content Management	Student Edition Activities
■ Section 4–1 Chemical Energy and Life, pp. 75–77 Cells and Energy ATP Chemical Energy	
■ Section 4–2 Making ATP Without Oxygen, pp. 78–80 Glycolysis Fermentation	MINI LAB: Temperature and Fermentation, p. 80 Laboratory Investigation: Tiny Bubbles, pp. 94–95
■ Section 4–3 Respiration, pp. 81–85 The Process of Respiration The Krebs Cycle The Electron Transport Chain	
■ Section 4–4 Photosynthesis, pp. 86–91 The Process of Photosynthesis Light-Dependent Reactions The Light-Independent Reactions	MINI LAB: Breaking Out of Prism, p. 88
◆ BRANCHING OUT • In Depth Section 4–5 ATP Synthesis, pp. 92–93 Membranes and ATP Chemiosmosis	

■ These sections cover all the necessary content and concepts for a basic course in biology.
◆ This section covers content and concepts that are either applications or extensions of the basic material.

Integration Strategies

SE Chemistry, p. 77

Assessment Strategies

SE Chapter Review, pp. 96–99
TR Section Reviews
Chapter Test
BL Chapter Review
Practice Test
CTB Chapter 4 Test

Tech Prep

Teaching strategies appropriate for students who are in technical/vocational programs or who are considering post-secondary technical education can be found on the following **TE** pages: 81 and 85.

Meeting the Standards

Sections 4–1 through 4–5 cover three of the six content standards under **The Cell** and four of the six content standards under **Matter, Energy, and Organization in Living Systems** as described on pages 184–187 of the National Science Education Standards.

Chapter Planning Guide

Teacher's Edition Activities	Other Activities	Media and Technology
Chapter Discovery Learning Activity, p. 74 **Inquiry Activity:** A Potential for Energy, p. 76	**TR** Writing in Biology: It Keeps Going and Going Explore: Of Bonds and Rubber Bands **BL** Inquiry Activity: What's the Word? Energy!	
Inquiry Activity: Bubbles in the Bread, p. 78 **Investigate:** Research, p. 78	**TR** Enrich: Last but Not Yeast **BL** Inquiry Activity: Feed Your Muscles	
Inquiry Activity: At the End of Respiration, p. 82	**LM** Observing Respiration, #8 **TR** Apply: Food Fun **BL** Inquiry Activity: Do Plants Breathe?	CD-ROM: Cellular Respiration **TB** Visualizing Respiration, #5
Inquiry Activity: A Product of the Sun?, p. 86 **Investigate:** Cooperative Learning, p. 87	**LM** Observing Photosynthesis, #7 **TR** Explore: Tiny Green Energy Machine **BL** Inquiry Activity: Colors of the Season	CD-ROM: Photosynthesis **TB** Visualizing Photosynthesis, #4
Investigate: Research, p. 92	**TR** Enrich: Cell Power for Cities **BL** Inquiry Activity: Jumping Breakfast Cereal	

KEY: **SE** Student Edition **TE** Teacher's Edition **LM** Laboratory Manual **TR** Teaching Resources **BL** BioLog **TB** Transparency Box **CTB** Computer Test Bank

Materials List

TE Chapter Discovery Learning Activity, p. 74 (15–20 minutes); solar-powered instruments, such as calculators, clocks, and heaters.

TE Inquiry Activity: A Potential for Energy, p. 76 (15–20 minutes); rubber bands.

TE Inquiry Activity: Bubbles in the Bread, p. 78 (10–15 minutes); unleavened bread, leavened bread.

SE MINI LAB: Temperature and Fermentation, p. 80 (30 minutes); test tubes, stoppers with rubber tubes, beakers, Bromthymol blue solution, glass-marking pencils, thermometers, warm water, ice, yeast suspension.

TE Inquiry Activity: At the End of Respiration, p. 82 (20 minutes); beaker, water, Bromthymol blue powder, drinking straw.

TE Inquiry Activity: A Product of the Sun?, p. 86 (15 minutes for initial setup; 15–20 minutes for conclusion); water, small *Elodea* plants, beaker, glass funnels, test tubes, matches, toothpicks.

SE MINI LAB: Breaking Out of Prism, p. 88 (30 minutes); white paper, flashlight or lamp, prism.

Energy and the Cell

Introducing the Chapter

. . . In Pictures

All living things need energy to carry out the processes of life. The opening photograph of cows in a Texas field highlights the two main ways of obtaining that needed energy. Have students examine the photograph and answer the following questions.

- **How do the cows gain energy by eating the plants?** (Once digested, the energy in the plants is distributed to all of a cow's cells.)
- **Where do the plants get their energy?** (Through photosynthesis.) In this chapter, students will learn about how some organisms, including plants, obtain energy directly from the sun and how other organisms, including animals, convert the chemical energy of plants into energy for their cells.

Teaching Strategy

In the first four sections of this chapter, students will learn about the ways in which cells obtain the energy needed for life processes, including glycolysis, fermentation, respiration, and photosynthesis. Use the BRANCHING OUT section to give students an in-depth understanding of the production of ATP molecules in mitochondria and chloroplasts.

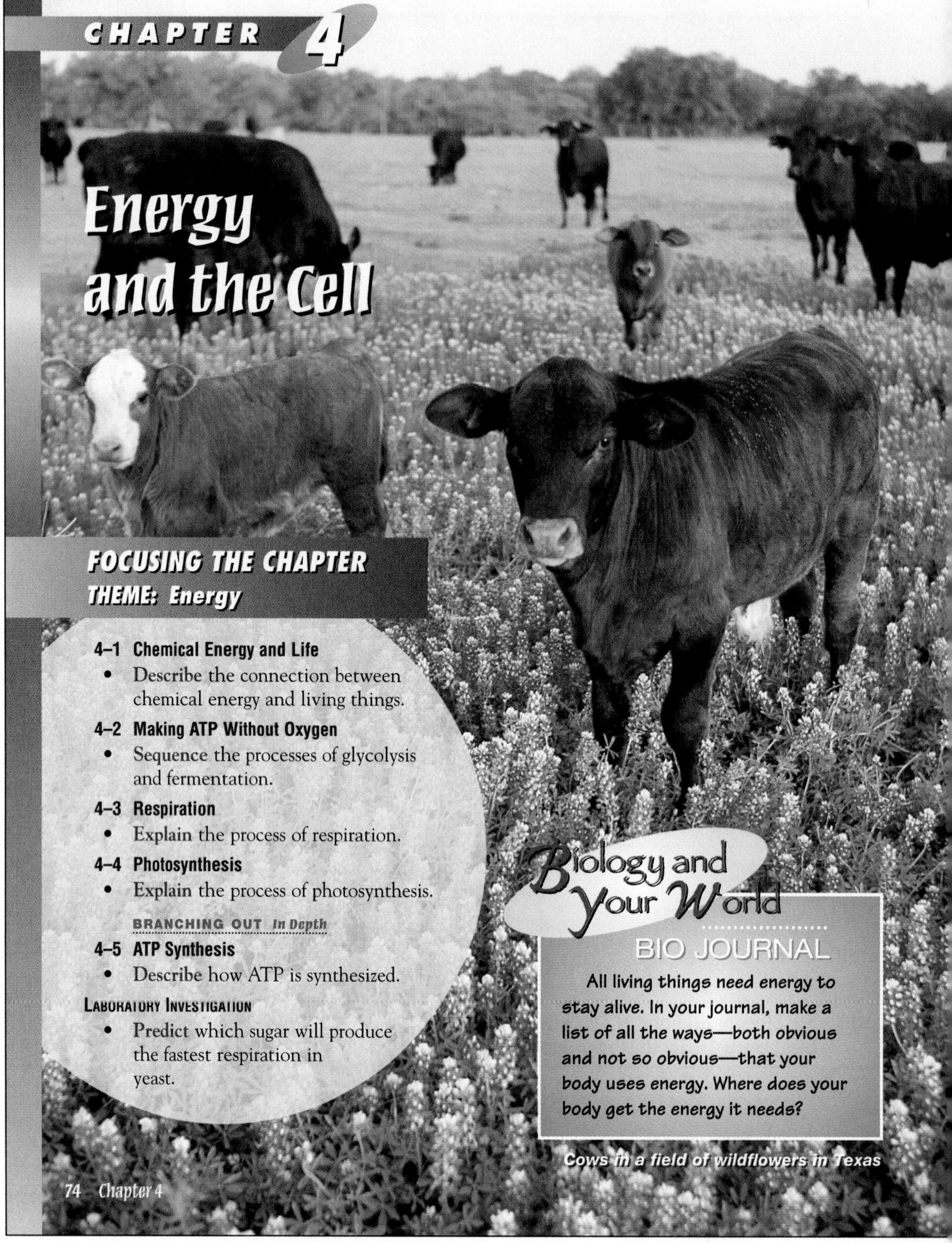

CHAPTER 4

Energy and the Cell

FOCUSING THE CHAPTER
THEME: Energy

4–1 Chemical Energy and Life
- Describe the connection between chemical energy and living things.

4–2 Making ATP Without Oxygen
- Sequence the processes of glycolysis and fermentation.

4–3 Respiration
- Explain the process of respiration.

4–4 Photosynthesis
- Explain the process of photosynthesis.

BRANCHING OUT *In Depth*

4–5 ATP Synthesis
- Describe how ATP is synthesized.

LABORATORY INVESTIGATION
- Predict which sugar will produce the fastest respiration in yeast.

Biology and Your World

BIO JOURNAL

All living things need energy to stay alive. In your journal, make a list of all the ways—both obvious and not so obvious—that your body uses energy. Where does your body get the energy it needs?

Cows in a field of wildflowers in Texas

74 Chapter 4

BIO JOURNAL

The Bio Journal topic can be used to stimulate classroom discussion about what living things need energy for and how they obtain that energy. Discuss with students their everyday energy needs. Then expand the discussion to the energy needs of plants and animals. Instruct students to keep their entries in their portfolios.

TEACHER SUPPORT

Chapter Discovery Learning Activity

Have students examine several solar-powered instruments, such as a calculator, a clock, or a heater. Then ask each student to write a paragraph explaining how he or she thinks such technology is powered. Have several students present their explanations to the class. Finally, discuss how the energy of sunlight can be used for the activities of living things, just as it is used to run solar technology.

Chemical Energy and Life

SECTION 4–1

GUIDE FOR READING

- **Explain** why energy is so important to living things.
- **Describe** how energy is stored in ATP and released from ATP.

EVERYTHING THAT IS ALIVE needs energy. The need for energy is easy to see in a group of athletes sprinting for the finish line, in a cheetah chasing a herd of antelopes, or in a flock of geese flying southward. Energy also is required for less obvious tasks. A tree standing in a meadow is silently using enormous amounts of energy to draw water from deep inside the Earth. A sleeping fox draws on its energy reserves to rebuild and replace the cells and tissues that were lost during the day's hunting.

Cells use energy for virtually everything they do. Energy is required to build new proteins, to pump ions across the cell membrane, to copy genetic information, and even to move. Where do your cells get their energy? The simple answer is that energy comes from the food you eat. And the energy in that food ultimately came from the sun.

Cells and Energy

Why is energy so important to living things? **Without the ability to produce and use energy, living things would cease to exist.** Living cells need supplies of energy for thousands of activities at the same time. How do they get it? Imagine thousands of construction workers needing energy for their power drills and sanders. How could you supply energy to them? One way would be via a battery-recharging center that supplied the workers with batteries for their power tools. Each battery would carry a small amount of energy. When that energy was used up, the worker would snap in a new battery and send the spent battery back for recharging.

Figure 4–1
All organisms use energy. (a) Although it is not obvious, these flowers need a tremendous amount of energy to transport materials throughout the plants. (b) In order to fly, these Canada geese also need a great deal of energy.

SECTION 4–1

Chemical Energy and Life

Performance Objectives

- Describe how energy is important to living things.
- Explain how energy is stored in and released from ATP.

1 ENGAGE

Ideas Through Images

Have students examine Figure 4–1, read the caption, and answer the following questions.

- **What are some of the ways in which these Canada geese use energy?** (Students might mention a variety of ways, including flying, eating, and reproducing.)
- **How does a Canada goose get the energy it needs?** (It eats and digests food.)
- **How do the individual cells of the goose obtain the energy for cell processes?** (Students might suggest that the cell takes in molecules of digested food.)
- **What are some of the ways in which plants use energy?** (Students might mention a variety of ways, including growing and reproducing.)
- **How does a plant get the energy it needs?** (Most students will know that plants get their energy from the sun. Some might mention photosynthesis.)

TEACHER SUPPORT

Managing Classroom Diversity

AT-RISK STUDENTS
Some students may not understand the difference between potential and kinetic energy. Review with the students the basics of these concepts. Provide a simple physical science text for them to read, and then ask them to describe an example of potential energy turning into kinetic energy, such as when a rock rolls down a hill. Explain to students that chemical bonds are a form of potential energy for cells.

Ancillary Support

The resource below can be used to support your teaching strategy for these two pages.

BL Inquiry Activity: What's the Word? Energy!

2 EXPLORE

Inquiry Activity

Designing Experiments

A Potential for Energy

Ask students how a rubber band can be made to store the energy of work. Give each student a rubber band to manipulate. Then ask them to make a series of labeled drawings of the rubber band that shows (1) how work can be done on the rubber band in such a way that it stores energy, and (2) how that stored energy can be released to do work. Encourage students to share their drawings with the class and to discuss the difference between potential and kinetic energy.

3 TEACH

Ideas Through Images

Have students examine Figures 4–2 and 4–3, read the captions, and answer these questions.

- **What are the three parts of a molecule of ATP?** (The amino acid adenine, a sugar called ribose, and three phosphate groups.)
- **Where is energy stored in a molecule of ATP that can be used by living things?** (Energy is stored in the bonds that hold the phosphate groups to the rest of the molecule.)
- **How do such organisms as fireflies and bacteria gain energy from ATP molecules?** (They use enzymes to break one phosphate bond, converting ATP to ADP.)

ATP

Obviously, cells don't have batteries, but they do have a compound that works almost like a battery. This compound is called **ATP,** or adenosine triphosphate. As its name suggests, ATP has three phosphate groups. A similar compound, ADP (adenosine diphosphate), has two phosphates, and AMP (adenosine monophosphate) has just one. Try to think of AMP as an uncharged battery. **It takes a significant amount of energy to attach a phosphate to AMP to make ADP. This energy is stored in the phosphate bond, in much the same way that electricity is stored in a battery.**

A similar amount of energy is required to attach the third phosphate, converting ADP to ATP. Why is ATP so important? ATP is similar to a fully charged battery, ready to supply energy to do the work of the cell. How does ATP do this? **Throughout the cell, enzymes that require energy have binding sites for ATP and similar energy-carrying molecules. When one of these enzymes needs energy to complete a chemical reaction, one phosphate breaks off, converting ATP to ADP.** Breaking the phosphate bond releases just enough energy to pump an ion across a membrane, attach an amino acid to a growing protein, or flick a cilium a fraction of a micrometer. The molecule of ADP is then available to store energy by forming ATP again. This process continues over and over—storing energy and then releasing it as needed.

☑ ***Checkpoint*** What makes up an ATP molecule? ❶

How Do Cells Make ATP?

It might seem remarkable that so many different functions within the cell are energized by ATP, but it also makes good sense. The energy released by converting ATP to ADP enables the cell to power just about everything it does. To meet its potential energy needs in everything from growth to movement, all that a cell has to do is recharge its chemical batteries by attaching phosphates to AMP and ADP to make ATP.

Figure 4–2
A molecule of ATP consists of the amino acid adenine, a sugar called ribose, and three phosphate groups.

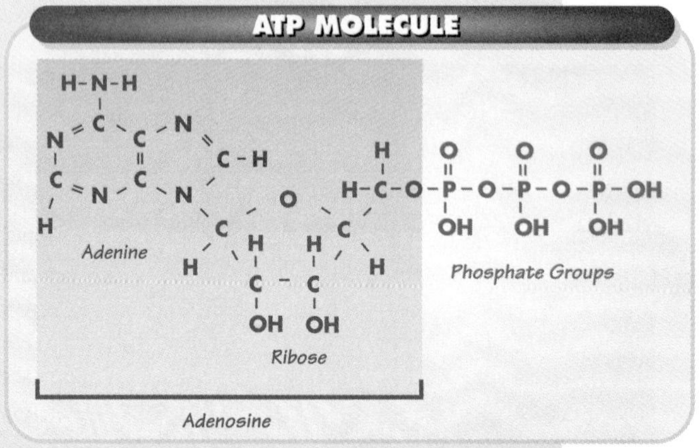

Releasing Energy From Food

Where do cells get the energy they need to replenish their supply of ATP? Animal cells get that energy from the food that is consumed. Most food molecules contain a great deal of energy. For example, a single glucose molecule contains more than 90 times the chemical energy released by splitting the third phosphate off ATP to make ADP.

TEACHER SUPPORT

Background Information

ATP molecules hold the energy that a cell needs to carry out the processes of life. These molecules have often been compared to batteries, but they also might be compared to the change in your pocket. Whenever you need to buy something, you reach for the change stored in your pocket; whenever a cell needs to do something, it reaches for the energy stored in its ATP molecules. That energy can be found in the covalent bonds that hold the second and third phosphate groups to the ATP molecule. Because those bonds release a relatively great amount of energy when they are broken, they are known as high-energy bonds. The cell is the beneficiary of the energy released when that occurs.

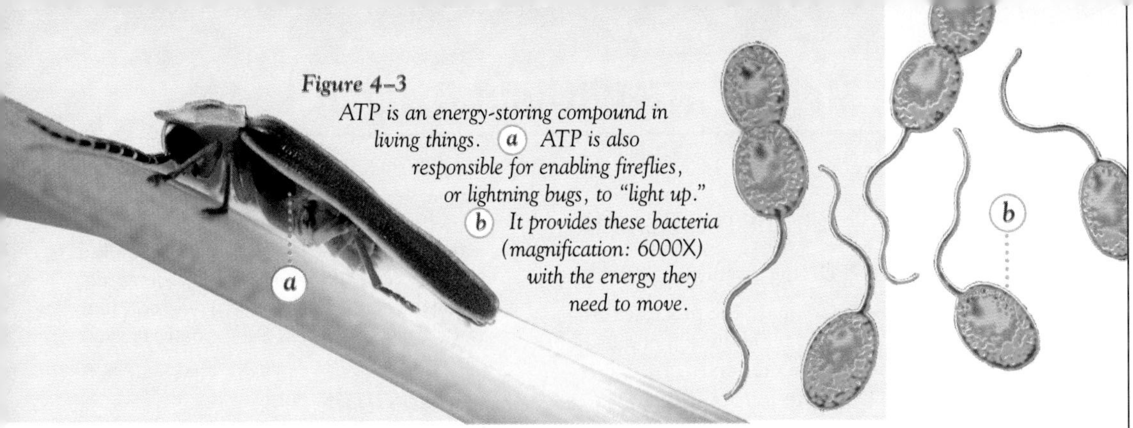

Figure 4–3 ATP is an energy-storing compound in living things. (a) ATP is also responsible for enabling fireflies, or lightning bugs, to "light up." (b) It provides these bacteria (magnification: 6000X) with the energy they need to move.

In the laboratory, the chemical energy in glucose can be released by burning it. This chemical reaction requires oxygen and produces carbon dioxide and water. In fact, the reaction of glucose with oxygen releases so much energy that it gives off heat and light—it burns. But a living cell has to control that reaction and release the energy a little bit at a time. This is where ATP comes in. It helps to trap the energy.

Checkpoint What kinds of energy are produced in the reaction of oxygen and glucose? (2)

Chemical Energy

Before you consider how cells go about trapping the energy in glucose, it might be useful to think about where that energy comes from. It certainly does not come from the nuclei of the atoms involved in the reaction. The nuclei are unchanged by the reaction. The only possible source of all that energy are the electrons that surround the carbon, hydrogen, and oxygen nuclei—the ones that form the chemical bonds between those atoms.

Compounds such as glucose store energy in their chemical bonds. This energy is released when the bonds are broken and new bonds storing less energy are formed. In other words, all that heat and light energy comes simply from rearranging the electrons that form the chemical bonds between the atoms of glucose.

How can cells capture energy from the chemical bonds of glucose? Recall that the reaction of glucose and oxygen releases an enormous amount of energy. Cells, however, need to capture energy in small amounts. Therefore, the reactions in living things take place in small steps, releasing small amounts of energy at a time. This enables cells to make the ATP they need.

INTEGRATING CHEMISTRY

What is the chemical formula for this reaction? What are the reactants? The products?

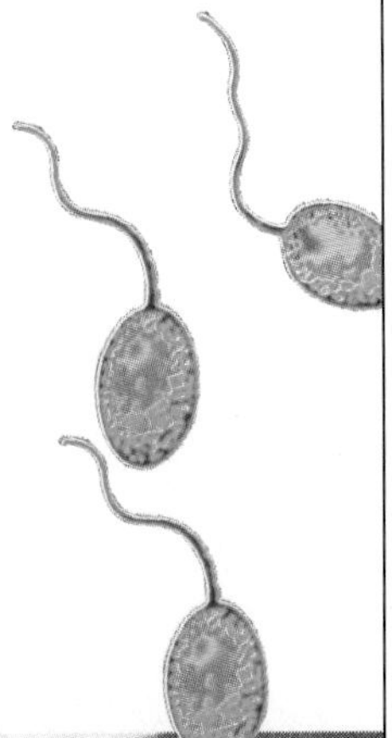

Section Review 4–1

1. **Explain** why energy is so important to living things.
2. **Describe** how energy is stored in ATP. How is it released?
3. **Critical Thinking—Drawing Conclusions** What is the relationship between energy and chemical bonds?

INTEGRATING CHEMISTRY

The chemical formula for the reaction known as respiration is:
$C_6H_{12}O_6 + 6O_2 \rightarrow 6CO_2 + 6H_2O$
The reactants are glucose and oxygen; the products are carbon dioxide and water.

4 ASSESS

Quick Check

Have students make a flow chart that shows the steps by which a cell makes an ATP molecule from food and then releases the energy in the phosphate bond of the ATP molecule to carry out an activity.

Section Review 4–1

1. Without the ability to produce and use energy, living things would cease to exist.

2. Energy is stored within the bonds of ATP's three phosphate groups. The energy is released when the bonds are broken.

3. Energy is needed to create a chemical bond, and that is where energy is stored. Therefore, energy is released when the bond is broken.

Checkpoints

(1) An ATP molecule consists of the amino acid adenine, a sugar called ribose, and three phosphate groups.

(2) The reaction produces energy in the form of heat and light.

Learning Modality

Visual Learning Ask students to make a drawing of an ATP molecule using Figure 4–2 as an example. Ask them to label the drawing as to where a cell stores energy in this molecule.

Ancillary Support

The resources below can be used to support your teaching strategy for these two pages.

TR Writing in Biology: It Keeps Going and Going

Explore: Of Bonds and Rubber Bands

SECTION 4–2

Making ATP Without Oxygen

Performance Objectives

- Discuss the reactions that make up glycolysis.
- Describe the processes of lactic acid and alcoholic fermentation.

Mini Lab Skill: Predicting
Laboratory Investigation Skill: Predicting

1 ENGAGE

Inquiry Activity

Comparing

Bubbles in the Bread

Give student groups a slice of unleavened bread and a slice of leavened bread. Have them examine both slices. Ask students what they see as the main difference in the two slices of bread. Then have each group write a comparison of the two and hypothesize about what caused the difference. Have each group share their hypothesis with the class.

2 EXPLORE

Investigate

Research Have groups of students work together on a report about aerobic and anaerobic exercise. Ask that they provide a comparison, examples of each, and an explanation of what occurs on the cellular level when a person participates in such activities. Have each group share their information with the class.

SECTION 4–2

Making ATP Without Oxygen

GUIDE FOR READING

- **Define** glycolysis.
- **Compare** the processes of lactic acid fermentation and alcoholic fermentation.

MINI LAB

- **Predict** the effect temperature has on the rate of fermentation.

TO RELEASE ENERGY FROM glucose a little bit at a time, the cell must take apart the glucose a little at a time. The cell does this by breaking the glucose down in a series of chemical reactions. These reactions take place in the cytoplasm of the cell, and they happen very quickly. It takes no more than a few milliseconds for most cells to produce thousands of molecules of ATP in this way. These ATP molecules provide quick energy for many cellular activities, including muscle contraction.

Each of these reactions is catalyzed by its own enzyme, and each is carefully controlled by the cell. Surprisingly, the first few reactions require energy—that is, the cell must use 2 molecules of ATP to begin the process.

Glycolysis

The series of reactions in which a molecule of glucose is broken down is called glycolysis. The word **glycolysis** means "sugar-breaking." The process of glycolysis, shown in ***Figure 4–5,*** begins when 2 molecules of ATP are used to convert the glucose molecule into a high-energy 6-carbon sugar with 2 phosphates. The 6-carbon sugar is broken down into two 3-carbon molecules (PGAL). The 2 PGAL molecules go through several more chemical reactions and produce pyruvic acid. These reactions produce 4 molecules of ATP for each molecule of glucose. This is a net gain of 2 molecules of ATP for each glucose molecule broken down.

Figure 4–4 (a) *Although the burning of wood is somewhat similar to the breakdown of glucose because energy is produced, the energy that is released from burning wood is much more dramatic.* (b) *In the absence of oxygen, the breakdown of glucose occurs by fermentation. The air bubbles in bread are a result of the fermentation of tiny yeast.*

TEACHER SUPPORT

Background Information

The oxidation of glucose—the way in which cells make ATP—begins with glycolysis. Glycolysis is often considered the first stage of a two-stage process whose second stage is respiration, which includes the Krebs cycle and the electron transport chain, and that is the organization presented in this text. Some works present cellular respiration as a three-stage process that includes glycolysis, the Krebs cycle, and the electron transport chain.

Glycolysis encompasses a series of nine chemical reactions that take place in the cytoplasm. Each reaction is catalyzed by a specific enzyme, and none of the reactions requires the presence of free oxygen. Compounds involved in this process include phosphoglyceraldehyde (PGAL) and the electron carrier nicotinamide adenine dinucleotide (NAD^+).

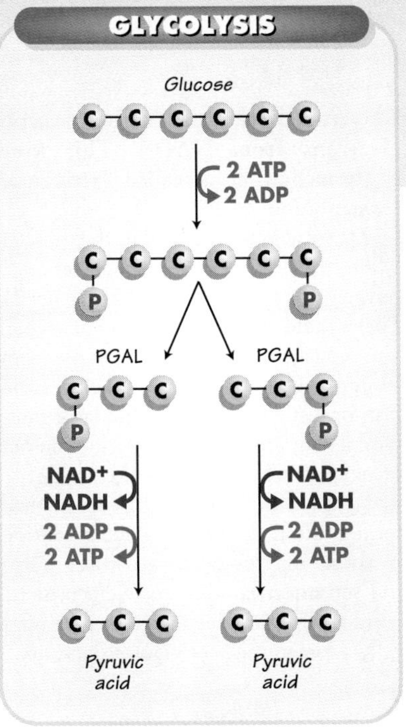

Figure 4–5
The complete process of glycolysis generates 4 molecules of ATP and 2 NADH molecules. NADH is formed when NAD^+ accepts a pair of high-energy electrons and a hydrogen ion (H^+).

In addition to the net gain of 2 molecules of ATP, glycolysis also produces 2 pairs of high-energy electrons. These electrons are passed to NAD^+, an electron carrier, to form NADH. In order for glycolysis to continue, there must be a constant supply of NAD^+.

The energy in these electrons can only be utilized when oxygen is available. However, if oxygen is not available, NADH cannot get rid of the high-energy electrons. Within a few seconds, all the cell's available NAD^+ molecules would be converted to NADH. Lacking a constant supply of NAD^+, ATP production would stop, and the cell would be in peril.

☑ **Checkpoint** What is the net gain of ATP in glycolysis? ①

Fermentation

Not surprisingly, the cell has a mechanism to get rid of the electrons if oxygen is not available. It passes the high-energy electrons from NAD^+ back to the same carbon atoms from which they came. What does this accomplish? It allows the cell to keep using its NAD^+ molecules over and over again, and that allows glycolysis to continue. It also has an interesting consequence—the cell accumulates the compounds that accept those electrons.

This process—the regeneration of NAD^+ to keep glycolysis running—is called **fermentation.** If oxygen is present, the cell can use the high-energy electrons in NAD^+ to make ATP, so fermentation is not necessary. Therefore, in nature, fermentation occurs only in cells and organisms that lack oxygen. There are two basic types of fermentation.

Lactic Acid Fermentation

In most animals, the pyruvic acid that accumulates due to glycolysis is

Figure 4–6
(a) During rapid exercise, such as running, muscle cells begin to produce lactic acid by lactic acid fermentation. This process provides these runners with the energy they need. (b) The process of alcoholic fermentation is responsible for turning the grapes in this vineyard into wine.

3 TEACH

Ideas Through Images

Have students examine Figure 4–5, read the caption, and answer the following questions.

- **What kind of molecule is broken down in glycolysis?** (A glucose molecule.)
- **What is used to provide the energy for this series of reactions?** (2 molecules of ATP.)
- **What is the net gain of ATP molecules in glycolysis?** (2 ATP molecules.)
- **What chemical compound is the final product of glycolysis?** (2 molecules of pyruvic acid.)
- **What else is produced in these reactions?** (2 molecules of NADH.)

Discussion

Lead students in a discussion of fermentation. Through this discussion, emphasize the following points.
- Fermentation occurs in cells after glycolysis has occurred.
- Fermentation occurs only when there is no oxygen present.
- The two basic types of fermentation are lactic acid fermentation and alcoholic fermentation.

Laboratory Investigation

The Laboratory Investigation, Tiny Bubbles, on pages 94–95, is appropriate to use at this point in the chapter.

☑ Checkpoint

① 2 molecules of ATP for each glucose molecule broken down.

TEACHER SUPPORT

Historical Perspective

If oxygen is available to the cell, then the breakdown of glucose continues on to respiration—the Krebs cycle and the electron transport chain. If oxygen is unavailable, then an alternative, anaerobic ("without oxygen") pathway is followed. Alcoholic fermentation is one such pathway, and it has been utilized for millennia to make alcoholic beverages. Evidence of beer- and wine-making has been found by archaeologists in many ancient cultures, including ancient Egypt thousands of years BC. A maker of beer or wine ferments a grain or fruit by adding yeast, which breaks down pyruvic acid into ethanol (an alcohol) and carbon dioxide. The carbon dioxide is the source of the bubbles in beer and sparkling wines, including champagne.

Ancillary Support

The resource below can be used to support your teaching strategy for these two pages.

BL Inquiry Activity: Feed Your Muscles

MINI LAB **Predicting**

Teacher Notes

- For time required and materials needed, see page 74b.
- Prepare a yeast solution by adding half a packet of yeast to 100 mL of 10% sugar solution an hour before the lab if rapid-acting yeast is used, several hours before if regular dry yeast is used.

Answers to Analyze and Conclude

1. Beaker A.
2. A higher temperature increased the rate of fermentation.
3. The rate would be slower because the lower temperature caused a slower reaction.

Skills Trace
Predicting
- Focus p. 80
- Practice p. 80
- Assess p. 99

4 ASSESS

Quick Check

Have students compare the two basic types of fermentation according to basic definitions, reactants, products, and the kinds of cells where each occurs.

Section Review 4–2

1. The series of reactions in which a molecule of glucose is broken down.
2. In lactic acid fermentation, the accumulated pyruvic acid is converted to lactic acid. In alcoholic fermentation, the accumulated pyruvic acid is converted to produce alcohol and carbon dioxide.
3. The fermentation of wine would cease because fermentation occurs only in cells that lack oxygen, and air contains oxygen.
4. Students should predict that the rate of fermentation will increase with an increase in temperature.

Skills Trace
Predicting
- Focus p. 80
- Practice p. 80
- Assess p. 99

MINI LAB ········ Predicting ········

Temperature and Fermentation

PROBLEM *How can you* ***predict*** *the effect of temperature on the rate of fermentation?*

PROCEDURE

1. Add enough yeast suspension to two test tubes so that it comes to within 3 cm of the top. Place a stopper with a rubber tube into each test tube. Put the test tubes aside for now.
2. Obtain 4 beakers from your teacher. Fill two of the beakers halfway with Bromthymol blue solution. **CAUTION:** *Bromthymol blue can stain your skin and clothing.*
3. Using a glass-marking pencil, label the remaining beakers A and B. Fill beakers A and B about two-thirds full with warm water. Using a thermometer and very warm water or ice, try to keep the temperature of the water in beaker A at 30°C and the water in beaker B at 20°C.
4. Place one test tube in beaker A and the other in beaker B. Put the free end of each rubber tube into a beaker of Bromthymol blue.
5. Record the time that it takes for each beaker of Bromthymol blue to change color.

ANALYZE AND CONCLUDE

1. Which beaker of Bromthymol blue turned color faster?
2. What effect did temperature have on the rate of fermentation?
3. If a third water bath with a temperature of 10°C was included in the experiment, would the rate of fermentation be faster or slower than that of beaker A or B? Explain your answer.

converted to lactic acid when it accepts electrons from NAD^+. This kind of fermentation is called lactic acid fermentation.

Lactic acid is produced in the muscles when the body cannot supply enough oxygen to muscles to meet their needs. **Lactic acid fermentation** occurs when you engage in vigorous exercise. For example, if you run, ride a bike, or swim fast for just a few seconds, the large muscles of your arms and legs quickly run out of oxygen. These muscles then begin to make the ATP they need by lactic acid fermentation. Lactic acid accumulation in these muscles causes a painful, burning sensation familiar to every athlete. This is why muscles may feel sore after only a few minutes of vigorous activity.

Alcoholic Fermentation

Another kind of fermentation occurs in yeasts. Yeasts are one-celled organisms that are used in baking or brewing. **In the absence of oxygen, pyruvic acid is broken down to produce alcohol and carbon dioxide instead of lactic acid. This process is known as alcoholic fermentation.**

Alcoholic fermentation causes bread dough to rise. When the yeast in the dough is starved for oxygen, it gives off tiny bubbles of carbon dioxide. The same carbon dioxide is the source of bubbles in beer and sparkling wines. To brewers, alcohol is a welcome byproduct of fermentation.

Section Review 4–2

1. **Define** glycolysis.
2. **Compare** lactic acid fermentation and alcoholic fermentation.
3. **Critical Thinking—Inferring** What would happen to wine if there was an air leak in the fermentation tank?
4. **MINI LAB** **Predict** the effect that temperature has on the rate of fermentation.

Learning Modality

Auditory Learning Have students explain orally the series of reactions that make up glycolysis. Make sure students pronounce the terms correctly and provide appropriate explanations for each step in the process.

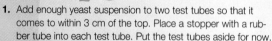

GUIDE FOR READING

- **Define** respiration.
- **Explain** the Krebs cycle.

AS USEFUL AS IT IS, GLYCOLYSIS releases only a small amount of the chemical energy that was originally stored in glucose. Most of that energy—about 90 percent—is still unused. To convert the rest of that chemical energy to ATP, the cell needs oxygen. Why does the cell need oxygen? In a sense, oxygen is the best electron acceptor. If a cell has access to oxygen, it can tap nearly all the energy available for its purposes.

The Process of Respiration

How does the cell use oxygen? You may recall that outside the cell, when glucose reacts with oxygen, it produces carbon dioxide and water and releases so much energy that it actually burns. The cell cannot afford to waste energy on a bonfire. Instead, it takes apart the pyruvic acid molecule formed in glycolysis, a little at a time. In the breakdown of pyruvic acid, the cell takes a few high-energy electrons with every step and uses their energy to make ATP. This process, called **respiration,** requires oxygen. **Respiration is the release of energy from the breakdown of food molecules in the presence of oxygen.**

In eukaryotic cells, respiration takes place inside the mitochondrion. You may recall that the mitochondrion is the cell organelle where energy is produced. The process of respiration begins when the pyruvic acid enters the mitochondrion.

The Krebs Cycle

The chemical bonds in pyruvic acid are broken apart in a series of reactions called the Krebs cycle, named for its discoverer, Dutch scientist Hans Krebs.

Figure 4–7
In order to release the maximum amount of energy from glucose, animals need oxygen. (a) All animals, including this grizzly bear, get the energy they need from the food—in this case, salmon—that they eat. (b) Dolphins must come to the surface of the water in order to get the oxygen they need.

TEACHER SUPPORT

Managing Classroom Diversity

TECH PREP STUDENTS
Have students who are planning careers in food service investigate how fermentation is used in the preparation of bread and alcoholic beverages. Ask that they research and describe specific processes, including the type of yeast added to breads and grains and fruits. Have them write a report on their findings, complete with illustrations.

SECTION 4–3
Respiration

Performance Objectives
- Describe the process known as respiration.
- Discuss the Krebs cycle and the electron transport chain.

1 ENGAGE

Ideas Through Images

Have students examine Figure 4–7, read the caption, and answer the following questions.

- **What do animals need to release the maximum amount of energy from glucose?** (They need oxygen.)
- **How do you think animals use oxygen to release energy from glucose?** (Students might suggest that the oxygen is transported by blood to the cells, where it is used in chemical reactions to break down glucose.)

Point out that the initial breakdown of glucose occurs in glycolysis. If oxygen is present in the cells, the products of glycolysis continue through a further series of reactions called respiration.

Technology

CD-ROM
Cellular Respiration

Ancillary Support

The resources below can be used to support your teaching strategy for these two pages.

TR Enrich: Last but Not Yeast
BL Inquiry Activity: Do Plants Breathe?

2 EXPLORE

Inquiry Activity

Experimenting

At the End of Respiration

Point out that humans inhale air to obtain the oxygen needed to release energy from glucose. Then ask students what they think is in the air that they exhale. Provide them with straws and beakers containing Bromthymol blue solution. Tell them that this solution turns yellow in the presence of carbon dioxide. Then have them experiment with their exhalation. Ask them to write an explanation of any changes they observe in the solution.

3 TEACH

Ideas Through Images

Have students examine Figure 4–8, read the caption, and answer these questions.

- **Where does the pyruvic acid come from that enters into the Krebs cycle?** (It is a product of glycolysis.)
- **What is the initial reaction that occurs to the pyruvic acid before it enters the cycle?** (It splits into carbon dioxide and a 2-carbon acetyl group, which attaches to Coenzyme A to form acetyl CoA.)
- **What does each turn of the Krebs cycle produce?** (2 molecules of carbon dioxide, 1 ATP molecule, 3 molecules of NADH, and 1 molecule of $FADH_2$.)

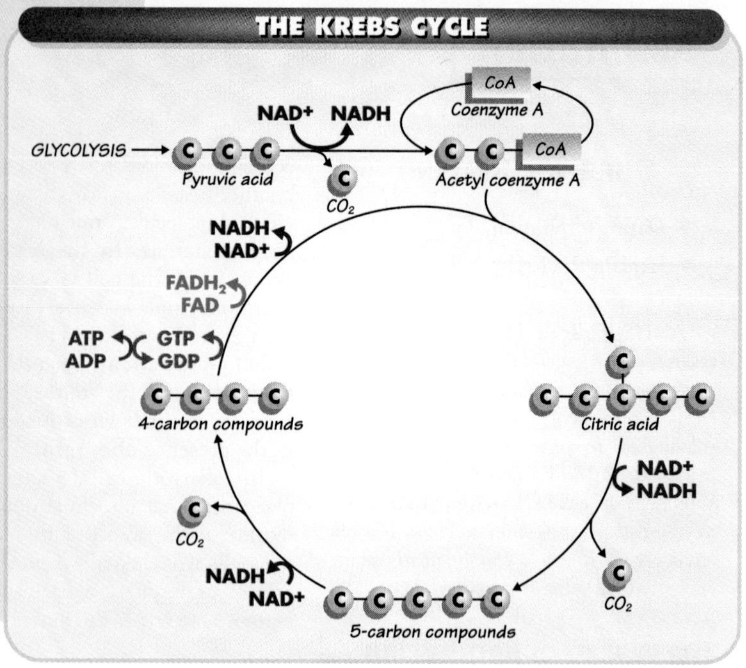

Figure 4–8
In the presence of oxygen, pyruvic acid gives off carbon dioxide and attaches to coenzyme A to form acetyl CoA. Acetyl CoA enters the Krebs cycle and joins with a 4-carbon compound to form citric acid. Each turn of the cycle produces 2 molecules of carbon dioxide, 1 molecule of GTP, which, in terms of energy, is equivalent to ATP, 3 molecules of NADH, and 1 molecule of $FADH_2$. $FADH_2$ is formed when FAD accepts a pair of high-energy electrons and H^+.

At first glance, the **Krebs cycle** may look complicated, but what actually happens is remarkably simple. Rather than break down pyruvic acid directly, the cell first breaks off 1 carbon atom and releases it in the form of carbon dioxide. Then it combines the remaining 2 carbons with a 4-carbon compound. The 2 carbons plus the 4 carbons make a 6-carbon compound. The 6-carbon compound formed in this way is called citric acid. For this reason, the Krebs cycle is sometimes called the citric acid cycle.

☑ ***Checkpoint*** How is citric acid formed? 1

The Breakdown of Citric Acid

Citric acid is gradually broken apart. First, one carbon is broken off, and then a second carbon breaks off. After a few more steps, the very same 4-carbon compound is produced that was used to start the cycle. The fact that it returns to its own starting point means that the Krebs cycle can go around and around, pulling apart the high-energy bonds that were left after glycolysis, and releasing carbon in the form of carbon dioxide.

In fact, the carbon dioxide that is released in the Krebs cycle is the source of all the carbon dioxide in your breath. Every time you exhale, you expel the carbon dioxide produced by the Krebs cycle in trillions of mitochondria throughout your body.

Electron Carriers

If the carbon atoms in glucose are exhaled in the form of carbon dioxide, what happens to all those high-energy electrons whose energy the cell hoped to trap? The electrons are passed to two electron carriers: NAD^+ and FAD. The two electron carriers can each accept a pair of high-energy electrons, hold them for a short time, and then pass them along to another compound. Between the two electron carriers, they

TEACHER SUPPORT

Background Information

The breakdown of a glucose molecule begins with glycolysis, which produces 2 molecules of pyruvic acid. Those molecules, produced in the cytoplasm, are completely broken down through a series of reactions, known as the Krebs cycle, in a mitochondrion. The link between the two series of reactions is the removal of the carbon and oxygen atoms from the pyruvic acid, which occurs as soon as the molecules enter the mitochondrion. That removal allows for the formation of acetyl CoA, which is the compound that enters the Krebs cycle.

The electron carriers that accept the high-energy electrons in the Krebs cycle are NAD^+ and flavin adenine dinucleotide (FAD^+). Most of the potential energy in the original glucose molecule remains in the high-energy electrons in these electron carriers.

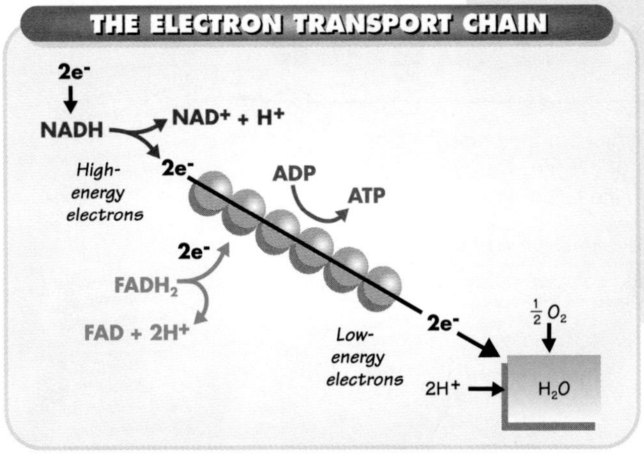

Figure 4–9
As electrons from the Krebs cycle move down the electron transport chain, their energy level is reduced. This energy is used to produce ATP. At the end of the electron transport chain, the energy-depleted electrons combine with oxygen and hydrogen ions to form water.

remove five pairs of high-energy electrons during each turn of the Krebs cycle. What does the cell do with the high-energy electrons? That's where oxygen comes in.

☑ **Checkpoint** What do the electron carriers do? ❷

The Electron Transport Chain

The electron carriers, NAD^+ and FAD, take the high-energy electrons directly to the inner membrane of the mitochondrion, where a series of special molecules is waiting for them. These molecules are known as the **electron transport chain,** and they receive the high-energy electrons from the carriers. The carriers then go back to the Krebs cycle for more electrons. Incidentally, the electrons that were passed to NAD^+ in glycolysis can also be brought into the mitochondrion and passed to the electron transport chain.

The high-energy electrons are then passed from one molecule in the electron transport chain to the next. With each transfer, the energy level of the electrons is gradually lowered. The energy of these electrons is used to produce ATP from ADP. Compared to the process of glycolysis, the amount of ATP produced in the mitochondrial electron transport chain is very large. Roughly 36 molecules of ATP are produced for each molecule of glucose, compared to just 2 molecules of ATP produced in glycolysis.

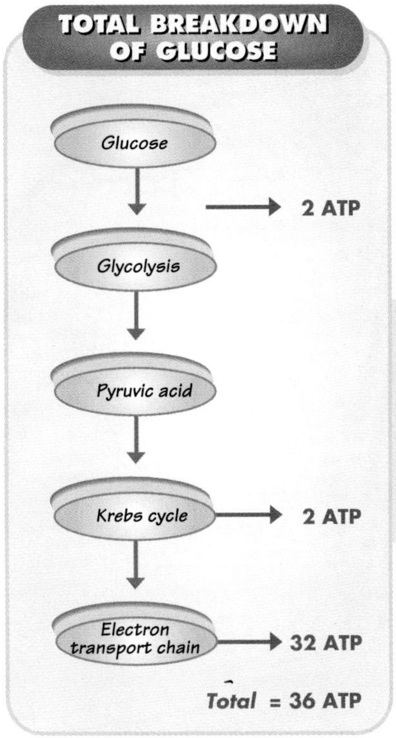

Figure 4–10
The complete breakdown of glucose in the presence of oxygen yields a total of 36 molecules of ATP.

Ideas Through Images

Have students examine Figures 4–9 and 4–10, read the captions, and answer these questions.

- **What do the electron carriers carry into the electron transport chain, and where did they get it?** (They carry high-energy electrons, which they got in the breakdown of citric acid in the Krebs cycle.)
- **What happens to the high-energy electrons in the electron transport chain?** (They are passed to special molecules in the chain.)
- **What changes occur in the electrons as they are passed from molecule to molecule in the chain?** (The energy level of the electrons is gradually lowered as they are passed through the chain.)
- **What molecules are produced by the energy lost from the electrons?** (ATP molecules.)
- **What series of chemical reactions in the breakdown of glucose produces the most ATP molecules?** (The electron transport chain produces the most by far.)

Correcting Misconceptions

Make sure students do not confuse the series of reactions known as respiration with the inhalation and exhalation of air, which is also often called respiration. Point out that the term can be correctly used for either process, though it should be clear by the context to which process the term refers. Explain that to avoid misunderstanding, the series of reactions described in this section is often referred to as cell or cellular respiration.

TEACHER SUPPORT

Background Information

The electron carriers in glycolysis and respiration are molecules that have the ability to accept the hydrogen atoms of the original glucose molecule in the form of electrons and protons. All of those hydrogen atoms are eventually transferred to oxygen molecules in the electron transport chain—a series of reactions whose result is the production of water and the release of energy. At three points in that series of reactions, enough energy is released to bond phosphate groups to ADP molecules, forming ATP molecules. The energy in those bonds is stored for the cell to use for its processes.

☑ Checkpoints

❶ During the Krebs cycle, 1 carbon atom breaks off from pyruvic acid and then the remaining 2 carbons combine with a 4-carbon compound, forming citric acid.

❷ The electron carriers, NAD^+ and FAD^+, remove five pairs of high-energy electrons during each turn of the Krebs cycle.

Visualizing Respiration

Energy is stored in the chemical bonds of molecules. To release this energy for use by the cell, organisms use a series of reactions known as respiration, or aerobic cellular respiration. Almost all organisms use this cellular process, including plants, animals, fungi, protists, and many bacteria. After students examine this visual essay, initiate a discussion about its major steps. Through this discussion, emphasize the following points.

- The breakdown of glucose begins with glycolysis. If there is no oxygen present in the cell, the product of glycolysis is further broken down through fermentation. But if oxygen is present, that product continues on to respiration.
- Glycolysis occurs in the cytoplasm of the cell. The pyruvic acid that results then passes into a mitochondrion, which is where respiration occurs. The high-energy electrons accepted by the electron carriers in the Krebs cycle are carried to the mitochondrial membranes, where further reactions occur in the electron transport chain.
- The intermediate step between glycolysis and the Krebs cycle occurs in the mitochondrion, where pyruvic acid is initially broken down.
- At four places in the Krebs cycle, high-energy electrons are accepted by electron carriers. The energy in these electrons is what is used by the electron transport chain to produce GTP (guanosine triphosphate), which, in terms of energy, is equivalent to ATP.
- The only place where oxygen is used in the process is at the end of the electron transport chain, where electrons, hydrogen ions, and oxygen atoms combine to form H_2O. Without this final step, respiration could not occur.

Visualizing Respiration

Respiration is the release of energy from the breakdown of food molecules in the presence of oxygen. The process of respiration can be summarized in the following equation:

$$C_6H_{12}O_6 + 6O_2 \rightarrow 6CO_2 + 6H_2O + \text{Energy}$$

Glucose + Oxygen → Carbon dioxide + Water + Energy (ATP + heat)

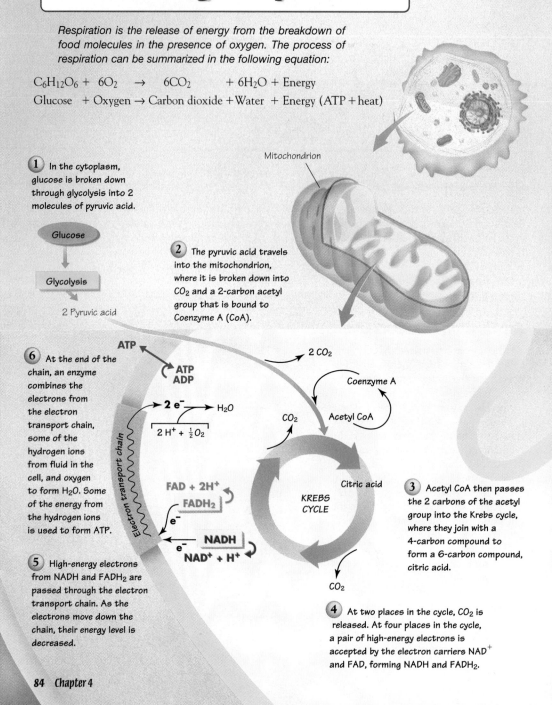

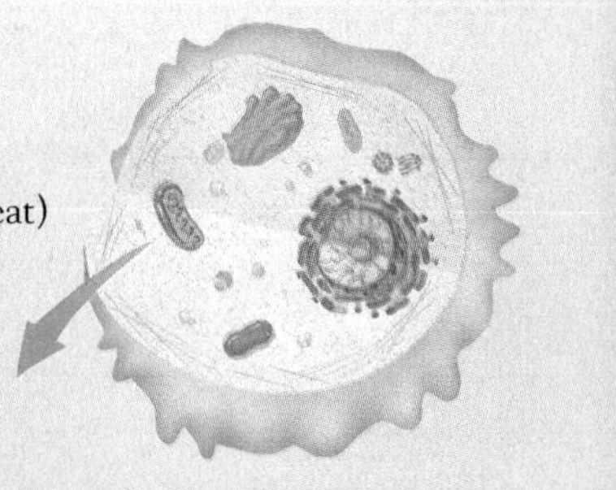

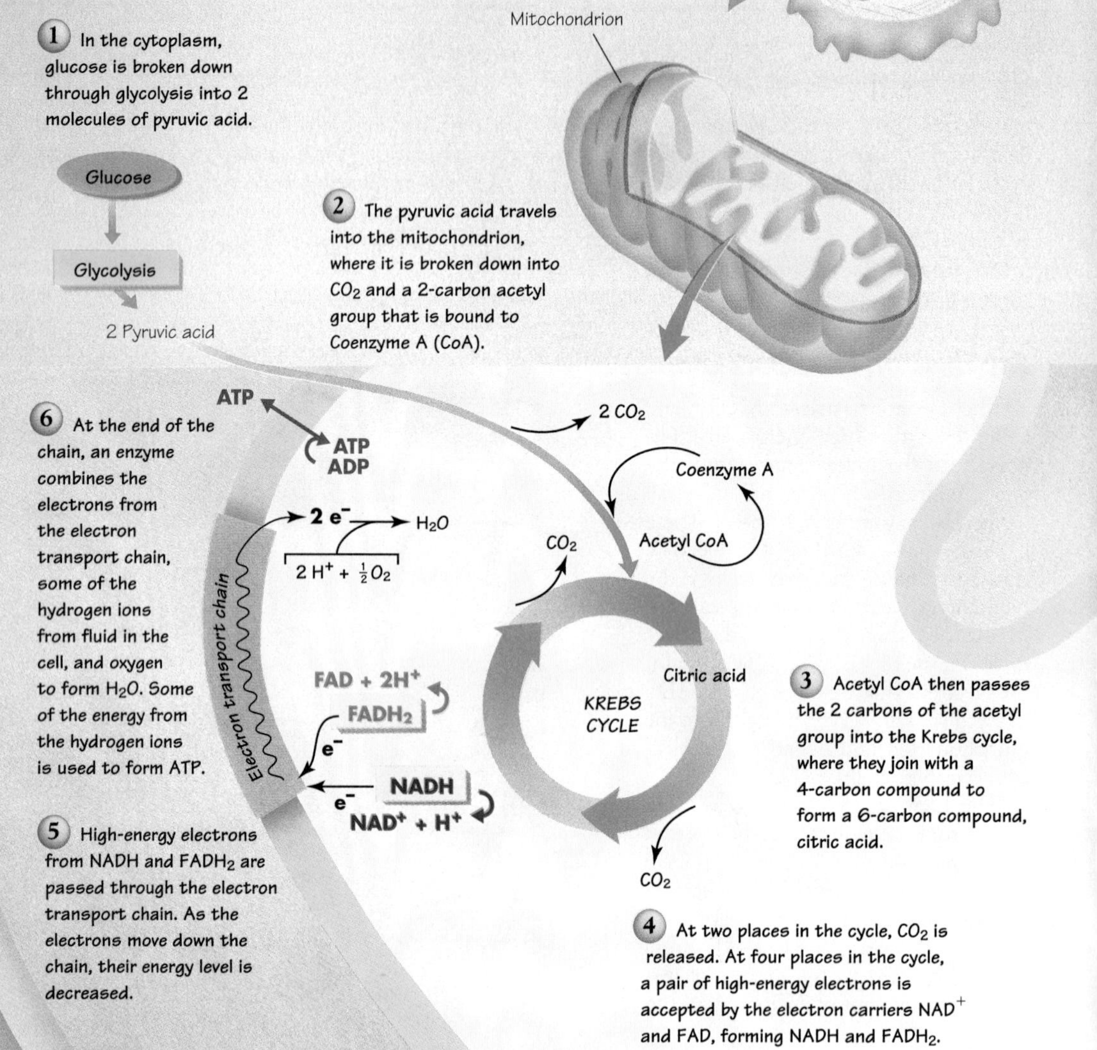

Mitochondrion
1 In the cytoplasm, glucose is broken down through glycolysis into 2 molecules of pyruvic acid.
Glucose
Glycolysis
2 Pyruvic acid
2 The pyruvic acid travels into the mitochondrion, where it is broken down into CO_2 and a 2-carbon acetyl group that is bound to Coenzyme A (CoA).
ATP
6 At the end of the chain, an enzyme combines the electrons from the electron transport chain, some of the hydrogen ions from fluid in the cell, and oxygen to form H_2O. Some of the energy from the hydrogen ions is used to form ATP.
ATP
ADP
2 e^-
H_2O
$2H^+ + \frac{1}{2}O_2$
Electron transport chain
FAD + $2H^+$
$FADH_2$
e^-
NADH
e^-
$NAD^+ + H^+$
2 CO_2
Coenzyme A
CO_2
Acetyl CoA
Citric acid
KREBS CYCLE
CO_2
3 Acetyl CoA then passes the 2 carbons of the acetyl group into the Krebs cycle, where they join with a 4-carbon compound to form a 6-carbon compound, citric acid.
5 High-energy electrons from NADH and $FADH_2$ are passed through the electron transport chain. As the electrons move down the chain, their energy level is decreased.
4 At two places in the cycle, CO_2 is released. At four places in the cycle, a pair of high-energy electrons is accepted by the electron carriers NAD^+ and FAD, forming NADH and $FADH_2$.

TEACHER SUPPORT

Facts and Figures

From the single glucose molecule that enters glycolysis, the cell nets a total of 36 ATP molecules through glycolysis, the Krebs cycle, and the electron transport chain.

- Glycolysis produces 2 ATPs.
- Glycolysis also produces two pairs of high-energy electrons, which are passed to NAD^+. The 2 NADHs that result are converted to 2 $FADH_2$s, which are used to make 4 ATPs in the electron transport chain.
- The Krebs cycle produces 2 ATPs directly.
- The $FADH_2$s produced in the Krebs cycle are used to make 4 ATPs in the electron transport chain.
- The NADHs produced in the Krebs cycle are used to make 24 ATPs in the electron transport chain.

Figure 4–11 *The delicious-looking food on this table is broken down into simple forms that can be used by the body to produce energy.*

The Role of Oxygen and Breathing

At the very end of the chain, the electrons are passed to oxygen. Each oxygen atom accepts a pair of electrons and takes a pair of hydrogen ions (H^+) from the material inside the cell to form water, H_2O. Believe it or not, this is the reason that we need to breathe oxygen. The steady supply of oxygen that is taken in is needed throughout the body for just one reason—to accept the electrons at the end of the electron transport chain. Without oxygen, electron transport could not take place, the Krebs cycle would stop, and ATP would not be produced.

Checkpoint What is the role of oxygen in the electron transport chain? (1)

Energy and Food

Even though glucose has been used as the example to show how food energy is utilized to produce ATP, the very same pathways are used for other food compounds. For example, a complex carbohydrate such as starch is broken down into simple sugars, most of which can then be converted into glucose. Most lipids and many proteins can be broken down into molecules that either enter glycolysis or the Krebs cycle at one of several places. Like a furnace that can burn wood, coal, or oil, the cell can generate chemical energy in the form of ATP from just about any source.

Figure 4–12 CAREER TRACK *In the laboratory, biological technicians help scientists by setting up equipment, performing experiments, and gathering information.*

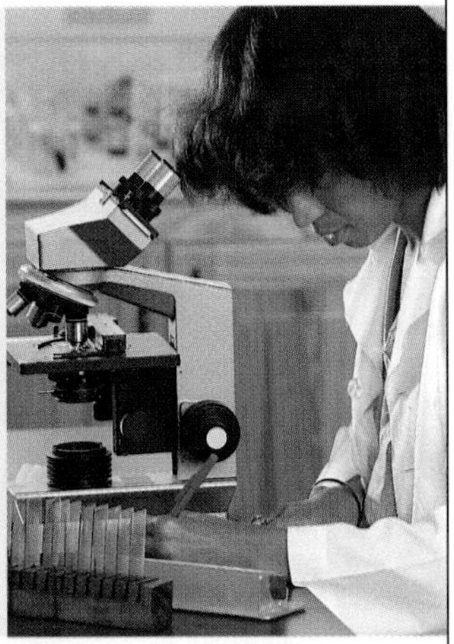

Section Review 4–3

1. **Define** respiration.
2. **Explain** the Krebs cycle.
3. **Critical Thinking—Analyzing** What is the relationship between breathing and the process of respiration?

4 ASSESS

Quick Check

Have students make an outline of the Krebs cycle and the electron transport chain.

Section Review 4-3

1. Respiration is the release of energy from the breakdown of food molecules in the presence of oxygen.
2. The Krebs cycle is a series of reactions in which the acetyl groups from the pyruvic acids produced by glycolysis are broken down to CO_2, accompanied by the formation of ATP and electron carriers NAD^+ and FAD^+.
3. Breathing brings into the body the oxygen needed for the Krebs cycle to continue. Breathing also exhales from the body the carbon dioxide and water produced during respiration.

Learning Modality

Auditory Learning Ask pairs of students to quiz each other orally about the steps and materials involved in the Krebs cycle and the electron transport chain.

Checkpoint

(1) To accept electrons and, with a pair of hydrogen ions, to form H_2O.

TEACHER SUPPORT

Managing Classroom Diversity

TECH PREP STUDENTS
Students who plan careers in food services and health care should know how different foods are utilized by the body. Have students research how the body handles proteins, carbohydrates, and lipids in the foods it consumes. Ask that they do library research to find out what occurs in the body when a diet is deficient in proteins, carbohydrates, or lipids.

Ancillary Support

The resources below can be used to support your teaching strategy for these two pages.

LM Observing Respiration, #8
TR Apply: Food Fun
TB Visualizing Respiration, #5

SECTION 4–4

Photosynthesis

Performance Objectives

- Describe the process known as photosynthesis.
- Discuss light-dependent reactions and light-independent reactions of photosynthesis.

Mini Lab Skill: Experimenting

1 ENGAGE

Inquiry Activity

Observing

A Product of the Sun?

Ask students whether they think a plant releases any gas into the atmosphere. Then have them follow these steps.

1. Fill two beakers three quarters with water. Place a small *Elodea* plant into each beaker and invert a glass funnel over each plant.

2. Fill two test tubes with water. Hold your thumb over the opening of a test tube, turn it over, and lower it into the beaker and over the inverted funnel. Repeat with the other test tube and beaker.

3. Place one beaker in a sunny place for six hours. Place the other beaker in a dark place for six hours.

4. Carefully remove the test tube from the beaker that was kept in the sun, keeping your thumb over the opening. Have a partner light a toothpick with a match and immediately blow it out. Then remove your thumb from the test tube and have the partner thrust the glowing toothpick into the test tube. Observe the results. Repeat the procedure with the other beaker and test tube. Compare the results and form a hypothesis to explain the difference.

SECTION 4–4

Photosynthesis

GUIDE FOR READING

- **Define** photosynthesis.
- **Compare** the light-dependent reactions and light-independent reactions of photosynthesis.

MINI LAB

- **Design an experiment** to find out what happens to white light as it passes through a prism.

WHERE DOES THE ENERGY IN food come from? This depends on the source of the food, of course. The ultimate source of all food energy is the sun. Green plants and microscopic organisms are able to trap the energy of sunlight and use that energy to build the high-energy complex molecules that make up food. Whether an animal is a meat-eater or a plant-eater, the source of energy in its diet can be traced back to plants. Plants obtain the energy they need from the sun.

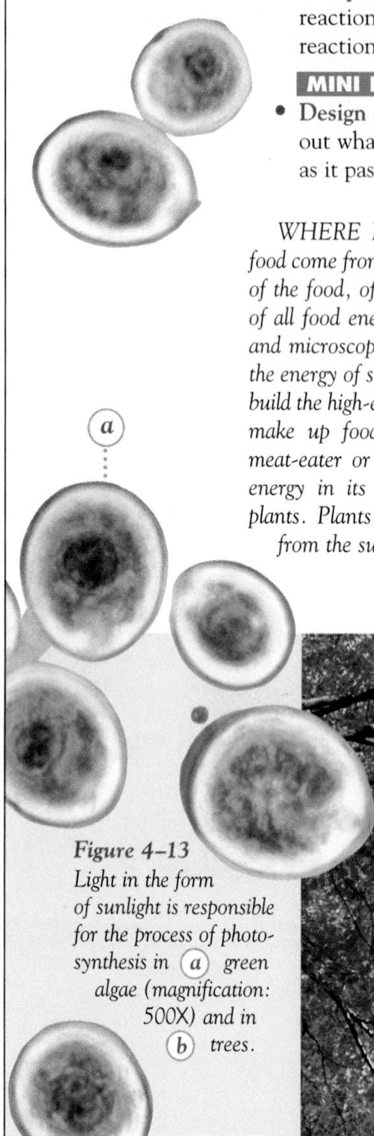

(a)

(b)

Figure 4–13 Light in the form of sunlight is responsible for the process of photosynthesis in (a) green algae (magnification: 500X) and in (b) trees.

The Process of Photosynthesis

Photosynthesis is the process by which green plants use the energy of sunlight to produce carbohydrates. In an overall sense, **photosynthesis** is the reverse of respiration. In respiration, the cell used the high-energy electrons found in glucose to provide energy to make ATP. The products of respiration—carbon dioxide and water—contain low-energy electrons. What does the cell have to do to make the process run in reverse? Quite simply, it must find a way to take those low-energy electrons and raise their energy levels to the point where their atoms can rearrange to form glucose. The cell must trap the sun's energy and pass it along to these electrons.

Sunlight

The sun bathes the Earth in a steady stream of sunlight. Sunlight provides

TEACHER SUPPORT

Ecology Note

The series of chemical reactions through which the element carbon circulates through Earth's ecosystem is known as the carbon cycle. The complementary processes of respiration and photosynthesis are part of that cycle. The carbon in carbon dioxide is used by plants in photosynthesis to make carbohydrates. Those carbohydrates become the building blocks of photosynthetic organisms, such as plants. Other organisms, such as animals, consume the plants as food. The plant carbohydrates are digested by the consuming organisms, and the glucose that results is used in the organisms' cells for respiration. A product of respiration is carbon dioxide, which is released into the atmosphere. Plants use that carbon dioxide in photosynthesis, and the cycle continues.

ABSORPTION OF LIGHT BY CHLOROPHYLL

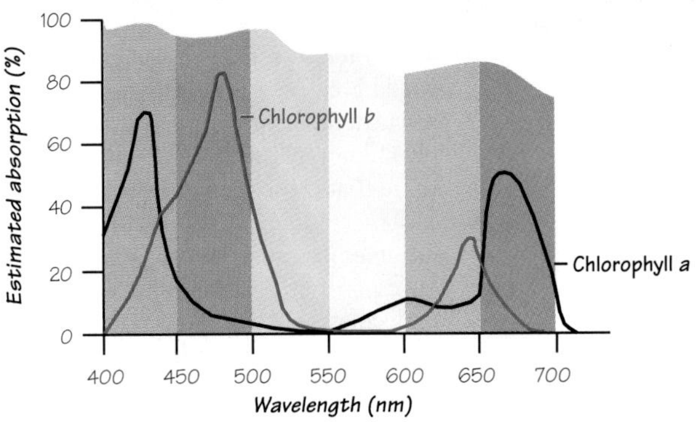

Figure 4–14
Chlorophyll a and chlorophyll b absorb slightly different wavelengths of light. The height of each line represents the amount of light of a particular color absorbed by each pigment. Neither form of chlorophyll absorbs light well in the middle of the spectrum, which is why plants are green.

the energy to warm the Earth and to drive the process of photosynthesis. What your eyes perceive as white light from the sun is actually a mixture of different wavelengths of light. Many of these wavelengths are visible to your eyes and make up what is known as the visible spectrum. Your eyes see the different wavelengths of the visible spectrum as different colors.

Chlorophyll

Plants contain **pigments.** Pigments are colored substances that reflect or absorb light. These pigments help plants to gather the sun's energy. The principal pigment of green plants is **chlorophyll.** Chlorophyll absorbs light very well in the blue and in the red regions of the spectrum, as you can see in *Figure 4–14.* However, chlorophyll does not absorb light in the green region of the spectrum. This is what gives chlorophyll its green color and explains why plants appear green to the human eye.

Because light is a form of energy, a compound that absorbs light also absorbs the energy from the light. When chlorophyll absorbs light, much of that energy is transferred directly to electrons in the chlorophyll molecule. In other words, chlorophyll absorbs light energy and produces its own high-energy electrons.

☑ *Checkpoint* What is chlorophyll? ①

Light-Dependent Reactions

There are two stages of photosynthesis. The first stage consists of the **light-dependent reactions.** Light-dependent reactions get their name because they require the direct involvement of light.

Electron Transport

The chlorophyll in green plants is found inside photosynthetic membranes of the chloroplast in clusters called photosystems. Light absorption by a photosystem produces high-energy electrons. These electrons move to an electron transport chain in the membrane, and are passed through the chain from one electron carrier to the next. As electrons are passed along the chain, their energy level is reduced. Some of this energy is used to produce ATP.

At the end of the photosynthetic electron transport chain, additional light energy is absorbed, raising the energy level of the electrons again. These high-energy electrons are passed to an electron carrier, $NADP^+$, forming NADPH. Then the NADPH transfers the electrons—energy and all—to a chemical reaction elsewhere in the cell.

Replacing Electrons

The electrons that were removed from the chlorophyll need to be replaced, or in just a few milliseconds, chlorophyll

2 EXPLORE

Investigate

Cooperative Learning Have cooperative learning groups research the carbon cycle in biology, ecology, and other books from the library. Ask each group to make a poster showing how respiration and photosynthesis are involved in this cycle.

3 TEACH

Ideas Through Images

Have students examine Figure 4–14, read the caption, and answer these questions.

- **What do the colors on this graph represent?** (The spectrum of visible light.)
- **What are two kinds of pigment in a plant?** (Chlorophyll *a* and chlorophyll *b*.)
- **Which parts of the spectrum does the graph show that each type of chlorophyll best absorbs?** (Chlorophyll *a* best absorbs violet and red light, while chlorophyll *b* best absorbs blue and orange light.)

☑ Checkpoint

① Chlorophyll is the main pigment of green plants.

Technology

CD-ROM
Photosynthesis

TEACHER SUPPORT — Background Information

The light-dependent reactions are sometimes known as the light-energy conversion stage of photosynthesis because in these reactions the energy of sunlight is converted into chemical-bond energy. This conversion occurs in essentially two pathways. In the first pathway, the electrons in the chlorophyll excited by sunlight move through an electron transport chain, and in so doing lose their energy, which is used to form ATP. This pathway utilizes the process called chemiosmosis described in Section 4–5. Other excited electrons are captured by nicotinamide adenine dinucleotide phosphate (NADP), forming NADPH. That is the second pathway by which sunlight is converted to chemical-bond energy. Both the ATP and the NADPH are used in the light-independent reactions of photosynthesis.

Ancillary Support

The resources below can be used to support your teaching strategy for these two pages.

LM Observing Photosynthesis, #7
TR Explore: Tiny Green Energy Machine
BL Inquiry Activity: Colors of the Season

MINI LAB Experimenting

Teacher Notes
- For time required and materials needed, see page 74b.
- Have students use sheets of white printer or copier paper.

Answers to Analyze and Conclude
1. The light split apart into a rainbow spectrum of colors that could be seen on the paper.
2. Students' responses may vary. Some might infer that the light splits into different parts of its spectrum as each different wavelength refracts, or bends, a different amount as it passes through the prism.
3. Students' responses may vary somewhat, though most should observe red, orange, yellow, green, blue, indigo, and violet.

Skills Trace
Experimenting
- Focus p. 88
- Practice p. 91
- Assess p. 99

Ideas Through Images
Have students examine Figure 4–15, read the caption, and answer these questions.

- **How does chlorophyll react to the energy of sunlight?** (Sunlight excites electrons in chlorophyll.)
- **What are the ways in which the energy of those excited electrons are used?** (Some of that energy is used as the excited electrons are passed down the photosynthetic transport chain. Some of that energy is also used to add electrons to an electron carrier to form NADPH. Finally, some of that energy is used to split water molecules.)

MINI LAB ...... Experimenting ....

Breaking Out of Prism

PROBLEM *How is white light separated into the colors of the visible spectrum?* ***Design an experiment*** *to find out.*

PROCEDURE

1. Obtain a sheet of white paper, a flashlight (or a lamp), and a prism.
2. Formulate a hypothesis to explain what will happen to the light when it is passed through a prism.
3. Design an experiment to test your hypothesis.

ANALYZE AND CONCLUDE

1. What happened to the light as it passed through the prism?
2. What do you think the prism does to the wavelengths of light, which enables you to see the different colors?
3. What colors of the visible spectrum did you observe?

would lose so many electrons that it would break apart. Fortunately, the photosynthetic membrane has a way to supply chlorophyll with electrons to replace those that are lost.

The source of electrons is water. Enzymes on the inner surface of the photosynthetic membrane split water molecules in two. Four electrons are removed from 2 molecules of water, leaving 4 hydrogen ions and 2 oxygen atoms. The electrons are returned to the chlorophyll. This reaction is the source of nearly all the oxygen in the Earth's atmosphere.

The light-dependent reactions produce two important products—ATP and high-energy electrons carried by $NADP^+$. These compounds have an important role in the plant cell: They provide energy to make carbohydrates.

Checkpoint What are the light-dependent reactions? 1

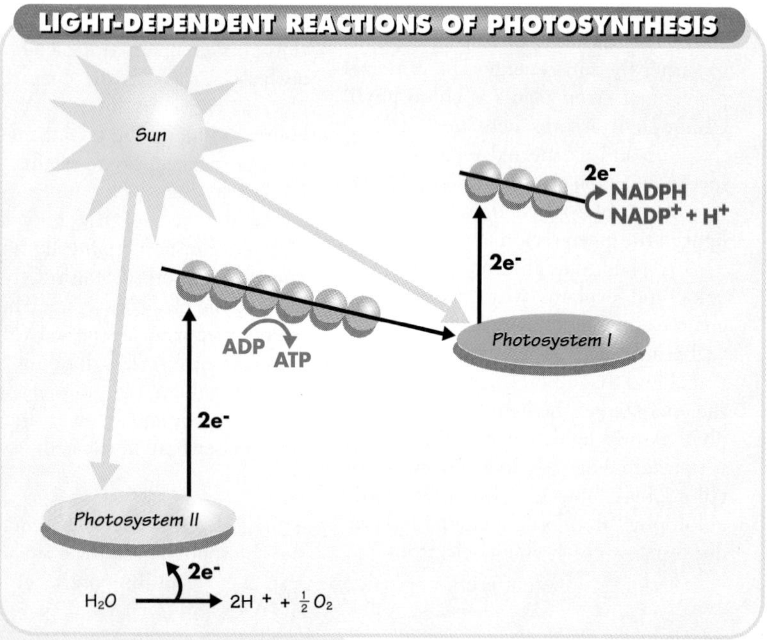

Figure 4–15
During the light-dependent reactions, light is absorbed by clusters within the photosynthetic membranes called photosystems. These photosystems (I and II) produce high-energy electrons that move to electron transport chains in the membrane. Here the electrons are passed from one electron carrier to the next, producing NADPH and ATP, both of which are needed for the second stage of photosynthesis.

TEACHER SUPPORT — Historical Perspective

By the latter part of the eighteenth century, European scientists knew that animals used the oxygen in air to sustain life. But if animals used the oxygen in air, why wasn't that gas eventually used up? Something had to be producing oxygen, since the oxygen in air remained constant. The answer to the riddle was discovered in 1779 by a Dutch plant physiologist named Jan Ingenhousz (1730–1799). His experiments showed that plants take in carbon dioxide and give off oxygen. He also discovered that this occurred only in sunlight.

In 1817, two French scientists, Pierre Pelletier (1788–1842) and Joseph Caventou (1795–1877), isolated the substance that makes plants green. They named it chlorophyll, or "green leaf."

Visualizing Photosynthesis

Photosynthesis is the process by which plants use the energy of sunlight to produce carbohydrates. Photosynthesis can be summarized in the following equation:

$$6CO_2 + 6H_2O + \text{Energy} \rightarrow C_6H_{12}O_6 + 6O_2$$

Carbon dioxide + Water + Energy (sun) → Glucose + Oxygen

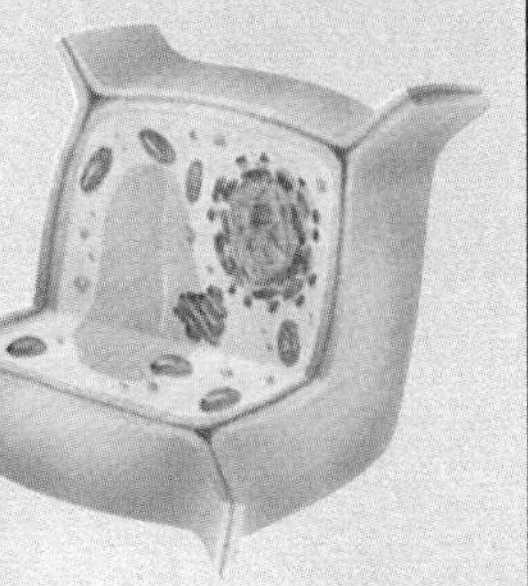

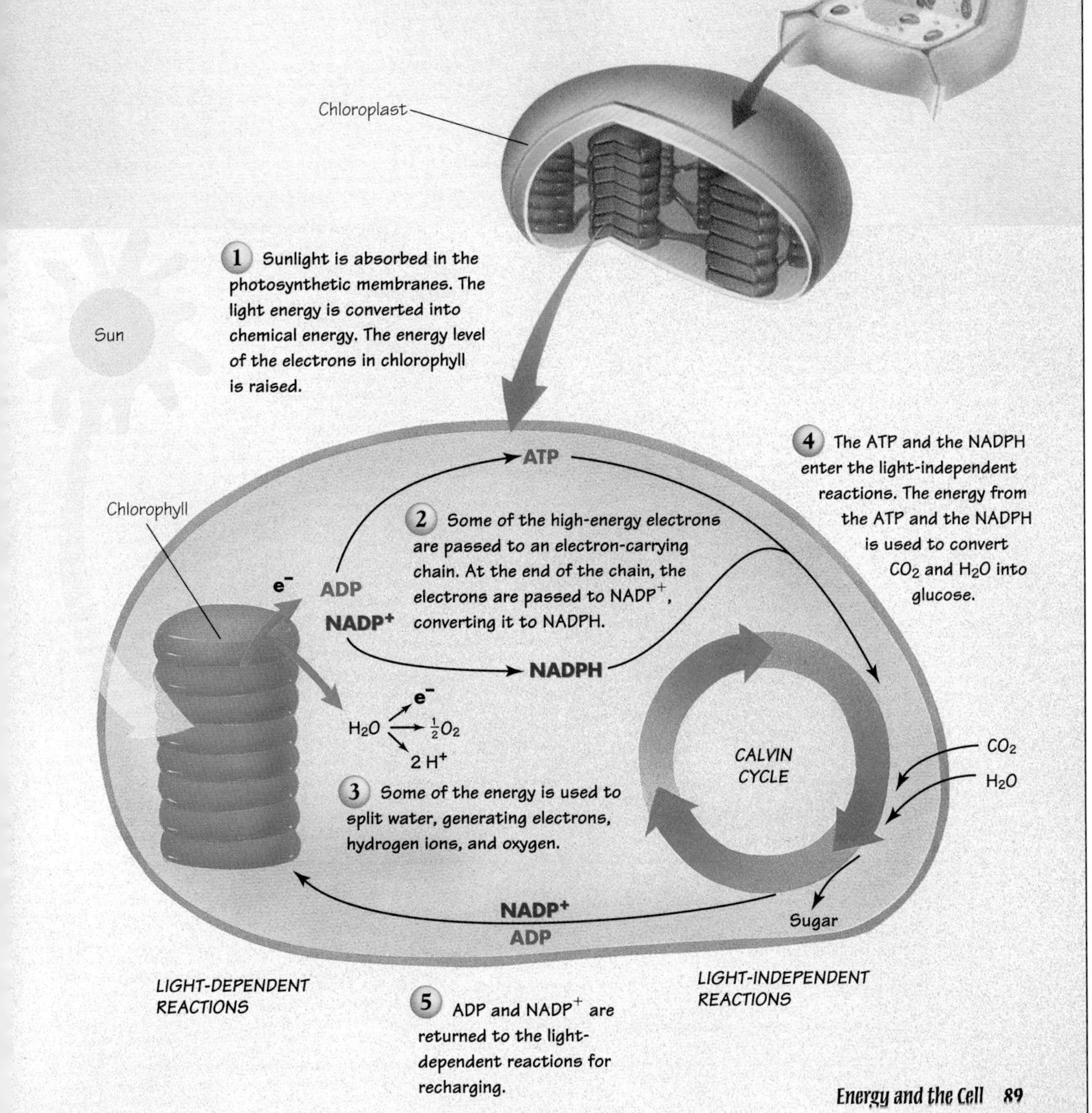

Chloroplast
Sun
1 Sunlight is absorbed in the photosynthetic membranes. The light energy is converted into chemical energy. The energy level of the electrons in chlorophyll is raised.
Chlorophyll
ATP
e⁻
ADP
NADP⁺
2 Some of the high-energy electrons are passed to an electron-carrying chain. At the end of the chain, the electrons are passed to NADP⁺, converting it to NADPH.
NADPH
H₂O
e⁻
½O₂
2 H⁺
3 Some of the energy is used to split water, generating electrons, hydrogen ions, and oxygen.
4 The ATP and the NADPH enter the light-independent reactions. The energy from the ATP and the NADPH is used to convert CO₂ and H₂O into glucose.
CALVIN CYCLE
CO₂
H₂O
Sugar
NADP⁺
ADP
LIGHT-DEPENDENT REACTIONS
LIGHT-INDEPENDENT REACTIONS
5 ADP and NADP⁺ are returned to the light-dependent reactions for recharging.

Visualizing Photosynthesis

Photosynthesis is the most important series of chemical reactions that takes place on Earth, for without these reactions energy from the sun could not be captured and almost all life on the planet could not be sustained. After students have examined the visual essay, initiate a discussion about the steps involved in the process, emphasizing the following points.

- Through photosynthesis, light energy is converted into chemical energy that can be utilized by cells.
- In the first, and most important, step in the process, the energy in sunlight excites the electrons in chlorophyll molecules.
- Some of the excited electrons are used to produce ATP in an electron transport chain that is much like the chain in respiration. Other excited electrons are used to form NADPH. These products are essential for use in the light-independent reactions.
- In the light-independent reactions, CO_2 and H_2O are converted into glucose, which the cells of organisms can utilize through respiration to make molecules of energy-storing ATP.

Checkpoint

1 The reactions of photosynthesis that require the direct involvement of light.

TEACHER SUPPORT

Facts and Figures

Here are some facts and figures related to photosynthesis.

- Each cell of a plant leaf contains about 40–50 chloroplasts.
- For each square mm of the surface of a leaf, there are about 500,000 chloroplasts.
- Each chloroplast thylakoid contains about 250–400 pigment molecules. (See Background Information on **TE** page 92.)

Ancillary Support

The resource below can be used to support your teaching strategy for these two pages.

TB Visualizing Photosynthesis, #4

Problem Solving

Designing an Experiment

Variations in Light and Dark

State The problem students are asked to solve is to determine whether photosynthesis takes place in the dark.

Solve Students know that the light-dependent reactions require light. Therefore, they might hypothesize that no photosynthesis takes place in the dark. They know that a product of respiration is CO_2, which will turn Bromthymol blue solution yellow. They also know that a product of photosynthesis is oxygen, and a plant placed in Bromthymol blue solution that contains CO_2 may cause the solution to change back to blue. Thus, students should predict that in sunlight the solution that has turned yellow will turn back to blue, whereas the solution containing the plant will remain yellow when kept in the dark.

Test Have students try out their designs.

Communicate Students should present their experimental designs, list the variable they tested, and explain the purpose of the control setup.

Answers to THINK ABOUT IT

1. Photosynthesis cannot take place in the dark.

2. Exhale through the straw to turn both beakers of Bromthymol blue solution yellow. Establish a control setup with a plant in one beaker and expose it to sunlight. Place a plant in the second beaker and place in a dark area. Observe the setups to see if either of the solutions turns back to blue.

3. To observe how the solution reacts to a plant when photosynthesis is occurring.

4. Students should conclude that photosynthesis does not take place in the dark.

Problem Solving

DESIGNING AN EXPERIMENT

Variations in Light and Dark

As you enter the laboratory, your teacher tells you that she has a mystery for you to solve. You are to determine if photosynthesis can take place in the dark.

You are to formulate a hypothesis for the mystery and then test your hypothesis by designing an experiment. Your experiment will require the materials and clues your teacher has given you.

The materials provided to you include Bromthymol blue, a drinking straw, *Elodea* (an aquatic plant), and beakers. Your teacher gives you two clues: (1) Bromthymol blue will turn yellow in the presence of carbon dioxide but remains blue when oxygen is present, and (2) drawings of the experimental setup and the control setup.

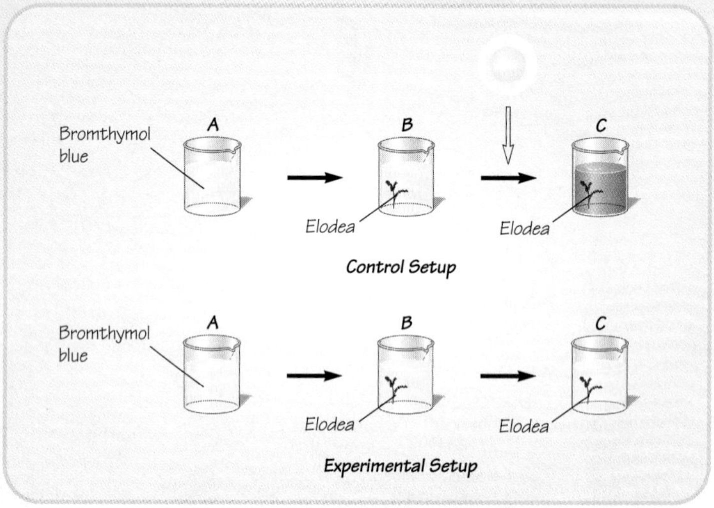

THINK ABOUT IT

1. Formulate a hypothesis for the mystery.
2. Outline your procedure.
3. What is the purpose of the control setup?
4. Based on the data provided and your knowledge of biology, does photosynthesis take place in the dark? Explain your answer.

TEACHER SUPPORT

Background Information

The electron carriers discussed in this chapter are usually represented in a more complicated fashion, such as this:

$NAD^+ + 2H \leftrightarrows NADH + H^+$

Students are sometimes confused about this reaction. They could think of the transfer of electrons like this:

$NAD^+ + 2e^- \leftrightarrows NAD^-$

Now the reaction is balanced and shows the 2-electron transfer. When the 2 electrons are transferred to NAD^+, of course, 2 protons are released into solution. One of those protons combines directly with NAD^- to produce NADH, while the other remains in solution. Thus, the products are shown as NADH + H^+. In order to avoid confusion, these electron carriers are shown in a simpler fashion, as NAD, NADP, and so on.

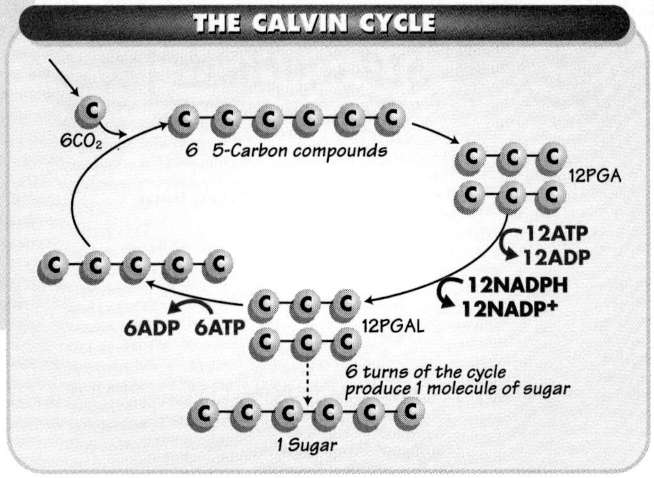

Figure 4–16
During the Calvin cycle, carbon dioxide combines with a 5-carbon compound to form 2 molecules of PGA. Using the energy provided by ATP and NADPH produced by the light-dependent reactions, PGA can then be converted into PGAL, which, in turn, is used to make sugars.

The Light-Independent Reactions

The second stage of photosynthesis consists of the **light-independent reactions.** This set of reactions gets its name because it does not directly involve light. **The light-independent reactions convert the energy from the ATP and NADPH into a form that can be stored indefinitely—sugars.**

The raw materials from which the cell builds sugars are carbon dioxide and water. Carbon dioxide from the atmosphere is combined with a 5-carbon sugar to produce two 3-carbon molecules called PGA. The 2 PGA molecules then enter a chemical pathway that uses the energy from ATP and NADPH. The pathway is called the **Calvin cycle,** after American scientist Melvin Calvin, who discovered it.

Each turn of the Calvin cycle uses 1 molecule of carbon dioxide and 2 atoms of hydrogen. After six turns, a 6-carbon sugar molecule is produced. As photosynthesis continues, the Calvin cycle works steadily, producing energy-rich sugars and removing carbon dioxide from the atmosphere. The plant is able to use the sugars produced in this way both to meet its energy needs and to build larger and more complex molecules, such as cellulose, that it needs for growth and development.

The products of the light-dependent reactions in photosynthesis are used to provide the energy to build energy-containing sugars from low-energy compounds. In this way, the two sets of reactions work together—the light-dependent reactions trap the energy of sunlight in chemical form and the light-independent reactions use that chemical energy to produce stable, high-energy sugars from carbon dioxide and water.

Section Review 4–4

1. **Define** photosynthesis.
2. **Compare** the light-dependent reactions and the light-independent reactions.
3. **Critical Thinking—Synthesizing** In the autumn, green plants stop producing chlorophyll. How does this explain why leaves turn color in the fall?
4. **MINI LAB** How would you **design an experiment** to find out what happens to white light when it passes through a prism?

Discussion

Lead a discussion about the light-independent reactions. Ask students to name the raw materials that are used to build the sugars that result from these reactions (carbon dioxide and water). Note for students that the ATP and the NADPH come from the light-dependent reactions, while the 5-carbon sugar, ribulose biphosphate (RuBP), is already present in the cell. It is to RuBP that CO_2 links, briefly forming an unstable 6-carbon molecule. This molecule quickly breaks down to form 2 molecules of PGA (phosphoglycerate). Have students explain the steps involved in the Calvin cycle. Ask how glucose is formed as a result.

4 ASSESS

Quick Check

Have students make a flowchart that begins with the energy of sunlight and ends with the making of glucose. Ask that they include as much detail as possible in the numerous steps.

Section Review 4–4

1. The process by which green plants use the energy of sunlight to produce carbohydrates.

2. The light-dependent reactions, which require the direct involvement of sunlight, produce ATP and the high-energy electrons carried by $NADP^+$. The light-independent reactions, which do not require light, convert the energy from the ATP and $NADP^+$ into sugars that can be stored indefinitely.

3. Chlorophyll is the green pigment of plants, and its reflection of the green region of the light spectrum makes leaves appear green. When plants stop production of chlorophyll, other pigments in the leaves reflect other colors of the spectrum.

4. Students' designs may vary. A possible experiment would involve measuring changes in the speed of light as it passes through the prism.

Skills Trace

Experimenting

- Focus p. 88
- Practice p. 91
- Assess p. 99

Learning Modality

Auditory Learning Ask students to respond orally to a series of questions about photosynthesis. Ask them to explain how sunlight affects chlorophyll, what occurs in the light-dependent reactions, and what occurs in the light-independent reactions.

Section 4–5

ATP Synthesis

Performance Objective

• Discuss the relationship between photosynthetic and mitochondrial membranes and ATP production.

1 ENGAGE

Ideas Through Images

Have students examine Figure 4–17, read the caption, and answer the following questions.

• **Where does photosynthesis occur in a cell?** (In the cell's chloroplasts.)

• **Where does respiration occur?** (In the mitochondria of a cell.)

• **In both processes, there is an electron transport chain that makes ATP molecules. Where do those reactions occur?** (The reactions occur in the membranes of the mitochondrion and the chloroplast.)

2 EXPLORE

Investigate

Research Have students research the structure of the chloroplast. Ask them to make a labeled drawing of a typical chloroplast, showing where chlorophyll is contained and where chemiosmosis occurs.

SECTION 4–5 BRANCHING OUT **In Depth**

ATP Synthesis

GUIDE FOR READING

- **Describe** the role that photosynthetic and mitochondrial membranes play in the production of ATP.

ATP PLAYS AN IMPORTANT ROLE in every living cell. ATP is also a central compound in both respiration and photosynthesis. As you have read, ATP is produced from ADP in both mitochondria and chloroplasts. In both places, ATP is made by an electron transport chain that is associated with a membrane. Is this just a coincidence or is there some special connection between these membranes and ATP production?

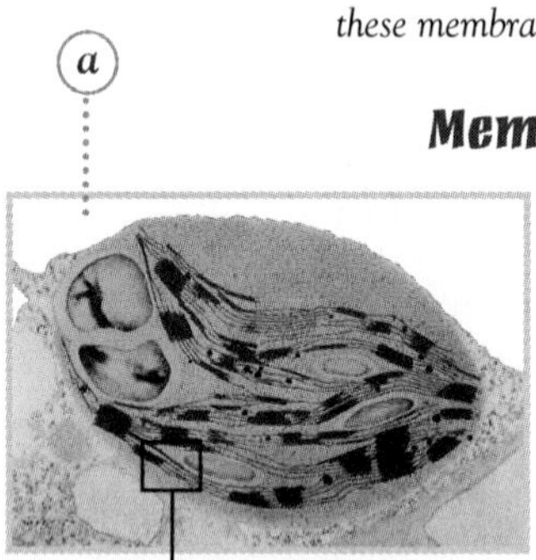

Membranes and ATP

In the early 1960s, British scientist Peter Mitchell thought that he could explain the connection between the membranes and ATP. Mitchell suggested that the changes that took place in the membrane during electron transport were essential in the production of ATP. In fact, Mitchell argued, the purpose of electron transport is to produce different electrical charges on each side of the membrane and then to use those differences to power the production of ATP.

ATP and Photosynthesis

Recall that during light-dependent reactions of photosynthesis, some of the high-energy electrons are passed to an electron-carrying chain. At the end of the chain, some of the energy is used to "split" water. When the water molecule is broken apart, the oxygen is released and the electrons are returned to chlorophyll. But where do the hydrogen ions go?

The hydrogen ions are released inside the photosynthetic membrane when the electrons are removed. This produces a high concentration of hydrogen ions (H^+) inside the membrane, giving it a positive charge. Outside the membrane, there is a low concentration of hydrogen ions, which gives it a negative charge.

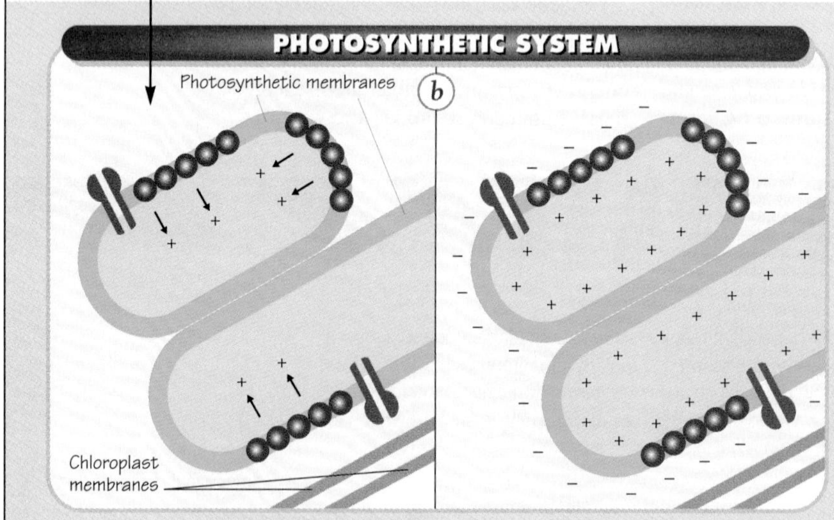

Figure 4–17 *(a) The boxed area shows part of a chloroplast's photosynthetic membrane (magnification: 4500X). (b) Electron transport pumps H^+ ions across this membrane (left), resulting in a high H^+ ion concentration inside the membrane (right). In mitochondria a similar process takes place. However, a high H^+ ion concentration builds up in the space between the inner and outer membrane.*

TEACHER SUPPORT

Background Information

The process of chemiosmosis is somewhat different in photosynthesis than it is in respiration. In respiration, the process involves a pumping of hydrogen ions to the space between the outer and inner mitochondrial membranes or even to the cytoplasm outside the outer membrane. In photosynthesis, the membrane involved in chemiosmosis is not the chloroplast's membrane, but rather the photosynthetic membrane around structures called thylakoids. These flattened sacs hold the molecules of chlorophyll that capture the sun's energy. Around the thylakoids, but still inside the double membrane of the chloroplast, is a solution called the stroma. The difference in ion concentration, then, is established on either side of the thylakoid membrane: within the thylakoids and outside in the surrounding stroma.

ATP and Respiration

During the process of respiration, something very similar takes place in the mitochondrion. The electron carriers, NADH and $FADH_2$, pass their electrons to the electron transport chain. As these electrons are passed down the chain, they provide the energy to pump hydrogen ions out of the membrane. Because there are more hydrogen ions outside the membrane, there is a more positive charge. Inside the membrane, where there are fewer hydrogen ions, there is a negative charge.

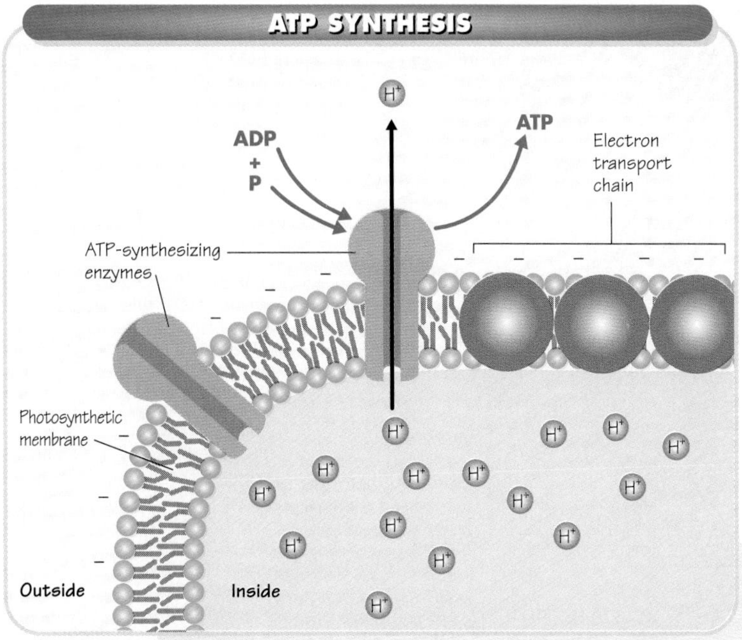

Figure 4–18
The force of the outward movement of H^+ ions that were pumped inside the photosynthetic membrane by electron transport provides the energy to produce ATP. A similar process produces ATP in mitochondria.

Chemiosmosis

The difference in electrical charges across the photosynthetic and mitochondrial membranes is a source of energy. This energy could be used to attach a phosphate to ADP to make ATP. *Figure 4–18* shows how this occurs. The photosynthetic and mitochondrial membranes are impermeable to hydrogen ions. However, there is an enzyme that seems to have a channel right through its center. The channel allows the hydrogen ions (H^+) to pass through it, drawn by the strong negative charges (from OH^- ions) on the other side of the membrane. This enzyme is called an ATP-synthesizing enzyme, meaning an "ATP-maker."

As the hydrogen ions pass through this channel, the energy from the movement is used to attach a phosphate to ADP, making ATP. This process of ATP formation in chloroplasts and mitochondria is called **chemiosmosis.**

Section Review 4–5

1. **Describe** the role of photosynthetic and mitochondrial membranes in the production of ATP.
2. **BRANCHING OUT ACTIVITY** Using reference books, find out more about Peter Mitchell. **Summarize** your findings in a brief report.

3 TEACH

Ideas Through Images

Have students examine Figure 4–18, read the caption, and answer the following questions.

- **In what structure are electron transport chain molecules located?** (In a mitochondrial or photosynthetic membrane.)
- **What provides a channel through the membrane for hydrogen ions?** (An enzyme called ATP-synthesizing enzyme.)
- **What is the product of chemiosmosis?** (ATP molecules.)

4 ASSESS

Quick Check

Have students make two flowcharts showing how chemiosmosis occurs in mitochondria and chloroplasts.

Section Review 4–5

1. The difference in electrical charges across the membranes is a source of energy, and that energy is used to attach a phosphate to ADP, making ATP.
2. Peter Mitchell (1920–1992) won the 1978 Nobel Prize in chemistry for his studies of the role of membranes in the production of ATP.

Learning Modality

Kinesthetic Learning Ask students to create a plan to act out chemiosmosis. Students could represent hydrogen ions. A door to the classroom could represent the channel made by the enzyme.

Ancillary Support

The resources below can be used to support your teaching strategy for these two pages.

TR Enrich: Cell Power for Cities
BL Inquiry Activity: Jumping Breakfast Cereal

TEACHER SUPPORT

Background Information

Since chloroplasts make so much ATP in the light, why do plants contain both mitochondria and chloroplasts? Some scientists have proposed that plants supply most of their ATP needs during the day by using the ATP produced in chloroplasts and need only to switch on their mitochondria at night. Thus, at night plants produce ATP from stored carbohydrates produced through photosynthesis. By that reasoning, nothing would take place in the mitochondria of plants grown in continuous artificial light—but that turns out not to be true.

Careful measurements in living cells seem to show that the rest of a plant cell gets few if any of its ATP molecules from its chloroplasts. Even in bright sunlight plant mitochondria are actively respiring and producing ATP from carbohydrates.

Laboratory Investigation

Tiny Bubbles

Before the Lab

1. Prepare 10% solutions of each of the dry sugars by adding 10 g of the dry sugar to 100 mL of water. Dilute the molasses by adding 10 mL of molasses to 90 mL of water.
2. Prepare yeast solutions by adding half a packet of yeast to 100 mL of sugar solution. If rapid-acting dry yeast is used, prepare solutions about an hour before use; if regular dry yeast is used, prepare solutions several hours before or the previous day.
3. Provide strips of modeling clay or flat metal washers to weight the pipette stems.
4. Have students place each test tube in a beaker of warm water if a constant temperature for the respiring yeast is desired.

Pre-Lab Discussion

Have students read the entire procedure for this investigation. Then ask students the following questions.

What is the purpose of this investigation? (To predict which kind of sugar produces the most fermentation in yeast cells.)

What occurs during fermentation in yeast cells, and what are the products of that process? (In yeast cells, the type of fermentation is called alcoholic fermentation, through which yeast breaks down pyruvic acid to produce alcohol and carbon dioxide.)

How do yeast cells obtain the pyruvic acid used in alcoholic fermentation? (They produce the pyruvic acid through glycolysis, a series of reactions in which a molecule of glucose is broken down.)

What is your prediction for which yeast solution will produce the most bubbles over a period of 10 minutes? (Most students will predict the yeast-glucose solution because glucose is what is broken down in glycolysis.)

Laboratory Investigation

Tiny Bubbles

Yeast are single-celled organisms that use sugar as a food source. In this investigation, you will observe the substances produced by yeast cells from the breakdown of food molecules.

Problem

Predict which kind of sugar produces the most rapid fermentation in yeast cells.

Materials (per group)

- 5 large test tubes
- 5 disposable plastic pipettes
- weight to fit on pipette stem
- thermometer
- yeast solutions
  - yeast-sucrose
  - yeast-glucose
  - yeast-lactose
  - yeast-molasses
  - yeast-water
- glass-marking pencil
- watch with second hand or timer

Procedure

1. **Label 5 test tubes from 1 to 5.**
2. **Fill the bulb section of a pipette with the yeast-sucrose solution. To fill the pipettes, pull up as much liquid as possible into the stem by squeezing the bulb and then slowly releasing it. Turn the pipette upside down and tap the pipette to move the liquid into the bulb. Keep the pipette upside down.**
3. **Attach a weight to the pipette stem just above the bulb and place the pipette (still upside down) into test tube 1, which is three-quarters**

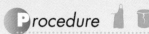

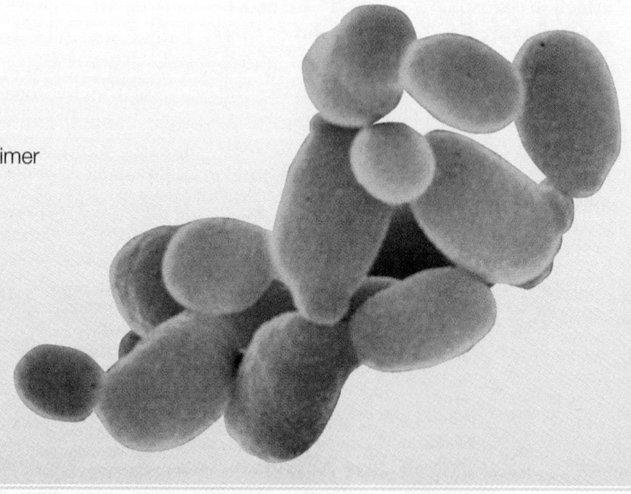

Safety Tips

Caution students not to taste any of the solutions and to keep their hands away from their mouths after handling the test tubes.

Remind students to be careful when handling glass as it may break and cut them.

full with warm water (about 37°C). The pipette should be completely covered by the water and have about 2 to 3 cm of water above the tip.

4. You should observe tiny bubbles being released from the tip of the pipette. Count the number of bubbles released over a period of 10 minutes and record your results.

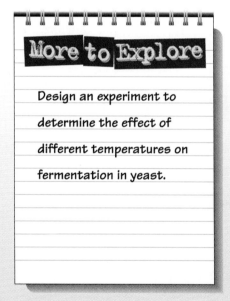

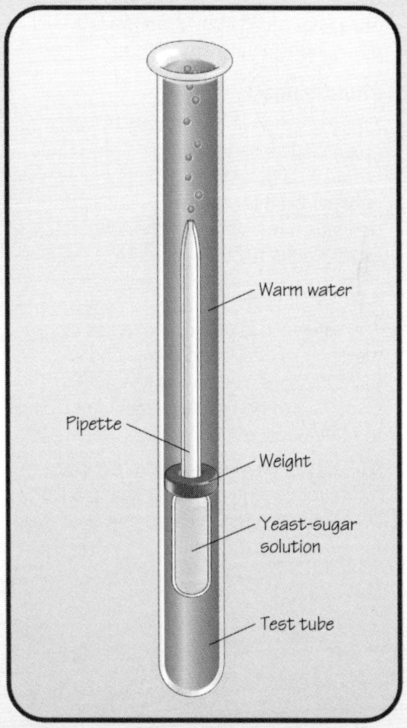

5. Repeat steps 2 to 4 for each of the remaining solutions. Record your observations for each.

6. Collect data from the class and calculate the average number of bubbles produced by each solution. Construct a graph of your data and the class average.

Observations

1. What differences do you note in the number of bubbles that you see?
2. How did your data compare with the class average?

Analysis and Conclusions

1. What was the purpose of the yeast-and-water solution?
2. What is the name of the gas that is inside the bubbles released from the solutions? Can you design a test to identify this gas?
3. Explain how the counting of the gas bubbles is a way of measuring fermentation.
4. Which sugar was the best food source for yeast? Give evidence to support your answer.
5. How does the molasses differ from the other sugars that you used?

More to Explore

Design an experiment to determine the effect of different temperatures on fermentation in yeast.

Answers to Observations

1. Students should observe that the number of bubbles varies with the type of nutrient used, with the yeast-glucose or yeast-molasses solutions producing the most bubbles and the yeast-water solution producing the least.
2. Students' data should be fairly close to the class average if they followed the procedure correctly.

Answers to Analysis and Conclusions

1. To act as a control.
2. The gas is carbon dioxide. Students might suggest collecting the gas by using a stopper for each test tube and then running the gas through a tube to an indicator solution that would turn color in the presence of carbon dioxide.
3. Counting the bubbles is a way of measuring the amount of gas produced. Since carbon dioxide is a product of fermentation, the more bubbles produced, the more fermentation has occurred.
4. Both glucose and molasses produce high levels of respiration, and either of those solutions should have produced the most bubbles.
5. Students may know that molasses is a combination of sugars and, in addition, contains vitamins and other trace nutrients.

More to Explore

Students' designs may vary. Most students should suggest using several pipettes of only one of the yeast solutions, such as the yeast-glucose solution, and then varying the temperature of the water in the test tubes in which the pipettes are placed.

Skills Development

Students will use these skills in the completion of this laboratory investigation: predicting, observing, communicating, comparing, interpreting, and inferring.

Teaching Strategies

1. Point out that by counting the number of bubbles over a set time (10 minutes), students are measuring the rate of fermentation.
2. Have groups assign a different member as the bubble counter for each of the yeast solutions, since no one student would be able to count bubbles for all solutions.
3. Discuss with students how to construct a graph of the results and how to find the class average for each of the solutions.

CHAPTER 4

Study Guide

Review Strategy

Have students in small groups collaborate on writing a play to represent either respiration or photosynthesis. Tell them they can base their play on the characters in a favorite television soap opera, drama, or situation comedy. Emphasize that the play can be serious or humorous, but it must in some way include the terminology and events of either photosynthesis or respiration. Have groups work on these plays for several days, and then ask them to perform their plays for the class.

Study Guide

Summarizing Key Concepts

The key concepts in each section of this chapter are listed below to help you review the chapter content. Make sure you understand each concept and its relationship to other concepts and to the theme of this chapter.

4–1 Chemical Energy and Life

- Without the ability to produce and use energy, living things could not survive.
- Energy in the cell comes from ATP. The high-energy bonds in ATP are used for storing and releasing energy.

4–2 Making ATP Without Oxygen

- Glycolysis is the series of reactions in which a molecule of glucose is broken down.
- Fermentation is the process that allows glycolysis to continue without oxygen, producing ATP. There are two types of fermentation—lactic acid and alcoholic fermentation.

4–3 Respiration

- Respiration is the release of energy from the breakdown of food molecules in the presence of oxygen.
- The pyruvic acid from glycolysis is broken down further in the Krebs cycle.

4–4 Photosynthesis

- Photosynthesis is the process by which green plants use the energy of the sun to produce carbohydrates. There are two sets of reactions that take place—the light-dependent reactions and the light-independent reactions.

4–5 ATP Synthesis

- The difference in electrical charges across the photosynthetic and mitochondrial membranes is a source of energy. This energy could be used to attach a phosphate to ADP to make ATP.
- ATP is generated when hydrogen ions move from a high concentration to a low concentration. This is called chemiosmosis.

Reviewing Key Terms

Review the following vocabulary terms and their meaning. Then use each term in a complete sentence.

4–1 Chemical Energy and Life

ATP

4–2 Making ATP Without Oxygen

glycolysis
fermentation
lactic acid fermentation
alcoholic fermentation

4–3 Respiration

respiration
Krebs cycle
electron transport chain

4–4 Photosynthesis

photosynthesis
pigment
chlorophyll
light-dependent reaction
light-independent reaction
Calvin cycle

4–5 ATP Synthesis

chemiosmosis

Inquiry-Based Strategy

Do plant cells produce ATP molecules in mitochondria at the same time they are producing sugars through photosynthesis? Have students research this question. Ask them to investigate whether plant cells contain mitochondria and whether those organelles function to produce ATP even in sunlight. Also ask students to design an experiment that would validate their answer to the question.

Recalling Main Ideas

Choose the letter of the answer that best completes the statement or answers the question.

1. The cell's main energy-storing compound is
   a. FADH. **c.** ATP.
   b. NAD. **d.** AMP.
2. Pyruvic acid is a product of
   a. respiration. **c.** fermentation.
   b. photosynthesis. **d.** glycolysis.
3. During vigorous activity, large body muscles produce
   a. alcohol. **c.** glucose.
   b. lactic acid. **d.** starch.
4. During respiration, the final acceptor of electrons in the electron transport chain is
   a. oxygen. **c.** water.
   b. carbon dioxide. **d.** ATP.
5. Carbon is released from the Krebs cycle in the form of
   a. glucose. **c.** citric acid.
   b. carbon dioxide. **d.** water.
6. The pigment in green plants, where photosynthesis takes place, is
   a. chlorophyll.
   b. mitochondrion.
   c. the ATP-synthesizing enzyme.
   d. the photosynthetic membrane.
7. The Calvin cycle is part of
   a. the light-dependent reactions.
   b. respiration.
   c. the light-independent reactions.
   d. fermentation.
8. The movement of hydrogen ions across a membrane to generate energy to form ATP is called
   a. chemiosmosis. **c.** respiration.
   b. photosynthesis. **d.** fermentation.

Putting It All Together

Using the information on pages xxx to xxxi, complete the following concept map.

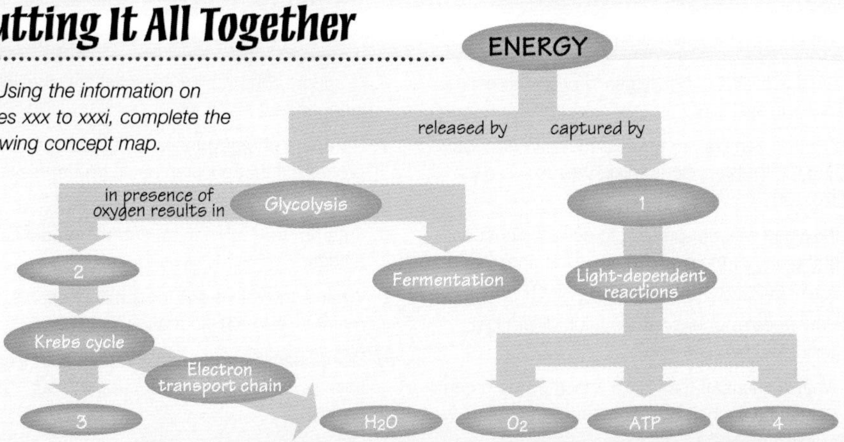

Putting It All Together

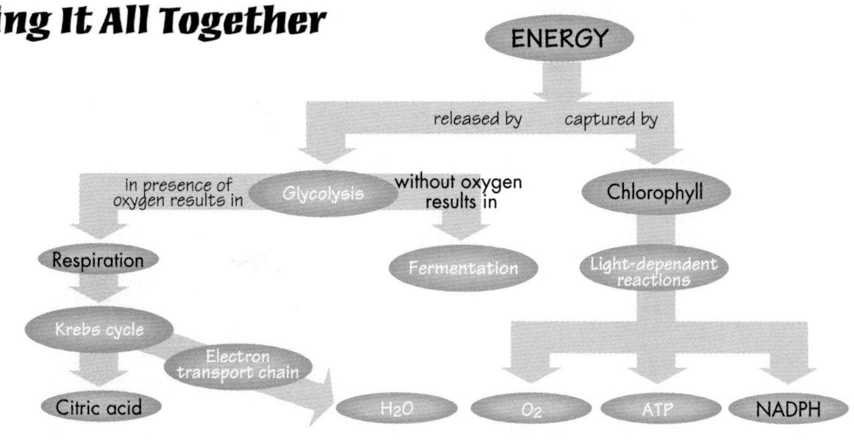

Recalling Main Ideas

1. c
2. d
3. b
4. a
5. b
6. a
7. c
8. a

Assessment

Reviewing What You Learned

1. The sun.
2. The ATP molecule consists of the amino acid adenine, a sugar called ribose, and three phosphate groups.
3. The products are carbon dioxide and water. The reactants are glucose and oxygen.
4. In the bonds of macromolecules.
5. A 3-carbon molecule that is formed when a 6-carbon sugar is broken down through glycolysis.
6. In the cytoplasm of a eukaryotic cell.
7. In the absence of oxygen, 4 ATP molecules are produced in the breakdown of glucose, with a net gain of 2 molecules. This process is called glycolysis.
8. A series of mitochondrial molecules that receive high-energy electrons from the electron carriers in the process of respiration.
9. Respiration.
10. They are all electron carriers.

Expanding the Concepts

1. To release energy from glucose, the cell breaks glucose apart in a series of chemical reactions. Each of these reactions is catalyzed by its own enzyme.
2. In glycolysis, the electron carrier NAD^+ accepts the 2 pairs of high-energy electrons produced during the breakdown of glucose, forming NADH. In the Krebs cycle, the electron carriers NAD^+ and FAD^+ remove 5 pairs of high-energy electrons during each turn of the cycle and take them to the electron transport chain.

Assessment (continued)

3. Without oxygen, electron transport could not take place, the Krebs cycle would stop, and ATP would not be produced.
4. In lactic acid fermentation, the pyruvic acid that accumulates due to glycolysis is converted to lactic acid. In alcoholic fermentation, the pyruvic acid is broken down to produce alcohol and carbon dioxide instead of lactic acid.
5. Green plants use many portions of the spectrum, especially the blue and red regions. These plants do not use the green region, which is reflected by the chlorophyll in the plants.
6. Light-dependent reactions require the direct involvement of sunlight, and they produce two important compounds, ATP and high-energy electrons carried by $NADP^+$. Light-independent reactions do not directly involve light, and they convert ATP and $NADP^+$ into sugars.
7. Respiration and photosynthesis each recycle a waste product of the other, just as an aluminum recycling plant recycles waste aluminum. Respiration uses the oxygen produced in photosynthesis, while photosynthesis uses the carbon dioxide produced in respiration.
8. Students' diagrams should reflect the diagram shown in Figure 4–16.
9. As hydrogen ions pass through channels in the membrane, the energy from the movement is used to attach a phosphate to ADP, making ATP.
10. Chemiosmosis occurs in the membranes of both mitochondria, which are found in plants and animals, and chloroplasts, which are found in plants. Therefore, chemiosmosis occurs in both plants and animals.

Assessment

Reviewing What You Learned

Answer each of the following in a complete sentence.

1. What is the ultimate source of all energy used by life on our planet?
2. Describe the components of an ATP molecule.
3. Observe the equation for respiration:

   $C_6H_{12}O_6 + 6O_2 \rightarrow 6CO_2 + 6H_2O$

   What are the products? The reactants?
4. Where is energy stored in macromolecules?
5. What is PGAL, and where do you find it?
6. Where does glycolysis occur in a eukaryotic cell?
7. How many molecules of ATP are produced in the breakdown of glucose in the absence of oxygen? What is this process called?
8. What is the electron transport chain?
9. In essence, photosynthesis is the reverse of what biological process?
10. How are the functions of FAD, NAD^+, and $NADP^+$ similar?

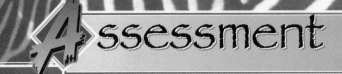

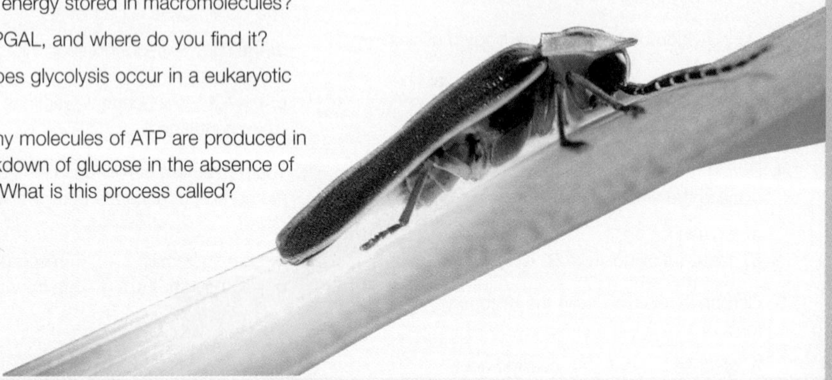

Expanding the Concepts

Discuss each of the following in a brief paragraph.

1. What is the role of enzymes in providing energy for living systems?
2. Electron carriers are key molecules in glycolysis and the Krebs cycle. Explain their role in each process.
3. If oxygen was not present to accept electrons at the end of the electron transport chain, what would happen to the overall reaction?
4. How does alcoholic fermentation differ from lactic acid fermentation?
5. What portions of the visible spectrum do green plants use as their energy source?
6. Compare light-dependent reactions and light-independent reactions.
7. Compare photosynthesis and respiration to the processes that occur in an aluminum recycling plant.
8. Diagram the Calvin cycle and the production of a sugar.
9. What is the role of the inner mitochondrial membrane in ATP formation?
10. Does chemiosmosis occur in both plants and animals? Give evidence to support your answer.

Extending Your Thinking

1. Both processes use energy to produce ATP molecules, which store the energy needed for cell functions. Respiration uses chemical energy to make ATP, whereas photosynthesis uses energy from the sun. Respiration uses oxygen and gives off carbon dioxide, while photosynthesis uses carbon dioxide and gives off oxygen.

2. The buildup of carbon dioxide in the atmosphere might aid photosynthesis because that process uses the chemical as a reactant. Such a buildup should concern us, though, because it might have bad effects on other processes of living things.

Skills Trace
Predicting

Focus p. 80
Practice p. 80
Assess p. 99

Extending Your Thinking

Use the skills you have developed in this chapter to answer the following.

1. **Comparing** Photosynthesis and respiration have often been described as opposite reactions. List both similarities and differences of these two major reactions.
2. **Predicting** How might the buildup of carbon dioxide in the atmosphere affect the process of photosynthesis? Is this something we need to be concerned about? Explain your answer.
3. **Observing** Write the chemical equation for the reaction of glucose and oxygen. What physical characteristic of this reaction can you observe? From what reactant is the oxygen in the resultant product, water, derived?
4. **Designing an experiment** Design an experiment to determine the optimal light wavelength for a plant.
5. **Applying concepts** Isotope tracer technology is a major tool used in understanding living reactions. How might Calvin have used this technology to better understand the many reactions of photosynthesis?

Applying Your Skills

The Energizer

Everything alive requires energy. Energy for the cell is stored in the compound ATP and is then released as needed. Actually, ATP energizes the cell in much the same way that a battery provides energy for a flashlight. Just as a battery needs to be recharged to provide that energy, cells need to replenish their supply of ATP. ATP is like a fully charged battery, ready to supply energy to the cell for the cell to do its work.

1. Working in a group, obtain a flashlight bulb, some insulated wire, and several D-cell batteries.
2. Connect one battery to the wire and the bulb. Is there any evidence that there is energy in your electrical system?
3. Now add a second battery, end to end with the first battery, and then add the wire and bulb to your system. Did the light bulb become brighter or did it stay the same?

• GOING FURTHER •

4. If you add a third battery, end to end to the other batteries, will the bulb get even brighter?
5. Explain how the chemical energy in the batteries is similar to the energy stored in the bonds of ATP.

3. The reaction is this:

$$C_6H_{12}O_6 + 6O_2 \rightarrow 6CO_2 + 6H_2O$$

Students might suggest that the physical characteristic that can be seen is the change of the solid sugar into a gas and a liquid. Students might logically predict that the oxygen in H_2O could be from either reactant. Scientists have discovered that it is actually derived from the free oxygen, not the sugar.

4. Students' designs will vary. A typical experiment will test how well a type of plant grows when the light it receives is limited to a specific region of the light spectrum.

Skills Trace

Experimenting

Focus p. 88
Practice p. 91
Assess p. 99

5. Calvin might have used isotope tracer technology to trace specific elements through the light-independent reactions of photosynthesis and thus better understand the steps of the cycle.

Applying Your Skills

Preparation

Collect a flashlight bulb, lengths of insulated telephone or large-gauge wire, and 3 batteries for each group. The lengths of wire will have to be stripped at both ends.

Suggestions

1. Demonstrate for students how to connect the lengths of wire to the batteries and to the exposed terminals of the flashlight bulb. Also demonstrate how to add batteries in series, positive end of one to the negative end of the next.
2. Students should find that the flashlight bulb will glow brighter with the addition of each battery. You may want one group to add more batteries to the series until the light burns out.
3. Before students write in their journals, you could discuss as a class how the bonds of ATP molecules are like the batteries and how a cell accumulates energy by accumulating ATP.

Scoring Rubric

4 Response is thorough, accurate, and creative; shows an in-depth understanding of science skills, procedures, and concepts.

3 Response is complete, mostly accurate, and original; shows a satisfactory understanding of science skills, procedures, and concepts.

2 Response is mostly complete but includes some inaccuracies; shows an adequate understanding of science skills, procedures, and concepts.

1 Response is only partially complete and has many inaccuracies; shows an incomplete understanding of science skills, procedures, and concepts.

0 Response is mostly incomplete and/or inaccurate; shows a lack of understanding of science skills, procedures, and concepts.

Chapter 5 Cell Division and Specialization

Content Management	Student Edition Activities
■ Section 5–1 Cell Growth and the Cell Cycle, pp. 101–104 Cell Growth The Cell Cycle Controlling Cell Growth	MINI LAB: How Big Is Too Big?, p. 104
■ Section 5–2 Cell Division, pp. 105–108 Interphase Mitosis	Laboratory Investigation: Mitosis, pp. 114–115
■ Section 5–3 Cell Specialization and Organization, pp. 109–111 Specialized Cells Levels of Organization	MINI LAB: Red, White, and Blood, p. 110
◆ BRANCHING OUT • In Depth Section 5–4 Controlling the Cell Cycle, pp. 112–113 Cyclins and the Cell Cycle The Cell Cycle and Cancer	

■ These sections cover all the necessary content and concepts for a basic course in biology.
◆ This section covers content and concepts that are either applications or extensions of the basic material.

Integration Strategies

SE Math, p. 101

Assessment Strategies

SE Chapter Review, pp. 116–119
TR Section Reviews
Chapter Test
BL Practice Test
Chapter Review
CTB Chapter 5 Test

Tech Prep

Teaching strategies appropriate for students who are in technical/vocational programs or who are considering post-secondary technical education can be found on the following **TE** page: 103.

Meeting the Standards

Sections 5–1 through 5–4 cover four of the six content standards under **The Cell** and one of the three content standards under **The Molecular Basis of Heredity** as described on pages 184–185 of The National Science Education Standards.

Chapter Planning Guide

Teacher's Edition Activities	Other Activities	Media and Technology
Chapter Discovery Learning Activity, p. 100 **Inquiry Activity:** How Does Volume Increase With Surface Area?, p. 102	**TR** Explore: Taking a Ride on the Cell Cycle **BL** Inquiry Activity: Keep on Growing	
Inquiry Activity: A Cell's Legacy, p. 105 **Inquiry Activity:** Putting Things in Order, p. 106	**LM** Measuring the Time Needed for Mitosis, #10 **TR** Writing in Biology: The Drama of Cell Division Apply: Let's Split **BL** Inquiry Activity: Unbroken Chains	CD-ROM: Mitosis **TB** Visualizing the Cell Cycle, #6
	LM Observing Specialized Cells, #9 **TR** Apply: Different Strokes for Different Folks **BL** Inquiry Activity: It's All Organized	
Inquiry Activity: A Regulation Cycle, p. 112	**TR** Enrich: Abnormal Cell Growth **BL** Inquiry Activity: Running Around In Cycles	

KEY: SE Student Edition **TE** Teacher's Edition **LM** Laboratory Manual **TR** Teaching Resources **BL** BioLog **TB** Transparency Box **CTB** Computer Test Bank

Materials List

TE Chapter Discovery Learning Activity, p. 100 (30 minutes); paramecium culture, microscope, slide, cover slip.
TE Inquiry Activity: How Does Volume Increase With Surface Area?, p. 102 (20 minutes); rectangular boxes of different sizes, meter stick.
SE MINI LAB: How Big Is Too Big?, p. 104 (30 minutes); plastic spoon, agar blocks (1 cm, 2 cm, 3 cm), 0.4% sodium hydroxide solution, tongs, paper towels, scalpel, metric ruler.
TE Inquiry Activity: Putting Things in Order, p. 106 (15 minutes); copies of photographs of the phases of mitosis.
SE MINI LAB: Red, White, and Blood, p. 110 (20 minutes); prepared slide of human blood, microscope.

CHAPTER 5

Cell Division and Specialization

Introducing the Chapter

. . . In Pictures

Have students examine the photomicrograph, read the caption, and answer the following questions.

• **What parts have been stained red in one of the cells at the top left?** (The nuclear membrane, the chromosome material within the nucleus, and organelles in the cytoplasm.)

• **How is the cell at the top right different from the cell to its left?** (The cell at the top right looks like two cells attached together. Some students may know that this cell is in the process of dividing. Lacking is a stained nuclear membrane. Each half of the doubled cell seems to have chromosome material, but it is flattened in comparison to the cell at the left.)

Teaching Strategy

In the first three sections of this chapter, students will learn about basic cell processes, including the optimum size of cells, the cell cycle, the phases of mitosis, and cell specialization. The BRANCHING OUT section provides students with a more in-depth understanding of how the cell cycle is regulated in a cell.

BIO JOURNAL

Ask students to think about how tasks or projects are accomplished in a large organization by small groups of members or by committees. Each member of the organization has different responsibilities, and in that way more is accomplished than if everyone did the same tasks. Help students make the analogy to how cells are specialized in organisms. Instruct students to keep their entries in their portfolios.

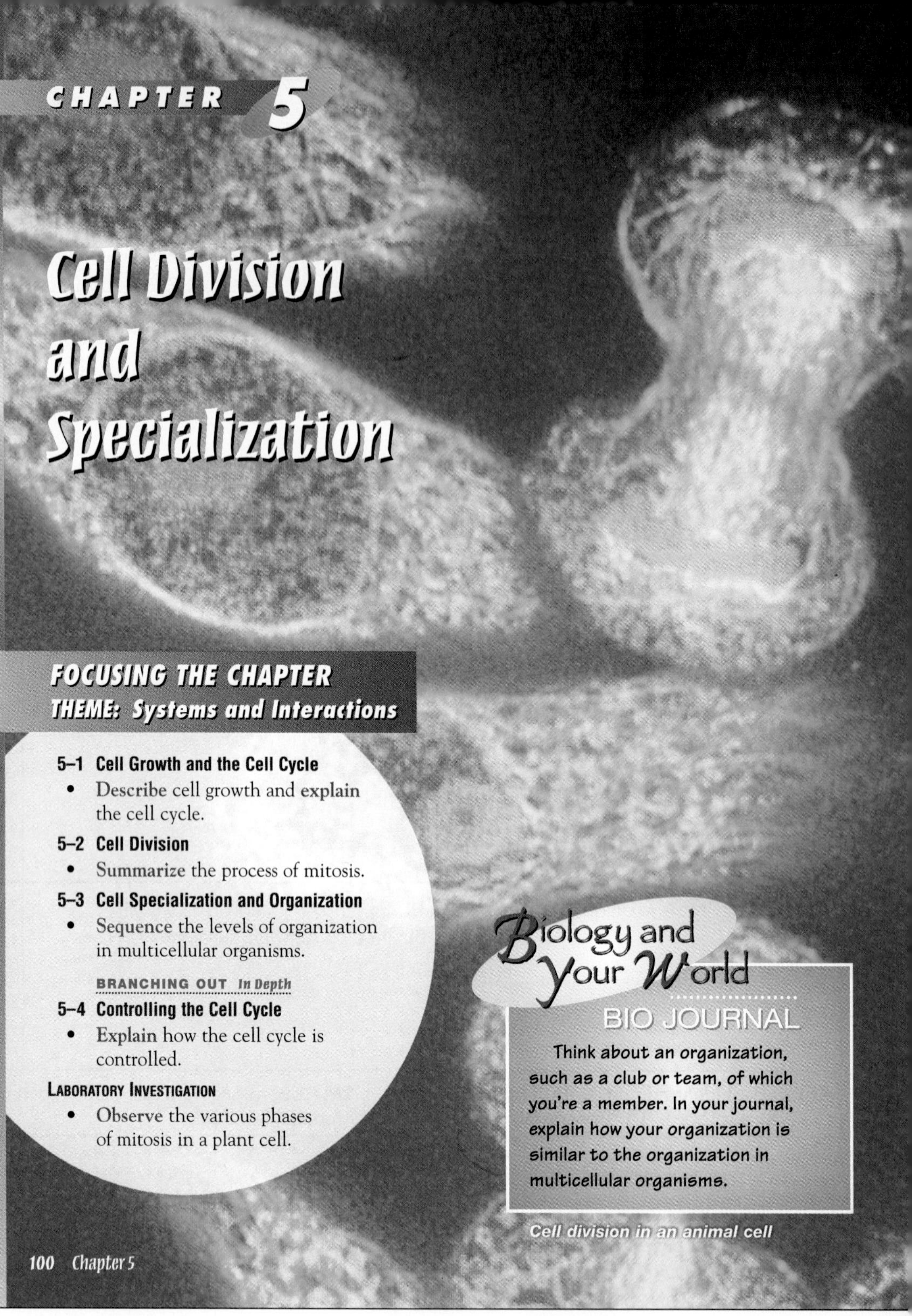

CHAPTER 5

Cell Division and Specialization

FOCUSING THE CHAPTER THEME: *Systems and Interactions*

5–1 Cell Growth and the Cell Cycle
- **Describe** cell growth and **explain** the cell cycle.

5–2 Cell Division
- **Summarize** the process of mitosis.

5–3 Cell Specialization and Organization
- **Sequence** the levels of organization in multicellular organisms.

BRANCHING OUT *In Depth*

5–4 Controlling the Cell Cycle
- **Explain** how the cell cycle is controlled.

LABORATORY INVESTIGATION
- **Observe** the various phases of mitosis in a plant cell.

Biology and Your World

BIO JOURNAL

Think about an organization, such as a club or team, of which you're a member. In your journal, explain how your organization is similar to the organization in multicellular organisms.

Cell division in an animal cell

TEACHER SUPPORT

Chapter Discovery Learning Activity

Provide students with a paramecium culture and ask each to make a slide. Have them search their slides, using low power, for paramecia that are pinched in the middle or look like doubled cells. Next, have students switch to high power to study and sketch one such pinched organism. Then ask students to write short explanations of the life process they think is occurring in the pinched paramecia.

SECTION 5–1

Cell Growth and the Cell Cycle

Guide for Reading

- Define the cell cycle.
- Describe the four phases of the cell cycle.

MINI LAB

- Analyze the relationship between the size of a cell and diffusion.

A BEAR, LIKE ALL animals, is made up of cells. Bear cubs, like other newborn animals, are much smaller than adults. What happens to the cells of a bear cub as it grows into an adult? Does a living thing get larger because its cells increase in size? Or does it get larger because it produces more and more cells? In most cases, a living thing grows because it produces more and more cells. On the average, the cells of an adult bear are no larger than those of a bear cub—there are just a lot more of them.

Cell Growth

Is there a reason why organisms grow by producing more cells? Couldn't an organism grow just by allowing its cells to get larger and larger? Or are there limits that prevent cells from getting too big? In a way, there are limits as to how large a cell can become.

Suppose that a cell were to double its diameter, as shown in *Figure 5–2* on the next page. As you can see, the internal volume of the cell is now eight times as great, while the surface area of the cell is only four times as great. Clearly, the larger a cell gets, the more difficult it is to get things in and out of it. If cells grew too large, they would not be able to supply their own needs, and growth would come to a stop. This is one of the main reasons why cells do not grow much larger even if the organism itself does.

Checkpoint Why is a small cell more efficient than a large cell? ①

INTEGRATING MATH

Calculate the volume/surface-area ratio for a cube in which each side is 4 cm.

Figure 5–1
(a) Although the cells in these bear cubs are the same size as the cells in the adult bear, the adult bear has many more cells. The same is true for (b) this adult oak tree and (c) the oak sapling.

Section 5-1

Cell Growth and the Cell Cycle

Performance Objectives

- Explain what the cell cycle is.
- Discuss the major events in the cell cycle, including the four phases.

Mini Lab Skill: Analyzing

1 ENGAGE

Ideas Through Images

Have students examine Figure 5–1, read the caption, and answer the following questions.

- **How does the size of cells compare in the bears shown?** (The cells are the same size in the adult as in the cubs.)
- **How does an organism grow to the size of an adult if its cells do not increase in size?** (Organisms produce more cells as they grow. The addition of cells, not an increase in cell size, increases the size of an organism.)

INTEGRATING MATH

Volume of a cube = length x width x depth; thus, the volume of the cube is 64 (4 x 4 x 4) cm^3. Surface area of a cube = length x width x number of sides; thus, the surface area of the cube is 96 (4 x 4 x 6) cm^2. Therefore, the volume/surface-area ratio is 64/96, or 2/3.

Checkpoint

① A small cell is more efficient because getting things into and out of a small cell is easier.

Ancillary Support

The resources below can be used to support your teaching strategy for these two pages.

TR Explore: Taking a Ride on the Cell Cycle

BL Inquiry Activity: Keep on Growing

TEACHER SUPPORT

Facts and Figures

Current thinking is that eukaryotic cells developed from prokaryotic cells, and, as one might expect, eukaryotic cells are larger than prokaryotic cells. After that development, organisms evolved into larger sizes through multicellularity, not through increasing the size of cells. Despite the tremendous variety of sizes in multicellular living things, most eukaryotic cells of most organisms are about 10 micrometers in diameter. There are some exceptions, but a closer look at those may convince one that they are not really exceptions to the rule. Consider a neuron that runs the length of a giraffe's neck. Certainly, the whole structure is larger than 10 micrometers. But the nucleus-containing cell body of that neuron remains about 10 micrometers. It's only the long axon of the neuron that is exceptional.

2 EXPLORE

Inquiry Activity

Drawing Conclusions

How Does Volume Increase With Surface Area?

Ask students to consider the way in which the volume of an object would increase if the surface area of that object were to increase. Give each group of students two rectangular boxes, one larger than the other. Ask that they find the surface area of each box by measuring with a meter stick. Ask that they also find the volume of each box. Then have them compare the measurements and draw a conclusion about how an increase in surface area affects the volume of an object.

3 TEACH

Ideas Through Images

Have students examine Figure 5–3, read the caption, and answer the following questions.

- **What happens at the end of every cell cycle?** (The cell divides into two independent cells.)
- **What event marks the end of the cell cycle?** (The end of the M phase.)
- **During which phase of the cycle does chromosome replication occur?** (The S phase.)

THE RATIO OF SURFACE AREA TO VOLUME IN CELLS

Cell Size	Volume (length x width x height)	Surface Area (number of surfaces x length x width)	Surface Area/ Volume Ratio
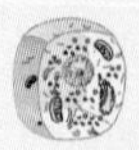	1 cm x 1 cm x 1 cm = 1 cm^3	6 x 1 cm x 1 cm = 6 cm^2	6 cm^2/1 cm^3 = 6/cm
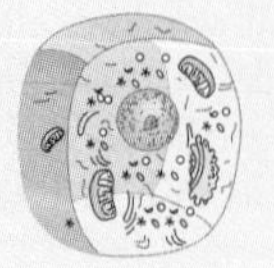	2 cm x 2 cm x 2 cm = 8 cm^3	6 x 2 cm x 2 cm = 24 cm^2	24 cm^2/8 cm^3 = 3/cm

Figure 5–2
As a cell doubles its diameter, its surface area increases by four, while its internal volume increases by eight.

The Cell Cycle

In most animals and plants, cells increase in size and then divide into two cells. These two new cells increase in size and then divide again. The process continues over and over. This regular series of events, called the **cell cycle,** occurs in eukaryotic cells. **The cell cycle is the period of time from the beginning of one cell division to the beginning of the next.** What happens to the cell during the cell cycle? Basically, the cell doubles its contents so that it is ready to divide into two completely independent cells.

The Cell Divides

Thousands of events take place during the cell cycle, but two of those events are so important that they are used as landmarks to define everything else. One of the events is **cell division.** Cell division is the process in which the cell divides into two independent cells, called daughter cells. In eukaryotic cells, this process is called **mitosis.** The period of time when mitosis takes place is the M phase of the cell cycle.

Checkpoint What is cell division? 1

The Cell Copies Its Chromosomes

The other major event in the cell cycle is the copying of the chromosomes that contain the cell's genetic information. When the cell copies this information, it synthesizes, or makes, a duplicate set of DNA molecules. As a result, this part of the cell cycle is called the S phase.

Because most cells do not begin DNA synthesis right after cell division, there is a time gap between the end of one M phase and the beginning of an S phase. This time gap is called the G_1 phase. A similar gap, the G_2 phase, occurs between the end of the S phase and the beginning of the M phase.

THE CELL CYCLE

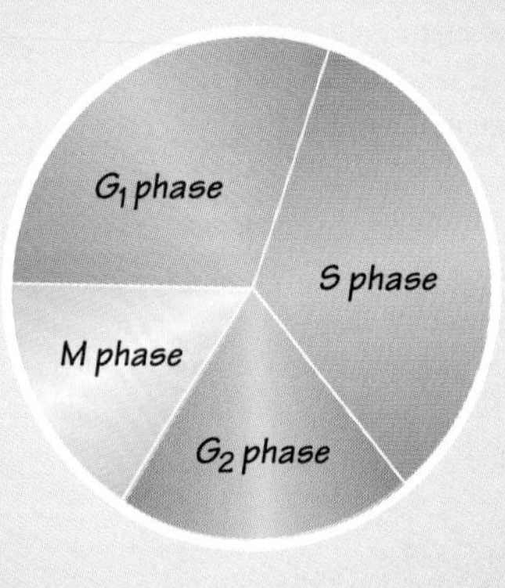

Figure 5–3
The cell cycle consists of four phases. During G_1, most of the cell's growth and activity take place. After the cell leaves G_1, it moves into the S phase, where chromosome replication takes place. After the S phase, the cell enters G_2, where it makes final preparations for cell division. Cell division takes place during the M phase.

TEACHER SUPPORT

Background Information

This text uses the same terminology that most scientists use when referring to the cell cycle. There are four phases to the cycle (G_1, S, G_2, M), and mitosis is further divided into four phases (prophase, metaphase, anaphase, telophase). All of this fits together quite nicely, but it leaves out one important process—cytokinesis, or the division of the cytoplasm. Some scientists consider it a fifth phase of the cell cycle or the fifth phase of mitosis, but that implies that there is a definable point when mitosis ends and cytokinesis begins. Such is not the case. In some cases, cytokinesis never occurs, as in embryonic mitosis in insects. In other cases, cytokinesis begins during telophase, anaphase, or even metaphase. Because the timing is so variable, it would be misleading to give it the status of a phase all by itself.

Problem Solving
INTERPRETING DATA

To Be or Not to Be . . .

On the fictional planet Cellmion, laboratory technicians are able to manufacture living boxes that can be used to create more complex life forms. The Cellmions have mastered this technology with one exception—the surface-area-to-volume ratio. If there is too little surface area for the volume of the living box, the substances needed for life are unable to enter the boxes in sufficient quantities. In addition, waste products, which are unable to leave the box quickly enough, will poison the box. As the head laboratory technician, you have determined that the optimal surface-area-to-volume ratio is 3:1. If a living box has a smaller ratio—for example, 2:1 or 1:1—the box will die because it has too little surface area to support its volume. Boxes with a 3:1 ratio or greater will live.

As the technicians create the boxes, you must check their surface-area-to-volume ratios. Laboratory technicians who have made boxes that will die because of a low surface-area-to-volume ratio must be retrained. The chart provides you with the names of the technicians and the dimensions of the boxes they have made.

LIVING BOXES

Technician	Box Length	Box Width	Box Height
Androm	1 cm	1 cm	1 cm
Shama	3 cm	3 cm	3 cm
Marcha	2 cm	1 cm	1 cm
Berich	4 cm	2 cm	1 cm

THINK ABOUT IT

1. How do you calculate the surface area of the boxes? The volume?
2. How do you calculate the surface-area-to-volume ratio?
3. Which technicians' boxes will live?
4. Which of the technicians will need to be retrained?

TEACHER SUPPORT

Managing Classroom Diversity

AT-RISK STUDENTS

Some students may not understand what ratios are and how they are expressed in the lowest common denominator. Help students understand these concepts by using a familiar example, such as the ratio of teachers to students in your school. Give them the raw figures (or have them ask at the main office) and help them work through the figures to find and express the ratio.

TECH PREP STUDENTS

Students planning careers in a great variety of fields will have to understand and work with ratios. Ask students to find out what ratios they might have to use in a career that interests them. They could discover such information through library research or by interviewing someone in the field.

Problem Solving
Interpreting Data
To Be or Not to Be . . .

Students will draw upon their knowledge of the relationship between surface area and volume. This activity will help students understand this concept more clearly.

State The problem to be solved is which of the four boxes have a surface-area-to-volume ratio of less than 3:1, because such a ratio will cause the death of a box.

Solve Students should calculate the surface area and volume of each box.

Androm's box has a surface area of 6 cm^2 and a volume of 1 cm^3. The ratio is 6:1.

Shama's box has a surface area of 54 cm^2 and a volume of 27 cm^3. The ratio is 2:1.

Marcha's box has a surface area of 10 cm^2 and a volume of 2 cm^3. The ratio is 5:1.

Berich's box has a surface area of 28 cm^2 and a volume of 8 cm^3. The ratio is 3.5:1.

Test Students could use poster board to construct four boxes, the specifications of which would match those in the table. Students could leave the tops open, seal the edges with wax, then pour water into each box and measure the volume of this water in a graduated cylinder.

Communicate Ask each student to say which technician(s) would need to be retrained. If any students disagree, have them show their calculations and then discuss their results.

Answers to THINK ABOUT IT

1. See Figure 5–2.
2. Find the surface area and the volume and then show their relative proportions as a fraction.
3. Androm, Marcha, and Berich.
4. Shama.

Checkpoint

1 The process in which the cell divides into two independent cells.

MINI LAB Analyzing

Teacher Notes

• For time required and materials needed, see page 100b.
• To prepare agar blocks, add 30 g of agar to 1000 mL of water and bring to a boil. Cool before adding 1 g of phenolphthalein, but add before the solution hardens. If the mixture turns pink, add dilute HCl until it turns colorless. Pour the mixture into a pan with a depth of 3 cm, let harden, and cut into blocks.

Answers to Analyze and Conclude

1. Answers will vary.
2. The smaller the surface-area-to-volume ratio, the greater the extent of diffusion.

Skills Trace
Analyzing
- Focus p. 104
- Practice p. 104
- Assess p. 118

4 ASSESS

Quick Check

Ask students to list the four phases in the cell cycle, define each, and describe the events that take place during each phase.

Section Review 5-1

1. The period of time from the beginning of one cell division to the beginning of the next.
2. Students' descriptions of the four phases should be similar to that found in the caption to Figure 5–3.
3. A typical response might suggest that a cell biologist could observe and compare the phases in a cell cycle many times, since in cancer cells cell growth is not regulated.

MINI LAB .... Analyzing ....

How Big Is Too Big?

PROBLEM *Analyze the relationship between cell size and diffusion.*

PROCEDURE

1. Using a plastic spoon, place three agar blocks of different sizes into a 250-mL beaker. Cover the blocks with 0.4% sodium hydroxide solution. **CAUTION:** *Do not touch the blocks or the solution. If the solution splashes on your skin, wash it off immediately.*
2. Calculate the surface-area-to-volume ratio for each block. Record your calculations.
3. After 10 minutes, use tongs to remove the agar blocks and gently blot them dry with paper towels.
4. Cut each block in half using a scalpel. **CAUTION:** *Be careful with sharp instruments.* You will see that a dark-pink color has diffused into each block.
5. Using a metric ruler, measure the distance the pink color has diffused in each block. Record your measurements.

ANALYZE AND CONCLUDE

1. Which block has the greatest proportion of pink color?
2. Compare your answer to the surface-area-to-volume ratios you computed. How does the ratio relate to diffusion?

The Length of the Cell Cycle

Not all cells move through the cell cycle at the same rate. In the human body, most muscle and nerve cells do not divide at all after they have developed. In contrast, the rapidly dividing cells of an embryo can complete the cell cycle in as little as 30 minutes. However, the average length of the cell cycle in a typical human adult cell is about 20 hours.

In general, when a cell stops growing, it stops in the G_1 phase. Although there are a few exceptions, when a cell leaves the G_1 phase and enters the S phase, it will continue through the rest of the cell cycle and enter cell division.

Controlling Cell Growth

One of the most striking aspects of cell behavior in multicellular organisms such as humans is how carefully cell division and cell growth are controlled. Cells in certain places of the body, including the brain and the heart, rarely divide—if they divide at all. In contrast, the cells of the skin and the digestive tract divide rapidly throughout life, replacing cells that have broken down due to daily wear and tear.

Why is the cell cycle in humans regulated so carefully? One important reason is that a mistake in regulating the cycle can be fatal. Cancer, a disease in which some of the body's cells grow uncontrollably, causes thousands of deaths every year. The various types of cancer seem to have one thing in common. To one degree or another, cancer cells have lost the normal ability to regulate the cell cycle.

Section Review 5-1

1. **Define** the cell cycle.
2. **Describe** each of the four phases of the cell cycle.
3. **Critical Thinking—Inferring** What could a cell biologist learn about the cell cycle by studying cancer cells?
4. **MINI LAB Analyze** the relationship between cell size and diffusion.

4. The smaller the surface-area-to-volume ratio of a cell, the greater the efficiency of diffusion in moving substances in and out of the cell.

Skills Trace
Analyzing
- Focus p. 104
- Practice p. 104
- Assess p. 118

Learning Modality

Tactile Learning Have students cut two different sizes of cubes from clay, measure their surface areas, and then predict their differences in mass by holding one cube in each hand. Have students find the masses of the cubes on a balance.

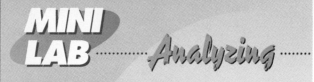

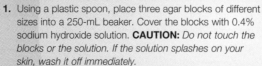

Cell Division

SECTION 5-2

GUIDE FOR READING

- Describe the four phases of mitosis.
- Compare cytokinesis in plant and animal cells.

IN MOST PROKARYOTIC CELLS, cell division is a simple matter of a single cell separating into two daughter cells. Most bacteria and other prokaryotes have a special mechanism that makes sure a cell copies its genetic information before cell division begins. Prokaryotes also ensure that each of the two daughter cells gets its own copy of that information before the cells completely separate.

In a sense, eukaryotic cells do much the same thing. But the more complex structure of eukaryotic cells and the fact that their nuclei contain many chromosomes explain why cell division in eukaryotes is more complex.

Interphase

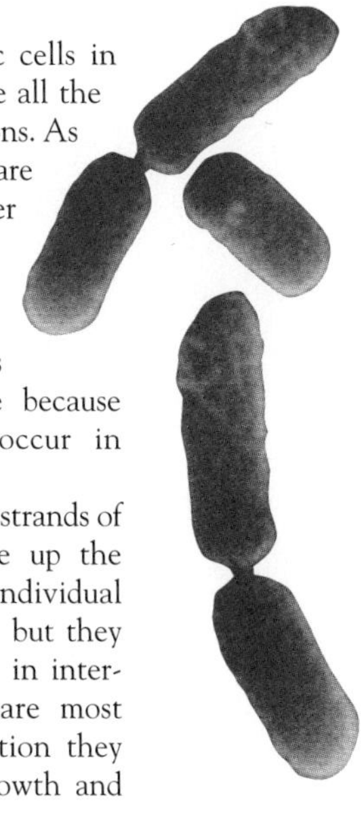

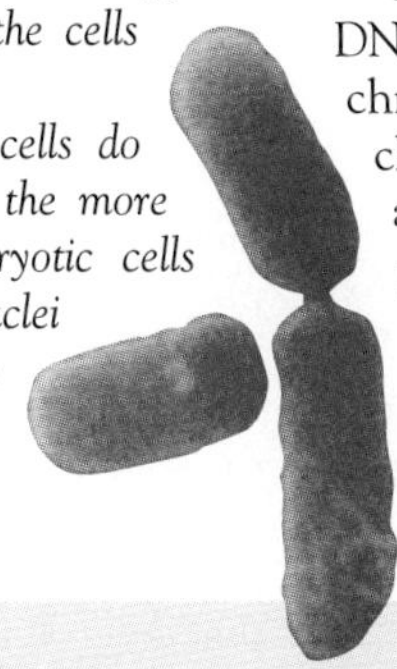

There are a few eukaryotic cells in which chromosomes are visible all the time, but these are the exceptions. As a general rule, chromosomes are not clearly visible—under either the light microscope or the electron microscope—during the G_1, S, and G_2 phases of the cell cycle. These three phases are usually called **interphase** because they are the phases that occur in between cell divisions.

During interphase, the long strands of DNA and protein that make up the chromosomes unfold. The individual chromosomes are still there, but they are difficult to see. In fact, in interphase the chromosomes are most active, using the information they contain to direct cell growth and development.

☑ **Checkpoint** What is interphase? ❶

Figure 5–4
Most cells undergo cell division. (a) These bacteria, which are magnified 30,000 times, are in the final stages of cell division. (b) The plant cells, on the other hand, are about to begin the process of cell division. The plant cells are magnified 1600 times.

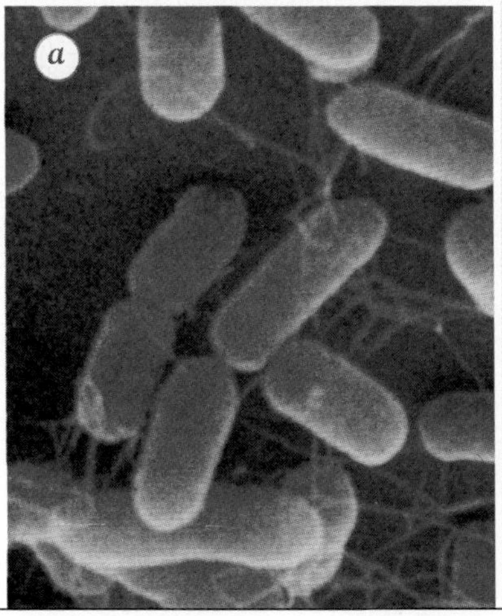

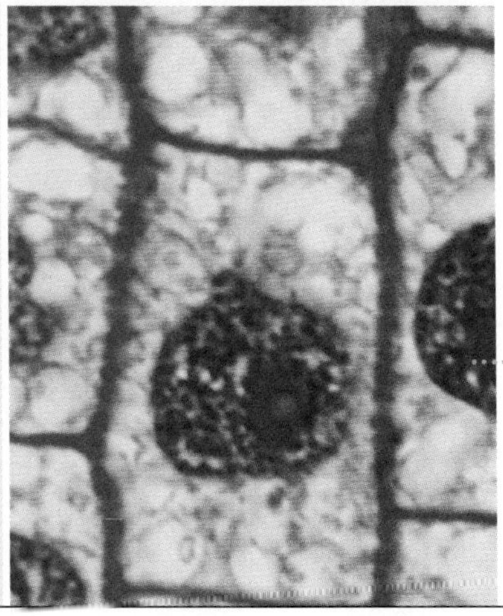

SECTION 5-2

Cell Division

Performance Objectives

- Discuss the four phases of mitosis.
- Describe cytokinesis in animal and plant cells.

Laboratory Investigation Skill: Observing

1 ENGAGE

Inquiry Activity

Hypothesizing

A Cell's Legacy

Remind students that during the M phase of the cell cycle, cell division takes place. Ask them how they think copies of all the instructions a cell needs to survive are given to each cell. As the students have learned, these instructions are contained in the cell's DNA molecules, which are found in the nucleus. Ask each student to form a hypothesis of how a cell provides a copy to each of the cells that results from cell division. Students should state a hypothesis in a sentence and then write a full description of the way in which the process might occur.

☑ Checkpoint

❶ The three phases of the cell cycle that occur between cell divisions.

TEACHER SUPPORT

Managing Classroom Diversity

LEP STUDENTS

To help students better understand the terminology introduced in this chapter, have them use a dictionary to find out the meaning of the word phase and these prefixes: *inter-*, *pro-*, *meta-*, *ana-*, and *telo-*. Once they have used the dictionary, ask them to write the meaning of interphase, prophase, metaphase, anaphase, and telophase.

Technology

CD-ROM
Mitosis

Ancillary Support

The resource below can be used to support your teaching strategy for these two pages.

BL Inquiry Activity: Unbroken Chains

2 EXPLORE

Inquiry Activity

Predicting

Putting Things in Order

Ask students if they can predict the order of events that occur during the M phase of the cell cycle. Find photographs of the phases of mitosis in biology texts. Make copies of those photographs, leaving off any captions or labels that explain what is occurring. Divide students into groups, and give each group a set of pictures that, if placed in order, would show the sequence of events in mitosis. Ask each group to come to an agreement about the sequence of the pictures that correctly represents the events in cell division. Have one or more groups present their prediction to the class.

3 TEACH

Ideas Through Images

Have students examine Figure 5–5, read the caption, and answer the following questions.

- **The human chromosome shown here consists of what?** (Two identical chromatids.)
- **Where can you see a centromere in this picture?** (The area of constriction where the two chromatids are attached.)
- **During which phase of mitosis can these chromatids first be seen under a light microscope?** (Prophase.)

Laboratory Investigation

The Laboratory Investigation, Mitosis, on pages 114–115 is appropriate to use at this point in the chapter.

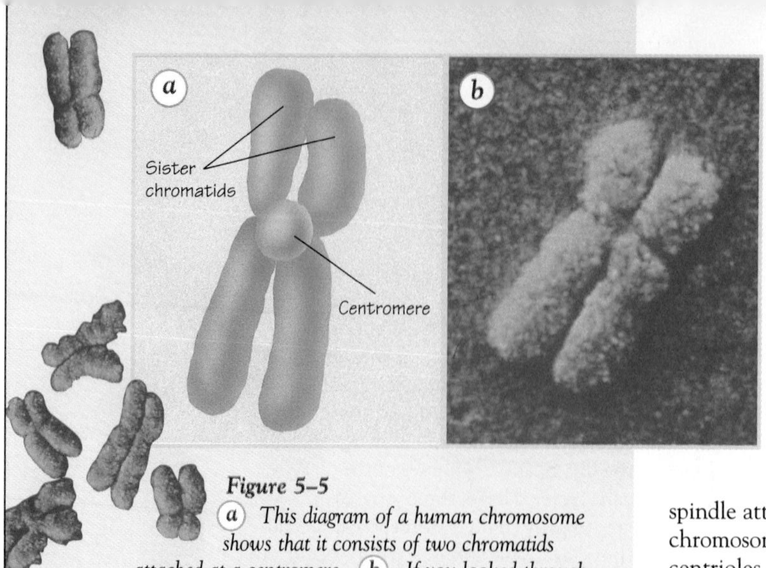

Figure 5–5 *(a) This diagram of a human chromosome shows that it consists of two chromatids attached at a centromere. (b) If you looked through a scanning electron microscope, this is what a human chromosome would look like (magnification: 40,000X).*

In animal cells, the **centrioles**—tiny structures that help to organize microtubules—separate from each other and move to opposite sides of the nucleus. Each pair of centrioles serves as a focal point for the growth of a cluster of microtubules that span the nucleus. This cluster of microtubules is called the **spindle.** Some of the microtubules of the spindle attach themselves directly to the chromosomes. Plant cells do not have centrioles, but they organize a nearly identical spindle in much the same way.

Checkpoint What are chromatids? 1

Mitosis

After interphase, the cell is ready for mitosis, or cell division. **Mitosis is divided into four phases: prophase, metaphase, anaphase, and telophase.** As you read about the process of mitosis, refer to page 107.

Prophase

The first phase of mitosis, **prophase,** is generally the longest of the four phases, taking as much as 50 percent of the total time required to complete mitosis. Often, the first clue that prophase has started is the appearance of chromosomes.

The cell nucleus changes dramatically in prophase, as the chromosomes come together and form thick, threadlike structures that are visible under the light microscope. At this point, each chromosome consists of two identical strands called **chromatids.** Because the chromatids are identical copies of the same chromosome, they are often called sister chromatids. The chromatids are attached at an area called the **centromere.**

Metaphase

The second phase of mitosis is called **metaphase.** Metaphase is the shortest phase of mitosis and may last only a few minutes. During metaphase, the chromosomes complete their attachment to the spindle and line up across the center of the cell. When metaphase is complete, each chromosome is aligned so that one of its chromatids is closer to one pole of the spindle and the other chromatid is closer to the other pole.

Anaphase

At the end of metaphase, the centromeres that hold the sister chromatids together suddenly split. The chromatids move toward the two poles of the spindle. This sudden movement marks the beginning of **anaphase.** Anaphase is the phase of mitosis in which the duplicated chromosomes separate from each other.

In a matter of a few minutes, the chromosomes move apart and are concentrated into two groups—one at each pole of the spindle. Anaphase is complete when the movement of chromosomes stops.

TEACHER SUPPORT

Background Information

Once a chromosome has been through the S phase, it is consistently referred to as being composed of two chromatids. This is part of an attempt by biologists to keep from getting confused, especially about how many chromosomes a cell contains. Human cells, for example, contain 46 chromosomes. At the end of the S phase, however, each of those has been duplicated. One does not say, however, that the G_2 cell contains 92 chromosomes, because the information content of the cell has not changed. Biologists continue to say that the cell has 46 chromosomes, but where once there was a single DNA molecule there are now two identical ones. That's where the verbal device of using the term chromatid comes into play. Each chromosome consists of one chromatid before the S phase and two chromatids after.

Visualizing the Cell Cycle

In eukaryotic cells, the cell cycle has two major phases—interphase and mitosis.

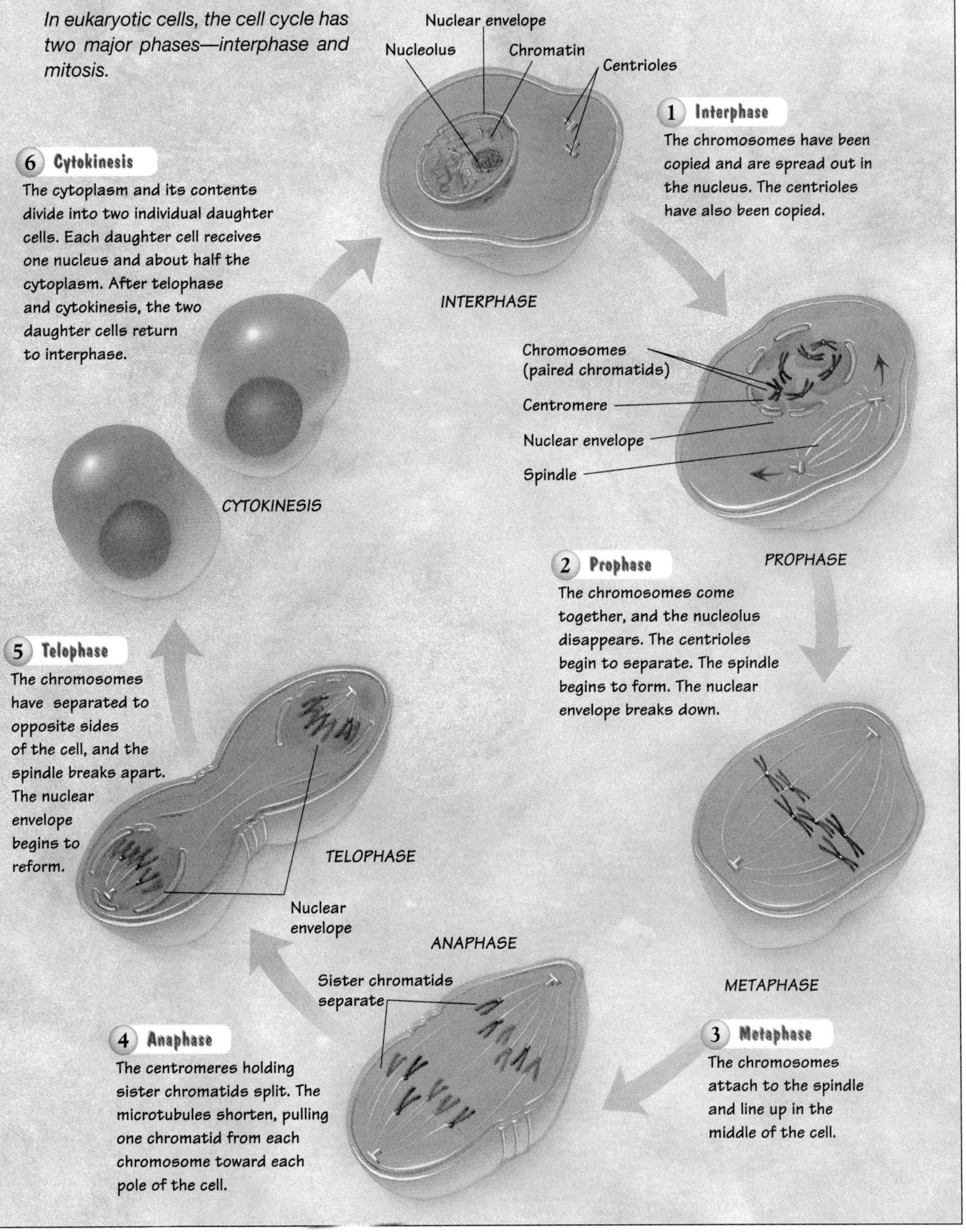

Nuclear envelope
Nucleolus
Chromatin
Centrioles
1 Interphase
The chromosomes have been copied and are spread out in the nucleus. The centrioles have also been copied.
INTERPHASE
Chromosomes (paired chromatids)
Centromere
Nuclear envelope
Spindle
PROPHASE
2 Prophase
The chromosomes come together, and the nucleolus disappears. The centrioles begin to separate. The spindle begins to form. The nuclear envelope breaks down.
METAPHASE
3 Metaphase
The chromosomes attach to the spindle and line up in the middle of the cell.
ANAPHASE
Sister chromatids separate
4 Anaphase
The centromeres holding sister chromatids split. The microtubules shorten, pulling one chromatid from each chromosome toward each pole of the cell.
TELOPHASE
Nuclear envelope
5 Telophase
The chromosomes have separated to opposite sides of the cell, and the spindle breaks apart. The nuclear envelope begins to reform.
CYTOKINESIS
6 Cytokinesis
The cytoplasm and its contents divide into two individual daughter cells. Each daughter cell receives one nucleus and about half the cytoplasm. After telophase and cytokinesis, the two daughter cells return to interphase.

Visualizing the Cell Cycle

The cell cycle shown is a generalized representation of a cycle that cells go through. The transition from one phase to the next is gradual. There is no exact point where the S phase ends and the G_2 phase begins, or when prophase ends and metaphase begins. These phases are somewhat arbitrary divisions of what takes place within a living cell.

Give students time to examine this visual essay, and then discuss its particulars, emphasizing the following points.

- Interphase, which here both ends and begins the cycle (step 1), encompasses the G_1, S, and G_2 phases of the cell cycle.
- The M phase, or mitosis, begins with prophase, when the chromosomes, in pairs of chromatids, come together, the spindle begins to form, and the nuclear envelope breaks down.
- Mitosis ends with telophase, by which time the cell's chromosomes have separated into two clusters. Mitosis, then, is a process by which a cell provides both daughter cells with the same instructions to carry out their life processes.
- Cytokinesis usually occurs during the same time as the last phase of mitosis. Thus, cytokinesis is not actually a separate step.

Checkpoint

1 The two identical strands that make up each chromosome.

TEACHER SUPPORT

Background Information

Where does the nuclear envelope go during mitosis? Some scientists thought that the two nuclear membranes "dissolved" during mitosis. When viewed with a high-powered light microscope, the membranes do indeed seem to disappear during prophase. Peter Helper, a scientist at the University of Massachusetts at Amherst, has solved this puzzle. By using an electron microscope, he discovered that nuclear membranes don't dissolve at all. Instead, the material of the envelope is rearranged into a series of tiny vesicles during prophase, and those vesicles are reassembled as membranes during telophase. Thus, although the membranes seem to disappear, they are actually broken apart and "kept out of the way" until the cell needs them again at the end of mitosis.

Ancillary Support

The resources below can be used to support your teaching strategy for these two pages.

LM Measuring the Time Needed for Mitosis, #10
TR Writing in Biology: The Drama of Cell Division
Apply: Let's Split
TB Visualizing the Cell Cycle, #6

Section 5–2 (continued)

Ideas Through Images

Have students examine Figures 5–6 and 5–7, read the captions, and answer the following questions.

• **What is cytokinesis?** (The division of the cytoplasm that occurs during cell division.)

• **When does cytokinesis occur during the cell cycle?** (During anaphase and telophase.)

• **Why is cytokinesis in a plant cell different from cytokinesis in an animal cell?** (A plant cell has a cell wall, while an animal cell does not.)

4 ASSESS

Quick Check

Have students add to the table they made for the Quick Check at the end of Section 5–1 by listing and describing the four phases of mitosis and the process of cytokinesis.

Section Review 5–2

1. Students should describe the major events as discussed on page 107.

2. In both animal and plant cells, cytokinesis is the process that occurs between anaphase and telophase in which the cytoplasm itself divides. In an animal cell, the cell membrane is pulled inward until the cytoplasm is pinched into two nearly equal parts. In a plant cell, a cell plate forms midway between the daughter nuclei and gradually forms a new cell wall between the daughter cells.

3. Students' responses should reflect the order of events described in steps 2–5 on page 107.

Learning Modality

Visual Learning Have pairs or small groups of students make a flipbook that shows the events of mitosis. They could draw the sequence of pictures on 3 x 5 cards, and then bind them together with string or staples.

CYTOKINESIS IN ANIMAL CELLS

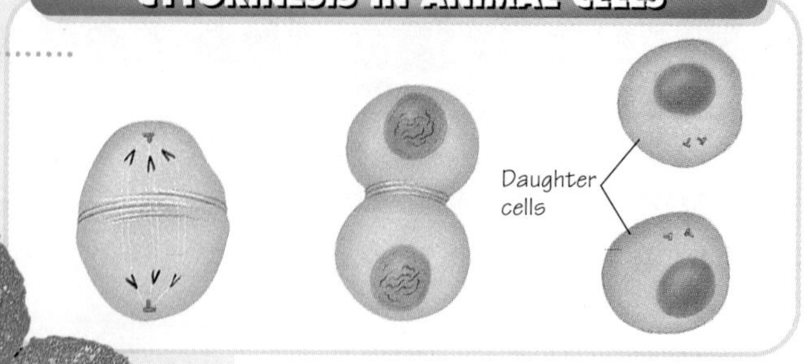

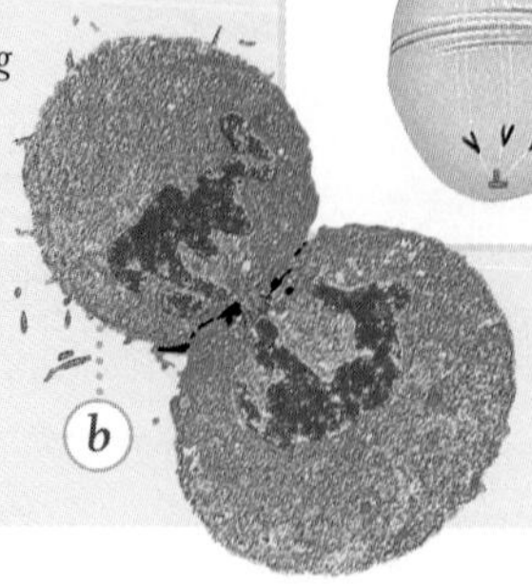

Figure 5–6
(a) During cytokinesis in most animal cells, the cell membrane is pulled inward by a ring of filaments. This continues until the cytoplasm is pinched into two nearly equal parts, each containing its own nucleus and cytoplasmic organelles.
(b) The process of cytokinesis is almost complete in this human kidney cell (magnification: 1740X).

Telophase

The fourth phase of mitosis is called **telophase.** In this phase, the microtubules of the spindle begin to break apart. The chromosomes that are clustered at each of the two poles begin to spread out. A nuclear membrane forms around each cluster, and two distinct nuclei gradually form within the cell. These two daughter nuclei will each go to one of the cells produced by the division, so that each of these new cells contains a nucleus.

Cytokinesis

In most cells, another process takes place during anaphase and telophase. Just as the two daughter nuclei are forming, the cytoplasm itself divides. This process is called **cytokinesis.** After telophase and cytokinesis are complete, the process begins again.

CYTOKINESIS IN PLANT CELLS

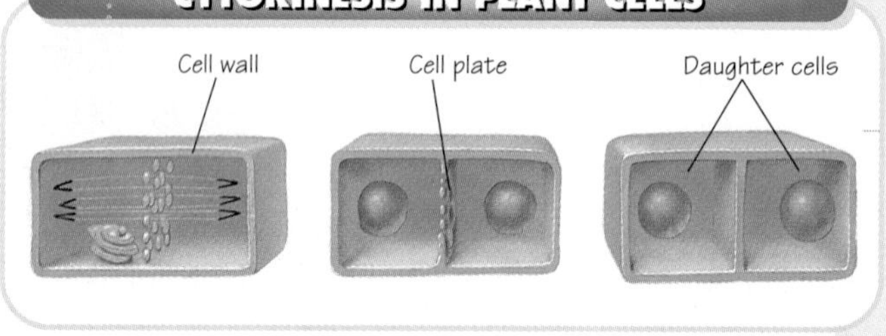

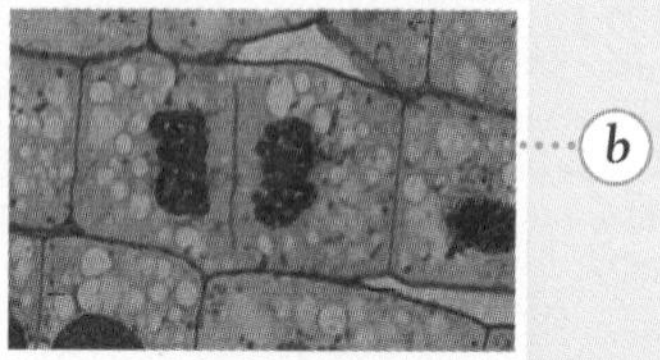

Figure 5–7
(a) In plant cells, a structure called the cell plate forms midway between the two nuclei. The cell plate grows gradually outward until a new cell wall appears between the daughter cells.
(b) In this plant cell, the cell plate has almost completely fused with the cell wall, creating two independent daughter cells (magnification: 1200X).

Section Review 5–2

1. **Describe** the four phases of mitosis.
2. **Compare** the process of cytokinesis in plant and animal cells.
3. **Critical Thinking—Sequencing** Describe the order of events in the process of mitosis.

TEACHER SUPPORT

Facts and Figures

Here are a few facts and figures about the cell cycle and cell division.

• In a mouse cell, a complete cell cycle takes about 22 hours. Of that time, the G_1 phase takes about 9 hours, the S phase takes about 10 hours, the G_2 phase takes about 2 hours, and the M phase takes about 1 hour.

• In a bean cell, a complete cell cycle takes about 19 hours. Of that time, the G_1 phase takes about 5 hours, the S phase takes about 7 hours, the G_2 phase takes about 5 hours, and the M phase takes about 2 hours.

• The minimum time for mitosis to occur in a cell is about 10 minutes.

• In an adult human being, about 2 trillion cell divisions occur in every 24-hour period, which translates to about 25 million divisions per second.

Cell Specialization and Organization

GUIDE FOR READING

- **Define** cell specialization.
- **List** the four levels of organization in a multicellular organism.

MINI LAB

- **Observe** the characteristics of blood.

EACH OF US BEGAN LIFE AS A single cell. By the time we were born, that single cell had gone through millions of cell divisions—proof of the importance of mitosis. A multicellular organism, however, is much more than a large group of cells, in the same way that a society is much more than just a large group of people. And just as a society is made up of individuals or groups of individuals who have certain specialties, each cell, or group of cells in a multicellular organism, has a different specialty. These different specialties allow the organism to continue functioning.

Specialized Cells

Cells in a multicellular organism tend to be specialized. **Cell specialization means that specific cells are uniquely suited to carry out specific functions.** Some cells may be specialized to move, while other cells may specialize in responding to the environment. Still other cells may make products that the rest of the organism needs.

What gives a cell the ability to do one job so much better than other cells? Let's take a close look at two important specialists from the hundreds of different types of cells in the human body.

Macrophages

In every large society there is a need for law and order, for protection. The trillions of cells in our bodies have a similar need, and one type of cell that provides this protection is the macrophage. The macrophages travel throughout the body in the bloodstream.

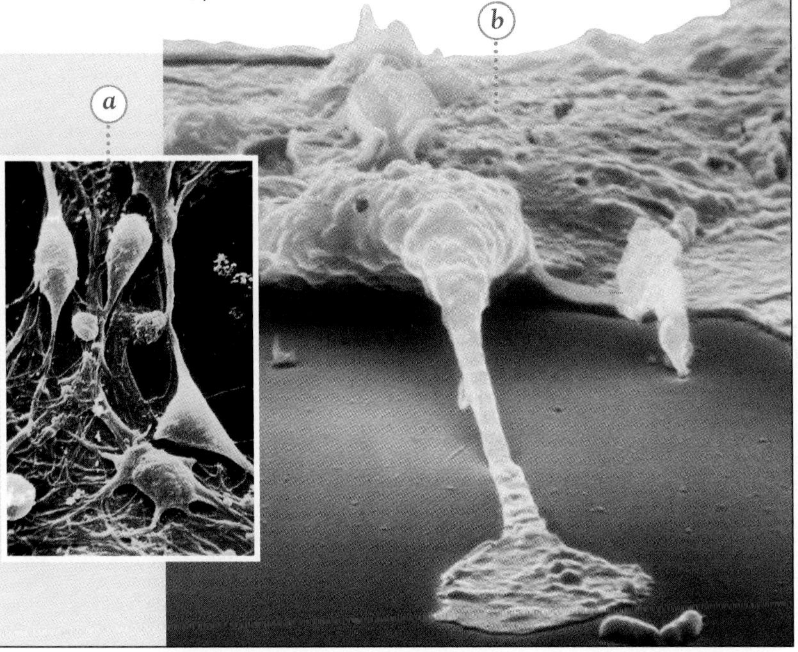

Figure 5–8 The human body has hundreds of specialized cells. (a) This false-color scanning electron micrograph shows the intricate network of neurons that carry messages throughout the human body. (magnification: 235X). (b) Macrophages help protect the body from disease. In this photograph, a macrophage is about to engulf a bacterium (magnification: 4000X).

TEACHER SUPPORT

Background Information

The specialized cells known as macrophages are one kind of the body's white blood cells, or leukocytes. An important way that they protect the body is through phagocytosis, the process by which a cell engulfs and destroys a foreign cell. A macrophage accomplishes this destruction by wrapping the foreign cell in a membrane-enclosed sac known as a vacuole. Once the invader is engulfed, lysosomes fuse with the vacuole and release enzymes that digest the invader. The process is quite similar to that used by paramecia to engulf and digest food particles. Students observed this process in the MINI LAB of Section 3–3, A Colorful Paramecium, on page 64.

SECTION 5-3

Cell Specialization and Organization

Performance Objectives

- Explain how cells are specialized in multicellular organisms.
- Describe the four levels of organization in a multicellular organism.

Mini Lab Skill: Observing

1 ENGAGE

Ideas Through Images

Have students examine Figure 5–8, read the caption, and answer the following questions.

- **What types of specialized cells are shown?** (Neurons and macrophages.)
- **What different functions do they carry out?** (Neurons send messages throughout the body, while macrophages protect the body from disease.)
- **How many other specialized cells do you think are in the body?** (Students should suggest that there are hundreds or thousands of different kinds.)
- **Do neurons work together in a system within the body?** (Most students will know that neurons function within the nervous system.)
- **What do specialized cells allow a multicellular organism to do that a unicellular organism cannot do?** (Most students should suggest that in general such cells allow the multicellular organism to carry out more complex tasks than a unicellular organism can.)

2 EXPLORE

MINI LAB Observing

Teacher Notes

- For time required and materials needed, see page 100b.
- Photographs of blood cells can serve as substitutes for prepared slides.
- Tell students that the macrophages shown in Figure 5–8 are a type of white blood cells.

Answers to Analyze and Conclude

1. White blood cells must be able to increase in number to meet a threat of invading organisms and therefore must have nuclei to reproduce.
2. A doctor might conclude that the patient has an infection in the body, since the number of white blood cells has increased to meet that threat.
3. Yes, red and white blood cells are similar cells that work together to perform similar functions, that is, to carry out the functions of blood.

Skills Trace
Observing
- Focus p. 110
- Practice p. 111
- Assess p. 118

3 TEACH

Ideas Through Images

Have students examine Figure 5–9, read the caption, and answer the following questions.

- **What are specialized cells?** (Cells that are uniquely suited to carry out specific functions.)
- **What are the levels of organization shown here in order of complexity?** (Specialized cells, tissues, organs, and organ systems.)

MINI LAB .... Observing ....

Red, White, and Blood

PROBLEM *Observe the characteristics of blood.*

PROCEDURE

1. Obtain a prepared slide of human blood.
2. Use the low-power objective to examine the slide under a microscope. Switch to high power.
3. Locate a field in which you can see both red and white blood cells. The nuclei of the white blood cells will appear purple due to the stain.

ANALYZE AND CONCLUDE

1. Why do you think is it necessary for white blood cells to have a nucleus? Why don't the red blood cells have a nucleus?
2. When an infection is present, the number of white blood cells increases. If your blood has a higher than normal percentage of white blood cells, what might a doctor conclude?
3. Should blood be considered a tissue? Explain why.

At the site of a wound or an infection, macrophages appear in great numbers and begin to disarm the "bad guys"—bacteria and other invading organisms. The cytoplasm of a macrophage is filled with specialized granules containing chemicals that attack the cell walls of bacteria. If these chemicals fail, the cell membrane of a macrophage may then surround the invader and completely engulf it. Within a few minutes the bacterium has been taken inside the macrophage, and in a few hours it is completely destroyed.

☑ *Checkpoint* Why are macrophages specialized cells? 1

Neurons

Communication is important in any large group of individuals, and it is just as important in a large group of cells. Without communication, one hand literally wouldn't know what the other hand was doing. How do cells in different parts of the body communicate? One of the most important ways is by means of the nervous system, a specialized network of cells that works almost like a network of telephone operators.

Some of these message-carrying cells, or neurons, are among the longest and thinnest cells in the body. Rapid movements of charged molecules across their cell membranes produce electrical impulses. These impulses carry messages from one end of the cell to the next, helping to relay information and control movements. These impulses also coordinate the activities of the most complicated society of cells in the entire world—the human brain.

Levels of Organization

Cell specialization is only part of the story of how a multicellular organism is put together. Many jobs are far too complex for a single cell to handle on its own. Groups of specialized cells may be necessary in such cases.

Tissues

A **tissue** is a group of similar cells that perform similar functions. The two specialized cells that you have just read about are, in fact, members of a tissue. The cells that protect the body from infection are one part of a tissue—blood. The cells that carry impulses from one neuron to the next are part of nerve tissue.

Organs

Although hundreds or even thousands of cells may make up a tissue, some tasks are too complicated to be carried

TEACHER SUPPORT

Ecology Note

In general, larger size would seem an advantageous adaptation from an evolutionary perspective. After all, a larger organism could eat a smaller organism. Thus, over time one might expect to see an increase in size among unicellular organisms. That did occur to a certain extent, but then cells hit the barrier that is discussed in Section 5–1, the problem of surface-area-to-volume ratio. The answer to this problem was multicellularity. Organisms could increase in size not through an increase in cell size but by cells' cooperating and specializing in a multicellular organism.

Although large size does have its advantages, that does not mean that larger organisms outnumber smaller. Actually, the opposite is true. In any given habitat, a general rule is that the larger the organism, the smaller its population.

out by just one type of tissue. In these cases, an **organ,** or a group of tissues that work together to perform a specific function, is needed. Each muscle in your body is an individual organ, and so are each of your eyes. These organs contain many different tissues that work together to carry out an essential task, such as movement or vision.

Organ Systems

In many cases, even a complex organ is not sufficient to carry out a series of specialized tasks. In these cases, an **organ system,** or a group of organs, performs several closely related functions. For example, the organs of the digestive system all work together to digest the food that you eat. There are eleven major organ systems in the human body, such as the muscular system, the skeletal system, and the nervous system.

The four levels of organization—cells, tissues, organs, and organ systems—are the same for nearly all multicellular organisms. The division of labor among the cells in these levels is one of the things that makes multicellular life possible. Specialized cells, such as nerve and muscle cells, are able to exist precisely because other cells are specialized to obtain the food and oxygen that these cells need. This overall specialization and interdependence is one of the remarkable characteristics of living things.

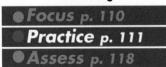

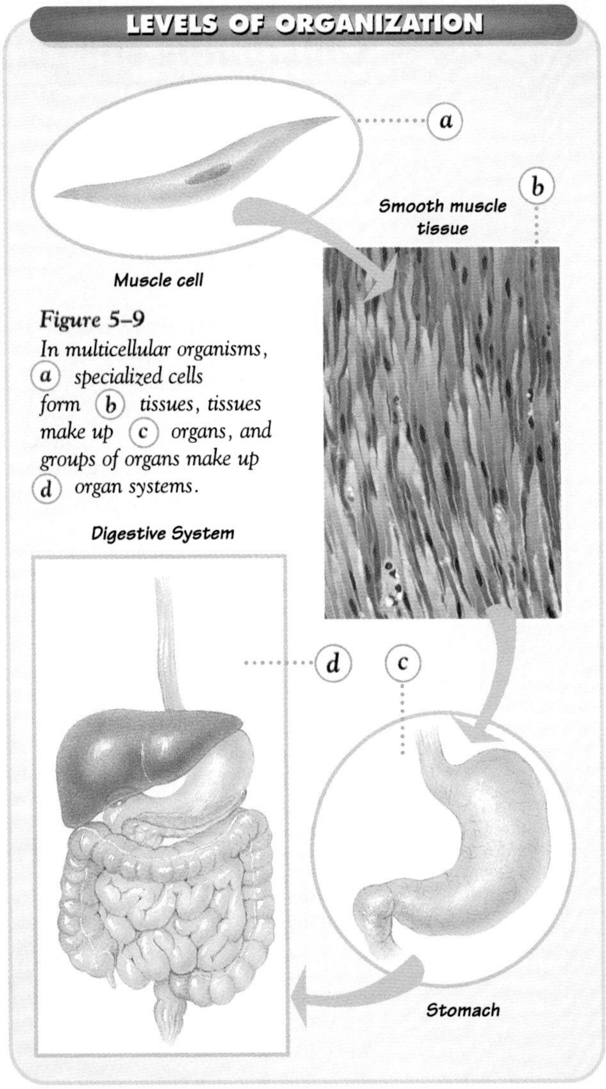

Figure 5–9
In multicellular organisms, (a) specialized cells form (b) tissues, tissues make up (c) organs, and groups of organs make up (d) organ systems.

Section Review 5–3

1. **Define** cell specialization.
2. **List** the four levels of organization in multicellular organisms.
3. **Critical Thinking—Applying Concepts** Why is blood classified as a tissue?
4. **MINI LAB** **Observe** the characteristics of blood.

Discussion

Initiate a discussion of how multicellularity depends on a division of labor among cells and the four levels of organization. Point out that an increasing level of complexity allows organisms to accomplish increasingly more complex tasks, such as distributing oxygen through the circulatory system to all the cells of the body so that they can perform respiration.

4 ASSESS

Quick Check

Have students make a Venn diagram of the four levels of organization in multicellular organisms. Such a diagram should be a series of larger and larger circles, each surrounding the previous one. Ask that students label these circles with a term and a brief definition.

Checkpoint

1 Macrophages are specialized cells because they are uniquely suited to provide protection in the body, either through chemicals that can attack the cell walls of bacteria or by engulfing invaders and destroying them.

Section Review 5–3

1. Cell specialization means that specific cells are uniquely suited to carry out specific functions.

2. Cells, tissues, organs, and organ systems.

3. It consists of a group of similar cells—red and white blood cells—that perform similar functions.

4. A typical response should describe blood as consisting of two similar types of cells—red and white blood cells—in a liquid medium.

Skills Trace

Observing

- Focus p. 110
- Practice p. 111
- Assess p. 118

Learning Modality

Auditory Learning Have students respond orally to questions about levels of organization within the human body. For example, ask a student to name an organ and then ask the student to explain the levels of organization above and below that organ.

Ancillary Support

The resources below can be used to support your teaching strategy for these two pages.

LM Observing Specialized Cells, #9
TR Apply: Different Strokes for Different Folks
BL Inquiry Activity: It's All Organized

SECTION 5–4

Controlling the Cell Cycle

Performance Objective
• Discuss how cyclins regulate the different phases of the cell cycle.

1 ENGAGE

Ideas Through Images

Have students examine Figure 5–10, read the caption, and answer the following questions.

• **Why would the cell cycle have to be controlled by anything?** (If the cell cycle were not controlled, the phases would occur haphazardly.)

• **What is cyclin?** (Cyclin is one of the proteins that can control the cell cycle.)

• **How do you think a protein could control the cycle?** (Students' responses may vary. Some might suggest that a phase of the cell cycle would begin when that protein built up to a certain level within the cell.)

2 EXPLORE

Inquiry Activity

Designing an Experiment

A Regulation Cycle

Ask students how they would go about discovering whether a certain substance within a cell regulated the time at which the cell entered each phase in the cell cycle. Have groups of students design experiments that could validate the hypothesis that Substance X was just such a cell-cycle regulator. Students' experiments could designate Substance X as the variable and either limit or increase its production in the cell, observing how such differences in level affect the cell cycle.

SECTION 5–4 BRANCHING OUT In Depth

Controlling the Cell Cycle

GUIDE FOR READING

• **Describe** the role of cyclin in the cell cycle.

CELL GROWTH AND DIVISION in a large organism are carefully regulated. This means that something must control whether a cell is allowed to divide or whether it can enter the next phase of the cell cycle. For years biologists wondered what that something might be. At long last, it seems as though they have the answer.

Nearly 20 years ago, scientists were trying to find out whether there was a signal that caused the egg cell of a frog to begin dividing after it was fertilized by a sperm cell. They discovered that the dividing cell contained a protein that would cause a spindle to form if it was injected into a nondividing egg cell. To their surprise, they discovered that the amount of this protein in the cell rose and fell in timing with the cell cycle.

Cyclins and the Cell Cycle

Scientists called the protein that caused a spindle to form **cyclin,** because the amount of this protein changed in time with the cell cycle. It turned out that cyclin was not just found in frogs. And injections of cyclin could cause just about any cell to enter mitosis!

Cyclins regulate the timing of the cell cycle in all eukaryotic cells that have been studied—from tiny yeast cells to humans. It just so happens that there are many different cyclins, including those that regulate different phases of the cell cycle. For example, the cyclins that were first discovered in frogs are now called M-phase cyclins because they regulate the entry of the cell into mitosis.

As a cell goes through the cell cycle, cyclin is made at a fairly constant rate and gradually builds up inside the cell. When the cyclin

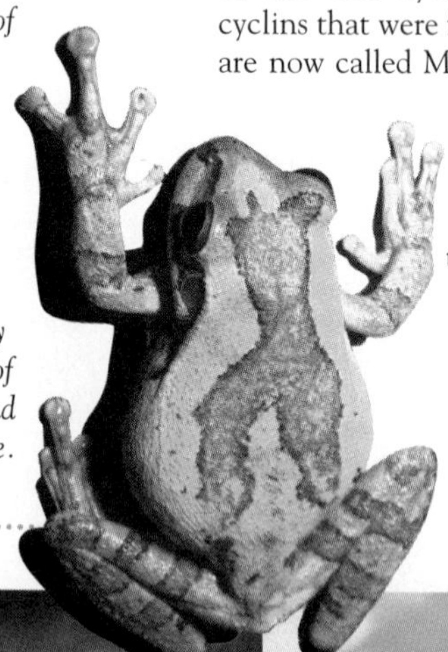

(a)

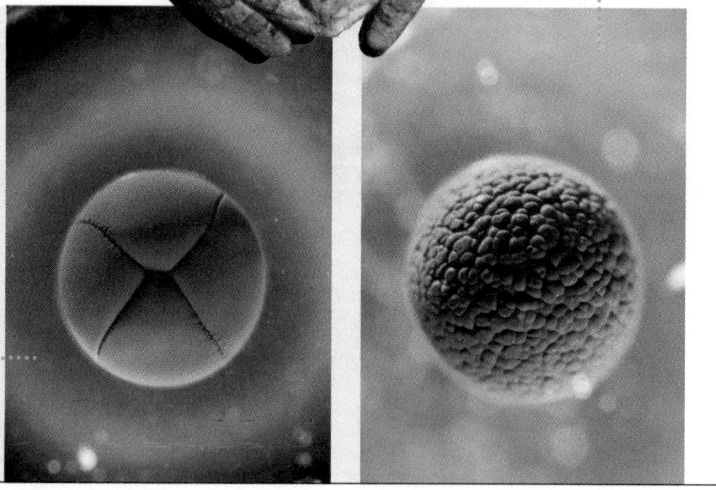

(b) (c)

Figure 5–10
Cyclin, one of the proteins that can control the cell cycle, was first discovered in (a) a frog's cells. This protein causes (b) a fertilized frog egg to undergo cell division, forming a few cells (magnification: 20X) and (c) then forming many more cells (magnification: 20X).

TEACHER SUPPORT

Background Information

The level of cyclins in a cell is not the only factor that regulates the cell cycle. Other factors include temperature, pH, the proximity of other cells, the availability of nutrients, and the kind of cell it is. A mature neuron never divides, whereas white blood cells will divide at a rapid rate when needed by the body to attack invading cells.

In cancer cells, regulation of the cell cycle has been lost for some reason. Such cells move through the cell cycle more rapidly than normal cells, and this fact can be utilized in the treatment of cancer. Radiation treatment, for example, can be effective because cells in the G_1 phase are not likely to be damaged by radiation. Normal cells pause for long periods in the G_1 phase, whereas cancer cells do not.

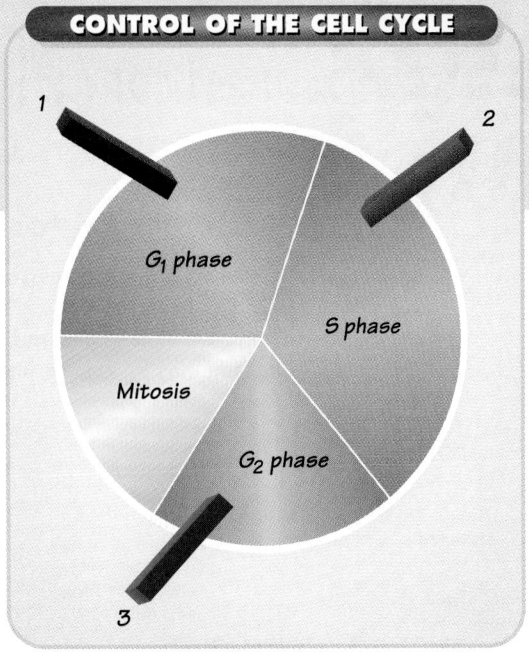

Figure 5–11
Cyclin can control the cell cycle at each of three main points: late in the G_1 phase, early in the S phase, and near the border between the G_2 phase and mitosis.

level reaches a critical point, it triggers the cell to enter mitosis. Then something remarkable happens. Once the cell has entered mitosis, it destroys nearly all its cyclin. This means that the cell must start to make cyclin again before it can enter mitosis a second time. The time it takes for a cell to make more cyclin determines how long it will take the cell to move through the cell cycle.

☑ **Checkpoint** What is cyclin? ①

The Cell Cycle and Cancer

You may recall that the ability to control cell growth is vital to an organism's survival, and that the cell cycle is the point at which growth is actually controlled. Cancer cells do not respond to the usual signals that keep other cells from growing uncontrollably. Very often, the reason they don't respond to the signals is because of a defect in cell cycle regulation. Cyclin and the proteins that interact with it have turned out to be the master proteins in regulating the cell cycle.

Figure 5–12
CAREER TRACK
Histologic technicians, who prepare tissue samples for further study, generally work in laboratories and hospitals.

Section Review 5–4

1. **Describe** the role of cyclin in the cell cycle.
2. **BRANCHING OUT ACTIVITY** Cyclin is a protein that regulates the timing of the cell cycle. Taxol is a powerful drug derived from the Pacific yew (*Taxus bervifolia*), an evergreen that grows in the northwestern United States. Research the role of taxol in fighting uncontrolled cell growth. **Communicate** your findings in a brief written summary.

3 TEACH

Ideas Through Images

Have students examine Figure 5–11, read the caption, and answer the following questions.

- **What can cyclin do besides regulate the entry of a cell into mitosis?** (It can control the cell cycle in the G_1 phase, the S phase, and the G_2 phase.)
- **What might happen if a cell were unable to produce cyclin?** (The cell might not be able to proceed from one phase of the cell cycle to the next, or to divide.)

4 ASSESS

Quick Check

Ask students to return to the table of the cell cycle they began at the end of Section 5–1 and place a notation at the appropriate places where cyclin controls the cycle.

Section Review 5–4

1. Cyclin regulates the timing of the cell cycle in eukaryotic cells, such as by regulating the entry of cells into mitosis.

2. Students should find that Taxol is the trade name of a drug whose generic name is paclitaxel. This drug is used in the management of ovarian cancer by attaching to the cell's microtubules and interfering with their function. That interference inhibits mitosis, thus causing the death of rapidly dividing cells, malignant cells in particular.

☑ Checkpoint

① Cyclin is a protein that can regulate the timing of the cell cycle.

Learning Modality

Visual Learning Ask students to make a sketch of the cell cycle using the visual essay on page 107 as a model. Then ask that they add arrows and labels in the sketch where cyclins regulate the cycle.

Ancillary Support

The resources below can be used to support your teaching strategy for these two pages.

TR Enrich: Abnormal Cell Growth
BL Inquiry Activity: Running Around in Cycles

CHAPTER 5

Laboratory Investigation

Mitosis

Before the Lab

1. Prepare the garlic cloves by piercing each clove on three sides with toothpicks, and then suspending the clove in a small glass of water so that the lower tip is in the water. Prepare 2 cloves per class, about three or four days ahead of time.
2. Garlic root tips seem to divide most abundantly at about noon or midnight. If your class meets close to noon, harvest fresh root tips directly into acid alcohol. Otherwise, collect the tips as close to noon as possible, and then fix them in 70% ethyl alcohol for later use.
3. Prepare the acid alcohol under a fume hood. Wear rubber gloves and goggles. Pour 1 part concentrated HCl into 1 part 95% ethyl alcohol. The solution may be kept in a closed container for later use.

Pre-Lab Discussion

Have students read the entire procedure for this investigation. Then ask them the following questions.

What is the purpose of this investigation? (To observe cells in the M phase of the cell cycle.)

When do a cell's chromosomes first appear as thick, threadlike structures? (In prophase, the first phase of mitosis.)

What are the phases of mitosis? (Prophase, metaphase, anaphase, and telophase.)

Review with students the major events of each of the phases of mitosis. Have them reexamine the visual essay on page 107 before beginning this lab.

Skills Development

Students will use the following skills while completing the laboratory investigation: measuring, observing, communicating, and drawing conclusions.

CHAPTER 5

Laboratory Investigation

Mitosis

The tip of a root is a good place to look for cells that are in the process of dividing because roots grow at the tip. In this investigation, you will prepare slides from garlic root tips. If your preparation is a good one, you may be able to find all the phases of mitosis.

Problem

How many phases of mitosis can you **observe** in a plant cell?

Materials (per group)

- forceps
- garlic root tips
- 2 watch glasses or Petri dish covers
- 50% hydrochloric acid-50% ethyl alcohol solution (HCl-EtOH solution)
- Carnoy's fixative
- microscope slide
- scalpel
- medicine dropper
- aceto-orcein stain
- coverslip
- paper towel
- compound microscope

Procedure

1. **Using the forceps, obtain a garlic root tip from your instructor. Place the root tip in a watch glass.**
2. **Carefully pour HCl-EtOH solution over the root tip so that the entire tip is immersed in the solution. CAUTION: *If the solution touches your skin, wash the area immediately with running water.* Soak the root tip in the solution for 5 to 6 minutes.**
3. **Using the forceps, transfer the root tip to the second watch glass. Pour Carnoy's fixative over the root tip. Leave the root tip in the fixative for 3 minutes.**
4. **Using the forceps, transfer the tip to a microscope slide.**

Safety Tips

- Caution students to be very careful when pouring the hydrochloric acid–ethyl alcohol solution. Tell them that if the solution touches their skin, they should immediately wash the area with running water. Ask them to inform you immediately if there is any spill or any other problem with the solution.
- Caution students to be careful when using the scalpel and immediately inform you if there is an accidental cut.
- Inform students that the aceto-orcein stain will stain their clothing so they should be careful when using the medicine dropper.

5. Holding the root tip with the forceps, use the scalpel to cut off 2 cm from the root tip. CAUTION: *Be careful when using sharp instruments.* Discard the rest of the root tip.

6. Use the medicine dropper to add just enough aceto-orcein stain to cover the remaining tip. CAUTION: *Aceto-orcein will stain clothing.* Leave the root tip in the stain for 5 minutes.

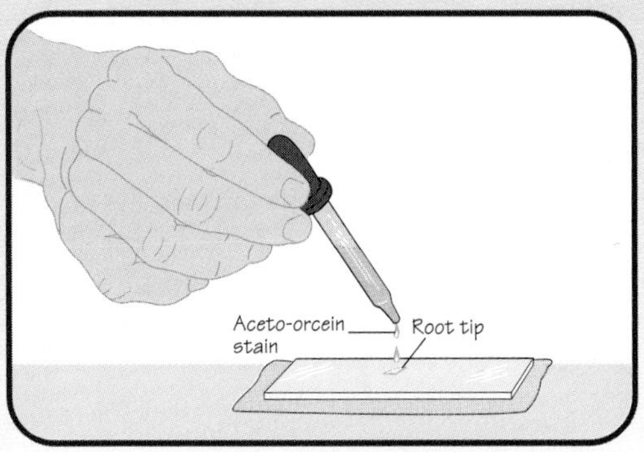

7. Place a clean coverslip over the root tip. Place a folded paper towel on a flat surface and fold the paper towel over the slide. Gently press down on the paper towel with your thumb so the paper towel will absorb the excess liquid.

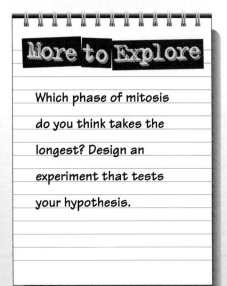

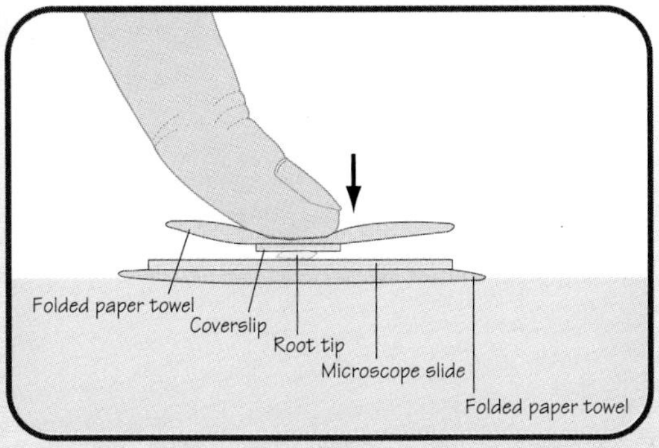

8. Place the slide under low power on your microscope. Focus the microscope. Then scan the slide until you find some stained cells.

9. Switch the microscope to high power and locate as many phases of mitosis as you can.

Observations

1. Sketch any cells that are in a phase of mitosis.
2. Label the sketch with the name of the appropriate phase.

Analysis and Conclusions

1. How do the cells that are in a phase of mitosis differ from cells that are not dividing?
2. What was the purpose of the hydrochloric acid-ethyl alcohol solution? (*Hint:* Consider how plant cells are held together.)
3. Did the aceto-orcein stain one part of the cell more than any other? If so, which one?
4. In which phase of mitosis were most of the cells you observed? Why do you think this was so?

More to Explore

Which phase of mitosis do you think takes the longest? Design an experiment that tests your hypothesis.

Teaching Strategies

1. Demonstrate how to slice off 2 cm from the root tip while holding it with the forceps.
2. Remind students to use the low power on the microscope first in order to find some stained cells to observe at high power.

Answers to Observations

1. Students should make several sketches and at least one for each of the four phases of mitosis.
2. Students' labels for each sketch should match the phase shown in that sketch.

Answers to Analysis and Conclusions

1. Most students should be able to recognize those cells that are in mitosis by observing the visible chromosomes and by noting a lack of nuclear membrane.
2. Students should infer that this solution serves to dissolve the layer between cells that holds them together.
3. Students should observe that the aceto-orcein stains chromosomes and the nuclei but not the cytoplasm or the cell walls.
4. Most students should have observed cells in prophase more frequently than cells in the other three phases—the reason being that prophase is the longest phase of mitosis.

More to Explore

Most students will build upon their answer to question 4 in Analysis and Conclusions and suggest that counting many cells in all phases will give an indirect measurement of which phase is the longest.

CHAPTER 5

Study Guide

Review Strategy

Divide students into groups of two or three and ask them to work together to construct a complex crossword puzzle. Provide each group with an example of a well-done puzzle, such as one from a national magazine or newspaper. Tell them that in their puzzle they can use any of the terms or concepts introduced in the chapter. Each group should construct a puzzle with at least 25 entries. Once the puzzles are completed, make copies and pass them around the class. Have the class choose one or two as the most well done and send those to another class in the school working on the same chapter.

Study Guide

Summarizing Key Concepts

The key concepts in each section of this chapter are listed below to help you review the chapter content. Make sure you understand each concept and its relationship to other concepts and to the theme of this chapter.

5–1 Cell Growth and the Cell Cycle

- As a cell increases in size, its volume increases at a faster rate than its surface area.
- The cell cycle is the period of time from the beginning of one cell division to the beginning of the next.
- Cell division is the process in which the cell divides into two independent cells. In eukaryotic cells, this process is called mitosis.
- There are four stages in the cell cycle—G_1, S, G_2, and M—during which a cell duplicates its contents and divides.

5–2 Cell Division

- The four phases of mitosis are prophase, metaphase, anaphase, and telophase.
- The two identical parts of a chromosome, called chromatids, are attached to each other at a centromere.
- In most cells, the cytoplasm divides as well as the nucleus.

5–3 Cell Specialization and Organization

- Many cells are specialized, or uniquely suited, to carry out specific functions.
- In multicellular organisms, cells are grouped into tissues, organs, and organ systems.

5–4 Controlling the Cell Cycle

- Cyclins are proteins that regulate the timing of the cell cycle.

Reviewing Key Terms

Review the following vocabulary terms and their meaning. Then use each term in a complete sentence.

5–1 Cell Growth and the Cell Cycle

cell cycle
cell division
mitosis

5–2 Cell Division

interphase
prophase
chromatid
centromere
centriole
spindle
metaphase
anaphase
telophase
cytokinesis

5–3 Cell Specialization and Organization

tissue
organ
organ system

5–4 Controlling the Cell Cycle

cyclin

Inquiry-Based Strategy

Have groups of students research the development of a human being before birth. How soon after fertilization does mitosis occur? What causes that mitosis to occur? When do cells begin to become specialized? What kinds of tissues develop and when? When do organs and organ systems develop? Ask that group members work together to complete a report or visual essay that answers these and related questions. Allow students to find out for themselves what kinds of sources contain the information they need.

CHAPTER 5

Recalling Main Ideas

Choose the letter of the answer that best completes the statement or answers the question.

1. When a cell doubles its diameter, its internal volume increases by
   a. 2. **c.** 6.
   b. 4. **d.** 8.
2. G_1, G_2, and S are often called
   a. interphase. **c.** metaphase.
   b. prophase. **d.** telophase.
3. Chromosomes first appear in the longest phase of mitosis, called
   a. cytokinesis. **c.** anaphase.
   b. metaphase. **d.** prophase.
4. Chromosomes line up across the middle of the cell during
   a. prophase. **c.** anaphase.
   b. metaphase. **d.** telophase.
5. Each chromosome contains two strands, called
   a. centromeres. **c.** chromatids.
   b. centrioles. **d.** microtubules.
6. Duplicated chromosomes separate from each other during
   a. prophase. **c.** anaphase.
   b. metaphase. **d.** telophase.
7. The cytoplasm divides during
   a. cytokinesis. **c.** anaphase.
   b. telophase. **d.** metaphase.
8. What regulates the timing of the cell cycle?
   a. cyclin **c.** chromatids
   b. centromeres **d.** centrioles
9. A group of tissues that work together form a
   a. cell. **c.** muscle.
   b. organ. **d.** organ system.

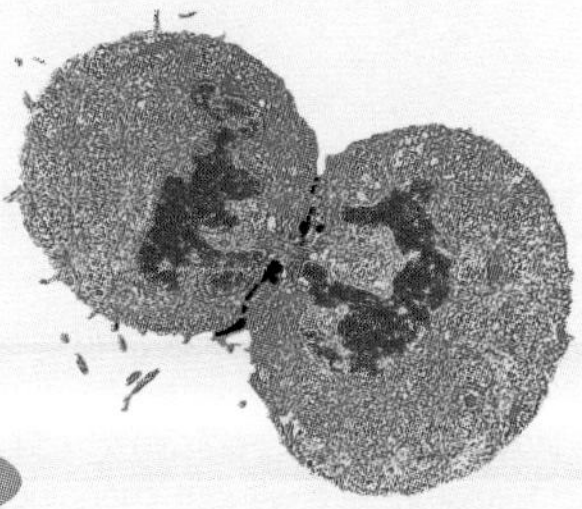

Putting It All Together

Using the information on pages xxx to xxxi, complete the following concept map.

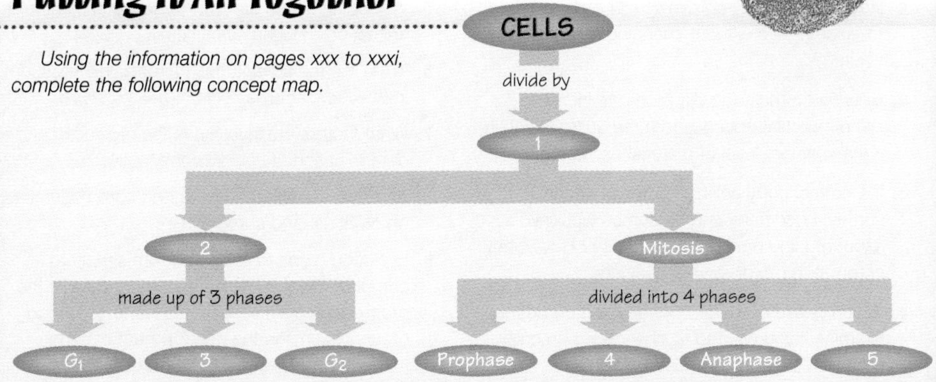

Recalling Main Ideas

1. d
2. a
3. d
4. b
5. c
6. c
7. a
8. a
9. b

Assessment

Reviewing What You Learned

1. The larger a cell gets, the more difficult it is to get things in and out of it.
2. The cell cycle is the period of time from the beginning of one cell division to the beginning of the next.
3. During the S phase, chromosome replication takes place.
4. Cancer is a disease in which some of the body's cells grow uncontrollably.
5. Interphase consists of the G_1 phase, S phase, and G_2 phase.
6. The phases of mitosis are prophase, metaphase, anaphase, and telophase.
7. Chromosomes are composed of DNA molecules and proteins; and during prophase they appear as thick, threadlike figures, each chromosome consisting of two chromatids.
8. Each pair of centrioles serves as a focal point for the growth of a cluster of microtubules that span the nucleus during mitosis.
9. Macrophages provide protection for the cell by destroying invading organisms, either by attacking them with chemicals or by engulfing them.
10. In multicellular organisms, groups of specialized cells work together in a division of labor that includes four levels of organization.
11. Cells, tissues, organs, and organ systems.
12. Cyclins regulate the timing of the cell cycle in eukaryotic cells.

Putting It All Together

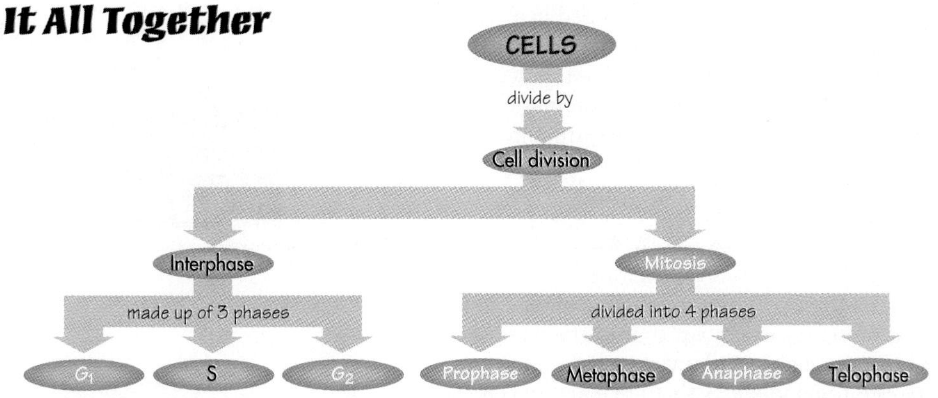

Assessment (continued)

Expanding the Concepts

1. A typical response might suggest that the cell could flatten itself, stretching its cell membrane in the process.
2. If the diameter of a cell doubles, its internal volume becomes 8 times as great, or 2^3. Therefore, if the diameter of a cell triples, its internal volume becomes 27 times as great, or 3^3. To supply its needs, then, the cell would have to increase the diffusion rate by a factor of 27.
3. An organism with 23 pairs of chromosomes would have 46 total chromosomes. Since replication of the chromosomes takes place in the S phase, during the G_2 phase the organism would have 92 chromatids, or double its number of chromosomes.
4. The M phase would be best for examining an organism's chromosomes because during prophase the chromososmes form thick, threadlike structures that are visible under a light microscope.

5. In an animal cell, you can observe the cell membrane pulled in by a ring of filaments, eventually pinching the cytoplasm into two nearly equal parts. In a plant cell, you can observe the formation of a cell plate, which gradually grows until a new cell wall appears between daughter cells.

Skills Trace
Observing
- Focus p. 110
- Practice p. 111
- Assess p. 118

6. Specialized tissues allow organisms to carry out functions that would be far too complex for single cells to handle on their own.
7. Factors involved in the regulation and determination of cell division include the type of organism, the type of cell within the organism, and the cyclin level inside the cell.

8. During interphase, a cell's coded instructions are spread out in the nucleus in a material called chromatin, which consists of DNA molecules and proteins. During the M phase, chromatin condenses to form thick, threadlike structures called chromosomes. Each chromosome consists of two identical strands called chromatids.

Skills Trace
Analyzing
- Focus p. 104
- Practice p. 104
- Assess p. 118

9. As organisms evolve, their cells become specialized in response to the more complex tasks that must be carried out; that is, the complexity of tissues, organs, and organ systems allows an organism to handle jobs that are equal in complexity.

Assessment

Reviewing What You Learned

Answer each of the following in a complete sentence.

1. Why is a large cell less efficient than a small cell?
2. What is the cell cycle?
3. What happens during the S phase of the cell cycle?
4. What is cancer?
5. What three phases make up interphase?
6. What are the phases of mitosis?
7. Describe the chemical and physical structure of a chromosome.
8. What function do centrioles have in a dividing animal cell?
9. What do macrophages do?
10. Describe multicellularity and the division of labor.
11. What are the four levels of organization in a multicellular organism?
12. What functions do cyclins have?

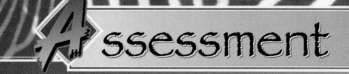

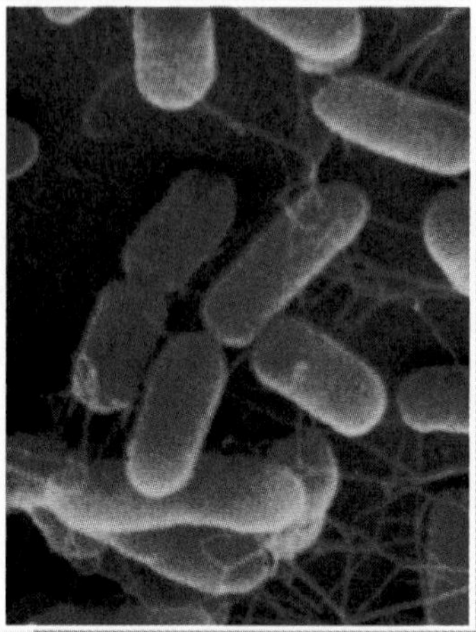

Expanding the Concepts

Discuss each of the following in a brief paragraph.

1. How might a cell improve its cell surface-area-to-volume ratio without changing its actual volume?
2. How much must the diffusion rate increase if a cell of one unit enlarges to three units, maintaining a constant level of material exchange?
3. If a normal body cell had 23 pairs of chromosomes, how many chromosomes would you expect to find during the G_2 phase? How many chromatids? Explain your answers.
4. Which phase of the cell cycle would be best to examine if you wanted to observe a particular organism's chromosomes? Explain why.
5. What differences can you **observe** in plant and animal cells during cytokinesis?
6. What are the advantages of specialized tissues in multicellular organisms?
7. What factors are involved in the regulation and determination of cell division?
8. **Analyze** the differences among chromosomes, chromatids, and chromatin.
9. Evolution tends to progress from simple to complex. How does this statement parallel the progression from cells to tissues to organs to organ systems in the development of living things?

Extending Your Thinking

Use the skills you have developed in this chapter to answer the following.

1. **Interpreting data** During an experiment in which you were calculating the mass of nuclear DNA, you came across a group of cells that contained twice the normal DNA. Suggest what is happening to these cells.
2. **Designing an experiment** Design an experiment in which you could estimate the relative length of each phase of mitosis.
3. **Inferring** Mitosis is often called duplication division. Discuss abnormalities in mitosis that might lead to variation within a species that reproduces asexually.
4. **Using the writing process** Discuss the role of both microtubules and microfilaments in plant and animal mitosis. Write a three- or four-paragraph summary.
5. **Applying concepts** Cancer is characterized by abnormal cell division. Using the information you have learned about cell division, suggest reasons why it is difficult to cure cancer.

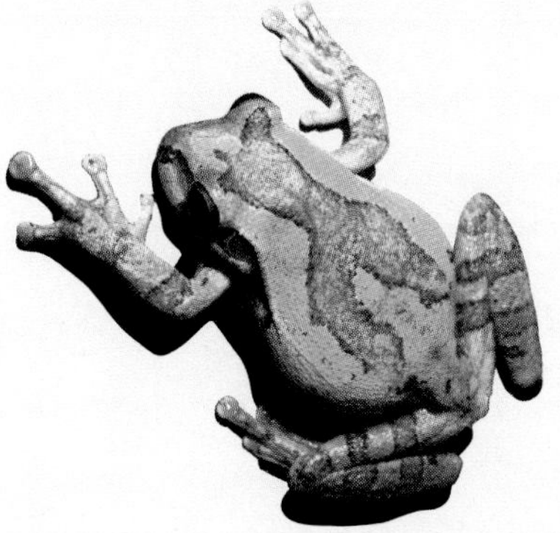

Applying Your Skills

Only Skin Deep

Your body requires new cells to be made to replace worn-out or damaged cells. These new cells must be identical to the original cells. An example of this process occurs any time your skin becomes damaged from sunburn or worn out through normal, everyday washing or aging. How does your body make more of the same kind of skin cells?

1. Obtain 60 cm of yarn, 100 cm of string, and a pair of scissors.
2. Cut four pieces of yarn in 3-cm lengths, four pieces in 5-cm lengths, and four pieces in 7-cm lengths.
3. Cut two 25-cm lengths of string. Then cut the rest as needed.
4. Using the yarn and string, illustrate the processes of interphase and mitosis. Begin with six pieces of yarn—two of each length.
5. Explain to your teacher what each step is and what the yarn and string represent.

• GOING FURTHER •

6. Using glue, paste your yarn representation of one of the phases of the cell cycle onto a piece of poster board. Display your poster in the classroom.

5. Cancer is a disease in which some of the body's cells grow uncontrollably because those cells have lost the ability to regulate the cell cycle. The difficulty in curing cancer lies in finding a way to keep cancer cells from dividing uncontrollably while at the same time allowing normal cells to divide at their normal rate.

Applying Your Skills

Preparation

Provide students with several different colors of yarn and string so that their posters will be clear and interesting. Also provide scissors, glue, and poster board.

Suggestions

1. Have students work in groups of two or three.
2. Ask students to examine illustrations of mitosis in several other textbooks or encyclopedias before they begin making their models.

Scoring Rubric

4 Response is thorough, accurate, and creative; shows an in-depth understanding of science skills, procedures, and concepts.

3 Response is complete, mostly accurate, and original; shows a satisfactory understanding of science skills, procedures, and concepts.

2 Response is mostly complete but includes some inaccuracies; shows an adequate understanding of science skills, procedures, and concepts.

1 Response is only partially complete and has many inaccuracies; shows an incomplete understanding of science skills, procedures, and concepts.

0 Response is mostly incomplete and/or inaccurate; shows a lack of understanding of science skills, procedures, and concepts.

Extending Your Thinking

1. A group of cells that contains twice the normal DNA would most likely be in the G_2 phase of the cell cycle, after the chromosomes have doubled but before mitosis begins.
2. A typical design might suggest observing cell division in numerous live cells and timing the events that occur. Another design might suggest counting the number of cells in each phase of mitosis in a large sample of cells of the same organism. The phase with the highest number could be inferred to have the greatest relative length.
3. Students should suggest that some mistake in the duplication of chromosomes that takes place during the S phase could result in a variation within a species.
4. In discussing the role of microtubules, students should mention the formation of the spindle during prophase and the role of that cluster of microtubules through the next three phases of mitosis. Students might infer that the cell's microfilaments increase in number in preparation for cell division and also play a role in animal cytokinesis.

UNIT 2

Genetics

Introducing the Unit

. . . In Words

Max Delbruck (1906–1981), a German-born American, is known as the founder of molecular biology. He was a pioneer in research on bacteriophages. In 1969, Delbruck won the Nobel Prize in physiology or medicine for his findings regarding the mechanism of replication in viruses and their genetic structure.

Delbruck said that any organism "is but a link in an evolutionary chain of changing forms." He believed the challenge to scientists was to learn how living matter manages to record and perpetuate its experiences. Today we know that the answer is DNA.

• **What do you think it means that cells carry the experiences of their ancestors?** (Help students understand that every cell is linked to its ancestors through the genetic material it inherits.)

• **Do you think cells will continue to change in the future?** (Students may realize that cells will continue to evolve as they adapt to changes in their environment.)

. . . In Pictures

These hybrid roses are a good example of genetics in action because they are so dramatically different from their wild rose ancestors. Wild roses are brambly plants that bear simple, single-layered blossoms in pale colors. Over the past few centuries, humans have bred roses to develop thousands of different varieties in a wide range of forms and colors. After students have examined the photograph, ask the following questions.

• **What kind of flower is shown in the photograph?** (Students should identify the flowers as roses.)

UNIT 2

Genetics

CHAPTERS

"(A)ny living cell carries with it the experiences of a billion years of experimentation by its ancestors."

— Max Delbruck

TEACHER SUPPORT

Unit Discovery Learning Activity

NATURE OR NURTURE?

Stimulate students to begin thinking about genetics by having them develop a list of human traits and consider whether the traits are inherited or influenced by environment. Follow these steps to carry out the activity.

1. Introduce the activity by showing students a photograph of a biological family. Ask how the children are like the parents. Point out that some traits, such as hair color, are inherited, or passed from parents to offspring. Suggest that one of the children in the family is very skilled at gymnastics. Ask students if they think that trait is inherited or influenced by environment.

CAREER TRACK

As you explore the topics in this unit, you will discover many different types of careers associated with biology. Here are a few of these careers:

- Horticulturist
- Genetic Counselor
- Geneticist
- Genetic Engineering Research Assistant

Roses growing in a garden

2. Have students work in small groups and brainstorm for a list of 15 to 20 human traits.
3. Challenge students to consider each trait on their list and make an inference about whether it is inherited or influenced by the environment. Ask students to provide support for their inferences.
4. Have students share their lists. Create a class list and have students reach some consensus about whether each trait is inherited or influenced by the environment. Encourage students to research the traits to make sure their inferences are correct.

By considering the inheritance of human traits and the role the environment plays in the development of individuals, students should begin to recognize and describe concepts of **systems and interactions** and **unity and diversity,** two themes developed in this unit.

- **Why are there so many different kinds of roses?** (Some students may know that humans have bred roses to develop different varieties.)
- **How do you think the quotation from Delbruck relates to the roses in the photograph?** (The modern rose shown is the result of experimentation by humans on its ancestors. Humans selectively bred roses for certain characteristics to develop this outstanding variety. Though it is quite different from its ancestors, the rose is still linked to them through heredity.)

CAREER TRACK

Throughout this unit, you will find a broad range of biology-related careers that vary in educational and training requirements. You may wish to have your students find out more about the following careers:

- Horticulturist, p. 125
- Genetic Counselor, p. 161
- Geneticist, p. 178
- Genetic Engineering Research Assistant, p. 201

Technology

BioVue
Genetics at Cold Spring Harbor Labs
Videodisc Side 2

Go to Chapter 2

Ancillary Support

The resource below can be used to support your teaching strategy for these two pages.

BL Integrating the Media
Unit Discovery Learning Activity

Chapter 6 Introduction to Genetics

Content Management	Student Edition Activities
■ Section 6–1 The Science of Inheritance, pp. 123–130 Parents and Offspring Gregor Mendel Genes Mendel's Principles	MINI LAB: You and Your Genes, p. 130
■ Section 6–2 Meiosis, pp. 131–134 Chromosomes The Phases of Meiosis Meiosis and Genetic Diversity	MINI LAB: Toothpick Meiosis, p. 132 Laboratory Investigation: Mapping a Chromosome, pp. 140–141
■ Section 6–3 Analyzing Inheritance, pp. 135–137 Probability Probability and Genetics	
◆ BRANCHING OUT • In Depth Section 6–4 A Closer Look at Heredity, pp. 138–139 Incomplete Dominance and Codominance Multiple Alleles Polygenic Traits	

■ These sections cover all the necessary content and concepts for a basic course in biology.
◆ This section covers content and concepts that are either applications or extensions of the basic material.

Integration Strategies

SE Mathematics, p. 135
BL Investigating Careers
Involving the Community
Science Through Art

Tech Prep

Teaching strategies appropriate for students who are in technical/vocational programs or who are considering post-secondary technical education can be found on the following **TE** pages: 123, 131.

Assessment Strategies

SE Chapter Review, pp. 142–145
TR Section Reviews
Chapter Test
Performance-Based Assessment
BL Investigating Further
Chapter Review
Practice Test
CTB Chapter 6 Test

Meeting the Standards

Sections 6–1 through 6–4 cover two of the three content standards under **The Molecular Basis of Heredity** as described on page 185 of The National Science Education Standards.

Chapter Planning Guide

Teacher's Edition Activities	Other Activities	Media and Technology
Chapter Discovery Learning Activity, p. 122 **Inquiry Activity:** It Runs in the Family, p. 123 **Investigate:** Cooperative Learning, p. 123 **Inquiry Activity:** The Inheritance of Taste, p. 124 **Activity:** The Parts of a Flower, p. 125 **Investigate:** Role-Playing, p. 126 **Investigate:** Model Building, p. 127 **Investigate:** Long-Term Project, p. 128 **Investigate:** Cooperative Learning, p. 129	**LM** Observing Phenotypes, #12 **TR** **Writing in Biology:** If These Genes Could Talk **Explore:** Marshan Genetics **BL** **Inquiry Activity:** Why Do We Look Like Our Parents?	**BioVue Plus CD-ROMs:** Genetics at Cold Spring Harbor Labs **CD-ROM:** Mendel's Principles of Heredity
Inquiry Activity: The Case of the Missing Genes, p. 131 **Investigate:** Research, p. 131	**TR** **Apply:** Everyone Is Falling Apart **BL** **Inquiry Activity:** Special Cell Division	**CD-ROM:** Meiosis **TB** Visualizing Meiosis, #7
Inquiry Activity: A Flip of the Coin, p. 135 **Investigate:** Cooperative Learning, p. 135	**LM** Investigating Probability, #11 **TR** **Explore:** The Ups and Downs of Probability **BL** **Inquiry Activity:** Practicing Probability	**CD-ROM:** Investigating Heredity
Inquiry Activity: Who's Taller Than Whom?, p. 138 **Investigate:** Long-Term Project, p. 138	**TR** **Enrich:** The Tale of a Cat **BL** **Inquiry Activity:** Testing Genetic Theories	

KEY: SE Student Edition **TE** Teacher's Edition **LM** Laboratory Manual **TR** Teaching Resources **BL** BioLog **TB** Transparency Box **CTB** Computer Test Bank

Materials List

TE Chapter Discovery Learning Activity, p. 122 (15 minutes); several different varieties of the same kind of flower.

TE Investigate: Cooperative Learning, p. 123 (30 minutes); sets of corn cobs showing inheritance of a single trait.

TE Inquiry Activity: The Inheritance of Taste, p. 124 (20 minutes each to develop procedures and share observations); taste test papers such as sodium benzoate and thiourea, control papers.

TE Activity: The Parts of a Flower, p. 125 (30 minutes); flowers such as lilies, knife or scalpel, hand lenses.

TE Investigate: Model Building, p. 127 (30 minutes); beads.

TE Investigate: Long-Term Project, p. 128 (3 weeks); corn seeds, soil, pots.

SE MINI LAB: You and Your Genes, p. 130 (20 minutes); mirror.

TE Inquiry Activity: The Case of the Missing Genes, p. 131 (20 minutes); photographs, diagrams, prepared slides of different kinds of cells in various stages of the cell cycle, microscopes.

SE MINI LAB: Toothpick Meiosis, p. 132 (20 minutes); colored toothpicks or pipe cleaners.

TE Inquiry Activity: A Flip of the Coin, p. 135 (15–20 minutes); coins.

TE Investigate: Cooperative Learning, p. 135 (30 minutes); deck of cards or a die.

TE Investigate: Long-Term Project, p. 138 (3 weeks); soybean seeds, soil, pots.

Introduction to Genetics

Introducing the Chapter

. . . In Pictures

In this family of Irish setters, the puppies have many of the same characteristics as their parent.

- **What differences between the puppies and their parent might change as the puppies grow?** (Possible answers include size and ear shape.)
- **Why don't Irish setters have Dalmatian puppies, or even kittens?** (Accept all logical responses. Some might explain that the egg and sperm from the parents have information that directs the embryo to develop into an Irish setter.)

Teaching Strategy

In the first three sections of this chapter, students will learn about the Mendelian principles of inheritance, the production of gametes in meiosis, and the use of probability to predict the outcome of a genetic cross. In the BRANCHING OUT section, students will study four other types of gene expression. This section gives students a broader understanding of genetics.

BIO JOURNAL

Discuss with students how family members of any organism can look both similar to and different from one another. Challenge students to think about biological processes that might cause these similarities and differences. Also point out that the environment can cause differences. Instruct students to keep their entries in their portfolios.

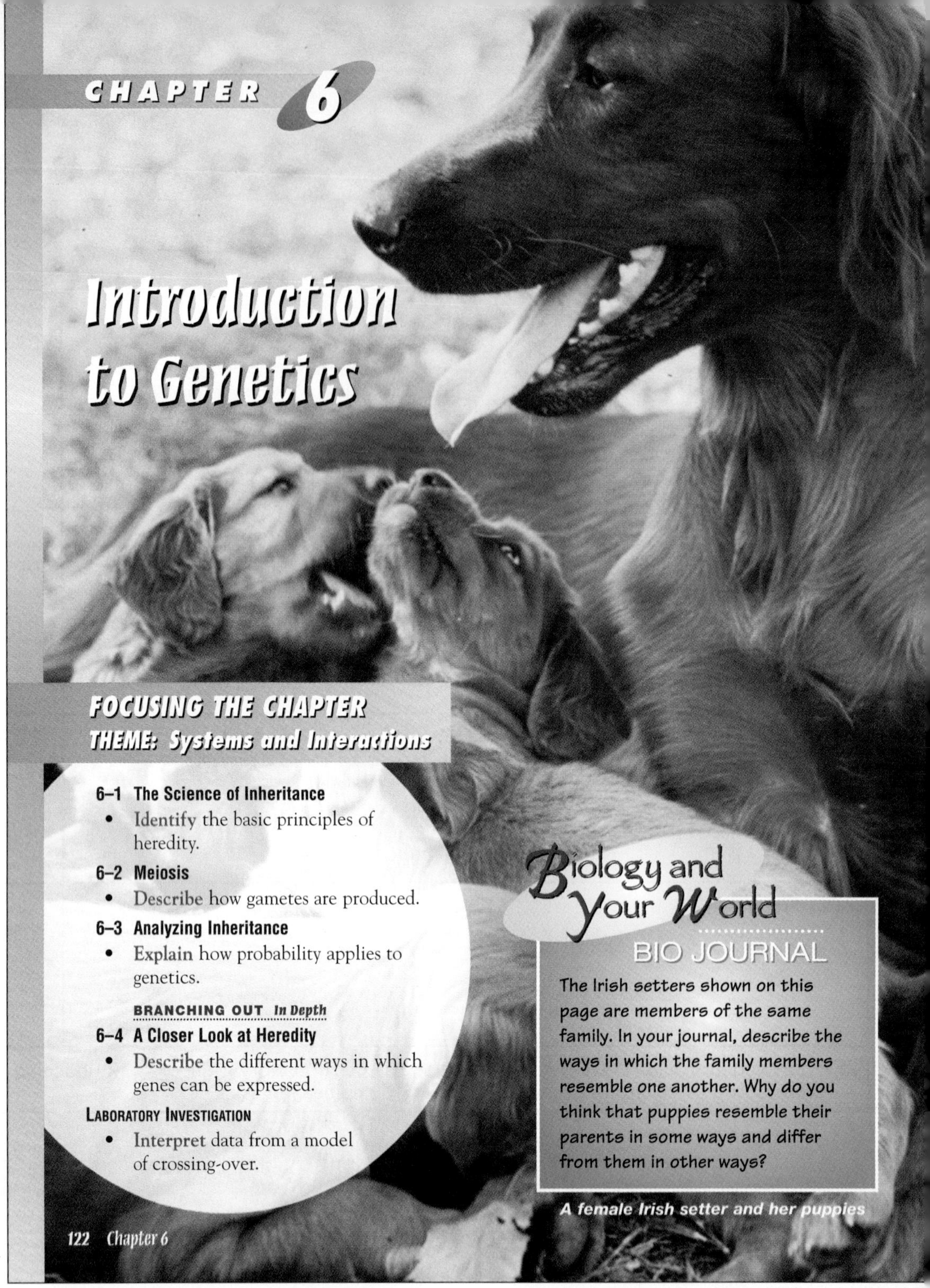

CHAPTER 6

Introduction to Genetics

FOCUSING THE CHAPTER THEME: *Systems and Interactions*

6–1 The Science of Inheritance
- Identify the basic principles of heredity.

6–2 Meiosis
- Describe how gametes are produced.

6–3 Analyzing Inheritance
- Explain how probability applies to genetics.

BRANCHING OUT *In Depth*

6–4 A Closer Look at Heredity
- Describe the different ways in which genes can be expressed.

LABORATORY INVESTIGATION
- Interpret data from a model of crossing-over.

Biology and Your World

BIO JOURNAL

The Irish setters shown on this page are members of the same family. In your journal, describe the ways in which the family members resemble one another. Why do you think that puppies resemble their parents in some ways and differ from them in other ways?

A female Irish setter and her puppies

TEACHER SUPPORT

Chapter Discovery Learning Activity

Display several different varieties of the same type of flower, such as carnations or petunias. Instruct students to design a chart in which they list characteristics of the flowers that are the same and those that are different. Invite students to share their observations with the class. Discuss reasons why they think the same type of flower can have different characteristics. Relate the similarities of the different flower varieties to the similarities of the Irish setter family in the chapter opening photograph. Explain that the same biological processes cause parents and offspring to have both similar and different characteristics.

The Science of Inheritance

SECTION 6–1

GUIDE FOR READING

- **Define** heredity and **identify** the units of heredity.
- **Explain** the principles of dominance, segregation, and independent assortment.

MINI LAB

- **Classify** dominant and recessive traits.

HAVE YOU EVER WONDERED why offspring resemble their parents? For example, why will puppies grow up to look like the adult dogs that produced them? Why will new maple trees grow from the seeds of adult maple trees?

If you have asked questions such as these, you are not alone. Since the beginning of recorded history, people have wondered why humans, animals, and plants grow up the way they do.

Parents and Offspring

Offspring resemble their parents because of their **heredity**—their biological inheritance. **An organism's heredity is the set of characteristics it receives from its parents.** Today, the study of heredity is known as **genetics.** As you will discover, genetics is one of the most important and useful branches of biology. By applying the principles of genetics, farmers are raising more useful animals and plants, physicians are preventing and treating many diseases, and scientists are discovering some of the secrets of life on our planet.

For thousands of years, people thought that the heredity of a living thing was merely a blend of the characteristics of its parents. After all, most animals look a little bit like the mother and a little bit like the father. In addition, if a big animal and a small animal produced offspring, the offspring would typically be medium-sized—a blend of the sizes of the two parents.

Figure 6–1
The same basic principles of genetics apply to a wide variety of organisms, including flowering plants, such as (a) this maple tree, and animals, such as (b) humans and (c) grizzly bears.

TEACHER SUPPORT

Managing Classroom Diversity

TECH PREP STUDENTS
To help students understand the relevance of genetics to various career fields, have them create a word map to show specific careers that may require knowledge of genetic concepts. Encourage students to use resource materials from the library or guidance office or interview guidance or vocational counselors to help them complete their maps. Students should discover that genetics is relevant to some careers in the fields of agribusiness, biotechnology, health care, and natural resources.

SECTION 6–1

The Science of Inheritance

Performance Objectives

- Explain what heredity is and tell what role genes play in inheritance.
- Relate the principles of dominance, segregation, and independent assortment to heredity.

Mini Lab Skill: Classifying

1 ENGAGE

Inquiry Activity

Observing

It Runs in the Family
Ask students what characteristics they think are common in families. (Some examples include hair color, eye color, dimples, and chin shape.) Challenge students to develop a procedure to identify and observe which family characteristics tend to be similar in both parents and children. They should also devise a way to present their data to the class in a clear and creative manner.

2 EXPLORE

Investigate

Cooperative Learning Give student pairs a set of corn cobs that show the inheritance of a single trait, such as purple or yellow kernels, and smooth or rough kernels. Challenge pairs to work together to form inferences that explain why the offspring look like only one parent, not both. Students should brainstorm for a list of inferences, and then select one or two they think are best. Randomly choose a member of each pair to report its inferences to the class.

Inquiry Activity

Observing

The Inheritance of Taste

Ask students if they think the characteristics of taste are similar or different in members of a family. To help students answer this question, give them taste papers, such as sodium benzoate and thiourea, as well as control papers that do not contain any taste chemicals. Instruct students to develop a procedure in which they use the taste papers to answer the question. Remind them to develop a method for collecting and organizing their observations. Students should analyze their observations to find any similarities or differences in the taste responses within families. (Most people will detect a bitter taste with thiourea. Sodium benzoate may taste sweet or salty, or have no taste.)

3 TEACH

Discussion

Initiate a class discussion about the importance of controlled experiments and systematic procedures to scientific research. Throughout the discussion, emphasize these points.

- Mendel was one of the first scientists to analyze his data systematically, using a mathematical approach.
- Mendel was successful because he studied only one inherited characteristic at a time. Many scientists of that era were studying more than one characteristic or were not using true-breeding stocks.

Have students imagine what it would be like if humans had only one of two hair colors: brown and blond.

- **If both parents had brown hair, predict what the hair color of their offspring would be. If both parents had blond hair?** (Brown hair; blond hair.)
- **If one parent had brown hair and the other had blond hair, predict the hair color of their offspring?** (There are no individuals with light-brown hair. Observations would have to be made to see the hair color of the offspring.)

Figure 6–2 *Although organisms resemble their parents in many ways, sometimes their characteristics are quite different. Deer with brown fur were the parents of this white deer, called an albino.*

Is heredity really that simple? No, it isn't. For example, two deer with brown fur were the parents of the white deer shown in **Figure 6–2.** The white fur of this deer could hardly be described as a blend of the colors of both of its parents' fur.

☑ ***Checkpoint*** What is heredity? ①

Gregor Mendel

For heredity to be truly explained, it needed to be studied carefully and objectively. And in Europe in the mid 1800s—about the same time as the Civil War in the United States—one man did just that. His name was Gregor Mendel.

Gregor Mendel was born in 1822. He lived for most of his life in the town of Brno, which is now part of the Czech Republic. After becoming a priest, he spent several years studying science and mathematics at the University of Vienna. When Mendel left Vienna, he returned to the monastery in Brno, where he taught science in a local high school and supervised the monastery's garden. History tells us little about Mendel's work as a teacher, but we know a great deal about his work in the garden.

☑ ***Checkpoint*** What was Mendel's contribution to the study of biology? ②

Mendel's Work on True-Breeding Pea Plants

Before Mendel arrived at the monastery, the previous gardeners had developed different true-breeding stocks of pea plants. A true-breeding stock always passes its characteristics to the next generation. For example, one true-breeding stock of pea plants might always produce tall plants with green pods, while another stock might always produce short plants with yellow pods.

What would you do if you had different stocks of true-breeding pea plants? Would you mate them and observe their offspring? That is exactly what Mendel did. (a)

Figure 6–3 (a) *Gregor Mendel may have looked like an ordinary gardener, but his achievements were far from ordinary. His work provides the basis of our understanding of heredity.* (b) *Mendel performed his experiments on* Pisum sativum, *the garden pea plant.*

TEACHER SUPPORT

Historical Perspective

Two of the most important studies in the history of biology were published at the time of the American Civil War. Charles Darwin published *On the Origin of Species* in 1859, and Mendel published his paper on plant breeding and inheritance in 1865. Darwin's work was received with a great deal of public acclaim and controversy, but Mendel's work went virtually unnoticed. Ironically, Darwin subscribed to the journal that published Mendel's paper and even had a copy in his study, but he never recognized that Mendel's work could be applied to the study of evolution. In fact, Mendel's law of segregation and independent assortment provided the biological basis for the evolution of species as described by Darwin.

CONTROLLING REPRODUCTION IN PEA PLANTS

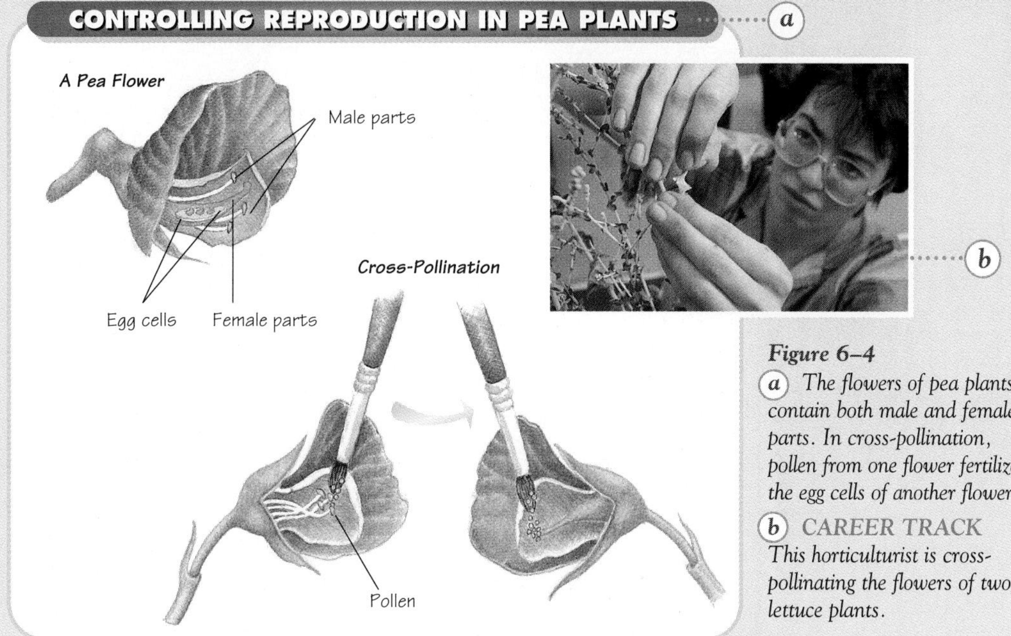

Figure 6–4
ⓐ *The flowers of pea plants contain both male and female parts. In cross-pollination, pollen from one flower fertilizes the egg cells of another flower.*
ⓑ CAREER TRACK
This horticulturist is cross-pollinating the flowers of two lettuce plants.

Reproduction in Pea Plants

Like many plants, pea plants use parts of their flowers to reproduce. One part produces pollen—the male sex cells—and another part produces egg cells—the female sex cells. When pollen fertilizes an egg cell, a seed for a new plant is formed.

Pea plants normally reproduce by self-pollination, in which pollen fertilizes egg cells on the same flower. In effect, seeds that are produced from self-pollination have only one plant as a parent.

However, pea plants can also cross-pollinate. In cross-pollination, pollen from the flower on one plant fertilizes the egg cells of a flower on another plant. The seeds produced from cross-pollination have two plants as parents.

To perform his experiments, Mendel had to select the pea plants that mated with each other. Therefore, he needed to prevent flowers from self-pollinating and to control their cross-pollinating. How did Mendel accomplish this task? First, he cut away the male parts of a flower. Then, as shown in ***Figure 6–4,*** he dusted that flower with pollen from a second flower.

☑ ***Checkpoint*** What is self-pollination? Cross-pollination? ③

Seven Traits

With this technique, Mendel could choose any two pea plants to cross-pollinate—or cross, for short. But how did he choose which type of pea plants to cross? Mendel had several different stocks of pea plants, and each was true-breeding for a variety of different characteristics.

To simplify his investigation, Mendel chose to study only seven **traits** in pea plants, illustrated in ***Figure 6–5*** on page 126. A trait is a characteristic that distinguishes one individual from another.

Looking back at Mendel's work, we realize that one of his most important decisions was to study just a small number of traits. Also, each of these traits has two contrasting forms. For example, seed shape is either round or wrinkled and pod color is either green or yellow.

Ideas Through Images

Have students examine Figure 6–4, read the caption, and answer the following questions.

- **What parts of a flower produce egg cells?** (Female parts.)
- **What parts of a flower produce pollen?** (Male parts.)
- **Why was cutting away the male parts of the flower an important part of Mendel's procedure?** (In this way, he knew exactly which plant was the male parent.)
- **What do you think would have happened if Mendel cross-pollinated a flower without removing the male flower parts?** (He would not have been sure which male plant was the parent. He would have had offspring from both males, which would have confused the results.)

☑ Checkpoints

① Biological inheritance—the set of characteristics an organism receives from its parents.

② He studied heredity carefully and objectively.

③ In self-pollination, pollen fertilizes egg cells on the same flower. In cross-pollination, pollen from one plant fertilizes the egg cells of another plant.

Technology

CD-ROM
Mendel's Principles of Heredity

TEACHER SUPPORT — Activity

THE PARTS OF A FLOWER
Give each student group a flower, such as a lily, in which the pistils and stamens are easily observable. Instruct students to carefully examine the structure of the flower, noting the location of the male (stamen) and female (pistil) flower parts. They may use Figure 6–4 as a guide. Students should diagram the flower and label the petals, stamen, and pistil. Encourage them to dissect the flower using a knife or scalpel and examine the parts with a hand lens. Caution students to be careful when handling the knife or scalpel. They should record their observations on their diagrams.

Ancillary Support

The resources below can be used to support your teaching strategy for these two pages.

TR Writing in Biology: If These Genes Could Talk
BL Inquiry Activity: Why Do We Look Like Our Parents?

Investigate

Role-Playing Give students pea pods to examine. Then challenge them to think as Gregor Mendel might have while observing the traits of the pea pod. Have them list as many traits of the pea pod and seeds as they can observe. (Possible answers include size, color, shape, seed color, seed shape, and seed coat color.) Then have students examine the results of the F_1 crosses in Figure 6–5. Challenge them to write inferences to explain why Mendel got those results. Have students compare their inferences to Mendel's principles at the end of this section.

Correcting Misconceptions

Students may not understand how two identical parents could produce offspring that look different in the F_2 cross. Review the genetic cross shown in Figure 6–6. Remind students that the parents of this cross were the F_1 generation produced when a true-breeding plant with wrinkled seeds was crossed with a true-breeding plant with smooth seeds. Point out that the trait for wrinkled seeds was present in the P generation, but disappeared in the F_1 generation. Show students examples of other F_2 crosses in which the offspring have traits different from those of the parents. Ask students to identify the traits present in the P generation, F_1 generation, and F_2 generation.

Discussion

Display corn cobs that show a cross between yellow (pp) and purple (PP) corn produces purple (Pp) offspring. Also display a cross between smooth (SS) and wrinkled (ss) corn that produces smooth (Ss) offspring. Ask students to identify the characteristics of the parents and the F_1 generation for each cross. Then ask these questions.

- **Which traits are dominant and which are recessive?** (Purple and smooth are dominant; yellow and wrinkled are recessive.)

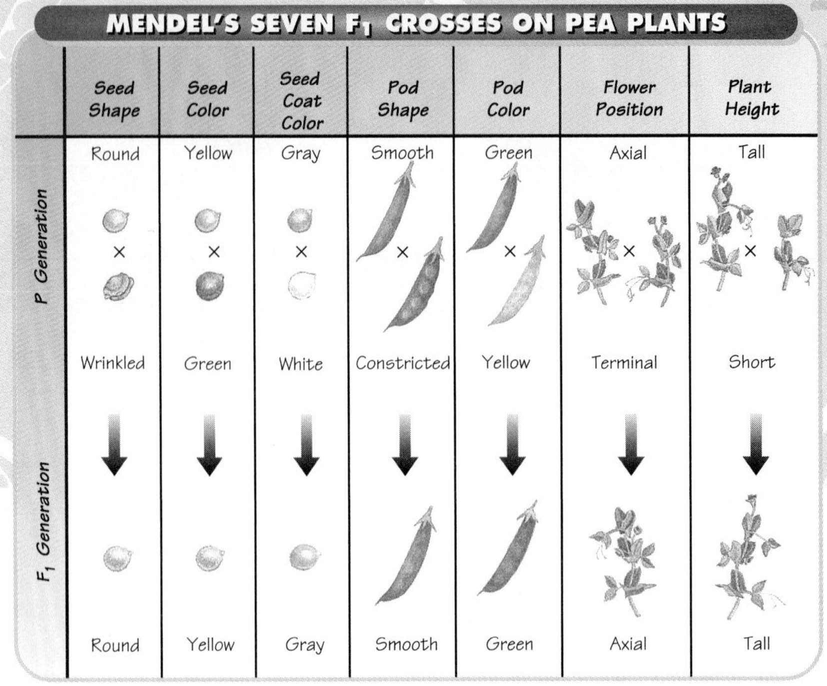

MENDEL'S SEVEN F_1 CROSSES ON PEA PLANTS
Seed Shape
Seed Color
Seed Coat Color
Pod Shape
Pod Color
Flower Position
Plant Height
P Generation
Round
Yellow
Gray
Smooth
Green
Axial
Tall
Wrinkled
Green
White
Constricted
Yellow
Terminal
Short
F_1 Generation
Round
Yellow
Gray
Smooth
Green
Axial
Tall

Figure 6–5 Mendel performed F_1 crosses for each of the seven traits shown here. To Mendel's surprise, the traits of just one parent appeared in the F_1 generation.

The F_1 Generation

Using true-breeding stocks for each of the seven traits, Mendel crossed pea plants that showed one form of a trait with pea plants that showed the other form, as illustrated in ***Figure 6–5.*** The offspring of these crosses are called **hybrids.** A hybrid is an offspring of parents with different characteristics.

Mendel called the hybrids the F_1 generation, and he called the cross that produced them an F_1 cross. The letter F stands for *filius*, which in Latin means "son." The true-breeding plants Mendel called the P generation. The letter P stands for the Latin word *parentis*, meaning "of the parent."

To Mendel's surprise, the traits of the parents did not blend in the F_1 generation. Instead, the traits of just one parent appeared in the offspring. The traits of the other parent seemed to have vanished!

☑ **Checkpoint** What are hybrids? 1

The F_2 Generation

If Mendel had stopped with the F_1 cross, he might not be remembered today. But he was curious about what had happened to the traits that seemed to have disappeared in the F_1 generation. So he decided to take the next logical step. He crossed the plants of the F_1 generation among themselves. This second cross he called the F_2 cross, and the plants that resulted he called the F_2 generation.

Incredibly enough, for each of the seven traits, the form that had vanished in the F_1 generation reappeared in the F_2 generation! Moreover, as illustrated in ***Figure 6–6,*** they reappeared in approximately one fourth of the plants in the F_2 generation.

Mendel knew that this pattern could not be a simple coincidence. Indeed, he realized that it signified something important about the nature of heredity.

☑ **Checkpoint** What is the F_1 generation? The F_2 generation? 2

TEACHER SUPPORT

Managing Classroom Diversity

LEP STUDENTS

Students might confuse the words gene and jean. Point out that although the words sound the same, they have different meanings. Explain that these words are homonyms—words that sound the same but have different meanings. Challenge students to think of other examples of homonyms, such as see and sea and meat and meet.

GIFTED STUDENTS

Have students choose a research organism, such as *Brassica rapa* or *Drosophila melanogaster*, and use reference materials to find out how to set up genetic crosses. Help them to obtain the materials they will need and guide them as they set up and maintain their crosses. Students' reports should include their hypotheses, procedure and experimental setup, results, and analysis and conclusions.

Genes

Because the traits did not blend, Mendel reasoned that some indivisible unit must determine each of the traits he investigated. Mendel called this unit a *Merkmal,* which is the German word for "character." Today, the unit that determines traits is called a **gene.** Therefore, true-breeding tall pea plants contain genes for tallness, and true-breeding short pea plants contain genes for shortness.

☑ ***Checkpoint*** What is a gene? ③

Alleles

How many copies of each gene does a pea plant contain? Mendel concluded that for each of the seven traits he investigated, a pea plant must contain at least two genes—one from each parent.

Today, the different forms of a gene are called **alleles** (uh-LEELZ). For example, the gene that determines height in pea plants has two alleles. One allele produces a tall plant and another allele produces a short plant. While some genes have only two alleles, many genes have three, four, or even dozens of different alleles.

As illustrated in ***Figure 6–7*** on page 128, all the plants in the P generation contain two copies of an allele. Each tall plant contains two copies of the allele for tallness. And each short plant contains two copies of the allele for shortness.

When pea plants reproduce, each parent produces sex cells—either pollen or egg cells. Unlike other cells, the sex cells contain only one copy of each gene. Therefore, when a sex cell from a true-breeding tall plant unites with one from a true-breeding short plant, the seed it produces contains one allele for tallness and one allele for shortness.

Dominant and Recessive

As Mendel had observed, all the plants in the F_1 generation were just as

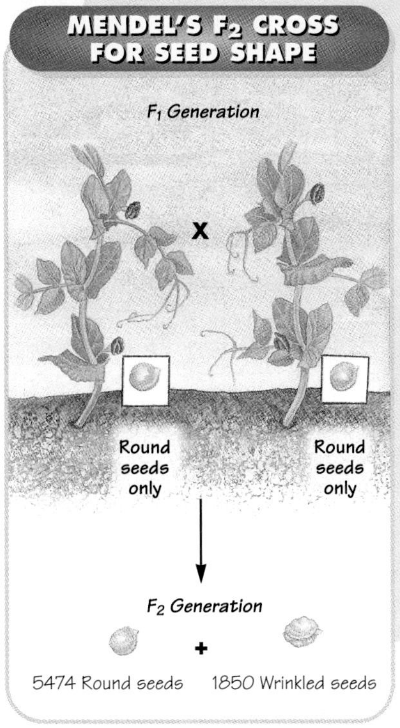

Figure 6–6
In his crosses for seed shape, Mendel found that wrinkled seeds disappeared in the F_1 generation but reappeared in roughly one fourth of the plants of the F_2 generation. Mendel believed that this pattern was significant—and he was right!

tall as the tall plants in the P generation. But according to his model, the plants in the two generations contained different alleles. Why does a plant with two alleles for tallness grow to the same height as a plant with only one allele for tallness?

To answer this question, Mendel proposed a simple but very important idea. Mendel called the allele for tallness the **dominant** allele. The allele for shortness he called the **recessive** allele. In other words, in pea plants that have both alleles, only the dominant allele—the allele for tallness—is expressed.

Today, biologists represent a dominant allele with a capital letter and a recessive allele with a lowercase letter. Thus, for pea plants, a capital letter T represents the allele for tallness and a lowercase letter t represents the allele for shortness.

Phenotype and Genotype

An organism's **phenotype** is the form of a trait that it displays. Pea plants, for

• **Predict the results of a cross between purple corn (PP) and yellow corn (pp).** (All of the offspring would be hybrid purple.)

Investigate

Model Building Students can model the inheritance of traits using beads to represent the alleles for a specific trait. Have them set up F_1 and F_2 crosses and show how the genes from each parent combine to produce the traits shown in the offspring. Ask students to explain what happened to the trait that "vanished" in the F_1 generation. (It was masked by the dominant allele.) Challenge students to demonstrate how Mendel's results would have been affected if he had not used true-breeding plants. (The F_1 generation might not all have the same phenotype.)

☑ Checkpoints

① Offspring of parents with different characteristics.

② The F_1 generation is the first generation of offspring from the P generation. The F_2 generation is the second generation, which is produced when the F_1 generation plants are crossed among themselves.

③ The unit that determines traits.

TEACHER SUPPORT

Background Information

Pea plants are useful organisms for genetic study because they have a large number of variable traits that are easy to identify. Mendel was able to easily study seven different traits that had two distinct forms. Pea plants also reproduce sexually, as opposed to asexually, so the offspring are genetically different from both parents, instead of being identical to them. More important, Mendel could easily set up controlled mating between parent plants with the traits he wanted to study. Each cross he set up produced large numbers of offspring, allowing Mendel to analyze his data statistically.

Ancillary Support

The resources below can be used to support your teaching strategy for these two pages.

LM Observing Phenotypes, #12
TR Explore: Marshan Genetics

Discussion

Initiate a class discussion about the segregation of alleles. Use Punnett squares, as shown in Figure 6–8, as a guide during the discussion. In the discussion, emphasize these points.

- The segregation of alleles for other traits in pea plants.
- Identify the sex cells for each parent in the cross and the possible genotypes of the offspring.

Ideas Through Images

Have students examine Figure 6–9, read the caption, and answer the following questions.

- **What is the phenotype of each F_1 parent?** (Both have round, yellow seeds.)
- **What is the ratio of yellow seeds to green seeds in the F_2 generation?** (¾ yellow: ¼ green.)
- **What is the ratio of round seeds to wrinkled seeds in the F_2 generation?** (¾ round: ¼ wrinkled.)
- **Why did Mendel conclude that the alleles for seed shape and color segregate independently?** (Mendel observed every possible combination of the four different alleles; certain alleles did not stay together.)

Investigate

Long-Term Project Have students plant corn seeds that were produced in a cross between two heterozygous green corn plants (Gg) that both have alleles for green color and white color. Ask students to predict the genotypes and phenotypes of the plants that will sprout. After the seeds sprout, have students count the number of offspring for each color and compare that number to the expected ratio of 3 green: 1 white.

ALLELES IN AN F_1 CROSS

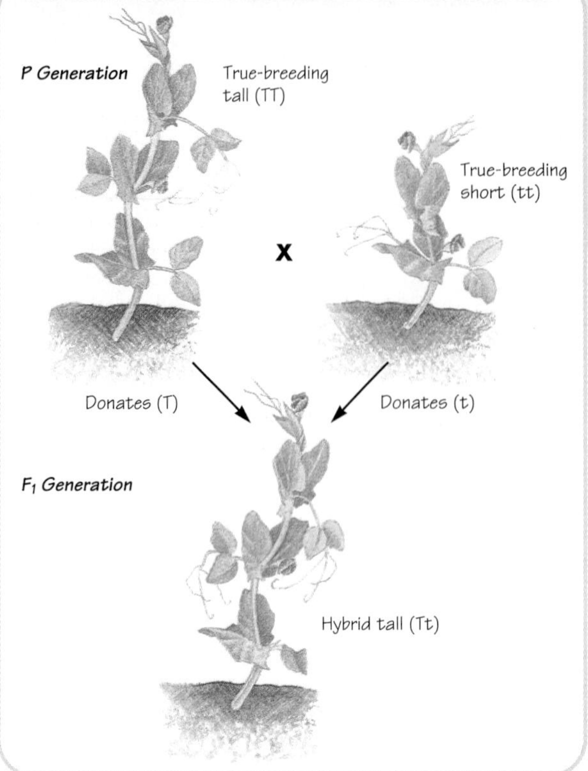

Figure 6–7 *Mendel used the idea of dominant and recessive alleles to explain the results of his experiments. He concluded that a pea plant contains two alleles for each of the seven traits that he studied. When the alleles differ, the dominant allele determines the form of the trait.*

example, express either the phenotype for tallness or the phenotype for shortness. But Mendel had the insight to conclude that identical phenotypes could be produced by more than one **genotype**—an organism's genetic composition.

Today, organisms that have an identical pair of alleles for a trait—such as TT or tt—are said to be **homozygous** (hoh-moh-ZIGH-guhs) for the trait. The prefix *homo-* means "same," and the suffix *-zygous* means "joined together." Organisms that have a mixed pair of alleles—such as Tt—are said to be **heterozygous** (heht-er-oh-ZIGH-guhs) for the trait. The prefix *hetero-* means "different."

In his F_1 cross, Mendel crossed plants that were homozygous for tallness (TT) with plants that were homozygous for shortness (tt). All the offspring were heterozygous for height (Tt), yet were just as tall as the homozygous tall plants.

Checkpoint What is the difference between genotype and phenotype? 1

Segregation

Mendel reasoned that when plants produced pollen and egg cells, the two copies of each gene would need to undergo **segregation**—a process that separates the two alleles of a gene. Remember that all the plants in the F_1 generation have the heterozygous genotype for height (Tt). Therefore, when a plant with the genotype Tt produces pollen or egg cells, half the sex cells will carry the allele for tallness (T) and the other half will carry the allele for shortness (t).

In an F_2 cross, half the pollen cells and half the egg cells carry the recessive allele (t), so exactly $1/2 \times 1/2$, or $1/4$ of the offspring, should have two copies of the recessive allele (tt). Therefore, $1/4$ of the offspring should be short plants (tt) and $3/4$ of the offspring should be tall plants (TT or Tt). Indeed, these ratios are almost exactly what Mendel's F_2 cross produced.

Independent Assortment

Mendel's first experiments left one important question about genes unanswered: Does the inheritance of one gene affect the inheritance of another? To answer this question, he performed an experiment to follow two different genes as they passed from one generation to the next.

TEACHER SUPPORT

Managing Classroom Diversity

AT-RISK STUDENTS

Some students might find the vocabulary in this section difficult to remember or comprehend. These students will find it helpful to make a set of flashcards for the following words: homozygous, heterozygous, gene, allele, trait, dominant, recessive, phenotype, and genotype. Have students write the word on one side of an index card and a definition or word association that will help them understand the meaning of the word more easily on the other side.

PUNNETT SQUARE FOR AN F_2 CROSS

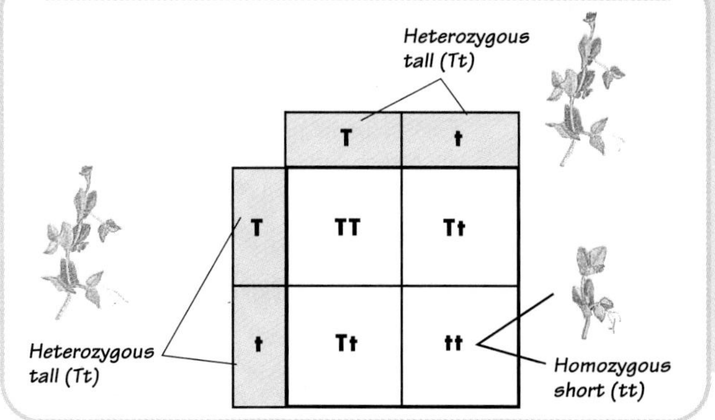

Figure 6–8
This Punnett square illustrates Mendel's F_2 cross for plant height. The possible gametes from one parent (Tt) are written along the top of the square, and the possible gametes from the other parent (Tt) are written along the left. The boxes in the square show the four possible genotypes of the offspring.

From his earlier experiments, Mendel knew that the gene for seed shape had two forms—round (R) and wrinkled (r)—and that the allele for roundness was dominant. He also knew that the gene for seed color had two forms—yellow (Y) and green (y)—and that the allele for yellow color was dominant.

To follow both genes, Mendel first performed an F_1 cross between plants that were true-breeding for round yellow seeds (RRYY) and plants that were true-breeding for green wrinkled seeds (rryy). As he expected, every plant in the F_1 generation had round yellow seeds. Mendel reasoned that each of these plants received the dominant alleles (RY) from one parent and the recessive alleles (ry) from the other parent, providing them with the heterozygous genotype for both traits (RrYy).

Mendel then crossed the F_1 plants. When the F_1 plants produce pollen and egg cells, would the allele for round seeds (R) always stay with the allele for yellow seeds (Y)? Would the allele for wrinkled seeds (r) always stay with the allele for green seeds (y)? Or instead, would the alleles segregate independently, allowing for other combinations of alleles?

As shown in ***Figure 6–9,*** Mendel's second cross produced plants with distinct ratios of different combinations of

MENDEL'S F_2 CROSS FOR TWO TRAITS

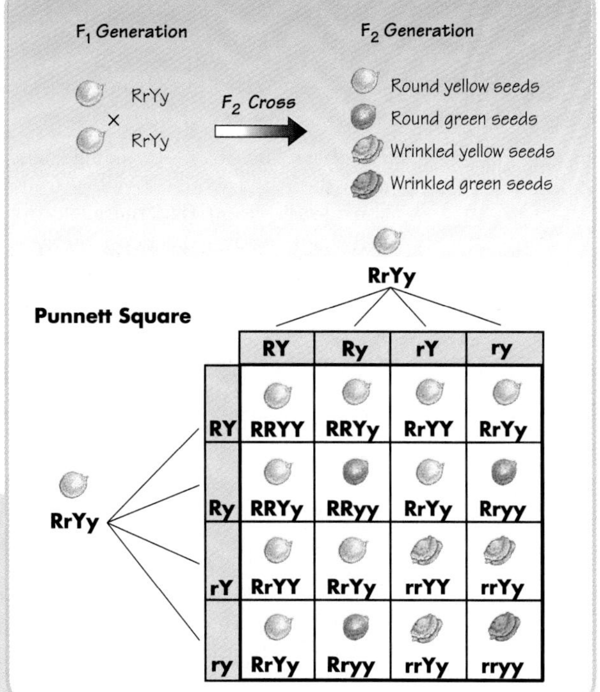

Figure 6–9
Mendel's F_2 cross for seed shape and seed color produced four seed phenotypes in a 9:3:3:1 ratio. This result showed that the genes for seed color and seed shape assort independently.

Discussion

Have a student copy Figure 6-8 on the chalkboard. Emphasize that in a Punnett square the dominant allele is always written as a capital (uppercase) letter. In Figure 6-8, tall is written as T. The recessive allele, on the other hand, is written as the corresponding lowercase letter. In this case, short is written as t. The gametes that are produced by each parent are placed along the top and the left-hand side of the Punnett square. Each box is completed by inserting the gamete that appears above and to the left of each box.

Investigate

Cooperative Learning Give student pairs a genetics problem for which you tell them the F_2 cross and the phenotypic ratios of the F_2 generation. (Example: A cross between two red-eyed fruit flies (Rr) produces 3 red-eyed:1 rosy-eyed offspring.) Instruct students to work together to determine the dominant and recessive alleles, the possible genotypes of the F_2 generation, and the genotypes and phenotypes of the P generation. Encourage students to practice active listening techniques while solving the problem.

Checkpoint

1 Genotype is an organism's genetic composition. Phenotype is the form of a trait that it displays.

TEACHER SUPPORT

Background Information

Gregor Mendel carried out extensive breeding experiments and kept very accurate records. But in recent years, some scientists have wondered if something might have been amiss in Mendel's data. His data from thousands of peas fall closer to a perfect 3:1 ratio than one might expect—so close that some historians suggest that Mendel, or perhaps more likely his assistant, may have adjusted some of the numbers. For now there is no way to know if Mendel's numbers were fudged or if he was just very lucky.

MINI LAB Classifying

Teacher Notes
- For time required and materials needed, see page 122b.
- Point out each phenotype on student volunteers.

Answers to Analyze and Conclude
1. Answers will vary based on students' phenotypes.
2. Recessive traits; dominant phenotypes can be either heterozygous or homozygous.

Skills Trace
Classifying
- Focus p. 130
- Practice p. 130
- Assess p. 145

4 ASSESS

Quick Check

Give students various genetic crosses for which they must identify genotypes and phenotypes of the parents and offspring and tell which individuals are homozygous and heterozygous. (Example: A cross between corn with purple kernels (PP) and corn with yellow kernels (pp) produces offspring with all purple kernels (Pp). The F_2 generation has a ratio of 3 purple:1 yellow.)

Section Review 6–1

1. Heredity is the set of characteristics an organism receives from its parents. The units of heredity are genes.
2. One allele masks the expression of another in dominance. Segregation is the process that separates the two alleles of a gene. In independent assortment, genes do not influence each other's inheritance.
3. All offspring will be RrYy.
4. Answers will vary based on students' traits.

Skills Trace
Classifying
- Focus p. 130
- Practice p. 130
- Assess p. 145

MINI LAB Classifying

You and Your Genes

PROBLEM *How can you **classify** the genotypes and phenotypes for four traits that you display?*

PROCEDURE

1. Using the information in the table, classify your phenotype as dominant or recessive for each trait.

	Dominant	Recessive
Freckles	Present	Absent
Earlobes	Free	Attached
Hair	Curly	Straight
Fingers	Mid-digit hair	Hairless

2. Poll the class to find out how many students display each phenotype.

ANALYZE AND CONCLUDE

1. For which traits do you have the dominant phenotype? The recessive phenotype?
2. For which traits can you determine your genotype? Explain your answer.

seed shape and color—including round green seeds and wrinkled yellow seeds. This clearly meant that the alleles for seed shape segregated independently of those for seed color—a principle known as **independent assortment.** Put another way, genes that segregate independently—such as the genes for seed shape and seed color in pea plants—do not influence each other's inheritance.

Checkpoint What is independent assortment? 1

Mendel's Principles

You might think that the publication of Mendel's work brought him fame and led to an immediate revolution in biology. But science doesn't always work that way.

In fact, Mendel's work went almost unnoticed for more than 30 years. Then, around the early 1900s, a number of scientists rediscovered Mendel's work and saw that its principles could be applied to animals as well as to plants.

Today, biologists can look back on Mendel's work and note four important principles that he developed:

- **Individual units, called genes, determine biological characteristics.**
- **For each gene, an organism receives one allele from each parent. The alleles separate from each other—a process called segregation—when reproductive cells are formed.**
- **If an organism inherits different alleles for the same trait, one allele may be dominant over the other.**
- **Some genes segregate independently.**

Section Review 6–1

1. **Define** heredity and **identify** the units of heredity.
2. **Explain** dominance, segregation, and independent assortment.
3. **Critical Thinking—Constructing Diagrams** A geneticist crosses a pea plant that is true-breeding for round green seeds (RRyy) with one that is true-breeding for wrinkled yellow seeds (rrYY). Construct a Punnett square to describe this cross. Compare it to ***Figure 6–9*** on page 129.
4. **MINI LAB** **Classify** yourself as expressing the dominant or recessive form for each of the four traits you investigated.

Learning Modality

Auditory Learning Some students may understand the vocabulary in this section better by listening to the words and their meanings on an audiocassette. These students might also find it helpful to hear difficult parts of the section read aloud to them.

Meiosis

SECTION 6–2

GUIDE FOR READING

- **Define** meiosis.

MINI LAB
- **Construct a model** of meiosis.

BECAUSE OUR KNOWLEDGE OF genetics has increased so much since Mendel's time, it's easy to overlook the fact that Mendel's genes were just hypothetical units. Mendel was not at all sure where genes might be located or how he would identify them. Fortunately, his descriptions of how genes behave were so specific that it was not long before biologists were certain they had found the location of genes in the cell.

Chromosomes

Because genes affect the entire organism, you might suspect that every cell has a copy of every gene. Where in the cell might you find genes? Remember that during mitosis—the process in which eukaryotic (yoo-kar-ee-AHT-ihk) cells (cells with a nucleus) produce daughter cells—structures called chromosomes appear. The chromosomes separate from each other when the cell divides, with one chromosome given to each daughter cell.

Could chromosomes actually contain genes? When chromosomes separate from each other during mitosis, are they in fact dividing genetic information between the two daughter cells? The idea that chromosomes contain genes is certainly an intriguing one—to say the least!

Forming Gametes

The best way to answer these questions is to watch what happens when an organism forms **gametes.** The term gamete is another name for a reproductive cell, such as a pollen cell or an egg cell.

According to Mendel's principles, an organism has two copies of each gene, but only one copy is passed on to an offspring. This means that when an organism forms gametes, the two copies of each gene need to separate precisely from each other.

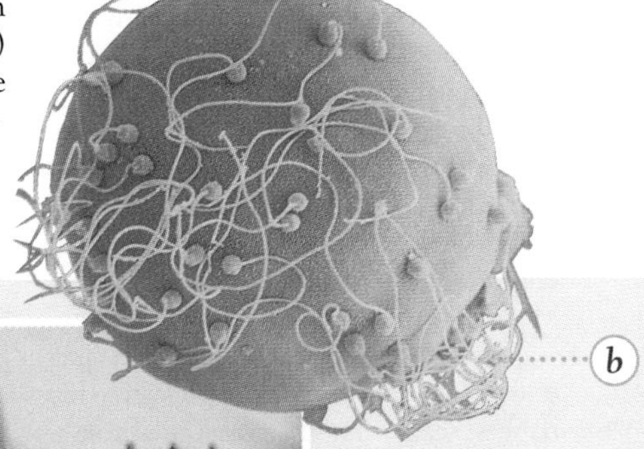

Figure 6–10
Both flowering plants and animals reproduce through gametes—specialized reproductive cells. (a) Each of these lilies contains a central pistil, which houses egg cells, and several stamens, which produce pollen. (b) This animal egg cell is surrounded by sperm cells. Typically, only one sperm fertilizes an egg (magnification: 480X).

TEACHER SUPPORT

Managing Classroom Diversity

TECH PREP STUDENTS
Modeling is a skill used frequently in this chapter to help make difficult biological concepts easier to understand. By practicing modeling, students can use their hands to learn difficult concepts. They can also learn how to use modeling to solve real-world problems in a creative way. Have students find out about as many careers as possible that use modeling in some form as a problem-solving technique. Encourage students to speak with a vocational counselor to help them get started.

SECTION 6–2
Meiosis

Performance Objective
- Describe the process of meiosis.

Mini Lab Skill: Modeling
Laboratory Investigation Skill: Interpreting

1 ENGAGE

Inquiry Activity
Inferring
The Case of the Missing Genes
Ask students where genes are located in the cell. Give them photographs, diagrams, and/or microscope slides of different kinds of cells in various stages of the cell cycle. Challenge students to infer where genes are located in the cells. Students should describe the evidence that supports their inferences. Encourage students to revise their inferences, as needed.

2 EXPLORE

Investigate
Research Have students use resource materials to research the scientific contributions of William Sutton, who made the connection between Mendel's hereditary units and chromosomes. Challenge students to write a newspaper article that describes Sutton and his important discovery as if it were a current event.

Checkpoint
1 Genes that segregate independently.

3 TEACH

MINI LAB Modeling

Teacher Note

• For time required and materials needed, see page 122b.

Answers to Analyze and Conclude

1. Four haploid cells.
2. In Metaphase I, homologous chromosomes form pairs. In Metaphase II, two copies of the same chromosome pair up.
3. Anaphase I; the pairs of homologous chromosomes separate randomly to produce two haploid cells.

Skills Trace
Modeling
- Focus p. 132
- Practice p. 134
- Assess p. 145

Correcting Misconceptions

Some students might confuse mitosis and meiosis. The most difficult point to understand is that the daughter cells produced after meiosis I are already haploid; they contain only one set of chromosomes. Have students compare diagrams of mitosis and meiosis. Point out that DNA replication occurs in prophase I and that the chromosome copies do not separate until meiosis II.

Tell students that the terms diploid and haploid can be misleading. Because the diploid number of chromosomes is 2n, it is logical to assume that n should be called the monoploid number. And, the haploid number should be called 1/2n. Unfortunately, logic does not apply here. Make sure that students understand that diploid is 2n and haploid is n.

MINI LAB .... Modeling ....

Toothpick Meiosis

PROBLEM *How can you **construct a model** of meiosis?*

PROCEDURE

1. Construct a model of a diploid cell that has 6 chromosomes. To model the chromosomes, use colored toothpicks, pipe cleaners, or other materials.
2. Move the chromosomes and redraw the cell boundaries to model the different stages of meiosis.
3. Repeat steps 1 and 2, this time aligning the chromosomes differently in Metaphase I.

ANALYZE AND CONCLUDE

1. What are the end products of meiosis?
2. Compare Metaphase I with Metaphase II.
3. Which step of meiosis determines the genetic composition of the gametes? Explain your answer.

Haploid and Diploid Cells

Gametes, in fact, contain exactly half the number of chromosomes found in other cells in the organism. For example, most human cells contain 46 chromosomes, but human gametes—sperm and egg cells—contain 23 chromosomes. The fusion of sperm and egg brings together chromosomes from both parents, just as Mendel's principles require.

The gametes, which contain just one set of chromosomes, are described as **haploid** cells. The number of chromosomes in a haploid cell is often represented by the letter n. In humans, n=23.

Cells that contain a double set of chromosomes are described as **diploid.** The number of chromosomes in a diploid cell is represented by the term 2n. For humans, 2n = 46.

☑ *Checkpoint* What is a haploid cell? A diploid cell? (1)

The Phases of Meiosis

How does a diploid organism produce haploid gametes? It does so by **meiosis** (migh-OH-sihs)—a special process of cell division. **In meiosis, the number of chromosomes in a diploid cell is reduced by half, producing haploid gametes.**

At one time, meiosis was called reduction division. Reduction division is not a bad name for meiosis, because meiosis reduces the number of chromosomes in the cell by one half—from diploid (2n) to haploid (n).

Study the sequence of steps in meiosis, presented in the feature on the next page. At first, you may think that meiosis looks much like mitosis—the process by which eukaryotic cells divide. And unfortunately, the words meiosis and mitosis sound just enough alike to make it easy to confuse the two. But don't be fooled. There is something very different about meiosis—something that would have made Gregor Mendel smile.

☑ *Checkpoint* What is meiosis? (2)

Meiosis and Genetic Diversity

In the first division of meiosis, the separation of each homologous chromosome pair is a random event. As a result, the haploid gametes could contain a great many different combinations of chromosomes.

Chromosome Combinations

How many chromosome combinations are possible? If an organism's cells have 6 chromosomes (2n = 6) that means that they have 3 pairs of homologous chromosomes. Because each pair can segregate in two different ways, there are 2^3 ($2 \times 2 \times 2$), or 8, possible combinations of chromosomes in the gametes.

TEACHER SUPPORT — Facts and Figures

DIPLOID (2n) NUMBER OF VARIOUS ORGANISMS

Organism	Chromosomes	Organism	Chromosomes
dog	78	corn	20
horse	64	common wheat	42
chimpanzee	48	cultivated cotton	52
fruit fly	8	chicken	78
garden pea	14	cat	38
cabbage	18	Adder's green tongue fern	over 1200
potato	48	yeast	34

Visualizing Meiosis

Meiosis takes place in two stages, called meiosis I and meiosis II. Let's take a look at the steps of each stage, using a cell that has 6 chromosomes (or 2n = 6) as an example.

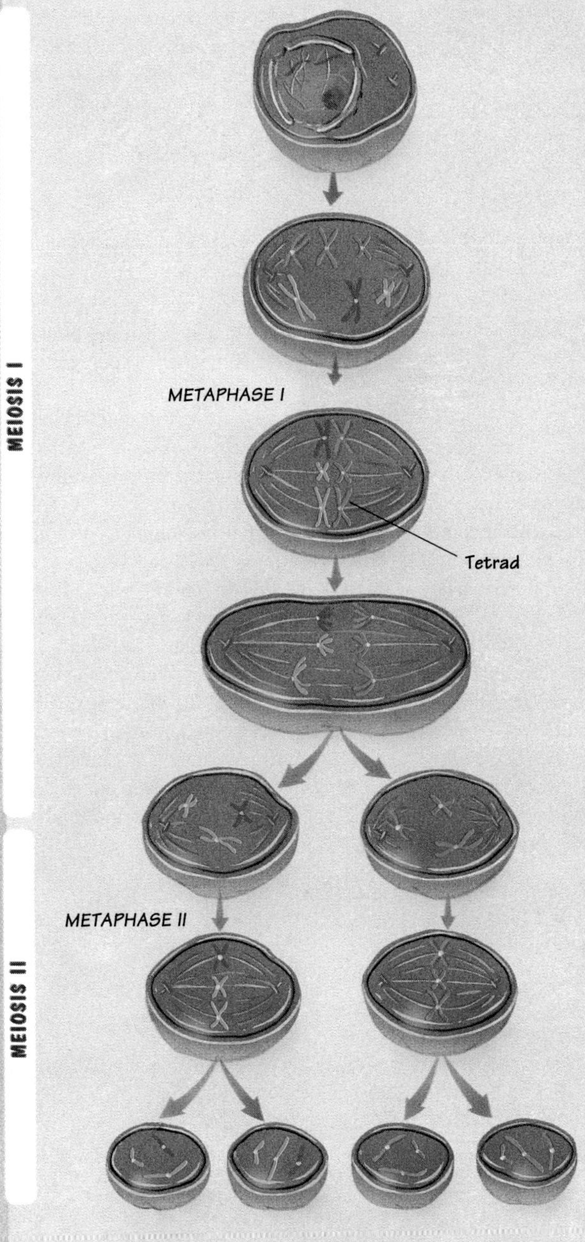

1. At the beginning of meiosis, each chromosome is replicated, forming duplicate chromatids joined at their centromeres.

2. Prophase I resembles prophase of mitosis. Chromosomes uncoil and the spindle apparatus forms.

3. At metaphase I, corresponding chromosomes, called **homologous chromosomes**, pair together and line up in the center of the cell. The paired chromosomes form structures called **tetrads.**

4. At anaphase I, the homologous chromosomes are pulled toward opposite sides of the cell.

5. The end products of meiosis I are two haploid (n) daughter cells. For the cells shown here, n = 3. In meiosis II, the two daughter cells undergo a second round of cell division.

6. In metaphase II, notice that chromosomes line up just as they line up in the metaphase stage of mitosis.

7. The end products of meiosis II are four haploid cells that may develop into gametes. In most male animals, all four cells develop into gametes. In females, only one cell does so.

Visualizing Meiosis

Have students study the stages of meiosis in the diagram and read the captions. Make sure students understand the difference between meiosis I and meiosis II. Ask them to explain in their own words what is happening in each stage. Then initiate a class discussion about meiosis and the segregation of alleles. Emphasize the following points.

- Mendel's principle of independent assortment is modeled by meiosis. Demonstrate this by marking two alleles for a gene on homologous chromosomes and tracing them through meiosis.
- Meiosis also shows how each parent contributes one allele for each gene to its offspring.

Review the process of mitosis. Ask students to point out ways in which the two processes are different. (Only sister chromatids separate in mitosis to form two diploid cells.)

Checkpoints

1. A haploid cell contains only one set of chromosomes, whereas a diploid cell contains a double set of chromosomes.

2. The process by which the number of chromosomes in a diploid cell is reduced by half, producing haploid gametes.

Technology

CD-ROM
Meiosis

TEACHER SUPPORT — Background Information

Polyploid organisms have three or more sets of chromosomes. A 3x individual is triploid, a 4x individual is tetraploid, and so on. Polyploidy is relatively common in plants. Many ferns are polyploid, and almost half of all flowering plants are polyploid. For example, bananas are triploid (3n = 9), potatoes are tetraploid (4n = 48), boysenberries are heptaploid (7n = 49), and strawberries are octoploid (8n = 56).

Polyploidy in animals is very rare. Only hermaphrodites (such as earthworms) and parthenogenetic females (such as some beetles, shrimp, and salamanders) are polyploid.

Ancillary Support

The resources below can be used to support your teaching strategy for these two pages.

TR Apply: Everyone Is Falling Apart
BL Inquiry Activity: Special Cell Division
TB Visualizing Meiosis, #7

Laboratory Investigation

The Laboratory Investigation, Mapping a Chromosome, on pages 140–141 is appropriate to use at this point in the chapter.

4 ASSESS

Quick Check

Ask students to diagram meiosis for an organism in which 2n = 6. Have them use different colors for each chromosome.

Section Review 6-2

1. The process of cell division that produces four haploid cells.

2. Meiosis I: Homologous chromosomes pair up to form tetrads in metaphase I. At anaphase I, the homologous chromosomes separate to produce two haploid daughter cells. Meiosis II: The chromosomes line up during metaphase II and separate at anaphase II to produce four haploid daughter cells.

3. Crossing-over switches alleles from one chromosome to another.

4. The gametes will have too many chromosomes.

5. Students might describe moving toothpicks to represent the movement of chromosomes during meiosis.

Skills Trace
Modeling

- Focus p. 132
- Practice p. 134
- Assess p. 145

Learning Modality

Kinesthetic Learning Have students demonstrate the movement of the chromosomes in meiosis. Students who represent homologous chromosomes should wear tags with the same number. Students who represent sister chromatids should wear tags of the same number and color. Sister chromatids should hold a circle that represents a centromere.

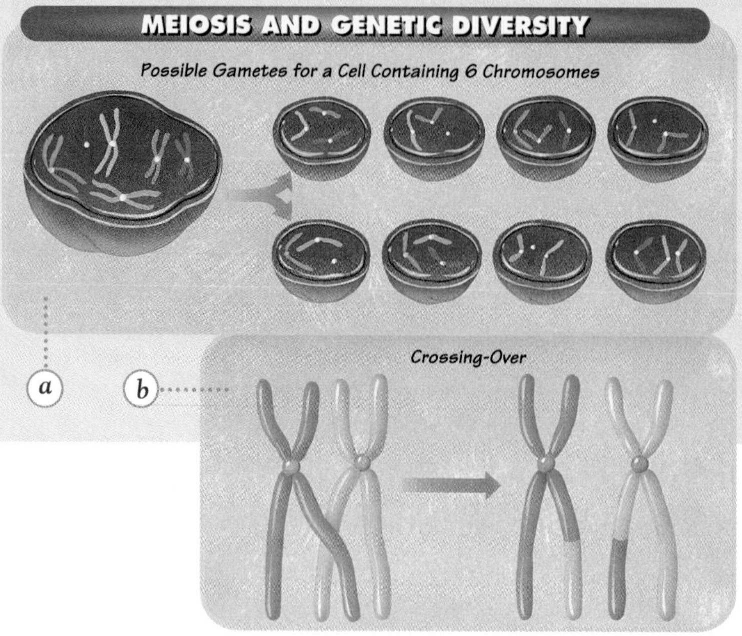

Figure 6–11
(a) Through meiosis, a cell with 6 chromosomes can produce any of 2^3, or 8, different gametes. Human cells, which have 46 chromosomes, could produce any of 2^{23} different gametes! (b) During meiosis, homologous chromosomes may exchange pieces of themselves. This process is called crossing-over, and it further increases the genetic diversity of gametes.

Although eight combinations is not that many, think about the combinations in a human cell. Human cells have 23 pairs of chromosomes. Thus, the chromosomes can segregate in 2^{23} possible ways. That is more than 8 million possibilities!

Crossing-Over

You might think that 8 million ways to segregate 23 chromosome pairs is more than enough to shuffle the genetic deck. But that is just the beginning. Think about groups of genes that are found on the same chromosome. These genes often are inherited together, and therefore are said to be linked genes. But there is an important exception to gene linkage.

During meiosis, when homologous chromosomes are paired in a tetrad, a piece of one chromosome may change places with a piece of the other. This exchange between homologous chromosomes is called **crossing-over.** As shown in ***Figure 6–11,*** the effect of crossing-over is the switching of alleles from one chromosome to another.

When a crossing-over event occurs between two alleles on the same chromosome, the alleles could become located on different chromosomes. This means that crossing-over produces even more possible combinations of genetic material!

Section Review 6–2

1. **Define** meiosis.
2. **Sequence** and **describe** the process of meiosis.
3. **Explain** how crossing-over increases genetic diversity.
4. **Critical Thinking—Predicting** Suppose that a pair of homologous chromosomes fails to separate during the first round of meiotic division. How will this affect the gametes that are produced?
5. **MINI LAB** How can you **construct a model** of meiosis?

TEACHER SUPPORT

Ecology Note

Biodiversity is the variety that exists among organisms and their environment. Genetic diversity is the most specific type of biodiversity because it is the variety of genes present in all the members of a species. Meiosis is important to genetic diversity because cross-over events and the separation of homologous chromosomes shuffle and redistribute the alleles of genes within a species. This shuffling and redistributing not only increase the genetic diversity of a species but also help species adapt to changes in the environment. As the climate changes, for example, only those individuals of a species with a particular trait will survive and produce offspring. And only those offspring will survive and produce more offspring carrying that certain trait.

Analyzing Inheritance

GUIDE FOR READING

- **Relate** probability to genetics.

IF YOU KNOW THE GENOTYPES of both parents in a cross, can you determine the most likely genotypes of their offspring? The answer is yes. Indeed, one of the most useful aspects of genetics is that it has predictive value. Put another way, we can use genetics and mathematical principles to tell us the chances that certain events will happen.

Probability

Think about an ordinary event with an uncertain outcome, such as the flip of a coin. Flipping a coin has two possible outcomes—the coin may land either heads up or tails up. Each outcome has an equal probability, or likelihood, of occurring. Therefore, the probability of a single coin flip landing heads up is 1 out of 2, or 1/2. ●

If you flip a coin four times in a row, what is the probability that it will land heads up each time? Because each coin flip is an independent event, the probability of each coin landing heads up is 1/2. Therefore, the probability of flipping four heads in a row is

$$1/2 \times 1/2 \times 1/2 \times 1/2 = 1/16$$

As you can see, you have 1 chance in 16 of flipping heads four times in a row. The fact that we multiplied the individual probabilities together illustrates an important point—past outcomes do not affect future ones. Even if you flipped three heads in a row, the probability of the fourth coin landing heads up is still 1/2.

INTEGRATING MATHEMATICS

If you flipped a coin 50 times, how many times would you expect it to land heads up?

Probability and Genetics

Does probability apply to events in genetics? It definitely does. **Probability applies to genetics because the formation of gametes depends on random events.** Remember that a gamete is equally likely to contain one chromosome or its homologous chromosome,

Figure 6–12
Probability applies to outcomes in genetics, such as (a) whether a sheep has white wool or black wool and (b) whether a Persian cat has long hair or short hair.

TEACHER SUPPORT

Managing Classroom Diversity

LEP STUDENTS
Some students have difficulty understanding probability and thus interpret Punnett squares incorrectly. These students mistakenly believe that a Punnett square shows the definite outcome of four separate events. Stress that the ratios predicted by a Punnett square represent the probability of the result for each event. Each event is completely independent of the results of every previous event.

SECTION 6–3

Analyzing Inheritance

Performance Objective
- Describe how probability applies to genetics.

1 ENGAGE

Inquiry Activity

Designing an Experiment

A Flip of the Coin
Ask students what is the chance that a coin will land heads up when they flip it. Give students a coin and instruct them to devise their own procedure to find an answer to the question. Encourage students to record their conclusions and refer to them while studying the section.

2 EXPLORE

Investigate

Cooperative Learning Give student groups a deck of cards or a die. Challenge them to determine the chance of drawing one particular card, or throwing a certain number. (Cards: 1:52; die: 1:6.) Instruct students to first devise a procedure to solve the problem, then compare their procedure with that of other groups in the class. Randomly call on group members to share their results with the class.

INTEGRATING MATHEMATICS
Approximately half the coin tosses, or 25 times.

3 TEACH

Problem Solving
Interpreting Diagrams
Cystic Fibrosis

Students will use their understanding of dominance, independent assortment, and probability to solve a genetics problem.

State Students must determine the probabilities of certain outcomes in genetic crosses.
Solve Students can solve the problem by first determining all the possible outcomes of the cross, and then counting the number of outcomes that would have the cystic fibrosis phenotype.
Test Students can test their solutions with a Punnett square. It shows all the possible combinations of alleles from the parents.
Communicate Discuss the results with the class. Encourage students to share their answers and their methods for solving the problem.

Answers to THINK ABOUT IT

1. Both parents are Cc, and the child is cc.
2. $\frac{1}{2} \times \frac{1}{2} = \frac{1}{4}$, or 25%.
3. The probability would be the same as for the first and second child, $\frac{1}{4}$, or 25%.
4. If a genetic disease were caused by a dominant allele, individuals with just one allele would have the disease and would probably not survive long enough to have children. Eventually, the allele would no longer exist in the population.

Problem Solving
INTERPRETING DIAGRAMS
Cystic Fibrosis

Cystic fibrosis is an example of a genetic disease, or a disease that is inherited. A recessive allele causes cystic fibrosis, which means that a person who inherits only one copy of the allele will be unaffected. If two such people have a child, however, the child could inherit two copies of the allele. This genotype causes the disease.

Cystic fibrosis affects the glands that produce mucus, which is a slick, slimy liquid that coats the lining of the lungs, intestines, and other organs. In people with cystic fibrosis, the mucus is significantly thicker and stickier than normal. The abnormal mucus clogs the breathing and digestive passages, which typically leads to infections and malnutrition. Fifty years ago, a baby born with cystic fibrosis usually would die within a few years. Today, thanks to better diagnosis and treatment, many people with cystic fibrosis survive into adulthood and lead productive lives. Researchers continue to study this disease.

To learn more about the way cystic fibrosis is inherited, study the hypothetical cross presented in the Punnett square shown below. Identify the phenotype of each parent and potential offspring, then calculate the probability that a child of these parents would have cystic fibrosis.

PUNNETT SQUARE

	C	c
C	CC	Cc
c	Cc	cc

Key: **C** normal allele
c disease allele

THINK ABOUT IT

1. A healthy man and a healthy woman have a child who has cystic fibrosis. Identify the genotypes for this trait for both parents and for their child.
2. This man and woman want another child. Calculate the probability that the second child would have cystic fibrosis.
3. Calculate the probability that a third child would have cystic fibrosis.
4. More serious genetic diseases are caused by recessive alleles than by dominant alleles. Explain why this is the case.

TEACHER SUPPORT

Historical Perspective

Although Mendel's paper in which he set forth his discovery of the laws of inheritance was published in 1865, his work was unrecognized by the scientific community until 1900, 16 years after his death. It was then that Hugo DeVries, known best for his development of the theory of mutation, carried out experiments that resulted in the rediscovery of Mendel's work and brought it to light.

Why did Mendel's tremendously important work remain unknown for so long? When he presented his results to a local natural history society in Brunn, he was disappointed by their lack of response. Undeterred, he then sent his paper to the eminent Swiss botanist Karl Nägeli, whose cold reception probably discouraged Mendel from further efforts at recognition.

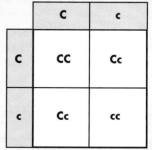

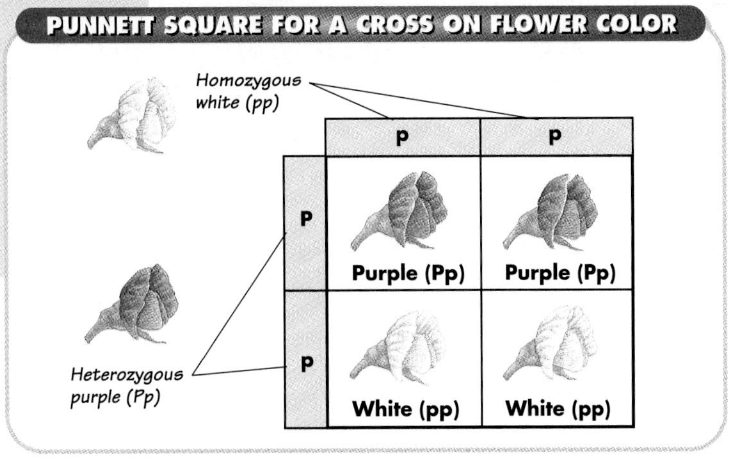

Figure 6-13
In this cross, 2 of the 4 possible offspring have white flowers. Therefore, the probability that the cross will produce a plant with white flowers is 2 out of 4, or 1 out of 2, or 1/2.

PUNNETT SQUARE FOR A CROSS ON FLOWER COLOR

Homozygous white (pp)

Heterozygous purple (Pp)

	P	P
P	Purple (Pp)	Purple (Pp)
P	White (pp)	White (pp)

just as a coin is equally likely to land heads up or tails up. Therefore, if an organism has two different alleles for the same gene, the chances are 1 in 2, or 1/2, that one of its gametes carries one of the alleles.

Purple Flowers or White Flowers?

Let's take flower color in pea plants as an example. Suppose you cross a plant that is heterozygous for purple flowers (Pp) with one that is homozygous recessive for white flowers (pp). What is the probability that a single seed from this cross will produce a plant with white flowers?

As shown in *Figure 6-13,* the white flower produces only gametes that contain the allele for white flowers (p), while the purple flower produces two types of gametes—one with the allele for purple flowers (P) and one with the allele for white flowers (p). Therefore, half the seeds will be heterozygous for purple flowers (Pp) and half will be homozygous

recessive for white flowers (pp). The probability that an offspring will produce white flowers is 1 out of 2, or 1/2.

Four Seeds

Suppose you plant four seeds from the cross just described. What is the probability of producing four plants with white flowers? Like flipping coins and getting four heads in a row, the probability is $1/2 \times 1/2 \times 1/2 \times 1/2 = 1/16$.

These numbers give an idea of what the term probability means. If you plant four seeds from this cross, you would expect half to produce white flowers and half to produce purple flowers. However, that doesn't mean that the seeds will always produce two plants with white flowers and two with purple ones. As you've just seen, there is a probability of 1 in 16 that all four will have white flowers.

Section Review 6-3

1. **Relate** probability to genetics.
2. **Calculate** the probability that a cross between individuals that are heterozygous for a trait (Aa × Aa) will produce a heterozygous offspring.
3. **Critical Thinking—Interpreting Data** In cats, the allele for short hair (S) is dominant over the allele for long hair (s). A cat with short hair is mated with a cat with long hair, producing five kittens with short hair. Can you identify the genotypes of both parents and their offspring? How certain can you be of your answers?

Introduction to Genetics **137**

Discussion

Initiate a class discussion about expected outcomes and actual outcomes of a genetic cross. Emphasize that each offspring is the result of a random event. The genotype of one offspring does not affect the genotype of another.

4 ASSESS

Quick Check

Set up a "Probability Bowl" in which student teams make up various genetics and probability problems for other teams to solve. Instead of speed, rate team answers on correctness and creativity.

Section Review 6-3

1. Probability applies to genetics because the formation of gametes depends on random events.
2. ½, or 50%
3. The long hair parent must be ss. All the short hair kittens are heterozygous, Ss, because they could receive only the recessive allele from the long hair parent. The short hair parent is probably SS, but there are not enough offspring to be absolutely sure that this genotype is correct. The short hair parent could also be Ss.

Learning Modality

Tactile Learning To help reinforce the principles of probability and the ability to predict the outcome of random events, have students work on probability problems using a die, a deck of cards, or a container filled with colored beads. Be sure students record the outcomes of each trial.

TEACHER SUPPORT

Managing Classroom Diversity

AT-RISK STUDENTS

Some students may need more practice with the principles of probability. Emphasize that probability can be used only to predict the outcome of random events. For example, flipping a weighted coin will not turn up heads or tails with equal probability. Give students time to observe and record the results of random events in coin flipping. Then they can

relate their knowledge of probability to genetics by determining outcomes of genetic crosses. Have them set up Punnett squares for crosses, then flip a coin, with each side representing one of the alleles for a gene. After 50 flips, have them compare their observed results with the expected results.

Ancillary Support

The resources below can be used to support your teaching strategy for these two pages.

LM Investigating Probability, #11
TR Explore: The Ups and Downs of Probability
BL Inquiry Activity: Practicing Probability

Section 6-4

A Closer Look at Heredity

Performance Objective

• Describe some factors that cause genes to be expressed in different ways.

1 ENGAGE

Inquiry Activity

Inferring

Who's Taller Than Whom?

Ask students why people are not just tall or short like Mendel's peas. Challenge them to think about how the trait for height is inherited in humans. Students should devise their own procedure for observing height in a large number of people. Then have students infer how height is inherited.

2 EXPLORE

Investigate

Long-Term Project Give students soybean seeds that will produce offspring with the phenotypic ratio 1 green: 2 yellow-green: 1 yellow. Explain that the seeds are the offspring of a cross between two heterozygous green plants (Gg). After the seeds sprout, have students determine the phenotypic ratio of the offspring and compare it to Mendel's 3:1 ratios. Encourage them to infer how this trait for color is inherited. (Students will learn that this is an example of incomplete dominance.)

SECTION 6–4 BRANCHING OUT In Depth

A Closer Look at Heredity

Guide for Reading

- **Identify** the factors that cause genes to be expressed in different ways.

A COMPLEX ORGANISM MAY *have thousands or tens of thousands of genes. As you might suspect, some of those genes have patterns of inheritance that are a little more complicated than others. These complications make life interesting, and they explain why not every inherited trait follows exactly the same pattern.*

Incomplete Dominance and Codominance

Many genes have more than one allele or have alleles that are neither dominant nor recessive. Genes with these kinds of alleles give rise to a variety of different phenotypes.

Snapdragons, for example, have two alleles for flower color—red (R) and white (r). Snapdragons that are homozygous red (RR) produce red flowers, and those that are homozygous white (rr) produce white flowers. However, the heterozygous plants (Rr) are neither red nor white. They're pink!

Which allele is dominant? The answer is that neither allele is completely dominant. Although the presence of the red allele does produce red color in the heterozygous plant (Rr), the red color is not as intense as it is in the homozygous plant (RR). Therefore, the red allele displays **incomplete dominance** over the white allele. In incomplete dominance, the heterozygous phenotype is somewhere in between the two homozygous phenotypes.

Another case in which both alleles affect phenotype is known as **codominance.** Interesting examples of codominance are found in roan horses and erminette chickens, as illustrated in *Figure 6–16.* In codominance, both alleles of a gene are expressed.

Figure 6–14 Not all genes display the simple behavior that you have studied so far. (a) In rabbits, the gene that determines coat color has four alleles. (b) In snapdragons, neither of the alleles that control flower color is dominant.

TEACHER SUPPORT

Managing Classroom Diversity

MULTICULTURAL STRATEGY

Instruct students to look around the classroom and observe the differences in individual students' hair color, skin color, height, weight, and eye color. Point out that these traits are polygenic traits and are determined by more than one gene.

Explain that a person's skin color is determined by the amount of a pigment called melanin that is produced in the body. Skin color also give clues to the environment of a person's ancestors. People with darker skin usually have ancestors who lived in areas near the equator, where summers are long. People with lighter skin usually have ancestors who lived in areas where summers are short. Darker skin has more melanin than lighter skin. Be sure to point out that all humans are more alike than they are different, despite differences in coloring.

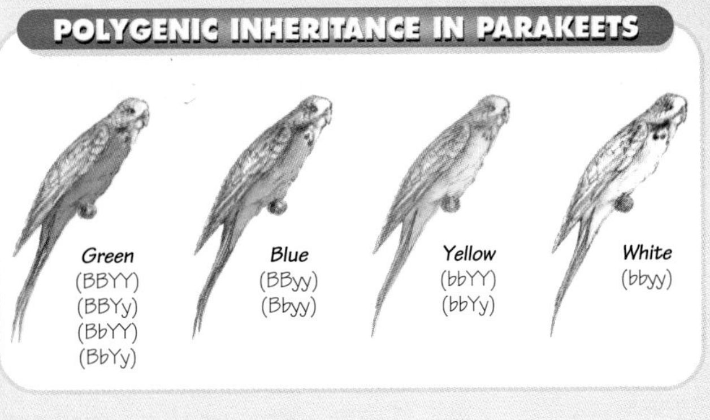

Figure 6–15
In parakeets, feather color is controlled by two genes—one that controls blue color and one that controls yellow color. Green parakeets have at least one dominant allele for each gene, whereas white parakeets have only the recessive alleles.

Multiple Alleles

As you learn the basic principles of genetics, it's easy to focus on genes that have just two alleles. But genes that have multiple alleles are very common in nature. For example, coat color in rabbits is determined by a single gene that has four well-known alleles. In humans, genes that have multiple alleles include the genes for blood group and eye color.

Polygenic Traits

Many inherited traits are controlled by more than one gene. This is particularly true of the genes that control body shape and form. For example, although your facial appearance is inherited, no single gene determines the exact shape of your mouth or the position of your ears. Traits that are controlled by more than one gene are said to be **polygenic traits.** Feather color in parakeets is one example of a polygenic trait, as shown in ***Figure 6–15.***

Because polygenic traits are controlled by more than one gene, their inheritance can be complicated. Polygenic traits often show a very wide range of phenotypes. For example, the range of skin colors in humans comes about partly because at least four different genes control this trait.

Figure 6–16
(a) In Erminette chickens, the gene for feather color has two codominant alleles—one for black feathers and one for white feathers. Thus, heterozygous chickens have both types of feathers.
(b) Roan horses have two colors in their coats—another result of codominant alleles.

Section Review 6–4

1. **Identify** the factors that cause genes to be expressed in different ways.
2. **Describe** four different types of genetic expression.
3. **BRANCHING OUT ACTIVITY** **Organize** a scheme of inheritance for three different traits in a mythical animal or plant. Each trait should follow one of the patterns of inheritance discussed in this section.

3 TEACH

Discussion

Initiate a discussion about the alleles of traits that show incomplete dominance. Emphasize that these alleles are neither dominant nor recessive; they work together to produce a "dosage effect." Explain that if a plant has one allele for red pigment and one allele for no pigment, then only half as much red pigment is produced, making the flowers pink.

Ideas Through Images

Have students examine Figure 6–15, read the caption, and answer the following questions.

- **What color offspring would you expect from a cross between a homozygous green parakeet (BBYY) and a white parakeet (bbyy)?** (Only green parakeets.)
- **Could a cross between blue and yellow parakeets produce a white parakeet?** (Yes, if both parents were heterozygous.)

4 ASSESS

Quick Check

Give students various examples of genetic crosses, with only the phenotypes of the parents and offspring. Have students identify the inheritance of the traits as polygenic, codominance, incomplete dominance, simple dominance, or multiple alleles.

Section Review 6–4

1. Genes with more than one allele or with alleles that are neither dominant nor recessive can be expressed in different ways.

2. Incomplete dominance: heterozygotes have an in-between phenotype; codominance: both alleles affect the phenotype; multiple alleles: genes with more than two alleles; and polygenic traits: traits controlled by more than one gene.

3. Accept all logical answers that correctly reflect one of the patterns of inheritance discussed in the section.

Learning Modality

Visual Learning Use Punnett squares to help students determine the phenotypic and genotypic outcomes of crosses involving traits showing different kinds of expression.

Ancillary Support

The resources below can be used to support your teaching strategy for these two pages.

TR Enrich: The Tale of a Cat
BL Inquiry Activity: Testing Genetic Theories

Laboratory Investigation

Mapping a Chromosome

Before the Lab

Gather enough pipe cleaners, metric rulers, and unlined paper for students to work in groups of two to four.

Pre-Lab Discussion

Have students read the entire procedure for this investigation. Then ask students the following questions.

What will you accomplish in this investigation? (Mapping the location of genes on a chromosome.)

What process are you modeling? (Crossing-over events in meiosis.)

Is the crossing-over event that you are modeling a random event? Why? (Yes, because each toss of the pipe cleaner does not affect any other toss.)

Skills Development

Students will use these skills while completing the laboratory investigation: measuring, modeling, interpreting, and drawing conclusions.

Teaching Strategies

1. Suggest to students that they toss the pipe cleaner underhanded. This will decrease their control over where the pipe cleaner lands, making their tosses a little more random.
2. If individual or group results are disappointing, pool the class data to get a larger amount of data and more accurate results.

CHAPTER 6

Laboratory Investigation

Mapping a Chromosome

How do scientists determine the location of a gene on a chromosome? One method is to study an event called crossing-over—the exchange of genes between homologous chromosomes. As you will see, the farther apart that genes are located on a chromosome, the more often that crossing-over separates them.

Problem

How are chromosomes mapped? **Interpret** the results of an experiment to discover the answer.

Materials (per group)

- pipe cleaner
- metric ruler
- paper
- pencil or pen

Procedure

1. **With a metric ruler, draw a vertical line 15 cm long on a sheet of paper. This line represents a chromosome. The pipe cleaner represents its homologous chromosome.**
2. **Mark the bottom of the line with a small horizontal line. Measuring from the horizontal line, mark off points 1 cm, 3 cm, 6 cm, 10 cm, and 15 cm. Draw a small horizontal line at each point. The horizontal lines represent the locations of genes on the chromosome.**
3. **Label the horizontal lines A through F, starting from the bottom horizontal line.**
4. **Construct a data table similar to the one shown above Observations.**
5. **Place the sheet of paper 15 cm from the edge of the table. Standing at least 30 cm away from the table, toss the pipe cleaner so it crosses the chromosome—the vertical line on the sheet of paper.**
6. **Assume a crossing-over occurs at the point where the pipe cleaner touches the line. Determine which genes (B through F) have separated from gene A. For example, if the pipe cleaner falls between genes C and D, then genes D, E, and F have separated from gene A. If the pipe cleaner falls between genes D and E, then genes E and F have separated from gene A. Place a check mark in each appropriate box in your data table.**
7. **Repeat steps 5 and 6 to produce 50 crossing-overs.**
8. **Count the total number of check marks for each gene. Record each total in the second column of your data table.**

DATA TABLE

Gene	Times Separated From Gene A		Frequency of Separation From Gene A	Gene Location	
	Check	Total		Calculated	Actual
B					
C					
D					
E					
F					

Observations

1. To calculate each gene's frequency of separation from gene A, divide the total number of separations by 50. Record the frequency of separation in the third column of your data table.
2. To calculate the location of each gene, multiply its frequency of separation by 15. Record these values in the fourth column of your data table.

Analysis and Conclusions

1. Which genes separated most frequently from gene A? Which genes separated least frequently from gene A?
2. Describe the relationship between the locations of two genes on a chromosome and the frequency with which crossing-over separates them. Use the data generated to support your answer.
3. How accurately did this procedure determine the locations of the genes? Explain why the procedure did not determine the exact locations of the genes.

More to Explore

Research other ways in which biologists determine a gene's location on a chromosome.

Answers to
Observations

1. Answers will vary depending on the results of pipe cleaner tosses.
2. Answers will vary depending on students' observations.

Answers to
Analysis and Conclusions

1. Genes F, E, and D; genes B and C.
2. The farther apart two genes are located on a chromosome, the higher the frequency of crossing-over.
3. Answers will vary. Tosses might not have been random enough, or more tosses were needed.

More to Explore

Many scientists map genes to chromosomes using genetic engineering techniques. They use special enzymes (restriction enzymes) to cut the genetic material (DNA) into many small fragments, one of which contains the gene being mapped. They use a combination of different restriction enzymes to produce a variety of fragments. Then they piece these fragments together like a puzzle to map the gene on the chromosome.

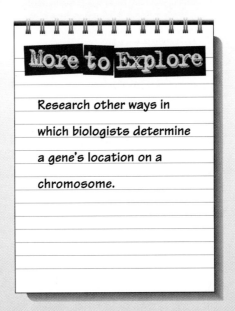

CHAPTER 6

Study Guide

Review Strategy

Divide the class into groups of two or three. Instruct each group to develop a concept map that shows how Mendel's principles are related to the process of meiosis. Also have groups show how incomplete dominance, codominance, multiple alleles, and polygenic traits fit into that relationship if they completed Section 6–4. Encourage students to be creative. Groups should present their concept maps to the rest of the class.

Study Guide

Summarizing Key Concepts

The key concepts in each section of this chapter are listed below to help you review the chapter content. Make sure you understand each concept and its relationship to other concepts and to the theme of this chapter.

6–1 The Science of Inheritance

- An organism's heredity is the set of characteristics it receives from its parents. Today, the study of heredity is known as genetics.
- As Mendel's experiments showed, traits are determined by units called genes. An organism contains two copies of every gene because it receives one copy from each parent.
- Genes have different forms, called alleles. When an organism receives two different alleles for the same trait, only the dominant allele is expressed.
- An organism's phenotype is the form of a trait it displays, and its genotype is its genetic composition. Different genotypes can produce the same phenotype.
- When sex cells are formed, the alleles undergo segregation, or separate from each other. Genes that are assorted independently do not influence each other's inheritance.

6–2 Meiosis

- Genes are located on chromosomes. Gametes contain a single set of chromosomes and are described as haploid cells. Cells that contain a double set of chromosomes are described as diploid.
- In meiosis, the number of chromosomes in a diploid cell is reduced by half, producing haploid gametes.

6–3 Analyzing Inheritance

- Probability applies to genetics because the formation of gametes depends on random events.

6–4 A Closer Look at Heredity

- Many genes have more than one allele, or have alleles that are neither dominant nor recessive. Genes with these kinds of alleles give rise to a variety of diffferent phenotypes.

Reviewing Key Terms

Review the following vocabulary terms and their meaning. Then use each term in a complete sentence.

6–1 The Science of Inheritance

heredity, genetics, trait, hybrid, gene, allele, dominant, recessive, phenotype, genotype, homozygous, heterozygous, segregation, independent assortment

6–2 Meiosis

gamete, haploid, diploid, meiosis, crossing-over

6–4 A Closer Look at Heredity

incomplete dominance, codominance, polygenic trait

142 Chapter 6

Inquiry-Based Strategy

Explain to students that a new mutation in pea plants produces plants with purple seeds. Challenge students to devise a research protocol that would answer the following question: How is this mutation inherited? Encourage students to use Mendel's approach as a guide. Remind them to consider modes of inheritance other than simple dominance.

Students will use various approaches to answer this question. A likely approach would begin with crosses between plants with purple seeds and plants with green seeds and plants with yellow seeds.

Recalling Main Ideas

Choose the letter of the answer that best completes the statement or answers the question.

1. Who was the first person to study heredity scientifically?

a. Mendel **c.** Watson
b. Punnett **d.** Calvin

2. Crossing different true-breeding stocks produces offspring called

a. the P generation. **c.** cross-overs.
b. the F_2 generation. **d.** hybrids.

3. The different forms of a gene are called

a. traits. **c.** gametes.
b. alleles. **d.** hybrids.

4. Which represents a heterozygous genotype for height in pea plants?

a. (TT) **c.** (tt)
b. (Tt) **d.** (T) or (t)

5. Gametes are described as

a. haploid cells. **c.** triploid cells.
b. diploid cells. **d.** adult cells.

6. During meiosis, homologous chromosomes pair together to form structures called

a. chromatids. **c.** gametes.
b. tetrads. **d.** centromeres.

7. What are the end products of meiosis?

a. 2 diploid cells **c.** 2 haploid cells
b. 4 diploid cells **d.** 4 haploid cells

8. Crossing-over is the exchange of genetic information between

a. reproductive cells.
b. diploid cells.
c. any 2 chromosomes.
d. homologous chromosomes.

9. The red, pink, and white colors of snapdragons are controlled by a gene that shows

a. incomplete dominance.
b. codominance.
c. polygenic dominance.
d. multiple alleles.

Putting It All Together

Using the information on pages xxx to xxxi, complete the following concept map.

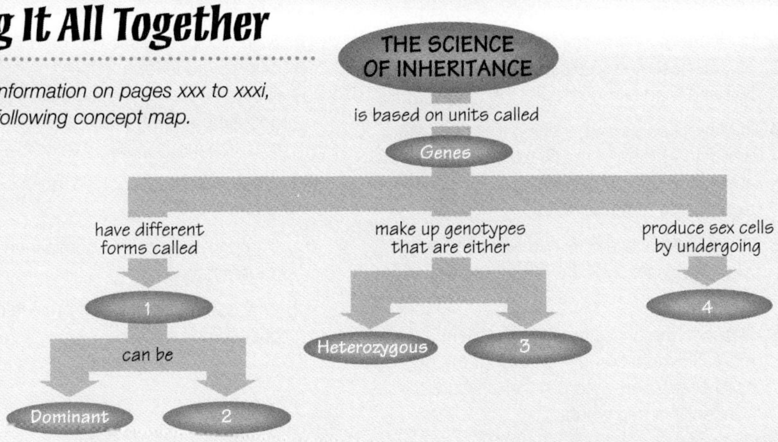

Recalling Main Ideas

1. a
2. d
3. b
4. b
5. a
6. b
7. d
8. d
9. a

Putting It All Together

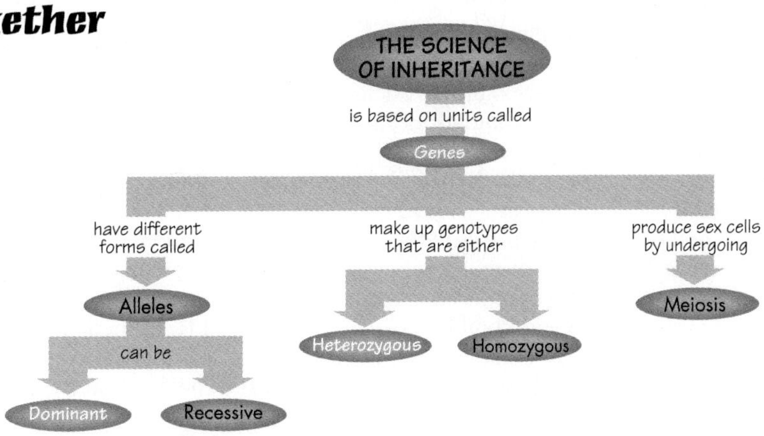

CHAPTER 6

Assessment

Reviewing What You Learned

1. The set of characteristics it receives from its parents.
2. He was the first to study heredity carefully and objectively, and his experiments resulted in the discovery of basic principles of heredity.
3. In self-pollination, pollen fertilizes egg cells on the same flower. In cross-pollination, pollen fertilizes egg cells on flowers of a different plant.
4. P generation: true-breeding parent plants; F_1 generation: hybrid offspring from crossing true-breeding parents; F_2 generation: offspring produced by crossing F_1 plants.
5. Organisms with only one dominant allele will have the same phenotype as those with two dominant alleles.
6. Haploid cells have one set of chromosomes. Diploid cells have two sets.
7. Four haploid cells.
8. The exchange of genetic material between homologous chromosomes during meiosis.
9. Homozygous: has an identical pair of alleles for a trait. Heterozygous: has a pair of alleles that are unlike.
10. The separation of two alleles of a gene during meiosis.
11. Traits that are controlled by more than one gene.

Expanding the Concepts

1. True-breeding stocks always pass the same characteristics to the next generation. Because of this, Mendel could assume that any differences he observed in the offspring resulted from crossing two different plants.
2. He did not want any offspring that might be produced by self-pollination to affect the results of his cross.
3. One form of the trait was recessive. It was masked by the dominant allele in the F_1 generation. It reappeared in the F_2 generation because some of the offspring were homozygous recessive.
4. Of the four possible combinations of the parental alleles, three result in tall plants and one results in short plants.
5. No. Some genes have multiple alleles or have alleles that are neither dominant nor recessive.
6. Genes that segregate independently do not influence each other's inheritance. When Mendel crossed true-breeding plants with round yellow seeds and true-breeding plants with green wrinkled seeds, F_1 plants with round yellow seeds were produced. The F_2 cross produced offspring with all four possible phenotypic combinations.
7. Tetrads form when homologous chromosomes pair together at metaphase I. Crossing-over occurs when tetrads form, which produces more possible combinations of genetic material.
8. Each pair of homologous chromosomes can segregate in two different ways, so there are 2^5 (2 x 2 x 2 x 2 x 2), or 32, possible gametes.
9. Genotypes: 1 AA (homozygous dominant), 2 Aa (heterozygous), 1 aa (recessive). Phenotypes: 3 dominant, 1 recessive.
10. Probability is the likelihood that a certain random event will occur. Probability can be used to predict the outcomes of a genetic cross because gamete formation depends on random events.
11. In incomplete dominance, the heterozygote has a phenotype that is somewhere in between the two homozygous phenotypes. In codominance, the heterozygote displays the traits for both alleles.

Assessment

Reviewing What You Learned

Answer each of the following in a complete sentence.

1. What is an organism's heredity?
2. Describe the contributions that Gregor Mendel made to the study of biology.
3. Explain the difference between self-pollination and cross-pollination.
4. In Mendel's experiments, what was the P generation? The F_1 generation? The F_2 generation?
5. Why can organisms that have the same phenotype for a trait have different genotypes for the trait?
6. What are haploid cells? Diploid cells?
7. What are the end products of meiosis?
8. What is crossing-over?
9. Compare a homozygous genotype and a heterozygous genotype.
10. What is segregation?
11. Define polygenic traits.

Expanding the Concepts

Discuss each of the following in a brief paragraph.

1. Why did Mendel use true-breeding stocks of pea plants in his experiments?
2. When Mendel cross-pollinated two pea plants, why did he cut off the male flowering parts of one pea plant?
3. In Mendel's F_1 crosses, explain why one form of a trait seemed to disappear in the F_1 generation and then reappeared in the F_2 generation.
4. In Mendel's F_2 cross on height in pea plants, 3/4 of the plants in the F_2 generation were tall and 1/4 of the plants were short. Discuss the significance of these ratios.
5. Do all genes have only two alleles, with one allele dominant over the other? Explain your answer.
6. Describe the principle of independent assortment. How did Mendel show that the genes for seed shape and seed color are assorted independently in pea plants?
7. What is a tetrad? Discuss why the formation of tetrads is important in meiosis.
8. If an organism has 5 chromosomes, how many different gametes could it produce? Explain your answer.
9. A geneticist crosses two organisms that are heterozygous for a trait (Aa × Aa). Construct a Punnett square for this cross. Then identify the genotype and phenotype of each of the possible offspring.
10. What is probability? How does it relate to genetics?
11. Compare incomplete dominance with codominance.
12. Why can multiple alleles provide many different phenotypes for a trait?

Extending Your Thinking

Use the skills you have developed in this chapter to answer the following.

1. **Relating** Describe how Mendel's principles of inheritance relate to the segregation of chromosomes in meiosis.
2. **Calculating** In fruit flies, the allele for a gray body (G) is dominant over the allele for a black body (g). In a cross between a black fruit fly (gg) and a heterozygous gray fruit fly (Gg), what is the probability that one offspring will have a gray body? That two offspring will have gray bodies?
3. **Interpreting data** In hamsters, the allele for black fur (B) is dominant over the allele for brown fur (b), and the allele for long hair (L) is dominant over the allele for short hair (l). A student performs an F_1 cross for these traits (BBLL × bbll), then performs an F_2 cross. Of the 102 offspring in the F_2 generation, 77 have long black hair and 25 have short brown hair. Explain the significance of this result.
4. **Classifying** In snapdragons, the allele for red flowers shows incomplete dominance over the allele for white flowers. If you know the color of a snapdragon flower, can you classify the genotype as homozygous or heterozygous? Explain your answer.
5. **Drawing conclusions** In humans, the allele for free earlobes (F) is dominant over the allele for attached earlobes (f). In one family, both parents and three of the children have free earlobes and one child has attached earlobes. From this information, can you conclude that each parent is heterozygous for ear shape? Explain your answer.
6. **Constructing a model** Construct a model of crossing-over. You may use straws, pipe cleaners, or toothpicks to represent the chromosomes. Why does crossing-over increase genetic diversity?

Applying Your Skills

Dog Breeding

In dogs, the allele for a spotted coat (S) is dominant over the allele for a solid coat (s). Suppose that you own a male dog with a spotted coat and a female dog with a solid coat and you allow the dogs to mate.

1. Can you calculate the probability that the first offspring will have a solid coat? Explain your answer.
2. Suppose that one parent of the female dog had a solid coat. Does this information change your answer to question 1? Explain.
3. Suppose that one parent of the male dog had a solid coat. Does this information change your answer to question 1? Explain.

• GOING FURTHER •

4. Other traits in dogs include hair length (short is dominant over long), hair texture (wiry is dominant over silky), and hair curliness (curly is dominant over straight). Is the dominant form of these traits necessarily more common than the recessive form? Explain why or why not.

12. Multiple alleles are genes that have more than two alleles for a trait. As a result, many more different phenotypes can occur than could normally occur if there were only two alleles.

Extending Your Thinking

1. Mendel thought that an organism received two alleles—one from each parent. Meiosis produces gametes that contain only one allele for each gene. Mendel also observed that some traits assort independently. In meiosis, homologous chromosomes segregate randomly, allowing any possible combination of alleles.

2. One offspring: ½; two offspring: ½ x ½ = ¼

3. These genes are not assorting independently because the F_2 generation does not have all four possible phenotypes.

4. Yes, each genotype has a different phenotype.

Skills Trace
Classifying
- Focus p. 130
- Practice p. 130
- Assess p. 145

5. Yes. In order to produce a child with the recessive phenotype, each parent had to contribute one recessive allele.

6. Students' models will vary. Crossing-over increases genetic diversity by redistributing the alleles that are carried together on homologous chromosomes.

Skills Trace
Modeling
- Focus p. 132
- Practice p. 134
- Assess p. 145

Applying Your Skills

1. No. The male dog could be either homozygous or heterozygous.
2. No. The female must be homozygous recessive, since she has a solid coat. We already know her genotype.
3. Yes. If one parent of the male dog has a solid coat, then that parent could contribute only a recessive allele to the male dog. So the male dog is heterozygous and the probability that the first offspring will have a solid coat is ½, or 50%.
4. No. If a particular dominant allele were very rare in the population of dogs, then dogs with the dominant phenotype would be in the minority.

Scoring Rubric

4 Response is thorough, accurate, and creative; shows an in-depth understanding of science skills, procedures, and concepts.

3 Response is complete, mostly accurate, and original; shows a satisfactory understanding of science skills, procedures, and concepts.

2 Response is mostly complete but includes some inaccuracies; shows an adequate understanding of science skills, procedures, and concepts.

1 Response is only partially complete and has many inaccuracies; shows an incomplete understanding of science skills, procedures, and concepts.

0 Response is mostly incomplete and/or inaccurate; shows a lack of understanding of science skills, procedures, and concepts.

Chapter 7 Human Inheritance

Content Management	Student Edition Activities
■ Section 7–1 The Human Genetic System, pp. 147–150 A Model System? Pedigree Analysis Genes and People	Laboratory Investigation: Only the Prints Can Tell, pp. 164–165
■ Section 7–2 Sex-Linked Inheritance, pp. 151–154 Sex Determination Sex-Linked Genes in Humans	MINI LAB: Human Beans, p. 153
■ Section 7–3 Human Genetic Disorders, pp. 155–159 Autosomal Genetic Disorders Chromosome Number Disorders Prenatal Diagnosis	MINI LAB: Climbing a Family Tree, p. 157
◆ BRANCHING OUT • In Depth Section 7–4 Special Topics in Human Genetics, pp. 160–163 X-Chromosome Inactivation Gene Imprinting Ethical Issues in Genetics	

■ These sections cover all the necessary content and concepts for a basic course in biology.
◆ This section covers content and concepts that are either applications or extensions of the basic material.

Integration Strategies

SE Careers, p. 150
Health, pp. 154, 158
Social Studies, p. 156

Assessment Strategies

SE Chapter Review, pp. 166–169
TR Section Reviews
Chapter Test
BL Chapter Review
Practice Test
CTB Chapter 7 Test

Tech Prep

Teaching strategies appropriate for students who are in technical/vocational programs or who are considering post-secondary technical education can be found on **TE** pages 149 and 158.

Meeting the Standards

Sections 7–1 through 7–4 cover all three of the content standards under **The Molecular Basis of Heredity** as described on page 185 of The National Science Education Standards.

Chapter Planning Guide

Teacher's Edition Activities	Other Activities	Media and Technology
Chapter Discovery Learning Activity, p. 146 **Inquiry Activity:** Studying Human Inheritance, p. 148 **Investigate:** Long-Term Project, p. 148 **Activity:** Karyotyping, p. 148	**LM** Investigating Inherited Traits, #13 **TR** **Apply:** Special Traits **BL** **Inquiry Activity:** Nature or Nurture?	
Inquiry Activity: Sex and Baldness, p. 151 **Investigate:** Cooperative Learning, p. 152	**LM** Observing Human Sex Chromosomes, #14 **TR** **Explore:** Gene Spy **BL** **Inquiry Activity:** Blood Relatives	**TB** Sex-Linked Inheritance, #8
Inquiry Activity: The Inheritance of Genetic Disorders, p. 156 **Investigate:** Research, p. 158 **Investigate:** Role-Playing, p. 158	**TR** **Writing in Biology:** In Sickness and in Health **Enrich:** Therapy for Bad Genes **BL** **Inquiry Activity:** A Sticky Situation	
Inquiry Activity: Research Topics in Human Genetics, p. 160 **Investigate:** Role-Playing, p. 160 **Investigate:** Cooperative Learning, p. 163	**TR** **Explore:** X Marks the Spot **BL** **Inquiry Activity:** Do You Really Want to Know?	

KEY: **SE** Student Edition **TE** Teacher's Edition **LM** Laboratory Manual **TR** Teaching Resources **BL** BioLog **TB** Transparency Box **CTB** Computer Test Bank

Materials List

TE Chapter Discovery Learning Activity, p. 146 (15–20 minutes); mixture of photographs of people that includes members of one family and nonfamily members.
TE Investigate: Long-Term Project, p. 148 (2 weeks), culture bottles containing fruit flies.
TE Activity: Karyotyping, p. 148 (15–20 minutes); photocopies of metaphase chromosomes, scissors, paper, paste.
SE MINI LAB: Human Beans, p. 153 (20 minutes); jars or other containers, marking pencil or labels, red beans, white beans.

CHAPTER 7

Human Inheritance

Introducing the Chapter

. . . In Pictures

Have students examine the photograph and read the caption. Then ask these questions.

- **In what ways do some of the people in the photograph resemble one another?** Students may mention similarities in size, age, hair color, gender, or other characteristics.)

- **In what ways is each person in the photograph unlike all the others?** (Students may mention differences in face and body structures, hair, or other characteristics.)

Teaching Strategy

In the first three sections of this chapter, students will learn how human traits are inherited and what causes some genetic disorders. In the BRANCHING OUT section, students find out about recent advances in the field of genetics and ethical issues raised by these advances. You may wish to assign this section to gifted students and students who have a special interest in human genetics.

BIO JOURNAL

Encourage students to infer what causes people to look both similar and different. Also point out that the environment affects a person's appearance. Have students describe how they think the environment affects the resemblance of people. Instruct students to keep their entries in their portfolios.

CHAPTER 7

Human Inheritance

FOCUSING THE CHAPTER THEME: *Unity and Diversity*

7–1 The Human Genetic System
- Explain why humans are not ideal organisms for the study of genetics.

7–2 Sex-Linked Inheritance
- Describe some of the genetic disorders carried on the sex chromosomes.

7–3 Human Genetic Disorders
- Classify some genetic disorders based on their cause.

BRANCHING OUT *In Depth*

7–4 Special Topics in Human Genetics
- Describe some of the recent advances in the field of genetics.

LABORATORY INVESTIGATION
- Observe the differences among fingerprints of different people.

Biology and Your World

BIO JOURNAL

People often resemble each other but don't look exactly alike, except for identical twins. Think about the people you know. In what ways are they similar? In what ways are they different? Answer these questions in your journal.

A group of teenagers

TEACHER SUPPORT

Chapter Discovery Learning Activity

Give student groups a mixture of photographs of people from the same family and people who are not in that family. Instruct students to determine which people belong to the family and which do not. After students have sorted their pictures, ask them to explain what criteria they used to sort the pictures.

Point out that family resemblances are often easy to see, but not always. Explain that in this chapter they will learn how human traits are inherited, which will help explain why family members often resemble and differ from one another.

The Human Genetic System

SECTION 7–1

Guide for Reading

- **Explain** how most human traits are inherited.
- **Define** multiple allele.

WHAT MAKES EACH PERSON unique and different? Obviously, every individual has a different set of experiences. Each person grows up with different surroundings and with a different viewpoint of the world. Added to these, however, are the biological differences that individuals inherit in their genes. These also help to make each person unique. Each one of us is born with a biological inheritance so large that it would take a library full of books to do it justice.

How much do we know about the library of human genetics? Today, it's fair to say that we have just begun to understand how large that library is and have begun to read some of its books. They are interesting, to be sure, but we have a lot of reading to do.

A Model System?

Are humans ideal organisms to use for the study of genetics? Unfortunately, they are not. If you wanted a perfect organism to study inheritance, you would surely pick something that was much simpler, that reproduced more quickly, that produced more offspring, and that took up less space in the lab! You might even make the same choice that geneticists made years ago—the common fruit fly, *Drosophila melanogaster*.

The fruit fly was first suggested as the perfect organism for genetic studies nearly 100 years ago by the American geneticist Thomas Hunt Morgan. Morgan realized that the fruit fly had several advantages for the study of genetics. First, it can produce a new generation in just a few weeks, making it possible to conduct experiments in a reasonable amount of time. Second, a fruit fly is small and thus easy to maintain in large numbers in the laboratory. Third, a fruit fly has a relatively simple genetic system, with just 8 chromosomes in a diploid cell.

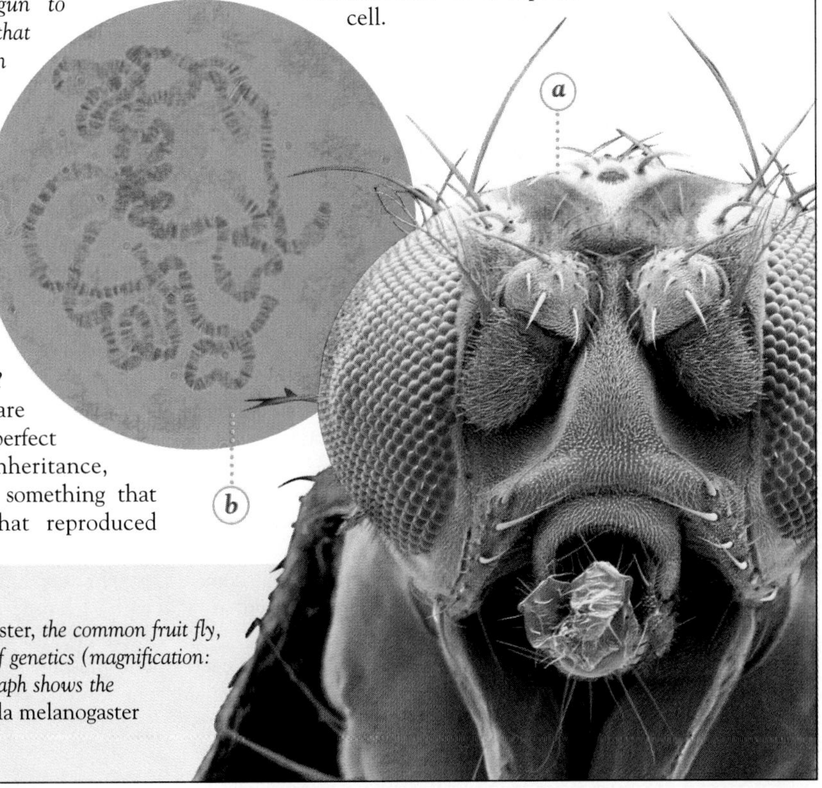

Figure 7–1
(a) Drosophila melanogaster, *the common fruit fly, is often used in the study of genetics (magnification: 140X).* (b) *This photograph shows the chromosomes of* Drosophila melanogaster *(magnification: 500X).*

TEACHER SUPPORT

Historical Perspective

Thomas Hunt Morgan was a professor of biology at Columbia University from 1904 to 1928. During that time, his "fly room," as it was affectionately called, was the site of many important genetic discoveries. In the same decade as Mendel's paper was rediscovered, Morgan showed that chromosomes are chains of genes. He also showed that genes located closely together are more likely to be inherited together. By using certain genetic traits, Morgan was able to map the locations of genes on the fruit fly chromosomes.

Section 7–1

The Human Genetic System

Performance Objectives

- Describe how the human genetic system works.
- Explain the role of a multiple allele in human genetics.

Laboratory Investigation Skill: Observing

1 ENGAGE

Ideas Through Images

Have students examine Figure 7–1, read the caption, and answer the following questions.

- **What are some characteristics of *Drosophila melanogaster* that you observe?** (Students might mention color of eyes, the presence of hairs on the thorax, the shape and number of wings, the color of the body, or the number of body segments. Accept all logical responses.)
- **How might the genetic study of *Drosophila melanogaster* help scientists understand the inheritance of human traits?** (Some students might mention that the inheritance of traits in both *Drosophila* and humans follows the principles of Mendelian genetics. Accept all logical responses.)
- **Do you think the techniques used to study the inheritance of traits in *Drosophila* are the same as those used to study human traits?** (Some students might mention that it is not possible to set up controlled genetic crosses in humans like it is in *Drosophila*. Accept all logical responses.)

2 EXPLORE

Inquiry Activity

Observing

Studying Human Inheritance
Ask students to consider how traits are inherited. Suggest they follow the inheritance of one trait in their family. They should choose a visible trait to study, such as tongue rolling, widow's peak, attached or unattached ear lobes, dimples, freckles, or any other similar trait. Instruct students to observe the trait in as many generations of their family as possible. Students should record their observations in charts of their own design. After students analyze their data, ask them to infer the kind of inheritance the trait shows.

3 TEACH

Investigate

Long-Term Project Have student groups set up a culture of fruit flies to observe the stages in the fruit fly life cycle. Give each group a culture bottle filled with media and a few males and females. Students should check their cultures daily and record their observations. When students first observe eggs laid across the top of the media, they may discard the adults. Instruct students to diagram each stage of the fruit fly life cycle and the number of days between each stage. After the project, discuss the characteristics of *Drosophila melanogaster* that make it a good model organism for genetic studies.

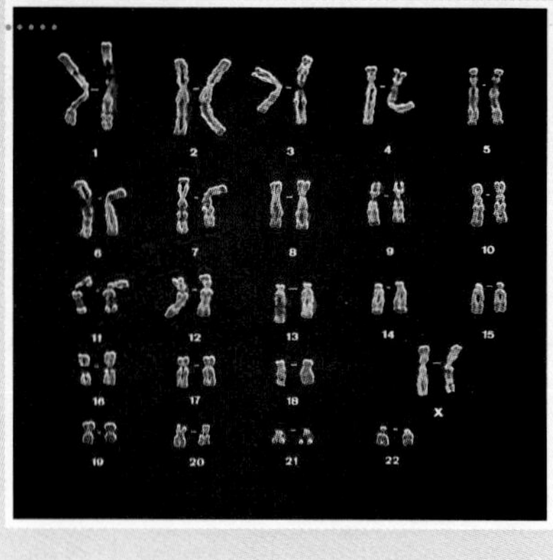

Figure 7–2
(a) In order to prepare a karyotype, a geneticist will literally cut out each individual chromosome from a photograph, match it to its corresponding homologous pair, and then arrange them in numerical order. (b) This photograph shows a complete karyotype of a female, with all the chromosomes arranged in numbered homologous pairs.

Biologists have used the fruit fly as a model system for the study of genetics for many years. These tiny animals have helped biologists learn how heredity functions in other organisms, including humans. In fact, many major discoveries in genetics were made in the fruit fly first and then were applied to the more complex genetic system—the human—later.

☑ **Checkpoint** Why is the fruit fly a model organism for the study of genetics? 1

The Human Cell

Diploid human cells have a total of 46 chromosomes—23 from each parent. As you may recall, chromosomes are easiest to see during mitosis. However, in order to see all 46 chromosomes at once, cell biologists have to use a special process. This process involves growing a sample of cells in colchicine, a poison that breaks down microtubules. This action prevents cells from completing mitosis. Before long, most of the cells are trapped in metaphase, and their chromosomes are fully condensed and easy to see and photograph. To analyze the chromosomes, cell biologists will literally cut out the photograph of each chromosome and then group them together, as shown in ***Figure 7–2.*** A picture of chromosomes put together this way is known as a **karyotype** (KAR-ee-uh-tighp).

A human karyotype reveals that each cell has 22 pairs of homologous (similar in structure) chromosomes that are numbered from 1 to 22 in order of decreasing size—chromosome 1 being the largest. The 22 pairs are called **autosomes,** or autosomal chromosomes. Each cell also has one pair of **sex chromosomes,** called the X and Y chromosomes. Female cells have two X chromosomes. Male cells have one X chromosome and one Y chromosome.

☑ **Checkpoint** What is a karyotype? 2

Human Reproductive Cells

The human reproductive cells—sperm and eggs—are produced by meiosis in the male and female reproductive systems. Sperm and eggs are both haploid—that is, they contain 23 chromosomes, only half the total number of chromosomes in human body cells. Therefore, they normally carry just one sex chromosome each. During fertilization, a sperm and an egg unite to form a zygote that contains 46 chromosomes.

Just like any other organism, human reproductive cells go through meiosis. Homologous chromosomes pair during the first meiotic division, and crossover events between human chromosomes produce genetic recombinations.

The sex chromosomes form tetrads with each other. This action ensures that each egg normally carries a single X chromosome. During meiosis in males, the X and Y chromosomes pair and then

148 Chapter 7

TEACHER SUPPORT

Activity

Karyotyping Have students construct a karyotype using a photocopy of metaphase chromosomes from any organism. You can draw the chromosomes yourself, or find a picture of them in a reference book. Instruct students to make the karyotype by cutting out the chromosomes, pairing up homologous chromosomes, and arranging the pairs in order of size (largest to smallest) on a separate sheet of paper. Challenge them to infer the sex of the individual by examining the chromosome pairs.

SEX DETERMINATION

		Male	
		X	Y
Female	X	XX	XY
	X	XX	XY

Figure 7–3
Female cells contain only X chromosomes, and male cells contain both X and Y chromosomes. As a result, the male cells determine the sex of a baby. As you can see from this Punnett square, there is a 50-50 chance of having one sex or the other.

are separated in the first meiotic division. This means that half of a male's sperm cells carry an X chromosome and the other half carry a Y chromosome. Think about this fact as you look at **Figure 7–3,** and see if you can explain why males and females are born in nearly equal numbers.

☑ *Checkpoint* Is an egg haploid or diploid? ③

Pedigree Analysis

A human generation spans more than 20 years, making it almost impossible to carry out the kinds of experiments that are possible with other organisms, such as fruit flies. In order to study the inheritance of human traits, biologists have to rely on family histories and medical records to provide the information they need. One of the best ways to summarize this information is to construct a **pedigree.** A pedigree is a diagram that follows the inheritance of a single trait through several generations in a family.

In a pedigree, squares represent males and circles represent females. Vertical lines connect parents and their children, and horizontal lines connect male and female parents. In a family, the symbols for the children are placed from left to right in birth order, with the oldest child on the extreme left. If a pedigree illustrates an inherited recessive trait, the squares or circles representing males and females with this trait are shaded. If a person is heterozygous for the trait (or a hybrid), the square or circle is half shaded.

☑ *Checkpoint* What is a pedigree? ④

Genes and People

Because Mendel's principles of genetics also apply to humans, it is possible to use genetics to analyze human inheritance. **Many human traits are inherited by the action of genes that have dominant and recessive alleles.** Other traits are determined by genes that have more than two alleles.

Dominant and Recessive Alleles

The Rh blood group is one example of a trait that is determined by a single-gene, two-allele system—positive and negative. The positive allele (Rh^+) is dominant, so persons who have two positive alleles (Rh^+/Rh^+) or one positive (Rh^+) allele and one negative (Rh^-) allele are said to be Rh-positive. Those with two negative alleles (Rh^-/Rh^-) are Rh-negative.

Figure 7–4
This pedigree traces the inheritance of a single recessive trait in a family.

INHERITANCE OF A RECESSIVE TRAIT

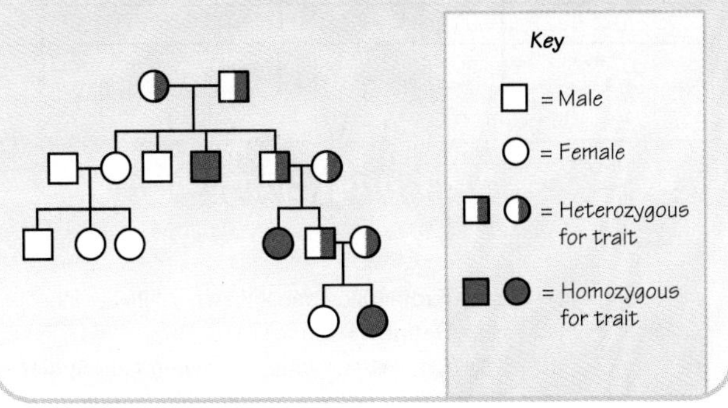

Laboratory Investigation

The Laboratory Investigation, Only the Prints Can Tell, on pages 164–165 is appropriate to use at this point in the chapter.

Ideas Through Images

Have students examine Figure 7–4 and read the caption. Draw a Punnett square on the board showing the cross between the two heterozygous parents in the first generation. Remind students that each child is the result of an independent event, so the actual phenotypic frequencies do not necessarily match those predicted in the Punnett square. Then ask students these questions.

- **If the homozygous recessive son in the second generation marries a heterozygous woman, what is the chance they will have a child with the trait?** (Fifty percent.)
- **If the mother of the male in the first generation does not have the recessive trait, then what could be her genotype?** (The mother is either homozygous dominant or heterozygous.)

☑ Checkpoints

① The fruit fly has a short generation time, small size, and a simple genetic system.

② A picture of an organism's chromosomes arranged in numbered homologous pairs.

③ Haploid.

④ A diagram that traces the inheritance of a single trait through a family.

TEACHER SUPPORT

Managing Classroom Diversity

AT-RISK STUDENTS

Have students diagram the process of meiosis to show how a gamete ends up with only one X or one Y chromosome. Then challenge them to diagram the process of fertilization in which the chromosomes from the gametes come together to form a diploid organism. Ask them which sex cell is contributed by the female (X chromosome), by the male (either X or Y chromosome), and which parent determines the sex of the offspring (the male).

TECH PREP STUDENTS

For those students who are especially interested in human genetics and inheritance, encourage them to learn about in which career fields they could put this information to use. (Biotechnology and health care are two such areas.) Challenge them to find out about the skills and educational requirements needed for various careers. With the information, have them make a bulletin board display on careers in genetics.

Ancillary Support

The resources below can be used to support your teaching strategy for these two pages.

LM Investigating Inherited Traits, #13
TR Apply: Special Traits
BL Inquiry Activity: Nature or Nurture?

INTEGRATING CAREERS

To become a phlebotomist, a person must have a high school education with classes in biology and chemistry. Further training in a medical assistant program at a technical school or junior college may also be required. Most phlebotomists work at hospitals or medical clinics.

4 ASSESS

Quick Check

Have students construct a pedigree showing the inheritance of the ABO blood group in a family over three or four generations. After students finish, have them compare their pedigrees.

Section Review 7–1

1. Most human traits are inherited by the action of genes that have dominant and recessive alleles.
2. A multiple allele is a gene with more than two alleles.
3. Because all other blood types can safely receive a blood transfusion from people with blood group O.

Learning Modality

Visual Learning Use Punnett squares and pedigrees to help students visualize the inheritance of human traits. Show how the alleles for both parents are split up in a Punnett square as they would segregate during gamete formation. The resulting offspring show all possible outcomes from a certain cross. Encourage students to practice identifying genotypes of individuals in a pedigree chart and predicting the genotypes of the offspring.

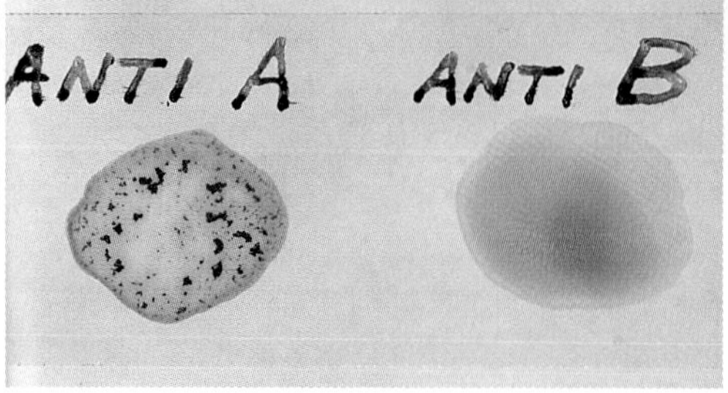

Figure 7–5
Blood groups are one example of a multiple allele. The blood sample on the left has formed clumps, indicating that two incompatible blood groups were mixed. The blood sample on the right has no clumps, indicating that compatible blood groups were mixed.

INTEGRATING CAREERS

A phlebotomist is a person trained to withdraw blood. What kind of training does a phlebotomist need?

Multiple Alleles

A multiple allele is a type of gene that is determined by more than two alleles. The ABO blood group is an example of a **multiple allele.** There are three alleles for this gene—I^A, I^B, and i. To complicate matters further, the I^A and I^B alleles are codominant, meaning they are both dominant over the allele i. Alleles I^A and I^B are responsible for producing molecules called antigens, which can be recognized by the immune system on the surface of the red blood cell. Allele i does not produce any antigens.

When medical workers describe blood groups, they usually mention both groups at the same time. For example, they may say that a patient has AB-negative blood, meaning that the person has both A and B antigens from the ABO gene and the negative allele from the Rh blood group.

Blood groups are very important, especially in medical procedures involving blood transfusions. ● Physicians must take care to be sure that the blood groups of the donor and the recipient are compatible. A transfusion of incompatible blood could cause a violent, or even fatal, reaction.

Figure 7–6
A person with blood group AB can safely receive a blood transfusion from any of the other blood groups. A person with blood group O, on the other hand, can receive a blood donation only from another individual with blood group O.

BLOOD GROUPS

Blood Group	Alleles	Antigen on Red Blood Cell	Safe Transfusions	
			To	From
A	I^AI^A or I^Ai	A	A, AB	A, O
B	I^BI^B or I^Bi	B	B, AB	B, O
AB	I^AI^B	A, B	AB	A, B, AB, O
O	ii	none	A, B, AB, O	O

Section Review 7–1

1. **Explain** how most human traits are inherited.
2. **Define** multiple allele.
3. **Critical Thinking—Drawing Conclusions** Why do you think that people with blood group O are called universal donors? (*Hint:* Look at ***Figure 7–6***).

TEACHER SUPPORT

Background Information

Human traits that are determined by more than one gene are polygenic traits. These include height, skin color, and eye color. None of the genes for a polygenic trait are dominant. Each gene has an active allele and an inactive allele. Active alleles have an additive effect on the phenotype. Inactive alleles do not affect the phenotype. Because of these additive effects, a continuous range of phenotypes is possible. Environmental conditions also affect the phenotype of polygenic traits. For example, height and weight are affected by nutrition, disease, and exercise.

Sex-Linked Inheritance

SECTION 7–2

Guide for Reading

- **Describe** how sex is determined in fruit flies.
- **Explain** why the sex-linked disorders are more common in males than in females.

MINI LAB

- **Construct a model** showing the inheritance of sex.

GENES THAT ARE LOCATED ON the 22 pairs of autosomes are inherited according to the principles described by Mendel. Does this also apply to genes located on the sex chromosomes? Should you expect to find a special pattern of inheritance for genes located on the X or the Y chromosome? The answer to these questions is yes, although it may surprise you that the answers did not come from studies of human inheritance. The understanding that genes could be sex-linked came from work on the fruit fly.

Sex Determination

The diploid cells of a fruit fly have only 8 chromosomes, but like human cells, they contain 2 sex chromosomes. **Female fruit flies have two X chromosomes, and male fruit flies have one X chromosome and one Y chromosome.** Like humans, the segregation of sex chromosomes in fruit fly meiosis ensures that male and female fruit flies will be born in nearly equal numbers.

This means that in fruit flies and in humans, the determination of sex is chromosomal. In other words, whether an individual is male or female depends on the sex chromosomes that the individual inherits. This has some very interesting consequences for the **sex-linked genes,** or the genes located on the sex chromosomes.

Morgan's Experiments

One day in 1909, Thomas Hunt Morgan noticed something strange in one of the bottles of fruit flies that he had in his lab. Normally, the flies have deep-red eyes. But in this bottle, one of the male flies had white eyes, which

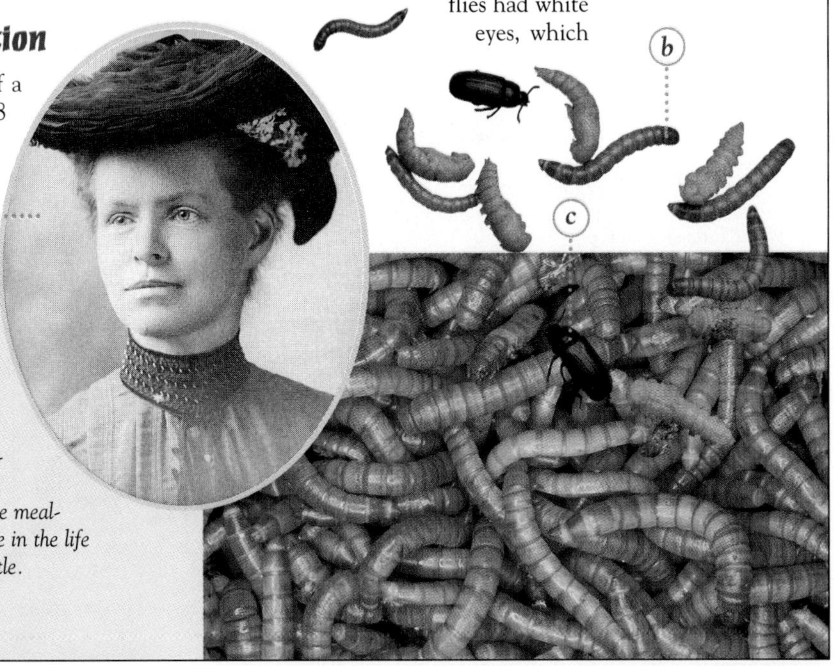

Figure 7–7 In the early part of the twentieth century, (a) Nettie Stevens discovered the sex chromosomes, X and Y. When Stevens first made her discovery, she was studying (b) mealworms. (c) The mealworm is actually one stage in the life cycle of the Tenebria beetle.

Section 7–2

Sex-Linked Inheritance

Performance Objectives

- Explain how sex determination occurs in humans.
- Describe why sex-linked recessive traits are expressed more often in males than in females.

Mini Lab Skill: Modeling

1 ENGAGE

Inquiry Activity

Observing

Sex and Baldness

Ask students whether they think baldness is inherited and, if so, if they think it is related to sex. Challenge students to design a procedure in which they observe a large number of people and record their observations. Encourage students to use their data to form inferences about the inheritance of baldness and its relationship to the sex of an individual.

2 EXPLORE

Discussion

Display karyotypes of a male and a female for students to compare. Then ask these questions.

- **How are the karyotypes similar?** (Both have 22 sets of autosomes; both have an X chromosome.)
- **How do the karyotypes differ?** (The sex chromosomes are different. Some students might explain that the male has one X and one Y chromosome; the female has two X chromosomes.)

Encourage students to infer how the differences in the karyotypes might affect the differences in traits between men and women.

TEACHER SUPPORT

Managing Classroom Diversity

EDUCATIONAL EQUITY

Some students may be interested to learn more about Nettie Stevens, her work with mealworms, and her contributions to scientific knowledge. Encourage those students to write a short biography about her. Point out that in 1905, when Nettie Stevens discovered the sex chromosomes, women scientists, even women with a Ph.D., were something of an oddity. Explain that women like Nettie Stevens have made it easier for women today to make major contributions to scientific research.

3 TEACH

Investigate

Cooperative Learning Challenge student groups to work cooperatively to design a pedigree that traces the inheritance of a sex-linked dominant or recessive trait in a family over several generations. Students can invent the trait and its phenotype, as well as the family in which it is inherited. Then have groups write three questions about their pedigree chart and the inheritance of the invented trait. Groups should switch charts and answer the questions. When completed, bring the groups together to discuss the answers to the questions, as well as the inheritance of the traits.

Discussion

Remind students of the Inquiry Activity, Sex and Baldness, on page 151 and initiate a class discussion about their inferences and data. Through the discussion, emphasize the following points.

- Male pattern baldness is a sex-influenced trait, not a sex-linked trait, because the gene for this trait has been mapped to an autosome.
- Scientists do not really know why the gene is expressed differently in men and women. Some scientists suspect that sex hormones, estrogen and testosterone, play a role in the gene's expression.

Correcting Misconceptions

Students might think that colorblind people see the world only in black and white. Show students charts used to diagnose colorblindness. Explain that a colorblind person either cannot see the object in the pattern or might see a different object. Help students realize that people who are red-green colorblind do see objects as blue or yellow or shades of red; they cannot see objects as green.

immediately caught Morgan's attention. He decided to find out how the white-eye trait was inherited.

Morgan crossed the white-eyed male with a female that had the normal red eye color. All the flies in the F_1 generation had red eyes. This meant that red eye color probably was a dominant allele, and therefore white was a recessive allele.

Morgan then took two flies from the F_1 generation and crossed them. Because each of these flies should be heterozygous for eye color—a white allele from the male and a red allele from the female—Morgan expected that 1/4 of the F_2 offspring would have white eyes and 3/4 would have red eyes. When he did this cross, this is exactly what happened. However, something very strange also occurred—all the white-eyed flies were male!

Morgan thought that these results had to be more than a coincidence. He quickly realized what was going on, and he made two assumptions—the allele for white eye color was recessive and the gene for eye color was located on the X chromosome. Suddenly, everything fell into place.

Genes on the Sex Chromosomes

Look at ***Figure 7–8***. Because the original white-eyed fly was a male, only the females in the F_1 generation inherited its X chromosome with the white-eye allele. All the male flies inherited a Y chromosome from their white-eyed male parent and an X chromosome from their red-eyed female parent. When the F_1 generation of fruit flies were crossed, producing the F_2 generation, there was only one way to produce a white-eyed fly—half the egg cells produced by the F_1 females must carry an X chromosome with the white-eye allele. When one of those egg cells was fertilized by a sperm carrying a Y chromosome, a white-eyed male was produced.

Because male flies have just one X chromosome, each allele on that chromosome helps to determine the fly's phenotype. A female that inherits a recessive allele on one X chromosome may inherit a dominant allele on the other X chromosome. However, any allele that a male inherits on its X chromosome is expressed, whether or not it is recessive.

What sort of cross would be needed to produce a white-eyed female? Recall that

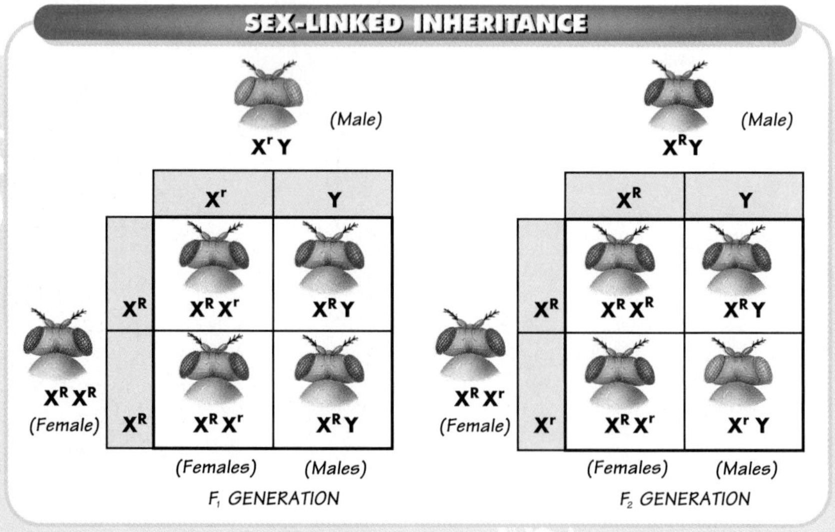

Figure 7–8
The Punnett squares illustrate Morgan's experiments of sex-linked inheritance in fruit flies. White-colored eyes are symbolized by X^r, and red-colored eyes are symbolized by X^R.

TEACHER SUPPORT

Managing Classroom Diversity

GIFTED STUDENTS

Encourage students to repeat Morgan's experiment with white-eyed fruit flies. Help them obtain the supplies and the flies they need to carry out the crosses. All supplies are readily available from biological supply companies. Make sure students write down their procedures and devise a way in which to record their data. Point out to them that it is important to use virgin females when setting up their crosses. (Females will not mate the first few hours after emerging.) Students should clear the culture bottles of flies in the morning, then collect the flies they wish to cross a few hours later. Encourage students to try different combinations of crosses.

the white-eye allele is recessive. Therefore, in order to have white eyes, a female fly needs to inherit two X chromosomes with the recessive allele.

☑ *Checkpoint* Why is a recessive allele carried on the X chromosome always expressed in a male? (1)

Sex-Linked Genes in Humans

Although the details of sex determination in humans are a bit different from fruit flies, the way in which genes on the human X chromosome are inherited is very much the same. In humans, sex-linked genes are almost always located on the large X chromosome. Although both males and females carry a copy of the X chromosome, only males carry the smaller Y chromosome that contains a few genes related to male sexual development. Therefore, the most important genes—those needed in both males and females—cannot be located on the Y chromosome.

How can you recognize sex-linked inheritance? **Because males have just one X chromosome, any X-chromosome-linked gene a male inherits, recessive or not, is expressed.** In addition, because males pass their X chromosomes along to their daughters, sex-linked genes will tend to move from fathers to their daughters. Then these genes may show up in the sons of those daughters.

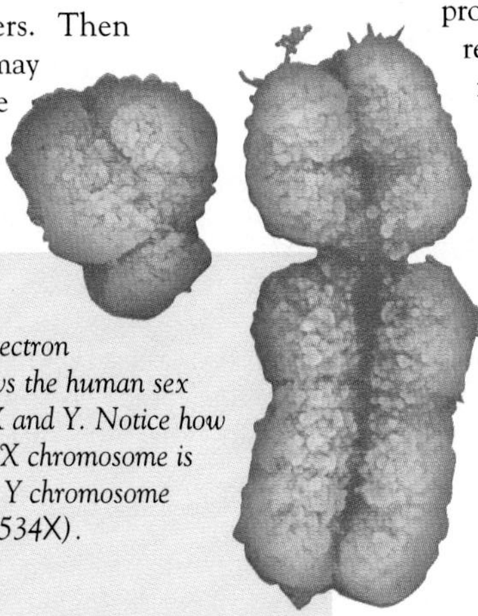

Figure 7–9
This scanning electron micrograph shows the human sex chromosomes, X and Y. Notice how much larger the X chromosome is compared to the Y chromosome (magnification: 534X).

MINI LAB ········ Modeling ······

Human Beans

PROBLEM *How can you construct a model of the inheritance of sex?*

PROCEDURE

1. Obtain two jars and label one "female" and the other "male."
2. Place 10 red beans in the jar labeled "female."
3. Place 5 red beans and 5 white beans in the jar labeled "male." The red beans will represent X chromosomes, and the white beans will represent Y chromosomes.
4. With your eyes closed, pick a pair of beans, one from each jar. Record the color of each bean.
5. Repeat step 4 until all the beans have been picked.

ANALYZE AND CONCLUDE

1. Why was one bean selected from each jar?
2. How many male offspring were produced? How many female offspring?
3. What does this tell you about the chances of an individual offspring being born either male or female?

Colorblindness

One of the important genes carried on the X chromosome is responsible for normal color vision. The dominant allele produces normal color vision. The recessive allele causes colorblindness. As many as 10 percent of all males in the United States suffer from at least one form of colorblindness, which is an inability to see certain colors properly.

Like the white-eyed fruit flies, a colorblind human male carries a single X chromosome with a recessive allele for colorblindness. How did he inherit this X chromosome? A human male inherits

MINI LAB Modeling

Teacher Notes
- For time required and materials needed, see page 146b.
- Students should keep their eyes closed while picking so that they choose randomly.

Answers to Analyze and Conclude
1. Each parent contributes one chromosome to its offspring.
2. 5 males and 5 females.
3. A child has a 50 percent chance of being either male or female.

Skills Trace
Modeling
- Focus p. 153
- Practice p. 154
- Assess p. 168

☑ *Checkpoint*

(1) Because males have only one X chromosome, any allele on that chromosome, whether dominant or recessive, is expressed.

TEACHER SUPPORT

Background Information

Not all organisms have an X-Y system of sex determination in which females are homogametic (XX) and males are heterogametic (XY). In grasshoppers, the Y chromosome does not exist. Grasshoppers with one X chromosome are male. Those with two are female.

Birds, butterflies, and moths have sex chromosomes, but the males are homogametic and the females are heterogametic. Scientists differentiate this system by notating males as ZZ and females as ZW.

In honey bees, sex is determined by being heterozygous at many different chromosome locations, not by the presence or absence of one chromosome. The worker bees and the queen bee are females with 32 chromosomes. Drones are males with 16 chromosomes. They develop from unfertilized eggs.

Ancillary Support

The resources below can be used to support your teaching strategy for these two pages.

LM Observing Human Sex Chromosomes, #14
TR Explore: Gene Spy
BL Inquiry Activity: Blood Relatives
TB Sex-Linked Inheritance, #8

INTEGRATING HEALTH

Some infectious diseases, such as hepatitis and HIV, can be transmitted from one person to another through blood. Screening the blood for these diseases prevents them from spreading to blood recipients.

4 ASSESS

Quick Check

Have students construct a pedigree showing the transmission of a sex-linked recessive trait through several generations of a family. Challenge students to identify the genotypes of certain individuals and to predict the genotypes of certain crosses.

Section Review 7–2

1. Sex is determined by the presence of X and Y chromosomes.
2. Males have one X chromosome, so recessive traits on the X chromosome cannot be masked by another allele.
3. The gene would never occur in females, who have only X chromosomes. If the gene is recessive and if it occurred on the Y chromosome, it would still not be expressed, because of the presence of the normal gene on the male's X chromosome.
4. The male determines the sex of a child, which has a 50 percent chance of being either sex.

Skills Trace

Modeling

- Focus p. 153
- Practice p. 154
- Assess p. 168

Learning Modality

Tactile Learning Have students manipulate pipe cleaner chromosomes to trace the inheritance of sex-linked traits during meiosis and fertilization. Give students beads of different shapes and colors to represent different genes and alleles on the pipe cleaners.

Figure 7–10
Queen Victoria of England was a carrier for the hemophilia gene. She passed the gene on to her offspring, who then passed it on to their offspring, spreading hemophilia through most of the royal families of Europe.

the X chromosome from his mother and the Y chromosome from his father.

Red-green colorblindness is about ten times more common among males than it is among females. Can you figure out why this is the case? If you think about the alleles that would have to be present on the X chromosomes of the parents of a colorblind female, you should be able to explain why only 1 female in 100 shows red-green colorblindness.

Checkpoint Is colorblindness caused by a dominant or a recessive allele? 1

INTEGRATING HEALTH

Why must blood be carefully screened for infectious diseases before being given to anyone?

Hemophilia

Two other important genes carried on the X chromosome help to control blood clotting. Individuals with the recessive allele for one of these genes are unable to produce one of the clotting factor proteins that normally help blood to clot. This condition is called hemophilia. For a person with hemophilia, even small cuts can present serious problems.

Hemophilia affects roughly 1 male in every 10,000. On the other hand, few females—less than 1 in 1 million—suffer from this disorder. Although no cure has been developed, it is possible to treat this disorder with injections of clotting factor proteins taken from the blood of healthy individuals. ●

Checkpoint What is hemophilia? 2

Duchenne Muscular Dystrophy

In the United States, 1 out of 3000 males between the ages of 3 and 6 develops Duchenne muscular dystrophy, a genetic disorder that causes a sudden weakness in muscles. The gene that is responsible for this disorder is also carried on the X chromosome. The recessive allele produces a defective protein that causes the muscles to weaken and break down, eventually causing death.

Researchers are trying to find a cure for this disorder. One possibility involves inserting a normal allele into the muscle cells of people with muscular dystrophy.

Section Review 7–2

1. **Describe** how sex is determined in fruit flies.
2. **Explain** why sex-linked disorders are more common in males than in females.
3. **Critical Thinking—Relating Concepts** If the gene for colorblindness were carried on the Y chromosome, what kind of pattern would you expect to see among males? Among females?
4. **MINI LAB** After **constructing your model** of the inheritance of sex, what can you conclude?

TEACHER SUPPORT

Background Information

Scientists have identified the protein, called dystrophin, whose absence causes Duchenne muscular dystrophy. The DNA sequence for this protein has also been identified. Now researchers are trying to insert normal copies of the dystrophin gene into the abnormal muscle cells of patients with the disease. Researchers hope this treatment will increase the production of dystrophin and improve muscle function in the patients.

Human Genetic Disorders

GUIDE FOR READING

- **Describe** why many genetic disorders are carried on autosomes.
- **Identify** some genetic disorders caused by nondisjunction.

MINI LAB

- **Interpret the data** from a pedigree of a recessive trait in a family.

SOMETIMES THE EXISTENCE OF a gene is discovered because one of its alleles produces an unusual trait—one that is very different from the rest of the population. Other genes are noticed because their alleles produce genetic disorders. From this information, you may get the impression that human genetics is nothing more than the study of everything that can go wrong. This is not the case, however. For every allele that causes a genetic disorder, there is also a normal, functional allele that works just fine in most people.

Autosomal Genetic Disorders

Most human genes are located on 1 of the 22 pairs of autosomes, rather than on the X and Y sex chromosomes. As you have read, some genetic disorders—colorblindness, hemophilia, and Duchenne muscular dystrophy—are carried on the sex chromosomes. **However, the majority of human genes, and therefore the majority of genetic disorders, are carried on the autosomes.** Albinism, cystic fibrosis, Tay-Sachs disease, sickle cell anemia, PKU, and Huntington disease are some examples of genetic disorders that are carried on autosomes.

Albinism

Albinism (AL-buh-nihz-uhm) is a genetic disorder caused by a recessive allele on chromosome 11. Individuals who have two copies of this allele are unable to produce melanin, the pigment responsible for most human skin color. People with albinism have no pigment in their hair or skin. In addition,

(a)

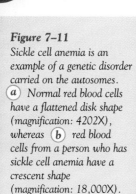

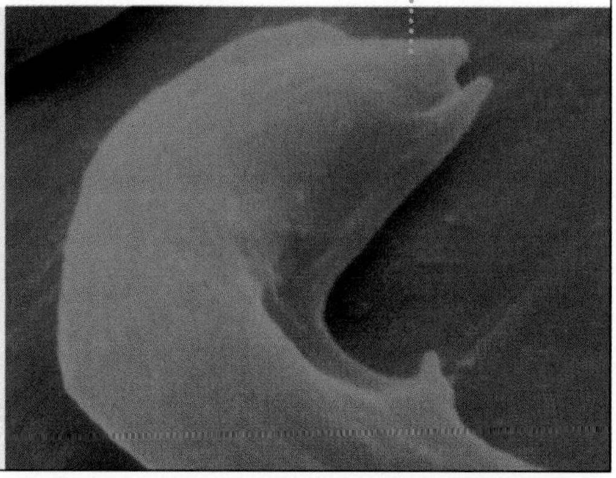

(b)

Figure 7–11 *Sickle cell anemia is an example of a genetic disorder carried on the autosomes. (a) Normal red blood cells have a flattened disk shape (magnification: 4202X), whereas (b) red blood cells from a person who has sickle cell anemia have a crescent shape (magnification: 18,000X).*

TEACHER SUPPORT

Managing Classroom Diversity

LEP STUDENTS
Students with limited English proficiency can organize the details for the genetic disorders described in this chapter with colored index cards. Students should choose a separate color for each type of disorder: autosomal and abnormal chromosome. Instruct students to list the main characteristics of each disorder on a separate card. They may include notes in their native language, if they wish.

SECTION 7–3
Human Genetic Disorders

Performance Objectives
- Explain the relationship between autosomes and genetic disorders.
- Relate nondisjunction to genetic disorders.

Mini Lab Skill: Interpreting

1 ENGAGE

Ideas Through Images

Have students examine Figure 7–11, read the caption, and answer the following questions.

- **What problems might a person with sickled red blood cells have?** (Some students might suggest that sickled red blood cells could cause pain or not function properly.)
- **How would the inheritance of sickle cell anemia differ from sex-linked traits?** (Males and females will both exhibit this trait with equal frequency.)

Checkpoints

1. Colorblindness is caused by a recessive allele.
2. Hemophilia is a genetic disorder in which clotting factor protein is not produced.

2 EXPLORE

Inquiry Activity

Inferring

The Inheritance of Genetic Disorders

Ask students to consider what could cause genetic disorders. Challenge them to brainstorm as many causes for genetic disorders as possible. They should list their ideas on a piece of paper. If students cannot think of any causes, have them consider meiosis and the principles of Mendelian genetics. Encourage students to keep their lists and update them while studying this section.

3 TEACH

Ideas Through Images

Have students examine Figure 7–12, read the caption, and answer the following questions.

- **How might the color of the albino giraffe affect its survival?** (Accept all logical responses, including that it would be more vulnerable to predators because it isn't well camouflaged.)
- **What are the chances that this giraffe will have albino offspring?** (If it mates with a heterozygous giraffe, there is a 50 percent chance of albino offspring. If it mates with a homozygous normal giraffe, none can be albino.)

INTEGRATING SOCIAL STUDIES

In Africa, malaria is most common along the Nile River in Egypt and Sudan, on the island of Madagascar, and in most of central Africa from about 10°N to 25°S. This region includes Liberia, Ghana, Nigeria, Chad, Ethiopia, Somalia, Kenya, Cameroon, Gabon, Congo, Angola, Zambia, Mozambique, and Botswana. Malaria is also prevalent in the Mediterranean basin.

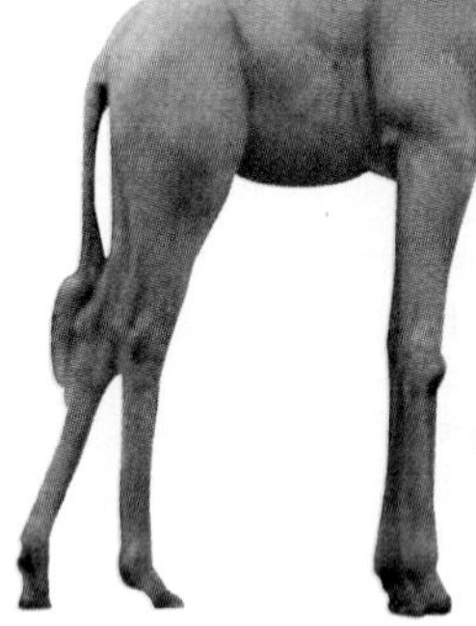

Figure 7–12 *(a) This giraffe has inherited the allele for albinism. As a result, its coat is white rather than (b) spotted, as in the other giraffes.*

they are sensitive to light and, therefore, must avoid excessive exposure to bright sunlight.

Cystic Fibrosis

In the United States, cystic fibrosis (SIHS-tihk figh-BROH-sihs) is the most common fatal genetic disease. It is found in people of European ancestry and affects approximately 1 child in 2500. Cystic fibrosis is caused by a recessive allele on chromosome 7.

Individuals with two copies of this allele make a defective cell membrane protein that interferes with the movement of chloride ions into and out of the cell. Soon chloride ions begin to build up inside the cells, causing water from the surrounding liquid to enter the cells. As a result, the surrounding liquid becomes thick and heavy, clogging the lungs and breathing passageways.

INTEGRATING SOCIAL STUDIES

In which parts of Africa is malaria common? Use reference books to find out.

Tay-Sachs Disease

Like cystic fibrosis, Tay-Sachs (TAY SAKS) disease is a fatal genetic disorder caused by a recessive allele. Tay-Sachs disease is most common in Jewish families of Eastern European ancestry. Children who are born with Tay-Sachs disease suffer from a rapid breakdown of the nervous system beginning at age 2 or 3.

Sickle Cell Anemia

Sickle cell anemia is a blood disorder that is characterized by crescent, or sickle-shaped, red blood cells. Sickle cell anemia is caused by a recessive allele that produces an alternate form of hemoglobin—the red blood cell protein. Interestingly, sickle cell anemia is common in those parts of the world where malaria is also common. Malaria is an infectious disease that causes severe chills and fevers, and may even cause death.

Individuals with two copies of the sickle cell allele suffer from sickle cell anemia and have serious medical problems. People who are heterozygous for the sickle cell allele, however, are generally healthy. In addition, they have the important benefit of being resistant to malaria. In the United States, sickle cell anemia is most common among people of African ancestry whose families trace their ancestry to regions of Africa where malaria is common. ●

Checkpoint What is sickle cell anemia? (1)

PKU

Roughly 1 child in every 15,000 is born with phenylketonuria (fehn-uhl-keet-oh-noor-ee-uh), or PKU. PKU is another genetic disorder caused by a recessive allele. PKU can cause severe mental retardation. Fortunately, there is both a test and a treatment for PKU. In fact, most states require all newborn infants to be tested for PKU. If the infant has the disorder, a special diet can help prevent damage to the nervous system.

TEACHER SUPPORT

Background Information

Sickle cell anemia is caused by a mutated gene that forms an abnormal hemoglobin protein. When the abnormal hemoglobin is deoxygenated, it becomes insoluble and crystallizes, causing the blood cells to become sickled. Symptoms of this disease, which include pain, sores that never heal, and swollen hands and feet, are caused when sickled blood cells block capillaries and prevent body tissues from receiving oxygen.

People heterozygous for the disease do produce abnormal hemoglobin, along with normal hemoglobin. However, they will show symptoms only if their bodies are deprived of oxygen, which could occur during vigorous exercise or at high altitudes. Heterozygotes are resistant to malaria because sickled cells are frequently removed from the circulation and destroyed, along with the malaria parasites.

Huntington Disease

Not all genetic disorders are carried on recessive alleles. Huntington disease, for example, is a rare genetic disorder caused by a dominant allele located on chromosome 4. Most individuals with this disorder have no symptoms until their late 30s or 40s, when they begin to lose control over their muscles. Later, as the disease progresses, the nervous system begins to break down, and most patients die within 15 years after symptoms of the disorder first appear.

Because Huntington disease appears in middle age, most people who are at risk for the disorder have already had children by the time they find out that they carry the allele. Because the allele is dominant, a heterozygous person with Huntington disease has a 50-50 chance of passing the disorder along to one of his or her children.

☑ *Checkpoint* What kind of allele causes Huntington disease? (2)

Chromosome Number Disorders

Every human life begins with a single cell, the zygote, which is formed by the fusion of a sperm and an egg. Normally, a human sperm and egg each contain 22 autosomes and 1 sex chromosome. As you have seen, when these sex cells are formed in meiosis, each chromosome pair separates during the first meiotic division.

Every now and then, however, something goes wrong and a chromosome pair fails to separate correctly. The most common error of this type in meiosis is called **nondisjunction,** which literally means "not coming apart." When nondisjunction occurs, abnormal numbers of chromosomes are produced in the sex cells. If such a sex cell produces a zygote, a genetic disorder results.

☑ *Checkpoint* What is nondisjunction? (3)

Turner Syndrome

One type of nondisjunction in which sex chromosomes fail to separate in meiosis can result in Turner syndrome. During meiosis, either a sperm or an egg is produced without a sex chromosome. When such a cell fuses with a sex cell carrying a single X chromosome, the zygote will be XO. The O

MINI LAB ······ *Interpreting* ······

Climbing a Family Tree

PROBLEM *How can you **interpret the data** from a pedigree showing inheritance of a recessive trait in a family?*

PROCEDURE

1. Draw a pedigree for a family showing 2 parents and 4 children. Include the following in the pedigree:
   - **a.** The 2 oldest children should be males and the 2 youngest children should be females.
   - **b.** The second son has sickle cell anemia.
   - **c.** The older son is married and has a daughter.
   - **d.** The oldest daughter is married and has a normal daughter and a son who has sickle cell anemia.
2. Using this information and your knowledge about constructing pedigrees, fill in the pedigree. Record the genotypes for each member of the pedigree next to his or her symbol. Use N for a normal allele and n for the sickle cell allele.

ANALYZE AND CONCLUDE

1. Can you determine the genotype for the people whose symbols are not shaded in? Explain your answer.
2. If the youngest daughter married, what would be the probability of her having a child with sickle cell anemia? Explain your answer.

MINI LAB **Interpreting**

Teacher Notes

- For time required and materials needed, see page 146b.
- Student pedigrees should look similar to the one below.

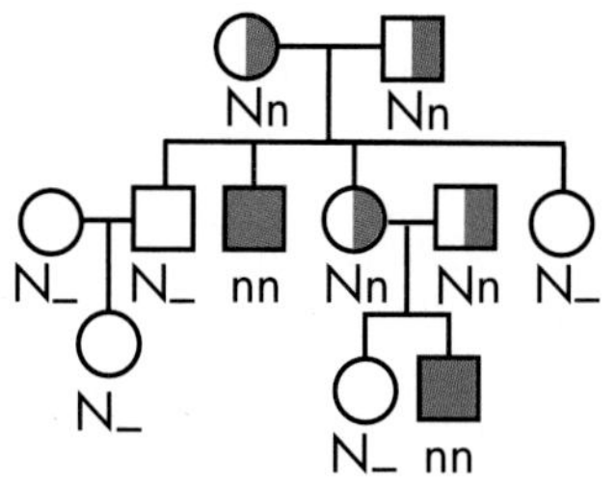

Answers to Analyze and Conclude

1. No, they could be either homozygous dominant or heterozygous.

2. If she is NN, then the chance is 0 percent. If she is Nn, 0 percent would have sickle cell anemia if her husband is NN. If her husband is Nn, they have a 25 percent chance of having a child with the disease. If her husband is nn, they have a 50 percent chance of having a child with the disease.

Skills Trace

Interpreting

- **Focus** p. 157
- **Practice** p. 159
- **Assess** p. 169

☑ **Checkpoints**

(1) A blood disorder characterized by sickle-shaped red blood cells.

(2) A dominant allele.

(3) When a chromosome pair fails to separate during meiosis.

TEACHER SUPPORT

Managing Classroom Diversity

MULTICULTURAL STRATEGY

Point out to students that some genetic disorders tend to be more common in certain cultural groups. For example, Tay-Sachs disease is most common in Jewish families of Eastern European ancestry and sickle cell anemia is most common among people of African ancestry. Lead a discussion that emphasizes the following points.

- The allele for the disorder becomes concentrated in one cultural group because spouses primarily come from only that group.
- Choosing spouses from different cultural groups will help disperse the allele for the disorder.
- The environment of the cultural group can actually select for the allele for the disorder, as in the case of sickle cell anemia.

INTEGRATING HEALTH

Women are born with all the eggs they will ever produce. These eggs remain arrested in prophase I of meiosis until they are released. As women get older, the cell machinery in their older eggs is more likely to malfunction. These eggs have also been exposed more often to radiation and viruses, which could also weaken the cellular machinery involved in meiosis.

Investigate

Research Explain to students that chromosomes can also be changed by duplications and inversions. Encourage students to research how duplications and inversions affect the expression of traits. Have students report their findings to the class.

Discussion

Explain to students that scientists know that the Y chromosome is required for maleness because individuals develop as females when the Y chromosome is absent. Genes on the Y chromosome include those that are present only on the Y chromosome itself, as well as those that are also present on the X chromosome. These homologous sites enable the X and Y chromosome to pair up in meiosis.

Investigate

Role-Playing Have students take turns playing the roles of a genetic counselor and a couple concerned that their developing baby might have a genetic disorder. Encourage students who are acting as the genetic counselors to recommend prenatal testing and to make up karyotypes. Help students realize that the difficult decisions begin after a genetic disorder is diagnosed.

indicates that a sex chromosome is missing. The karyotype for people who have Turner syndrome is written as 45XO.

Only females can be afflicted with Turner syndrome. Because their sex organs do not fully develop, these females cannot have children. However, most people with Turner syndrome are able to lead otherwise full and healthy lives.

Klinefelter Syndrome

Nondisjunction can also produce males whose cells contain an extra chromosome. This abnormality, symbolized as 47 XXY, is called Klinefelter syndrome. Mental retardation is often associated with Klinefelter syndrome, although its extent varies from one person to the next. The extra X chromosome interferes with meiosis and prevents these individuals from reproducing.

Down Syndrome

INTEGRATING HEALTH

Why is Down syndrome more common in infants of mothers over the age of 35? Use reference material to find out.

Nondisjunction can occur in autosomes as well as in sex chromosomes. If the two copies of an autosome do not separate correctly in meiosis, an individual can be born with cells that contain three copies of a chromosome. This condition is called **trisomy.** The most common form of trisomy is Down syndrome. ● **In Down syndrome, there is an extra copy of chromosome 21.**

Down syndrome results in heart and circulatory problems, a weakened immune system, and mental retardation. The degree of retardation varies greatly. Although some people who have Down syndrome are severely retarded, others are able to function quite well in society.

Scientists are only beginning to learn why a little extra genetic information causes so many problems. Current theories suggest that an extra copy of so many genes upsets the balance by which genes are regulated, leading to the disorders associated with trisomy.

Chromosome Deletions and Translocations

As you may recall, crossing-over during meiosis results in genetic recombination. When you read about crossing-over, it may have occurred to you that if something went wrong with the process, chromosomes might break. Well, occasionally, this does happen.

Many genetic disorders result from pieces of chromosomes breaking off and getting lost in meiosis. These are called **chromosome deletions.** Other disorders arise when pieces of broken chromosomes become reattached to another chromosome. These are called **chromosome translocations.**

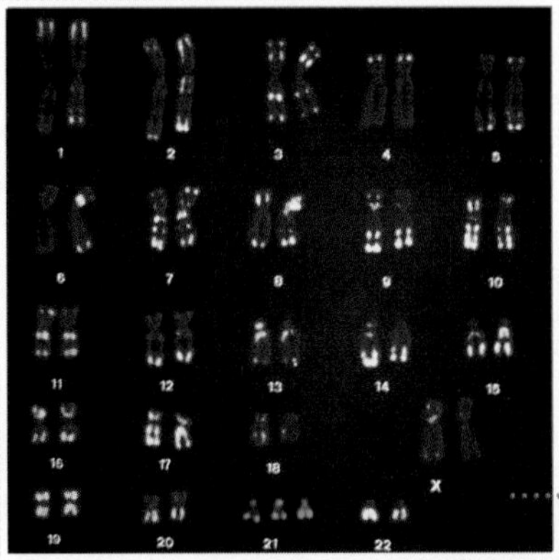

(a)

(b)

Figure 7–13 *(a) Down syndrome is characterized by the presence of an extra copy of chromosome 21, as shown in this karyotype. (b) Many people with Down syndrome, including the television star Christopher Burke, live active lives.*

TEACHER SUPPORT

Managing Classroom Diversity

TECH PREP STUDENTS

Ask students to identify the career areas that are involved in all aspects of prenatal testing (biotechnology and health care). Encourage students to find out about the training required and the career opportunities available in one of these fields. Some students might wish to interview a person currently working in the field.

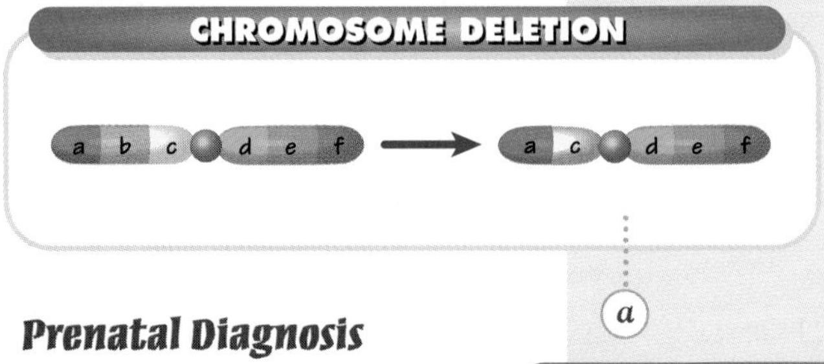

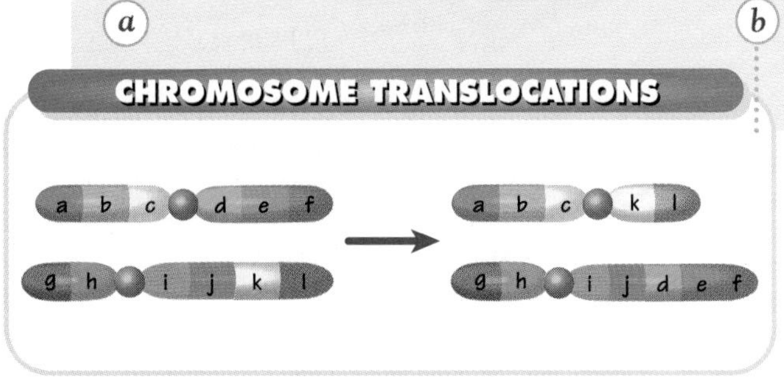

Figure 7–14
(a) A chromosome deletion occurs when a piece of the chromosome is broken off. (b) In some cases, pieces of chromosomes become attached to another chromosome. This is called chromosome translocation.

Prenatal Diagnosis

A rapidly expanding list of genetic disorders—including Down syndrome, Tay-Sachs disease, and Huntington disease—can now be detected before birth in the cells of a developing fetus. These cells can be grown in the laboratory for a few days and then analyzed by a variety of techniques to determine whether a baby is likely to be born with a genetic defect. The problem is how to collect such cells without harming either the mother or the developing fetus.

Currently, there are two ways to do this. One technique, **amniocentesis** (am-nee-oh-sehn-TEE-sihs), involves withdrawing a small amount of fluid from the sac surrounding the fetus. The fluid contains cells from the fetus which can be examined for abnormalities. Cells from a fetus can also be obtained by another technique, called **chorionic villus** (kor-ee-AHN-ihk VIHL-uhs) **sampling.** In this technique, tissue surrounding the fetus is removed and examined. Because the cells come directly from the fetus, chorionic villus sampling provides a quicker way to examine cells than does amniocentesis.

Both of these techniques have made it possible to detect a large number of genetic disorders, enabling at-risk parents to know before birth whether their child may suffer from a genetic disorder. As the understanding of genetics advances, careful testing may even make it possible to treat such disorders before birth to maximize the chances of delivering a healthy baby.

Section Review 7-3

1. **Describe** why many genetic disorders are carried on autosomes.
2. **Identify** some genetic disorders caused by nondisjunction.
3. **Critical Thinking—Synthesizing Information** Why do people with Huntington disease have a greater chance of passing this disorder on to their children than people who have Tay-Sachs disease or cystic fibrosis?
4. **MINI LAB Interpret the data** from a pedigree of a recessive trait in a family.

4 ASSESS

Quick Check

Challenge students to draw diagrams that show how nondisjunction, chromosome deletions, and translocations can cause genetic disorders. Also have them diagram how autosomal genetic disorders can be inherited.

Section Review 7-3

1. The 22 pairs of autosomes carry many more genes than the single pair of sex chromosomes.

2. Turner syndrome, Klinefelter syndrome, Down syndrome.

3. The symptoms of Huntington disease do not usually appear until after the individual has children. Tay-Sachs disease and cystic fibrosis show up in children. In addition, the allele for Huntington disease is dominant. Therefore, a heterozygous person has a 50-50 chance of passing the disorder to one of his or her children.

4. By using the pedigree they constructed for the Mini Lab on page 157, students should observe that some family members can pass on the sickle cell allele even when they do not exhibit the recessive trait. Accept other reasonable interpretations.

Skills Trace

Interpreting

- Focus p. 157
- **Practice p. 159**
- Assess p. 169

Learning Modality

Tactile Learning Students can use different colored pieces of clay or paper strips to simulate the formation of chromosome deletions and translocations. Have students use Figure 7–14 as a guide. Encourage them to move the chromosome models through meiosis to find out how the genetic make-up of the gametes is affected.

Ancillary Support

The resources below can be used to support your teaching strategy for these two pages.

TR Writing in Biology: In Sickness and in Health
Enrich: Therapy for Bad Genes
BL Inquiry Activity: A Sticky Situation

Special Topics in Human Genetics

SECTION 7–4

Special Topics in Human Genetics

Performance Objective

• Identify advances made in genetic research and explain how they may lead to treatments for genetic disorders.

1 ENGAGE

Inquiry Activity

Hypothesizing

Research Topics in Human Genetics

Ask students to formulate a question about human genetics. Challenge them to use their question and their knowledge of human genetics to write a hypothesis that could be used to start a research project. For example, students might ask how sickle cell anemia could be treated using genetics. Then they might formulate this hypothesis: Inserting a normal copy of the hemoglobin gene into a patient will relieve the symptoms of sickle cell anemia. Have students share their questions and hypotheses with the class.

2 EXPLORE

Investigate

Role-Playing Have students use their hypothesis from the Inquiry Activity as they play the role of a genetic researcher. Challenge students to predict what the implications might be if they successfully proved their hypothesis. Students should record their predictions and update them while studying this section.

GUIDE FOR READING

• **Define** what a Barr body is and explain why it is not found in males.

"KNOW THYSELF" IS SOMETIMES given as a philosopher's first challenge to students. It's wonderful advice. How can we hope to know the world around us if we don't seek to understand ourselves first?

In one sense, knowing ourselves is precisely what we try to do when we study human genetics. Understanding our own inheritance helps us to understand more completely our place in the world of living things.

Can we look back on all that we have learned about human genetics and conclude, after so much scientific effort, that now we really do know ourselves? Not at all. In this section, we will briefly examine some questions about human genetics that remain unanswered and continue to puzzle biologists.

X-Chromosome Inactivation

Human cells normally contain two copies of each autosome. However, the X chromosome is different. Recall that females have two copies of the X chromosome, while males have just one. As you have read, the X chromosome contains important genes that control everything from color vision to blood clotting. If just a single X chromosome is enough to regulate these tasks in male cells, how does the cell adjust to the extra X chromosome in female cells?

Turning Off the X

The answer to this question was discovered by the British geneticist Mary Lyon. She noted that most cells from human females have a dense region in the nucleus, called a Barr body. **Lyon suggested that the Barr body was**

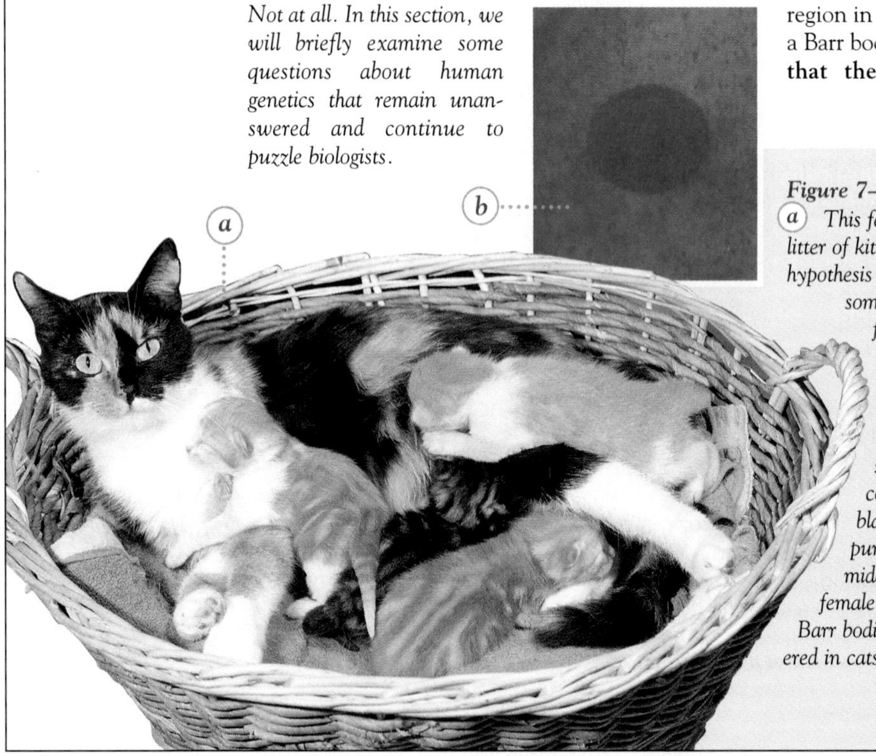

Figure 7–15 (a) *This female cat and her litter of kittens illustrates the hypothesis that one X chromosome is inactivated in females. The female cats are calico with spots of orange and black, whereas the male cats have spots of only one color—orange or black.* (b) *The dark-purple sphere in the middle of this human female cell is a Barr body. Barr bodies were first discovered in cats.*

TEACHER SUPPORT — Managing Classroom Diversity

LEP STUDENTS

Help students with difficult vocabulary in this section, such as the words inactivation, condensed, and imprinted. When using these words for the first time, repeat them and give a definition that students will understand.

Students might also find the names of syndromes such as Angelman and Prader-Willi difficult to understand. Explain that these syndromes, as well as most genetic disorders, are named for the person who first identified and described the disorder. Point out that the name does not really have anything to do with the symptoms or characteristics of the syndrome.

Figure 7–16
CAREER TRACK
Genetic counselors often review family histories and provide advice to people who are considering having children.

actually a condensed turned-off X chromosome. The reason Barr bodies aren't found in male cells is that their single X chromosome is still active.

It happens that the same process also occurs in other mammals. In cats, for example, a gene controlling the color of coat spots is located on the X chromosome. As a cat embryo develops, a single X chromosome in many of its cells is randomly and permanently switched off. If one X chromosome has an allele for brown spots and the other X chromosome has an allele for black spots, the cat's white fur will have a mixture of brown and black spots.

Interestingly, male cats, which have just one X chromosome, can have spots of a single color only. In fact, this is an almost foolproof way to tell the sex of a spotted cat! If a cat with a spotted coat has three colors—white with spots of tan and black—you can be sure it's a female.

☑ **Checkpoint** What is a Barr body? 1

What Turns Off the X?

Careful studies of female human cells show that one of the X chromosomes has been inactivated in nearly every tissue in the body. The X chromosome that has been inactivated varies from tissue to tissue and sometimes from cell to cell. How does this happen? This is the big question, and it remains unanswered.

Recent research has shown that a handful of genes is still functioning in the X chromosome that has been turned off. Maybe these genes control the activity of the rest of the chromosome. If this is the case, biologists may learn how to turn off all the genes in a single chromosome at once. This and many other discoveries could be very helpful in the treatment of genetic disorders.

Gene Imprinting

Should it make any difference whether you inherit a gene from your mother or from your father? You may not think so. In fact, until a few years ago, any geneticist would have told you that once a sperm and an egg fuse, there is no way to tell whether a particular gene came from one parent or the other.

Now, however, it turns out that this may not be true. A few years ago, a team of researchers traced a genetic disorder called Angelman syndrome to a mutation of chromosome 15. Patients with this disorder are quite short and suffer from obesity. Meanwhile, another group of researchers studying Prader-Willi syndrome, another genetic disorder, traced it to chromosome 15 as well. Individuals suffering from Prader-Willi syndrome are usually hyperactive, very thin, and of normal height. When the two groups

TEACHER SUPPORT

Historical Perspective

Barr bodies were named for Murray Barr, who first observed them in the nerve cells of female cats in 1949. It was not until the early 1960s that Mary Lyon proposed that one X chromosome is randomly inactivated. In body cells, she observed that one X chromosome replicated later than the other. The late-replicating X chromosome is inactivated when the embryo implants in the uterine wall. All body cells have the same inactivated X chromosome as the embryonic cell from which they were derived.

3 TEACH

Ideas Through Images

Have students examine Figure 7–15, read the caption, and answer the following questions.

- **Why do male cats have spots of only one color?** (Males have only one X chromosome.)
- **Is the same X chromosome inactivated in every body cell of females?** (No.)
- **Which X chromosome is inactivated in the orange spots of female cats?** (The one with the allele for black spots.)

Correcting Misconceptions

Make sure students understand how gene imprinting differs from sex-linked and sex-influenced traits.

- **Why are the Prader-Willi syndrome and the Angelman syndrome not sex-linked traits?** (The defective gene causing these disorders is located on chromosome 15, not the X chromosome.)

Explain that a sex-influenced trait, like baldness, is linked to an autosome and its expression differs in males and females.

- **How is gene imprinting different from a sex-influenced trait?** (In gene imprinting, the trait expressed is determined by the sex of the parent from which the allele is inherited. In sex-influenced traits, the trait expressed is determined by the sex of the individual with the allele.)

☑ Checkpoint

1 A condensed, inactive X chromosome.

Ancillary Support

The resource below can be used to support your teaching strategy for these two pages.

TR Explore: X Marks the Spot

Connections

A number of ethical and legal questions have been raised since the beginning of the Human Genome Project in 1990. Many doctors and researchers are anxiously awaiting the DNA sequences for genes responsible for genetic disorders. Once the DNA sequence is known, it might be possible for researchers to find a treatment or a cure. Currently, medical research is not progressing as quickly as gene mapping and sequencing. Many genetic diseases have genetic tests, but no treatments.

Answers to Making the Connection

Accept all reasonable responses regarding submitting to prenatal genetic testing. Pros of genetic testing include treating genetic diseases before symptoms appear, or choosing not to have children. Cons include possibly losing insurance coverage, or facing the onset of a disorder for which there is no treatment.

Discussion

Remind students of some of the genetic disorders they have studied in this chapter. Then initiate a class discussion about how scientists study the inheritance of human traits by studying genetic disorders. Through the discussion emphasize these points.

- Genetic disorders teach researchers the functions of different genes and the inheritance of certain traits, which leads to the development of genetic tests and treatments for disorders.
- Finding the answer to one research question often leads to more questions.

Bio FRONTIER Connections

Who Owns Your Genes?

Arthur had just graduated from college and was looking for a job. He found an ad in the newspaper, applied for the job, and went on the interview. The woman interviewing Arthur told him that in order to be hired and covered under the health insurance plan, he had to agree to a complete physical examination and some genetic testing. Arthur agreed and had the tests done.

Test Results

The test results came back and showed that Arthur was a carrier of the gene for cystic fibrosis. Because Arthur only carried the gene, the company wasn't concerned by his test results. The company did mention to Arthur that if he married and had children, his wife and children would have to be tested as well.

Five years later, Arthur got married, and his wife was tested. The results of her test were disturbing. She, too, carried the gene for cystic fibrosis. Again, the company was not concerned because she too was just a carrier. However, if Arthur and his wife were to have a baby, the company wanted the baby to be tested prenatally because the child would have a one in four chance of having cystic fibrosis.

Future Testing

In the future, there will be tests for many, if not all, genetic diseases. The Human Genome Project is identifying and mapping all the human chromosomes. All the genes will be located in their position on each chromosome and identified. Once the genes have been identified, scientists will try to develop tests for identifying any problems. Only then can possible cures for these diseases be found.

DNA sequencing machine

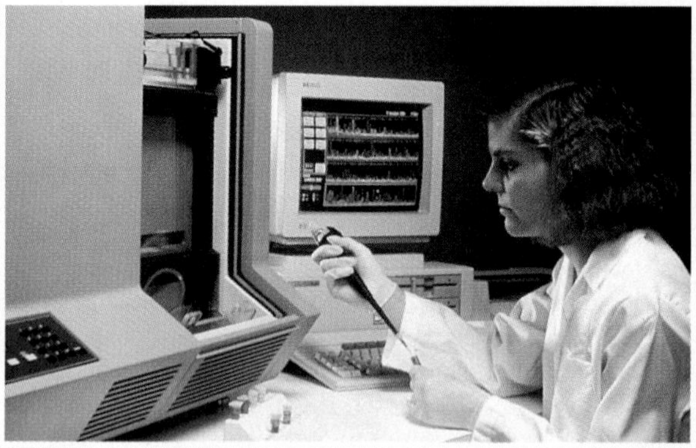

Scientists at universities, private companies, and the government are working together to map all our genes. Many genes have been placed in their proper locations, but there are at least 100,000 genes to map. It may take years, but when this project is over, human heredity will no longer be a mystery.

If employers and insurance companies gain access to genetic information, they might raise insurance rates or refuse to employ or insure people who carry certain genes. Today, medical records and all test results are private. But in the future, companies may make genetic testing a requirement for employment.

Making the Connection

If you were Arthur, would you allow the company to test your child prenatally? What if the company threatened to fire you if you didn't submit to the test? What are some of the pros and cons of genetic testing?

TEACHER SUPPORT

Historical Perspective

The Human Genome Project officially began in 1990 with two ultimate goals: identify and map every gene to its chromosome and determine the entire DNA sequence for the human genome, which has about 6 million base pairs. Research centers, universities, and private companies in the United States and around the world are working on this multibillion-dollar project, which is estimated to take 20 years to complete. The first step of this project was completed in 1993, when a French group completed a rough map of genetic markers for the entire genome. These markers will be used to help researchers map the locations of various DNA fragments.

compared notes, they were shocked. Both disorders were caused by exactly the same gene!

Why are the disorders different even though they are caused by the same apparent defect? As it turns out, a person with Prader-Willi syndrome inherits the defective allele from the mother, whereas someone with Angelman syndrome inherits the defective allele from the father. Why should these findings make a difference? That's a good question. Some researchers suggest that certain genes are marked, or imprinted, with a genetic marker that is different in males and in females—which could account for the difference. It will be interesting to find out how widespread gene imprinting is and whether it plays an important role in human genetics.

Ethical Issues in Genetics

An important new set of ethical issues has been raised by the rapid advances in human genetics. Simply stated, these questions revolve around the proper ways to use genetic information. Does anyone own genetic information? When a new gene is found, do its discoverers have special commercial rights? Do insurance companies have the right to conduct genetics tests before they issue policies? Do individuals have a right to keep their genetic information to themselves?

Many people have already had to face these questions. For example, in 1989 a test for the Huntington disease allele was developed. For the first time, it was possible for people who might carry a copy of the allele to be tested before they developed symptoms. The test was a great relief to many people who wanted to know whether or not they could pass the disorder along to their children. However, because there is no way to treat Huntington disease, many people chose not to be tested. Quite simply, they did not wish to find out whether or not they carried this fatal allele. What is the right choice in such a situation? Do people have an obligation to be tested for such alleles? If the test is positive, what are their responsibilities to their children or potential children?

These questions don't have easy answers. But in a democracy, every citizen should be prepared to play a role in determining the rules that we will live by. Science can help to shed some light on these important issues, and you owe it to yourself to develop an understanding of them. However, science by itself cannot provide the moral values or judgments that will be needed to make these important choices and decisions. Answers to these ethical questions will not come from scientific experts, but from the wisdom and strength of people in a free society.

Section Review 7-4

1. **Define** what a Barr body is and explain why it is not found in males.
2. **BRANCHING OUT ACTIVITY** Find a recent newspaper or magazine article written about one of the genetic disorders in this chapter. **Summarize** the article in a few paragraphs.

Investigate

Cooperative Learning Divide the class into pairs and give each pair a situation in which an ethical issue in genetics is raised. Instruct each pair to choose one side of the issue and prepare a case for it. Encourage them to collaborate with students from other groups who will be defending the same side of the same issue. Then each pair should present its side of the issue to the other. Encourage students to practice active listening so that they will be prepared to describe their debate to the rest of the class. After the debates, point out that there are no "right" answers to these issues. Stress the importance of understanding science in order to make informed choices based on personal needs.

4 ASSESS

Quick Check

Instruct students to choose a topic in genetics and briefly describe its implications for society. Challenge them to explain how an understanding of science will help them make informed choices.

Section Review 7-4

1. A Barr body is a condensed turned-off X chromosome. The reason that Barr bodies are not found in males is that their single X chromosome is still active.

2. Students' summaries will vary depending on the article selected.

Learning Modality

Auditory Learning Have students debate the issue of genetic testing. Halfway through the debate, switch the students who are on the pro side and the con side to reinforce that there are no "right" or "wrong" answers to this issue.

Ancillary Support

The resource below can be used to support your teaching strategy for these two pages.

BL Inquiry Activity: Do You Really Want to Know?

CHAPTER 7

Laboratory Investigation

Only the Prints Can Tell

Before the Lab

Gather enough ink pads, hand lenses, and index cards for students to work in groups of two to four.

Pre-Lab Discussion

Have students read the entire procedure for this investigation. Then ask students the following questions.

What is the purpose of this investigation? (To observe how fingerprints are unique to individuals and how they can be used to identify a person.)

Why do you think you need to make fingerprints of all your fingers? (Each finger has a different print.)

How does this investigation relate to this chapter about human genetics? (Fingerprint patterns are inherited traits and are unique to individuals.)

Skills Development

Students will use these skills while completing the laboratory investigation: observing, interpreting, classifying, and comparing.

CHAPTER 7

Laboratory Investigation

Only the Prints Can Tell

Fingerprints are often used to solve mysteries and crimes. Although there are similar patterns in fingerprints, no two fingerprints are alike. In this investigation, you will identify what makes fingerprints unique.

Problem

Observe how fingerprints can be used to identify a person.

Materials (per group)

ink pad
2 index cards
magnifying glass

Procedure

1. Obtain an ink pad, two index cards, and a magnifying glass.

2. On an index card like the one shown below, write your name, the words left hand, and the numbers 1 to 5.

3. On the second index card, include the same information except write the words right hand instead of left hand.

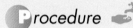

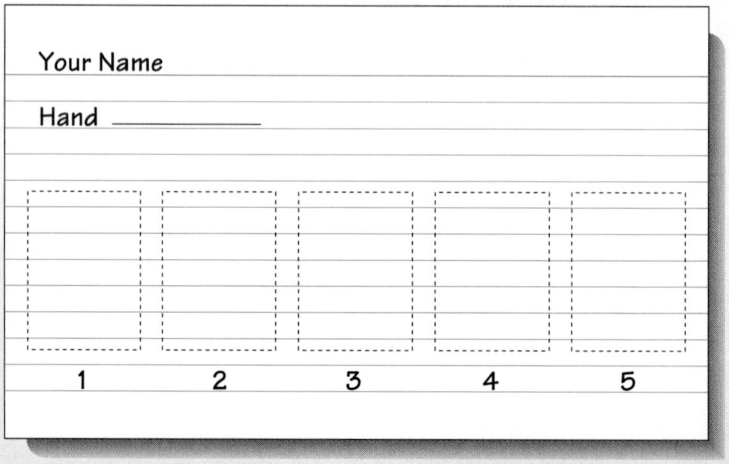

Safety Tips

Remind students not to touch anything while they have ink on their fingers. Make sure they wash their hands immediately after making the prints.

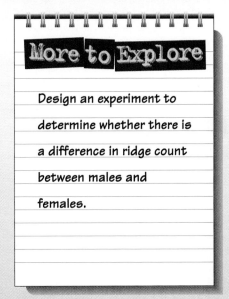

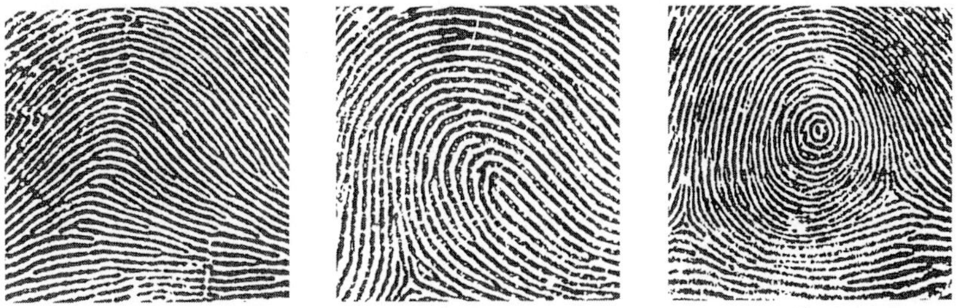

4. Carefully roll the tip of one finger from left to right on the ink pad.

5. Roll the inked fingertip on the index card in the spot numbered 1. Lift your finger straight up after making the print to avoid smudging the print.

6. Repeat steps 4 and 5 until all fingertips of both hands appear in order on the index card.

Observations

1. For each fingerprint, determine whether you have an arch, a loop, or a whorl, and record it under the prints.
2. Fingerprints are formed before birth. The genotype LL forms a whorl, Ll forms a loop, and ll forms an arch pattern. For each fingerprint, record your genotype for each fingertip.
3. For each fingerprint, draw an imaginary line from the center of your pattern to the triradius. The triradius is the triangular area formed by intersecting ridges. Count the number of ridges for each fingertip and record the number under your prints.

Analysis and Conclusions

1. Study each of your fingerprints and describe any patterns you notice.
2. Compare your fingerprints with those of others in the class and describe the results.
3. How can fingerprints be used to identify a person? Explain your answer.

More to Explore

Design an experiment to determine whether there is a difference in ridge count between males and females.

Teaching Strategies

1. If inkpads are unavailable, students can scribble on an index card with pencil until the card is thick with pencil lead. Then have them roll their fingers through the lead, place clear tape on the print, lift the tape, and place it on the index card.
2. An arch fingertip pattern does not have a triradius, so the ridge count is 0.
3. To count the ridges on a loop pattern, students should start counting from the center of the pattern along an imaginary line until reaching the triradius. Do not count the triradius.
4. A whorl with two triradii has two ridge counts (from the center of the pattern to each triradius). Have students record only the larger of the two ridge counts.

Answers to Observations

1. Answers will vary. Be sure students identify their prints correctly.
2. Genotypes will vary. Be sure students assign the correct genotype to each fingerprint pattern.
3. Ridge counts will vary. See Teaching Strategies for more information about ridge counts.

Answers to Analysis and Conclusions

1. Most students will find that their fingerprints don't show any patterns; each fingerprint could be different.
2. Students should find that everyone has a different set of fingerprints.
3. No one has a fingerprint pattern identical to that of another person, so comparing an unknown fingerprint with known fingerprints will identify a person.

More to Explore

Students can use the classroom data, as well as fingerprint data from volunteers outside of class. Encourage students to use their data to form conclusions about differences between male and female ridge counts.

CHAPTER 7

Study Guide

Review Strategy

Divide the class into teams of two or three. Have each team write ten answers and questions about concepts in this chapter that can be used to play Jeopardy. Encourage teams to write answers for three or four different categories. When students complete their answers and questions, have teams take turns playing the game, in which one team gives the questions for the other team's answers.

Study Guide

Summarizing Key Concepts

The key concepts in each section of this chapter are listed below to help you review the chapter content. Make sure you understand each concept and its relationship to other concepts and to the theme of this chapter.

7–1 The Human Genetic System

- Many human traits are inherited by the action of genes that have dominant and recessive alleles.
- Other traits are determined by more than two, or multiple, alleles.

7–2 Sex-Linked Inheritance

- The sex of an individual—male or female—depends on the sex chromosomes that the individual inherits.
- Because males have only one X chromosome, any X-chromosome-linked gene a male inherits, recessive or not, is expressed.
- Colorblindness, hemophilia, and Duchenne muscular dystrophy are examples of disorders carried on the sex chromosomes.

7–3 Human Genetic Disorders

- The majority of human genes, and therefore the majority of genetic disorders, are carried on the autosomes.
- Albinism, cystic fibrosis, Tay-Sachs disease, sickle cell anemia, PKU, and Huntington disease are examples of autosomal genetic disorders.
- When a chromosome pair fails to separate during meiosis, it is called nondisjunction.
- Many genetic disorders can be detected before birth by either amniocentesis or chorionic villus sampling.

7–4 Special Topics in Human Genetics

- New discoveries in human genetics may help in the treatment of genetic disorders.

Reviewing Key Terms

Review the following vocabulary terms and their meaning. Then use each term in a complete sentence.

7–1 The Human Genetic System

karyotype
autosome
sex chromosome
pedigree
multiple allele

7–2 Sex-Linked Inheritance

sex-linked gene

7–3 Human Genetic Disorders

nondisjunction
trisomy
chromosome deletion
chromosome translocation
amniocentesis
chorionic villus sampling

Inquiry-Based Strategy

A researcher has a patient with a disorder that has never before been described. Have students design a research procedure that would answer these questions: Is this disorder an inherited trait? If so, how is this disorder inherited? Students may develop different approaches to find the answers to these questions. A likely research procedure would include karyotyping the patient and developing a pedigree to trace the disorder through the patient's family.

Recalling Main Ideas

Choose the letter of the answer that best completes the statement or answers the question.

1. How many chromosomes do human cells have?

a. 46 **c.** 22
b. 23 **d.** 2

2. An example of a multiple allele is

a. the Rh blood group.
b. trisomy.
c. nondisjunction.
d. the ABO blood group.

3. A genetic disorder in which the blood does not clot properly is

a. PKU. **c.** hemophilia.
b. Huntington disease. **d.** Tay-Sachs disease.

4. People who are resistant to malaria often are heterozygous for which genetic disorder?

a. sickle cell anemia **c.** PKU
b. Turner syndrome **d.** colorblindness

5. When cells contain three copies of a chromosome, it is called a

a. chromosome deletion.
b. trisomy.
c. chromosome translocation.
d. multiple allele.

6. Down syndrome results from a(an)

a. extra chromosome.
b. chromosome translocation.
c. chromosome deletion.
d. missing chromosome.

7. A Barr body is a(an)

a. turned-off X chromosome.
b. trisomy.
c. turned-off Y chromosome.
d. autosome.

Putting It All Together

Using the information on pages xxx to xxxi, complete the following concept map.

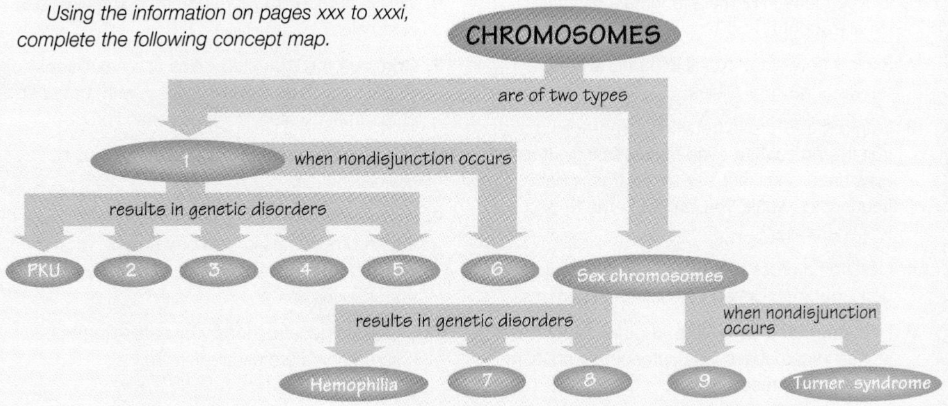

Putting It All Together

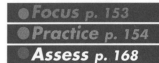

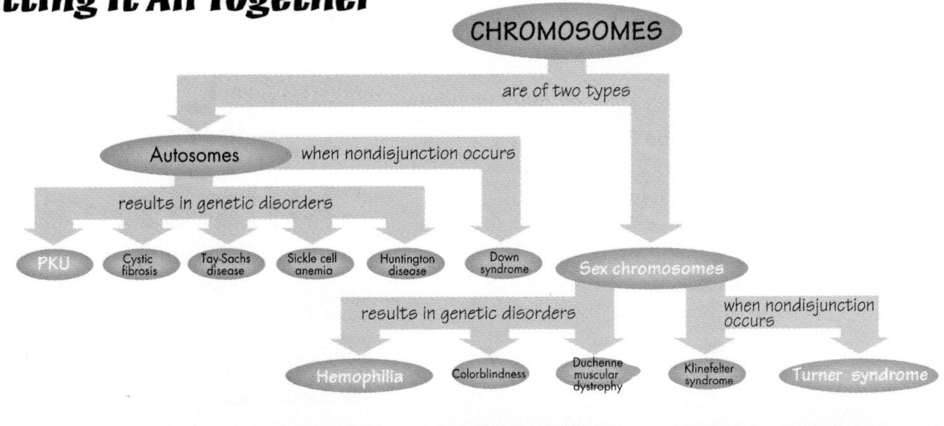

Recalling Main Ideas

1. a
2. d
3. c
4. a
5. b
6. a
7. a

Assessment

Reviewing What You Learned

1. It can produce a new generation in a short time, is easy to maintain in large numbers because of its small size, and has a simple genetic system with only 8 chromosomes.
2. Diploid cells have two copies of each chromosome. All body cells are diploid; only gametes are not diploid.
3. A normal human karyotype has 22 pairs of autosomes and one pair of sex chromosomes, for a total of 23 homologous pairs.
4. An autosome is any chromosome that is not a sex chromosome. A sex chromosome is either the X or the Y chromosome. The presence of these chromosomes determines the sex of an individual.
5. Hemophilia: caused by sex-linked gene; sickle cell anemia: caused by an autosomal gene; Klinefelter syndrome: caused by nondisjunction of chromosomes.
6. Answers might include the ABO blood group.
7. Sickled cells are frequently removed from the circulation and destroyed, killing the malaria parasites with them.

8. Students' models should show that either homologous chromosomes fail to separate at anaphase I or sister chromatids fail to separate at anaphase II, resulting in gametes with an abnormal number of chromosomes.

Skills Trace
Modeling

- Focus p. 153
- Practice p. 154
- Assess p. 168

CHAPTER 7

Assessment (continued)

9. No. Barr bodies are condensed, inactive X chromosomes. Since males have just one copy of the X chromosome, it does not need to be inactivated.

10. Imprinted genes are marked with a genetic marker that is different in males and females, causing the gene to give a different phenotype in males and females.

Expanding the Concepts

1. Sex is determined by the presence of X and Y chromosomes. The mother always contributes an X chromosome. The father will contribute either an X or a Y chromosome with equal probability.

2. The four blood types—O, A, B, and AB—are determined by one gene that has three alleles: O, A, B.

3. Crosses should look similar to the following.
$X^rX^r \times X^RY \rightarrow X^RX^r \quad X^rY$ (F_1)
F_1 frequency: females—100% red eyes; males—100 % white eyes.
$X^RX^r \times X^rY \rightarrow X^RX^r \quad X^rX^r \quad X^RY \quad X^rY$ (F_2) F_2 frequency: females—50% red eyes, 50% white eyes; males—50% red eyes, 50% white eyes.

4. Possible answers include a cross between a colorblind female and a normal male. All sons will be colorblind; all daughters will have normal vision.

5. Self-pollinate the plant. If some offspring do not have peppermint stripes, the plant is heterozygous and the trait is dominant. If all the offspring have stripes, then the plant is homozygous. In this case, cross the peppermint stripe and a carnation without stripes.

6. Hemophilia is a sex-linked trait. Males inheriting one recessive allele will have the disease. Females must inherit two recessive alleles to have the disease.

7. More males than females would be expected to inherit a sex-linked disease. Males and females have an equal chance of inheriting an autosomal disease.

8. Nondisjunction of sex chromosomes can result in Turner syndrome (45XO) or Klinefelter syndrome (47XXY). Nondisjunction of autosomes can produce Down syndrome, caused by an extra copy of chromosome 21.

9. The offspring could have either more or less genetic material than normal.

10. Spot color in cats is determined by a sex-linked gene with two alleles. Female cats have two X chromosomes, but one is randomly inactivated, forming a Barr body. The allele for spot color on the active X chromosome will produce either orange or black spots, depending on which allele is present. Male cats have only one X chromosome, so they can have only one possible spot color.

Extending Your Thinking

1. Pedigrees will vary, but must include three generations, or three rows of symbols; a key that defines the symbols for hair color and sex; and shaded symbols appropriate to the inheritance of hair color (either autosomal or sex-linked).

Skills Trace

Interpreting

- Focus p. 157
- Practice p. 159
- Assess p. 169

Assessment

Reviewing What You Learned

Answer each of the following in a complete sentence.

1. Why is *Drosophila melanogaster* an excellent organism for the study of genetics?
2. What are diploid cells? Where would you expect to find them in your body?
3. What can you observe in a normal human karyotype?
4. What is an autosome? What is a sex chromosome?
5. How do the following disorders—hemophilia, sickle cell anemia, and Klinefelter syndrome—differ from one another?
6. Give one example of a multiple allele.
7. Why are people who have sickle cell anemia resistant to malaria?
8. **Construct a model** of meiosis in which nondisjunction has occurred.
9. Do males have Barr bodies? Explain your answer.
10. What is gene imprinting?

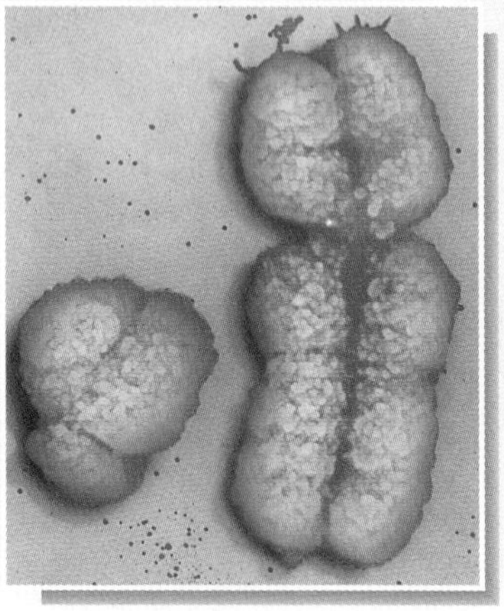

Expanding the Concepts

Discuss each of the following in a brief paragraph.

1. Why is the ratio of male to female offspring usually about 50-50?
2. Explain how blood types in humans are the results of multiple alleles.
3. Diagram a P_1 cross between a red-eyed male fruit fly and a white-eyed female fruit fly. If red eyes are a dominant sex-linked trait, what frequencies would you expect in the F_1 and F_2 generations?
4. Describe a cross that would clearly show the concept of sex-linked inheritance in humans.
5. How could you determine whether peppermint stripes in carnations was autosomal dominant or autosomal recessive?
6. Why is hemophilia more common in males than in females?
7. Compare the expected ratios of a sex-linked disease, such as colorblindness, with that of an autosomal disease, such as cystic fibrosis.
8. Describe three genetic disorders caused by nondisjunction.
9. If a translocation occurred between two different chromosomes in only one parent, what would be the possible genetic combinations of the offspring?
10. Explain in genetic terms why cats with three-colored coats are usually female.

CHAPTER 7

Extending Your Thinking

Use the skills you have developed in this chapter to answer the following.

1. **Interpreting** Draw a three-generation pedigree of an imaginary family that addresses hair color and sex.
2. **Comparing** For the purpose of blood transfusions, why is O blood considered the universal donor, whereas AB is considered the universal acceptor?
3. **Making judgments** You are the director of a research team that has just developed a new strain of genetically engineered cattle with a new gene that produces excessive growth hormone. These animals reach maturity in three fourths the usual time and their meat is of exceptional quality. However, they have many bone deformations. Should these animals be made available to ranchers to help solve the food requirements of humans around the world? Support your position.
4. **Hypothesizing** Discuss how the trait for sickle cell anemia could develop and become prevalent in the gene pool.
5. **Evaluating** If you were a genetic counselor, what types of information would you seek in counseling a couple that had cystic fibrosis and Huntington disease in their respective family histories?
6. **Applying concepts** Some diseases are carried as dominant genes. Marfan's syndrome is a dominant allele that causes extreme height and a weakened aorta in both sexes. Explain how a pedigree for a family with Marfan's syndrome would differ from the pedigree for a recessive disease.

Applying Your Skills

Genetic Disorders

Cystic fibrosis is the most common fatal genetic disorder in the United States. People with cystic fibrosis have difficulty breathing due to an accumulation of thick mucus in the lungs. Researchers doing genetic research at the University of Michigan are hopeful that they will be able to isolate some of the DNA mutations that cause cystic fibrosis.

1. Working in a group, research the topic of cystic fibrosis. Find out what causes this disorder and why cystic fibrosis patients rarely live past the age of twenty.
2. People with cystic fibrosis have an excess amount of sodium chloride in their sweat, making it very salty. What effect does the sodium chloride in the lung cells have on the mucus?

• GOING FURTHER •

3. In your journal, describe your group's findings regarding cystic fibrosis.
4. What new research is being conducted that may help to find a cure for cystic fibrosis?

2. O blood does not have antigens, so it can be mixed with any other blood group and the blood will not clump. AB blood has both A and B antigens, so it can mix with A, B, and O blood and the blood will not clump.
3. Accept all answers that are logically supported. Students should consider the pain and suffering of the animals along with the possible effects of growth hormone on humans.
4. Accept all logical responses. Those without the allele would die from malaria. Those with the allele would survive and pass the allele to their offspring.
5. Possible answers include a family history of the diseases, genetic testing for the couple, and prenatal testing of the couple's baby.
6. Heterozygous individuals will also have completely shaded symbols, not half-shaded ones.

Applying Your Skills

Preparation

Groups should decide what tasks will be needed to complete the research required, then divide these tasks among group members.

Suggestions

1. Encourage students to use various resource materials, such as encyclopedias, science periodicals, and newspaper articles.
2. Students should learn the following about cystic fibrosis: Patients usually die in childhood from lung problems, organ failure, or blockage in the intestines. Cystic fibrosis is a disease of the endocrine glands that affects the pancreas, sweat glands, and respiratory system. The genetic defect prevents chloride from passing through cell membranes. This causes salt to build up and clog the chloride channels in lung cells. This causes the mucus layer in the lungs to be very thick and viscous.
3. Group members should pool their research findings and work together to write their journal entries.
4. Currently, cystic fibrosis does not have a cure. Most treatments concentrate on relieving the symptoms. Some researchers have used gene therapy to replace the abnormal gene with copies of the normal gene. A genetically engineered drug called DNase, which helps break up mucus in the airways, is also being tested.

Scoring Rubric

4 Response is thorough, accurate, and creative; shows an in-depth understanding of science skills, procedures, and concepts.

3 Response is complete, mostly accurate, and original; shows a satisfactory understanding of science skills, procedures, and concepts.

2 Response is mostly complete but includes some inaccuracies; shows an adequate understanding of science skills, procedures, and concepts.

1 Response is only partially complete and has many inaccuracies; shows an incomplete understanding of science skills, procedures, and concepts.

0 Response is mostly incomplete and/or inaccurate; shows a lack of understanding of science skills, procedures, and concepts.

Chapter 8 DNA and RNA

Content Management	Student Edition Activities
■ Section 8–1 Discovering DNA, pp. 171–174 The Language of Genes Griffith and Transformation Avery and DNA The Hershey-Chase Experiment	
■ Section 8–2 DNA Structure and Replication, pp. 175–180 DNA Structure DNA Replication DNA and Chromosomes	Laboratory Investigation: Extracting DNA, pp. 190–191 MINI LAB: Build Your Own DNA, p. 180
■ Section 8–3 RNA, pp. 181–186 RNA Structure Transcription Forms of RNA Genetic Code Translation Genes and Proteins	MINI LAB: Left to Right or Right to Left?, p. 186
◆ BRANCHING OUT • In Depth Section 8–4 Controlling Gene Expression, pp. 187–189 Gene Expression Expressing Lac Genes Genes in Pieces	

■ These sections cover all the necessary content and concepts for a basic course in biology.
◆ This section covers content and concepts that are either applications or extensions of the basic material.

Integration Strategies

SE Language Arts, p. 171
Health, p. 174
Mathematics, p. 183

Assessment Strategies

SE Chapter Review, pp. 192–195
TR Section Reviews
Chapter Test
BL Chapter Review
Practice Test
CTB Chapter 8 Test

Tech Prep

Teaching strategies appropriate for students who are in technical/vocational programs or who are considering post-secondary technical education can be found on the following **TE** page: 171.

Meeting the Standards

Sections 8–1 through 8–4 cover three of the six content standards under **The Cell** and one of the three content standards under **The Molecular Basis of Heredity** as described on pages 184–185 of The National Science Education Standards.

Chapter Planning Guide

Teacher's Edition Activities	Other Activities	Media and Technology
Chapter Discovery Learning Activity, p. 170 **Inquiry Activity:** Which Molecule Is It?, p. 172 **Investigate:** Research, p. 173	**TR** Enrich: Tuning in to Radioisotopes **BL** Inquiry Activity: I Spy	
Inquiry Activity: Molecules and Information, p. 175 **Investigate:** Long-Term Project, p. 176 **Investigate:** Cooperative Learning, p. 177 **Investigate:** Model Building, p. 179	**TR** Explore: Doublin' DNA **BL** Inquiry Activity: DNA Data Bank	**CD-ROM:** DNA: The Molecule of Life **BioVue Animation:** DNA Replication, Videodisc Side 2 **BioVue Plus CD-ROMs:** DNA Replication **TB** DNA Replication, #10
Inquiry Activity: Genes and Proteins, p. 181 **Investigate:** Cooperative Learning, p. 181 **Investigate:** Research, p. 182 **Investigate:** Cooperative Learning, p. 184 **Investigate:** Model Building, p. 184 **Activity:** Sequencing, p. 184	**LM** Constructing a Model of a Protein Molecule, #15 Constructing a Model of Protein Synthesis, #16 **TR** Apply: Constructing a Protein Sentence **BL** Inquiry Activity: Breaking the Code	**BioVue Animation:** DNA Transcription, Videodisc Side 2 **BioVue Plus CD-ROMs:** DNA Transcription **CD-ROM:** From DNA to Protein **TB** Visualizing Protein Synthesis, #9 The Genetic Code, #11
Inquiry Activity: Gene Expression, p. 187 **Investigate:** Research, p. 188	**TR** Writing in Biology: Biology Acrostics Apply: Making Sense of Introns and Exons **BL** Inquiry Activity: Fits Like a Glove	

KEY: **SE** Student Edition **TE** Teacher's Edition **LM** Laboratory Manual **TR** Teaching Resources **BL** BioLog **TB** Transparency Box **CTB** Computer Test Bank

Materials List

TE Inquiry Activity: Molecules and Information, p. 175 (20–30 minutes); beads, yarn, pipe cleaners, toothpicks, or any other material students might choose.

TE Investigate: Model Building, p. 179 (10 minutes); 30-to 50-cm lengths of yarn, beads, short wooden dowels, very small containers.

SE MINI LAB: Build Your Own DNA, p. 180 (30 minutes); pipe cleaners, plastic straws, toothpicks, or any other suitable materials.

TE Inquiry Activity: Genes and Proteins, p. 181 (20–30 minutes); resource containing description of Beadle-Tatum *Neurospora* experiment.

TE Investigate: Cooperative Learning, p. 181 (15–20 minutes); diagram of object to build, colored blocks or construction toys.

Chapter 8

DNA and RNA

Introducing the Chapter

. . . In Pictures

Have students examine the RNA molecule in the photograph and read the caption. Explain that the transfer RNA molecule plays an important role in heredity and the expression of genetic traits. Then ask the following questions.

- **What do you think genes are made up of?** (Some students might suggest that genes are made of DNA, since they have learned that chromosomes are made of DNA.)
- **How do you think genes actually determine the traits an organism has?** (Genes specify the proteins that make up an organism.)

Teaching Strategy

In the first three sections of this chapter, students will study the structure and function of DNA and RNA and the significant experiments leading to the discovery that genes are made of DNA. In the BRANCHING OUT section, students will find out how cells can control gene expression. You may wish to assign this section to gifted students and students who are interested in molecular genetics.

BIO JOURNAL

You might have students give their coded messages to another student in the class. Challenge students to crack the code to find out what the messages say. Then point out that codes store information but that stored information can be used only if it is decoded. Instruct students to keep their entries in their portfolios.

CHAPTER 8

DNA and RNA

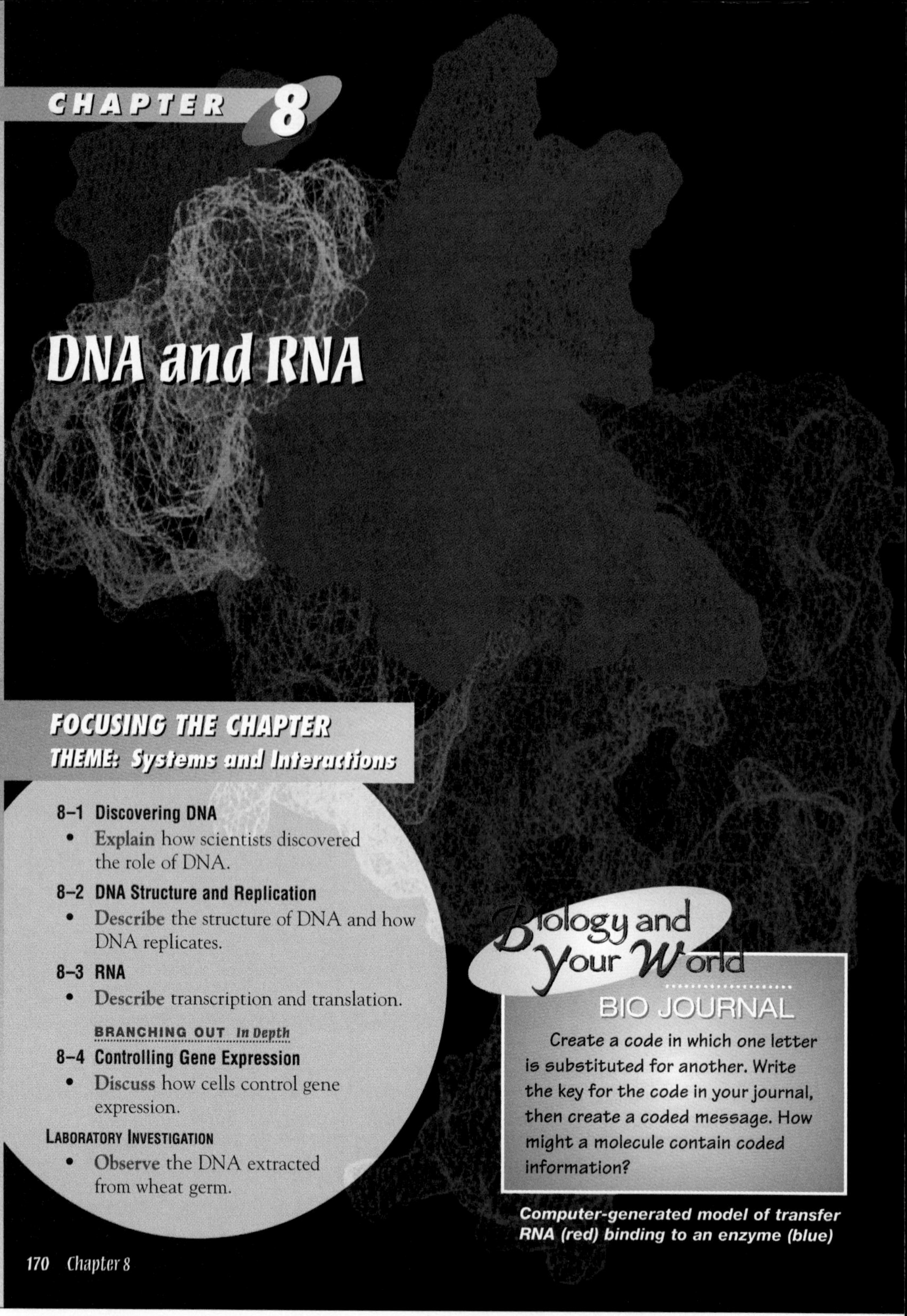

FOCUSING THE CHAPTER

THEME: Systems and Interactions

8–1 Discovering DNA
- **Explain** how scientists discovered the role of DNA.

8–2 DNA Structure and Replication
- **Describe** the structure of DNA and how DNA replicates.

8–3 RNA
- **Describe** transcription and translation.

BRANCHING OUT *In Depth*

8–4 Controlling Gene Expression
- **Discuss** how cells control gene expression.

Laboratory Investigation
- **Observe** the DNA extracted from wheat germ.

Biology and Your World

BIO JOURNAL

Create a code in which one letter is substituted for another. Write the key for the code in your journal, then create a coded message. How might a molecule contain coded information?

Computer-generated model of transfer RNA (red) binding to an enzyme (blue)

TEACHER SUPPORT

Chapter Discovery Learning Activity

Have student groups determine the flow of information among a cook, a waitress, a diner, and a menu in a restaurant. Emphasize that students should follow only the flow of information about the food, such as the orders and the menu, not the food itself. Instruct students to diagram how this information flows. Ask them to describe the processes required to transfer information (speaking, reading, and writing). Help students understand that a code—language—is required to transfer the information. Explain that in this chapter students will learn how a special code in cells carries and transfers information about an organism's phenotype.

Discovering DNA

SECTION 8–1

GUIDE FOR READING

- **Identify** the composition of genes.
- **Describe** the results of experiments by Griffith, Avery, and Hershey and Chase.

VISIT A LARGE PUBLIC LIBRARY and you will find novels, magazines, newspapers, and a host of books that contain information on almost any subject—including science, art, travel, history, and sports, to name just a few. In fact, a public library might best be described as a storehouse of information for the community.

Do cells have libraries? In a sense, yes. The library of a cell is its genetic information—information organized on chromosomes. If we compare chromosomes to the stacks of shelves in a library, then each gene would be a book on a shelf—a book that contains the information that is needed to produce a trait.

The Language of Genes

The information in books consists of marks on paper—marks that we recognize as letters, punctuation, or other symbols of language. But these marks are useless unless the reader knows the language in which the book was written. The word ostrich, for example, signifies a long-necked, flightless bird, but it does so only to someone who can read the English language.

How is genetic information stored in chromosomes? And by what code—or language—does the cell interpret this information? To answer these questions, biologists first had to learn which molecule contains genetic information. In other words, they had to find the molecule of heredity.

INTEGRATING LANGUAGE ARTS

Do all written languages use letters and words? Research this interesting topic.

Figure 8–1 (a) *In this false-color photograph, the blue structures are chromosomes (magnification: 2200X).* (b) *Like a stack of shelves in a library, a chromosome contains highly organized information.* (c) *You can compare a book on a stack of shelves to a gene on a chromosome.*

SECTION 8–1

Discovering DNA

Performance Objectives

- Explain what genes are made of.
- Describe the experiments that led to the discovery of DNA.

1 ENGAGE

Ideas Through Images

Have students examine Figure 8–1, read the caption, and answer the following questions.

- **What do you think scientists had to look for while searching for the chemical composition of genes?** (Some students might mention that scientists had to find a molecule that could encode the information.)
- **If you found a molecule in a cell that you thought made up genes, what experiment might you set up to test it?** (One possible response is to remove the molecule from one organism and insert it into another to see if it affects the organism's phenotype.)

INTEGRATING LANGUAGE ARTS

Some languages, such as Chinese and Japanese, use characters to symbolize objects and ideas.

TEACHER SUPPORT

Managing Classroom Diversity

LEP STUDENTS

Encourage students with limited English proficiency to make a code book of terms or phrases used in genetics. In their code books, students should write the term or phrase in English, then write the definition or meaning in their native language. Help them realize that language is a code, and they can use their own language to help "break" the code for the English language.

TECH PREP STUDENTS

Explain to students that most career areas use special codes whose meanings are really understood only by people in those fields. In many cases, the code is simply lingo, or vocabulary. However, the code could also be a technical procedure. Encourage students to choose one career that interests them and find out a code that is used in that field.

2 EXPLORE

Inquiry Activity

Inferring

Which Molecule Is It?
Explain that cells are made up of proteins, lipids, nucleic acids, carbohydrates, and water. Encourage students to determine the characteristics of these molecules. Have students make inferences from their findings about which molecule makes up genes. Encourage students to check their inferences at the end of the section.

3 TEACH

Ideas Through Images

Have students examine Figure 8–2, read the caption, and answer the following questions.

- **What was Griffith trying to learn in his experiments with smooth and rough pneumonia bacteria?** (He wanted to find the cause of pneumonia.)
- **What were the controls in Griffith's experiment?** (Injecting mice with smooth bacteria and with rough bacteria were the controls.)
- **How could Griffith show that heat actually killed the bacteria?** (By trying to grow a sample of bacteria from the heated test tube in a Petri dish. If bacteria grew, then the heat did not kill the bacteria.)
- **What do you think Griffith expected to observe when he injected mice with the mixture of live rough bacteria and heat-killed smooth bacteria?** (He expected the mice to live.)

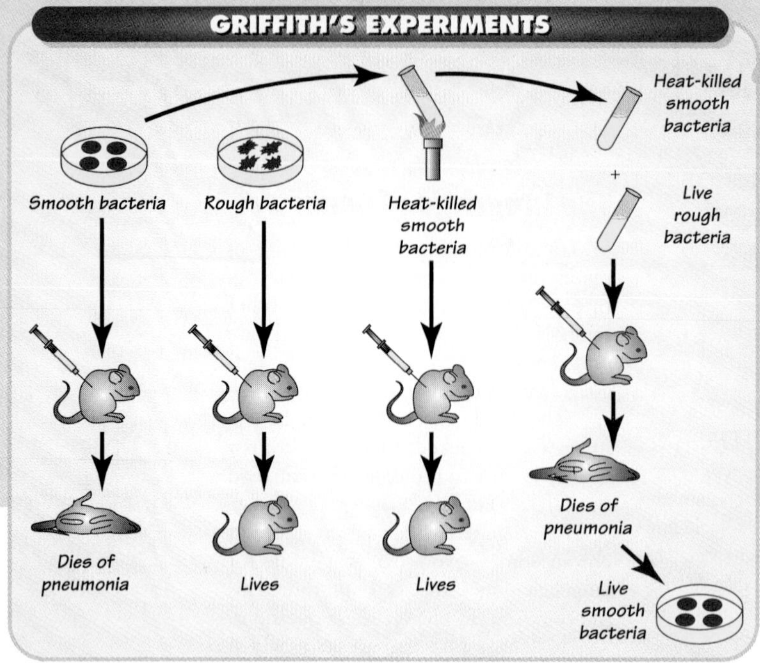

Figure 8–2
Griffith injected mice with the different samples of bacteria shown here. He found that heat-killed smooth bacteria and live rough bacteria were harmless individually but lethal in combination! Griffith concluded that some factor changed the live bacteria from rough to smooth—a process he called transformation.

Griffith and Transformation

One of the first important steps in finding the molecule of heredity was taken in 1928 by a British scientist named Frederick Griffith. Griffith was trying to find better ways to fight pneumonia—a serious and sometimes fatal infection of the lungs.

In his laboratory, Griffith had isolated two types of bacteria that cause pneumonia. He called these types "smooth" and "rough" because the smooth bacteria produced shiny, smooth colonies, whereas the rough bacteria produced dull, rough-edged colonies.

Griffith found that when samples of each type of bacteria were injected into laboratory mice, pneumonia developed only in the mice injected with the smooth type. The mice injected with the rough bacteria remained healthy.

Griffith's Experiments

In one experiment, Griffith heated a sample of smooth bacteria until all the bacteria were dead, then injected the sample into mice. The mice did not develop pneumonia, so Griffith concluded that smooth bacteria needed to be alive to cause pneumonia.

Griffith then mixed a sample of heat-killed smooth bacteria with a sample of live rough bacteria. By themselves, neither type of bacteria should have caused the mice to develop pneumonia. But when Griffith injected mice with the mixture of the two types of bacteria, something remarkable happened. The mice became sick with pneumonia, and many of them died.

Which type of bacteria caused the pneumonia in these mice? Griffith removed the lungs of the dead mice, recovered live bacteria from them, and grew colonies of the bacteria in laboratory culture dishes. The colonies that developed were the glistening, smooth type of the pneuomia-causing bacteria.

Griffith's Conclusions

Griffith immediately recognized what had happened. Some molecule or group of molecules had changed the harmless rough bacteria into

TEACHER SUPPORT

Historical Perspective

Today, it seems that Avery's results show without a doubt that DNA makes up genes. However, in 1944 the results were questionable. At that time, most scientists thought DNA was a very simple molecule and did not have enough complexity to contain all the information required to direct the development of an organism. Scientists were more excited about Hershey and Chase's results with bacteriophages in 1952. By that time, genetic studies showed that bacteriophages had properties of heredity similar to those of higher organisms. Also, experiments showed DNA was much more complex than originally thought. The results of the Hershey and Chase experiment, in effect, prompted scientists to rediscover Avery's results.

deadly smooth bacteria. Because one type of bacteria was transformed into another, Griffith called this process **transformation.**

Checkpoint What is transformation? 1

Avery and DNA

In 1944, Canadian biologist Oswald Avery realized that studying the process of transformation might be the key to identifying the molecule of heredity. Avery and his co-workers assumed that in Griffith's experiments, genes had been transferred from the dead smooth bacteria to the live rough bacteria. They reasoned that if they found out which molecule was needed for transformation to occur, they might be able to identify the molecule that makes up genes.

In a series of experiments, Avery's team carefully treated heat-killed bacteria with enzymes that destroyed proteins, lipids, carbohydrates, and other molecules. None of these treatments affected transformation. But transformation was blocked when they destroyed a molecule called **DNA**—deoxyribonucleic acid.

From these experiments, Avery reached a simple conclusion about DNA and genes. Genes are made of DNA.

The Hershey-Chase Experiment

Although many biologists accepted Avery's conclusion, a few were still skeptical. In 1952, American scientists Alfred Hershey and Martha Chase carried out another experiment that further supported the conclusion that genes are made of DNA.

Viruses

Hershey and Chase were investigating viruses—tiny particles that can invade and replicate within host cells. A type of virus that infects bacteria is known as a bacteriophage, or phage, for short.

Hershey and Chase knew that a phage contains both protein and DNA. They reasoned that if they could determine which of these molecules enters a bacterium during an infection, they would know which molecule makes up the genes of the phage.

Checkpoint What is a bacteriophage? 2

Radioactive Isotopes

How can protein and DNA molecules be followed, or traced, when a phage attacks a bacterium? One way to trace molecules is to take advantage of an interesting property of matter—that not all of an element's atoms are identical!

Elements have different isotopes, or atoms that have the same numbers of protons but different numbers of neutrons in their nuclei. For example, while the nuclei of the different hydrogen isotopes each contain 1 proton, they contain 0, 1, or even 2 neutrons.

Although the common isotopes of many elements are stable, some isotopes are unstable, which means that their nuclei release small particles or rays of energy. This release of particles or energy is called radioactivity.

Figure 8–3
Are genes made of DNA or protein? Martha Chase and Alfred Hershey answered this question with a clever experiment.

Discussion

Begin a discussion about the importance of communication among scientists and how small bits of information added together over time form the pool of scientific knowledge. Emphasize the following points.

- Avery was trying to identify the substance that made up genes. He was not interested in pneumonia.
- Avery repeated Griffith's experiments 16 years later but added one more step; he treated the heat-killed bacteria with different enzymes that destroyed specific cellular substances.

Investigate

Research Scientists have studied many different bacteriophages. Encourage students to learn more about phages. Have them choose one, such as lambda (temperate phage) or T4 (virulent phage), which was the phage studied by Hershey and Chase. Students should learn about the phage's life cycle, the kinds of bacteria it infects, and its structure and composition. Students can pool their knowledge to construct a bulletin board display of the life cycles of different types of bacteriophages.

Checkpoints

1 The process by which one type of bacteria has changed into a different type of bacteria.

2 A virus that infects bacteria.

TEACHER SUPPORT

Managing Classroom Diversity

EDUCATIONAL EQUITY

Some female students might notice that Alfred Hershey's name is always first when referring to the famous bacteriophage experiment conducted by Martha Chase and Alfred Hershey. In fact, some students may have even assumed that Chase was a man. Point out that even though Alfred Hershey headed the laboratory, much of the actual work was done by Martha Chase.

Ancillary Support

The resources below can be used to support your teaching strategy for these two pages.

TR Enrich: Tuning in to Radioisotopes

BL Inquiry Activity: I Spy

INTEGRATING HEALTH

Iodine-131 is used to study the function of the thyroid gland. Sodium-24 is used to detect diseases in the circulatory system. Iron-59 is used to study blood circulation. Cobalt-60 is the most commonly used radioisotope for cancer radiation treatment. Carbon-14 is used to treat brain tumors.

4 ASSESS

Quick Check

Have students construct a concept map to summarize the experiments carried out by Griffith, Avery, and Hershey and Chase.

Section Review 8-1

1. Genes are composed of DNA.
2. Students should summarize the descriptions in the text of the three important experiments that showed that genes are made of DNA.
3. In this experiment, radioactive bacteria would be produced only by the phage grown in the radioactive nitrogen isotope. However, the results would not definitively show that genes were made of DNA, because both DNA and proteins contain nitrogen; both the DNA and the protein coat of the phage grown in the nitrogen isotope would be radioactively labeled.

Learning Modality

Visual Learning Some students might understand the Griffith experiment and the Hershey-Chase experiment more easily by studying Figures 8–2 and 8–4. Encourage these students to draw diagrams that summarize these experiments.

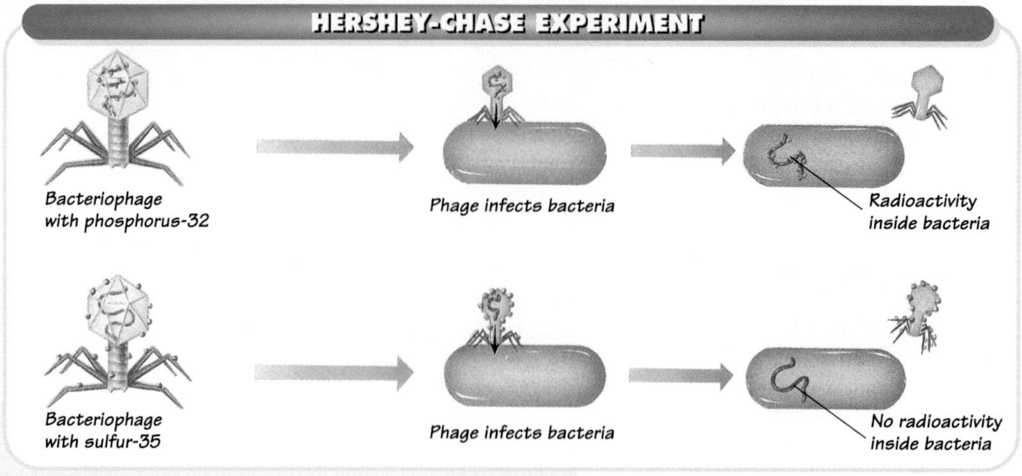

Figure 8–4
Hershey and Chase used radioactive isotopes to label the DNA and proteins of bacteriophages. Because only the phages' DNA entered the bacteria, they concluded that the phages' genes are made of DNA.

INTEGRATING HEALTH

Which radioactive isotopes are used in the diagnosis or treatment of certain illnesses? Write a report on your findings.

Radioactive isotopes become part of molecules just as stable isotopes do. And under the proper safety conditions, radioactivity can be readily observed in the laboratory. As a result, radioactive isotopes provide biologists with a useful way to label molecules, allowing them to be identified as they move from one place to the next. ●

Checkpoint What are isotopes? 1

Labeling DNA and Proteins

As shown in ***Figure 8–4***, Hershey and Chase prepared two samples of the phage: one with phosphorus-32, a radioactive isotope of phosphorus, and one with sulfur-35, a radioactive isotope of sulfur. Phosphorus is part of DNA but not of proteins, so phosphorus-32 labeled the phages' DNA. And sulfur is part of proteins but not of DNA, so sulfur-35 labeled the phages' proteins.

Hershey and Chase allowed both samples of bacteriophages to infect bacteria, then analyzed the bacteria for radioactivity. Only one of the samples made the bacteria radioactive. This was the sample grown in phosphorus-32—the isotope that labeled DNA.

The Conclusions

Hershey and Chase concluded that the genetic material of a bacteriophage was DNA, not protein. In fact, their experiment convinced biologists around the world that genes were made of DNA.

Section Review 8–1

1. **Identify** the composition of genes.
2. **Describe** the results of experiments by Griffith, Avery, and Hershey and Chase.
3. **Critical Thinking—Predicting Results** A biology student repeats the Hershey-Chase experiment using a radioactive nitrogen isotope instead of phosphorus-32. Describe the results of this experiment. Would the results show that genes were made of DNA?

TEACHER SUPPORT

Background Information

The three isotopes of hydrogen are:

^1H	protium	1 proton, 0 neutrons
^2H	deuterium	1 proton, 1 neutron
^3H	tritium	1 proton, 2 neutrons

Each of these three isotopes is still hydrogen because they each have one proton and one electron. Their chemical properties are identical. However, their physical properties are not the same. Tritium has almost three times the atomic mass of protium and is radioactive.

One of the potential problems related to radioactive materials is that radiation can damage or kill living things. Therefore, it is very important that these materials be handled with great care to prevent harm to those who work with them and to prevent their release into the environment.

DNA Structure and Replication

GUIDE FOR READING

- **Identify** the structure of the DNA molecule.
- **Explain** how DNA replicates.

MINI LAB
- **Construct** a model of DNA.

YOU MIGHT BE THINKING THAT Hershey and Chase solved the great mystery of heredity. However, the really difficult questions had yet to be asked. If genes are made of DNA, then the information that genes contain must be coded in the DNA molecule. How can a molecule carry information? And how can that information be copied every time a cell divides? To begin answering these questions, let's take a look at the structure of the DNA molecule.

DNA Structure

DNA is a nucleic acid—one of the four major classes of large molecules called macromolecules. All nucleic acids are polymers of **nucleotides.** A nucleotide is made of three parts: a phosphate group, a nitrogenous (nitrogen-containing) base, and a 5-carbon sugar, which in DNA is deoxyribose (dee-ahks-ee-RIGH-bohs).

DNA is made of four different types of nucleotides. These nucleotides are adenine (AD-uh-neen), cytosine (SIGHT-oh-seen), guanine (GWAH-neen), and thymine (THIGH-meen). As shown in *Figure 8–5*, each of these nucleotides contains a different nitrogenous base.

Chargaff's Rules

In 1950, American biochemist Erwin Chargaff discovered a curious fact about the nucleotides in DNA. Chargaff studied the nucleotide composition of many different samples of DNA, and he found

DNA NUCLEOTIDES

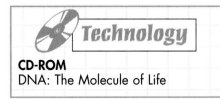

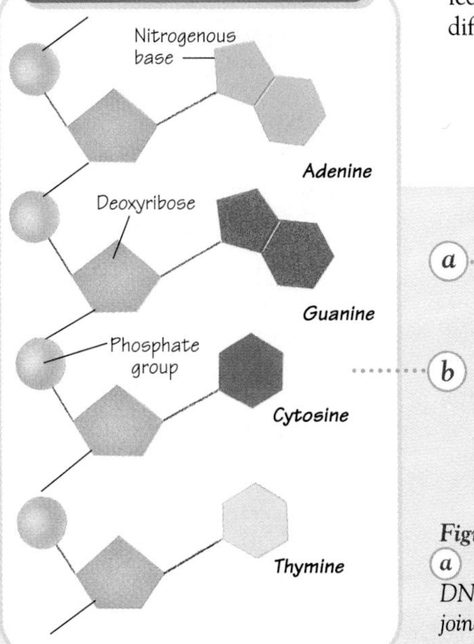

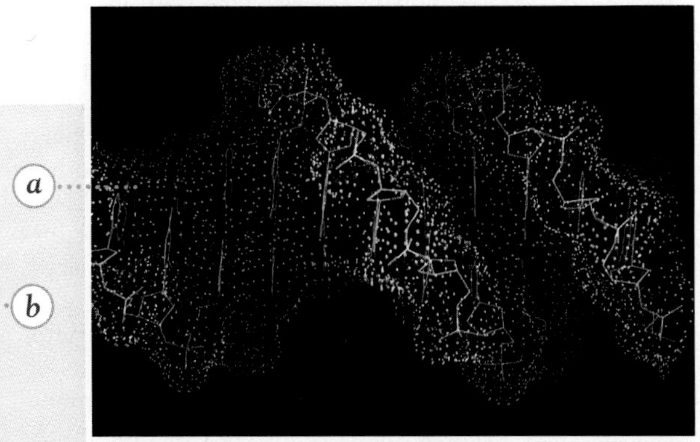

Figure 8–5
(a) A computer generated this image of the structure of DNA. (b) The backbone of DNA is a chain of nucleotides joined together by bonds between the phosphate group of one nucleotide and the deoxyribose sugar of another.

TEACHER SUPPORT

Managing Classroom Diversity

GIFTED STUDENTS
Some students may be interested in learning how DNA is analyzed. Encourage them to research how restriction enzymes (which cut DNA at specific sites) and gel electrophoresis (which separates DNA fragments according to size) are used to study the DNA of different organisms. Have students share their findings with the class.

AT-RISK STUDENTS
The chemistry in this section might be difficult for some students. Encourage students to construct their own diagrams of the DNA molecule in which they define and label each part of a nucleotide and show how nucleotides join together to form a polymer—the DNA double helix.

SECTION 8–2

DNA Structure and Replication

Performance Objectives
- Describe the structure of the DNA molecule.
- Discuss the process of DNA replication.

Laboratory Investigation Skill: Observing
Mini Lab Skill: Modeling

1 ENGAGE

Inquiry Activity
Modeling
Molecules and Information
Ask students to consider how molecules can carry information. To help students answer this question, challenge them to create a chainlike molecule that stores and transmits information and give them some examples of chains that carry information. For example, Morse code is a chain with two units—dots and dashes. Computer language—zeros and ones—is also a chain with two units. The English language is a chain with 26 units. Point out how a chain with only one unit cannot carry information. When students have completed their chain molecules, have them exchange their molecule models and try to decipher the information carried by the molecule—first without the code, and then with the code.

Checkpoint

1 Atoms of the same element that have different numbers of neutrons.

Technology
CD-ROM
DNA: The Molecule of Life

2 EXPLORE

Investigate

Long-Term Project Have students read *The Double Helix: A Personal Account of the Discovery of the Structure of DNA* by James Watson. Watson gives his personal viewpoint of the race to discover the structure of DNA. The book also gives students insight into the everyday workings of a scientist. After students have read the book, invite them to discuss what they think of the story and the people involved. Remind them that they read only one viewpoint of the story, and challenge them to consider how Rosalind Franklin might tell the same story.

3 TEACH

Ideas Through Images

Have students examine the X-ray image of DNA in Figure 8–6, read the caption, and answer the following questions.

- **Can you tell what the structure of DNA is from this X-ray image?** (Most students won't be able to make much sense out of this image.)
- **What do you think scientists learned from this X-ray image?** (Some students might explain that the image gave scientists important clues to the structure of DNA.)

Explain to students that the image itself does not show the structure of the DNA molecule. It is more like a shadow that gives hints of its possible structure. Point out that the regular spacing of the dark spots and the X-shaped pattern indicate that the DNA molecule is twisted in a regular pattern—like a helix.

(a)

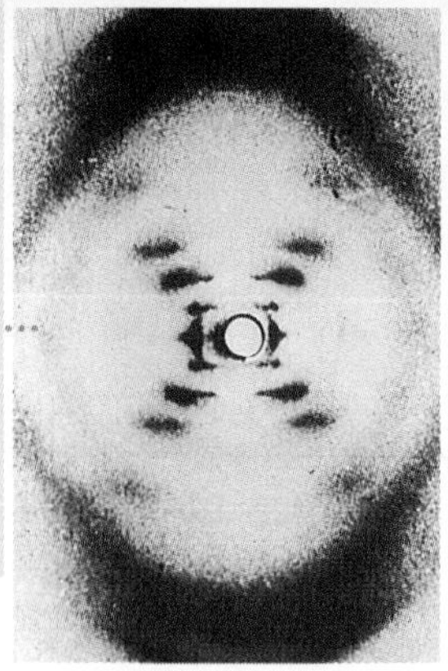

(b)

Figure 8–6 *(a) Rosalind Franklin used X-rays to study all sorts of substances, including viruses and coal. (b) Franklin's X-ray image of DNA provided a vital clue to determining DNA's structure.*

that the amount of each type of nucleotide differed in each sample. However, the amounts also followed a distinct pattern. The amounts of adenine (A) and thymine (T) were almost always equal, as were the amounts of cytosine (C) and guanine (G).

This pattern has proven true for the DNA of almost every organism, and it is now known as Chargaff's rules. However, neither Chargaff nor any of his contemporaries had any idea why DNA should follow this pattern.

Rosalind Franklin

In 1951, the English scientist Rosalind Franklin was studying the DNA molecule with a technique called X-ray diffraction. In this technique, a powerful X-ray beam is aimed at a sample, then the scattering pattern of the X-rays is recorded on film. Working with Maurice Wilkins, another English scientist, Franklin produced better and better scattering patterns of the DNA molecule. In 1952, she produced the image shown in ***Figure 8–6.***

By itself, Franklin's X-ray pattern does not reveal the structure of DNA. But the pattern does contain important clues, similar to the clues that footprints provide at the scene of a crime.

In the winter of 1953, Franklin's work came to the attention of the American scientist James Watson. Watson and Francis Crick, a British scientist, had also been investigating the structure of DNA. When Watson saw Franklin's X-ray patterns for the first time, he realized they contained just the clues that he needed. Watson wrote: "The instant I saw them my mouth fell open and my heart began to race."

The Watson-Crick Model

Only a few weeks after seeing Franklin's X-ray work, Watson and Crick had solved the structure of DNA. They believed that Franklin's X-ray pattern suggested that DNA contains two strands, each twisted around the other. This twisted pattern, which is similar to the threads on a screw, is called a helix.

To see if DNA could have such a structure, Watson and Crick built models of two short strands of nucleotides and placed them next to each other, keeping the sugar-phosphate chains on the outside. They then wound the two strands around each other, producing a model with two helix-shaped strands, as shown in ***Figure 8–7.*** **The structure of the DNA molecule is a double helix.** The double-helix model of DNA accounts for most of the features seen in Franklin's X-ray diffraction pattern.

Bonds Between the Strands

However, Watson and Crick faced one big question: What held the two strands together? It took the scientists only a few days to find the answer.

TEACHER SUPPORT

Managing Classroom Diversity

EDUCATIONAL EQUITY
Students might be interested in learning more about Rosalind Franklin and her struggles to learn the structure of the DNA molecule. One source students might try is *Rosalind Franklin and DNA: A Vivid View of What It Is Like to Be a Gifted Woman in an Especially Male Profession* (Anne Sayre, 1975).

As shown in ***Figure 8–7,*** the nitrogenous bases of each strand were arranged very close to each other along the center of the double helix. When Watson and Crick sketched the structures of the nitrogenous bases, they found that hydrogen bonds could form between adenine (A) and thymine (T), and also between cytosine (C) and guanine (G). These pairs of nitrogenous bases are called base pairs, and the hydrogen bonds between the nitrogenous bases in a base pair provide the force that holds the two strands together.

Suddenly, everything became clear to Watson and Crick. The sequence of nucleotides on one strand is matched perfectly to a complementary sequence on the other strand. In addition, they realized that base-pairing explained Chargaff's rules. Chargaff's rules state that DNA contains equal amounts of adenine and thymine, as well as equal amounts of cytosine and guanine. These are exactly the same pairs that form hydrogen bonds with each other. Therefore, for every adenine in a double-stranded DNA molecule, there had to be one thymine. And for every cytosine, there had to be one guanine.

☑ **Checkpoint** What is the shape of the DNA molecule? ❶

Significance of the Double Helix

Solving the structure of DNA was one of the great scientific achievements of the century. In 1962, the Nobel prize—the highest award the international community can give for a scientific discovery—was given to Watson, Crick, and Wilkins. Rosalind Franklin

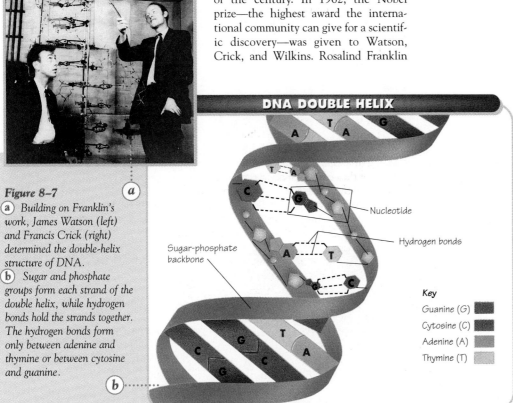

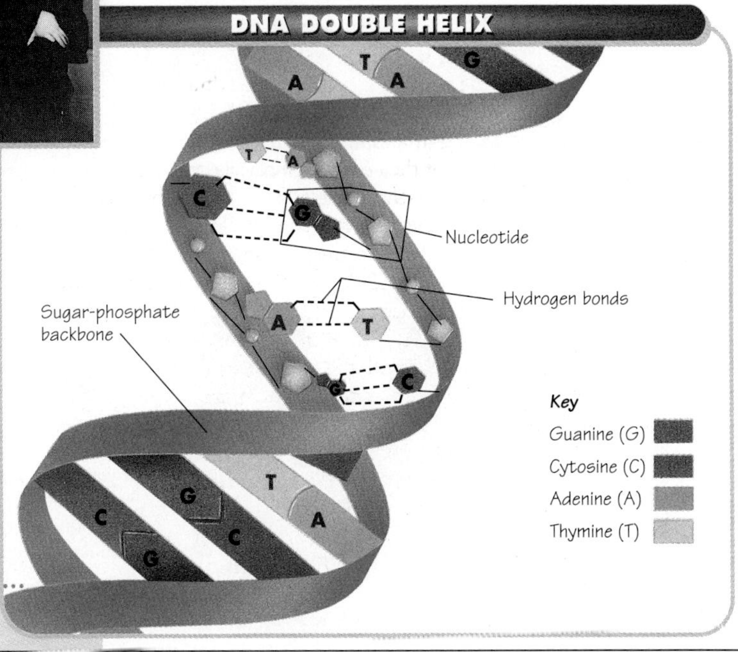

Figure 8–7
ⓐ *Building on Franklin's work, James Watson (left) and Francis Crick (right) determined the double-helix structure of DNA.*
ⓑ *Sugar and phosphate groups form each strand of the double helix, while hydrogen bonds hold the strands together. The hydrogen bonds form only between adenine and thymine or between cytosine and guanine.*

Laboratory Investigation

The Laboratory Investigation, Extracting DNA, on pages 190–191 is appropriate to use at this point in the chapter.

Ideas Through Images

Have students examine the structure of the DNA double helix in Figure 8–7, read the caption, and answer the following questions.

- **How does the number of hydrogen bonds between the bases relate to Chargaff's rules?** (Adenine and thymine could not successfully bind to either guanine or cytosine, because the number of possible hydrogen bonding sites is not equal, which would lead to an unstable molecule.)
- **Hydrogen bonds are very weak bonds. Why might this be important?** (Accept all logical responses. Students will learn that the two DNA strands separate—the hydrogen bonds break—during replication.)

Investigate

Cooperative Learning Divide the class into groups of two and instruct each student to write a base pair sequence for one strand of DNA. Partners should exchange their DNA sequences and write the sequence of the complementary strand. Monitor students to be sure they understand the process.

☑ Checkpoint

❶ The DNA molecule is a double helix.

TEACHER SUPPORT

Background Information

All the genes in a cell are not located in the nucleus, although for many years, scientists thought they were. Then scientists noticed that a few genes seem to follow a pattern of inheritance that is quite unusual for genes in the nucleus. Could those genes be located somewhere else in the cell? In the 1970s, researchers found that mitochondria and chloroplasts have their own DNA molecules, containing anywhere from 10 to 50 genes. These genes code for proteins found in the organelles, some of them quite important.

In 1989, Douglas Wallace of Emory University in Atlanta discovered a mitochondrial genetic disorder known as Leber's disorder—a rare condition that leads to blindness. Since then, six more human mitochondrial genetic disorders have been discovered.

Ancillary Support

The resource below can be used to support your teaching strategy for these two pages.

TB DNA Structure, #10

Connections

DNA fingerprinting is based on the idea that it is extremely unlikely that any two people have identical DNA. (Identical twins are the exception.) When DNA is used to identify a person who was at a crime scene, the DNA can be isolated from samples of blood, semen, bone, hair, and saliva. If the samples are very small, the DNA can be amplified using a very simple process. However, if the sample is contaminated by bacteria, unsterile equipment, or other samples from the same crime scene, the material contaminating the DNA will also be amplified and can affect the results.

After the DNA from the sample is processed, its gel banding pattern is compared to that of the suspect's DNA. The more bands that match, the more likely it is that the suspect left the sample at the crime scene. However, if only one band is different, the suspect is cleared.

Answers to Making the Connection

Accept all reasonable responses on accepting the results of DNA fingerprinting as evidence in a criminal trial, as well as the questions students might want to ask about DNA fingerprinting.

Bio Frontier Connections

DNA Fingerprinting

Every human has a different set of physical characteristics, which means that every human has unique DNA. Therefore, in theory, people can be conclusively identified from samples of their DNA—just as they can be identified from their fingerprints.

In fact, scientists have developed several procedures to identify a DNA sample, and these procedures are called DNA fingerprinting. Using DNA fingerprinting, the DNA from a drop of blood or a skin sample can be matched to the person who left the sample behind.

Techniques of DNA Fingerprinting

You might think that DNA fingerprinting involves identifying all the nucleotides in a DNA molecule. However, such a technique is not feasible—at least not with today's technology. Why is this so? A molecule of human DNA contains billions of nucleotides—far too many to analyze quickly.

How is DNA fingerprinting done today? In one technique, a DNA molecule is split apart at specific locations, creating fragments that vary in length from one person to the next. Proponents of this technique believe it to be sensitive enough to identify one person from 100 thousand to 100 million others.

CAREER TRACK *This geneticist is preparing DNA for electrophoresis—one step in DNA fingerprinting.*

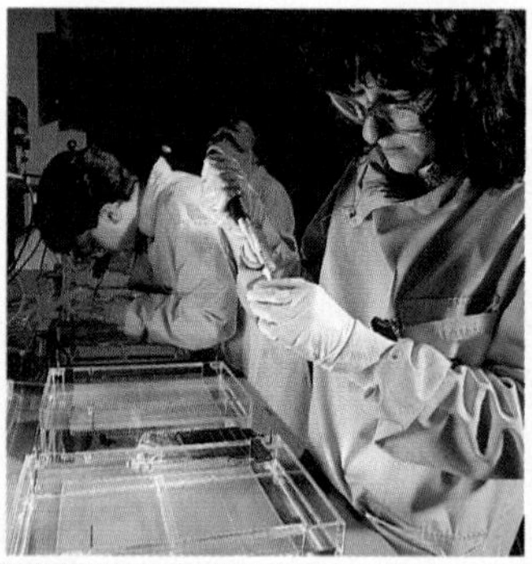

Uses of DNA Fingerprinting

DNA fingerprinting and other types of DNA analysis are being used for a variety of interesting purposes. Geneticists are analyzing DNA to study hereditary diseases. Archaeologists are analyzing DNA to identify blood stains on ancient artifacts and in caves. And one group of historians is using DNA to trace the lineages of European royal families.

But arguably the most controversial applications of DNA fingerprinting have been in the criminal justice system. Although the police often use DNA evidence to identify suspects, juries have not always accepted this evidence when a case comes to trial. Observers have argued that many jury members do not trust DNA fingerprinting because it is too new or too difficult to understand.

The Debate Ahead

Although DNA fingerprinting impresses many experts, others argue that, at best, it is an imperfect means of identification. The strengths and weaknesses of DNA fingerprinting are sure to be debated and tested in the years ahead.

The results of DNA fingerprinting are often presented as evidence in criminal trials.

Making the Connection

If you were on a jury, would you accept the results of DNA fingerprinting as evidence? What questions about DNA fingerprinting would you want to ask?

Teacher Support: Background Information

DNA fingerprinting focuses in on the large amount of "junk DNA"— repeating units of DNA that do not code for protein synthesis. The number of repeats between genes varies from individual to individual. The greater the number of repeated units, the longer the strand of DNA between the genes.

During analysis, the DNA is split into fragments with the use of restriction enzymes. Then the DNA fragments are injected into a gel, in which they can be separated by their lengths. Radioactive probes match up to the repeat units and adhere to them. The radioactivity is then detected in order to allow the number of repeat units to be measured.

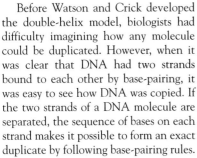

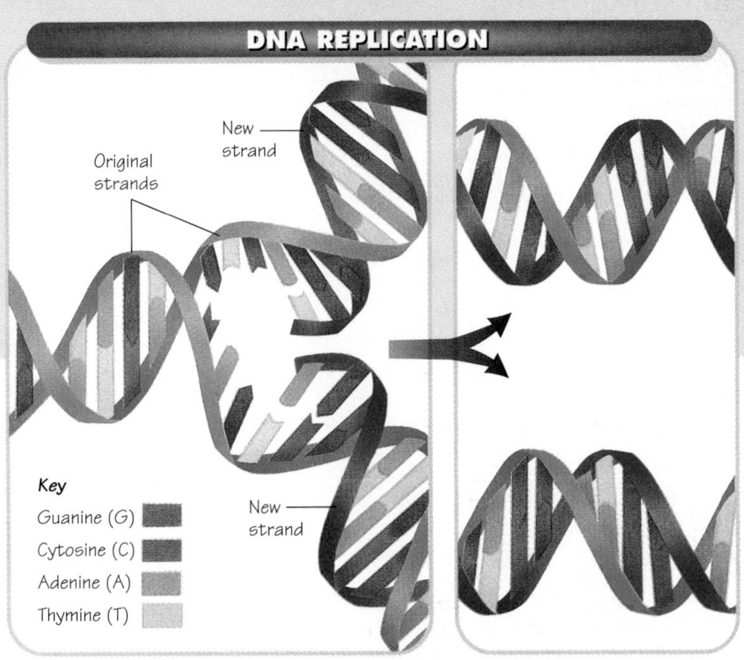

Figure 8–8
In DNA replication, each strand serves as a pattern for the synthesis of a complementary strand. The result is two double-stranded DNA molecules, each an exact copy of the original molecule.

undoubtedly would have shared in this prize, but she died in 1958, and Nobel prizes are given only to living scientists.

Watson and Crick published their model of DNA structure in a scientific paper that was just one page long. However, that brief paper contained a sentence that explained one more thing about DNA: how the molecule could copy itself. "It has not escaped our notice," wrote Watson and Crick, "that the specific pairing we have postulated immediately suggests a possible copying mechanism for the genetic material."

DNA Replication

Before Watson and Crick developed the double-helix model, biologists had difficulty imagining how any molecule could be duplicated. However, when it was clear that DNA had two strands bound to each other by base-pairing, it was easy to see how DNA was copied. If the two strands of a DNA molecule are separated, the sequence of bases on each strand makes it possible to form an exact duplicate by following base-pairing rules.

DNA is copied in a process called **DNA replication.** DNA replication takes place during the synthesis phase (S-phase) of the cell cycle, and the replication is carefully controlled by a group of enzymes. **In DNA replication, enzymes separate the two strands, then synthesize new strands that base-pair to the original strands.** This process is illustrated in ***Figure 8–8.***

When DNA replication is complete, a cell has duplicated all its genetic information. The cell is then ready to begin cell division.

☑ **Checkpoint** How does DNA replicate? ❶

DNA and Chromosomes

In eukaryotic cells, genetic information is contained in chromosomes located in the cell nucleus. Does this mean that chromosomes are made of DNA? Although chromosomes do contain DNA, their structure is significantly more complex. In fact, eukaryotic chromosomes actually contain more protein than DNA.

Discussion

Begin a class discussion about how DNA replication relates to Mendel's principles. Emphasize the following points.

- DNA is located in the nucleus.
- Through DNA replication, the parents' genes are copied and passed to the offspring in gametes. Make sure students understand that chromosomes are composed of double-stranded DNA; gametes do not contain single strands of DNA.
- All new body cells that form during mitosis, either as a response to repair or to growth, will be genetically identical to the parent cell because of DNA replication.

Investigate

Model Building Give students a very long piece of yarn (30–50 cm), some beads, short wooden dowels, and a very small container. Challenge students to use the materials to help them fit the yarn inside the container, making sure that the yarn can be unwound fairly easily. Encourage students to make comparisons between their models and chromatin.

☑ Checkpoint

❶ Enzymes separate the two DNA strands, then synthesize new strands that base-pair to the original strands.

Technology

BioVue
Animation: DNA Replication
Videodisc Side 2

Go to Chapter 20

TEACHER SUPPORT

Facts and Figures

- If all of the DNA in one human cell were laid out end to end, it would be almost 2 m long.
- The same single human cell contains about 6 billion nucleotide base pairs of DNA. The letters for these base pairs would fill over a million pages of type.
- Human cells encode about 20,000 different kinds of protein molecules.
- One chromosome contains about 3,000 genes.

Ancillary Support

The resources below can be used to support your teaching strategy for these two pages.

TR Explore: Doublin' DNA
BL Inquiry Activity: DNA Data Bank
TB DNA Replication, #10

MINI LAB Modeling

Teacher Notes
- For time required and materials needed, see page 170b.
- Have ring stands and clamps available to hold student models.

Answers to Analyze and Conclude

1. Responses will vary depending on student models.
2. Chargaff's rules state that an organism has equal amounts of adenine and thymine and equal amounts of guanine and cytosine. Students should pair thymine with adenine and guanine with cytosine in their models.
3. Students should observe that the sequence of one DNA strand can specify the sequence of the complementary strand.

Skills Trace
Modeling
- Focus p. 180
- Practice p. 180
- Assess p. 195

4 ASSESS

Quick Check

Have students draw a diagram of the DNA molecule that shows the nitrogenous bases and the sugar-phosphate backbone.

MINI LAB Modeling

Build Your Own DNA

PROBLEM *How can you **construct a model** of DNA?*

PROCEDURE

1. Construct a three-dimensional model of DNA. The model should clearly show sugars, phosphate groups, and the four different nitrogenous bases. Use pipe cleaners, plastic straws, toothpicks, or any other materials available.
2. Create a key that identifies the different parts of your model.

ANALYZE AND CONCLUDE

1. In what ways does your model accurately represent DNA? In what ways is it inaccurate?
2. What are Chargaff's rules? How does your model follow these rules?
3. Watson and Crick believed that their model of DNA held clues to how DNA was copied. Do you see any such clues? Explain your answer.

Chromatin

Chromosomes are made of a material called **chromatin.** Chromatin consists of DNA and a number of different proteins. Some of the most important of these proteins are histones, a class of proteins that bind directly to DNA.

Nucleosomes

In 1973, the American scientists Don and Ada Olins and Christopher Woodcock discovered that histones form tiny particles that they called nucleosomes. What do nucleosomes do? They may help to fold and package DNA. Folding and packaging DNA is an important job, because the DNA in a single chromosome may be as much as 10,000 times as long as the chromosome itself! In addition, recent evidence suggests that nucleosomes play a role in regulating the way genes are transcribed into RNA.

Scientists have learned a great deal about the structure of DNA and the way DNA and proteins are organized in chromosomes. However, we still have a long way to go in understanding DNA.

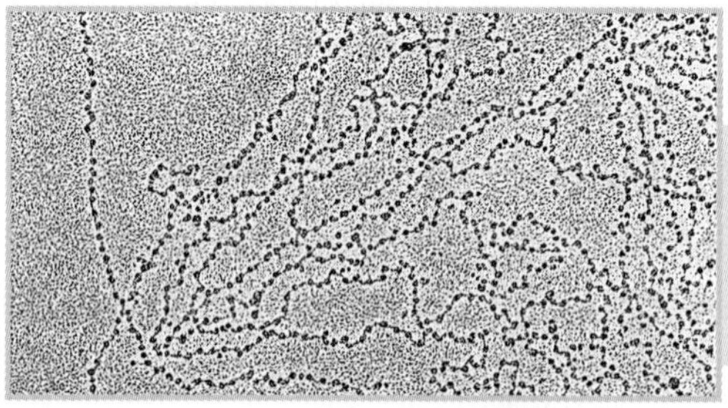

Figure 8–9 *Nucleosomes look like beads on a string when viewed through an electron microscope (magnification: 100,000×).*

Section Review 8–2

1. **Identify** the structure of the DNA molecule.
2. **Explain** how DNA replicates.
3. **Describe** the different components of chromatin.
4. **Critical Thinking—Interpreting Models** How does the double-helix model of DNA explain Chargaff's rules?
5. **MINI LAB** How can you **construct a model** of DNA?

Section Review 8–2

1. A double helix.
2. Enzymes separate the two strands, then synthesize new strands that base-pair to the original strands.
3. Chromatin consists of DNA and a number of different proteins.
4. In the DNA model, only adenine and thymine can bind together and only guanine and cytosine can bind together.
5. Answers should relate to the models students constructed for the MINI LAB.

Skills Trace
Modeling
- Focus p. 180
- Practice p. 180
- Assess p. 195

Learning Modality

Tactile Learning Encourage students to manipulate their DNA models from the MINI LAB to show how DNA replication occurs.

GUIDE FOR READING

- **Identify** the role of RNA.
- **Compare** RNA with DNA.
- **Describe** the processes of transcription and translation.

MINI LAB

- **Interpret** the genetic code.

THE DOUBLE-HELIX MODEL shows that a DNA molecule can be replicated, just as you might expect for a molecule that is found in every cell and that contains genetic information. But how is the genetic information decoded? And after it is decoded, what does it say?

As you will see, the sequence of nucleotides in DNA really does contain a code. And to put that code to use, the cell first makes a copy of the coded message.

RNA Structure

To decode the genetic information contained in DNA, the cell uses a molecule called **RNA**—ribonucleic acid. **RNA is the principal molecule that carries out the instructions coded in DNA.**

Like DNA, RNA is a nucleic acid—a macromolecule formed by nucleotides. However, RNA differs from DNA in three principal ways:

- **The sugar in RNA is ribose. In DNA, the sugar is deoxyribose.**
- **RNA is generally single-stranded. Recall that the structure of DNA is a double-stranded helix.**
- **RNA contains uracil** (YOOR-uh-sihl) **instead of thymine. Like thymine, uracil can form hydrogen bonds with adenine.**

☑ *Checkpoint* How does RNA differ from DNA? 1

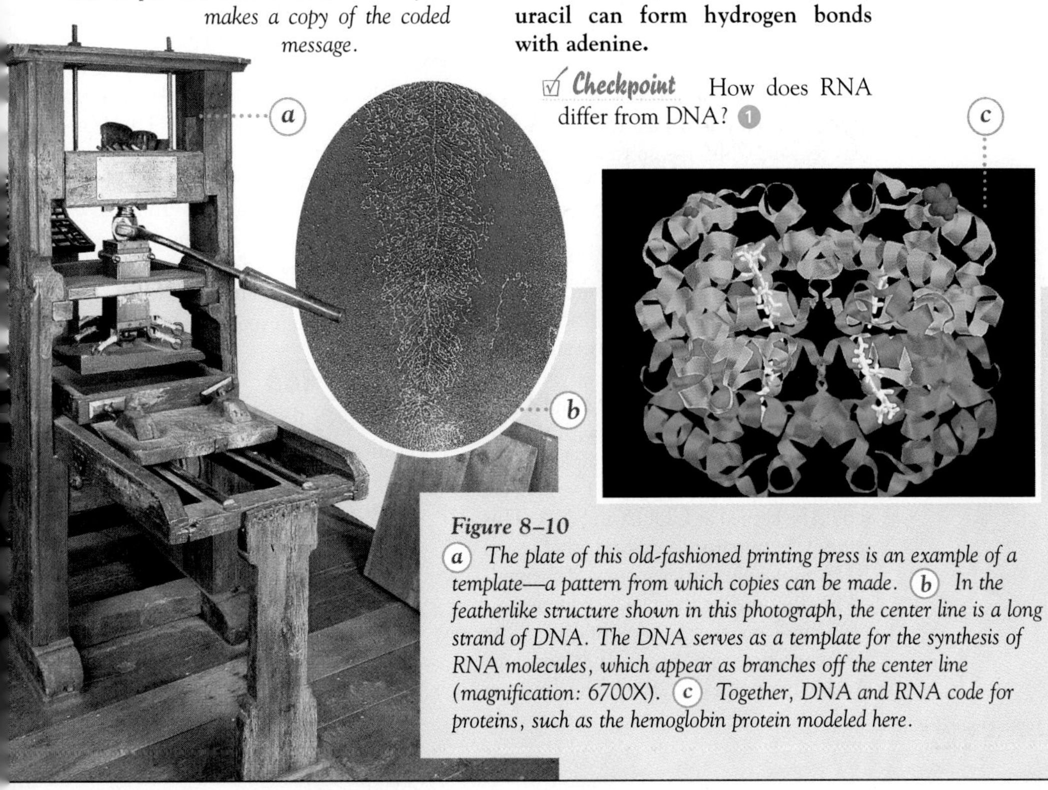

Figure 8–10
(a) The plate of this old-fashioned printing press is an example of a template—a pattern from which copies can be made. (b) In the featherlike structure shown in this photograph, the center line is a long strand of DNA. The DNA serves as a template for the synthesis of RNA molecules, which appear as branches off the center line (magnification: 6700X). (c) Together, DNA and RNA code for proteins, such as the hemoglobin protein modeled here.

TEACHER SUPPORT

Managing Classroom Diversity

AT-RISK STUDENTS

Make sure the vocabulary in this section is not preventing students from understanding the processes of transcription and translation. Encourage students to make up flash cards for each word they find difficult. Use the visuals in this section to help students understand the steps in these two processes and describe how these processes relate to DNA replication. Be clear about where these processes occur in the cell, and relate the protein end product of translation to the phenotype of an organism.

SECTION 8–3

RNA

Performance Objectives

- Describe what RNA does.
- Explain how RNA differs from DNA.
- Discuss the processes of transcription and translation.

Mini Lab Skill: Interpreting

1 ENGAGE

Inquiry Activity

Hypothesizing

Genes and Proteins

Explain that two scientists, George Beadle and Edward Tatum, used bread mold (*Neurospora*) to show that one gene controls the production of one protein. Encourage students to read about Beadle and Tatum's experiment. Then have students write a hypothesis that explains the relationships among DNA, proteins, genes, and the phenotypes of organisms.

2 EXPLORE

Investigate

Cooperative Learning Give groups of four a diagram of a simple object to build using colored blocks, Legos®, Tinkertoys®, or other building sets. Explain that the diagram must stay in one spot and the building materials and building site must be in a different spot. Instruct students to devise a method by which they can build the object accurately despite the distance between the building plan and site.

☑ Checkpoint

1 RNA has ribose, not deoxyribose; it is single-stranded, not double-stranded; and it has uracil, not thymine.

3 TEACH

Ideas Through Images

Have students examine Figure 8–11, read the caption, and answer the following questions.

- **Why do you think the cell makes an RNA copy of the DNA molecule?** (In this way, specific sequences of DNA—genes—can be copied over and over again, and it helps to protect DNA from damage.)
- **In what part of the cell does transcription occur?** (It occurs in the nucleus.)
- **Is the entire DNA molecule transcribed to RNA at the same time?** (No, only those genes whose products are needed at the time are transcribed.)
- **Are both strands of the DNA molecule transcribed?** (No, only one strand for each gene is transcribed. However, different genes can be transcribed from different strands.)

Discussion

Begin a class discussion in which you compare and contrast DNA replication and transcription. In the discussion, emphasize these differences.

- The product of each process is different (RNA vs. DNA).
- Transcription is carried out by one enzyme (RNA polymerase), and replication is carried out by a number of different enzymes.
- Only one or a few genes are transcribed at one time, whereas the entire genome is replicated at once.

Also point out the similarity between replication and transcription: The DNA double helix is opened up and single-stranded DNA acts as a template for the new nucleotide chain.

Investigate

Research Encourage students to choose one form of RNA and research its role in the cell. Students should present their findings to the class as diagrams.

TRANSCRIPTION

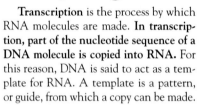

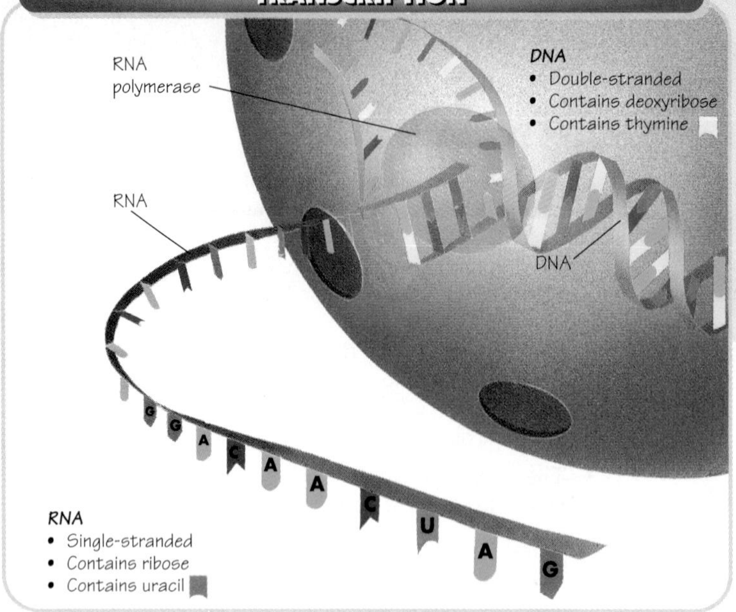

Figure 8–11 *In transcription, DNA serves as a template to produce RNA. The RNA then enters the cytoplasm and is used to make proteins. While DNA and RNA are very similar, they differ in the ways listed in the diagram.*

Transcription

Transcription is the process by which RNA molecules are made. **In transcription, part of the nucleotide sequence of a DNA molecule is copied into RNA.** For this reason, DNA is said to act as a template for RNA. A template is a pattern, or guide, from which a copy can be made.

RNA Polymerase

Transcription is carried out by RNA polymerase, an enzyme that binds directly to a molecule of DNA. As shown in *Figure 8–11,* RNA polymerase produces a strand of RNA, one nucleotide at a time, by matching base pairs with the nucleotides in DNA. For example, a nucleotide sequence of AACT in DNA would be copied as UUGA in RNA. This careful base-pairing ensures that each RNA molecule carries a copy of the coded instructions in the DNA sequence.

Where on the DNA molecule does RNA polymerase begin transcription? And where does it stop? The answers lie in special "start" and "stop" sequences in DNA. These sequences determine exactly which parts of the DNA will be copied into RNA.

Checkpoint What does RNA polymerase do? 1

RNA as a Message

By making RNA, the cell achieves at least two goals. First, a single sequence in DNA may be copied again and again into RNA, making hundreds or even thousands of identical copies. This is especially important for a cell that is growing rapidly and might need multiple copies of the instructions that DNA contains. Second, by making RNA, the cell is able to keep its DNA in reserve, controlling access to it and carefully regulating its use and replication.

Forms of RNA

What does RNA do? It does quite a few things, but in most cells the main forms of RNA are all involved in making proteins. There are three principal forms of RNA:

- **Messenger RNA** Most genes contain instructions for the assembly of amino acids into polypeptides, which are long chains of amino acids. The form of RNA that carries copies

182 Chapter 8

TEACHER SUPPORT

Background Information

Transcription of a segment of DNA begins at an initiation site, called a promoter. Special proteins that control RNA polymerase recognize this site and help RNA polymerase bind to the DNA molecule and begin transcription. To transcribe DNA, about two turns of the DNA helix (16–18 nucleotides) are unwound and opened up. Only one strand, the template strand, is transcribed to RNA. The other DNA strand actually has the same sequence as the RNA molecule (except DNA has thymine instead of uracil). RNA polymerase transcribes the DNA molecule in only one direction. As the RNA molecule grows, it separates from the template strand of DNA. When RNA polymerase reaches the termination site, called a terminator, RNA polymerase dissociates from the DNA molecule, and the DNA helix closes up. The completed RNA molecule moves into the cytoplasm where translation occurs.

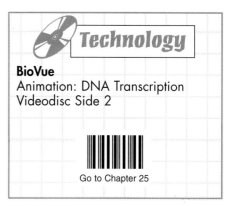

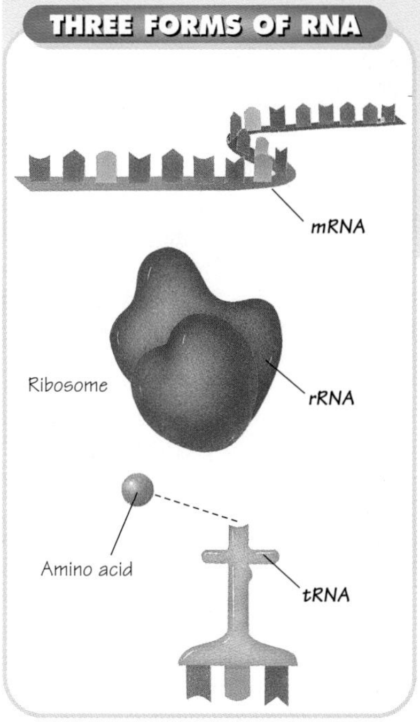

Figure 8–12
Cells use three main forms of RNA. The nucleotide sequence in messenger RNA (mRNA) determines the amino acid sequence of a polypeptide. Ribosomal RNA (rRNA) is an important component of ribosomes. And each type of transfer RNA (tRNA) binds to a specific amino acid.

of these instructions is known as **messenger RNA** (mRNA). As its name implies, mRNA serves as a messenger from DNA to the rest of the cell.

- **Ribosomal RNA** Proteins are assembled at particles called ribosomes. Ribosomes are made of several dozen proteins, as well as a form of RNA known as **ribosomal RNA** (rRNA).
- **Transfer RNA** When a protein is assembled, molecules of another form of RNA transfer one amino acid after another to the ribosome. This form of RNA is called **transfer RNA** (tRNA).

The mRNA, rRNA, and tRNA in a cell are each produced by transcription of their own genes in DNA. As you will see, each form of RNA plays a distinct role in the production of proteins.

☑ ***Checkpoint*** What are the three main forms of RNA? ❷

Genetic Code

Proteins are made from polypeptides, and polypeptides are made from 20 different amino acids. The order of the amino acids determines the polypeptide's properties.

What do the bases in DNA have to do with the sequence of amino acids in a polypeptide? The instructions coded in DNA specify the order in which the 20 different amino acids are put together. The language of the instructions in DNA and RNA is called the **genetic code.**

Only 4 Letters

As you have read, RNA contains 4 different nucleotides: A, U, C, and G. In effect, this means that the code is written in a language of only 4 letters.

How can a code that uses only 4 letters carry instructions for 20 different amino acids? The answer is that the nucleotides in mRNA are read in groups of 3. Put another way, each word of the genetic code is 3 letters long. Thus, in theory, the genetic code could signify 64 different words, because 4^3 equals 64. ●

INTEGRATING MATHEMATICS

How many different 3-letter words can 4 letters signify? How many different 2-letter words can 4 letters signify?

Codons

The group of 3 nucleotides in mRNA that specifies an amino acid is known as a **codon.** You can think of codons as the words of the genetic message. For example, consider the following sequence of nucleotides in mRNA:

AAACACGGU

This sequence is read as 3 codons:

AAA–CAC–GGU

Correcting Misconceptions

Some students might have the misconception that mRNA is transcribed from DNA and then turned into tRNA or rRNA. Review the roles and the structures of each form of RNA. Point out that both rRNA and tRNA must bind to other proteins in the cytoplasm of the cell before they are activated. Emphasize that mRNA is transcribed only from genes that encode proteins. Ribosomal RNA and transfer RNA are transcribed from special genes that cannot be translated into proteins.

INTEGRATING MATHEMATICS

Four letters can signify 64 different 3-letter words (4 x 4 x 4 = 64). Four letters can signify only 16 different 2-letter words (4 x 4 = 16).

Checkpoints

❶ It transcribes DNA sequences to produce RNA.

❷ Messenger RNA, ribosomal RNA, and transfer RNA.

Technology

BioVue
Animation: DNA Transcription
Videodisc Side 2

Go to Chapter 25

TEACHER SUPPORT

Background Information

Breaking the Code In 1961, two scientists, Marshall Nirenberg and Johann Matthaei, identified the first codon for an amino acid—UUU specified phenylalanine. After their discovery, many other scientists joined the search, and all 61 codons that specify amino acids were identified by 1965.

tRNA Wobble Cells do not produce 61 tRNA molecules—one for each codon. Most cells produce between 22 and 30 kinds of tRNA. The third nucleotide base in a codon is often called the wobble position because the strength of the bond between the codon and the anticodon is weak. Because of this weakness, Chargaff's rules can be broken, and bases that would not normally pair up, do. This wobble effect is evident in the genetic code. In many cases, the first two bases are the most important in specifying an animo acid. It often does not matter what the third base is.

Ancillary Support

The resources below can be used to support your teaching strategy for these two pages.

LM Constructing a Model of a Protein Molecule, #15

BL Inquiry Activity: Breaking the Code

Investigate

Cooperative Learning Give student groups different sequences of DNA, and tell them that a mutation has occurred that changed one of the nucleotide bases. Have students show two possible sites for this mutation, one that affects the protein product and one that does not. Ask students to explain how the genetic code can help prevent some DNA mutations from affecting an organism's phenotype. (The mutation changed a nucleotide base, but the resulting codon specifies the same amino acid as the original codon.)

Investigate

Model Building Ask students to make concept maps or diagrams that describe what is occurring during transcription and translation. Students should show where in the cell each process occurs and what the end product of each process is. They should also include any enzymes or building blocks required for each process.

Ideas Through Images

Have students examine Figure 8–13, read the caption, and answer the following questions.

- **What is the codon for tryptophan?** (UGG.)
- **What are the two possible codons for glutamine?** (CAG, CAA.)
- **What does the codon GGG stand for?** (Glycine.)
- **What are the codons for the three stop signals?** (UAA, UAG, UGA.)

And each codon represents a different amino acid:

AAA–CAC–GGU
Lysine–Histidine–Glycine

Figure 8–13 shows all 64 possible codons of the genetic code. Notice that more than one codon can specify the same amino acid. For example, 6 different codons specify the amino acid leucine, and 6 others specify the amino acid arginine.

In most molecules of mRNA, the AUG codon is the start signal, or initiator codon. AUG also codes for the amino acid methionine, which means that methionine is usually the first amino acid when a polypeptide chain is assembled.

Three codons—UAA, UAG, and UGA—serve as stop signals. Like a period at the end of a sentence, these codons signify the end of a genetic message—and the end of the polypeptide.

Checkpoint What is a codon? 1

Translation

In eukaryotic cells, mRNA emerges from the nucleus and enters the cytoplasm. There, the codons in mRNA are translated into amino acids—and **translation** is exactly what biologists call this process. **In translation, nucleotides in mRNA are decoded into a sequence of amino acids in a polypeptide.**

You can think of mRNA as a plan or blueprint for a polypeptide. However, blueprints do not produce buildings all by themselves—builders are needed to follow them.

In cells, the polypeptide builders are the ribosomes—small particles made of rRNA and protein. And the molecules that actually bind the individual amino acids are molecules of tRNA. In effect, ribosomes "read" the codons in mRNA, allowing tRNA molecules to bring the proper amino acids to form a polypeptide chain. To better understand this process, study the illustration on the next page.

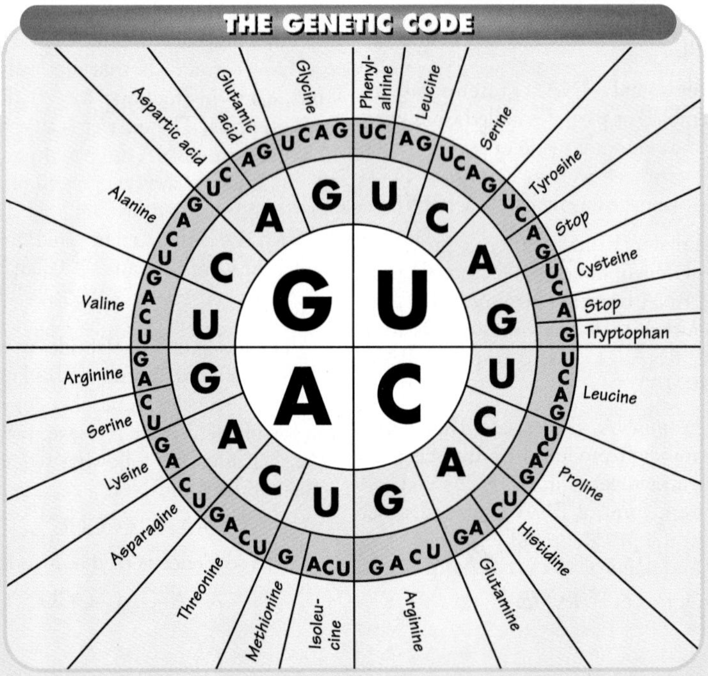

Figure 8–13
You can use this table to "decode" a codon by starting at the middle of the circle and moving outward. For example, the codon GAU codes for aspartic acid.

TEACHER SUPPORT — Activity

Sequencing Give students a sequence of DNA, such as:
ATGCCTAAGGCACGGTAAAAG
Challenge them to give the DNA sequence of the other strand, the mRNA sequence, and the protein sequence.

Complementary DNA sequence:
TACGGATTCCGTGCCATTTTC
mRNA sequence:
UACGGAUUCCGUGCCAUUUUG
Protein sequence:
tyrosine—glycine—phenylalanine—arginine—alanine—isoleucine—leucine

Visualizing Protein Synthesis

The different forms of RNA work together to change a coded message into a protein—a process called translation.

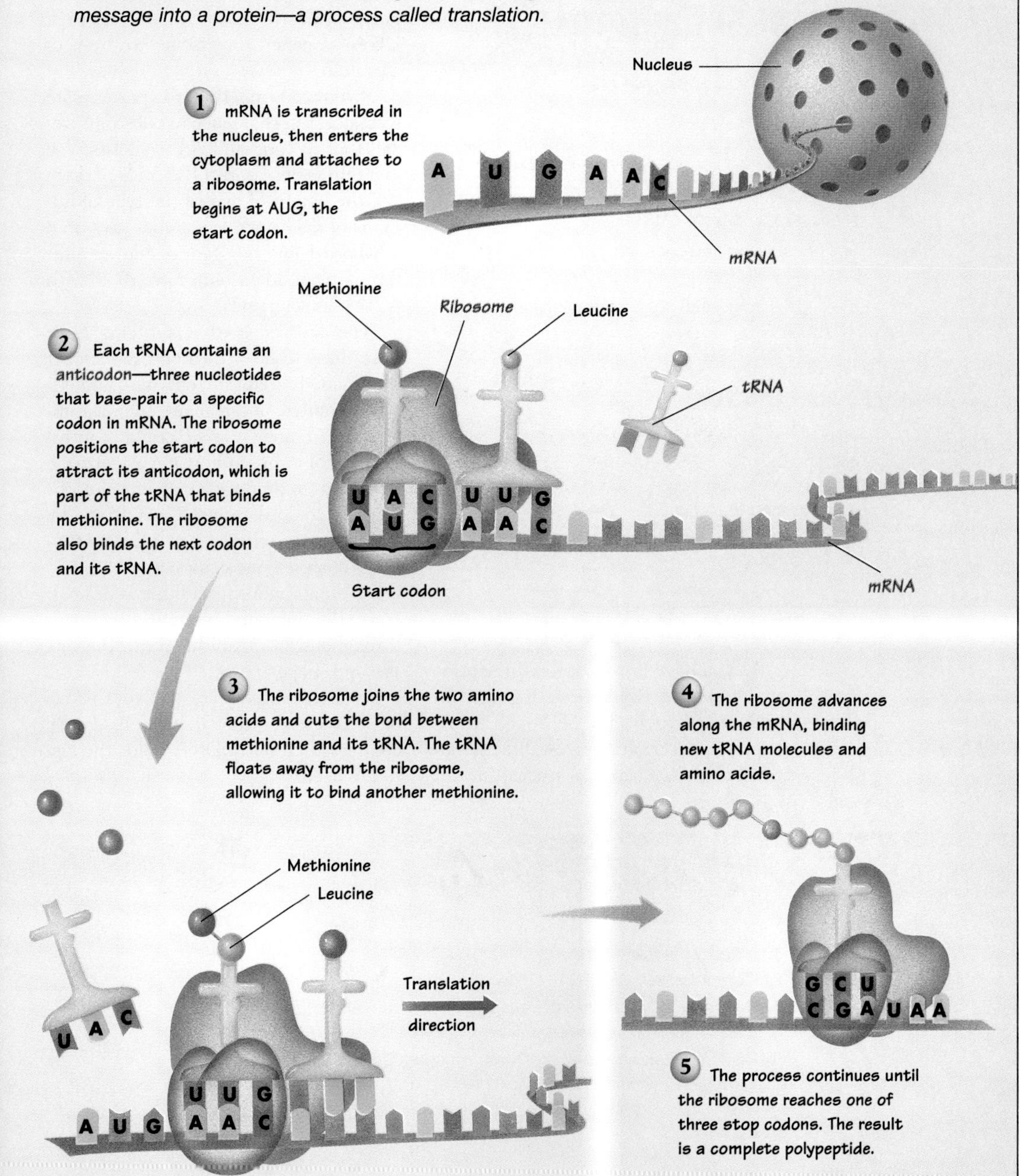

Nucleus
1 mRNA is transcribed in the nucleus, then enters the cytoplasm and attaches to a ribosome. Translation begins at AUG, the start codon.
A U G A A C
mRNA
Methionine
Ribosome
Leucine
2 Each tRNA contains an anticodon—three nucleotides that base-pair to a specific codon in mRNA. The ribosome positions the start codon to attract its anticodon, which is part of the tRNA that binds methionine. The ribosome also binds the next codon and its tRNA.
tRNA
U A C U U G
A U G A A C
Start codon
mRNA
3 The ribosome joins the two amino acids and cuts the bond between methionine and its tRNA. The tRNA floats away from the ribosome, allowing it to bind another methionine.
Methionine
Leucine
U A C
Translation direction
U U G
A U G A A C
4 The ribosome advances along the mRNA, binding new tRNA molecules and amino acids.
G C U
C G A U A A
5 The process continues until the ribosome reaches one of three stop codons. The result is a complete polypeptide.

Visualizing Protein Synthesis

Have students study the process of translation shown in the diagram. Ask them to identify the roles for mRNA, tRNA, and rRNA. Explain that ribosomes begin translation by binding to mRNA at an initiation site, which includes the start codon, AUG. Once bound, the ribosome moves along the mRNA molecule, one codon at a time. Point out that as soon as the initiation site is open on mRNA, another ribosome binds to it and begins translating another polypeptide. Encourage students to infer why multiple ribosomes translate an mRNA molecule at the same time. (It is more efficient for the cell; more proteins can be made in a shorter period of time.)

Have students consider where mistakes could be made during translation and what effect these mistakes might have on an organism. (Wrong amino acid binds tRNA. Wrong anticodon binds mRNA. If the wrong protein is made, it could affect the phenotype of the organism.) Explain that many accessory proteins in translation verify and proofread the tRNA-amino acid complexes and the polypeptide chains.

☑ Checkpoint

1 A group of three nucleotides in mRNA that specifies an amino acid.

TEACHER SUPPORT

Background Information

The synthesis of proteins is a carefully orchestrated and controlled process that begins with a coded message on a DNA molecule. The cell goes to a lot of trouble to synthesize proteins correctly because proteins define what the cell looks like, how it functions, how it grows, and how it passes this information to its daughter cells. Some of the specific roles played by proteins include enzymatic action, transport, motion, protection, support, communication, and regulation.

Ancillary Support

The resources below can be used to support your teaching strategy for these two pages.

LM Constructing a Model of Protein Synthesis, #16
TR Apply: Constructing a Protein Sentence
TB Visualizing Protein Synthesis, #9
The Genetic Code, #11

MINI LAB Interpreting

Teacher Note
- For time required and materials needed, see page 170b.

Answers to Analyze and Conclude
1. Different codons produce different amino acids.
2. Student hypotheses will vary.

Skills Trace
Interpreting
- Focus p. 186
- Practice p. 186
- Assess p. 195

4 ASSESS

Quick Check

Have students list the three forms of RNA and describe their roles.

Section Review 8-3

1. RNA carries out the instructions coded in DNA.
2. See page 181.
3. In transcription, part of the DNA molecule is copied into RNA. In translation, mRNA is decoded into a polypeptide sequence.
4. Proteins regulate the chemical reactions in the body, as well as the rate and pattern of growth.
5. Messenger RNA carries the instructions for assembling a protein; ribosomal RNA makes up ribosomes, which assemble proteins; and transfer RNA brings the correct amino acid to the ribosome for the growing polypeptide. Transfer RNA and ribosomal RNA are reused to produce different polypeptides; they are not as specific to one polypeptide as messenger RNA is.

MINI LAB .... Interpreting .....

Left to Right or Right to Left?

PROBLEM *How does a cell **interpret** DNA?*

PROCEDURE

1. Assume that a gene contains the following sequence of nucleotides: **GACAAGTCCACAATC**
   Write this sequence on a piece of paper.
2. Reading from left to right, transcribe the gene into a molecule of mRNA.
3. Reading the codons from left to right, translate the mRNA into a polypeptide.
4. Repeat step 3 reading the codons from right to left.

ANALYZE AND CONCLUDE

1. Why did steps 3 and 4 produce different polypeptides?
2. Do cells decode nucleotides in one direction only or can they decode them in either direction? Formulate a hypothesis to answer this question.

Genes and Proteins

As you have just read, the three principal forms of RNA work together to produce polypeptides. Through transcription, a section of DNA directly determines the sequence of nucleotides in a molecule of mRNA. And through translation, the nucleotides in mRNA are translated into the amino acids of a polypeptide. In this way, a section of DNA—a gene—directs the synthesis of a protein.

If you are wondering why proteins are so important, that's a good question! Recall that in your studies of genetics, you saw that genes control the color of flowers, the height of plants, the type of human blood, and even the sex of a newborn baby. But genes code for proteins—what do proteins have to do with these characteristics?

The answer is that proteins have everything to do with them! Remember that many proteins are enzymes, and enzymes catalyze and regulate chemical reactions. Thus, a gene could control flower color by coding for an enzyme that helps to produce a pigment. Another gene could determine blood type by coding for an enzyme that helps to produce complex molecules in red blood cells. The proteins from other genes regulate the rate and pattern of growth throughout an organism, controlling its size and shape.

In fact, proteins are the keys to almost everything that living cells do. By coding for proteins, DNA holds the key to life itself.

Section Review 8-3

1. **Identify** the role of RNA.
2. **Compare** RNA with DNA.
3. **Describe** the processes of transcription and translation.
4. **Explain** the importance of proteins.
5. **Critical Thinking—Making Comparisons** Compare the three different forms of RNA. Which forms could be used over and over again to produce different polypeptides?
6. **MINI LAB** How does a cell **interpret** the genetic code?

6. The sequence of base pairs in an mRNA molecule is read in one direction to produce a polypeptide.

Skills Trace
Interpreting
- Focus p. 186
- Practice p. 186
- Assess p. 195

Learning Modality

Tactile Learning Give students such materials as yarn, pipe cleaners, straws, and beads to build a model of a molecule of RNA. Remind them to show how RNA differs from DNA.

Controlling Gene Expression

Guide for Reading

- **Explain** why cells control gene expression.
- **Describe** how mRNA is edited.

EVEN THE SIMPLEST LIVING organism contains thousands of genes. Are all those genes active all the time? Do cells copy every gene into mRNA?

The answer to both questions is no. Like the thousands of books in a library, not all the genes on a cell's chromosomes are read at the same time. In fact, only a small fraction of the cell's genes are actively copied at any given time.

Gene Expression

A cell that transcribed all its genes at the same time would be making lots of proteins that it did not need, thus wasting energy and raw materials. Fortunately for cells, they use their genes more efficiently. **Cells regulate gene transcription because they do not always need a gene's product.**

A gene that is transcribed into mRNA is said to be expressed, and a gene that is not being transcribed is said to be unexpressed. Put another way, an expressed gene is "turned on" and an unexpressed gene is "turned off."

How does a cell efficiently regulate gene transcription? How does a cell recognize when to turn genes on and when to turn them off? The first answers to these questions came from studies done on the genes of a bacterium called *Escherichia coli*.

Expressing Lac Genes

Escherichia coli—*E. coli*, for short—contains about 2000 genes. Three of these genes are called the *lac* genes. Each *lac* gene codes for a protein, and

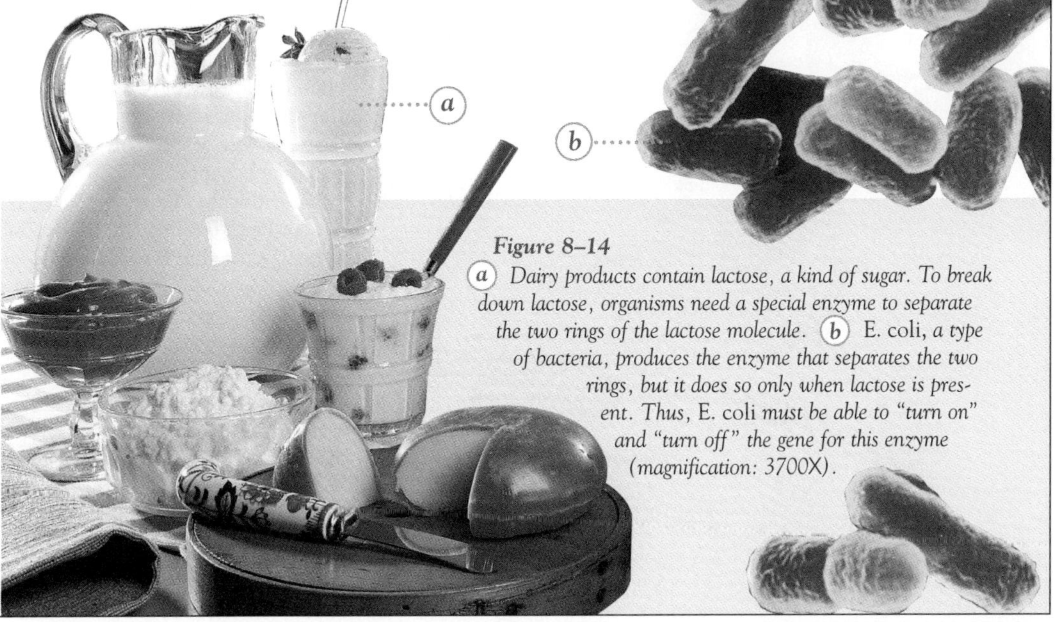

Figure 8–14
(a) Dairy products contain lactose, a kind of sugar. To break down lactose, organisms need a special enzyme to separate the two rings of the lactose molecule. (b) E. coli*, a type of bacteria, produces the enzyme that separates the two rings, but it does so only when lactose is present. Thus,* E. coli *must be able to "turn on" and "turn off" the gene for this enzyme (magnification: 3700X).*

TEACHER SUPPORT — Ecology Note

Being able to control gene expression is an advantage to an organism because it is more energy-efficient. Transcription and translation require both energy and building blocks. An organism acquires the energy and building blocks needed for these processes from food.

In nature there is great competition for food among various members of a community. The most efficient organisms are better able to survive and reproduce because they can successfully complete all of their essential body processes using the least amount of energy. If food sources in a community are scarce, the more efficient organisms have an advantage and are less vulnerable to predators, parasites, and disease.

Section 8–4

Controlling Gene Expression

Performance Objectives

- Explain the importance of controlling gene expression.
- Describe introns and exons.

1 ENGAGE

Inquiry Activity

Hypothesizing

Gene Expression

Ask students if they think that cells transcribe every gene into mRNA all the time. Encourage students to consider how a cell works and what is required to build a protein. Challenge students to hypothesize a method by which cells control the expression of genes. Invite students to share their hypotheses with the class.

2 EXPLORE

Discussion

Begin a class discussion about how the body regulates many functions without our conscious control. Invite students to name as many auto-controlled functions as possible. (Heartbeat, digestion, growth and repair, and respiration are some examples.) Emphasize that in all of these functions, the body regulates itself so that energy and body building blocks are not wasted. For example, the body produces antibodies to fight a certain virus only when the virus has invaded the body.

3 TEACH

Ideas Through Images

Have students examine Figure 8–15, read the caption, and answer the following questions.

- **What happens to the *lac* repressor when lactose is present?** (When lactose binds to the repressor, the repressor changes shape and falls off the operator.)
- **How do you think expression of the *lac* genes is stopped after all the lactose has been broken down?** (A *lac* repressor that is translated in the absence of lactose will be able to bind to the *lac* operator.)
- **What do you think might happen if a defect in the *lac* repressor prevented it from binding lactose?** (The *lac* genes would never be transcribed, and the cell could not use lactose for food.)

Investigate

Research Many other systems that control gene expression have been studied in bacteria, as well as in more complex organisms. Encourage students to find out about another method of controlling gene expression. Have students conduct miniseminars to present their findings to the class. Encourage students to use models or visual aids to help explain the regulatory system.

4 ASSESS

Quick Check

Have students diagram the control of gene expression for the *lac* genes of *E.coli*.

each protein must be expressed for the cell to use lactose, a type of sugar.

When does it make sense for *E. coli* to express *lac* genes? Obviously, it makes sense only when lactose is actually present! In fact, because of the energy needed to make the three proteins, expressing the *lac* genes might even be a waste of precious resources. Therefore, an efficient bacterium would express the *lac* genes only when lactose is present. And that is exactly what the bacterium does!

The Promoter

To one side of the three *lac* genes is a special region of DNA called the **promoter.** The promoter is a binding site for RNA polymerase.

RNA polymerase is able to recognize the promoter, and there it attaches itself to the chromosome. It then moves along the DNA molecule until it finds the first gene. At that point it starts transcription, making a single mRNA molecule from the three genes that can be translated into three proteins.

The Repressor and Operator

To regulate the expression of the *lac* genes, the bacterium uses a protein called a *lac* **repressor.** A repressor is a DNA-binding protein that blocks a gene's transcription.

The *lac* repressor binds to another special region of DNA called the **operator.** When the *lac* repressor binds to the operator, RNA polymerase cannot move past the operator to reach the *lac* genes. Like a lock on the library door, the repressor blocks the expression of the *lac* genes.

Checkpoint What is the *lac* repressor? The operator? 1

Unlocking the Padlock

Once the repressor is bound to the operator, how can the *lac* genes be expressed? In fact, when lactose is not present, the repressor remains bound to the operator and the genes' transcription is blocked. However, when lactose is present, something remarkable happens.

As shown in ***Figure 8–15,*** the repressor has a binding site for lactose. When lactose binds to the repressor,

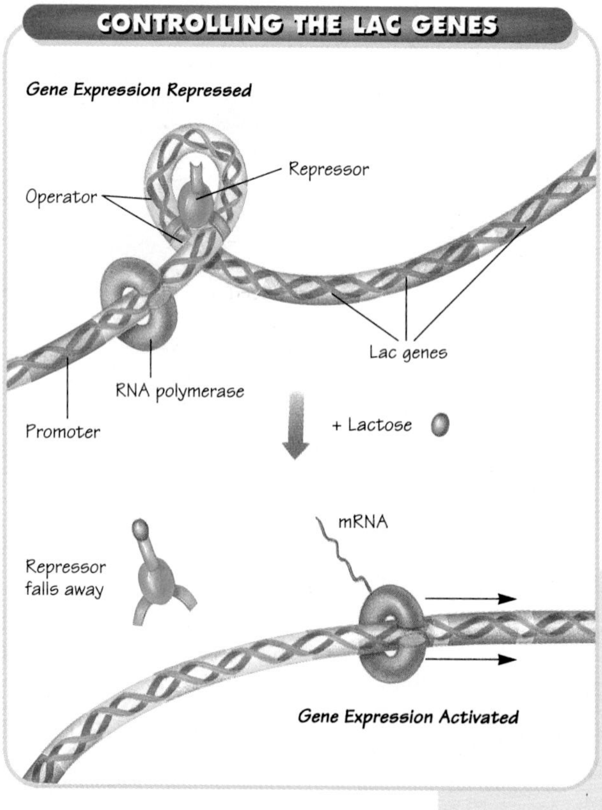

Figure 8–15
How does the repressor "turn off" the lac genes? Researchers have shown that it binds to the gene at two different places, thus tying the gene in a knot! Gene expression is repressed only when lactose is not present.

TEACHER SUPPORT

Managing Classroom Diversity

GIFTED STUDENTS
The regulation of the *lac* genes in the *lac* operon is actually more complex than described here. For example, the *lac* repressor regulates the operon negatively, and a cyclic AMP complex is a positive regulator. Encourage students to learn more about the *lac* operon and the genetic analysis of this system by François Jacob and Jacques Monod. Have students share their findings with the class.

LEP STUDENTS
Students might confuse the meanings of the words operator, repressor, and promoter. Encourage students to diagram the regulation process of the *lac* genes. They may include notes in their native language for the process and for the functions of the promoter, operator, and repressor. Have students find other meanings for these words and relate those meanings to their functions in the *lac* genes.

INTRONS AND EXONS

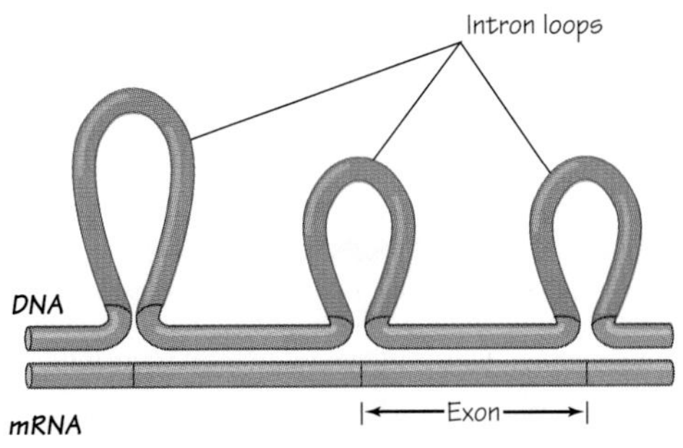

Figure 8–16
After a molecule of mRNA is transcribed, sequences called introns may be removed. The remaining sequences, called exons, are then spliced together. As a result, the final version of mRNA matches to separate pieces of the DNA that coded for it, not to the entire gene.

the repressor changes shape and falls off the DNA. Suddenly, the lock is gone, and the *lac* genes are ready to be transcribed.

Not all genes work exactly as the *lac* genes do. In eukaryotic cells, for example, the control of gene expression can be especially complicated. However, many genes follow the general pattern of DNA-binding proteins—such as the *lac* repressor—that control where and when transcription happens.

☑ *Checkpoint* Why are the *lac* genes expressed when a lactose molecule is present? ②

Genes in Pieces

In 1976, scientists Philip Sharp and Susan Berget made a surprising discovery about gene expression in eukaryotes. They carefully compared the DNA sequence of a gene with the base sequence of mRNA for the very same gene. They expected the two sequences to match perfectly—but they were amazed to see something quite different!

As Sharp and Berget discovered with further research, mRNA often undergoes a process similar to editing, in which parts of the molecule are removed and discarded. The discarded parts are called **introns**—short for intervening sequences. **After the introns are removed, the remaining parts are spliced together to form the final version of mRNA.** The remaining parts are called **exons**—short for expressed sequences.

Why do genes make mRNA with introns and exons? Biologists still have no good answer for this question. Some mRNA molecules may be spliced in different ways, making it possible for a single gene to produce several different molecules of mRNA. In addition, introns and exons may play a role in evolution, making it possible for very small changes in DNA sequences to have dramatic effects in gene expression.

Section Review 8–4

1. **Explain** why cells control gene expression.
2. **Describe** how mRNA is edited.
3. **BRANCHING OUT ACTIVITY** **Construct a model** of the *lac* genes and the promoter, repressor, and operator. Use your model to explain how the expression of the *lac* genes is controlled.

Section Review 8–4

1. Cells regulate gene transcription because they do not always need a gene's product.

2. Introns are the intervening sequences that are removed from mRNA. Exons are the expressed sequences of mRNA that are spliced together after the introns are removed. Introns and exons could allow one gene to produce different proteins, and they may also play a role in evolution.

3. Students' models will vary. See Figure 8–15 for a description of how the *lac* genes are controlled.

Learning Modality

Kinesthetic Learning Have student groups model the processing of pre-mRNA as shown in Figure 8–16. Group members should divide the parts to play—intron, exon, cap, and tail. Encourage groups to determine the best way to choreograph the process. Videotape each group as they perform the process. Then have the class compare and contrast the performances.

☑ Checkpoints

① The *lac* repressor is a protein that binds to DNA to block transcription of the *lac* genes. The operator is the DNA sequence to which the *lac* repressor binds.

② When lactose is present, it binds to the repressor, which changes shape and falls off the operator, allowing transcription to occur.

TEACHER SUPPORT

Background Information

RNA Splicing The removal of introns and the joining of exons is called RNA splicing. RNA splicing occurs in the nucleus of the cell after the molecule has been capped and the tail added. Introns are removed one by one, with the exons joining before the next intron is removed. After RNA splicing is complete, the mRNA is transported to the cytoplasm for translation.

Number of Introns in Genes The number of introns in a gene is highly variable. Some genes, such as the gene encoding interferon, do not have any introns. Others have a large number of introns. For example, the mRNA molecule for collagen has 52 introns. In either case, introns usually are much longer than exons.

Ancillary Support

The resources below can be used to support your teaching strategy for these two pages.

TR Writing in Biology: Biology Acrostics
Apply: Making Sense of Introns and Exons

BL Inquiry Activity: Fits Like a Glove

CHAPTER 8

Laboratory Investigation

Extracting DNA

Before the Lab

1. Gather enough 200-mL plastic cups, hot plates, 1000-mL beakers, thermometers, 10-mL graduated cylinders, glass stirring rods, ice buckets, and tongs for students to work in groups of two to four.
2. Check supplies of ice, distilled water, raw wheat germ (not roasted; available at health food stores), liquid dishwashing detergent (such as Palmolive®), and meat tenderizer (Adolph's®, unseasoned).
3. Prepare the following solutions.

- Baking soda solution (1 N sodium bicarbonate at pH 8.0): Add 8.4 g baking soda to 100 mL distilled water.
- Alcohol solution (95% ethanol or isopropanol): Add 5 mL of distilled water to 95 mL of 100% ethanol or isopropanol.

Pre-Lab Discussion

Have students read the entire procedure for this investigation. Then ask students the following questions.

What is the purpose of this investigation? (To observe the characteristics of DNA.)

Why is it important to check the temperature of the water bath frequently? (If the water temperature rises above 60°C, DNA will break down.)

Skills Development

Students will use these skills while completing the laboratory investigation: observing, measuring, and drawing conclusions.

Laboratory Investigation

Extracting DNA

DNA is stored in the nucleus of every eukaryotic cell. In this investigation, you will perform a DNA extraction—a procedure that removes the DNA from cells. In this investigation, you will extract the DNA from wheat germ, the fat-rich part of the seed of the wheat plant. A similar procedure, however, could extract the DNA from many different organisms.

Problem

How can you **observe** DNA?

Materials (per group)

- 200-mL plastic cup
- distilled water
- 1.5 g raw wheat germ
- hot plate
- 1000-mL beaker
- thermometer
- liquid dishwashing detergent
- 3 g meat tenderizer
- baking soda solution
- ice
- 10-mL graduated cylinder
- 10 mL alcohol solution
- glass stirring rod
- tongs

Procedure

1. Mix 100 mL of distilled water and the wheat germ in the 200-mL plastic cup.

2. Place the plastic cup in a water bath, as shown in the diagram.

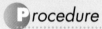

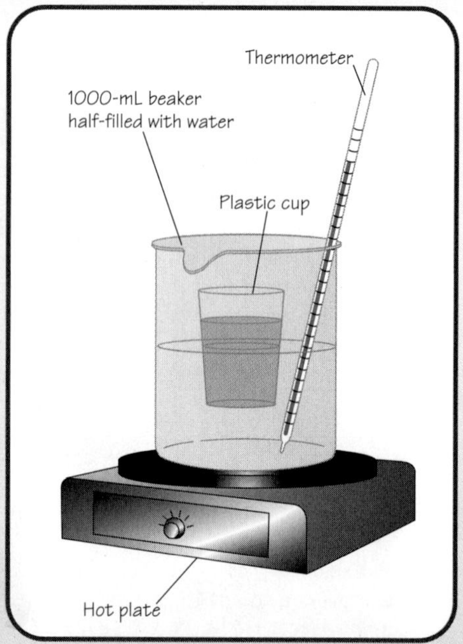

Safety Tips

- Students should wear lab aprons and goggles.
- Remind students to use caution while using the hot plate and while handling the hot plastic cup.
- Caution students not to spill the alcohol solution on themselves or on the laboratory benches.
- Have students wash their hands immediately after completing the investigation.

3. **Heat the water bath to 50°C. As you perform steps 4 through 6, adjust the hot plate as necessary to maintain the water temperature near 50°C. DNA will denature, or lose its structure, at temperatures above 60°C.**
4. **Add 5 mL of liquid dishwashing detergent to the plastic cup. Liquid dishwashing detergent breaks apart cell membranes.**
5. **Add the meat tenderizer to the plastic cup.**
6. **Add 10 mL of the baking soda solution to the plastic cup. Stir the mixture, then wait 10 minutes.**
7. **Turn off the hot plate. Using the tongs, transfer the plastic cup to a container of ice. Keep the plastic cup in the ice for 15 minutes.**
8. **Using the 10-mL graduated cylinder, slowly add the alcohol solution to the plastic cup. The alcohol solution should form a second layer on top of the wheat germ solution.**
9. **The DNA of the wheat germ precipitates at the interface of the two layers. Place the tip of the glass stirring rod at the interface and twist it to spool the DNA.**

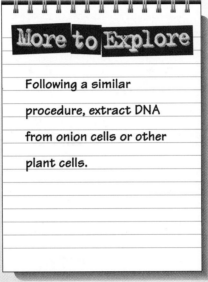

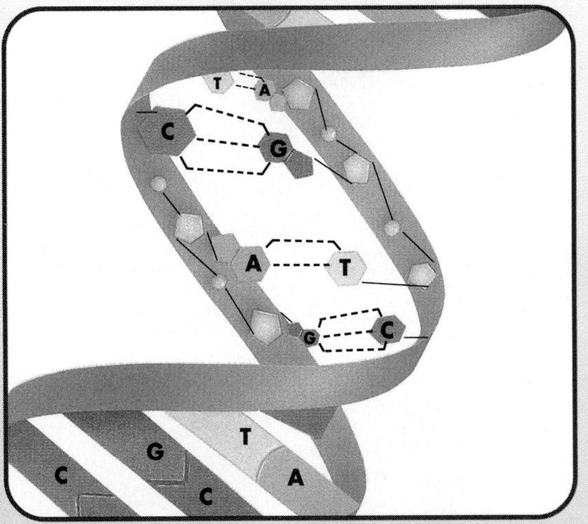

Observations

Describe the DNA you produced.

Analysis and Conclusions

1. What is the role of DNA in the cell?
2. Explain the purpose of adding liquid dishwashing detergent in step 4.
3. Can you directly observe the double-helix structure in the DNA sample you produced? Explain your answer.
4. Explain why a procedure similar to the one in this investigation could be used to extract DNA from the cells of other organisms.

More to Explore

Following a similar procedure, extract DNA from onion cells or other plant cells.

Teaching Strategies

1. The detergent disrupts the lipids in the cell membrane. The meat tenderizer contains papain, an enzyme that breaks down proteins.
2. The alcohol solution should be kept ice cold in the refrigerator and removed just before using it. When students add the alcohol solution, they should hold the cup at a slight angle and pour the alcohol very slowly down the side of the cup.

Answer to Observations

Students should observe and describe the DNA as white and gelatinous. They might even be able to observe thin, hairlike strands. If the DNA is damaged during the extraction process, it will precipitate as a white fuzzy mass that cannot be collected on a glass rod.

Answers to Analysis and Conclusions

1. DNA makes up genes; it holds the information that determines how an organism looks and functions.
2. Liquid dishwashing detergent breaks apart the cell membrane.
3. No, the molecular structure of DNA is so small that it cannot be observed directly.
4. Cells that make up all organisms have basically the same structure, except that plant cells have cell walls and animal cells do not.

More to Explore

Prepare an onion cell solution by blending pieces of a yellow onion with 1.5 g of noniodized salt, 10 mL of liquid dishwashing detergent, and 90 mL of distilled water. Filter the blended mixture through cheesecloth and give each student group 4 mL. Students can follow the laboratory procedure from step 2, skipping step 4.

Chapter 8

Study Guide

Review Strategy

Divide the class into small groups and have each group work together to write a study guide for this chapter. Students can use the key concepts of the chapter to help them get started. Encourage students to write a wide range of questions, including simple review questions and critical thinking questions. After groups have completed their study guides, they can exchange the questions and practice answering them.

Study Guide

Summarizing Key Concepts

The key concepts in each section of this chapter are listed below to help you review the chapter content. Make sure you understand each concept and its relationship to other concepts and to the theme of this chapter.

8–1 Discovering DNA

- Frederick Griffith discovered transformation, a process that changes one type of bacteria into another type.
- DNA is the molecule of heredity—the molecule that forms genes. The role of DNA was demonstrated by the work of Oswald Avery and the Hershey-Chase experiment.

8–2 DNA Structure and Replication

- Watson and Crick determined that DNA has the structure of a double helix. Hydrogen bonds between base pairs link the two strands together.
- In DNA replication, enzymes separate the two strands, then synthesize new strands that base-pair to the original strands.
- Chromosomes are made of chromatin, which contains DNA and proteins. Biologists suspect that proteins help to fold and package DNA.

8–3 RNA

- RNA carries out the instructions coded in DNA. The three principal forms of RNA are mRNA, rRNA, and tRNA.
- In transcription, a nucleotide sequence in DNA is copied into RNA. Transcription is carried out by an enzyme called RNA polymerase.
- A codon is a group of three nucleotides in mRNA that codes for an amino acid. In translation, the codons in mRNA are translated into a polypeptide.

8–4 Controlling Gene Expression

- Cells regulate gene transcription because they do not always need the genes' products.
- After an mRNA molecule is transcribed, sections of it may be cut away. These sections are called introns. The remaining sections, called exons, are expressed.

Reviewing Key Terms

Review the following vocabulary terms and their meaning. Then use each term in a complete sentence.

8–1 Discovering DNA

transformation
DNA

8–2 DNA Structure and Replication

nucleotide
DNA replication
chromatin

8–3 RNA

RNA
transcription
messenger RNA
ribosomal RNA
transfer RNA
genetic code
codon
translation
anticodon

8–4 Controlling Gene Expression

promoter
repressor
operator
intron
exon

Inquiry-Based Strategy

Mitochondria and chloroplasts have been found to contain their own DNA molecules, having anywhere from 10 to 50 genes. Have students design an experiment that answers this question: Are the inheritance patterns for mitochondrial DNA the same as for nuclear genes? Encourage students to determine what research is necessary to answer the question. Then they should develop an appropriate procedure for answering it. Students are likely to develop different procedures. One procedure will involve following the inheritance of a mutation that involves a gene in an organelle.

Recalling Main Ideas

Choose the letter of the answer that best completes the statement or answers the question.

1. What did Griffith name the process that changed rough bacteria to smooth bacteria?
   a. transformation c. translation
   b. transcription d. replication

2. Hershey and Chase showed that the genetic material of a bacteriophage is
   a. protein. c. DNA.
   b. sugar. d. RNA.

3. According to Chargaff's rules, the amount of adenine (A) in DNA equals the amount of
   a. thymine (T).
   b. cytosine (C).
   c. guanine (G).
   d. cytosine (C) and guanine (G).

4. In the Watson-Crick model of DNA, the two strands of the double helix are united by hydrogen bonds between
   a. sugar molecules. c. nitrogenous bases.
   b. phosphate groups. d. nitrogen atoms.

5. Which molecule(s) are found in chromosomes?
   a. DNA only c. proteins only
   b. RNA only d. DNA and proteins

6. RNA polymerase is the enzyme that carries out
   a. transcription. c. transformation.
   b. translation. d. DNA replication.

7. In translation, amino acids bond to molecules of
   a. DNA. c. rRNA.
   b. mRNA. d. tRNA.

8. The *lac* repressor falls off the operator in the presence of
   a. lactose. c. rRNA.
   b. RNA polymerase. d. tRNA.

9. The portions of mRNA that are removed and discarded are called
   a. introns. c. nucleosomes.
   b. exons. d. tRNA.

Putting It All Together

Using the information on pages xxx to xxxi, complete the following concept map.

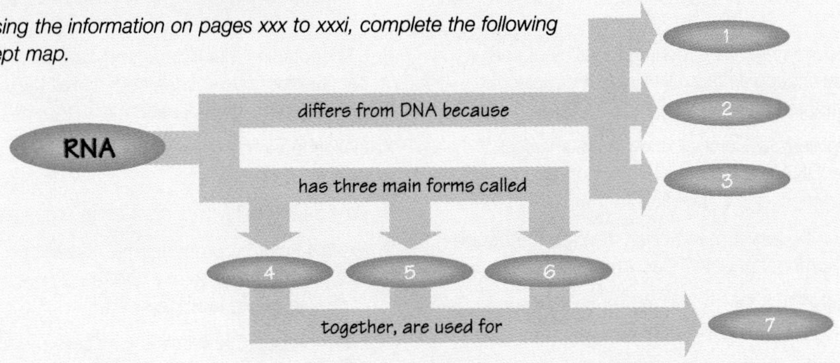

Putting It All Together

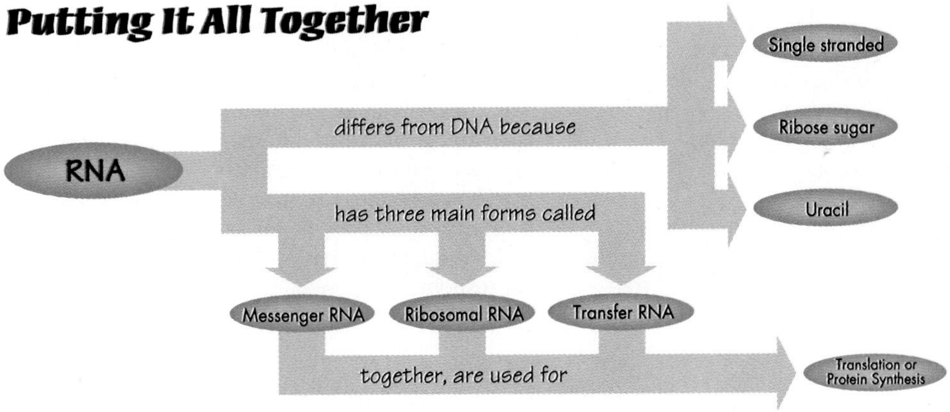

Recalling Main Ideas

1. a
2. c
3. a
4. c
5. d
6. a
7. d
8. a
9. a

Assessment

Reviewing What You Learned

1. The process that changes one type of bacteria into another type.
2. By the number of neutrons in their nuclei.
3. Radioactive isotopes can become part of a molecule just as stable isotopes can.
4. Phage DNA entered the bacterial cell. Hershey and Chase used radioactive isotopes to label the molecules.
5. She produced X-ray diffraction images of the DNA molecule, which led to the discovery of DNA structure.
6. A nucleotide is composed of a phosphate group, a nitrogenous base, and a 5-carbon sugar (deoxyribose). The four nucleotides in DNA are adenine, thymine, guanine, and cytosine.
7. RNA is single-stranded, not double-stranded; has ribose, not deoxyribose; and has uracil, not thymine.
8. Messenger RNA, ribosomal RNA, and transfer RNA.
9. In the cytoplasm.
10. A group of three nucleotides in mRNA that specifies an amino acid.
11. Transfer RNA has three nucleotides called an anticodon that bind the codon of mRNA.
12. Only when lactose is present in the cell.
13. An intron is an intervening sequence of mRNA that is removed and discarded. An exon is an expressed sequence of mRNA that is spliced to other exons when the introns are removed to form the final version of mRNA.

Assessment

Reviewing What You Learned

Answer each of the following in a complete sentence.

1. What is bacterial transformation?
2. How do the isotopes of an element differ?
3. How can radioactive isotopes be used to label molecules?
4. In the Hershey-Chase experiment, which phage molecule entered the bacteria? How did Hershey and Chase identify this molecule?
5. How did Rosalind Franklin contribute to the understanding of the structure of DNA?
6. Describe the composition of a nucleotide and name the four different nucleotides in DNA.
7. Identify three ways in which RNA differs from DNA.
8. Identify the three main forms of RNA.
9. Where in the cell does translation take place?
10. What is a codon?
11. How does tRNA recognize a codon in mRNA?
12. When does *E. coli* express the *lac* genes?
13. What is an intron? An exon?

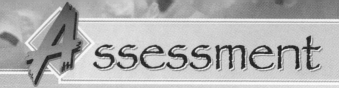

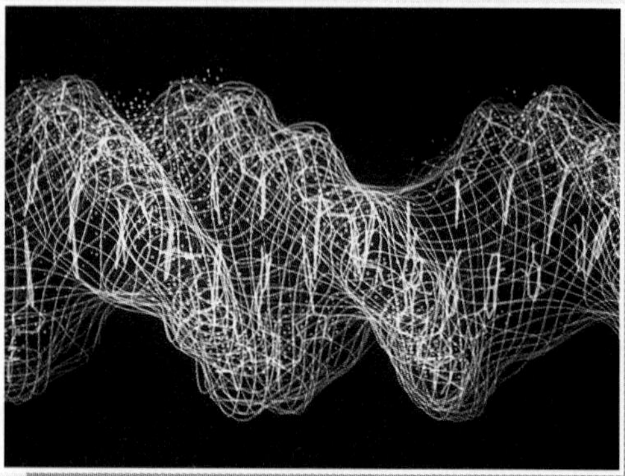

Expanding the Concepts

Discuss each of the following in a brief paragraph.

1. Describe Avery's experiments. Why did his results suggest that DNA was the molecule of transformation?
2. Explain how Hershey and Chase showed that DNA is the molecule that contains a bacteriophage's genetic information.
3. How did Watson and Crick develop the double-helix model of DNA? Describe this model.
4. Is DNA the only molecule that chromosomes contain? Explain your answer.
5. Compare transcription with DNA replication.
6. DNA contains four different nucleotides. How can just four nucleotides code for all the different proteins in a cell?
7. Describe the role of each form of RNA in protein synthesis.
8. Why are proteins important to an organism?
9. Explain how the promoter, repressor, and operator combine to regulate the expression of the *lac* genes in *E. coli*.
10. Describe possible reasons why cells produce mRNA with introns and exons.

194 Chapter 8

Assessment (continued)

Expanding the Concepts

1. Avery treated heat-killed smooth bacteria with enzymes that destroyed proteins, lipids, carbohydrates, and DNA and used these treatments to transform live rough bacteria. Transformation was prevented only when Avery destroyed DNA, which suggests that DNA is the molecule of transformation.
2. Hershey and Chase prepared one sample of phage labeled with phosphorus-32, which labels only DNA, and another sample labeled with sulfur-35, which labels only proteins. They allowed both phage samples to infect bacteria and observed that only the phage labeled with phosphorus-32 made the bacteria radioactive.
3. Watson and Crick studied X-ray diffraction images of the DNA molecule and built models of the molecule. DNA is a double helix in which sugar and phosphate groups form each strand of the double helix, while hydrogen bonds hold the strands together. The hydrogen bonds form only between adenine and thymine or between cytosine and guanine.
4. No. Chromosomes also contain a number of different proteins that help to fold and package DNA so it can fit inside a cell.
5. In transcription, one protein, RNA polymerase, separates the two strands of DNA and uses one strand as a template to make a single-stranded RNA molecule. In DNA replication, a number of different enzymes separate the two strands of DNA and use both strands as templates to make another double-stranded DNA molecule.
6. The nucleotides are read in groups of three, called codons. There are 64 different codons, enough to allow each of the 20 amino acids to be specified by at least one codon.
7. The nucleotides in mRNA are decoded to form the amino acid sequence of the protein. Each tRNA binds a specific amino acid, and it has three nitrogenous bases, called an anticodon, that bind to the codon in mRNA. Ribosomes are composed of rRNA and proteins. As the ribosomes advance along the mRNA, they bind tRNA, join amino acids in a polypeptide chain, and cut tRNA from its amino acid.
8. Proteins make up cell structures, and they are the enzymes that catalyze and regulate chemical reactions in the cell.
9. When lactose is not present, the repressor binds to the operator, which prevents RNA polymerase from binding to the promoter, and transcription is blocked. When lactose is present, lactose binds to the repressor, and it falls off the operator, allowing RNA polymerase to bind to the promoter and transcribe the *lac* genes.
10. Introns and exons allow some mRNA molecules to be spliced in different ways to produce different polypeptides from one sequence of DNA. Introns and exons may also play a role in evolution, making it possible for small changes in the DNA sequence to have a large effect on gene expression.

Extending Your Thinking

Use the skills you have developed in this chapter to answer the following.

1. **Identifying assumptions** A biology student identifies the nucleotide sequence AAC in a strand of mRNA. In the genetic code, AAC codes for asparagine. Will asparagine necessarily appear in the polypeptide? Explain your answer.
2. **Interpreting data** A polypeptide contains the amino acid sequence of histidine–isoleucine–valine–glycine. Using the genetic code and the rules of base-pairing, identify a sequence of nucleotides in DNA that code for this amino acid sequence. Is more than one such sequence possible in DNA?
3. **Observing** Look at the X-ray diffraction pattern shown in ***Figure 8–6*** on page 176 and describe what you observe. What evidence can you see of the double-helix structure of DNA in this pattern?
4. **Constructing models** Using construction paper, pipe cleaners, straws, or other materials available in your classroom, construct models of mRNA, tRNA, and amino acids. Use your models to explain protein synthesis.
5. **Interpreting diagrams** The table below lists the percentages of the four nucleotides in the DNA of different organisms. What conclusions can be drawn from this table? How does the structure of DNA explain these conclusions?

NUCLEOTIDE PERCENTAGES

Source of DNA	A	T	G	C
Streptococcus	29.8	31.6	20.5	18.0
Yeast	31.3	32.9	18.7	17.1
Herring	27.8	27.5	22.2	22.6
Human	30.9	29.4	19.9	19.8

Applying Your Skills

DNA Replication

DNA replication relies on the principles of base-pairing—adenine pairs with thymine, and cytosine pairs with guanine.

1. Construct a model of the following double-stranded sequence of DNA:

   AAGCTTATGG
   | | | | | | | | | |
   TTCGAATACC

   Model the nucleotides with colored paper clips, straws, pipe cleaners, or any other materials available.
2. Separate the strands of your model. Using ***Figure 8–8*** on page 179 as a guide, construct models of the new strands that DNA replication would produce.
3. Describe the products of DNA replication.

• GOING FURTHER •

4. If DNA were single-stranded instead of double-stranded, could it be replicated by the procedure you just modeled? Explain your answer.
5. Using your model as a visual aid, present a report to your class on DNA replication.

Extending Your Thinking

1. No. It is possible that the sequence is part of two adjacent codons that specify different amino acids.
2. Possible DNA sequences include
GTG-TAT-CAC-CCA
GTA-TAG-CAT-CCG
GTG-TAA-CAG-CCT
GTA-TAT-CAA-CCC
Yes, since more than one codon can specify an amino acid, more than one DNA sequence is possible.

3. Students might describe that the pattern looks like a large X with equally spaced dots. Evidence students might observe is the X-shaped pattern.

4. Student models should reflect the information shown in Figure 8–12.

Skills Trace
Modeling
- Focus p. 180
- Practice p. 180
- Assess p. 195

5. Only adenine can form hydrogen bonds with thymine to hold together the two DNA strands, and only cytosine can form hydrogen bonds with guanine.

Skills Trace
Interpreting
- Focus p. 186
- Practice p. 186
- Assess p. 195

Applying Your Skills

Teacher Notes

- Students can use the models of DNA they constructed for the MINI LAB on page 180 and modify them.
- Students might color-code the sugar-phosphate backbones of the new DNA strands to differentiate them from the original DNA strands.

Answers

3. Two double-stranded DNA molecules that are composed of one newly synthesized strand and one of the original strands.
4. No, the double strands would not have to be separated for replication to occur, and the product would be one single strand of DNA that has the complementary DNA sequence, not the identical DNA sequence.

Scoring Rubric

4 Response is thorough, accurate, and creative; shows an in-depth understanding of science skills, procedures, and concepts.

3 Response is complete, mostly accurate, and original; shows a satisfactory understanding of science skills, procedures, and concepts.

2 Response is mostly complete but includes some inaccuracies; shows an adequate understanding of science skills, procedures, and concepts.

1 Response is only partially complete and has many inaccuracies; shows an incomplete understanding of science skills, procedures, and concepts.

0 Response is mostly incomplete and/or inaccurate; shows a lack of understanding of science skills, procedures, and concepts.

Chapter 9 Genetic Engineering

Content Management	Student Edition Activities
■ Section 9–1 Breeding New Organisms, pp. 197–200 Breeding the Appaloosa Selective Breeding Mutations	Laboratory Investigation: The Effects of Radiation on Seeds, pp. 210–211 MINI LAB: Mind Your Mutations!, p. 200
■ Section 9–2 Manipulating DNA, pp. 201–204 The Tools of Editing Cell Transformation	MINI LAB: So Many Restrictions!, p. 202
■ Section 9–3 Engineering New Organisms, pp. 205–206 Manipulating Genes Human Gene Therapy	
◆ BRANCHING OUT • In Action Section 9–4 The New Human Genetics, pp. 207–209 "RIHF-lihps" The Human Genome Project	

■ These sections cover all the necessary content and concepts for a basic course in biology.
◆ This section covers content and concepts that are either applications or extensions of the basic material.

Integration Strategies

SE Social Studies, p. 197
Health, p. 205

Assessment Strategies

SE Chapter Review, pp. 212–215
TR Section Reviews
Chapter Test
BL Chapter Review
Practice Test
CTB Chapter 9 Test

Tech Prep

Teaching strategies appropriate for students who are in technical/vocational programs or who are considering post-secondary technical education can be found on the following **TE** pages: 198 and 202.

Meeting the Standards

Sections 9–1 through 9–4 cover two of the six content standards under **The Cell** and two of the three content standards under **The Molecular Basis of Heredity** as described on pages 184–185 of The National Science Education Standards.

Chapter Planning Guide

Teacher's Edition Activities	Other Activities	Media and Technology
Chapter Discovery Learning Activity, p. 196 **Inquiry Activity:** Mutations, p. 197 **Investigate:** Research, p. 197 **Investigate:** Cooperative Learning, p. 198	**LM** Observing Cloning, #17 **TR** **Enrich:** A Risky Business? **BL** **Inquiry Activity:** Designer Dogs	**TB** Chromosomal and Gene Mutations, #12
Inquiry Activity: The Tools of Editing, p. 201 **Investigate:** Cooperative Learning, p. 202 **Investigate:** Research, p. 203 **Activity:** Analyzing DNA, p. 204	**LM** Investigating Gel Electrophoresis, #18 **TR** **Apply:** How'd They Do That? **BL** **Inquiry Activity:** Changing Directions	
Inquiry Activity: Genetic Engineering, p. 206	**TR** **Writing in Biology:** Speak Out! **Enrich:** Will Transgenics Save the World? **BL** **Inquiry Activity:** The Creating Game	**BioVue Mini Doc:** Gene Therapy, Videodisc Side 2
Inquiry Activity: Inheritance and Genetic Engineering, p. 207 **Investigate:** Role-Playing, p. 208	**TR** **Explore:** Probing for Prints **BL** **Inquiry Activity:** Updating the Human Genome Project	**BioVue Mini Doc:** The Human Genome Project, Videodisc Side 2

KEY: **SE** Student Edition **TE** Teacher's Edition **LM** Laboratory Manual **TR** Teaching Resources **BL** BioLog **TB** Transparency Box **CTB** Computer Test Bank

Materials List

TE **Chapter Discovery Learning Activity,** p. 196 (20 minutes); photographs of various breeds of dogs.
TE **Inquiry Activity: Mutations,** p. 197 (20–30 minutes); genetic code.
SE **MINI LAB: Mind Your Mutations!,** p. 200 (20–30 minutes); genetic code.
SE **MINI LAB: So Many Restrictions!,** p. 202 (20–30 minutes); scissors, different-colored pencils or paper.
TE **Activity: Analyzing DNA,** p. 204 (several hours over a few days); DNA restriction analysis kit, water bath, gel electrophoresis chamber, power supply, micropipetor.

CHAPTER 9

Genetic Engineering

Introducing the Chapter

. . . In Pictures

Have students examine the photograph and read the caption. Explain that gel electrophoresis is a method scientists use to separate pieces of DNA according to their size.

- **What does it look like the researcher in the photograph is doing?** (She is adding DNA samples to the gel to begin the gel electrophoresis procedure.)

- **Why can't you see the DNA in the photograph?** (The DNA molecule is very small; it is also in solution.)

Point out that gel electrophoresis is one of the important tools that geneticists use to study DNA.

Teaching Strategy

In the first three sections of this chapter, students will learn how new organisms can be produced by selective breeding, by mutations, and by manipulating DNA. In the BRANCHING OUT section, students find out how scientists use probes to identify and classify human DNA. You may wish to assign this section to students who are especially interested in human genetics.

BIO JOURNAL

Have students think about what the genetic code specifies. Then challenge them to brainstorm for a list of reasons why scientists would want to know the DNA sequence of a gene. Encourage students to relate what they have learned about genes, phenotypes, and human genetics in previous chapters to the advantage of actually knowing the nucleotide sequence of a gene. Instruct students to keep their entries in their portfolios.

CHAPTER 9

Genetic Engineering

FOCUSING THE CHAPTER
THEME: Systems and Interactions

9–1 Breeding New Organisms
- Describe how selective breeding and mutations can produce new organisms.

9–2 Manipulating DNA
- Explain how recombinant DNA is produced.

9–3 Engineering New Organisms
- Describe the achievements of genetic engineering.

BRANCHING OUT *In Action*

9–4 The New Human Genetics
- Identify RFLPs and discuss the Human Genome Project.

LABORATORY INVESTIGATION
- Design an experiment to determine the effects of radiation on seeds.

Biology and Your World

BIO JOURNAL

The researcher in this photograph is performing gel electrophoresis—one step toward identifying the nucleotide sequence in a strand of DNA. In your journal, explain why this information might be useful.

A laboratory technician performing gel electrophoresis on DNA

TEACHER SUPPORT

Chapter Discovery Learning Activity

Display photographs of various breeds of dogs. Have students compare and contrast the characteristics of each breed. Encourage them to make inferences about why each breed has been developed with those particular characteristics. You might wish to point out that many dog breeds have been developed to perform certain tasks. For example, collies were developed to herd animals, and Labrador retrievers were developed to retrieve birds shot by hunters. Challenge students to speculate about the process by which breeders have developed these certain characteristics in breeds of dogs.

Breeding New Organisms

GUIDE FOR READING

- **Describe** the process of selective breeding.
- **Define** a mutation.

MINI LAB

- **Construct a model** to show the effects of a point mutation.

WHEN THE EUROPEANS FIRST settled the beautiful, rugged land that is now the northwestern United States, they noticed that the Palouse and Nez Percé owned an exceptional breed of spotted horses. The horses were strong, durable, and gentle, as well as unusually colorful and attractive. The English-speaking settlers named these animals palouse horses. Over time, the name palouse was slurred first to palousey and, eventually, to appaloosa—the name by which the breed is known today.

Breeding the Appaloosa

Spaniards introduced horses to North America in the early 1500s. Over a span of 200 years, both the Palouse and Nez Percé had acquired horses and learned how to train and breed them. ● From Spanish horses of mixed color and temperament, the two tribes produced the appaloosa—the first recognized breed of horses in North America and still a favorite among horse owners today.

How did the tribes accomplish this feat? First, they realized that the Spanish horses showed a great deal of variability. Some of the horses were fast, and others were slow. Many horses bore plain colors, but a few had bright, attractive colors.

Then, as people of many cultures have done, the Palouse and Nez Percé set about to breed the kind of animal they wanted. Over the years, colorful horses must have been mated with horses that were very easy to handle. Naturally, the goal was to produce offspring that would have the best characteristics of both parents.

INTEGRATING SOCIAL STUDIES

What was the relationship between the Spanish explorers and the Native Americans they encountered?

Figure 9–1
(a) *The Palouse and Nez Percé well understood the principles of selective breeding, as demonstrated by how quickly they bred the appaloosa horse.* (b) *Appaloosa horses are prized for their beauty, strength, and gentleness.*

SECTION 9–1

Breeding New Organisms

Performance Objectives

- Explain how selective breeding is used to produce new organisms.
- Discuss what a mutation is.

Mini Lab Skill: Modeling
Laboratory Investigation Skill: Designing an experiment

1 ENGAGE

Inquiry Activity

Inferring

Mutations
Ask students to infer how changes in the DNA sequence of an organism affect its phenotype. You might wish to give each student an arbitrary DNA sequence and have students determine how a change in the sequence changes the protein it encodes. Challenge students to propose various changes to the DNA sequence and infer how these changes could affect the organism.

2 EXPLORE

Investigate

Research People have changed many animals and plants through the process of selective breeding. Encourage students to choose one animal or plant and find out how breeders have changed it. They should also find out what characteristics the breeders were selecting for. Invite students to present their findings to the class.

INTEGRATING SOCIAL STUDIES

Spanish explorers tried either to convert Native Americans to the Spanish way of life or conquer them. Native Americans were resistant to giving up their customs and their land.

TEACHER SUPPORT

Managing Classroom Diversity

MULTICULTURAL STRATEGY
Native Americans living in what is now central or southern Mexico selectively bred corn from wild plants to make it a more useful food crop. Encourage students to learn more about how advances in farming techniques changed the customs and lifestyles of Native Americans, such as the Pueblo people. Have students consider why it was important for Native Americans to improve the wild plants and animals around them to help them to survive. Challenge students to compare these Native Americans to present-day breeders. Ask them to explain how their methods are similar. (Both selected plants or animals with the desired traits and used them to set up controlled matings.)

3 TEACH

Discussion

Begin a class discussion about the reasons why breeders practice selective breeding. Emphasize the following points.

- Breeders are working to increase the food supply and improve the nutritional quality of foods.
- Breeders are breeding plants that are better suited to mechanized farming, such as thick-skinned tomatoes.
- Breeders are breeding plants or animals for qualities that have nothing to do with food, such as drought-resistant flowers, and fast race horses.

Investigate

Cooperative Learning Give pairs of students a breeding problem to solve. For example, wheat cannot grow in hot, dry areas, but breeders want to develop a strain of wheat that can. Challenge students to develop a hypothetical procedure in which they produce a strain of heat- and drought-resistant wheat. Instruct students to explain when they should use hybridization and when they should use inbreeding. Encourage students to break the problem down into smaller parts, with each person working on separate parts. You may want students to present their solutions to the class.

Ideas Through Images

Have students examine Figure 9–3, read the caption, and answer the following questions.

- **During what cell process would chromosomal mutations most likely occur?** (During crossing-over events in meiosis I.)
- **Will a frameshift mutation in one gene affect the gene next to it?** (Probably not; the next gene will most likely have its own RNA polymerase binding site, so the mRNA will by synthesized in the correct frame.)

Figure 9–2 *Perhaps the greatest selective breeder of all time was Luther Burbank, shown here holding a tuber that he developed. Burbank developed more than 800 varieties of plants, including many important crops.*

Selective Breeding

The breeding of the appaloosa is an example of **selective breeding**—one of the oldest ways in which humans have produced organisms that best suit their purposes. **In selective breeding, individual organisms with desired characteristics are chosen to produce a new generation.** Selective breeding has produced nearly all domestic animals—including cats, dogs, and horses—as well as most crop plants.

Checkpoint How was the appaloosa produced? ①

Hybridization

A cross between dissimilar individuals is known as **hybridization.** Hybridization is one of the breeder's most important tools because it provides a way to combine the best characteristics of two organisms. For example, hybridization could be used to combine the disease resistance of one plant with the food-producing capacity of another.

Inbreeding

When a breed of organisms has been established, the breeder must decide how to maintain it. Sometimes this is done by **inbreeding**—the continued breeding of closely related individuals. The many breeds of dogs—from beagles to poodles to schnauzers—are each maintained by inbreeding.

Inbreeding helps to ensure that the characteristics that make each breed special will be preserved. However, inbreeding also carries with it a special set of problems. Because most members of a breed are genetically similar, crossing individuals of the same breed may bring together two recessive alleles for a genetic defect. Excessive inbreeding has caused several problems in many dog breeds, including blindness and joint deformities in both shepherds and retrievers.

Checkpoint What is inbreeding? ②

Mutations

Selective breeding is a powerful tool for producing new organisms, but it depends entirely on the variation that already exists in a species. Where does that variation come from? And is there a way to increase the variation in a species? The answers to both questions involve a molecule that you have already studied—DNA.

DNA codes for an organism's genetic characteristics, and it is found in every cell of the organism. As you have read earlier, a cell copies its DNA before it divides. But although the copying procedure usually works perfectly, every now and then it produces a mistake. These mistakes are called **mutations**—from a Latin word meaning "change." **A mutation is an inheritable change in genetic information.** Mutations may occur in any cell and in any gene.

TEACHER SUPPORT

Managing Classroom Diversity

TECH PREP STUDENTS

The principles of selective breeding are used in career areas, such as agribusiness and natural resources. Challenge students to use their knowledge of inbreeding and hybridization to explain how they might prevent an endangered plant or animal from extinction in a region. Encourage students to speak with a naturalist or environmentalist from a local nature reserve or state park to help them solve the problem.

LEP STUDENTS

Students with limited English proficiency might need extra practice with the words selective breeding, hybridization, and inbreeding. Have students write these words in their journals or make flashcards for them. Students should write synonyms or definitions for these words in both English and their native languages.

Chromosomal Mutations

Changes involving the number or structure of a cell's chromosomes are called **chromosomal mutations.** As shown in ***Figure 9–3,*** chromosomal mutations may move a gene's location on a chromosome or change the number of copies of a gene.

Some chromosomal mutations take place during meiosis. When a whole set of chromosomes fails to separate during meiosis, gametes with extra sets of chromosomes can be produced. These gametes may produce triploid (3n) or even tetraploid (4n) organisms. An organism with 3 or more sets of chromosomes in its cells is said to be polyploid.

In animals, polyploidy is usually fatal. However, for unknown reasons, plants tolerate polyploidy much better than animals do. In fact, it is a healthy condition in many plants—often making them larger and stronger than diploid (2n) plants. Crops such as bananas, wheat, and citrus fruits are each produced from polyploid plants.

Gene Mutations

While a change that affects an entire chromosome is called a chromosomal mutation, a change that affects only an individual gene is known as a **gene mutation.** A gene mutation may involve only one nucleotide or many nucleotides. But no matter how large or how small the change, a gene mutation can have dramatic consequences for an organism.

A gene mutation that involves a single nucleotide—such as the substitution of one nucleotide for

Figure 9–3
Chromosomal mutations include the four types shown here, as well as mutations that involve whole sets of chromosomes. Gene mutations affect only a single gene. Notice that a nucleotide substitution produces fewer changes than a nucleotide deletion.

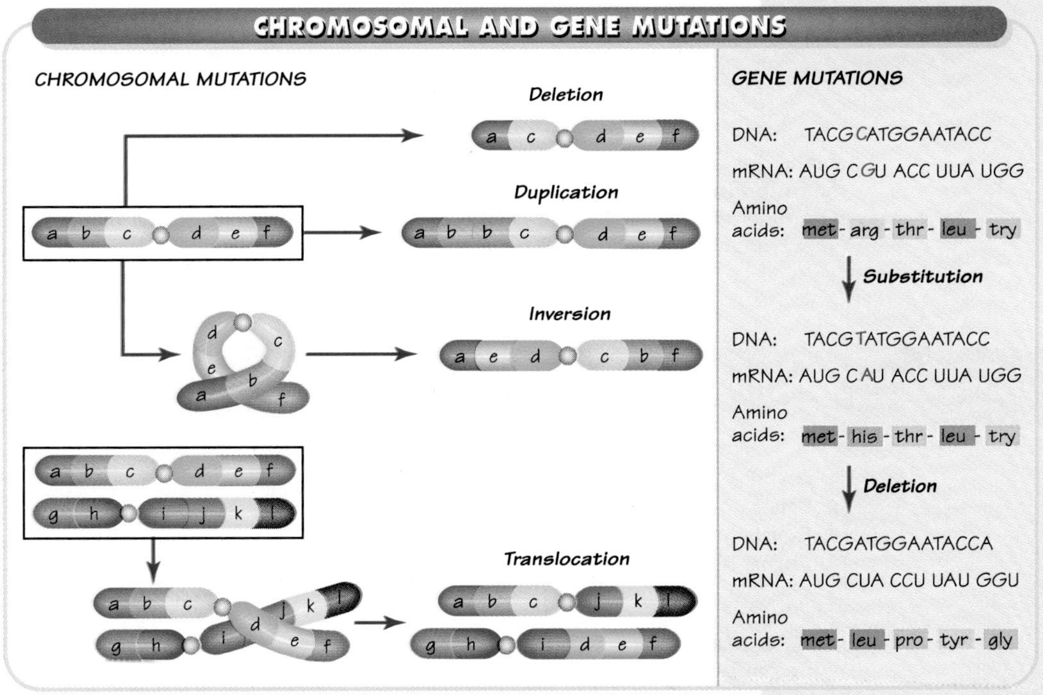

Discussion

Point out how a frameshift mutation causes much more damage than a point mutation. Explain that in some cases, a point mutation may not have a large effect on an organism, especially if the changed amino acid is chemically similar to the original one or if it is not critical to protein structure or function. Write on the board the following sentence: The fat cat ate the rat. Then cross out the letter h in the first word and invite students to explain how the "deletion" changes the "reading frame." Regroup the remaining letters into groups of three and ask students to explain what the sentence says. Point out that this is very similar to what occurs in a frameshift mutation.

Laboratory Investigation

The Laboratory Investigation, The Effects of Radiation on Seeds, on pages 210–211 is appropriate to use at this point in the chapter.

Checkpoints

1. The appaloosa was produced by selective breeding—individual horses with the desired traits were chosen to produce a new generation.
2. Inbreeding is the mating of individuals with similar characteristics.

TEACHER SUPPORT

Ecology Note

Agents that cause mutations, or mutagens, such as radon gas or ultraviolet radiation, can occur naturally in the environment. Other mutagens, such as some pesticides and pollutants, can be introduced by the action of humans. Such mutagens affect not only people but also wildlife in the area. In most cases, mutations caused by exposure to mutagens are harmful to an organism. Common mutagenic effects include cancers, tumors, and abnormal growth and development. In some cases, however, a mutation may actually help an organism better survive in a changing environment. In this instance, the descendants of the organism with the mutation are more likely to survive and pass the mutation to their offspring. The mutation will eventually become more common in the population.

Ancillary Support

The resources below can be used to support your teaching strategy for these two pages.

LM Observing Cloning, #17
TR Enrich: A Risky Business?
BL Inquiry Activity: Designer Dogs
TB Chromosomal and Gene Mutations, #12

MINI LAB Modeling

Teacher Note

• For time required and materials needed, see page 196b.

Answers to Analyze and Conclude

1. Insertion and deletion mutations change the polypeptide most because they change the reading frame of the codons.

2. A substitution may not have any effect, because the mutated codon specifies the same amino acid as the original codon.

Skills Trace
Modeling
- Focus p. 200
- Practice p. 200
- Assess p. 215

4 ASSESS

Quick Check

Have students draw a concept map in which they show the different kinds of mutations that can affect an organism.

Section Review 9–1

1. Individual organisms with desired characteristics are chosen to produce a new generation.

2. A mutation is an inheritable change in genetic information.

3. To increase the chance of producing a desirable trait.

4. A mutation that deletes only one nucleotide will have a much larger effect because it changes the reading frame of the mRNA, causing more amino acids to be different in the polypeptide. A mutation that deletes three nucleotides may affect only one or two amino acids in the polypeptide.

5. Most students will describe writing random changes in a nucleotide sequence of DNA on paper, then determining the resulting polypeptide sequence.

Skills Trace
Modeling
- Focus p. 200
- Practice p. 200
- Assess p. 215

MINI LAB .... Modeling ....

Mind Your Mutations!

PROBLEM *How can you* ***construct a model*** *of the effects of a point mutation?*

PROCEDURE

TACTGTCTCACCATT

1. Assume that the letters above represent the nucleotide sequence of a gene. Using the rules of base-pairing and the genetic code, determine the polypeptide for which this gene codes.
2. Design a procedure to show how the polypeptide is affected by a random point mutation in the gene.
3. Repeat the procedure at least five times. Include one substitution, one insertion, and one deletion mutation.

ANALYZE AND CONCLUDE

1. Which mutation changed the polypeptide the most? The least? Discuss the significance of your answers.
2. Can a gene mutation not affect a polypeptide? Explain your answer.

another—is called a **point mutation.** As shown in ***Figure 9–3*** on page 199, the substitution of a nucleotide can change one of the amino acids for which the gene codes.

However, much bigger changes can result from another kind of point mutation—the insertion or deletion of a nucleotide. Why is this so? Recall that the genetic code is read in groups of three nucleotides known as codons. When a nucleotide is inserted or deleted, the grouping of the nucleotides is shifted. This type of mutation is known as a **frameshift mutation**—so called because it shifts the "reading frame" of the genetic message. Frameshift mutations can cause tremendous changes to a polypeptide.

☑ ***Checkpoint*** What is a point mutation? A frameshift mutation? 1

Mutations and Breeding

Most mutations are harmful. However, mutations occasionally produce very desirable characteristics. For this reason, breeders sometimes try to increase the rates at which mutations occur, thus increasing the chances of producing a beneficial one. X-rays, ultraviolet light, and certain chemicals can each increase an organism's mutation rate.

Another way to increase the chances of obtaining beneficial mutations is to work with large numbers of organisms. Bacteria can be grown in the millions, allowing researchers to study even the rarest mutations in bacterial genes.

Section Review 9–1

1. **Describe** the process of selective breeding.
2. **Define** a mutation.
3. **Explain** why breeders may increase an organism's mutation rate.
4. **Critical Thinking—Comparing** Compare a mutation that deletes a sequence of three nucleotides from a strand of DNA with a mutation that deletes only one nucleotide.
5. **MINI LAB** How can you **construct a model** to show the effects of a point mutation?

Learning Modality

Tactile Learning Encourage students to practice making gene mutations on paper using written nucleotide sequences of DNA. Students can also simulate chromosome mutations using pipe cleaners strung with beads to represent different gene segments.

Manipulating DNA

SECTION 9–2

GUIDE FOR READING

- **Explain** how biologists edit a DNA molecule.
- **Define** cell transformation.

MINI LAB

- **Construct a model** of restriction enzymes.

SELECTIVE BREEDING IS A SIMPLE way to influence which genes are passed on to new individuals. But what would the world be like if farmers and ranchers didn't have to wait for generations of selective breeding to produce the combinations of genes they seek? What if genes could be cut from one organism, then spliced into another? What if scientists could read the genetic message, then rewrite it any way they chose?

In many ways, we do not need to imagine any of these things as science fiction. It is possible to do every one of them right now.

The Tools of Editing

When a movie or television show is put together, film editors usually combine pieces from several videotapes in order to assemble different scenes for their proper impact. What tools do film editors need to accomplish this task? First, they need a way to view the videotape—to translate the encoded information into pictures or sounds. Second, they need a way to cut out and separate different sections of the videotape. And third, they need a way to splice the different sections together.

In a sense, a chromosome is like a reel of videotape—both contain long stretches of information in a coded form. And not surprisingly, editing a piece of DNA requires tools that work in a similar way to the tools of film editing.

Are tools actually available for editing DNA? Yes, they are! **Biologists have tools to cut, separate, and read DNA sequences and to splice together these sequences in almost any order.** Let's take a look at each of the tools that biologists use to edit DNA.

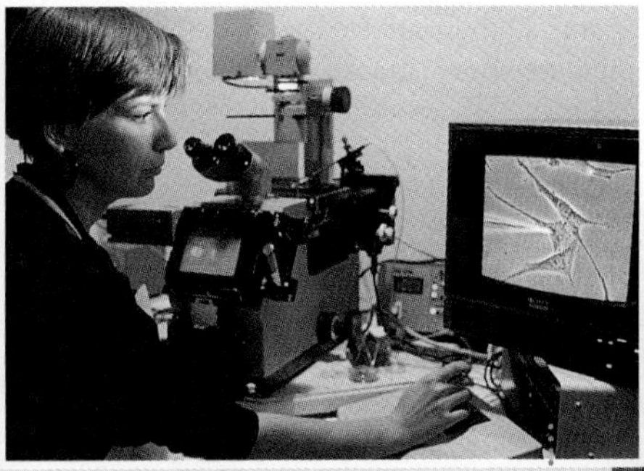

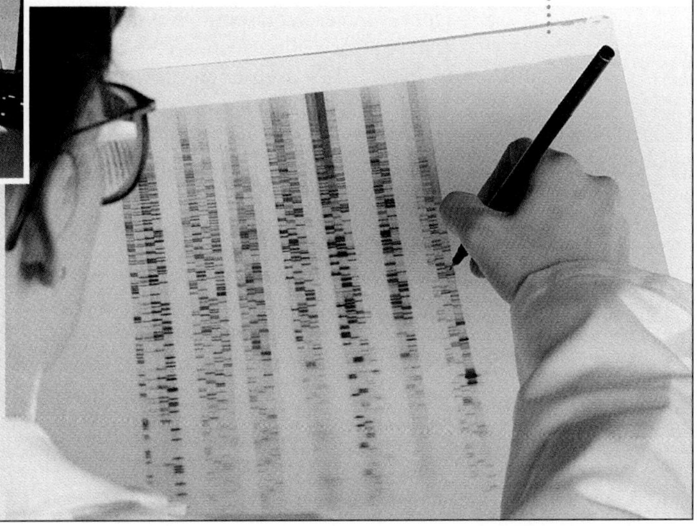

Figure 9–4
(a) With the aid of a microscope and a television monitor, a tiny needle can be used to inject DNA into an animal cell.
(b) CAREER TRACK This genetic engineering research assistant is interpreting the results of a DNA sequencing procedure.

SECTION 9–2
Manipulating DNA

Performance Objectives
- Describe how biologists can manipulate a DNA molecule.
- Explain what occurs during cell transformation.

Mini Lab Skill: Modeling

1 ENGAGE

Inquiry Activity
Modeling
The Tools of Editing
Ask students to determine what tools are necessary to edit a code. Students may choose any kind of code they wish and devise a model of editing to help them identify the required tools. Begin a discussion about the process of editing to make sure students understand what is involved. Point out that students do not need to name a specific tool; they can give the tool a generic name that describes its function. After students complete their models, encourage them to share their editing tools with the class.

Checkpoint
1 A point mutation involves a change in a single nucleotide. A frameshift mutation occurs when a nucleotide is inserted or deleted and the grouping of nucleotides is shifted.

TEACHER SUPPORT

Historical Perspective

From the time Watson and Crick discovered the structure of the DNA molecule in 1953, it took ten years for researchers to crack the genetic code. Ten years later, in the early 1970s, researchers first developed the techniques for manipulating DNA, including the use of restriction enzymes and gel electrophoresis. In the late 1970s, researchers successfully engineered bacteria to produce insulin and interferon. In 1982, the first drug produced by recombinant bacteria, insulin, was approved for use on people. It was also in 1982 that researchers were successful in transferring genes between plant and animal species. In the early 1990s, researchers began inserting DNA into human patients to treat genetic diseases.

2 EXPLORE

MINI LAB Modeling

Teacher Note

• For time required and materials needed, see page 196b.

Answers to Analyze and Conclude

1. Answers will vary depending on students' sequences and their choices of restriction enzymes.

2. It enables biologists to cut DNA into smaller and more numerous fragments.

Skills Trace
Modeling

- Focus p. 202
- Practice p. 204
- Assess p. 215

3 TEACH

Investigate

Cooperative Learning Challenge groups of three or four students to construct a list of reasons why scientists would want to manipulate the DNA molecule. Encourage groups to begin with a brainstorming session in which one student takes notes. Then instruct students to modify their brainstorming ideas in an editing session in which another student acts as the moderator. Remind students to practice active listening skills and to use positive language when evaluating each idea on the list. Make sure students realize that they can still add ideas to the list if they wish. Finally, have a spokesperson from each group share the group's list with the class. Keep a class list on the chalkboard and add or subtract ideas as you study the section.

MINI LAB Modeling

So Many Restrictions!

PROBLEM *How can you **construct a model** of the action of restriction enzymes?*

PROCEDURE

1. Write a 100-character sequence of the letters A, C, G, and T in a random order.
2. Copy the sequence onto each of three different strips of paper. Use different-colored pencils or paper to identify each copy.
3. Cut the strips to model the action of the three restriction enzymes shown in ***Figure 9–5.*** Use a different strip for each enzyme.

ANALYZE AND CONCLUDE

1. Which restriction enzyme produced the most pieces? The fewest pieces?
2. Why do biologists use more than one restriction enzyme to cut DNA?

Tool #1—Cutting DNA

DNA can be cut at specific places by proteins known as **restriction enzymes.** More than 100 restriction enzymes are known, and each one cuts DNA at a specific sequence of nucleotides. As shown in ***Figure 9–5,*** restriction enzymes are amazingly precise. Like a key that fits only one lock, a restriction enzyme will cut a DNA sequence only if it matches the sequence perfectly.

Restriction enzymes make it possible to cut enormous DNA molecules into smaller, precisely sized fragments. Biologists can then work on pieces of DNA that contain a few hundred nucleotides, instead of many millions.

☑ *Checkpoint* What is a restriction enzyme? 1

Tool #2—Separating DNA

What good is a mixture of DNA fragments of various sizes? It's not much good at all—unless it is possible to separate them. Fortunately, DNA fragments can be separated by a technique known as electrophoresis (ee-lehk-troh-fuh-REE-sihs). In electrophoresis, DNA fragments separate as they move through a special gel—a watery solid with a consistency similar to dessert gelatin.

First, DNA fragments are placed at one end of the gel. Then the gel is placed in an electric field. Because DNA fragments carry negative charges, they move toward the positively charged electrode. This separates the fragments because the smaller fragments slip through the gel faster than the larger fragments.

Tool #3—Reading DNA

More than 20 years ago, researchers developed a way to read the sequence of small, single-stranded pieces of DNA—typically fewer than 200 nucleotides. First, the pieces are placed in test tubes with the enzyme DNA polymerase. The enzyme is then allowed to make a new complementary strand, occasionally using chemically modified nucleotides that halt the assembly of the new strand at certain places. The new strands are then separated from each other by electrophoresis, producing a pattern of bands such as the one shown in ***Figure 9–4*** on page 201. This pattern reveals the base sequence of the original strand.

DNA sequencing has become a routine laboratory procedure. It is so routine, in fact, that automated machines now carry out the sequencing reactions, and computers analyze the sequencing gels.

Tool #4—Splicing DNA

To a film editor, the term "splicing" means joining two sections of film by taping their ends together. Can

TEACHER SUPPORT — Managing Classroom Diversity

TECH PREP STUDENTS

Although the tools for editing DNA are specific to genetic engineering, the procedures in the editing process are similar in many career areas. Encourage students to find the steps in the editing process for career areas in which they are interested. For example, an automotive technician must first determine which part is not working properly. Then the technician must remove the part and replace it with a new part. Have each student make a flowchart to show the steps in the editing process for his or her field of interest.

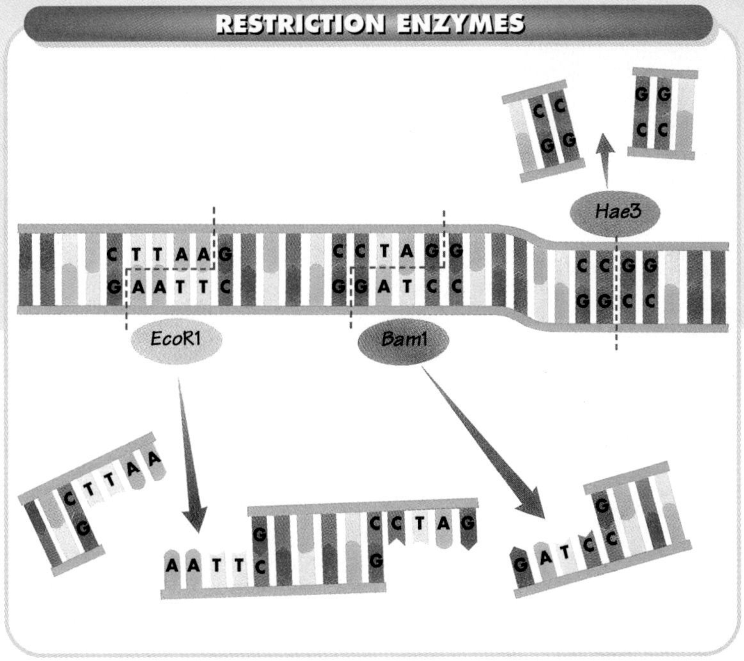

Figure 9–5
Restriction enzymes cut DNA only at specific sequences. In this diagram, the labeled nucleotides indicate how the restriction enzymes EcoR1, Bam1, *and* Hae3 *each cut DNA.*

sections of DNA also be spliced? The answer is yes, they can!

When some restriction enzymes cut DNA, they leave a short, single-stranded region on each side of the cut, and these regions act like the sticky side of a piece of tape. So by mixing two DNA fragments cut with the same enzyme, the single-stranded regions hold the ends of the fragments together. Other enzymes can then be used to permanently join the fragments.

The joined pieces of DNA act like a single DNA molecule. This kind of DNA is known as **recombinant DNA** because it is made by combining DNA from two different sources.

Why would anyone want to join together two pieces of DNA? Doing so makes it possible to design DNA

Figure 9–6
ⓐ *Plasmids are circular pieces of DNA found in bacteria (magnification: 160,000X).* ⓑ *Plasmids can be isolated, cut, and combined with DNA from other organisms. Any DNA made from two or more sources is called recombinant DNA.*

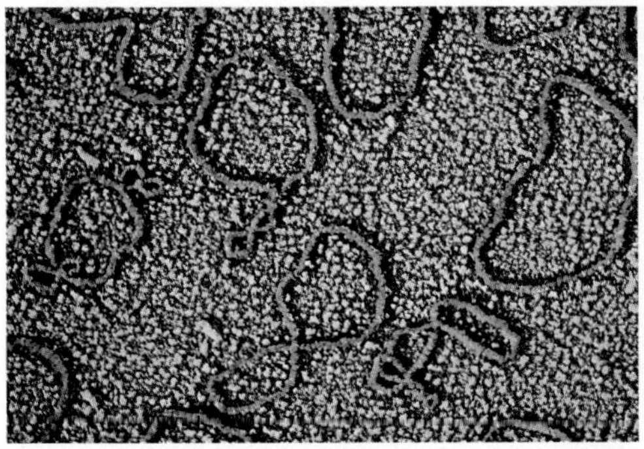

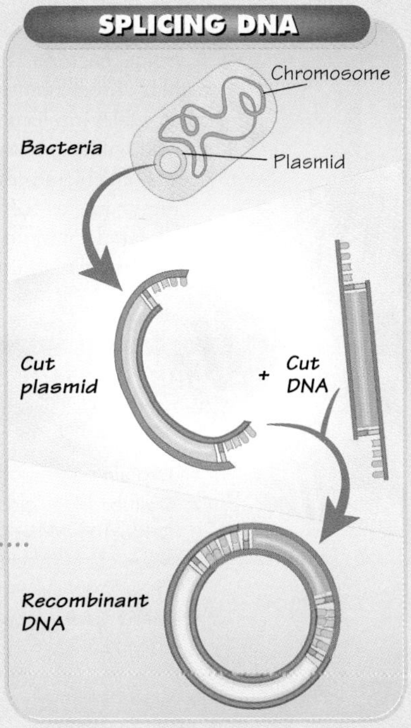

Investigate

Research Have students choose one of the tools for editing DNA and learn more about it. Encourage students to prepare short presentations to the class in which they give some of the details about the tool they studied. You may wish to have students who studied the same tool work together in a group on their presentation.

Ideas Through Images

Have students examine Figure 9–6, read the caption, and answer the following questions.

- **What do biologists use plasmids for?** (They use plasmids as a vehicle to insert DNA into a bacterial cell.)
- **Which restriction enzymes should be used to cut the plasmid and the DNA to be inserted?** (Both should be cut with the same enzyme, one that leaves a short, single-stranded region on both sides of the cut.)
- **How do you think biologists isolate the DNA fragment they wish to insert into a plasmid?** (They cut the band of DNA out of a gel.)

Checkpoint

1 A restriction enzyme cuts DNA at a specific nucleotide sequence.

TEACHER SUPPORT

Background Information

Restriction enzymes were discovered in bacteria that were able to protect themselves against bacteriophages. Scientists studying these bacteria found that they had special enzymes that recognized phage DNA as being foreign and then cut the phage DNA into pieces. These enzymes did not cut the bacterial DNA, because the bacterium modifies its own DNA in a special way. These special enzymes were called restriction enzymes because they restrict the multiplication of bacteriophages. After further study, different classes of restriction enzymes have been characterized, and they have become very important tools in the manipulation of the DNA molecule.

Ancillary Support

The resources below can be used to support your teaching strategy for these two pages.

LM Investigating Gel Electrophoresis, #18
TR Apply: How'd They Do That?
BL Inquiry Activity: Changing Directions

4 ASSESS

Quick Check

Have students create a table in which they list and describe the tools used for editing DNA.

Section Review 9–2

1. Biologists have tools to cut, separate, and read DNA sequences and to splice together these sequences in almost any order.

2. New genes are inserted into a cell, changing the cell's genetic makeup.

3. Because most organisms have DNA with the same four nucleotides, DNA from one organism can be inserted into another, and the gene is successfully expressed to produce the same protein.

4. One likely answer is to write a DNA sequence, then find the sequence recognized by a particular restriction enzyme and cut the DNA sequence at the proper site.

Skills Trace
Modeling

- Focus p. 202
- **Practice p. 204**
- Assess p. 215

Learning Modality

Tactile Learning Have students use Figure 9–6 to help them model the processes involved in creating recombinant DNA plasmids. Students can use different-colored yarn or pipe cleaners to represent the two different DNA molecules.

Figure 9–7
This tree tumor, called a crown gall, is caused by bacteria that insert plasmids into the tree's cells. In laboratories, researchers are using a similar process to transform a variety of plant cells.

molecules for all sorts of special purposes. Two genes could be fused into one, the control region of one gene could be placed next to another, and several genes from different sources could be assembled into the same DNA molecule.

☑ **Checkpoint** What is recombinant DNA? (1)

Cell Transformation

After a recombinant DNA molecule is assembled, the next step is **cell transformation**—putting the recombinant DNA inside a live cell. **In cell transformation, new genes are inserted into a cell, thus changing the cell's genetic makeup.**

Recombinant DNA can be used to transform cells in many ways. Let's take a look at some of them.

Transforming Bacteria

Some bacteria, in addition to their regular chromosomes, contain small circular DNA molecules called **plasmids.** As you will see, plasmids can be used as agents of cell transformation.

First, pieces of DNA are joined to isolated plasmid molecules. These recombinant plasmids are mixed with a culture of bacteria that do not contain plasmids. Under the right conditions, a few of the bacteria in the culture will take up the plasmids.

The transformed bacteria can be isolated, then used to grow millions of transformed bacteria. Each of the bacteria inherits both the plasmid and the recombinant DNA.

☑ **Checkpoint** What are plasmids? (2)

Transforming Eukaryotes

Biologists routinely transform bacteria, which are prokaryotes. Eukaryotes are more complex than prokaryotes, however, and it is significantly harder to make their cells accept new DNA molecules. But the task is not impossible. Yeasts, which are single-celled eukaryotes, have plasmids of their own. Yeast plasmids are now used to transform yeast cells in a way that is very similar to bacterial transformation.

In addition, biologists have developed ways to transform animal and plant cells, which do not have plasmids. One way is to use a tiny needle to inject new DNA into a cell, as shown in ***Figure 9–4*** on page 201. Sometimes the cell breaks down and destroys the new pieces of DNA, but at other times the cell takes them into the nucleus and inserts them into chromosomes. The result is a transformed cell.

Section Review 9–2

1. **Explain** how biologists edit a DNA molecule.
2. **Define** cell transformation.
3. **Critical Thinking—Analyzing** Almost every organism has DNA that is made of the same four nucleotides and translated by the same genetic code. Explain why this fact is significant in cell transformation.
4. **MINI LAB** How can you **construct a model** of the effects of restriction enzymes?

TEACHER SUPPORT

Activity

Analyzing DNA You can demonstrate DNA restriction analysis to the class, or even allow student groups to perform the procedure if you have enough resources. Some biological supply companies have prepared kits that contain restriction enzymes, DNA, agarose gel materials, electrophoresis equipment, and all the other supplies and detailed instructions required for this procedure. You might wish to perform a restriction map analysis in which a DNA sequence is cut separately with two different restriction enzymes, and then cut with a mixture of the two enzymes. These three different samples are run together on a gel along with a sample of uncut DNA and marker DNA with fragments of known lengths. From the bands on the gel, the order of fragments in the DNA sequence can be determined.

Engineering New Organisms

GUIDE FOR READING

- Describe the achievements of genetic engineering.

BY MANIPULATING DNA, ARE biologists now able to create a griffin—a mythical creature that is half eagle and half lion? For many reasons, the answer is no. However, biologists have been able to produce some fascinating organisms that may be just as remarkable as any mythical one.

Manipulating Genes

The cutting and splicing of genes and DNA from different sources is sometimes called **genetic engineering**—one of the newest branches of the biological sciences. **Through genetic engineering, researchers are able to insert new genes into almost any organism.**

Organisms that have been transformed with genes from other organisms are said to be **transgenic.** As you have read, plasmids can be used to produce transgenic bacteria and transgenic yeasts. And if a complete organism is grown from a transformed animal or plant cell, the result is a transgenic animal or a transgenic plant.

What good will come from genetic engineering? How will it affect your life? These are important questions, and we will present some answers in this section.

Genetically Engineered Proteins

If a gene is properly inserted into a yeast or a bacterium, the yeast or bacterium is "tricked" into producing large amounts of the protein for which the gene codes. For example, transgenic bacteria are now producing a human protein called insulin. People with a disease called diabetes do not make enough insulin of their own, and the insulin produced by the bacteria is both inexpensive and effective. ●

In fact, transgenic cells are used to make proteins for treating cancer, heart attacks, and other diseases and disorders. Researchers are also trying to create transgenic bacteria to produce vaccines.

INTEGRATING HEALTH

What are the different forms of diabetes? How are they treated?

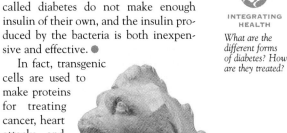

Figure 9–8
(a) This griffin is a combination of an eagle and a lion. While genetic engineering cannot produce creatures from mythology, it has created (b) a giant mouse, shown to the right of a mouse of normal size.

SECTION 9–3

Engineering New Organisms

Performance Objective

- Discuss the achievements of genetic engineering.

1 ENGAGE

Ideas Through Images

Have students examine Figure 9–8, read the caption, and answer the following questions.

- **Why do you think scientists could not produce a griffin?** (The griffin is made up of two genetically distinct parts.)
- **What might be some limitations for creating genetically engineered organisms?** (The ability to introduce the new DNA into a cell or the amount of DNA that can be added to a cell.)

INTEGRATING HEALTH

In diabetes mellitus, the body cannot use sugar normally. Type I diabetics do not produce normal levels of insulin. They are treated with daily doses of insulin. Type II diabetes is controlled by diet, insulin, or drugs.

Checkpoints

1. Recombinant DNA is formed by combining DNA from two different sources.
2. Small, circular DNA molecules found in bacteria.

TEACHER SUPPORT

Managing Classroom Diversity

AT-RISK STUDENTS
Be sure students make the transition from editing DNA molecules to engineering new organisms. Go through an example using the mice shown in Figure 9–8 and the procedure for splicing DNA in Figure 9–6. Explain that scientists transformed a mouse egg cell with rat DNA containing the gene for rat growth hormone. Another example to show students is the transformation of a bacterial cell with a recombinant plasmid containing the gene for human insulin.

Ancillary Support

The resources below can be used to support your teaching strategy for these two pages.

TR Writing in Biology: Speak Out!
Enrich: Will Transgenics Save the World?

BL Inquiry Activity: The Creating Game

2 EXPLORE

Inquiry Activity

Hypothesizing

Genetic Engineering

Ask students to form a hypothesis about how they could manipulate, or edit, DNA to produce an organism that would serve a useful purpose. Point out that the engineered organism does not have to be a plant or animal; it could also be bacterium or yeast. Encourage students to refine their hypotheses as they study the section.

3 TEACH

Discussion

Initiate a class discussion about the advantages of genetic engineering over selective breeding. Begin by asking students to compare the goals of each technique. (To produce an organism with the desired characteristics.) Point out that selective breeding is less precise than genetic engineering, and breeders must often wait several generations before developing the desired organism.

4 ASSESS

Quick Check

Ask students to describe two examples of transgenic plants or animals and their uses. (Refer to the section content for specific examples.)

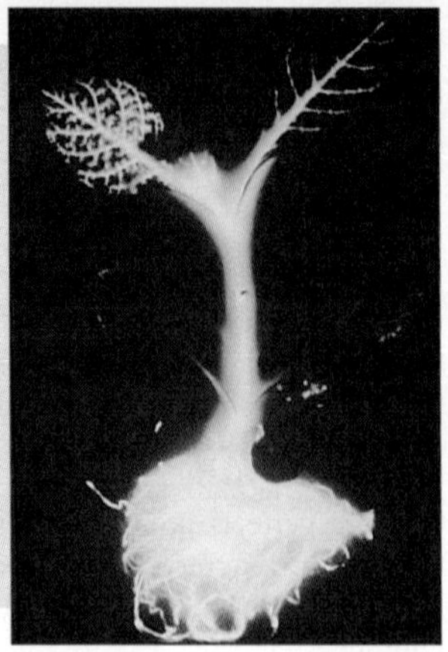

Figure 9–9 *By transferring a gene from a firefly to a tobacco plant, researchers created this transgenic tobacco plant that glows in the dark! The gene codes for the enzyme luciferase, the catalyst for a reaction that produces light.*

Transgenic Plants and Animals

Researchers have found ways to stimulate transformed plant cells to grow into transgenic plants. Their results include a tomato that stays fresher longer than other tomatoes, a strain of soybeans that is highly resistant to weed-killing chemicals, and the unusual tobacco plant shown in ***Figure 9–9***. Currently, work is underway to produce transgenic plants that resist insect pests, make their own fertilizer, or produce more food than ordinary plants do.

To produce a transgenic animal, researchers first transform an animal's egg cell, then allow the egg to be fertilized and to mature. In the future, this procedure may be used to create all sorts of useful animals. Transgenic cattle, for example, could be created with a gene that increases milk production.

☑ **Checkpoint** How can a transgenic animal be produced? 1

Human Gene Therapy

In the laboratory, human cells can be transformed just like other animal cells. However, transforming cells in a living human has not proved to be as easy a task.

For example, consider the latest efforts in treating cystic fibrosis (CF)—a serious genetic disease that is inherited as an autosomal recessive trait. In one experimental treatment, researchers transformed viruses with healthy alleles for the CF gene. Then they sprayed the viruses into the air passageways of CF patients. Sure enough, the viruses carried the healthy allele into the patients' cells, and their symptoms improved! Unfortunately, when the transformed cells were replaced by other cells, the symptoms of cystic fibrosis reappeared.

The experiments in gene therapy raise many important questions. Should researchers carry out experiments that permanently change human DNA? Should we use genetic engineering only to cure certain disorders? Or should we also try to make people taller, stronger, or more disease resistant?

Genetic engineering will affect everyone, and you should expect to play a role in forming public policy about it. We urge you to learn as much as you can about genetic engineering, then to use both your knowledge and your ethical and moral training to address the important questions that will be raised.

Section Review 9–3

1. **Describe** the achievements of genetic engineering.
2. What are some of the ethical questions that genetic engineering raises? **Discuss** these questions.
3. **Critical Thinking—Inferring** To produce a transgenic animal, scientists typically transform an unfertilized egg cell. Why is the cell transformation done at such an early stage of an animal's life?

206 Chapter 9

Section Review 9–3

1. Through genetic engineering, researchers are able to insert new genes into almost any organism.

2. Possible ethical questions include: Should researchers permanently change human DNA? Should genetic engineering be used only to cure disorders?

3. When an unfertilized egg is transformed, every body cell in the developing organism will contain the recombinant DNA. If transformation is done later, some body cells will not have the recombinant DNA.

Learning Modality

Auditory Learning Have small groups of students debate genetic engineering issues such as the following.

- Recombinant proteins in foods, such as recombinant bovine growth hormone in milk, could cause health problems for humans.
- Transgenic disease-resistant plants could force out native plants that cannot successfully compete in the environment.

The New Human Genetics

Guide for Reading

- **Define** RFLPs and **explain** why biologists study them.
- **Describe** the purpose of the Human Genome Project.

A NEW KIND OF GENETICS IS taking shape. In the old genetics, researchers could only observe the effects of genes. They recorded plant size, flower color, blood type—anything that provided clues about the genes that were hidden and invisible within the cell.

The new genetics, however, is not restricted to indirect clues. Rather than looking for the effects of genes, biologists now can look at the genes themselves. As you will see, the new genetics is already affecting everyday life, and it will become even more important in the years ahead.

"RIHF-lihps"

How can a specific nucleotide sequence be isolated from a huge DNA molecule? One way is to cut the DNA into small pieces and separate the pieces on a gel. Then, a specific sequence can be located with a probe—often, a chemically treated sequence of nucleotides. The probe binds to complementary sequences in the DNA pieces, revealing the sequences as dark bands.

The bands identified in this procedure are sometimes called **RFLPs** (RIHF-lihps), which stands for Restriction Fragment Length Polymorphism. Like a gene, a RFLP is inherited, and different individuals have different sets of RFLPs in their DNA. **By using probes to identify RFLPs, biologists can identify and classify an individual's DNA.** Let's take a look at some applications of this technique.

☑ **Checkpoint** What is a RFLP? ❷

Probing for Genetic Diseases

Consider people at risk for Huntington disease—a serious genetic disease caused by an autosomal dominant allele. Huntington disease slowly damages the nervous system, eventually leading to death. However, the disease's symptoms do not appear until late middle age.

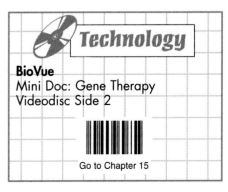

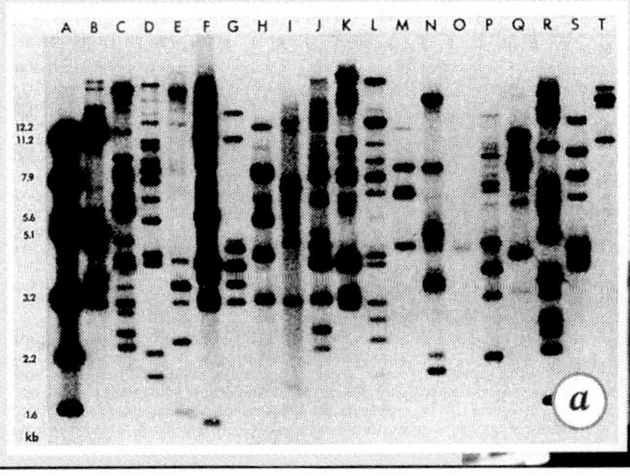

Figure 9–10
Researchers probe for RFLPs to distinguish the DNA of individuals of the same species. (a) This photograph shows how one probe bound to the DNA of 20 different Xanthomonas *bacteria, labeled A through T. The dark bands indicate the RFLPs to which the probe attached. (b) Each of these young women has a different set of RFLPs in her DNA.*

TEACHER SUPPORT

Managing Classroom Diversity

EDUCATIONAL EQUITY
Encourage students to learn about Barbara McClintock, a very important geneticist who discovered transposons, or jumping genes, in corn. For her work with transposons, McClintock was awarded the Nobel Prize in 1983. In 1996, a transposon was found to be responsible for a human genetic disorder. Encourage students to read the biography of Barbara McClintock, *A Feeling for the Organism* by Evelyn Fox Keller.

SECTION 9–4

The New Human Genetics

Performance Objectives

- Explain what RFLPs are and why biologists study them.
- Describe the goals of the Human Genome Project.

1 ENGAGE

Inquiry Activity

Inferring

Inheritance and Genetic Engineering

Ask students to make inferences about how genetic engineering has changed the way in which geneticists study inheritance. Encourage students to compare and contrast Mendel's methods of studying inheritance (setting up controlled crosses to study inheritance) with the methods of genetic engineering. Invite students to share their inferences with the class. (An example of an inference students might make is that genetic engineering can be used to learn the DNA sequence of the alleles of a gene, but it cannot be used to determine whether the alleles are dominant or recessive.)

☑ Checkpoints

❶ Researchers transform an animal's egg cell, then allow the egg to be fertilized and to mature.

❷ A specific sequence of DNA that is identified by a probe as a band on a gel.

Technology

BioVue
Mini Doc: Gene Therapy
Videodisc Side 2

Go to Chapter 15

2 EXPLORE

Investigate

Role-Playing Challenge students to play the role of a genetic researcher who is writing a research proposal in order to gain funding for a research project. Proposals should describe what students want to study and what they expect to learn.

3 TEACH

Connections

Patenting small fragments of the human genome has become highly controversial. Some researchers believe that patenting these fragments will speed up the process of sequencing the human genome. They think it allows researchers to share their results without worrying about other researchers' using them. Others contend that these fragments are simply an intermediate step in the research process and are not even worthy of a patent. (In order to be patented, a discovery must be useful, novel, and nonobvious.) Since patent owners could prevent anyone from using their fragments for 17 years, they would control all uses of the discoveries related to their DNA fragments.

Answers to Making the Connection

Answers will depend on your state. Encourage students to contact your state legislators for more information. Disease-resistant crops need fewer chemicals for protection, which is better for the environment. However, new strains of diseases could appear over time to which these plants are not resistant.

Biology and You ... Connections

Patenting Life

When inventors produce a new machine or a new way of doing something, they can protect their inventions with a patent. A patent provides the exclusive rights to build and sell an invention. Thomas Edison, for example, held a patent on the phonograph for many years.

Should it be possible to patent living things? At the beginning of the twentieth century, it was not. Therefore, when a plant breeder produced a new high-yielding strain of a crop plant, anyone who acquired a few seeds could produce that plant. As a result, breeders had little financial incentive to develop better plants.

Patent laws now protect the developers of improved crop plants such as this high-yielding cotton.

Changes to the Patent Laws

In 1930, however, the United States government changed the patent laws so that some plants and other organisms could be protected. This law benefited many plant breeders, as well as the descendants of Luther Burbank, arguably the greatest plant breeder of all time. Burbank's estate was granted 17 patents on the varieties of plants he had produced.

Today, patents are granted not only for plants bred by ordinary means, but also for those created by genetic engineering. Without patents, genetic researchers might not have developed these plants—many of which are potentially very beneficial.

For example, one company has engineered a strain of soybeans that is resistant to weed-killing chemicals. Other companies have developed strains of cotton plants and potato plants that actually produce a bug-killing compound. And one laboratory has produced plants that absorb mercury and other harmful compounds. These plants may prove useful in clearing pollutants from contaminated soil.

Patent Laws Today

Under the patent laws of 1930, any genetically engineered organism can be patented. Although these laws are more than half a century old, they are helping to protect the rights of genetic researchers and are spurring the growth of whole new industries.

However, no one in 1930 could have foreseen what is happening in biology today. Indeed, biotechnology companies are testing the limits of the old laws every day. Some companies have even filed for patents on parts of the human DNA sequence!

The Future

What can you expect in the future? As biologists continue to develop the techniques of genetic engineering, laws will be needed to deal specifically with the kinds of organisms that researchers will be creating. We hope that you—the decision makers of the future—will find the best ways to prosper from this new technology.

Making the Connection

Does your state have laws to regulate genetic engineering? What advantages and disadvantages do disease-resistant crops offer?

Teacher Support: Facts and Figures

- In 1976, the National Institutes of Health (NIH) issued safety guidelines for techniques in genetic engineering. These guidelines have been relaxed because this research has proved to be safe.
- In 1986, the first patent was issued on a genetically engineered plant. It was a variety of corn with an increased nutritional value.
- In 1987, the National Academy of Sciences concluded that transferring genes between organisms posed no serious environmental hazards.
- In 1988, the first patent was issued on a genetically engineered animal—a mouse developed for use in cancer research.

Figure 9–11
Computers are routinely used to determine the sequence of short pieces of DNA. However, even with the aid of computers and other tools, the Human Genome Project is an extraordinarily complex undertaking.

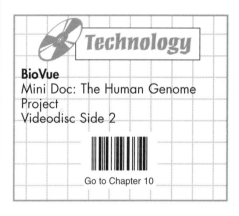

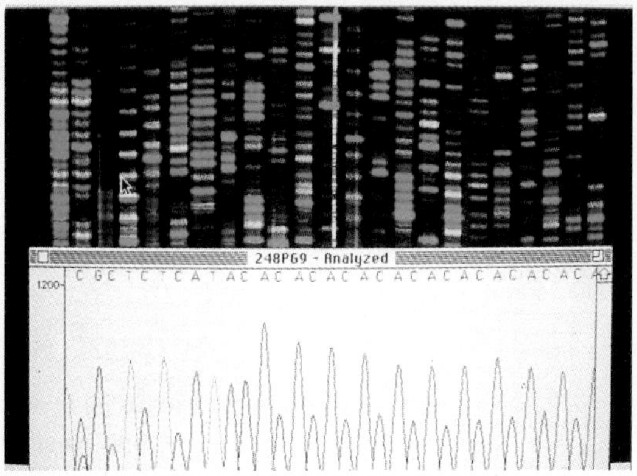

Before genetic testing, the children of people who had Huntington disease had to wait many years before learning whether they, too, would suffer from this condition. Today, however, researchers have identified RFLPs that are inherited with the allele that causes Huntington disease. Thus, by probing DNA for these RFLPs, geneticists can determine whether a person carries this allele.

Similar tests have been developed for other genetic disorders, including cystic fibrosis, sickle cell anemia, and Tay-Sachs disease. These tests are particularly useful for couples deciding whether they should have children.

DNA Fingerprinting

Some probes detect RFLPs that are highly variable from one individual to another. Researchers quickly realized that identifying these RFLPs could make it possible to distinguish the DNA of one individual from another. Today, using RFLPs to identify individuals is popularly known as **DNA fingerprinting.**

DNA fingerprinting is used for all sorts of purposes, including criminal investigations. DNA fingerprinting can identify suspects of serious crimes—as well as clear people of crimes that they did not commit.

The Human Genome Project

A human cell contains 46 chromosomes, with 3 billion pairs of DNA nucleotides. Such a tremendous amount of information certainly seems overwhelming. **However, a number of years ago, scientists throughout the world decided to identify the complete nucleotide sequence in human DNA. This project is now known as the Human Genome Project.** Its goal is huge, but one that many scientists feel is worth achieving.

What good will come from the Human Genome Project? Information from the project has already identified a host of genes associated with genetic disorders. It has provided clues to the genetic basis of cancer and heart disease, and it may eventually give important clues to that most interesting of all questions—what is there about our genes that truly makes us who we are?

Section Review 9–4

1. **Define** the term RFLP. **Explain** why biologists study RFLPs in DNA.
2. **Describe** the purpose of the Human Genome Project.
3. **BRANCHING OUT ACTIVITY** Research the progress of the Human Genome Project. **Discuss** the findings of your research with your class.

Correcting Misconceptions

Some students might think that the human genome has only one DNA sequence. Help students realize that scientists are analyzing DNA from many different human samples. Remind them that the different alleles of a gene encode slightly different proteins, causing different phenotypes. These different alleles also have different DNA sequences. Point out that when the entire genome is sequenced and mapped, scientists probably will not have sequenced every possible allele for every gene. But they will have identified the location of every gene on every chromosome in the human genome.

4 ASSESS

Quick Check

Have students write three questions about the concepts from this section. Then instruct them to exchange questions and answer them. Encourage students to discuss the answers with one another.

Technology

BioVue
Mini Doc: The Human Genome Project
Videodisc Side 2

Go to Chapter 10

Section Review 9–4

1. RFLP, or Restriction Fragment Length Polymorphism, is a specific sequence of DNA that is identified by a probe as a band on a gel. By using probes to identify RFLPs, biologists can determine if an individual carries the allele for a genetic disorder, or distinguish the DNA of one individual from another.

2. The purpose of the Human Genome Project is to identify the complete nucleotide sequence in human DNA.

3. Research findings will vary. Most students should learn that genetic markers have been mapped to each chromosome and that researchers are isolating small fragments of DNA that they can use as probes to help them find and characterize every gene in the entire genome.

Learning Modality

Visual Learning Have students draw a diagram or flowchart that shows the steps in the process that biologists use to identify RFLPs. Diagrams should illustrate the steps of the process as described in the section.

Ancillary Support

The resources below can be used to support your teaching strategy for these two pages.

TR Explore: Probing for Prints
BL Inquiry Activity: Updating the Human Genome Project

CHAPTER 9

Laboratory Investigation

The Effects of Radiation on Seeds

Before the Lab

1. A few weeks before the lab, order irradiated seeds from a biological supply company, or arrange to have your seeds irradiated at a local university or medical clinic.
2. A few days before the investigation, have groups design their experiments and list the materials they need.
3. At least one day prior to the investigation, gather the materials required for each group, or have each group gather its own materials.

Pre-Lab Discussion

After students have read the entire procedure for this investigation and have designed their experiment, ask them the following questions.

- **What is the purpose of this investigation?** (To see the effects of radiation on seeds.)
- **What is the purpose of having a control in an experiment?** (A control allows you to differentiate between the effects of the experimental organism and the effects of the environment and natural variations in growth.)
- **What is the control group in this experiment?** (The nonirradiated seeds are the control group.)

Skills Development

Students will use these skills while completing the laboratory investigation: designing an experiment, observing, comparing, communicating, and hypothesizing.

Teaching Strategies

1. Review each group's experimental design before students proceed with their experiment. Make sure all variables are controlled except for the one being tested.
2. Place the Petri dishes in a warm, dark place while the seeds are germinating.

Laboratory Investigation

DESIGNING AN EXPERIMENT

The Effects of Radiation on Seeds

Mutations occur naturally in all organisms. However, an organism's mutation rate increases when it is exposed to certain chemicals or types of radiation. In this investigation, you will design an experiment to show the effects of X-ray exposure on seeds.

Problem

Do irradiated seeds grow differently from nonirradiated seeds? **Design an experiment** to answer this question.

Suggested Materials

irradiated seeds and nonirradiated seeds from the same organism
2 Petri dishes
paper towels
pots with soil
glass-marking pencil

Suggested Procedure

1. **Design an experiment to determine whether irradiated seeds grow differently from nonirradiated seeds. Include two test groups in your experiment, with one test group as a control. Make sure that the test groups are treated identically.**
2. **To grow the seeds, follow any special directions on the seeds' packages. Otherwise, place the seeds in Petri dishes and cover the seeds with water, as shown in the diagram.**

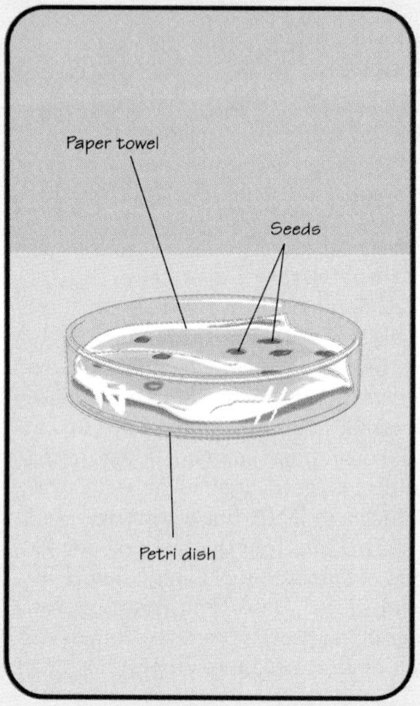

3. **Use the glass-marking pencil to label each Petri dish. Every Petri dish that your class uses in this experiment should have a unique label. Store the Petri dishes in a location designated by your teacher.**

Safety Tip

Remind students to wash their hands after handling the seeds and the potting soil.

4. **Observe the growth of the seeds over the course of 2 weeks. Record your observations in a data table similar to the one shown. Add water to the Petri dishes as necessary to keep the seeds moist.**

5. **After 2 weeks, carefully transfer five young plants in each test group from the Petri dishes to pots containing soil.**

6. **Label the pots and place them in sunlight or under a fluorescent lamp. Water the plants regularly. Observe their growth for the next few weeks. Record your observations in a data table similar to the one shown.**

DATA TABLE

Day	Nonirradiated Seeds	Irradiated Seeds
1		
2		
3		
4		

Observations

1. Describe the roots produced by the seeds. In what ways are they similar? Different?
2. Describe any leaves that the young plants produced. In what ways are the leaves similar in the two groups? In what ways are they different?
3. Note any other similarities or differences among the plants that the seeds produced.

Analysis and Conclusions

1. Compare how the irradiated seeds and the nonirradiated seeds grew into plants.
2. Did the irradiated seeds contain mutant DNA? How certain can you be of your answer? Explain.
3. How could you best determine whether a seed contains mutant DNA?
4. Formulate a hypothesis to explain the results of your experiment. Could a different hypothesis also explain the results? Discuss this possibility.

More to Explore

Repeat your experiment with irradiated seeds of other plants.

Answers to
Observations

1. Students should observe uniform root growth from the nonirradiated seeds. Root growth from irradiated seeds might be variable.
2. Students might observe that irradiated seeds produce leaves that look different from those of nonirradiated seeds.
3. In general, the nonirradiated seeds will show normal growth. The irradiated seeds will produce variable growth and development.

Answers to
Analysis and Conclusions

1. Some irradiated seeds will grow into plants that look like those from the nonirradiated seeds. Other irradiated seeds may not even grow.
2. The irradiated seeds may or may not have mutant DNA. It is difficult to be certain, because a seed with mutant DNA will not necessarily have a mutant phenotype.
3. A seed that produces a mutant plant probably has mutant DNA.
4. Many students might hypothesize that irradiation caused mutations in the DNA of the seeds, causing the seeds to grow and develop differently. A different hypothesis that would explain the same results is that the seeds contained mutant DNA before they were irradiated. If students did not observe mutant plants, they might hypothesize that the mutation occurred in a gene that is not required for growth and development, or that the DNA was not affected by irradiation.

More to Explore

Remind students to repeat the test conditions they used in the first experiment. Encourage them to compare the number of differences between the irradiated seeds and nonirradiated seeds from all the plants. Ask them to consider if some seeds are more susceptible to mutations from radiation than other seeds. Then ask them to consider some characteristics of a seed that could protect it from radiation.

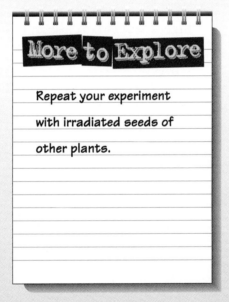

CHAPTER 9

Study Guide

Review Strategy

Divide the class into teams of four or five and have them compete against one another in a "Genetics Bowl" game. Each group should submit ten questions and answers based on the concepts in this chapter. Use these questions in the game, allowing students 30 seconds to answer each question. The team that gives the first correct answer wins a point.

Study Guide

Summarizing Key Concepts

The key concepts in each section of this chapter are listed below to help you review the chapter content. Make sure you understand each concept and its relationship to other concepts and to the theme of this chapter.

9–1 Breeding New Organisms

- In selective breeding, individual organisms with desired characteristics are chosen to produce a new generation.
- A mutation is an inheritable change in genetic information. A chromosomal mutation involves a change in the number or structure of chromosomes. A gene mutation affects only an individual gene.
- Breeders may stimulate mutation rates to increase the chance of finding a beneficial mutation.

9–2 Manipulating DNA

- Biologists have tools to cut, separate, and identify DNA sequences, as well as to splice together these sequences in almost any order.
- In cell transformation, new genes are inserted into a cell, thus changing the cell's genetic makeup. Small DNA molecules called plasmids can be used to transform bacteria and other organisms.

9–3 Engineering New Organisms

- Through genetic engineering, researchers are able to insert new genes into almost any organism.
- An organism with new genes is said to be transgenic. Scientists have produced many transgenic organisms, and they are working to put new genes in human cells to cure genetic disorders.

9–4 The New Human Genetics

- By using probes to identify RFLPs, biologists can identify and classify an individual's DNA.
- The goal of the Human Genome Project is to identify the complete nucleotide sequence of human DNA.

Reviewing Key Terms

Review the following vocabulary terms and their meaning. Then use each term in a complete sentence.

9–1 Breeding New Organisms

selective breeding
hybridization
inbreeding
mutation
chromosomal mutation
gene mutation
point mutation
frameshift mutation

9–2 Manipulating DNA

restriction enzyme
recombinant DNA
cell transformation
plasmid

9–3 Engineering New Organisms

genetic engineering
transgenic

9–4 The New Human Genetics

RFLP
DNA fingerprinting

Inquiry-Based Strategy

A research group has just identified the DNA sequence for the gene that encodes dystrophin, the protein that is abnormal in patients with muscular dystrophy. Ask students to outline a procedure in which they could test people for the presence of the abnormal dystrophin gene. Encourage students to determine what research is necessary to develop the procedure. Students will most likely develop different procedures. (One possibility is to use probes developed from restriction fragments of the abnormal dystrophin gene to find corresponding fragments in the DNA of people being tested.)

Recalling Main Ideas

Choose the letter of the answer that best completes the statement or answers the question.

1. Selective breeding involves
   a. inbreeding only.
   b. hybridization only.
   c. inbreeding and hybridization.
   d. mutations only.

2. Polyploidy is an example of a
   a. chromosomal mutation.
   b. gene mutation.
   c. point mutation.
   d. frameshift mutation.

3. The substitution of a thymine (T) for an adenine (A) in a gene is an example of a
   a. chromosomal mutation.
   b. point mutation.
   c. frameshift mutation.
   d. RNA mutation.

4. To cut DNA at specific sequences, biologists use
   a. restriction enzymes. **c.** DNA polymerase.
   b. electrophoresis. **d.** recombinant DNA.

5. What is the name of DNA that is made from two different sources?
   a. mutant DNA **c.** RFLPs
   b. plasmid DNA **d.** recombinant DNA

6. Inserting new genes into a cell is a process called
   a. DNA replication. **c.** cell transformation.
   b. RNA transcription. **d.** gene therapy.

7. Transgenic bacteria that produce insulin were transformed with
   a. insulin.
   b. the virus that produces insulin.
   c. the gene that produces insulin.
   d. the mRNA that is translated into insulin.

8. An individual's DNA can be classified by identifying special sequences called
   a. RNA. **c.** RFLPs.
   b. restriction enzymes. **d.** polymerases.

Putting It All Together

Using the information on pages xxx to xxxi, complete the following concept map.

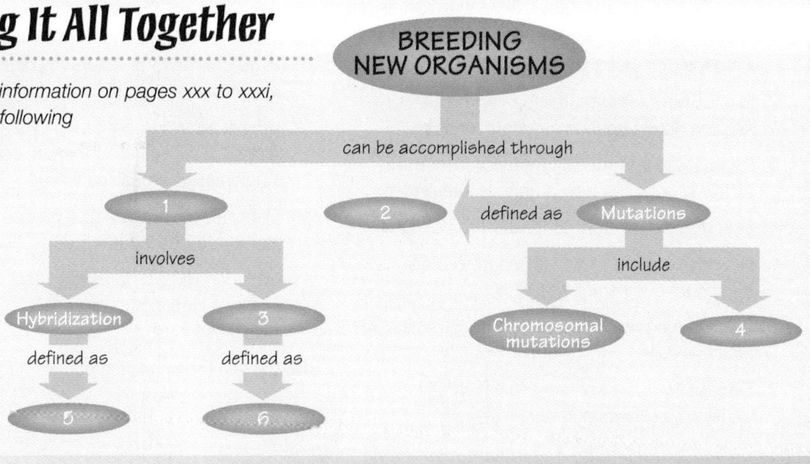

Recalling Main Ideas

1. c
2. a
3. b
4. a
5. d
6. c
7. c
8. c

Assessment

Reviewing What You Learned

1. The purpose of selective breeding is to produce organisms that best suit their functions.
2. In hybridization, dissimilar individuals are crossed to combine the best characteristics of both organisms. In inbreeding, similar individuals are crossed to maintain the characteristics of a specific breed.
3. Mutations are inheritable changes in DNA. Examples of chromosomal mutations include polyploidy, insertions, inversions, translocations, and deletions. Examples of gene mutations include point mutations and frameshift mutations.
4. A frameshift mutation occurs when a single nucleotide is inserted or deleted, causing the reading frame of the codons to shift.
5. Biologists use restriction enzymes to cut a DNA molecule into smaller fragments.
6. DNA fragments with short, single-stranded regions on each end will easily stick to other fragments with the complementary ends because the nucleotides will pair up.
7. Recombinant DNA is a DNA molecule composed of DNA from two different sources.
8. Cell transformation is the process in which new genes are inserted into a living cell, thus changing its genetic makeup.
9. Bacterial cells are easiest to transform.
10. A plasmid is a small, circular DNA molecule that is found in some bacteria and yeast.
11. Examples include transgenic bacteria that produce proteins used to treat diseases, transgenic animals that produce more food, and transgenic plants that produce more food or are resistant to pests.

Putting It All Together

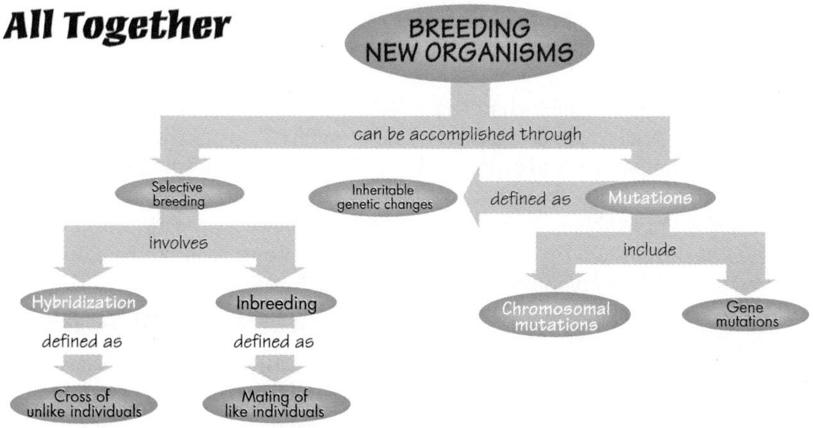

Assessment (continued)

12. A RFLP, Restriction Fragment Length Polymorphism, is a specific sequence of DNA identified by a probe as a band on a gel. By using probes to identify RFLPs, biologists can determine if an individual carries the allele for a genetic disorder, or distinguish the DNA of one individual from another.
13. In the Human Genome Project, scientists are working to identify the complete nucleotide sequence in human DNA.

Expanding the Concepts

1. Breeders use hybridization to combine the best characteristics of two organisms to establish a breed. Then inbreeding helps to ensure that the characteristics that make the breed special will be preserved.
2. If a mutation occurs in an intron, a sequence that is spliced from an mRNA transcript, it will not affect the protein product. A point mutation that produces a codon that specifies the same amino acid as before will also be a silent mutation.
3. A frameshift mutation changes the reading frame of the triplet codons, causing new triplets to form after the mutation point. All amino acids specified after the mutation can be very different from those of the normal protein.
4. Students should summarize the different tools used to edit DNA as described in Section 9–2.
5. As negatively charged DNA fragments move toward the positively charged electrode, the smaller fragments slip through the gel faster than the larger fragments, and the fragments are separated.
6. Plasmids act as the vehicles that bring recombinant DNA into bacterial cells. DNA fragments are joined to plasmids, and these recombinant plasmids are used to transform the bacterial cells.
7. Biologists transform eukaryotic cells such as yeast with plasmids. In animal and plant cells that do not have plasmids, biologists insert DNA fragments into a cell with a tiny needle.

Assessment

Reviewing What You Learned

Answer each of the following in a complete sentence.

1. What is the purpose of selective breeding?
2. Compare hybridization and inbreeding.
3. What are mutations? Give an example of a chromosomal mutation and a gene mutation.
4. Describe a frameshift mutation.
5. For what purpose do biologists use restriction enzymes?
6. Why can two DNA fragments be spliced together easily?
7. What is recombinant DNA?
8. Define cell transformation.
9. Of bacterial cells, plant cells, and animal cells, which are easiest to transform?
10. Describe a plasmid.
11. Give three examples of transgenic organisms and their uses.
12. What is a RFLP? Why do biologists probe DNA for RFLPs?
13. Describe the Human Genome Project.

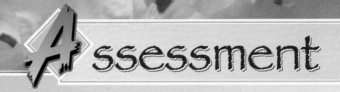

Expanding the Concepts

Discuss each of the following in a brief paragraph.

1. Why do breeders use both hybridization and inbreeding to maintain a breed?
2. Explain how some mutations can be silent, causing no changes in a gene's function.
3. Explain why a frameshift mutation can completely change the way a gene is interpreted.
4. Describe the different tools used to edit DNA.
5. How does electrophoresis separate DNA fragments of different sizes?
6. Discuss the role of plasmids in transforming bacterial cells.
7. Discuss two different ways in which biologists transform eukaryotic cells.
8. How can bacteria be "tricked" into producing large quantities of a human protein, such as insulin?
9. Why is replacing genes in human cells more difficult than replacing them in bacteria or other single-celled organisms?
10. Describe how radioactive probes are used to identify RFLPs in DNA.
11. Why can RFLPs be used to test a person's DNA for Huntington disease and other genetic diseases?
12. Explain the principles of DNA fingerprinting.

8. If a recombinant plasmid is properly inserted into a bacterium, it is "tricked" into producing the protein for which the gene codes.
9. Human cells are more complex than the cells of bacteria and other single-celled organisms, and it is harder to make human cells accept new DNA molecules. Also, the human body is made of many more cells, and it is impossible to insert new DNA into all of them at once.
10. A probe will bind only to complementary sequences in the DNA fragments on a gel. These sequences, the RFLPs, appear as dark bands on the gel.
11. Certain RFLPs have been identified to be inherited with Huntington disease and other genetic diseases. By probing DNA for these RFLPs, geneticists can determine whether an individual carries the allele for one of these diseases.
12. Because some probes detect RFLPs that are highly variable from one person to another, researchers can use RFLPs to distinguish the DNA of one individual from another.

Extending Your Thinking

1. Students should disagree. Possible explanations include: Too many genetic differences exist

Extending Your Thinking

Use the skills you have developed in this chapter to answer the following.

1. **Analyzing arguments** Your friend proposes that by using the techniques of genetic engineering, biologists should be able to produce an organism with any combination of characteristics, such as the body of a frog and the wings of a bat. Do you agree or disagree with this proposal? Explain.
2. **Relating ideas** Compare the tools used in editing DNA with the tools used in editing videotape.
3. **Interpreting data** A certain gene codes for a protein made of 195 amino acids. After the gene undergoes a point mutation, it codes for a protein made of only 101 amino acids. Explain how this is possible.
4. **Predicting** Predict three ways in which transgenic organisms will be used in the future.
5. **Constructing a model** Using construction paper, pipe cleaners, straws, or other materials available in your classroom, construct a model of the electrophoresis of DNA fragments. Use your model to explain this process to your class.
6. **Designing an experiment** In a grassy field, you discover a patch of dandelions that are each roughly 2 centimeters longer than the other dandelions in the field. Design an experiment to determine whether this difference is caused by a mutation.

Applying Your Skills

The Debate About DNA

Should researchers combine DNA from any organisms of their choice? Should they try to transform human cells to cure genetic diseases? Should the government keep DNA records of its citizens? These questions—and questions like them—are sure to be debated in the years ahead, just as you will debate them now.

1. Select one of the above questions or formulate a similar question. Organize class members into two teams to debate the question. Assign each team one position to argue.
2. Research evidence that supports your team's position. Good sources of evidence include encyclopedias, magazines, textbooks, and scientific journals.
3. Conduct the debate, with your teacher as moderator.

• GOING FURTHER •

4. Create a policy statement that you feel offers a reasonable answer to the issue you debated.
5. Present your policy statement in a letter to your state legislator. Ask the legislator for his or her opinions on how genetic engineering and genetic testing should be regulated.

between frogs and bats. It is too difficult to control the expression of so many genes in such a specific location.
2. Students should compare the tools used in editing DNA and those used in editing videotape as described in Section 9–2.
3. A deletion or insertion of one nucleotide will shift the reading frame of the codons, causing a stop codon to form at a different location.
4. Some predictions might include bacteria that produce certain proteins or vaccines, plants that are resistant to certain diseases or pests, and animals that grow faster.

5. Models will vary but should demonstrate that smaller DNA fragments move more quickly through the gel toward the positive electrode than larger fragments.

Skills Trace
Modeling
- Focus pp. 200, 202
- Practice pp. 200, 204
- Assess p. 215

6. One possible experiment would be to use restriction enzymes to cut the DNA from both kinds of dandelions and separate the fragments using gel electrophoresis. Then use probes to identify and compare the RFLPs of both dandelions. If the RFLPs of the two kinds of dandelions are different, then the height difference is due to a mutation.

Applying Your Skills

Teacher Notes

- You may wish to have the entire class debate one question, or divide the class into teams to debate more than one question.
- Encourage students to divide the research tasks so that each student researches one topic. Then students should share their research results with the rest of their team.
- After the debate has ended, help students formulate a statement that both teams feel addresses the issue.
- Teams should work together to write the letter to your state legislator. Be sure to share the legislator's response with the class.

Scoring Rubric

4 Response is thorough, accurate, and creative; shows an in-depth understanding of science skills, procedures, and concepts.

3 Response is complete, mostly accurate, and original; shows a satisfactory understanding of science skills, procedures, and concepts.

2 Response is mostly complete but includes some inaccuracies; shows an adequate understanding of science skills, procedures, and concepts.

1 Response is only partially complete and has many inaccuracies; shows an incomplete understanding of science skills, procedures, and concepts.

0 Response is mostly incomplete and/or inaccurate; shows a lack of understanding of science skills, procedures, and concepts.

UNIT 3

Evolution

Introducing the Unit

. . . In Words

The quotation is from Charles Darwin's work *On the Origin of Species by Means of Natural Selection*, published in 1859. Darwin (1809–1882) was the British naturalist who created a scientific revolution with his theories on evolution. He developed these theories through his observations of plants, animals, and fossils while serving as naturalist aboard the HMS *Beagle*. The variation he observed among similar species led him to question the widely held theory of the immutability of the species and to consider the idea that one species evolves from another.

- **What do you think Darwin meant by the phrase "each slight variation, if useful"?** (Darwin meant that each trait or characteristic of an individual organism helps it succeed in its environment.)
- **How do you think a variation is "preserved"?** (Any trait or characteristic of an organism is preserved when it is passed genetically to its offspring.)
- **How would you define natural selection in your own words?** (Accept all reasonable responses.)

. . . In Pictures

The marine iguana (*Amblyrhynchus cristatus*) is the only lizard that lives in the sea. It can hold its breath for 10 to 15 minutes while it dives to the sea floor to feed on green algae. A relative, the land iguana, is also found on the Galapagos Islands, but it never goes near the water, and it eats cactuses and other land plants. After students have examined the photograph, ask the following questions.

UNIT 3

Evolution

CHAPTERS

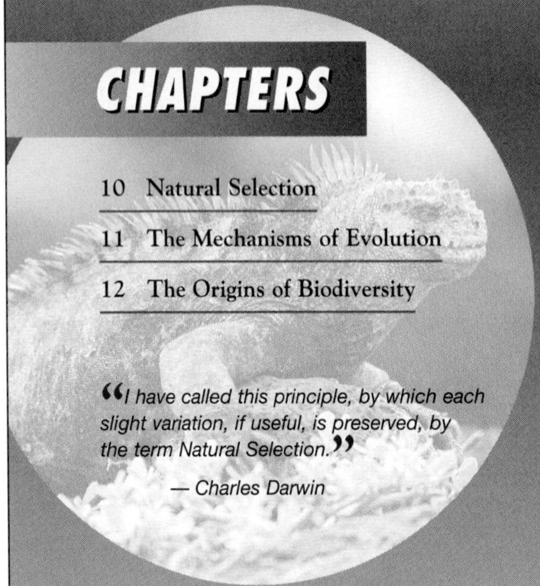

"*I have called this principle, by which each slight variation, if useful, is preserved, by the term Natural Selection.*"

— *Charles Darwin*

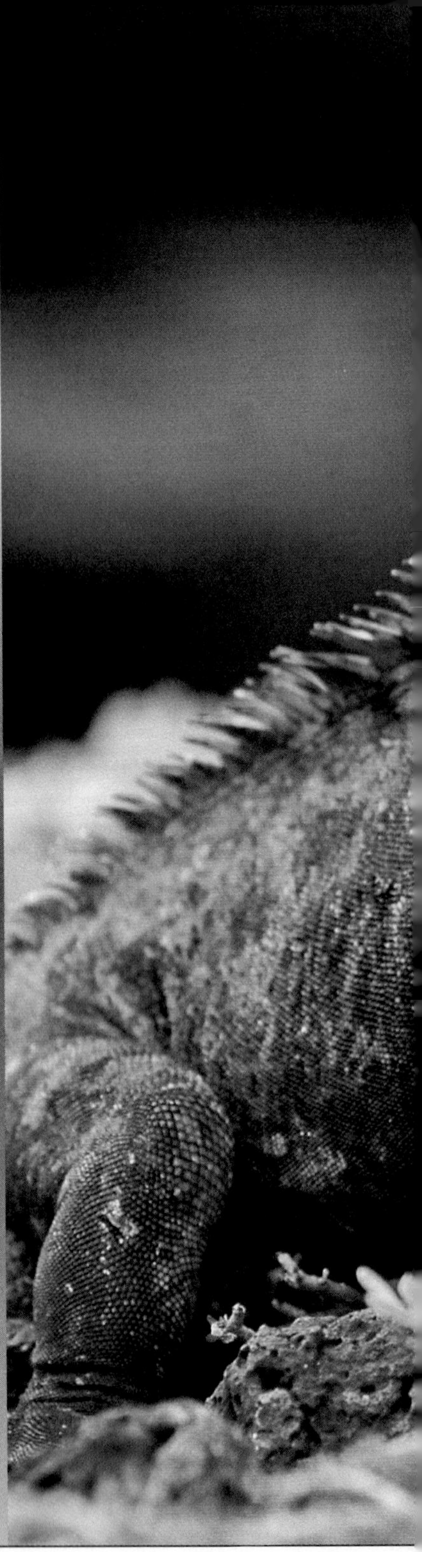

TEACHER SUPPORT

Unit Discovery Learning Activity

EYEWITNESSES TO EVOLUTION

Even in students' relatively short lifetimes, they have undoubtedly witnessed change around themselves. This activity will encourage students to observe change more closely and consider its causes and effects. Follow these steps to carry out this activity.

1. Introduce the activity by pointing out a student's athletic shoes and asking the student to describe the particular features of the shoes. Then ask students if they can remember the first pair of athletic shoes they owned and how they were different from ones people wear today. Ask students if they have seen photographs of athletic shoes their parents and grandparents wore when they were young and how those shoes were different.

CAREER TRACK
As you explore the topics in this unit, you will discover many different types of careers associated with biology. Here are a few of these careers:
• Zoologist
• Genetic Engineer
• Taxonomist

A marine iguana in the Galapagos Islands

• **What trait of the marine iguana is useful for its survival? Explain.** (The ability to dive into the ocean and eat algae.)

• **What might happen to the marine iguana if the algae died or a stronger competitor dominated the algae beds?** (The marine iguana would have to change or it would become extinct. The marine iguanas with a useful variation, such as the ability to also eat land plants, might then be the ones to survive.)

Explain to students that in Unit 3 they will learn how evolution is carried out through natural selection.

CAREER TRACK

Throughout this unit, you will find a broad range of biology-related careers that vary in educational and training requirements. You may wish to have your students find out more about the following careers:

- Zoologist, p. 228
- Genetic Engineer, p. 249
- Taxonomist, p. 271

Technology

BioVue
Do Modern Dinosaurs Fly?
Videodisc Side 3

Go to Chapter 2

2. Instruct students to work in pairs and choose some item, such as athletic shoes, automobiles, or audio equipment, for which they can trace changes over the years.
3. Students should research the item to find out how it has changed and why.
4. Have students create a poster to show and explain the series of changes the item has gone through over the years. The posters may have pictures cut from magazines or drawings students have made, as well as text.
5. Ask each group to present its poster to the class, explaining how the item has changed, the causes for the changes, and the effects of the changes.

By observing change and considering its causes and effects, students will be introduced to concepts of **evolution,** a theme developed in this unit.

Ancillary Support

The resource below can be used to support your teaching strategy for these two pages.

BL Integrating the Media
Unit Discovery Learning Activity

Chapter 10 Natural Selection

Content Management	Student Edition Activities
■ Section 10–1 A Riddle: Life's Diversity and Connections, pp. 219–225 A Daring Voyage Pieces of the Puzzle The Galapagos Islands Exciting Time, Exciting Thoughts	
■ Section 10–2 Darwin's Solution, pp. 226–231 The Findings Of Farmers and Pigeons Selection in Nature Common Descent The Test of Time	Laboratory Investigation: Simulating Natural Selection, pp. 234–235 MINI LAB: The Tall and Short of It, p. 229
◆ BRANCHING OUT • In Depth Section 10–3 Darwin's Revolution, pp. 232–233 Evolution Life in Constant Motion	MINI LAB: Now You See Me, Now You Don't, p. 233
■ These sections cover all the necessary content and concepts for a basic course in biology. ◆ This section covers content and concepts that are either applications or extensions of the basic material.	

Integration Strategies

SE Earth Science, p. 224
Biology and Society, p. 233
BL Investigating Careers
Involving the Community
Science Through Art

Assessment Strategies

SE Chapter Review, pp. 236–239
TR Section Reviews
Chapter Test
Performance-Based Assessment
BL Investigating Further
Practice Test
Chapter Review
CTB Chapter 10 Test

Tech Prep

A teaching strategy appropriate for students who are in technical/vocational programs or who are considering post-secondary technical education can be found on the following **TE** page: 229.

Meeting the Standards

Sections 10–1 through 10–3 cover all of the five content standards under **Biological Evolution** and two of the four content standards under **The Behavior of Organisms** as described on pages 185 and 187 of The National Science Education Standards.

Chapter Planning Guide

Teacher's Edition Activities	Other Activities	Media and Technology
Chapter Discovery Learning Activity, p. 218 **Inquiry Activity:** Requirements for Survival, p. 220 **Investigate:** Research, p. 220 **Investigate:** Cooperative Learning, p. 222 **Investigate:** Role-Playing, p. 222 **Investigate:** Research, p. 224 **Activity:** Super Reproduction, p. 225	**LM** Interpreting Events from Fossil Evidence, #19 Comparing Amino Acid Sequences in Vertebrates, #20 **TR** **Writing in Biology:** Aboard the *Beagle* **Enrich:** Unique Islands **BL** **Inquiry Activity:** A Strange Structure	**BioVue Mini Doc:** Whale Evolution, Videodisc Side 3 **BioVue Plus CD-ROMs:** Whale Evolution **TB** Similarities in Organisms, #13
Inquiry Activity: Pigeon Toes and Duck Feet, p. 226 **Investigate:** Model Building, p. 226 **Investigate:** Cooperative Learning, p. 228 **Activity:** Vegetable Comparisons, p. 228 **Investigate:** Research, p. 231	**TR** **Apply:** An Early Evolutionist **BL** **Inquiry Activity:** Survival of the Fittest	**CD-ROM:** Evolution: The $3\frac{1}{2}$ Billion Year Journey
Inquiry Activity: Evolution in Progress, p. 232	**TR** **Explore:** Evolution—What's in a Word? **BL** **Inquiry Activity:** Horsing Around With Evolution	
KEY: SE Student Edition **TE** Teacher's Edition **LM** Laboratory Manual **TR** Teaching Resources **BL** BioLog **TB** Transparency Box **CTB** Computer Test Bank		

Materials List

TE Chapter Discovery Learning Activity, p. 218 (20 minutes); photographs of various animals and separate photographs of their environments.
TE Investigate: Research, p. 220 (20–30 minutes for groups to organize, 30–40 minutes for presentations; have students carry out research on their own time); various art materials.
TE Investigate: Cooperative Learning, p. 222 (15 minutes for groups to organize, 40 minutes to create visual displays, 40 minutes for group presentation); various art materials.
TE Activity: Super Reproduction, p. 225 (20 minutes); green pepper, knife.
TE Inquiry Activity: Pigeon Toes and Duck Feet, p. 226 (20–30 minutes); photographs of different kinds of bird feet.
TE Investigate: Model Building, p. 226 (20–30 minutes); various photograghs or drawings showing different designs in the evolution of a machine or appliance.
TE Activity: Vegetable Comparisons, p. 228 (20–30 minutes); cut-up and whole samples of cabbage, kale, broccoli, kohlrabi, cauliflower, and Brussels sprouts.
SE MINI LAB: The Tall and Short of It, p. 229 (30 minutes); meterstick, graph paper.
SE MINI LAB: Now You See Me, Now You Don't, p. 233 (20–30 minutes); graph paper.

CHAPTER 10

Natural Selection

Introducing the Chapter

. . . In Pictures

Have students examine the puffins in the photograph and read the caption. Then ask the following questions.

• **What characteristics do these puffins share?** (Possible responses include shape of beak, body shape, and coloring.)

• **In what way are puffins distinct from other kinds of birds?** (Possible responses include coloration, body shape, diet, habitat, breeding behaviors, method of getting food.)

Explain that puffins, which mainly eat fish, are strong swimmers and divers. Like penguins, they use their wings to swim, and steer with their feet. However, puffins can fly. Point out that the characteristics of puffins make them able to live successfully in their environment.

Teaching Strategy

In the first two sections of this chapter, students will learn about Charles Darwin and his observations of living things that led him to develop his theory of evolution based on natural selection. In the BRANCHING OUT section, students find out about the significance of evolution.

BIO JOURNAL

Have students consider the different roles people play in their community. Point out that people in different roles have specific talents and skills that help them to perform those roles successfully. Also challenge them to consider what life might be like if everyone were the same. Instruct students to keep their entries in their portfolios.

CHAPTER 10

Natural Selection

FOCUSING THE CHAPTER THEME: Evolution

10–1 A Riddle: Life's Diversity and Connections
- Discuss Darwin's observations of the living world.

10–2 Darwin's Solution
- Explain natural selection.

BRANCHING OUT *In Depth*

10–3 Darwin's Revolution
- Examine the significance of evolution.

LABORATORY INVESTIGATION
- Construct a model of natural selection.

Biology and Your World

BIO JOURNAL

Have you heard the saying "Variety is the spice of life"? What does it mean to you? In your journal, write a short essay about how the differences among people—their interests, abilities, and talents—can enrich more than divide a community.

Atlantic puffins on a sea cliff in Scotland

TEACHER SUPPORT

Chapter Discovery Learning Activity

Display individual photographs of various animals, such as insects, fish, amphibians, reptiles, birds, and mammals, and photographs of the environments in which they live. Challenge students to match each animal with its environment. Ask them to explain what characteristics of the animal gave them clues about the environment in which it lives. You may wish to list their responses on the board or have students list their responses on their own papers to share with the class later. Explain to students that in this chapter, they will learn how animals become adapted to live successfully in their environments.

A Riddle: Life's Diversity and Connections

SECTION 10–1

GUIDE FOR READING

- **Define** the term evolution.
- **Identify** the observations of living things that puzzled Darwin on his voyage.

THE LIVING WORLD PRESENTS us with an extraordinary puzzle. Humans share the Earth with millions of other species—from bacteria to blue whales. What's more, among the vast majority of multicellular species, no two individuals are exactly alike. Yet all forms of life are regulated by similar messages of molecular instructions written in the living code of DNA. What scientific process can account for the incredible diversity on one hand and the unity of life on the other?

A Daring Voyage

The answer to this question lies in a process known as **evolution**—a collection of facts, observations, and hypotheses about the history of life. **Evolution means a change over a period of time.** And a systematic study of evolution began on one of the most important adventures in all of human history.

In late December 1831, the research ship HMS *Beagle* set sail from England for a five-year cruise around the world. There was nothing out of the ordinary about the

Figure 10–1 *(a) A group of flamingoes in Florida, (b) plant life in a cypress swamp in South Carolina, and (c) the bacteria that cause food poisoning—*Staphylococcus aureus *(magnification: 50,000X)—are examples of the variety of life forms that inhabit the Earth.*

SECTION 10–1

A Riddle: Life's Diversity and Connections

Performance Objectives

- State the meaning of the term evolution.
- Describe the puzzling observations of living things that Darwin made on his voyage.

1 ENGAGE

Ideas Through Images

Have students examine Figure 10–1, read the caption, and answer the following questions.

- **In what ways are these organisms different? In what ways are they similar?** (Differences include plant vs. animal vs. bacteria, eukaryote vs. prokaryote, food sources, role in the environment. Similarities include contain DNA, must reproduce for the species to survive, are adapted to live in their environment.)
- **What is the biological basis for differences among these three organisms?** (Their genetic make-up.)
- **Since the DNA molecules of these organisms have similar characteristics, what processes might cause each of these organisms to possess different genes?** (Some students might mention that the environment or the effect of mutations can cause genetic diversity among organisms.)

TEACHER SUPPORT

Background Information

Charles Darwin was born in Shrewsbury, England, on February 12, 1809. Like his father and grandfather, Darwin studied medicine at the University of Edinburgh but found he did not like it. He then entered Christ's College in Cambridge to study theology in order to become a clergyman. His interest in natural history prompted him to study biology and geology also. After Darwin graduated in 1831, one of his professors recommended him for a post as an unpaid naturalist on the HMS *Beagle*, a surveying ship heading for the coasts of South America. Initially, Darwin refused the position. However, he later changed his mind and wrote a letter of acceptance, only to find that another candidate had also accepted. Robert FitzRoy, the captain of the HMS *Beagle*, chose Darwin over the other candidate only because FitzRoy believed that Darwin would make a better companion.

Section 10–1 (continued)

2 EXPLORE

Inquiry Activity

Inferring

Requirements for Survival
Ask students to make inferences about what a particular species of animal needs to survive. Make sure students understand that a species is a group of organisms with similar characteristics that produces fertile offspring when bred. Point out to students that not only the physical characteristics of an organism help it to survive but also the organism's behaviors and relationship with its environment. Have students choose a particular organism and list its requirements for survival. Invite students to share their lists in a class discussion.

Investigate

Research Have students create a time line in which they chronicle the various evolution theories over time. Encourage students to research different theories of evolution and when they were proposed. Some theories students might include are Lamarckism (1809), Darwin's theory (1858), mutationism (1900–1910), and the synthetic theory (1937). Instruct students to write a brief description of each theory on the time line.

3 TEACH

Discussion

Initiate a class discussion about the causes of living diversity. Through the discussion emphasize these points.

- DNA is the basis for all diversity among living things.
- Fossil evidence shows the kinds of diversity that failed to adapt to environmental changes.

THE VOYAGE OF THE BEAGLE

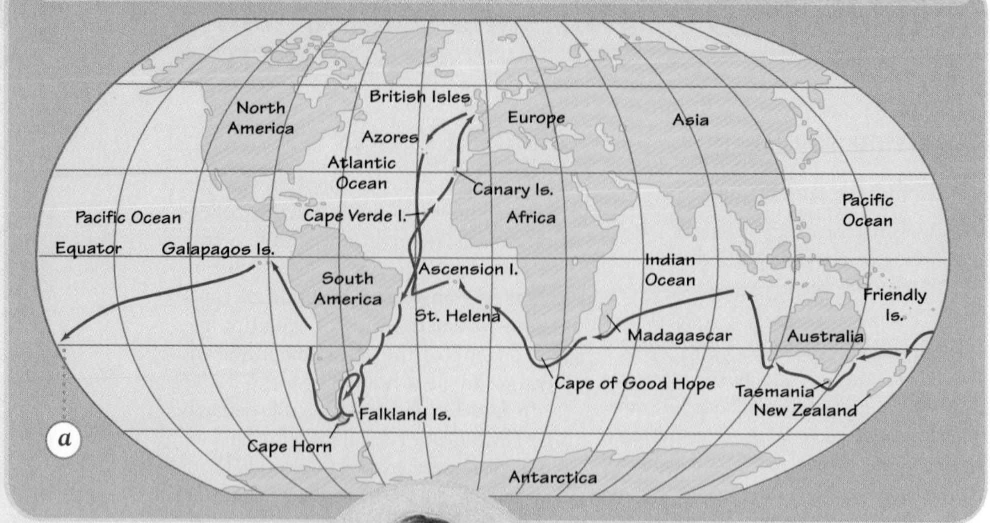

Figure 10–2
(a) The Beagle's voyage around the world lasted for a little over four years. Although the stop at the Galapagos Islands was for just one month, (b) Charles Darwin made the wealth of observations that led to his revolutionary hypothesis about the history of life on Earth.

Beagle, its captain, or its crew. But on this trip, the *Beagle* carried an educated, self-enlightened 22-year-old ship's naturalist named Charles Robert Darwin. No one—not even Darwin himself—knew that this voyage would begin a revolution in scientific thought that would radically change the way scientists look at life.

Darwin loved natural history. During the voyage of the *Beagle*, Darwin's powers of observation helped him to notice things that others had missed. At sea, Darwin studied specimens, read scientific books, and gave a great deal of thought to what he had seen. This was the key to his great contribution. Other explorers made long lists of little discoveries. But to Darwin, every individual find seemed to be another piece in a great puzzle that kept him involved for decades.

Pieces of the Puzzle

Wherever the *Beagle* went, Darwin collected plant and animal specimens. Time and again, he was thrilled by extraordinary sights that few people had imagined. The things that excited Darwin so long ago are just as astonishing today.

Living Diversity

As Darwin traveled, he was amazed by the tremendous variety of animals and plants that inhabited the Earth. Just one day's work in a Brazilian rain forest produced a collection of more than 68 different species of beetles! **Darwin called the variety of living things the diversity of life, or living diversity.** He wondered how this diversity came to be. Today, scientists know that living diversity is far greater than Darwin imagined. They estimate that Earth is home to between 5 and 50 million different species. Where did they come from?

TEACHER SUPPORT

Managing Classroom Diversity

MULTICULTURAL STRATEGY
Instruct students to find where they live on the map in Figure 10–2. Then challenge them to locate where their ancestors lived. Ask students if they have lived or had ancestors who lived in the areas where Darwin traveled. Then have students choose a plant or animal from their country of origin that is different from plants and animals native to the United States. Students should draw a picture of that plant or animal and describe how it differs from a comparable plant or animal native to the United States.

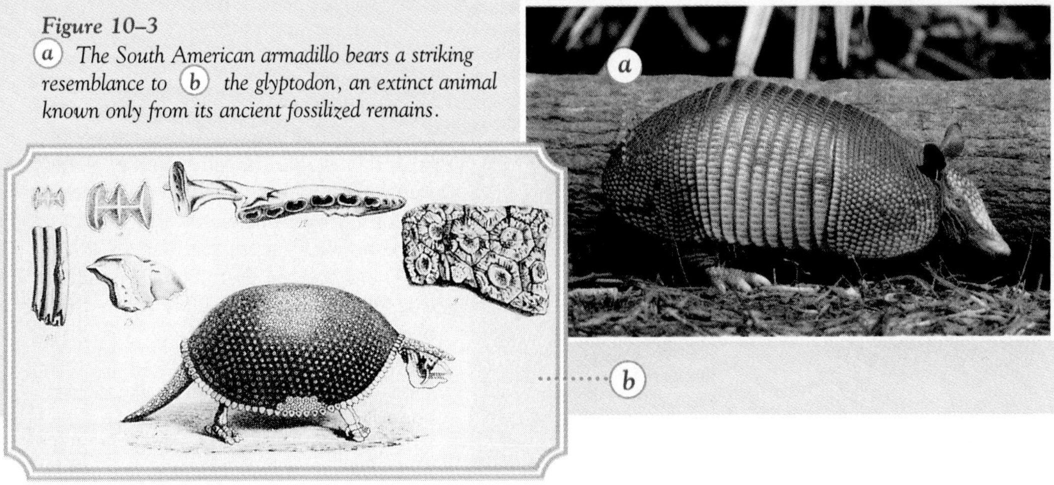

Figure 10–3
(a) The South American armadillo bears a striking resemblance to (b) the glyptodon, an extinct animal known only from its ancient fossilized remains.

Fossil Diversity

In many places, Darwin collected bones and other traces of ancient organisms, called **fossils.** Some of these were rather ordinary, but many looked as strange as dragons or other imaginary beasts. **Since Darwin's time, researchers have uncovered the fossilized remains of many more unusual creatures.** In fact, scientists estimate that 99.9 percent of all species that have ever lived are now extinct. If that is correct, hundreds of millions of species have appeared, lived for a time, and vanished. Where did these marchers in the parade of life come from? And why did so many disappear?

Adaptation

As Darwin studied plants and animals, he noticed that every species seemed remarkably well suited to the life it leads. Each species had a combination of physical characteristics and behaviors that helped it catch food, withstand harsh conditions, or reproduce. These characteristics and behaviors, called **adaptations,** are found at every level of biology—from cell chemistry to animal behavior. **Biologists use the word adaptation to describe physical and behavioral traits that enable organisms to survive.**

Fitness

Darwin realized that for a species to survive, its members must do more than just stay alive. They must also reproduce. **Darwin used the word fitness to describe the ability of an individual to survive and reproduce.** Evolutionary biologists today define **fitness** in a more precise way. Fitness now is based on an organism's ability to successfully pass on its genes to its offspring.

☑ ***Checkpoint*** What is meant by the term adaptation? By the term fitness? ①

Figure 10–4
Although the hawk might not have much success with this prey, its sharp talons and hooked beak are adaptations that are essential for its survival.

Ideas Through Images

Have students examine Figure 10–4, read the caption, and answer the following questions.

- **Besides its talons and beak, what other adaptations enable a hawk to catch prey?** (Large wings for soaring at high altitudes to scan for prey, sharp eyesight, strong limbs.)
- **What adaptations does the tortoise have to protect itself from predators?** (Its hard shell, large size, and the ability to hide inside the shell.)
- **Hawks can catch animals for food because of their adaptations. What kind of food do tortoises most likely eat?** (Because tortoises are slow-moving and close to the ground, students should infer that tortoises most likely eat plants.)

☑ Checkpoint

① An adaptation is a physical characteristic or behavior that helps an organism get food, reproduce, or survive in the environment. Fitness is the ability of an individual to survive and reproduce, passing its genes to its offspring.

TEACHER SUPPORT

Managing Classroom Diversity

GIFTED STUDENTS
The extinction of dinosaurs is probably the most significant mass extinction in the history of Earth. Encourage interested students to research the various theories for the extinction of dinosaurs and find a common theme to these theories. (A change in the climate.) Challenge students to make inferences about why dinosaurs could not survive these changes. They should include living diversity, adaptations, and fitness in their discussions.

LEP STUDENTS
Some students might confuse the meaning of the word fitness as defined by Darwin and its common usage, being physically healthy with good cardiopulmonary strength and endurance. Have students use their native language to describe both meanings of fitness.

Ancillary Support

The resources below can be used to support your teaching strategy for these two pages.

LM Interpreting Events From Fossil Evidence, #19
TR Writing in Biology: Aboard the *Beagle*
Enrich: Unique Islands

Investigate

Cooperative Learning Have student groups work together to learn about the Galapagos Islands. Instruct groups to divide the research assignments so that each member is responsible for a particular topic, such as location, climate, plant life, and animal life. Encourage students who are researching the same topic for different groups to work together. Groups should present their findings to the class using visual displays, such as a map, model, bulletin board, or poster. Discuss how diverse environments might have caused the development of diverse species.

Discussion

Encourage students to discuss Darwin's thought processes as he developed his theory of evolution. Include the following points in the discussion.

- When Darwin began his voyage, he was not looking to find evidence for evolution. He was simply observing the variety of characteristics of organisms native to different parts of the world.
- Darwin was a religious man and believed that all living species were divine creations.
- Darwin later found out that the very different Galapagos birds were actually a group of closely related finches.

Investigate

Role-Playing Challenge students to imagine that they are Charles Darwin in the mid-1800s. Impress upon them how radical Darwin's ideas were for that period of time. Then instruct students to develop an approach for introducing a radical idea to the community, whether it is the scientific community or a neighborhood community. Encourage students to consider which approach might work best so that the community would accept the new idea. Invite students to share their approaches with the class.

Figure 10–5
The Galapagos Islands are the tips of undersea volcanoes that reach from the ocean floor to just above sea level.

The Galapagos Islands

The *Beagle* visited so many different places that the captain's log filled several books. But of all the *Beagle's* ports of call, Darwin was most influenced by his visit to a group of islands located 1000 kilometers west of South America. All these islands are small—some mere specks on the map. Several of them have climates that are quite different from the rest. The smallest islands at the lowest elevation above sea level are hot, dry, and nearly barren. Yet a strange assortment of plants and animals live there, including giant tortoises, marine iguanas, and some odd birds. These islands in the Pacific Ocean are the Galapagos Islands, and their inhabitants provided Darwin with his greatest inspiration.

Peculiar Creatures

Darwin was fascinated by the Galapagos wildlife, especially land tortoises and marine iguanas. He also saw several types of small brown birds looking for seeds. Although he collected several, he didn't find them unusual or important. As he examined these specimens, however, he noted that the birds showed a variety of beak shapes. He thought some of them were wrens, others were warblers, and still others were blackbirds. But that was all he noticed—at least at first.

There was another zoological tidbit that Darwin noted but did not think important at the time. The Vice-Governor of the islands told Darwin that giant tortoises varied in predictable ways from one island to another. Furthermore, the Vice-Governor boasted to Darwin that he could tell which island a particular tortoise came from by looking at its shell. Darwin later admitted in his notes that "I did not for some time pay sufficient attention to this statement."

The Journey Home

While heading home, Darwin had plenty of time—between bouts of seasickness—to look at his Galapagos specimens and think more about them. While examining several mockingbirds, he noticed that individuals collected from the islands of Floreana and Santiago looked different from one another. They also looked different from individuals collected on other islands. Darwin remembered what the Vice-Governor had told him about the tortoises. Darwin began to wonder whether animals living on different islands had once been members of the same species and had changed after they were isolated from one another. Was that possible? How could it be? If it were true, it would turn his whole view of the natural world upside down!

Exciting Time, Exciting Thoughts

Darwin made his voyage during one of the most exciting periods in the history of Western science. Many explorers were

TEACHER SUPPORT

Background Information

The Galapagos Islands lie in the Pacific Ocean about 970 km off the coast of Ecuador, the country to which they belong. Fifteen islands, totaling about 7800 square km, make up the Galapagos. These islands are all volcanic peaks rising out of the ocean at different elevations, some as high as 1500 m. The climate on each island varies with its elevation. Those with higher elevations have lush, green environments at their peaks. All have hot, dry lava rock at sea level.

Almost 10,000 people live on the islands, whose most notable resources are the unusual animals living there. These islands were once known as the Enchanted Isles and have a very colorful history. Pirates buried their treasures there and ships dropped off their mutineers there. During World War II, Ecuador allowed the United States to establish a military base there to guard the Panama Canal.

traveling the world, expanding the horizons of knowledge. Great thinkers in several fields of science had begun to challenge established views about the natural world. To understand just how radical Darwin's thoughts would soon become, you must understand a few things about the world in which he lived.

The vast majority of Europeans in Darwin's day believed that the Earth and all forms of life were divine creations, produced a few thousand years ago over a span of one week. Since that original creation, both the Earth and its living species were thought to have remained fixed and unchanged. By the time Darwin set sail on the *Beagle*, there were numerous discoveries of evidence—fossils of extinct animals, for example—that this traditional view could not explain. Some scientists adjusted their beliefs to include not one period of creation but several creations—each preceded by a catastrophe, such as the Flood described in the Book of Genesis.

At first, Darwin accepted these beliefs. But as he traveled, much of what he observed did not fit neatly into this view of unchanging life. The more he saw, the more he wondered whether all species really did remain the same. Could living things change over time? If Darwin had lived a century earlier, he might have done little more than think about such things, as others had before him. But as Darwin wondered, he also read the latest scientific books and discussed his findings with other scientists interested in natural history. Slowly, his thinking began to follow a dramatically different path.

Figure 10–6
(a) No matter how different the limbs of many animals look, their bones are incredibly similar to one another. (b) The earliest stages of these three embryos look so similar that it is difficult to tell them apart. As these embryos grow, their homologous structures develop in very different ways, producing infant animals that can easily be recognized.

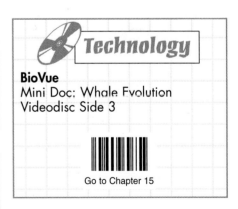

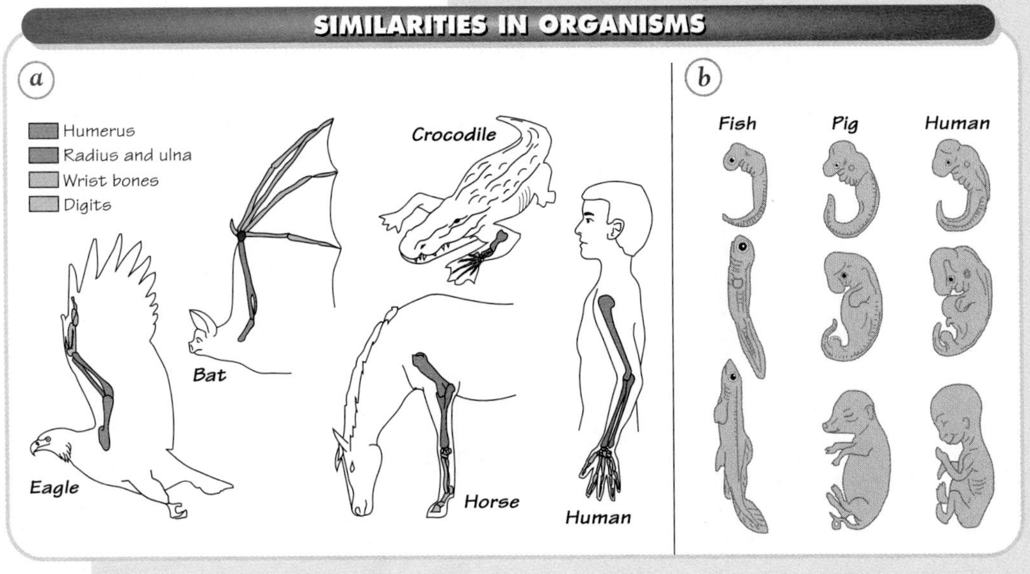

Ideas Through Images

Have students examine Figure 10–6, read the caption, and answer the following questions.

- **How are differences in the forelimbs of the horse and the human related to their functions?** (The digits and wrist bones of the horse are elongated for speed, and all bones in the forelimb are fused for strength. Human digits are separated for dexterity.)
- **Compare the forelimbs of the bat and the eagle. How did both develop differently to support flight?** (The digits of the bat are elongated to support the membranous wing. The entire eagle forelimb supports the wing structure, and the digits are greatly reduced.)
- **Compare the fish, pig, and human embryos. Which animals are probably more closely related and why?** (Human and pig are more closely related because the embryos share common development for a longer period of time.)

Technology

BioVue
Mini Doc: Whale Evolution
Videodisc Side 3

Go to Chapter 15

TEACHER SUPPORT

Historical Perspective

From ancient times, most people believed that all living things were created by a divine entity. Once the world was created, these living things remained unchanged, with no new species appearing. One of the first scientists to propose a theory of biological evolution was Jean Baptiste Lamarck (1744–1829). His theory of acquired characteristics proposed that organisms change because they want to be better adapted to their environments. He also thought that by using their bodies in different ways, organisms could change their forms, and these changes were inherited. For example, if a giraffe stretched its neck longer and longer to reach the leaves at the top of a tree, its offspring would have longer necks. Lamarck's ideas helped to influence Darwin's thinking in the development of his theory of evolution.

Ancillary Support

The resource below can be used to support your teaching strategy for these two pages.

TB Similarities in Organisms, #13

Discussion

Begin a discussion about vestigial organs. Encourage students to make inferences about why some animals have vestigial organs. You might want to list their inferences on the board. Then explain that vestigial organs give clues to the species from which an animal has evolved. For example, the presence of tiny hip bones in snakes suggests that snakes evolved from ancestors with hips. Have students consider what Darwin might have thought upon learning about vestigial organs. Ask them how they think these organs are related to Darwin's ideas about gradual changes in organisms over time.

Investigate

Research Point out to students that insects and birds have different wing structures. Explain that these structures are analogous—they have similar functions but different forms. Encourage students to find other examples of analogous structures and the clues they give to the ancestors of an organism.

INTEGRATING EARTH SCIENCE

Rain, heat, cold, earthquakes, and volcanic eruptions gradually change rocks, mountains, and valleys. Fossils of marine animals in desert areas show that Earth's environment and climate have changed over time. Earthquakes are symptoms of the movement of large plates of Earth's surface, causing mountains to grow higher and rock layers to become twisted or buried.

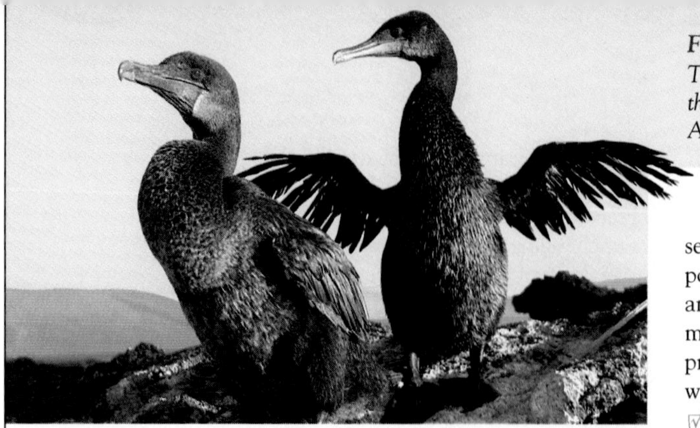

Figure 10–7
These flightless cormorants are found on the islands off the western coast of South America.

Living Questions

During Darwin's lifetime, several interesting observations were made by anatomists who studied the structure of adult animals and by biologists who studied developing embryos. Among their findings were many phenomena that needed to be explained.

When looking at adult animals with four limbs, anatomists saw striking similarities among the bones of very different types of arms and legs. Structures such as those that are color-coded in ***Figure 10–6*** on page 223 are called **homologous structures.** Homologous structures develop from similar tissues in the early developmental stages of the organism. As you can also see, studies of developing embryos revealed even more surprising similarities.

INTEGRATING EARTH SCIENCE
What evidence did scientists uncover to support the hypothesis that Earth was constantly changing?

Anatomists also found structures that seemed to have little or no obvious purpose in the organism. These structures are known as **vestigial organs.** As more of these structures were found, they presented real puzzles to scientists, who were unable to explain their presence.

☑ **Checkpoint** What are homologous structures? 1

An Ancient, Changing Earth

While on board the *Beagle*, Darwin read the recent works of Charles Lyell, a geologist who agreed with a revolutionary proposal that had been made nearly a century earlier. Lyell put forth some convincing arguments that Earth had to be older than people thought. He argued that the modern world must have been shaped by the same geological forces that can be seen in action today. Thus, if river valleys were dug by a process as slow as erosion, Earth had to be older than a few thousand years. ●

Lyell then extended his thinking beyond geology to all of science. He proposed that scientists must explain the past in terms of events and processes that they could observe themselves.

Figure 10–8
Charles Lyell's hypothesis about the age of the Earth and the forces that shape it was based on observations such as (a) volcanic eruptions and (b) erosion.

TEACHER SUPPORT

Background Information

When Charles Lyell proposed his theory of uniformitarianism, he essentially drew a line between scientific analysis and religious convictions. His theory included three principles that were based on his observations of geologic forces, but they easily translate to all fields of science. In the first principle, Lyell argued that natural laws must be constant in space and time; otherwise, science can have no explanatory or predictive power. The second principle stated that scientists must always explain past events in terms of observable events. The third principle stated that most geologic change occurs slowly and gradually, not through catastrophic events. Darwin considered these principles when he developed his theory of evolution.

Figure 10–9
(a) *Plants such as the Australian* Eugenia corniflora, *laden with fruit, and* (b) *animals such as the spadefoot toad, whose young are shown here, illustrate the huge reproductive capacity of many organisms.*

In other words, Lyell argued that science could not call upon miracles and supernatural events to explain observed phenomena. For if that were the case, a scientific approach could never enable scientists to explain the past or make reliable predictions about the future.

Lyell's arguments made sense to Darwin after he witnessed a few geological events. In South America, Darwin observed a volcanic eruption—from a safe distance. Later, he wrote about a violent earthquake that lifted a stretch of rocky coastline more than 3 meters into the air.

With Lyell's ideas fresh in his mind, Darwin was able to understand how the fossils of marine animals, which he had found in rock layers several meters above sea level, got there. Geological phenomena such as volcanic eruptions and earthquakes could change the face of the Earth. And if Earth itself could change over time, why not life on Earth as well?

The Problem of Reproduction

Another influence on Darwin's thinking was the English economist Thomas Malthus. In 1788, Malthus observed that babies were being born faster than people were dying. If this growth continued, he realized, the world would be overrun with humans. And if that happened, Malthus suggested that war, famine, and disease would limit human populations.

When Darwin read Malthus's work, he realized that this reasoning applied even more to plants and animals, because they produce many more offspring than humans do. A mature maple tree can produce thousands of seeds in a single summer. One oyster can produce millions of eggs each year. If all the offspring of any species survived for several generations, they would overrun the world.

Obviously, this doesn't happen. Continents aren't covered with maple trees, and oceans aren't filled with oysters. The majority of the offspring of a species die, and only a few that survive succeed in reproducing. But what causes the death of those individuals? And what factor or factors determine which survive and reproduce and which do not? These questions will be answered in the next section.

Section Review 10-1

1. **Explain** what is meant by the term evolution.
2. **Identify** the observations of living things that puzzled Darwin on his voyage.
3. **Critical Thinking—Drawing Conclusions** What evidence do homologous structures and vestigial organs offer about the patterns of change in living things?

4 ASSESS

Quick Check

Ask students to define the terms evolution, adaptation, and fitness.

Section Review 10-1

1. Evolution means a change over a period of time.

2. The observations that puzzled Darwin on his voyage included the extent of living diversity, fossils of organisms unlike any alive at time, and the differences between animals found on nearby islands.

3. Students may conclude that organisms having homologous structures may have common ancestry and that the pattern of change is one in which diversity increases. Vestigial organs may suggest that change in living things is often gradual.

Learning Modality

Visual Learning For each photograph in the section, have students write an explanation about how the subject of the photograph influenced Darwin's thinking about living things and evolution.

Checkpoint

(1) Homologous structures are parts of different organisms that develop from similar tissues in the early developmental stages of the organisms.

TEACHER SUPPORT

Activity

SUPER REPRODUCTION
Have student pairs cut open a green pepper and count all the seeds inside. Ask students to calculate the number of seeds that would be produced if they planted all the seeds from their pepper and every seed grew into a plant that produced eight peppers, each containing the same number of seeds as their original pepper. (8 x y = 8y = the number of peppers produced. 8y x y = the total number of seeds, where y equals the number of seeds from the pepper students cut open.) Have pairs record their data on a chart on the chalkboard and calculate a class total. Then discuss with the class why pepper plants are not found growing everywhere, even though they produce so many seeds.

Ancillary Support

The resources below can be used to support your teaching strategy for these two pages.

LM Comparing Amino Acid Sequences in Vertebrates, #20
BL Inquiry Activity: A Strange Structure

Section 10–2
Darwin's Solution

Performance Objectives
- Explain what is meant by the term artificial selection.
- Relate natural selection to evolution.

Laboratory Investigation Skill: Constructing a model
Mini Lab Skill: Interpreting

1 ENGAGE

Inquiry Activity
Inferring

Pigeon Toes and Duck Feet
Display photographs of various bird feet, such as duck, hawk, chicken, and finch. Do not identify the birds to which the feet belong. Ask students to infer the function of each type of foot. You might have them record their observations as they compare the characteristics of the feet. Challenge students to make inferences about how each type of foot helps the bird to survive. Invite students to share their inferences with the class. You might record their inferences on the chalkboard.

2 EXPLORE

Investigate
Model Building Give student groups various photographs or drawings showing different designs in the evolution of a machine or appliance, such as an airplane, automobile, tractor, or refrigerator. Challenge students to work together to sequence the various stages of the design from the oldest to the most current design. Encourage students to choose a few specific items of the design and trace how they have changed over time. Challenge them to describe why those changes were made and how they made the object work more efficiently. Invite groups to present their models to the class.

SECTION 10–2 **Darwin's Solution**

GUIDE FOR READING

- **Describe** artificial selection.
- **Explain** evolution by natural selection.

MINI LAB
- **Interpret** the variation in height of students in your class.

AFTER DARWIN RETURNED TO England, the scientific community was soon buzzing with excitement. Darwin had turned over many specimens, including the Galapagos birds, to specialists at the Zoological Society of London. He soon learned that the mockingbirds he had collected were actually three separate species. Even more exciting was the news that these three species live only on the Galapagos Islands. And there were more surprises to come.

The Findings

To Darwin's astonishment, the small seed-eating birds he had thought were wrens, warblers, and blackbirds were actually all finches. And they too, like the mockingbirds, live only on the Galapagos Islands. The same was true of the tortoises, marine iguanas, and all the plants that Darwin had collected on the islands. For all these new species, the story was the same—each island species looked a great deal like a species on the mainland of South America. Yet the island species were distinctly different—both from the mainland species and from each other.

Not only was Darwin stunned by these discoveries, he was also disturbed by them. Years later, he wrote, "It was evident that such facts as these . . . could be explained on the supposition that species gradually became modified, and the subject haunted me." He began to record his thoughts and observations on the process that would later be called evolution.

Figure 10–10 (a) *The blue-footed booby,* (b) *the sally light-foot crab, and* (c) *the giant tortoise are some examples of the wildlife that inhabits the Galapagos Islands.*

TEACHER SUPPORT

Facts and Figures

- The word *galapagos* is the Spanish word for turtles. The Galapagos Islands are named for the giant tortoises that live there. These are among the largest species of tortoises and grow up to 1.2 m long and have masses over 230 kg.
- Sunflower plants that grow in the Galapagos Islands have evolved into tall trees.
- Marine iguanas living in the Galapagos Islands grow as long as 1.2 m. Many of these iguanas eat algae on the rocks along the coasts of the islands.
- Penguins are also found living in the Galapagos Islands.

Figure 10–11

Taken from Darwin's The Origin of Species by Means of Natural Selection, *these sketches clearly illustrate the difference in beak shape and size found among the finches of the Galapagos Islands.*

Although Darwin returned to England in 1836, it wasn't until 1844 that he first wrote down most of his ideas on how evolution might work. Then in 1859, nearly 30 years after he began his voyage on the *Beagle*, Darwin published his explanations in a book entitled *The Origin of Species by Means of Natural Selection*. Darwin published his work at that time only because someone else was about to be given credit for the same ideas. That someone was Alfred Russel Wallace, who had been studying natural history in Malaysia. Wallace sent Darwin a short essay in which he summarized exactly what Darwin had been thinking about for almost 25 years.

In *The Origin of Species*, Darwin accomplished two important tasks. First, he assembled an enormous quantity of evidence supporting the idea that life has changed, or evolved, over time. Second, he proposed a scientific hypothesis to explain how and why evolution occurs.

Darwin's book caused an immediate sensation. The first printing sold out the day it was released! Some people questioned or rejected Darwin's message. Others found his arguments brilliant. Let's look at what Darwin actually proposed in his book.

☑ **Checkpoint** What were Darwin's findings concerning the birds of the Galapagos Islands? ①

Of Farmers and Pigeons

Darwin began his discussion of evolution not with his discoveries on the Galapagos Islands but with observations made closer to home—observations of farm animals and agricultural crops in England. He knew that over the years, farmers had greatly altered and improved domesticated plants and animals. How did they do it?

No Two Alike

Plant and animal breeders told Darwin that no two individuals among their livestock and crop plants were exactly alike. Some were larger or smaller, heavier or lighter than others of their kind. Some cows and sheep gave more milk than others. Some plants produced larger fruit than others of their kind. Often this variation was inheritable, which means that it could be passed on to the next generation. Farmers told Darwin that although they could not cause this variation, they did know how to use it when they found it.

Artificial Selection

What the farmers did was simple. Looking over their stock, they decided which animals and plants had the characteristics they wanted to use for breeding. The farmers called this process picking, or selection. Generation after

3 TEACH

Ideas Through Images

Have students examine Figure 10–11, read the caption, and answer the following questions.

- **Why do you think these finches have different-shaped beaks?** (Each beak is shaped to help the bird get and eat the kind of food available on its island.)
- **Why do you think each island has different variations of the same kind of bird?** (Each island has a different environment with different plant life, climate, and terrain. Each bird species evolved to live successfully in its environment.)
- **Why do you think these birds caused a sensation in the scientific community in Darwin's time?** (These birds showed that species could become modified from one another, an idea that was exactly the opposite of common beliefs.)

Discussion

Discuss with students how artificial selection relates to genetics. Emphasize the following points in the discussion.

- Variations between animals in the same species occur because of differences in the DNA sequence of different genes. These mutations form different alleles for each gene.
- Artificial selection is the same as selective breeding. Review the processes involved in selective breeding—inbreeding and hybridization.

☑ Checkpoint

① Each island species looked similar to a species on mainland South America. Yet the island species were distinctly different from one another and the mainland species.

TEACHER SUPPORT

Historical Perspective

When Darwin wrote his basic ideas for the theory of evolution in 1844, he realized how controversial they were. Because of this, he did not publish them. However, he continued to develop his theory by making additional observations. Alfred Russell Wallace (1823–1913) was a British naturalist who explored the Amazon and the East Indies, collecting data and observations of the animal species living there. In the 1850s, he independently came up with the same ideas about natural selection as Darwin had. Wallace wrote to Darwin about his ideas, and they jointly published their ideas in a paper in 1858. Then Darwin went ahead and published his book, *The Origin of Species*, in the following year.

Ancillary Support

The resource below can be used to support your teaching strategy for these two pages.

TR Apply: An Early Evolutionist

Investigate

Cooperative Learning Instruct small groups of students to choose a species of organism to study its variations. Students should determine the trait they will study, the method for determining how individuals vary, and a method for recording data. Group members can collect data on their own, then pool their data to make a bar graph showing their results. Encourage students to make inferences about how the variations in the trait they observed might help the organism survive. Invite a member from each group to present its data to the class.

Correcting Misconceptions

Some students might think that only the physically strongest individuals of a species will survive. Give students some examples of conditions that would favor smaller animals, such as when food or water is scarce, when a large number of individuals live in a small area, or when smaller animals are able to escape predators more successfully than larger animals. Then ask students to make inferences about which individual would be more successful in those conditions, the larger individual or the smaller one.

Laboratory Investigation

The Laboratory Investigation, Simulating Natural Selection, on pages 234–235 is appropriate to use at this point in the chapter.

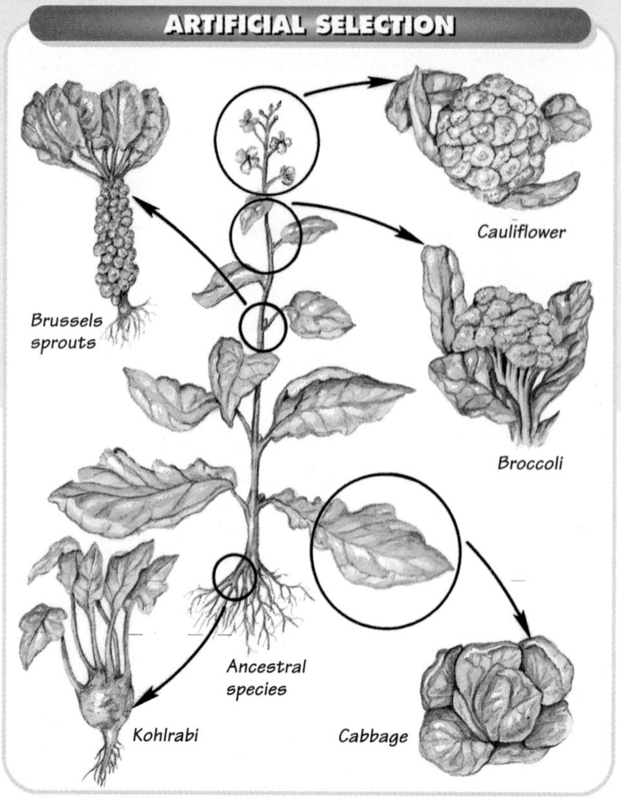

Figure 10–12
The vegetables shown here are the descendants of a single species. They have been produced from generations of artificial selection for leaves (kale), buds (Brussels sprouts and cabbage), flowers and stem (broccoli), stem (kohlrabi), and flower clusters (cauliflower).

generation, the farmers would select only the largest hogs, the fastest horses, or the cows that gave the most milk. **As Darwin put it, nature provided the variation and humans allowed only selected organisms to produce offspring. He called this process artificial selection.** Using **artificial selection** over many years, breeders had produced a wide range of plants and animals that looked very different from their ancestors.

☑ ***Checkpoint*** What is artificial selection? ❶

Selection in Nature

Darwin was convinced that a process such as artificial selection occurred in nature. But how did this process work? His explanation of the process is where Darwin made his greatest contribution.

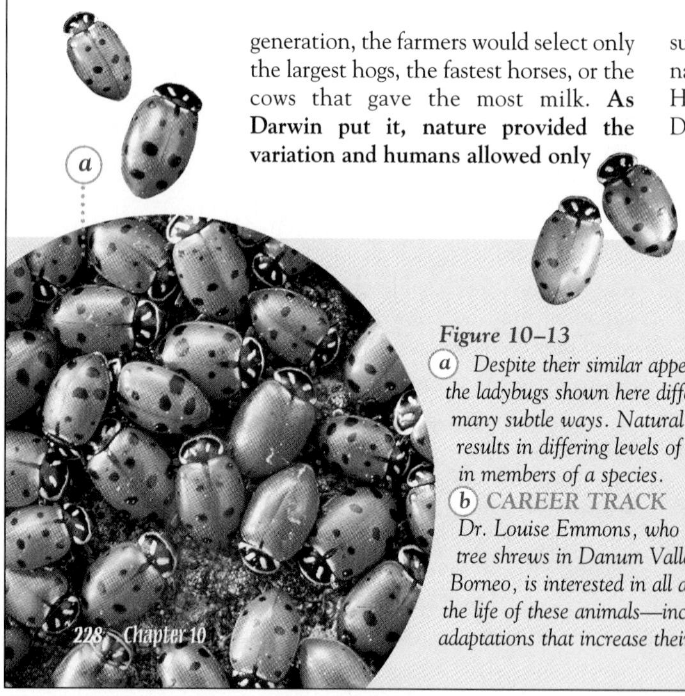

Figure 10–13
(a) *Despite their similar appearance, the ladybugs shown here differ in many subtle ways. Natural variation results in differing levels of fitness in members of a species.*
(b) CAREER TRACK *Zoologist Dr. Louise Emmons, who studies tree shrews in Danum Valley, Sabah Borneo, is interested in all aspects of the life of these animals—including adaptations that increase their fitness.*

TEACHER SUPPORT

Activity

VEGETABLE COMPARISONS

Display whole and cut-up samples of cabbage, kale, Brussels sprouts, broccoli, cauliflower, and kohlrabi. Encourage students to use all of their senses (especially touch, smell, sight, and taste) to compare and contrast the characteristics of each vegetable. Have students use Figure 10–12 as a guide while they examine the vegetables. Challenge them to relate the similarities and differences among the vegetables to the parts of the ancestral plant from which each vegetable was developed. Ask them if kale and cabbage are more similar to each other than are kale and cauliflower. (Kale and cabbage are more similar because they were both developed from leaves of the ancestral plant.)

Variation in Nature

Darwin pointed out that in nature, as in domesticated plants and animals, inheritable variation was common. Today this seems obvious because we can see variation in almost any plant or animal species. In Darwin's time, however, this was a revolutionary statement because living things, as part of creation, were thought to be perfect. Variations were occasional defects and nothing more. Of course, no one knew just yet why variation occurred or even how inheritance worked. Although Gregor Mendel had done work in genetics, his work was not published until 1866, and it was not widely recognized until much later.

Struggle for Existence

Darwin recognized a process in nature that could operate in much the same way as artificial selection did on farms and in fields. It was in this thinking that Darwin made his sharpest break with the past. Instead of calling upon a mysterious force to take the place of the farmer, Darwin searched for a scientific hypothesis to explain selection in nature. Remembering the work of Malthus, Darwin realized that high birth rates and a shortage of life's basic needs forced organisms into a constant struggle for existence. The fastest predators could catch the most prey. Only the best camouflaged, or best protected, prey survived the hunt.

Natural Selection

Here is the heart of Darwin's insight. Because each individual differs from all other members of its species, each has slightly different advantages and disadvantages in the struggle for existence. During that struggle, individuals that are well-suited to their environment will survive and reproduce more often than individuals not well-suited. Because individuals that survive and reproduce are the best-suited, or fittest, this process is called survival of the fittest.

Darwin proposed that generation after generation, the struggle for existence selects the fittest individuals to survive in nature. Darwin called this process **natural selection.** Natural selection explains how over time, species become better suited to their environment as they respond to various selection pressures. Thus, natural selection explains the riddles of adaptation and fitness.

☑ *Checkpoint* How do artificial selection and natural selection differ? 2

MINI LAB ········ Interpreting ········

The Tall and Short of It

PROBLEM *How does height vary in a small human population? **Interpret data** to answer this question.*

PROCEDURE

1. Working with a partner, use a meterstick to measure your partner's height to the nearest centimeter. Record this information.
2. Reverse roles with your partner and repeat step 1.
3. Obtain the heights of all class members. Then construct a data table that contains 3-cm ranges from the smallest height recorded to the tallest height recorded. For example, if you had a 152- to 155-cm range, a person who is 154 cm tall would fit into this range.
4. Record the number of students who fall within each height range.
5. Plot the number of students within a height range as a function of height.

ANALYZE AND CONCLUDE

1. What is the range of heights and the average height?
2. Why do you think there is a variation in height?
3. How can you interpret the shape of the graph?
4. Are there any selective advantages to being very tall or very short?

MINI LAB Interpreting

Teacher Notes

• For time required and materials needed, see page 218b.

• Students may construct either bar graphs or line graphs. All graphs should have height on the X axis and number of students on the Y axis.

Answers to Analyze and Conclude

1. Answers will depend on the variation of the class.

2. Some students might mention environmental influences. Others might describe a genetic basis.

3. The shape of the graph is determined by the number of people having a certain height. The highest point of the graph indicates the most common height among students.

4. In modern human populations, there is probably no selective advantage to being tall or short.

Skills Trace

Interpreting

Focus p. 229
Practice p. 231
Assess p. 238

☑ Checkpoints

1 The process of choosing animals or plants with the desired characteristics to produce offspring.

2 In natural selection, selection pressures in the environment determine which organisms will survive and produce offspring. In artificial selection, people make that choice.

TEACHER SUPPORT

Managing Classroom Diversity

TECH PREP STUDENTS

Point out to students that Darwin could very easily have dismissed all of his observations, or simply attributed them to a mysterious force or a deity. However, he trusted his observations and tried to find a scientific explanation for them. Encourage students to learn about the role that observation plays in their career area of interest. Have them prepare a poster or other visual that summarizes the role of observation in a method or process commonly used in their field of interest.

Ancillary Support

The resource below can be used to support your teaching strategy for these two pages.

BL Inquiry Activity: Survival of the Fittest

Problem Solving

Interpreting Graphs

What's So Different About Pill Bugs and Cattails?

Students will use their knowledge of species variation and natural selection to interpret data collected from two different species.

State The problem is to determine whether a similar pattern of variation exists in two species and, if so, to determine how this pattern relates to natural selection.

Solve Students can solve the problem by plotting the two sets of data. The pattern common to both is the bell-shaped curve.

Test To test whether species variation for any characteristic follows a bell curve, students can collect data for another trait from any organism and plot their data on a graph.

Communicate Invite student volunteers to present their graphs to the class. As a class, discuss the pattern common to both graphs. Ask students to suggest what the implications might be for such a distribution pattern of traits within a population with respect to natural selection.

Answers to THINK ABOUT IT

1. Both graphs have a bell-shaped curve.

2. The most common variation in a population is the one that makes individuals best suited to live in the environment. If selection pressures change, individuals with different variations may become better suited, and the number of individuals with a certain variation will change.

3. Over time, the number of medium-size and large-size pillbugs in the population will decrease, and the number of small pillbugs will increase. If pillbugs could reproduce when only 4 mm long, then the medium-size and large-size pillbugs could reproduce before the predator caught them, and there would be no change in the distribution of size within the population.

Problem Solving

INTERPRETING GRAPHS

What's So Different About Pill Bugs and Cattails?

John and Sasha's teacher asked them if all living things of the same species were exactly the same. "Of course not," they said. So their teacher asked them to pick a species and then choose a characteristic of that species to study. She asked them to collect data as evidence to share with their class.

John went to a wooded area and lifted a rotting log from the forest floor. Tiny pill bugs dashed to and fro. He collected about 50 pill bugs, placed them in a jar, and brought them back to his classroom. There he fed and observed them until he was sure they were fully grown. Then he measured their body length.

Sasha walked to a pond and noticed that many cattails were growing near the edge of the water. Her teacher told her that the cattails were fully grown at that time of year. Sasha measured their long brown combs.

John's and Sasha's data are shown in the data table. Plot each data set to see whether they share any common features.

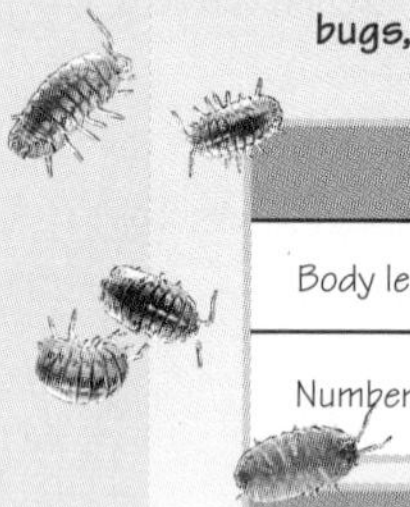

Pill Bug Measurements

Body length (in mm)	4	5	6	7	8	9	10	11	12
Number of pill bugs	3	4	5	8	10	9	6	4	1

Cattail Comb Measurements

Length of comb (in cm)	21	22	23	24	25	26	27	28	29	30	31	32	33
Number of combs	1	1	2	3	5	7	8	6	4	3	2	2	1

THINK ABOUT IT

1. Compare the pill bug and cattail graphs. Describe the pattern common to both graphs.
2. What is the significance of this pattern with respect to the process of natural selection?
3. A new predator that eats pill bugs has emigrated to the forest. This predator's vision allows it to see only medium-sized and large-sized pill bugs. If pill bugs do not reproduce until they are fully grown, what changes might take place (over many generations) in the population of pill bugs? Predict what would happen if the pill bugs were able to reproduce when they were only 4 mm in length.

TEACHER SUPPORT

Managing Classroom Diversity

AT-RISK STUDENTS

Some students may require extra help with the math terms and procedures used in this graphing exercise. You might ask these students to give you the range for each data set and to calculate the average for each. Have students compare the graph from the MINI LAB on page 229 with the graphs from Problem Solving. Explain that a graph with a bell curve is a typical pattern seen in a population of individuals. Point out how the average is close to the highest point of the curve, but the average is not necessarily the midpoint of the range.

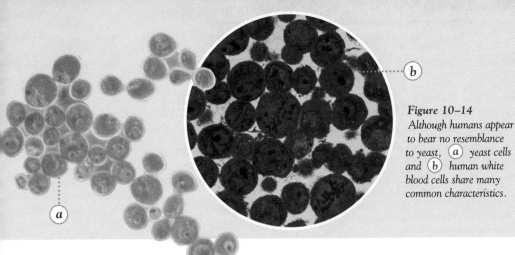

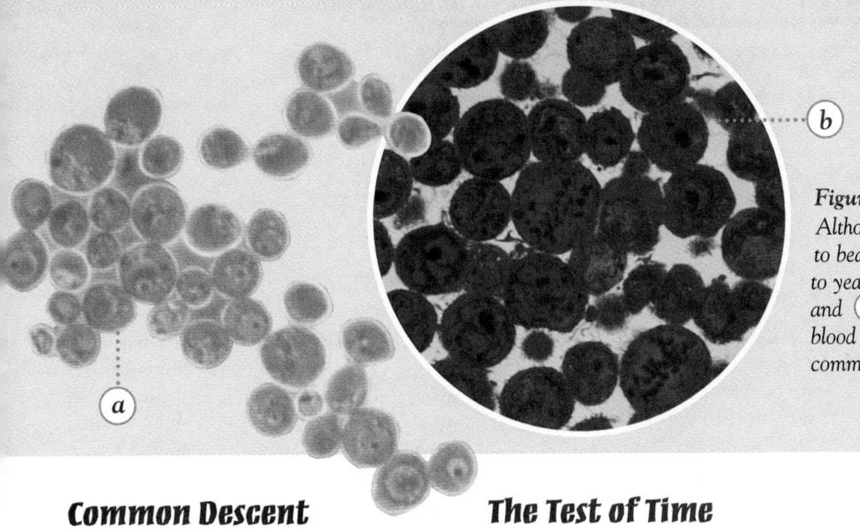

Figure 10–14
Although humans appear to bear no resemblance to yeast, (a) yeast cells and (b) human white blood cells share many common characteristics.

Common Descent

Finally, Darwin argued that living species were not spontaneously produced as we know them. Instead, modern organisms have been produced through a long, slow process of evolutionary change. Darwin further argued that just as each living organism is the descendant of its parents and grandparents, each living species has descended from other species over time.

Look back in time, and you will find ancestors that were common to humans and monkeys. Look farther back, and you will find ancestors that were common to humans, alligators, and fishes. And if you could look even farther back, you would find that all living things share common ancestors. Therefore, this principle is called **common descent.**

The Test of Time

Today, more than a century after Darwin, the overwhelming scientific evidence has caused virtually all scientists to agree that life has evolved. Evolutionary change is undeniable from a scientific perspective. Explaining how and why evolution occurs, however, is much more difficult. Evolution by natural selection has, over time, grown into an enormous collection of carefully reasoned and tested hypotheses.

As you will learn in the next chapter, a new generation of experiments and observations is supplying even more evidence that evolution has occurred in the past and is continuing, day by day, in the natural world around us. These experiments and observations reinforce the power and beauty of Darwin's insight.

Section Review 10–2

1. **Describe** artificial selection. Explain why it is practiced.
2. **Explain** evolution by natural selection.
3. **Critical Thinking—Analyzing and Evaluating** What are the key elements of Darwin's explanation of evolution? Can they be verified experimentally?
4. **MINI LAB** How does height vary in a small human population? **Interpret data** to answer this question.

Investigate

Research Have students choose an organism and determine the ancestors from which it evolved. Challenge students to find out how the organism and its ancestors responded to changes in the environment as it evolved. Invite students to present their findings to the class.

4 ASSESS

Quick Check

Ask students to make a chart in which they list the similarities and differences between natural selection and artificial selection and give one example of each.

Section Review 10–2

1. In artificial selection, people select to breed only the organisms with the characteristics they want. In this way they can improve and change domesticated plants and animals to suit their needs.

2. Individuals who are well suited to the environment will survive and reproduce more often than individuals who are not well suited. Over time the species will evolve to look more like the well-suited individuals. Adaptation and fitness are the underlying processes of natural selection. Individuals with certain adaptations are better suited to their environment and are more likely to survive and produce more offspring.

3. The key elements are variations in traits, adaptation, fitness, natural selection, and common descent. These elements have been observed and tested experimentally in the past and continue to be tested.

4. Students should refer to their data from the MINI LAB on page 229 and describe the range of heights and average height of students in their class, and note that the range of variation, when graphed, forms a bell curve.

Skills Trace

Interpreting

- Focus p. 229
- Practice p. 231
- Assess p. 238

Learning Modality

Auditory Learning Instruct one student in each student pair to explain evolution and natural selection in his or her own words. Have each partner record the explanation, and then give his or her own explanation of evolution, filling in any details the first partner might have missed. Then have pairs repeat the procedure, incorporating the terms fitness, adaptation, and variation in their explanations.

Section 10-3
Darwin's Revolution

Performance Objective
• Explain why evolution is important to the study of biology.

Mini Lab Skill: Inferring

1 ENGAGE

Ideas Through Images
Have students examine Figure 10–15, read the caption, and answer the following questions.

• **Which animals of those shown are probably more closely related?** (The giant weevil and the butterfly are more closely related.)

• **Which animals were probably the first to split away, or evolve different adaptations, from the common ancestor?** (The lions, because they have more differences in adaptations than the two insects—the weevil and the butterfly.)

2 EXPLORE

Inquiry Activity
Predicting

Evolution in Progress

Ask students to predict how an organism will change in the next 1000 years. Have students choose any organism to show how it might evolve in response to its environment. Students should draw pictures of the organism in different stages of its evolution and give reasons for the changes.

INTEGRATING BIOLOGY AND SOCIETY

People should use antibiotics for the entire prescribed course, and use both antibiotics and pesticides sparingly.

SECTION 10–3 BRANCHING OUT In Depth

Darwin's Revolution

Guide for Reading

• **Discuss** the importance of evolution in the study of biology.

MINI LAB

• **Make an inference** about selection pressure and adaptation in peppered moths from population data.

EVOLUTION IS CONTROVERSIAL enough in certain circles that some people wonder why biologists insist on teaching it. The answer is simple. Evolution is the most powerful general statement ever made about living things.

Figure 10–15 Despite obvious differences, all living things—from (a) giant weevil beetles to (b) morpho butterflies to (c) lions—share ancestors and are linked by the underlying thread of evolution.

Evolution

Evolution provides a single common language that enables biologists in all fields to share information with one another. Why is it that researchers can learn about human DNA by studying the genes of yeasts? Because humans and yeasts share common ancestors—and a surprising number of genes! Why is it so important to preserve endangered species? Because each living species has been produced by millions of years of evolution and may contain irreplaceable knowledge about how life works. **Quite simply, evolution provides a unifying principle that underlies all of biology—from the micro level of molecular genetics to the macro level of global ecology.**

The body of powerful and complex scientific thought that has built on the concept of evolution is constantly changing. Some of Darwin's original ideas have proved to be right on target. Others have been revised. But revision does not mean that evolutionary change itself is in question or that evolutionary concepts are a collection of vague guesses.

By comparison, consider that physicists still do not understand how gravity works, despite the fact that no one doubts

TEACHER SUPPORT

Ecology Note

Evolution provides the basis for discussing relationships between living things and their environments. Ecology provides the terminology and the examples for discussing how living things change over time. A common topic in ecology is the balance of nature, or the stability of a population of organisms within a community. The stability of a population depends on the fitness, adaptations, and genetic diversity of the population in relation to the competition for resources, predators, and disease and parasites. If this balance is ever disrupted by a climatic change or by human action, the survival of a species is put at risk. Whether or not the species survives depends on the genetic diversity, fitness, and adaptations of the individuals in the population that will enable the species to evolve successfully.

the existence of this powerful force. There is no doubt that if you jump up into the air, you will end up on the ground below. It makes no difference whether you understand or even believe in gravity. What goes up must come down. Just as definitely, life on Earth has evolved and is continuing to evolve all around us all the time.

Life in Constant Motion

One of the most powerful predictions concerning evolution is that under certain circumstances life may be constantly changing. If enough variation exists in a species and if environmental conditions change, the species will evolve. One of the first examples to be documented of evolution in progress was a fascinating color change in peppered moths in England around 1760.

The idea of changing species also helps explain why disease-causing bacteria become resistant to every antibiotic that is used against them and why crop-damaging insects become resistant to pesticides. Concepts about evolution also set the stage for understanding that variety is indeed the spice of life! For most organisms, inheritable variation is essential to species survival.

INTEGRATING BIOLOGY AND SOCIETY

How can we slow the rate of development of antibiotic-resistant bacteria and pesticide-resistant insects?

MINI LAB ········ Inferring ········

Now You See Me, Now You Don't

PROBLEM *What can you* ***infer*** *about selection pressure and adaptation in peppered moths from population data?*

PROCEDURE

Graph the data presented in the data table.

ANALYZE AND CONCLUDE

1. What has happened to the population of light-colored moths over the course of the study? Dark-colored moths?
2. What do you think caused these changes?
3. What is the adaptation in this species? What is the selection pressure in this study?

Year	Light-Colored Moths	Dark-Colored Moths
1	537	112
2	484	198
3	392	210
4	246	281
5	225	357
6	193	412
7	147	503
8	84	594
9	56	638
10	38	673

Section Review 10-3

1. **Discuss** the importance of evolution in the study of biology.
2. **Examine** evolution in action.
3. **MINI LAB** What can you **infer** from population data about the selection pressure and adaptation in peppered moths?
4. **BRANCHING OUT ACTIVITY** Find out how the overuse of antibiotics can cause bacteria to become drug resistant. **Write** a short report on your findings.

3 TEACH

MINI LAB Inferring

Teacher Note

• For time required and materials needed, see page 218b.

Answers to Analyze and Conclude

1. Light-colored moths decreased; dark-colored moths increased.
2. A change in the environment made light-colored moths easier for predators to see and dark-colored moths more difficult to see.
3. The adaptation is their protective coloration; the selective pressure is predation.

Skills Trace
Inferring
- Focus p. 233
- Practice p. 233
- Assess p. 239

4 ASSESS

Quick Check

Ask students to write a description of a species evolving in response to selection pressures.

Section Review 10-3

1. See page 232.
2. Students should summarize one of the two examples on page 233.
3. Changes in the environment caused predators, the selection pressure, to find light-colored moths more easily than dark-colored moths, causing the color of moths in the population, the adaptation, to change over time.

Skills Trace
Inferring
- Focus p. 233
- Practice p. 233
- Assess p. 239

4. Students should find that overusing antibiotics actually selects for resistant bacteria, especially when antibiotics are prescribed too frequently or not taken properly.

Learning Modality

Visual Learning Have students create a flowchart to summarize the evolution of peppered moths from light-colored to dark-colored.

Ancillary Support

The resources below can be used to support your teaching strategy for these two pages.

TR Explore: Evolution—What's in a Word?
BL Inquiry Activity: Horsing Around With Evolution

CHAPTER 10

Laboratory Investigation

Simulating Natural Selection

Before the Lab

1. At least one day prior to the laboratory investigation, find paper or cloth of various colors and patterns to cover a lab table for each group of four.
2. Cut enough 3-cm by 3-cm squares from colored paper for each group to have ten squares of each color.
3. Have available additional colored paper and scissors so that students can cut more squares when they get to step 7.

Pre-Lab Discussion

Have students read the entire procedure for this investigation. Then ask students the following questions.

What is the purpose of this investigation? (To model the process of natural selection.)

Why do you think it is important for the "predators" to keep their backs to the table while the gamekeeper sets up the game? (It prevents the "predators" from studying the positions of the colored squares and forces them to choose only the colored squares that are most prominent to them when they turn around.)

What results do you expect to observe? (Some students might expect that the colored squares that are most in contrast to the table cover color will be "preyed" on first, resulting in the dominance of the colored squares that match the color of the cloth.)

Skills Development

Students will use these skills while completing the laboratory investigation: modeling, observing, communicating, inferring, and drawing conclusions.

Laboratory Investigation

Simulating Natural Selection

Natural selection can be observed in nature. However, studying selection in nature takes a very long time. In this laboratory investigation, you will play a game that will simulate natural selection.

Problem

How can you **construct a model** for the process of natural selection?

Materials (per group)

paper or cloth to cover lab table

10 paper squares of each of the following 10 colors: brown, green, yellow, gray, black, white, blue, purple, violet, and red

additional paper squares as needed

Procedure

1. **Working in groups of 4, spread your cloth "habitat" on your lab table and obtain 10 paper squares of each of the 10 colors.**
2. **Have 1 person of your group act as the gamekeeper and the other 3 as the predators.**
3. **While the predators have their backs turned to the habitat, have the gamekeeper distribute the square pieces of colored paper, which represent the prey, on the table. The pieces must be randomly placed and must not overlap or hide other pieces.**
4. **When the gamekeeper says "Go!" the predators should turn around, face the habitat, and quickly pick up the first piece of paper they see, then turn their backs again.**
5. **Repeat step 4 until there are only 10 prey remaining in the habitat.**
6. **Count the number of "survivors" of each color. Record these numbers.**
7. **Allow each "survivor" to reproduce by adding 9 more pieces of the same color.**
8. **Repeat steps 2 to 7 until each person in the group has had a turn being the gamekeeper.**

Teaching Strategies

1. You might wish to give groups different colors of cloth or paper to cover their table. Try both solid colors and prints.
2. Stress the importance of "predators" keeping their backs to the table, then quickly turning and picking up a square.

Observations

1. Construct a graph that shows the results of the simulation. The graph should include the original populations and the survivors at the end of each round.
2. How long did it take for any color to become extinct?
3. How long did it take for any color to become dominant (more than 50 percent of total)?

Analysis and Conclusions

1. What represents the selection pressure in this game?
2. What is the adaptation mechanism of the prey?
3. Does one color eventually become dominant? Why does this happen?

More to Explore

Design an experiment in which survival depends on escaping predators that must "feel" for their prey because the predators are blind. What kinds of variations in the prey will be significant for natural selection?

Answers to Observations

1. Student graphs should show the number of each color on the Y axis and the number of rounds on the X axis. A line graph with a different line for each color will best represent these data.
2. Some colors can become extinct after the fourth round.
3. For any color to exceed 50 percent of the total population would take at least until the end of the twenty-seventh round.

Answers to Analysis and Conclusions

1. The "predators" represent the selection pressure.
2. The adaptation mechanism of the prey is protective coloration.
3. In most cases, one color will eventually become dominant because it blends in most successfully with the table cover color, making it more difficult for a predator to see.

More to Explore

One possible experiment students might design is setting up a game in which squares of cloth with different textures are placed randomly on a cloth that has the same texture as one of the squares. The game could be played in the same way except that the "predators" are blindfolded and sit at the table with their hands in their laps until the gamekeeper says "Go!"

CHAPTER 10

Study Guide

Review Strategy

Solicit from the class different words and terms that are used in this chapter. Examples include fitness, adaptation, selection, and diversity. Write these words on the chalkboard, generating a list of at least ten words. Then divide the class into pairs. Have each pair play a word association game in which one partner says one of the words on the class list and the other partner responds by giving another word that means the same thing or is an example of the word. After doing half of the words on the list, partners should switch roles.

Study Guide

Summarizing Key Concepts

The key concepts in each section of this chapter are listed below to help you review the chapter content. Make sure you understand each concept and its relationship to other concepts and to the theme of this chapter.

10–1 A Riddle: Life's Diversity and Connections

- The variety of living things is called living diversity.
- Fossil diversity is the variety of the fossilized remains of creatures that lived long ago.
- Adaptations are physical and behavioral traits that enable organisms to survive.
- Fitness is the ability of an individual to survive and reproduce.

10–2 Darwin's Solution

- Artificial selection is a process used by breeders to produce a wide range of plants and animals that are functionally different from their ancestors.
- The struggle for existence and the survival of the fittest serve to select organisms for survival in nature. This is called natural selection.
- The principle of common descent states that each living species has descended from other species over time.

10–3 Darwin's Revolution

- Evolution provides a unifying principle that underlies all of biology—from the micro level of molecular genetics to the macro level of global ecology.
- A color change evolved by peppered moths in response to a change in their environment is a modern example of evolution at work.

Reviewing Key Terms

Review the following vocabulary terms and their meaning. Then use each term in a complete sentence.

10–1 A Riddle: Life's Diversity and Connections

evolution
fossil
adaptation
fitness
homologous structure
vestigial organ

10–2 Darwin's Solution

artificial selection
natural selection
common descent

Inquiry-Based Strategy

Arctic hares are white in the winter and turn brown in the spring. Cottontail rabbits also live in climates where there is snow in winter, but they remain brown all winter long. Ask students to determine what selection pressures have selected for white arctic hares and brown cottontail rabbits in winter. Encourage students to conduct any research they feel is required to answer this question. Students may approach the answer in a variety of ways. Some students might look at the climate of both rabbits and the amount of vegetation in their environments. Other students might look at the predators in the environment of each or the number of offspring produced by both.

CHAPTER 10

Recalling Main Ideas

Choose the letter of the answer that best completes the statement or answers the question.

1. The collection of facts, observations, and hypotheses about the history of life is called
   a. survival of the fittest.
   b. adaptation.
   c. evolutionary theory.
   d. artificial selection.
2. Charles Darwin was unaware of the works of
   a. Malthus.
   b. Lyell.
   c. Mendel.
   d. Wallace.
3. Which of the following puzzled Darwin the least?
   a. diversity in living things
   b. adaptation of organisms to their environment
   c. fossils of strange creatures
   d. similarities among organisms
4. During Darwin's time, many people believed that the
   a. Earth constantly changed.
   b. Earth and its organisms did not change.
   c. Earth was hundreds of millions of years old.
   d. living things on Earth changed gradually.
5. Vestigial structures in organisms
   a. look the same.
   b. perform the same function.
   c. serve little or no apparent function.
   d. develop from the same embryonic tissues.
6. Farmers improve domestic plants and animals by
   a. providing proper nutrients.
   b. selective breeding.
   c. common descent.
   d. survival of the fittest.
7. Darwin proposed that natural selection occurs because of
   a. natural variation.
   b. the struggle for existence.
   c. the survival of the fittest.
   d. all of the above.
8. The principle that states that all living things share common ancestors is called
   a. common descent.
   b. natural selection.
   c. artificial selection.
   d. adaptive radiation.

Putting It All Together

Using the information on pages xxx to xxxi, complete the following concept map.

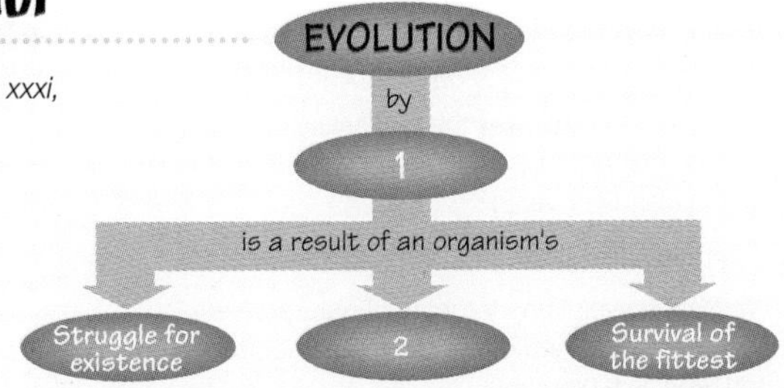

Putting It All Together

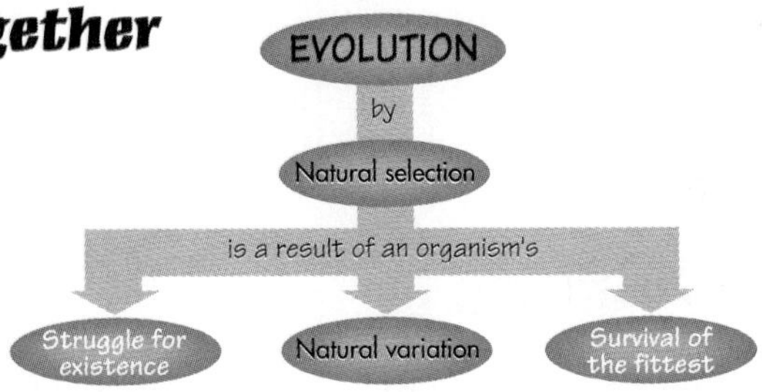

Recalling Main Ideas

1. c
2. c
3. d
4. b
5. c
6. b
7. d
8. a

Assessment

Reviewing What You Learned

1. Evolution is the process by which living things change over time.
2. Scientists estimate that 99.9 percent of all species that have ever lived on Earth are extinct.
3. Generation after generation, the struggle for existence selects the fittest individuals to survive in nature.
4. Possible examples include the forearm of a human and a bat wing.
5. Vestigial organs are structures that have little or no obvious purpose in an organism.
6. Natural history is the study of Earth and its living things.
7. Fitness is the ability of an individual to survive and reproduce.
8. All living things share common ancestors.
9. Wallace was a naturalist who independently came up with the same ideas as Darwin, prompting Darwin to publish his work.
10. Possible examples include hair color, skin color, eye color, and height.

Expanding the Concepts

1. Adaptations are the physical characteristics and behaviors that help an organism catch food, reproduce, withstand harsh conditions, and avoid predators, thus helping the species to survive.
2. The organisms from the Galapagos Islands were very closely related; however, they had specific adaptations that enabled them to survive in the specific, isolated environment of each island.

Assessment (continued)

3. Charles Lyell's arguments that scientists must explain the past in terms of observable events and processes led Darwin to search for a scientific hypothesis to explain selection in nature. The ideas of Malthus made Darwin realize that high birth rates and a shortage of life's basic needs forced organisms into a constant struggle for existence.

4. Similarities among species that have been isolated for a long time indicate that the species descended or evolved from a common ancestor.

Skills Trace
Interpreting

- Focus p. 229
- Practice p. 231
- Assess p. 238

5. In artificial selection, people select to breed organisms with certain desired traits. In natural selection, organisms with adaptations that are best suited to their environment will survive and produce more offspring.

6. The theory of natural selection helps tie together all concepts in biology, such as DNA and the inheritance of traits, and food chains and an organism's role in its habitat.

7. The peppered moths evolved in certain areas of England from being light-colored to dark-colored in response to their visibility to predators. The moths were a clear demonstration of the process of natural selection.

8. Beak shapes and sizes are adaptations to the kind of food that is available on each island. Each island has different food sources available, and birds living on each island evolved a beak shape to help them get that food most efficiently.

9. Variations in traits are encoded in the DNA of an organism. In the process of natural selection, the variations that make an individual best suited to its environment are selected. Different variations are best for different environments, thus accounting for the great diversity of life.

Assessment

Reviewing What You Learned

Answer each of the following in a complete sentence.

1. What is evolution?
2. Of all the species that have lived on Earth, what percentage are now extinct?
3. State Darwin's theory of natural selection.
4. Give examples of two or more homologous structures.
5. What are vestigial organs?
6. What is meant by natural history?
7. In the context of the survival of a species, what did Darwin mean by the term fitness?
8. What is the principle of common descent?
9. Who was Alfred Russel Wallace and what role did he play in the publication of Darwin's findings?
10. Give an example of an inheritable variation in humans.

Expanding the Concepts

Discuss each of the following in a brief paragraph.

1. What is the role of adaptation in a species' survival?
2. How did the organisms that Darwin observed on the Galapagos Islands help him to formulate his theory of natural selection?
3. What impact did the works of Charles Lyell and Thomas Malthus have on Darwin's thinking?
4. How can you **interpret** the similarities among species that have been geographically isolated for thousands of years?
5. Compare artificial selection and natural selection.
6. Why is the evolutionary theory of natural selection considered one of the ten most important concepts in biology?
7. Why is the peppered moth example often termed "Darwinism in Action"?
8. Why do the birds of the Galapagos Islands demonstrate a great diversity of beak shapes and sizes?
9. If all living things are controlled by DNA, how does evolution account for the great diversity of life?
10. Generally, only a few of the many offspring produced in the reproductive cycle of an organism survive. What happens to the other offspring? Relate your answer to the theory of natural selection.

238 *Chapter 10*

10. The other offspring are either caught by predators or do not survive to adulthood because of environmental conditions. These offspring did not have adaptations that made them fit to survive in the environment.

Extending Your Thinking

1. Students' time lines should incorporate at least the following dates and events: December 1831, the HMS *Beagle* left England. In 1836, Darwin returned home from the voyage. In 1844, Darwin first wrote down most of his ideas about how evolution worked. In 1859, Darwin published *The Origin of Species*.

2. Island environments are isolated from any other environment, so the species of organisms living on the island must adapt quickly to the environment on the island, or they will not survive.

Skills Trace
Inferring

- Focus p. 233
- Practice p. 233
- Assess p. 239

Extending Your Thinking

Use the skills you have developed in this chapter to answer the following.

1. **Sequencing** Develop a time line of important events for Darwin, beginning with the voyage of the *Beagle* and ending with his publication of *The Origin of Species by Means of Natural Selection.*
2. **Inferring** Explain why the study of life on islands usually demonstrates great living diversity and rapidly evolving species.
3. **Evaluating** Discuss the concept that adaptation on the organism's part is not an active process but a passive one. Use specific examples in your discussion.
4. **Constructing a model** Construct a model to simulate natural selection.
5. **Evaluating** Discuss how sudden changes in the environment—such as the release of radioactivity in the Chernobyl disaster—set evolution in motion.

Applying Your Skills

A Survival Scenario

Adaptations are inherited physical and behavioral traits that enable an organism to survive in its environment. What if an organism's environment were to suddenly change or be disrupted? Would the organism be able to survive?

1. Select an adaptive trait of an animal or plant and write a scenario describing how the trait might have evolved.
2. Write a second scenario reflecting the work of Malthus or Wallace.

• GOING FURTHER •

3. Have other students read the scenarios and identify the theory upon which each one is based.

3. An organism is born with a particular set of adaptations that it inherited from its parents. Whether or not the organism survives depends on how its adaptations make it suited to live in the environment. If the environment changes, as happened to peppered moths, the organism's adaptations may make it more vulnerable to predators in the new environment—just as light-colored moths became less protected from predators than the dark-colored moths in the changing environment.
4. A likely model students will describe is the process used in the Laboratory Investigation to model natural selection.

5. Sudden changes in the environment change the selection pressures on the populations of organisms. Many individuals immediately die off, leaving the organisms with adaptations that make them better suited to live in the changing environment. These remaining organisms evolve to replace the organisms that did not survive.

Applying Your Skills

Teacher Notes

- You may wish to have students work on their scenarios individually, or divide students into cooperative groups of two or three.
- Encourage students to research various organisms to find a trait that shows a unique adaptation.

Answers

1. Students should describe the adaptation and give a logical explanation about how it might have occurred, taking into account possible changes in the organism's environment.
2. Students should use the same adaptation as the one used to write the first scenario. Wallace, like Darwin, described a theory of evolution based on natural selection and the survival of the fittest. Malthus suggested that human populations would be limited by war, famine, and disease.
3. Student responses will be based on the scenarios they read. They should identify the scenarios as being based on the theories of Darwin, Wallace, or Malthus.

Scoring Rubric

4 Response is thorough, accurate, and creative; shows an in-depth understanding of science skills, procedures, and concepts.

3 Response is complete, mostly accurate, and original; shows a satisfactory understanding of science skills, procedures, and concepts.

2 Response is mostly complete but includes some inaccuracies; shows an adequate understanding of science skills, procedures, and concepts.

1 Response is only partially complete and has many inaccuracies; shows an incomplete understanding of science skills, procedures, and concepts.

0 Response is mostly incomplete and/or inaccurate; shows a lack of understanding of science skills, procedures, and concepts.

Chapter 11 The Mechanisms of Evolution

Content Management	Student Edition Activities
■ Section 11–1 Darwin "Meets" DNA, pp. 241–245 How Does Variation Arise? Inheritable Variation Genes, Fitness, and Adaptation	MINI LAB: It's All Relative to Broccoli, p. 244
■ Section 11–2 Evolution as Genetic Change, pp. 246–252 Evolution—Genetically Defined Natural Selection on Single-Gene Traits Natural Selection on Polygenic Traits The Role of Chance The Birth of New Species The Pace of Evolution	Laboratory Investigation: Mutations in Bacteria, pp. 256–257 MINI LAB: Catch the Drift, p. 252
◆ BRANCHING OUT • In Action Section 11–3 How Species Change, pp. 253–255 Darwin's Finches A Galapagos Study	

■ These sections cover all the necessary content and concepts for a basic course in biology.
◆ This section covers content and concepts that are either applications or extensions of the basic material.

Integration Strategies

SE Math, p. 244

Assessment Strategies

SE Chapter Review, pp. 258–261
TR Section Reviews
Chapter Test
BL Chapter Review
Practice Test
CTB Chapter 11 Test

Tech Prep

A teaching strategy appropriate for students who are in technical/vocational programs or who are considering post-secondary technical education can be found on the following **TE** page: 254.

Meeting the Standards

Sections 11–1 through 11–3 cover two of the three content standards under **The Molecular Basis of Heredity,** two of the five content standards under **Biological Evolution,** and one of the four content standards under **The Behavior of Organisms** as described on pages 185 and 187 of The National Science Education Standards.

Chapter Planning Guide

Teacher's Edition Activities	Other Activities	Media and Technology
Chapter Discovery Learning Activity, p. 240 **Inquiry Activity:** Causes of Variation, p. 241 **Investigate:** Research, p. 242 **Investigate:** Model Building, p. 243	**LM** Measuring Variation Within a Population, #21 Observing the Effect of Environment on Seedling Growth, #22 **TR** **Apply:** Designer Organism **BL** **Inquiry Activity:** What Darwin Didn't Know	
Activity: Diagramming Evolution, p. 246 **Inquiry Activity:** Evolution and Genetics, p. 247 **Investigate:** Cooperative Learning, p. 248 **Investigate:** Model Building, p. 248	**TR** **Enrich:** Laying Down the Law **BL** **Inquiry Activity:** Determining Frequency	**TB** Natural Selection on Normal Distributions, #14
Inquiry Activity: Form Follows Function, p. 253 **Investigate:** Research, p. 254 **Investigate:** Role-Playing, p. 254	**TR** **Writing in Biology:** Making Sense of Change **Explore:** Get a Grip **BL** **Inquiry Activity:** Looking for Natural Selection	

KEY: **SE** Student Edition **TE** Teacher's Edition **LM** Laboratory Manual **TR** Teaching Resources **BL** BioLog **TB** Transparency Box **CTB** Computer Test Bank

Materials List

TE Chapter Discovery Learning Activity, p. 240 (20 minutes); photographs of monarch and viceroy butterflies.

TE Investigate: Model Building, p. 243 (20–30 minutes); 100 or more beads of various colors, graph paper.

SE MINI LAB: It's All Relative to Broccoli, p. 244 (30 minutes); several examples of *Brassica* plants such as kale, cauliflower, kohlrabi, cabbage, rutabaga, turnips, Brussels sprouts, and broccoli.

TE Inquiry Activity: Evolution and Genetics, p. 247 (20–30 minutes); similar objects of different colors such as beads, buttons, or toothpicks.

TE Investigate: Model Building, p. 248 (15–20 minutes); graph paper.

SE MINI LAB: Catch the Drift, p. 252 (15–20 minutes); container with 10 types of beans and 10 beans of each type such as pinto, kidney, black, garbanzo, navy, white, lima, black-eyed peas, green peas, and lentils.

TE Inquiry Activity: Form Follows Function, p. 253 (15 minutes); photographs or drawings of several different species of Darwin's finches.

Chapter 11

The Mechanisms of Evolution

Introducing the Chapter

. . . In Pictures

Poison dart frogs' common name comes from the practice of South American rain forest hunters' tipping their darts with the poison from some species. Have students examine the photograph and read the caption. Then ask the following questions.

- **Why do you think some of the frogs are very brightly colored? How could it improve their fitness?** (Their bright colors serve as a warning to predators. Predators learn to avoid these frogs because they are poisonous.)
- **What might cause the differences among the frogs?** (The interaction between their genotypes and their environment.)

Explain that in this chapter students will study the role of genetics in the evolution of a species.

Teaching Strategy

In the first two sections of this chapter, students will learn that genes cause the variation in species on which natural selection acts and that mechanisms, such as natural selection and genetic drift, cause the evolution of new species. In the BRANCHING OUT section, students can study an example of speciation.

CHAPTER 11

The Mechanisms of Evolution

FOCUSING THE CHAPTER THEME: *Patterns of Change*

11–1 Darwin "Meets" DNA
- Examine Darwin's concepts of evolution in genetic terms.
- Compare natural variation produced by single-gene and polygenic traits.

11–2 Evolution as Genetic Change
- Discuss patterns of evolution.
- Describe the process of speciation.

BRANCHING OUT *In Action*

11–3 How Species Change
- Describe how natural selection can lead to the formation of new species.

Laboratory Investigation
- Formulate a hypothesis to explain drug resistance in bacteria.

Biology and Your World

BIO JOURNAL

Look at old photograph albums showing a family—siblings, parents, uncles, aunts, and grandparents—at various times in their lives. In your journal, write about the similarities you observed and share your thoughts on why you think the similarities range from significant to none.

Variation in poison dart frogs, Panama

240 Chapter 11

BIO JOURNAL

Have students consider the amount of variation in traits among the family members. Review how traits are inherited. Encourage students to relate this to the variations in phenotypes they observe in the family pictures. Then challenge students to describe the evolutionary importance of this variation. Instruct students to keep their entries in their portfolios.

TEACHER SUPPORT — Chapter Discovery Learning Activity

Display photographs of monarch and viceroy butterflies for students to study and compare. Explain that birds do not like the taste of monarch butterflies. Then ask students to explain why they think the butterflies look so similar. (The viceroy is protected from predators because it looks like the monarch, which predators avoid.) Challenge students to infer what might happen to viceroy butterflies if a mutation caused monarch butterflies to have white spots instead of orange. Then ask if they would expect the same outcome if viceroy butterflies had the white mutation. Encourage students to reassess their inferences throughout the chapter. Explain that in this chapter, they will learn how natural selection acts on genetic variation to cause evolution.

Darwin "Meets" DNA

SECTION 11–1

GUIDE FOR READING

- **Identify** the source of inheritable variation in organisms.
- **Define** species, fitness, and adaptation in genetic terms.

MINI LAB

- **Relate** common vegetables to the parts of the ancestral species from which they were artificially selected.

NEARLY A CENTURY after Darwin proposed his theory of natural selection to explain evolution, the theory itself went through an incredible period of growth and change. Biologists interested in evolution combined Darwin's insights with new developments in the study of inheritance. Indeed, scientists could now explain how evolution worked far better than Darwin ever could.

How Does Variation Arise?

Darwin knew nothing about how inheritable traits were passed from one generation to the next. He also had no idea where the inheritable variation that his theory of natural selection depended on might come from. When geneticists rediscovered Mendel's work during the early part of this century, evolutionary biologists realized that they had stumbled onto a gold mine.

When biologists recognized that genes in an organism's cells are carriers of traits, they realized that genes are also the source of inheritable variation. Because inheritable variation provides the raw material for natural selection, genes quickly became the center of attention in hypotheses and experiments aimed at understanding the mechanisms

Figure 11–1 (a) A mother duck and her ducklings, (b) an Egyptian goose, and (c) a wood duck are remarkably similar and, at the same time, are distinctly different. What mechanism can explain how they evolved? The science of inheritance was instrumental in answering this question.

TEACHER SUPPORT

Historical Perspective

Scientists were intrigued with Darwin's theory of evolution, and many embraced it. However, Darwin could not explain the mechanism that produced inheritable variation, prompting many scientists to search for a workable theory of inheritance. Mendel's principles of inheritance were not published until shortly after Darwin published *The Origin of Species*. Unfortunately, Darwin never learned of Mendel's paper. Darwin attempted to explain the inheritance of traits in a process that he called pangenesis, in which body cells produce minute particles, called pangenes, that circulate throughout the body and pass into male and female gametes. This idea was quickly disproved by other scientists, some of whom eventually rediscovered Mendel's work.

SECTION 11–1

Darwin "Meets" DNA

Performance Objectives

- Identify mutations and gene shuffling as the primary sources of inheritable variation in organisms.
- Explain the meanings of variation, species, fitness, and adaptation in genetic terms.

Mini Lab Skill: Relating

1 ENGAGE

Ideas Through Images

Have students examine Figure 11–1, read the caption, and answer the following questions.

- **In what ways are these birds similar? How are they different?** (They all have adaptations for living in water. They have different colors, body shapes, and sizes.)
- **What causes the differences among these birds?** (The genes that they inherit from their parents.)
- **What role do you think genetics plays in evolution?** (Accept all logical responses. Genes determine the variation in traits among individuals of a population. It is on this variation that natural selection acts.)

2 EXPLORE

Inquiry Activity

Hypothesizing

Causes of Variation

Ask students to form a hypothesis about what causes variations among individuals of a population. Suggest that students consider what they know about genetics and the inheritance of traits. (One hypothesis students might develop is that variations in traits are caused by mutations in the DNA molecule.) Encourage students to adjust their hypothesis as they study the section.

3 TEACH

Discussion

Begin a class discussion about the difference in the mutation rates between bacteria and humans. Encourage students to give their opinions about the following points.

- Bacteria can evolve more quickly because of their higher rate of mutations, leading to strains that are resistant to certain antibiotics.
- A higher mutation rate is an adaptive mechanism for the survival of bacteria.
- Sexual reproduction in humans produces more inheritable variation than rare, beneficial mutations. So a high mutation rate is not required for survival of humans.

Investigate

Research Have small groups of students work together to find out how scientists measure the genetic variability of organisms. (Scientists use gel electrophoresis to find differences in the amino acid sequence of proteins. Then they determine the average frequency of heterozygotes per gene.) Encourage students to summarize what they found in a short report.

Correcting Misconceptions

Students might have difficulty understanding that natural selection does not affect an organism's genotype. Ask students what causes an organism's phenotype. (The interaction of its genotype and the environment.) Emphasize that natural selection acts only on an organism's phenotype. Then ask students to describe how they think natural selection acts on an organism's phenotype. (Organisms with adaptations that help them better survive in their environment are more likely to produce more offspring with those traits.)

of evolution. The result was a new view of the principles of evolution—one based on genes. **Scientists now know that inheritable variation comes primarily from two kinds of changes in an organism's genetic material—mutations and gene shuffling.**

Mutations

Sometimes changes in the structure of an organism's DNA cause changes in the information carried in one or more of its genes. Such changes in DNA are called **mutations.** The rate at which mutations occur varies a great deal from one group of organisms to another. Bacteria, for instance, have fairly high mutation rates, whereas humans have fairly low mutation rates. Mutations are one source of variation in nature, and they can have powerful effects—both positive and negative—on organisms.

Gene Shuffling

Mutations are not the only source of inheritable variation. You do not look exactly like either of your biological parents, even though they provided you with all your genes. You probably look even less like any brothers or sisters you may have (except an identical twin). Yet mutant genes are not the likely source of differences among you. Instead, the differences are probably due to the extensive shuffling of genes that occurs when egg and sperm are produced. When the same genes are combined in different ways, they often interact differently and produce different results. Thus, sexual reproduction is an important source of variation in nature.

☑ **Checkpoint** What are the sources of variation in nature? 1

Figure 11–2 *Studying heredity in (a) the evening primrose, Hugo de Vries, a Dutch botanist, was the first to recognize the nature of mutations. Mutations—random changes in an organism's DNA—have given rise to (b) the dramatic variation in the color of the tigers. Variation, although less obvious in (c) these emperor penguins, is very common in populations of organisms, and it arises in large part due to the shuffling of genes in sexual reproduction.*

TEACHER SUPPORT

Managing Classroom Diversity

AT-RISK STUDENTS
Some students may need to review the process of meiosis. Refer them to diagrams of meiosis. Point out that gene shuffling refers to the cross-over event that occurs during the first stage of meiosis. Discuss how crossing over shuffles the alleles of genes so that the resulting chromosomes look nothing like the parent chromosomes. Some students might also need to review the different kinds of mutations that occur in DNA and how they affect gene expression.

How Common Is Genetic Variation?

Darwin realized that inheritable variation is common in nature, but he had no way to measure how common it is. Today, biologists know that a significant percentage of genes in natural populations have at least two different forms, called alleles (uh-LEELZ). In insects, as many as 15 percent of all genes have more than one allele. In fishes, reptiles, and mammals, about 5 percent of all genes have more than one allele. This level of genetic difference between organisms is a very important source of raw material that can be influenced by natural selection.

Inheritable Variation

There are many kinds of inheritable variation. Some you can see with the unaided eye, such as the flower colors of Mendel's pea plants. Others are invisible because they involve hidden biochemical processes, such as enzyme action and protein synthesis. In addition, some traits are controlled by a single gene, and others are controlled by several genes. This makes a big difference in the way genetic variation is expressed in individual organisms.

Of course, natural selection never "sees" individual genes. In fact, natural selection doesn't even act directly on an organism's genotype—its complete genetic makeup. "Survival of the fittest" refers to whether or not an individual organism manages to survive and reproduce. For this reason, natural selection can affect only variations in phenotype—the characteristics produced by the interaction of an organism's genes and its environment. Not surprisingly, natural selection can have different effects on different kinds of traits.

Traits Controlled by Single Genes

If a trait is controlled by a single gene with two alleles, there are three possible genotypes. Depending on the trait involved and the way the gene operates, these genotypes may produce either two or three phenotypes, which in turn may have very different fitness. A distribution for three phenotypes of a single-gene trait is shown in ***Figure 11–3.***

Traits Controlled by Several Genes

Many important traits, however, are polygenic, which means that they are

Figure 11–3
The graphs illustrate the distribution of phenotypes that would be expected for a trait if one, two, or many genes contributed to the trait. The last graph is a bell-shaped curve characteristic of a normal distribution.

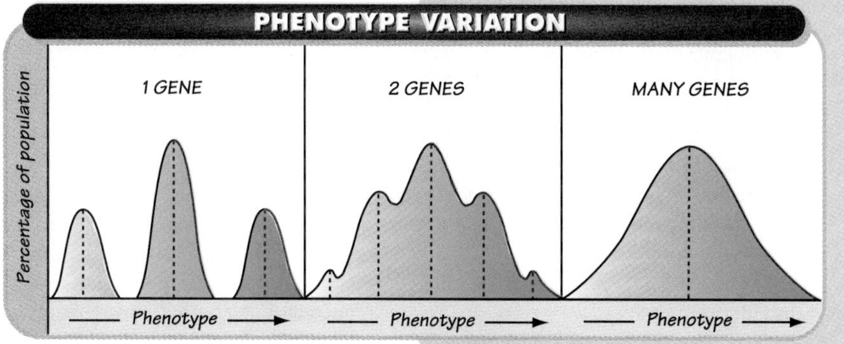

Ideas Through Images

Have students examine Figure 11–3, read the caption, and answer the following questions.

- **Which graph shows a population with the largest amount of variation?** (The bell-shaped graph.)
- **On which traits would natural selection have the most effect?** (Polygenic traits, because they have the largest range of variation.)
- **If a trait controlled by one gene is homozygous recessive lethal, how would the graph change?** (Only two distinct curves would exist on the graph because the population will exhibit only two phenotypes for the trait.)

Investigate

Model Building Give small groups of students containers of at least 100 beads of various colors. Instruct each group to sort the beads by color and then count them. Students should work together to graph their data, as well as calculate the frequency of each color in the population of beads. Point out that each bead represents the allele for a trait in a population. Encourage students to simulate 50 genetic crosses by randomly choosing beads. Ask them if the frequency of alleles in the population changed. (No, the alleles were simply shuffled around.) Challenge them to infer one method that would cause the allele frequency of the population to change. Invite groups to share their inferences with the class.

Checkpoint

1 Mutations and gene shuffling.

TEACHER SUPPORT

Background Information

Make sure students understand the meaning of different terms commonly used in population genetics. For example, a population is a group of the same species living in an area at the same time. Emphasize throughout the chapter that the effects of natural selection are visible in the population of organisms, not on individuals in the population. Also make sure students are aware that selection pressures from the environment include both living and nonliving things. Explain that an organism's environment is made up of climate, soil type, water, air quality, nutrients, as well as plants and animals and the interactions among them.

Ancillary Support

The resource below can be used to support your teaching strategy for these two pages.

LM Measuring Variation Within a Population, #21
Observing the Effect of Environment on Seedling Growth, #22

MINI LAB Relating

Teacher Notes

• For time required and materials needed, see page 240b.

• Students should observe the following. Selection for leaves (kale), stems (kohlrabi), flowers (broccoli and cauliflower), buds (Brussels sprouts and cabbage), roots (turnips and rutabagas).

Answers to Analyze and Conclude

1. They are different species because they cannot be bred to produce fertile offspring.

2. Some hybrids have been produced, such as broccoflower. These hybrids are sterile from the lack of homology between chromosomes, causing a breakdown in meiosis.

Skills Trace

Relating

- Focus p. 244
- Practice p. 245
- Assess p. 261

INTEGRATING MATH

A normal distribution is characterized by a bell-shaped curve—a line defined by the number of individuals along the y-axis and the phenotype on the x-axis. The highest point on the line represents the most common, or average, phenotype in the population. Traits that exhibit normal distribution are generally polygenic traits such as height, weight, hair color, and skin color in humans.

MINI LAB .... Relating ....

It's All Relative to Broccoli

PROBLEM *How can you **relate** common vegetables to the parts of the ancestral plant from which they were artificially selected?*

PROCEDURE

1. Working in a group, examine each vegetable and discuss its main features.
2. Decide on the feature of the ancestral *Brassica* plant—belonging to the cabbage and turnip group—that you think was artificially selected to breed this vegetable. Record this as your observation.
3. Organize your observations under these categories: selection for leaves, stem, flowers, roots, and buds.

ANALYZE AND CONCLUDE

1. All of the *Brassica* vegetables you observed have 18 chromosomes per cell, yet they are considered separate species. Why?
2. Do you think that hybrids (such as hybrid broccoli-Brussels sprouts) can be produced from two of the species?

controlled by two or more genes. Often, each of these genes has two or more alleles. As a result, there are a large number of possible genotypes and an even larger number of possible phenotypes for such traits. Height in humans is a good example of a trait controlled by several genes. If you were to measure and graph the height in a group of people, you would find that people aren't just tall, medium, or short. Instead, there is a wide range of heights. In fact, the graph would be shaped like a bell. This characteristic bell-shaped curve—called a normal distribution—is observed quite commonly in nature. ●

INTEGRATING MATH

What are the characteristics of a normal distribution? Discuss examples of traits that exhibit such a distribution.

✓ **Checkpoint** What is a normal distribution? 1

Genes, Fitness, and Adaptation

Today, an understanding of genetics makes it possible to define fitness and adaptation in a more meaningful and measurable way. Each time an organism reproduces, it passes copies of its alleles on to its offspring. **An organism's evolutionary fitness can be defined as its success in passing genes to the next generation. An adaptation can be described as any genetically controlled trait that increases an individual's ability to pass along copies of its genes.**

Genes Also Define Species

In Darwin's time, biologists defined a species as a group of organisms that looked alike. **Today, a species is defined as a group of similar-looking organisms that can breed with one another and produce fertile offspring.** Members of two different species cannot interbreed. This is known as **reproductive isolation.**

Why is this genetic definition important? When members of a species interbreed, they share genes with one another. Researchers therefore say that individuals within a species share a group of alleles called a **gene pool.** Because of that common gene pool, a genetic change that occurs in one member of a species can spread through the population, as ***Figure 11–4*** illustrates. On the other hand, because members of different species do not share genes, each species evolves as a separate unit.

Swimming in the Gene Pool

The gene pool of each species contains a certain number of alleles for each trait. In a species that is not under pressure from natural selection, each allele typically occurs at a particular relative frequency. Put another way, this means

TEACHER SUPPORT Managing Classroom Diversity

LEP STUDENTS

Students with limited English proficiency may misinterpret the meanings of the terms gene pool and normal distribution. Point out that the word pool as it is used in gene pool refers to a grouping of resources. Emphasize that a gene pool is the entire collection of individual genomes in a population of organisms. Make sure students realize that the word normal in normal distribution means the same as standard or average. Encourage students to define the terms in their native language to help them differentiate between the various shades of meaning.

that each allele occurs a certain number of times compared with other alleles for the same gene.

Sexual reproduction by itself does not change the relative frequency of alleles in a population. Why? Think of the allele combinations produced by sexual reproduction as being similar to the different hands that can be dealt from a deck of playing cards. Shuffling and reshuffling the cards can produce an enormous number of different hands. But shuffling will not change the relative numbers of aces, kings, or jokers in the deck. The only way that this can be done is if hands containing certain cards are discarded. As you will soon discover, something similar to this happens when a species evolves.

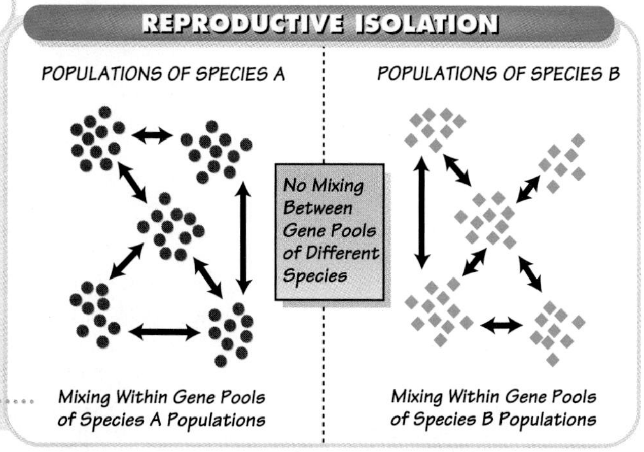

Figure 11–4
(a) The parent bird with five nestlings is more fit than its neighbor with only two nestlings. Fitness is defined as an organism's success in passing genes to the next generation.
(b) Species A and B are reproductively isolated. Within each of the two separate gene pools of species A and species B, mixing occurs. However, no mixing occurs between the gene pools of the two species.

Section Review 11-1

1. **Identify** the source of inheritable variation in organisms.
2. **Define** species, fitness, and adaptation in genetic terms.
3. **Critical Thinking—Hypothesizing** How does variation depend on the size of the gene pool?
4. **MINI LAB** How do common vegetables **relate** to the parts of the ancestral species that were used in artificial selection?

4 ASSESS

Quick Check

Have each student write two questions about the concepts in the section and exchange questions with another student. After students have answered the questions, have them review the answers with their partners.

Section Review 11-1

1. Mutations and gene shuffling.
2. A species is a group of similar-looking organisms that can breed with one another and produce fertile offspring. Fitness is an organism's success in passing genes to the next generation. An adaptation is any genetically controlled trait that increases an individual's ability to pass along copies of its genes.
3. Genetic variation increases as the size of the gene pool increases.

Checkpoint

(1) The characteristic bell-shaped curve observed when there is continuous variation of a phenotype in the population.

4. Possible answers include that kale came from the leaves of the ancestral species, kohlrabi from the stem, broccoli and cauliflower from the flowers, Brussels sprouts and cabbage from the buds, and turnips and rutabagas from the roots.

Skills Trace

Relating

- Focus p. 244
- **Practice p. 245**
- Assess p. 261

Learning Modality

Auditory Learning Instruct students to write an outline of the section that includes the main ideas presented in it. Then divide the class into pairs and have each pair summarize the content of the section in their own words, using their outlines as a guide. Make sure students listen critically to their partners and discuss any misinterpreted ideas.

Ancillary Support

The resources below can be used to support your teaching strategy for these two pages.

TR Apply: Designer Organism
BL Inquiry Activity: What Darwin Didn't Know

SECTION 11-2
Evolution as Genetic Change

Performance Objectives

- State the meaning of evolution in terms of genetics.
- Describe the process of genetic drift.
- Describe what must occur for speciation to take place.

Mini Lab Skill: Modeling
Laboratory Investigation Skill: Formulating a hypothesis

1 ENGAGE

Ideas Through Images

Have students examine Figure 11–5, read the caption, and answer the following questions.

- **In what ways do the similar organisms pictured vary?** (Dahlias differ in color and in petal size and shape. Dogs differ in markings and in size. Palms differ in size and in the number of fronds.)
- **What is the allele frequency of a trait?** (It is the total number of copies of a certain allele in an entire population.)
- **What might cause the allele frequency of a trait in a population to change?** (Natural selection and genetic drift can both cause the allele frequency to change.)

SECTION
11–2 Evolution as Genetic Change

GUIDE FOR READING

- **Define** evolution in genetic terms.
- **Define** genetic drift.
- **Explain** how speciation can occur.

MINI LAB

- **Construct a model** of genetic drift.

WHAT DOES IT MEAN TO SAY that a species evolves? Of course, individual organisms of a species do not evolve. But a population of organisms, slowly, over many generations, does undergo changes due to inheritable variations and the forces of natural selection. Does this mean that evolution occurs in all species at all times and at the same rate? And is natural selection the only means by which evolutionary change takes place?

Evolution—Genetically Defined

Today, evolutionary biologists view evolution as a natural consequence of the nature of genes and DNA and the interactions between organisms and their environment. **In modern genetic terms, evolution can be defined as any change in the relative frequencies of alleles in the gene pool of a species.** You may recall that sexual reproduction alone will not cause such a change. What then can cause the allele frequencies in a gene pool to change? Let's examine some possibilities, or mechanisms, beginning with Darwin's choice—natural selection.

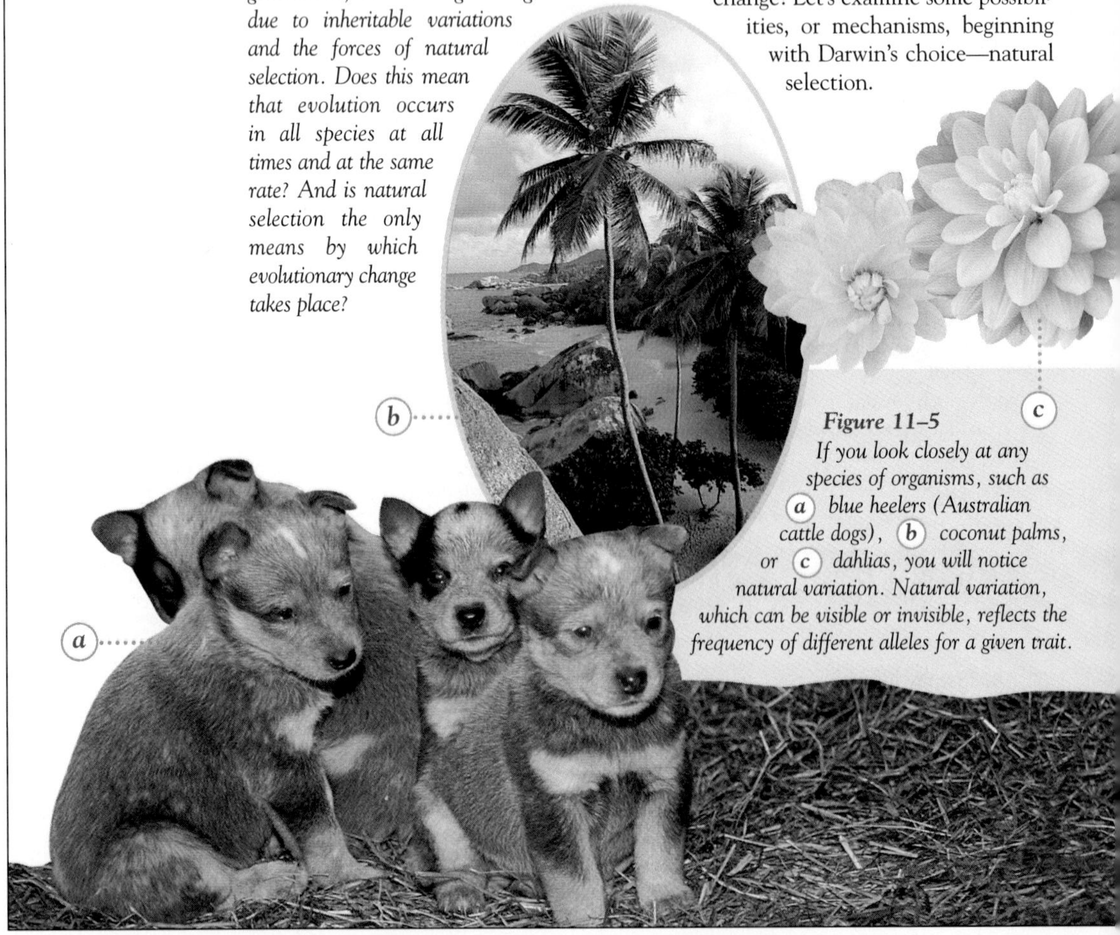

Figure 11–5 If you look closely at any species of organisms, such as (a) blue heelers (Australian cattle dogs), (b) coconut palms, or (c) dahlias, you will notice natural variation. Natural variation, which can be visible or invisible, reflects the frequency of different alleles for a given trait.

TEACHER SUPPORT

Activity

DIAGRAMMING EVOLUTION
Challenge students to imagine what the wild ancestor of a domesticated plant or animal looked like. Then have students draw stages in its evolution from the wild ancestor to its domesticated state. For each stage, students should list or describe the selection pressures, either artificial or natural, that might have caused the organism to evolve. Invite students to present their drawings to the class. Challenge students to find evolutionary trends, such as an increase or decrease in size as it relates to function.

Natural Selection on Single-Gene Traits

As mentioned earlier, some traits important to evolutionary fitness are controlled by a single gene. What happens if a mutation occurs in one copy of that gene carried by a single individual? The answer depends on several factors, including chance. For starters, let's look at the role natural selection can play.

Assume that the mutation is not lethal. Or at least, assume that a single copy of this new allele doesn't kill an individual that carries it before that individual can reproduce.

Harmful Mutations

If a mutation decreases the ability of some member of a species to survive and reproduce, fewer copies of the allele will be passed on to future generations. Members of the same species that do not carry the allele will survive and reproduce. Thus, the allele will tend to become even less common in the population.

Helpful Mutations

Now suppose that the new allele increases the evolutionary fitness of individuals that carry a single copy. Over time, carriers of this allele would produce more offspring than the individuals that do not have the allele. As a result, over a few generations, the relative frequency of this allele would increase in the population. And if the allele has no negative effects, it may sooner or later be found in nearly all members of the species.

Natural Selection on Polygenic Traits

The situation with polygenic traits is both more interesting and more complicated. As you have read, the action of alleles on traits such as height produces a wide range of phenotypes. In most cases, the graphs of the variation of such traits display a bell-shaped curve, or normal distribution. The fitness of individuals located near one another on the curve will be similar. However, fitness can vary a great deal from one end of the curve to the other. And if fitness varies, natural selection can act. When it does act, natural selection can affect these distributions in any of three ways: It can stabilize the distribution, it can shift the distribution in one direction or the other, or it can disrupt the distribution.

Stabilizing Selection

Stabilizing selection occurs when organisms near the center of the curve are more fit than organisms at either end. This situation keeps the center of the curve at its current position and may or may not decrease the amount of variation above and below the average. Evolution as defined in this chapter is either minor or absent. See ***Figure 11–6*** on page 248.

The mass of human infants at birth seems to be under the influence of stabilizing selection. Infants that are born much smaller or larger than average are less healthy and have a greater chance of developing serious complications that may lead to death. Obviously, the fitness of those individuals is low. Data show that the average mass of humans at birth coincides quite well with the mass at which mortality is lowest.

Directional Selection

Directional selection occurs when individuals at one end of the curve have higher fitness than individuals in the middle or at the other end. This situation will cause the entire curve to move as the trait changes. This means both a change in the allele frequencies in the gene pool and that evolution occurs.

2 EXPLORE

Inquiry Activity

Modeling

Evolution and Genetics

Ask students how they would define evolution using genetic terms. To help them develop their definitions, encourage students to explore the mechanism of evolution in a population by using objects, such as colored beads or buttons, to represent the alleles for a particular phenotype. Then students should employ some sort of selection pressure that affects one of the alleles in the gene pool. Suggest to students that they describe what has occurred in their models, using genetic terms. Then they can use their descriptions to help them write definitions of evolution. Have students revise their definition as they study the section.

3 TEACH

Discussion

Begin a class discussion about the genetic definition of evolution. Make sure students understand what relative frequencies are. Also emphasize that individuals in a population do not evolve. Rather, the species evolves when the entire population shows a shift in the relative frequencies of alleles. Use examples to help reinforce this point, such as the evolution of peppered moths in which the allele for dark color had a very low relative frequency until the environment changed. Then the relative frequency of the allele for light color began to decrease while that of the dark allele increased.

TEACHER SUPPORT

Background Information

Stabilizing selection causes a population to maintain a relatively constant genetic composition with many of its individual traits. When the relative frequency of a trait is changed during artificial selection, natural selection will often cause the relative frequency to return to the original state after artificial selection is stopped. For example, if breeders select sheep that produce two or more offspring, they will successfully create a flock that produces a large number of offspring per ewe. However, when the breeders stop artificial selection, natural selection gradually changes the number of offspring back to one or two per ewe—the phenotype that is naturally most common in the population.

Ancillary Support

The resources below can be used to support your teaching strategy for these two pages.

TR Enrich: Laying Down the Law
BL Inquiry Activity: Determining Frequency

Investigate

Cooperative Learning Have small groups of students work together to make inferences about the action of natural selection on a particular trait. Groups can choose either a single-gene trait or a polygenic trait. (Students do not have to choose real traits; they can simply make up one of their own that is a logical choice for their organism.) Encourage students to devise at least two different scenarios in which natural selection affects the frequency of alleles for the trait in the population. Have groups present their scenarios to the class.

Investigate

Model Building Assign a different trait—such as beak size, birth weight, number of offspring per birth, or height—to each group of students. Instruct them to use graphs to show how the allele frequencies differ in periods of stabilizing selection and directional selection. They should also describe the selection pressures and the traits that are being selected in each type of selection. Have students compare the graphs and explain how different kinds of selection affect the distribution of phenotypes in a population.

Ideas Through Images

Have students examine Figure 11–6, read the caption, and answer the following questions.

- **If the fitness of the intermediate phenotype is very high in a case of stabilizing selection, how might the bell curve change over time?** (The bell curve will become narrower because the more extreme phenotypes are less fit.)
- **Which types of selection will result in evolution over time?** (Directional and disruptive selection will result in evolution.)

Laboratory Investigation

The Laboratory Investigation, Mutations in Bacteria, on pages 256–257 is appropriate to use at this point in the chapter.

Among Darwin's seed-eating finches, the size of a bird's beak determines the size of the hard-shelled seeds it can crack open to eat. Larger beaks enable birds to feed on larger seeds. If the number of available small- and medium-sized seeds decreases, birds that are able to open larger seeds will have more access to food and therefore have higher fitness. The average beak size in this population of birds would be expected to increase as the species evolves.

Disruptive Selection

Disruptive selection occurs when individuals at both the upper and lower ends of the curve have higher fitness than individuals near the middle. In such situations, natural selection acts most strongly against individuals of an intermediate type. If the pressure of natural selection is strong enough and lasts long enough, this situation can cause the single curve to split into two curves, as illustrated in ***Figure 11–6,*** causing evolution to occur.

Sometimes an insect species that predators find tasty gains protection because it resembles another insect species that contains poisonous or distasteful chemicals. If the tasty species inhabits a very large geographical area, it may be under pressure from disruptive selection to imitate two different poisonous species in different places. In this situation, insects that resemble neither of the poisonous species have lower fitness than those who resemble either of the poisonous species. As a result, the population may be split into different forms as it evolves.

☑ ***Checkpoint*** How do stabilizing selection and disruptive selection differ? 1

NATURAL SELECTION ON NORMAL DISTRIBUTIONS

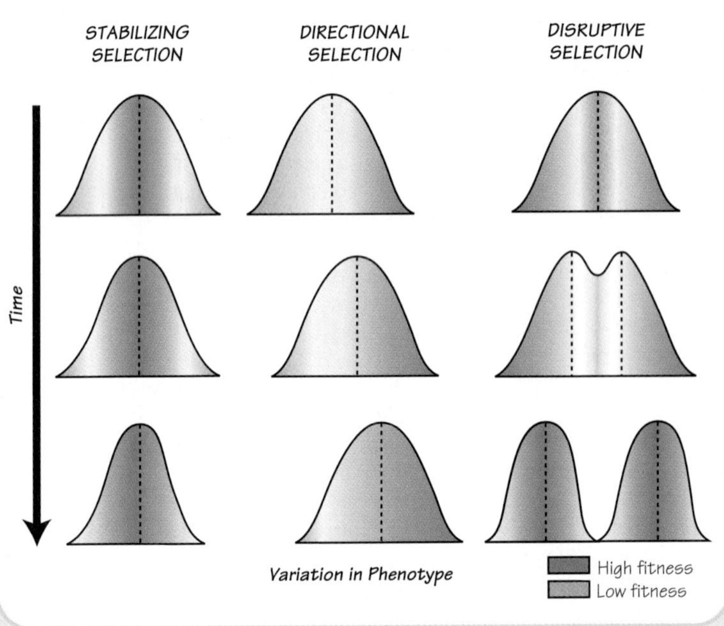

Figure 11–6 The effect of natural selection on a normal distribution of phenotype depends on how fitness varies with phenotype. Stabilizing selection occurs when the fitness of individuals is high near the center and low toward the ends of the distribution. Directional selection occurs when fitness is high at one end and low at the other end of the distribution. Disruptive selection occurs when fitness is high at both ends but low around the center of the distribution.

TEACHER SUPPORT

Background Information

Directional selection occurs in a population when the environment changes or when organisms move into a new environment. Directional selection can also act over long periods of time, in which it is translated into evolutionary trends. For example, the size of the human cranium has increased over time. The evolution of the horse is another example of directional selection. People play a role in causing directional selection when they change the environment. For example, when people spray insecticides over large areas, they inadvertently select insects that are resistant to the insecticide. Insecticide-resistant insects are most fit, and the insect population evolves.

Bio FRONTIER Connections

Altering the Human Gene Pool

Cathy Sullivan couldn't believe it. A California team of doctors was working on preventing cystic fibrosis, a condition with which Cathy's 10-year-old daughter, Melissa, was born. Mel, as her parents called her, took various experimental drugs, had her back pounded three times a day to loosen the mucus that filled her lungs, and yet couldn't do all the things a normal 10-year-old can do.

Because cystic fibrosis is a genetic disorder caused by a recessive gene, both Cathy and her husband, Al, were carriers of the gene. But they were not sick. Melissa's sickness was an unfortunate consequence of nature's random actions.

Modern Treatment

Cystic fibrosis, or CF, is a condition whose treatment has come a long way. Today, there are drugs to help reduce the risk of lung diseases, thus enabling children with CF to live to adulthood. There is even a gene therapy for the condition, still experimental, whereby the non-CF gene is introduced into the patient's body in order to replace the CF gene.

Is Prevention Better Than the Cure?

Scientists have found a way to test an egg or a sperm for the gene for CF. In this procedure, eggs are removed from the mother and examined for a smaller cell that contains a set of chromosomes, called the polar body, that is discarded just before fertilization occurs. An egg will discard a polar body so that it will have half the number of chromosomes needed for fertilization. If a woman is a carrier, her polar body may or may not have the gene for CF. If the polar body does not have the gene, the egg does. By the same token, if the polar body has the gene for CF, the egg does not. Consequently, when this egg is fertilized by a sperm that does not have the CF gene, a child without CF will be produced.

The procedure seems to offer the perfect solution—at least in theory. But many people find the procedure, called preimplantation testing, questionable in principle. Why? Because although the notion of manipulating human genes to achieve desirable outcomes is intriguing to some, it is frightening to others. No one actually knows what the altering of human genes may mean to our future.

CAREER TRACK *The genetic engineer is isolating gene-sized fragments of DNA in order to conduct recombinant DNA research, which has important applications in medicine, industry, and agriculture.*

Making the Connection

How will altering human genes affect human evolution? Should we forge ahead with such medical practices before we learn more about their long-term effects? What do you think?

Connections

Preimplantation testing is a genetic test that genetic counselors can use to advise carriers of genetic diseases. This test is sometimes preferred over amniocentesis because the pregnancy can be prevented if the egg has the defective gene.

People who oppose the idea of preimplantation testing wonder how selecting against a certain allele will affect the human gene pool. They point out that not only is the defective allele selected against, but so are other gene alleles carried on the same chromosome. Opponents also wonder about the moral issues involved in selecting for certain genes. What if someone decides to select for or against certain physical appearances or certain behaviors?

Answers to Making the Connection

Students' answers will vary. Students should explain why they think procedures, such as preimplantation testing, that could alter the human gene pool should or should not be used. They should also infer how these procedures could affect human evolution.

Checkpoint

1 In stabilizing selection, the fitness of individuals is high near the center of the distribution. In disruptive selection, fitness is high at both ends of the distribution and low in the center.

TEACHER SUPPORT — Background Information

Eugenics is the science and practice of changing the genetic composition, or gene pool, of humans. Even though scientists have the capability to manipulate the genetic composition of humans, they will never totally control the evolutionary destiny of humans. The reason is that the phenotype of an individual is the result of its genotype and its environment. This is especially true with humans because people respond to whatever is around them. For example, identical twins raised in two different environments will have different phenotypes and behaviors.

Ancillary Support

The resource below can be used to support your teaching strategy for these two pages.

TB Natural Selection on Normal Distributions, #14

Ideas Through Images

Have students examine Figure 11–7, read the caption, and answer the following questions.

- **If you flipped a coin two times and got heads both times, what is the relative frequency of heads? Of tails?** (The relative frequency of heads is 1 and of tails is 0, which is not close to the expected 50:50 ratio.)
- **If you flipped a coin 1000 times and got 504 heads and 496 tails, what is the frequency of each?** (The frequency of heads is 0.504 and of tails is 0.496, which is close to the expected 50:50 ratio.)
- **How can you relate the frequencies from flipping the coin to the frequency of alleles in a large population? A small population?** (In a large population, a larger number of parents produce offspring, so the observed frequency of alleles in the offspring will be close to the allele frequency of the parents. In small populations, the observed frequency is more likely to be different from the allele frequency of the parents simply because of chance.)

Discussion

Initiate a class discussion about the factors that cause speciation. Emphasize that speciation occurs not only because of geographic isolation but also because of the following factors.

- Individuals of the same species that live in the same area but occupy different habitats will not meet, and therefore not mate.
- Temporal isolation can separate individuals of a population when mating or flowering occurs at different times—either seasonally or at different times of the day.
- Differences in courtship and mating rituals.

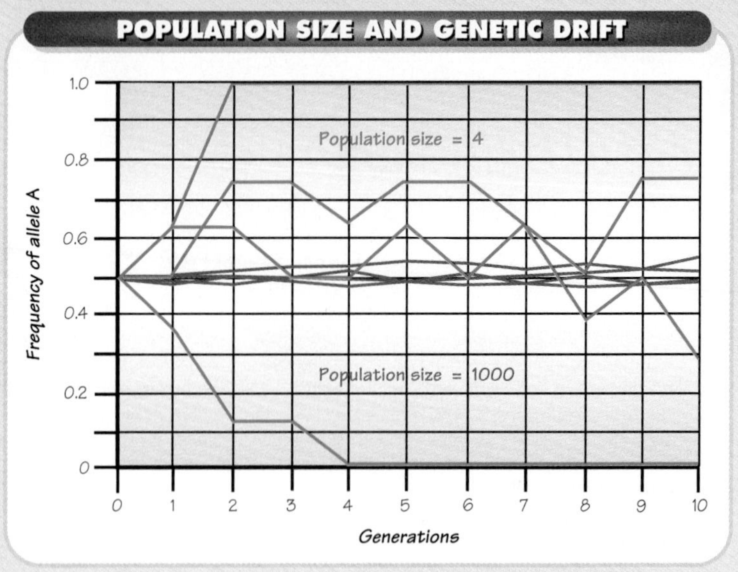

Figure 11–7
These computer simulations illustrate the effect of population size on genetic drift. The green lines represent an initial population of 4 individuals, and the red lines represent an initial population of 1000. In both cases, the initial population was composed of half A and half a alleles. After 10 generations, notice that in two simulations for population size 4, one allele became extinct by chance. All four simulations for a population size of 1000 show that the allele frequencies remained fairly constant.

The Role of Chance

Over the century and a half since Darwin, experiments and observations have supported natural selection in a remarkable number of cases. However, evolutionary biologists today also recognize the existence of other mechanisms of evolutionary change.

Recently, researchers realized that organisms can sometimes evolve whether or not natural selection is operating. **Studies have shown that an allele can become more or less common in a population simply by chance. Such a random change in allele frequency is called genetic drift.** How can this happen?

In some cases, individuals that carry a particular allele may leave more descendants than other individuals—not because they are more fit but just because of chance. Look at ***Figure 11–7*** to see how **genetic drift** is more likely to occur in small populations than in larger ones.

Often a small group of organisms will colonize a new habitat. These organisms may carry alleles in different relative frequencies from the larger population from which they came. Thus, the offspring they produce will be genetically different from the original population simply by chance.

☑ **Checkpoint** What is genetic drift? 1

The Birth of New Species

So far you have seen several ways in which changes may occur within a species. But how do these changes lead to **speciation**—the formation of new species? Remember that, by definition, members of a species can interbreed with one another but not with members of other species. This is called reproductive isolation. **Therefore, for speciation to take place, a population must evolve enough genetic changes—by mechanisms such as natural selection—so that breeding cannot occur between the emerging, genetically different groups.**

Speciation in animals and most plants usually occurs when two groups of individuals are physically separated from one another by a geographical barrier.

TEACHER SUPPORT

Managing Classroom Diversity

MULTICULTURAL STRATEGY
Encourage students to choose a small population of people, such as aborigines from New Zealand, native Hawaiians, or American Eskimos, and learn about their culture and their environment. Challenge students to make inferences about why these small populations of people are diverse from other populations of people. Students should explain their inferences using evolutionary terms, such as natural selection, adaptation, genetic drift, and geographic isolation. Encourage students to find examples of each in the cultures of the population they chose.

Visualizing Evolution in Galapagos Finches

From a small ancestral group of birds, the 13 species of birds known as Darwin's finches evolved. The following steps outline the probable mechanism of their evolution.

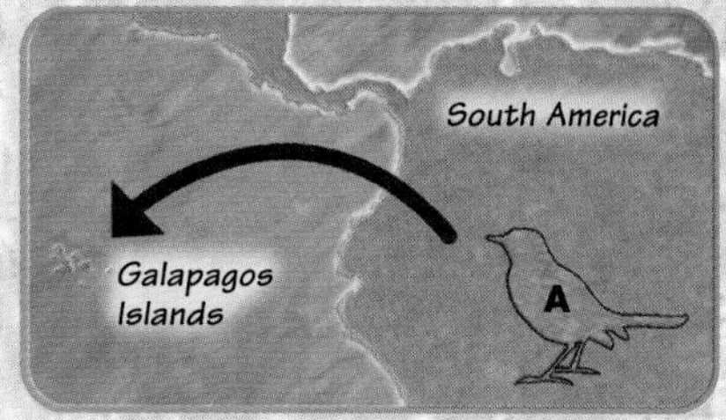

1 Arrival of the founders

A few finches, A, find their way to one of the islands. There they survive and reproduce.

2 Separation of populations

A few of the species A travel to another island. These two populations no longer share a common gene pool.

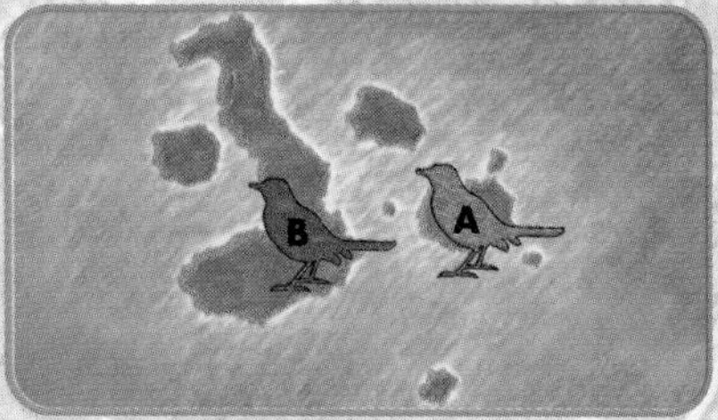

3 Changes in the gene pool

Over time, the isolated populations begin to evolve into two species, A and B, in ways determined by the conditions on their island home.

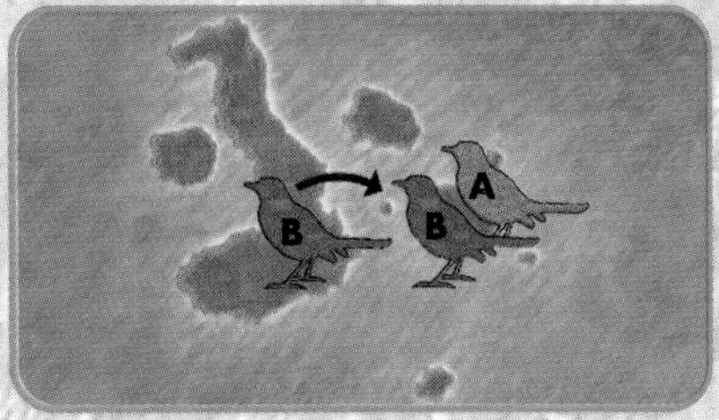

4 Reproductive isolation

Some of the birds, B, travel back to the original island, home to the founder species, A. Because the finches prefer to mate with birds that display similar phenotypes, A and B probably will not interbreed. The two gene pools are now separate, and the birds belong to different species.

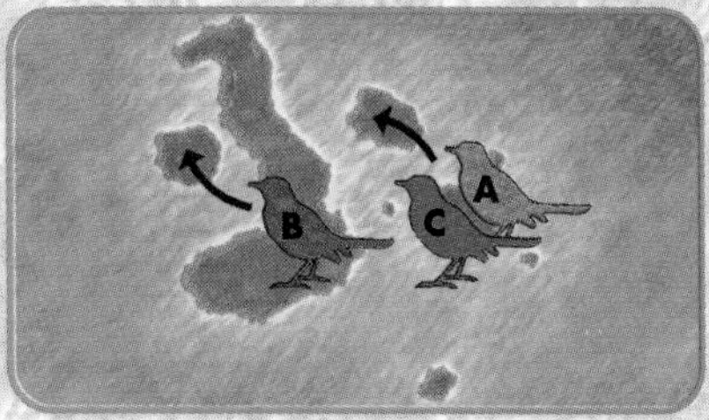

5 Sharing the same island

As the two birds, A and B, continue to share a single island, they compete with each other for food in times of drought. Directional selection leads to further changes in the species, causing B to evolve into C.

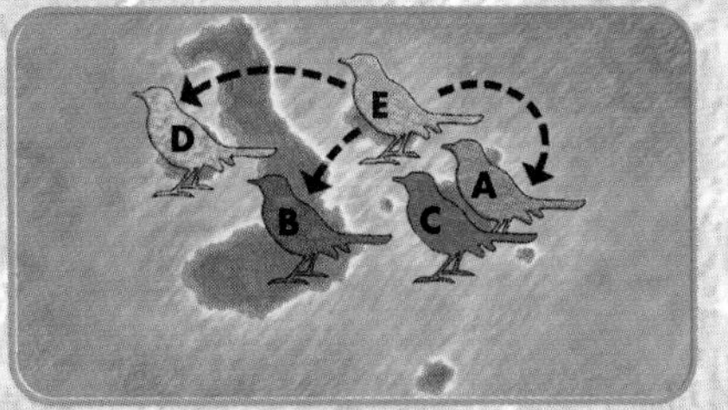

6 Repeating the process

If this process is repeated on the different islands, it could easily produce the 13 living species and the several extinct forms known as Darwin's finches on the Galapagos Islands.

Visualizing Evolution in Galapagos Finches

Have students examine the steps in the evolution of Darwin's finches and read the captions. Discuss examples of genetic drift and natural selection in the evolution of the finches. Emphasize the following points.

- Genetic drift occurs in step 1 and step 2 when small groups of finches first land on new islands and begin evolving.
- Natural selection occurs in steps 1, 3, and 5 as the species evolve in response to the new or changing environment.
- Because finches do not usually fly over large expanses of water, those individuals that were separated from the main population—probably due to storms—tended to remain isolated.

Review what occurs in the process of speciation. Ask students to explain in their own words why the finches from the different islands did not interbreed, as described in step 4. (The two species looked different from each other.) Remind students that reproductive isolation can occur at many different levels, and one of the first levels is attracting and accepting a mate.

Checkpoint

1 Genetic drift is a random change in allele frequency that occurs in a population simply by chance.

TEACHER SUPPORT

Managing Classroom Diversity

AT-RISK STUDENTS

Some students might find the mathematical content of Section 11–2 difficult to relate to real-life situations. To help students become more involved in the graphing and statistical details of natural selection, you might have them read Section 11–3 first. This section describes basically the same ideas as those in Section 11–2 without using graphs and frequencies. Once students understand the relationships between the organisms and their environment during the process of speciation, they will better understand the statistical details.

MINI LAB Modeling

Teacher Note
• For time required and materials needed, see page 240b.

Answers to Analyze and Conclude
1. 10 percent.
2. In most cases, the percentages of each sample will differ from each other and from those in the container.
3. In most cases no, because the percentages of beans in the small samples are different from the percentages in the container.

Skills Trace
Modeling
- Focus p. 252
- Practice p. 252
- Assess p. 261

4 ASSESS

Quick Check

Have students diagram the stages in the speciation of two geographically isolated populations—one for gradualism and the other for punctuated equilibrium.

Section Review 11-2

1. Any change in the relative frequencies of alleles in the gene pool of a species.
2. See page 250.
3. See page 250, column 2.
4. It can stabilize the distribution when the fitness of individuals is high near the center of the bell curve. It can shift the distribution when the fitness of individuals is high at one end of the curve. It can disrupt the distribution when fitness is high at both ends of the curve, but low around the center.
5. Students may describe the model from the MINI LAB.

Skills Trace
Modeling
- Focus p. 252
- Practice p. 252
- Assess p. 261

MINI LAB ······ Modeling ······

Catch the Drift

PROBLEM *How can you* ***construct a model*** *of genetic drift?*

PROCEDURE

1. Without looking, scoop out a handful of beans from the container provided by your teacher.
2. Place the beans on your table. Count and record the number of beans of each type.
3. Repeat steps 1 and 2 two more times and record your observations in a data table.

ANALYZE AND CONCLUDE

1. If the container has 10 types of beans and 10 beans of each type, what is the percentage of each type of bean in the container?
2. Calculate the percentage of each type of bean in each handful of beans. How do these percentages compare with the percentages of the beans in the container? With each other?
3. Are the small samples (handfuls) representative of the larger sample (container)? Explain your results.

The illustration on page 251 shows how speciation might have occurred among the finches of the Galapagos Islands.

Checkpoint When does speciation usually occur? 1

The Pace of Evolution

Evolutionary biologists agree that evolution occurs as the result of forces such as natural selection and genetic drift. But they differ on the relative importance of these forces and on the pace at which evolutionary change occurs.

Darwin may have overestimated the connection between geology and biology. Like Lyell, who argued that geological change was slow and steady, Darwin believed that evolutionary change also had to work the same way—very slowly. The view that evolutionary change occurs slowly and steadily over long periods of time is known as **gradualism.**

As researchers came to know the fossil record in greater detail, they discovered that evolutionary change did not always seem to proceed at the same rate. Sometimes species seemed to remain unchanged for very long periods of time. Now and again, there seemed to be periods of evolution that proceeded relatively quickly. This pattern is known as **punctuated equilibrium,** because it involves long periods of stability that are interrupted by episodes of rapid change.

Gradualism and punctuated equilibrium represent two extreme views of evolution. Most evolutionary biologists hold the view that evolution follows both patterns—in varying degrees at various times in evolutionary history.

Section Review 11-2

1. **Define** evolution in genetic terms.
2. **Define** genetic drift and **explain** how it can occur.
3. **Explain** how speciation can occur.
4. **Critical Thinking—Relating** How does natural selection affect the relative frequencies of alleles in a gene pool for each of the three distributions representing variation in a polygenic trait?
5. **MINI LAB** How can you **construct a model** of genetic drift?

Learning Modality

Kinesthetic Learning Students can model genetic drift by playing the role of an allele in a population of organisms. Have students wear different-colored paper squares to represent different alleles of a trait. Help them choreograph how genetic drift occurs when part of a population colonizes a new environment and when some alleles are randomly lost.

How Species Change

GUIDE FOR READING

- **Explain** how natural selection can lead to speciation in Darwin's finches.

DAPHNE MAJOR IS A TINY island—even for the Galapagos. The tip of this dead volcano is so small that you could walk around its crater rim in less than 20 minutes. It is a lonely, desolate place. Black lava rock bakes in the sun. There is no fresh water. There are no palm trees. But there are flocks of Darwin's finches. Thanks to these birds, researchers are studying processes that Darwin thought no one ever could. They are seeing natural selection in action. Day by day, as they watch, some birds survive and some die. Some reproduce and others don't. Species evolve—right before their eyes!

Darwin's Finches

On the desolate Galapagos Islands, Peter and Rosemary Grant have spent more than 20 years of their married life watching evolution in action. Before you can appreciate what they have been doing and why it is important, you need to learn a little more about the remarkable birds they study.

Researchers now know that the 13 species known today as Darwin's finches all evolved from a common ancestor. Darwin thought some of them were wrens, others were warblers, and still others were blackbirds because their beaks looked very different. Then as other researchers observed these birds, some interesting facts came to light. Each species has body structures—including beaks—and behaviors that enable it to exist in a very different way from its neighbors.

Some of these adaptations are difficult to believe. Some species eat different kinds of seeds, while others eat various types of insects. Some use their beaks as tools and others use cactus spines as tools. These species pick up a spine, shape it

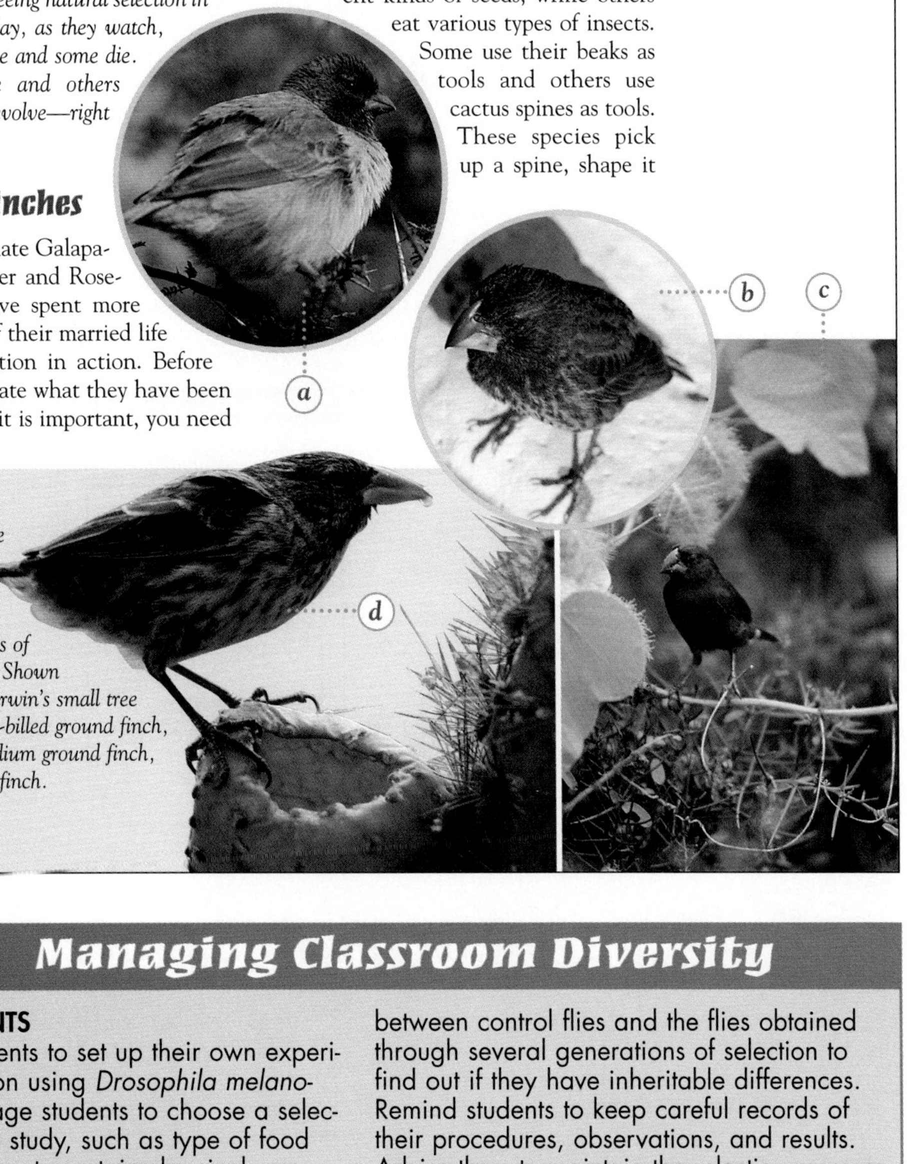

Figure 11–8 *The beaks of these Galapagos finches differ greatly as a result of the slow process of natural selection. Shown here are (a) Darwin's small tree finch, (b) large-billed ground finch, (c) Darwin's medium ground finch, and (d) cactus finch.*

SECTION 11–3

How Species Change

Performance Objective

- Describe the role of natural selection in the speciation of Darwin's finches.

1 ENGAGE

Inquiry Activity

Inferring

Form Follows Function

Display photographs or drawings of several different species of Darwin's finches. Ask students to infer what kinds of food each species eats based on the shape of its beak. Suggest to students that they think of the beaks as tools used to find and get food. Have students write their inferences for each species of finch. You might want to make a class list of inferences and refer to them throughout the section.

Checkpoint

1 Speciation usually occurs when two groups of individuals are physically separated from each other by a geographic barrier. It can also occur through reproductive isolation.

TEACHER SUPPORT — Managing Classroom Diversity

GIFTED STUDENTS

Challenge students to set up their own experiment in evolution using *Drosophila melanogaster*. Encourage students to choose a selection pressure to study, such as type of food offered, exposure to certain chemicals, or temperature at which the flies are grown. Make sure students maintain a control culture of wild flies. Suggest that they set up crosses between control flies and the flies obtained through several generations of selection to find out if they have inheritable differences. Remind students to keep careful records of their procedures, observations, and results. Advise them to maintain the selection pressure for at least four generations, if not longer. Have students write a scientific report describing their investigation.

Ancillary Support

The resource below can be used to support your teaching strategy for these two pages.

TR Writing in Biology: Making Sense of Change
Explore: Get a Grip

2 EXPLORE

Investigate

Research Have students find out what features are common only to finches. Point out that Darwin originally thought some of the birds he collected from the Galapagos Islands were warblers, wrens, and blackbirds. Ask students to describe how these birds are different from finches. Instruct students to diagram a generic finch in which they point out all features specific only to finches.

3 TEACH

Ideas Through Images

Have students examine Figure 11–9, read the caption, and answer the following questions.

- **Which beaks would be best suited for crushing large seeds?** (The large, heavy beaks of *Platyspiza* and *Geospiza*.)
- **What might a beak shaped like needle-nose pliers be best suited for?** (Accept all logical responses. This beak is well suited for picking out food from small holes or crushing small seeds.)
- **One of Darwin's finches uses its beak to hold a cactus spine to help it get food. Which beak would be best suited for holding other tools?** (The beak shaped like curved needle-nose pliers.)

Investigate

Role-Playing Challenge students to assume the role of an evolutionary biologist. First have them choose an organism that they will study. Then ask them to list the kinds of observations they would make as they study the organism evolving into a new species. Advise students to consider the organism's environment, food sources, and selection pressures as they list their observations.

with their beaks, and use it to pull hidden grubs (larvae of some insects) out of dead branches. One species survives by eating leaves, a feat accomplished by only one other bird species in the world. Another species pulls bark from twigs and branches to expose the nutritious living tissue beneath. There is even a vampire finch that sits on the backs of larger birds, pecks them until they bleed, and then drinks their blood!

The variety of beak sizes and shapes that confused Darwin has evolved in ways that help the birds accomplish these varied tasks. If you think of beaks as tools, these birds began with a common set of pliers and evolved a whole tool kit. But how did these beaks diversify this way? Could these 13 species really have evolved from a single founding species?

A Galapagos Study

To show that this is a reasonable hypothesis—that the 13 species could have evolved from a single species—Peter and Rosemary Grant needed to do two things. First, they had to show that there is enough variation within each finch species so that natural selection can operate. Second, they had to document natural selection in action—something that had never been done before.

☑ **Checkpoint** What was the objective of the Grants' study? ❶

Studying the Flock

The first task was to catch and identify as many birds as possible. That is why the Grants chose Daphne Major. The island is large enough to support fairly big finch populations. Yet it is small enough to allow the Grants to catch and identify nearly every bird. And once the birds were caught and tagged, the Grants could return, year after year, to keep a record of the individuals that lived and those that died, the ones that succeeded in breeding and those that did not. Today, the Grants not only know the age of all the birds they watch, they also know the history of each of these birds for three generations.

Looking for Variation

As the Grants catch each bird, they record the colors of their beaks and feathers, the body mass, and the lengths of

Figure 11–9
Notice the striking similarity between the beaks of some finches and these tools designed by human technology.

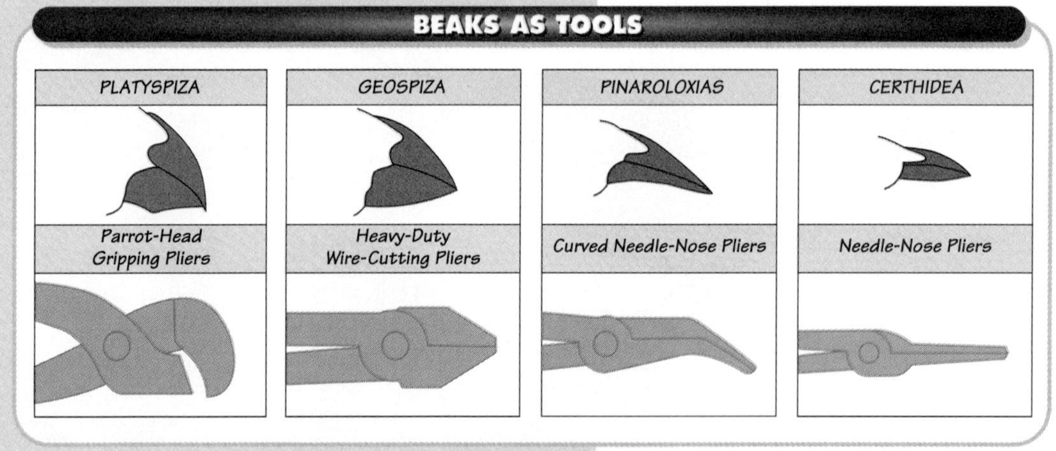

TEACHER SUPPORT

Managing Classroom Diversity

TECH PREP STUDENTS
Point out that the Grants used the scientific method in their experimental approach to studying the evolution of Darwin's finches. Have students identify the steps in the scientific method. (State the problem, gather information, form a hypothesis, experiment, record and analyze data, state a conclusion.) Then challenge students to think of a situation in which they can use these steps or adapt them to solve a problem that they might encounter in their career area of interest. Suggest that students construct a poster to show the problem and the steps they would use to solve it.

their wings, legs, and beaks. What they have found is fascinating. Many traits produce just the sort of normal distribution that is characteristic of polygenic traits such as human height. And individuals regularly vary by as much as 10 percent from the average measurements for their species—plenty of variation.

Looking for Natural Selection

According to Darwin, natural selection is constantly inspecting "... the slightest variations; rejecting those that are bad, preserving and adding up all that are good; silently ... working, whenever and wherever opportunity offers. . . ." Yet when Darwin visited the Galapagos Islands, he did not see variation and selection in action. In fact, he often saw several species eating the same food. How could that be?

Actually, there is a simple explanation. Darwin visited these islands during the rainy season, when plant food is plentiful. At such times, many finches eat whatever they fancy. But it doesn't rain throughout the entire year. During the dry season, the food situation is dramatically different. Some types of food disappear. Other foods are scarce. Then different beaks come in handy.

As food becomes scarce, birds become feeding specialists—each selecting the type of food its beak is best suited to handle. The birds with big, heavy beaks go after big, thick seeds that no other species can crack open. Nevertheless, every year during the dry season, many birds die. Many young birds hatched during the wet season do not survive. Some older birds die, too. The situation is sometimes even more severe. During a long drought that lasted from 1976 through 1977, the Grants observed a population of 1200 birds dwindle to 180! Individual birds they had identified and measured survived and reproduced or died.

☑ *Checkpoint* Why did Darwin not observe natural selection in action? ❷

What Selection Does

The results of the Grants' study were fascinating. When a large-beaked species encountered food scarcity, the birds that survived were those that had the largest beaks. Individuals with small beaks—falling at the other end of the bell curve—did not survive. So the average beak size in the surviving population increased. The change was so large and happened so quickly that a colleague made a startling calculation. It might take only between 12 and 20 droughts to change one species of finch into another! **From this study, you can imagine how several species of finches can, over time, evolve from an ancestral finch species—by the action of the environment on individual organisms with varying fitness.**

Section Review 11-3

1. **Explain** how natural selection can lead to speciation in Darwin's finches.
2. **Explain** the importance of variation to natural selection.
3. **BRANCHING OUT ACTIVITY** **Identify** the selection that occurred in the large-beaked bird species studied by the Grants as either stabilizing, directional, or disruptive selection. Construct a graph to illustrate the appropriate selection process.

Learning Modality

Visual Learning Some students may be able to visualize the speciation process better if they draw diagrams or flowcharts that summarize the Grants' observations and findings. Advise students to include examples of variation and the effects of the drought and rainy seasons on the different bird species.

4 ASSESS

Quick Check

Have student pairs list the Grants' observations of the variations in the traits among the finch species. Also have them list the incidences when natural selection acted on the different finch populations. Encourage each group to make an inference describing how variation and natural selection lead to speciation.

Section Review 11-3

1. When food became scarce on Daphne Major, the finches became specialized in the types of food they ate. Only those finches with big, heavy beaks survived during times of drought and food shortages. Birds with smaller beaks died, and over time, the beak size in the population changed and a new species of finch was formed.

2. Variation of traits must be present in the gene pool of the population so that natural selection can act. If all individuals in the population have identical traits, there are no alternative traits to select for.

3. Directional selection occurred in the large-beaked bird species studied by the Grants. Students should draw a graph similar to the graph shown for directional selection in Figure 11–6.

☑ Checkpoints

❶ Their objective was to show that the 13 species of Darwin's finches could have evolved from a single species.

❷ Darwin visited the Galapagos Islands during the rainy season when plenty of food was available.

Ancillary Support

The resource below can be used to support your teaching strategy for these two pages.

BL Inquiry Activity: Looking for Natural Selection

CHAPTER 11

Laboratory Investigation

Mutations in Bacteria

Before the Lab

1. Several weeks in advance, order from a biological supply company stock cultures of either *Bacillus cereus* or *Bacillus subtilis*, streptomycin filter paper disk, sterile swabs, and prepared Petri plates (if needed). You can substitute other antibiotics, except for penicillin because it may not be effective against *Bacillus*.
2. Prepare the broth culture of bacteria 24 hours ahead of time. Prepare sterile nutrient agar plates by adding 5 g peptone, 3 g beef extract, and 15 g agar to 1 L distilled water in a flask and mix well. Heat gently and stir until solids are dissolved. Boil the dissolved mixture for 1 minute. Plug the flask with cotton and sterilize at 120°C, 15 pounds pressure, for 15 minutes. While the solution is hot, pour it into sterile Petri plates. Prepared Petri plates may also be purchased from biological supply companies. Prepare the broth culture by dissolving 5 g peptone and 3 g beef extract into 1 L distilled water. Heat gently if necessary. Sterilize at 120°C, 15 pounds pressure, for 15 minutes.
3. Gather enough glass marking pencils, forceps, transparent tape, and metric rulers for each group.
4. Check the incubator and set the temperature to 37°C.

Pre-Lab Discussion

Have students read the entire procedure for this investigation. Then ask the following questions.

What is the purpose of this investigation? (To observe that not all the bacteria in a population are affected in the same way by an antibiotic.)

Why must Petri plates be stored upside down? (So condensing water does not drop from the lid onto the agar surface.)

Laboratory Investigation

Mutations in Bacteria

The environment of bacteria that live in the human body undergoes a significant change when antibiotics, such as penicillin or streptomycin, are used. Although most bacteria are killed by an antibiotic, some may survive because they are genetically resistant to the drug. These resistant forms can be thought of as mutants.

Problem

How do antibiotics affect the growth of bacteria? **Formulate a hypothesis** to answer this question.

Materials (per group)

- culture of bacteria
- sterile swabs
- sterile nutrient agar plate
- glass-marking pencil
- antibiotic filter paper discs
- forceps
- transparent tape
- metric ruler

Procedure

1. **CAUTION:** ***Before and after working with bacteria, you must wash your hands and working surfaces with soap and water and disinfectant.*** **Carefully turn the sterile nutrient agar plate over and place it on your table. Do not open the plate.**
2. **With a glass-marking pencil, draw two lines at right angles to each other so that the plate is divided into four equal areas, or quadrants. Label the quadrants from 1 to 4.**
3. **Remove the covering from the sterile swab. Carefully dip the swab in the culture of bacteria. CAUTION:** ***Be very careful when working with bacterial cultures.***
4. **Remove the cover of a nutrient agar plate and rub the bacteria-containing swab over the entire surface of the agar. Follow the directions of your teacher as to how to dispose of the swab.**
5. **With clean forceps, place the antibiotic discs on the nutrient agar, making certain that each disc is placed in the center of a numbered quadrant.**

Safety Tips

- Remind students to wash their hands thoroughly before and after working with the bacteria.
- Students should wash all work surfaces with soap and water and disinfectant before and after working with the bacteria.
- Caution students to handle glass items carefully and to notify you immediately if anything breaks.
- Sterilize all contaminated swabs and Petri plates before disposal using a 15% bleach solution or a 95% ethanol solution, or by autoclaving at 120°C, 15 pounds pressure, for 15 minutes.

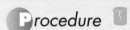

6. **Cover the plate and tape the plate closed.**
7. **Using the glass-marking pencil, write your initials on the bottom of the plate.**
8. **Place the plate upside down in the area designated by your teacher.**
9. **After 24 hours, observe the growth of bacteria around each disc. Record your observations.**
10. **Using a metric ruler, measure in millimeters the diameter of the zone of no bacterial growth, or zone of inhibition, that surrounds each of the antibiotic discs. Construct a data table and record the diameters of the zones of inhibition.**
11. **Carefully observe the zone of inhibition. Do you see a hazy secondary zone of bacterial growth? Record your observations in your data table.**

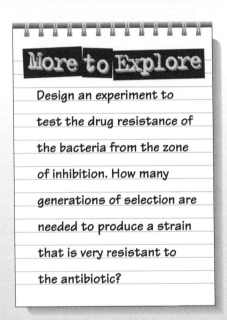

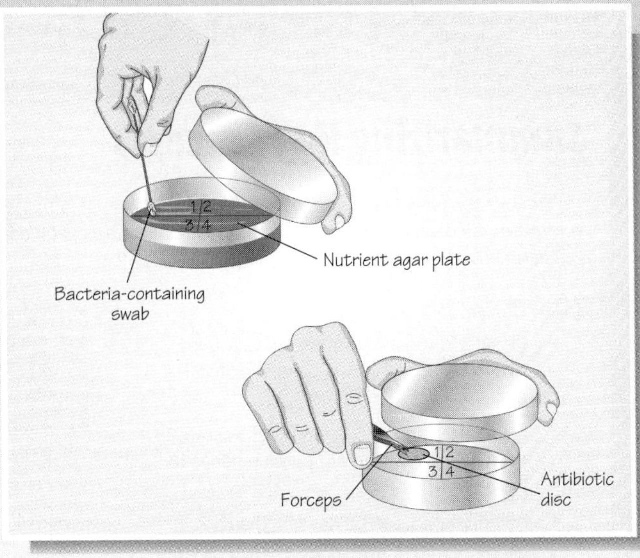

Observations

How is the growth of bacteria affected by the antibiotic discs?

Analysis and Conclusions

1. What factor represents the selection pressure in this experiment?
2. Many of the infectious bacteria—such as *Staphylococcus*—have evolved a resistance to antibiotics. How has this occurred? What is the selection pressure? The adaptation?
3. Do the results of your experiment support your hypothesis?

More to Explore

Design an experiment to test the drug resistance of the bacteria from the zone of inhibition. How many generations of selection are needed to produce a strain that is very resistant to the antibiotic?

Answers to Observations

Students should observe the bacteria growing in a dense lawn, except in areas around the antibiotic disks. Around each disk there will be a halo in which bacterial growth has been inhibited by the antibiotic. There will also be a hazy zone where colonies that are partially resistant to the antibiotic will grow.

Answers to Analysis and Conclusions

1. The antibiotic is the selection pressure.
2. The genes for resistance probably existed in the population of bacteria as mutations. The incorrect use or overuse of antibiotics has selected for mutant bacteria that carry antibiotic-resistant genes.
3. Answers will depend on students' hypotheses. Students should explain why their results did or did not support their hypotheses.

More to Explore

Students' experimental designs might suggest using sterile swabs to collect bacteria growing in the hazy halo around the antibiotic disk, inoculating a new Petri plate, and repeating the investigation. They should repeat this procedure until they observe no zones of inhibition around the disks.

What is the zone of inhibition? (It is a clear or hazy ring around the antibiotic disk in which bacterial growth is inhibited.)

What is your hypothesis about the effect of antibiotics on the growth of bacteria? (Some students may hypothesize that antibiotics prevent the growth of most bacteria, but mutant bacteria may grow in the presence of the antibiotic.)

Skills Development

Students will use these skills while completing the laboratory investigation: hypothesizing, observing, measuring, communicating, and interpreting.

Teaching Strategies

1. Demonstrate the sterilizing technique before the investigation. Tell students to hold the stopper with one hand and to replace it quickly after they have finished.
2. Demonstrate how to inoculate the Petri plate by running the swab gently over the surface of the agar in a zigzag pattern, then covering the Petri plate immediately.
3. Collect used swabs in a jar containing 95% ethanol or 15% bleach.
4. Caution students not to touch the surface of the agar with the forceps.

CHAPTER 11

Study Guide

Review Strategy

Divide the class into small teams to play the following game: One team draws a picture of a word, and another team tries to guess the word. Drawers cannot speak or use letters or words in the drawings. Use the key terms for this chapter, as well as other terms, such as directional selection, mutation, and adaptation. Write each word on a card and have the drawers randomly pick a card. Give a time limit, such as 30 seconds to 1 minute, for teams to guess the word. A student on the drawing team can be timekeeper. If the guessers do not guess the word in the time limit, then the teams switch roles. If you wish, have teams keep score by tallying the number of words guessed correctly.

Recalling Main Ideas

1. c	5. c
2. a	6. d
3. b	7. a
4. a	8. b

Assessment

Reviewing What You Learned

1. Genetics.
2. A gene is the carrier of an inheritable trait. An allele is a different form of a gene.
3. A change in the structure of DNA.
4. A significant percentage of genes in natural populations have more than one allele. Therefore, genetic variation in nature is fairly common.
5. A trait controlled by two or more genes.
6. Darwin's definitions did not consider the role that genes play in fitness or adaptation.
7. Reproductive isolation occurs when two different species cannot interbreed. A species is a group of organisms that can breed only with one another to produce fertile offspring.

Study Guide

Summarizing Key Concepts

The key concepts in each section of this chapter are listed below to help you review the chapter content. Make sure you understand each concept and its relationship to other concepts and to the theme of this chapter.

11–1 Darwin "Meets" DNA

- Inheritable variation comes primarily from two kinds of changes in genetic material—mutations and gene shuffling.
- An organism's evolutionary fitness can be defined as its success in passing genes to the next generation.
- An adaptation can be described as any genetically controlled trait that increases an individual's ability to pass along copies of its genes.
- A species is defined as a group of similar-looking organisms that can breed with one another and produce fertile offspring. The members of two different species cannot interbreed and are therefore said to be reproductively isolated from one another.

11–2 Evolution as Genetic Change

- In genetic terms, evolution is defined as any change in the relative frequencies of alleles in the gene pool of a species.
- Natural selection alters the allele frequencies in a gene pool by selecting helpful mutations and by selecting variations that represent the highest fitness.
- A random change in allele frequency is called genetic drift.
- For speciation to take place, a population must evolve enough genetic changes so that breeding cannot occur between the emerging genetically different groups.
- Gradualism and punctuated equilibrium are two views of the pattern of evolution.

11–3 How Species Change

- Organisms display a variation in phenotypes. The variation in phenotypes often corresponds to a variation in fitness. Natural selection chooses the fittest individuals to survive and reproduce, slowly causing the distribution of phenotypes to change. When the change is large enough to prevent interbreeding between the populations, a distinct species has evolved.

Reviewing Key Terms

Review the following vocabulary terms and their meaning. Then use each term in a complete sentence.

11–1 Darwin "Meets" DNA

mutation
reproductive isolation
gene pool

11–2 Evolution as Genetic Change

genetic drift
speciation
gradualism
punctuated equilibrium

Inquiry-Based Strategy

Sometimes when a species moves into a new environment, it encounters no selection pressures and reproduces rampantly, eventually forcing out native species. Most of these opportunistic organisms have been introduced by human action. Some examples are purple loosestrife in northern lakes and waterways, and gypsy moths in eastern forests. Allow students to choose one of these organisms, or another with similar characteristics, and research it in order to answer the following question: What can be done to keep this organism from destroying the ecosystem?

Students may approach finding the answer to this question in many different ways. One might be to introduce natural predators into the environment. Students should be aware of how their solutions will affect the environment.

Recalling Main Ideas

Choose the letter of the answer that best completes the statement or answers the question.

1. Which is a source of inheritable variation in organisms?
   - **a.** climate
   - **b.** struggle for existence
   - **c.** gene shuffling
   - **d.** punctuated equilibrium
2. A normal distribution of phenotypes is observed for traits controlled by
   - **a.** many genes. **c.** 1 gene.
   - **b.** 2 genes. **d.** 0 genes.
3. In genetic terms, evolution is
   - **a.** the diversity of living things.
   - **b.** a change in the relative frequencies of alleles in the gene pool of the species.
   - **c.** natural selection acting on inheritable variation.
   - **d.** a combination of gradual and rapid change in living things.
4. A helpful mutation causes the corresponding allele's frequency to
   - **a.** increase. **c.** remain unchanged.
   - **b.** decrease. **d.** double over 10 generations.
5. Natural selection acting on a normal distribution of phenotypes in which the fittest individuals correspond to the center of the graph is called
   - **a.** disruptive selection. **c.** stabilizing selection.
   - **b.** directional selection **d.** artificial selection.
6. A random change in the frequency of an allele in a gene pool is called
   - **a.** gradualism. **c.** speciation.
   - **b.** gene shuffling. **d.** genetic drift.
7. Speciation in nature usually occurs because
   - **a.** populations become separated by a geographical barrier.
   - **b.** only the fittest organisms survive.
   - **c.** of artificial selection.
   - **d.** of genetic drift.
8. Two populations that occupy the same habitat but do not share a gene pool
   - **a.** belong to the same species.
   - **b.** are reproductively isolated.
   - **c.** are geographically isolated.
   - **d.** undergo disruptive selection.

Putting It All Together

Using the information on pages xxx to xxxi, complete the following concept map.

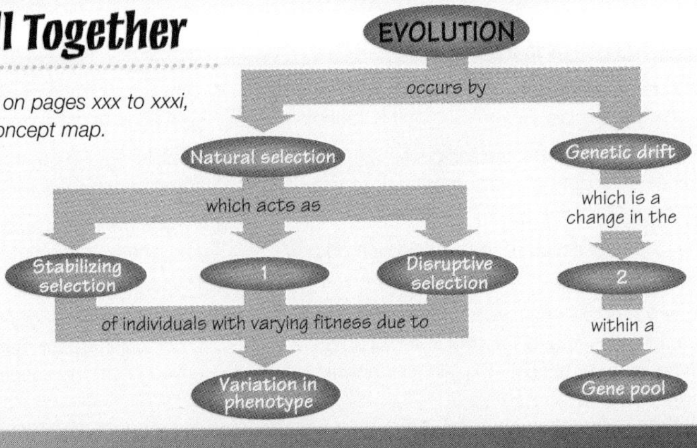

Putting It All Together

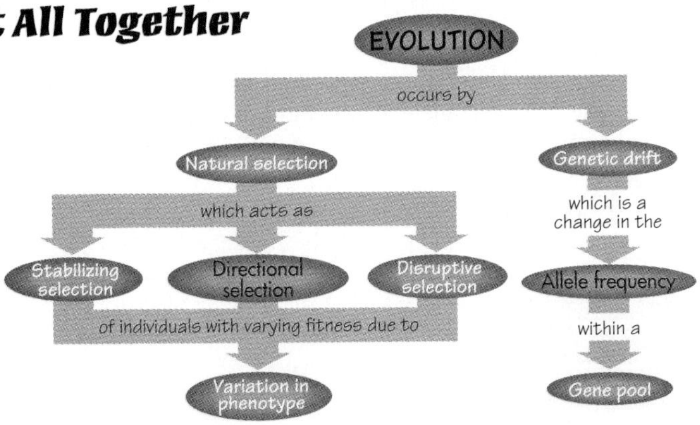

8. A gene pool is the group of alleles shared by the individuals of a species.
9. The frequency of an allele for a harmful mutation will decrease, and it will increase for a helpful mutation.
10. By stabilizing selection, directional selection, and disruptive selection.
11. Genetic drift is the random change in allele frequency in a population. It is most likely to occur in small populations or when a small group of organisms colonizes a new habitat.
12. Geographic isolation and reproductive isolation.
13. Gradualism is the idea that evolution occurs slowly and steadily over long periods of time. Punctuated equilibrium is the idea that evolution occurs in a pattern involving long periods of stability interrupted by episodes of rapid change.
14. During periods of food scarcity, only those birds with the largest beaks survived. Those with small beaks did not survive, causing the average beak size in the population to increase. These observations provided evidence that several species of finches can evolve over time from an ancestral finch species.

Expanding the Concepts

1. Traits controlled by single genes with two alleles produce two or three possible phenotypes. Polygenic traits produce a continuous variation of phenotypes, which is characterized by a bell-shaped curve.
2. The phenotype of an organism determines whether it will survive and reproduce. Natural selection affects only the variations in phenotypes within a population. These variations are produced by the interaction between an organism's genes and its environment.
3. Shuffling the genes within a gene pool does not change the relative number of alleles for a particular gene. The relative allele frequencies will change only if some of the alleles in the gene pool are lost because of the inability to pass the genes to offspring.

CHAPTER 11

Assessment (continued)

4. The fitness of individuals at different locations on a bell-shaped curve varies, allowing natural selection to act. Figure 11–6 gives a good description of stabilizing selection, directional selection, and disruptive selection.
5. Stabilizing selection; because the most fit individuals also have the highest relative allele frequency in the population. Evolution occurs only when there is a change in the allele frequency.
6. Genetic changes might cause one organism to look different from another, so they will not be attracted as mates. These genetic changes have led to reproductive isolation; breeding cannot occur between the two groups, so the two groups have become two different species.
7. Isolating mechanisms keep two groups of organisms from interacting with each other, as well as enabling natural selection to work differently on each group. This allows the two groups to become genetically different from each other.
8. Natural selection acts only on the phenotype of an organism, which is the result of the interaction between the organism's genotype and its environment. As natural selection changes the allele frequency of a population, evolution occurs.
9. A smaller population may carry alleles in relative frequencies different from those of a larger original population. Thus, the offspring they produce will be genetically different from the original population simply by chance.
10. An organism that is better adapted to its environment has inheritable traits and behaviors that make it more fit than another individual of that species.

Assessment

Reviewing What You Learned

Answer each of the following in a complete sentence.

1. What area of biology has made possible a better understanding of evolution?
2. What is a gene? An allele?
3. What is a mutation?
4. How common is genetic variation in nature?
5. What is meant by a polygenic trait?
6. How are the genetic definitions of fitness and adaptation different from Darwin's?
7. What is meant by reproductive isolation? Define the term species in this context.
8. Explain the concept of a gene pool.
9. What happens to the frequency of an allele as a result of a harmful mutation? A helpful mutation?
10. Identify three ways in which natural selection affects the distribution of variation in polygenic traits.
11. What is genetic drift? In what kinds of situations is it more likely to occur?
12. What conditions give rise to speciation?
13. What is gradualism? Punctuated equilibrium?
14. Describe the results of the study of birds on Daphne Major, one of the Galapagos Islands.

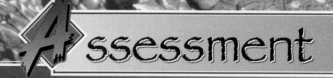

Expanding the Concepts

Discuss each of the following in a brief paragraph.

1. Compare the variations produced by single-gene and polygenic traits.
2. Natural selection acts on phenotype and not on genotype. Explain the meaning of this statement.
3. Sexual reproduction shuffles genes within a gene pool, causing variation. Why does this not cause a change in relative allele frequencies?
4. Describe the action of natural selection on polygenic traits.
5. In which of the three types of selection (stabilizing, directional, or disruptive) is evolution likely to be minor or absent? Explain your answer.
6. How might genetic changes lead to the formation of new species?
7. Why are isolating mechanisms important to the formation of new species?
8. Explain why an organism's phenotype is usually the driving force for its evolution.
9. Why is the role of chance as the mechanism for genetic change more significant in smaller populations?
10. What does a biologist mean when stating that a particular organism is better adapted to its environment than another of that species?

Extending Your Thinking

1. Some students might hypothesize that those tortoises with high neck arches could reach food that was located higher up on bushes or trees. Those with low neck arches could reach food only on the ground. The scarcity of food might have selected for tortoises that had some variation in their neck arch.

2. It is almost impossible to remove the allele from the population because it will always be masked by the dominant normal allele. Natural selection cannot select against the recessive allele. It can select against only the harmful phenotype.

Skills Trace
Relating

- Focus p. 244
- Practice p. 245
- Assess p. 261

3. Organisms that cause diseases, such as bacteria, viruses, and fungi, have enough natural variation and high mutation rates to produce resistance to any kind of medicine.

Extending Your Thinking

Use the skills you have developed in this chapter to answer the following.

1. **Hypothesizing** In a small group of islands, it was noted that tortoise shells were of two major types—those with high neck arches and those with low neck arches. Formulate a hypothesis to explain the evolution of this difference. Then discuss the role of environmental and genetic factors that might have had selective value.
2. **Relating** Harmful gene mutations are normally harmful only in the homozygous recessive condition, in which the individual has two copies of the recessive allele. Discuss why the removal of the harmful gene from the population is almost impossible.
3. **Evaluating** "The complete control of detrimental diseases is highly unlikely." Discuss the validity of this statement.
4. **Constructing a model** Construct a model to simulate genetic drift due to a small population separating from a large population and establishing a new, distinct gene pool. Will evolution occur? Explain your reasoning.
5. **Hypothesizing** Orchids and insects are often quoted as examples of coevolution—the evolution of two or more closely interacting species that serve as the selection force for one another. Formulate a hypothesis to explain how species might coevolve.

Applying Your Skills

Natural Selection in Action

A mouse population exhibits variation in fur color. Mice that have more white fur are easier prey for hawks, and those with darker fur are better camouflaged in their environment. The allele for dark fur is dominant to the allele for white fur.

1. Over a number of years, there was an increase in hawk population. What will this do to the allele frequencies for fur color in mice? Write a paragraph to answer the question.
2. Draw a graph to help explain your answer.

• GOING FURTHER •

3. Over many generations of mice in this environment, what adaptation will allow the mice to survive and reproduce? Will this affect the hawk population? Explain your answer.

4. Some student models might use colored beads to represent the alleles in a gene pool. Evolution will occur because there will be a change in the allele frequency of the new, distinct gene pool.

Skills Trace

Modeling

- Focus p. 252
- Practice p. 252
- Assess p. 261

5. Some students might hypothesize that species coevolve because the two species rely on each other for survival. Any variation that increases the fitness of one species will affect the fitness of the other.

Applying Your Skills

Teacher Notes

• You might wish to have students work in pairs or cooperative groups to answer these questions.

Answers

1. An increased number of hawks will require more mice to feed them. Those mice that are easier prey will be less fit than those mice that are better camouflaged. Over time, most mice in the population will have dark fur. However, the white allele will never completely vanish from the population because it is masked by the dominant dark allele.
2. Students should draw a graph that looks similar to the graph in Figure 11–3 for a trait controlled by one gene. However, the graph should show that the number of individuals with the homozygous dominant genotype is increasing and the number of individuals with the homozygous recessive genotype is decreasing, and almost absent. The number of heterozygotes will probably remain about the same.
3. Darker fur better camouflages the mice so that the hawks cannot catch them. This adaptation will allow the mice to survive and reproduce. The hawk population might decrease because individual hawks may not be able to find and catch enough food to survive.

Scoring Rubric

4 Response is thorough, accurate, and creative; shows an in-depth understanding of science skills, procedures, and concepts.

3 Response is complete, mostly accurate, and original; shows a satisfactory understanding of science skills, procedures, and concepts.

2 Response is mostly complete but includes some inaccuracies; shows an adequate understanding of science skills, procedures, and concepts.

1 Response is only partially complete and has many inaccuracies; shows an incomplete understanding of science skills, procedures, and concepts.

0 Response is mostly incomplete and/or inaccurate; shows a lack of understanding of science skills, procedures, and concepts.

Chapter 12 The Origins of Biodiversity

Content Management	Student Edition Activities
■ Section 12–1 The Unity of Life, pp. 263–267 Evolving Differences The Molecular Unity of Life	MINI LAB: Structure or Function?, p. 266 Laboratory Investigation: Who's Related to Whom?, pp. 274–275
■ Section 12–2 Biodiversity, pp. 268–271 What Is Biodiversity? Importance of Biodiversity Importance of Genetic Diversity	
◆ BRANCHING OUT • In Depth Section 12–3 DNA: A Storehouse of History, pp. 272–273 Molecular Clocks Slow Clocks, Fast Clocks	MINI LAB: Molecular Clocks, p. 273

■ These sections cover all the necessary content and concepts for a basic course in biology.
◆ This section covers content and concepts that are either applications or extensions of the basic material.

Integration Strategies

SE Chemistry, p. 266
Biology and Society, p. 271

Assessment Strategies

SE Chapter Review, pp. 276–279
TR Section Reviews
Chapter Test
BL Chapter Review
Practice Test
CTB Chapter 12 Test

Tech Prep

Teaching strategies appropriate for students who are in technical/vocational programs or who are considering post-secondary technical education can be found on the following **TE** pages: 264 and 270.

Meeting the Standards

Sections 12–1 through 12–3 cover three of the six content standards under **The Cell,** two of the three content standards under **The Molecular Basis of Heredity,** all five of the content standards under **Biological Evolution,** and two of the five content standards under **The Interdependence of Organisms** as described on pages 184–186 of The National Science Education Standards.

Chapter Planning Guide

Teacher's Edition Activities	Other Activities	Media and Technology
Chapter Discovery Learning Activity, p. 262 **Inquiry Activity:** One Common Ancestor, p. 264 **Investigate:** Model Building, p. 264	**LM** Observing the Effects of Temperature on the Growth of Yeast, #23 **TR** **Writing in Biology:** Similarity and Diversity **Apply:** Backyard Evolution **BL** **Inquiry Activity:** Jurassic Mall	**BioVue Plus CD-ROMs:** Do Modern Dinosaurs Fly? **TB** Cytochrome-c Family Tree, #15
Inquiry Activity: Discovering Diversity, p. 268 **Investigate:** Cooperative Learning, p. 268 **Investigate:** Research, p. 269	**LM** Observing Organisms in Soil Samples, #24 **TR** **Explore:** Desktop Estuary **BL** **Inquiry Activity:** Nature's Variety	**BioVue Mini Doc:** Genetic Diversity and Endangered Species, Videodisc Side 3 **BioVue Plus CD-ROMs:** Genetic Diversity and Endangered Species
Inquiry Activity: Marking Time, p. 272	**TR** **Enrich:** Ancient DNA, Modern Techniques **BL** **Inquiry Activity:** Time Marches On	

KEY: SE Student Edition **TE** Teacher's Edition **LM** Laboratory Manual **TR** Teaching Resources **BL** BioLog **TB** Transparency Box **CTB** Computer Test Bank

Materials List

TE Chapter Discovery Learning Activity, p. 262 (20 minutes); models, preserved specimens, and/or photographs of various winged animals, such as grasshoppers, beetles, dragonflies, bats, penguins, chickens, sparrows, ducks, and ostriches.
SE MINI LAB: Structure or Function?, p. 266 (15–20 minutes); photographs of various organisms that have homologous and/or analogous structures, such as winged animals, plants with different leaf shapes, and animals with homologous forelegs.
TE Investigate: Cooperative Learning, p. 268 (1–2 hours); poster board and various art supplies, such as markers, colored pencils, scissors, colored paper, old magazines, and glue.
TE Inquiry Activity: Marking Time, p. 272 (20 minutes); various timekeeping devices, such as a pendulum clock, kitchen timer, metronome, hourglass, and stopwatch.
SE MINI LAB: Molecular Clocks, p. 273 (15–20 minutes); calculator.

CHAPTER 12

The Origins of Biodiversity

Introducing the Chapter

. . . In Pictures

The chapter opening photograph shows three different species of colorful butterflies that exist in nature. Have students examine the photograph, read the caption, and answer the following questions.

- **What causes these butterflies to be similar yet different?** (Their inherited traits and their environment cause their similarities and differences.)
- **How might their differences benefit these butterflies?** (Accept all reasonable responses. Their differences provide the inheritable variation on which natural selection acts, making these butterflies better able to adapt to changes in the environment.)

Explain that although evolution increases the variation among organisms, their DNA molecules have some surprising similarities.

Teaching Strategy

In the first two sections of this chapter, students learn that many different organisms have similar DNA sequences and that evolution contributes to biodiversity. The BRANCHING OUT section explains how scientists use changes in DNA to determine the evolutionary relationships of organisms.

BIO JOURNAL

Students should be able to identify several differences among the various species of butterflies in the photograph, including wing color, wing patterns, size, and shape. Similarities may include the number of wings, legs, and antennae. Instruct students to keep their entries in their portfolios.

CHAPTER 12

The Origins of Biodiversity

FOCUSING THE CHAPTER
THEME: *Unity and Diversity*

12–1 The Unity of Life
- **Discuss** adaptive radiation and convergent evolution as origins of biodiversity.
- **Examine** genetic evidence for the unity of life.

12–2 Biodiversity
- **Define** biodiversity and **explain** its importance.

BRANCHING OUT *In Depth*

12–3 DNA: A Storehouse of History
- **Explore** how changes in DNA can be used to mark time.

LABORATORY INVESTIGATION
- **Predict** the relatedness of several species from their amino acid sequences.

Biology and Your World

BIO JOURNAL

How do these butterflies differ from one another? How are they the same? Write the answers to these questions in your journal.

A display of diversity among butterflies

TEACHER SUPPORT

Chapter Discovery Learning Activity

COMPARING STRUCTURES

Display models, preserved specimens, and/or photographs of different kinds of animals with wings, such as grasshoppers, beetles, dragonflies, bats, penguins, chickens, sparrows, ducks, and ostriches. Instruct students to compare and contrast the wing structures and functions in all of the animals. Encourage them to make inferences about which animals are more closely related based on wing structure. Make sure they explain what criteria they used to determine those relationships. Explain to students that they will study how scientists use similar structures to help them determine the common ancestors of organisms.

The Unity of Life

SECTION 12–1

Guide for Reading

- **Compare** adaptive radiation and convergent evolution.
- **Examine** molecular evidence for the unity of life.

MINI LAB

- **Classify** various parts of organisms by structural or functional similarity.

THE VOLCANIC CRATER OF Solfatarra near Naples, Italy, isn't the sort of place you would expect to find much life. Superheated steam bubbles out of boiling mud that is laced with sulfuric acid. Yet these bubbling mud pots are home to bacteria that are as different from humans as any form of life could be. Unlike humans, the bacteria are poisoned by oxygen. Yet they thrive in water that would boil humans alive, and they eat sulfur. Nevertheless, some of their genes are astonishingly similar to genes in your cells! The story behind this remarkable genetic similarity is nothing less than the story of life itself.

Evolving Differences

Ever since Darwin, biologists have known that all organisms on Earth are related. But relationships among some organisms are easier to see than others. A chimpanzee looks a lot like its siblings, a bit less like a gorilla, and even less like a dog, a bird, or a dolphin. Yet if you were to look closely at all these animals, you would see similarities in body structures. One such similarity is that they all have backbones. Their arms, legs, wings, and flippers are formed from similar bones that have been modified in different ways.

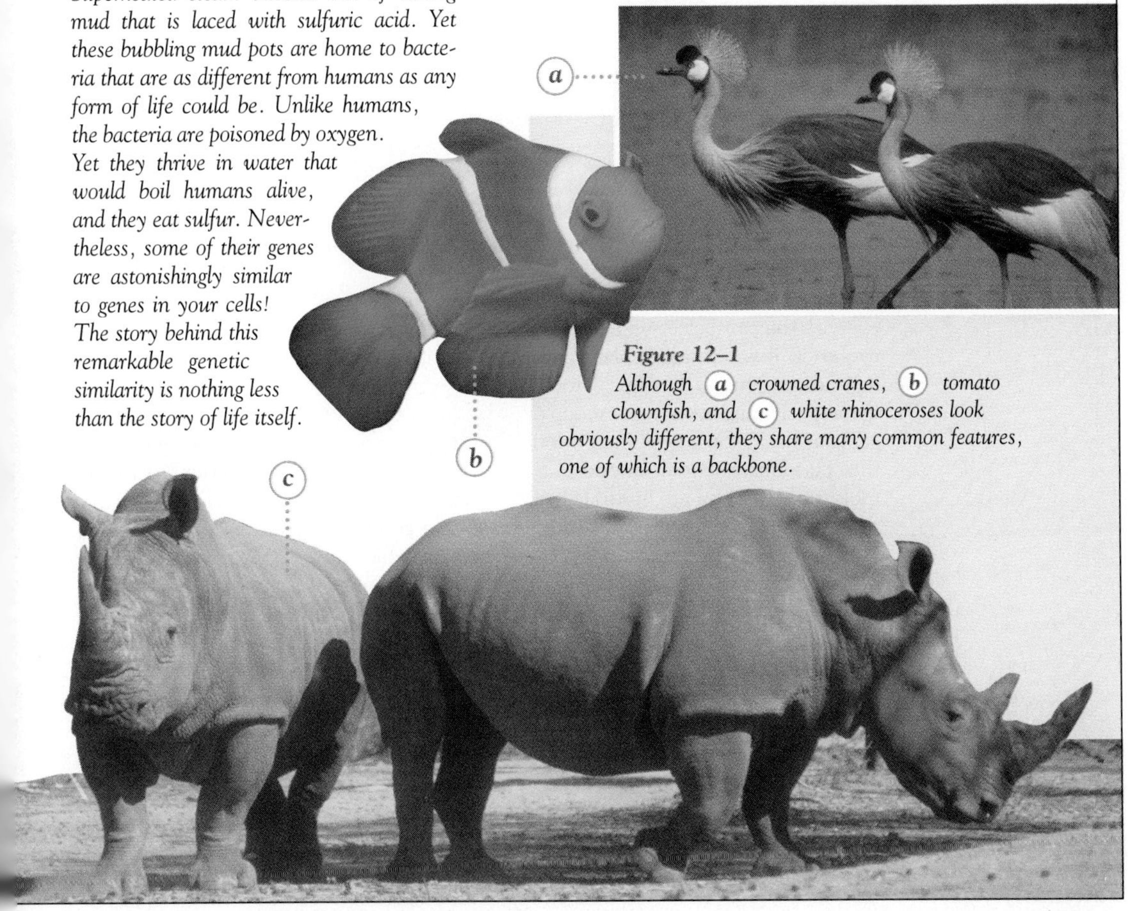

Figure 12–1
Although (a) crowned cranes, (b) tomato clownfish, and (c) white rhinoceroses look obviously different, they share many common features, one of which is a backbone.

Section 12–1

The Unity of Life

Performance Objectives

- Differentiate between adaptive radiation and convergent evolution.
- Give examples of the molecular evidence for the unity of life.

Mini Lab Skill: Classifying
Laboratory Investigation Skill: Predicting

1 ENGAGE

Ideas Through Images

Have students examine Figure 12–1, read the caption, and answer the following questions.

- **Can you recall from Chapter 10 what homologous structures are?** (Structures in different organisms formed from similar tissues or bones that have been modified.)
- **What are some homologous structures in these animals?** (The front legs of the rhinoceroses and the wings of the cranes, as well as the fish scales and the crane feathers.)
- **Why do these animals have such diverse shapes and body structures?** (Responses may include that each animal has structures that help it to best survive in its environment.)

TEACHER SUPPORT

Background Information

You might want to share these facts with students to give examples of similarities between vastly different organisms.

- Chlorophyll, the pigment molecule in plants that absorbs light and captures the energy from the sun, is very similar to hemoglobin, the pigment molecule that transports oxygen in an animal's bloodstream.
- The genes in fruit flies that control the development of the fruit fly body share a very similar nucleotide sequence with genes that perform the same function in many other animals, although each species has its own unique sequence.

Ancillary Support

The resource below can be used to support your teaching strategy for these two pages.

TR Writing in Biology: Similarity and Diversity

2 EXPLORE

Inquiry Activity

Inferring

One Common Ancestor Ask students to infer whether all living organisms could have evolved from one common ancestor. Encourage students to observe as many living things as possible before making their inferences. Students should reassess their inferences at the end of the section.

3 TEACH

Discussion

Discuss with students the similarities among such diverse organisms as bacteria and humans. Point out how the process of natural selection has tinkered with an original group of molecules to produce all organisms living on Earth. And because of this, all the diverse organisms on Earth share some very common biological processes, such as the Krebs cycle, cellular respiration, and protein synthesis.

Investigate

Model Building Challenge students to diagram the adaptive radiation of a group of common objects, such as balls, shoes, clothes, motor vehicles, or writing utensils. They should show how the object has evolved to be specific for different uses. Have students use Figure 12–2 as a model for their own diagrams.

Correcting Misconceptions

To help students better understand homologous and analogous structures, draw two arrows on the chalkboard that begin at the same point, then diverge. Explain that this illustrates adaptive radiation and how homologous structures form. Then draw two arrows that begin at two different points and converge at the same point to illustrate how analogous structures form in convergent evolution.

ADAPTIVE RADIATION

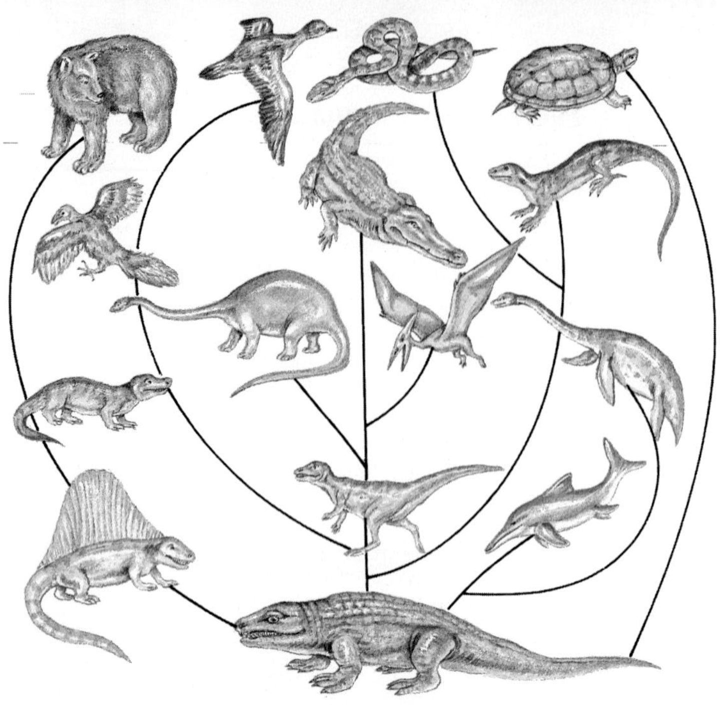

Figure 12–2 The illustration shows the formation of several different species from an adaptive radiation of ancient reptiles. Dinosaurs were some of the most spectacular products of this adaptive radiation.

You may recall that these homologous structures are formed from similar tissues.

How and why do such structures evolve? You can better understand their evolution if you think of plant and animal adaptations as biological tool kits. Each species and each major group of organisms has its own version of a tool kit that performs essential functions. Some tools in the tool kit are invisible because they involve biochemical processes such as respiration and protein synthesis. More visible parts—such as lungs, claws, or wings—are used for breathing, catching food, and moving around.

Recall that natural selection works by selecting inheritable variations in plant and animal characteristics. It is therefore easy for natural selection to change the shape or size of a particular tool in ways that change its function. You have seen how this process can increase beak size in Galapagos finches. Natural selection can work the same way for almost any trait that is under genetic control. But it is much more difficult (and therefore much less common) for natural selection to produce a kit with an entirely new set of tools. Simply put, evolution can modify existing tool kits much more easily than it can generate entirely new ones.

Adaptive Radiation

Every now and then, however, a new tool kit does evolve. Fossil records show several instances of diversity occurring in a newly evolved species in a relatively short period of time. This process is known as **adaptive radiation.** Adaptive radiation also occurs when an organism or a group of organisms colonizes a new area where other species that compete for life's necessities are lacking. In both these situations, selection and adaptation lead to the formation of a new species. **When a newly evolved species or a group of organisms in a new area evolve—sometimes somewhat quickly—into different species that live in different ways, this pattern of evolution is known as adaptive radiation.**

TEACHER SUPPORT

Managing Classroom Diversity

TECH PREP STUDENTS
Have students list the skills required for their career area of interest. Then have them make a list of the skills they already have. Encourage students to list all their skills, even if they are not required for their career. Then challenge students to show how they can develop the skills they need from the skills they have. Point out that skill development, like natural selection, builds on skills that already exist.

LEP STUDENTS
Students with limited English proficiency may have difficulty with some of the scientific terminology in this section. Pair LEP students with other students who understand the concepts. Instruct LEP students to list the words that they do not understand. Then have partners draw pictures to describe the meanings of the words.

Figure 12–3
Although the wings of the (a) bald eagle, the (b) fishing bat, and the (c) dragonfly serve the same function, they have evolved from different parts of the animals' tool kits. The wings of these animals are an example of analogous structures.

Darwin's finches are an example of the type of adaptive radiation that often happens on isolated island groups. In this case, more than a dozen species evolved from a single founding species that colonized the islands from the mainland of South America.

☑ ***Checkpoint*** What is the process of adaptive radiation? (1)

Convergent Evolution

Often, adaptive radiations in different groups of organisms produce species that are adapted to similar feeding habits or ways of moving from place to place. **Convergent evolution** is the name given to this process. **In convergent evolution, unrelated species may independently evolve superficial similarities because of adaptations to similar environments.**

For example, woodpeckers get their food by drilling into tree bark to uncover grubs and other insects. But several other animals—such as the honeycreeper, the striped opossum, and the aye-aye—also obtain their food in this way. There are also several groups of animals that fly. Bird and bat wings are similar but not identical. Close observation reveals that their front limb bones support flight structures in different ways. Insect wings are completely different. Structures such as these—which are similar in appearance and function but are developed from anatomically different parts—are called **analogous structures.** Analogous structures are the hallmark of convergent evolution.

☑ ***Checkpoint*** What is convergent evolution? (2)

Problems With Distant Relations

Homologous structures in adult organisms and fossils often enable biologists to piece together evolutionary history and determine how various species are related. But this approach has its limits. Adult body parts cannot offer much help in deciding how humans might be related to animals such as insects or snails.

Looking at structures in the early stages of embryo development can help in some cases. But similarities in embryo development cannot help with single-celled organisms because they have neither embryos nor body parts that correspond to those of humans. Interestingly, the most exciting clues to evolutionary history and relationships among these organisms have come from the work of researchers who weren't even studying these topics!

Ideas Through Images

Have students examine Figure 12–3, read the caption, and answer the following questions.

- **Why are the animal wings pictured here considered to be analogous structures?** (The wings resemble one another because they have similar functions, not similar structures.)
- **How are these animal wings an example of convergent evolution?** (These animals are unrelated species that have independently evolved a similar method of moving.)
- **Why do you think each of these species evolved adaptations for flight?** (Accept all reasonable responses. Flight enables these animals to get food and escape predators.)

Discussion

Start a class discussion about how the molecular unity of life helps medical researchers learn more about human health. For example, explain that researchers can study certain genes and proteins in yeast to find treatments for cancer. Then describe one experiment in which researchers inserted a normal human gene into mutant yeast whose cells would not stop dividing. The inserted gene caused the yeast to stop dividing.

☑ Checkpoints

(1) Adaptive radiation occurs when a newly evolved species or group of organisms in a new area evolves somewhat quickly into different species that live in different ways.

(2) In convergent evolution, unrelated species independently evolve superficial similarities because of adaptations to similar environments.

TEACHER SUPPORT

Managing Classroom Diversity

AT-RISK STUDENTS

Some students might miss the relationships among DNA, diversity, molecular unity, and natural selection. Suggest that these students make flowcharts to show the connections among these concepts. You might pair these students with others who fully grasp the relationships and encourage both to work together to design the flowcharts. (Flowcharts might look like this: DNA → molecular unity → natural selection → diversity.)

Ancillary Support

The resources below can be used to support your teaching strategy for these two pages.

TR Apply: Backyard Evolution
BL Inquiry Activity: Jurassic Mall

MINI LAB Classifying

Teacher Note
- For time required and materials needed, see page 262b.

Answers to Analyze and Conclude
1. Homologous structures and analogous structures.
2. Answers will depend on the organisms students classify.
3. Analogous structures indicate that convergent evolution has occurred. Homologous structures indicate that adaptive radiation has occurred.

Skills Trace
Classifying
- Focus p. 266
- Practice p. 267
- Assess p. 278

INTEGRATING CHEMISTRY

Proteins contain carbon, oxygen, hydrogen, nitrogen, and sulfur. They function as antibodies, enzymes, and cell components. All amino acids have four groups of atoms bound to a central carbon atom. These groups are the amino group (NH_2), the carboxyl group (COOH), an atom of hydrogen (H), and the R group (specific to each of the 20 different amino acids). Amino acids are joined together to form proteins. DNA is a chain of nucleotides. Each nucleotide is made up of three parts: a five-carbon sugar, a nitrogenous base, and a phosphate group. DNA is the code from which proteins are made.

Laboratory Investigation

The Laboratory Investigation, Who's Related to Whom? on pages 274–275 is appropriate to use at this point in the chapter.

MINI LAB Classifying

Structure or Function?

PROBLEM *How can you **classify** various parts of organisms by structural or functional similarity?*

PROCEDURE

1. Examine the photographs of the organisms provided by your teacher.
2. Identify a part in each organism that could be similar in structure or function to a part in another organism. Record this information.

ANALYZE AND CONCLUDE

1. What are the terms used to indicate these structures?
2. Classify the organisms into two groups: those with parts exhibiting structural similarities and those with parts exhibiting functional similarities.
3. What patterns of evolution are indicated by these similarities?

The Molecular Unity of Life

INTEGRATING CHEMISTRY

What is the chemical structure and function of proteins, amino acids, and DNA?

Recently, molecular biologists developed techniques to read information coded in DNA letter by letter. When that information first began to accumulate, most researchers used it to answer questions about the workings of genes, genetic diseases, or cell chemistry. These applications continue today, of course. But as more and more DNA data were gathered, evolutionary biologists became fascinated with DNA, and molecular biologists were astonished to find themselves interested in evolution. Thus began an entirely new age of exploration in evolution.

Reading DNA

What information did molecular biology provide? **As information on DNA sequences accumulated, biologists realized that many genes were shared by a wide range of organisms.** Researchers knew that amino acids—the basic building blocks of proteins—were common to all forms of life. But new data have shown that whole stretches of DNA and, therefore, entire sequences of amino acids in many proteins were practically identical in nearly every organism studied!

Of course, as you can see in ***Figure 12–4,*** the more closely two organisms are related, the more closely their genes resemble each other. And organisms that differ as much as bacteria differ from humans contain many different genes. Bacteria that live in hot springs and mud pots, for example, carry genes that help them to survive high temperatures. Humans lack those genes, but they do have genes that carry instructions on how to walk upright on two legs.

Checkpoint What did researchers discover by studying DNA? 1

Identical Tool Kits

Interestingly, certain genes in bacteria that live in hot springs are almost identical to genes and proteins found in every other living organism—from yeast to fruit flies to humans. One common feature of all living things, for example, is the ribosome—the part of life's molecular tool kit that serves as a protein factory. When molecular biologists compared DNA sequences that build bacterial ribosomes with genes that direct the assembly of human ribosomes, they found them to be astonishingly similar. Certainly, these genes and proteins are homologous.

Now think about that for a minute. First, you should know that some hot-springs' bacteria are more similar to the very first forms of life on Earth than any other living organisms. Yet the genes that carry instructions to build their ribosomes are incredibly similar to ours! Both molecular biologists and evolutionary biologists find this fact amazing.

266 Chapter 12

TEACHER SUPPORT Background Information

Genealogical trees, like the one in Figure 12–4, are constructed with the assumption that species share common ancestors. Scientists compare the amino acid sequences or nucleotide sequences of certain proteins or genes from different species to determine their evolutionary relationships. The length of the branches on a genealogical tree, which symbolize the distance from a common ancestor, is approximately equal to the number of amino acid or nucleotide differences. When molecular evolutionists have compared their trees to those made by paleontologists studying fossilized remains, they have found that the trees are remarkably similar.

Figure 12–4
Cytochrome-c is a protein molecule that organisms need for cellular respiration. Each number in this illustration represents the number of amino acid substitutions in the cytochrome-c of various organisms, measured from the previous branch point.

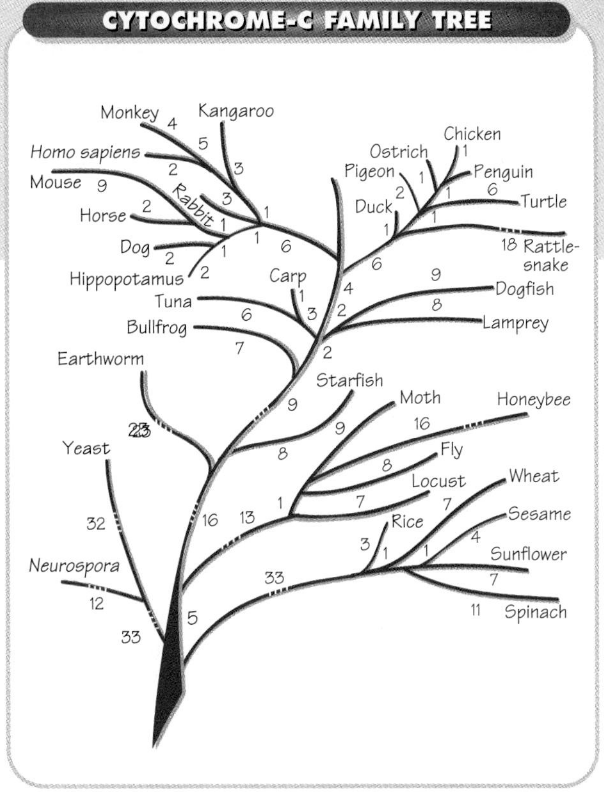

Muscle Proteins—In Yeast!

The molecular unity of life doesn't end there. Researchers were surprised to find a yeast gene that codes for a protein called myosin. Why were they surprised? Because most biologists know that myosin is found in the muscle cells of humans and other multicellular animals. In our bodies, long fibers of myosin interact with other proteins to cause muscles to contract, which enables us to move. But yeasts don't have muscles. And they don't move.

Or do they? Well, even in yeasts, certain cellular components move around within the cell. Myosin in yeasts interacts with other cell proteins to make that movement possible. Molecular biologists have found similarities among many other genes in a wide range of organisms, including plants. How can scientists explain these observations?

The original form of myosin made it possible for parts of cells to move. Since then, as life diversified, evolution of the original myosin genes produced the forms that help your body to move. Time and time again, diversity evolved by adding up changes in original tools, rather than by inventing new tools from scratch. Over time, the bits and pieces of different tool kits were mixed and modified to produce the great variety of living organisms on Earth.

Section Review 12–1

1. How do adaptive radiation and convergent evolution **compare?**
2. **Examine** molecular evidence for the unity of life.
3. **Critical Thinking—Relating** How can adaptive radiation explain the unity as well as the diversity of life?
4. **MINI LAB** How can you **classify** structures of organisms by structural and functional similarity?

4 ASSESS

Quick Check

Ask students to list the clues that scientists use to trace the evolution of organisms. Have them describe the information these clues give to scientists.

Section Review 12–1

1. In adaptive radiation, organisms evolve into different species that live in different ways. In convergent evolution, different groups of organisms evolve structures with similar functions to adapt to similar environments.
2. Many genes and proteins have practically identical sequences in a wide range of organisms.
3. In adaptive radiation, evolved organisms share similar structures and protein and gene sequences with an ancestor. However, the evolved organisms often look and behave very differently from the common ancestor in order to survive in different environments.
4. Structures can be classified as homologous structures—those with structural similarities—and as analogous structures—those with functional similarities.

Checkpoint

1 That many genes were shared by a wide range of organisms.

Skills Trace
Classifying

- Focus p. 266
- Practice p. 267
- Assess p. 278

Learning Modality

Visual Learning Have students look at the cytochrome-c family tree in Figure 12–4, and determine which organisms are more closely related. Have them explain what pattern of evolution occurred at the tree branches. (Adaptive radiation.)

Ancillary Support

The resources below can be used to support your teaching strategy for these two pages.

LM Observing the Effects of Temperature on the Growth of Yeast, #23

TB Cytochrome-c Family Tree, #15

SECTION 12-2
Biodiversity

Performance Objectives
- Explain what biodiversity is.
- Describe why genetic diversity is important.

1 ENGAGE

Inquiry Activity
Predicting

Discovering Diversity

Ask students to predict how many different organisms they think exist in a certain area, such as a park or the school grounds. Students should choose an area and record their prediction. Then students should go to that area and record their observations of organisms. You might suggest that students devise a systematic method for observing organisms and recording their observations. After students have made their observations, have them compare their predictions with their observations. As a class, discuss the amount of diversity observed compared with that predicted.

2 EXPLORE

Investigate
Cooperative Learning Have groups of students design and create a poster that illustrates what biodiversity is. Encourage students to decide first what biodiversity means to them and plan what they want to include on their posters. Some students in the group might even wish to do some research to learn more about biodiversity. Have groups present their posters to the class, with one spokesperson from the group describing the poster.

SECTION 12–2 **Biodiversity**

GUIDE FOR READING
- **Define** biodiversity.
- **Explain** the importance of genetic diversity.

IN THE WORDS OF EDWARD O. Wilson, Professor of Science at Harvard University, *". . . imagine yourself on a journey upward from the center of the Earth, taken at the pace of a leisurely walk. For the first twelve weeks you travel through furnace-hot rock and magma devoid of life. Three minutes to the surface—five hundred meters to go—you encounter the first organisms: bacteria feeding on nutrients that have filtered into the deep water-bearing strata. You breach the surface and for ten seconds glimpse a dazzling burst of life—tens of thousands of species of microorganisms, plants, and animals within horizontal line of sight. Half a minute later almost all are gone. Two hours later only the faintest traces remain. . . ."*

The thin layer teeming with life at the Earth's surface is called the biosphere. And the diversity of life in the biosphere is a subject of utmost importance to humans.

What Is Biodiversity?

During the billions of years since life first appeared on Earth, genes and the organisms they produce have been constantly changing. Yet the similarities in the genes and DNA of all organisms testify that life got going only once, then diversified by evolving, combining, and shuffling changes in the molecular makeup of living organisms. One adaptive radiation after another has generated this **biodiversity**—the variety of living organisms. **Biodiversity is the variety of organisms, the genetic information they contain, and the biological communities in which they live.**

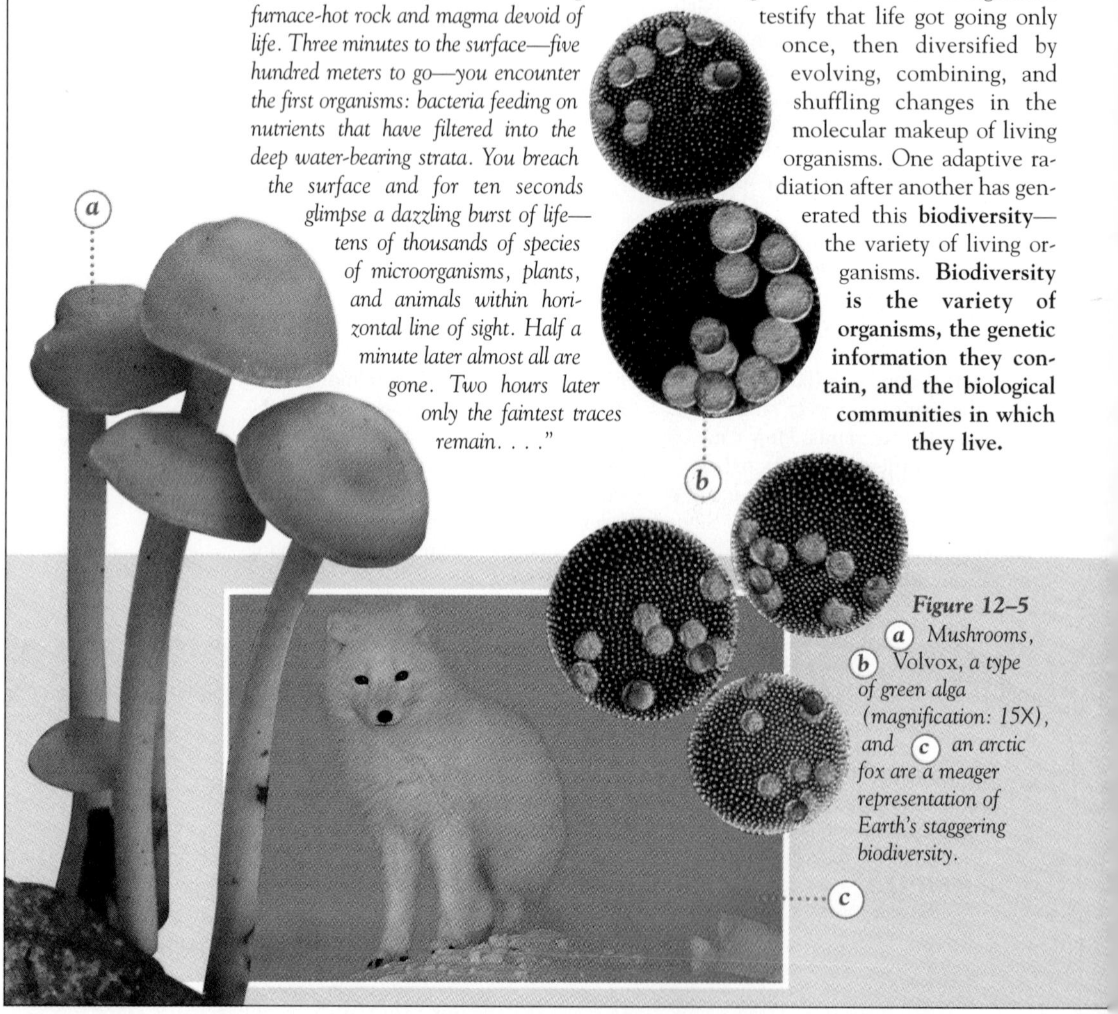

Figure 12–5 (a) *Mushrooms,* (b) *Volvox, a type of green alga (magnification: 15X), and* (c) *an arctic fox are a meager representation of Earth's staggering biodiversity.*

TEACHER SUPPORT

Background Information

Most scientists think life originated about 4 billion years ago when amino acids and nucleotides began interacting with each other. Over time, these molecules were encased by other molecules that protected them from the outside environment, and DNA became the information carrier. After another billion years, these primitive cells evolved methods of producing energy by photosynthesis and respiration. The cells continued to evolve, and about 2 billion years ago the first prokaryotic cells as we know them appeared. Not long after, simple cells moved into the larger prokaryotic cells, forming the first eukaryotic plant and animal cells. About 1 billion years ago, these cells began congregating to form organisms with very simple body plans. From there, body plans become more diverse and complex, leading to the formation of modern plant and animal species.

Biodiversity is an important part of the living world as we know it. Biodiversity is also an enormous and invaluable treasure.

☑ **Checkpoint** What is biodiversity? (1)

Importance of Biodiversity

Although all forms of biodiversity are interconnected, researchers often talk about biodiversity on three levels: **ecosystem diversity, species diversity,** and **genetic diversity.** Biodiversity is important in sustaining many species, including the human species *Homo sapiens*. Unfortunately, human activity around the world seriously threatens diversity at each of these levels.

Ecosystem Diversity

Ecosystems are communities of organisms and their environments. Ecosystem diversity includes the variety of habitats, living communities, and ecological processes in the living world. The diversity of ecosystems on Earth is remarkable because organisms have adapted to nearly every part of our planet. And everywhere there is life, there are complex combinations of organisms.

Species Diversity

When most people talk about the diversity of life, they are probably referring to species diversity. Species diversity refers to the enormous variety of living organisms on Earth, and it is the easiest kind of diversity to see and relate to. About 1.4 million species have been identified and named so far, but different estimates suggest that there may be anywhere from 4 to 50 million more species awaiting discovery. The number and variety of species in an ecosystem can profoundly influence that system's stability, productivity, and value to humans. Sometimes the presence or absence of a single species can completely change the nature of life in an area.

Figure 12–6
Elephants feeding on and trampling through trees in the Moremi Wildlife Reserve in Botswana play a vital role in shaping the ecosystem. When elephants are eliminated from an area by actions such as poaching, trees grow and change what was once grassland into woodland.

Genetic Diversity

Genetic diversity refers to the sum total of all the different forms of genetic information carried by all organisms living on Earth today. Within each species, genetic diversity refers to the total variety of all alleles, which are the different forms of all the genes present in the gene pool of that species.

Sometimes genetic diversity in a species is found between groups of organisms living in different places. In India, farmers have traditionally cultivated thousands of different varieties of rice with different alleles and allele frequencies in their gene pools. In South America, the same is true of potatoes. Other times, the genetic makeup of individual organisms within a population may vary a great deal.

☑ **Checkpoint** What are the three levels of biodiversity? (2)

3 TEACH

Investigate

Research Have students find out what the major ecosystems are on Earth. (Some of these include fresh water, salt water, desert, tundra, grassland, woodland, and wetland.) Students should choose one ecosystem and learn about its characteristics, as well as the major types of adaptations that enable organisms to live there. Challenge students to present their findings in a poster, a collage, or even a short story or poetry.

Ideas Through Images

Have students examine Figure 12–6, read the caption, and answer the following questions.

- **Why do you think the ecosystem would change if elephants were eliminated from the area?** (There would be nothing to stop the growth of trees and bushes, so these plants would eventually take over the environment.)
- **Why would the changing ecosystem affect the other organisms living there?** (The organisms in the ecosystem are adapted to the environmental conditions there. If the ecosystem changes, these organisms will no longer be adapted to the environment.)

☑ Checkpoints

(1) The variety of organisms, the genetic information they contain, and the biological communities in which they live.

(2) Ecosystem diversity, species diversity, and genetic diversity.

TEACHER SUPPORT

Ecology Note

Biodiversity is important in maintaining the balances of energy and nutrients on Earth. The increasing human population is a threat to biodiversity. Some scientists believe that Earth is experiencing an era of mass extinctions. In the past, mass extinctions had natural causes, such as climatic or geologic changes. However, the current extinctions are due to human activities, such as overhunting, habitat destruction, introduction of nonnative species, wildlife trade, and chemical pollutants. Conservation efforts have slowed but not stopped these extinctions. As individual ecosystems begin failing due to the loss of diversity, the balance of energy and nutrients in Earth's biosphere is affected, which threatens human existence.

Ancillary Support

The resources below can be used to support your teaching strategy for these two pages.

LM Observing Organisms in Soil Samples, #24
TR Explore: Desktop Estuary
BL Inquiry Activity: Nature's Variety

Problem Solving

Interpreting Data

Measuring Biodiversity

Students will use their knowledge of ecosystem diversity and species diversity to interpret data collected from various ecosystems.

State The problem students are asked to solve is to develop methods for measuring, comparing, and displaying biodiversity on a high school campus.

Solve Students can solve the problem by first brainstorming for methods to measure the number and distribution of different organisms. Then they should devise several methods of comparison, such as comparing numbers of organisms or comparing their density in different areas. Finally, students can design a way to present their data.

Test Students might suggest that to test the reliability of the method used to determine biodiversity, other methods, such as a belt transect or a line transect, can be used to resample the ecosystems. In these methods, the students would record the number and location of all organisms located within the belt or those touching the line.

Communicate Have each student group present its methods for measuring, comparing, and displaying biodiversity to the class.

Answers to THINK ABOUT IT

1. It would be best if students used the same methods. However, if students express biodiversity as the number of different organisms per unit area, they may compare data but should note that the methods differed.

2. Yes, because the number and distribution of organisms within ecosystems vary throughout the year.

3. Some students might choose to present their data as a drawing of the ecosystem and its location with the organisms shown as drawings, student photographs, magazine pictures, or preserved specimens.

Problem Solving

INTERPRETING DATA

Measuring Biodiversity

As the culmination of the year's activities, a teacher wanted her biology class to develop a display that showed the biodiversity on the high school campus. She issued this challenge to her students: Develop a way of measuring and displaying campus biodiversity.

First, the entire class had a discussion regarding this task and possible methodologies. After developing a method of measuring the number and distribution of different organisms, the class was divided into working groups to sample the various ecosystems surrounding the school. Then the groups worked together to compare the diversity among ecosystems and to display their work. If you were in this class, how would you suggest that the class accomplish each of these tasks?

NUMBER OF CURRENTLY KNOWN LIVING SPECIES

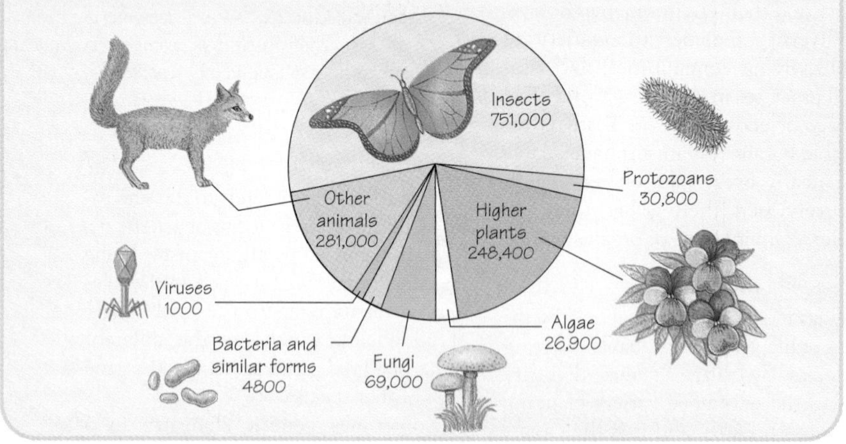

THINK ABOUT IT

1. Should each group's method of measuring biodiversity and the distribution of organisms be the same in order to make comparisons among ecosystems? Explain your answer.
2. If more than one class was involved in this project, would measurements of biodiversity and the distribution of organisms need to be done at the same time of year for valid comparisons to be made among ecosystems? Explain your answer.
3. How would you organize and present the data of the various groups so that the main findings, comparisons, and conclusions could be easily seen in the class display?

TEACHER SUPPORT

Managing Classroom Diversity

MULTICULTURAL STRATEGY

Help students understand the importance of human diversity by making them aware that every individual can contribute something special to society. To demonstrate this, ask students to write one way in which they can contribute to society. Collect their responses and read them to the class, attributing them to individuals. Point out that both diversity and open-mindedness enrich our society.

TECH PREP STUDENTS

Ask students to consider how diversity relates to their career interest. Point out that diversity in careers arises from the interaction of co-workers and clients, as well as from the characteristics of the career. For example, a computer technician is often asked to solve different computer problems daily. Have students ask persons in their careers of interest how they manage diversity in their jobs.

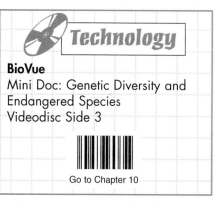

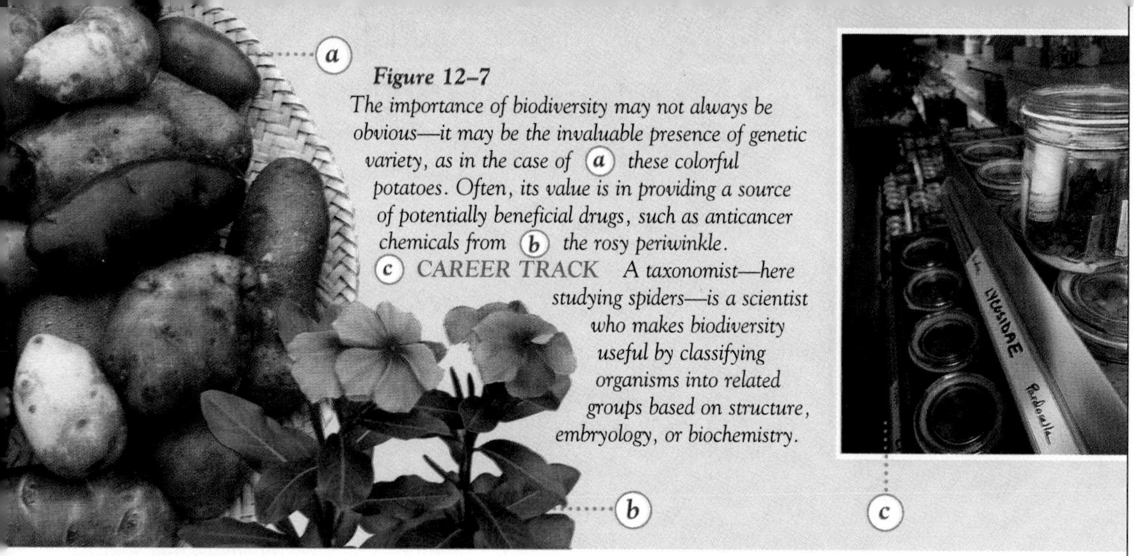

Figure 12–7
The importance of biodiversity may not always be obvious—it may be the invaluable presence of genetic variety, as in the case of (a) these colorful potatoes. Often, its value is in providing a source of potentially beneficial drugs, such as anticancer chemicals from (b) the rosy periwinkle.
(c) CAREER TRACK *A taxonomist—here studying spiders—is a scientist who makes biodiversity useful by classifying organisms into related groups based on structure, embryology, or biochemistry.*

Importance of Genetic Diversity

In a sense, genetic diversity provides the foundation on which the rest of biodiversity is built. **Genetic diversity gives rise to inheritable variation, which, as you have learned, provides the raw material for evolution.** Without inheritable variation on which natural selection can operate, the ability of most species to adapt to changing environments is limited. Because human activity is altering both local and global environments faster than ever, this adaptability may be essential for many species to survive.

What's more, if the genetic diversity within a species decreases too much, an individual organism's strength, ability to combat disease, and ability to reproduce may be seriously threatened. Thus, decreased genetic diversity can threaten a species with extinction.

An important point to remember is that the variety of genes carried by all living species is the result of millions of years of random mutation, natural selection, and genetic drift. An enormous number of diverse and potentially useful characteristics in different plants and animals have evolved as a result of these changes—a priceless and irreplaceable genetic resource for plant and animal breeders and genetic engineers. ●

Thomas Eisner captures the potential of genetic diversity in this metaphor: "A biological species is not merely a hardbound volume of the library of nature. It is also a loose-leaf book, whose individual pages, the genes, might be available for selective transfer and modification of other species."

INTEGRATING BIOLOGY AND SOCIETY

In what ways is genetic diversity important to society?

Section Review 12–2

1. **Define** biodiversity.
2. **Explain** the importance of genetic diversity.
3. **Critical Thinking—Hypothesizing** Formulate a hypothesis to explain why small populations of species are more likely to be threatened with extinction.

INTEGRATING BIOLOGY AND SOCIETY

Genetic diversity provides the inheritable variation through which evolution occurs, and ultimately provides for the survival of a species. Many species carry genetic traits that can benefit human lives, either by their medicinal value or their value as food sources, or simply for pleasure.

4 ASSESS

Quick Check

Have student pairs work together to list the three types of biodiversity and give examples of each. Ask them to explain why genetic diversity is important to the survival of a species.

Section Review 12-2

1. Biodiversity is the variety of organisms, the genetic information they contain, and the biological communities in which they live.
2. Genetic diversity gives rise to inheritable variation, which provides the raw material for evolution. Without inheritable variation, species could not easily adapt to changes in their environment.
3. Some students might hypothesize that small populations of species have smaller gene pools, which translates to less genetic diversity. With less genetic diversity, a species' ability to respond to changes in the environment decreases because there is less inheritable variation on which natural selection can act.

Learning Modality

Tactile Learning Have students create a model of biodiversity in which they use colored beads or buttons to represent the genetic diversity of a species. Have students manipulate the beads to show how decreased genetic diversity could threaten a species with extinction. Then instruct them to repeat the exercise using the beads to represent different species. Ask them to infer how decreased species diversity might affect an ecosystem. (It could cause the ecosystem to change.)

Technology

BioVue
Mini Doc: Genetic Diversity and Endangered Species
Videodisc Side 3

Go to Chapter 10

Section 12–3

DNA: A Storehouse of History

Performance Objective
• Describe molecular clocks.

Mini Lab Skill: Modeling

1 ENGAGE

Ideas Through Images

Have students examine Figure 12–8, read the caption, and answer the following questions.

• **How does a clock mark the passage of time?** (Clocks mark time by the regular movement of their hands.)

• **How might DNA be used to mark time in the evolution of organisms?** (Researchers compare the number of mutations in homologous DNA sequences from different organisms to learn how long ago the organisms shared a common ancestor.)

2 EXPLORE

Inquiry Activity

Comparing

Marking Time

Ask students to compare different ways in which time is measured. Provide them with various timekeeping devices, such as a pendulum clock, a kitchen timer, an hourglass, a stopwatch, and a metronome. Encourage students to examine each timepiece and record how it keeps time. Allow students to devise their own criteria for comparison. Suggest that they design a chart for recording their observations. In a class discussion, have students describe how the timekeepers are similar and how they are different.

SECTION 12–3 BRANCHING OUT In Depth

DNA: A Storehouse of History

Guide for Reading

- **Explain** the concept of molecular clocks.

MINI LAB

- **Construct a model** to show how mutations in genes determine the degree to which species are related.

WHAT DO A QUARTZ CRYSTAL clock and a pendulum clock have in common? Any instrument used to mark time requires a periodically repeating process. In a pendulum clock, that process is the periodically swinging pendulum. In a quartz clock, that process is the periodic vibrations of a quartz crystal under certain conditions. What do pendulum clocks and quartz crystal clocks have to do with DNA and history?

Believe it or not, researchers have reason to think that changes in DNA that occur with some regularity may be a process they can use to mark time in their study of evolution. They hope that in the DNA sequences of various organisms they will find a record of the very deepest and most ancient links between all living organisms.

Molecular Clocks

Scientists hope that changes in DNA can act as **molecular clocks**—biological timekeepers that record how long ago living organisms shared a common ancestor. **The idea of molecular clocks comes from the notion that simple mutations in DNA should occur at a somewhat constant rate.** If the mutations are neither helpful nor harmful, they might accumulate at a constant rate over time. And if that's the case, it should be possible to look at homologous DNA sequences in different organisms to determine how long ago those genes branched off from a common ancestor.

In practice, this idea is complicated for several reasons. First, different positions in DNA sequences accumulate mutations faster than others. Second, although no one knows why, different branches on the evolutionary tree accumulate mutations at different rates. And third, some genes more than others are under stronger pressure from

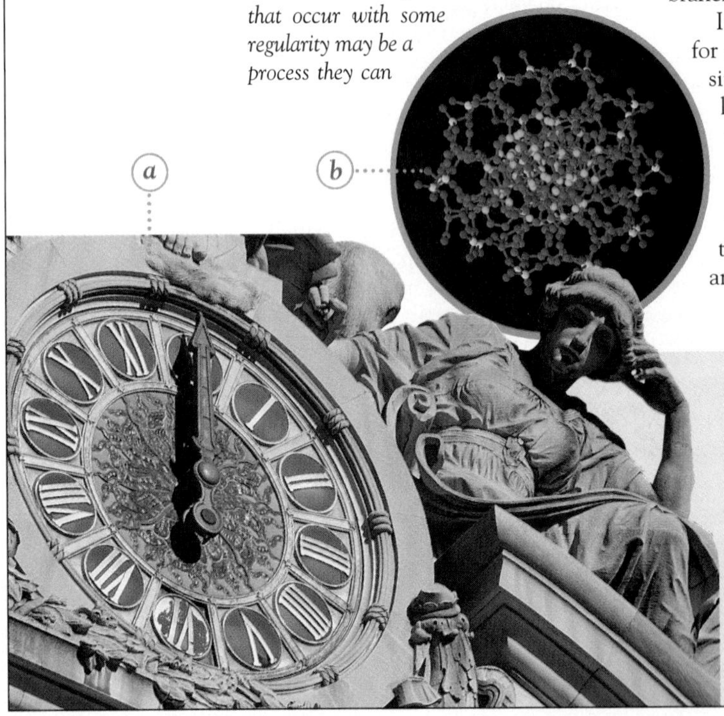

Figure 12–8
The connection between (a) the clock in Grand Central Station in New York and (b) a DNA model is simply that changes in the DNA of organisms may give scientists a way to mark time in Earth's living history.

TEACHER SUPPORT

Managing Classroom Diversity

EDUCATIONAL EQUITY
Invite some of your former students currently enrolled in college to describe to the class what college life is like. Try to invite minority students and female students in nontraditional fields. Ask the college students to describe their experiences of starting college, being away from home, making new friends, and dealing with homesickness. Allow time for students to speak individually to the college students.

GIFTED STUDENTS
Encourage interested students to learn more about molecular clocks and how researchers use them to study evolution. Advise students to find out what kinds of mutations researchers use to mark evolutionary time and what homologous DNA sequences they study. You might want students to present their findings to the class or write a newspaper article describing what they learned.

natural selection not to change. Thus, there is not just one molecular clock in the genome—a complete set of chromosomes of an organism—but many, all "ticking" at different rates.

☑ *Checkpoint* What changes in DNA serve to mark the passage of time? (1)

Slow Clocks, Fast Clocks

Now here's the interesting point: As long as researchers can get some clues on the speed with which clocks in different parts of the genome "tick," differences in speed can be very useful for timing different kinds of evolutionary events.

To understand why, think of a conventional clock with an hour hand, a minute hand, and a second hand. If you want to time a very brief event—say, a 100-meter dash—you must pay close attention to the second hand because it's the only hand that ticks fast enough to tell the difference between one runner and another. However, if you want to time a marathon that lasts more than two hours, you need not only the minute hand but the hour hand as well. Why? Because the second hand and minute hand both move too quickly to time the entire event by themselves. Only the hour hand moves slowly enough to be in a unique position at both the beginning and the end of the race.

The same is true of molecular clocks. To time recent evolutionary events, researchers will use a clock that ticks fairly quickly. But to estimate how long ago humans and bacteria shared a common ancestor, they must use clocks that tick very slowly, because they are trying to time something that happened long ago.

MINI LAB ········ Modeling ········

Molecular Clocks

PROBLEM *How can mutations in genes help determine the degree to which species are related? **Construct a model** to answer this question.*

PROCEDURE

Answer the questions on the basis of the following hypothetical information: Gene A is composed of a DNA sequence that mutates at the rate of one mutation every 4 hours, gene B is composed of a DNA sequence that mutates at the rate of one mutation every 10 minutes, and gene C is composed of a DNA sequence that mutates at the rate of one mutation every 10 seconds.

ANALYZE AND CONCLUDE

1. After 24 hours, how many mutations would each gene have accumulated?
2. Which of the three genes in this model would be the best one to determine how long ago modern humans shared a common ancestor with a paramecium and a dog? Explain your answer.
3. Would there be any limitations to this model? Explain your answer.

Section Review 12-3

1. **Explain** the concept of molecular clocks.
2. **MINI LAB** How do mutations in genes determine the degree to which species are related? **Construct a model** to answer this question.
3. **BRANCHING OUT ACTIVITY** Make a list of various timekeeping methods that are used today. **Identify** the periodically repeating processes that serve to measure time.

3 TEACH

MINI LAB Modeling

Teacher Note
- For time required and materials needed, see page 262b.

Answers to Analyze and Conclude
1. Gene A: 6, gene B: 144, gene C: 8640.
2. Gene A. Because it has the slowest mutation rate.
3. Possible answer: The model assumes constant rates of mutation over a long period of time.

Skills Trace
Modeling
- **Focus p. 273**
- Practice p. 273
- Assess p. 279

4 ASSESS

Quick Check

Ask students to compare a molecular clock to a clock in the classroom.

☑ Checkpoint

(1) Simple mutations in homologous sequences of DNA.

Section Review 12-3

1. See page 272.

2. Students might devise a model in which they compare the number of mutations in homologous DNA sequences from different species.

Skills Trace
Modeling
- Focus p. 273
- **Practice p. 273**
- Assess p. 279

3. Possible timekeeping methods include pendulum clocks with the moving pendulum, metronome with the moving pendulum, carbon dating with the radioactive decay of a carbon isotope, wind-up clocks with moving gears, and a tree trunk with annual rings.

Learning Modality

Auditory Learning Have student pairs take turns explaining to each other when a fast-ticking clock should be used to time evolutionary events and when a slow-ticking clock should be used. Partners should listen critically to each other and develop a rule to explain the relationship.

Ancillary Support

The resources below can be used to support your teaching strategy for these two pages.

TR Enrich: Ancient DNA, Modern Techniques
BL Inquiry Activity: Time Marches On

Laboratory Investigation

Who's Related to Whom?

Before the Lab

You might wish to photocopy the amino acid sequences on page 275 so that each student has a copy that can be marked on.

Pre-Lab Discussion

Have students read the entire procedure for this investigation. Then ask students the following questions.

What is the purpose of this investigation? (To determine evolutionary relationships between species by analyzing the amino acid sequence of a homologous protein.)

How do you calculate the percentage difference between two species? (Determine the number of amino acids that differ between the two species, then divide that number by the total number of amino acids in the sequence; in this case 60 amino acids are given.)

What species do you predict to be the most closely related? (Some students might predict human and chimpanzee, chicken and turkey, or horse and donkey.)

What species do you predict to be the most distantly related? (Some students might predict baker's yeast and human.)

Skills Development

Students will use these skills while completing the laboratory investigation: calculating, predicting, communicating, interpreting data, inferring, and concluding.

Teaching Strategies

1. Have students work in pairs. To more easily compare two amino acid sequences, recommend that one student in a pair read one sequence while the partner follows along the other sequence and counts the number of different amino acids.

Laboratory Investigation

Who's Related to Whom?

Natural selection and evolution would predict that species which diverged from one another relatively recently in the history of life on Earth will share more genetic similarities than species that diverged from one another earlier. Because proteins are programmed by genes, a comparison of the amino acid sequences of their proteins would indicate the relatedness among species.

Problem

How can you **predict** the degree to which species are related from the amino acid sequences in their proteins?

Materials

Data table of amino acid sequences of the protein cytochrome-c

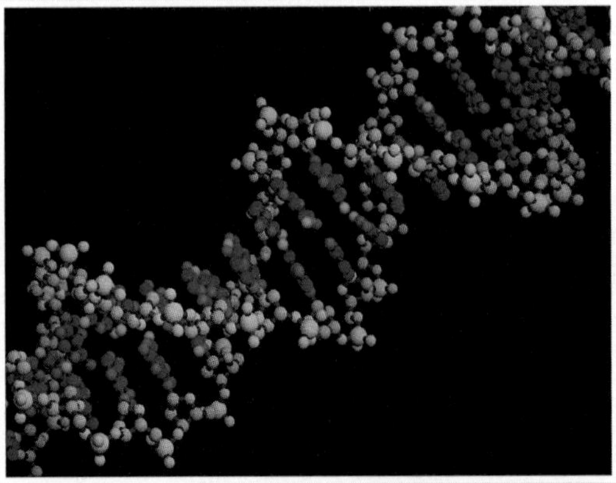

Procedure

1. **Use the amino acid sequences to calculate the percentage difference between a fruit fly and a sunflower. To calculate the percentage difference between two species, determine the number of amino acids that differ between the two species, then divide that number by the total number of amino acids in the sequence. (The sequences provided have 60 amino acids.)**
2. **Make an approximate prediction regarding the percentage difference of the cytochrome-c amino acid sequences of a human and a chimpanzee. Record this information in a data table.**
3. **To test your prediction, repeat step 1 for a human and a chimpanzee.**
4. **Repeat steps 1 to 3 using the amino acid sequences of a horse and a donkey.**
5. **Repeat steps 1 to 3 using the amino acid sequences of a chicken and a turkey.**
6. **Repeat steps 1 to 3 using the amino acid sequences of birds, rattlesnakes, and mammals.**
7. **Repeat steps 1 to 3 using an animal and the sunflower (plant) or yeast (fungus).**

2. The percentage difference for step 1 and steps 3 to 7 are the following:
   1. fruit fly/sunflower: 43.3 percent
   3. human/chimpanzee: 0 percent
   4. horse/donkey: 1.7 percent
   5. chicken/turkey: 0 percent
   6. turkey/horse: 8.3 percent; rattlesnake/horse: 13.3 percent; turkey/rattlesnake: 10 percent
   7. animal (horse)/plant (sunflower): 40 percent; animal (horse)/fungus (yeast): 41.6 percent

AMINO ACID SEQUENCES IN CYTOCHROME-C

Human	GDVEKGKKIFIMKCSQCHTVEKGGKHKTGPNLHGLFGRKTGQAPGYSYTAANKNKGIIWG
Chimpanzee	GDVEKGKKIFIMKCSQCHTVEKGGKHKTGPNLHGLFGRKTGQAPGYSYTAANKNKGIIWG
Rhesus monkey	GDVEKGKKIFIMKCSQCHTVEKGGKHKTGPNLHGLFGRKTGQAPGYSYTAANKNKGITWG
Horse	GDVEKGKKIFVQKCAQCHTVEKGGKHKTGPNLHGLFGRKTGQAPGFTYTDANKNKGITWK
Donkey	GDVEKGKKIFVQKCAQCHTVEKGGKHKTGPNLHGLFGRKTGQAPGFSYTDANKNKGITWK
Chicken	GDIEKGKKIFVQKCSQCHTVEKGGKHKTGPNLHGLFGRKTGQAEGFSYTDANKNKGITWG
Turkey	GDIEKGKKIFVQKCSQCHTVEKGGKHKTGPNLHGLFGRKTGQAEGFSYTDANKNKGITWG
Rattlesnake	GDVEKGKKIFTMKCSQCHTVEKGGKHKTGPNLHGLFGRKTGQAVGYSYTAANKNKGITWG
Fruit fly	GDVEKGKKLFVQRCAQCHTVEAGGKHKVGPNLHGLIGRKTGQAAGFAYTNANKAKGITWQ
Baker's yeast	GSAKKGATLFKTRCELCHTVEKGGPHKVGPNLHGIFGRHSGQAQGYSYTDANIKNVLTWD
Sunflower	GDPTTGAKIFKTKCAQCHTVEKGAGHKQGPNLNGLFGRQSGTTAGYSYSAANKNMAVIWE

The letters represent the amino acids as shown:
G = glycine, A = alanine, V = valine, L = leucine, I = isoleucine, M = methionine, F = phenylalanine, W = tryptophan, P = proline, S = serine, T = threonine, C = cysteine, Y = tyrosine, N = asparagine, Q = glutamine, D = aspartic acid, E = glutamic acid, K = lysine, R = arginine, H = histidine

Observations

1. How different are humans and chimps in the first 60 amino acids of the cytochrome-c sequence?
2. What pattern of relatedness did you observe from the percentage differences among various species?

Analysis and Conclusions

1. Which species share recent common ancestors? Distant common ancestors?
2. Would you be able to draw a "family tree" of the organisms named, showing when they diverged from one another? Would such a family tree be very accurate?
3. Some positions on the amino acid sequence are the same for all cytochrome-c molecules shown. Why might this be so?
4. As a rule, what general conclusion can you draw regarding how closely related species are and how their cytochrome-c amino acid sequences compare?

More to Explore

Research data on the gene sequences of various proteins. Use this data to construct a family tree of related organisms.

Answers to Observations

1. There are no differences.
2. Birds are more closely related to one another than they are to different organisms. Animals are more closely related to one another than they are to plants or fungus. Humans and chimps are closely related to one another. Birds and mammals are more closely related than reptiles and mammals.

Answers to Analysis and Conclusions

1. Human and chimpanzee, horse and donkey, and chicken and turkey share recent common ancestors. Animals and plants, animals and fungus, and plants and fungus share distant common ancestors.
2. A family tree could be drawn, but it would not be very accurate, because the comparisons between species were made using the amino acid sequences for only one protein.
3. The amino acids that are the same for most of the species in the chart are probably critical to the structure and function of the protein.
4. The more closely related the species, the more similar are their cytochrome-c amino acid sequences.

More to Explore

Students can calculate the percentage difference between gene sequences as they did in this investigation. Some proteins students might research include tubulin, albumin, or myosin. Students can use the cytochrome-c family tree in Figure 12–4 as a guide for constructing a family tree.

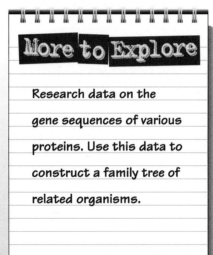

CHAPTER 12

Study Guide

Review Strategy

Have student pairs play a game of Twenty Questions using the key terms and other terms from this chapter. Remind students that in Twenty Questions, the guesser can ask questions that have only a yes or no answer. You might want to limit the number of questions to five to make the game more challenging. The partner who has chosen the term should give a clue to help the guesser begin. Partners should take turns asking and answering questions.

Study Guide

Summarizing Key Concepts

The key concepts in each section of this chapter are listed below to help you review the chapter content. Make sure you understand each concept and its relationship to other concepts and to the theme of this chapter.

12–1 The Unity of Life

- When a newly evolved species or a group of organisms in a new area evolve—sometimes somewhat quickly—into different species that live in different ways, the pattern of evolution is known as adaptive radiation.
- Unrelated species independently evolve superficial similarities because of adaptations to similar environments by a process known as convergent evolution.
- Analogous structures are similar in appearance and function but are developed from anatomically different parts.
- Information gathered on DNA sequences reveals that many genes are shared by a wide range of organisms. New data have shown that whole stretches of DNA and, therefore, entire sequences of amino acids in many proteins are practically identical in nearly every organism studied.
- A comparison of the amino acid sequences in the proteins of organisms can indicate the degree to which species are related.

12–2 Biodiversity

- Biodiversity is the variety of all the organisms, the genetic information they contain, and the biological communities in which they live.
- Ecosystem diversity consists of the variety of habitats, living communities, and ecological processes in the living world.
- Species diversity refers to the enormous variety of living organisms on Earth.
- Genetic diversity refers to the sum total of all the different forms of genetic information carried by all organisms living on Earth.
- Decreased genetic diversity can threaten a species with extinction.

12–3 DNA: A Storehouse of History

- Changes in DNA can act as molecular clocks—biological timekeepers that record how long ago living organisms shared a common ancestor.
- The idea of molecular clocks comes from the notion that simple mutations in DNA should occur at a somewhat constant rate.

Reviewing Key Terms

Review the following vocabulary terms and their meaning. Then use each term in a complete sentence.

12–1 The Unity of Life
adaptive radiation
convergent evolution
analogous structure

12–2 Biodiversity
biodiversity
ecosystem diversity
species diversity
genetic diversity

12–3 DNA: A Storehouse of History
molecular clock

Inquiry-Based Strategy

Endangered species are not only threatened with extinction; they also threaten the balance in their ecosystems. Have students choose an endangered species and research it in order to answer the following question: What can be done to save this species from extinction? Students may approach answering this question in different ways. One approach would be to breed the species in captivity until sufficient numbers are built up. Another might be to protect the habitat of the species from destruction.

Recalling Main Ideas

Choose the letter of the answer that best completes the statement or answers the question.

1. A new species or a species in a new area giving rise to many species, sometimes in a relatively short period of time, is called
   a. convergent evolution. **c.** stabilizing selection.
   b. adaptation. **d.** adaptive radiation.
2. Analogous structures are a sign of
   a. directional selection. **c.** divergent evolution.
   b. convergent evolution. **d.** adaptive radiation.
3. The more closely related two organisms are, the
   a. greater the similarity in their genes.
   b. less the similarity in their genes.
   c. greater the occurrence of analogous structures.
   d. greater the differences in their DNA sequences.
4. Structures that are similar in appearance and function but differ anatomically are said to be
   a. analogous. **c.** vestigial.
   b. homologous. **d.** convergent.
5. Which of the following is not a level of biodiversity?
   a. genetic diversity **c.** species diversity
   b. ecosystem diversity **d.** habitat diversity
6. Species diversity refers to the variety of
   a. living organisms.
   b. Earth's ecosystems.
   c. alleles in the gene pool of a species.
   d. species already extinct.
7. Genetic diversity refers to
   a. the variety of alleles in the species.
   b. phenotype variation.
   c. genotype variation.
   d. normal distribution.
8. Changes in DNA can mark time because
   a. amino acid sequences in DNA change.
   b. mutations occur at fairly constant rates.
   c. mutations do not cause amino acid sequences to change.
   d. all organisms have DNA.

Putting It All Together

Using the information on pages xxx to xxxi, complete the following concept map.

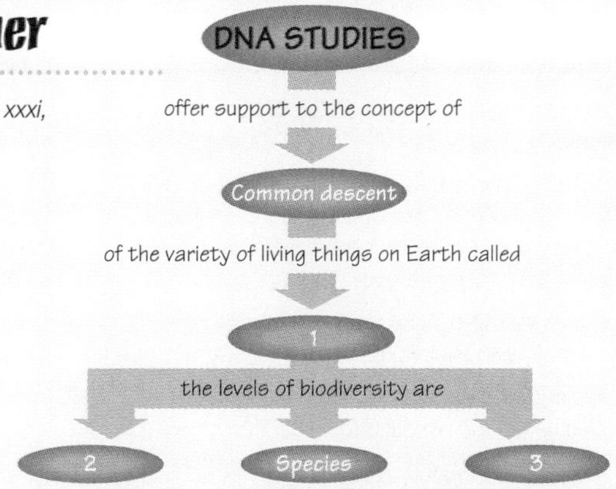

Recalling Main Ideas

1. d
2. b
3. a
4. a
5. d
6. a
7. a
8. b

Assessment

Reviewing What You Learned

1. Adaptive radiation is a pattern of evolution in which a newly evolved species or a group of organisms in a new area evolves somewhat quickly into different species that live in different ways.
2. In convergent evolution, unrelated species evolve similarities because of adaptations to similar environments. In adaptive radiation, a species evolves differences because of adaptations to different environments.
3. Possible examples of homologous structures include arms, legs, wings, and flippers; backbones; and bird beaks. Possible examples of analogous structures include bird, bat, and insect wings; and structures for getting food by drilling into tree bark. Analogous structures are similar in appearance and function but are anatomically different. Homologous structures have different functions but are anatomically similar.

Skills Trace
Classifying

- Focus p. 266
- Practice p. 267
- Assess p. 278

4. Applications of DNA studies include answering questions about the workings of genes, genetic diseases, cell chemistry, and evolution.
5. Certain genes in bacteria and humans are almost identical, such as the DNA sequences that direct the assembly of ribosomes. Many genes in bacteria and humans are completely different. For example, some bacteria have genes that help them survive high temperatures, and humans have genes that enable them to walk upright on two legs.

Putting It All Together

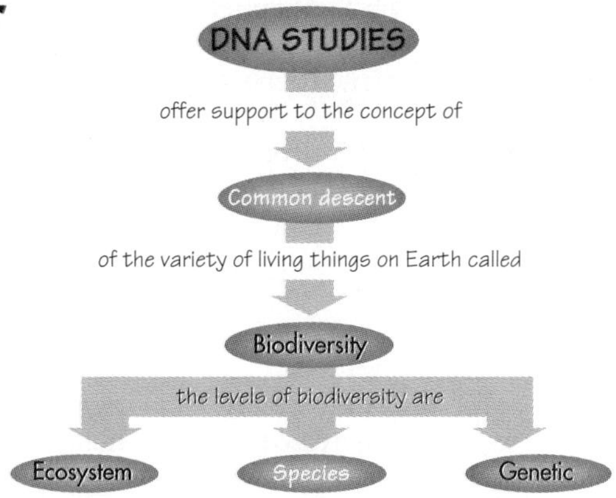

Assessment

Reviewing What You Learned

Answer each of the following in a complete sentence.

1. Characterize adaptive radiation.
2. How do convergent evolution and adaptive radiation differ?
3. Give two examples of homologous and analogous structures. What criterion did you use to **classify** structures as analogous or homologous?
4. What are the applications of DNA studies?
5. How are the genes of bacteria and humans similar? How are they different?
6. How can common descent be considered evidence for evolution?
7. What are the levels of biodiversity? Which level is the foundation for the other two?
8. How might DNA act as a molecular clock?
9. What is a genome?
10. Why might some genes mutate at a faster rate than others?

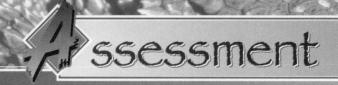

Expanding the Concepts

Discuss each of the following in a brief paragraph.

1. Why is the study of DNA important to evolutionary biologists?
2. Can genes be homologous? Explain your answer.
3. If some human genes are similar in code and function to certain yeast genes, is it reasonable to assume that humans and yeasts share a common ancestor? Explain your answer.
4. How might gene modification be a key to understanding evolution?
5. Give evidence to support this statement: "Evolution can modify existing tool kits much more easily than it can generate entirely new ones."
6. How has human activity threatened each level of biodiversity?
7. Give evidence to support this statement: "The greater the genetic diversity, the greater the survival potential of a species."
8. Only a small portion of the DNA within a human cell is actually functional. What might be the purpose of the excess?
9. How might the number and variety of species actually influence an ecosystem's stability?
10. How can a molecular clock be used to determine the length of shared ancestry?

Assessment (continued)

6. If unrelated species have homologous structures, it indicates that they once had a common ancestor because natural selection cannot produce entirely new structures—it can only modify existing structures.
7. The levels of biodiversity are ecosystem diversity, species diversity, and genetic diversity. Genetic diversity is the foundation for the other two.
8. DNA acts as a molecular clock because simple mutations in DNA can occur at a somewhat constant rate.
9. A genome is the complete set of chromosomes of an organism.
10. Some genes are not under a strong pressure from natural selection to stay the same.

Expanding the Concepts

1. Evolutionary biologists have learned that many genes are shared by a wide range of organisms. By comparing gene sequences from different organisms, they can determine how closely related those organisms are.
2. Yes, a mutation can cause a gene in one species to have a different function in a different species, even though they are still the same gene.
3. Yes. Natural selection cannot invent new "tools" from scratch. However, it can make changes to the original "tools" to increase the diversity of life. Since humans, which are a more highly complex organism, do share some DNA sequences with yeast, it shows that humans did share a distant ancestor with yeast.
4. Mutations in genes, or gene modifications, create inheritable variation on which natural selection can act, and evolution occurs.
5. Natural selection works by selecting inheritable variations in the characteristics of an organism. Natural selection can easily change the shape or size of a certain tool in ways that change its function, such as it did with beak size in Galapagos finches.
6. Possible answers include that overpopulation, mining, logging, and pollution have threatened ecosystem diversity. Illegal hunting and habitat destruction decrease species diversity. Toxic waste and selective breeding have threatened genetic diversity.
7. Without genetic diversity, the ability of most species to adapt to changing environments is limited because there is less inheritable variation on which natural selection can act.
8. Some students might suggest that some of the excess DNA is left over from ancestral species and has no function in the evolved species.
9. The larger number of species and the more variety within the species lead to increased genetic diversity. Increased diversity enables a species to respond to environmental changes because it gives natural selection inheritable variation on which to work. Because the species will have a better chance of surviving, the ecosystem will be more stable.
10. If simple mutations occur at a somewhat constant rate, then these mutations should accumulate in DNA sequences at a constant rate over time. By comparing homologous DNA sequences in different organisms, it should be possible to determine how long ago those genes branched off from a common ancestor by determining the number of differences between the two sequences.

Extending Your Thinking

Use the skills you have developed in this chapter to answer the following.

1. **Hypothesizing** Ribosomes are remarkably similar throughout the six kingdoms. Formulate a hypothesis to explain this observation. Suggest a way to support your hypothesis.
2. **Analyzing** Obtaining and using energy is the primary function of all living things. Would you expect to find energy flow and control in genes or gene products from diverse organisms to be similar?
3. **Inferring** Homeoboxes are a series of repeatable DNA sequences in organisms. Find out how mutations to individual homeoboxes produce complex organisms such as an earthworm or a fruit fly.
4. **Constructing a model** Construct a model to simulate mutations in DNA as timekeepers.
5. **Evaluating** An enormous amount of money and time is being spent to collect, study, and use DNA for various purposes—such as to treat diseases and alter crop characteristics. Discuss the pros and cons of the collection, storage, and use of diverse genetic material.

Applying Your Skills

Observing Diversity in Action

Ecosystems usually contain an amazing diversity of species. Species diversity is the number of species living within an ecosystem.

1. Select an ecosystem in your area—a forest, field, pond, lake, grassland, or desert.
2. Within that ecosystem, identify as many species as possible.

• GOING FURTHER •

3. What might happen to the ecosystem if a new species with no natural predators was introduced?

Extending Your Thinking

1. Some students might hypothesize that ribosomes are very similar among different kingdoms because they perform the same function in every living organism. To support their hypothesis, students might suggest making changes in the DNA sequence of ribosomes and testing the mutant ribosomes for proper function.
2. Yes, since obtaining and using energy is a primary function, the proteins that control these processes would be under strong selective pressures not to change.
3. Mutations in specific homeoboxes produce different structures with different functions, leading to the segmentation of organisms.
4. Students might devise a model in which they compare the number of mutations that occur in homologous DNA sequences from different species.

Skills Trace
Modeling
- Focus p. 273
- Practice p. 273
- Assess p. 279

5. Pros include that genetic material holds information that can never be replaced. All uses for genetic information have not been realized. For example, potential drugs for new diseases might be produced by endangered organisms. Cons include that the money could be better spent solving the problems of society and not saving a species that does not directly affect human lives.

Applying Your Skills

Teacher Notes

• You might divide the class into small groups, each selecting a different kind of ecosystem.
• Students should select a specific area within their ecosystem. Within that area, students should identify and record as many different plant and animal species as they can. Data will vary depending on which ecosystem students select.

Answers

3. Without natural predators, the new species will reproduce prolifically while there is a sufficient food supply. This new species could conceivably become the dominant species in the ecosystem, forcing out the native species that cannot compete as easily for resources. Eventually, the species diversity in the ecosystem could change, which could completely change the nature of life in the area.

Scoring Rubric

4 Response is thorough, accurate, and creative; shows an in-depth understanding of science skills, procedures, and concepts.

3 Response is complete, mostly accurate, and original; shows a satisfactory understanding of science skills, procedures, and concepts.

2 Response is mostly complete but includes some inaccuracies; shows an adequate understanding of science skills, procedures, and concepts.

1 Response is only partially complete and has many inaccuracies; shows an incomplete understanding of science skills, procedures, and concepts.

0 Response is mostly incomplete and/or inaccurate; shows a lack of understanding of science skills, procedures, and concepts.

UNIT 4

Ecology

Introducing the Unit

. . . In Words

Baba Dioum, a forest manager in Senegal, made this statement at a conference on environmental education in Africa in the 1970s. Since then, it has been widely quoted.

By learning about ecology, students will come to a better understanding not only of their own immediate environment, but also of all the different environments in the biosphere. From this understanding comes appreciation and respect for the living things and natural systems in our world. When we appreciate these organisms and systems, we will work to protect them from harm.

- **How does this quotation relate education to protecting the environment?** (It says that humans will only conserve—or protect—what they know about.)
- **Can you think of examples of educating the public that have helped to conserve the environment?** (Accept all reasonable responses, including educating the public about endangered species so that there is support for protecting them.)

. . . In Pictures

This photograph illustrates a coastal rain forest in the American Northwest—a lush environment that may be unfamiliar to most students. At first glance, students may think this is a tropical rain forest. Make sure they read the caption and note the forest location.

- **What types of living things do you see in this photograph?** (Plants, specifically trees, mosses, and ferns.)

UNIT 4

Ecology

CHAPTERS

"In the end, we will conserve only what we love, we will love only what we understand, we will understand only what we are taught."

— Baba Dioum

TEACHER SUPPORT

Unit Discovery Learning Activity

MAKING MINI-HABITATS

To provide sources for direct observation and discussion throughout this unit, have student teams set up a variety of classroom "mini-habitats" with living and nonliving things they have collected outdoors. You could take students on a class collecting trip or have them collect the organisms and materials on their own.

To ensure that organisms ordinarily found in different habitats are not mixed together, emphasize that each team should collect living things from only one immediate area. Also make sure that at least one team constructs the rotting log habitat described below so students can observe examples of decomposers. Caution students about the handling of living organisms.

1. Put a layer of pebbles in the bottom of a small aquarium, a clear-plastic shoe box, or a gallon jar turned on its side. (If using a jar, tape two pencils to it to keep it from rolling.)

CAREER TRACK

As you explore the topics in this unit, you will discover many different types of careers associated with biology. Here are a few of these careers:

- Ecologist
- Wildlife Biologist
- Oceanographer
- Botanist

Rain forest in Olympic National Park in Washington State

- **What nonliving things do you see?** (Soil and the trunk of a fallen tree. Some students may mention sunlight, a form of energy.)
- **How is this location different from where you live?** (Answers will vary depending on students' location. Guide them to identify specific differences, such as the types and density of the vegetation. Some students may infer a difference in precipitation levels. Also make sure they note the apparent absence of human impact on this forest.)
- **How is the location similar to where you live?** (Depending on students' location, similarities may be more difficult for them to identify than differences. Help them conclude that soil and sunlight are also found in their own surroundings and that both locations contain plants, although the specific types may differ greatly.)

CAREER TRACK

Throughout this unit, you will find a broad range of biology-related careers that vary in educational and training requirements. You may wish to have your students find out more about the following careers:

- Ecologist, p. 286
- Wildlife biologist, p. 320
- Oceanographer, p. 350
- Botanist, p. 373

Technology

BioVue
Bringing Back the Prairie
Videodisc Side 4

Go to Chapter 2

2. Mix damp soil, peat moss, and sand in 2–1–1 proportions. Spread the mixture over the pebbles in a layer 5–7 cm deep.
3. Add the living organisms and the nonliving and once-living materials collected from outdoors. (For a **rotting log habitat**, add a piece of rotting log, some decomposing leaves, and a few of the plants, fungi, wood lice, earthworms, and other organisms that were found under or around the log.)
4. Cover the container's opening with screening, and secure with tape or an elastic band.
5. Place the mini-habitat where it will get natural light but not long periods of direct sunlight. As needed, add water by misting.
6. When observations are complete, return the living things to their original location.

By observing and evaluating their mini-habitats over time, students should be able to recognize, describe, and explain specific examples of the key concepts of **systems and interactions** and **patterns of change** that are developed in this unit.

Ancillary Support

The resource below can be used to support your teaching strategy for these two pages.

BL Integrating the Media
Unit Discovery Learning Activity

Chapter 13 Energy and Nutrients

Content Management	Student Edition Activities
■ Section 13–1 Ecology: Studying Nature's Houses, pp. 283–286 Ecological Research Why Study Ecology?	
■ Section 13–2 Energy: Essential for Life's Processes, pp. 287–290 Energy From the Sun Energy Flow Through the Biosphere	MINI LAB: Life in Your Neighborhood, p. 289
■ Section 13–3 Nutrients: Building Blocks of Living Tissue, pp. 291–296 What Are Nutrients? Nutrient Cycles Nutrient Limitation	MINI LAB: Fertilizers–Nutrients Unlimited?, p. 296
■ Section 13–4 Food Webs: Who Eats Whom?, pp. 297–299 Food Chains and Webs Food Web Diversity	Laboratory Investigation: Food or Feeders?, pp. 304–305
◆ BRANCHING OUT • In Depth Section 13–5 The Carbon Cycle: A Closer Look, pp. 300–303 The Greenhouse Effect Major Carbon Pathways	
■ These sections cover all the necessary content and concepts for a basic course in biology. ◆ This section covers content and concepts that are either applications or extensions of the basic material.	

Integration Strategies

SE Careers, p. 284
Earth Science, p. 301
BL Investigating Careers
Involving the Community
Science Through Art

Assessment Strategies

SE Chapter Review, pp. 306–309
TR Section Reviews
Chapter Test
Performance-Based Assessment
BL Investigating Further
Practice Test
Chapter Review
CTB Chapter 13 Test

Tech Prep

Teaching strategies appropriate for students who are in technical/vocational programs or who are considering post-secondary technical education can be found on the following **TE** pages: 287, 291, and 302.

Meeting the Standards

Sections 13–1 through 13–5 cover four of the five content standards under **The Interdependence of Organisms** and three of the six content standards under **Matter, Energy, and Organization in Living Systems** as described on pages 186–187 of The National Science Education Standards.

Chapter Planning Guide

Teacher's Edition Activities	Other Activities	Media and Technology
Chapter Discovery Learning Activity, p. 282 **Inquiry Activity:** Asking Scientific Questions, p. 284 **Activity:** Modeling Wetlands, p. 285	**TR Apply:** Choosing the Right Method **BL Inquiry Activity:** Where Are the Frogs?	**BioVue Mini Doc:** Adopt-a-Reef, Videodisc Side 4 **BioVue Plus CD-ROMs:** Adopt-a-Reef **CD–ROM:** The Wetlands
Investigate: Long-Term Project, p. 288	**LM** Observing the Effects of Sunlight on Plant Growth, #26 **TR Writing in Biology:** Ecological Conversations **Enrich:** Dark Secrets **BL Inquiry Activity:** The Energy of Life	
Activity: Identifying Plant and Human Nutrients, p. 292	**LM** Investigating the Effects of Water Pollution on Plants, #25 **TR Explore:** Cycle in a Bottle **BL Inquiry Activity:** Water Roundup	**BioVue Animations:** The Water Cycle, Videodisc Side 4 The Nitrogen Cycle, Videodisc Side 4 The Oxygen/Carbon Dioxide Cycle, Videodisc Side 4 **BioVue Plus CD-ROMs:** The Water Cycle, the Nitrogen Cycle, the Oxygen/Carbon Dioxide Cycle **CD-ROM:** Food Chains and Food Webs **TB** Visualizing the Water Cycle, #16 Visualizing the Nitrogen Cycle, #17 Visualizing the Carbon Cycle, #18
Inquiry Activity: Food Chains for People, p. 298	**TR Explore:** All Linked Together **BL Inquiry Activity:** Nature's Supermarket	
Investigate: Model Building, p. 300 **Activity:** Do Plants Need Carbon Dioxide?, p. 301	**TR Enrich:** Bubbling Up **BL Inquiry Activity:** Climate in a Cup	

KEY: SE Student Edition **TE** Teacher's Edition **LM** Laboratory Manual **TR** Teaching Resources **BL** BioLog **TB** Transparency Box **CTB** Computer Test Bank

Materials List

TE Chapter Discovery Learning Activity, p. 282 (20 minutes for initial set-up, 10 minutes for each subsequent observation and recording); glass jars, soil, bean seeds, marker, aphids, ladybird beetles, screening, elastic bands.

TE Inquiry Activity: Asking Scientific Questions, p. 284 (30 minutes); pencil and paper.

TE Activity: Modeling Wetlands, p. 285 (two 45-minute sessions); students' choice of materials.

TE Investigate: Long-Term Project, p. 288 (10 minutes for initial set-up, 10 minutes for each subsequent observation and recording); wooden board.

SE MINI LAB: Life in Your Neighborhood, p. 289 (30–45 minutes); magnifier optional.

TE Activity: Identifying Plant and Human Nutrients, p. 292 (two 45-minute sessions); resource materials for researching human nutrients, plant fertilizer labels.

SE MINI LAB: Fertilizers–Nutrients Unlimited?, p. 296 (20 minutes for initial set-up, 10 minutes for each subsequent observation and recording); wide-mouthed jars, water from pond or aquarium, *Elodea* or other aquatic plants, marking pencil, lawn fertilizer, disposable latex gloves.

TE Inquiry Activity: Food Chains for People, p. 298 (30 minutes); pencil and paper.

TE Investigate: Model Building, p. 300 (Part A: 10 minutes, Parts B, C, D: 10 minutes each for initial set-up, 5 minutes for each observation and recording); plastic cups, distilled water, bromthymol blue solution, marker, plastic wrap, aquatic snails, *Elodea*.

TE Activity: Do Plants Need Carbon Dioxide?, p. 301 (15 minutes for initial set-up, 10 minutes for each subsequent observation and recording); houseplants, large glass jars, marking pencil, soda lime crystals, small cup.

Chapter 13

Energy and Nutrients

Introducing the Chapter

. . . In Pictures

Have students examine the photograph, read the caption, and answer the following questions.

- **What is happening in this photograph?** (A ladybug is eating aphids.)
- **What do you think the aphids are doing on the plant?** (The aphids are eating the plant.)

The photograph actually shows a simple food chain that illustrates the three trophic levels introduced in Section 13–2.

Teaching Strategy

In the first section of this chapter, students are introduced to the study of ecology, the research methods employed by ecologists, and the importance of studying ecology. The next two sections describe the flow of energy and the cycling of various nutrients through the biosphere, leading to a discussion of food chains and webs in the fourth section. The BRANCHING OUT section describes the carbon cycle in greater detail, including how the cycle is affected by human activities.

BIO JOURNAL

Students should be able to identify several basic needs shared by plants, insects, and humans, at least in simple, general terms such as air, water, and food. If students have difficulty thinking beyond these obvious needs, you could divide the class into several "brainstorming" groups and then have students share their ideas in a class discussion. Instruct students to keep their entries in their portfolios.

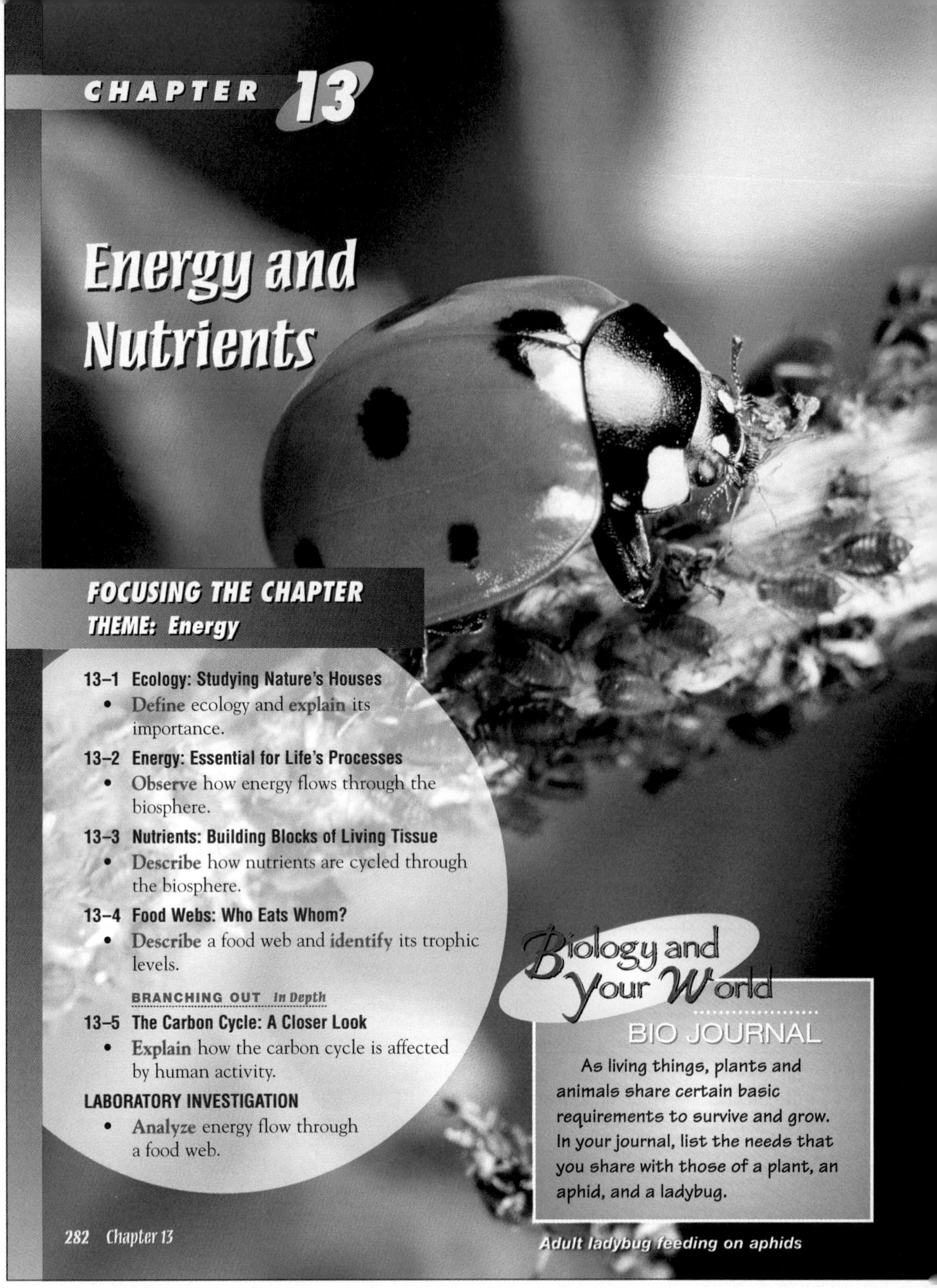

CHAPTER 13

Energy and Nutrients

FOCUSING THE CHAPTER

THEME: Energy

13–1 Ecology: Studying Nature's Houses

- **Define** ecology and **explain** its importance.

13–2 Energy: Essential for Life's Processes

- **Observe** how energy flows through the biosphere.

13–3 Nutrients: Building Blocks of Living Tissue

- **Describe** how nutrients are cycled through the biosphere.

13–4 Food Webs: Who Eats Whom?

- **Describe** a food web and **identify** its trophic levels.

BRANCHING OUT *In Depth*

13–5 The Carbon Cycle: A Closer Look

- **Explain** how the carbon cycle is affected by human activity.

LABORATORY INVESTIGATION

- **Analyze** energy flow through a food web.

Biology and Your World

BIO JOURNAL

As living things, plants and animals share certain basic requirements to survive and grow. In your journal, list the needs that you share with those of a plant, an aphid, and a ladybug.

Adult ladybug feeding on aphids

TEACHER SUPPORT

Chapter Discovery Learning Activity

This activity can be set up as a demonstration or done by student teams. It will give students an opportunity to directly observe the plant → aphid → ladybug food chain. (Aphids and ladybugs may be collected from outdoors or purchased from a biological supply house.)

1. Plant a bean seedling in each of two large glass jars labeled A and B.
2. Put about 20 aphids in each jar.
3. Add several ladybugs to jar B.
4. Cover both jars with a piece of screening and place in a sunny location. Water the plants regularly.
5. Observe the jars every day for a week, and note the number of aphids and the condition of the plant in each one.

Results: The unchecked aphids in jar A will feed on and eventually kill the bean plant. The ladybugs in jar B will eat the aphids, thus protecting the plant.

Ecology: Studying Nature's Houses

SECTION **13–1**

Guide for Reading

- **Define** ecology.
- **Explain** the importance of studying ecology.

THE STORIES SEEM TO POP UP in newspapers and on television everywhere nearly every day. "Mississippi Floods Hit the Midwest!" "American Songbirds Vanish . . . Why?" "New England Fisheries Disappear!" "As Ozone Holes Get Larger, Skin Cancer Risk Rises!" "Coral Reefs Die in the Florida Keys!"

At first glance, these headlines seem to deal with very different events. Do they have anything in common? And why are they mentioned here? Read on to find out the answers to these questions.

Ecological Research

All the events mentioned in these headlines have to do with **ecology**—its issues and concerns. **Ecology is the scientific study of interactions between different kinds of living things and between living things and the environments in which they live.** Ecology is named after the Greek word *oikos*, meaning "house," because ecology is the study of our house—the planet Earth—with all its living and nonliving parts.

Ecologists, the scientists who study ecology, examine different things in different ways, depending on the questions they ask. Ecologists ask questions about phenomena and organisms that range in size and scope from a single cell to the entire living planet.

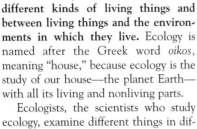

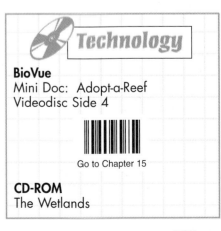

Figure 13–1 (a) This baby gorilla from Central Africa, (b) underwater coral reefs near Australia, and (c) forests in North Carolina represent examples of living things threatened by various changes in their environment.

Section 13–1

Ecology: Studying Nature's Houses

Performance Objectives

- Define the term ecology.
- Explain ecology's importance as a scientific field of study.

1 ENGAGE

Ideas Through Images

Have students examine Figure 13–1, read the caption, and answer the following questions.

- **What needs do all of the living things in these photographs share?** (Students should mention the basic needs they identified earlier in the Bio Journal discussion.)
- **What type of animals are shown in photograph *b*?** (Fish and coral. If students do not mention the coral, explain that coral are animals, not plants.)
- **What kind of environmental changes might be affecting the coral and the gorilla?** (Point out that the animals' continued existence in the wild is threatened by human activity.)
- **What has happened to the trees shown in photograph *c*? What could have caused this?** (The trees have died. Accept all reasonable explanations, including acid rain.)

TEACHER SUPPORT

Historical Perspective

The English word *ecology* is derived from *oekologie*, a term devised in the 1860s by German biologist Ernst Haeckel to refer to the study of living things in their natural surroundings. The same root, *oikos*, also gave us the term *economics*, which is the study of human household management. These two disciplines ran in parallel for a time, borrowed from each other, and were sometimes studied by the same people. In fact, Adam Smith, the founder of economics, was a follower of Linnaeus.

In his 1749 essay, "The Oeconomy of Nature," Linnaeus argued that nature's economy was created exclusively for human benefit. When Adam Smith developed economics, he incorporated the viewpoint that nature exists to be exploited by humans. For this reason, most classical economic models, although they describe human economies fairly well, concern themselves only with human activity and human wealth, paying little heed to biological and environmental wealth.

Technology

BioVue
Mini Doc: Adopt-a-Reef
Videodisc Side 4

Go to Chapter 15

CD-ROM
The Wetlands

2 EXPLORE

Inquiry Activity

Relating

Asking Scientific Questions
Ask students to think of various interactions they have observed between different types of living things, including the plant/aphid/ladybug relationships pictured on page 282 and investigated in the Chapter Discovery Learning Activity. Then have each student choose one such interaction and list three scientific questions that might be asked about it, for example: What other types of insects do ladybugs eat? How many aphids does one ladybug usually consume in one day? What types of animals prey on ladybugs? Guide students to suggest how they might go about answering these questions.

3 TEACH

Discussion

Guide students to relate the information presented in Figure 13–2 to the steps in the scientific method. Point out that as ecologists study an issue, they may alternate between the three different inquiry methods described in this table, with the results obtained with one method generating hypotheses that are then tested using another method. For example, data gathered through observation may lead researchers to create a model. The model may generate predictions that can be tested in experiments. Experimental results may prompt further questions to be answered through observation, and so on.

INTEGRATING CAREERS

Ecologists must have a solid background in biology, animal physiology, morphology, chemistry, and geology. A Bachelors degree in science is required for nonresearch positions, a Masters degree for applied research or management positions, and a Ph.D. degree for independent research positions or teaching at the college level.

To study different parts of the biosphere, or the living world, ecologists use a wide range of techniques. Some use genetic fingerprints to identify single-celled organisms that inhabit the mud of coastal marshes. Others use radio transmitters to track migrating wildlife across continents. Still others use data gathered from satellites to monitor the temperature of the oceans. Today, ecological research makes use of three basic methods, summarized in ***Figure 13–2.*** ●

INTEGRATING CAREERS
What kind of educational preparation is required for a career in ecology?

Why Study Ecology?

Scientists are becoming increasingly aware of the important role that ecology plays in our lives. **Today, ecological research provides us with information that is necessary to understand and resolve many of the environmental and ecological issues that confront us.** In order to ask and answer the appropriate questions, gain an appreciation of the short-term and long-term effects of your actions, and make wise choices on controversial issues, you need an understanding of ecology.

Some Examples

To start your thinking, here are a few questions for you to consider:

- What has happened to the populations of certain food fishes in parts of the North Atlantic? How can families continue to earn a living from the sea? To answer these questions,

Figure 13–2
The table presents three research methods of ecology.

RESEARCH METHODS OF ECOLOGY

	Observations	Experiments	Models
Method	Careful observations of the natural world form the foundations of ecological science.	Hypotheses based on prior observations are tested by intelligently designed and carefully performed experiments. The effect of different variables is studied independently.	Models useful in studying ecological phenomena—such as the flow of energy and nutrients and the way in which organisms reproduce—usually consist of mathematical formulas and equations that are manipulated by computer. The best models are those that are driven by data gathered by observation, experimentation, or both.
Advantages	Observations often lead to valuable understanding of situations and phenomena. Making observations is usually the first step in asking important questions.	Experiments allow control of important variables and the chance to manipulate each variable separately.	Models allow tests of hypotheses over long periods of time. Models also allow simple manipulation of variables that may be difficult or impossible to vary in nature.
Disadvantages	Although observations often suggest connections between various events in nature, usually observations alone cannot prove those links.	When trying to study large, complex collections of organisms, it is possible that laboratory experiments differ from the real world in ways that experimenters do not realize.	Models are only as good as the data and thought that go into them. Models based on faulty hypotheses or incomplete data make faulty predictions.

TEACHER SUPPORT

Managing Classroom Diversity

EDUCATIONAL EQUITY
Two of the most notable field researchers of this century have been women: Jane Goodall and Dian Fossey. Jane Goodall's patient and meticulously documented observations of wild chimpanzees in East Africa since the 1960s have revealed surprising discoveries: Chimpanzees make and use simple tools, work cooperatively to obtain meat, and wage war.

Dian Fossey—a controversial figure whose book *Gorillas in the Mist* was the basis for a movie in the late 1980s—studied wild mountain gorillas in Africa for 18 years. When some of her research subjects were killed by poachers, Fossey redirected her work toward protecting wild gorillas and their habitat.

Encourage interested students to learn more about these famous field researchers and the challenges they faced as they tried to observe their shy and elusive subjects in the wild.

Biology AND YOU .... Connections

The Mississippi River Floods—How Can Wetlands Help?

The summer of 1993 was a nightmare for the Midwest. Heavy rains swelled the Mississippi River system to five times normal widths. Levees burst. Millions of hectares of land were flooded, destroying homes, farms, and businesses.

The Role of Wetlands

As anyone who lives near the Mississippi knows, the river has always been prone to flooding. Nutrient-rich sediment spread by flood waters over thousands of years has made the region fertile for growing crops. But in the old days, the river's banks and tributaries were surrounded by habitats called wetlands. Wetlands—swamps, marshes, seasonal creeks, and wet-footed woods—act like giant sponges. During heavy rains, wetlands soak up enormous quantities of water and then release it slowly.

Over the last century, development projects drained and filled wetlands for farming and housing. Without natural "safety valves" in the water cycle, the river became more prone to rising suddenly during rainy spells. To contain it, many miles of dikes and levees were built. This simply moved the flood zone downstream, making it worse.

Hope for the Future

Applied ecological research is offering hope that future floods might not be as devastating. Researchers are finding out that restoring former wetlands to their original condition can be fast and inexpensive. They calculate that if only about 3 percent of the land in the upper Mississippi watershed is returned to its former wetland condition, disastrous floods could be avoided. Do you think we will put our understanding of ecology to use and test the scientists' hypothesis?

Making the Connection

What are the advantages of building levees and dikes? What are the benefits of preserving wetlands?

RESTORING WETLANDS

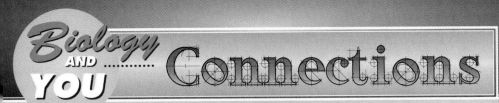

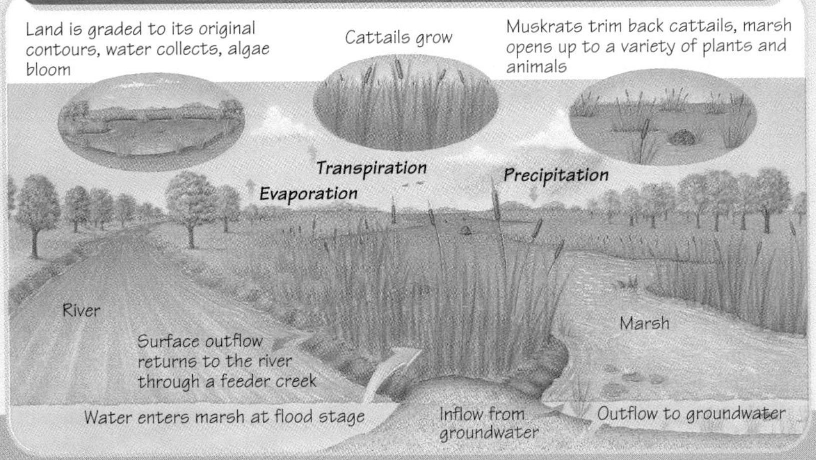

Connections

The floods that struck the Missouri and upper Mississippi River basins in 1993—the result of abnormally high levels of rainfall over an eight-month period—claimed more than 40 lives, displaced more than 30,000 people in eight states, and caused an estimated $10 billion in damage.

To help students appreciate the extent of the 1993 flooding, have them locate the upper Mississippi River on a U.S. map and find the states that are affected when the river overflows its banks or breaks through levees and dikes. Point out that flooding also occurs along the rivers and streams that flow into the Mississippi. Thus, widespread flooding affected eight states in 1993: Minnesota, South Dakota, Nebraska, Wisconsin, Illinois, Missouri, Iowa, and Kansas.

Make sure students understand the stages of wetland restoration shown in the illustration. Emphasize that these stages occur naturally once artificial barriers and drainage systems are removed. You may want to return to this illustration when students learn about ecological succession in Chapter 15, Section 15–2.

Answers to Making the Connection

Levees and dikes make land available for farming and housing while helping to contain water during moderate flooding. Wetlands soak up enormous quantities of water and release it slowly, preventing the devastating floods that can break through levees and dikes.

TEACHER SUPPORT

Activity

MODELING WETLANDS

This activity is appropriate for use as a follow-up to the Connections feature. Challenge student teams to design and build a model that demonstrates the role of wetlands in preventing flooding by absorbing heavy rainfall and releasing the water slowly.

The models can be as simple or as complex as students choose, from a tilted cookie sheet with a large household sponge on it, to dishpans of "wetlands" made of clumps of weeds and sod. Give each team an opportunity to demonstrate and explain its model to the rest of the class.

Ancillary Support

The resources below can be used to support your teaching strategy for these two pages.

TR Apply: Choosing the Right Method

BL Inquiry Activity: Where Are the Frogs?

4 ASSESS

Quick Check

Identify a specific ecology-related question or issue that could be investigated using the inquiry methods described in Figure 13–2. Have each student draw a flow chart to show the steps a scientist might go through in applying two or all three inquiry methods to the question or issue.

Section Review 13-1

1. The scientific study of interactions between different kinds of living things and between living things and the environments in which they live. Provides us with the necessary information to understand and resolve environmental and ecological issues.

2. Students' answers should include the information in Figure 13–2.

3. Accept all reasonable responses. Students may cite the examples given on pages 284 and 286 of the student text.

Learning Modality

Auditory Learning Ask volunteers with fluent reading skills to tape-record the information presented in Figure 13–2. Make the tape available for independent use by students who learn best when material is presented through auditory means. To check students' understanding, follow up with small-group discussions of the material.

Figure 13–3
Ⓐ *Earth is home to an amazing variety of living and nonliving things that are closely connected.*

CAREER TRACK
Ⓑ *Ecologists study the biosphere to understand these connections so that humans can use Earth's resources without causing long-term harm.*

you must come to understand what fishes need in order to grow and reproduce in abundance.

- Is the Earth getting warmer? If so, how will this affect the way we live? To grasp this important and complicated question, you must piece together various kinds of information that you will learn while studying ecology. Even then, the answer may not be clear.

✓ **Checkpoint** Why is it important for you to have an understanding of ecology? ❶

Web of Interdependence

As a result of the work of dedicated ecologists, people around the world have begun to understand two fundamental ecological truths. First, our planet is home not only to humans but to many other forms of life as well. Second, the health of human society depends on the well-being of much of that life. From microscopic organisms to tall trees and from swamps to coral reefs, living things affect each other in many ways. To take care of our planet and ourselves properly, we must understand how and why organisms affect one another and their environment as they do.

At the core of every organism's interaction with its environment and with other organisms is the organism's need for energy and nutrients—energy to power life's processes and raw materials to build and maintain living tissue. As you study this chapter, you will discover that the processes of acquiring energy and nutrients join all life together in an intricate web of interdependence and coexistence. Therefore, the study of ecology must begin with the study of how different organisms obtain and use the energy and nutrients on which all life depends.

Section Review 13-1

1. **Define** ecology. **Explain** why it is important to study ecology.
2. **Describe** three methods that ecologists use in their studies. What are the advantages and disadvantages of each?
3. **Critical Thinking—Relating** Give two examples of the kinds of questions ecologists ask. Explain why they are important.

TEACHER SUPPORT

Ecology Note

Recognizing the need to prevent habitat destruction, many nations attending the Earth Summit held in Rio de Janeiro in 1992 signed a pact called the Biodiversity Convention. The Convention's purpose is to provide money to help countries preserve their unique species and manage them as valuable natural resources.

Overhunting endangers other species. For example, some whale species were brought to the brink of extinction before a whaling ban was instituted in 1986. Unfortunately, a few countries continue to hunt whales. The African rhinoceros, although protected, is killed for its horns. Elephants are slaughtered for their tusks, despite a ban on the ivory trade.

Other species are at risk because they are taken from the wild to be sold as pets. The Convention on International Trade in Endangered Species (CITES) and other international agreements restrict the trade of wild plants and animals but are often difficult to enforce.

Energy: Essential for Life's Processes

GUIDE FOR READING

- **Explain** how energy flows through the biosphere.
- **Describe** how energy flows through the different trophic levels in the biosphere.

MINI LAB

- **Classify** the living things you see in your neighborhood.

ALL OF LIFE'S PROCESSES require energy. Although both animals and plants require energy, only plants and certain bacteria can collect energy from their environment and harness it to do biological work. An animal can store energy in its body in the form of complex chemicals such as carbohydrates, fats, or proteins, but the only way an animal can obtain energy is to eat other organisms. To understand how energy moves through the biosphere, you must begin where most energy enters living systems—in green plants.

Energy From the Sun

Green plants can do something that no animals can do. They can harness the energy from sunlight by a process called photosynthesis. Ultimately, the plants assemble simple substances into the building blocks of living tissue, such as carbohydrates, fats, and proteins.

Primary Producers

Plants are **primary producers** because they produce living tissue from nonliving sources, such as water, carbon dioxide, and energy. Primary producers are also called **autotrophs,** meaning "self-feeding." While plants get their energy from the sun, the chemoautotrophs, a group of bacteria, harvest energy from certain chemicals.

Consumers

Animals, as well as most bacteria, cannot capture energy from the sun as plants do. Yet animals need energy for their life processes. Animals also cannot make all the building blocks of living tissue from simple nonliving chemical substances

Figure 13–4 (a) Swans, (b) seals, and even (c) sunflowers must obtain energy to live.

SECTION 13–2

Energy: Essential for Life's Processes

Performance Objective

- Describe the flow of energy from primary producers to consumers to decomposers in the biosphere.

Mini Lab Skill: Classifying

1 ENGAGE

Ideas Through Images

Have students examine Figure 13–4, read the caption, and answer the following questions.

- **Which of the organisms shown in these photographs must eat other organisms to obtain food?** (The swan and seals.)
- **What do swans eat?** (Aquatic plants and insects. Students' answers may vary depending on their prior experience. Accept all reasonable responses.)
- **What do seals eat?** (Fishes and other marine animals.)
- **Which organisms in the photographs do not eat other organisms?** (The sunflowers and all other plants shown.)

Checkpoint

1 In order to ask and answer appropriate questions, gain an appreciation of the short- and long-term effects of actions, and make wise choices on controversial issues.

TEACHER SUPPORT

Managing Classroom Diversity

TECH PREP STUDENTS

Encourage students who are interested in a career in agriculture or horticulture to research common plant pests that attack crops and vegetation in your area. Such pests might include Japanese beetles, gypsy moth larvae, aphids, boll weevils, corn borers, fruit flies, mites, and bud worms. Also suggest that students find out about the methods that are presently being used to control these pests and new controls that are being investigated.

AT-RISK STUDENTS/LEP STUDENTS

To make the terms *herbivore, carnivore,* and *omnivore* more meaningful to students, ask them to use a dictionary to find the derivations of the words. (From the Latin *herba,* meaning "grass"; *carn,* "flesh"; *omni,* "all"; and *vorus,* "to devour.")

Ancillary Support

The resources below can be used to support your teaching strategy for these two pages.

TR Writing in Biology: Ecological Conversations

LM Observing the Effects of Sunlight on Plant Growth, #26

2 EXPLORE

Investigate

Long-Term Project Have student teams observe what happens to plants when they are deprived of sunlight. Based on these observations, students should discover that plants need sunlight to carry on photosynthesis and remain healthy.

1. Start the experiment in the morning on a sunny day. Choose a grassy spot outdoors that gets sun most of the day. Cover a small patch of grass with a wooden board.
2. The next morning, lift the board and observe the color of the grass underneath it. If the grass is still green, replace the board and continue to check the patch each morning. As soon as the grass starts to turn yellow, remove the board. (Depending on the type of grass and your location, it may take from one to several days for the covered grass to start to turn color.)
3. After the board is removed, continue to observe the patch each morning for several more days and notice what happens. (In two or three days, the grass will begin to turn green again.)

3 TEACH

Ideas Through Images

Have students examine Figure 13–5, read the caption, and answer the following questions.

- **Which of the organisms are primary producers?** (The trees, grass, and other plants.) **Consumers?** (The sheep, leopard, and impala.)
- **What type of consumers are the sheep?** (Herbivores.) **The leopard?** (A carnivore.)

Discussion

Ask students to classify each organism in the mini-habitats they set up in the Unit Discovery Learning Activity on pages 280–281 as a producer, a consumer, or a decomposer.

Figure 13–5
(a) Energy from the sun is captured by green plants and other primary producers. (b) Herbivores such as sheep and (c) carnivores such as leopards are consumers and get their energy by eating other organisms.

available to them in the environment. As a result, animals must eat other organisms to obtain their energy and nutrients. For this reason, animals are called **consumers.** Animals are also called **heterotrophs,** because they must feed on other organisms to obtain energy.

Heterotrophs

There are many kinds of heterotrophs in the natural world. Herbivores obtain energy by eating autotrophs that have manufactured and stored proteins, carbohydrates, and other high-energy substances. Carnivores obtain energy by eating other animals. Omnivores are animals that eat both plants and animals. Parasites are organisms that live in or on other organisms and obtain their

Figure 13–6
Organisms depend on one another for food. Ecologists use the concept of trophic levels to study this interdependence.

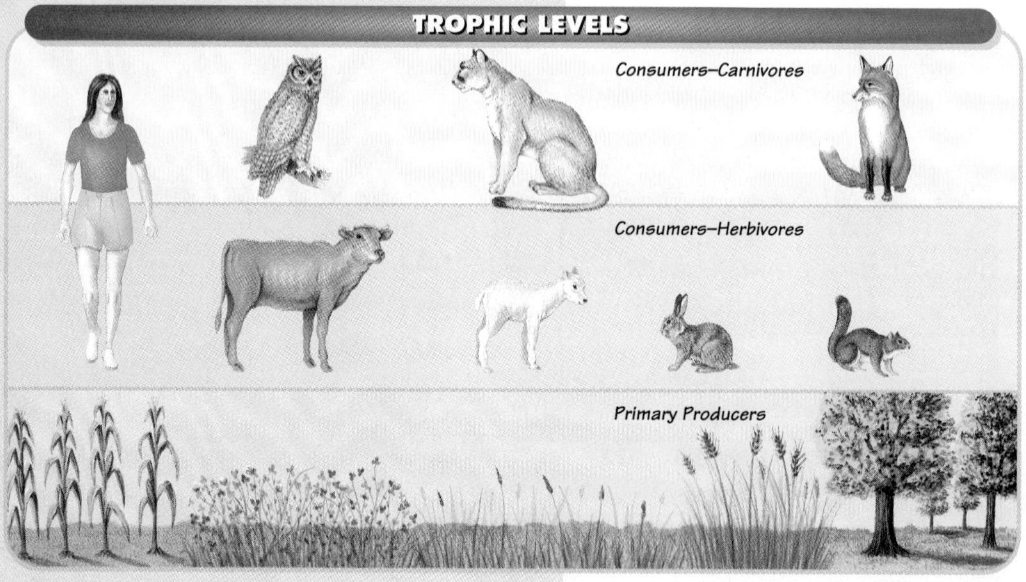

TEACHER SUPPORT

Background Information

Chlorophyll, the pigment that gives plants their green color, is constantly being made in the plants' leaves. When plants are deprived of sunlight, both photosynthesis and chlorophyll production stop, and the chlorophyll already present in the leaves starts to break down. This lack of chlorophyll exposes yellow and orange pigments, called carotenoids, that are also present in leaves but normally masked by the green chlorophyll. Thus, plants deprived of sunlight turn yellow or orange.

If a yellowing plant is soon exposed to sunlight again, it begins producing chlorophyll again and turns green.

A similar process creates the changes in leaf color associated with autumn. As days become shorter in the fall, the leaves of deciduous trees stop making pigments. Chlorophyll is the first pigment to break down. The fading of the green color exposes red, yellow, orange, and purple pigments also present in the leaves.

nutrients from their living host. Although parasites "eat their victims alive," they do not necessarily kill them—at least not right away. Still other organisms, called **decomposers,** feed on the dead bodies of animals and plants or on their waste products.

Checkpoint What is the difference between autotrophs and heterotrophs? ❶

Energy Flow Through the Biosphere

Because energy cannot be recycled, or used again in the biosphere, it can be thought of as a flow—a one-way flow. **Arriving as sunlight, energy flows through the tissues of primary producers to the tissues of consumers and then to the tissues of decomposers.** In a sense, you can think of energy in the biosphere as a stream that flows steadily downhill, powering a series of water wheels (primary producers, consumers, and decomposers) along the way.

Trophic Levels

Each step in this series of organisms eating other organisms makes up a **trophic level,** or a feeding level. Theoretically, there is no limit to the number of trophic levels in the biosphere. **However, the greater the number of trophic levels between consumers and primary producers, the smaller the amount of energy that is available to the consumers compared to the energy originally captured by the primary producers.** This is because every time one organism eats another, much of the energy obtained is used up rather than stored. Why does this happen? Because all life's processes—from growth and reproduction to the powering of simple daily activities—require energy. In addition, most animals cannot use 100 percent of the energy potentially contained in the foods they eat.

As a result of these energy losses, only about 10 percent of the energy at one trophic level can be used by the consumers at the next trophic level. Thus, only 10 percent of the energy contained in plants ends up stored in the tissues of herbivores, and only 10 percent of the energy in herbivores can be stored in the tissues of carnivores. Further, only 10 percent of the energy in carnivores—that is, 10 percent of 10 percent of 10 percent, or 1 part in 1000 of the original amount—is available to carnivores that eat other carnivores!

Checkpoint How can you explain the decrease in the energy that is available at successive trophic levels? ❷

MINI LAB ..... Classifying

Life in Your Neighborhood

PROBLEM *How can you* ***classify*** *the organisms in your area?*

PROCEDURE

1. Choose an area around your school or around your home. Make a list of the different kinds of organisms—such as plants, insects, animals, and people—that you see.
2. Classify each organism as either a primary producer or a consumer.
3. Further classify each consumer as a carnivore or herbivore.

ANALYZE AND CONCLUDE

1. What organisms did you classify as primary producers? Consumers?
2. Did you observe any herbivores? What were they?
3. Did you observe any carnivores? If so, what were they?
4. What do you think would happen if all the primary producers in the area died out?

MINI LAB Classifying

Teacher Notes

- For time required and materials needed, see page 282b.
- If students do not already know what types of food a particular animal eats, tell them to do some research to find out.

Answers to Analyze and Conclude

1. All plants are primary producers, all animals are consumers. Make sure students do not identify fungi, which are decomposers, as either producers or consumers.

2. Accept answers that identify omnivores, such as crows, as herbivores.

3. Accept answers that identify omnivores as carnivores.

4. All the herbivores would die, and in turn all the carnivores that feed on them would die.

Skills Trace

Classifying

- **Focus** p. 289
- **Practice** p. 290
- **Assess** p. 308

Checkpoints

❶ Autotrophs produce their own food using energy from the sun. Heterotrophs must eat other organisms to obtain energy and nutrients.

❷ Every time one organism eats another, much of the energy obtained is used up rather than stored.

TEACHER SUPPORT

Managing Classroom Diversity

MULTICULTURAL STRATEGY

Humans are often cited as an example of omnivores, but this is not entirely accurate. For a variety of reasons—cultural practices, religious beliefs, personal convictions, health considerations—many people choose not to eat meat or other foods derived from animals. Such people are called vegetarians, although not all vegetarians eat only plants and plant products.

Encourage students to research different types of vegetarian diets. Strict vegetarians eat no animal foods of any kind. Other vegetarians eat fish, poultry, eggs, and dairy products but do not eat red meat. Lacto-ovo vegetarians eat eggs, milk, and milk products but do not eat red meat, fish, or poultry.

Vegetarian diets are healthy so long as they contain all essential nutrients. Because their diets are low in fat, vegetarians are less likely to be overweight or to develop diseases associated with high fat consumption.

Ancillary Support

The resources below can be used to support your teaching strategy for these two pages.

TR Enrich: Dark Secrets
BL Inquiry Activity: The Energy of Life

4 ASSESS

Quick Check

Have students reexamine the chapter opener photograph on page 282 and Figure 13–4 on page 287. Ask them to identify each organism shown in the pictures as a primary producer or a consumer and, if the latter, as a herbivore or a carnivore.

Section Review 13-2

1. Arriving as sunlight, energy flows through the tissues of primary producers to the tissues of consumers and then to the tissues of decomposers.

2. Primary producers use solar energy to change simple nonliving chemical nutrients into living tissue. Consumers feed on other organisms to obtain energy. Decomposers feed on the dead bodies of animals and plants or on their waste products.

3. Only about 10 percent of the energy at one trophic level can be used by the consumers at the next trophic level. An ecological pyramid shows this decreasing amount of energy at successive trophic levels.

4. Animals at higher trophic levels must eat more food as a result of the pattern of energy loss between levels. A large animal such as a whale obtains the maximum amount of energy by feeding on primary producers.

5. Accept all reasonable classifications of trophic levels. The sequence is called an ecological pyramid.

Skills Trace
Classifying

- Focus p. 289
- Practice p. 290
- Assess p. 308

ECOLOGICAL PYRAMIDS

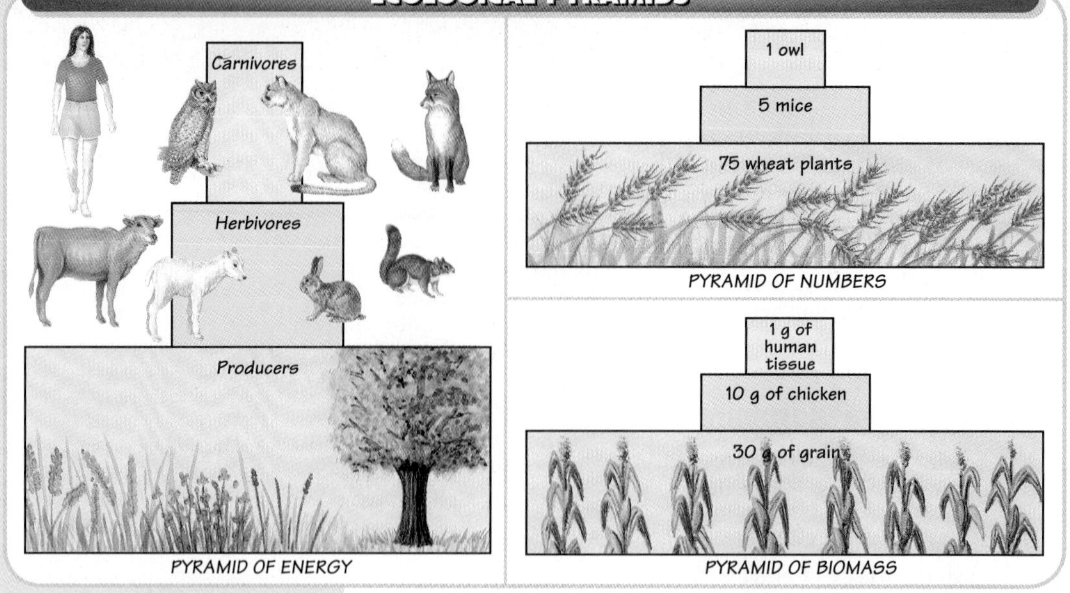

Figure 13–7 *Ecological pyramids show the decreasing amounts of energy, living tissue, or number of organisms at successive trophic levels.*

Ecological Pyramids

Figure 13–7 shows the ecologically important result of the energy flow from plants to the carnivores on the highest trophic level. The less energy available at any trophic level, the less living tissue that trophic level can have. Thus, the energy chain from primary producers to herbivores to carnivores creates what are called **ecological pyramids.** Three types of ecological pyramids are shown in **Figure 13–7.**

In summary, only primary producers such as green plants can make the sun's energy available to the rest of Earth's living things. But energy is not all that organisms need. Organisms also need materials for growth and maintenance. And the foods they eat give them both—energy and nutrients. In the following section, you will learn more about nutrients, how organisms obtain them, and how they cycle through the biosphere.

Section Review 13–2

1. **Explain** how energy flows through the biosphere.
2. **Describe** how energy flows through the different trophic levels in the biosphere.
3. **Compare** the loss of energy at each trophic level. **Relate** this to ecological pyramids.
4. **Critical Thinking—Hypothesizing** What is the significance of the pattern of energy loss for animals on higher trophic levels? Following this line of reasoning, why might it be advantageous for a large animal such as a whale to feed on plankton, or tiny marine primary producers?
5. **MINI LAB** **Classify** the organisms you observed in your neighborhood into trophic levels based on who eats whom. What might you call such a sequence?

Learning Modality

Visual Learning Use the following activity to help students visualize energy transfer from producers to herbivores to carnivores. Divide the class into teams of three. Give one student on each team a sheet of graph paper, and tell the student that he or she represents a plant. Have the student outline a 10×10 block of squares on the graph paper and cut it out. Then tell the student to cut a row of 10 squares from the block and hand the row to a second student, who represents a herbivore. Tell the "herbivore" to cut one square from the row and hand it to the third student, who represents a carnivore. Students will see that only a small portion of the original food energy stored in the plant (1 square of the original 100) reaches the carnivore.

Nutrients: Building Blocks of Living Tissue

SECTION 13–3

GUIDE FOR READING

- **Describe** how nutrients are recycled in the biosphere.
- **Define** nutrient limitation.

MINI LAB

- **Formulate a hypothesis** to explain the effect of fertilizer on plant growth.

AS YOU HAVE JUST READ, organisms need more than energy in order to survive. Organisms also need nutrients—the chemical building blocks of life. Nutrients are the substances that organisms use to build living tissues and to grow.

What Are Nutrients?

Autotrophs can manufacture substances such as carbohydrates, fats, and proteins from simple chemical nutrients that they can readily obtain from their environment. Green plants, for example, take up water, carbon dioxide, nitrogen, phosphorus, and potassium from their environment in substantial quantities. They require other substances, such as iron and magnesium, in smaller, or trace, amounts. Making use of the sun's energy, primary producers assemble these relatively simple nutrients into complex substances such as carbohydrates, proteins, and fats for their growth and maintenance.

Heterotrophs, on the other hand, cannot manufacture all the complex substances that they need from simple ingredients such as water and carbon dioxide. Therefore, animals must eat other organisms in order to obtain the nutrients—such as carbohydrates, fats, and proteins—they need. For the most part, carbohydrates

Figure 13–8
From (a) a seed in a pine cone to (b) seedling to (c) fully-grown pine tree—nutrients enable organisms to grow.

SECTION 13–3

Nutrients: Building Blocks of Living Tissue

Performance Objectives

- Describe how nutrients—including water, nitrogen, and carbon—are re-cycled among organisms and ecosystems in the biosphere.
- Explain the effect of nutrient limitation on ecosystem productivity.

Mini Lab Skill: Hypothesizing

1 ENGAGE

Ideas Through Images

Have students examine Figure 13–8, read the caption, and answer the following questions.

- **What does this series of photographs show?** (Students should recognize that the photographs show the life cycle of a pine tree, from seeds [in the cone], to seedling, to mature tree.)
- **How are nutrients important to this life cycle?** (Accept all reasonable responses, including that nutrients are needed to build living tissues so the pine tree can grow and reproduce.)
- **How do living organisms get the nutrients they need?** (Accept all reasonable responses, including plants get nutrients from the soil they grow in and the water they absorb; animals get nutrients from the food they eat.)

TEACHER SUPPORT

Managing Classroom Diversity

TECH PREP STUDENTS

Encourage students who are considering careers in horticulture to research the nutrient needs of various types of nursery plants and houseplants. Agriculture students could investigate the nutrient requirements of different crops and the methods used to supply those nutrients—not only applying fertilizers to fields but also rotating crops, planting winter wheat in the fall and plowing it under in the spring, and so forth. Also suggest that these students learn more about irrigation methods that conserve water and reduce evaporation.

Students in a culinary arts program or those who plan to become dieticians or dietary aides could find out about the USDA's Food Guide Pyramid and how it is used in planning a healthy diet. Also suggest that they investigate food-preparation methods that conserve nutrients in foods, such as steaming vegetables instead of boiling them.

2 EXPLORE

Discussion

Ask students to define the term *cycle* in their own words. Definitions may vary but should focus on the idea that a cycle consists of a specific sequence of steps or stages that repeat over and over again. Ask students to describe various cycles that are familiar to them. Students may cite the seasons, the days of the week, the firing of pistons in an engine, and the life cycles of plants and animals, including humans. Point out that in life cycles, individual organisms do not repeat the stages of birth/germination, growth, reproduction, and death, but rather the species as a whole experiences the cycle.

3 TEACH

Ideas Through Images

Have students examine Figure 13–9, read the caption, and answer the following questions.

- **What are some of the nutrients that are recycled through the biosphere?** (Water, carbon dioxide, nitrogen, phosphorus, and potassium. Students also might name iron and magnesium, mentioned on page 291 of the student text.)
- **Where do autotrophs get the nutrients they need?** (From their environment; from soil and air.)
- **What do autotrophs do with these nutrients?** (Manufacture carbohydrates, proteins, fats, and vitamins for growth and maintenance.)
- **Where do heterotrophs get the nutrients they need?** (From the plants and other heterotrophs they consume.)
- **What type of energy continually enters the biosphere?** (Light energy from the sun.)
- **What type of energy is continually released by heterotrophs as a waste product?** (Heat energy.)

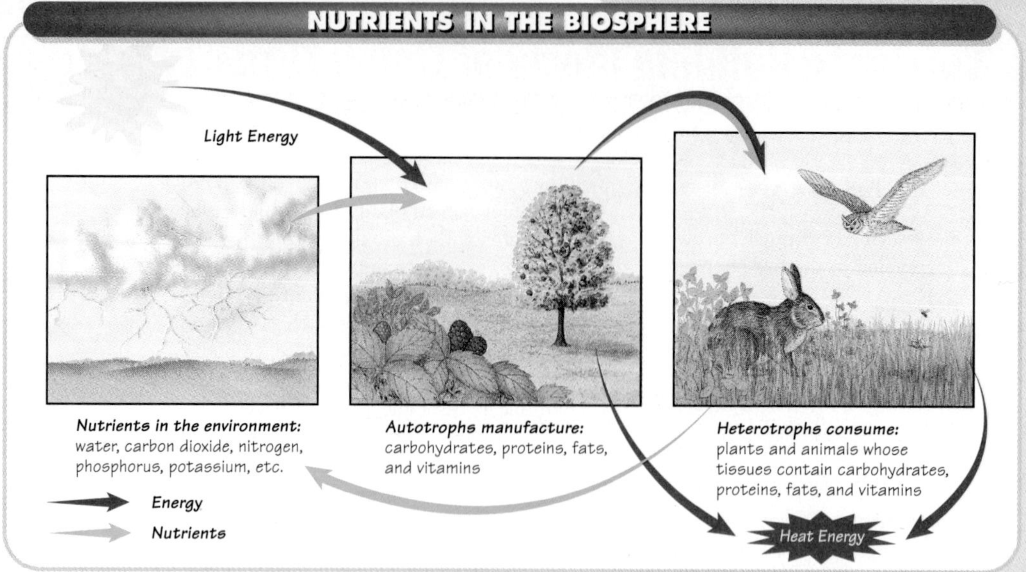

Figure 13–9
The arrows show the movement of nutrients and energy through the biosphere. Notice that nutrients are recycled, whereas energy is not.

and fats provide immediate energy or are stored in the animal's body, providing energy when it is needed. Proteins are broken down into amino acids, which can be reassembled into the particular protein the organism needs. Animals also need several vitamins manufactured by plants and many of the same trace elements that plants need.

Earlier in this chapter, you read that organisms in each trophic level eat members of the level beneath them to obtain both energy and nutrients. Put another way, energy and nutrients move together from one trophic level to the next in the form of plant or animal tissue. However, energy and nutrients move through the biosphere in very different ways.

You may recall that energy is always arriving from the sun and is continually being used by organisms to perform work. Strictly speaking, energy is not destroyed as organisms use it—it is converted into a different form. Ultimately, the energy ends up as the heat that is released into the biosphere. However, living things cannot harness and then reuse this heat energy. So although energy is conserved, it cannot be recycled. As a result, the energy that all living things need must be continually captured from its original source—the sun.

✓ **Checkpoint** What are nutrients? 1

Nutrient Cycles

Nutrients, unlike energy, do not arrive on Earth from outer space. Like energy, however, nutrients are not destroyed as a result of their use by Earth's organisms. Nutrients either become part of living tissue or they are eliminated from the organism as waste products.

Nutrients that are available in fixed quantities on Earth are passed from one organism to another and from one part of the biosphere to another through the

TEACHER SUPPORT

Activity

Identifying Plant and Human Nutrients
Provide—or ask students to bring from home—labels from different types of plant fertilizers. Have students examine the labels and list the nutrients contained in each fertilizer. Ask volunteers to create a class master list of all the plant nutrients they find.

Next have students focus on the nutrients that humans need: carbohydrates, fats, proteins, vitamins, minerals, and water. Provide a variety of age-appropriate resource materials, and suggest that students research each nutrient's major dietary sources and its role in maintaining good health. Again have students compile their findings in a class master list.

In a follow-up class discussion, ask students to compare the two lists and identify the nutrients that are needed by both plants and humans (water and certain minerals, primarily phosphorus and potassium).

pathways of nutrient cycles. These **nutrient cycles** pass the same nutrients over and over again through the different parts of the biosphere. As you may expect, understanding nutrient cycles is essential to understanding the biosphere.

Three important nutrient cycles are illustrated below and on the following two pages. As you examine these cycles, keep in mind that cycles are closed loops in which something flows continuously without a beginning or an end. Often, cycles consist of several processes that are going on at the same time.

☑ *Checkpoint* How do nutrient cycles differ from energy flows? 2

Nutrient Limitation

Although nutrient cycles are ultimately global processes, over the short term they may be limited to smaller parts of the biosphere, called ecosystems. Ecosystems might appear to be self-contained and to function independently of one another. In fact, sometimes just the opposite is true. As nutrients move through ecosystems, they often have some interesting consequences.

An ecosystem's productivity is a measure of the rate at which energy is captured by its autotrophs. This productivity may be limited by a single nutrient

Visualizing Nutrient Cycles

The Water Cycle

The water cycle consists of the processes of evaporation, condensation, and precipitation.

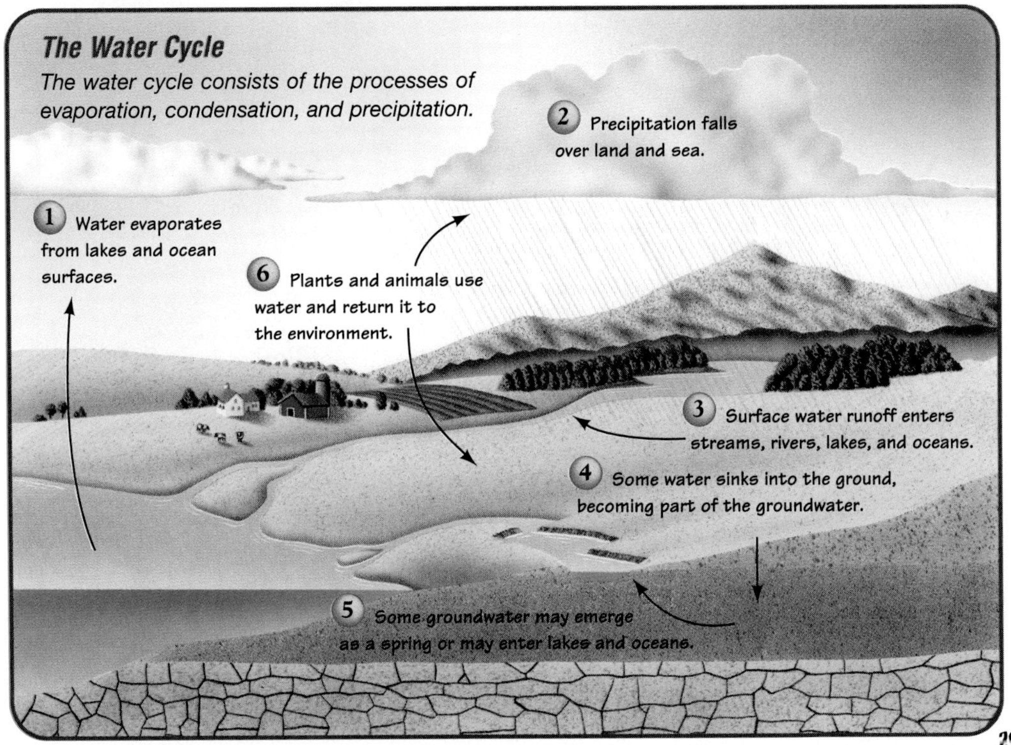

1 Water evaporates from lakes and ocean surfaces.
2 Precipitation falls over land and sea.
3 Surface water runoff enters streams, rivers, lakes, and oceans.
4 Some water sinks into the ground, becoming part of the groundwater.
5 Some groundwater may emerge as a spring or may enter lakes and oceans.
6 Plants and animals use water and return it to the environment.

Visualizing Nutrient Cycles

The Water Cycle

Explain the processes of evaporation, condensation, and precipitation in greater detail. Solar energy heats liquid water on the Earth's surface, causing it to change state to a gas, water vapor, that rises into the atmosphere. When the vapor is cooled at higher atmospheric levels, it condenses, or changes state to liquid water again, forming tiny droplets that collect on microscopic particles of dust and other solids in the air. A cloud is simply a mass of such water droplets and solid particles. As more droplets collect on the particles, they eventually fall as precipitation in the form of rain, snow, sleet, or hail depending on the air temperature. Water that has fallen to Earth is again subject to evaporation, and the cycle repeats.

☑ Checkpoints

1 Substances that organisms use to build living tissues and to grow.

2 Nutrient cycles move the same nutrients over and over again through the biosphere, whereas energy flows in only one direction and does not recycle.

Technology

BioVue
Animation: The Water Cycle
Videodisc Side 4

Go to Chapter 25

TEACHER SUPPORT

Ecology Note

Human activity affects the global water cycle in a variety of ways. For example, one source of atmospheric water is transpiration from the dense vegetation that makes up tropical rain forests. When rain forests are destroyed to clear land for farming, ranching, and mining—as is happening at an alarming rate today—transpiration is reduced and less water vapor is released into the atmosphere. The long-range effect of this process on local and global weather patterns is uncertain.

Another human activity that affects the water cycle is large-scale pumping of groundwater to the surface for irrigation. More water on the surface increases the evaporation rate over land. If this loss is not balanced by increased rainfall on land, groundwater supplies may be depleted. In the United States, large areas of the Midwest, the southwestern desert, parts of California, and areas bordering the Gulf of Mexico already face serious water shortages as a result of groundwater depletion.

Ancillary Support

The resources below can be used to support your teaching strategy for these two pages.

LM Investigating the Effects of Water Pollution on Plants, #25
TR Explore: Cycle in a Bottle
BL Inquiry Activity: Water Roundup
TB Visualizing the Water Cycle, #16

Visualizing Nutrient Cycles

The Nitrogen Cycle

Point out to students that nitrogen is the most plentiful gas in the air around us, making up almost 80 percent of the atmosphere. Despite its abundance, however, atmospheric nitrogen is unusable by most plants and thus cannot directly enter an ecosystem's nutrient flow. Emphasize that it is the action of bacteria—microscopic organisms we cannot even see—that makes nitrogen available to plants and in turn to the animals, including ourselves, that feed directly or indirectly on them.

Discussion

For the sake of clarity and simplicity, only the three most important nutrient cycles are discussed in the student text. Note that they are presented in their order of increasing complexity. You could point out to students that all nutrients pass through such cycles, many of which are even more complex than the nitrogen and carbon cycles. As an example of another cycle, ask students whether they have ever smelled the distinctive "rotten eggs" odor of swamp or marsh mud. Explain that what they smelled was hydrogen sulfide, a gas produced by bacteria that live in anaerobic environments such as swamp mud. This action is part of the sulfur cycle.

As you discuss the water, nitrogen, and carbon cycles, emphasize that when an organism gives off waste products or dies and decomposes, the released molecules do not cycle together through the same pathway but split up and follow different pathways.

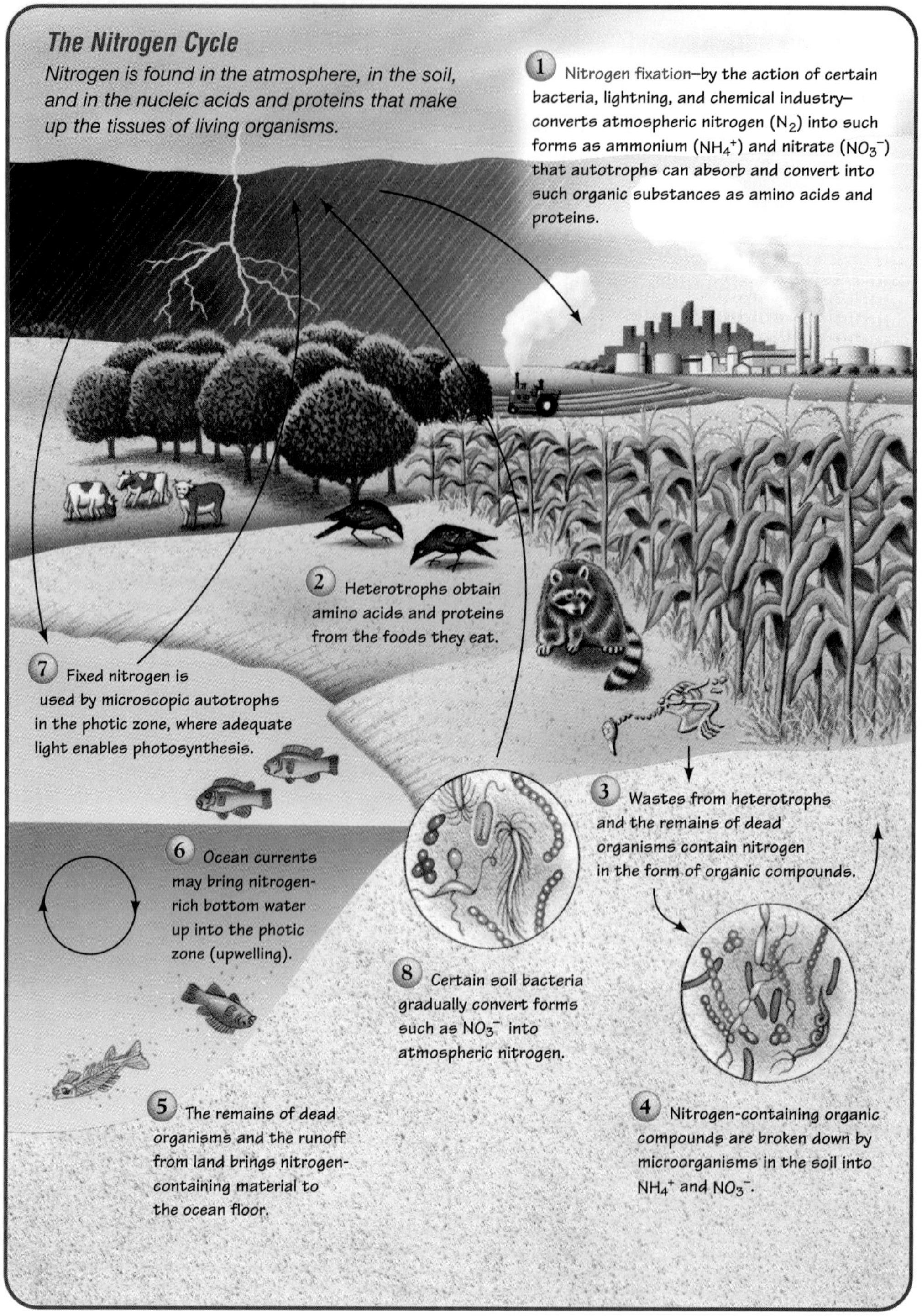

The Nitrogen Cycle
Nitrogen is found in the atmosphere, in the soil, and in the nucleic acids and proteins that make up the tissues of living organisms.
1 Nitrogen fixation—by the action of certain bacteria, lightning, and chemical industry—converts atmospheric nitrogen (N_2) into such forms as ammonium (NH_4^+) and nitrate (NO_3^-) that autotrophs can absorb and convert into such organic substances as amino acids and proteins.
2 Heterotrophs obtain amino acids and proteins from the foods they eat.
3 Wastes from heterotrophs and the remains of dead organisms contain nitrogen in the form of organic compounds.
4 Nitrogen-containing organic compounds are broken down by microorganisms in the soil into NH_4^+ and NO_3^-.
5 The remains of dead organisms and the runoff from land brings nitrogen-containing material to the ocean floor.
6 Ocean currents may bring nitrogen-rich bottom water up into the photic zone (upwelling).
7 Fixed nitrogen is used by microscopic autotrophs in the photic zone, where adequate light enables photosynthesis.
8 Certain soil bacteria gradually convert forms such as NO_3^- into atmospheric nitrogen.

294

TEACHER SUPPORT — Ecology Note

As with the water cycle, human activity affects the balance of the natural nitrogen cycle in many ways. For example, sewage treatment plants release large amounts of dissolved inorganic nitrogen compounds into rivers, streams, and oceans. Vast quantities of inorganic nitrogen fertilizers are applied to crops, lawns, and golf courses. Although the fertilized plants absorb some of the nitrogen compounds, and denitrifying bacteria convert some into atmospheric nitrogen, the huge quantities of chemical fertilizers exceed the soil's natural recycling capacity.

Runoff from precipitation and irrigation carries the excess nitrogen compounds into streams, rivers, and lakes, where they cause algae overgrowth. Nitrogen compounds also leach through the soil and enter groundwater supplies. In the human digestive tract, nitrates in drinking water are converted to nitrites, which can be toxic.

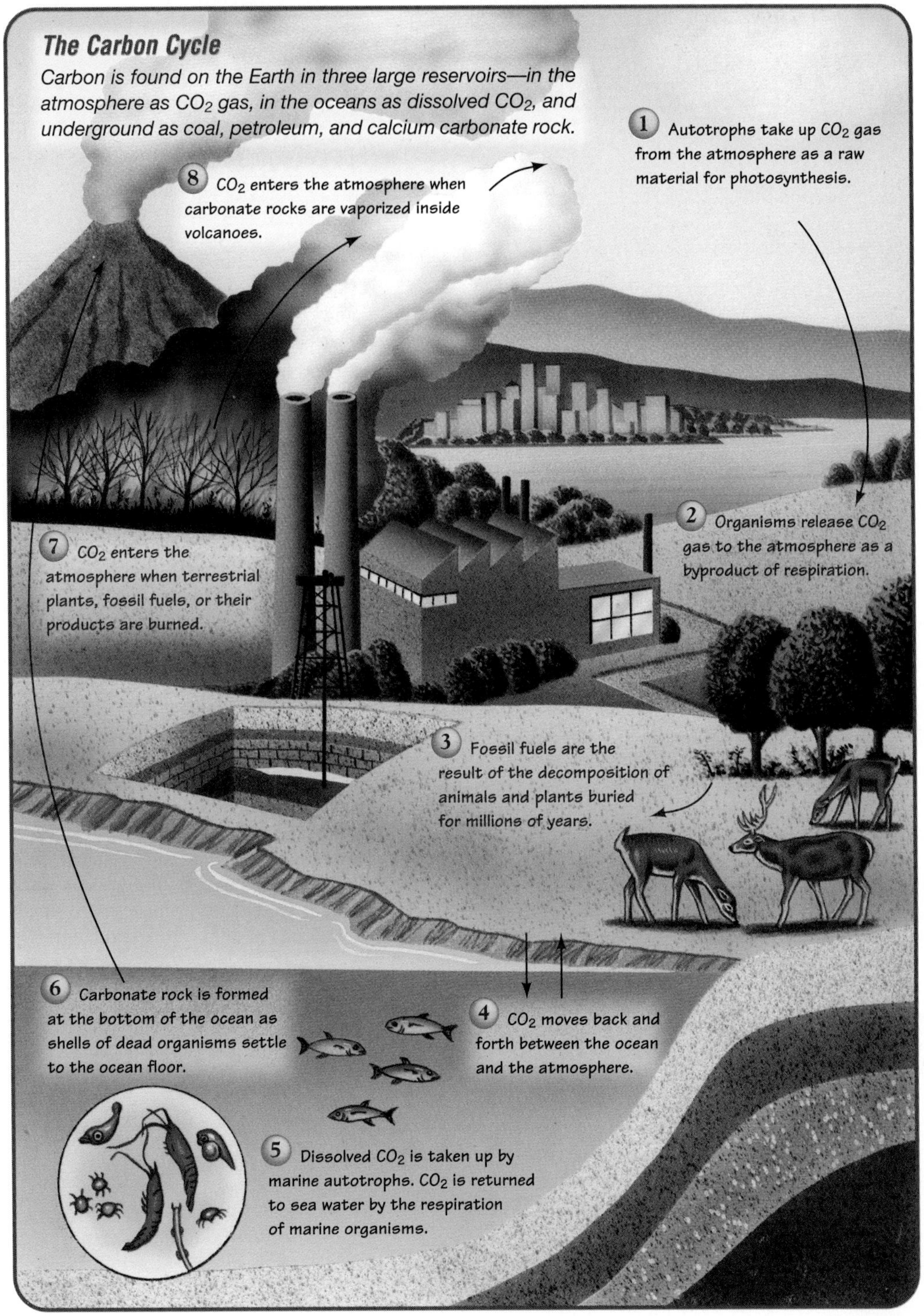

The Carbon Cycle
Carbon is found on the Earth in three large reservoirs—in the atmosphere as CO_2 gas, in the oceans as dissolved CO_2, and underground as coal, petroleum, and calcium carbonate rock.
1 Autotrophs take up CO_2 gas from the atmosphere as a raw material for photosynthesis.
2 Organisms release CO_2 gas to the atmosphere as a byproduct of respiration.
3 Fossil fuels are the result of the decomposition of animals and plants buried for millions of years.
4 CO_2 moves back and forth between the ocean and the atmosphere.
5 Dissolved CO_2 is taken up by marine autotrophs. CO_2 is returned to sea water by the respiration of marine organisms.
6 Carbonate rock is formed at the bottom of the ocean as shells of dead organisms settle to the ocean floor.
7 CO_2 enters the atmosphere when terrestrial plants, fossil fuels, or their products are burned.
8 CO_2 enters the atmosphere when carbonate rocks are vaporized inside volcanoes.

Visualizing Nutrient Cycles

The Carbon Cycle

Ask students if they have ever noticed the sooty black material that is left over when a piece of paper or wood burns, and tell them that this material is carbon. Make sure students note that most of the carbon in the atmosphere is in the form of carbon dioxide gas, CO_2, a compound of carbon and oxygen. Also explain that the amount of carbon dioxide returned to the atmosphere by respiration roughly balances the amount removed from the atmosphere by photosynthesis. The burning of fossil fuels, however, increases the amount of carbon dioxide released into the atmosphere, destroying this natural balance. (Section 13–5 presents this issue in greater detail.)

Technology

BioVue

Animation: The Nitrogen Cycle
Videodisc Side 4

Go to Chapter 30

Animation: The Oxygen/Carbon Dioxide Cycle
Videodisc Side 4

Go to Chapter 35

TEACHER SUPPORT

Managing Classroom Diversity

GIFTED STUDENTS

Ask students to imagine that they are a molecule of water in the water cycle, an atom of carbon in the carbon cycle, or an atom of nitrogen in the nitrogen cycle. Tell them to think of themselves at one point in the cycle and then imagine all the changes they would experience and all the places they could go as they traveled through the complete cycle. Encourage each student to write a short story based on these imaginary experiences. Students could also work in cooperative groups, with each student writing about a different stage in the cycle.

LEP STUDENTS

Ask fluent bilingual volunteers to translate the captions for each cycle illustration into students' native languages, and let students use these translations to study the cycles.

Ancillary Support

The resource below can be used to support your teaching strategy for these two pages.

TB Visualizing the Nitrogen Cycle, #17

Visualizing the Carbon Cycle, #18

MINI LAB Hypothesizing

Teacher Note

- For time required and materials needed, see page 282b.

Answers to Analyze and Conclude

1. Control: Jar A (without fertilizer). Variable: Jar B (with fertilizer).
2. The excess of nutrients in jar B, coupled with ample sunlight, promoted rapid growth of the aquatic plant and overgrowth of the algae already present in the pond or aquarium water.
3. Overgrowth of aquatic plants and algae.

Skills Trace
Hypothesizing
- Focus p. 296
- Practice p. 296
- Assess p. 309

4 ASSESS

Quick Check

Have students draw simple flow charts to show the nutrient pathways in the water, nitrogen, and carbon cycles. Let them check their flow charts against the figures on pages 293–295.

Section Review 13-3

1. Nutrients that are available in fixed quantities on Earth are passed from one organism to another and from one part of the biosphere to another.
2. See Visualizing the Water Cycle, page 293.
3. Productivity is limited by a single nutrient that is either in short supply or moves through the ecosystem very slowly.
4. Levels of atmospheric CO_2 will increase, and less CO_2 will be removed from the atmosphere due to the destruction of the trees.
5. Students' answers should demonstrate an understanding of the nutrient role of fertilizers. Accept all reasonable responses to the second question.

Skills Trace
Hypothesizing
- Focus p. 296
- Practice p. 296
- Assess p. 309

MINI LAB .... Hypothesizing ....

Fertilizers—Nutrients Unlimited?

PROBLEM *How does lawn fertilizer affect the balance in an ecosystem? **Formulate a hypothesis.***

PROCEDURE

1. Fill two wide-mouthed jars with pond water or water from an aquarium.
2. Add a few strands of *Elodea* or other living aquatic plants to each jar.
3. With a marking pencil, label one jar A and the other jar B.
4. Add one teaspoon of fertilizer to jar B. **CAUTION:** *Always wear protective gloves when working with fertilizer.*
5. Place the jars in a sunny location.
6. Observe the jars each day for 2 to 3 weeks. Record your observations.

ANALYZE AND CONCLUDE

1. Which jar was the control? Which jar contained the variable?
2. Describe any changes that occurred in the jars. What may have caused these changes?
3. Based on your results, what do you think happens when large amounts of fertilizers are washed into ponds and other bodies of water?

that is either in short supply or moves through the ecosystem very slowly. This phenomenon is called nutrient limitation. Farmers—well aware of this phenomenon—use fertilizers to boost productivity. Fertilizers usually contain varying amounts of three important plant nutrients—nitrogen, phosphorus, and potassium. These nutrients help plants grow larger and more quickly than they would in unfertilized soil.

Most lakes and streams carry moderate amounts of nitrogen and potassium but little phosphorus. When the detergent industry developed phosphate detergents, what do you suppose happened? As waste water containing these detergents made its way into lakes and streams, the added phosphates caused the algae in those bodies of water to grow at alarming rates. Soon algae covered the surfaces of ponds, lakes, and even some rivers. As a result, underwater plants died because sunlight could not penetrate the layers of algae. Bacteria began growing on the dying plants, using up much of the oxygen. As oxygen levels in the water decreased, fishes and other animals suffocated and died. Luckily, when investigators understood what was causing this problem, a solution was easily found. Detergent manufacturers simply developed nonphosphate detergents.

Section Review 13-3

1. **Describe** how nutrients are recycled in the biosphere.
2. **Sequence** the path of a drop of water through the water cycle.
3. **Define** nutrient limitation.
4. **Critical Thinking—Predicting** Based on the carbon cycle, what do you think might happen if vast areas of forest are cleared by burning?
5. **MINI LAB** **Formulate a hypothesis** to explain the effect of fertilizers on productivity. Can you think of any reasons why fertilizers should be used with caution?

Learning Modality

Visual and Kinesthetic Learning Write—or ask volunteers to write—the stages (not numbered) of each nutrient cycle presented in this section on separate index cards and label the back of each card with the name of the cycle to which the stage belongs. Let students arrange each set of cards in correct order to show the sequence of stages in the cycle.

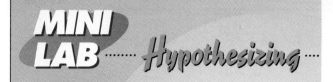

Food Webs: Who Eats Whom?

SECTION 13–4

Guide for Reading

- Describe a food web.

HOW DOES ENERGY FLOW AND how do nutrients cycle in a particular ecosystem? As you may already know, animals and plants don't flow or cycle through different ecosystems. Instead, they eat, grow, reproduce, eliminate their wastes, and die within the same ecosystem. In fact, many organisms have developed unique methods of obtaining food, growing, and reproducing. The intriguing question here is how these various methods interact to cause the energy flows and the nutrient cycles of Earth's biosphere. Read on to find out how this happens.

Food Chains and Webs

In the biosphere, all organisms are linked together into complex networks based, more or less, on who eats whom. At first these relationships were thought of as simple, straight-line **food chains.** A food chain is a sequence of organisms related to one another as predator and prey. In other words, the old "big fish eats little fish" story. But as you might have guessed, things in nature rarely happen this simply.

Almost every place you look in nature, you can find more than one type of primary producer. Often, you can find dozens. As you look closer, you will see that most plant-eating animals feed on at least two different kinds of plants and often more. Carnivores usually eat at least two different kinds of herbivores—and sometimes even each other. Scavengers eat leftovers from other animals. Bacteria and fungi decompose dead tissue and release essential nutrients in different forms.

(a)

(b)

Figure 13–10
(a) The squirrel feeds on acorns produced by (b) an oak tree. The squirrel in turn may become food for another organism.

TEACHER SUPPORT

Managing Classroom Diversity

GIFTED STUDENTS

Some students may wish to explore other types of symbiotic relationships besides parasitism, described in this section. Begin by telling students that parasitism is a type of symbiosis—an interaction between species in which one species lives in or on another species. Explain that there are two other major types of symbiosis, mutualism and commensalism. Suggest that students research these types of symbiotic relationships and give examples of each.

- In mutualism, both partners benefit. Examples include legume plants and the nitrogen-fixing bacteria on their roots, cows and the cellulose-digesting bacteria in their stomachs, and flowering plants and their pollinators.
- In commensalism, one partner benefits without harming or benefiting the other. Examples include bats roosting in a tree, an epiphyte growing on another plant, and birds feeding on insects flushed out of the grass by grazing animals.

Section 13–4

Food Webs: Who Eats Whom?

Performance Objective

- Describe the feeding relationships in a food web.

Laboratory Investigation Skill: Analyzing

1 ENGAGE

Ideas Through Images

Have students examine Figure 13-10, read the caption, and answer the following questions.

- **Which of the things shown in these photographs are primary producers or come from producers?** (The trees, grass, other plants, and the acorn.)
- **Which are consumers?** (The squirrel.)

2 EXPLORE

Discussion

Ask students to think about a meal they ate recently and to list all the foods in it. Explain that if any of the foods were combinations of different items—a bologna and cheese sandwich, for example, or pasta with meat sauce—they should list each item separately. Then have students review their lists and identify whether each item was derived directly from a plant or from an animal. Have students save their lists for use in the Inquiry Activity on page 298.

Technology

CD-ROM
Food Chains and Webs

3 TEACH

Inquiry Activity

Communicating

Food Chains for People

Ask students whether every food chain begins with a primary producer. Using their lists from the Explore activity, have students trace each "from an animal" item back through its food chain to a primary producer. Students could show each chain by listing all the organisms in it and connecting them with arrows. Make sure students draw each arrow from the organism being consumed to the organism doing the consuming.

Discussion

To ensure that students understand the overlapping nature of food webs, have students take turns identifying the organisms in each of the possible food chains shown in Figure 13–11. When they have exhausted all possibilities, ask a volunteer to name another organism that could be part of that same ecosystem, and have other students identify additional food chains that could include that organism.

Laboratory Investigation

The Laboratory Investigation, Food or Feeders?, on pages 304–305 is appropriate to use at this point in the chapter.

Correcting Misconceptions

Students may think that plants are the only primary producers in ecosystems. You can use Figure 13–12 to help dispel this misconception. Explain that the primary producers shown at the bottom of each pyramid are phytoplankton. These organisms carry on photosynthesis just as plants do. Emphasize that phytoplankton are important producers in aquatic food webs.

TERRESTRIAL FOOD WEB

Figure 13–11
This diagram shows a simplified forest food web. Notice that the organisms belong to at least three trophic levels.

Detritus (dee-TRIGHT-uhs) feeders, such as earthworms, are animals that digest a combination of bacteria, bodily wastes, and bits of decaying organisms. And different kinds of parasites draw their food from many different types of hosts.

A **food web** is the best way to illustrate how organisms feed on one another. **Food webs show the complex feeding relationships that result from interconnecting food chains.** As *Figure 13–11* shows, food webs have many crisscrossing strands.

In spite of the complexity of typical food webs, it is helpful to remember that they can all be described in terms of three categories of organisms—primary producers, consumers, and decomposers. Note that consumers as well as decomposers are classified as heterotrophs because they obtain their energy by feeding on other organisms.

☑ **Checkpoint** What is the difference between a food chain and a food web? 1

Food Web Diversity

Although the general rules of energy flow and food web interactions hold true in all ecosystems, some variations arise due to interactions that are unique to an ecosystem. Temperate woodlands in the United States and in Germany differ very little. Although they are home to different types of animals and plants, from an ecological standpoint they are almost identical.

Other ecosystems, however, can differ from one another significantly. In the terrestrial ecosystem shown in *Figure 13–11,* the predominant pathway of energy and nutrient cycling is from primary producers to herbivores to carnivores. Now let's examine two very different kinds of food webs.

Coastal Salt Marsh Food Web

Think of a typical Atlantic Coast salt marsh. At first, this ecosystem may appear much like any terrestrial grassland. However, few of the animals eat grasses directly. Instead, energy and nutrients take a different route, which supports a

TEACHER SUPPORT

Background Information

DETRITIVORES

Detritus feeders play an important role in both aquatic and terrestrial ecosystems. Detritivores break down dead organisms and organic wastes into smaller particles that can then be broken down completely by decomposers, primarily bacteria and fungi. Aquatic detritivores include zooplankton, clams, mussels, crayfish, shrimp, and crabs. Terrestrial detritivores include earthworms, snails, and slugs.

RED TIDES

In coastal ecosystems, an overabundance of nutrients may cause a red tide, a bloom of algae called dinoflagellates that contain poisonous compounds. Filter-feeding animals such as clams and mussels that feed on these algae are not harmed themselves, but the toxins accumulate in their tissues. If people eat these shellfish, the toxins can have serious effects. Red tides have also been implicated in the illness and death of certain whales.

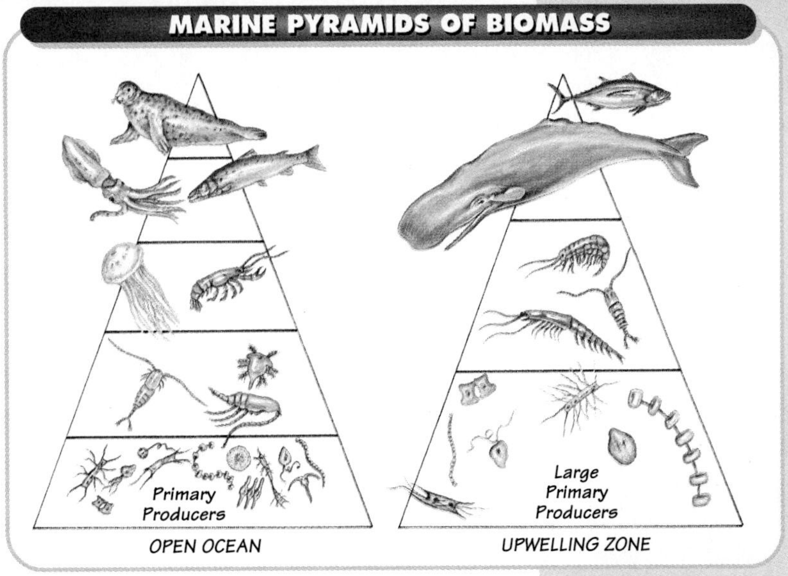

host of aquatic animals. Although some of the primary producers (plants) are eaten by herbivores (grasshoppers and snails), most of the primary producers die, decompose, and are converted into detritus. Each detritus particle acts as a tiny ecosystem because it consists of a piece of dead plant or animal matter coated with microscopic organisms of decay. As the detritus is eaten by detritus feeders that are eaten by carnivores, energy and nutrients are transferred from one organism to another. Such food webs are common in many coastal marine ecosystems.

☑ **Checkpoint** Identify the main energy and nutrient pathway in a coastal marsh ecosystem. ②

Marine Food Web

Consider the "big fish eats little fish" scenario as an example of a food chain. How many trophic levels do you see in the first part of ***Figure 13–12***—between the primary producers and carnivores such as salmon and tuna? With so many different primary producers and consumers, this simple chain becomes an extremely tangled web. But that's not all, as the second half of ***Figure 13–12*** shows.

In parts of the open sea where nitrogen is in short supply, only tiny primary producers can grow. These primary producers are so small that only small consumers can eat them. But in areas where ocean currents bring up nitrogen-rich water from the depths to the surface, greater amounts of nitrogen can support larger primary producers. Notice the smaller number of trophic levels between the primary producers and the largest consumers in the second pyramid shown in ***Figure 13–12***.

Figure 13–12 *Nitrogen-rich ocean water in the upwelling zone supports larger primary producers. As a result, fewer trophic levels separate large consumers, such as tuna and seal, from the first trophic level.*

Section Review 13–4

1. **Compare** a food web and a food chain.
2. **Explain** how the food web in a typical salt marsh differs from one in a terrestrial grassland.
3. **Critical Thinking—Relating** Why do upwelling areas support more fish life than most parts of the open sea?

4 ASSESS

Quick Check

Have each student draw a diagram of a food web with two final consumers, at least four different types of lower-level consumers, and various producers.

Section Review 13–4

1. The complex feeding relationships that result from interconnecting food chains; a sequence of organisms related to one another as predator and prey.
2. Few animals in a salt marsh eat grasses directly. Most primary producers die, decompose, and are converted into detritus, which becomes the first level for many food chains.
3. In areas where ocean currents bring up nitrogen-rich water from the depths to the surface, greater amounts of nitrogen can support larger primary producers, so fewer trophic levels separate large consumers from the first trophic level.

☑ Checkpoints

① A food chain is a simple, straight-line sequence of organisms. A food web shows interconnecting food chains.

② Detritus, the substance that results from decomposition, is the main energy and nutrient pathway.

Learning Modality

Tactile and Kinesthetic Learning Choose one student to represent each plant, plant product, and animal shown in Figure 13–11. Have students stand at their desks and recreate the food web by stretching colored yarn between one another, using a different color for each possible food chain—for example, red yarn for the grass → rabbit → owl chain, yellow for the nuts → squirrel → mountain lion chain, green for the grass → deer → mountain lion chain, blue for the trees → deer → person chain, and so forth.

Ancillary Support

The resources below can be used to support your teaching strategy for these two pages.

TR Explore: All Linked Together
BL Inquiry Activity: Nature's Supermarket

Section 13–5

The Carbon Cycle: A Closer Look

Performance Objective
- Describe the effect of human activities on the global carbon cycle.

1 ENGAGE

Ideas Through Images

Have students examine the photographs in Figure 13–13, read the caption, and answer the following questions.

- **What gas is being released in all of these photographs?** (Carbon dioxide.)
- **What else is being released?** (Water vapor and solid particles such as soot.)
- **What effects do you think the increased release of carbon dioxide by humans might have?** Increased carbon dioxide in the atmosphere could possibly affect Earth's climate.)

2 EXPLORE

Investigate

Model Building The simple models in the following four-part activity will enable students to detect the presence of CO_2 released by humans and other animals during respiration and absorbed by plants during photosynthesis.

PART A: Humans Exhale CO_2

1. Half-fill a cup with distilled water, and add 12–15 drops of Bromthymol blue (BTB) solution.
2. Blow into the water with a straw. (The water will turn yellow.)

Results: The air we exhale contains carbon dioxide. When CO_2 is blown into distilled water, which is neutral, a weak acid is formed. BTB, an acid indicator, changes color to show the presence of the acid.

SECTION 13–5 BRANCHING OUT In Depth

The Carbon Cycle: A Closer Look

Guide for Reading

- **Explain** how the global carbon cycle is affected by human society.

About forty years ago, two scientists named R. Revelle and H. Seuss published an article describing an unplanned planetwide experiment. Human activity had begun "returning to the atmosphere and oceans the concentrated organic carbon stored in sedimentary rocks over hundreds of millions of years." What does that statement mean? Why is it important? And how has our understanding of this issue changed over the years? Read on.

The Greenhouse Effect

The article by Revelle and Seuss drew attention to a phenomenon called the greenhouse effect. If you have experienced the warmth inside a glass greenhouse on a sunny day even when the outside air temperature was much lower, you have a good idea of what the greenhouse effect is. What causes the air inside the greenhouse to be warmer than the air outside? The glass allows the sun's energy to enter the greenhouse, where it is transformed into heat energy. The glass, however, does not allow the heat energy to leave the greenhouse as easily. The energy thus trapped causes the temperature inside the greenhouse to rise. What does the greenhouse effect have to do with the carbon cycle?

Greenhouse gases, such as carbon dioxide, trap energy in the atmosphere

Figure 13–13 Human activities such as (a) the combustion of fossil fuels, (b) the burning of forests, and (c) deforestation contribute to the increase of the levels of greenhouse gases in Earth's atmosphere.

TEACHER SUPPORT

Ecology Note

Other gases besides carbon dioxide contribute to the greenhouse effect. Methane, for example, the major component of natural gas, is produced in large quantities by rotting vegetation in dumps. Fertilizers release nitrous oxide. The primary polluting gases, however, are chlorofluorocarbons, or CFCs—carbon compounds containing chlorine and fluorine.

CFCs enter the atmosphere in various ways. Some aerosol spray cans contain CFCs as propellants. Refrigerators and air conditioners use CFCs as coolants, and industrial solvents contain CFCs. CFCs are also produced during the manufacture of plastic foam.

Since 1978, the United States, Canada, and most Scandinavian countries have prohibited the use of CFCs in aerosol spray cans, and the U.S. is phasing out CFC use in refrigerators and air conditioners. An international agreement to phase out the use of CFCs was reached in 1987, but developing alternatives has been difficult and costly.

just as the glass in a greenhouse traps heat energy inside the greenhouse. Atmospheric carbon dioxide allows the sun's energy to reach the Earth's surface, where it is absorbed and ultimately converted to heat energy. Later, the heat energy radiates back into outer space. But carbon dioxide and other gases in the atmosphere absorb some of this heat energy, forming a "heat trap" around the Earth.

If Earth's temperature and climate are to remain stable, the planet must lose energy to space at the same rate at which energy arrives. If heat leaves faster, the planet will cool. (Without the presence of greenhouse gases, Earth would be 30°C cooler than it is today!) If heat leaves more slowly, extra energy in the form of heat will build up.

With this background information, you are now ready to examine some data to help you determine how the carbon cycle—and therefore the carbon dioxide in the atmosphere—has changed over the course of the last 100 years.

Checkpoint How does the Earth's atmosphere act like a greenhouse? ❶

Figure 13–14
The Earth's atmosphere acts something like the glass in a greenhouse, allowing energy in the form of sunlight to enter, but absorbing and holding some of that energy once it is converted to heat. This atmospheric effect is largely due to the presence of carbon dioxide gas.

Major Carbon Pathways

If you refer back to pages 294 and 295, you will notice that there are four different kinds of pathways that are simultaneously occurring in the carbon cycle:

1. Biological pathways: photosynthesis, respiration, and death and decay of plants and animals.

2. Geochemical pathways: release of carbon dioxide to the atmosphere by volcanic activity and weathering of rocks, and the carbon dioxide exchange between the ocean and the atmosphere. ●

3. Biogeochemical pathways: burial and conversion of carbon from once-living organisms into fossil fuels (coal and petroleum).

4. Human-initiated pathways: mining and burning of fossil fuels, and the cutting and burning of forests.

By studying these processes over many years, scientists are attempting to find out how much carbon travels along the various pathways and the rate at which it travels. They also want to know how much carbon is stored in the atmosphere, in the oceans, on land, in carbonate rocks, and in living tissues. Measurable data such as these are necessary in order to predict the effects that human activities have on the carbon cycle.

Some researchers believe that most carbon travels through geochemical pathways. If this is true, the clearing of forests and the burning of coal and oil will not affect the global scheme of things much. Other scientists, however, think that a significant amount of carbon travels through biological and biogeochemical pathways. If this is true, then human activities that influence

INTEGRATING EARTH SCIENCE

How does CO_2 cycle through the atmosphere, the oceans, and the rocks in the Earth's crust?

PART B: Animals Release CO_2

1. Prepare two cups, labeled #1 and #2, as described in Part A, step 1.
2. Add a large aquatic snail to cup #1. Cover both cups and observe them at regular intervals.

Results: The water in cup #1 will turn green/yellow, indicating the presence of an acid and demonstrating that animals release CO_2 in respiration.

PART C: Plants Do Not Release CO_2

1. Prepare two labeled cups as in Part B. Add a sprig of *Elodea* to cup #1. Cover both cups and leave them in a well-lighted area. Observe the cups at regular intervals.

Results: The water in both cups will remain blue. Students should conclude that plants do not release CO_2.

PART D: Plants Absorb CO_2

1. Prepare one cup as described in Part A. Add both a snail and an aquatic plant.
2. Cover the cup and leave it in a well-lighted area. Observe the cup at regular intervals for several days.
3. If the water changes from blue to green or yellow, add more plants.

Results: With both a CO_2-releaser (the snail) and one or more CO_2-absorbers (the plants) in the cup, the water will remain blue.

INTEGRATING EARTH SCIENCE

Answers should address the geochemical pathways in #2 on the student page.

Checkpoint

❶ Greenhouse gases trap heat energy in the atmosphere as does the glass in a greenhouse.

TEACHER SUPPORT

Activity

DO PLANTS NEED CARBON DIOXIDE?

This activity will allow students to determine what happens to plants deprived of carbon dioxide.

1. Put two healthy coleus or geranium plants where they will receive ample light. Cover one plant with a large glass jar labeled A.
2. Pour soda lime crystals into a small cup and place it next to the other plant. Cover that plant and the cup with another, identical jar labeled B.
3. Observe both plants for several weeks. Once each week, record the appearance of each plant. Every other week, change the soda lime in jar B.

Results: The plant in jar B will eventually die because the soda lime absorbs the CO_2 available to the plant and prevents it from carrying on photosynthesis. From this result, students should conclude that CO_2 in the atmosphere is necessary to sustain plant life.

Ancillary Support

The resource below can be used to support your teaching strategy for these two pages.

BL Inquiry Activity: Climate in a Cup

3 TEACH

Discussion

Ask students to describe what they felt when they got into an automobile that had been left in sunlight for a long time with its windows closed. Explain that this is the same type of overheating that occurs in an unventilated greenhouse.

Ideas Through Images

Have students examine Figures 13–15 and 13–16, read the captions, and answer the following questions.

- **In Figure 13–15, what is the greatest source of carbon in the atmosphere?** (The sea-surface gas exchange.)
- **On land, how is carbon returned to the atmosphere?** (Through respiration, decay of residues, fossil fuel burning, and land use.)
- **How does the amount of carbon in the atmosphere compare to the amount of carbon on land and in oceans?** (The amounts are roughly equal.)
- **In Figure 13–16, why do you think the amount of carbon dioxide varies slightly within each year?** (The concentration of carbon dioxide fluctuates between winter and summer because of seasonal variations in photosynthesis.)
- **When you consider both figures, can you infer why the concentration of carbon dioxide in the atmosphere has increased over the past 30 years?** (Students should conclude that all factors except human activities remain fairly constant. The gradually increasing concentration is due mainly to burning fossil fuels and deforestation.)

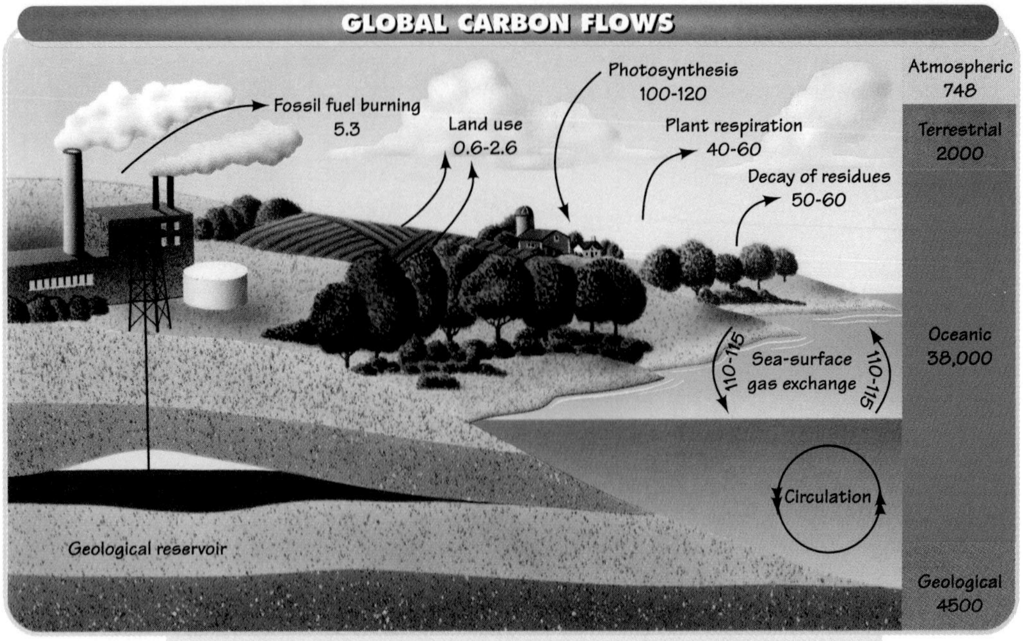

Figure 13–15
Carbon flows between the three major carbon reservoirs—oceans, atmosphere, and deposits in the Earth—are shown in units of gigatons per year. Although the amount of carbon entering the atmosphere as a result of human activity is relatively small, its cumulative effect in the

these pathways could have significant effects on how much carbon ends up in various places—specifically, as carbon dioxide in the atmosphere.

Checkpoint What are the ways in which human activities affect the carbon cycle? 1

Experimental Data

What data have scientists gathered so far? If you look at ***Figure 13–15,*** you will see information about rates of carbon flow along different pathways. ***Figure 13–15*** also shows the relative amounts of carbon stored in different parts of the biosphere. What do these data show? Notice that the amount of carbon returned to the atmosphere by the burning of fossil fuels and human land use is small in comparison with the other pathways. Also note that most of the carbon is stored in the oceans, very little is in the atmosphere, and a small but significant amount is in terrestrial ecosystems and fossil fuels.

Although many questions still remain—particularly about the future—certain things are becoming more clear. Notice that the amount of carbon that is cycled in and out of the ocean is roughly equal to the amount that is cycled in and out of terrestrial environments. Therefore, any process that significantly affects the biological pathways for

TEACHER SUPPORT

Managing Classroom Diversity

TECH PREP STUDENTS

Encourage students interested in automobile mechanics to investigate the various types of emission control systems in use today, how they work, and the type of maintenance they require. For example, spark timing is a vital factor in both fuel economy and pollution control. To determine the optimum timing, today's engines use electronic sensors to gather data on engine temperature, speed, throttle rate, vacuum, exhaust oxygen content, and more.

In general, an efficient engine reduces pollution. However, one type of emission—oxides of nitrogen—forms at high combustion temperatures. To control these emissions, modern automobiles have a catalytic converter, which passes the exhaust gas through chemicals that convert the pollutants to CO_2, nitrogen, and steam. Students should note that catalytic converters do not resolve the problem of CO_2 release in automobile exhaust and the resultant effect on the carbon cycle.

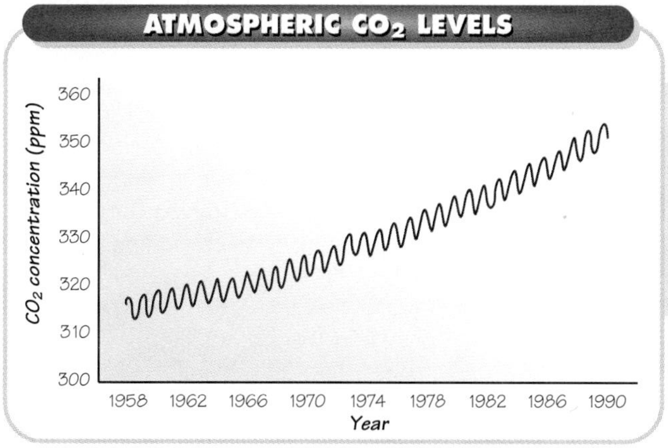

Figure 13–16 The graph shows atmospheric carbon dioxide concentrations measured over the past 30 years.

carbon on land, such as major deforestation, could affect the global flow of carbon. Also note that human activities—which did not amount to much until a century ago—now account for a small percentage of the carbon flow each year. Interestingly, this flow is one way, without a reverse human process that takes it back. Although one year's worth of such activity may not make much of a difference on a global scale, its effect could be significant and damaging if the activity continues year after year.

Atmospheric CO_2 Levels

Let's look at a final bit of data. ***Figure 13–16*** shows a graph of atmospheric carbon dioxide concentrations in parts per million measured at Mauna Loa, Hawaii, from 1958 through 1990. This graph clearly shows that the average concentration of carbon dioxide is rising slowly but steadily over time. **This gradual increase in atmospheric carbon dioxide levels is probably due to human activity. And as the insulating carbon dioxide blanket gets thicker, it could have a warming effect on Earth.**

As your knowledge of ecology grows, you will learn that your environment is not static. You will learn that the biological activity of organisms can affect even environments as large as Earth's atmosphere. As living organisms, humans too have a part in this activity. We affect our environment and are affected by it in ways that we are just now beginning to understand.

Section Review 13–5

1. **Explain** the greenhouse effect.
2. **Describe** how the global carbon cycle is affected by humans.
3. **BRANCHING OUT ACTIVITY** **Formulate a hypothesis** to explain the periodic fluctuation in atmospheric carbon dioxide levels. Suggest ways to test this hypothesis.

4 ASSESS

Quick Check

Have each student write the names of the four major carbon pathways across the top of a sheet of paper and then list the processes in each pathway below its heading.

Section Review 13–5

1. Atmospheric carbon dioxide allows the sun's energy to reach the Earth's surface, where it is absorbed and ultimately converted to heat energy that later radiates back into outer space. Greenhouse gases absorb some of this heat energy, trapping it in the atmosphere.
2. Mining, burning of fossil fuels, and the cutting and burning of forests releases more carbon into the atmosphere.
3. Accept a variety of reasonable hypotheses and tests. Seasonal fluctuations are due mainly to variations in photosynthesis.

Learning Modality

Visual and Kinesthetic Learning

Mark off four equal-sized sections on a bulletin board and label them with the four types of carbon pathways listed on page 301. In each section, have students attach pictures they have cut from magazines or drawn showing examples of the processes involved in each pathway.

Checkpoint

1 Mining, burning fossil fuels, and cutting and burning forests increases the concentration of carbon dioxide in the atmosphere.

TEACHER SUPPORT

Background Information

The material presented in Figures 13–15 and 13–16 and their accompanying text not only expands the coverage of carbon cycling in the biosphere but also leads students through some scientific reasoning, demonstrates the need for and interpretation of quantitative data, and exposes students to an approximation of the real-world level of complexity and uncertainty about global ecological issues. To follow this material, students must interpret different types of visually presented numerical information and apply what they learn in answering questions about ecological issues.

Covering this material has an additional advantage for more advanced students, who may be frustrated if they are asked to consider the global warming controversy without an understanding of the underlying issues. Introducing the complexity of the issue here lays the groundwork for explanations concerning why it is difficult to resolve ecological issues that have major socioeconomic impact.

Ancillary Support

The resource below can be used to support your teaching strategy for these two pages.

TR Enrich: Bubbling Up

Chapter 13

Laboratory Investigation

Food or Feeders?

Before the Lab

Optional: Collect field guides and other source materials so students can research the food preferences of the animal species listed in the chart.

Pre-Lab Discussion

Have students read the entire procedure for this investigation. Then ask students the following questions.

Which of these communities occurs naturally? (The hickory/oak forest community.)

Why is the other one not a natural community? (A cultivated field requires human activity to create and maintain it.)

Which community has a greater variety of producers? (The forest community.)

How do you think its greater variety of producers will affect the feeding relationships in this community? (Accept a variety of answers, but students should recognize that a greater variety of producers will support a greater variety of consumers at all trophic levels.)

Skills Development

Students will use these skills while completing the laboratory investigation: analyzing, applying concepts, classifying, developing models, and making judgments.

Teaching Strategies

1. Review and explain any terms that are unfamiliar to students, such as the following:

Temperate (step 1): Describes the ecosystem's climate; a temperate climate is a mild climate, neither very hot nor very cold.

Deciduous (step 1): Refers to trees that shed their leaves at the end of the growing season (in autumn in North America).

Invertebrate (both Animal Species sections of chart): Literally means "without a backbone"; name for animals without an internal skeleton.

2. If students do not know what some of the listed animals normally eat, guide them to make reasonable assumptions. You may want to provide field guides and other source materials so they can research the information and more accurately determine feeding relationships.

Laboratory Investigation

Food or Feeders?

Within a community, organisms interact in many ways. Tracing the flow of energy within a community can help you to understand how the organisms interact.

Problem

How does the energy flow through a community affect the community's complexity and stability? **Analyze** the feeding relationships among organisms from two terrestrial communities.

Materials (per group)

2 large sheets of unlined paper
plain notebook paper
pen or pencil
several colored markers
tape or glue

Procedure

1. **On the next page, you will find a chart that contains two lists of organisms. One list includes organisms from a hickory/oak forest community in a temperate deciduous forest. The other is from a cultivated cornfield community.**
2. **Carefully read the lists and identify as many feeding relationships as you can. In many cases, one species may be linked to several others—either as food or as feeder.**
3. **Write the names of the organisms from the first community on a sheet of notebook paper. Cut the names out and arrange them on one of the large sheets of paper. Note: *Do not attach them to the sheet yet.***
4. **Discuss how the organisms are to be arranged. Keep in mind that the names have to be connected to one another to indicate feeding links.**
5. **When you have decided on the arrangement, attach the names of the organisms to the large sheet with tape or glue.**

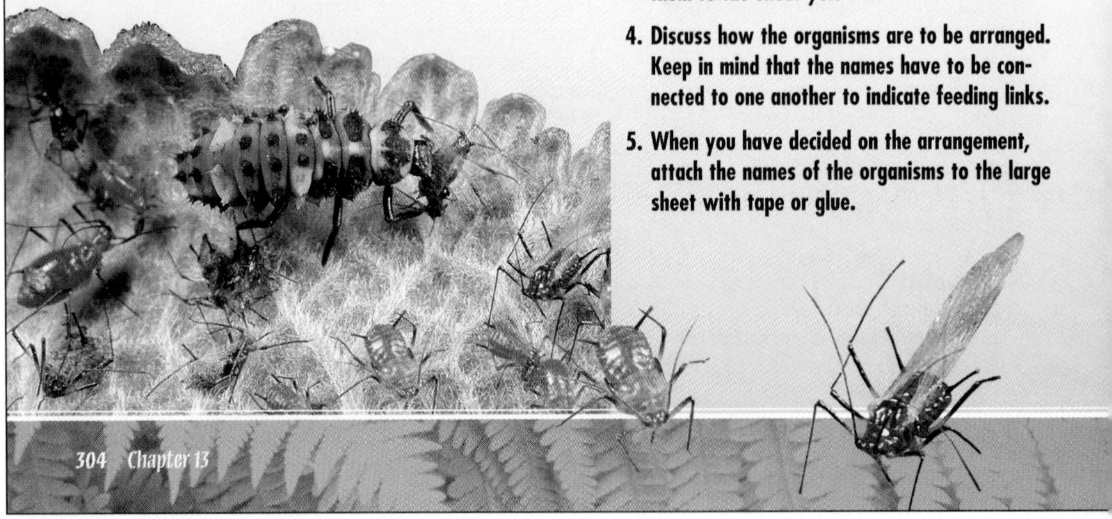

ORGANISMS IN DECIDUOUS FOREST AND CORNFIELD COMMUNITIES

	Hickory/Oak Forest Community	Cultivated Cornfield Community
Plant Species	White oak, black oak, tulip tree, white pine, birch, big tooth aspen, dogwood, sassafrass, viburnum	Corn
Animal Species	Invertebrates, such as a beetle, ant, sow bug, earthworm, snail, termite, moth, centipede, and spider; birds, such as cardinal, warbler, chickadee, woodpecker, flycatcher, and owl; other animals, such as raccoon, squirrel, chipmunk, black bear, opossum, wood mouse, vole, deer, and black racer (snake)	Raccoon, corn snake, woodchuck, field mouse, deer; invertebrates, such as corn borer, grasshopper, cricket, earthworm, butterfly, moth, fly; birds, such as sparrow, meadowlark, crow, hawk
Fungi and Bacteria	Various fungi and bacteria	Various fungi and bacteria

6. Use the markers to construct food chains by drawing arrows from the food source to the feeder. Use different-colored markers to indicate different food chains. Make your food web as complex as possible.

7. Repeat steps 3 through 6 for the second list of organisms.

Observations

1. Compare your webs to those created by other groups.
2. Which community—the hickory/oak forest or the cornfield—seems to be more complex?

Analysis and Conclusions

1. Are the food webs for the hickory/oak forest community the same for different groups? How are they different?
2. Are the food webs for the cornfield community the same for different groups? How are they different?
3. Which community has the greater variety of primary producers? The greater number of trophic levels?
4. Suppose a parasite destroyed most of the oak trees in the forest community and the corn plants in the cultivated field. How would each community be affected?

More to Explore

Choose one animal species from each of the two communities and assume that it has become extinct. Predict the effect the loss of each animal would have on its community. Which community do you think would be less affected by the loss? Why?

Answers to
Observations

1. Groups' food webs may vary.
2. The hickory/oak forest.

Answers to
Analysis and Conclusions

1. Answers will vary; groups may have slightly different food webs.
2. Answers will vary; groups may have slightly different food webs.
3. The hickory/oak forest for both.
4. The forest ecosystem would continue, although it would change as different trees take the place of the oaks. The cornfield ecosystem would be virtually destroyed, since it contains no other major producers.

More to Explore

Students could indicate their responses by simply crossing out the names of the two animal species on the food webs they created and then deciding whether the animals that feed on those animals would have any other sources of food. The specific effects on each community will, of course, depend on the animal species chosen. In general, however, students should realize that the cultivated cornfield community—in which all consumers depend directly or indirectly on the same producer and the food web is less complex—would be more affected by the extinction of one species.

Chapter 13

Study Guide

Review Strategy

Suggest that students create simple card games—perhaps based on childhood favorites such as "Go Fish"—using sets of index cards labeled with vocabulary terms and definitions, stages in the nutrient cycles, the research approaches used by ecologists, producers and consumers in food chains and webs, various processes in the four major types of nutrient pathways, and other chapter concepts. Have students review the chapter in small groups using their card games.

Study Guide

Summarizing Key Concepts

The key concepts in each section of this chapter are listed below to help you review the chapter content. Make sure you understand each concept and its relationship to other concepts and to the theme of this chapter.

13–1 Ecology: Studying Nature's Houses

- Ecology is the scientific study of interactions between different types of organisms and between organisms and their environments.
- Ecologists typically use one or more of three different research approaches—observations, experiments, and models—when studying the biosphere.

13–2 Energy: Essential for Life's Processes

- Primary producers (autotrophs) are able to make their own food. Consumers and decomposers (heterotrophs) must obtain energy from other organisms.
- Energy moves through the biosphere in a one-way flow. Arriving as sunlight, energy flows through the tissues of primary producers to the tissues of consumers and then to the tissues of decomposers.
- Only a small fraction of the energy at any trophic level can be used by the organisms in the next higher trophic level. This gives rise to ecological pyramids.

13–3 Nutrients: Building Blocks of Living Tissue

- Nutrients that are available in fixed quantities on Earth are passed from one organism to another and from one part of the biosphere to another through nutrient cycles.
- Three major nutrient cycles are the water cycle, the nitrogen cycle, and the carbon cycle.
- Productivity in an ecosystem may be limited by a single nutrient. This is called nutrient limitation.

13–4 Food Webs: Who Eats Whom?

- Organisms in an ecosystem are linked together by food webs.
- A food web shows the complex feeding relationships that result from interconnected food chains.

13–5 The Carbon Cycle: A Closer Look

- The gradual increase in atmospheric carbon dioxide levels is probably due to human activities. This increase could have a warming effect on Earth.

Reviewing Key Terms

Review the following vocabulary terms and their meaning. Then use each term in a complete sentence.

13–1 Ecology: Studying Nature's Houses
ecology

13–2 Energy: Essential for Life's Processes
primary producer
autotroph
consumer
heterotroph
decomposer
trophic level
ecological pyramid

13–3 Nutrients: Building Blocks of Living Tissue
nutrient cycle

13–4 Food Webs: Who Eats Whom?
food chain
food web

Inquiry-Based Strategy

Review the interactions that students have observed between the plants, aphids, and ladybugs in the Chapter Discovery Learning Activity and between organisms in the mini-habitats they set up in the Unit Discovery Learning Activity. Then ask students to decide on a question they would like to investigate involving these organisms—perhaps one of the questions generated in the Explore activity for Section 13–1—and to design and carry out an experiment to answer the question.

Review each group's question and experimental design to make sure the proposed investigation focuses on a clear objective and does not involve subjecting organisms to undue stress or harm. Supervise the groups as they work, guiding students with their record keeping, data analysis, and conclusions. In a follow-up session, give each group an opportunity to present its question, experimental design, observations, and conclusions to the rest of the class.

Recalling Main Ideas

Choose the letter of the answer that best completes the statement or answers the question.

1. Green plants are also called
   a. autotrophs. **c.** herbivores.
   b. heterotrophs. **d.** carnivores.
2. Animals that eat only other animals are called
   a. herbivores. **c.** carnivores.
   b. omnivores. **d.** decomposers.
3. In a food chain, herbivores are known as
   a. consumers. **c.** producers.
   b. decomposers. **d.** carnivores.
4. The process of converting atmospheric nitrogen into a form producers can use is called
   a. nitrogen fixation. **c.** denitrification.
   b. respiration. **d.** photosynthesis.
5. A hawk eats a snake that has eaten a mouse that has eaten some vegetation. This is an example of a
   a. food web. **c.** pyramid of numbers.
   b. food chain. **d.** pyramid of biomass.
6. In a series of trophic levels, the organisms farthest from the producers usually
   a. constitute the least biomass.
   b. are herbivores.
   c. are autotrophs.
   d. constitute the greatest biomass.
7. Most carbon on Earth is stored
   a. in fossil fuels. **c.** in the oceans.
   b. in the atmosphere. **d.** on land.
8. Measurements of carbon dioxide concentrations in the air over past decades have shown a
   a. leveling off.
   b. slow but steady increase.
   c. dramatic increase.
   d. slow but steady decline.

Putting It All Together

Using the information on pages xxx to xxxi, complete the following concept map.

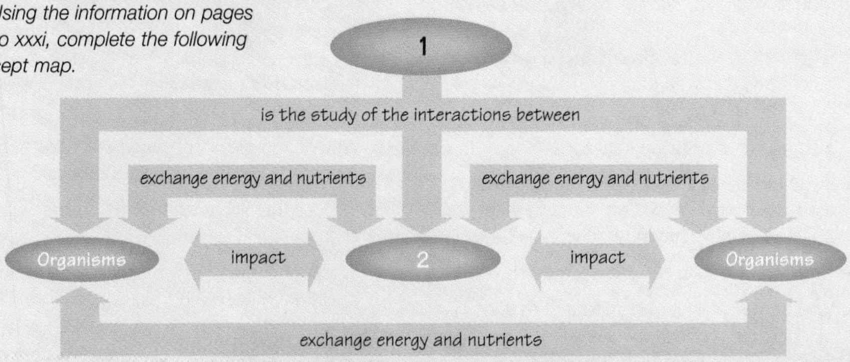

Recalling Main Ideas

1. a
2. c
3. a
4. a
5. b
6. a
7. c
8. b

Putting It All Together

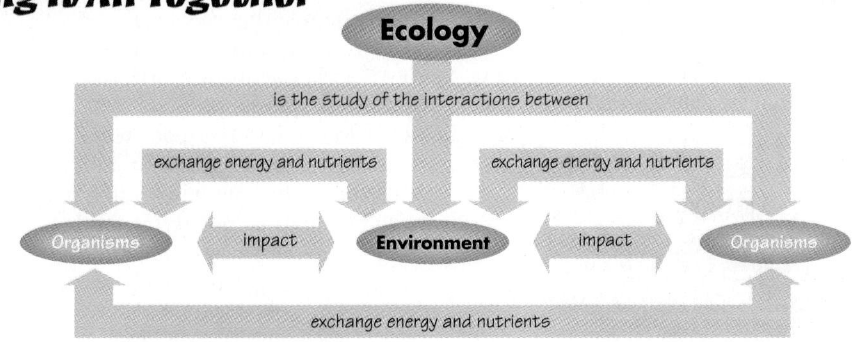

CHAPTER 13

Assessment

Reviewing What You Learned

1. Ecology is the scientific study of interactions between different kinds of living things and between living things and their environments.
2. The three basic methods are observations, experiments, and models.
3. It is true because neither is a primary producer; both are consumers.
4. A plant is a primary producer.
5. It is used for life processes, such as growth, reproduction, and daily activities.
6. A nutrient cycle is a pathway in which nutrients are passed over and over again through different parts of the biosphere.
7. The three states of water are liquid, solid ice, and water vapor, a gas.
8. Decomposers break down organic matter into simple molecules that can be reused as nutrients.
9. All food webs consist of interconnecting food chains that begin with primary producers. All include three major types of organisms: primary producers, consumers, and decomposers.
10. The three forms are free nitrogen gas (N_2), ammonia (NH_3), and nitrates (NO_3).
11. Eliminating phosphates from detergents helped prevent algae overgrowth, which kills aquatic plants and animals.
12. Most of Earth's carbon is stored in the oceans.
13. A geochemical pathway releases CO_2 through volcanic activity, weathering of rocks, and exchange between the ocean and the atmosphere. A biogeochemical pathway releases CO_2 through the burial and conversion of carbon from once-living organisms into fossil fuels.
14. In the greenhouse effect, atmospheric carbon dioxide allows the sun's energy to reach the Earth's surface, where it is absorbed and converted to heat energy, but the carbon dioxide and other gases in the atmosphere trap some of this heat energy.

Assessment

Reviewing What You Learned

Answer each of the following in a complete sentence.

1. Give a brief definition of ecology.
2. What are the research methods used by ecologists?
3. Neither herbivores nor carnivores are autotrophs. Is this statement true? Explain your answer.
4. What type of organism would be considered a primary producer?
5. What happens to the energy lost at each trophic level?
6. What is meant by a nutrient cycle?
7. Name the three states of water observed in the water cycle.
8. What is the primary role of a decomposer?
9. What are the common features of all food webs?
10. What are the different forms of nitrogen in the nitrogen cycle?
11. Why did the removal of phosphates in household detergents improve the quality of our nation's waterways?
12. Where is most of the carbon on Earth located?
13. What is the difference between a geochemical and a biogeochemical pathway?
14. What is the greenhouse effect?

Expanding the Concepts

Discuss each of the following in a brief paragraph.

1. Explain the basis for **classifying** organisms as autotrophs and heterotrophs.
2. Trace the flow of energy from its origin in the foods you ate for lunch today.
3. If you are located at the fourth trophic level in a food chain, how would you compare with organisms at the second trophic level?
4. Compare a food chain and a food web.
5. Why is nutrient limitation important to understanding the productivity of an ecosystem?
6. Why is it possible that a carbon atom in your ear lobe might once have been part of a dinosaur?
7. Why do most overpopulated countries base their diets on plants or plant products?
8. Discuss the difference between nutrients and energy.
9. Without nitrogen-fixing bacteria, what would be the future of life on this planet?

Expanding the Concepts

1. Autotrophs can produce their own food using energy from the sun. Heterotrophs must feed on other organisms to obtain energy and nutrients.

Skills Trace
Classifying
- Focus p. 289
- Practice p. 290
- Assess p. 308

2. Answers will vary. Make sure students begin each chain with a producer.
3. Organisms at the second trophic level are herbivores. Those at the fourth trophic level are carnivores or omnivores.
4. A food chain is a sequence of organisms related to one another as predator and prey. A food web shows the complex feeding relationships that result from interconnecting food chains.
5. Productivity may be limited by a single nutrient that is either in short supply or moves through an ecosystem very slowly. An ecosystem's productivity can be increased by adding one or more nutrients to the system.

CHAPTER 13

Extending Your Thinking

Use the skills you have developed in this chapter to answer the following.

1. **Predicting** In which areas of the world would you expect to find a large fishing industry and why?
2. **Relating** Recent Mississippi floods have been much worse than those in previous years. How can an understanding of ecology help to prevent similar occurrences in the future?
3. **Analyzing** Why must people be extremely careful when using insecticides to control unwanted pests in the environment?
4. **Relating** Burning tropical rain forests to provide space for farming has had many serious consequences on the environment. Discuss two of these consequences.
5. **Hypothesizing** Filling in salt marshes for new home sites has caused a noticeable decline in fishing industries hundreds of kilometers away. Discuss the factors that are associated with this scenario.

Applying Your Skills

The Food Web in Your Community

Food webs exist in every ecosystem. What does the food web in your surrounding ecosystem look like?

1. Form three groups to collect information on the following organisms living around your school. List five primary producers, three herbivores, two omnivores, one carnivore, two detritus feeders, and two decomposers.
2. Combine your information with the information from the other groups.
3. Combine the information from all three groups to make a poster of a food web.

• GOING FURTHER •

4. Write a paragraph explaining how this food web would be different from one in your backyard.

6. Carbon atoms are continually recycled in the biosphere.
7. Because energy is lost at each trophic level, overpopulated countries base their diets on the trophic level containing the most stored energy, autotrophs.
8. There is a fixed supply of nutrients in the biosphere, whereas energy continually enters the biosphere from the sun. Nutrients are not lost as they recycle; energy is lost to heat and life processes at each trophic level.
9. Plants and animals, which need nitrogen in the form of nitrates, would die.

Extending Your Thinking

1. Large fishing industries would be located in areas that have significant upwelling of nutrient-rich bottom water to the ocean's surface. Such upwellings support larger aquatic producers and, in turn, greater numbers of fish.
2. An understanding of ecology helps you consider the interactions between different kinds of living things and their environment, which might provide clues, such as the role of wetlands, for reducing the extent of the flooding.
3. Nonbiodegradable pesticides accumulate in the food chain and reach harmful or deadly levels at the top of the chain.
4. Two consequences are the destruction of species living in the rain forest and the global effect of rising carbon dioxide levels in the atmosphere.
5. Filling in salt marshes eliminates organisms on which fish at higher trophic levels ultimately depend. Salt marshes also serve as protected breeding grounds for many species.

Skills Trace
Hypothesizing

Focus p. 296
Practice p. 296
Assess p. 309

Applying Your Skills

1. Primary producers include grasses, roses, tulips, maple trees, and sunflowers. Herbivores include squirrels, rabbits, and aphids. Omnivores include humans and dogs. An example of a carnivore is a wolf. Examples of detritus feeders are earthworms and beetles. Examples of decomposers are bacteria and fungi.
3. The food web should show all trophic levels and the interconnecting feeding relationships of all the organisms.
4. Students' paragraphs will vary depending on how the environment where they live differs from the environment around the school.

Scoring Rubric

4 Response is thorough, accurate, and creative; shows an in-depth understanding of science skills, procedures, and concepts.

3 Response is complete, mostly accurate, and original; shows a satisfactory understanding of science skills, procedures, and concepts.

2 Response is mostly complete but includes some inaccuracies; shows an adequate understanding of science skills, procedures, and concepts.

1 Response is only partially complete and has many inaccuracies; shows an incomplete understanding of science skills, procedures, and concepts.

0 Response is mostly incomplete and/or inaccurate; shows a lack of understanding of science skills, procedures, and concepts.

Chapter 14 Populations

Content Management	Student Edition Activities
■ Section 14–1 Populations and How They Grow, pp. 311–314 Changing Populations A Baby Boom Growth With Limits Boom and Bust	MINI LAB: But Not a Drop to Drink, p. 313 Laboratory Investigation: The Rise and Fall of Yeast, pp. 326–327
■ Section 14–2 Why Populations Stop Growing, pp. 315–318 Density-Dependent Limiting Factors Density-Independent Limiting Factors	
■ Section 14–3 Human Population Growth, pp. 319–321 Growth Increases Growth Slows Down	
◆ BRANCHING OUT • In Depth Section 14–4 Population Growth and Carrying Capacity, pp. 322–325 World Population Growth Future Population Growth Earth's Carrying Capacity	MINI LAB: A Baby Boom?, p. 325

■ These sections cover all the necessary content and concepts for a basic course in biology.
◆ This section covers content and concepts that are either applications or extensions of the basic material.

Integration Strategies

SE Careers, p. 311
Health, p. 319
Careers, p. 323

Assessment Strategies

SE Chapter Review, pp. 328–331
TR Section Review
Chapter Test
BL Chapter Reviews
Practice Test
CTB Chapter 14 Test

Tech Prep

Teaching strategies appropriate for students who are in technical/vocational programs or who are considering post-secondary technical education can be found on **TE** page 313.

Meeting the Standards

Sections 14–1 through 14–4 cover three of the five content standards under **The Interdependence of Organisms** and one of the six content standards under **Matter, Energy, and Organization in Living Systems** as described on page 186 of The National Science Education Standards.

Chapter Planning Guide

Teacher's Edition Activities	Other Activities	Media and Technology
Chapter Discovery Learning Activity, p. 310 **Activity:** Comparing Germination Rates, p. 314	**LM** Observing the Effects of Crowding on Seedlings, #27 **TR Enrich:** Uninvited Guests **BL Inquiry Activity:** My, How You've Grown	**CD-ROM:** Population Ecology
Investigate: Research, p. 316 **Activity:** Comparing Seedling Growth, p. 318	**LM** Estimating a Population, #28 **TR Apply:** Limiting Factors **BL Inquiry Activity:** Don't Pop Your Balloon	**TB** Predator–Prey Relationship, #19
Investigate: Research, p. 320	**TR Writing in Biology:** Reports From the Front **Explore:** Population in Balance **BL Inquiry Activity:** The Growing World	
Inquiry Activity: Changes in Family Size, p. 322 **Investigate:** Cooperative Learning, p. 324	**TR Apply:** A Population Picture **BL Inquiry Activity:** How Many Can Fit?	

KEY: SE Student Edition **TE** Teacher's Edition **LM** Laboratory Manual **TR** Teaching Resources **BL** BioLog **TB** Transparency Box **CTB** Computer Test Bank

Materials List

TE Chapter Discovery Learning Activity, p. 310 (10–15 minutes for initial set-up, 5 minutes for observation every other day for 2–3 weeks); 2 cups, marker, potting soil, 18 bean, pea, or corn seeds.

SE MINI LAB: But Not a Drop to Drink, p. 313 (30 minutes); large bowls, masking tape and marker, water, 1-cup and ¼-cup measuring cups.

TE Activity: Comparing Germination Rates, p. 314 (15–20 minutes); cups with sprouted seeds from Chapter Discovery Learning Activity.

TE Activity: Comparing Seedling Growth, p. 318 (15–20 minutes); cups with seedlings from Chapter Discovery Learning Activity.

TE Inquiry Activity: Changes in Family Size, p. 322 (30–40 minutes); pencil and paper.

SE MINI LAB: A Baby Boom?, p. 325 (30 minutes); pencil and paper, calculator.

CHAPTER 14

Populations

Introducing the Chapter . . . In Pictures

Have students examine the photograph, read the caption, and answer the following questions.

- **How can you tell that all the lupines in the photograph are the same species of organism?** (Responses should focus on the plants' identical appearance.)
- **What environmental factors might cause the lupines to spread even more widely?** (Sunlight, good soil, adequate rainfall, appropriate temperatures, and the absence of animals that feed on them.)
- **What factors might cause the lupines to decline or die out?** (Drought, periods of extreme heat or cold, attacks by insect pests or plant diseases, or grazing by herbivores.)

Teaching Strategy

In the first section of this chapter, students are introduced to the concept of population and examine different patterns of population growth. Factors that limit population growth are presented in the second section and applied to the human population in the third section. The BRANCHING OUT section discusses human population growth as it relates to Earth's carrying capacity.

BIO JOURNAL

Encourage students to think about specific needs of people in their community—food, water, housing, clothing, medical treatment, schools, and so forth—and to consider how each of these needs would be affected if the community's population doubled. Have them think of ways in which the doubling of populations in other regions and in other countries would affect these needs. Instruct students to keep their entries in their portfolios.

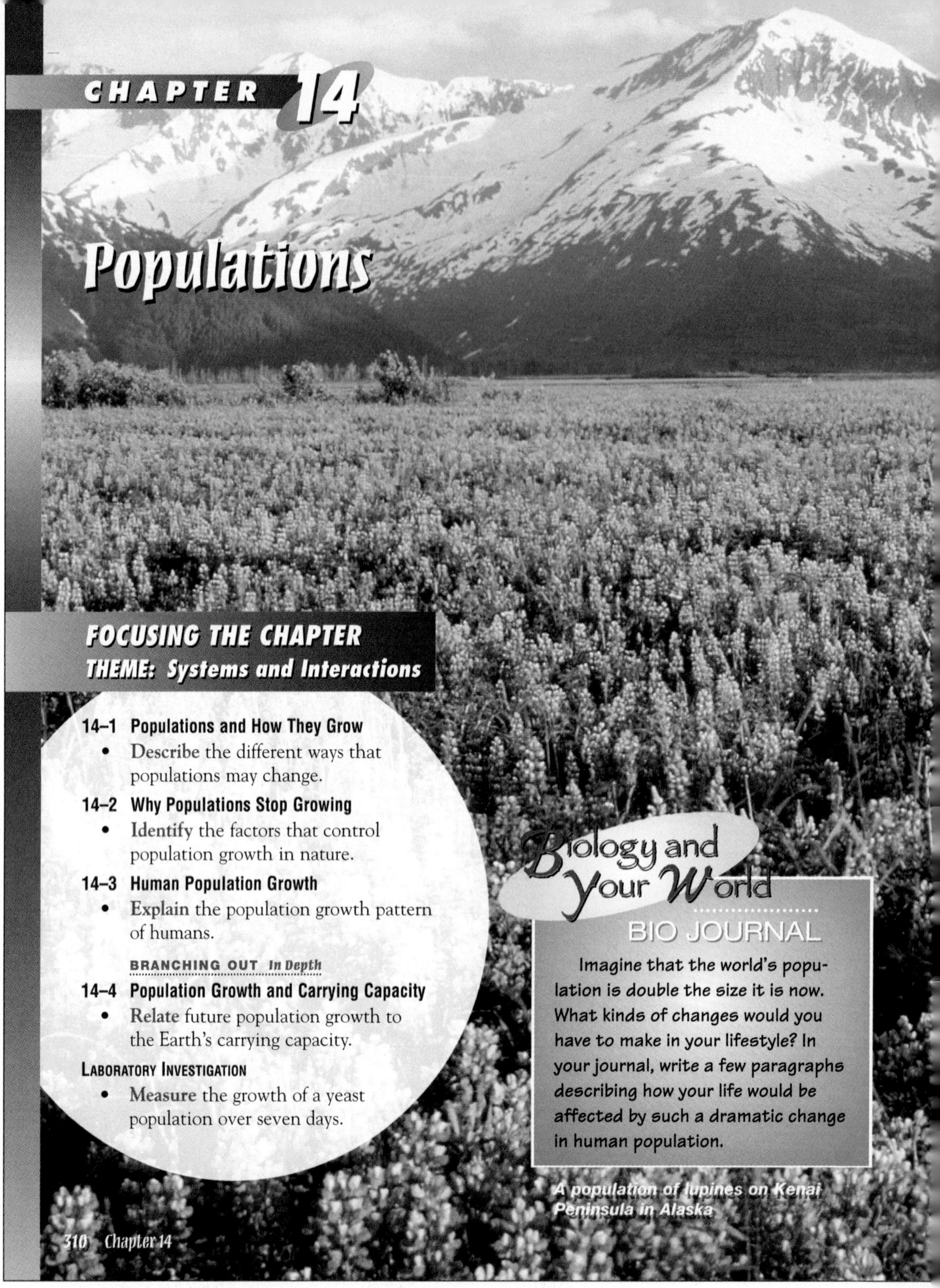

CHAPTER 14

Populations

FOCUSING THE CHAPTER THEME: Systems and Interactions

14–1 Populations and How They Grow
- **Describe** the different ways that populations may change.

14–2 Why Populations Stop Growing
- **Identify** the factors that control population growth in nature.

14–3 Human Population Growth
- **Explain** the population growth pattern of humans.

BRANCHING OUT *In Depth*

14–4 Population Growth and Carrying Capacity
- **Relate** future population growth to the Earth's carrying capacity.

LABORATORY INVESTIGATION
- **Measure** the growth of a yeast population over seven days.

Biology and Your World

BIO JOURNAL

Imagine that the world's population is double the size it is now. What kinds of changes would you have to make in your lifestyle? In your journal, write a few paragraphs describing how your life would be affected by such a dramatic change in human population.

A population of lupines on Kenai Peninsula in Alaska

TEACHER SUPPORT

Chapter Discovery Learning Activity

CARRYING CAPACITY AND COMPETITION

Discuss the results of this investigation when students study those sections. (See Activity: Comparing Germination Rates, page 314, and Activity: Comparing Seedling Growth, page 318.)

1. Fill two identical cups labeled A and B about two thirds full with potting soil.
2. Using bean, pea, or corn seeds, plant 3 seeds in cup A and 15 seeds in cup B.
3. Water each cup so the soil is moist but not wet.
4. Put both cups in a location where they will get bright light but not long periods of direct sunlight. Water the cups regularly as needed.
5. When the seeds sprout, count the seedlings in each cup every other day for two or three weeks.

Populations and How They Grow

SECTION **14–1**

GUIDE FOR READING

- **Define** population.
- **Compare** population growth under ideal conditions and actual conditions.

MINI LAB

- **Construct a model** of human population growth.

THROUGHOUT FLORIDA, THE waterways are being strangled by hydrilla. In rivers, the tangled stems of this plant prevent boats from passing. In lakes, the hydrilla grows so thick that birds can walk across the water's surface. About 40 years ago, hydrilla plants made their way into a canal. The offspring of those plants now cover more than 45 square kilometers.

Meanwhile, in the Northeast, families who make their living from the sea are in trouble. For more than 300 years, their ancestors harvested cod, haddock, and flounder from the rich fishing ground called Georges Bank. In the last 20 years, the present-day families have noticed a drastic decrease in their fishing catch. Many of these families are afraid they'll lose the only jobs they have ever known.

Changing Populations

At first glance, these two stories seem to be very different. One is about plants growing out of control and the other is about disappearing fishes. Yet both situations involve changes in the size of what ecologists call a **population.** What is a population? ● **A population is a group of organisms of a single species that live in a given area.** A species is a group of organisms that reproduce fertile offspring.

INTEGRATING CAREERS

What are some of the different jobs open to an ecologist?

In nature, populations often stay about the same size from year to year. Sometimes, however, a particular population will grow very rapidly, like the hydrilla in Florida. Other times, populations shrink quickly, like the fish on Georges Bank. What accounts for these different situations?

Figure 14–1
These photographs show two different stories of population growth. (a) Hydrilla plants, which were brought to this country from Sri Lanka because they grew so well in aquariums, were accidentally tossed into a canal in Florida. This action caused the hydrilla population to grow rapidly. (b) Overfishing in many areas has caused the fish population to decrease sharply.

TEACHER SUPPORT

Ecology Note

Another example of unchecked population growth is starlings. In 1890, during a period when introducing foreign species was a popular and unregulated activity in North America, about 120 European starlings were released into New York's Central Park as part of a campaign to bring all the birds mentioned in Shakespeare's works to the New World. During the next century, starlings spread rapidly throughout the United States and Canada, with the North American starling population now numbering about 100 million.

Starlings foul their roosting areas, devour grain in fields and feedlots, and displace native birds. The U.S. spends millions of dollars every year trying to control starlings with traps, poisons, electrified wires on buildings, and barrages of noise, but all methods have proven ineffective. Because of this and other harsh lessons, the government now closely regulates the introduction of foreign species.

SECTION 14–1

Populations and How They Grow

Performance Objectives

- Define the term population.
- Compare exponential population growth and growth with limits.

Mini Lab Skill: Modeling
Laboratory Investigation Skill: Measuring

1 ENGAGE

Ideas Through Images

Have students examine Figure 14–1, read the caption, and answer the following questions.

- **Why do you think the hydrilla spread over such a large area?** (Students should realize that the unchecked growth was due to two main factors: favorable living conditions, such as ample nutrients, and the absence of consumers that feed on hydrilla.)
- **What could be done to solve the problem of hydrilla overgrowth?** (Accept all reasonable responses, such as introducing a consumer species.)
- **What could be done to reverse the decline in fishing catches?** (Accept all reasonable responses, such as imposing limits on catches.)

INTEGRATING CAREERS

Ecologists may be employed as teachers, as researchers, and as consultants with private companies and government agencies.

Ancillary Support

The resources below can be used to support your teaching strategy for these two pages.

TR Enrich: Uninvited Guests
LM Observing the Effects of Crowding on Seedlings, #27

2 EXPLORE

Discussion

Introduce the basic concepts (but not the terms) developed in this section by having students utilize the mini-habitats they created in the Unit Discovery Learning Activity to answer the following questions. You may want to return to these questions when students have completed this section.

1. How many different species does your mini-habitat contain?
2. How many organisms of each species did you put into the habitat at the beginning? How many of each species are in it now?
3. Which groups of organisms are larger now than when you started? Which groups are smaller? Which stayed the same?
4. Do you think the groups that got larger will continue to increase? Why or why not? What about the groups that got smaller?

3 TEACH

Ideas Through Images

Have students compare Figures 14–2 and 14–3, read the captions, and answer the following questions.

• **Which of these graphs shows the type of growth that occurred when hydrilla entered Florida waterways?** (Figure 14–2, exponential growth.)

• **What do you think a hydrilla graph would look like 25 years from now, and why?** (Students may think the population will level off, as in Figure 14–3; or that it will continue to increase, as in Figure 14–2; or that using controls such as herbicides will reduce the population and produce a graph showing a decline.)

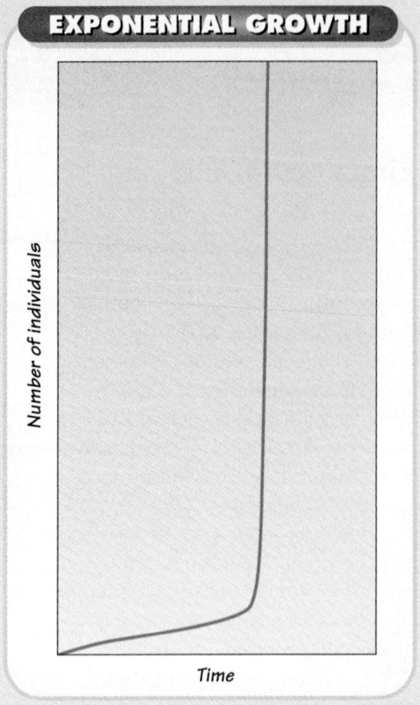

Figure 14–2
This J-shaped graph shows the exponential growth of bacteria. If ideal conditions continue, the population of bacteria will continue to grow rapidly.

Growth Rate

Simply put, a population will change size depending on how many organisms are added to it and how many organisms are removed from it. This change in population size is called **growth rate.** Growth rate can be positive, negative, or zero.

You may recall that producers, consumers, predators, and prey are linked by complex food webs. So it should not surprise you to learn that an organism's population growth rate depends in large part on the other organisms with which it interacts.

☑ *Checkpoint* What is growth rate? ①

Why Populations Grow

If you provide a population of any species with ideal conditions, it will increase, or grow. That's because all healthy organisms—from bacteria to humans—reproduce faster than their death rate. Of course, that is only to be expected. If a species' characteristics did not include the ability to produce offspring faster than its members die, that species would quickly become extinct!

In general, a population will grow if more organisms are born in a given period of time than die during the same period. An ecologist would say that such a population's birth rate is higher than its death rate. Because birth rates usually are higher than death rates for healthy organisms, populations tend to grow unless something stops them.

☑ *Checkpoint* How does birth rate affect population size? ②

A Baby Boom

If a population lives with ideal conditions—such as an adequate food supply, protection from predators, and shelter—something interesting happens. First, the existing organisms reproduce. Soon, their offspring reproduce. And then, their offspring's offspring reproduce. **As long as ideal conditions continue, the larger a population gets, the faster it grows.** This type of growth is called **exponential growth.**

Let's examine a typical instance of exponential growth. Suppose a single bacterium divided every half hour. After the first half hour, there would be two cells. Half an hour later, there would be four cells. And after another half hour, there would be eight cells. Can you grasp what is happening? Look at ***Figure 14–2*** to see the number of bacteria that could result from one cell if nothing were to stop it. If this growth continued, bacteria would cover the planet!

☑ *Checkpoint* What is exponential growth? ③

TEACHER SUPPORT — Background Information

GROWTH RATE

The ability of a given population to replenish itself is essential to the population's survival. This is why monitoring the population size of endangered species is so important. If natural or human-caused environmental changes result in a steady, unchecked decline in population size, first individual populations and then the entire species will be at risk for extinction.

SLOW INITIAL GROWTH

Reasons for the slow initial growth of populations that are introduced to a new environment include short-term adaptation to new conditions and the time needed for juveniles to mature to reproductive age. In addition, for some species that reproduce sexually, the time required to find a suitable mate may be longer because the individuals are more spread out in the new environment.

Growth With Limits

Bacteria do not cover the planet; therefore, we conclude that exponential growth does not continue in natural populations for long. Something eventually stops it or at least slows it down. The graph in *Figure 14–3* shows a different type of growth curve. If you were to introduce a few organisms into a new environment, their numbers would begin to grow slowly. Soon the population would enter an exponential growth phase. **But because exponential growth does not continue for long, population growth would begin to slow down.**

Zero Population Growth

As you will see, there are several reasons why growth slows down. In the meantime, what do you think would happen to a population if its birth rate and death rate were the same? Population growth would stop. In other words, the population would enter a state called **zero population growth.** Zero population growth does not mean that the number of individuals in the population is zero. Rather, it means that the size of the population stays the same

MINI LAB .... Modeling ....

But Not a Drop to Drink

PROBLEM *How many people can the Earth hold? What will happen if the birth rate keeps increasing? Will the Earth overflow with people? How can you **construct a model** of population growth?*

PROCEDURE

1. With a partner, label three large bowls Birth, Earth, and Death. Fill the Birth and Earth bowls three-quarters full with water. Leave the Death bowl empty.
2. Using a one-cup measuring cup, begin adding water from the Birth bowl to the Earth bowl. At the same time, have your partner use a quarter-cup measuring cup to remove water from the Earth bowl and put it into the Death bowl.
3. Continue this process until the Earth bowl is about to overflow.

ANALYZE AND CONCLUDE

1. Does this activity model positive or negative population growth?
2. What does the change in water level in the Earth bowl symbolize? How does it relate to population growth?
3. **Design an experiment** to model zero population growth. What modifications would have to be made to the experiment?

Figure 14–3
*In a growth-with-limits curve, the number of organisms begins to grow slowly, as shown in segment **a** of the graph. This slow growth is followed by an exponential growth phase, shown in segment **b**. As shown in segment **c**, eventually the population growth slows down, and at segment **d**, it levels off at carrying capacity.*

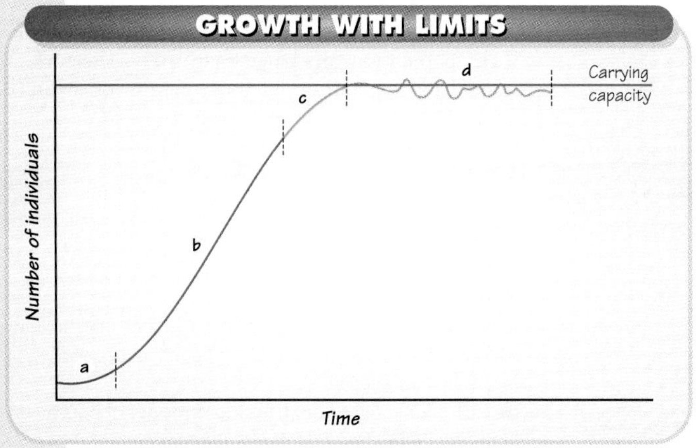

MINI LAB Modeling

Teacher Notes
- For time required and materials needed, see page 310b.
- Both students should add and remove cupfuls at the same rate.

Answers to Analyze and Conclude

1. Positive.
2. The changing size of Earth's population. If the birth rate remains higher, the population will continue to grow.
3. The two cups would have to be the same size.

Skills Trace
Modeling
- Focus p. 313
- Practice p. 314
- Assess p. 330

Checkpoints

1. A change in population size.
2. If it exceeds the death rate, population increases; if it is less than the death rate, population decreases; if the two rates are the same, population growth is zero.
3. Under ideal conditions, the larger a population gets, the faster it grows.

TEACHER SUPPORT

Managing Classroom Diversity

TECH PREP STUDENTS
Students who are interested in careers in horticulture and landscaping may want to find out about the appropriate spacing of new plantings so that an area will be filled in within a reasonable amount of time without crowding the initial plants. Students could also research types of plant reproduction (seeds, runners, bulbs, rhizomes) and how long it takes for various plant species, particularly groundcovers, to spread and cover an area.

Students who are interested in careers in animal husbandry could investigate the methods used to ensure that an animal population remains stable or increases over time. For example, how much grazing land is needed to support a dairy herd of 50 cows? What conditions must a pig farmer provide in order to breed and raise 200 young pigs for slaughter while still maintaining a stable core population of breeding adults?

Ancillary Support

The resource below can be used to support your teaching strategy for these two pages.

BL Inquiry Activity: My, How You've Grown

Section 14–1 (continued)

Laboratory Investigation

The Laboratory Investigation, The Rise and Fall of Yeast, on pages 326–327 is appropriate to use at this point in the chapter.

4 ASSESS

Quick Check

Briefly describe two populations experiencing different environmental conditions—for example, a pair of guppies placed in an aquarium with no other fish as predators, and a pair placed in an aquarium with predators. Have each student draw the shape of the graph for each population and explain why the graph would be that shape.

Section Review 14–1

1. A group of organisms of a single species that live in a given area.

2. Exponential growth: The larger a population gets, the faster it grows. Growth with limits: Population growth slows down and levels off at the carrying capacity.

3. Accept all reasonable responses, such as an increase in available nutrients, the introduction of new and more productive primary producers, and (in the case of humans) new agricultural methods or other technological advances.

4. If birth rate is greater than death rate, the population size will increase.

Skills Trace
Modeling
- Focus p. 313
- Practice p. 314
- Assess p. 330

Learning Modality

Visual and Kinesthetic Learning

Let students use plastic chips, dry beans, or other objects as counters to demonstrate the example of exponential growth described on page 312 of the student text.

BOOM AND BUST

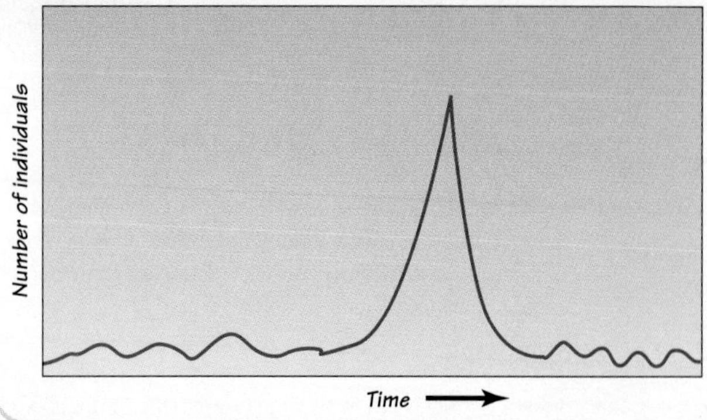

Figure 14–4
In a boom-and-bust growth curve, the population remains steady at a low rate before growing rapidly. When the population reaches its peak, the organisms die off dramatically. The population remains steady again until the next peak.

because its growth rate is zero. This situation is called the steady state.

Checkpoint What is zero population growth? ❶

Carrying Capacity

If you were to draw a horizontal line through the middle of the steady-state region, the line would tell you how large this stable population is. This line represents the largest number of individuals that can survive over long periods of time in a given environment. Scientists call this the **carrying capacity** of a particular environment for a particular species. When a population reaches the carrying capacity of its environment, a variety of factors act to stabilize it at that size.

If the population gets larger than the carrying capacity, either its birth rate falls or its death rate rises. If the population falls below the carrying capacity, its birth rate rises, its death rate drops, or both occur. In most natural populations, the steady state is not absolutely steady. It rises and falls somewhat from one year to the next.

Checkpoint What is meant by carrying capacity? ❷

Boom and Bust

Although many species in nature increase until they reach carrying capacity and then level off, it would be wrong to think that all species do. Some species grow exponentially until they reach a peak population size (the boom) and then crash dramatically (the bust). After the crash, the population may build right up again or may stay low for some time.

Section Review 14–1

1. **Define** population.
2. **Compare** the features of exponential growth and growth with limits.
3. **Critical Thinking—Inferring** What might cause the carrying capacity of a population to change?
4. **MINI LAB** After **constructing a model** of population growth, what can you conclude?

TEACHER SUPPORT

Activity

COMPARING GERMINATION RATES

Ask students to compare the numbers of seeds that have sprouted in the two cups they planted in the Chapter Discovery Learning Activity, page 310, and note any differences in their germination rates. (All three seeds in cup A probably will sprout, but some of the 15 seeds in cup B may not.)

Ask students to explain any differences in the germination rates in terms of the two cups' carrying capacities. (The large number of seeds in cup B exceeds the cup's carrying capacity.)

Why Populations Stop Growing

SECTION **14-2**

GUIDE FOR READING

- **List** four density-dependent limiting factors.
- **Compare** density-dependent limiting factors and density-independent limiting factors.

WHAT KINDS OF FACTORS IN AN environment actually control population growth in nature? Population growth may be limited by several factors—some that depend on the size and density of the population and others that do not. Population density is the number of organisms in a given area. Acting separately or together, the population-limiting factors keep natural populations somewhere between extinction and covering the entire planet.

Density-Dependent Limiting Factors

Some population-limiting factors operate more strongly on large, dense populations than on small, less-crowded ones. These factors are called **density-dependent limiting factors.** Species whose populations are controlled by density-dependent limiting factors tend to have fairly stable populations. **Competition, predation, parasitism, and crowding are examples of density-dependent limiting factors.**

Competition

When populations become crowded, individual plants or animals may compete with one another for food, water, space, sunlight, or other things essential to life. Some individuals may obtain enough of what they need to survive and reproduce. Others may obtain enough to live but not enough to enable them to raise offspring. Still others may starve to death or die from lack of shelter.

Figure 14–5
Population growth may be limited by several factors. (a) An example of a density-dependent limiting factor—predation—is shown here between a marine iguana and a Galapagos hawk. (b) Populations such as orange trees, on the other hand, are controlled by density-independent limiting factors, such as snow and ice.

SECTION 14-2
Why Populations Stop Growing

Performance Objective
- Identify and compare various density-dependent and density-independent factors that limit population growth.

1 ENGAGE

Ideas Through Images
Have students examine the photographs in Figure 14–5, read the caption, and answer the following questions.

- **What type of feeding relationship is shown between the hawk and the iguana?** (Predator-prey.)
- **What might happen to the size of the hawk population if the iguana population increased? Why?** (The hawk population would increase because more food would be available.)
- **How might cold weather affect a population of orange trees?** (It may kill orange trees and reduce the population.)

Checkpoints

1. A state in which a population's size stays the same because its birth and death rates are the same.
2. The largest number of individuals that can survive over long periods of time in a given environment.

TEACHER SUPPORT

Managing Classroom Diversity

GIFTED STUDENTS
Suggest that students do independent research on the various types of defenses that have evolved in prey species as protection against predators. Have students share their findings with the class.
- **Camouflage**—coloration that blends with the background—allows organisms to escape the notice of predators. Example: The resemblance of the desert plant *Lithops* to stones lying on the ground.
- **Mechanical defenses** make attack by most predators uncomfortable, difficult, or impossible. Example: A porcupine's quills.
- **Chemical defenses** include toxins and caustic agents; may be combined with warning coloration. Examples: A honeybee's sting; deadly alkaloids in a poison-arrow frog's skin.
- In **mimicry**, a palatable species looks like an unpalatable one. Example: The stingless flower fly's resemblance to a honeybee.

Ancillary Support
The resources below can be used to support your teaching strategy for these two pages.

LM Estimating a Population, #28
BL Inquiry Activity: Don't Pop Your Balloon

2 EXPLORE

Investigate

Research Suggest that students research species that were introduced to an area and then proved to be harmful or destructive but had no known predators or other natural controls in their new environment. Examples include rabbits in Australia; starlings in the United States (see Ecology Note, page 311); Africanized honeybees in South America, Central America, and southern North America; and Nile perch in East Africa's Lake Victoria. Encourage students to find out why or how the species were introduced, whether they competed with native species, and if so, what were the effects on the native species.

3 TEACH

Ideas Through Images

Have students examine Figure 14–6, read the caption, and answer the following questions.

- **What do you think the lines on the graph would look like for the lynx and hare populations in 1950? in 1965?** (For 1950, lines would dip to deep valleys; for 1965, lines would climb to high peaks.)
- **Which type of population growth do the lynx and hare cycles show?** (Boom and bust. If students do not agree, have them compare this graph with Figure 14–4 on page 314.)

Competition can thus lower birth rates, increase death rates, or do both.

How can competition among members of a species be considered a density-dependent limiting factor? The more individuals there are in an area, the sooner they will use up the available resources. The fewer individuals there are, the less competition they have for the resources and the longer they will last. Competition for limited resources is often one of the most important factors in determining the carrying capacity of an environment for a particular species.

☑ **Checkpoint** What is the relationship between competition and carrying capacity? ❶

Predation

You may recall that energy in the biosphere flows through producers and consumers. Most species serve as food for some other species. In nature, predators and the organisms they prey upon usually coexist over long periods of time. Over time, predator and prey become accustomed to each other's strengths and weaknesses.

Prey develop some remarkable defenses against predators. Predators in turn develop their own defenses, or counterdefenses. Strong jaws and sharp teeth, powerful digestive enzymes, or keen eyesight are examples of counterdefenses that have developed.

The presence of defenses and counterdefenses does not mean, however, that the number of predators and prey will always reach a balance. As you can see in ***Figure 14–6,*** populations of predators and prey almost always change in size over time.

☑ **Checkpoint** If an entire wolf population is killed off, what may happen to the deer population on which it preys? ❷

Parasitism

Parasites are similar to predators in many ways. A **parasite** is an organism that takes nourishment from its host. Parasites live at the expense of their hosts, weakening them and causing disease and, in some cases, death.

You may wonder why parasitism acts as a density-dependent control on population size. Parasites work most effectively when hosts are present in large numbers. Why is this so? Parasites are often host-specific. This means that they grow best in members of a single species. Crowding helps parasites travel from one suitable host to another.

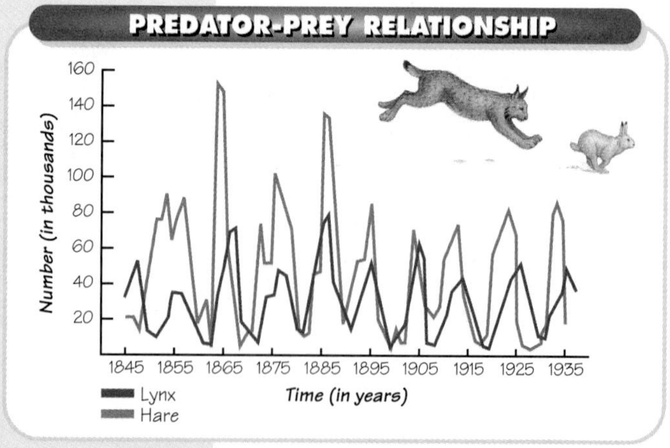

Figure 14–6
The relationship between populations of lynx (predators) and snowshoe hares (prey) changes over many years. As the number of hares increases, the number of lynx increases as well. The lynx eat more hares than the number being born, and the hare population decreases. As a result, the lynx begin to starve, causing their population to drop. With a decreased lynx population, the hares begin to recover and the cycle repeats itself.

TEACHER SUPPORT

Background Information

The sizes of the lynx and hare populations shown in Figure 14–6 are based on counts of pelts that trappers sold to the Hudson's Bay Company over a 90-year period. Both hare and lynx populations experience a 10-year cycle of boom and bust. However, other factors besides predation by lynx may also influence the hare cycle.

For example, researchers have found that the hare population fluctuates dramatically about every 10 years whether or not lynx are present. The hare population's periodic crashes may be associated with changes in the hares' own food supply. As food becomes more scarce, hares must take greater risks to reach the remaining food plants, increasing their exposure to predators. Another proposed hypothesis, based on laboratory studies of mice and other small rodents, suggests that stress from overcrowding may alter the hares' hormonal balance and reduce their fertility, thus precipitating a crash.

Problem Solving

INTERPRETING DIAGRAMS

Flowering Plants

The sophomore class needs to raise money for their year-end dance. One Biology class decided to have a plant sale. The class reasoned that if they planted the seeds themselves and then transplanted the flowering plants into decorative flowerpots, they could make a lot of money.

Based on the prices for the seeds, fertilizer, potting soil, flats, and flowerpots, they determined that in order to break even, they would need to grow 25 to 29 plants per flat. If they grew 30 or more plants per flat, the class would make a profit.

Two different groups planted seeds. The students in Group A decided to try to grow 30 plants per flat. They carefully counted out enough seeds and evenly spaced the seeds in the potting soil. Those in Group B decided to try to grow more than 30 plants. They planted enough seeds for 50 plants in the same amount of space. The two groups' flats were placed next to each other on a windowsill and given the same amount of water and fertilizer each week. The results of each group's plant flats are shown below.

THINK ABOUT IT

1. What density-dependent factors might have affected the plant growth? Were these factors equally strong on both groups' plants?
2. What density-independent factors might have affected the plant growth? Were these factors equally strong on both groups' plants?
3. **Design an experiment** to determine the maximum number of plants per flat that would flower and grow if the flat measured 1' × 2' × 3".

Problem Solving
Interpreting Diagrams
Flowering Plants

Students will apply their understanding of limiting factors to an experiment on plant growth. The problem can be solved by using the four-step problem-solving strategy.

State The problem is to determine the optimum number of plants to grow per flat of a given size.
Solve Students should identify all the factors that could affect plant growth. They must isolate the one factor that should be changed: the number of seeds.
Test Let students carry out their experiments.
Communicate Have groups describe their experimental designs, explain how they controlled each factor, and state their results.

Answers to THINK ABOUT IT

1. The amount of sunlight, water, and nutrients; they were stronger for Group B.
2. Species of plants used, type of soil, amount of watering, fertilizer concentration, temperature, and light. These factors were equally strong for both groups.
3. All designs should involve changing only the seed number.

Checkpoints

1. Competition for limited resources can decrease the population of a species and thus the carrying capacity of an environment for that species.
2. It will increase.

TEACHER SUPPORT

Background Information

Natural selection generally favors the evolution of less virulent parasite strains that do not kill their hosts too quickly, as explained in the student text. However, recent investigations into host-parasite relationships indicate that there are some exceptions.

One exception occurs when large numbers of hosts are crowded very tightly together. Under such conditions, some parasites can spread efficiently even though they kill very quickly. This may have been the reason that the bubonic plague in Europe and Asia in the 1300s remained deadly for so long.

Crowded conditions also may have accounted for the deadly influenza epidemic of 1918. During World War I, large numbers of soldiers were tightly crowded into trenches under unsanitary conditions. When individuals fell ill, they were carried—sneezing and coughing—through the crowded trenches, affording ample opportunity for the disease to spread rapidly.

Ancillary Support

The resources below can be used to support your teaching strategy for these two pages.

TR Apply: Limiting Factors
TB Predator–Prey Relationship, #19

4 ASSESS

Quick Check

Have students examine again the photographs in Figure 14–5 and identify the type of limiting factor (density-dependent or density-independent) shown in each.

Section Review 14–2

1. Competition, predation, parasitism, and crowding and stress.

2. Density-dependent limiting factors (see #1) operate more strongly on large, dense populations than on small, less-crowded ones. Density-independent factors (weather, fires, droughts, floods, hurricanes, harmful human activities) affect organisms regardless of how large the population is.

3. Answers will vary. Example: A hurricane may kill many people outright, destroy homes, crops, and livestock, and contribute to malnutrition and the spread of disease.

Learning Modality

Visual Learning This section's tight focus and clear structure make it particularly appropriate for outlining as a learning/study aide. If needed, help students decide which ideas are most important, which ideas support those major ideas, and which ideas are minor details. Some students may find it helpful to write the major ideas, supporting ideas, and minor details on separate index cards or strips of paper and then arrange them in outline format before writing the entire outline.

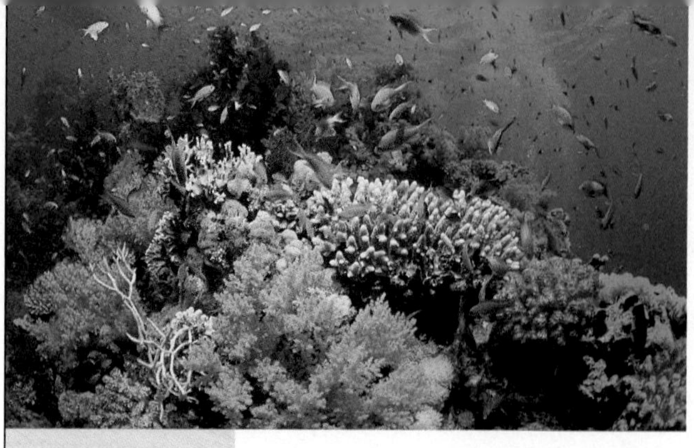

Figure 14–7 *Stress caused by crowding is an example of a density-dependent limiting factor.*

Note that few parasites kill their hosts—at least, not right away. If a parasite killed its host too quickly, the parasite would have to find another host or it too would die. That's why under most circumstances, it is to a parasite's advantage not to be too deadly.

☑ ***Checkpoint*** Why is parasitism a density-dependent limiting factor? (1)

Crowding and Stress

Most animals, including humans, have a built-in behavioral need for a certain amount of space. Both the males and the females of a species may need room to hunt for food. They may need a certain amount of space for nesting, or they may need a territory of a certain size. In such cases, the number of suitable territories regulates population size in a density-dependent manner.

Some organisms fight among themselves if they become overcrowded. Fighting can cause high levels of stress, which disturbs the finely tuned system of hormones that coordinate body functions. Often, the immune system may become weakened. Hormonal changes from stress can also upset animals' behavior so that they neglect, kill, or even eat their own offspring. All these factors limit population growth.

☑ ***Checkpoint*** How does crowding act as a density-dependent limiting factor? (2)

Density-Independent Limiting Factors

Not all populations are controlled by density-dependent limiting factors. **Species that have boom-and-bust growth curves may be affected by factors that kill organisms regardless of how large the population is.** Because the density of the population does not matter in such cases, these factors are called **density-independent limiting factors.**

Weather is probably the most important density-independent limiting factor. An entire insect population can be destroyed by a rainstorm. They may also be harmed by unusually hot or cold weather, by disturbances such as fires, or by droughts, floods, or hurricanes. Human activities—such as a toxic waste spill, the spraying of pesticides, or clear-cutting a forest—may also act as density-independent limiting factors.

Section Review 14–2

1. **List** four density-dependent limiting factors.
2. **Compare** density-dependent limiting factors and density-independent limiting factors.
3. **Critical Thinking—Relating Concepts** Give an example of a density-independent limiting factor that has impacted a human population. Explain how it has impacted the population.

TEACHER SUPPORT

Activity

COMPARING SEEDLING GROWTH

Have students examine the cups they planted in the Chapter Discovery Learning Activity and compare the seedlings in each. (All seedlings in cup A should be thriving, but some in cup B may be dying or at least may be noticeably smaller than others.)

Ask students to explain this observation in terms of the limiting factors discussed in this section and to decide which factor is affecting cup B. (The seedlings in cup A have ample space, sunlight, nutrients, and water. The seedlings in cup B must compete with one another for these resources. Thus, competition—not the crowding itself—is the limiting factor.)

Human Population Growth

SECTION 14–3

GUIDE FOR READING

- **Describe** how the human population is growing exponentially.
- **List** the three stages of demographic transition.

LIKE THOSE OF OTHER organisms, human populations tend to increase with time in the same ways and for the same reasons. What, if anything, will stop humans from covering the planet? How and why do human populations stop growing? Read on to find the answers to these questions.

Growth Increases

For most of human existence, human populations grew slowly. Why was this so? Population-limiting factors kept populations at a low level. Life was harsh. Food was difficult to find. Predators and parasites were everywhere. Death rates, therefore, for humans were quite high. Until recently, only half the children survived to adulthood. Families had many children, just to make sure that some of them would survive.

Human Population Grows Quickly

About 300 years ago, the world's human population started growing more rapidly. Over several hundred years, agricultural and industrial revolutions made human life easier. People developed ways to control some population-limiting factors. Thanks to modern agriculture, more nutritious foods became available. Recently, doctors learned to cure or prevent diseases that once killed large numbers of people. Better health care and nutrition dramatically reduced the number of infants who died. People started living healthier, longer lives.

INTEGRATING HEALTH

How do the leading causes of death today differ from those in 1900?

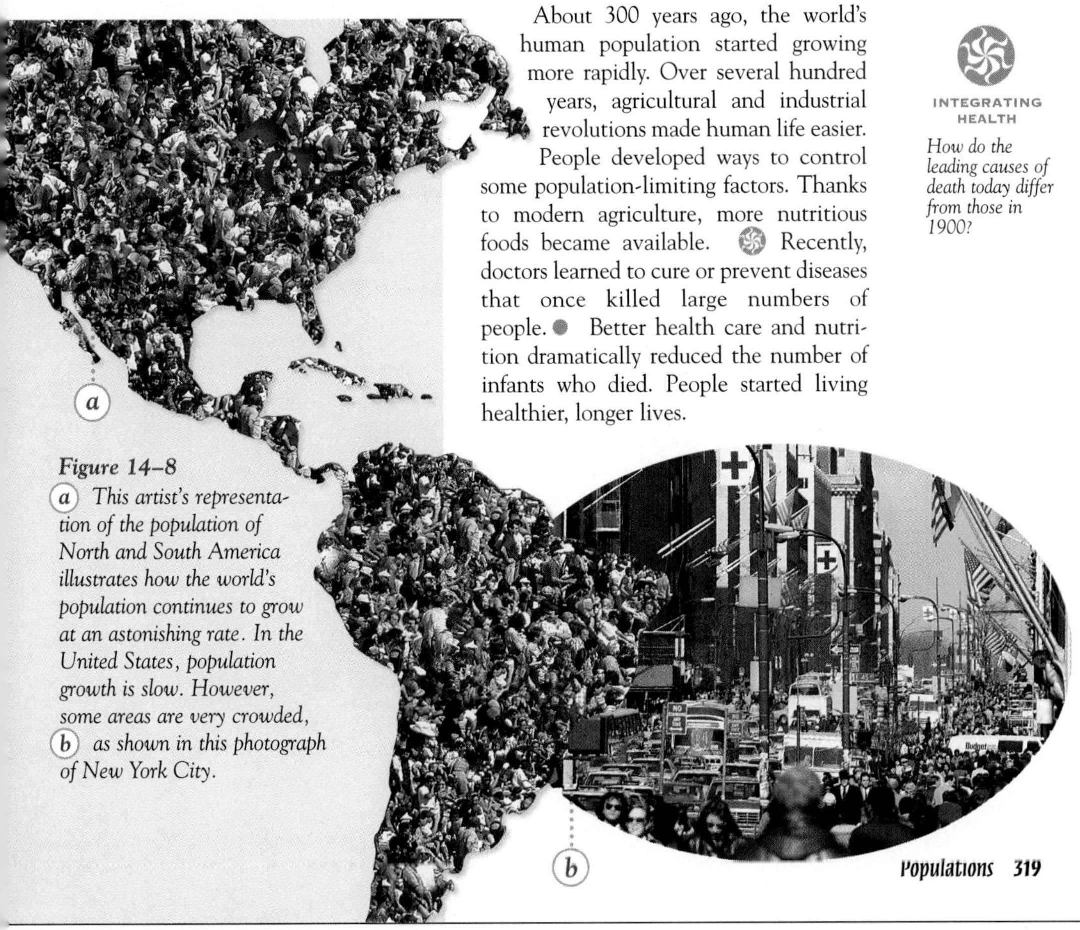

Figure 14–8
(a) This artist's representation of the population of North and South America illustrates how the world's population continues to grow at an astonishing rate. In the United States, population growth is slow. However, some areas are very crowded, (b) as shown in this photograph of New York City.

SECTION 14-3

Human Population Growth

Performance Objectives

- Describe the world's human population growth as exponential.
- Identify the three stages of demographic transition as human population growth slows.

1 ENGAGE

Ideas Through Images

Have students examine Figure 14–8, read the caption, and answer the following questions.

- **Which areas of the United States are very crowded?** (Areas such as New York, Los Angeles, Miami, Dallas, and Chicago.)
- **How would you categorize the population density of the area where you live?** (Answers will depend on your location.)

INTEGRATING HEALTH

Infectious diseases—pneumonia, influenza, and tuberculosis—headed the list in 1900, while heart disease, stroke, and cancer head today's list.

Checkpoints

1. Parasites work most effectively when hosts are present in large numbers.
2. May cause fighting, high levels of stress, and disruptions in behavior that limit population growth.

TEACHER SUPPORT

Facts and Figures

INFANT DEATH RATES
More than 8 million infants worldwide die each year before reaching their first birthday, according to a World Health Organization study released in 1996. Most of these deaths are due to disease or inadequate care in the first weeks of life. About 98 percent of infant deaths occur in developing countries, where an average of 57 babies per 1000 births are born dead or die within the first week of life. The highest rates are in African nations, followed by south-central Asian countries. In contrast, the average infant death rate in developed nations is 11 per 1000 live births.

DECLINING BIRTH RATES
The idea that birth and death rates reach a balance in Stage 3 of the demographic transition is not true of all countries. For example, Italy's birth rate, already one of the lowest in the world, is continuing to decline.

Ancillary Support

The resource below can be used to support your teaching strategy for these two pages.

TR Writing in Biology: Reports From the Front
Explore: Population in Balance

2 EXPLORE

Investigate

Research Suggest that students interview older family members and friends about their experiences with serious diseases that were once fairly common in the U.S. but are now rare, such as rubella (German measles), diphtheria, poliomyelitis, pertussis (whooping cough), and virulent strains of influenza. Encourage students to find out what it was like when an epidemic struck, what treatments were used, and what precautions, such as quarantining, were taken to prevent further spread.

3 TEACH

Ideas Through Images

Have students examine Figure 14–10, read the caption, and answer the following questions.

- **If its growth continues at the same rate, how large will the human population be in the year 2000?** (About 6.2 billion. Calculation: 1990 population of 5.3 billion plus 0.9 billion [92 million per year, as stated in student text, times 10 years].)
- **The world population doubled between 1800 and 1900. What will the increase be from 1900 to 2000?** (Triple.)

Discussion

Ask students to identify major historical events that could be added to Figure 14–10. You could have volunteers make a large copy of the graph and add these events.

Figure 14–9
CAREER TRACK
As human population growth impacts animals and other wildlife, care must be taken to prevent organisms from becoming extinct. Here a wildlife biologist tags a frog-eating bat in a Panama rain forest. This enables wildlife biologists to monitor the bat population.

In other words, several factors combined to lower human death rates. More children than ever before survived to marry and have children of their own. At the same time, birth rates in most places continued to be as high as they had ever been. Because the birth rate was higher than the death rate, the human population grew. **Today, the world's human population is still growing exponentially.** At present, 180 people are born every minute. This means that there are 92 million more humans each year.

☑ **Checkpoint** Why has the human death rate decreased? ❶

Controlling Human Populations

Human population size cannot increase exponentially forever for the same reason that populations of bacteria don't do so. That much is obvious. Exactly why and how will human growth slow down? The answer to this question is far less obvious.

You have seen that the human population grows for the same reasons that

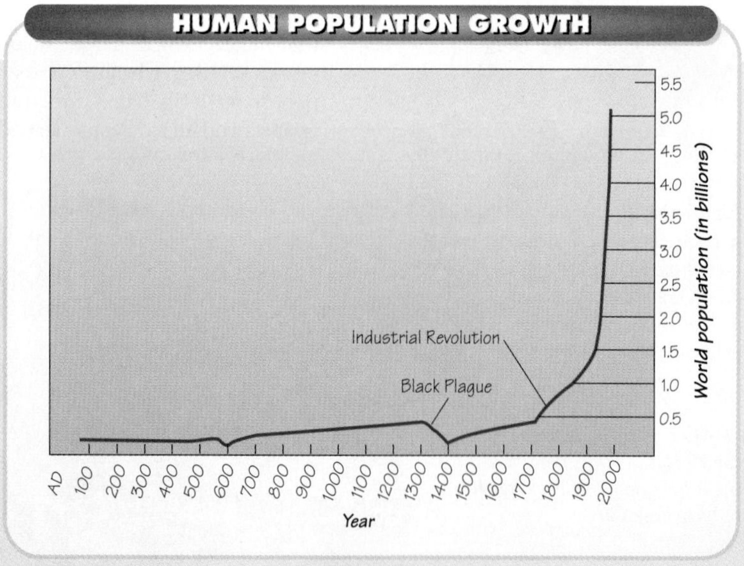

Figure 14–10
The global human population reached 1 billion in 1800. In a little more than 100 years, the population doubled to 2 billion, then doubled again to 4 billion less than 50 years later. And 13 years later, the population reached 5 billion. Notice the growth decrease in the 1300s due to the Black Plague and the beginning of the rapid increase in the 1700s due to the Industrial Revolution.

320 Chapter 14

TEACHER SUPPORT

Background Information

The demographic transition is a useful concept in human population biology. When applied to western nations, it can be considered a simple, factual, historical description of changes in birth and death rates as cultures passed through various stages. When applied to global population growth, however, demographic transition may be considered a theory—a prediction that nonwestern cultures will pass through similar stages for more or less the same reasons as western cultures did.

If you wish to explore the demographic transition with students in more depth, you could point out that the applicability of the theory to cultures in sub-Saharan African nations, India, and some nations in southeast Asia is open to dispute. There is also considerable controversy about whether all cultures will pass through Stage 2 to complete Stage 3.

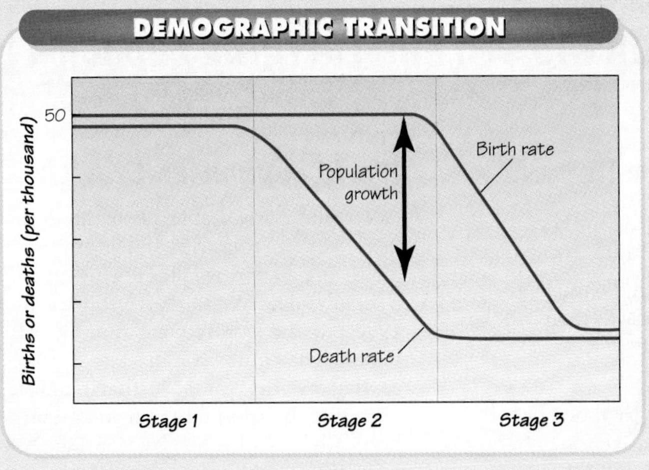

Figure 14–11
Before the Industrial Revolution in the eighteenth century, populations in North America and Europe were in Stage 1 of the demographic transition. After industrialization, death rates decreased due to improved medical and scientific advances. Birth rates remained high, and Stage 2 was reached. As the economy began to improve and education became more widespread, birth rates began to decrease to match the death rate. North America and Europe are now in Stage 3.

animal populations grow. The human population would stop growing if birth rates fell, death rates rose, or both occurred. But do human birth and death rates change for the same reasons as they do in other animal populations? To answer this question, let's look at some situations in which human population growth has indeed slowed or stopped.

Growth Slows Down

Over the last century, human population growth has slowed down dramatically in some countries. What factors have caused this change? Biologists say that these populations passed through the **demographic transition.** The demographic transition is a change in growth rate resulting from changes in birth rate.

The demographic transition consists of three stages. During the first stage, there is a high birth rate and a high death rate. Families have many children to make sure some will survive. Because both the birth rate and death rate are high, population growth is slow during this stage.

During the second stage, improvements are made in living conditions. Food production increases, there are advances in medicine, and sanitation is improved. As a result, more children live to adulthood and the death rate decreases. Because the birth rate remains high, the population grows rapidly.

In the third stage, the birth rate decreases for a variety of reasons. Because more children are surviving, families begin to have fewer children. The birth rate and death rate reach a balance at a lower level. Population growth slows down and may stabilize.

Section Review 14–3

1. **Describe** how the human population is growing exponentially.
2. **List** the three stages of demographic transition.
3. **Critical Thinking—Inferring** In what stage of the demographic transition is the United States?

4 ASSESS

Quick Check

Have students summarize the characteristics of each stage of the demographic transition in a chart.

Section Review 14–3

1. Several factors have combined to lower human death rates (see Checkpoint below). At the same time, birth rates in most places continue to be high.
2. Stage 1: high birth rate and high death rate. Stage 2: death rate decreases, birth rate remains high. Stage 3: birth rate decreases to balance death rate; population growth slows down and may stabilize.
3. Stage 3.

Learning Modality

Visual and Kinesthetic Learning

The following activity provides a model of the human population growth graph, Figure 14–10. (The model requires a total of 215 counters, such as plastic chips or pennies.)

1. Use a meterstick (0 end at the left) to represent the time span from A.D. 1 through A.D. 2000. Each centimeter represents 100 years. The counters represent the human population. One counter stands for 100 million people.

Checkpoint

❶ More nutritious foods, medical advances in the cure and prevention of diseases, better health care and nutrition for infants

2. Have students lay counters above marks on the meterstick to indicate the size of the population at various points in time, as listed in the table below. (Students should arrange the counters in vertical rows upward from the meterstick like bars on a graph, not in stacks.)
3. To create a line graph, connect the top points of the "bars" with string or yarn.

HUMAN POPULATION

Year	Population	Number/Position of Counters
1	200 million	2 at 0 cm
1000	300 million	3 at 10 cm
1650	600 million	6 at 16.5 cm
1750	700 million	7 at 17.5 cm
1800	1000 million	10 at 18 cm
1850	1200 million	12 at 18.5 cm
1900	2000 million	20 at 19 cm
1950	4000 million	40 at 19.5 cm
1990	5300 million	53 at 19.9 cm
2000	6200 million	62 at 20 cm

Ancillary Support

The resource below can be used to support your teaching strategy for these two pages.
BL Inquiry Activity: The Growing World

SECTION 14–4 Population Growth and Carrying Capacity

Performance Objectives

• Explain why the world's human population continues to grow exponentially.

• Make a prediction about the future growth of the world's human population.

Mini Lab Skill: Comparing

1 ENGAGE

Inquiry Activity

Hypothesizing

Changes in Family Size

Ask each student to write a list of reasons that couples in the United States today generally have few children, and another list of reasons that couples in the past generally had large families. (If students seem to focus on the unavailability of reliable family planning and birth control methods as the reason for large families in the past, encourage them to think about other issues, such as needing children to help support the family on the farm or in paid employment, having many children to compensate for a high infant mortality rate, and so forth.) Let students share their lists in a class discussion and compare the factors influencing the two family-size choices.

14–4 Population Growth and Carrying Capacity

GUIDE FOR READING

- **Explain** why the world's population continues to grow.
- **Predict** the kind of human population growth there will be in the future.

MINI LAB

- **Compare** the total number of offspring over five generations in one-, two-, and three-children families.

FUTURE HUMAN POPULATION growth is an important issue. To many ecologists, the size of the human population is the single most important factor in determining the overall health of the Earth. Why? Because human activities have profound effects on both local and global environments. And population size affects all these activities.

World Population Growth

Despite fairly stable populations in most western countries and Japan, the global population is still growing exponentially. The last serious estimate in 1990 put the world's population at 5.3 billion. The United Nations has predicted that by the year 2100 that number may reach between 6 billion and 19 billion. Why will this number continue to grow? **The world's population continues to grow because most people live in countries that have not yet completed the demographic transition.**

The United States, Canada, Japan, and the countries of Europe have gone through all three stages of the demographic transition. In these countries, there is slow population growth. The population of the United States, for example, is still growing, but it is growing much more slowly than in the past. In some European countries, populations are even declining slightly.

Countries in Asia, Africa, and South America have not yet completed the demographic transition. These areas are home to approximately 80 percent of the world's population. As you can see in ***Figure 14–13,*** these areas are still undergoing rapid growth. This rapid

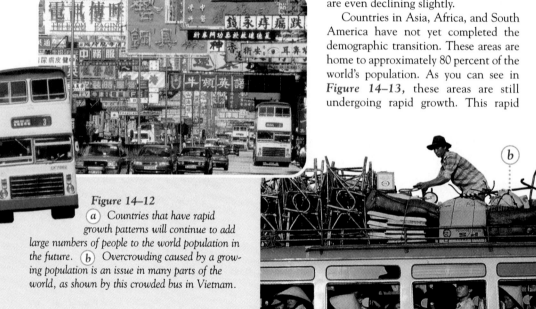

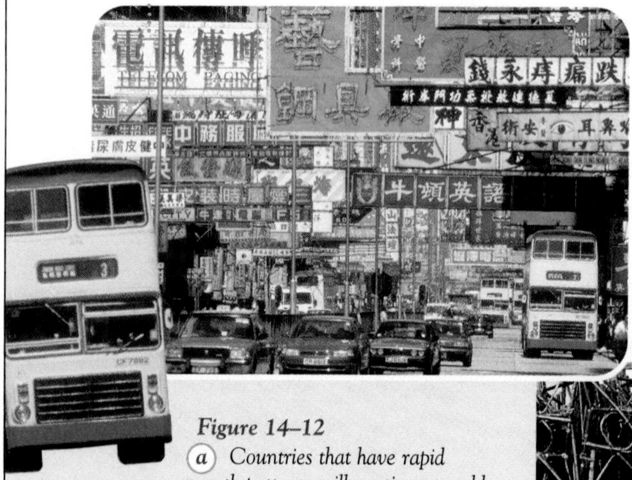

Figure 14–12 (a) *Countries that have rapid growth patterns will continue to add large numbers of people to the world population in the future.* (b) *Overcrowding caused by a growing population is an issue in many parts of the world, as shown by this crowded bus in Vietnam.*

TEACHER SUPPORT

Historical Perspective

Two examples illustrate the complexities of controlling human population growth in developing nations. In India, most people do not have adequate food, shelter, or medical care. Due largely to family resistance, government-sponsored population control programs have not done well. In desperation, the government enacted a law subjecting some men to compulsory vasectomy. Public outrage was so great that the law was rescinded. India's population continues to grow.

China—a nation that has experienced repeated famines and mass starvations—has instituted the most extensive family planning program in the world. Couples who pledge to have only one child are given extra food, better housing, free medical care, and salary bonuses. Couples who break this pledge lose their benefits. These policies have curtailed explosive population growth, but growth is still rapid, due primarily to the large number of women in or entering their reproductive years.

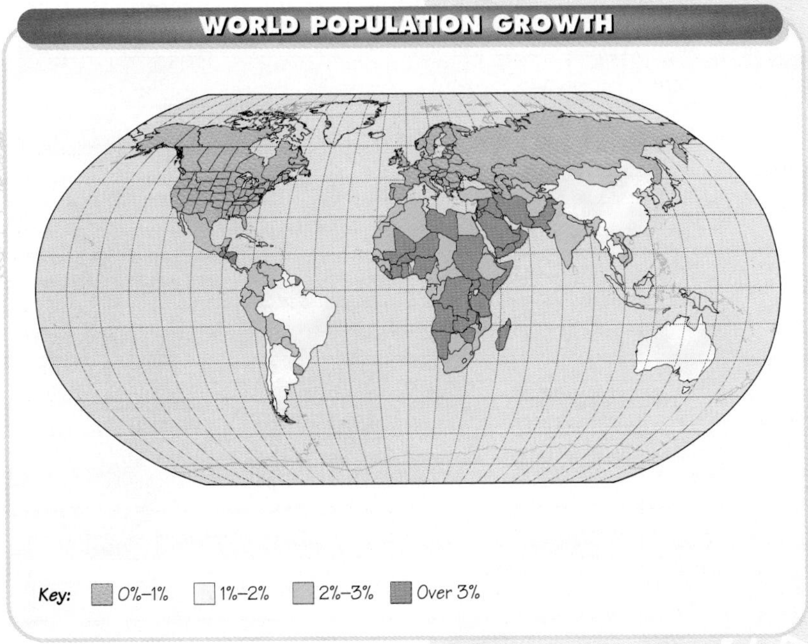

Figure 14–13
This map shows population growth rates in different parts of the world. Notice the high growth rate in Asia, Africa, and South America.

growth, coupled with a declining death rate, has intensified economic problems.

Future Population Growth

Future population growth in various countries depends, in part, on how many people of different ages are living in that country today. On the next page, ***Figure 14–14*** shows what are called the **age-structure diagrams** of human populations in three different countries. Demographers, or people who study population growth, use age-structure diagrams to make predictions about future growth.

Rapid Growth

In a country with rapid growth, such as Mexico, the majority of the population is under the age of 15. Older groups represent a much smaller percentage of the population. Although the birth rate in Mexico has decreased, there is still great potential for growth. How can you tell? The largest percentage of people has not yet reached their childbearing years. As this group reaches reproductive age, Mexico can expect to grow even more.

Slow Growth

In a country such as Sweden, there is slow population growth. There are almost equal numbers of people in each age group. The growth rate in Sweden is almost zero.

In the United States, too, there are almost equal numbers of people in each age group. This pattern predicts a slow, steady growth for the near future. Do you see the large number of people in the age

INTEGRATING CAREERS

What kind of degree must demographers have? What kinds of courses should they take?

2 EXPLORE

Ideas Through Images

Have students examine Figure 14–13, read the caption, and answer the following questions.

- **How does the population growth rate in the United States compare to the rest of North America?** (The annual population growth rate in the U.S. is 0% to 1%. The growth rate is the same in Canada, but in Mexico it is 2% to 3%.)
- **What areas other than the United States and Canada have low growth rates? High growth rates?** (Europe, Australia, Russia, and Japan; Africa.)

3 TEACH

INTEGRATING CAREERS

A college degree in sociology with an emphasis in demography or a related area is usually required to work as a demographer. Some positions require a master's degree or doctorate in sociology.

Correcting Misconceptions

Although the text states that about 80 percent of the world's population lives in developing nations, many students may still believe that most people live in developed countries. To help dispel this misconception, have students research and compare the populations of several developing nations with the populations of the United States, Canada, and Japan.

TEACHER SUPPORT

Facts and Figures

The population growth of developed countries, although slow, is in many ways a greater threat to the biosphere than the rapid growth of undeveloped countries. India, for example, has 16 percent of the world's population; the United States, less than 5 percent. Yet the U.S. consumes more resources and causes more ecological damage.

The average person in the U.S. consumes 50 times as much in resources as the average person in India. The U.S. consumes about 25 percent of the world's processed minerals and nonrenewable energy resources; India, 3 percent. And the U.S. produces at least 25 percent of the world's trash and pollution; India, 3 percent. Extrapolating from these figures, it would take 12.9 billion people in India to match the present consumption rate and environmental impact of 258 million average Americans.

Ancillary Support

The resource below can be used to support your teaching strategy for these two pages.

TR Apply: A Population Picture

Ideas Through Images

Have students examine Figure 14–14, read the caption, and answer the following questions.

- **In Sweden's age structure diagram, why are the bars about the same size?** (The numbers of people in the different age groups are about the same.)
- **What does the "bulge" in the United States diagram represent?** (The baby boom that occurred after World War II.)
- **Would an age structure diagram for an African nation look more like the diagram for Mexico, Sweden, or the United States. Why?** (Mexico, because African nations have rapid growth rates. Students should determine this information about Africa's growth rates from the text on page 322 and the world map on page 323.)
- **What would the diagram for a nation with a declining population look like?** (An inverted pyramid; like an upside-down version of Mexico's diagram.)

Investigate

Cooperative Learning Ask each group of three students to research population statistics by age group for your community, county, and state. (Population-by-age statistics for states, counties, and large cities are included in *Statistical Abstract of the United States* and *County and City Data Book*, both published by the U.S. Department of Commerce and available in the reference section of most libraries. Statistics for your community may be available from your town/city hall.) Have group members exchange the data they researched and use the information to construct three age structure diagrams. Ask students to compare their diagrams with the diagram for the United States in Figure 14–14 and note any differences. Based on their diagrams, students also should be able to make some general predictions regarding future population growth in your area. (Also see the Multicultural Strategy included in Managing Classroom Diversity on this page.)

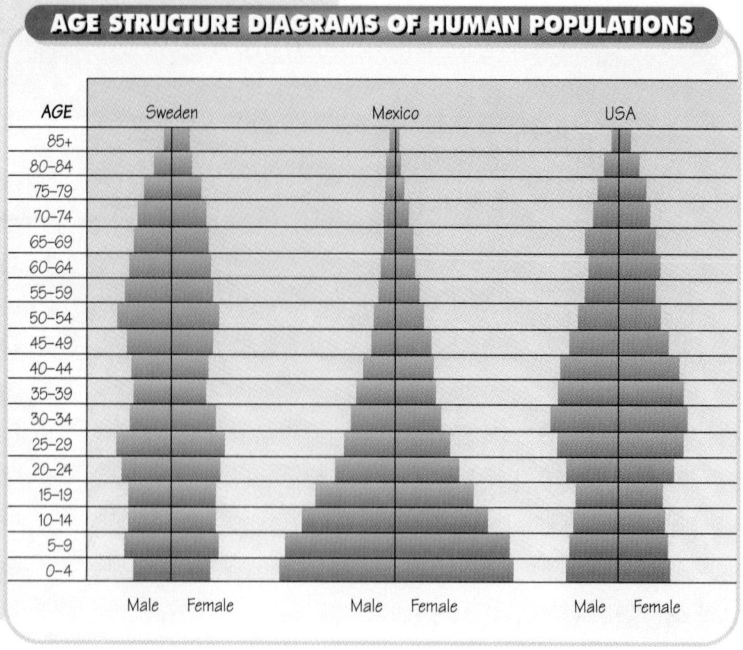

Figure 14–14
On an age structure diagram, each bar represents the percentage of the population of individuals within a 5-year age group. The percentage of males in that age group is found to the left of the center line, and the percentage of females is to the right. In a country with slow growth, such as Sweden, there are almost equal numbers of people in each age category. In a country with rapid growth, such as Mexico, the larger percentage of people is under the age of 15. The United States has fairly stable growth.

groups born just after World War II? These people, called the baby boomers, belong to the largest segment of the population.

Baby boomers have hit their childbearing years and yet population growth is still slow. How can that be? Due to many social changes, many women are delaying childbirth and having fewer children.

Earth's Carrying Capacity

Is world population growth going to be a problem in the future? Opinions differ about how long population growth will continue, whether it is a problem, and how important it is to slow it down. Ecologists argue that if population growth doesn't slow down, there could be serious and lasting damage to both the local and global ecology. Others disagree. Economists think that science,

Figure 14–15
The city of Nairobi in Kenya provides a backdrop to this topi and impala buck, illustrating how human growth is beginning to have an impact on other natural populations.

TEACHER SUPPORT

Managing Classroom Diversity

MULTICULTURAL STRATEGY

The reference books listed for the Investigate activity on this page include population-by-age statistics for five racial groups—Hispanic, Non-Hispanic White, Black, American Indian/Eskimo/Aleut, and Asian/Pacific Islander. You might want to have students create age structure diagrams based on these statistics as well.

GIFTED STUDENTS

Paul Ehrlich, author of *The Population Bomb*, and Julian Simon, author of *The Ultimate Resource*, exemplify the debate described in the student text. Ehrlich predicts dire consequences for the biosphere if present population growth continues. Simon contends that global conditions will improve as the result of human ingenuity and technological advances. Suggest that students read both books to learn more about their views.

technology, and changes in society will help to control the human impact on the environment. The most important question, however, is what the Earth's carrying capacity for humans might be. And that is an incredibly difficult question to answer.

As a group, ecologists feel strongly that human population should not be viewed in isolation. Instead, human activity should be looked at as it affects the Earth's ability to provide the essentials of life, such as food, water, air, land, shelter, and minerals. That is easily said. But just how much human, plant, and animal life can a particular area support? How much of the biosphere can be covered by homes, farms, and highways without interfering with global life-support systems?

Different experts, using different approaches, have suggested that the Earth can hold anywhere between 5 billion and 20 billion people. It is interesting to note that the actual human population has now reached the lower part of that range. Within your lifetime, the number of people on Earth will double at least once.

How long will this growth continue? What does it mean for the future? Finding answers to these and many other questions is vital to the future of humans on Earth.

MINI LAB ······ Comparing

A Baby Boom?

PROBLEM *How would the number of offspring in one-, two-, and three-children families over five generations **compare** if each offspring bears the same number of offspring as its parents had?*

PROCEDURE

1. Calculate the number of offspring that could be born in each generation for a one-child family over five generations. Record your calculations.
2. Repeat Step 1 for a two-child family and then a three-child family.

ANALYZE AND CONCLUDE

1. In the third generation, how many total offspring are there in the two-child family? In the three-child family?
2. In the fifth generation, how many total offspring are there in the one-child family? In the three-child family?
3. In a four-child family, how many offspring could there be in the fifth generation?

Section Review 14–4

1. **Explain** why the world's population is still growing rapidly.
2. **Predict** the kind of human population growth there will be in the future.
3. **MINI LAB** **Compare** the total number of offspring in one-, two-, and three-children families over five generations. Assume that each child will have the same number of offspring as its parents had.
4. **BRANCHING OUT ACTIVITY** In the age-structure diagram of the United States, there is a decrease in the percentage of people in the age category before the baby boom. **Formulate a hypothesis** to explain this decrease. Use reference material to find out what happened during that time that could account for a low birth rate.

MINI LAB Comparing

Teacher Notes

- For time required and materials needed, see p. 310b.
- Students may find it helpful to organize their calculations in a table.

Answers to Analyze and Conclude

1. Two-child: 8. Three-child: 27.
2. One-child: 1. Three-child: 243.
3. 1024.

Skills Trace
Comparing
- Focus p. 325
- Practice p. 325
- Assess p. 330

4 ASSESS

Quick Check

Ask students to draw rough sketches of the age structure diagrams for three nations: one with a rapidly growing population, one with a stable population, and one with a slowly growing population.

Section Review 14–4

1. Most people live in countries that have not yet completed the demographic transition.

2. In countries that have gone through all three stages of the demographic transition, growth will be slow. In countries that have not yet completed the transition, growth will continue to be rapid.

3. One-child: 5. Two-child: 62. Three-child: 363.

Skills Trace
Comparing
- Focus p. 325
- Practice p. 325
- Assess p. 330

4. Students' answers should focus on the effects of World War II. Fewer children were born during this period because many husbands and wives were separated while one served in the military.

Learning Modality

Visual Learning With students who have difficulty understanding the format of age structure diagrams, point out that the vertical midline on these diagrams is similar to the horizontal baseline on a bar graph. If students turn the textbook 90 degrees to the right and cover the bottom half of the diagram with a piece of paper, they will see that the diagram's upper half looks just like an ordinary bar graph.

Ancillary Support

The resource below can be used to support your teaching strategy for these two pages.

BL Inquiry Activity: How Many Can Fit?

CHAPTER 14

Laboratory Investigation

The Rise and Fall of Yeast

Before the Lab

1. Prepare enough molasses solution and yeast solution for the class by multiplying the number of groups by the amount needed per group, given below, plus an additional amount in case of mistakes.
   - Molasses solution: 8 mL molasses to 32 mL water
   - Yeast solution: ⅛ tsp dry yeast to 4 mL water
2. For each group, pour 40 mL molasses solution into one cup and 4 mL yeast solution into another cup.
3. Set up several microscopes—preferably one for each group—with low- and high-power objectives.

Pre-Lab Discussion

Have students read the entire procedure for this investigation. Then ask students the following questions.

Are yeast living organisms or a nonliving material? (Living organisms.)

Why do you think a molasses solution is used instead of plain water? (As living organisms, the yeast need a food source, and the molasses provides it.)

Why should you take yeast from a different beaker each time you count samples? (Some yeast were removed from the previous beaker when sampling was done, and this affects the size of that population and thus its rate of reproduction and the sample count.)

Skills Development

Students will use these skills while completing the laboratory investigation: measuring, developing models, interpreting data, making predictions, making inferences, and designing experiments.

Laboratory Investigation

The Rise and Fall of Yeast

The population of yeast varies over time. In this investigation, you will monitor the population of a yeast culture over seven days. Will the yeast population grow and thrive? Perform this experiment to find out.

Problem

How can you **measure** the population of a yeast culture over a period of seven days?

Materials (per group)

4 25-mL beakers
glass-marking pencil
40 mL molasses solution
4 mL yeast solution
2 pipettes
microscope slide
coverslip
microscope
graph paper

Procedure

1. **Use the glass-marking pencil to label each beaker with the following information: group name and beaker number (1 through 4).**
2. **Add 10 mL of the molasses solution to each of the beakers.**
3. **Stir the yeast solution, then add 10 drops to each of the beakers.**
4. **Use a clean pipette to transfer 1 drop of solution from beaker 1 to a clean microscope slide. Cover with a coverslip.**
5. **Use the low-power objective to examine the slide under a microscope. Switch to high power. Use the fine adjustment to locate some yeast cells.**
6. **Count the number of yeast cells in the field of view. Each bud counts as a single yeast cell. Record your number in a data table similar to the one shown.**
7. **Repeat step 6 three more times. Calculate an average of the four counts. This is the average population of yeast in the culture.**

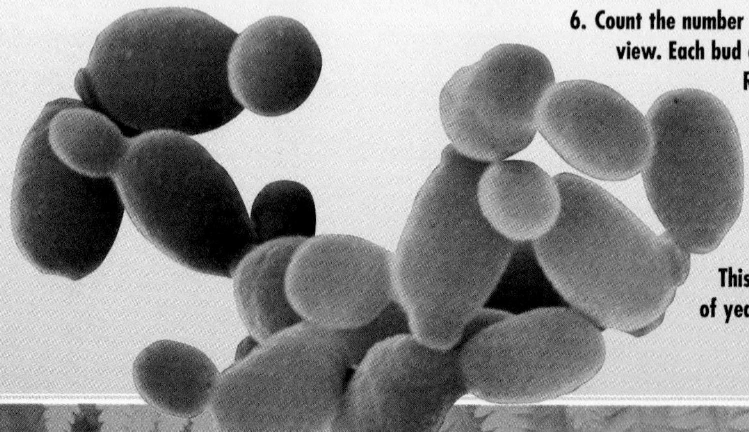

Safety Tips

Students should wear aprons and safety goggles. Caution students to be careful when using glassware and handling microscope slides as glass can break easily and cut students. Students should always handle the microsope with extreme care.

DATA TABLE

Populations	Day 1	Day 3	Day 5	Day 7
	Beaker 1	Beaker 2	Beaker 3	Beaker 4
View 1				
View 2				
View 3				
View 4				
Average				

8. Store beakers 2, 3, and 4 in a dark, warm area where they can remain undisturbed for seven days.

9. On the third day, repeat steps 4 through 7 using beaker 2.

10. On the fifth day, repeat steps 4 through 7 using beaker 3.

11. On the seventh day, repeat steps 4 through 7 using beaker 4.

Observations

1. Use the graph paper to construct a graph representing the population growth of the yeast culture by plotting time horizontally and average population vertically.
2. Using your graph, identify the period of time when the population of yeast increased. Did the yeast population ever decrease?
3. Summarize the population density of the yeast over the seven-day period.
4. Predict what might happen to the yeast population after another two days.

Analysis and Conclusions

1. Identify and label the stages of growth on your graph.
2. What kind of growth does the yeast population follow?
3. Why does the population density of yeast in this culture change over time?

More to Explore

Design your own experiment to determine the effect of light on the growth of a yeast population.

Answers to Observations

1. Groups' average yeast populations may vary. The graph should show a population increase through day 3, a stable population on day 5, and a population decrease through day 7.
2. Increase from days 1 through 3; decrease from days 5 through 7.
3. The population density increased for the first three days, then leveled off, and then decreased.
4. The population will decrease further.

Answers to Analysis and Conclusions

1. Days 1–3: positive growth, or exponential growth. Days 3–5: zero growth. Days 5–7: negative growth.
2. Growth with limits.
3. At first, food is abundant and the yeast organisms are not crowded, so population increases. When the population size reaches the carrying capacity of the containers, the population levels off. As the food supply is depleted and wastes accumulate, the crowded organisms begin to die, and the population declines.

More to Explore

Students' experimental designs may vary, but all should involve changing only the light conditions for each beaker (the manipulated variable) and holding all other variables constant for all four beakers. Check each group's experimental design beforehand to make sure that such is the case. Also make sure each group writes up its experiment—stating the problem, the procedure to be followed, observations, and conclusions—and designs a table for recording results. In a follow-up class discussion, let groups share their experimental designs, observations, and conclusions, with their results presented in graph form.

Teaching Strategies

1. You may need to demonstrate the use of a pipette, particularly how to control the number of drops released.
2. Stress the importance of putting the same amount of yeast solution in all four beakers. If students accidentally put too many drops in any of the beakers, let them discard the beaker contents and try again.
3. When students use the microscope, have them compare what they see on their slides with the photograph of budding yeast on page 326. Explain that they should not expect to see such high magnification with their own slides, since the photograph was taken with a type of microscope that is much more powerful than the microscope they are using. They will, however, be able to discern individual yeast cells and buds.

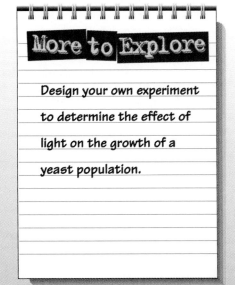

CHAPTER 14

Study Guide

Review Strategy

Have students work in groups of two to four. Divide the first three sections of the chapter (or all four sections, if you presented the Branching Out section) into as many parts as there are groups. Begin a chapter concept map on a large sheet of blank newsprint attached to the bulletin board or chalkboard. Beginning with the first assigned part of Section 14–1 and continuing through the chapter, have each group in turn add to the map the concepts and linkages covered in its assigned part of the chapter. When all groups have made their entries, review the completed concept map with the entire class, and ask students to make any changes they think are needed in order to incorporate all of the chapter's major ideas.

Study Guide

Summarizing Key Concepts

The key concepts in each section of this chapter are listed below to help you review the chapter content. Make sure you understand each concept and its relationship to other concepts and to the theme of the chapter.

14–1 Populations and How They Grow

- A population is a group of organisms of a single species that live in a given area.
- Given ideal conditions, a population will grow rapidly and without limits. This kind of growth is called exponential growth.
- In nature, most populations will grow exponentially for a short time and then level off at a steady state. The steady state represents the carrying capacity of the population.

14–2 Why Populations Stop Growing

- Population growth may be controlled by limiting factors—some that depend on population size and density and others that do not.
- Population-limiting factors that act more strongly on large, dense populations are called density-dependent limiting factors.
- Limiting factors that act on a population regardless of its size and density are called density-independent limiting factors.

14–3 Human Population Growth

- Human population has been steadily increasing since the beginning of time. The human population is now growing exponentially.
- Humans, unlike other organisms, have the ability to alter the carrying capacity of the environment in which they live.
- The demographic transition is a change in growth rate from a high birth rate and death rate to a low birth rate and death rate.

14–4 Population Growth and Carrying Capacity

- Most people in the world live in countries that have not yet completed the demographic transition. Therefore, the population continues to grow.
- An age-structure diagram is a graphic illustration of the distribution of males and females in a country according to age.

Reviewing Key Terms

Review the following vocabulary terms and their meaning. Then use each term in a complete sentence.

14–1 Populations and How They Grow
population
growth rate
exponential growth
zero population growth
carrying capacity

14–2 Why Populations Stop Growing
density-dependent limiting factor
parasite
density-independent limiting factor

14–3 Human Population Growth
demographic transition

14–4 Population Growth and Carrying Capacity
age-structure diagram

Inquiry-Based Strategy

Provide each group with three or four fruit fly cultures, and have each group design and conduct an experiment to answer a question about fruit fly population growth. If students have difficulty thinking of questions, suggest the following:

- **How long will it take for the population size to reach the container's carrying capacity?**
- **What effect do different light conditions have on the population's growth?**
- **What effect does temperature have on the population's growth?** (Caution students not to cool the flies so much that they become inactive.)

Explain that the easiest way to count the flies is to immobilize them by putting the vials in a freezer for one to two minutes and then shake the flies onto a piece of paper. If they become active again during counting, students should brush them back into the vial and recool them.

Recalling Main Ideas

Choose the letter of the answer that best completes the statement or that answers the question.

1. A population that has a death rate greater than its birth rate is said to be
   a. increasing. **c.** growing exponentially.
   b. decreasing. **d.** staying the same.

2. A growth curve characterized by a population that starts growing slowly and then increases rapidly before leveling off is a(an)
   a. boom-and-bust curve.
   b. exponential curve.
   c. growth-with-limits curve.
   d. age-structure curve.

3. In most situations, predators and their prey
   a. destroy each other.
   b. coexist over a long time.
   c. cannot coexist.
   d. compete for the same limited resources.

4. About 500 years ago, the human population
   a. began to grow slowly.
   b. began to grow exponentially.
   c. reached carrying capacity.
   d. reached zero population growth.

5. A group of organisms of a single species that live in a given area is called a
   a. community. **c.** food web.
   b. niche. **d.** population.

6. Density-dependent limiting factors act most strongly on which populations?
   a. dense **c.** large
   b. small **d.** scattered

7. The world's human population is currently in which phase?
   a. zero population growth
   b. slow population growth
   c. rapid population growth
   d. carrying capacity

8. In the second stage of the demographic transition,
   a. birth rate is high and death rate is high.
   b. birth rate is high and death rate is low.
   c. birth rate is low and death rate is high.
   d. birth rate is low and death rate is low.

Putting It All Together

Using the information on pages xxx–xxxi, complete the following concept map.

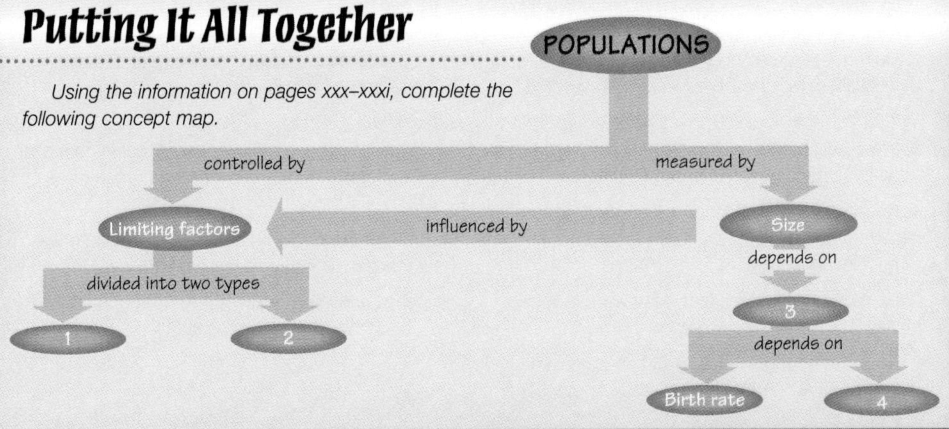

Recalling Main Ideas

1. b
2. c
3. b
4. b
5. d
6. a
7. c
8. b

Assessment

Reviewing What You Learned

1. Accept all answers that identify a population—a group of organisms of a single species that live in a given area.
2. The major factors are birth rate and death rate.
3. Carrying capacity is the largest number of individuals that can survive over long periods of time in a given environment.
4. When a population gets larger than its carrying capacity, either its birth rate falls or its death rate rises.
5. Competition, predation, parasitism, crowding, and stress are examples of density-dependent limiting factors.
6. Competition can lower birth rates, increase death rates, or both.
7. A parasite is an organism that takes nourishment from its host.
8. Density-dependent limiting factors are competition, predation, parasitism, crowding, and stress. Density-independent factors are weather, fires, droughts, floods, hurricanes, and human activities.

Skills Trace
Comparing
- Focus p. 325
- Practice p. 325
- Assess p. 330

9. Weather can destroy an entire population in a short amount of time.

Putting It All Together

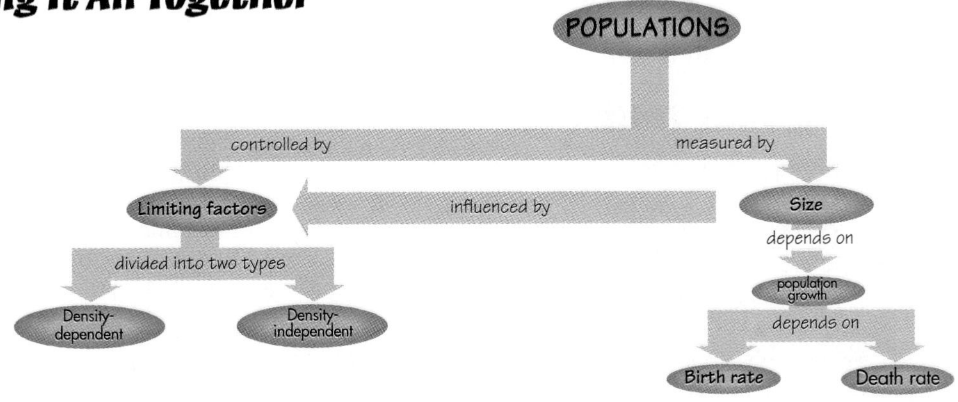

Assessment (continued)

10. The demographic transition is a change in growth rate resulting from changes in birth rate.
11. An age structure diagram shows the percentage of the population of individuals within 5-year age groups.
12. A demographer studies population growth.
13. The baby boomers are people who were born in the period just after World War II.

Expanding the Concepts

1. Populations of organisms at higher trophic levels may decrease due to food shortages. Those at lower levels may increase due to less predation.
2. Competition for resources, predation, parasitism, crowding/stress, weather, and human activities influence exponential growth in a typical deer population.
3. Accept all reasonable answers that involve a density-dependent limiting factor: competition, predation (uncommon with humans today), parasitism, and crowding/stress.
4. If parasites killed their hosts too quickly, they would have to find other hosts or they too would die.
5. Hormonal changes can upset animals' behavior so they neglect, kill, or even eat their own offspring.
6. Accept all answers that involve a density-independent limiting factor: weather, fire, drought, flood, or human activities.

Skills Trace
Modeling
- Focus p. 313
- Practice p. 314
- Assess p. 330

7. Improvements in living conditions have resulted in an increase in the birth rate and a decrease in the death rate of the human population, causing exponential growth.
8. Human growth rates must be understood because the biosphere has limited resources.
9. Human activity affects the Earth's ability to provide the essentials of life, such as food, water, air, land, shelter, and minerals.

Extending Your Thinking

1. Answers will vary. Modern medicine has had the most direct effect on the density-dependent limiting factors of parasitism and crowding/stress and on the density-independent limiting factor of the effects of human activities.
2. Answers will vary. Population control in humans is more of a conscious decision than an effect of the density-dependent limiting factors of competition, predation, and parasitism that control deer populations.
3. Answers will vary. Initial research should focus on the pest's life cycle and on natural limiting factors in its native environment. If the researcher can find a means of interfering with the pest's life cycle—such as by introducing a host-specific parasite or disease—or can find a natural predator that is harmless to other organisms, then pesticides would not have to be used.

Assessment

Reviewing What You Learned

Answer each of the following in a complete sentence.

1. Define and identify a population in your community.
2. What major factors influence population growth rates?
3. What is meant by the carrying capacity of an environment?
4. What happens when a population gets larger than its carrying capacity?
5. What are five examples of density-dependent limiting factors?
6. How does competition help to maintain a stable population?
7. What is a parasite?
8. **Compare** the density-dependent and density-independent factors that influence a population.
9. Why is weather an important density-independent limiting factor for certain organisms under certain conditions?
10. What is the demographic transition?
11. What is an age-structure diagram?
12. What kind of work does a demographer do?
13. Who are the baby boomers?

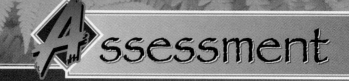

Expanding the Concepts

Discuss each of the following in a brief paragraph.

1. How does the removal of an organism in a food web affect the other organisms with which it interacts?
2. What factors influence exponential growth in a typical deer population in a natural forest?
3. Choose one of the density-dependent limiting factors and explain how it applies to human populations.
4. Parasites generally do not kill their host quickly. Why?
5. How can hormonal changes in an organism limit population growth?
6. **Construct a model** that illustrates the effect of one density-independent limiting factor on a plant population.
7. What have been the effects of improvements in living conditions on the birth and death rates of humans?
8. Why is it essential to understand human growth rates for the future of this planet?
9. Why can we not view the human population in isolation?

Extending Your Thinking

Use the skills you have developed in this chapter to answer the following.

1. **Drawing conclusions** Modern medicine has had a pronounced effect on both density-dependent and density-independent factors for humans. Explain how.
2. **Making judgments** What generally controls birth and death rates in humans? Are these factors similar to those that influence a deer population in a natural environment? Support your answer.
3. **Using the writing process** If you were the leader of a research group assigned to control a nonnative animal pest, what would be the focus of your initial research and why?
4. **Making predictions** You have observed the population growth curves of two different species of *Paramecia* in isolation. In identical environments, species *A* had a doubling time of 24 hours and species *B* had a doubling time of 18 hours. When placed together in a limited environment, what would you predict would happen to their growth rates?
5. **Drawing conclusions** In many isolated environments, such as the islands of Hawaii, most plant populations grew without predation from grazing animals. What would be the consequences of the introduction of sheep?

Applying Your Skills

What Goes Up Always Comes Down—Or Does It?

How do births and deaths in a population affect the population size? On a yearly basis, wildlife biologists collect information on certain animals that live in the wild. This information is used to help determine regulations to help control the size of the population through various management practices. You are going to collect some fictional data, graph your results, analyze the information, and then suggest future guidelines for this population.

1. Roll two dice. Each roll of the two dice is equal to one year's birth rate when multiplied by 1000. Record the birth rate. Roll the dice a total of ten times, recording the birth rate each time.
2. Repeat step 1. This time, however, the number represents the death rate.
3. Calculate the growth rate for each of the 10 years. Record this information.
4. Construct a graph that shows the growth rate over a 10-year period. The population size began at 100,000. (This is the carrying capacity.)
5. Graph the growth rate for 10 years.

• GOING FURTHER •

6. Analyze your data. Based on your population size after 10 years, write a paragraph on the future management of the population.

Applying Your Skills

Preparation

Find out if changes in the population of any animal species in your geographical area are a matter for concern. Gather data and material that can help students address the management of the populations of organisms.

Suggestion

Ask students how their randomly generated data could differ from real-world data.

Scoring Rubric

4 Response is thorough, accurate, and creative; shows an in-depth understanding of science skills, procedures, and concepts.

3 Response is complete, mostly accurate, and original; shows a satisfactory understanding of science skills, procedures, and concepts.

2 Response is mostly complete but includes some inaccuracies; shows an adequate understanding of science skills, procedures, and concepts.

1 Response is only partially complete and has many inaccuracies; shows an incomplete understanding of science skills, procedures, and concepts.

0 Response is mostly incomplete and/or inaccurate; shows a lack of understanding of science skills, procedures, and concepts.

4. Some students may say that species A would be more successful and increase steadily because its population would take longer to reach the carrying capacity of the limited environment. Other students may say that species B, with a faster doubling time, would outcompete species A and show more rapid population growth. Accept either response, but students should realize that both populations would level off in time due to the environment's limitations.
5. Populations of plants that have developed no adaptations as protection against grazing animals would be greatly reduced, perhaps even eliminated.

Chapter 15 Our Living Planet

Content Management	Student Edition Activities
■ Section 15–1 Climate and Life, pp. 333–336 Climate Environments and Ecosystems	Laboratory Investigation: Greenhouse in a Bottle, pp. 352–353
■ Section 15–2 Environments and Life, pp. 337–340 Life Affects Environments Changes in Ecosystems	MINI LAB: Successful Succession?, p. 339
■ Section 15–3 Earth's Biomes, pp. 341–345 What Is a Biome? Terrestrial and Aquatic Biomes	MINI LAB: Do Leaves Have Waxy Skin?, p. 345
◆ BRANCHING OUT • In Depth Section 15–4 Climate: A Complex Story, pp. 346–351 What Causes Climate? The Climate Controversy	

■ These sections cover all the necessary content and concepts for a basic course in biology.
◆ This section covers content and concepts that are either applications or extensions of the basic material.

Integration Strategies

SE Physics, p. 347

Assessment Strategies

SE Chapter Review, pp. 354–357
TR Section Reviews
Chapter Test
BL Chapter Review
Practice Test
CTB Chapter 15 Test

Tech Prep

Teaching strategies appropriate for students who are in technical/vocational programs or who are considering post-secondary technical education can be found on **TE** page 333.

Meeting the Standards

Sections 15–1 through 15–4 cover four of the five content standards under **The Interdependence of Organisms** and two of the six content standards under **Matter, Energy, and Organization in Living Systems** as described on pages 186–187 of The National Science Education Standards.

Chapter Planning Guide

Teacher's Edition Activities	Other Activities	Media and Technology
Chapter Discovery Learning Activity, p. 332 **Inquiry Activity:** Identifying Microclimates, p. 335	**LM** Constructing Climographs, #29 **TR** **Apply:** Finding Your Niche **BL** **Inquiry Activity:** Holding in the Heat	**CD-ROM:** The Biosphere
Investigate: Long-Term Project, p. 338 **Investigate:** Model Building, p. 338	**TR** **Enrich:** Giants of the Forest **BL** **Inquiry Activity:** A Recipe for Succession	
Inquiry Activity: Identifying Types of Climate Regions, p. 341 **Investigate:** Model Building, p. 342 **Investigate:** Research, p. 343 **Investigate:** Cooperative Learning, p. 344	**LM** Observing Plant Adaptations, #30 **TR** **Writing in Biology:** On the Road **Apply:** The Tundra Next Door **BL** **Inquiry Activity:** Where in the World?	**BioVue Plus CD-ROMs:** Bringing Back the Prairie
Inquiry Activity: Mini-Habitat Climate Conditions, p. 346 **Inquiry Activity:** Testing Climate Changes, p. 347 **Activity:** Why Do Wind Patterns Curve?, p. 347 **Investigate:** Research, p. 348 **Investigate:** Role-Playing, p. 348 **Investigate:** Research, p. 349	**TR** **Explore:** Whirling Winds **BL** **Inquiry Activity:** Colorful Currents	**TB** What Causes Climate?, #20

KEY: SE Student Edition **TE** Teacher's Edition **LM** Laboratory Manual **TR** Teaching Resources **BL** BioLog **TB** Transparency Box **CTB** Computer Test Bank

Materials List

TE Chapter Discovery Learning Activity, p. 332 (1 hour); large outdoor area, metric tape measure, pencils, string, graph paper.

TE Investigate: Model Building, p. 338 (2 weeks); gravel, dishpan, soil, shallow dish, water, grass seeds, birdseeds.

SE MINI LAB: Successful Succession?, p. 339 (15 minutes for initial set-up, 5–10 minutes each day for follow-up pH testing, 30–45 minutes for final session); clear jar with cover, dried plant material, boiled pond water or sterile spring water, pH paper, microscope slides, pipette, microscope.

TE Inquiry Activity: Identifying Types of Climate Regions, p. 341 (30 minutes); photocopy of U.S. map that includes Alaska and Hawaii, marker, pencil and paper.

SE MINI LAB: Do Leaves Have Waxy Skin?, p. 345 (20 minutes for initial set-up, 15 minutes for follow-up observation and recording); 3 paper towels, water, waxed paper, paper clips, tray.

TE Inquiry Activity: Mini-Habitat Climate Conditions, p. 346 (20–30 minutes); mini-habitats from Unit Discovery Learning Activity, pp. 280–281.

TE Inquiry Activity: Testing Climate Changes, p. 347 (20–30 minutes for designing experiments, 1–2 weeks for conducting experiments, 45 minutes for reporting results); mini-habitats from Unit Discovery Learning Activity, pp. 280–281.

TE Activity: Why Do Wind Patterns Curve?, p. 347 (10 minutes); Earth globe on stand, washable markers.

CHAPTER 15

Our Living Planet

Introducing the Chapter

. . . In Pictures

The growth of this high-altitude evergreen has been distorted by strong prevailing winds from one direction. Have students examine the photograph, read the caption, and answer the following questions.

- **What has caused the tree to grow in a strange shape?** (Strong winds.)
- **Why do you think all the branches are growing in the same direction?** (The wind must blow primarily in one direction.)

Teaching Strategy

The first section of this chapter describes the influence of climate, biotic factors, and abiotic factors on organisms in ecosystems and habitats. Students learn about ecological succession and climax communities in the second section and about terrestrial and aquatic biomes in the third section. The BRANCHING OUT section at the end of the chapter describes the causes of climate conditions and discusses climate changes, the greenhouse effect, and global warming.

BIO JOURNAL

Before students begin, ask them what they think climate means. Make sure they understand the difference between climate (an area's typical long-term conditions) and weather (varying short-term conditions). Encourage students to question older family members and friends to get a sense of what the climate was like in your area 25, 50, or more years ago. Instruct students to keep their entries in their portfolios.

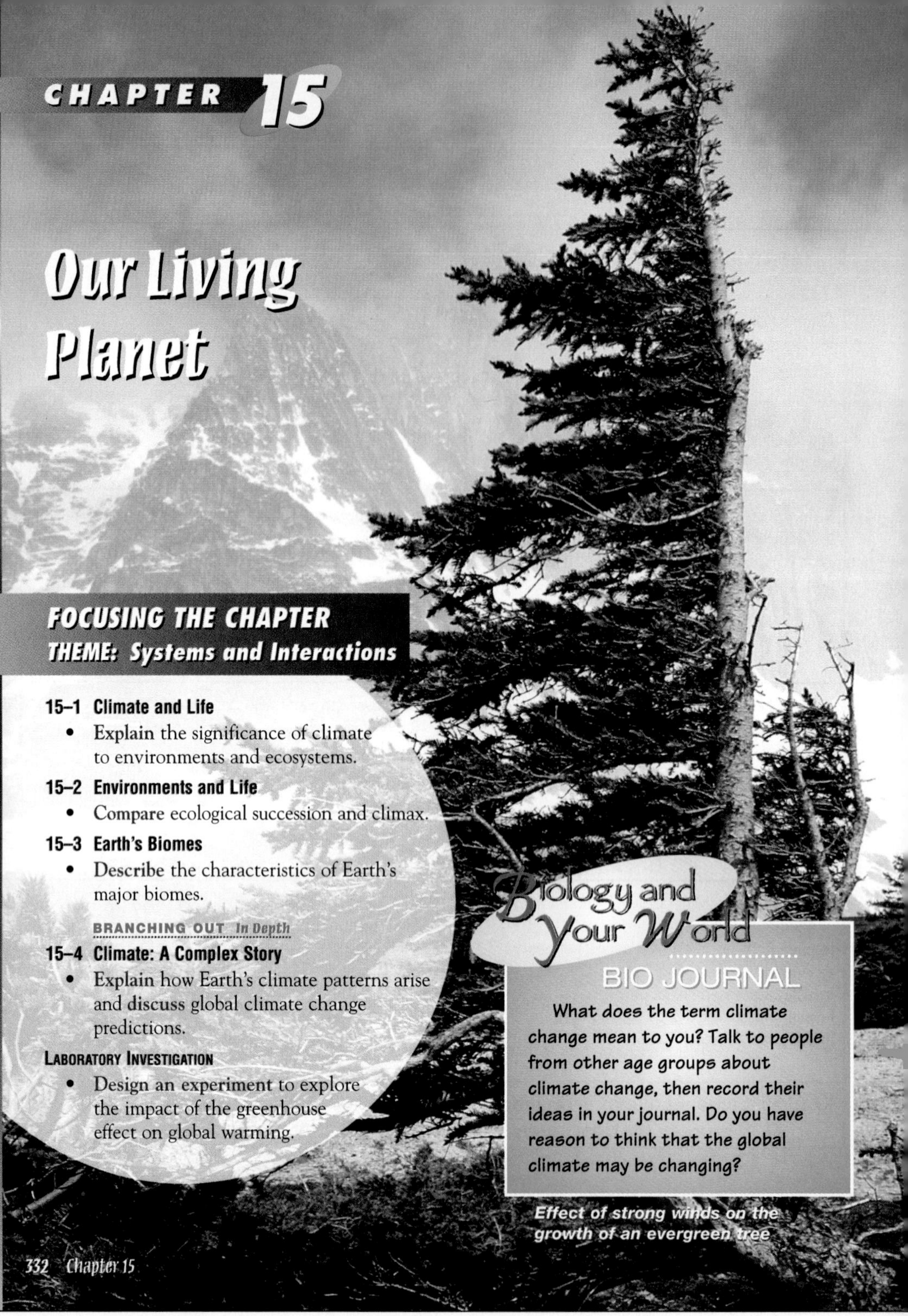

CHAPTER 15

Our Living Planet

FOCUSING THE CHAPTER
THEME: Systems and Interactions

15–1 Climate and Life
- **Explain** the significance of climate to environments and ecosystems.

15–2 Environments and Life
- **Compare** ecological succession and climax.

15–3 Earth's Biomes
- **Describe** the characteristics of Earth's major biomes.

BRANCHING OUT *In Depth*

15–4 Climate: A Complex Story
- **Explain** how Earth's climate patterns arise and discuss global climate change predictions.

LABORATORY INVESTIGATION
- **Design** an experiment to explore the impact of the greenhouse effect on global warming.

Biology and Your World

BIO JOURNAL

What does the term climate change mean to you? Talk to people from other age groups about climate change, then record their ideas in your journal. Do you have reason to think that the global climate may be changing?

Effect of strong winds on the growth of an evergreen tree

332 Chapter 15

TEACHER SUPPORT

Chapter Discovery Learning Activity

The following activity will give students an opportunity to observe and classify living (biotic) and nonliving (abiotic) factors in an ecosystem. Before students begin, select an outdoor area that is large enough for each group to mark off a 4m² section.

1. Measure a 2m x 2m square on the ground, drive pencils into the ground to mark the corners, and stretch string around the pencils. Then divide the large square into four 1m² squares (one for each student in the group).

2. On graph paper, roughly sketch everything you see in one small square; label the sketch with the names of the items.

Back in the classroom, have students name all the items they found and classify each as living/once-living or nonliving. If necessary, remind students to include air, sunlight, and subsurface water. Compile a class master chart with the items listed in two columns.

SECTION 15-1

Climate and Life

GUIDE FOR READING

- Explain the importance of climate to life.
- Define environment and ecosystem.

HAVE YOU EVER WONDERED *why banana trees cannot grow in Anchorage, Alaska, or why tulips and blueberries do not grow in Hilo, Hawaii? Thanks to tropical sunshine, plenty of rain, and frost-free temperatures, bananas do, of course, grow well on the island of Hawaii. Tulips and blueberries, on the other hand, grow well in Alaska, where they find the cold winters they need. Why do different parts of the world support different kinds of plants and animals?*

Climate

Different parts of the globe have different **climates.** Climate is the temperature range, the average annual precipitation (rain or snow), humidity, and the amount of sunshine that a region typically experiences. The climate of an area is a powerful factor in determining the types of living organisms that the area can support. **Populations of plants and animals grow, remain stable, or vanish, depending in part on climate conditions such as temperature and rainfall. These conditions also affect the structure of food webs and the flow of nutrients.**

Figure 15–1 (a) Conifers, (b) bananas, and (c) wheat naturally grow in parts of the world where climate conditions suit them best.

SECTION 15-1
Climate and Life

Performance Objectives

- Describe how climate conditions affect living things.
- Define the terms environment and ecosystem.

Laboratory Investigation Skill: Designing an experiment

1 ENGAGE

Ideas Through Images

Have students examine the photographs in Figure 15–1, read the caption, and answer the following questions.

- **What type of area is shown in photograph *a*?** (Snowy, cold; the winter season in a northern area.)
- **What type of area is shown in photograph c?** (A wheat field in a mild area, in summer or early fall.)
- **In what type of area do banana trees live?** (A tropical area. If students do not know, have them refer to the section's opening paragraph to find the answer.)
- **Do these three photographs show the same type of area or different areas? How can you tell?** (Different areas. The kinds of plants and the types of growing conditions are very different.)

TEACHER SUPPORT

Managing Classroom Diversity

TECH PREP STUDENTS

In conjunction with their study of climate, students who are considering careers in horticulture, nursery management, or landscaping could find out about the types of plants that do well in various climate zones.

Field guides used by landscape designers and nursery workers—and some planting guides intended for a general audience—include a map of climate zones to assist in the selection of appropriate plantings. Particularly good sources are *Taylor's Encyclopedia of Gardening* (1961) and the smaller, topic-specific field guides (*Perennials, Ground Covers, Shrubs,* and so forth) derived from the complete encyclopedia. Try to obtain copies of these books, as well as general-audience planting guides, for students to use in their research. If any students have designed planted areas, ask them to present their designs to the rest of the class and explain why they chose the particular plants they did.

Ancillary Support

The resource below can be used to support your teaching strategy for these two pages.

BL Inquiry Activity: Holding in the Heat

2 EXPLORE

Discussion

Introduce the concepts of biotic and abiotic factors by having students consider the mini-habitats they created in the Unit Discovery Learning Activity. Ask each group to make a two-column chart showing all the things included in its mini-habitat, with the columns labeled Living/Once-Living and Nonliving and each type of organism or material listed in the appropriate column. Remind students to include forms of energy (sunlight, heat) and nonsolid materials (air, water). Give each group an opportunity to present its chart to the rest of the class for comparison.

3 TEACH

Discussion

To review the concept of the greenhouse effect, remind students of their previous discussion (Section 13–5, pages 300–303) comparing the greenhouse effect to the interior of a car left in the sun with its windows closed. Point out the importance of the greenhouse effect to living organisms on Earth in regulating Earth's temperatures. Without this effect, the average surface temperature of Earth would be about 33°C lower.

Laboratory Investigation

The Laboratory Investigation, Greenhouse in a Bottle, on pages 352–353 is appropriate to use at this point in the chapter.

What gives rise to a region's climate? The sun's energy, as it interacts with Earth's air, water, and land, causes global climate patterns. You will see that these global climate patterns, in turn, shape all life on Earth.

Earth's Thermostat

Earth is the only planet in the solar system that has temperatures that are acceptable to life as we know it, day in and day out, throughout the year. This is because the Earth's atmosphere serves as a natural thermostat. Carbon dioxide, water vapor, and a few other gases in the atmosphere allow solar energy to reach the Earth's surface, where it is absorbed and later converted into heat. These gases, however, do not allow the heat energy to leave the Earth quite as readily, keeping the heat energy trapped inside for a period of time. This natural function of the atmosphere is called the **greenhouse effect.**

☑ *Checkpoint* What is the greenhouse effect? ❶

Figure 15–2
This diagram shows examples of different microclimates within a temperate forest.

Earth's Climate Zones

Interactions between solar energy and the atmosphere are responsible for much more than the Earth's temperature. Solar energy is what powers global winds and ocean currents, which give rise to the variety of climate zones on the Earth.

For instance, tropical regions are much warmer than temperate regions, which are warmer than polar regions. Rainfall patterns arise in large part due to the interaction of prevailing winds, ocean currents, and landmasses.

How Climate Varies

Climate and its effects are often quite complicated. Locations that are hundreds of kilometers apart can have similar climates. For example, gardeners know that some plants that can grow in Mississippi and Louisiana can also be grown along the coastline of Oregon and Washington. And certain areas of central Alabama and Georgia can occasionally get as cold in winter as some of the islands off the coast of Alaska.

On the other hand, some locations that are quite close to one another can have dramatically different climates. In Hawaii, orchid and banana plants can grow just kilometers from the snow-covered Mauna Loa volcano. Parts of California's northern coast have lush redwood forest growth, yet areas a short distance inland are desertlike.

Climate also can vary on a much smaller scale. If you look closely at tree trunks in a North

TEACHER SUPPORT

Facts and Figures

Earth's moderate temperature range (–70°C to +55°C), oxygen/nitrogen-based atmosphere, and abundance of water make it unique in the solar system in its ability to support life as we know it. Encourage students to research temperatures on the other eight planets (see list) and compare them with temperatures on Earth. (*Note*: Surface temperatures are given for Mercury, Venus, and Mars; temperatures at cloud tops for the remaining planets.)

Mercury: –180°C to +425°C
Venus: +465°C; Venus's carbon dioxide atmosphere produces an extreme greenhouse effect, making it the hottest planet in the solar system.
Mars: –120°C to +25°C
Jupiter: –150°C
Saturn: –180°C
Uranus: –210°C
Neptune: –210°C
Pluto: –220°C

Figure 15–3 *The biotic factors of an environment include all the organisms that live there. The abiotic factors are the pond and soil as well as factors such as humidity and sunlight, which are not easily shown in a drawing.*

American forest, you will find moss growing on their northern sides. And if you walk through a city in the Northern Hemisphere in early spring, you will see that trees growing in the sun next to south-facing buildings have leaves, but similar trees growing across the street won't put out leaves until several days later. Conditions such as these that vary over small distances are referred to as the **microclimate** for that location.

☑ *Checkpoint* What is microclimate? ②

Environments and Ecosystems

An environment is a combination of physical and biological factors that influence life. Physical environmental factors, called **abiotic factors,** are the area's climate, the type of soil and its acidity, and the availability of nutrients. Biological environmental factors, called **biotic factors,** include all the living things with which an organism might interact.

When you look carefully at an organism in its **environment,** it is often difficult to separate the biotic and the abiotic factors. This is because organisms in nature affect each other's environments. A tree growing in a forest shades the ground beneath it. By dropping leaves that decay, the tree contributes to the amount of moisture-holding material in the soil. In this case, are shade and moisture in the soil abiotic factors or biotic factors? They are abiotic factors that arise due to the biotic factors in the environment.

Ecosystem

If you ask an ecologist where a particular organism lives, he or she might say "on a Caribbean coral reef," "in a temperate beech-maple forest," or "in an Amazon rain forest." These answers can be thought of as the biological "street address" of an organism. Like your street address, a biological address tells you more than just where an organism lives.

Figure 15–4 *Too much or too little of an abiotic factor such as heat, light, and humidity can be difficult for an organism to tolerate, as shown in this graph.*

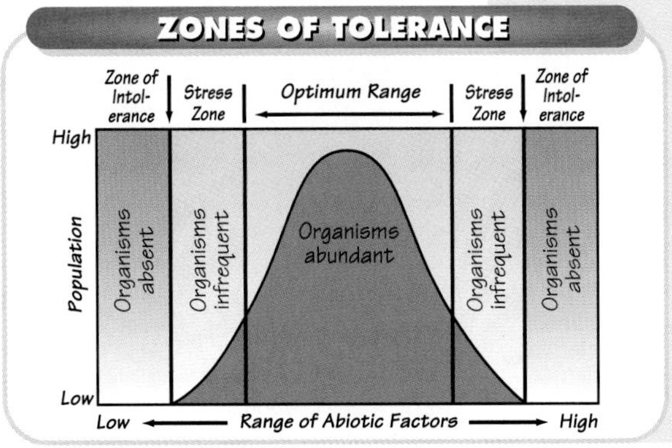

Inquiry Activity

Making Inferences

Identifying Microclimates
Ask students to look for microclimates on the school grounds, around their homes and neighborhoods, or in a nearby field, vacant lot, or park. In a follow-up discussion, have students describe the microclimates they observed and identify the factors they think are responsible for each one—for example, protection from north winds and increased exposure to sunlight on a south-facing embankment.

Ideas Through Images

Have students examine Figure 15–3, read the caption, and answer the following questions.

- **Are sunlight and air biotic or abiotic factors?** (Abiotic.)
- **What biotic factors might exist in this environment that you cannot see in the photograph?** (Accept all reasonable responses that refer to living organisms, including bacteria and other microscopic organisms, organisms living in the water or the soil, and so forth.)
- **What are some ways the abiotic and biotic factors affect each other in this environment?** (Accept all reasonable responses, including that animals remove oxygen from the air and add carbon dioxide to it during respiration, and that the acidity of the soil helps to determine what plants can grow there.)

Checkpoints

① The heat-trapping effect of carbon dioxide and other atmospheric gases.

② A microclimate consists of conditions that vary over small distances.

TEACHER SUPPORT

Managing Classroom Diversity

LEP STUDENTS/AT-RISK STUDENTS
You could use the following procedure to help students understand the terms biotic and abiotic. Write *bio* on the chalkboard. Ask students to list words that begin with *bio* and to write a definition of each term in their own words. Let students check their definitions against a dictionary and the glossary in this text, refine their definitions, and add any other terms they find to their lists. Discuss the terms and definitions with students as a group, emphasizing that *bio* means life or living thing.

Next, discuss common prefixes (*dis-*, *sub-*, *mis-*, *un-*, and so forth, making sure you include *a-* and *ab-*) and the meaning of each. Emphasize that the prefixes *a-* and *ab-* mean "not" or "opposite to," as in abnormal and asymmetrical.

When students clearly understand the meanings of *bio* and *a-*, write the terms biotic and abiotic on the board, and have students analyze the meanings of the terms.

Ancillary Support

The resource below can be used to support your teaching strategy for these two pages.

LM Constructing Climographs, #29

Correcting Misconceptions

Students sometimes have difficulty understanding what a niche is: the role an organism or species plays in an ecosystem. Use simple analogies to help develop this understanding. For example, each player on a baseball team has a specific niche: a different position to play. Ask students to suggest other analogies.

4 ASSESS

Quick Check

Using photographs of ecosystems that you have selected from other chapters of this text or from other sources, have students list the biotic and abiotic factors in other ecosystems besides the one included in this section.

Section Review 15-1

1. Climate is the temperature range, average precipitation, humidity, and amount of sunshine that a region experiences. Populations grow, remain stable, or vanish depending in part on climate conditions, which affect the structure of food webs.

2. Environment: a combination of physical and biological factors that influence life. Ecosystem: a collection of organisms interacting with each other and with their physical environment.

3. Biotic: all living things with which an organism might interact. Abiotic: physical environmental factors.

4. They would compete for the same resources, and the less successful species would die or move out.

Learning Modality

Visual Learning Write various biotic and abiotic factors on separate strips cut from index cards. Include the factors identified in the Chapter Discovery Learning Activity on page 332 and the Explore Discussion on page 334. Make two heading strips labeled Biotic and Abiotic. Have students arrange the factor strips below the appropriate headings.

Figure 15–5
(a) The scarlet macaw lives in the tropical rain forest of Central America, whereas (b) the black-tail prairie dog lives in the western grasslands of the United States.

It tells you the type of climate the organism is accustomed to and the kinds of neighbors it is likely to have. **In the natural world, a combination of biotic and abiotic factors is called an ecosystem.** An **ecosystem** is a collection of organisms—producers, consumers, and decomposers—interacting with each other and with their physical environment.

☑ ***Checkpoint*** What is an ecosystem? 1

Niche

An address by itself does not tell you a great deal about a person—for example, what the person does for a living or what her favorite foods are. In a similar way, knowing an organism's ecosystem in itself does not tell you everything about the organism. A description of an organism's **niche,** however, does. A niche is the full range of physical and biological conditions in which the organisms in a species can live and the way in which the organisms use those conditions.

The biotic factors of the niche identify other organisms that a species interacts with in any way. They include the plants that an animal rests on or makes a home in, the prey it eats, the predators it may encounter, and so on. Besides a description of what it eats, an animal's niche also includes information about when it eats and where and how it finds its food.

Habitat

Many fishes that live on coral reefs eat plankton, or tiny marine animals, that swim or drift in the ocean current. You might be tempted to say that all these fishes have the same niche. But some species feed only during the daytime, while others feed only at night, making for distinctly different niches. What the fishes do share, however, is the same **habitat.** Habitat simply indicates the type of surroundings in which a species lives and thrives—defined in terms of the plant community and the abiotic factors. Organisms that share the same habitat do not necessarily compete with one another if they have different niches.

Section Review 15-1

1. **Define** climate and **explain** its significance to living things.
2. **Define** environment and ecosystem.
3. **Compare** biotic and abiotic environmental factors.
4. **Critical Thinking—Predicting** What do you think will happen if two species with similar niches move into the same habitat?

TEACHER SUPPORT

Historical Perspective

Two species cannot coexist in a community if they occupy identical niches. When two species vie for the same resource—a process called interspecific competition—one population will most likely be eliminated. This principle was first postulated by Russian ecologist G.F. Gause in 1934.

In laboratory experiments, Gause studied the effect of interspecific competition on two closely related species of protists. When he cultured the two species separately, both populations grew rapidly and then leveled off at the culture's carrying capacity. When he cultured the two species together, however, one species apparently had a competitive edge in obtaining food, and the other species was driven to extinction in the culture.

Gause concluded that two species so similar that they compete for the same limited resources cannot coexist in the same place. His ideas, termed the competitive exclusion principle, were later confirmed.

Environments and Life

GUIDE FOR READING

- Explain ecological succession.
- Define climax community.

MINI LAB

- Observe ecological succession and a climax community.

EVER SINCE LIFE APPEARED ON this planet, organisms have been gradually changing the environments in which they live. Some organisms have had minor effects on ecosystems, and others have had profound effects on the entire planet.

You have seen how an environment's biotic and abiotic factors jointly determine and shape all life within it. Yet that is only part of what happens in the biosphere.

Life Affects Environments

Consider a forest or a grassland. Each of these is associated with a particular set of plants, shrubs, and trees that are most common to that ecosystem. Once these plants are established, they become part of the environment for all other plants and animals living in the area. For example, they offer food, nesting sites, and protection from the weather for the organisms that live there.

A remarkable example of organisms affecting the environment began nearly three billion years ago, when bacteria appeared that could photosynthesize in much the same way that plants do today. The bacteria released a dangerous toxic waste product that had never before been present in the atmosphere. This toxic waste product was oxygen. Of course, new forms of life eventually evolved aerobic respiration, which puts oxygen to good use. But that first global "pollution" changed the entire course of life on Earth.

Figure 15–6 (a) *The Whitsunday Islands are part of* (b) *the Great Barrier Reef, Australia. The Great Barrier Reef and the organisms it shelters, such as* (c) *the fish shown here, are an example of the interdependence between living things and their environment.*

SECTION 15-2
Environments and Life

Performance Objective

- Explain how the process of ecological succession eventually culminates in a stable climax community.

Mini Lab Skill: Observing

1 ENGAGE

Ideas Through Images

Have students examine the photographs in Figure 15–6, read the caption, and answer the following questions.

- **What kind of material is a reef made of?** (Coral. If students do not know, have them turn back to Figure 13–1 on page 283 and reread its caption.)
- **What other kinds of animals besides fish would you expect to find living in a coral reef?** (Accept all reasonable responses.)
- **What do you think might be some examples of interdependence between living things and their environment in this coral reef?** (Accept all reasonable responses.)

☑ Checkpoint

1 A collection of organisms interacting with each other and their physical environment.

TEACHER SUPPORT

Background Information

Photosynthetic bacteria dominated the Earth's shallow seas for nearly 2 billion years. Their populations formed large mats in which sediments collected. These mats slowly accumulated on top of one another, creating structures called stromatolites. In Western Australia today, one can find stromatolites that formed between 2000 and 1000 years ago in shallow seawater. Calcium deposits preserved their structure.

One group of photosynthetic bacteria are the cyanobacteria, common in lakes, ponds, and tropical oceans, where they undergo population explosions called blooms. Blooms of a reddish species give the Red Sea its name and, with other microorganisms, often tint the Gulf of California. Blooms in lakes usually indicate polluted water conditions, such as an overabundance of wastes from agricultural runoff. The molecular processes in cyanobacteria today are likely similar to those that introduced oxygen to Earth's atmosphere.

Ancillary Support

The resource below can be used to support your teaching strategy for these two pages.

TR Apply: Finding Your Niche

2 EXPLORE

Investigate

Long-Term Project Take the class to an area that exemplifies an ecosystem undergoing change—for example, a wood lot where all the trees were recently cut down, an abandoned field or garden, or a vacant lot where a building was recently torn down. Ask students to describe the changes they would expect to see over time if the area were left undisturbed. Encourage students to return to the area periodically to observe the actual changes and compare them with their predictions.

3 TEACH

Investigate

Model Building The following activity models the stages of succession shown in Figure 15–8.

1. Put a 1-inch layer of gravel in the bottom of a dishpan and cover it with about 4 inches of soil.
2. Create a pond by sinking a shallow dish in the soil so its top is even with the soil surface. Put about ½ inch of soil in the bottom of the pond.
3. Slowly pour water into the dishpan until the pond is completely full and the soil surrounding it is wet.
4. Sprinkle a handful of grass seed over the entire dishpan.
5. Leave the dishpan on a table near a sunny window and observe it regularly.
6. Every 3 to 4 days, sprinkle grass seed over the dishpan again. Lightly water the soil to keep it damp, but do not refill the pond or clean it out. (Due to evaporation of the water in it and buildup of dead material at its bottom, the pond will become shallower and will eventually fill in with growing grass.)
7. When the pond has filled in, sprinkle a handful of mixed birdseed over the dishpan once a week for two weeks. (The birdseed plants will be larger than the grass plants, representing the gradual invasion of shrubs and trees and the succession from a meadow to a forest.)

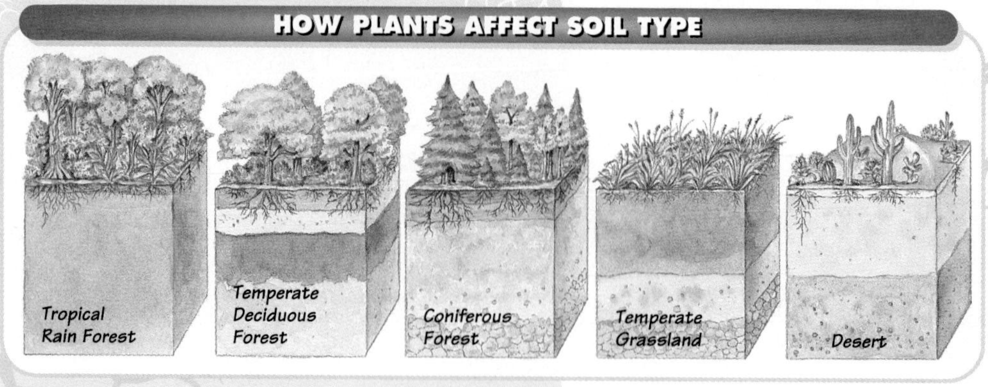

Figure 15–7
Plants affect the soil upon which they grow. Along with different patterns of rainfall, plants produce different types of soils in various ecosystems.

As you can see, the biotic and the abiotic factors of an environment continually interact with and affect each other. These interactions as well as their capacity to change ecosystems usually operate slowly, over a very long time scale. As you read ahead, you will discover that ecosystems respond to change by undergoing more changes!

Changes in Ecosystems

On the time scale of a human life, most ecosystems seem stable. But because organisms alter their surroundings, many ecosystems are constantly changing. As an ecological system changes, older inhabitants gradually die out and new plants and animals move in, causing further changes in the ecosystem.

Ecological Succession

Rakata Island in Indonesia was created by a violent volcanic eruption that destroyed the larger island of Krakatau (Krakatoa) in 1883. At first, only the hardiest of organisms—mosses, fungi, and a few tough grasses—were able to survive on the newly cooled lava rock. Over time, these organisms caused the

Figure 15–8
This series of diagrams illustrates how ecological succession gradually changes a pond into dry land covered with a forest.

TEACHER SUPPORT

Background Information

Many biologists once believed that succession in a particular type of ecosystem was invariable. That is, if a given ecosystem were disturbed, its successionary path would always follow the same route through the same types of transitional communities and would culminate in the same type of climax community. We now know that this is not true in all cases.

As a result of an area's precise location, climate, and other factors, the process of succession may take different paths. Depending on the area's specific conditions, the new succession may or may not go through all the same stages again and may not even produce the same climax community.

The classic example of succession in abandoned fields is based on studies of former agricultural land in parts of the United States where soil types and climates support recovery. Unfortunately, those conditions do not hold true of many other ecosystems throughout the world, including tropical areas.

rock to break down, producing a thin layer of soil. Further changes took place in the soil, enabling other types of plants to survive and grow. As the plant community grew and changed the soil, trees appeared. Soon animals that flew, swam, or drifted in from the nearby islands of Java and Sumatra made a home on Rakata. In less than 100 years, the new volcanic island was transformed into a tropical rain forest. This process, known as **ecological succession,** often occurs in natural environments for physical as well as biological reasons. **Ecological succession is the process by which an existing ecosystem is gradually and progressively replaced by another ecosystem.**

Ecological succession can also occur when human activities disturb an area. If a cleared field is left abandoned, grasses, wildflowers, and field animals move in. Over time, the seeds of bushes and small trees sprout. As these taller plants mature, birds and small mammals move into the area. Over many years—if soil and climate conditions are favorable—the field may become a forest.

☑ *Checkpoint* What is the process of ecological succession? ①

Climax Community

Ecological succession proceeds until a relatively stable state is reached in the interaction between organisms and their environment. **The relatively stable collection of plants and animals that results when an ecosystem reaches such a state is called a climax community.**

To say that a **climax community** is stable does not mean that it never changes. On the contrary, fires, floods, or winds may destroy large areas of climax communities on land. Similarly, tsunamis, which are mistakenly called tidal waves, and hurricanes can destroy marine climax communities. When a small area within a larger ecosystem disappears because of any of these disasters, ecological succession begins and continues along toward a climax. It is interesting to note that most climax communities are not uniform over large areas. Rather, they are similar to a patchwork quilt and consist of different areas in different stages of ecological succession.

MINI LAB ········ Observing

Successful Succession?

PROBLEM *How can you **observe** ecological succession and a climax community?*

PROCEDURE

1. Obtain a clean jar with a cover and place a handful of dried plant material into the jar.
2. Fill the jar with boiled pond water or sterile spring water. Determine the initial pH of the water with pH paper.
3. Cover the jar and place it in an area that receives indirect light.
4. Examine the jar every day for the next few days. Test and record the pH each day.
5. When the jar appears cloudy, prepare microscope slides of water from various levels of the jar. Use a pipette to collect the samples.
6. View the slides under the low-power objective of a microscope and record your observations.

ANALYZE AND CONCLUDE

1. Why did you use boiled or sterile water?
2. Where did the organisms you saw come from?
3. Did the pH of the water change?
4. Was ecological succession occurring? Give evidence to support your answer.
5. Did your community reach a stable, or climax, condition?

MINI LAB Observing

Teacher Notes
- For time required and materials needed, see page 332b.
- Check to make sure students know how to prepare microscope slides correctly.

Answers to Analyze and Conclude
1. To make sure there were no organisms already in the water.
2. The dried plant material.
3. Yes; it became more acid.
4. Yes; bacteria grew initially, followed by protists.
5. After several weeks, the cultures should reach a stable condition.

Skills Trace
Observing
- Focus p. 339
- Practice p. 340
- Assess p. 356

Discussion

After students learn about succession, have them look back at the Connections feature about wetlands on page 285 in Chapter 13. Point out that restoring former wetlands to their original condition is the reverse of the succession stages shown in Figure 15–8. Emphasize that this figure illustrates natural succession, whereas the wetland destruction described in the Connections feature was caused by human activity.

☑ **Checkpoint**

① The process by which an ecosystem is replaced by another ecosytem.

TEACHER SUPPORT

Ecology Note

Human activity has destroyed climax communities worldwide. Logging, oil drilling, agriculture, mining, road construction, and ranching all contribute to destruction of tropical rain forests. Some countries have placed strict controls on the use of their forests, but the damage has already been done. In many areas, soil erosion is already so severe that the land can no longer support tall trees. Even where conditions are favorable, regrowth of the climax community is a very slow process.

The effects of deforestation are worse in hilly areas. Without trees to anchor the soil, rain washes soil from the hillsides, leaving steep-sided gullies. Soil is washed into rivers, carried downstream, and deposited, choking irrigation channels and smothering fields.

In temperate regions, large areas of deciduous forest have been replanted with quick-growing conifers to provide a renewable source of lumber. Conifers turn the soil acidic and can harm drainage patterns.

Ancillary Support

The resource below can be used to support your teaching strategy for these two pages.

BL Inquiry Activity: A Recipe for Succession

4 ASSESS

Quick Check

Have students select one example of ecological succession—either one described in the student text or one of their own choice—and describe the sequence of changes that the ecosystem would undergo.

Section Review 15–2

1. The process by which an existing ecosystem is gradually and progressively replaced by another ecosystem.
2. The collection of plants and animals that results when an ecosystem proceeds through ecological succession to a relatively stable state.
3. Fires, floods, winds, tsunamis, hurricanes, droughts, and other natural disasters. Students may also mention human activities.
4. Lichens, mosses, weeds and grasses, shrubs, birch and pine.
5. By beginning with sterile water and dried plant material, succession could be observed from the initial growth of bacteria through a climax community containing protists.

Skills Trace
Observing
- Focus p. 339
- Practice p. 340
- Assess p. 356

Learning Modality

Auditory Learning Ask a volunteer to tape-record the definition of ecological succession on page 339 of the student text, the caption for Figure 15–8, and a brief description of each stage of succession shown in the figure. Let students use the recording in conjunction with the figure to study succession.

Figure 15–9 (a) *The temperate forest in Nova Scotia, Canada, and* (b) *the lowland rain forest in Borneo, Indonesia, are examples of climax communities.* (c) *A climax community damaged by a fire—such as this one in Yellowstone National Park—begins to recover by the gradual process of ecological succession.*

Don't think of natural disasters such as fire and drought as necessarily bad or harmful to a community. Some climax communities and the species that live in them are dependent on such catastrophes. The seeds of some plants—such as jack pines—will not sprout unless exposed to the heat of a fire. Other plants need the heat of a fire to make certain nutrients in the soil available to them.

Consider one final observation about ecological succession. Why does it occur slowly? Remember that ecological succession occurs because living things modify their environment. With the exception of humans, organisms usually modify their environment a little at a time, so ecosystem change is gradual. But what about situations in which human impact causes a more substantial change in the environment? Might this lead to an ecological upset or an ecological collapse and not ecological succession? These are questions that ecologists are trying to answer.

Section Review 15–2

1. **Explain** what is meant by ecological succession.
2. **Define** climax community.
3. **List** some ways in which climax communities can be disturbed.
4. **Critical Thinking—Sequencing** Arrange the following organisms according to their appearance in a process of ecological succession on a rock: mosses, shrubs, weeds and grasses, birch and pine, lichens.
5. **MINI LAB** How were you able to **observe** ecological succession and a climax community?

TEACHER SUPPORT

Ecology Note

For many years, the National Park Service's policy in Yellowstone Park was to put out all fires. But in 1972, park officials were given discretion in handling fires ignited by natural causes. Fires were not extinguished unless they threatened life or property.

This new policy recognized that fires can perform a vital role in ecosystems. Fires promote regrowth of diverse plant life of different ages, which in turn supports diverse animal life. The lodgepole pine, common in Yellowstone, produces some cones that open only when heated. Fires also clear out deadfall and other fuels periodically.

Unfortunately, the old policy's 90-year reign in Yellowstone had already produced a vast accumulation of deadwood and huge stands of closely spaced, insect-infested trees—an enormous fuel supply. In the summer of 1988, eight huge fires swept through nearly half the park's 2.2 million acres—45 times the acreage burned in any other recorded year.

Earth's Biomes

SECTION 15-3

GUIDE FOR READING

- **Define** biome.
- **List** and **describe** some terrestrial and aquatic biomes.

MINI LAB

- **Predict** how leaves control the amount of water lost to the environment.

NOW YOU ARE READY TO answer the question posed in the first section of this chapter: Why don't bananas grow in Alaska and why can't blueberries grow in Hawaii? Each of these plants is adapted to and therefore thrives in a particular ecosystem—bananas are unique to a hot and wet tropical ecosystem, whereas blueberries are unique to a cooler, less wet ecosystem. Thus, bananas also grow well in Central America and Indonesia, where there are tropical rain forests.

What Is a Biome?

Earth's diverse living organisms inhabit a wide range of ecosystems. The type of ecosystem in a particular part of the world depends primarily on the climate conditions of the region. For the sake of convenience, biologists often refer to the world's major ecosystems by the name of their most common climax communities. **Ecosystems identified by their climax communities are called biomes.**

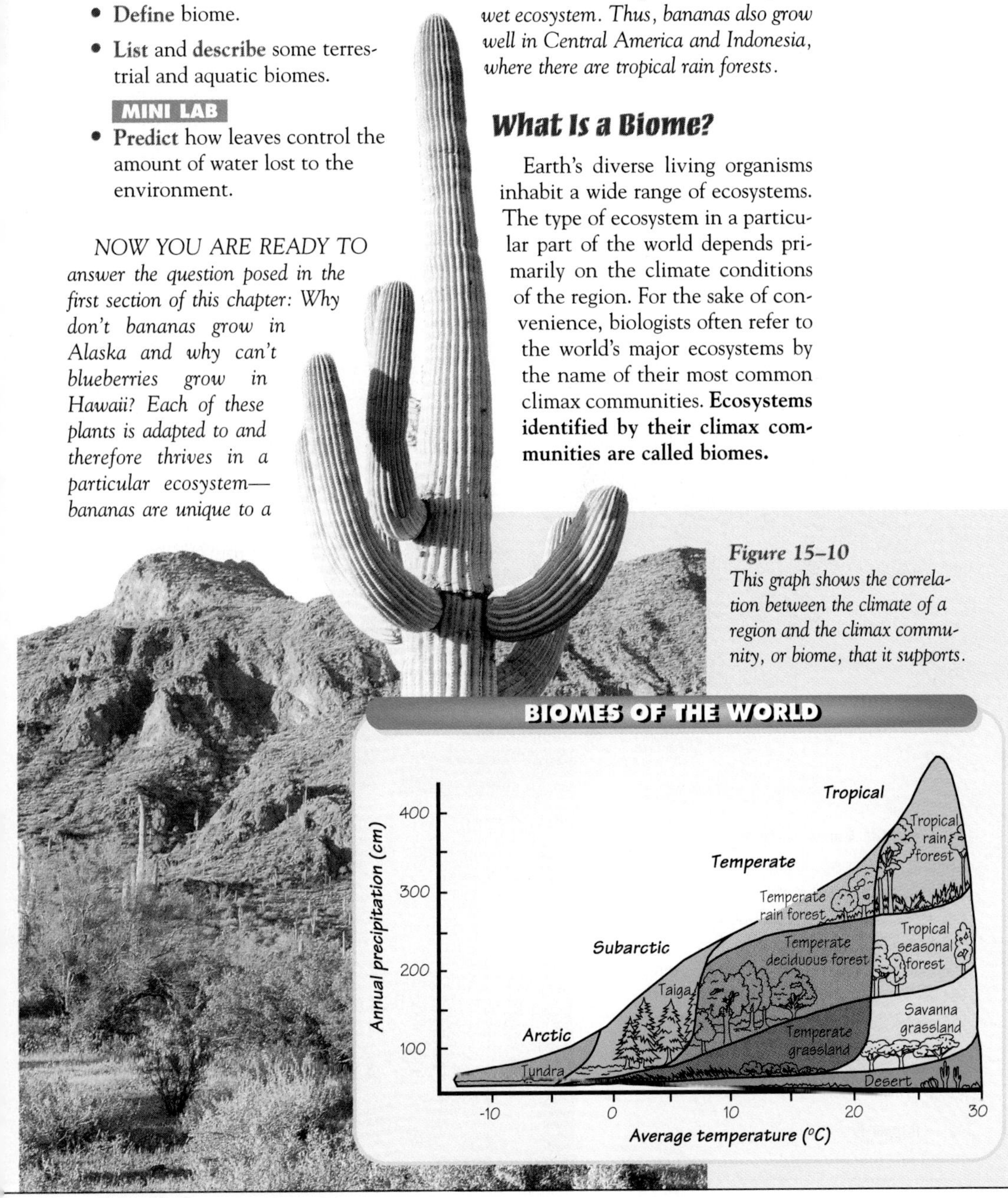

Figure 15–10 This graph shows the correlation between the climate of a region and the climax community, or biome, that it supports.

Managing Classroom Diversity

MULTICULTURAL STRATEGY

The indigenous peoples of the present United States, including Alaska and Hawaii, have inhabited all major biomes, adapting to and making use of the biotic and abiotic factors in their environment. Encourage students to research Native American cultures. Two useful sources of information are *The Encyclopedia of North American Indian Tribes* by Bill Yenne (1986) and *Atlas of the North American Indian* by Carl Waldman (1985).

You could make this a cooperative learning activity, with one group researching Hawaii and each of the other groups researching one of the geographic regions into which Native American groups are generally divided (Northeast, Southeast, Plains, Southwest, Great Basin, Plateau, California, Northwest Coast, Subarctic, and Arctic). Each group member might research a different tribe or culture. Have groups share their findings in class presentations.

SECTION 15-3
Earth's Biomes

Performance Objectives

- Define the term biome.
- Describe characteristics of terrestrial and aquatic biomes.

Mini Lab Skill: Predicting

1 ENGAGE

Inquiry Activity

Classifying

Identifying Types of Climate Regions

Ask students how many different types of climate regions they think there are in the United States, including Alaska and Hawaii. Give each group a copy of a U.S. map. Tell students to outline each climate region that they think has its own unique combination of climate conditions and to list the specific characteristics of each region.

Ideas Through Images

Have students examine Figure 15–10, read the caption, and answer the following questions.

- **Based on the graph, what type of biome has the highest average temperatures and the lowest average annual precipitation?** (Desert.)
- **What is the average temperature range of temperate biomes?** (From about 20°C to about 3°C.)
- **What is the range of annual precipitation that can be found in deserts?** (From about 80 cm to about 1 cm.)

Ancillary Support

The resources below can be used to support your teaching strategy for these two pages.

LM Observing Plant Adaptations, #30

TR Enrich: Giants of the Forest

2 EXPLORE

Investigate

Model Building The following activity models the function of hair, fur, and feathers in protecting animals against the cold—a vital adaptation for life in biomes with low temperatures.

1. Let a thermometer sit for 10 minutes so it shows room temperature.
2. Hold the thermometer in one hand with your thumb gently pressing against the bulb for 5 seconds. Observe and record the new temperature.
3. Submerge the same hand in a bowl of ice water for 5 seconds. Dry your hand with paper towels and immediately hold the thermometer for 5 seconds again with your thumb pressed against the bulb. Observe and record the new temperature.
4. Put on a wool glove and hold the thermometer for 5 seconds again.
5. Cover your gloved hand with a plastic bag and repeat step 3. (The glove acts as an insulator, keeping the hand's heat from being lost to the ice water.)

Discussion

Display photographs of animals and plants from each of the major terrestrial biomes. Ask students to guess where they think each animal and plant can be found. Have students make a list of each animal and plant. Ask students to match the animals with the plants and place them in their appropriate biome.

Visualizing Terrestrial Biomes

Biomes are the Earth's major types of ecosystems. Six terrestrial biomes are presented, along with a list of their main characteristics.

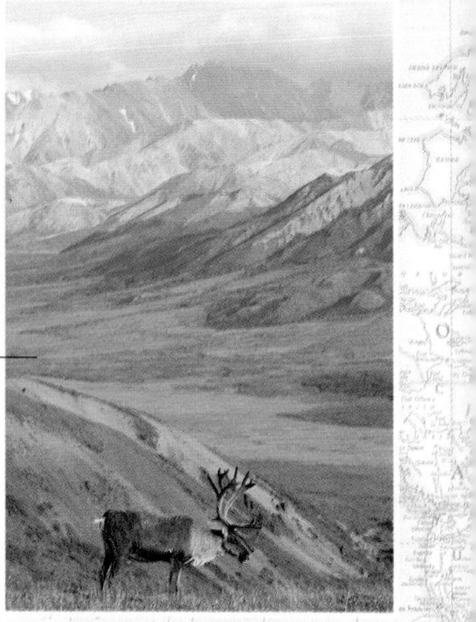

1 Tundra

ABIOTIC FACTORS: temperature range −40°C to 10°C, annual precipitation less than 25 cm, windy, permafrost (frozen ground)

BIOTIC FACTORS: vegetation—nearly treeless, mainly grasses, sedges, low flowering herbs and lichens; animals—arctic hare, lemming, arctic fox, musk ox, rock ptarmigan, snowy owl

6 Taiga

ABIOTIC FACTORS: temperature range −30°C to 20°C, annual precipitation 50 to 125 cm, soil thaws completely during summer

BIOTIC FACTORS: vegetation—coniferous trees, ferns, mosses, fungi (mushrooms); animals—snowshoe hare, timber wolf, shrew, lynx, weasel, black bear, woodchuck, woodpecker, chickadee, crossbill

5 Temperate Deciduous Forest

ABIOTIC FACTORS: temperature range −10°C to 25°C, annual precipitation 75 to 125 cm

BIOTIC FACTORS: vegetation—sugar maple, beech, yellow birch, pine, oak, shrubs, flowering plants, mosses, and ferns; animals—white-tailed deer, cottontail rabbit, gray squirrel, beaver, raccoon, opossum, woodpecker

TEACHER SUPPORT

Historical Perspective

Taiga Taiga once covered great stretches of the state of Michigan, but these coniferous forests were almost completely destroyed by logging. Today, visitors to Michigan can tour a living "taiga museum." On an estate surrounding a former logger-baron's home, visitors can see a preserved portion of the vast forests that once covered the entire region.

Temperate deciduous forests Our deciduous forests have also seen several major disturbances. Chestnut blight and Dutch elm disease, accidentally imported on infected plants and timber in the early 1900s, destroyed nearly all eastern American chestnut trees and millions of elms. Other species of trees have since taken their place, disrupting forest ecology. Today, the ravenous gypsy moth caterpillar is chewing its way through deciduous forests. Introduced to the United States from Europe, this caterpillar has no natural enemies here. Ecologists still do not know how this pest will affect our forests in years to come.

2 Tropical Rain Forest

ABIOTIC FACTORS: temperature range 20°C to 30°C, annual precipitation greater than 200 cm

BIOTIC FACTORS: vegetation—broad-leafed evergreen trees, ferns, tangled lianas; animals—monkey, colorful birds, flying squirrel, tapir, anteater, ocelot, jaguar, agouti, and armadillo

3 Desert

ABIOTIC FACTORS: average annual temperature is 10°C in cool deserts to 20°C in hot deserts, annual precipitation less than 25 cm

BIOTIC FACTORS: vegetation—brush, cacti, small plants; animals—road runner, jack rabbit, kit fox, lizard, scorpion

4 Grassland

ABIOTIC FACTORS: temperature range −10°C to 25°C, but daily fluctuations more extreme than deciduous forest, annual precipitation 25 to 75 cm

BIOTIC FACTORS: vegetation—various grasses, small plants, mosses, and lichens; animals—large grazing herbivores such as bison and antelope in North America, zebra, wildebeest, elephant, and giraffe in Africa

3 TEACH

Visualizing Terrestrial Biomes

Guide students through the wealth of information on these pages by having them focus on a single factor at a time across all six biomes. First have students compare the biomes' temperature ranges and sequence them from lowest to highest (tundra, taiga, temperate deciduous forest and grassland, desert, tropical rain forest). Then have them compare the biomes' precipitation amounts and sequence those from lowest to highest (desert and tundra, grassland, taiga, temperate deciduous forest, tropical rain forest). Next have them compare the types of vegetation found in the biomes, and finally the types of animals.

Discuss any plants and animals that are unfamiliar to students. You may want to supply field guides in book and/or CD-ROM format so students can see what those organisms look like and find out more about them.

Investigate

Research In the 1930s, mismanagement of America's great midwestern prairie stripped land of vegetation and exposed topsoil to the effects of windstorms. Ask students to do research and report on the effects this action had on the history of the United States.

TEACHER SUPPORT

Background Information

There are two other types of tropical forests besides the tropical rain forest included among the six major biomes presented on these pages. Rainfall, rather than temperature, determines the kind of vegetation that grows in a particular type of tropical forest. **Tropical rain forests** are found in very humid equatorial areas, such as Indonesia and the Amazon River basin, where rainfall is abundant and the dry season lasts no more than a few months.

Tropical deciduous forests dominate areas with distinct wet and dry seasons, such as central West Africa and much of India and Southeast Asia. Trees and shrubs drop their leaves during the long dry season and releaf only during the following heavy rains. **Tropical thorn forests,** common in eastern Africa and northwestern India, have prolonged dry seasons. Vegetation consists of thorny shrubs and trees and nonwoody plants that retain water for long periods.

Ancillary Support

The resources below can be used to support your teaching strategy for these two pages.

TR Writing in Biology: On the Road Apply: The Tundra Next Door

BL Inquiry Activity: Where in the World?

Visualizing Aquatic Biomes

As suggested for the terrestrial biomes, guide students through this information by having them focus on one factor at a time—temperature range, light and nutrient availability, and characteristic organisms—across all four biomes. Also discuss any unfamiliar organisms and provide field guides so students can research them. Encourage students to share any personal experiences they have had with the different aquatic biomes.

Make sure students note the similarities between the types of organisms found in the freshwater biome and those found in estuaries. Ask students whether the same species of aquatic animals could live in both biomes and have them explain their answers. (No. Estuaries are saltwater environments; species are usually adapted to either a saltwater or a freshwater environment, not both.)

Investigate

Cooperative Learning Ask students what aquatic biomes exist in your area. If possible, arrange for students to visit the biomes and observe and record the types of living things found there. Have student groups make maps to show the location of the aquatic biomes in your county or state.

Visualizing Aquatic Biomes

Biomes are the Earth's major types of ecosystems. Four aquatic biomes are presented along with a list of their main characteristics.

1 Open Water

ABIOTIC FACTORS: temperature range slight, little seasonal variation, light and nutrient availability slight to moderate

BIOTIC FACTORS: phytoplankton, fishes, dolphins, and whales

2 Fresh Water

ABIOTIC FACTORS: temperature range moderate (temperate freshwater) to slight (tropical freshwater), light and nutrient availability usually good

BIOTIC FACTORS: vegetation—algae, mosses, lichens; animals—insects, fishes, amphibians, and often reptiles and mammals

3 Estuaries

ABIOTIC FACTORS: temperature range extreme, annual precipitation highly seasonal, good light and nutrient availability

BIOTIC FACTORS: vegetation—algae, mosses, lichens, abundance of aquatic plants; animals—insects, shrimps, crabs, fishes, amphibians, birds

4 Rocky Intertidal

ABIOTIC FACTORS: exposure to air and sunlight alternating with being submerged by ocean water

BIOTIC FACTORS: algae, barnacles, snails, sea urchins, starfish, mussels

TEACHER SUPPORT

Managing Classroom Diversity

EDUCATIONAL EQUITY

Much of what is known about open water biomes comes from explorations and studies done by marine biologists, geologists, and archaeologists who have dived deep below the ocean's surface. Sylvia Earle, a marine biologist, has earned international recognition for her underwater explorations using scuba equipment, the deep-diving Jim suit (named for Jim Jarratt, the first person to use a rigid, pressure-resistant diving suit), and the *Deep Rover* and *Star II* submersibles.

Earle's background and experiences are detailed in *Window on the Deep: The Adventures of Underwater Explorer Sylvia Earle* by Andrea Conley. Obtain a copy of the book so that interested students can learn more about this pioneering underwater scientist.

Terrestrial and Aquatic Biomes

The relationship between the major terrestrial **biomes** and two of the most important climate conditions—namely, temperature and rainfall—is graphically shown in *Figure 15–10* on page 341. The tundra biome on Earth is found above the Arctic Circle. The taiga biome is found in a wide band just below the Arctic Circle. Tropical rain forests and seasonal forests abound in the Earth's equatorial land areas. Temperate deciduous forests thrive throughout much of Europe and the eastern part of the United States. The desert biome occurs in large parts of Africa and the southwestern United States and in small parts of South America, Asia, and Australia. Savanna grasslands cover much of South America, Africa, and Australia, while temperate grasslands are found in the central United States, western Canada, and in a wide belt across southern Asia.

Aquatic biomes are classified as freshwater or marine ecosystems. It may surprise you to know that only 3 percent of the water on Earth is fresh water! And 98 percent of the fresh water (98 percent of 3 percent) is frozen in icecaps. Freshwater biomes are important not only because they provide us with water for drinking, they also provide us with water for irrigating crops and habitats for food fishes.

MINI LAB .... Predicting ....

Do Leaves Have Waxy Skin?

PROBLEM *Can you **predict** how leaves control the amount of water loss to the environment?*

PROCEDURE

1. Obtain three paper towels and dampen them with water so they are wet but not dripping.
2. Cut two pieces of waxed paper the same size as a towel and sandwich one wet towel between the two pieces of waxed paper. Fasten the corners with paper clips and place this flat on a tray.
3. Roll up the two remaining towels. Place one roll on the tray uncovered and the other covered with a length of waxed paper. Secure the edges with paper clips.
4. Place the tray in direct sunlight. Predict which paper towel setup will lose the least amount of water.

ANALYZE AND CONCLUDE

1. How did the towels differ after 24 hours?
2. Which of the setups conserved water best?
3. Was your prediction correct? Explain your answer.
4. Explain how the leaves of desert plants conserve water.

Major marine biomes include estuaries (a zone in which a river joins the sea), rocky intertidal zones, and open water. The characteristics of aquatic biomes are presented on the previous page.

Section Review 15–3

1. **Define** biome.
2. **List** and **describe** some terrestrial and aquatic biomes.
3. **Critical Thinking—Relating** Use examples to illustrate how plants and animals within a given biome are suited to that biome.
4. **MINI LAB** How can you **predict** how leaves control the amount of water lost to the environment?

MINI LAB Predicting

Teacher Note

• For time required and materials needed, see page 332b.

Answers to Analyze and Conclude

1. The flat towel protected by waxed paper will be damp. The unprotected rolled towel will be dry on the edges and on the surface but damp inside. The rolled towel covered with waxed paper will be damp throughout.
2. The rolled towel covered with waxed paper.
3. Answers may vary. The waxed paper prevented evaporation. Rolling up the towels exposed less surface area to the air, reducing evaporation.
4. The leaves are narrow, flat, and covered with a waxy material that reduces evaporation.

Skills Trace
Predicting
- Focus p. 345
- Practice p. 345
- Assess p. 357

4 ASSESS

Quick Check

Have students list the six major biomes in order from the lowest temperature range to the highest and then number them in order from the lowest precipitation amount to the highest.

Learning Modality

Kinesthetic Learning Have students make a set of abiotic and biotic factor cards for each terrestrial biome. Have six students hold a sheet of paper labeled with the name of a biome. Have students take turns reading one card's factor description aloud, identifying the biome to which the factor belongs, and giving that card to the appropriate "biome" student.

Section Review 15–3

1. Ecosystems that are identified by their climax communities.

2. See pages 342–344.

3. Accept all reasonable responses. Desert plants have narrow leaves or spines that reduce water loss. Many desert animals are active during the night instead of the day; this behavior protects them from the intense heat.

4. By testing and comparing water loss by protected and unprotected materials.

Skills Trace
Predicting
- Focus p. 345
- Practice p. 345
- Assess p. 357

Section 15–4

Climate: A Complex Story

Performance Objectives

- Describe the causes of global climate patterns.
- Identify global warming as one possible climate change, and explain why such changes are difficult to predict.

1 ENGAGE

Inquiry Activity

Making Predictions

Mini-Habitat Climate Conditions

Ask students to identify the primary climate conditions that affect the mini-habitat they created in the Unit Discovery Learning Activity. (The significant conditions are the amount of moisture in each habitat, its temperature, and the amount of light it receives.) Ask students to predict what might happen if they changed one climate condition. Let each group share its predictions with the rest of the class. Follow up with the Explore activity on page 347.

Ideas Through Images

Have students examine Figure 15–11, read the caption, and answer the following questions.

- **How could the greenhouse effect lead to climate changes?** (If increased levels of carbon dioxide and other greenhouse gases enter the atmosphere, more heat will be trapped, and temperatures on Earth could increase.)
- **What climate changes have you read or heard about?** (Students may have heard about the severe drought conditions in mid- and southwestern U.S. or global warming predictions.)

SECTION 15–4 BRANCHING OUT In Depth

Climate: A Complex Story

Guide for Reading

- **Distinguish** between climate change and global warming.
- **Explain** why climate changes are difficult to predict.

IN 1995, A SEVERE SUMMER drought parched the northeastern part of the United States, Europe, and Australia. Torrential rains flooded the Mississippi basin and the west coasts of North and South America. In central England, the month of August was 3.4°C warmer than average, breaking all records since record keeping began in 1659. And the hurricane season in the Atlantic was one of the most severe in 125 years of record keeping.

Were these events unrelated? Or was there a common cause behind them? Are human actions changing global climate? If so, how will those changes affect the biosphere and human life?

What Causes Climate?

Ecologists are hard at work trying to find the answers to the questions just posed. In order to understand the issues and controversies that surround the subject of global climate, you must first learn what causes climate. This will help you understand how climate changes.

Global climate patterns are caused by the action of winds and ocean currents. Winds and ocean currents are in turn powered by solar energy that makes its way to Earth. How does this happen?

Winds

Because the Earth's surface is curved, different parts of the surface receive different amounts of solar energy. Near the equator, solar energy is more concentrated than it is at the North and South poles. As a result, the surface of the Earth is warmer at the equator than it is at the poles. See **Figure 15–12.**

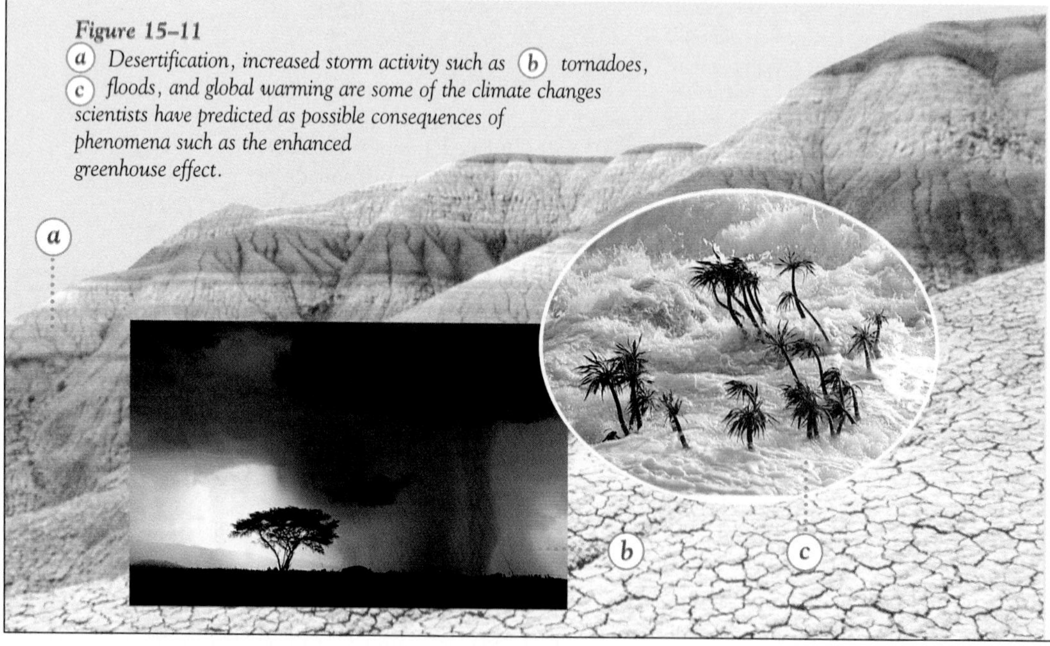

Figure 15–11 (a) *Desertification, increased storm activity such as* (b) *tornadoes,* (c) *floods, and global warming are some of the climate changes scientists have predicted as possible consequences of phenomena such as the enhanced greenhouse effect.*

TEACHER SUPPORT — Managing Classroom Diversity

LEP STUDENTS/AT-RISK STUDENTS

If students are unfamiliar with the term desertification in the caption for Figure 15–11, help them figure out the meaning as follows:

- First, write the word on the board and draw a slash to separate its parts: *desert/ification.* Ask students if they recognize either part. When they mention desert, ask them to define the word.
- Next, ask them to suggest other words that end with *-ification*—for example, mummification and amplification. If students have difficulty thinking of words, suggest one or two to get them started. List all the words on the board, and ask students to define each one. Guide them to recognize that *-ification* means "the process of" or "the process of turning into."
- Finally, erase the slash in *desert/ification*, and ask students to explain what the word means—"the process of turning into a desert." Let students use a science dictionary to verify their definition.

Perhaps you already know that warm air rises and cool air sinks. Therefore, the warmer air near the equator rises, while the cooler polar air sinks to the ground. Cool air then moves toward the equator, where it warms up and rises again. As shown in ***Figure 15–12***, this great solar heat pump sets up three large circuits of rising and falling air on each side of the equator.

As the Earth rotates on its axis beneath the atmosphere, the air flows move east or west relative to the ground. Especially important are surface air flows, called the trade winds. Trade winds have been the power behind sailing vessels for hundreds of years.

Checkpoint What causes wind? (1)

INTEGRATING PHYSICS

Why does warm air rise and cool air sink?

Figure 15–12
Winds and ocean currents are the results of uneven solar heating of Earth's air and water. The interaction of these air and water flows with Earth's landmasses produces the rainfall patterns of the world.

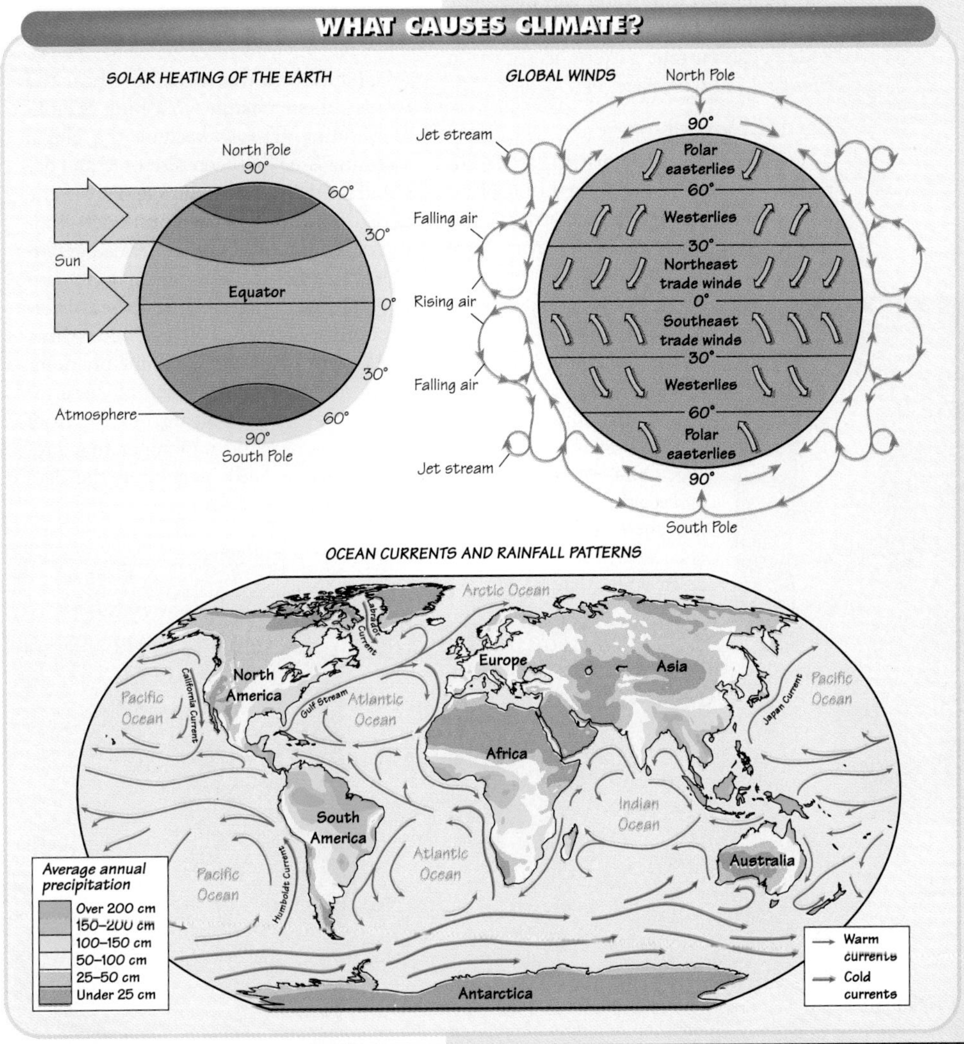

2 EXPLORE

Inquiry Activity

Designing an Experiment

Testing Climate Changes
Challenge groups to design experiments to test the predictions they made in the Engage activity on the previous page. Before students proceed, review each group's design to ensure that the new climate condition will not subject any animals to stress or kill an entire population. Give each group an opportunity to describe its experimental design, observations, results, and conclusions to the rest of the class.

3 TEACH

INTEGRATING PHYSICS

Warm air is lighter than cool air. The molecules in warm air are spread farther apart than the molecules in an equal volume of cool air.

Ideas Through Images

Have students examine Figure 15–12, read the caption, and answer the following questions.

- **Why are the sun's rays strongest at the equator?** (Sunlight strikes Earth more directly at the equator.)
- **In which direction do the trade winds blow?** (From east to west.)

Checkpoint

(1) Uneven solar heating and Earth's rotation.

TEACHER SUPPORT Activity

Why Do Wind Patterns Curve? Students may have some difficulty understanding that the direction of air flow is the result of Earth's rotation on its axis. You can use the following activity to help students visualize this effect.

One student should slowly turn a globe in the same direction that Earth rotates on its axis. As the globe turns, a second student should use a washable marker to draw a line directly down from the North Pole to the equator, and a third student should draw a line directly up from the South Pole to the equator.

Results: When the first student stops turning the globe, students will see that the two lines are not straight but curve to the west, due to Earth's rotation. Explain that this curving is called the Coriolis effect. The westward curving air flows that it creates are the trade winds.

Ancillary Support

The resources below can be used to support your teaching strategy for these two pages.

TR Explore: Whirling Winds
BL Inquiry Activity: Colorful Currents
TB What Causes Climate?, #20

Investigate

Research Emphasize that ocean currents have a powerful effect on climate worldwide. For example, although Scotland and eastern Canada are at about the same latitude, Scotland is much warmer in winter due to the warming effect of the Gulf Stream flowing past its western coast. Ask students to research and report on the effects of other ocean currents—including the Humboldt Current but not its periodic disruption known as El Niño, which is covered later in the Connections feature on page 350.

Ideas Through Images

Have students examine Figure 15–13, read the caption, and answer the following questions.

- **How does the windward slope of a mountain have more moisture than the leeward slope?** (Winds force moist air up and over a mountain, causing large amounts of rain to fall.)
- **What happens to the air as it flows to the leeward side of a mountain?** (Once over the top of a mountain, the air becomes dry and picks up moisture from its surroundings, causing the area to become dry.)

Investigate

Role-Playing Ask students to find out more about the climate controversy described on pages 348, 349, and 351, particularly scientists' arguments supporting or refuting the prediction that the enhanced greenhouse effect will cause an increase in Earth's average temperature. Let each student choose whether to research the supporting or the refuting viewpoint, but make sure neither side is overwhelmingly represented. Encourage students to use articles in recent issues of scientific journals—*Nature*, *Science*, *BioScience*, *Scientific American*, and so forth—as sources so they obtain the latest information. When students have completed their research, convene a "global warming symposium" in which students play the roles of scientists debating the long-term results of the enhanced greenhouse effect.

Ocean Currents

Like the atmosphere, oceans experience more solar heating at the equator than at the poles. As a result, warmer water at the ocean surface moves from the equator toward the cooler water at the poles. On the other hand, cold water near the poles sinks to the bottom of the ocean and travels along the ocean floor toward the equator. Surface water is also pushed around by the action of winds. Of course, continents get in the way and affect the path that water can take. The result of all these flows is the worldwide ocean current pattern, as shown in *Figure 15–12* on page 347.

Earth's Geography

As you have read earlier, Earth's climate is caused by the interaction of air and water currents with Earth's landmasses. As warm air moves over warm water, it picks up moisture in the form of water vapor. If the warm, moist air rises and later cools, the water vapor condenses and falls to the Earth as fog, rain, snow, or sleet. This often happens when warm, moist air meets high mountain ranges—such as the Sierra Madre and Rocky Mountains in North America, the Andes in South America, and the Himalayas in Asia.

☑ **Checkpoint** How do mountain ranges create rainfall patterns? ❶

The Climate Controversy

Chances are that when you hear the words climate change, you think of global warming. This is because the global warming issue has been discussed and debated for more than a decade. Part of the controversy stems from a misunderstanding of basic terms. The enhanced greenhouse effect, climate change, and global warming are often used interchangeably, as if they were three different names for the same phenomenon. Let's examine each of these individually, separating facts from predictions. And remember that predictions are only as good as the data they are based upon.

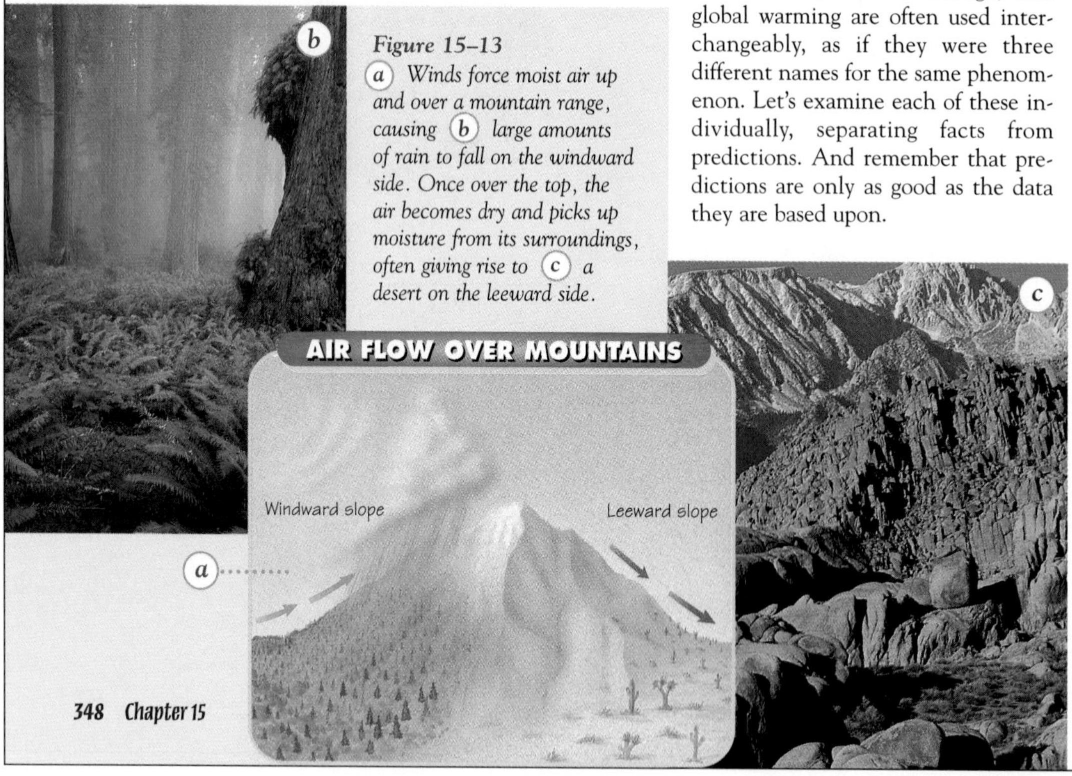

Figure 15–13 (a) *Winds force moist air up and over a mountain range, causing* (b) *large amounts of rain to fall on the windward side. Once over the top, the air becomes dry and picks up moisture from its surroundings, often giving rise to* (c) *a desert on the leeward side.*

TEACHER SUPPORT

Historical Perspective

Prevailing winds and ocean currents played a vital role in Europeans' world explorations in the fifteenth through eighteenth centuries. In some cases, sailors followed prevailing winds and currents to reach their desired location. In many cases, however, explorers discovered new lands by chance when they were carried off their intended course by unexpected winds or currents. Some voyagers encountered difficulty or disaster when their ships entered the equatorial area of calm winds known as the doldrums or when they had to sail against prevailing winds and currents.

Encourage students to research the routes sailed by some early European explorers and compare the routes with the directions of the ocean currents and surface winds. Descriptions of many explorers' voyages and maps of their routes are included in *Exploring the Oceans* by Derek Cullen and John Murray-Robertson.

Enhanced Greenhouse Effect

Earlier in this chapter, you learned that the greenhouse effect is a natural phenomenon occurring in Earth's atmosphere. This effect has maintained a nearly stable temperature range on Earth for millions of years. However, when scientists discuss the **enhanced greenhouse effect,** they are referring to the fact that human activities are adding greenhouse gases to the atmosphere. There is little scientific debate that this is happening. Because humans are adding carbon dioxide and other greenhouse gases to the atmosphere, Earth will retain more heat from the sun than it has in the past.

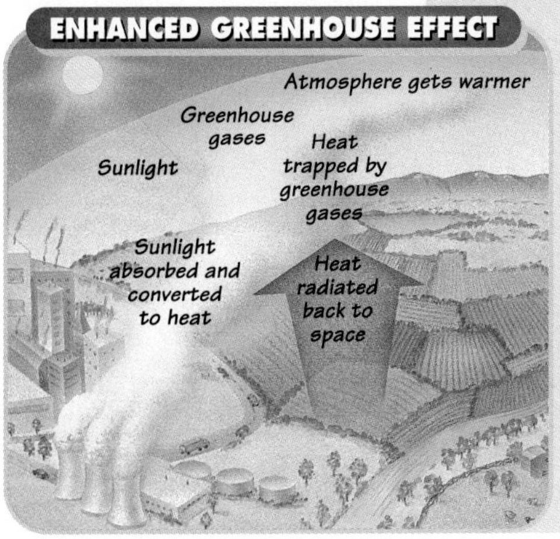

Figure 15–14 Various human activities, such as the burning of fossil fuels, add to the greenhouse gases released to the atmosphere. As a result, the Earth will retain more heat than it has in the past.

Researchers predict that concentrations of greenhouse gases in the atmosphere will double during the early part of the twenty-first century. You may want to take a look at ***Figure 13–16*** on page 303, which shows the atmospheric carbon dioxide levels for the past 35 years. This doubling of greenhouse gases will reduce the rate at which Earth loses energy to space by about 2 percent. If the rate at which energy is returned to space decreases, energy will build up in the atmosphere. You may not think that a 2-percent change is anything to worry about. But given the amount of energy the Earth receives and ultimately returns to space, the 2-percent reduction is equivalent to adding the energy content of 3 million metric tons of oil to the atmosphere every minute!

Most experts agree that energy will be added to the biosphere and the biosphere will adjust to it. Just how the biosphere will adapt is the question. As you can imagine, the worldwide system of atmospheric and oceanic currents carrying heat around the globe is complicated. The global carbon cycle that links various carbon reservoirs is also complex. Exactly what will the accumulation of energy do to these cycles and systems? This is where scientific questions and debates arise.

☑ **Checkpoint** What is the enhanced greenhouse effect? ②

Global Warming

Many scientists believe that a significant amount of the extra energy will remain in the biosphere in the form of heat, causing Earth's average temperature to rise. You may have heard of **global warming** scenarios, predicting the melting of polar icecaps, the rising of sea levels, and the flooding of coastal cities. **When the enhanced greenhouse effect (a fact) is used to predict a significant rise in Earth's average temperature (a possibility), the prediction is called global warming.**

What evidence do scientists have to support this prediction? All over the world, temperature records, similar to those shown in ***Figure 15–15*** on page 351, offer evidence that Earth has been warming over the last century.

Predicting how global temperatures will change in the future is not easy. Climate researchers rely on computer models of the oceans and atmosphere, trying to take into account as many relevant factors as possible, such as volcanic and

Investigate

Research As pointed out in the student text, carbon dioxide is not the only gas that contributes to the greenhouse effect. Have students research the other major greenhouse gases and their sources. Ask volunteers to create a class master chart of students' findings.

Discussion

Point out to students that there is nothing new or unusual in the suggestion that humans are changing the environment. Emphasize that all organisms have done so to a greater or lesser degree. As an example, remind students of the dramatic change in Earth's atmosphere that resulted when new forms of bacteria began producing oxygen as a waste product (Section 15–2, page 337). The major difference between what humans are doing now and what other organisms have done in the past is not the extent of human-caused changes but the speed with which those changes are occurring. Unlike changes caused by other organisms, the global effects of human activity are becoming evident not in billions, millions, or even thousands of years but mere decades.

☑ Checkpoints

① When warm, moist air rises and meets high mountain ranges, the water vapor cools and condenses.

② The enhanced greenhouse effect includes human activities that add greenhouse gases to the atmosphere.

TEACHER SUPPORT

Background Information

Most climatologists would agree with the conservative prediction for global warming presented in the student text. However, the level of confidence in the results of predictive models depends on how well the climate system can be represented and on how many other factors can be included. Thus, the observation that global temperatures are rising does not by itself prove that the enhanced greenhouse effect is responsible for the rising temperatures.

Many other factors can affect global climate: The sun does not always release the same amount of energy. The global climate network has natural cycles that could raise and lower temperatures over time. Variations in Earth's orbit could affect temperature. Volcanic eruptions, periodic occurrences of El Niño (discussed on the next page), and other natural events also cause climate changes—although generally not of the long-term duration indicated by Figure 15–15.

Connections

El Niño was first recorded as far back as the early 1500s and since that time has recurred about every two to seven years. El Niño was for many years considered to be only a local phenomenon, but in the late 1960s, scientists discovered a connection between El Niño and a change in the wind pattern over the entire tropical Pacific Ocean. In 1975, scientists used this information for the first time to predict a recurrence—and indeed El Niño struck again, as predicted, in 1982–83.

In addition to its effect on global climate conditions, the massive warming kills many fish and sea birds by preventing nutrient-rich cold waters from rising to the surface. This effect damages the economies of Peru and Ecuador, whose coastal waters are one of the world's largest fishing grounds.

Answers to Making the Connection

The enhanced greenhouse effect may increase the number of El Niño occurrences in the future. El Niño occurs when normally quickly disappearing warm ocean water is spread by winds. Because El Niño deals with increasing temperatures, the warming caused by the enhanced greenhouse effect may help in spreading the warm water, thereby creating more widespread disasters.

Biology and Earth Science Connections

El Niño

Usually the tropical region of the Pacific Ocean is subject to strong winds that blow from east to west. Sometimes, however, the winds are weaker than normal, allowing the warmer waters of the western Pacific to move toward the eastern end of the ocean and South America. This change of wind flow and water current is an event commonly called El Niño, meaning "the male child" in Spanish.

The red areas in the equatorial regions of the Pacific Ocean indicate the presence of the warmer waters of El Niño.

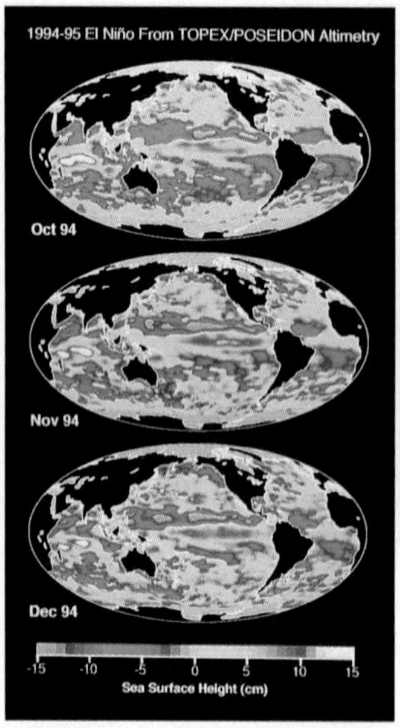

CAREER TRACK Oceanographers gather and interpret data such as ocean water temperatures to understand the importance of climate change.

Effects of El Niño

What changes can El Niño cause? It is often associated with increased thunderstorms and other climate changes in western South America and beyond. Moreover, off the coast of Peru, El Niño reduces a phenomenon called upwelling—the rising of cold, nutrient-filled water toward the surface. With fewer nutrients, the higher levels of water support smaller populations of fishes and other marine life.

In fact, the effects of an El Niño event are felt all over the world. Usually an El Niño event coincides with drought in Australia, floods in western North and South America, and a mix of heavy rain and drought in Africa.

Climate Change?

An El Niño event may last from a few weeks to several months. Until recently, the events occurred approximately once every 3 to 7 years. To the concern of scientists around the world, however, the frequency and severity of El Niño events seem to be increasing. Some researchers wonder whether this is a coincidence or one of the first signs of climate change. More data are needed before questions about such phenomena can be answered for certain.

Making the Connection

How might the enhanced greenhouse effect impact on El Niño occurrences in the future? Do you think the El Niño effects are short term or long term? Give evidence to support your answer.

TEACHER SUPPORT

Background Information

The term *El Niño Southern Oscillation (ENSO)*, as meteorologists call it, refers to a seesaw in atmospheric pressure over the equatorial Pacific Ocean. The oscillation may be triggered by pulses of heat from Earth, possibly at clusters of active volcanoes recently discovered on the ocean floor.

The western equatorial Pacific is Earth's largest reservoir of warm water. More warm, moisture-laden air rises here than anywhere else, and the resultant heavy rainfall releases much of the heat energy that drives Earth's air circulation system. Normally, the reservoir and rainfall move westward. When El Niño occurs, however, they move eastward.

This movement causes prevailing surface winds in the equatorial Pacific to pick up speed, "dragging" the ocean surface waters eastward with them. This reversal in air flow and water displaces the cold, deep Humboldt Current flowing northward along South America's west coast.

Figure 15–15
This graph shows the annual surface temperature of the Earth from the years 1856 to 1991. Notice the warming trend during the last two decades.

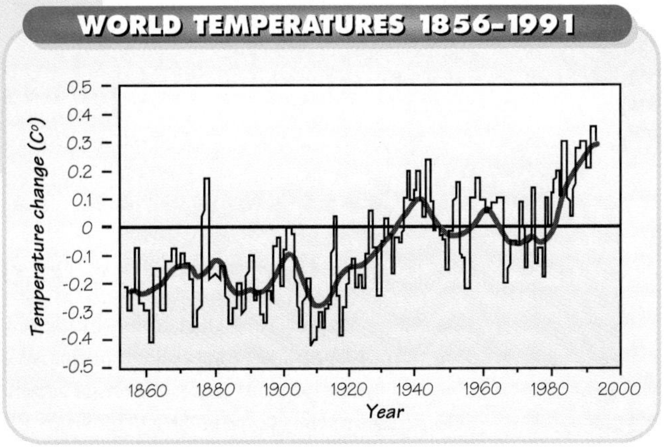

other geologic activities. The most recent models suggest that the average global surface temperature will increase by about 1 to 2°C by the year 2050.

Other scientists question whether the Earth's temperature will rise by a significant amount. But most scientists involved in this research agree that the Earth will undergo some change in climate. **Climate change includes any significant change in patterns of temperature, rainfall, humidity, storm activity, and cloud formation that occurs in any part of the world.** As you see, temperature is only one factor in the larger picture of global climate.

Climate Change: Is It a Problem?

Global warming is not the only possible climate change. Acting like giant conveyor belts, winds and ocean currents carry heat from warmer places to cooler ones. Many scientists are concerned that adding energy to the biosphere—a result of the enhanced greenhouse effect—will influence the air and water flows in ways that they do not yet understand.

They point out that such changes may not be gradual and predictable. Several climate models also suggest that these changes may begin long before there is any clear indication that the Earth is warming up. Why should we be concerned about climate change? The following example may provide the beginnings of an answer.

Recent observations of marine environments raise troubling questions for ocean ecosystems. Since 1950, surface currents off the coast of California have been warming up. This warming trend has caused populations of zooplankton—tiny marine organisms that are part of marine food chains—to decline. Some of these populations have decreased as much as 80 percent over the last 40 years! Not surprisingly, the populations of animals on higher trophic levels have also been declining. Is this trend permanent? Will it continue? No one knows for sure. But can we afford to ignore it?

Section Review 15–4

1. **Distinguish** between climate change and global warming.
2. **Explain** why climate changes are difficult to predict.
3. **Describe** the greenhouse effect. Why has it increased during the past decades?
4. **BRANCHING OUT ACTIVITY** Working in a group, **predict** some of the effects that rising temperatures could have on the Earth. Compare your predictions with those of your classmates.

Ideas Through Images

Have students compare Figure 15–15 with Figure 13–20 on page 303 of Chapter 13 and answer the following question.

- **What general trend do you see in both graphs?** (Both atmospheric CO_2 levels and surface air temperatures have increased.)

4 ASSESS

Quick Check

Ask each student to write a brief explanation, in his or her own words, of how solar heating causes global wind patterns and ocean currents.

Section Review 15–4

1. Climate change includes any significant change in patterns of temperature, rainfall, humidity, storm activity, and cloud formation in any part of the world. Global warming is one possible climate change.
2. Because many factors are involved in climate change.
3. Carbon dioxide and other gases in Earth's atmosphere trap heat energy and prevent it from dissipating into space. Human activities have added greenhouse gases to the atmosphere.
4. Sample prediction: The polar ice caps will melt, and rising ocean levels will flood coastal areas.

Learning Modality

Visual and Tactile Learning Let students use an Earth globe and water-soluble markers of two different colors to re-create the global wind patterns and ocean currents shown in Figure 15–12, page 347.

TEACHER SUPPORT

Ecology Note

In 1996, scientists reported what one specialist called the clearest evidence to date that human activity may contribute to global warming and other changes in Earth's climate.

Researchers used computer simulations to investigate the effects of carbon dioxide buildup, atmospheric particulates from the burning of fossil fuels, and chemical depletion of high-altitude ozone. They found that patterns of temperature change in the computer-simulated atmosphere resembled patterns observed in the actual atmosphere from 1963 to 1987.

One temperature pattern was cooling in the upper atmosphere and warming at lower altitudes, apparently the result of carbon dioxide buildup. These changes seemed too great to be entirely the result of natural variations in climate. A second pattern was less low-altitude warming in the Northern Hemisphere than in the Southern Hemisphere, apparently from the shading effect of industrially produced particles in the North.

CHAPTER 15

Laboratory Investigation

Greenhouse in a Bottle

Before the Lab

1. Collect (or ask students to bring in) enough empty 2-L plastic bottles so each group can have two. Make sure the bottles are thoroughly washed, rinsed, and dried.
2. Obtain sufficient potting soil for each group to have about 350 g.
3. Be prepared to supply whatever additional materials (water, ice cubes, and so forth) are needed for groups to carry out the experiments they design.

Pre-Lab Discussion

Begin by asking students to tell what the greenhouse effect is. If students confuse the natural greenhouse effect with the enhanced greenhouse effect, have them review the paragraph on page 334 below the heading "Earth's Thermostat." Then have students read the entire procedure for this investigation and answer the following questions.

In step 3, what does the plastic wrap represent? (Greenhouse gases in the atmosphere.)

Should you put plastic wrap over just one jar when you test one of the hypotheses in step 7? Why, or why not? (No. All variables except the one being tested—water vs. land, ice vs. bare soil, or plants vs. bare soil—should be kept the same for both jars. Therefore, both jars should be covered with plastic wrap.)

Skills Development

Students will use these skills while completing the laboratory investigation: designing an experiment, making comparisons, developing hypotheses, making predictions, and evaluating experimental results.

Laboratory Investigation

DESIGNING AN EXPERIMENT

Greenhouse in a Bottle

Scientists often find that using models of ecosystems is a convenient and useful way to collect information and make predictions. In this investigation, you will construct model ecosystems in plastic soda bottles to test the effects of a warming environment.

Problem

Design an experiment to observe the impact of the greenhouse effect on global warming.

Suggested Materials

2 outdoor thermometers
2 2-liter plastic bottles
dry potting soil
clear plastic wrap
rubber band
100-watt bulb on a ring stand
scissors
tape
graph paper
cardboard
one of the following:
- water
- wet and dry soil
- ice cubes
- sod or other plants

Suggested Procedure

1. **Remove all labels from the 2-liter bottles. Cut the tops from each bottle just where they begin to narrow.**
2. **Put 350 g of potting soil into one bottle. Tape an outdoor thermometer to the inner wall of the bottle, making sure the thermometer does not touch the soil and the calibrations face outward. Tape a piece of cardboard directly over the bulb of the thermometer.**
3. **Cover the opening of the bottle with plastic wrap and secure it with a rubber band.**
4. **Record the temperature in the bottle.**
5. **Hang the light bulb from a ring stand, then position the bottle on one side of the light.**
6. **Turn the light on for 15 minutes. Record the temperature in the bottle every 3 minutes. If necessary, extend the time until the temperature increases noticeably in the bottle.**
7. **Using a setup similar to the one you used in steps 1 to 6, design an experiment to test one of the following hypotheses:**

Safety Tips

- Students should wear aprons. Make sure that students are careful when using scissors.
- Caution students to be careful when handling a thermometer as it may break and cut them.
- Have students properly dispose of all materials and wash their hands thoroughly at the end of the investigation.

- **Air over water heats up at a different rate than that over land.**
- **Air over ice-covered surfaces heats up at a different rate from that over land that is not covered with ice.**
- **The presence of plants affects the rate of warming.**

8. Be sure to include a control in your experiment. After you write out the procedure, have your teacher check it.

9. Write out your hypothesis and predict the results of your experiment.

10. Carry out your planned experiment and record your results.

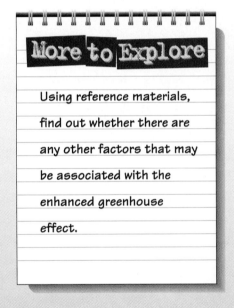

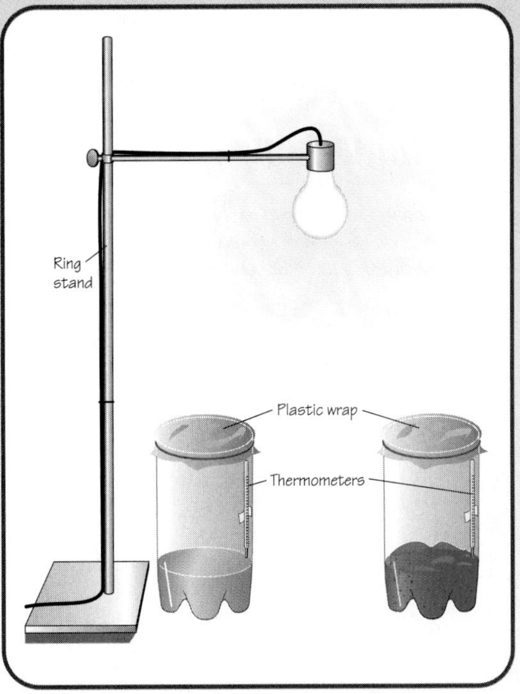

Observations

1. Make line graphs of the data from your experiments.
2. Compare the changes in temperature in each set of bottles over time.
3. What was the control in the experiment? What was the variable?

Analysis and Conclusions

1. How would your results have been affected if you had used two pieces of plastic wrap to cover the bottle?
2. Identify the parts of Earth that each part of the experimental setup represents.
3. In what real-life situations have you observed the greenhouse effect?
4. How did your prediction compare with the data you collected? Was your hypothesis supported?
5. Compare your results with those of your classmates. Was there a difference in the amount of warming in different environments?

More to Explore

Using reference materials, find out whether there are any other factors that may be associated with the enhanced greenhouse effect.

Teaching Strategies

1. In step 7, you may need to help some groups decide how to set up the two jars to test the particular hypothesis they have chosen. The most obvious possibilities for testing the hypotheses are as follows:
First hypothesis: One jar with water and the other with soil, or one jar with wet soil and the other with dry soil.
Second hypothesis: One jar with ice cubes over soil, the other with bare soil.
Third hypothesis: One jar with soil and plants, the other with soil only.

2. When you check students' experimental designs in step 8, make sure each group has remembered to put plastic wrap over both jars, as noted in the Pre-Lab Discussion.

More to Explore

Factors associated with the enhanced greenhouse effect include human activities that generate the greenhouse gases carbon dioxide, methane, and nitrous oxide in quanitities that are greater than those that enter the atmosphere as a result of natural processes. In addition, humans generate chlorofluorocarbons (CFCs) and other halocarbons, which do not occur naturally.

Answers to Observations

1. Check students' graphs to make sure they accurately represent the data.
2. First experiment (steps 1–6): The covered bottle will show a greater increase in temperature. Second experiment (steps 7–10): Answers will vary depending on students' experimental designs.
3. First experiment: Control—uncovered bottle; variable—covering. Second experiment: Answers will vary depending on students' experimental designs.

Answers to Analysis and Conclusions

1. An additional layer may cause a somewhat greater temperature increase.
2. Soil: Earth's surface. Air in bottles: atmosphere; greenhouse gases.
3. Responses will vary but may include a closed car on a sunny day or a sunny room with closed windows.
4. Answers will vary. Make sure students cite specific observations to support or refute their hypotheses.
5. Answers will vary depending on students' experimental designs.

Study Guide

Review Strategy

Have students work in small groups to create crossword puzzles, word-search puzzles, and other word games using the vocabulary terms in this chapter. (Remind each group to create an answer key for its puzzle.) Make photocopies of each group's puzzle to distribute to the rest of the class, and provide copies of the answer keys so students can check their work.

Study Guide

Summarizing Key Concepts

The key concepts in each section of this chapter are listed below to help you review the chapter content. Make sure you understand each concept and its relationship to other concepts and to the theme of this chapter.

15–1 Climate and Life

- A region's climate is the temperature range, average annual precipitation, humidity, and amount of sunshine that the region has.
- Populations of plants and animals grow, remain stable, or vanish depending in part on climate conditions such as temperature and rainfall. These conditions also affect the structure of food webs and the flow of nutrients.
- Climate is one of the physical (abiotic) environmental factors that influence life. Biological (biotic) environmental factors are all the living things with which an organism might interact.
- An ecosystem is a particular combination of a physical environment and the organisms that live in that environment.

15–2 Environments and Life

- Ecological succession is the process by which an existing ecosystem is gradually and progressively replaced by another ecosystem.
- A fairly stable collection of organisms in an ecosystem is called a climax community.

15–3 Earth's Biomes

- Ecosystems identified by their climax communities are called biomes.

15–4 Climate: A Complex Story

- Winds and ocean currents are caused by differential solar heating of the Earth's surface. Winds and ocean currents, as they interact with Earth's geography, give rise to climate.
- Global warming is a prediction based on the enhanced greenhouse effect, or the increased heat in the biosphere due to an increase in levels of greenhouse gases.
- Climate change includes any significant change in patterns of temperature, rainfall, humidity, and storm activity that occurs in any part of the world.

Reviewing Key Terms

Review the following vocabulary terms and their meaning. Then use each term in a complete sentence.

15–1 Climate and Life

climate
greenhouse effect
microclimate
abiotic factor
biotic factor
environment
ecosystem
niche
habitat

15–2 Environments and Life

ecological succession
climax community

15–3 Earth's Biomes

biome

15–4 Climate: A Complex Story

enhanced greenhouse effect
global warming

Inquiry-Based Strategy

Discuss the mini-habitats that student groups created in the Unit Discovery Learning Activity—the habitats' climate conditions; their biotic and abiotic factors; the growth, decline, or stability of their populations; and the factors responsible for any changes—including the climate factors that students investigated in the Explore activity on page 347 if you presented Section 15–4.

Challenge each group to design an experiment to answer the question: **How will the greenhouse effect change the mini-habitat and affect the populations in it?** Remind students of the technique they used in the Laboratory Investigation, Greenhouse in a Bottle, on pages 352–353, to simulate the greenhouse effect. Before they proceed, review each group's experimental design to ensure that it will not subject any animals to stress or harm. Give the groups an opportunity to describe their experimental techniques and report their observations, results, and conclusions to the class.

Recalling Main Ideas

Choose the letter of the answer that best completes the statement or answers the question.

1. A region's climate does not depend on its
   - a. annual rainfall.
   - b. population.
   - c. average temperature.
   - d. distance from the equator.
2. The greenhouse effect occurs in the Earth's
   - a. atmosphere.
   - b. oceans.
   - c. ozone layer.
   - d. plant life.
3. Earth's climate patterns arise due to
   - a. the water cycle.
   - b. global warming.
   - c. Earth's biomes.
   - d. winds and ocean currents.
4. The process of slow change by which a forest recovers after a fire is called
   - a. ecological succession.
   - b. microclimate.
   - c. climate change.
   - d. climax.
5. Which of the following biomes receives the least annual precipitation?
   - a. rain forest
   - b. grasslands
   - c. taiga
   - d. desert
6. An organism's niche is a description of
   - a. its physical environment.
   - b. its biological environment.
   - c. the range of physical and biological conditions in which it can live.
   - d. its habitat.
7. Winds and ocean currents are caused by the
   - a. differences in solar heating of Earth's land and ocean surfaces.
   - b. unevenness of Earth's landmasses.
   - c. tilt of the Earth's axis.
   - d. cutting of tropical rain forests.
8. The enhanced greenhouse effect is due in large part to
   - a. global warming.
   - b. climate change.
   - c. human activity that adds greenhouse gases to the atmosphere.
   - d. microclimate change.

Putting It All Together

Using the information on pages xxx to xxxi, complete the following concept map.

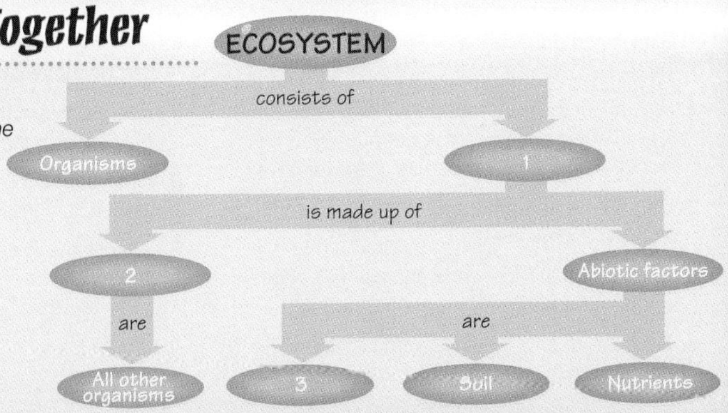

Recalling Main Ideas

1. b
2. a
3. d
4. a
5. d
6. c
7. a
8. c

Putting It All Together

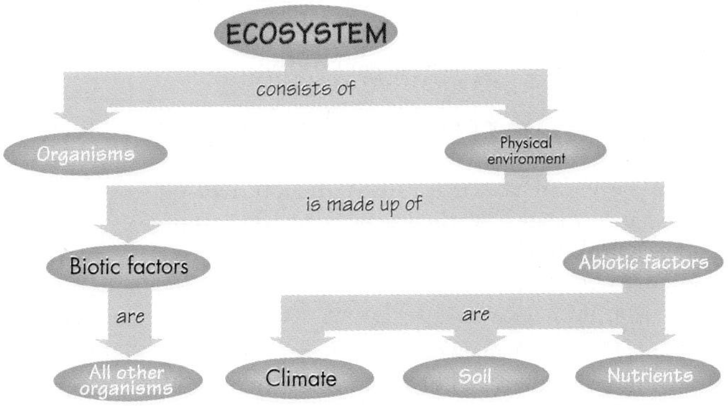

Assessment

Reviewing What You Learned

1. The temperature range, average annual precipitation, humidity, and amount of sunshine that a region typically experiences. Students' descriptions of the climate in your area will vary but should include specific observations of the above conditions.

Skills Trace
Observing
- Focus p. 339
- Practice p. 340
- **Assess p. 356**

2. Answers will vary but should show that students understand the concept of microclimate.
3. Biotic factors: all living things with which an organism might interact. Abiotic factors: physical factors such as climate, soil type and acidity, and availability of nutrients.
4. Answers will vary but should show that students understand the concept of ecosystem.
5. Some abiotic factors include amount of light, temperature range, humidity, and availability of water and nutrients.
6. An organism's niche is the way in which it uses the physical and biological conditions in its environment. Its habitat is the type of surroundings in which it lives.
7. The process by which an existing ecosystem is gradually and progressively replaced by another ecosystem. Occurs for both physical and biological reasons.
8. An oak forest is a stable ecosystem that will not naturally progress to a different ecosystem.
9. Students should address any three of the biomes presented on pages 342–344.
10. Enhanced greenhouse effect: The addition of greenhouse gases to the atmosphere by human activities. Global warming: The prediction that the enhanced greenhouse effect will cause a significant rise in Earth's average temperature. Climate change: Any significant change in patterns of temperature, rainfall, humidity, storm activity, and cloud formation that occurs in any part of the world.

Expanding the Concepts

1. The curvature of Earth causes uneven heating of the air and water, producing winds and currents.
2. Accept all reasonable answers. The area covered by leaves would remain damp and dark, unlike the rest of the forest.
3. No. The organisms would compete with each other for the same resources, and one would be eliminated.
4. Yes. Explanations will vary but should include the effects of interactions between organisms and the biotic and abiotic factors in their environment.
5. Answers will vary. Clearing a wooded area to build a housing development or shopping mall.
6. Natural disasters begin the process of ecological succession once again, ensuring that the planet is not dominated by climax communities.
7. Winds force moist air up and over a mountain range, causing large amounts of rain to fall on the windward side. Once over the top, the air becomes dry and picks up moisture from its surroundings, often giving rise to a desert on the leeward side.

Assessment

Reviewing What You Learned

Answer each of the following in a complete sentence.

1. Define climate and briefly describe the climate you **observe** in your area.
2. Give examples from your neighborhood of locations with different microclimates.
3. Contrast biotic and abiotic factors of an environment.
4. Characterize any four ecosystems, one of which represents the area in which you live.
5. What abiotic factors are associated with an organism's niche?
6. How does an organism's niche differ from its habitat?
7. Define ecological succession. Why does it occur?
8. Why might an oak forest be considered a climax community?
9. Identify and characterize three major biomes.
10. Distinguish between the enhanced greenhouse effect, global warming, and climate change.

Expanding the Concepts

Discuss each of the following in a brief paragraph.

1. Explain the significance of Earth's curvature to climate.
2. Why might the microclimate under a layer of leaves at the base of a tree be much different from the characteristic climate of the forest?
3. Can two organisms occupy the same niche? Support your answer.
4. Do organisms influence or change their habitat? Explain your answer.
5. Describe an area in your community in which human activity has altered natural succession.
6. How might one consider natural disasters as part of nature's order?
7. How do mountain ranges affect the climate on either side of the range?
8. What is meant by the "Earth's heat pump," and what is its connection to Earth's climate?
9. Discuss the role of carbon dioxide in the atmosphere and the predictions based on its rising concentrations.

CHAPTER 15

Extending Your Thinking

Use the skills you have developed in this chapter to answer the following.

1. **Hypothesizing** Explain why the ocean currents in the Northern Hemisphere travel in a clockwise direction whereas those in the Southern Hemisphere travel in a counterclockwise direction.
2. **Relating** Why are the biomes at subsequent elevations of a mountain range similar to those you would encounter while traveling from the equator to the North Pole?
3. **Sequencing** The lava flows of the seventeenth century greatly devastated areas of the island of Hawaii. Trace the probable steps in ecological succession to the climax community that now exists.
4. **Evaluating** Why is global warming called prediction and not fact? Justify your answer.
5. **Predicting** Predict what might happen if a new species were to arrive in a habitat and begin to occupy the same niche as one of the species in that habitat.

Applying Your Skills

Designing a City of the Future

Through this activity you will explore how air pollution in a city can be minimized by the arrangement of living areas, work areas, and landscaping.

1. Design appropriate symbols for the following elements: single-family home, office building, apartments and townhouses, industrial plant, parks and forests, playground and ballfield, school, gas station, restaurant, highway, shopping mall, bus and subway routes, and walking, jogging, and bike trails.
2. Working in groups, imagine that you are urban planners and design a city. Decide on the placement of the elements in order to minimize air pollution. Make sufficient copies of the elements and mount them on cardboard. Then cut and paste these elements, following your design.
3. Present your design to other groups, giving the rationale for your layout.

• GOING FURTHER •

4. Invite an urban planner to your class to discuss and evaluate the layouts of all the groups.

8. Warmer air near the equator rises, while cooler polar air sinks to the ground. Cool air then moves toward the equator, where it warms up and rises again. This "heat pump" sets up three large circuits of rising and falling air on each side of the equator.
9. Carbon dioxide traps heat in Earth's atmosphere. Human activities have added carbon dioxide and other greenhouse gases to the atmosphere. Some scientists predict that this enhanced greenhouse effect will result in global warming, a significant rise in Earth's average temperature.

Extending Your Thinking

1. Because of Earth's rotation, the water in the oceans tends to slip along the equator. This causes water to move from east to west. When the water hits a land mass, it is diverted toward the poles. This action continues so that the water moves clockwise in the Northern Hemisphere and counterclockwise in the Southern Hemisphere.
2. Biomes are greatly influenced by two factors: temperature and humidity. As you travel up a mountain or toward the poles, the climate effects of altitude and latitude are similar.
3. Students should describe a succession process similar to that of Krakatoa on pages 338–339.
4. Exactly how the biosphere will adapt to rising levels of greenhouse gases in the atmosphere is unknown. The worldwide system of atmospheric and oceanic currents carrying heat around the globe is quite complicated, as is the global carbon cycle that links various carbon reservoirs.

5. Two species cannot occupy the same niche in a habitat. They would compete with each other for the same resources, and the less successful species would be eliminated.

Skills Trace
Predicting
- Focus p. 345
- Practice p. 345
- Assess p. 357

Applying Your Skills

Preparation

1. Gather art materials, including construction paper, colored markers, scissors, paste, and posterboard.
2. Provide aerial photos of cities for students to examine before designing their own city.

Suggestion

Encourage students to identify all potential sources of pollution before laying out their city.

Scoring Rubric

4 Response is thorough, accurate, and creative; shows an in-depth understanding of science skills, procedures, and concepts.

3 Response is complete, mostly accurate, and original; shows a satisfactory understanding of science skills, procedures, and concepts.

2 Response is mostly complete but includes some inaccuracies; shows an adequate understanding of science skills, procedures, and concepts.

1 Response is only partially complete and has many inaccuracies; shows an incomplete understanding of science skills, procedures, and concepts.

0 Response is mostly incomplete and/or inaccurate; shows a lack of understanding of science skills, procedures, and concepts.

Chapter 16 Humans in the Biosphere

Content Management	Student Edition Activities
■ Section 16–1 This Island Earth, pp. 359–362 Human Activity and the Environment Charting a Course	**MINI LAB:** When a Little Can Mean a Lot, p. 361 **Laboratory Investigation:** Turn Your Garbage Around, pp. 378–379
■ Section 16–2 Agriculture, pp. 363–369 The Green Revolution Environmental Impact Agriculture in the Future	**MINI LAB:** Holding Your Own, p. 366
■ Section 16–3 Resources at Risk, pp. 370–374 Environmental Pollution Biodiversity	
◆ BRANCHING OUT • In Depth Section 16–4 Conserving Biodiversity, pp. 375–377 Island Size Conservation Biology	

■ These sections cover all the necessary content and concepts for a basic course in biology.
◆ This section covers content and concepts that are either applications or extensions of the basic material.

Integration Strategies

SE Technology and Society, p. 364
Health, p. 372

Assessment Strategies

SE Chapter Review, pp. 380–383
TR Section Reviews
Chapter Test
BL Chapter Review
Practice Test
CTB Chapter 16 Test

Tech Prep

Teaching strategies appropriate for students who are in technical/vocational programs or who are considering post-secondary technical education can be found on **TE** pages 363 and 373.

Meeting the Standards

Sections 16–1 through 16–4 cover four of the five content standards under **The Interdependence of Organisms** and two of the six content standards under **Matter, Energy, and Organization in Living Systems** as described on pages 186–187 of The National Science Education Standards.

Chapter Planning Guide

Teacher's Edition Activities	Other Activities	Media and Technology
Chapter Discovery Learning Activity, p. 358 Inquiry Activity: Changes in Ecosystems, p. 359 Investigate: Research, p. 359 Investigate: Model Building, p. 360 Investigate: Research, p. 361	**TR** Explore: Good as New **BL** Inquiry Activity: Here Today, Here Tomorrow	BioVue Mini Doc: Raising Condors, Videodisc Side 4 **TB** Biological Magnification, #21
Investigate: Model Building, p. 364 Activity: Comparing Soil Types, p. 368	**TR** Apply: Cope With the Slope **BL** Inquiry Activity: Washing Away	BioVue Mini Doc: Cattle Ranching and the Environment, Videodisc Side 4
Inquiry Activity: How Does Acid Affect Plants? p. 370 Activity: Evaluating Air and Water Quality, p. 370 Investigate: Model Building, p. 371 Investigate: Research, p. 372 Investigate: Research, p. 373	**LM** Investigating Air and Water Pollution, #31 Observing the Effects of Acid Rain on Seed Germination and Plant Growth, #32 **TR** Writing in Biology: Writing, Reading, and Speaking Out About the Environment Explore: Oil and Water Don't Mix **BL** Inquiry Activity: Raindrops Keep Falling	
Inquiry Activity: Preserving Natural Habitats, p. 375 Investigate: Research, p. 375 Investigate: Model Building, p. 376 Investigate: Role-Playing, p. 377	**TR** Enrich: Conservation Conundrum **BL** Inquiry Activity: In Your Own World	**TB** Island Size and Biodiversity, #22

KEY: **SE** Student Edition **TE** Teacher's Edition **LM** Laboratory Manual **TR** Teaching Resources
BL BioLog **TB** Transparency Box **CTB** Computer Test Bank

Materials List

TE Chapter Discovery Learning Activity, p. 358 (20 minutes at home for trash collection, 30 minutes for class session); plastic bag containing 4.5 lbs clean trash collected by student, calculator.

TE Investigate: Model Building, p. 360 (30 minutes); 6 vials, medicine dropper, red food coloring.

SE Mini Lab: When a Little Can Mean a Lot, p. 361 (45 minutes); bowl containing 75 red beans and 75 white beans, 10 small plastic bags, 1 large plastic bag, grease pencil or tape and marker to label bags, calculator.

TE Investigate: Model Building, p. 364 (40 minutes); modeling clay, plastic knife, blue, yellow, and green paint or markers.

SE Mini Lab: Holding Your Own, p. 366 (15–20 minutes for the initial planting session and 5–10 minutes for each subsequent observation); plastic cups, potting soil, annual rye grass seed, radish seeds; optional: magnifier.

TE Activity: Comparing Soil Types, p. 368 (20 minutes for soil collecting, 20–30 minutes for in-class investigation); soil samples collected by students, clear jars, water, ruler.

TE Inquiry Activity: How Does Acid Affect Plants? p. 370 (20–30 minutes for designing experiments, 1–2 weeks for conducting tests, 45 minutes for class presentations); plants and acid solutions chosen by students.

TE Activity: Evaluating Air and Water Quality, p. 370 (20–30 minutes for each investigation); Examining new and used air filters: magnifier; Testing for acid rain: rainwater samples collected by students, litmus paper.

TE Investigate: Model Building, p. 371 (20 minutes); paper-towels, paper cups, dark molasses.

TE Investigate: Model Building, p. 376 (40 minutes); graph-paper, string, metric ruler.

CHAPTER 16

Humans in the Biosphere

Introducing the Chapter

. . . In Pictures

Have students examine the photograph, read the caption, and answer the following questions.

- **What type of biome is shown in the picture?** (A temperate deciduous forest.)
- **Besides the trees that are being cut down, how might other living things be affected by this human activity?** (Accept all reasonable responses. Students should consider the effects of habitat loss on animals that depend on the trees for food, nesting sites, and shelter; the effects of cutting roads through the forest; and the effects of noise and exhaust from trucks and machinery.)

Teaching Strategy

In the first section of this chapter, students learn about the ability of humans to change environments. In the second section, they identify strategies for sustainable agriculture, which help to protect the environment. In the third section, they identify the role of pollution in placing resources at risk and ways to protect those resources. In the BRANCHING OUT section at the end of the chapter, they examine how conservation biology aims to maintain biodiversity through the preservation of wildlife habitats.

BIO JOURNAL

To prompt students' thoughts about what their world might look like in the future, briefly discuss the changes they have already witnessed in their lifetime—for example, clearing of wooded areas to build new highways or housing developments, or increasing smog levels as a result of more cars, factories, and power plants. Instruct students to keep their entries in their portfolios.

CHAPTER 16

Humans in the Biosphere

FOCUSING THE CHAPTER THEME: Patterns of Change

16–1 This Island Earth
- **Examine** the capacity of human actions to change environments.

16–2 Agriculture
- **List** several strategies for sustainable agriculture.

16–3 Resources at Risk
- **Name** resources at risk and **identify** ways to protect the environment.

BRANCHING OUT *In Depth*

16–4 Conserving Biodiversity
- **Examine** the role of conservation biology in preserving wildlife habitats.

LABORATORY INVESTIGATION
- **Construct a model** compost column and **predict** the suitability of various materials for composting.

Biology and Your World

BIO JOURNAL

Imagine that it is the year 2020. In what ways might the world look different than it does now? How much of that change do you think may be caused by human activity? In your journal, write your predictions along with your reasons.

Loading lumber on a truck in Canada

TEACHER SUPPORT

Chapter Discovery Learning Activity

The following activity illustrates the environmental impact of a common human activity: trash disposal.

One student in each group: Fill a plastic bag at home with 2 kilograms of clean trash (no food scraps) and bring it to class. (To find the mass of the trash, first find your mass, then find your mass while holding the bag; adjust the amount of trash in the bag so it has a mass of 2 kilograms.) Each student in group: **(1)** Lift the bag; 2 kilograms is the average amount of trash produced each day by one person in the United States. **(2)** Calculate how much trash your family produces in one day, one week, one month, and one year. **(3)** Find out how many people live in your city or town. Calculate how much trash those people produce in one day, one week, one month, and one year. **(4)** Find out what is done with the trash collected in your city or town.

This Island Earth

SECTION 16–1

GUIDE FOR READING

- **Explain** how human actions alter environments.
- **Define** sustainability.

MINI LAB

- **Calculate** the concentration of DDT at several aquatic trophic levels.

CENTURIES AGO, THE FIRST humans to settle the islands we now call Hawaii learned to live on tiny specks of land. They had limited amounts of fresh water and land on which to live and grow crops. But more importantly, the culture and customs of these people reflected their awareness of the limitations. Their society was completely self-supporting, although the population was greater than it is today.

In a far different environment, the Anasazi, which in Navajo means "ancient people," built great cities in the canyons of the American Southwest. As their population grew, however, the Anasazi required more from the desert than the ecosystem could supply. When a 30-year drought struck, the Anasazi were forced to abandon their canyon cities—never to return.

Human Activity and the Environment

In the past, human cities were islands of humanity in the sea of the biosphere. The impact of individual cultures was limited to their immediate environment. But exponential human population growth has changed all that.

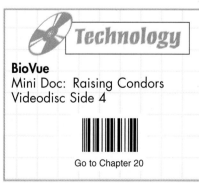

Figure 16–1 *(a) Despite limited resources such as fresh water, ancient Hawaiian cultures thrived. The Anasazi civilization built (b) elaborate cities and created (c) beautiful objects but did not survive a long period of drought. Perhaps these cultures offer important lessons as we look to the future.*

SECTION 16–1
This Island Earth

Performance Objectives

- Define the term sustainability.
- Explain how human activity can adversely affect physical and biological systems in the biosphere.

Mini Lab Skill: Calculating
Laboratory Investigation Skill: Constructing a model

1 ENGAGE

Inquiry Activity
Making Inferences

Changes in Ecosystems
Ask each group to think of one example of human activity changing an ecosystem. Have students list all the original ecosystem's biotic and abiotic factors and briefly describe how each factor would be affected by the human-caused changes. Let groups share their ideas in a class discussion.

2 EXPLORE

Investigate

Research Ask students to read the labels on various pesticides and herbicides found at home or in a store, paying particular attention to the safety precautions and environmental hazards listed on each container. Have students share their findings in class.

TEACHER SUPPORT

Managing Classroom Diversity

MULTICULTURAL STRATEGY
The Anasazi were the direct ancestors of modern Pueblo Indians, the Hopi and Zuni. For more than 1000 years, the Anasazi flourished across the American Southwest where the present states of Utah, Colorado, Arizona, and New Mexico meet. These ancient people first settled the area in about AD 100. By AD 1200 they numbered well into the tens of thousands. Then, shortly before AD 1300, they suddenly abandoned their cities and moved south.

Despite more than a century of research, archaeologists still do not completely understand this sudden move. The prolonged drought and resulting famine and disease certainly played a major role. Other factors most likely included deforestation, soil depletion, and the scarcity of wild game and other resources as the population grew. Encourage students to find out more about the Anasazi way of life and about the reasons they abandoned their homeland.

Technology

BioVue
Mini Doc: Raising Condors
Videodisc Side 4

Go to Chapter 20

3 TEACH

Discussion

Emphasize that DDT affects terrestrial food chains as well as aquatic chains like the one shown in Figure 16–3. Also make sure students understand that DDT does not have to kill predatory birds directly to have disastrous consequences. Birds with high concentrations of DDT in their bodies produce eggs with brittle shells that break before the chicks hatch, thus eliminating the next generation. Even today, more than 20 years after DDT was banned in the United States, some bird populations are still being affected. (See Ecology Note below.)

Ideas Through Images

Have students examine Figure 16–3, read the caption, and answer the following questions.

- **Except for the arrow showing DDT concentration, what does this diagram look like?** (An ecological pyramid, like the one shown in Figure 13–7 on page 290 in Chapter 13. Have students look at that diagram again, if necessary.)
- **What does parts per million mean?** (You could use the Investigate activity below to explain or clarify the term's meaning.)

Investigate

Model Building The following activity illustrates the meaning of the term parts per million used in Figure 16–3.

1. Number six clear vials 1 through 6.
2. Put 10 drops of red food coloring in vial 1. (Food coloring is already diluted 1:10, or 1 part dye per 10 parts water.)
3. Take one drop of food coloring from vial 1, put it in vial 2, and add nine drops of water. Calculate the ratio of dye to water in vial 2. (1:100)
4. Repeat the procedure with vials 3–6. (The ratio of dye to water in vial 3 is 1:1000; in 4, 1:10,000; in 5, 1:100,000; and in 6, 1:1,000,000. Vial 6 illustrates parts per million.)

Figure 16–2
Although this eaglet managed to hatch from its egg, its sibling will not be as lucky. High concentrations of DDT in the tissues of its mother at the time of egg production results in thin-shelled eggs that may never hatch.

Today, roughly half of all land on Earth not covered with ice and snow has been used and altered in some way by human actions. **According to a recent study, human actions now use almost as much energy and transport almost as much material as all other species on Earth—plants and animals combined. Humans have become the greatest source of change in the biosphere.**

Yet the human species is still a part of the biosphere and depends on global food webs, nutrient cycles, and energy flows. You can think of the biosphere as an island, and although its resources and space are abundant, they are not limitless. What's more, because our understanding of the biosphere's life-support systems is still incomplete, we should be cautious about actions we take. The following example illustrates how the physical and biological systems in the biosphere sometimes respond to human actions in ways that threaten human health and well-being.

Poisons in the Food Web

Decades ago, researchers discovered an insect-killing chemical, called DDT. At first, DDT seemed to be the perfect weapon for insect control. Once sprayed in an area, it remained active for a long time and killed many different types of insects. By killing mosquitoes, DDT helped to reduce the spread of deadly diseases, such as malaria. DDT was found to be effective against body lice and common household insects. It was also sprayed over large areas of farmland to control agricultural pests.

For a while, everything appeared to be fine. But as the insecticide became part of the water runoff from farmland, it entered nearby rivers and streams.

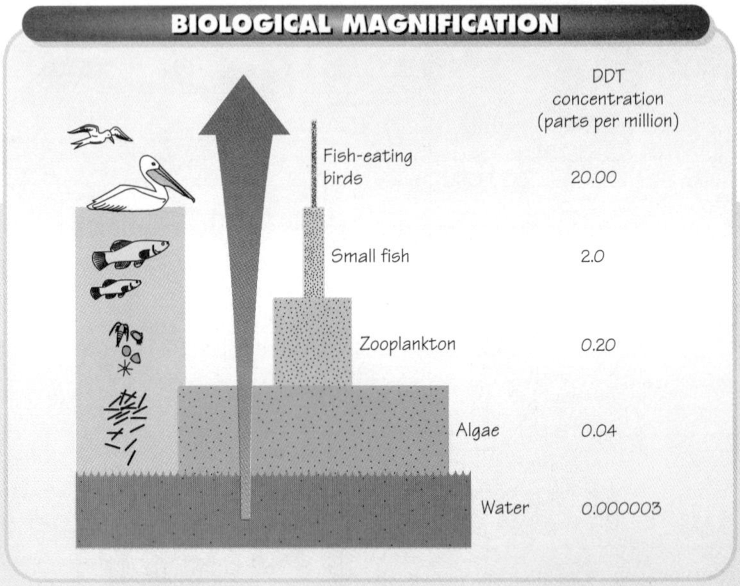

Figure 16–3
Studies show that DDT concentration was magnified almost 7 million times as it passed from primary producers, such as algae, to the highest level of consumers, such as fish-eating birds.

TEACHER SUPPORT

Ecology Note

DDT, the first synthetic organic pesticide, is a relatively stable hydrocarbon compound that is nearly insoluble in water. However, winds can carry DDT in vapor form, and water can transport fine particles. DDT is highly soluble in fats, which accounts for its accumulation in body tissues. In addition, many organisms can partially metabolize DDT to DDE and other modified compounds with different but still disruptive effects, such as fragile eggshells.

Although it has been banned in the United States since the 1970s and many endangered species have partially recovered from its devastation, DDT is still affecting animal populations. For example, some migratory birds pick up DDT at their winter ranges in Latin America. In 1990, the California State Department of Health recommended that a commercial fishery off the coast of Los Angeles be closed due to contamination by DDT from industrial waste discharges that ended more than 20 years ago.

First, the fishes in those streams began to die. Soon, fish-eating birds—such as eagles, pelicans, and ospreys—began to lay eggs that failed to hatch. Then, to their surprise, scientists discovered DDT in human body fat! Traces of DDT were even found in the flesh of penguins as far from civilization as the South Pole! What had happened?

After careful study, scientists discovered two characteristics that made this insecticide hazardous in the biosphere. First, DDT is **nonbiodegradable,** meaning that it cannot be broken down by the life processes of living things. This characteristic makes it much more potentially dangerous than **biodegradable** substances, which are broken down in the environment. Second, when an organism picks up DDT from its environment, it does not eliminate it from its body. In combination, these two characteristics led to a surprising chain of events.

Biological Magnification

Although DDT may be present in lakes and streams in very low concentrations, it can be picked up and stored by aquatic primary producers, such as algae. When herbivores eat the algae, they collect and store the DDT. The more they eat, the more DDT they store. In fact, in herbivores, the levels of DDT are ten times greater than they are in plants. When carnivores eat herbivores, DDT is concentrated even more. This process, called **biological magnification,** continues throughout the food web. Through the process of biological magnification, substances such as toxic metals and chemicals accumulate over time and are passed up the trophic levels at higher and higher concentrations.

Luckily, the trace amounts of DDT found in humans were discovered before any people were harmed. But the situation was far different for other species, such as fishes and birds. The American bald eagle, for example, was threatened with extinction due largely to the harmful effects of DDT on its eggs.

Today, the use of DDT is strictly controlled. Similar controls also apply to many other pesticides and potentially toxic substances that can be released into the environment.

Checkpoint What is biological magnification? 1

MINI LAB ········ Calculating

When a Little Can Mean a Lot

PROBLEM *How would you **calculate** the amount of DDT that accumulates in organisms of an aquatic food chain?*

PROCEDURE

1. Obtain a bowl of red and white beans. The beans represent two different types of algae, or primary producers.
2. Label 10 small plastic bags "zooplankton," and number the bags 1 through 10. Zooplankton are tiny organisms that feed upon algae.
3. Place any combination of the red and white beans—up to a total of 15—into each plastic bag. Record the number of each type of bean in each bag.
4. Label a large plastic bag "killfish." Place the 10 zooplankton bags into the large plastic bag.

ANALYZE AND CONCLUDE

1. If a red bean represents 5 ppm of DDT and a white bean represents 10 ppm of DDT, calculate the ppms in each of the zooplankton.
2. Calculate the ppms of DDT the killfish could accumulate in a day if the killfish consumes an average of 10 zooplankton per hour.
3. If a flounder (a larger fish) consumes 10 killfish per day, how much DDT could the flounder accumulate in 30 days?
4. Predict how much DDT a human could accumulate in a year by eating a flounder each month.

MINI LAB Calculating

Teacher Notes

- For time required and materials needed, see page 358b.
- Make sure students know that ppm means "parts per million."

Answers to Analyze and Conclude

1. 75–150 ppm
2. 18,000–36,000 ppm
3. 540,000–1,080,000 ppm
4. 6,480,000–12,960,000

Skills Trace
Calculating

Focus p. 361
Practice p. 362
Assess p. 383

Investigate

Research Have students research other pesticides and herbicides that were once commonly used but are now controlled or banned.

Checkpoint

1 Toxic substances accumulate over time and are passed up the trophic levels at higher and higher concentrations.

TEACHER SUPPORT

Historical Perspective

A tragic example of biological magnification involves mercury, a byproduct in the manufacture of batteries. In humans, mercury affects the central nervous system, causing paralysis, mental illness, and even death. Some years ago, factories located around Minamata Bay in Japan discharged mercury into the sea in a supposedly safe insoluble form. Microorganisms in the bay changed the mercury's form, making it soluble in seawater. The dissolved mercury was taken in by phytoplankton, passed up the food chain, and reached dangerously high concentrations in fishes such as tuna and swordfish on higher trophic levels.

Because the Japanese diet typically includes a great deal of fish, people in the Minamata area ingested large quantities of mercury and many became terribly ill and died. Also, mothers gave birth to deformed and retarded children. This tragedy is a good example of why careful scientific studies are needed before disposing of waste products into the environment.

Ancillary Support

The resources below can be used to support your teaching strategy for these two pages.

TR Explore: Good as New
BL Inquiry Activity: Here Today, Here Tomorrow
TB Biological Magnification, #21

Laboratory Investigation

The Laboratory Investigation, Turn Your Garbage Around, on pages 378–379 is appropriate to use at this point in the chapter.

4 ASSESS

Quick Check

Ask students to write a brief outline of the process of biological magnification described on pages 360–361.

Section Review 16-1

1. Human actions now use almost as much energy and transport almost as much material as all other species on Earth combined.
2. A condition in which practices are in harmony with the biosphere and do not damage its living and nonliving parts.
3. Consequences are unexpected because people sometimes fail to think about the long-term effects of their actions and because haste or human error can lead to oversights.
4. Multiply the concentration (ppm) in one organism at a lower trophic level by the number of those organisms eaten by a consumer at the next higher trophic level.

Skills Trace

Calculating

- Focus p. 361
- Practice p. 362
- Assess p. 383

Learning Modality

Visual and Tactile Learning Using Figure 16–3 as a model, students could create poster-size diagrams showing the process of biological magnification. Encourage students to use a variety of unusual materials—such as different colors and patterns of fabric for the bars in the ecological pyramid and sandpaper for the arrow—rather than simply drawing the diagram.

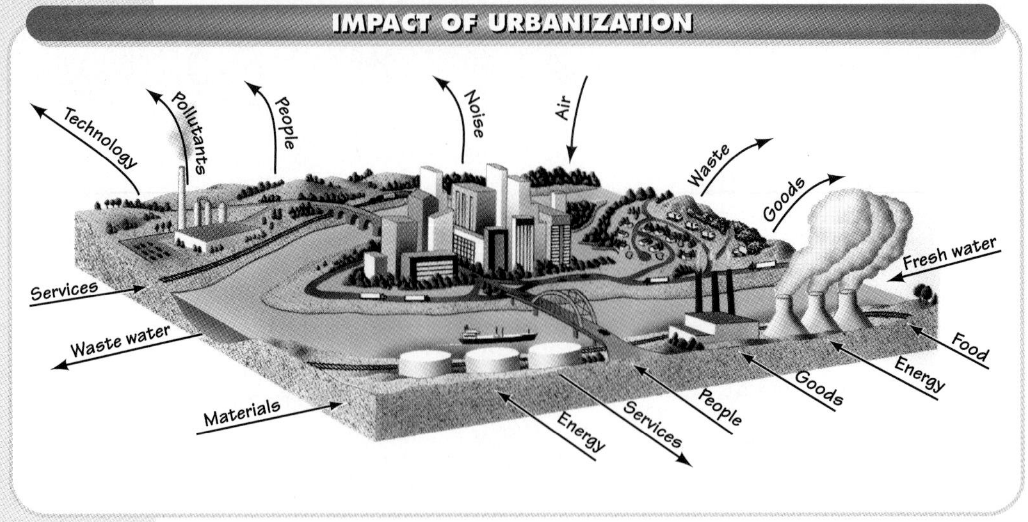

Figure 16–4 *Cities rely heavily on exchanging large quantities of materials and energy with the environment.*

Charting a Course

The DDT disaster is one of several examples that has taught humanity a valuable lesson—we do not yet know enough about the workings of the biosphere to predict all the consequences of our actions. Given these limitations, can an understanding of ecology help us shape a positive future for ourselves and the biosphere? The answer is yes. And it centers on **sustainability,** a fundamental and important concept of ecology.

Human ways of living that are based on the principles of ecology will be ecologically sustainable. Ways of living that pursue economic growth while ignoring these principles are less likely to be ecologically sustainable. **Sustainable practices are in harmony with the biosphere and do not deteriorate its living and nonliving parts.** Simply put, we must realize that we are a part of an interdependent world and must learn to live within the limits of nature's systems in order for them to support us.

As you read the next sections of this chapter, you will have an opportunity to examine several human activities along with their consequences. This will help you to understand the role and the responsibility of humans in the biosphere.

Section Review 16-1

1. **Explain** how human actions are potentially more powerful than the actions of Earth's other organisms.
2. **Define** sustainability.
3. **Critical Thinking—Evaluating** Biological magnification is frequently quoted as an example to show the unexpected consequences of some human actions. Discuss the use of the word unexpected.
4. **MINI LAB** How can you **calculate** the concentration of DDT in organisms related by a food chain?

TEACHER SUPPORT

Facts and Figures

The following information relates to the Laboratory Investigation to be used with this section. You may want to share this information with students when they do the investigation.

As noted in the Chapter Discovery Learning Activity on page 358, each person in the United States produces an average of 2 kilograms of trash every day. Multiplying this by 365 days and then by 260 million people shows that the U.S. population produces approximately 200 billion kilograms of solid waste per year—enough to fill a line of gar-bage trucks reaching one fifth of the way from Earth to the moon.

Most of this waste is taken to sanitary landfills, where it is dumped, compacted, covered with soil, and left to decompose. However, as students learn in the Laboratory Investigation, many wastes are nonbiodegradable. In addition, some waste products release toxic fumes into the atmosphere and toxic chemicals into groundwater supplies.

Agriculture

GUIDE FOR READING

- **Describe** the key practices of the green revolution and **relate** them to their environmental impact.
- **Identify** several strategies for sustainable agriculture.

MINI LAB

- **Design an experiment** to see how planting winter rye grass in a summer-cultivated cornfield helps prevent soil erosion.

THE ORIGIN OF AGRICULTURE was among the most important events in human history. Why? Agriculture supplies humans with one of their most basic needs—a dependable supply of food. Without the concentrated and predictable food supply that farming provides, humans could not gather into cities in such overwhelming numbers. Today, even if we stopped driving cars and recycled everything we use, producing food for humanity would still have an enormous impact on the biosphere.

The Green Revolution

The Earth would not be able to support as many people as it does today if it were not for a dramatic improvement in the way humans grow food. During the 1950s, governments and researchers looked at the rapidly growing world population with alarm. How could farmers possibly grow enough food to prevent mass starvation? A global effort to increase food production resulted in what is called the **green revolution.** The green revolution led to a substantial increase in crop yields as a result of a few key practices.

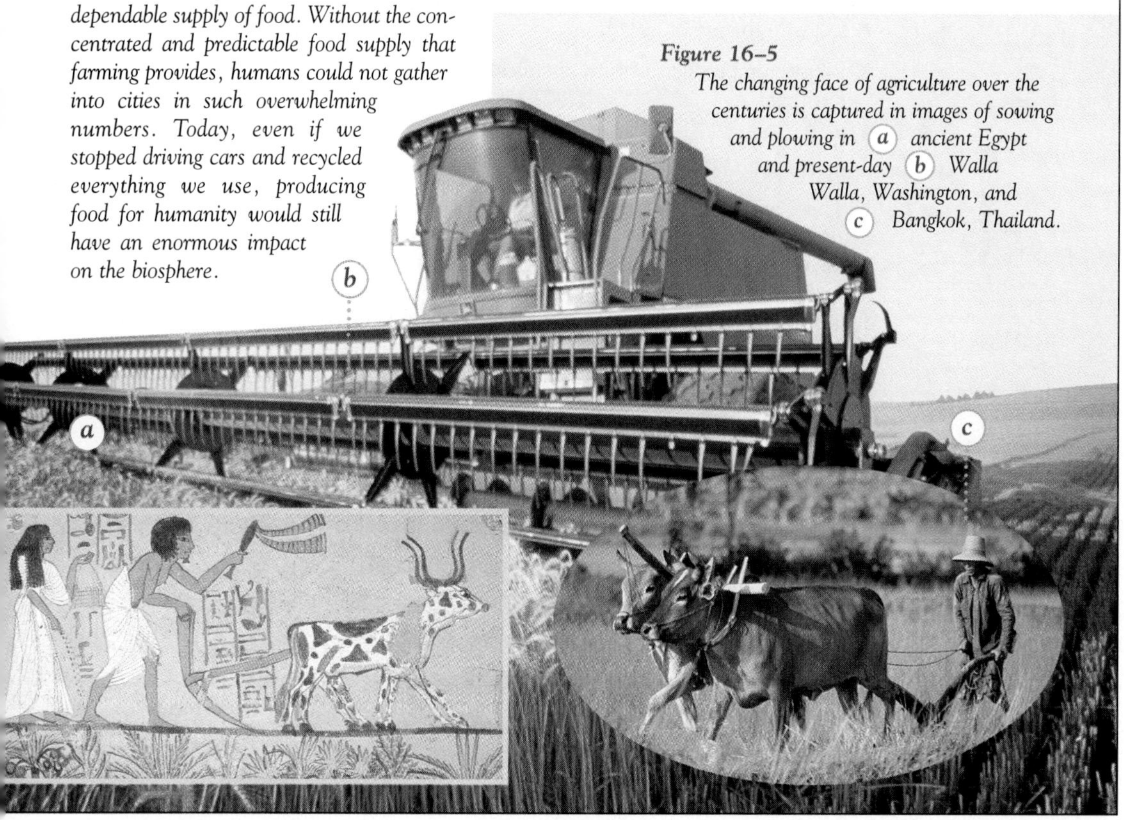

Figure 16–5
The changing face of agriculture over the centuries is captured in images of sowing and plowing in (a) ancient Egypt and present-day (b) Walla Walla, Washington, and (c) Bangkok, Thailand.

SECTION 16–2
Agriculture

Performance Objectives

- Describe environmental problems arising from green revolution practices.
- Identify characteristics of a sustainable agricultural system.

Mini Lab Skill: Experimenting

1 ENGAGE

Ideas Through Images

Have students examine the photographs in Figure 16–5, read the caption, and answer the following questions.

- **What similarity do you see between the plowing methods used in ancient Egypt and in present-day Thailand?** (Both methods use a hand-held plow pulled by oxen.)
- **What similarity do you see between the fields in Thailand and in Washington?** (Both appear to be planted with one crop.)
- **What are the advantages of using agricultural machines such as this wheat-harvesting combine?** (Vast acreages can be plowed, sown, and harvested in less time and with fewer people, enabling farmers to produce larger crops.)
- **What are the disadvantages of these machines?** (Accept a variety of responses, including their cost and the exhaust gases they release into the air.)

TEACHER SUPPORT

Managing Classroom Diversity

TECH PREP STUDENTS

Encourage students who are interested in careers in agriculture to research farming practices in your area. Sources of information include 4-H clubs, state and county agricultural agencies, and agricultural organizations listed in the *Encyclopedia of Associations,* including its separate volumes *Regional, State, and Local Organizations* for different regions.

Also suggest that students identify and interview farm owners and managers who represent different viewpoints and approaches, including both those farmers who employ green revolution practices such as chemical fertilizers and pesticides and those who rely on organic practices with low environmental impact.

Ask students to present their findings to the rest of the class in oral presentations or bulletin board displays. Challenge students to develop a specific farming plan that incorporates the sustainable-agriculture characteristics described on pages 368–369.

2 EXPLORE

Investigate

Model Building The following activity provides a visual representation of the amount of Earth's land surface that is suitable for agriculture.

1. Mold clay into a ball about the size of a grapefruit. The ball represents Earth.
2. Cut a ¼ wedge out of the ball. With paint or a marker, color the outer curved surface of the remaining ¾ section blue. This blue section represents the amount of Earth's surface covered by water.
3. Color the surface of the remaining ¼ section yellow. This section represents Earth's total land surface.
4. Cut the yellow section into two ⅛ wedges. One section represents land areas such as polar regions and deserts, where crops cannot be grown.
5. Cut a ¼ wedge out of the other ⅛ section to make a 1/32 section and a 3/32 section. Color the surface of the 3/32 section brown. This section represents land that is too wet, hot, or rocky for agriculture or that has soil too poor to grow crops.
6. Color the surface of the remaining 1/32 section green. This section represents the total land area available for agriculture.

3 TEACH

Discussion

Ask students to describe various green revolution practices that they have seen being used in their area—whether on large farms, small farms, or in household vegetable gardens—or practices they may have used themselves.

INTEGRATING TECHNOLOGY AND SOCIETY

Students should cite the five key practices listed on page 364.

Figure 16–6 (a) *Soaring crop yields were a result of several green revolution efforts, such as* (b) *large-scale irrigation.*

- Clear and plow large fields and plant a single highly productive crop. This strategy, called **monoculture,** makes sowing, tending, and harvesting more efficient.
- Use machinery powered by fossil fuels.
- Increase the use of irrigation.
- Boost crop production with chemical fertilizers.
- Control plant pests with chemical pesticides.

INTEGRATING TECHNOLOGY AND SOCIETY
How do the green revolution practices make use of technology to improve conditions for human society?

These practices produced remarkable results worldwide. In 20 years, Mexican farmers increased their production of wheat tenfold. The world's most densely populated countries—China and India—were able to produce most of the food they needed for the first time in years. The green revolution, probably more than any other single effort, helped to prevent global food shortages.

☑ **Checkpoint** How did the green revolution produce high crop yields? 1

Environmental Impact

In many places, green revolution techniques continue to be enormously successful. But constant use of these techniques can cause problems. With what you know now about ecology, you should be able to understand why and how those problems have arisen. **The green revolution practices can cause a number of pressing environmental problems—such as pesticides in the environment, loss of soil fertility, and the dwindling of water resources.** Some of these problems are outlined in the pages that follow.

Pests and Diseases

To an insect that eats the leaves of corn plants, much of the farmland in the United States looks like a huge dinner table set with endless fields of identical tasty corn plants! Once a population of corn-eating insects gets established in such an area, it can grow unchecked because it is surrounded by an almost unlimited supply of food. The same is true for bacterial and fungal plant diseases.

The first response to the problem of pests and diseases was the use of chemical pesticides—a key green revolution practice. Pesticides were relatively cheap and seemed to solve the problem easily and cleanly. So they were applied in large quantities to field after field, year after year.

TEACHER SUPPORT

Facts and Figures

In 1988–90, the latest years for which figures are available, there were 841 million chronically undernourished people worldwide. Obviously, the green revolution has not affected all nations equally.

According to a report released in 1996 by the UN Food and Agriculture Organization, human population growth will cause an average 75 percent increase in food-supply needs worldwide by the year 2050. The situation is most critical in African nations (sub-Saharan countries in particular), which will need to boost food production by 300 percent to satisfy growing population demands. Latin American and Caribbean countries will need to boost food production by 80 percent, Asian countries by 69 percent, and North American countries by 30 percent. European demand for food production is expected to decline during this period.

Bio FRONTIER Connections

Good Guys in the Badlands

Joe R. Weatherly isn't someone most people would think of as an environmentalist. He is a cattle rancher in Wheeler, Texas. Like more than 90 percent of American cattle ranches, his company—Heritage Beef Cattle Company—is a family operation. And in order to be able to pass the business on to future generations, the Weatherly family wants to keep the land healthy. So they use as many sustainable agriculture techniques as they can. For their work, the Weatherly family won the 1995 Environmental Stewardship Award from the National Cattlemen's Association. Since 1991, this award has recognized ranchers who practice environmentally sound strategies.

Cattle grazing on properly managed rangeland

The Problem

Unlike the grazing habits of antelope, elk, deer, and bighorn sheep, beef cattle do not graze for a while in one area and then move on. Instead, left to themselves, beef cattle overgraze range land and destroy the streams that run through it. As a result, many areas of grassland became scrub brush unsuitable for grazing, and water supplies were in trouble.

The Solution

Soon ranchers began working with ecologists to see if they shared common ideas. Together they agreed that a solution must combine good science, workable conservation strategies, and economic sense. Because fire is an important part of prairie ecosystems, both groups worked out plans to allow some areas to burn in controlled ways. They also developed strategies to move cattle from place to place so they would not overgraze any single area. In addition, ranchers learned how to protect streams to guard water supplies.

Thanks to this combined effort, most range land today is either stable or in the process of improving. What's more, many ranchers are now working with environmental groups to protect endangered species that are found on their property.

Making the Connection

What are other uses of land that can cause lasting harm to our resources or the environment? How can people begin to adopt sustainable ways of using their land?

Connections

Overgrazing results when too many animals graze an area or when animals stay in one place too long. When land is overgrazed, the grasses die and are replaced by scrub, weeds, and toxic plants that do not provide good pasture for livestock. The death of grasses with wide-branching roots increases runoff of water, resulting in soil erosion. Overgrazing also ruins wildlife habitats. For example, livestock trample the fertile areas that border streams, killing plants, causing erosion of the stream banks, and making the water too muddy to support aquatic life.

Moving livestock herds at intervals allows grasses in the vacated areas to regrow. Controlled burning destroys scrub brush and toxic plants without harming the grass, whose roots soon sprout new forage for the livestock herds that will return to the area later.

Answers to Making the Connection

The building of residential and commercial structures can be detrimental to our resources and environment. Involved parties can discuss ways to save ecosystems. Land might be set aside for wildlife reserves.

Checkpoint

1 By using monoculture, machinery powered by fossil fuels, increased irrigation, and chemical fertilizers and pesticides.

TEACHER SUPPORT — Background Information

In 1991, a research team from the World Resources Institute conducted a study comparing conventional U.S. farming systems that rely on heavy use of fertilizers and pesticides with systems that use sustainable practices to maintain soil fertility, control moisture, and manage pests. In a follow-up study reported in 1994, researchers concluded that federal farm policies do not encourage sustainable practices.

The basic incentive structure of the U.S. farm program in fact works against sound resource management because farmers are paid incentives based on how much of the defined "program crops" they produce. Farmers who plant nonprogram crops to control pests and increase soil fertility receive less government support than farmers who adhere to the program while ignoring its environmental impact. Farm policy critics suggest that incentives be tied to farmers' financial needs and environmental stewardship, not simply to how much of a program crop they produce.

Technology

BioVue
Mini Doc: Cattle Ranching and the Environment
Videodisc Side 4

Go to Chapter 10

MINI LAB Experimenting

Teacher Notes

- For time required and materials needed, see page 358b.
- Remind students to control all variables except the one they want to test.
- If students wish to remove the plants from the soil, show them how to do so without damaging the roots: Gently loosen the soil with a fork and pry up a clump of plants. Lightly shake the plants to dislodge excess soil covering the roots without disturbing any soil particles clinging to them.
- Optional: Provide magnifiers so students can examine the exposed roots more closely.

Answers to Analyze and Conclude

1. Students' answers will vary depending on their hypotheses and experimental results.

2. Annual rye grass germinates quickly in the fall, preventing soil erosion during the winter months. It can then be plowed under in the spring before the new crop is planted.

Skills Trace
Experimenting

Focus p. 366
Practice p. 369
Assess p. 383

MINI LAB Experimenting

Holding Your Own

PROBLEM *How can planting winter rye grass in a summer-cultivated cornfield help to prevent soil erosion? **Design an experiment** to answer the question.*

SUGGESTED PROCEDURE

1. Formulate a hypothesis about the effect that planting rye grass has on soil.
2. Use plastic cups, potting soil, rye grass seed, radish seeds, and water to design and conduct an experiment to test your hypothesis.
3. Allow yourself two weeks to make observations and draw conclusions.

ANALYZE AND CONCLUDE

1. Did your experiment support your hypothesis? Explain your answer.
2. Why do you think farmers would plant an annual rye grass during the winter?

What's Wrong With Pesticides?

Over time, however, problems began to surface. The first to be noticed was biological magnification. But other problems were brewing as well. As farmers continued to use a pesticide, insects became resistant to it. At first, higher doses of pesticide worked. Then farmers switched to more powerful poisons. But sooner or later, the insects become immune to nearly any pesticide. Meanwhile, as more pesticides were used, streams, lakes, and underground water supplies were contaminated. The total environmental cost of pesticide use in this country is estimated at $8 billion each year. Still, insect damage continues to rise.

And there are other problems. Not only do pesticides kill the target pests, they also kill insects that are their natural predators. Because of biological magnification, pesticides often affect these beneficial insects on a higher trophic level more adversely than they affect the destructive pests at the lower trophic level. This means that as soon as pesticide use is stopped, destructive pests multiply uncontrollably because their natural predators are gone. Researchers estimate that the destruction of natural predators by pesticides costs farmers more than $500 million each year.

The Good Earth

Farmland in the United States is productive largely because vast areas of the country are covered with excellent topsoil. The Midwest was once a prairie ecosystem covered by rich soil. Tough, deep roots of long-lived grasses held the soil in place against the actions of wind and rain. When the prairie was converted to farmland, these grasses were removed. Today, single-season crops are planted and harvested, leaving large fields exposed to wind and rain between crops. As a result, soil is eroded faster than it can be replaced.

Just how rapid is soil loss? A typical field on the high plains of the Midwest loses an average of about 4 million kilograms of topsoil per square kilometer every year. In parts of the tropics, the situation is much worse. Poor farmers often must plant crops on steep hillsides. Some of these fields lose up to 150 million kilograms of topsoil per square kilometer each year. An astonishing 30 percent of the world's cropland has been abandoned over the last 40 years because erosion has stripped it of useful soil. Some researchers estimate the cost of soil erosion in the United States to be as high as $27 billion every year.

☑ ***Checkpoint*** How does cultivation of single-season crops lead to soil loss? 1

TEACHER SUPPORT — Ecology Note

The deterioration of large tracts of grassland or cropland to more desertlike conditions, with a 10 percent or greater drop in agricultural productivity, is known as desertification. In the past 50 years, 9 million square kilometers of land worldwide has become desertified, and at least 200,000 square kilometers are being added to that number annually.

Overgrazing on marginal lands is the main cause of large-scale desertification. For example, the Sahel—a region of West Africa that forms a belt of savanna between the Sahara and tropical rain forests—is rapidly undergoing desertification as a result of overgrazing by cattle and overfarming.

Prolonged drought can accelerate the desertification process, as it did in the American Great Plains during the 1930s, giving the region a new nickname: the Dust Bowl. Today, without massive irrigation and intensive conservation farming, desertlike conditions could reclaim this region.

Figure 16–7
Prairie grass ecosystems—which once protected the rich topsoil from erosion by rain and wind—have been converted to farmland, leaving fields vulnerable to soil loss throughout the winter months.

Water, Water Everywhere?

Agriculture across much of the world depends on large-scale watering, called irrigation. More than 70 percent of all water consumed in the United States is used for agriculture. In some states, such as California, river water is transported by pipes and aqueducts over long distances to farmlands. Farmlands in Texas, Oklahoma, Kansas, Colorado, South Dakota, New Mexico, and Nebraska get their water from a huge underground deposit called the Ogalalla aquifer.

In many places, however, water is becoming scarce. Water in the Ogalalla aquifer, for example, is often described as "fossil water" because it has collected over millions of years and is not replaced each year by rainfall. In fact, so much water in this aquifer is being pumped out and used for agriculture that the entire aquifer is expected to run dry within 20 to 40 years!

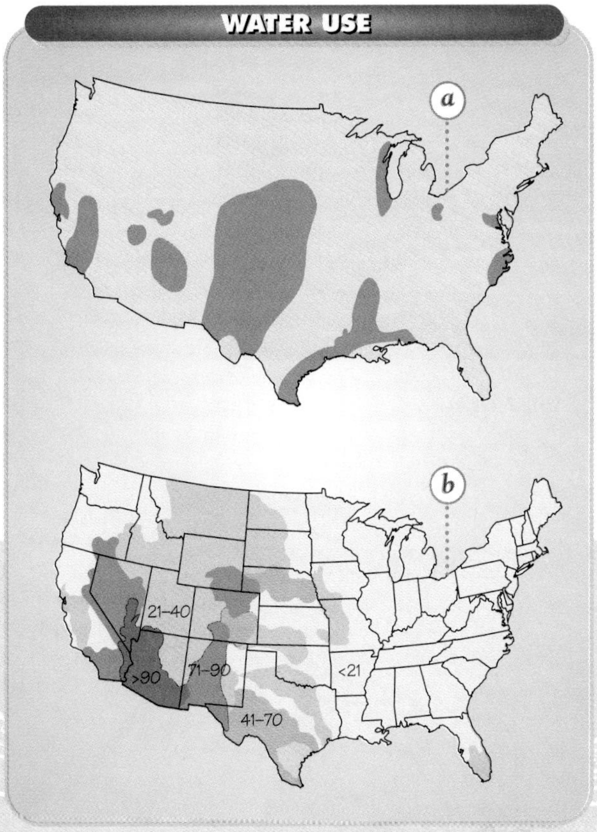

Figure 16–8
(a) This map shows areas of groundwater depletion, while (b) this map identifies areas where a high percentage of surface water is used.

Ideas Through Images

Have students examine Figure 16–8, read the caption, and answer the following questions.

- **What do the terms groundwater and surface water in the caption refer to?** (Groundwater is water that is held in underground reservoirs deep below Earth's surface. Surface water is the fresh water contained in lakes, rivers, streams, and other bodies on the surface.)
- **Which part of the United States has the largest groundwater supplies?** (The eastern half of the country.)
- **Which part depends most heavily on surface water supplies?** (The western half.)
- **Which regions or states are using much more than 30 percent of their surface water supplies each year?** (The Southwest, California, Nevada, Wyoming, Colorado, Nebraska.)
- **What is happening to water supplies in the area where we live?** (Answers will vary depending on your location. If you live near the Atlantic, Pacific, or Gulf coasts, you may want to point out that many aquifers in coastal locations are being contaminated by the intrusion of saltwater.)

☑ Checkpoint

1 When single-season crops are harvested, large fields are exposed to wind and rain, resulting in soil loss.

TEACHER SUPPORT

Managing Classroom Diversity

GIFTED STUDENTS

Suggest that students research desalination processes and technologies that are used to remove salt from seawater and obtain fresh water for drinking, irrigation, and other uses. Encourage them to find out why the United States does not use desalination to solve its water shortages, although the supply of seawater is virtually unlimited and desalination technologies already exist.

Desalination is feasible only in countries with limited population sizes, large energy reserves, and ample financial resources. In some situations, desalination may be the only alternative to running completely out of water, as some southern California cities nearly did recently during a severe, prolonged drought. However, desalination is not at present cost-effective for large-scale agriculture, which accounts for the majority of water use in this country as well as almost two thirds of the water use worldwide.

Ancillary Support

The resource below can be used to support your teaching strategy for these two pages.

BL Inquiry Activity: Washing Away

Visualizing Agriculture in the Future

Point out to students that some of the strategies described on this page have been known and used worldwide for many years. These strategies include contour plowing, strip cropping, crop rotation, maintaining good topsoil and mulch cover, growing crops suited to local rainfall, and using natural predators as biological controls. Other strategies—such as drip irrigation and some biological controls—are newer, often the result of recent scientific discoveries and new technology. Emphasize that what makes agriculture of the future significantly different from methods used today and in the past is that these strategies are used in combination as an integrated agricultural plan.

You may also want to point out that some of these methods are at present more costly than conventional farming techniques or require additional financial outlays to implement. For example, a farmer who uses spray irrigation (which wastes water through evaporation) but who wants to convert to drip irrigation must purchase and install new equipment. (For another example of financial issues, see Background Information on page 365.)

Visualizing Agriculture in the Future

Agriculture in the future must use practices that are compatible with the principles of sustainability. Planting alternating rows (strips) of crops, cultivating in contoured strips at right angles to the slope of the terrain, and rotating crops from year to year are practices that conserve soil. Delivering water, drop by drop, directly to the roots of plants that need it conserves water. Crop rotation and the use of predators and parasites to control destructive insects are some of the practices that jointly constitute what is known as Integrated Pest Management. Decreasing meat consumption and increasing the direct consumption of grains is a more efficient use of existing supplies.

3 Contour Plowing

2 **CROP ROTATION**

	Field A	Field B	Field C	Field D	Field E	Field F
Year 1	corn	corn	oats	alfalfa	alfalfa	alfalfa (plowed in)
Year 2	corn	oats	alfalfa	alfalfa	alfalfa (plowed in)	corn
Year 3	oats	alfalfa	alfalfa	alfalfa (plowed in)	corn	corn

1 Strip Cropping

6 Grain for Human Consumption

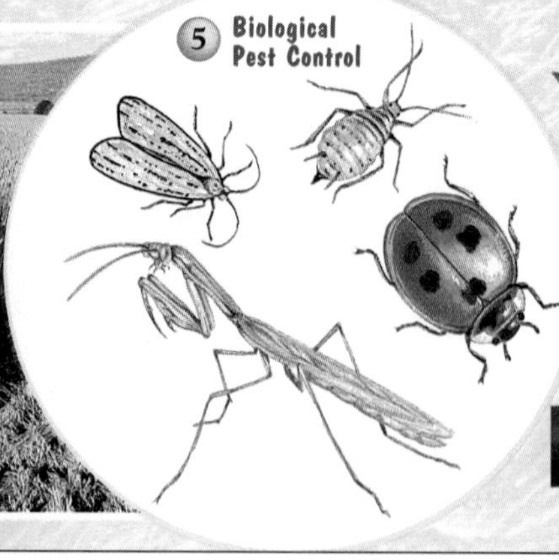

5 Biological Pest Control

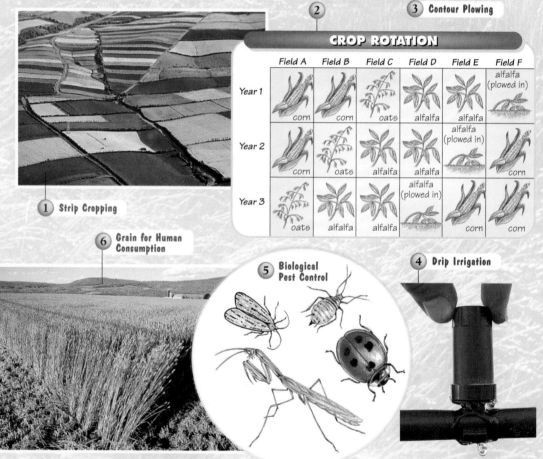

4 Drip Irrigation

TEACHER SUPPORT

Activity

COMPARING SOIL TYPES

The following activity demonstrates that humus-rich soil with lower proportions of clay and sand best supports plant life.

1. Collect soil samples from a variety of distinctive locations (a wooded area, a vacant lot, a ballfield or pathway with compacted soil, a garden, a bare road embankment, and the like). Label each sample to identify the type of area from which it was collected.

2. Place each sample in a clear jar, fill the jar with water, secure the lid, shake the jar, then leave it undisturbed until all the soil particles have settled.

3. For each sample, measure the depth of each layer and identify the type of soil material in it (pebbles, sand, clay, and so forth).

4. Compare each sample's characteristics with the plant growth in the area from which it was collected. Which soil type best supports plant growth?

States such as California, Arizona, and Nevada are also running short of water—river water. Interestingly, most researchers estimate that no more than 30 percent of a river's average flow should be taken out for use each year if water shortages are to be avoided. Take a look at ***Figure 16–8*** on page 367 to see if this is being followed.

Agriculture in the Future

Perhaps you are beginning to see the challenge facing agriculture in the future. The goal of sustainable agriculture is to provide an adequate supply of food to feed a growing global human population while, at the same time, protecting the environment. This sounds good, but what does it mean?

Most ecologists would define a sustainable agricultural system as having the following characteristics:

- **Stability** The system must be able to operate without causing long-term harm to the soil, water, and climate on which it depends.
- **Flexibility** The system must be flexible enough to survive environmental stresses—such as droughts, floods, and extreme heat or cold.
- **Appropriate Technology** The system's needs for equipment and energy must be suitable for local environments and compatible with the abilities and training of the people using them.
- **Efficiency** The system should consume as little energy and material as possible. There should be a shift away from a reliance on fossil fuel energy sources toward renewable energy sources, such as solar energy.

How are these principles translated into practice? Visualizing Agriculture in the Future on the previous page presents a few specific strategies, or practices, that address the environmental problems you have read about earlier in this chapter. In addition, such simple practices as planting crops appropriate to local rainfall and covering soil with mulch—dead organic matter such as leaves and grass—to further prevent soil loss will go a long way in conserving precious resources and protecting the environment.

With proper management based on accurate information, many agricultural systems could be made much more sustainable than they are today. Will you be one of the people who helps humanity achieve that goal?

Section Review 16-2

1. **Describe** the key practices of the green revolution and **relate** them to their environmental impact.
2. **Identify** several strategies for sustainable agriculture.
3. **Critical Thinking—Sequencing** Sequence the use of the following integrated pest management (IPM) strategies so that they cause the least harm to the environment: low-impact nontoxic sprays, biodegradable poisons, crop rotation, biological control.
4. **MINI LAB** What type of plants might be most effective in reducing the erosion of topsoil from vacant fields in winter? **Design an experiment** to answer the question.

Learning Modality

Auditory Learning Ask volunteers with fluent reading skills to tape-record the information presented in the visual essay on page 368. Let students use the recording in conjunction with the visuals to study the information.

4 ASSESS

Quick Check

Have students create a three-column table with the heads Soil Conservation, Water Conservation, and Integrated Pest Management, then list and briefly describe at least two specific strategies in each column.

Section Review 16-2

1. Monoculture: Increases soil loss. Machinery powered by fossil fuels: Increases atmospheric carbon dioxide and polluting gases. Increased irrigation: Depletes groundwater and surface water supplies. Chemical fertilizers: Pollute water supplies; stimulate algae blooms. Chemical pesticides: Biological magnification endangers other organisms; insects become resistant; pesticides contaminate water supplies.

2. Students should identify some of the specific soil conservation, water conservation, and pest management strategies described on page 368.

3. From least to greatest harm: biological control, crop rotation, low-impact nontoxic sprays, biodegradable poisons.

4. Plants that germinate quickly in the fall and can withstand the harshness of winter, such as annual rye grass. Students' experimental designs will vary but may be refined versions of their designs for the MINI LAB on page 366.

Skills Trace
Experimenting

- Focus p. 366
- Practice p. 369
- Assess p. 383

Ancillary Support

The resource below can be used to support your teaching strategy for these two pages.

TR Apply: Cope With the Slope

SECTION 16-3
Resources at Risk

Performance Objectives

- Identify the sources and effects of several major forms of environmental pollution.
- Differentiate between ecosystem diversity, species diversity, and genetic diversity.
- Explain the value of biodiversity to human society.

1 ENGAGE

Inquiry Activity
Designing an Experiment

How Does Acid Affect Plants?
Ask students what effect they think an acid solution would have on plants. Suggest that each group design and carry out an experiment to investigate the question. Explain that they can water plants with an acid solution to test its effect on plant growth, mist plants with it to test its effect on leaves, or devise another test method. They can also use acid solutions of different strengths. The only limitation is that they must use an acid that is completely safe for them to handle, such as vinegar or lemon juice. Check students' experimental designs to make sure they control all variables except the one being tested. Remind students to record all measurements, observations, and conclusions. When students have completed their experiments, give each group an opportunity to present its test design and results to the rest of the class.

SECTION 16–3 Resources at Risk

Guide for Reading

- **Identify** the major forms of pollution and their sources.
- **Define** biodiversity and **explain** its importance.

THE ALASKAN OIL PIPELINE cutting through untouched wilderness is symbolic of the dilemma human society faces today. Although we appreciate and love the beauty of natural ecosystems, we also manipulate and often exploit natural resources for our needs and wants. Can humans use our planet's resources without causing long-term harm to our environment or perhaps even to the biosphere?

Environmental Pollution

Although agriculture is the largest single human activity, many other things that people do also greatly affect the biosphere. In the past, cities and industries could grow rapidly and cheaply because people were not concerned about discarding waste products into the environment. When pollution problems became serious locally, solutions seemed simple. Too much liquid waste? Dump it into the ocean. Too much smoke? Build a higher smokestack so the wind will carry it away. This was not because people were careless about the environment—it was because no one really understood the long-term effects of these actions or what was at stake.

We now know that our waste products are polluting many parts of the continents we live on and the oceans around us. **A variety of human activities are affecting natural resources—such as clean air and water—that serve as the lifeblood of the biosphere.**

Some forms of pollution are caused by activities that are as basic to our lives as eating. We drive cars, heat homes, use electric lights, and keep food in refrigerators. We shop in malls filled with an amazing variety of products that go far

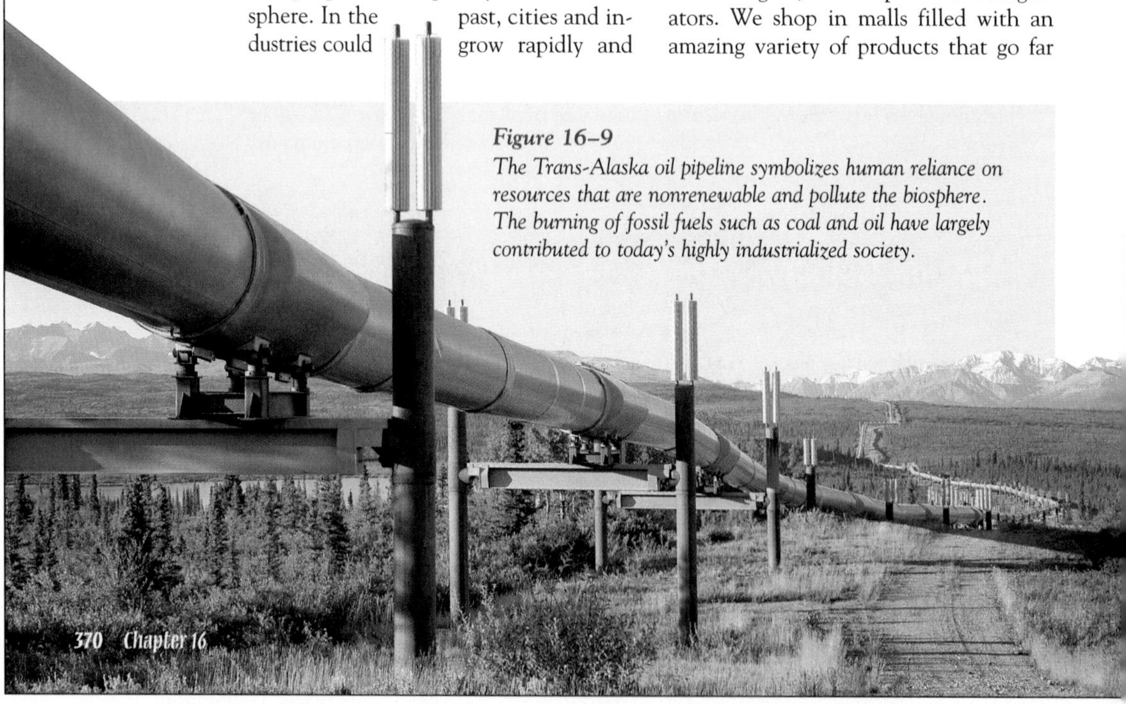

Figure 16–9
The Trans-Alaska oil pipeline symbolizes human reliance on resources that are nonrenewable and pollute the biosphere. The burning of fossil fuels such as coal and oil have largely contributed to today's highly industrialized society.

TEACHER SUPPORT

Activity

EVALUATING AIR AND WATER QUALITY
Students could investigate air and water quality in their own environment as follows.

- **Examining air filters:** Provide, or ask students to bring in, a variety of new and used air filters from automobile carburetors, heating and air-conditioning systems, room air-filtering units, kitchen or workshop exhaust fans, and the like. Have students examine the filters with a magnifier, comparing the appearance of the new filters with that of the used ones.
- **Testing for acid rain:** Have students collect samples of rainwater from various outdoor locations, test each sample's pH level with litmus paper, and compare it with the acidity of the water from a faucet. Explain that all rainwater is slightly acidic (pH 6–7) due to naturally occurring carbon dioxide in the air. If the rainwater that students test is less than pH 6, it qualifies as acid rain.

Figure 16–10
(a) The smog in Los Angeles, (b) the ozone hole over the Antarctic—shown by the red area in the image of the Earth—and (c) hazardous chemical dumps and spills are examples of some of the undesirable consequences of human actions.

beyond the simple needs of food, clothing, and shelter. Think of the energy and material requirements of the manufacturing industries and the waste products they generate—waste products that often end up polluting our air, water, and land resources.

One of the biggest sources of environmental pollution is the burning of fossil fuels—coal, oil, and natural gas. Nearly 90 percent of the energy used in the world today—for transportation, generating electricity, and heating buildings, for example—comes from fossil fuels.

Smog

Smog is due primarily to automobile exhausts and factory smokestacks. It threatens the health of the elderly and of people with asthma or other respiratory conditions.

Acid Rain

Many combustion processes, such as the burning of coal in power plants, release acidic gases into the atmosphere. Here gases combine with water vapor to form strong acids that fall to Earth as acid rain. Acid rain is harmful to plants as well as to animals.

Holes in the Ozone Layer

Ozone, a gas that is a pollutant at ground level, is a helpful barrier in the upper atmosphere. It shields the Earth from excessive, potentially harmful ultraviolet radiation. Pollutants such as CFCs (chlorofluorocarbons)

Figure 16–11
Precipitation that is 10 to 1000 times more acidic than normal is common in the northeastern United States. This diagram shows some of the effects of acid rain.

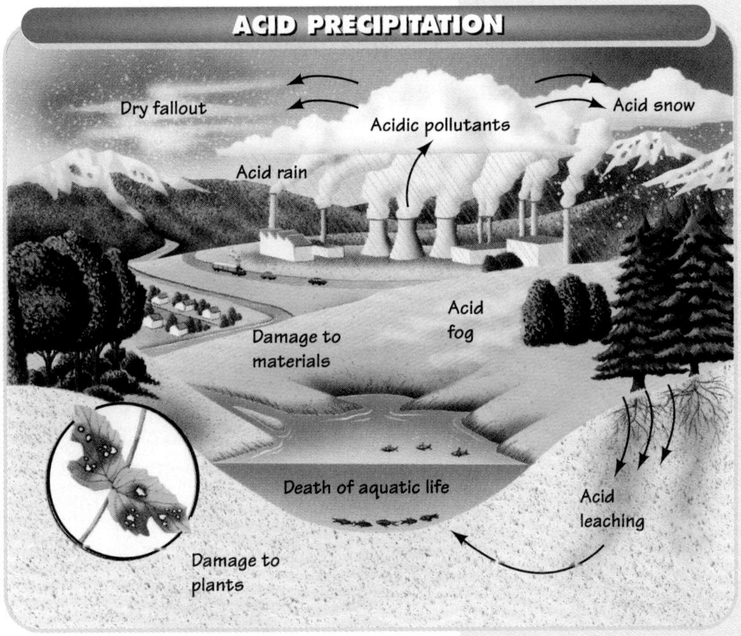

2 EXPLORE

Investigate

Model Building The following activity demonstrates the high viscosity of crude oil compared with that of motor oil and other common oils with which students may be familiar. This understanding will be helpful to students when they read on page 372 about oil spills . Give each student or group a paper towel, a small, empty paper cup, and an identical cup containing about 30 mL of dark molasses, but do not reveal what the substance is. Tell students to pour the substance from one cup to the other and try to pick some up with the paper towel. Students will discover that the substance does not pour easily and is not absorbed by the towel. Let students dip a finger into the molasses to see how thick it is. Identify the substance and explain that its consistency is similar to that of crude oil.

3 TEACH

Ideas Through Images

Have students examine Figure 16–11, read the caption, and answer the following questions.

- **What are the sources of acidic pollutants in the atmosphere?** (Factories, power plants, automobiles.)
- **Besides acid rain, what other forms of acidic pollution can affect living things?** (Acid snow, dry fallout, acid fog, acid leaching.)
- **What are some effects of acid precipitation?** (Death of aquatic life, damage to plants, damage to materials.)

Ancillary Support

The resource below can be used to support your teaching strategy for these two pages.

TR Writing in Biology: Writing, Reading, and Speaking Out About the Environment

TEACHER SUPPORT

Background Information

Two types of smog—"gray air" (industrial smog) and "brown air" (photochemical smog)—form in major cities. Where winters are cold and wet, industrial smog develops as a gray haze over industrialized cities that burn fossil fuels. The airborne pollutants include dust, smoke, soot, ashes, asbestos, oil, bits of lead and other heavy metals, and sulfur oxides. If the pollutants are not dispersed by winds and rain, they can reach lethal concentrations. New York, Pittsburgh, and Chicago were "gray air" cities until coal burning was restricted. Today, most industrial smog forms in cities of China, India, and other developing nations and in the coal-dependent countries of eastern Europe.

In warm climates, photochemical smog develops as a brown haze over large cities, particularly where the surrounding land forms a natural basin, as it does in Los Angeles and Mexico City. This type of smog is caused mainly by nitric oxide in automobile exhaust.

Ideas Through Images

Have students examine Figure 16–12, read the caption, and answer the following questions.

- **Particulates are tiny solid particles in air. What might some of these particles consist of?** (Dust, ash, soot, pollen, etc.)
- **Federal law has forced car manufacturers to reduce CO emissions. How might this show on the graph?** (The levels of carbon monoxide in the atmosphere have decreased in the last 20 years.)

INTEGRATING HEALTH

When lead is inhaled, ingested, or absorbed through the skin, it may cause lead poisoning, which affects the production of red blood cells and causes damage to the brain, liver, and other organs. Children are especially susceptable to lead poisoning.

Investigate

Research Ask students to research toxic waste sites that have been identified in the United States, particularly any that are located in your state or region. Encourage them to find out whether specific sites have already been cleaned up by the EPA, are scheduled for cleanup, or have simply been set aside for cleanup at some undetermined point in the future. Explain that in addition to their health hazards, toxic waste sites pose significant financial and emotional problems for the people most directly affected by them; suggest that students find out about this issue as well. (Love Canal is a classic example.)

Remind students of their experience handling molasses (Explore Activity, page 371) and its resemblance to crude oil. Encourage students to find out about the methods and technologies that are now in use or are being developed to clean up oil spills—not only to remove oil from the water but also to clean oil-coated beaches and wildlife.

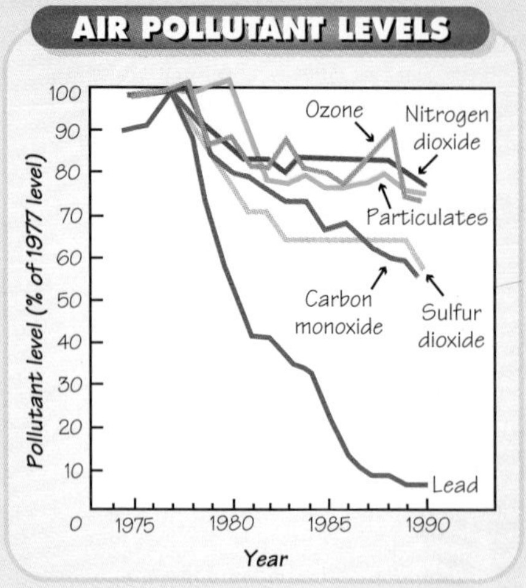

Figure 16–12
The graph shows the levels of major air pollutants in selected areas of the United States. The reason for the remarkable drop in the level of lead is due to the use of unleaded gasoline.

rise up into the upper atmosphere and destroy the ozone. International agreements on controlling CFC use are expected to halt the release of these gases by 1998.

Lead

INTEGRATING HEALTH

How is lead harmful to human health?

The levels of this toxic metal in the environment rose dangerously high largely due to the use of leaded gasoline in automobile engines. Adding lead to gasoline offered an inexpensive way of enhancing the performance of ordinary gasoline. Today, as you can see in **Figure 16–12,** the levels of lead in the environment are dropping as a result of the switch to lead-free gasoline. ●

Chemical Wastes and Oil Spills

Improperly discarded hazardous chemicals pollute streams, rivers, oceans, and underground water supplies. The chemicals are harmful to aquatic plants and animals and pose a threat to humans as they are consumed and pass up the food chain through the process of biological magnification. The Environmental Protection Agency now regulates toxic waste disposal and promotes sustainable strategies such as "reduce, reuse, recycle, and discard safely."

Oil can spill into the ocean if tankers or barges run aground, hit another ship, or are damaged by storms. Oil spilled at sea is difficult to recover—even in calm weather. When oil is spilled during stormy weather, very little can be done. Oil slicks and tar balls are deadly to marine animals that swallow them or are coated with the oil. When oil blows into estuaries, animals and plants are smothered or poisoned quickly.

Figure 16–13
Sustainable energy use must rely on renewable and less-polluting energy sources, such as solar, hydroelectric, geothermal, and biomass. Solar energy can be used to generate electricity (a) in a solar home and (b) in an experimental solar power station.

TEACHER SUPPORT

Background Information

About one twentieth of the world's energy is produced by nuclear power plants. Nuclear power, a virtually limitless renewable resource, has several distinct advantages over fossil fuels. However, nuclear reactors produce highly radioactive wastes that are difficult to handle and store safely. More importantly, safety precautions occasionally fail, and radioactive particles are accidentally released into the atmosphere, affecting not only the immediate vicinity but areas far from the power plant.

The world's worst nuclear reactor disaster occurred in April 1986 at the Chernobyl power plant in Ukraine when errors in judgment during a routine test led to runaway reactions. More than 30 people were killed instantly, many others died of radiation sickness during the weeks that followed, and radioactive fallout put an estimated 300 to 400 million people at risk of developing radiation-induced disorders and genetic defects. The effects of this disaster are still unfolding today.

Sustainable Strategies

How can we stop pollution without changing our lifestyles? It's a difficult question to answer. Just as there are strategies for sustainable agriculture, are there sustainable strategies for dealing with pollution? The answer is yes.

One significant step we can take to protect our environment is to shift from nonrenewable fossil fuel energy sources to renewable, nonpolluting energy sources such as solar and hydroelectric power. ***Figure 16–13*** offers a glimpse of the types of changes we must make if we are to protect our resources in the future.

☑ ***Checkpoint*** What are some sources of pollution in the environment? ❶

Biodiversity

You may be surprised to learn that one of Earth's greatest natural resources is **biodiversity,** or biological diversity. **Biodiversity is the genetically-based variety of living organisms in the biosphere.** The processes that bring forth new species as well as those that make species extinct have been occurring for hundreds of millions of years. The net result of these processes is the biodiversity you see all around you.

Value of Biodiversity

Biodiversity is considered a natural resource, and it is valuable to society in such diverse endeavors as agriculture, medicine, and recreation. Let's see how.

Many challenges facing agriculture may be solved with the help of wild plants. Most crop plants have surviving wild relatives around the world. Often, these wild plants contain valuable genes that can lend disease resistance, pest resistance, drought resistance, or other useful traits. Similarly, forestry, animal breeding, and aquaculture benefit from a diverse gene pool to draw upon as sources of desirable traits.

Modern medicine relies on a variety of plants as a source of a majority of commonly prescribed drugs. Painkillers, antibiotics, heart drugs, anticancer drugs, coagulants, anticoagulants, enzymes, hormones, and antidepressants are some of the drugs that have come from Earth's huge diversity of plant species.

Do you enjoy observing wild plants and animals in their natural habitats? Camping, hiking, birdwatching, visiting wild animal parks, zoos, and aquariums

(a)

(b)

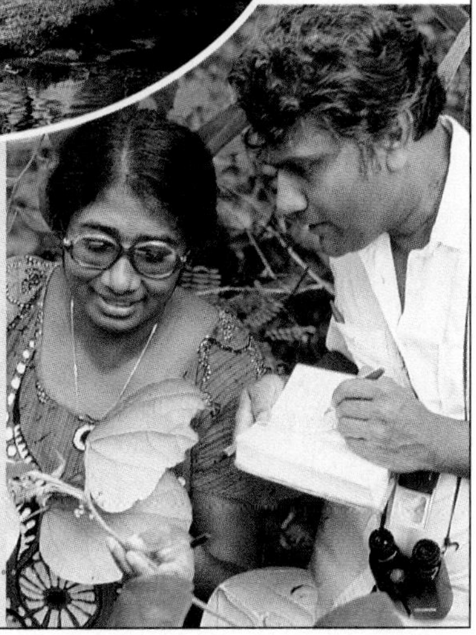

(c)

Figure 16–14
Conserving biodiversity is important for many reasons. (a) *Appreciating the beauty of wildlife, such as this resplendent quetzal from Costa Rica, and* (b) *camping in unspoiled, serene surroundings are examples of popular recreational activities.* (c) CAREER TRACK *Botanists in Sri Lanka study local plant life in order to explore possible medicinal uses.*

Discussion

Discuss nonrenewable and renewable energy sources to make sure students understand the difference between them. Nonrenewable energy sources are naturally occurring materials that are available in limited amounts. Fossil fuels—coal, oil, and natural gas—are nonrenewable resources. Because it takes millions of years for these resources to form naturally, they are essentially nonreplaceable. Renewable resources are essentially unlimited or are replaced naturally within a comparatively short period of time. Forests are one example of a renewable resource. If trees are harvested according to a well-considered plan that allows much of the forest to remain standing, and if seedlings are planted to replace harvested trees, a forest may last indefinitely. Discuss the other types of renewable energy sources identified in the caption for Figure 16–13.

Investigate

Research Challenge students to each find out about one specific example of how biodiversity is valuable to society. These examples may relate to agriculture, medicine, recreation, and other endeavors. Have students report their examples to the class or post them on a special bulletin board.

☑ Checkpoint

❶ Burning of fossil fuels, automobile exhaust, factory smokestacks, power plants, leaded gasoline, chemical wastes, oil spills.

Ancillary Support

The resources below can be used to support your teaching strategy for these two pages.

LM Investigating Air and Water Pollution, #31

Observing the Effects of Acid Rain on Seed Germination and Plant Growth, #32

TR Explore: Oil and Water Don't Mix

BL Inquiry Activity: Raindrops Keep Falling

TEACHER SUPPORT

Managing Classroom Diversity

TECH PREP STUDENTS

Students who are interested in agriculture or animal husbandry could research wild plants or animals that have been or might be crossbred with domesticated hybrid species in order to increase their desirable traits.

Our hybrid corn, for example, is an annual plant that matures, flowers, sets seed, and dies in a single season. This means that corn must be planted and harvested every year, leaving soil exposed and vulnerable between crops. Among the wild relatives of our domesticated corn are a few perennial species. These plants die back to the root each year but sprout again the next season. At this time, these perennial corn species bear only tiny cobs with rock-hard kernels. However, either plant breeding or genetic engineering might be used to add the perennial trait to our hybrid domesticated corn.

4 ASSESS

Quick Check

Ask each student to write a brief description of three harmful environmental effects of burning fossil fuels.

Section Review 16-3

1. Smog: Automobile exhaust and factory smokestacks. Acid rain: Gases from the burning of fossil fuels. CFCs: Released during the manufacture of certain products. Lead: Leaded gasoline. Chemical wastes: Factories and industrial processes. Oil spills: Tankers or barges running aground, hitting another ship, or being damaged by storms.

2. The genetically based variety of living organisms in the biosphere. Important because of its value to human society in medicine, agriculture, recreation, and knowledge.

3. Accept a variety of responses. The fact that the United States must obtain oil from Alaska despite huge stores in the continental states indicates that the United States relies too heavily on fossil fuels. The advantages of obtaining oil from within our own country, rather than relying on imported oil, cannot make up for the environmental damage caused by the pipeline.

Learning Modality

Visual Learning Have students outline this section using two major headings, Environmental Pollution and Biodiversity, with the main ideas listed below each major heading and supporting details listed below each main idea.

Figure 16–15
The value of genetic diversity extends beyond visible differences such as the height of these corn plants. A greater genetic diversity may offer benefits such as resistance to disease and drought.

or going on a whale watch are a source of joy to many of us.

In addition to the benefits just mentioned, the systematic study of biodiversity provides human society with an invaluable understanding of the workings of our living planet. Such knowledge is essential if we are to use our resources responsibly.

☑ ***Checkpoint*** What is biodiversity and its value to humans? 1

Biodiversity Threatened

Various types of human activity are causing a decrease in Earth's biodiversity. Scientists think of biodiversity as the variety at different levels of organization.

Ecosystem diversity is the variety of living ecosystems in the world, and it is threatened by the development of land for housing, industry, and agriculture. In the United States, only 5 percent of the old-growth forests, or forests that existed when the first colonists arrived, remain today. Wetlands are disappearing at an alarming rate. In the tropical regions of the world, rain forests are vanishing even more quickly.

The number and variety of different life forms, or **species diversity,** is also declining rapidly across the world. As habitats are destroyed, species living in those habitats are placed at risk. A species in danger of becoming extinct is called an endangered species. Today, many species around the world fall into this category.

Scientists also extend the concept of biodiversity to **genetic diversity**—the variety of different forms of genes present in a population. Such diversity is essential to the survival of most species. Genetic diversity in the biosphere is at risk for several reasons. When species are reduced to small populations, the populations lose genetic diversity. This tends to make individual organisms weaker and more prone to birth defects. It can also make breeding animals less fertile and less able to fight off parasites and disease. Populations that stay too small for too long thus become more vulnerable to extinction.

All forms of biodiversity are threatened by climate change today as never before in the history of life on Earth. Why? In the past when Earth's climate warmed or cooled or when patterns of rainfall shifted, living things could move around. They could extend their ranges to the north or the south. But today, most natural environments have been reduced to small patches surrounded by cities, suburbs, and farms. If climate changes now, many organisms will have no place to go.

Section Review 16-3

1. **Identify** major forms of pollution and their sources.
2. **Define** biodiversity and **explain** why it is important.
3. **Critical Thinking—Evaluating** What problem is symbolized by the Alaskan oil pipeline winding through pristine natural ecosystems? Do you think the advantages outweigh the disadvantages?

TEACHER SUPPORT

Ecology Note

Species are being lost today at a rate unprecedented in the history of life. Some biologists estimate that within the next century, half of Earth's current species may become extinct, primarily as the result of habitat loss, competition from foreign species, and overhunting. The Florida key deer is a case in point.

The key deer, a miniature species of the whitetail deer, has a unique gene pool. Key deer were cut off from whitetail populations on the mainland when sea levels rose after the last ice age. Confined to a few islands and never numerous, key deer were nearly exterminated by poachers in the early 1900s. Conservation efforts brought the species back from fewer than 50 individuals to about 400 in the early 1970s. Key deer are again declining as the human population in the Florida Keys mushrooms, housing developments destroy habitat, and highways carry more motorists. Key deer are now dying on the roads faster than they can reproduce.

BRANCHING OUT **In Depth**

Conserving Biodiversity

SECTION 16–4

GUIDE FOR READING

- **Explain** the relationship among habitat size, population size, and species diversity.
- **Examine** the role of conservation biology in land resource management.

WHEN YOU THINK OF AN ISLAND, you probably imagine a small plot of land in an ocean of water. But a lake, too, can be thought of as an island—an island of water surrounded by land. New York's Central Park is an island of trees and grass in a sea of concrete and asphalt. Even a patch of forest can be a biological island if it is surrounded by plowed fields, housing developments, or shopping malls. The concept of a biological island is important to conservation efforts aimed at preventing the loss of a species.

Island Size

To a biologist, an island is any patch of habitat surrounded by a different habitat—meaning that organisms living on the island stay confined to the island and do not move into the surrounding habitat. Studies of islands show that there are fewer species on small islands than there are on larger ones. Data indicate that the number of species on islands doubles for every tenfold increase in island size. Why does species diversity relate to island size this way? There are several reasons.

Habitat Diversity

The larger an island is, the more likely it is to have a variety of habitats. The greater the variety of habitats on the island, the greater the variety of species able to live there.

Habitat Size

The larger an island is, the larger its habitats can be. Larger habitats can support larger populations. And large populations are more likely to survive over the long term than small populations. Why? Recall that density-independent limiting factors such as unpredictable changes in environmental conditions can cause sudden increases in death rates or decreases in birth rates. The larger a

Figure 16–16
Examples of biological islands include (a) land surrounded by water and (b) New York's Central Park.

TEACHER SUPPORT

Ecology Note

In an effort to slow ecosystem destruction, a number of countries are creating megareserves—extensive regions that include one or more undisturbed areas surrounded by areas that are used by people for economic gain. These surrounding areas are protected from extensive alteration, thus serving as a buffer zone preventing further intrusion into the undisturbed areas.

The Central American nation of Costa Rica has become a world leader in this effort. In exchange for reductions in its international debt, the Costa Rican government has established eight megareserves. Their buffer zones provide a steady, lasting supply of forest products, water, and hydroelectric power and support sustainable agriculture and tourism. However, destructive practices that are incompatible with long-term ecosystem stability are discouraged in these zones. Costa Rica expects its megareserve system to maintain at least 80 percent of the country's native species.

SECTION 16–4

Conserving Biodiversity

Performance Objectives

- Explain the effect of habitat size on population size and species diversity.
- Describe the importance of habitat research and conservation management in maintaining wildlife habitats.

1 ENGAGE

Inquiry Activity

Constructing a Model

Preserving Natural Habitats Ask students to identify places in their own area where a patch of natural habitat is surrounded by a different type of habitat. Have each group choose one such habitat and then devise a plan to maintain it in as natural a state as possible. Have groups share their plans in oral presentations.

2 EXPLORE

Investigate

Research Have students research plant and animal species that are in danger of becoming extinct in the United States. (A list of endangered species can be obtained from the U.S. Fish and Wildlife Service, U.S. Department of the Interior, Washington, DC 20240.) Tell students to find out about the species' natural habitats, the reasons they are endangered, and any efforts now being made to protect them. Let students share their findings in oral reports or posters.

Checkpoint

1 Biodiversity contributes to human needs in medicine, agriculture, recreation, and knowledge.

3 TEACH

Ideas Through Images

Have students examine Figure 16–17, read the caption, and answer the following questions.

- **Based on this graph, what general statement can you make about the relationship between island size and biodiversity?** (Larger islands support a greater number of species than smaller islands do.)
- **How could this graph be used to make an argument for how to protect biodiversity in the United States?** (The graph shows that larger natural habitats are more favorable for biodiversity than smaller natural habitats are.)

Investigate

Model Building The following activity will show students the relationship between an island's perimeter and its interior area.

1. Draw two irregularly shaped "islands" on a sheet of graph paper—one large island that takes up most of the sheet and a second, much smaller island inside it.
2. Measure each island's perimeter by laying string along the line and then measuring the string with a ruler.
3. Count the number of squares inside each island. When the perimeter line divides a square, count more than half a square as a full square, and do not count less than half a square.
4. For each island, calculate the ratio of perimeter units to interior-area units: Divide the number of interior squares by the number of perimeter units and round off to the nearest tenth. (*Example:* If the larger island has a perimeter of 55 cm and an interior area of 395 squares, divide 395 by 55 and round off to get the ratio 1 to 7.2.)
5. Compare the two ratios. Which island has more interior area per unit of perimeter? (Regardless of the two islands' specific sizes, the larger island will always have a larger interior area per unit of perimeter.)

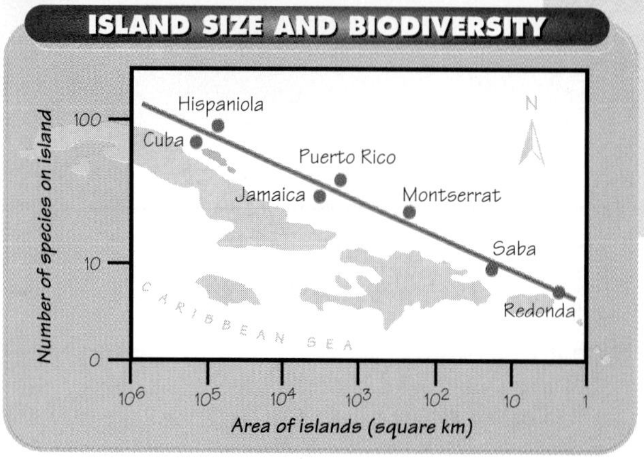

Figure 16–17 *The graph compares the diversity of reptiles and amphibians on seven Caribbean islands of various sizes. It shows that a 90-percent reduction in island size correlates with a 50-percent reduction in the number of species.*

population is, the more likely it is to survive these changes. On the other hand, the smaller a population is, the more likely it is to become extinct when stressed.

Edge Effects

An island's size has an interesting and important effect on the relationship between the island's area and its perimeter, or the length of its edge. Large islands of forest and jungle offer much more space in the interior relative to space near their edges. Small forest or jungle islands, on the other hand, have much more edge for each unit of their area.

Why is this distinction important? Here's an example to illustrate the idea. Songbirds that summer in North America thrive when they build their nests inside large areas of temperate forest. They are not as successful near the edge of forest patches for an interesting reason. Animals such as opossums, raccoons, blue jays, and cowbirds thrive in and around forest edges. In fact, these species prefer to live near neighborhoods where they can rummage through garbage cans for food. When a large patch of forest is divided by roads, shopping malls, and houses, local populations of these animals increase in size. How does this affect songbird populations? Jays, raccoons, and opossums prey on songbird eggs and hatchlings. Cowbirds are parasites that lay eggs in the nests of songbirds. Cowbird hatchlings either throw songbird hatchlings out of the nest or steal food brought back by songbird parents so the songbird chicks starve.

So when a large forest is cut up into smaller forest islands, the forest edge increases at the cost of interior forest area. Populations of predators and parasites increase and destroy so many songbird eggs and hatchlings that the size of the songbird population falls dramatically.

The lesson from several similar studies is clear. **Larger habitats support larger populations of organisms, which in turn promotes greater species diversity.** How will this understanding guide human society in deciding the best way to use land resources? Only time will tell.

☑ ***Checkpoint*** Why do larger islands support a larger number of species? 1

Conservation Biology

From the United States to Indonesia, what were once giant ecosystems are now being reduced to island habitats in a sea of human environments. Most people would like to see precious habitats preserved. Most people also want to save endangered plant and animal species. But as populations grow, it will be impossible to leave entire forests, jungles, or wetlands untouched, and compromises will have to be made.

Conservation biology is a new discipline that has emerged due to a growing understanding of the importance of habitats and biodiversity. The primary goal of this discipline is **conservation,** or the managing of natural resources

TEACHER SUPPORT

Managing Classroom Diversity

EDUCATIONAL EQUITY

One of the most influential people in raising global awareness of tropical rain forest destruction and species loss was not a trained ecologist but a rubber tapper, Chico Mendes, who lived and worked in the Amazon rain forest of Brazil. It was Mendes who created the concept of the "extractive reserve," a protected area from which forest products could be harvested without threatening the ecosystem's survival. Mendes was assassinated in 1988 by ranchers who wanted to clear vast tracts of rain forest for their own profit.

Encourage students to read about Mendes's transformation from rubber tapper to union organizer to worldwide spokesperson for the Amazon rain forest and its indigenous people. Two good sources are *Four Against the Odds: The Struggle to Save Our Environment* by Stephen Krensky (Scholastic, 1992) and *Chico Mendes: Defender of the Rain Forest* by Joann J. Burch (Millbrook Press, 1994).

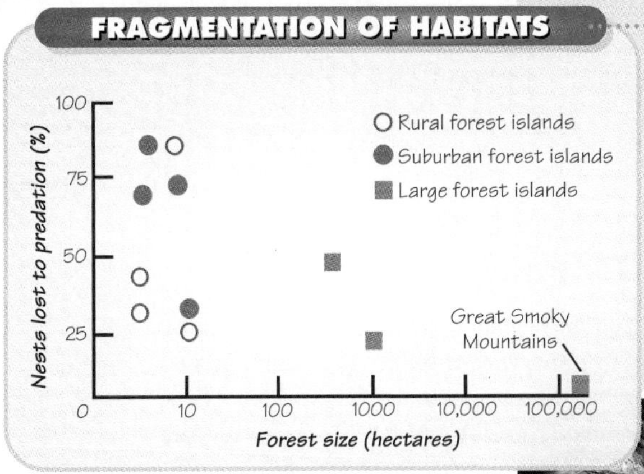

Figure 16–18
Recent research on island and habitat size is indicating that small forest fragments are a threat to many bird species. (a) *This graph shows that nest predation is significantly higher in rural and suburban forest fragments than in large forests.* (b) *A yellow warbler, victimized by cowbird parasitism, is caring for a cowbird hatchling at the cost of two of its own smaller hatchlings.*

in a way that maintains biodiversity. Knowledge and information from areas—such as genetics, ecology, and resource management—are integrated and used to achieve conservation goals.

How Big Is Big Enough?

Conservation management requires detailed information about the relationship between populations and habitat size. To save spotted owls in the Northwest, researchers must find out how large the fragments of old-growth forest must be for the birds to thrive. Is 1 hectare enough? Do they need 10? Or 100?

Habitat Conservation Research

One study designed to gather such data has been going on in Brazil since the 1970s, set up by the World Wildlife Fund. Brazilian landowners who wanted to develop jungle land were required by law to set aside half their land untouched. The landowners had to set aside the untouched land in chunks of different sizes! The jungle islands range in size from 1 hectare to nearly 1000 hectares.

Data gathered have revealed many fascinating interactions among populations in jungle islands. More experiments like this will provide the information we need to manage our world into the next century.

Section Review 16-4

1. **Explain** the relationship among habitat size, population size, and species diversity.
2. **Examine** the role of conservation biology in land resource management.
3. **List** a few examples of human behavior that may result in the loss of wildlife habitats.
4. **BRANCHING OUT ACTIVITY** Obtain a detailed map of your county. Of the following categories, **identify** the ones found in your county and **estimate** their percentage (by area): highly urban, suburban residential, rural/agricultural, and natural preserve.

Investigate

Role-Playing Ask students to imagine that they are conservation biologists or local builders, developers, and economists who are meeting to discuss the need to preserve natural areas in your community. Have students work in small groups to outline the major points and arguments they would want to make. Let the class role-play the meeting.

4 ASSESS

Quick Check

Ask students to explain why setting aside a 24-km^2 section of forest as a protected wildlife area is better than creating three separate 8-km^2 sections.

Section Review 16-4

1. Larger habitats support larger populations of organisms, promoting greater species diversity.
2. Conservation biology involves managing natural resources in a way that maintains biodiversity.
3. Students may cite activities such as road construction that divide large tracts of land into smaller "islands."
4. Answers will vary according to where students live.

Checkpoint

(1) Larger islands have larger habitats with larger populations, which promotes greater species diversity.

Learning Modality

Visual Learning Have students draw a large and a small irregular shape to represent two islands of different sizes, then label each island with the names and sizes of the populations it might contain. Make sure students list fewer species and smaller population numbers for the smaller island.

Ancillary Support

The resources below can be used to support your teaching strategy for these two pages.

TR Enrich: Conservation Conundrum
BL Inquiry Activity: In Your Own World
TB Island Size and Biodiversity, #22

Laboratory Investigation

Turn Your Garbage Around

Before the Lab

1. Collect (or ask students to bring in) enough empty 2-liter plastic bottles so each group can have two. Make sure the bottles are thoroughly washed, rinsed, and dried.
2. Ask students to collect and bring in various biodegradable and nonbiodegradable materials to put in their compost columns, including any plant materials they wish to use. (See Safety Tips below.) Students could include some of the materials they collected for the Chapter Discovery Learning Activity on page 358.
3. Each group will need brief access to an equal-arm balance for steps 8 and 16. Groups can share one balance.
4. To make the observations in step 13, each group will need to use a microscope for about 15 minutes each week.
5. Provide reference books for students to use in identifying organisms in step 13.

Pre-Lab Discussion

Begin by reviewing the terms biodegradable and nonbiodegradable to make sure students understand the difference between the two types of materials. Then have students read the entire procedure for the investigation and answer the following questions.

What types of materials are biodegradable, and what are some examples? (Once-living materials such as eggshells, food scraps, dead leaves, and grass clippings, and products made from living things, such as paper, cardboard, and cotton or wool fabric.)

What types of materials are nonbiodegradable, and what are some examples? (Materials not derived from living things, such as metals, plastics, and glass.)

CHAPTER 16

Laboratory Investigation

Turn Your Garbage Around

With the growing waste disposal problem, there is a great deal of interest in composting as a valuable way of reducing the amount of waste to be disposed and converting it into a useful product. Composting is a process by which biodegradable matter is decomposed by microorganisms such as bacteria and fungi. As a result, essential nutrients are recycled and make the soil more fertile.

Problem

Construct a model compost column and **classify** various materials according to their suitability for composting.

Materials (per group)

2 2-L plastic bottles
markers
knife
scissors
porous cloth
transparent tape
balance
rubber bands
pieces of cloth
materials for composting
water
slides
microscope

Procedure

1. **Prepare a list of materials to be composted—both biodegradable and nonbiodegradable.**
2. **Show your list to your teacher for approval.**
3. **Predict which material will decompose the fastest, the next fastest, and so on.**
4. **Record your predictions in a data table.**
5. **Remove the labels from the bottles. Using the knife, make the first cut and then use scissors to cut the bottles as indicated in the diagram. CAUTION:** ***Be careful when using a knife.*** **Make windows in the bottle tops as shown, taping strips of porous cloth over them to allow air to circulate.**
6. **Cover the mouth of the longer bottle top with a piece of porous cloth. Secure this with a rubber band. In this way, liquid can percolate through the bottom of the compost column.**
7. **Invert the bottle top into the bottle base and tape them together securely with transparent tape.**
8. **Determine and record the mass of the materials to be composted using a balance. Use enough material to fill approximately half of the inverted bottle section of the column.**

378 Chapter 16

Safety Tips

- Students should put on lab aprons before starting the procedure.
- Remind students to handle the knives carefully.
- Let students include food materials such as fruit and vegetable scraps, but make sure they do not include any meat, fish, or poultry scraps, which can attract rodents and other animals.
- Provide an ample supply of disposable latex gloves for students to wear when they examine the composted materials in steps 11–16. Have them wash their hands each time after they finish examining the compost.
- Make sure that students who are allergic to molds or spores avoid exposure when the groups examine and weigh the compost in steps 11–16.

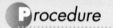

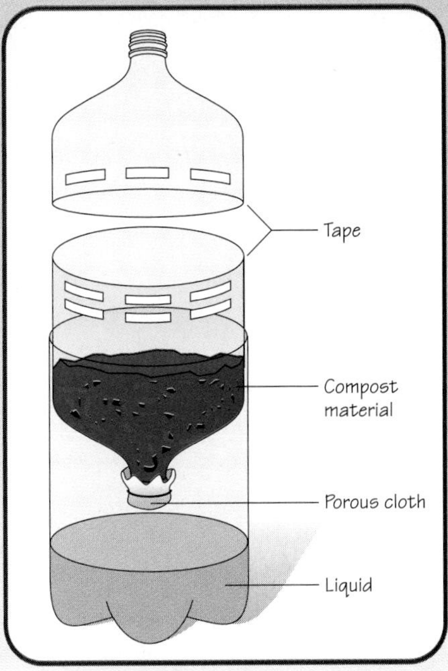

9. **Add approximately 250 mL of water to the material in the column. Then tape the remaining bottle top to the top of the column.**
10. **Place the column in an area that will provide the best environment for decomposition.**
11. **Examine the compost column every week for at least 4 weeks, and observe and record any changes.**
12. **During each observation, carefully loosen the tape from the bottom of the column to remove any liquid that has accumulated in the bottom section of the column.**
13. **Examine several drops of the liquid under the low-power objective of a microscope. Record your observations.**
14. **After 4 weeks, spread out a plastic trash bag on your table. Carefully empty the contents of the column onto the plastic bag.**
15. **Wearing rubber gloves, examine the compost and record your observations.**
16. **Record the mass of the compost material.**

Observations

1. Describe the changes you observed in your compost column.
2. Which material appears to decompose the fastest? The slowest?
3. What changes did you observe in the water samples from week to week?
4. How did the mass of the compost material compare with its initial mass?

Analysis and Conclusions

1. How do your results compare with your predictions? How can you explain any differences?
2. Calculate the percentage change in the mass of the compost material. How can you account for this difference?
3. Did the location of the compost column affect the results of the experiment in any way? You may consult with your classmates.
4. What can you conclude regarding the benefits of composting as one option for waste disposal?

More to Explore

Design an experiment using a variety of materials and investigate their suitability for composting.

Answers to Observations

1. Answers will vary depending on the materials chosen for composting and the conditions. Generally, the biodegradable materials will decompose and the nonbiodegradable materials will not change.
2. Specific answers will vary. Once-living materials will decompose the fastest, nonbiodegradable materials the slowest.
3. Water samples will contain increasing numbers of living organisms.
4. The final mass of the compost material will be less than its initial mass.

Answers to Analysis and Conclusions

1. Answers will vary depending on students' predictions and results.
2. The change in mass is due to the formation of the liquid.
3. The columns' locations should have little or no effect on the rate of decomposition, provided that they are placed according to the guidelines in Teaching Strategy 3.
4. Accept all reasonable responses, including that composting reduces the mass of biodegradable wastes and changes them into a form that can be reused.

More to Explore

The materials that are accepted for collection in recycling programs are generally nonbiodegradable materials such as glass, aluminum (but not all metals), and certain types of plastics. Most recycling programs also accept newspapers, which are biodegradable but highly recyclable; some programs also accept higher-grade paper such as glossy magazines, which decompose less readily than pulp newspaper. Suggest that students try composting various types of papers, for example, or different types of plastics or metals.

Skills Development

Students will use these skills while completing the laboratory investigation: constructing a model, classifying, making predictions, observing, and interpreting data.

Teaching Strategies

1. When you check each group's list of materials to be composted (step 2), make sure it includes only materials that are safe to handle as they decompose. (See Safety Tips on page 378.)
2. In step 5, students should first make a small slit with a knife, as indicated in the illustration, and then cut around the remaining circumference with scissors. The bottom part of the bottle should be cut just below where the label ends, to make the column more stable. The upper part of the bottle should be cut about 1 inch above the label. The unused top can be discarded. The remaining middle sleeve may be used to extend the height of the column if desired.
3. In step 10, students may need some help choosing an appropriate area to keep the compost columns. Explain that the bacteria, fungi, and other microorganisms that decompose materials do not need light, so the columns can be kept in a dark location. The temperature should be neither very hot nor very cold.

Study Guide

Review Strategy

Divide the class into eight groups (or ten groups, if you presented Section 16–4) and assign each group one of the key concepts listed on this student page. Explain that each group is to become the "class experts" on its assigned concept. Give students some time to review the text material; then have each group give a brief presentation on its concept, explaining the major ideas and using examples to clarify and support them. Encourage other groups to ask questions of the "expert" group.

Study Guide

Summarizing Key Concepts

The key concepts in each section of this chapter are listed below to help you review the chapter content. Make sure you understand each concept and its relationship to other concepts and to the theme of this chapter.

16–1 This Island Earth

- Human activities are the most important source of change in the biosphere.
- Nonbiodegradable substances accumulate in organisms and are passed up the trophic levels at higher and higher concentrations by the process of biological magnification.
- Humans must adopt ways of living that are ecologically sustainable—which means human actions must not cause deterioration of the environment.

16–2 Agriculture

- The green revolution is based on such key practices as monoculture (planting large fields with a highly productive crop), the use of chemical fertilizers and pesticides, machinery, and irrigation.
- Green revolution practices have harmful impacts on the environment, such as biological magnification of toxic substances, loss of soil, and the depletion and pollution of water resources.
- Sustainable practices—such as biological control of pests, crop rotation, contour strip farming, drip irrigation, and the cultivation of crops suitable to a region's rainfall—protect the environment.

16–3 Resources at Risk

- Environmental pollution occurs in large part because of the combustion of fossil fuels and the wastes generated by numerous manufacturing industries.
- Biodiversity is the genetically-based variety of living organisms in the biosphere.

16–4 Conserving Biodiversity

- Larger habitats support larger populations of organisms, which in turn allows greater species diversity.
- Conservation biology aims to maintain biodiversity by applying what we know about genetics, ecology, and resource management.

Reviewing Key Terms

Review the following vocabulary terms and their meaning. Then use each term in a complete sentence.

16–1 This Island Earth
nonbiodegradable
biodegradable
biological magnification
sustainability

16–2 Agriculture
green revolution
monoculture

16–3 Resources at Risk
biodiversity
ecosystem diversity
species diversity
genetic diversity

16–4 Conserving Biodiversity
conservation

Inquiry-Based Strategy

As a concluding activity with their mini-habitats from the Unit Discovery Learning Activity on page 280, students could design and carry out experiments related to the concepts presented in this chapter and, if you wish, earlier chapters in this unit. Some possible avenues of inquiry include the following.

- **How does acid rain affect the plants and animals in the habitat?**
- **Do common pesticides kill insects other than the ones for which they are intended?**
- **How can mold growth be controlled in the mini-habitat without using toxic substances?**

Review each group's experimental design to make sure it will not subject higher-order animals to harm. Let each group describe its experiment and explain its conclusions to the rest of the class. Make sure students return all their mini-habitat organisms to the natural habitats where they were collected.

CHAPTER 16

Recalling Main Ideas

Choose the letter of the answer that best completes the statement or answers the question.

1. A substance that is broken down by living things in the environment is said to be
- **a.** nonbiodegradable.
- **b.** biodegradable.
- **c.** sustainable.
- **d.** biologically magnified.

2. Which of the following is not a strategy central to the original green revolution?
- **a.** use of fertilizers
- **b.** monoculture
- **c.** irrigation
- **d.** crop rotation

3. A major cause of soil erosion is
- **a.** monoculture.
- **b.** inadequate irrigation.
- **c.** the use of chemical fertilizers.
- **d.** biochemical pest control.

4. Which is not a strategy for sustainable agriculture?
- **a.** crop rotation
- **b.** growing crops suited to local rainfall
- **c.** biological pest control
- **d.** monoculture

5. Which of the following pollutants poses a substantially lower threat today than it did 10 years ago?
- **a.** smog
- **b.** acid rain
- **c.** lead
- **d.** oil spills

6. The value of biodiversity to agriculture is mainly through
- **a.** genetic diversity.
- **b.** species diversity.
- **c.** ecosystem diversity.
- **d.** habitat diversity.

7. The main goal of conservation biology is to
- **a.** manage resources to conserve biodiversity.
- **b.** combine the fields of genetics, ecology, and resource management.
- **c.** save the spotted owl.
- **d.** do conservation research.

8. Studies show that species are most likely to be threatened in
- **a.** large rural forest fragments.
- **b.** small urban forest fragments.
- **c.** large urban forest fragments.
- **d.** small rural forest fragments.

Putting It All Together

Using the information on pages xxx to xxxi, complete the following concept map.

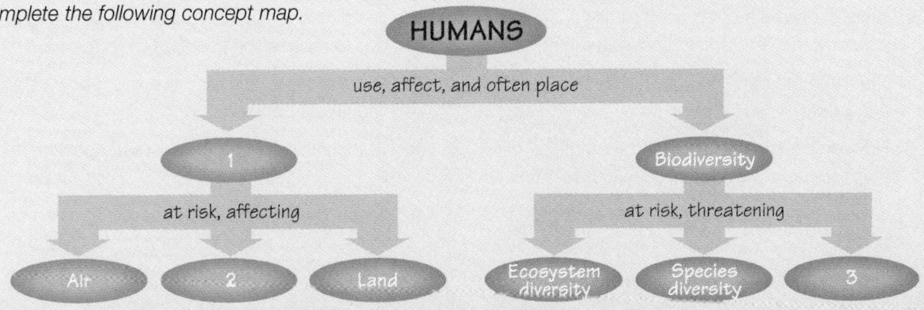

Recalling Main Ideas

1. b
2. d
3. a
4. d
5. c
6. a
7. a
8. b

Putting It All Together

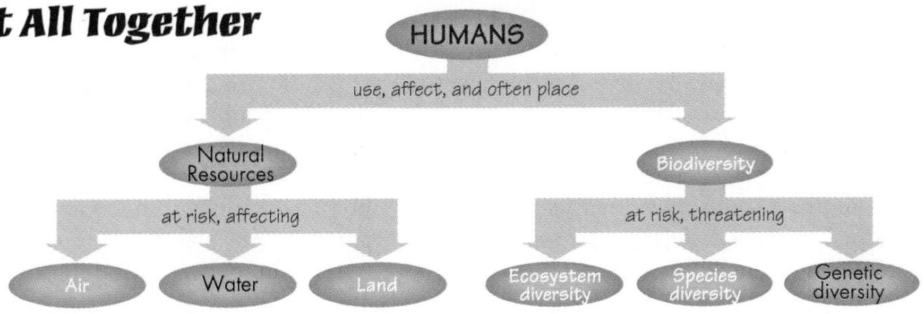

CHAPTER 16

Assessment

Reviewing What You Learned

1. Human activity.
2. If it can be broken down by natural processes in the environment.
3. The increasing concentration of DDT in the bodies of consumers at higher trophic levels.
4. The worldwide development of new farming techniques that dramatically increased food production.
5. Monoculture is the clearing and plowing of large fields and planting them with a single, highly productive crop; it makes sowing, tending, and harvesting more efficient.
6. Smog, acid rain, holes in the ozone layer, lead in the atmosphere, chemical wastes, and oil spills.
7. The genetically based variety of living organisms in the biosphere.
8. Students may answer an island surrounded by water and New York's Central Park as mentioned in caption on page 375. Accept all reasonable responses.
9. Smaller islands have more edge for each unit of area, fewer and smaller populations, and less species diversity.
10. The managing of natural resources in a way that maintains biodiversity.

Expanding the Concepts

1. One example is the continued heavy use of plastics, which are not biodegradable. Landfills will eventually fill up, forcing communities to find other ways to dispose of plastics.
2. Modern agriculture produces high crop yields to feed the world's human population. However, pesticides can enter food webs and harm organisms, topsoil is eroded from harvested fields, and crop irrigation depletes water supplies.
3. Sustainable agricultural practices protect the environment while providing an adequate food supply. Green revolution practices produce high crop yields at the expense of the environment.
4. As farmers continue to use a pesticide, a crop pest becomes resistant to it and in time becomes immune to nearly any pesticide.
5. Students may identify any three of the benefits discussed on student text pages 373–374.
6. Starting or expanding a recycling program, banning leaf burning, encouraging use of mass transit, building a waste-water treatment plant, and holding a special collection day for toxic waste materials.
7. They support larger populations of organisms, which in turn promotes greater species diversity.
8. Ecosystem diversity: The variety of living ecosystems in the world. Species diversity: The number and variety of different life forms. Genetic diversity: The variety of different forms of genes present in a population.
9. Water, soil, and air. Water can be protected by conserving its use and preventing its contamination. Soil can be conserved by drip irrigation and not using monoculture as a primary agricultural practice. Air quality can be controlled by reducing or eliminating various forms of air pollution.

Assessment

Reviewing What You Learned

Answer each of the following in a complete sentence.

1. What has been the greatest source of change in the biosphere?
2. When is a substance considered to be biodegradable?
3. Give an example of biological magnification.
4. What was the green revolution and where did it occur?
5. What is monoculture? What are its advantages?
6. What are some examples of environmental pollution?
7. Define biodiversity.
8. What is a biological island? Give two examples.
9. Speaking biologically, how do smaller islands differ from larger islands?
10. What is meant by conservation?

Expanding the Concepts

Discuss each of the following in a brief paragraph.

1. Give an example of an ecologically unsustainable practice. Predict its consequences.
2. Compare the benefits and the costs of modern agriculture.
3. How do sustainable agricultural practices differ from key green revolution practices?
4. Why is it impossible to eliminate a crop pest completely?
5. Identify and discuss three benefits of biodiversity.
6. Describe five actions your community might take to reduce the pollution in your area.
7. Why do larger habitats have more biodiversity than smaller ones?
8. Distinguish between ecosystem, species, and genetic diversity.
9. Identify three resources currently at risk and indicate what might be done to alleviate the problem.

CHAPTER 16

Extending Your Thinking

Use the skills you have developed in this chapter to answer the following.

1. **Hypothesizing** A monoculture of cotton was planted in the 1980s in many southern states. A new disease invaded the cotton plants, almost completely destroying them. Why did this occur?
2. **Evaluating** Water is often referred to as our most important resource. Do you agree? Why or why not?
3. **Calculating** A nonbiodegradable toxic substance is concentrated ten times at each trophic level. What will be its concentration in organisms at the fifth trophic level if the primary producers of the first trophic level store the substance at concentrations of 40 ppm?
4. **Experimenting** Can covering soil with mulch near the base of plants help reduce soil erosion? Design an experiment to answer the question.
5. **Evaluating** Some industries, such as agriculture, have established gene banks to maintain the genetic diversity important to that industry. Discuss the pros and cons of this practice.

Applying Your Skills

A Letter to the Editor

Humans are affecting the biosphere in many ways. In order to help maintain sustainability, everyone must become aware of the issues involved and be able to communicate information effectively and to express opinions based on facts.

1. Investigate a local problem that may affect the future ecology of your area.
2. Gather relevant facts and information from different sources to help you arrive at possible solutions.

• GOING FURTHER •

3. Write a letter about the problem to the editor of your local newspaper, stating your concern and offering one or more possible solutions.

Extending Your Thinking

1. Answers will vary. A monoculture is a single, highly productive crop. This means that all the cotton plants contained the same genetic material. When a new disease invaded the fields, it could spread unchecked.
2. Organisms are made up of at least 50 to 90 percent water; all biochemical reactions occur in a watery environment; photosynthesis requires water; and without water, recycling of nutrients would be impossible.
3. Assuming that only one organism is eaten by each organism at each trophic level, the concentration in organisms at the fifth trophic level would be 4,000,000 ppm.

Skills Trace
Calculating
- Focus p. 361
- Practice p. 362
- Assess p. 383

4. Students' experimental design should include two setups—one in which mulch is used and one in which it is not.

Skills Trace
Experimenting
- Focus p. 366
- Practice p. 369
- Assess p. 383

5. The use of gene banks would upset the natural gene pool, certain traits might be lost, and new species might arise. Ethical issues as well as questions about the feasibility of this technique would also be raised.

Applying Your Skills

Preparation

Gather research materials that students can use to get started on their investigations. Collect some examples of effective letters to the editor.

Suggestions

1. In a class discussion, brainstorm for a list of local environmental problems that students might investigate.
2. With students' permission, send the best letters to your local newspaper.

Scoring Rubric

4 Response is thorough, accurate, and creative; shows an in-depth understanding of science skills, procedures, and concepts.

3 Response is complete, mostly accurate, and original; shows a satisfactory understanding of science skills, procedures, and concepts.

2 Response is mostly complete but includes some inaccuracies; shows an adequate understanding of science skills, procedures, and concepts.

1 Response is only partially complete and has many inaccuracies; shows an incomplete understanding of science skills, procedures, and concepts.

0 Response is mostly incomplete and/or inaccurate; shows a lack of understanding of science skills, procedures, and concepts.

UNIT 5

Life on Earth: An Overview

Introducing the Unit

. . . In Words

Lewis Thomas (1913–1993) was a pathologist, president of the Memorial Sloan-Kettering Cancer Center, and dean of the medical schools at New York University and Yale. Thomas is remembered for his lucid essays that captured the range of natural phenomena from the unit of a cell to the relationship of Earth and the universe. These essays were collected into several books, including *The Lives of a Cell* and *The Medusa and the Snail*. Thomas viewed Earth as a kind of single living cell in a membrane of atmosphere. He countered the notion that humans are a lethal force to this fragile planet with the belief that Earth will endure and humans are the delicate, transient elements.

- **Is Earth alive? Explain.** (Some students might agree because all of Earth's surface is covered with living organisms.)
- **Why do you think the health of Earth is important?** (The condition of the land, air, and water is critical to the organisms living on Earth.)

. . . In Pictures

This photograph shows a vivid example of the coevolution of a plant and an animal. As the englossine bee gathers the golden poppy's nectar for food, pollen grains cling to the bee's body. When the bee moves to other flowers, it spreads the pollen, which leads to plants' reproduction. This interaction between bees and plants increases the evolutionary fitness of both organisms.

UNIT 5

Life on Earth: An Overview

CHAPTERS

". . . the astonishing thing about the Earth, catching the breath, is that it is alive."

— Lewis Thomas

TEACHER SUPPORT

Unit Discovery Learning Activity

ORDER OUT OF DISORDER

The following activity is designed to introduce students to classification systems, which they will study in Section 17–2 and use throughout the unit. In the course of this activity, students will compare various items for common characteristics, and then use these characteristics to design a classification scheme.

1. Gather a wide variety of classroom objects, such as pens, pencils, books, chalk, stapler, scissors, microscope, hand lens, and so on. Display the items for students to examine.

2. Have students work in pairs to look for common characteristics that they could use to sort the objects into two or three large groups. Students should list these groups on a sheet of paper.

3. Challenge students to look for common characteristics they could use to sort each large group into smaller groups. They should list

CAREER TRACK

As you explore the topics in this unit, you will discover many different types of careers associated with biology. Here are a few of these careers:

- Paleontologist
- Nursery Operation Technician
- Ocean Technician
- Animal Physiologist
- Anthropologist

A bee pollinating a poppy plant

these groups. Students should continue sorting in this way until they cannot make any more groups.
4. Ask each student group to make a chart on a large piece of paper showing its classification system, but without revealing the characteristics used to classify the objects.
5. Have students compare classification systems. Challenge them to identify the characteristics other groups used to classify the objects.

By identifying common characteristics among the wide variety of objects and using them to divide the objects into groups, students should begin to recognize and describe concepts of **unity and diversity,** one of the themes developed in this unit.

- **How do both these organisms benefit from their interaction?** (Lead students to conclude that the bee obtains food in the form of nectar and the flower receives pollen from the bee that enables it to reproduce.)
- **Can you think of other examples of interactions between different organisms?** (Students may suggest other relationships, such as birds spreading seeds of fruits they eat.)

CAREER TRACK

Throughout this unit, you will find a broad range of biology-related careers that vary in educational and training requirements. You may wish to have your students find out more about the following careers:

- Paleontologist, p. 391
- Nursery Operation Technician, p. 431
- Ocean Technician, p. 459
- Animal Physiologist, p. 487
- Anthropologist, p. 498

Technology

BioVue
Drug-Resistant Tuberculosis
Videodisc Side 5

Go to Chapter 2

Ancillary Support

The resource below can be used to support your teaching strategy for these two pages.

BL Integrating the Media
Unit Discovery Learning Activity

Chapter 17 The History and Diversity of Life

Content Management	Student Edition Activities
■ Section 17–1 The Changing Earth, pp. 387–392 The Changing Planet Fossils and Their Stories The Geologic Time Scale Wandering Continents	**MINI LAB:** When Can Half a Clock Tell Time?, p. 390 **Laboratory Investigation:** Constructing a Geologic Time Line, pp. 408–409
■ Section 17–2 Finding Order in Diversity, pp. 393–397 Why Do We Classify? Biological Classification Kingdoms of Life	**MINI LAB:** A Taxing Situation, p. 395
■ Section 17–3 Bacteria—The First Organisms, pp. 398–400 Ancient Prokaryotes Living Prokaryotes What Are Bacteria? How Do Bacteria Reproduce?	
■ Section 17–4 Viruses, pp. 401–403 What Is a Virus? Types of Viruses How Do Viruses Reproduce?	
◆ BRANCHING OUT • In Depth Section 17–5 How Did Life Begin? pp. 404–407 Building Blocks The Greatest Leap	

■ These sections cover all the necessary content and concepts for a basic course in biology.
◆ This section covers content and concepts that are either applications or extensions of the basic material.

Integration Strategies

SE Earth Science, p. 389
Math, p. 390
Careers, p. 394
Health, p. 400
Astronomy, p. 405

BL Investigating Careers Involving the Community
Science Through Art

Assessment Strategies

SE Chapter Review
TR Section Reviews
Chapter Test
Performance-Based Assessment
BL Investigating Further
Chapter Review
Practice Test
CTB Chapter 17 Test

Tech Prep

Teaching strategies appropriate for students who are in technical/vocational programs or who are considering post-secondary technical education can be found on **TE** pages 393, 399, and 401.

Meeting the Standards

Sections 17–1 through 17–5 cover three of the six content standards under **The Cell** and four of the five content standards under **Biological Evolution** as described on pages 184–185 of The National Science Education Standards.

Chapter Planning Guide

Teacher's Edition Activities	Other Activities	Media and Technology
Chapter Discovery Learning Activity, p. 386 **Investigate:** Research, p. 388 **Inquiry Activity:** How Relative Dating Works, p. 389 **Activity:** Making Model Fossils, p. 389	**TR** **Writing In Biology:** Where in the World Am I? **Apply:** The Dating Game **BL** **Inquiry Activity:** Time for a Change	**TB** Geologic History of the Earth, #23
Investigate: Cooperative Learning, p. 394	**TR** **Explore:** Who's Related to Whom? **BL** **Inquiry Activity:** The Right Address	
Investigate: Research, p. 398 **Activity:** Observing Bacteria, p. 398 **Investigate:** Research, p. 399	**LM** Observing Bacteria, #33 **TR** **Explore:** They're Everywhere! **BL** **Inquiry Activity:** A Simple Life	**BioVue Plus CD-ROMs:** Drug-Resistant Tuberculosis
Investigate: Research, p. 401	**TR** **Enrich:** Population Explosion **BL** **Inquiry Activity:** To Be or Not to Be	
Inquiry Activity: Describing Ancient Earth, p. 404 **Investigate:** Research, p. 404	**LM** Making Coacervates, #34 **TR** **Explore:** What's Cooking? **BL** **Inquiry Activity:** Soup's On	

KEY: **SE** Student Edition **TE** Teacher's Edition **LM** Laboratory Manual **TR** Teaching Resources **BL** BioLog **TB** Transparency Box **CTB** Computer Test Bank

Materials List

TE Chapter Discovery Learning Activity, p. 386 (20–30 minutes); copy of world map with continents outlined and labeled with their names, scissors, colored marker or pencil.

TE Inquiry Activity: How Relative Dating Works p. 389 (30 minutes for making models, 30 minutes for follow-up class presentations); materials of students' choice, such as colored clay or construction paper.

TE Activity: Making Model Fossils, p. 389 (1 hour or two 30-minute sessions); shell, leaf, fern frond, nut, or other organic specimen; plaster of Paris; small, flat-bottomed container; petroleum jelly.

SE MINI LAB: When Can Half a Clock Tell Time?, p. 390 (20–30 minutes); 3 pieces round filter paper.

TE Investigate: Cooperative Learning, p. 394 (30 minutes); field guide.

SE MINI LAB: A Taxing Situation, p. 395 (30 minutes); assorted common objects listed on page 395.

TE Activity: Observing Bacteria, p. 398 (15–20 minutes); at least one learning station with a microscope and prepared slides of bacteria, study sheet.

CHAPTER 17

The History and Diversity of Life

Introducing the Chapter

. . . In Pictures

The stromatolites shown in this photograph were formed by photosynthetic bacteria. Have students examine the photograph and read the caption. Point out that fossils of stromatolites are found throughout the world, and living stromatolites still exist in a few places.

Teaching Strategy

The first section of this chapter introduces some basic concepts regarding Earth's history: fossils as evidence of ancient life on Earth, relative and absolute dating, the geologic time scale, and continental drift. The biological classification system is introduced in the second section, laying the foundation for discussions of bacteria in the third section and viruses in the fourth section. The BRANCHING OUT section at the end of the chapter presents more detailed information on the origins of life on Earth.

BIO JOURNAL

Living fossils are organisms alive today that have remained essentially unchanged for millions of years. There are numerous plant and animal examples, including horsetails, club mosses, ginkgo trees, magnolias, dawn redwoods, chambered nautiluses, starfishes, horseshoe crabs, sharks, coelacanths, lungfish, stingrays, crocodiles, turtles and tortoises, tuataras, opossums, tarsiers, grebes, ants, dragonflies, and cockroaches. Students may mention organisms they learned about in previous science courses. Instruct students to keep their entries in their portfolios.

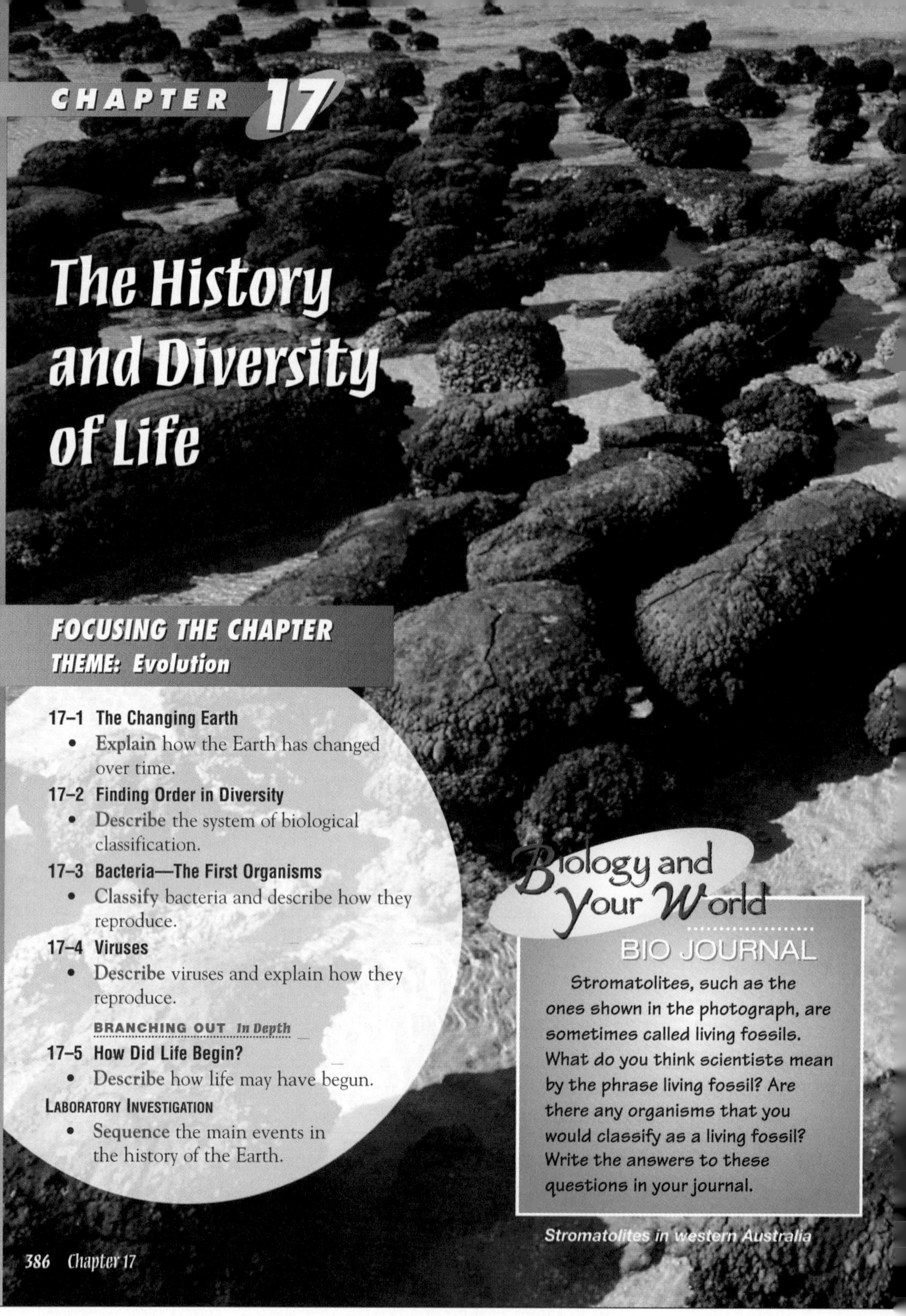

CHAPTER 17

The History and Diversity of Life

FOCUSING THE CHAPTER

THEME: Evolution

17–1 The Changing Earth
- **Explain** how the Earth has changed over time.

17–2 Finding Order in Diversity
- **Describe** the system of biological classification.

17–3 Bacteria—The First Organisms
- **Classify** bacteria and describe how they reproduce.

17–4 Viruses
- **Describe** viruses and explain how they reproduce.

BRANCHING OUT *In Depth*

17–5 How Did Life Begin?
- **Describe** how life may have begun.

LABORATORY INVESTIGATION
- **Sequence** the main events in the history of the Earth.

Biology and Your World

BIO JOURNAL

Stromatolites, such as the ones shown in the photograph, are sometimes called living fossils. What do you think scientists mean by the phrase living fossil? Are there any organisms that you would classify as a living fossil? Write the answers to these questions in your journal.

Stromatolites in western Australia

TEACHER SUPPORT

Chapter Discovery Learning Activity

In the following activity, students make a simple model of continental drift, discussed in Section 17–1, and observe how it affected the distribution of organisms.

1. Cut out the continents on a world map. Then try to fit them together in one large land mass, using their shapes as a guide. (Students' solutions may vary somewhat but should show South America joined with Africa, North America with Europe, and Australia with Africa and Asia.)

2. Color a band across South America, Africa, and Australia, and label it lungfish. Lungfish are ancient types of animals that have existed for millions of years.

3. Move the continents back to their present-day positions, and note the locations of the colored areas. Lungfish live today in Africa, South America, and Australia.

4. How can widely separated continents have the same unusual type of animal? (Lungfish evolved when the continents were joined. Also see Background Information, page 392.)

The Changing Earth

Guide for Reading

- **Describe** the importance of the fossil record.
- **Explain** the importance of the geologic time scale.

MINI LAB

- **Relate** an element's half-life to the amount of the original element that remains.

THE STORY OF LIFE ON EARTH is both fascinating and exciting. It is filled with mysteries and life-and-death struggles. The cast contains species as amazing as any monsters from science fiction. And Earth's changes over millions of years set the stage for this exciting drama.

Some of these changes were caused by sudden events, such as volcanic eruptions, collisions with meteors, or earthquakes. Other changes happened more slowly. Yet all these events—both sudden and gradual—are important to the history of life, because every change in our planet affects the daily lives of every man, woman, and child.

The Changing Planet

Many scientists hypothesize that our planet Earth was formed as pieces of cosmic debris became attracted to one another over hundreds of millions of years. As the Earth developed, it was struck by large objects, one of which may have been as large as the planet Mars. This catastrophic event produced incredible amounts of heat—enough, in fact, to melt the entire globe.

Once the Earth melted, the elements rearranged themselves according to their density. The most dense elements formed the Earth's core, while less dense elements formed the outer coverings of the Earth. Eventually, these elements cooled to form a solid crust. Still lighter elements, such as hydrogen and nitrogen, escaped from Earth's surface to form its first atmosphere.

Figure 17–1
(a) Although this view of the planet Earth from space doesn't show it, Earth has had a long and interesting history. (b) Many scientists now believe that an asteroid collided with Earth—similar to what is shown in this artist's representation—causing mass extinctions of some forms of life.

Section 17-1
The Changing Earth

Performance Objectives
- Explain how the fossil record has helped scientists learn about Earth's history.
- Describe the geologic time scale and tell why it is important.

Mini Lab Skill: Relating
Laboratory Investigation Skill: Sequencing

1 ENGAGE

Ideas Through Images

Have students examine Figure 17–1, read the caption, and answer the following questions.

- **What is an asteroid?** (A rocky body from outer space.)
- **How do you think an asteroid collision could have caused mass extinctions?** (Students may know that in addition to killing organisms in the impact area itself, such a collision would send vast amounts of dust, debris, and water vapor into Earth's atmosphere, blocking sunlight for a long period afterward and causing profound climate changes on Earth. These climate changes in turn could have made it impossible for many types of organisms to survive.)
- **What other natural events can cause climate changes that endanger organisms?** (Students may mention volcanic eruptions, which spew gases and particles into the atmosphere, and El Niño.)

TEACHER SUPPORT

Facts and Figures

Many scientists theorize that a massive asteroid impact caused the extinction of the dinosaurs at the Cretaceous-Tertiary (K-T) boundary about 65 million years ago. A layer of iridium-rich rock worldwide dates precisely to the K-T boundary. Iridium is rare on Earth's surface but is common in asteroids.

By analyzing gravity maps, iridium levels in soils, and other evidence, researchers have identified the asteroid's impact site as just off the northern coast of Mexico's Yucatán peninsula. The impact crater is 9.6 kilometers deep and 300 kilometers wide. Based on these dimensions, scientists calculate that the asteroid hit Earth at a speed greater than 160,000 kilometers per hour and threw more than 200,000 cubic kilometers of debris and dense gases into the atmosphere. Monstrous waves raced across the oceans, and the entire crust heaved with earthquakes.

2 EXPLORE

Investigate

Research Ask students to research and report on plant and animal extinctions that have occurred within the past hundred years and the reasons for the extinctions. Notable examples include the passenger pigeon, dodo, moa, auroch, and Tasmanian wolf. Students could also investigate organisms that are currently in danger of becoming extinct and the scientific efforts being made to maintain them. The California condor is a prime example.

3 TEACH

Ideas Through Images

Have students examine Figure 17–3, read the caption, and answer the following questions.

- **Would the entire fish be fossilized or only some of its parts? Why?** (Only hard parts such as bones, teeth, and possibly scales would fossilize. Soft parts such as muscles and internal organs would decay before they could be fossilized.)
- **If fossils commonly form in rock layers deep under water, how is it possible for people to discover them millions of years later?** (The ancient oceans, rivers, or lakes may dry up as the climate changes, or geologic processes can thrust the sedimentary rock layers upward over millions of years so the fossils are located on dry land.)

Figure 17–2
The history of life has been recorded in many ways. (a) Sometimes entire organisms, such as these ants, were trapped in plant sap that has solidified into amber. (b) Sometimes only footprints of an organism, such as these of a dinosaur, have been left behind.

Had you been there at that time, you never would have recognized the Earth—it was so different from today's Earth. When the crust cooled enough for water to stay in liquid form, oceans covered most of the surface. The Earth's first atmosphere lacked oxygen and was composed mainly of carbon dioxide, hydrogen sulfide, and methane. A few deep breaths would have killed you!

Fossils and Their Stories

What evidence do scientists have that helps them know when the Earth was formed? And how can they tell when organisms that are now extinct once lived? **To learn about life's past and to fully understand its present, researchers read the history preserved in the fossil record.** Unfortunately, the oldest rocks in this record are not very useful to scientists. Over time, most of these rocks have usually been subjected to enough heat and pressure to destroy any traces of life they may once have contained.

Layers of Rock

However, rocks formed about 3 billion years ago are a different story. These rocks often contain **fossils,** which are the remains or traces of ancient life.

Figure 17–3
Layers of sedimentary rock sometimes contain fossils that represent billions of years of Earth's history. (a) When a fish dies, for example, it sinks to the bottom of a body of water. Over time, sediments pile up on top of the fish's remains until it is covered. The soft parts of the fish disintegrate and only its hardest parts are left. Millions of years later, changing circumstances bring the fish's remains, or fossil, to the surface, where erosion exposes more of it. (b) The photograph shows the layers of sedimentary rock that make up the walls of the Grand Canyon.

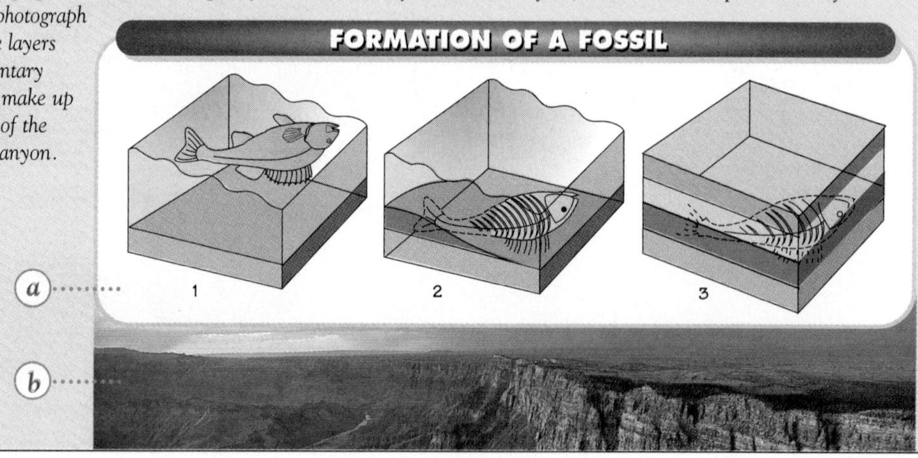

TEACHER SUPPORT

Historical Perspective

Students would probably be surprised to learn that the first dinosaur footprints ever discovered in the United States were found by a 12-year-old boy. In 1802, while plowing a field on his family's farm in western Massachusetts, Pliny Moody turned up a flat stone with footprints on it that resembled bird footprints but were much too large for any living bird. When news of Pliny's discovery spread, crowds came to view the prints. People thought they must be from giant ravens that Noah had released from the Ark and so called the creatures "Noah's ravens."

Prompted by Pliny's discovery, Edward Hitchcock, president of Amherst College, began a 30-year search throughout the Connecticut River Valley for more prints and eventually discovered tracks of 49 different types of dinosaurs. Believing the tracks to have been made by large, ostrichlike birds, Hitchcock called the prints ornithichites, meaning "stony bird tracks."

Fossils are most commonly found in **sedimentary rocks** that form when silt, sand, or clay builds up in the bottom of a river, lake, or ocean. ● As these sediments pile up, pressure on lower layers turns them into rocks such as sandstone or limestone. Over time, layers of sedimentary rocks can be laid down like layers in a cake. Each rock layer is identified with a time period in history, which is often named after a place where the rocks were found.

☑ *Checkpoint* What are fossils? ①

Figure 17–4
Fossils are usually found in sedimentary rocks. Because younger sedimentary rocks normally lie on top of older sedimentary rocks, scientists can determine the course of changes in living things on the Earth. Scientists often compare similar fossils found in rock layers in different areas.

Putting the Past in Order

Because each fossil species appears at some point in time and disappears at another, scientists can recognize distinct groups of fossils in specific rock layers. Often, the assortment of fossils in one rock layer differs from fossils in other rock layers. By matching rock layers and fossils, geologists can identify rocks that were formed at the same time. They can also arrange the rock layers in chronological order—from the deepest, oldest layers to more recent layers closer to Earth's surface. Scientists can then compare the ages of the fossils in one layer with the ages of fossils found in other layers. This is called relative dating.

☑ *Checkpoint* What is relative dating? ②

INTEGRATING EARTH SCIENCE

Igneous rocks are rocks formed from hot lava or magma. Why do you think fossils are usually not found in igneous rock?

Radioactive Dating

Relative dating cannot give the actual age of rocks and fossils, so how are scientists able to calculate the age of the Earth? About 100 years ago, scientists discovered that certain elements are radioactive—that is, they break down from an unstable form into a more stable form over time. In addition, geologists realized that these radioactive elements could provide a series of clocks by which they could measure the age of rocks.

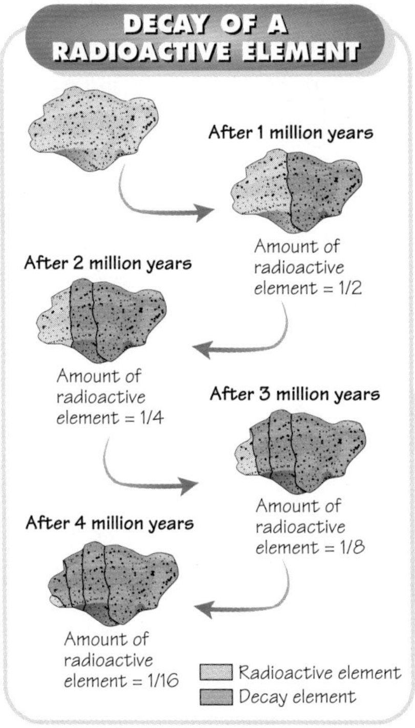

Figure 17–5
Radioactive elements break down, or decay, into stable elements at a steady rate, measured in a unit called a half-life. This sample element, for example, has a half-life of 1 million years. After 1 million years, 1/2 of the sample is radioactive and 1/2 is stable. After 4 million years, only 1/16 of the sample element remains radioactive.

Inquiry Activity

Building Models

How Relative Dating Works

Challenge small groups to each design and build a model showing how the fossils contained in one sequence of rock layers can be used to determine the relative ages of the fossils in another sequence of layers. To represent the rock layers, students could use slabs of clay or stacks of paper of different colors or any other materials of their own choice. They could label the layers with pictures of fossils they have drawn or have photocopied from Figure 17–4. Let each group present its model to the rest of the class and explain how relative dating can be done using the two sequences of rock layers.

INTEGRATING EARTH SCIENCE

The extreme heat of the molten rock destroys organisms' remains or traces before they can be fossilized.

Discussion

Ask students to identify the third major type of rock besides sedimentary and igneous. (Metamorphic.) Then ask whether they think metamorphic rock would be likely to contain fossils and to explain their answer. (As stated on page 388 of the student text, great heat and pressure have destroyed any traces of life that the oldest rocks on Earth may once have contained. Since metamorphic rocks are formed by extreme heat and pressure, students should be able to deduce that they rarely contain fossils.)

☑ Checkpoints

① The remains or traces of ancient life.

② The comparison of the ages of fossils in different rock layers.

TEACHER SUPPORT

Activity

MAKING MODEL FOSSILS

Have each student or group make a model fossil from a shell, leaf, fern frond, nut, or other organic specimen, as follows.

- *Making a mold:* Pour a plaster of Paris mixture into a small, flat-bottomed container. When the plaster just begins to harden, press the specimen into its surface. After the plaster hardens, carefully remove the specimen. The fossil imprint is called a mold.
- *Making a cast:* Cover the mold and the plaster just around it with petroleum jelly. Pour fresh plaster into the mold until it overflows slightly. Tap the container on the table to force air bubbles out of the plaster. When the plaster has hardened completely, carefully lift out the fossil duplicate, called a cast.

Explain that fossils also form when minerals replace organic materials in the decaying specimen. This process, called mineralization or petrification, creates a stony duplicate of the original specimen.

Ancillary Support

The resource below can be used to support your teaching strategy for these two pages.

BL Inquiry Activity: Time for a Change

MINI LAB Relating

Teacher Note

- For time required and materials needed, see page 386b.

Answers to Analyze and Conclude

1. After first fold, 6 g; after second fold, 3 g.
2. For C-14, 5770 years; U-238, 4.5 billion years; K-40, 1.3 billion years. The time period is called half-life.

Skills Trace
Relating
- Focus p. 390
- Practice p. 392
- Assess p. 412

INTEGRATING MATH

It will take 30 years.

Ideas Through Images

Have students examine Figure 17–6, read the caption, and answer the following questions.

- **Which evolved first—flowering plants or insects?** (Insects.)
- **During which period did mammals first appear?** (Triassic.)
- **When did the Cretaceous Period end?** (65 million years ago. Point out that dinosaurs became extinct at that time.)
- **Did dinosaurs and modern humans ever coexist?** (No.)
- **How old are the oldest known rocks?** (About 3.8 billion years old.)

MINI LAB .... Relating ....

When Can Half a Clock Tell Time?

PROBLEM *How does half-life **relate** to the amount of original element that remains?*

PROCEDURE

1. Place a round piece of filter paper in front of you. Label the center of the paper C-14 (carbon-14). At the top of the paper (the 12 o'clock position), write 0 years. At the 6 o'clock position, write 5770 years (the half-life of C-14). And at the 9 o'clock position, write 11,540 years.
2. Fold the filter paper in half down the middle, from top to bottom.
3. Repeat steps 1 and 2 using U-238 (half-life 4.5 billion years) and K-40 (half-life 1.3 billion years).

ANALYZE AND CONCLUDE

1. If the unfolded filter represents 12 g, what mass remains after folding the paper in half? After folding the paper in half again?
2. How many years does folding the paper in half represent? What is this time period called?

How might these clocks work? Each radioactive element decays at a constant rate. This rate is measured by a unit called **half-life.** The half-life of an element is the amount of time needed for half the original element to decay into its more stable form.

INTEGRATING MATH

If the half-life of an element is 10 years, how many years will it take until only 1/8 of the element remains?

The half-lives of radioactive elements vary enormously. Carbon-14, for example, has a half-life of 5770 years. At the end of 5770 years, one half of a given amount of carbon-14 decays to nitrogen-14. Carbon-14 is present in the atmosphere, so organisms are constantly taking it in. When the organism dies, it stops taking in carbon-14. By comparing the amounts of carbon-14 and nitrogen-14 in the organism, scientists can estimate its age. This kind of dating is called absolute dating because it allows scientists to calculate the actual age of the organism.

Carbon-14 is often used to date organic material, such as charcoal, that is less than 50,000 years old. Another radioactive element, Potassium-40, has a half-life of 1.3 billion years. It is used to date fossils that are at least 1 million years old. Because the half-life of uranium-238 is 4.5 billion years, it has been used to date the oldest rocks on Earth, roughly 4 billion years old.

☑ ***Checkpoint*** What is meant by the half-life of an element? 1

Figure 17–6
The geologic time scale is a record of the history of life. Many of the time periods get their names from the areas in which the rocks and fossils were found. For example, the Jurassic Period was named after the Jura Mountains of France and Switzerland, where rocks from that time period were discovered.

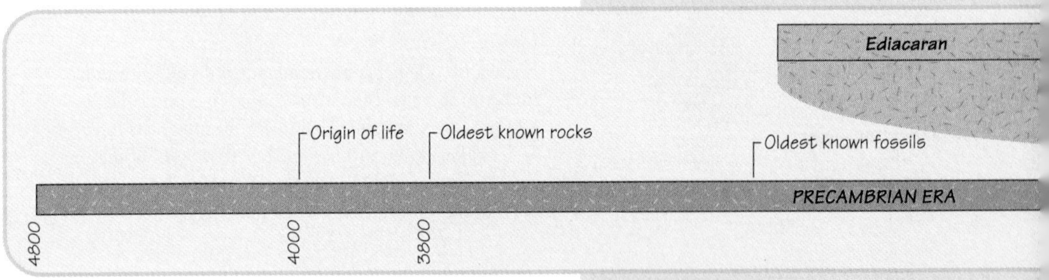

TEACHER SUPPORT Background Information

Students may not be familiar with the terms tetrapods and hominids used in Figure 17–6. Explain that tetrapods (literally, "four-footed") are four-legged animals. Hominids include modern humans and all of our ancient humanlike ancestors.

Students also may not know the difference between monkeys and apes. Explain that monkeys have a tail, and their forelimbs are about the same length as their hind limbs. In contrast, apes have no tail and have forelimbs that are longer than their hind limbs. Apes—including the gibbon, orangutan, gorilla, and chimpanzee—are closely related to humans, whereas monkeys are not.

The Geologic Time Scale

Scientists have put together a history of life from almost 4 billion years ago to the present. Four billion years is an incredibly long time. We don't usually talk about time periods longer than a century. But to geologists and paleontologists, a thousand years is like the blink of an eye. **To make Earth's long history more manageable and to show how organisms have changed over time, scientists developed the geologic time scale.** Each unit of the **geologic time scale**—eons, eras, periods, and epochs—is based on information contained in rocks studied around the world.

The fossil record also shows that the history of life has not been one of steady progress. You will see that during some periods, life didn't change much at all. During other periods, major changes took place that gave rise to many new species.

Figure 17–7
CAREER TRACK
If fossils of ancient organisms interest you, you may enjoy a career in paleontology, which is a branch of geology.

GEOLOGIC HISTORY OF THE EARTH

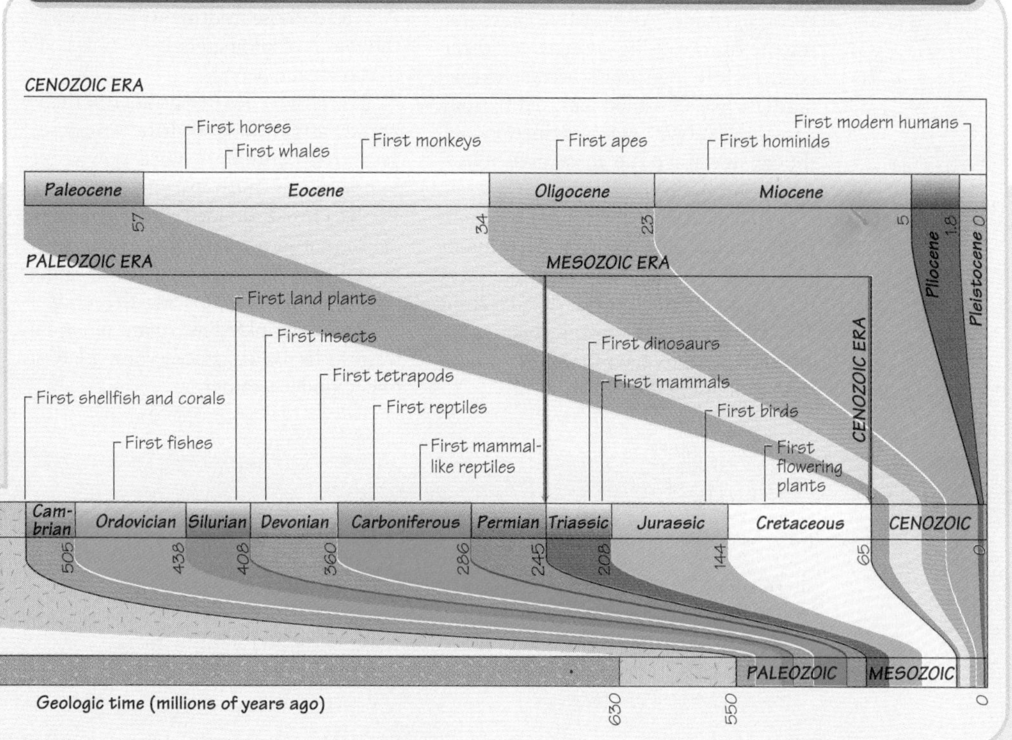

Discussion

Use the following analogy to help students understand the vast stretches of time represented by the geologic time scale: If a clock represented the entire history of Earth, with midnight as its formation, life forms would not exist until 6:30 AM, when the first microscopic organisms would appear. The first animals with backbones, such as fish and amphibians, would not appear until about 9:15 PM, followed by reptiles at about 10:30 PM. Mammals would appear at about 11:00 PM but would not become common until about 11:40 PM. Early humans would appear about 40 seconds before midnight. All recorded history would occur in the last tenth of a second of the day.

Laboratory Investigation

The Laboratory Investigation, Constructing a Geologic Time Line, on pages 408–409 is appropriate to use at this point in the chapter.

Checkpoint

1. Half-life is the amount of time needed for half the original element to decay into its more stable form.

TEACHER SUPPORT

Managing Classroom Diversity

AT-RISK STUDENTS/LEP STUDENTS
Use the following procedure to help students understand the term paleontology. Write the term on the board and draw slash marks to separate it into its three parts: pale/onto/logy. Explain that the suffix *logy* means "study of" and is used in many other words that students know, including "biology." Ask students to use a dictionary to find the meaning of the other two word parts. (Pale from the Greek *palaios*, meaning ancient; onto from the Greek *onta* meaning "existing things.") Thus, paleontology means the study of ancient existing things, or life forms.

GIFTED STUDENTS
Suggest that students use encyclopedias, textbooks, and other sources to find out the differences between paleontology, archaeology, and anthropology as fields of study. (Archaeology: the study of the remains of ancient human life and culture. Anthropology: the study of human origins, development, and behavior.)

Ancillary Support

The resources below can be used to support your teaching strategy for these two pages.

TR Writing In Biology: Where in the World Am I?
Apply: The Dating Game
TB Geologic History of the Earth, #23

4 ASSESS

Quick Check

Have students draw two sketches, without consulting Figures 17–4 and 17–5, showing fossil sequences used in relative dating and radioactive decay used in absolute dating.

Section Review 17–1

1. Studying the fossil record enables researchers to learn about life's past and fully understand its present.
2. The geologic time scale makes Earth's long history more manageable and shows how organisms have changed over time.
3. Relative dating involves comparing the ages of fossils in one rock layer with the ages of fossils found in other layers to determine which fossils are older and younger than others. Absolute dating involves measuring the amount of a radioactive element remaining in an organism to determine its actual age.
4. By comparing the amount of the element that remains with the amount that was originally present.

Skills Trace

Relating

- Focus p. 390
- Practice p. 392
- Assess p. 412

Learning Modality

Visual and Kinesthetic Learning

The following visualization will help students understand the relative lengths of the geologic eras shown in Figure 17–6. Have students work in groups of three. Two students should stretch a rope tightly between them with their hands 3.4 meters apart. The third student should measure and mark the rope at 5 cm, 15 cm, and 38 cm from the right-hand end of the rope. Explain that from left to right (largest to smallest), the rope sections represent the Precambrian, Paleozoic, Mesozoic, and Cenozoic Eras. Have students compare the relative lengths of the rope sections and the diagram sections.

Figure 17–8
Mountains such as these, beautifully reflected in a lake, are formed when continental plates collide.

Over time, huge numbers of species have disappeared over relatively short periods of time. At least five times during the history of life, as many as 50 percent of all living species became extinct during what are called mass extinctions. The best-known mass extinction—although it wasn't the most disastrous—ended the era of dinosaurs.

What causes mass extinctions? Some may have been caused by climate change. Others may have been caused by the effects of huge meteorites crashing into the Earth. Whatever their cause, mass extinctions have had powerful effects in shaping the history of life.

Wandering Continents

There was still a puzzle to be solved before scientists could fully understand the history of the Earth. Nearly 150 years ago, geologists looking at maps of the globe noticed that major landmasses resembled pieces of a jigsaw puzzle. They saw that the east coast of South America could comfortably fit against the west coast of southern Africa. In the same way, North America and Greenland could fit neatly into Europe and northern Africa.

As time went on, more curious information was revealed. For example, rocks and fossils of a certain age from South America closely resemble those found in Africa. If those continents were always thousands of kilometers apart, how could that have happened?

The answer lies in a geological theory known as **continental drift,** which suggests that continents move slowly over hundreds of millions of years. The Earth's crust is divided into eight major plates that move. In places where continental plates collide, one of two things happens. In some places, the crust is folded and wrinkled into giant mountain ranges. In other places, one plate is forced under another.

Section Review 17–1

1. **Describe** the importance of the fossil record.
2. **Explain** the importance of the geologic time scale.
3. **Critical Thinking—Comparing** Compare relative dating and absolute dating.
4. **MINI LAB** How can you **relate** an element's half-life to the amount of the original element that remains?

TEACHER SUPPORT

Background Information

Throughout Earth's history, continental movements have influenced the distribution of organisms. Two events in particular significantly influenced life. The first occurred about 250 million years ago, at the end of the Paleozoic Era, when plate movements brought all Earth's land masses together into the supercontinent known as Pangaea. Species that had evolved in isolation were brought together and had to compete for resources. The total amount of shoreline and shallow coastal areas was reduced, ocean currents changed, and the climate became more harsh. These changes forced great numbers of species to extinction.

The second event began about 180 million years ago, during the early Mesozoic Era, when Pangaea began to break apart again, causing tremendous changes for existing species. As the continents drifted apart, each became in effect a vast island on which species evolved into new forms in isolation from their original related neighbors.

Finding Order in Diversity

GUIDE FOR READING

- **Explain** the importance of classification systems.
- **Classify** living things into six kingdoms.

MINI LAB

- **Classify** common objects into groups.

HUNDREDS OF MILLIONS OF species have come and gone on Earth during the history of life. This is quite a lot to think about. In order to even begin to speak about this staggering diversity, we need to develop a classification system to help us identify specific living things. In this way, we can give names to individual organisms and see how they relate to other organisms.

Why Do We Classify?

A classification system identifies objects and gathers them into groups whose members are similar to one another. Whether you are aware of it or not, you use classification systems all the time. You might, for example, classify people as teachers, students, or auto mechanics if you are speaking about something that involves the work they do.

This simple way of naming things is similar to scientific classification in two ways. First, it is based on a logical method of naming things. Second, all classification systems group objects into categories based on some feature they have in common. For example, the objects might look alike, function in similar ways, or be related to one another—if they are living things. This combination of

Figure 17–9
These three organisms are all members of the cat family because they have some common characteristics. Yet they differ in several ways. For this reason, (a) *the common house cat is given the scientific name* Felis domesticus, (b) *the tiger is called* Panthera tigris, *and* (c) *the black leopard is called* Panthera pardus.

TEACHER SUPPORT

Managing Classroom Diversity

TECH PREP/EDUCATIONAL EQUITY
Students who enjoy working with animals might like to investigate career opportunities as veterinary technicians. Suggest that students research the educational requirements and experience necessary for employment in this field and the many different types of jobs available. Sources of this information include *Encyclopedia of Careers and Vocational Guidance* (William E. Hopke, editor; J.G. Ferguson Publishing Company, 1993), *Careers in Veterinary Medicine* by Jane Caryl (Rosen Publishing Group, 1994), and *Opportunities in Veterinary Medicine Careers* by Robert Swope (NTC Publishing Company, 1993).

Encourage students to read nonfiction books written by or about veterinary professionals detailing their experiences and daily work life. A source that would be particularly suitable for female students is *Women in Veterinary Medicine: Profiles of Success* by Sue Drum (Iowa State University Press, 1991).

SECTION 17-2

Finding Order in Diversity

Performance Objectives
- Describe how classification systems are helpful.
- Identify the six kingdoms used in biological taxonomy.

Mini Lab Skill: Classifying

1 ENGAGE

Ideas Through Images

Have students examine Figure 17–9, read the caption, and answer the following questions.

- **What characteristics do all these cats have in common?** (Accept a variety of answers, such as all have the same overall body shape, have the same body parts, are mammals, are carnivores, are predators, and so forth.)
- **What characteristics are different?** (Accept a variety of answers, such as the cats' sizes, coloration, and natural habitats and the fact that the housecat is domesticated and the others are wild.)
- **What other animals probably belong in this same family?** (Accept all reasonable possibilities, including African lions, mountain lions, cheetahs, and lynx.)
- **What animals that share some major characteristics with cats do not belong in the cat family?** (Students should name carnivorous mammals such as dogs, bears, hyenas, coyotes, and wolves.)

2 EXPLORE

Investigate

Cooperative Learning Prepare a list of 20–30 specific mammals representing several different families and orders, and give each group a copy of the list. Have students sort the animals into different categories (for example, cats, bears, canines, etc.) based on their apparent similarities and differences, listing each category and its animals on a preliminary master chart. Then have each group member choose one category and use a field guide to verify the group's decisions, noting any errors or questionable classifications on the chart. As a final step, group members should work together to revise the chart as needed and produce a final version. Let groups share their final charts.

3 TEACH

INTEGRATING CAREERS

Botanists study plants—their anatomy, physiology, classification, reproduction, heredity, and value to agriculture, horticulture, and medicine.

Ideas Through Images

Have students examine Figure 17–10 and read the caption. To make sure students recognize the similarities and differences between the animals in each classification category, ask the following questions for each category, beginning with Family in the illustration and working upward.

- **Which animal has been added in this category?** (From family through kingdom: tiger, polar bear, dolphin, bird, butterfly.)
- **Why does that animal belong with the others in this category?** (Tiger: Is a type of cat, a member of the cat family. Polar bear: Is a carnivore, eats other animals. Dolphin: Is a mammal. Bird: Is a chordate, or vertebrate; has a backbone. Butterfly: Is an animal.)

widely understood names and groupings allows us to communicate information about objects easily and efficiently among ourselves.

Biological Classification

Obviously, any useful system of classification requires universal rules. In biology, those rules begin with the name assigned to each species. First, scientists assign a single universally accepted name to each species. Then, they group species into larger categories that have biological significance. The science of naming organisms and assigning them to these groups is called **taxonomy.**

INTEGRATING CAREERS
What kinds of work do you think botanists do?

The classification system used today was established by the Swedish botanist Carolus Linnaeus in the eighteenth century. ● Linnaeus gave each organism a two-part name in Latin, the language of science at the time. The house cat, for example, is called *Felis domesticus*. The first part of the name, *Felis*, refers to the **genus** (plural: genera) to which this cat belongs. A genus refers to the small group of organisms that are quite similar to one another, though different in certain respects.

The second part of the cat's name, *domesticus*, refers only to one particular species. Often, this part of the name is a Latin description of some important characteristic of the organism. *Felis domesticus* literally means domesticated cat. In this textbook, as in other scientific books, the genus and species name is printed in italics. In addition, the genus name is capitalized.

Checkpoint What is taxonomy? 1

Species and Genus

The smallest group in the biological classification system is the **species,** which is a population of organisms that share similar characteristics and that interbreed in nature. If two species share many features but are different biological units, they are classified as different species within the same genus. For example, although the bobcat is a catlike animal, it is placed in a different species from the house cat and is called *Felis rufus*.

Checkpoint What is a species? 2

Other Groupings

The genus *Felis* and three other genera of cats are grouped into larger units

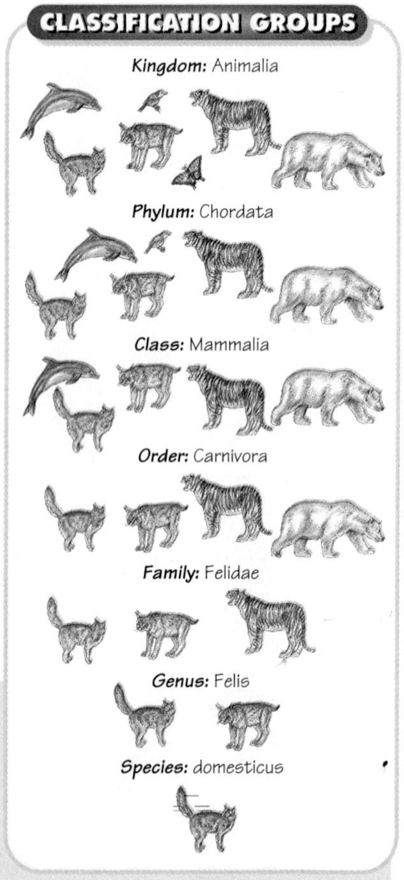

Figure 17–10
This illustration shows the classification of a house cat. Notice that as you go from species to kingdom, the house cat has less in common with members of each group.

TEACHER SUPPORT — Background Information

Although Carolus Linnaeus did not intentionally establish the system of binomial nomenclature, he is still known for developing it. He actually preferred to use the longer descriptive name for plants in his works. However, he would write a shorter two-word name for each organism in the margins of his notes. Other researchers found this shorthand so useful that they adopted it.

Strictly speaking, the second part of a scientific name is the specific epithet, or trivial name, and a species' name consists of both the genus and specific epithet. In this text, the term species name will be used because it is easier for students to understand and easier for them to remember.

called **families.** All genera of catlike animals belong to the family Felidae.

Several families of similar organisms make up the next larger group—an **order.** Members of the cat, dog, bear, and raccoon families are placed in the order Carnivora.

Orders are grouped into **classes.** All members of the order Carnivora are placed in the class Mammalia, along with other animals that are warmblooded, have body hair, and produce milk for their young. Several classes are placed in a **phylum** (FIGH-luhm), which has a large number of very different organisms. These organisms share some important characteristics. For example, mammals are grouped with the birds, reptiles, amphibians, and several classes of fishes into the phylum Chordata. Lastly, all phyla belong to one of six large groups called **kingdoms.** Animals make up the kingdom Animalia.

☑ ***Checkpoint*** To which class do humans belong? 3

MINI LAB .... Classifying

A Taxing Situation

PROBLEM *What rules do you use to* ***classify*** *common objects?*

PROCEDURE

1. As a group, think of a characteristic that will divide the following materials into two groups: plain straight pins, straight pins with colored plastic tops, safety pins of different sizes, buttons, a zipper, steel nails of various sizes, steel screws of various sizes, brass nails of various sizes, brass screws of various sizes, galvanized nails of various sizes, and galvanized screws of various sizes.
2. Divide each of the two groups into two smaller groups.
3. Further divide each smaller group into subgroups.
4. Continue this process until there is only one object in each group.

ANALYZE AND CONCLUDE

1. What characteristics do all these objects have in common? In what ways are they different?
2. How many groups does your classification system have?
3. On what basis did you choose to place each object?

Figure 17–11
Except for viruses, all organisms can be classified into one of the six kingdoms of life.

MAJOR CHARACTERISTICS OF THE SIX KINGDOMS

Kingdom	Archaebacteria	Eubacteria	Protista	Fungi	Plantae	Animalia
Cell Type	Prokaryotes	Prokaryotes	Eukaryotes	Eukaryotes	Eukaryotes	Eukaryotes
Cell Structures	Have cell walls that lack peptidoglycan	Have cell walls made up of peptidoglycan	Have a nucleus, mitochondria, some have chloroplasts	Have a nucleus, mitochondria, but no chloroplasts/ cell wall of chitin	Have a nucleus, mitochondria, chloroplasts/cell wall of cellulose	Have a nucleus, mitochondria, but no chloroplasts; no cell wall
Body Form	Unicellular	Unicellular	Mostly unicellular, some multicellular	Some unicellular, most multicellular	Multicellular	Multicellular
Nutrition	Autotrophic or heterotrophic	Autotrophic or heterotrophic	Autotrophic or heterotrophic	Heterotrophic (absorption)	Autotrophic	Heterotrophic
Examples	Methanogens, halophiles	Rhizobium	Amebae, paramecia	Yeasts, molds, mushrooms	Mosses, ferns, flowering plants, seaweeds	Sponges, worms, snails, insects, mammals

MINI LAB Classifying

Teacher Notes

• For time required, see page 386b.

• Make sure students use the division procedure described in Background Information below.

Answers to Analyze and Conclude

1. Accept all reasonable responses.
2. Answers will vary depending on the characteristic used for each division.
3. Answers will vary but should include only one characteristic for each division.

Skills Trace
Classifying

- Focus p. 395
- Practice p. 397
- Assess p. 412

☑ Checkpoints

1 Taxonomy is the science of naming organisms and assigning them to biological groups.

2 A species is the smallest group in the biological classification system.

3 Humans belong to the class Mammalia.

TEACHER SUPPORT

Background Information

A classification system in which each step divides objects into only two groups is known as a dichotomous key. Only one characteristic is used to make each division, and only two groups are produced. One contains all objects that do have that characteristic, and the other contains all objects that do not have that characteristic. Any single characteristic can be used for each division. In the MINI LAB, for example, students could use metal and not metal to divide the objects in step 1, sewing items and not sewing items in step 2, straight and not straight in step 3, and so on.

Stress this procedure before students begin, and supervise their work to make sure they are using only one characteristic for each division and are producing only two groups—for example, metal and not metal, not steel, brass, plastic, and cloth.

Ancillary Support

The resource below can be used to support your teaching strategy for these two pages.

BL Inquiry Activity: The Right Address

Ideas Through Images

Some students may feel overwhelmed by the vast amount of information in Figure 17–12, its rather complex format, and the numerous scientific terms used in it. Explain that only the most knowledgeable experts know all this information by heart, and reassure students that they are not expected to learn and remember all these details. Emphasize that the diagram's main purpose is simply to show the evolutionary relationships between different life forms. Then have students examine the diagram, read the caption, and answer the following questions.

- **In what order did chordates—animals with backbones—evolve?** (Fish, amphibians, reptiles, birds, mammals.)
- **According to this chart, from what type of animals did birds evolve?** (Dinosaurs.)

Correcting Misconceptions

Contrary to the belief of many people, scientists do not contend that humans evolved from apes. Rather, scientists postulate that both the earliest humans (hominids) and the earliest apes evolved from a common ancestor (a hominoid) in the ancient past but their evolutionary pathways diverged millions of years ago. The sequence of "first apes, then humans" shown in Figure 17–6 on pages 390–391 does not mean that humans evolved from apes but that the direct ancestors of modern humans appeared later in Earth's evolutionary history than the direct ancestors of modern apes.

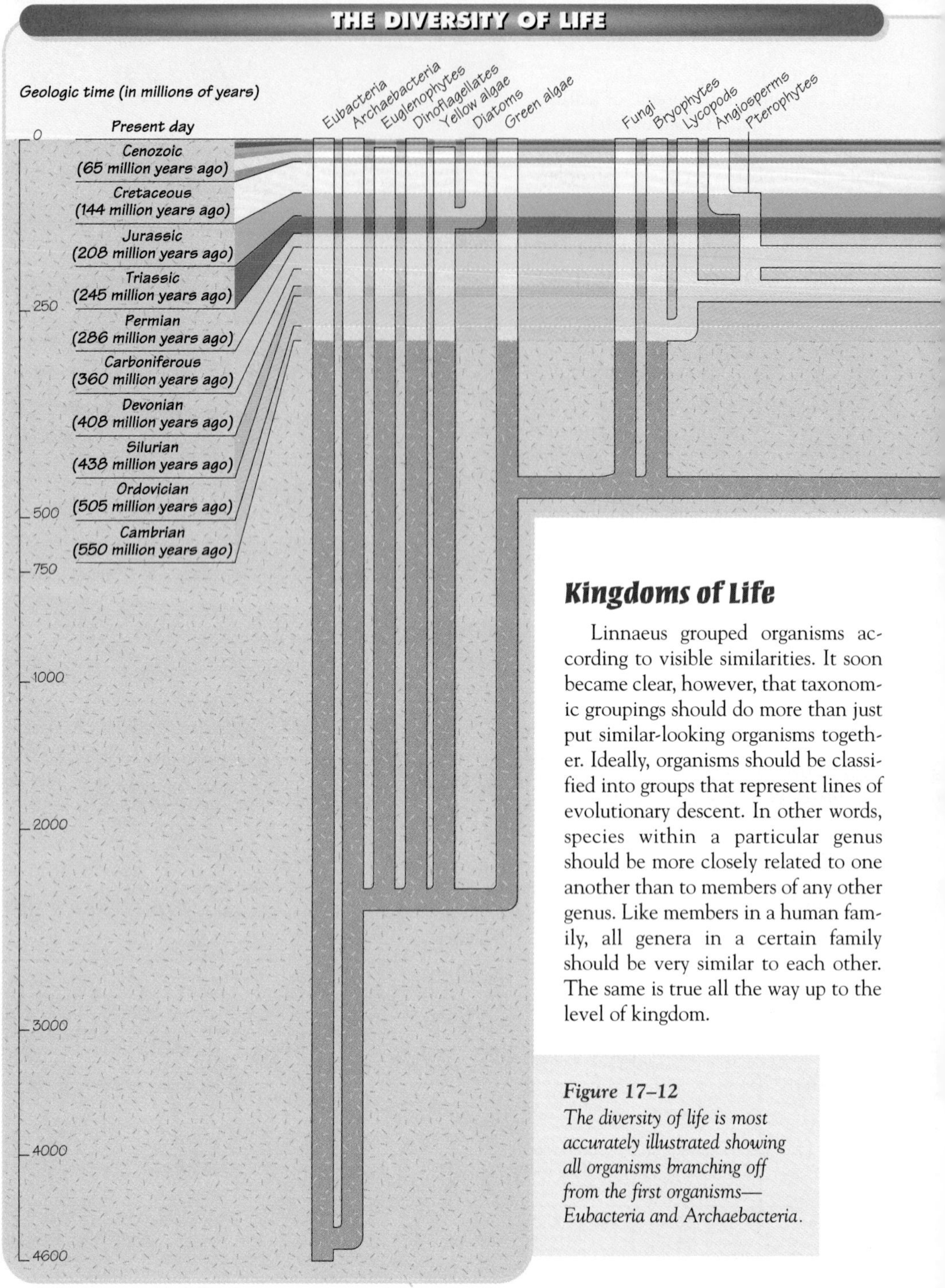

Kingdoms of Life

Linnaeus grouped organisms according to visible similarities. It soon became clear, however, that taxonomic groupings should do more than just put similar-looking organisms together. Ideally, organisms should be classified into groups that represent lines of evolutionary descent. In other words, species within a particular genus should be more closely related to one another than to members of any other genus. Like members in a human family, all genera in a certain family should be very similar to each other. The same is true all the way up to the level of kingdom.

Figure 17–12 *The diversity of life is most accurately illustrated showing all organisms branching off from the first organisms—Eubacteria and Archaebacteria.*

TEACHER SUPPORT

Facts and Figures

The most direct way to determine the relationship between two species is by comparing their DNA. The most precise (but also most tedious) method is DNA sequencing, in which the researcher first prepares comparable DNA segments from two species, and then determines the nucleotide sequences of the segments. Another method, DNA-DNA hybridization, measures the extent of hydrogen bonding between single strands of DNA from different species.

Amino acid sequencing—determining the sequence of amino acids in a polypeptide—is the most precise method for comparing proteins from different species. A close match indicates that the genes programming those proteins evolved from a common gene and thus a shared ancestor. For example, the sequences for humans and chimpanzees match perfectly for all 104 amino acid positions along the polypeptide chain for cytochrome c, an electron transport protein.

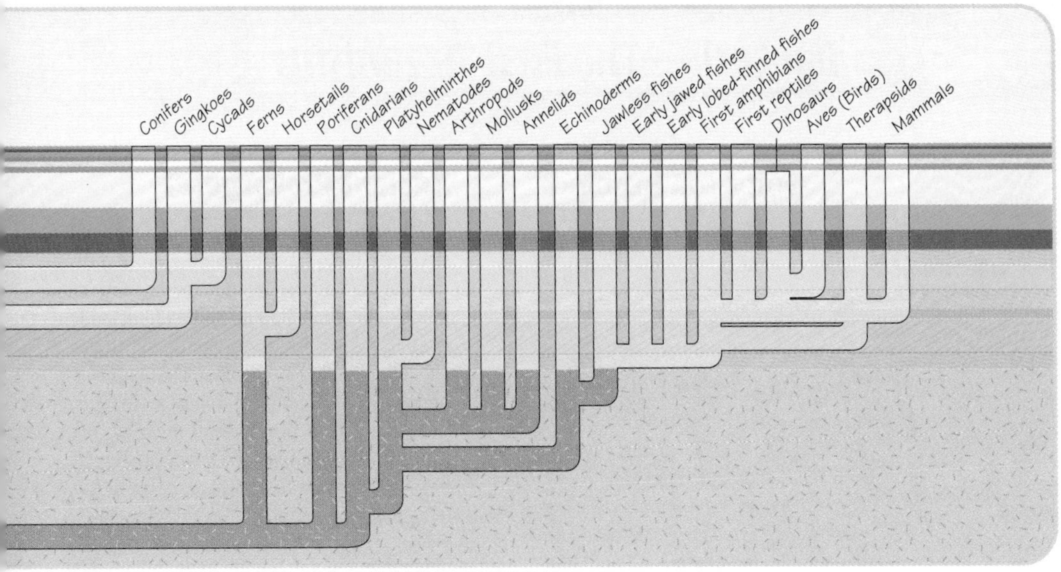

The Six Kingdoms

For decades, biologists recognized five kingdoms of life—Monera, Protista, Fungi, Plantae, and Animalia. In recent years, however, molecular techniques such as reading DNA and sequencing proteins were applied to evolutionary history and relationships. Biologists now realize that the two major groups of bacteria are so different that they deserve to be placed in two separate kingdoms—Eubacteria (yoo-bak-TEER-ee-uh) and Archaebacteria (ahr-kee-bak-TEER-ee-uh). **Today, most researchers agree that there should be at least six kingdoms—Eubacteria, Archaebacteria, Protista, Fungi, Plantae, and Animalia.** This textbook will use a six-kingdom classification system.

Diagramming Life's Diversity

What is the best way to represent life's diversity in pictures? A good way to start is to draw the evolutionary relationships among organisms to the best of our knowledge. This kind of diagram, shown in ***Figure 17–12,*** shows both that living organisms had common ancestors and that other descendants of those organisms are still living and evolving today.

Section Review 17–2

1. **Explain** the importance of classification systems.
2. Name the six kingdoms into which living things are **classified.**
3. **Critical Thinking—Drawing Conclusions** Why is taxonomy a continuing science?
4. **MINI LAB** What rules do you use to **classify** common objects?

4 ASSESS

Quick Check

Ask students to list the categories in the biological classification system in their correct order from species to kingdom and then give examples of organisms that could be included in each category.

Section Review 17–2

1. Classification systems allow people to identify objects and put them into groups whose members are similar to one another.

2. Eubacteria, Archaebacteria, Protista, Fungi, Plantae, and Animalia.

3. Accept all reasonable responses. Sample: As new technology enables scientists to learn more about living things, scientists may change their classifications to show relationships more accurately.

4. Answers will vary. Students may mention the dichotomous characteristics they used in the MINI LAB.

Skills Trace

Classifying

Focus p. 395
Practice p. 397
Assess p. 412

Learning Modality

Visual Learning Present the Explore activity on page 394 using individual pictures of animals rather than a list of their names. If you do not have a resource of animal pictures, ask volunteers to photocopy some in field guides and other sources and mount each on a separate index card. Let students physically arrange the pictures in separate groups before they list the animals' names on the master chart.

Ancillary Support

The resource below can be used to support your teaching strategy for these two pages.

TR Explore: Who's Related to Whom?

SECTION 17-3

Bacteria—The First Organisms

Performance Objectives

• Discuss the structure of bacteria.
• Differentiate between eubacteria and archaebacteria.

1 ENGAGE

Ideas Through Images

Have students examine Figure 17–13, read the caption, and answer the following questions.

• **Have you ever seen anything that looked like these pictures when you used a microscope? If so, what?** (Students may say that the pictures look like cells they have observed.)

• **Do you think bacteria are actually colored like this?** (Accept all responses. Explain that dyes and special microscopes were used to add color to these images so the bacteria's structures would be easier to see.)

2 EXPLORE

Investigate

Research Ask students to consult additional biology textbooks (including college texts), encyclopedias, and nonfiction library books to find photographs of other types of bacteria to compare with those shown in Figure 17–13. Tell students to list the full scientific name of each bacterium and its action or function. Have them summarize their findings in a table with columns labeled *Helpful Bacteria*, *Harmful Bacteria*, and *Not Sure*.

SECTION

17–3 Bacteria—The First Organisms

GUIDE FOR READING

• **Describe** the structure of bacteria.
• **Classify** bacteria into two kingdoms.

AS AMAZING AS IT MAY SOUND, life on Earth has existed nearly as long as the Earth itself. Fossils of single-celled organisms that look surprisingly similar to modern organisms have been found in rocks that are more than 3.5 billion years old. This is remarkable, because it is believed that until at least 4 billion years ago, volcanic eruptions and collisions with comets and asteroids made any form of life impossible. How then did life begin? What characteristics did the first life forms have? Although several hypotheses have tried to explain how life may have arisen, we may never know the answers.

Ancient Prokaryotes

Nearly 3.5 billion years ago, advanced single-celled organisms were common on the Earth. Microscopic fossils—or microfossils—of that age looked remarkably similar to certain living photosynthetic prokaryotes. Prokaryotes are unicellular organisms that do not have a nucleus. Scientists hypothesize that the first life forms must have evolved without oxygen because Earth's first atmosphere didn't contain that highly reactive gas.

Over time, some cells evolved that had the ability to use the sun's energy to produce food. These photosynthetic prokaryotes were common in the shallow seas of the Precambrian Period. By 2.2 to 2 billion years ago, these single-celled organisms were producing vast quantities of oxygen.

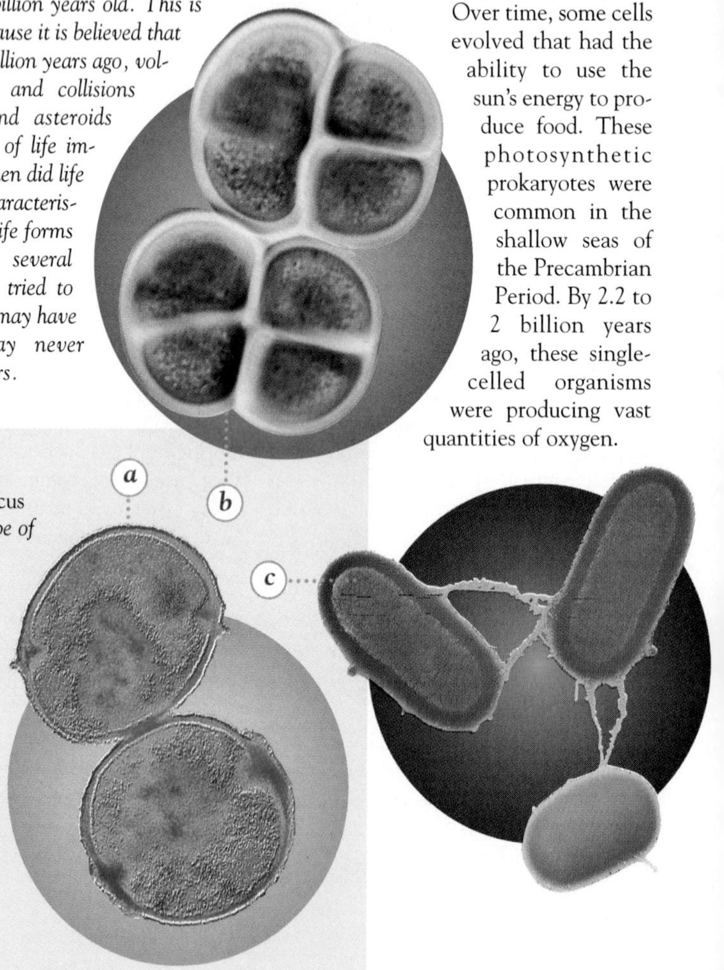

Figure 17–13
ⓐ *One type of bacteria,* Streptococcus pneumoniae *is responsible for one type of pneumonia in humans (magnification: 30,000X).* ⓑ *Cyanobacteria are photosynthetic bacteria that some scientists believe may have been the predecessor of chloroplasts (magnification: 600X).*
ⓒ *Bacteria reproduce by either binary fission or conjugation. In this photograph, the bacteria* E. coli, *which live in the intestines of humans, are undergoing conjugation (magnification: 11,250X).*

TEACHER SUPPORT

Activity

OBSERVING BACTERIA

Set up at least one learning station with a microscope and a number of prepared slides showing various species of bacteria. Provide opportunities for students to use the station during class periods. To guide students as they make their observations, prepare a study sheet to use with each slide, with the following questions and instructions and any others you wish to add.

1. What is the scientific name of this bacterium?

2. What magnification did you use in order to see the bacterium clearly?

3. Draw a picture of the bacterium in the space below. Label the cell wall.

4. Optional: Find out what this bacterium does in nature. For example, does it cause a certain disease? Does it decompose dead organic material? Does it take part in the nitrogen cycle?

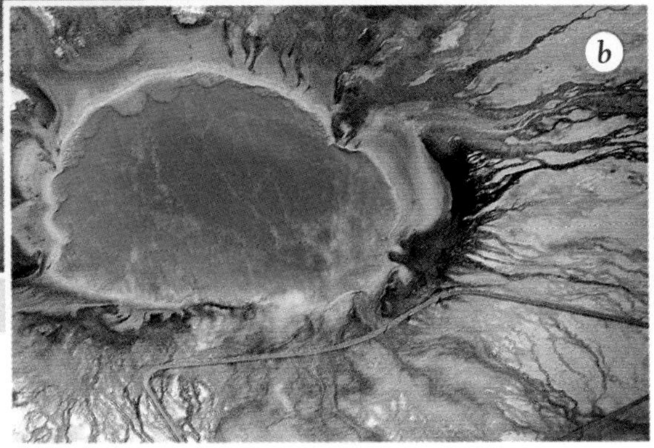

Figure 17–14
Bacteria can live in a variety of environments. (a) Some bacteria prefer cold environments and live on icebergs. (b) Other bacteria prefer the hot temperatures of these sulfur pools in Yellowstone National Park in Wyoming.

The oxygen gas started to accumulate in the atmosphere. As a result, the oxygen concentration in the atmosphere rose. Over several hundred million years, the oxygen concentration in the atmosphere continued to rise until it reached its present-day level.

This event brought about a worldwide crisis for organisms that had evolved in the absence of oxygen. The high level of free oxygen in the atmosphere drove some early life forms to extinction. Others were forced into deep, airless hiding places. And still others evolved new ways to use the oxygen to generate useful energy for the cell. The stage was set for the evolution of modern life.

☑ **Checkpoint** How old are the earliest fossils? ❶

Living Prokaryotes

If you look at the geologic time scale, you will see that prokaryotes were the only form of life for nearly half of Earth's history. So it shouldn't surprise you to learn that their descendants—modern **bacteria**—have evolved incredibly diverse lifestyles.

You may not think about them much, but bacteria are everywhere. They live on the tops of mountains and the bottom of the ocean floor, on the surfaces of melting glaciers, and in very hot water in volcanic hot springs. As a group, bacteria are incredibly adaptable. Many are nearly indestructible. And they play a greater role in your daily life than you probably imagine. The number of bacteria living in just one part of your body—your intestines—at this very moment is greater than the total number of human beings who have ever lived on the Earth!

What Are Bacteria?

All bacteria are prokaryotes. **Bacteria have a cell membrane that is surrounded by a tough, protective cell wall. Their genetic material is contained on a single strand of circular DNA that is not surrounded by a nuclear envelope.** Bacteria also lack mitochondria, chloroplasts, and other cellular structures enclosed in membranes.

3 TEACH

Investigate

Research If any students have observed the volcanic hot springs at Yellowstone National Park, ask them to describe what they saw. Suggest that students find out more about the types of bacteria that live in hot springs and in the other extreme conditions mentioned in the student text.

Discussion

Use students' findings in Explore and the Activity, Observing Bacteria, on the previous page to introduce information about the shapes of bacteria. Emphasize that a bacterium's shape helps an observer identify its species. Spherical bacteria are called cocci (singular: coccus). Cocci commonly occur in clusters or chains. Rod-shaped bacteria are called bacilli (singular: bacillus). Spiral-shaped bacteria are called spirilla (singular: spirillum). Have students examine prepared slides of bacteria and identify the shape of each bacterium. Ask students to review the drawings they made with what they see under the microscope.

☑ Checkpoint

❶ Nearly 3.5 billion years old.

TEACHER SUPPORT

Managing Classroom Diversity

TECH PREP STUDENTS

Students who are considering careers in health care could research antibiotics—their sources, actions, and possible side effects, their profound effect on the incidence and mortality rate of diseases since their development in the 1940s, examples, and precautions that must be taken in prescribing them.

Antibiotics, which are produced by certain microorganisms as normal metabolic products, kill or inhibit the growth of other microorganisms. Penicillin, for example, disrupts the formation of covalent bonds that hold bacterial cell walls together. Antibiotics are not effective against viruses.

Besides performing their intended function, some antibiotics disrupt normal populations of bacteria in the body, leading to secondary infections. In addition, overprescribing antibiotics can result in the development of resistant strains of bacteria, making some diseases more difficult to treat.

Ancillary Support

The resources below can be used to support your teaching strategy for these two pages.

LM Observing Bacteria, #33
TR Explore: They're Everywhere!
BL Inquiry Activity: A Simple Life

INTEGRATING HEALTH

Pneumonia is classified as viral or bacterial, depending on the pathogen. Bacterial pneumonia is treated with antibiotics. There are currently no medications to treat viral pneumonia, but symptoms can be alleviated.

4 ASSESS

Quick Check

Ask each student to sketch a bacterium (any type) from memory, label its cell wall, and add a caption describing bacteria's genetic material.

Section Review 17-3

1. Bacteria have a cell membrane that is surrounded by a tough, protective cell wall. Their genetic material is contained on a single strand of circular DNA that is not surrounded by a nuclear envelope.
2. Eubacteria and Archaebacteria.
3. They have evolved very diverse lifestyles, adapting to the most extreme conditions.

Learning Modality

Tactile Learning Have students use a variety of materials—yarn, sandpaper, textured fabrics, pipecleaners, and so forth—to make models of bacteria based on the photographs in Figure 17–13 and on the drawings they made when they observed bacteria with a microscope.

The classification and evolutionary relationships of bacteria have been completely changed in recent years. Why has this occurred? One reason is that researchers have examined the similarities and differences in ribosomal RNA, which serves as a "slow" molecular clock for timing evolutionary events. The data they gathered divide the major groups of living bacteria into two kingdoms. **The two kingdoms of bacteria are Eubacteria and Archaebacteria.** Members of these kingdoms evolved from a single, extinct common ancestor.

Checkpoint Are bacteria prokaryotes or eukaryotes? 1

Eubacteria

Members of the kingdom Eubacteria, or "true" bacteria, have thick, rigid cell walls made up of the carbohydrate peptidoglycan (pehp-tih-doh-GLIGH-kan). The cell wall surrounds a typical cell membrane. Eubacteria are extremely diverse in their ecology and metabolism. For example, some species of Eubacteria live in soil, while others infect larger organisms and produce disease. And still other species of Eubacteria are photosynthetic and make their own food using light energy.

INTEGRATING HEALTH

What are the different kinds of pneumonia? How are they treated?

Archaebacteria

Members of the kingdom Archaebacteria, or "ancient" bacteria, live in the most extreme environments imaginable—volcanic hot springs, brine pools, and black organic mud that lacks oxygen. Many can survive only in the absence of oxygen. Their cell wall lacks peptidoglycan, and their cell membrane contains certain lipids that are not found in any other organism.

How Do Bacteria Reproduce?

Bacteria have fairly simple reproductive lives. Most of the time, bacteria reproduce by **binary fission**—the division of the cell into two daughter cells, along with the duplication of their single chromosome. There are, however, some exceptions to this rule.

Certain bacteria, such as the common intestinal bacteria *Escherichia coli* (*E. coli*), sometimes undergo a process called **conjugation,** which is a simple form of sexual reproduction. During conjugation, part of the genetic information from one cell is transferred to another cell.

Certain other bacteria, such as *Streptococcus pneumoniae,* reproduce only by binary fission but have a habit of picking up bits and pieces of DNA from other bacteria. This process, which is called **transformation,** offers an unusual opportunity for a normally asexual organism to pick up new traits. Because *S. pneumoniae* can cause pneumonia in humans, particularly infants and toddlers, this ability can have serious consequences for human health.

Section Review 17-3

1. **Describe** the structure of bacteria.
2. What are the two kingdoms into which bacteria are **classified**?
3. **Critical Thinking—Hypothesizing** How have bacteria survived so successfully?

TEACHER SUPPORT

Ecology Note

Bacteria appear to have great potential to help solve environmental problems. For example, certain bacteria that occur naturally on ocean beaches can decompose petroleum. Spraying nitrogen and phosphorus fertilizers on oil-soaked beaches stimulates the growth of these oil-eating bacteria. Although there is some danger of water pollution from the fertilizers, this technique is the most rapid and inexpensive method yet devised to clean oil-fouled beaches.

The water that drains from old mines is highly acidic and laced with toxins such as arsenic, copper, zinc, lead, mercury, and cadmium. Researchers have found that species of the bacterium *Thiobacillus,* which thrives in acidic water, can absorb and accumulate the toxic metals. By seeding the water with bacteria or passing it through filters containing bacteria, the metals can be recovered.

Viruses

SECTION **17–4**

Guide for Reading

- **Describe** the structure of a virus.
- **Explain** how a virus reproduces.

THEY ARE INCREDIBLY SMALL and impossibly simple. They are not alive because they are not cells and are not composed of cells. Medical science has yet to devise foolproof ways to stop them once they have infected a cell.

No one knows where they came from. Because they cannot survive without invading living host cells, they cannot have appeared before the first true life forms. Yet because they infect virtually every known organism, including bacteria, it is likely that they evolved fairly soon after the appearance of the first prokaryotes.

What Is a Virus?

What are these mysterious objects? They are viruses. **A virus is a tiny particle—made up of genetic material and protein—that can invade and replicate within a living host cell.**

Viruses are so fundamentally different from living things that they are not even called organisms. In a sense, you can think of viruses as pure information, similar to a computer program stored on a disk with no hardware of its own. By itself, a virus can do absolutely nothing. It doesn't respire, eat, excrete, or reproduce. It simply holds onto its information and waits to infect a suitable host.

Each virus particle contains a core of either DNA or RNA, surrounded by a protein coat. The outer surface of the virus may also be covered with an envelope composed of lipids and proteins. Often, these compounds help the virus bind to the host cell membrane and "trick" the host cell into taking the virus inside, where it can do its harm.

Checkpoint What is a virus? (2)

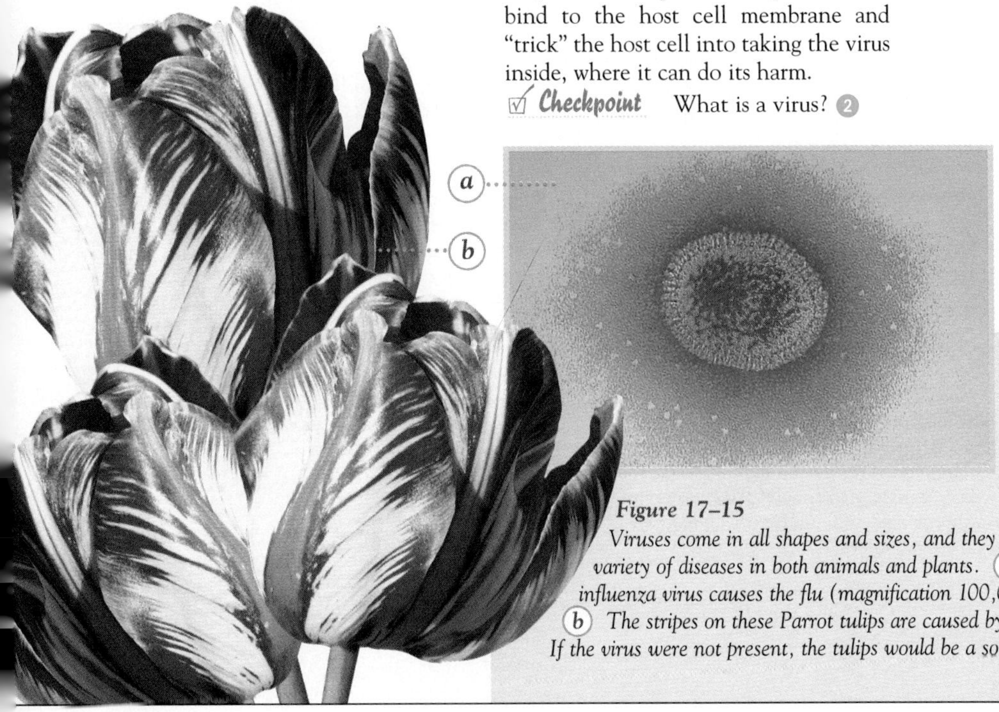

Figure 17–15
Viruses come in all shapes and sizes, and they cause a variety of diseases in both animals and plants. (a) The influenza virus causes the flu (magnification 100,000X). (b) The stripes on these Parrot tulips are caused by a virus. If the virus were not present, the tulips would be a solid color.

TEACHER SUPPORT

Managing Classroom Diversity

TECH PREP STUDENTS
Encourage students considering careers as veterinary technicians to research the names and effects of common viral diseases that affect cats and dogs. Such diseases in cats include rabies, panleukopenia (FPL), viral rhinotracheitis (FVR), calicivirus (FCV), and feline leukemia virus (FeLV). Viral diseases in dogs include rabies, distemper, parainfluenza, adenovirus type 2, viral hepatitis, parvovirus (CPV), and coronavirus (CCV).

Ask students considering careers in health care to research the names and effects of viral diseases that affect humans. These include the common cold, influenza, viral pneumonia, hepatitis, mumps, measles, genital warts, polio, and AIDS. Encourage students to find out why viral diseases are so difficult to treat.

Section 17–4
Viruses

Performance Objectives
- Discuss the structure of a virus.
- Describe the reproductive processes of viruses.

1 ENGAGE

Ideas Through Images

Have students examine Figure 17–15, read the caption, and answer the following questions.

- **What do you know about the structure of a virus?** (Some students may know that viruses are not composed of cells.)
- **How does the magnification of the influenza virus shown here compare to the magnifications of the bacteria shown in Figure 17–13?** (The magnification of the virus is much greater.)
- **Are viruses living or not?** (Some students may know that viruses are not alive.)

2 EXPLORE

Investigate

Research Ask students to consult additional sources to find pictures of other types of viruses to compare with those shown in Figure 17–15. Have students list the name of each virus and its action in a table.

Checkpoints

(1) Bacteria are prokaryotes.

(2) A tiny particle—made up of genetic material and protein—that can invade and replicate within a living host cell.

Ancillary Support

The resource below can be used to support your teaching strategy for these two pages.

TR Enrich: Population Explosion

3 TEACH

Connections

Point out to students that the combination of rapid mutation rate, cross-species transfer, and lack of effective treatments for the diseases they cause makes viruses as a group the most dangerous and lethal pathogens on Earth.

Many viral diseases originated in tropical regions where there are great concentrations and varieties of plants and animals to serve as hosts. The African rain forest, for example, was the origination site of AIDS (first recorded in 1959), Lassa fever (1969), and Ebola fever (1976).

Modern transportation enables viruses to travel faster and farther than ever before—from animals to humans, from rural areas to cities, and from nation to nation. For example, the Hantaan virus, which caused the mysterious flu-like disease that struck the Navajo people in the Four Corners region of the southwestern United States in 1993, was introduced to this country by infected soldiers returning home from the Korean War. (Also see Managing Classroom Diversity below.)

Answers to *Making the Connection*

Because flu viruses mutate rapidly, every year new strains evolve that are not recognized by the body's immune system, requiring new vaccines. Health-care workers are repeatedly exposed to flu viruses, including newly evolved strains. The elderly, people with circulatory and respiratory problems, and people with immune system disorders are particularly vulnerable to viral infections.

Biology and You ... Connections

Viral Evolution and the Flu

Most viruses are similar to organisms in that they constantly evolve in response to changes in their environment. The environment for viruses that infect humans includes our bodies, our domestic animals, and the medicines we take.

Some viruses, such as those that cause measles and smallpox, do not evolve quickly. Because of this slow evolution, vaccines were developed to help eliminate the viruses. A vaccine is an injection into the body of a weakened or mild form of the virus. Vaccines give the body the ability to recognize and attack an invading virus more quickly. Because viruses of this type don't change much, they always look the same to the body's immune system, so that a single vaccination can protect against infection for years.

Influenza viruses (magnification: 37,700X)

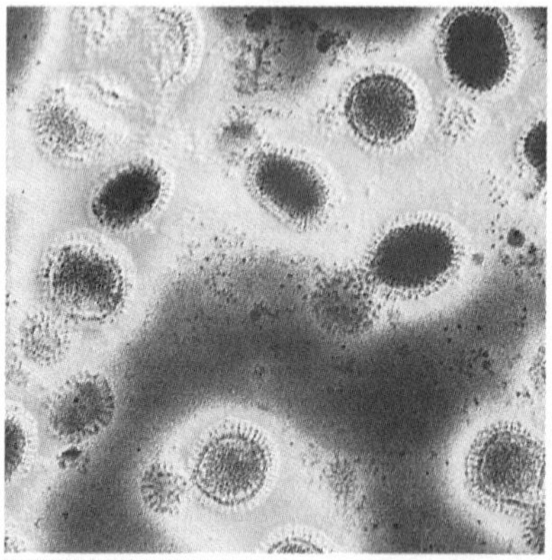

Flu Virus Adaptations

But some viruses—like those that cause influenza, the flu—have two survival adaptations that keep them in circulation. First, flu viruses mutate rapidly, constantly changing their appearance. So the strains of flu viruses that are present this year have evolved from last year, and they no longer look the same to the body. As a result, the body does not recognize the new viruses and so does not attack them, enabling them to infect the body.

More Than One Host

The second adaptation is that certain viruses have the ability to live in two or more different animal hosts. One strain of the virus, for example, may live in ducks and pigs, while another strain of the same virus may live in pigs and humans. If both these two strains infect the same cells in the same pig at the same time, it can spell trouble. Can you imagine why? Flu viruses happen to carry their genetic information on eight pieces of DNA. If two strains of the virus infect the same cell, some of those genes can get mixed up. If that happens, the result may be a new strain of the virus that can infect humans. This new strain carries proteins on its surface from the duck virus, which humans have never encountered before. And these new strains of viruses often cause the most serious diseases in the most people.

Making the Connection

Why are new flu vaccines developed every year? Why do you think flu vaccinations are recommended for health-care workers, the elderly, people with circulatory and respiratory problems, and people with immune system disorders?

TEACHER SUPPORT — Managing Classroom Diversity

GIFTED STUDENTS

Encourage interested students to read *The Hot Zone: A Terrifying True Story* by Richard Preston (1994), a highly readable and truly frightening account of an exotic filovirus that entered the United States in 1989.

The previously unknown virus first became evident in monkeys imported by a company in Reston, Virginia, that supplies research subjects to laboratories. In its primate hosts, the virus caused hemorrhagic fever and was 100 percent fatal. It then infected workers who had been exposed to the living monkeys and their postmortem tissues. Fortunately, the virus proved to be nonlethal in most, but not all, of its human hosts. Intensive research in Biosafety Level 4 ("hot") containment laboratories finally identified the virus as a mutated strain of Ebola, and it was given the name Ebola Reston virus. The virus's point of origin was traced back through its human victims to a remote cave in the central African rain forest.

Figure 17–16
The white blood cell in this electron micrograph is infected with the human immunodeficiency virus (HIV), the virus responsible for causing AIDS. The virus (shown here as green spheres) will continue to multiply and will eventually destroy the cell (magnification: 16,000X).

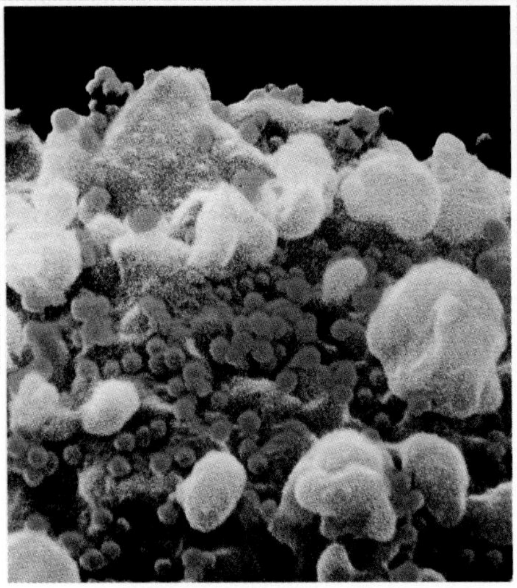

Types of Viruses

Just as living cells can have a variety of shapes and forms, so too can viruses. According to the nature of their genetic material and the way they infect cells, viruses can be divided into three groups—DNA viruses, RNA viruses, and retroviruses. Viruses infect virtually every known organism—from bacteria to plants to humans.

How Do Viruses Reproduce?

Because viruses are not alive, they can reproduce only when they invade, or infect, a living host cell. Viruses have three basic types of life cycles that occur within host cells.

In the lytic cycle, the virus injects its genetic material into a host and immediately takes over the cell's metabolic machinery. The host's DNA is used to make viral DNA, and the host cell manufactures new viral genes and proteins until it bursts, releasing many new viruses.

In the lysogenic cycle, viral genes do not go into action immediately. Instead, the viral DNA attaches to the circular DNA of a bacterium host. They may remain there for quite some time. When this occurs, viral genes are copied each time the infected cell divides.

The third type, retroviruses—which contain RNA—first make DNA copies of their RNA genes and then insert them into the host cell's chromosomes. There they may remain dormant for varying lengths of time before becoming active, directing the production of new viruses and causing the death of the host cell. Retroviruses were discovered only about 20 years ago. One example of a retrovirus is the Human Immunodeficiency Virus (HIV), which causes AIDS.

Section Review 17–4

1. **Describe** the structure of a virus.
2. **Explain** how a virus reproduces.
3. **Critical Thinking—Making Judgments** Why are viruses not classified into any of the kingdoms of life?

Discussion

Explain that although viruses reproduce in different ways, almost all of their replication pathways include five basic steps.

1. The virus attaches to a host cell.
2. Either the entire virus or its genetic material enters the cell.
3. The virus's DNA or RNA directs the host cell to produce multiple copies of its nucleic acids and proteins.
4. The nucleic acids and proteins are combined to form new virus particles.
5. The newly formed virus particles are released from the infected cell and travel to other cells, where they repeat the process.

4 ASSESS

Quick Check

Have each student write a paragraph explaining the major differences between viruses and living organisms.

Section Review 17-4

1. A virus is a tiny particle made up of genetic material and protein. Each particle contains a core of either DNA or RNA surrounded by a protein coat. The outer surface may be covered with an envelope composed of lipids and proteins.
2. Students should describe the three reproduction methods explained on this page of the student text and/or the five pathways presented in the Discussion above.
3. Viruses are not alive, because they are not cells or made of cells; they cannot survive or reproduce unless they invade living host cells.

Learning Modality

Tactile Learning As in the Learning Modality activity for the previous section on bacteria, have students use a variety of materials to make models of a typical virus. Tell students to include in their models all the structures described in the last paragraph on page 401 of the student text.

Ancillary Support

The resource below can be used to support your teaching strategy for these two pages.

BL Inquiry Activity: To Be or Not to Be

Section 17-5

How Did Life Begin?

Performance Objective

• Discuss the chemical conditions that may have led to the formation of Earth's first organic molecules.

1 ENGAGE

Inquiry Activity

Using the Writing Process

Describing Ancient Earth
Ask students what they think conditions on Earth might have been like before the first life forms appeared. Have each student or group write three or four paragraphs describing the conditions. Tell students they can use information they have learned from previous science courses, their general reading, television programs, or other sources, or they can simply use their imagination. Let students share their descriptions by reading them aloud or by displaying them on a bulletin board.

2 EXPLORE

Investigate

Research Ask students to consult science textbooks (including college texts), nonfiction library books, and other sources to find artists' illustrations that are based on scientific hypotheses about conditions on the early Earth. Let students compare these illustrations with the descriptions they wrote in the Engage activity above.

SECTION 17–5 BRANCHING OUT In Depth

How Did Life Begin?

GUIDE FOR READING

• **Describe** the chemical conditions on the early Earth.

ONLY 200 TO 300 MILLION YEARS after the Earth had cooled enough to carry water in its liquid form, prokaryotes similar to modern bacteria were growing everywhere. For a long time, scientists believed that this span of time was much too short for something as complicated as a living cell to have evolved from random molecules. But in recent years, new data have shown that this process—though still astonishing—is much more probable than anyone had thought.

Building Blocks

Living cells are composed of four major classes of complex organic molecules: lipids, carbohydrates, proteins, and nucleic acids. Atoms do not put themselves together into these complex organic molecules on modern Earth. There are many reasons why, but two are easy to understand. First, the presence of oxygen in the atmosphere makes it unlikely that any organic molecules could accumulate without being broken down, or oxidized. Second, no sooner would organic molecules begin to accumulate than something—bacteria or some other form of life—would probably come along and gobble them up!

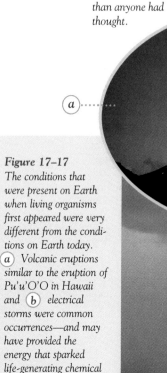

Figure 17–17 The conditions that were present on Earth when living organisms first appeared were very different from the conditions on Earth today. (a) Volcanic eruptions similar to the eruption of Pu'u'O'O in Hawaii and (b) electrical storms were common occurrences—and may have provided the energy that sparked life-generating chemical reactions on Earth.

TEACHER SUPPORT

Background Information

Recently, Graham Cairns-Smith at Glasgow University in Scotland proposed that the first so-called organisms were made of inorganic crystals. According to Cairns-Smith, the material was actually layered clay that could assemble itself into the appropriate pattern by the crystallization of dissolved materials. The pattern of each crystal would serve as a template for other dissolved minerals. These function as a kind of "clay gene" in that it would direct activity to make a copy of itself. In Cairns-Smith's plan, newly developed organic molecules probably assisted the clay replication process by increasing the solubility of minerals and acting as catalysts. Eventually, according to Cairns-Smith, the organic and inorganic clusters became compartmentalized, and shifted from inorganic dominance to organic dominance. The study of this process is still going on today.

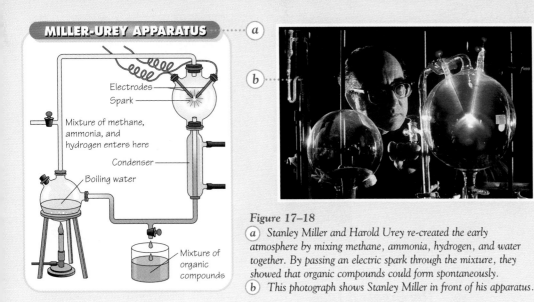

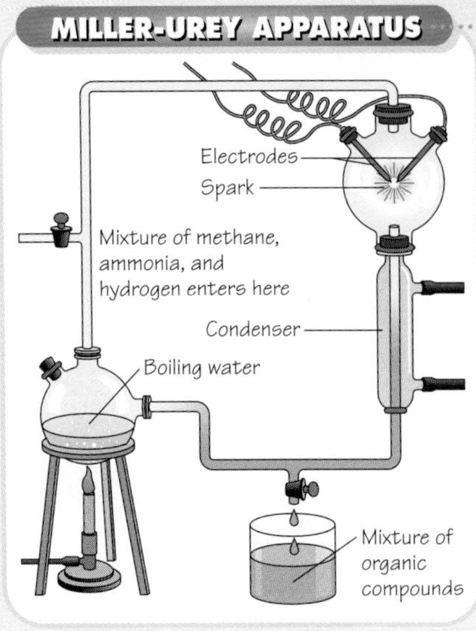

Figure 17–18
(a) *Stanley Miller and Harold Urey re-created the early atmosphere by mixing methane, ammonia, hydrogen, and water together. By passing an electric spark through the mixture, they showed that organic compounds could form spontaneously.*
(b) *This photograph shows Stanley Miller in front of his apparatus.*

On Early Earth

As you have read, the early Earth was a very different place from today's Earth. **Scientists hypothesize that Earth's early atmosphere was probably composed of hydrogen cyanide, carbon dioxide, carbon monoxide, nitrogen, hydrogen sulfide, and water vapor.** Could something have happened unexpectedly to cause organic molecules to form and accumulate in ways that they never could today?

In the early 1950s, American scientists Stanley Miller and Harold Urey tried to re-create the conditions that occurred on early Earth in a laboratory to see what might have occurred. They filled a flask with hydrogen, methane, ammonia, and water. They carefully kept oxygen out of the mixture and sterilized the equipment to make certain that no microorganisms could contaminate the results. Then they passed repeated electric sparks through the mixture to simulate the lightning storms that were probably a constant occurrence on the early Earth.

The First Organic Molecules

The results of this experiment were spectacular and exceeded Miller and Urey's wildest dreams. Over just a few days, their apparatus accumulated significant quantities of several amino acids—the building blocks of proteins that are produced only by living organisms. Since that time, similar experiments have produced a wide variety of surprisingly complex compounds. Not only does this list include sugars, but also the nitrogen bases—purines and pyrimidines that form the backbones of DNA and RNA!

Some years later, a sizable meteorite that crashed in Murchison, Australia, was carefully split open and analyzed. ● Among the compounds discovered were the same amino acids that had been produced in Miller and Urey's apparatus! Because these compounds were almost certainly not produced by living organisms, they supported Miller and Urey's experimental results.

Checkpoint What were the results of Miller and Urey's experiment? (1)

INTEGRATING ASTRONOMY

What is a meteorite?

3 TEACH

Ideas Through Images

Have students examine Figure 17–18, read the caption and the text description under the heading On Early Earth, and answer the following questions.

- **Why did Miller and Urey use methane, ammonia, and hydrogen?** (This mixture of gases resembles Earth's early atmosphere.)
- **Why did they keep oxygen out of the gas mixture?** (Oxygen was not present in the early atmosphere.)
- **Why did they boil water in the flask?** (To produce water vapor, which probably existed in the early atmosphere.)
- **Why did they create electrical sparks?** (To simulate electrical storms and lightning in the early atmosphere.)

INTEGRATING ASTRONOMY

A body from outer space that travels through Earth's atmosphere and strikes Earth's surface.

Checkpoint

(1) Their apparatus accumulated significant quantities of several amino acids—the building blocks of proteins that are produced only by living organisms.

TEACHER SUPPORT

Historical Perspective

Miller and Urey devised their experiment to test a hypothesis developed in the 1920s by Russian geochemist A. I. Oparin and British geneticist J.B.S. Haldane. Oparin and Haldane proposed that conditions on early Earth could have generated organic molecules that in turn could have given rise to the first living organisms. They reasoned that present-day conditions on Earth do not allow the spontaneous synthesis of organic compounds, simply because the atmosphere is rich in oxygen, which is corrosive and tends to disrupt chemical bonds.

In recent years, the hypothesis that Earth's early atmosphere was the original source of organic molecules has been criticized. Some scientists claim that Earth never had an atmosphere of methane and ammonia. A few biologists have suggested that the first organic molecules on Earth did not originate here but arrived with meteorites.

Ancillary Support

The resources below can be used to support your teaching strategy for these two pages.

TR Explore: What's Cooking?
BL Inquiry Activity: Soup's On

Discussion

Remind students that the primary function of the cell membrane is to control which substances move into and out of the cell. Without this control, cells cannot exist. Thus, the development of membranes in proteinoid microspheres was a significant step toward actual living cells.

With more advanced students, explain that membrane sacs are known to form spontaneously, perhaps to protect information-storage templates and metabolic agents against environmental conditions. In one experiment, a researcher heated amino acids until they formed protein chains, then put them in hot water. When the chains cooled, they assembled into small, stable spheres that were selectively permeable to different substances, as are cell membranes. The spheres also picked up lipids from the water, and a lipid-protein film formed at their surface. In experiments that simulated evaporating tidepools, fatty acids and glycerol combined to form long-tail lipids that self-assembled into small, water-filled sacs similar to cell membranes.

Ideas Through Images

To ensure student understanding of Figure 17–20 and the text that it summarizes, guide students to recall the information on DNA and RNA. Then have students examine Figure 17–20, read the caption, and answer the following question.

- **What recent discovery led scientists to question whether DNA or RNA developed first?** (The discovery that RNA molecules may be able to grow and duplicate themselves on their own.)

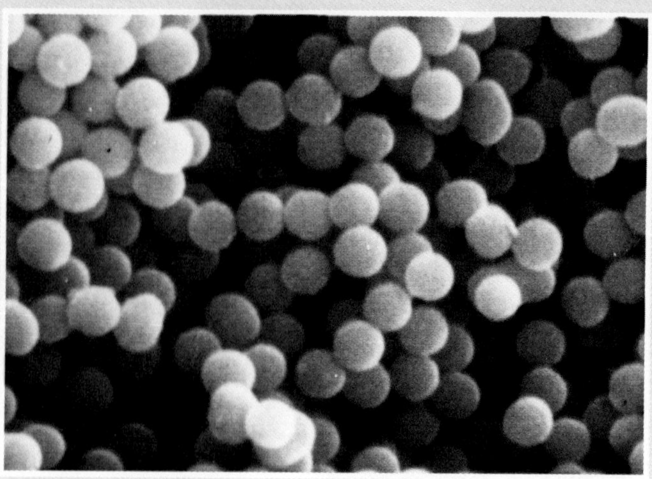

Figure 17–19
Proteinoid microspheres, shown in this scanning electron micrograph (magnification: 3000X), are hollow structures that have some of the characteristics of living systems. Under the right conditions, proteinoid microspheres can absorb material, grow, and even divide.

The Greatest Leap

Of course, a bubbling stew of organic molecules is a long way from a living cell. The leap from this point to the simplest forms of life we know is still the greatest gap in hypotheses about life's origins.

Studies have shown that large organic molecules can, under some conditions, organize themselves into tiny bubbles called proteinoid microspheres. Proteinoid microspheres aren't cells, but they do have some characteristics of living systems. They are surrounded by a two-layered membrane made of lipids, and they can grow in size by taking in more organic matter. Several hypotheses suggest different ways that these structures might have slowly acquired the characteristics of living cells.

The largest stumbling block in bridging the gap between nonliving and living still remains. All living cells are controlled by information stored in DNA, which is transcribed into RNA and then made into protein. This is a very complicated system, and each of these three molecules requires the other two—either to put it together or to help it work. DNA, for example, carries information but cannot put that information to use or even copy itself without the help of RNA and protein.

☑ **Checkpoint** What are proteinoid microspheres? 1

A Role for RNA?

How could this multi-step biochemical machinery ever have gotten started in the first place? The answer may have been found in the way that many scientific discoveries happen—by researchers who weren't even concerned with this question! Over the last 20 years, molecular biologists realized that they had not completely understood all the things RNA can do.

In protein synthesis, for example, one type of RNA—called messenger RNA—is usually described as a cross between a cellular copying machine and a messenger. Able to do nothing on its own, it simply copies the genetic information from DNA and brings it to the ribosomes—the cell structures in which proteins are made. What's more, in modern cells both messenger RNA and another type of RNA—transfer RNA—are produced only on instructions from DNA.

TEACHER SUPPORT

Background Information

After small organic molecules formed on prebiotic Earth, the second major chemical step before life appeared was most likely polymerization, the formation of organic polymers from monomers.

Polymers are synthesized by dehydration reactions. In living cells, specific enzymes catalyze these reactions. However, polymerization also occurs in laboratory situations without enzymes—for example, when dilute solutions of organic monomers are dripped onto hot sand, clay, or rock. The heat vaporizes the water in the solutions and concentrates the monomers on the underlying substance. Some of the monomers then spontaneously bond together in chains, forming polymers. In a similar way on early Earth, rain or waves may have splashed dilute solutions of organic monomers onto fresh lava or other hot rocks and then rinsed proteinoids and other polymers into the sea.

WHICH WAS THE FIRST MOLECULE—DNA OR RNA?

DNA

Stores and transmits information; replicates only with assistance from enzymes

RNA

Primarily serves to carry out DNA's instructions by mediating the synthesis of proteins; RNA synthesis now directed by DNA and mediated by enzymes

Protein

Provides structure and serves most functions in living systems; synthesis directed by DNA and mediated by RNA and other proteins

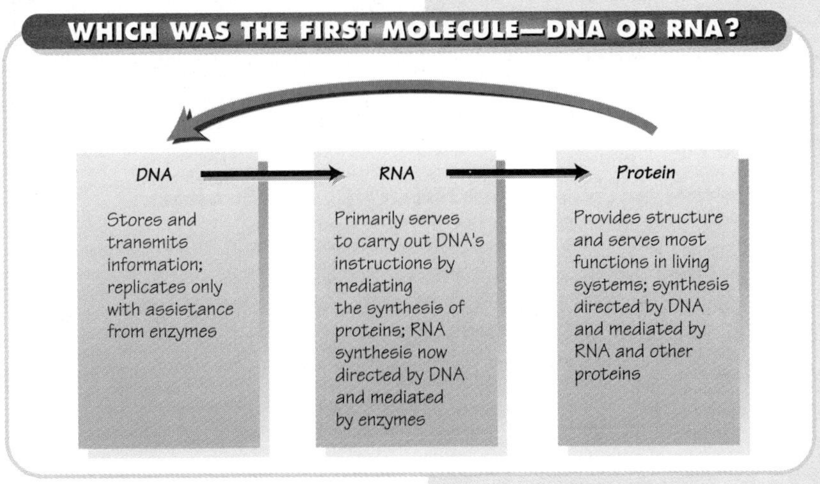

Figure 17–20
Some scientists hypothesize that RNA evolved first, followed by DNA and proteins.

More Than a Messenger

Yet under the right circumstances, RNA sequences can do some surprising things. Some sequences help DNA copy itself. Others process messenger RNA after it copies the information for DNA. Still others catalyze chemical reactions.

Recent evidence suggests that RNA molecules can grow and duplicate themselves entirely on their own! In a new series of experiments that duplicated probable conditions found on the early Earth, several scientists showed that small sequences of RNA could have formed on their own. Given enough time, the scientists think that these short RNA chains could have grown longer and may ultimately have taken on a life of their own.

As a result of these experiments, some scientsts now hypothesize that RNA, rather than DNA, may have been the first information-storage molecule. Such a molecule could also direct the formation of the first proteins.

At this point, several steps could have led to the modern system of DNA-directed protein synthesis. It may be possible—as many researchers now believe—that the modern DNA world evolved from an earlier RNA world. Perhaps future experiments will gather more data to confirm or refute this fascinating hypothesis.

Section Review 17–5

1. **Describe** the chemical conditions on the early Earth.
2. **Compare** proteinoid microspheres and living cells.
3. **BRANCHING OUT ACTIVITY** Look up the words biogenesis and abiogenesis. **Compare** the meanings of the two words.

Background Information

Life depends on intricate metabolic processes that require the cooperation of many complex organic molecules. It is therefore likely that some degree of molecular cooperation preceded the origin of life.

The earliest forms of molecular cooperation may have involved a primitive form of translation of simple RNA genes into polypeptides without using ribosomes or tRNA. Cooperative RNA-polypeptide associations ("co-ops") may have become common in aquatic environments, particularly in small puddles or films of water on clay surfaces.

Proteinoid microspheres on those clay surfaces may have taken in some of the RNA-polypeptide co-ops. Once a co-op was contained within a microsphere's membrane, it was isolated from other co-ops in its surroundings. Any membrane-enclosed co-ops that grew and replicated more efficiently than other co-ops would have been favored by natural selection and could have begun evolving.

Quick Check

Have each student write a brief description of Miller and Urey's experiment and their results, accompanied by a sketch of the apparatus.

Section Review 17–5

1. Earth's early atmosphere was probably composed of hydrogen cyanide, carbon dioxide, carbon monoxide, nitrogen, hydrogen sulfide, and water vapor.

2. Proteinoid microspheres have some characteristics of living cells—such as a two-layer membrane made of lipids and the ability to absorb material, grow, and divide—but are not actually alive. Living cells are controlled by information stored in DNA, which is transcribed into RNA and then made into proteins.

3. Biogenesis: The development of living organisms from other living organisms. Abiogenesis: The development of living organisms from nonliving matter.

Learning Modality

Visual Learning Have students draw a diagram to illustrate the hypothesis about life's origins based on the work of Miller and Urey. They should label their diagrams and point out where the gaps in the hypothesis are.

☑ Checkpoint

1 Tiny bubbles, formed from large organic molecules, that have some characteristics of living systems.

Ancillary Support

The resource below can be used to support your teaching strategy for these two pages.
LM Making Coacervates, #34

Chapter 17

Laboratory Investigation

Constructing a Geologic Time Line

Before the Lab

1. Cut a roll of adding machine paper into 5-m strips, one for each group.
2. Locate and photocopy illustrations and photographs of the life forms listed in the table, or ask volunteers to do this for you.

Pre-Lab Discussion

Have students read the entire procedure for this investigation. Then ask students the following questions.

How does the information in this table compare with the information in Figure 17–6 on pages 390–391? (The names of the eras, periods, and epochs and the sequence of events in the development of life forms are the same.)

What will you have to do in order to correctly position each major event listed in the table on your time line? (Multiply each age by 1 mm; for larger numbers on the table [first fishes through first birds], divide millimeters by 1000 to convert to meters.)

Skills Development

Students will use these skills while completing the laboratory investigation: sequencing, constructing a model, and interpreting diagrams.

Teaching Strategies

1. In addition to meter sticks, which usually do not show millimeters, provide small metric rulers that do include these units.
2. Allow students to draw their own pictures of the organisms in addition to or instead of using the photocopies you supply.
3. As needed, help each group decide on appropriate intervals for dividing the time line (step 2).

Laboratory Investigation

Constructing a Geologic Time Line

In order to develop a true perspective of the vast spans of Earth's history during which different life forms existed, it helps to construct a time line. In this investigation, you will construct a time line representing the Earth's history and identify the main events of the beginnings of life on Earth.

Problem

How can you **sequence** some of the main events in the history of life on Earth?

Materials (per group)

meterstick
5 m adding machine paper
colored markers
photographs and artwork of different life forms
index cards
transparent tape

Procedure

1. For your geologic time line, use a scale in which 1 mm = 1 million years, or 1 m = 1 billion years.

2. Mark the adding machine paper strip at appropriate intervals, such as every 25 million years, from the beginning of the Earth to the present.

3. **Using the table provided, identify and label the major geologic eras, periods, and epochs on the geologic time scale according to their relative lengths.**

4. **Decorate the geologic time scale using the paper strip and the art and photographs of the life forms. Write brief descriptions of the life forms on the index cards. Art, photographs, and descriptions should be affixed to the times during which the first fossils of a particular group were formed.**

Observations

1. How long did it take for the first life forms to leave fossils?
2. In which period did the first multicellular organisms begin to leave fossils?
3. When in Earth's history did photosynthetic organisms first appear?
4. During which periods did the dinosaurs rule the Earth?

Analysis and Conclusions

1. Where on the time line do most life forms exist?
2. What percentage of your time line accounts for the Precambrian Era?
3. Assume that humans have been around for about 250,000 years. What percentage of your time line accounts for the history of modern humans?

MAJOR EVENTS IN THE HISTORY OF LIFE

Event	Millions of Years Ago
First apes	23–34
First whales	34–57
First horses	34–57
First monkeys	34–57
First flowering plants	65–144
First birds	144–208
First dinosaurs	208–245
First mammals	208–245
First reptiles	286–360
First insects	360–408
First land plants	408–438
First fishes	438–505

More to Explore

Design an experiment that equates one year with the mass of one penny. What would be the mass, in grams, of all the pennies that represent the age of the Earth? In kilograms?

Answers to
Observations

1. About 1 billion years. Calculation: 4.5 billion years (approximate age of Earth) minus 3.5 billion years (approximate age of oldest fossils).
2. Precambrian Era.
3. Precambrian Era.
4. The Triassic, Jurassic, and Cretaceous periods.

Answers to
Analysis and Conclusions

1. During the Quaternary Period of the Cenozoic Era.
2. About 88 percent.
3. Less than 1 percent (specifically, 0.000055 percent).

More to Explore

To calculate the mass in grams of all the pennies that represent the age of Earth, students should multiply the mass in grams of one penny by 4.5 billion. To calculate the mass in kilograms, students should divide the first answer by 1000.

CHAPTER 17

Study Guide

Review Strategy

Have students write the characteristics listed in each box of the table in Figure 17–11 on a separate index card and make heading cards labeled with the names of the six kingdoms. Students should shuffle the characteristics cards and then arrange them under the heading cards to re-create the table from memory. Students could use a similar technique to review and check their knowledge of the names of the geologic eras in their correct order (Figure 17–6), the classification of the housecat from species to kingdom (Figure 17–10), the steps in Miller and Urey's experiment (Figure 17–18), and the major events in the history of life (Laboratory Investigation table).

Study Guide

Summarizing Key Concepts

The key concepts in each section of this chapter are listed below to help you review the chapter content. Make sure you understand each concept and its relationship to other concepts and to the theme of this chapter.

17–1 The Changing Earth

- To learn about life's past and to fully understand its present, researchers read the history preserved in the fossil record.
- Fossils are the remains or traces of ancient life, commonly found in sedimentary rocks.
- The age of fossils can be determined by two methods—relative dating and absolute dating.
- To make Earth's long history more manageable, scientists developed the geologic time scale.
- The theory of continental drift provides further evidence of evolution from matching rocks and fossils.

17–2 Finding Order in Diversity

- A classification system identifies objects and gathers them into groups.
- Taxonomy is the science of naming organisms and classifying them into groups.
- Living things are classified into six kingdoms: Eubacteria, Archaebacteria, Protista, Fungi, Plantae, and Animalia.

17–3 Bacteria—The First Organisms

- Bacteria have a cell membrane that is surrounded by a tough, protective cell wall. Their genetic material is contained on a single strand of circular DNA that is not surrounded by a nuclear envelope.
- There are two major kingdoms of bacteria—Eubacteria and Archaebacteria.
- Bacteria reproduce by binary fission, and some by conjugation or transformation.

17–4 Viruses

- A virus is a tiny particle—made up of genetic material and protein—that can invade and replicate within a living host cell.
- Because viruses are not alive, they can reproduce only when they invade, or infect, a living host cell.

17–5 How Did Life Begin?

- Scientists hypothesize that Earth's early atmosphere was composed of hydrogen cyanide, carbon dioxide, carbon monoxide, nitrogen, hydrogen sulfide, and water.

Reviewing Key Terms

Review the following vocabulary terms and their meaning. Then use each term in a complete sentence.

17–1 The Changing Earth

fossil
sedimentary rock
half-life
geologic time scale
continental drift

17–2 Finding Order in Diversity

taxonomy
genus
species
family
order
class
phylum
kingdom

17–3 Bacteria—The First Organisms

bacteria
binary fission
conjugation
transformation

17–4 Viruses

virus

Inquiry-Based Strategy

Ask students to imagine that they have just discovered a new type of organism, which they must now classify into one of the six kingdoms based on the characteristics presented in Figure 17–11. Have each group give its unknown organism a scientific name (genus and species) and list its characteristics, making sure the organism would fit into only one of the six kingdoms. (For example, students should not describe the organism as both unicellular and having a cell wall made of cellulose.)

When students have completed their descriptions, have groups exchange their lists. Then tell each group to decide into which kingdom the other group's organism should be classified. Let each group explain the organism's classification in a class discussion.

CHAPTER 17

Recalling Main Ideas

Choose the letter of the answer that best completes the statement or answers the question.

1. The Earth's first atmosphere did not contain

a. nitrogen. **c.** oxygen.
b. hydrogen sulfide. **d.** carbon dioxide.

2. Which is the most helpful element for determining the age of a 10,000-year-old fossil?

a. potassium-40 **c.** uranium-238
b. carbon-14 **d.** nitrogen-14

3. The system of taxonomy used today was developed by

a. Miller. **c.** Urey.
b. Linnaeus. **d.** Aristotle.

4. Related phyla are grouped into a

a. family. **c.** species.
b. genus. **d.** kingdom.

5. The first organisms on Earth were thought to be

a. viruses. **c.** prokaryotes.
b. mitochondria. **d.** eukaryotes.

6. All bacteria reproduce by

a. transformation. **c.** conjugation.
b. the lytic cycle. **d.** binary fission.

7. A virus particle contains a core of

a. DNA. **c.** DNA or RNA.
b. RNA. **d.** protein.

8. Viruses can reproduce by

a. the lytic cycle. **c.** conjugation.
b. transformation. **d.** binary fission.

Putting It All Together

Using the information on pages xxx to xxxi, complete the following concept map.

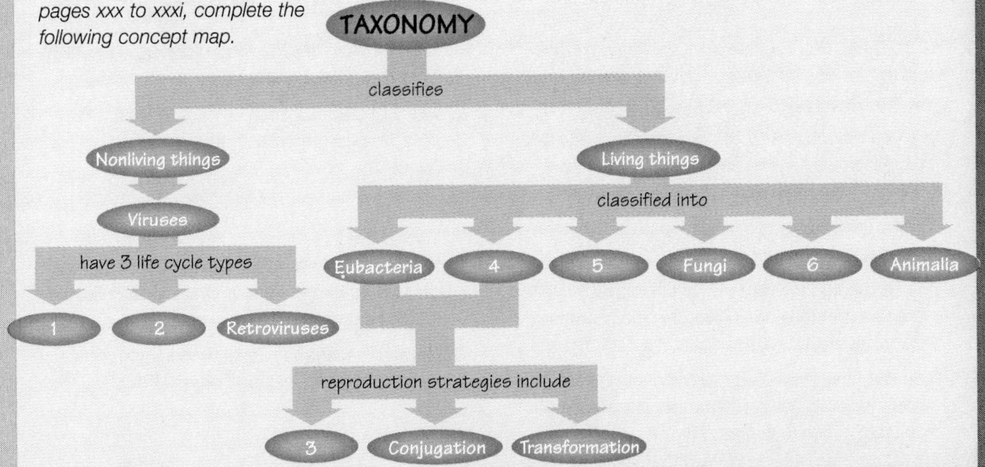

Recalling Main Ideas

1. c
2. b
3. b
4. d
5. c
6. d
7. c
8. a

Putting It All Together

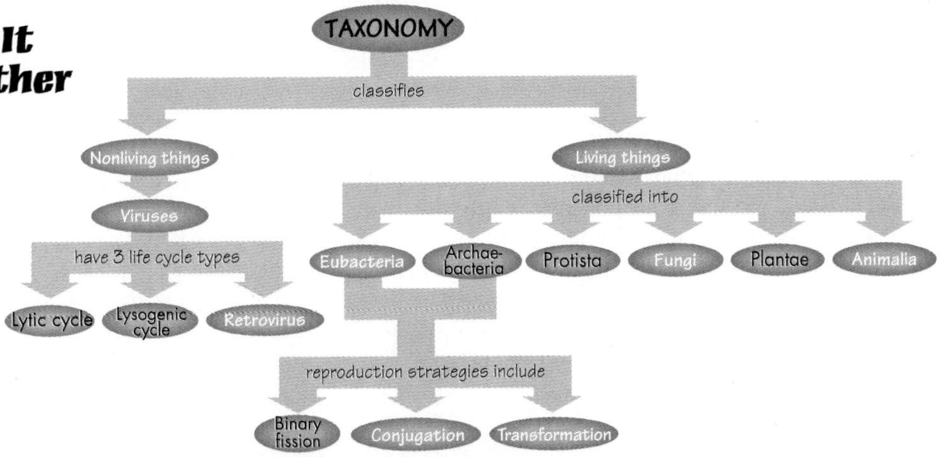

CHAPTER 17

Assessment

Reviewing What You Learned

1. Older.
2. 3.5 billion years.
3. A scale showing Earth's history, divided into units and based on information contained in rocks.
4. The Triassic, Jurassic, and Cretaceous Periods.
5. Linnaeus gave each organism a two-part Latin name, with the first part identifying the genus and the second part identifying the species.

Skills Trace
Classifying
- Focus p. 395
- Practice p. 397
- Assess p. 412

6. Eubacteria, Archaebacteria, Protista, Fungi, Plantae, and Animalia.
7. Oxygen.
8. Unicellular organisms that do not have a nucleus.
9. A virus that contains RNA and that replicates by making DNA copies of the RNA genes and inserting them into a host cell's chromosomes.
10. Tiny bubbles, formed from large organic molecules, that have some of the characteristics of living systems.

Expanding the Concepts

1. It will take 20 years. Students should explain that ½ of the original element will remain after the first 5 years, ¼ after 10 years, ⅛ after 15 years, and 1⁄16 after 20 years.

Skills Trace
Relating
- Focus p. 390
- Practice p. 392
- Assess p. 412

2. Absolute dating, because it can establish a fossil's exact age.
3. Only sedimentary rocks contain fossils. Organisms' remains are destroyed by the heat of magma and lava that form igneous rocks and by the heat and pressure that transform sedimentary and igneous rocks into metamorphic rocks.
4. That the two groups have many common characteristics, and thus they may have evolved from a common ancestor.
5. Students may identify classification systems such as those used to arrange products in a supermarket, hardware store, or department store and systems used to categorize segments of the general population for statistical purposes.
6. An example of asexual reproduction is binary fission, in which the cell divides into two daughter cells with duplicate chromosomes. An example of sexual reproduction is conjugation, in which part of the genetic information from one cell is transferred to another cell.
7. Bacteria are incredibly adaptable, surviving in even the most extreme conditions. Many are nearly indestructible. And bacteria have survived for over 3.5 billion years while many other forms of life have become extinct.

Assessment

Reviewing What You Learned

Answer each of the following in a complete sentence.

1. Are fossils that are found in the deepest layers of sedimentary rocks older or younger than fossils found closer to the surface?
2. Approximately how old are the oldest known rocks that contain fossils?
3. What is the geologic time scale?
4. During which geological periods did dinosaurs rule the Earth?
5. How did Linnaeus **classify** organisms?
6. What are the six kingdoms of life?
7. Which important gas was missing from the ancient or early atmosphere?
8. What are prokaryotes?
9. What is a retrovirus?
10. What are proteinoid microspheres?

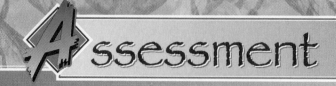

Expanding the Concepts

Discuss each of the following in a brief paragraph.

1. If the half-life of an element is 5 years, **relate** how long it will take until only 1/16 of the original unstable element remains.
2. If you were trying to find out the exact age of a fossil, which type of dating would you use—relative or absolute? Explain your answer.
3. Why are sedimentary rocks so important in studying the history of the Earth?
4. Two groups of organisms are in different genera, but they are included in the same family. What does this tell you about the two groups?
5. In a library, books are classified into different categories. What are two other classification systems used in everyday life?
6. Reproduction in prokaryotes can be asexual or sexual. Give an example of each type.
7. Why are bacteria often called the most successful organisms on the Earth?
8. Why are viruses unable to reproduce on their own?
9. Two of the three types of life cycles found in viruses are lytic and lysogenic. Describe these cycles and indicate which cycle is potentially more dangerous to humankind.
10. How did Miller and Urey's work explain how life might have developed on this Earth?

Extending Your Thinking

Use the skills you have developed in this chapter to answer the following.

1. **Comparing** Develop a chart that compares the similarities and differences of eubacteria and archaebacteria.
2. **Analyzing** Could viruses have been the first life form on Earth? Develop an argument that supports your position.
3. **Hypothesizing** Beginning with the gases of the primitive atmosphere, sequence the steps that might have led to the first living organism. Remember that chemical evolution would have had to precede biological evolution.
4. **Analyzing data** A scientist finds a new organism but is unsure to which kingdom it belongs. The organism's characteristics include: It is unicellular, has a cell wall made up of peptidoglycan, has a circular DNA and ribosomes, but it lacks a nuclear envelope. To which kingdom does the organism probably belong?

Applying Your Skills

Building a Model of a Bacteriophage

Viruses have a variety of shapes and forms. One type of virus is a bacteriophage. A bacteriophage is a virus that infects a bacterium. For this activity, you will build a model of a bacteriophage.

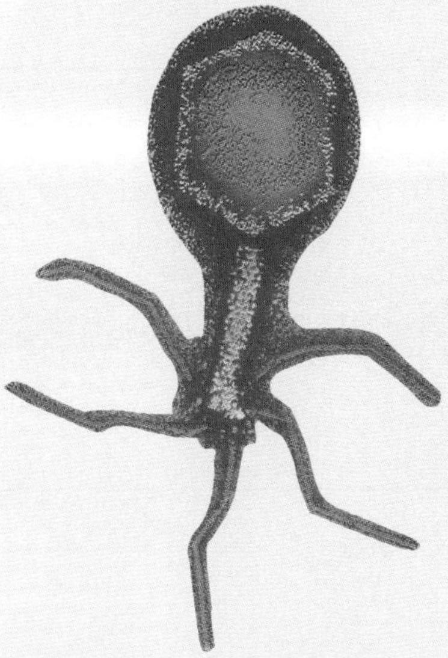

1. Look at the photograph of the bacteriophage.
2. Make a three-dimensional model of a bacteriophage using the following materials: machine screw, 2 acorn nuts that fit the screw, pliers, 3 pieces of floral wire, and a pipe cleaner.
3. Diagram the bacteriophage on a sheet of paper and label its parts.

• GOING FURTHER •

4. What part of your model represents the outer protein coat?
5. Where is the RNA or DNA located in your model virus?
6. Compare your model with models of other members of your group and other members of your class. How are the models alike? How are they different?
7. In your journal, write one or two paragraphs describing your model. State how your model is similar to and different from the virus in the photo. How could you improve your model?

8. Viruses are not alive, so they cannot reproduce unless they invade a living host cell.
9. In the lytic cycle, the virus injects its genetic material into a host cell and immediately takes over the cell's metabolic machinery. In the lysogenic cycle, viral genes do not go into action immediately but remain attached to the host cell's DNA and are copied each time the infected cell divides.
10. Their work showed that organic molecules could form and accumulate under conditions simulating early Earth's atmosphere.

Extending Your Thinking

1. Students' charts should include at least the similarities and differences summarized in Figure 17–11, page 395.
2. Viruses could not have been the first life forms on Earth, because they must invade living host cells in order to survive and reproduce. Therefore, living organisms—the first prokaryotes—must have evolved before viruses.
3. Students' hypotheses may vary. They should describe Earth's early atmosphere, energy from volcanic eruptions and electrical storms, formation of amino acids and other organic compounds, organization of large organic molecules into proteinoid microspheres, formation of DNA and RNA, synthesis of first proteins, formation of first living system.
4. The organism probably belongs to Archaebacteria.

Applying Your Skills

Teacher Notes

1. Before class, gather machine screws each with 2 acorn nuts that fit, pliers, floral wire, and pipe cleaners.
2. Have students work individually or in pairs.

Answers

4. Students should identify the outside of the acorn nut on top of the model as representing the outer protein coat of the bacteriophage.
5. Students should suggest that the RNA or DNA would be located inside the acorn nut.
6. Models should be somewhat similar, but may differ in size.
7. Students should be able to describe their model and suggest how they might improve it compared to the photograph.

Scoring Rubric

4 Response is thorough, accurate, and creative; shows an in-depth understanding of science skills, procedures, and concepts.

3 Response is complete, mostly accurate, and original; shows a satisfactory understanding of science skills, procedures, and concepts.

2 Response is mostly complete but includes some inaccuracies; shows an adequate understanding of science skills, procedures, and concepts.

1 Response is only partially complete and has many inaccuracies; shows an incomplete understanding of science skills, procedures, and concepts.

0 Response is mostly incomplete and/or inaccurate; shows a lack of understanding of science skills, procedures, and concepts.

Chapter 18 Protists, Fungi, and Plants

Content Management	Student Edition Activities
■ Section 18–1 Protists, pp. 415–419 What Is a Protist? Evolution of Protists Living Protists How Do Protists Reproduce?	
■ Section 18–2 Fungi, pp. 420–424 What Is a Fungus? Living Fungi Lichens How Do Fungi Reproduce?	MINI LAB: Fuzzy Food, p. 423
■ Section 18–3 Multicellular Plants, pp. 425–431 What Is a Plant? Evolution of Plants Challenges of Life on Land Bryophytes Tracheophytes Adapting to Land How Do Plants Reproduce?	Laboratory Investigation: Vascular Plant Tissues, pp. 436–437
◆ BRANCHING OUT • In Depth Section 18–4 The Coevolution of Plants and Animals, pp. 432–435 Pollination Seed Dispersal	MINI LAB: Traveling Seeds, p. 434

■ These sections cover all the necessary content and concepts for a basic course in biology.
◆ This section covers content and concepts that are either applications or extensions of the basic material.

Integration Strategies

SE Earth Science, p. 428

Assessment Strategies

SE Chapter Review, pp. 438–441
TR Section Reviews
Chapter Test
BL Chapter Review
Practice Test
CTB Chapter 18 Test

Tech Prep

Teaching strategies appropriate for students who are in technical/vocational programs or who are considering post-secondary technical education can be found on the following **TE** pages: 425 and 433.

Meeting the Standards

Sections 18–1 through 18–4 cover three of the six content standards under **The Cell,** one of the three content standards under **The Molecular Basis of Heredity,** all five of the content standards under **Biological Evolution,** and one of the five content standards under **The Interdependence of Organisms** as described on pages 184–186 of The National Science Education Standards.

Chapter Planning Guide

Teacher's Edition Activities	Other Activities	Media and Technology
Chapter Discovery Learning Activity, p. 414 **Inquiry Activity:** Observing a Slime Mold, p. 416 **Investigate:** Model Building, p. 418 **Activity:** Observing Protists, p. 418	**LM** Examining an Algal Bloom, #36 **TR** **Explore:** Life by the Drop **BL** **Inquiry Activity:** The Next Step	
Activity: Collecting Fungi, p. 420 **Investigate:** Cooperative Learning, p. 420 **Activity:** Making Spore Prints, p. 424	**LM** Classifying Fungi, #35 **TR** **Explore:** Frankly, It's Fungi **BL** **Inquiry Activity:** Fungus Among Us	
Inquiry Activity: Identifying Uses of Plants, p. 425 **Inquiry Activity:** Developing a Definition of Plant, p. 426 **Investigate:** Long-Term Project, p. 427 **Investigate:** Research, p. 428 **Activity:** Classifying Monocots and Dicots, p. 429 **Investigate:** Research, p. 429 **Investigate:** Long-Term Project, p. 430 **Investigate:** Cooperative Learning, p. 430 **Activity:** Calculating Water Loss, p. 430	**TR** **Writing in Biology:** Making Myths **Apply:** What a Re-leaf **BL** **Inquiry Activity:** The Seeds of Life	**BioVue Mini Doc:** Plant Diversity: Evolving for Survival, Videodisc Side 5 **TB** Differences Among Monocots and Dicots, #24
Inquiry Activity: Observing Insect Pollinators, p. 432 **Investigate:** Research, p. 432 **Activity:** What Attracts Insects to Flowers?, p. 432	**TR** **Enrich:** Abuzz With Orchids **BL** **Inquiry Activity:** Which Came First?	**BioVue Mini Doc:** Pollination and Coevolution, Videodisc Side 5

KEY: **SE** Student Edition **TE** Teacher's Edition **LM** Laboratory Manual **TR** Teaching Resources **BL** BioLog **TB** Transparency Box **CTB** Computer Test Bank

Materials List

TE Chapter Discovery Learning Activity, p. 414 (20 minutes for initial setup, 15 minutes for follow-up observations each day for a week), 3 small paper cups, dry yeast, radish seeds, brine shrimp eggs, 12 plastic cups, salt, sugar, potting soil, plastic wrap, hand lens, microscope.

TE Inquiry Activity: Observing a Slime Mold, p. 416 (5–10 minutes for each observation over several weeks); terrarium containing a slime mold.

TE Investigate: Model Building, p. 418 (15 minutes for research, 30 minutes for model building); books with photos of protists.

TE Activity: Observing Protists, p. 418 (45 minutes for setting up cultures, 15 minutes for each observation); jar of pond water, dried vegetation, uncooked rice, Timothy hay, medicine dropper, microscope, slides, coverslips.

TE Activity: Collecting Fungi, p. 420 (30–45 minutes for outdoor collecting, 30 minutes for examination in classroom); small self-sealing plastic bags, plastic forks, hand lenses, field guide.

TE Investigate: Cooperative Learning, p. 420 (30–40 minutes); mushrooms, ingredients specified in recipes, hot plate, cooking pan.

SE MINI LAB: Fuzzy Food, p. 423 (15 minutes each for initial setup and follow-up observations); 3 plastic containers, paper towels, 3 slices bread, hand lens.

TE Activity: Making Spore Prints, p. 424 (10 minutes for initial setup, 15 minutes for follow-up observations); mushroom, white or black paper, clear plastic cup, hand lens.

TE Investigate: Long-Term Project, p. 427 (30 minutes to set up terrarium, 5 minutes each day to care for the plants); terrarium, bryophyte specimens, books on plant care.

TE Activity: Classifying Monocots and Dicots, p. 429 (20–30 minutes); hand lens, plastic bag, corn kernels, bean seeds, acorns, tulip, oak leaf, bean leaf, tulip leaf, corn leaf, bean stem, corn stem, tulip stem, oak branch.

TE Investigate: Long-Term Project, p. 430 (10 minutes); terrarium with bryophytes.

TE Activity: Calculating Water Loss, p. 430 (15 minutes for initial setup, 15 minutes for follow-up calculations); twig with several leaves, graph paper, graduated cylinder, cooking oil.

TE Investigate: Research, p. 432 (20 minutes); flowers with pollen, plants with seeds, black paper, white paper, hand lenses.

TE Activity: What Attracts Insects to Flowers? p. 432 (45–60 minutes); stiff white paper, scissors, pink, red, and black markers or crayons, honey.

SE MINI LAB: Traveling Seeds, p. 434 (30–45 minutes); 3–4 maple seeds.

CHAPTER 18

Protists, Fungi, and Plants

Introducing the Chapter

. . . In Pictures

California redwoods (*Sequoia sempervirens*) are the world's tallest trees—they can reach a height of 112 m. Redwoods are conifers, or cone-bearers. Give students this information. Then have them examine the photograph, read the caption, and answer the questions below.

- **What average-sized trees are also conifers?** (Most students will know that pines, spruces, cedars, and firs are conifers.)
- **How do conifers differ from trees such as maples and oaks?** (Students will probably know that the conifers have needlelike leaves in contrast to the broad leaves of maples and oaks.)

Teaching Strategy

The first three sections of this chapter introduce the characteristics, evolution, classification, and life cycles of protists, fungi, and plants. The BRANCHING OUT section at the end of the chapter describes the coevolution of angiosperms and animals, focusing on pollination and seed dispersal.

BIO JOURNAL

Before students begin writing in their journals, have the class list the observations they can make about redwood trees and their surroundings from this photograph. In their journals, students may infer that the great height of the trees allows redwoods to collect more sunlight than other forest trees. They may also infer that the water droplets in the fog are trapped by the tree branches and drip down to the ground along the furrows. Instruct students to keep their entries in their portfolios.

CHAPTER 18

Protists, Fungi, and Plants

FOCUSING THE CHAPTER THEME: Scale and Structure

18–1 Protists
- **Classify** protists and **describe** their major characteristics.

18–2 Fungi
- **Describe** the characteristics of fungi.

18–3 Multicellular Plants
- **Identify** the major characteristics of plants.

BRANCHING OUT *In Depth*

18–4 The Coevolution of Plants and Animals
- **Describe** an example of the coevolution of plants and animals.

LABORATORY INVESTIGATION
- **Predict** the role of vascular tissue in plants.

Biology and Your World

BIO JOURNAL

How have these trees adapted to their surroundings? Answer this question in your journal.

Redwoods, firs, and rhododendrons in California

TEACHER SUPPORT — Chapter Discovery Learning Activity

Give each group of students three small paper cups labeled A, B, and C containing a spoonful of one of the following materials: A, dry yeast; B, radish seeds; C, brine shrimp eggs. Then have students follow these steps.

1. Put ¼ teaspoon of each material in a separate, numbered clear-plastic cup: cup 1, plain tap water; 2, saltwater solution; 3, sugar water solution; 4, potting soil. Also label each cup with the letter of the material it contains. (Altogether, you will have 12 cups.) Dampen the soil in each cup 4 and cover the cups with plastic wrap.

2. Each day for a week, examine each cup with a hand lens. Also examine drops of water from cups 1–3 with a microscope. Record your observations in a data table.

3. Which cups seem to contain living organisms? (A-3, B-4, C-2.) Classify each organism as a plant, an animal, or "other." (A-3, animals; B-4, "other" [fungus]; C-2, plants.)

Protists

SECTION 18–1

GUIDE FOR READING

- **Describe** the characteristics of protists.
- **Compare** algae and protozoans.
- **Explain** how protists reproduce.

SOME SWARM AT THE OCEAN'S surface. Others dig through mud in ponds and rivers. Some act like animals, feeding on smaller organisms. Some act like plants, producing complex organic compounds from sunlight, water, and inorganic nutrients. Others decompose dead organic matter. Many are deadly parasites. As the oldest eukaryotes, they have played vital roles in the history of life for more than a billion years.

What Is a Protist?

These eukaryotes, better known as **protists,** are a fascinating yet puzzling group of organisms. What is a protist? Surprisingly, there is no simple answer to that question because the organisms classified into the Protist kingdom are such a diverse group. **All protists are eukaryotes, but these organisms do not share a set of unique characteristics.** While most protists are unicellular, quite a few are multicellular. Many are microscopic, but the single-celled *Caulerpa* can grow up to a meter in length. And some multicellular species grow 70 meters long! Most protists need oxygen to survive, but a few are poisoned by it. Some protists are autotrophic, and others are heterotrophic. Some reproduce sexually, some asexually, and still others alternate between the two. The differences go on and on!

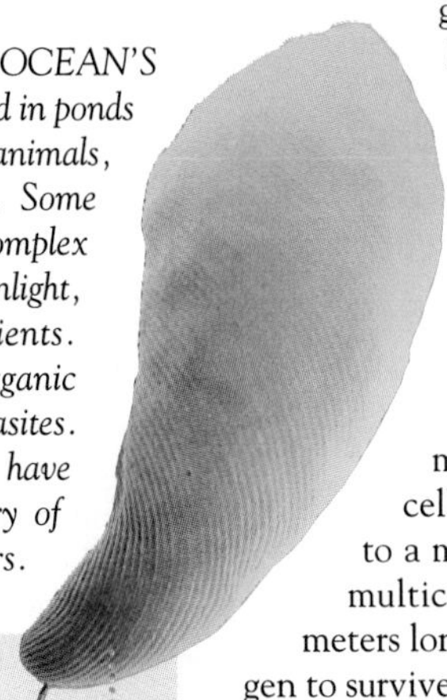

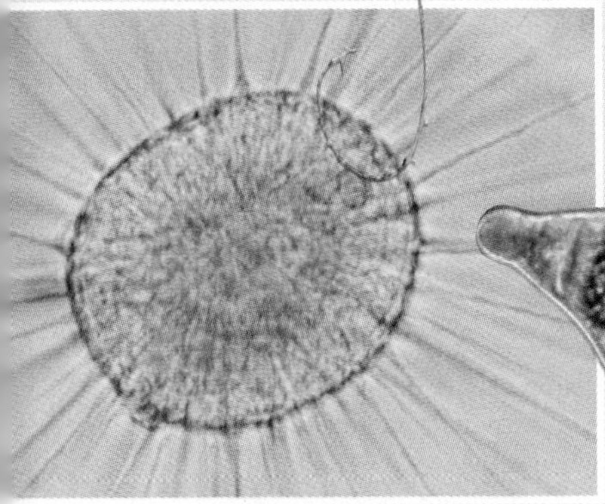

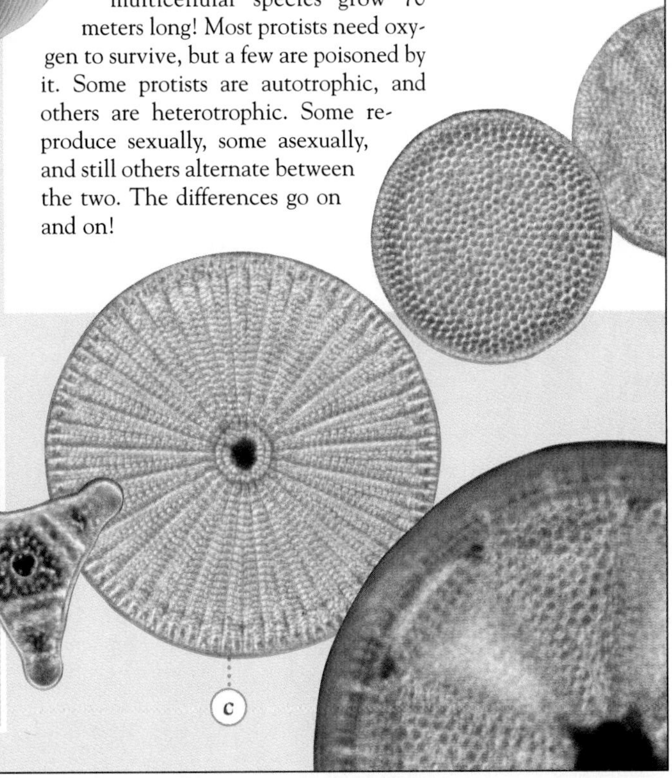

Figure 18–1
As a group, protists do not share any unique characteristics. These photographs of (a) a euglena (magnification: 2000X), (b) a heliozoan (magnification: 31X), and (c) diatoms (magnification: 63X) show just how diverse protists really are.

TEACHER SUPPORT

Background Information

Diatoms, most of which are photosynthetic, are unicellular algae with glassy cell walls containing silica, the mineral used to make glass. The cell wall consists of two halves that fit together like the top and bottom of a pillbox. Diatoms store their food reserves in the form of an oil, which also provides buoyancy and keeps the cells floating near the water surface in sunlight.

Diatoms are plentiful in both freshwater and saltwater environments. A pailful of water scooped from the surface of the ocean or almost any pond or lake may contain millions of these microscopic organisms. Massive accumulations of fossilized diatoms form thick sediments known as diatomaceous earth, which is mined for use as abrasives, a filtering medium, and an insulation material.

SECTION 18–1

Protists

Performance Objectives

- Identify characteristics of protists.
- Compare and contrast the characteristics of algae and protozoans.
- Describe the life cycles of protists.

1 ENGAGE

Ideas Through Images

Have students examine Figure 18–1, read the caption, and answer the following questions.

- **How are all these organisms alike?** (All consist of only one cell and are extremely small—evident from the magnifications identified in the caption.)
- **How are they different?** (Accept a variety of reasonable responses, including their shapes, structural features such as the euglena's tail, and actual size—evident from their different magnifications.)
- **Where do you think organisms like these might be found?** (Accept all reasonable responses, such as in freshwater ponds and streams, in oceans, in soil and mud, and even within other living things.)

2 EXPLORE

Discussion

Ask students to predict what would happen if they added fertilizer to a jar containing pond water and an aquatic plant. (The water would become greenish and cloudy due to an overgrowth of algae.) Point out that the algae in the jar is an example of an autotrophic protist. Ask students where they think the algae that grew in the jar came from. (They were already in the water, which was taken from a pond or aquarium.)

Section 18–1 (continued)

Inquiry Activity

Classifying

Observing a Slime Mold

Ask students if they think they can determine with certainty the difference between a plant, an animal, and a "neither plant nor animal" organism. Then show the class a terrarium containing a slime mold that you have collected from outdoors or obtained from a biological supply house. Tell students to observe the organism closely over a period of time, list the characteristics it shares with other types of organisms they are familiar with, and then try to classify it as a plant, an animal, or "other." Make sure you give students an opportunity to observe both the animallike mobile stage and the plant/funguslike reproductive stage. Note: If you are not familiar with the life stages of slime molds and the conditions that precipitate the reproductive stage, see Background Information below.

3 TEACH

Ideas Through Images

Have students examine Figure 18–2, read the caption, and answer the following questions.

- **Which kingdoms evolved before there was oxygen in Earth's atmosphere?** (Archaebacteria and Eubacteria.)

- **What was the source of the oxygen that was added to the atmosphere?** (Bacteria, photosynthetic prokaryotes. If students do not recall this information, have them look back at Chapter 17, page 398.)

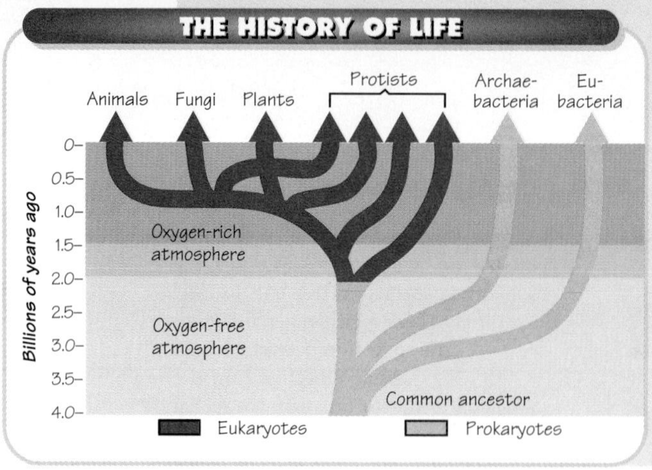

Figure 18–2 *This modern evolutionary tree illustrates the history and relationships of the six kingdoms of life. The base of the tree represents the common ancestor of all eukaryotic organisms. Notice that once oxygen became available, organisms quickly evolved.*

Evolution of Protists

The best way to approach the study of protists is to follow the evolutionary history of life. You may recall that the first living cells were prokaryotes, which resembled living bacteria. One of those ancient prokaryotes became the ancestor of all eukaryotes.

The First Eukaryotes

Sometime between 2 and 1.8 billion years ago, a great leap occurred in the evolution of life. As **Figure 18–3** illustrates, one form of prokaryotic cell grew larger and evolved internal cell membranes. Some of those membranes formed a nuclear envelope that surrounded its DNA. Other membranes became involved in producing and transporting proteins inside the cell. The result was the ancestor of all eukaryotes.

Then, something remarkable happened. One or more prokaryotic organisms entered this ancestral eukaryotic cell. But these invading organisms didn't infect their host, as parasites would have done. And the host didn't digest them, as it would have digested prey. Instead, the smaller prokaryotes began living inside the larger eukaryotic cell. Over time, a remarkable relationship called **symbiosis** (sihm-bigh-OH-sihs) evolved. This particular form of symbiosis, in which both the host and guest benefit, is called mutualism.

The smaller cells had the ability to use oxygen to generate the energy-rich molecule ATP. Over time, the smaller prokaryotes evolved together with their new hosts and became mitochondria—the cellular powerhouses of most protists and all multicellular organisms.

Other groups of prokaryotes moved into several different groups of evolving eukaryotic cells. These prokaryotes had the ability to perform photosynthesis. The prokaryotes within evolving eukaryotic cells further evolved into chloroplasts, and the partnerships gave rise to all photosynthetic eukaryotes, including algae and plants.

☑ ***Checkpoint*** What is symbiosis? 1

Evolution of Sexual Reproduction

About 300 million years after single-celled eukaryotes first appeared, the group started evolving very quickly. Why did this happen? Eukaryotes evolved the ability to reproduce sexually.

Prokaryotes, which reproduce by binary fission, simply copy their single chromosome and send one daughter chromosome to each daughter cell. This fast and effective means of reproduction

TEACHER SUPPORT

Background Information

There are two types of slime molds, cellular and plasmodial. In life cycles of both types, one stage consists of single cells that live on rotting leaves, logs, and other plant material, where they feed on bacteria, yeasts, and organic compounds. When food is scarce, the slime mold enters a second stage in which cells differentiate and form reproductive structures.

With cellular slime molds, the single ameboid cells collect in a sluglike colony covered with a slimy cellulose sheath. After moving about for a short time in this form, the colony develops into a stalked, spore-bearing structure.

A plasmodial slime mold is usually found on decaying matter in the form of a branching growth several centimeters in diameter. Despite its size, the organism consists of only one cell, called a syncytium, that extends pseudopodia for feeding. When food is scarce, the syncytium stops growing and differentiates into moldlike reproductive structures, as pictured in Figure 18–6, page 419.

EVOLUTION OF EUKARYOTIC CELLS

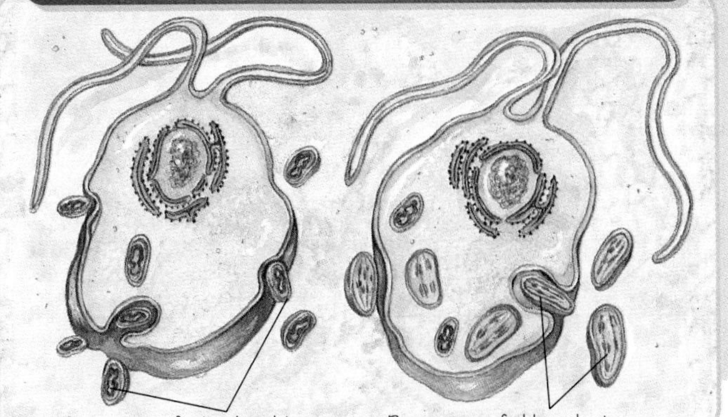

Figure 18–3
A widely accepted hypothesis states that the evolution of modern eukaryotic cells involved the formation of symbiotic relationships between two different kinds of ancient organisms. According to this hypothesis, mitochondria and chloroplasts are the descendants of ancient prokaryotes that took up residence inside the ancestors of modern eukaryotic cells.

has served bacteria well for billions of years. However, daughter cells produced in this way are exact replicas of their parents—unless a mutation occurs.

Eukaryotes that reproduce sexually, on the other hand, produce a lot of genetic variation among their offspring. You may recall that a great deal of chromosome shuffling occurs during independent assortment in meiosis. In addition, crossing-over can result in the exchange of pieces of DNA between members of a chromosome pair. This process can rearrange genes into different combinations. In this way, the next generation is formed by the fusion of gametes carrying genes from two different parents.

Because all these processes increase genetic variation, sexual reproduction provides more raw material for natural selection to operate. For that reason, soon after sexual reproduction evolved, eukaryotes experienced an extraordinary adaptive radiation—which is one species giving rise to many new species in a short period of time. Between 1.25 and 1 billion years ago, a great burst of evolutionary change produced the rest of living protist groups, as well as the ancestors of plants, animals, and fungi.

☑ **Checkpoint** Why did the eukaryotes suddenly begin to evolve quickly? 2

Living Protists

Ancestors of modern protists separated from one another a very long time ago. For that reason, living protists have been evolving alongside one another for about a billion years. That's an awfully long time, and many things have happened in each surviving group. Several groups have become photosynthetic, and others have become parasites. Still others have evolved varied ways of surviving.

Because differences among living protists are so extreme, most scientists agree that they should be divided into many different kingdoms. As a compromise, this chapter recognizes the diversity among protists but discusses the organisms in two groups—based on whether they are autotrophic or heterotrophic.

Autotrophic Protists

Algae are photosynthetic autotrophs that look and act like plants in certain ways. According to current estimates, there are about 30,000 species of algae in the oceans and in fresh water. Today, between 30 and 40 percent of all photosynthesis that takes place on Earth is performed by these protists. Major groups of algae, which vary greatly, are shown in **Figure 18–4** on page 418. Some are nearly as small as bacteria, while

Discussion

To reinforce the text explanation of genetic variation resulting from sexual reproduction, you may want to review the process of meiosis.

Ideas Through Images

Some students may not know the meaning of the term precursors, used in the labels for Figure 18–3. Explain (or ask students to use a dictionary to determine) that a precursor is something that comes before something else. After students examine the illustration, show them an illustration of a cell with mitochondria and chloroplasts. Ask students to identify the similarities and differences between these ancient symbiotic cells and modern eukaryotic cells.

Correcting Misconceptions

Students may think of the word primitive as meaning old, out-of-date, or somehow not up to snuff. To evolutionary biologists, primitive simply means "closest to the earliest appearing form."

☑ Checkpoints

1 A close relationship between two species.

2 They evolved the ability to reproduce sexually, thus producing genetic variation among their offspring.

TEACHER SUPPORT — Facts and Figures

A considerable amount of evidence supports the hypothesis that eukaryotic cells evolved from the symbiotic relationship described on page 416. For example, mitochondria and chloroplasts in eukaryotic cells today are similar to bacteria in many ways. They contain DNA, RNA, and ribosomes, all of which resemble their counterparts in prokaryotes more than those in eukaryotes. These components enable mitochondria and chloroplasts to act somewhat autonomously.

The endosymbiotic hypothesis also explains why mitochondria and chloroplasts have two membranes. Their inner membranes could have derived from the plasma membranes of the engulfed bacteria and their outer membranes from the infolded plasma membranes of the original host cells. In fact, the inner membranes of mitochondria and chloroplasts have several enzymes and electron transport molecules that resemble those found in the plasma membranes of prokaryotes today.

Ancillary Support

The resource below can be used to support your teaching strategy for these two pages.

BL Inquiry Activity: The Next Step

Ideas Through Images

Have students examine Figure 18–4, read the caption, and answer the following questions.

• **By what chararacteristic are the protists in the chart classified?** (Means of nutrition.)

• **Do you think it is likely that any photosynthetic protists are parasitic? Why or why not?** (Probably not, since photosynthetic protists can make their own food and do not need to obtain nutrients from other living organisms.)

• **Think about the appearance of the protists listed in the second column. Do you support the proposal that these organisms should each be in a separate kingdom? Why or why not?** (Students may agree that these organisms are so different from one another that they should be in separate kingdoms.)

Investigate

Model Building Ask students to look through this and other books to find additional color photographs of protists. Have each group choose one protist and construct a three-dimensional model of it using any materials they wish. Challenge students to be creative. For example, they could make a model of an ameba by filling a clear latex glove with corn syrup and adding marbles, sand, and other materials to represent the internal structures.

Discussion

If students have observed the reproductive stage of the slime mold you presented in the Inquiry Activity on page 416, have them compare the characteristics of the mobile and reproductive stages. If students have not yet observed the reproductive stage, tell them to keep observing the slime mold regularly and watch for the change.

CLASSIFICATION OF PROTISTS

Phylum	Examples	Nutrition
Euglenophyta (Euglenoids)	*Euglena*	Photosynthetic autotrophs
Pyrrophyta (Dinoflagellates)	*Gonyaulax* (causes red tide)	Photosynthetic autotrophs
Chrysophyta (Golden algae) (Diatoms)	*Orchromonas* *Navicula*	Photosynthetic autotrophs
Chlorophyta (Green algae)	*Chlamydomonas, Ulva*	Photosynthetic autotrophs
Rhodophyta (Red algae)	*Polysiphonia*	Photosynthetic autotrophs
Phaeophyta (Brown fungi)	*Fucus*	Photosynthetic autotrophs
Zoomastigina (Zooflagellates)	*Trypanosoma* (causes African sleeping sickness)	Heterotroph
Sarcodina	*Ameba*	Heterotroph
Sporozoa	*Plasmodium* (causes malaria)	Heterotrophic parasites
Ciliophora	*Paramecium*	Heterotroph
Myxomycota (Plasmodial slime molds)	*Physarum*	Heterotroph
Acrasiomycota (Cellular slime molds)	*Dictyostelium*	Heterotroph

Figure 18–4
Protists are often classified according to the way they obtain nutrients. Protists that make their own food by photosynthesis are called autotrophs, whereas those that get their food from another source are called heterotrophs.

others—such as giant kelp—form dense forests that may reach 70 meters.

Three groups of algae—Euglenophyta (yoo-glee-nuh-FIGHT-uh), Pyrrophyta (pigh-roh-FIGHT-uh), and Chrysophyta (krihs-uh-FIGHT-uh) are mostly single-celled. Chlorophyta (klor-oh-FIGHT-ah), Rhodophyta (roh-duh-FIGHT-uh), and Phaeophyta (fee-ah-FIGHT-uh) are mainly multicellular. Among multicellular species, most of the cells are nearly identical.

☑ ***Checkpoint*** What are algae? 1

Heterotrophic Protists

Heterotrophic protists, some examples of which are shown in ***Figure 18–6,*** have been commonly known as protozoans. Most protozoans are quite active and can usually be seen with a compound light microscope. **All heterotrophic protists spend most of their lives as unicellular organisms. Some species, such as slime molds, gather into groups at some time during their life cycle.**

Protozoans have evolved many different feeding strategies, and living species may act as predators, decomposers, or

Figure 18–5
Algae, the autotrophic protists, are found in moist and sunny environments where they can carry out photosynthesis. (a) *Notice the single chloroplast in the center of the Spirogyra, a strandlike green algae (magnification: 200X).* (b) *In most red algae, a red pigment masks the other pigments, such as chlorophyll, giving the algae its characteristic red color.*

(a)

(b)

TEACHER SUPPORT

Activity

OBSERVING PROTISTS

Have students observe living protists in drops of water they have taken from a culture and placed on a microscope slide. You or students can obtain protist cultures as follows. If both cultures are available, students can compare the types of organisms found in them.

• Collected culture: Half-fill a jar with pond water, and put in a handful of dried vegetation from the pond's bank. Add 12 grains of uncooked rice. Let the jar stand undisturbed out of direct sunlight for about a week before removing drops to examine.

• Hay infusion: Boil a liter of water. Add a handful of Timothy hay, and boil for an additional 10 minutes. When the water has cooled, add about 5 grams of uncooked rice or wheat grains. Let the container stand undisturbed in semidarkness. After about a week, students should see a dark area around the grains. Drops for examination should be removed from this dark area.

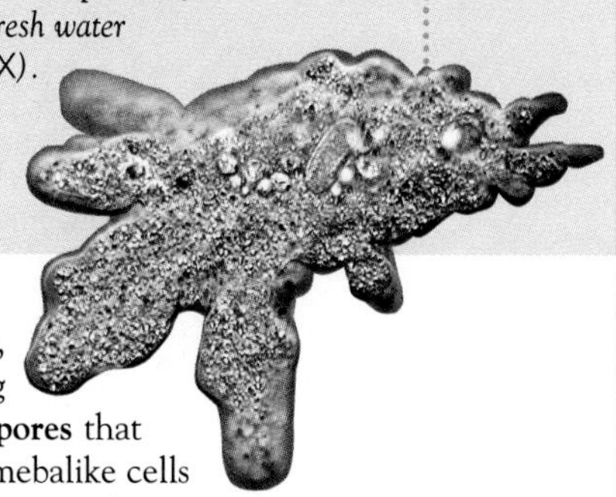

Figure 18–6
Some representative examples of heterotrophic protists include (a) Myxophyta, *a slime mold, and* (b) Amoeba proteus, *a sarcodine found in fresh water (magnification: 160X).*

parasites. Sporozoa may look like simple organisms, but they are complex parasites that cause serious diseases in humans and other animals. One species of sporozoa, the genus *Plasmodium*, causes malaria, a disease that kills more humans each year than any other disease.

Checkpoint What are protozoans? 2

How Do Protists Reproduce?

Life cycles among protists are enormously varied. Because these organisms have been evolving for a billion years, it isn't surprising that they have evolved more life-cycle variations than the fungi, plant, and animal kingdoms combined.

One group, Euglenophyta, branched off from the others before sexual reproduction evolved. *Euglena* and its relatives reproduce only asexually. All other groups reproduce sexually at least occasionally.

Cellular slime molds spend most of their lives as individual, free-moving amebalike cells. But under certain circumstances, they gather together and form a sluglike mass. This mass moves around for a while, then forms a fruiting body that releases **spores** that develop into new amebalike cells on their own, without needing to join with another cell.

Algae show several variations in a life cycle that alternates between a sexual stage and an asexual stage. The green algae *Ulva* shows a pattern of reproduction that also occurs in green plants. This species illustrates a process known as **alternation of generations.** In alternation of generations, diploid (2n) and haploid (n) cells switch back and forth. Diploid cells have the normal number of chromosomes for that species. Haploid cells have half the normal number of chromosomes. The diploid generation is called the sporophyte because it undergoes meiosis to produce haploid spores. These spores grow into haploid male and female cells called gametophytes (gah-MEET-uh-fights). Gametophytes produce gametes—eggs and sperm. When an egg and sperm fuse, they produce a diploid cell called a zygote (ZIGH-goht), which grows into a sporophyte again.

Section Review 18–1

1. How would you **describe** the characteristics of protists?
2. **Compare** algae and protozoans.
3. **Explain** how protists reproduce.
4. **Critical Thinking—Comparing** Describe the differences between the sporophyte and gametophyte generations in *Ulva*.

4 ASSESS

Quick Check

Have students create a two-column table summarizing the characteristics of algae and protozoans and identifying the major differences between the two groups.

Section Review 18–1

1. All protists are eukaryotes, but they do not share a unique set of characteristics. (Students may mention specific differences.)
2. Algae are photosynthetic autotrophs; protozoans are heterotrophs and spend most or all of their lives as unicellular organisms.
3. Asexual reproduction by mitosis, sexual reproduction, spore-producing fruiting bodies, and alternation between sexual and asexual stages (alternation of generations).
4. Diploid cells in the sporophyte generation have the normal number of chromosomes for that species. Haploid cells in the gametophyte generation have half the normal number of chromosomes.

Checkpoints

1 Photosynthetic autotrophs that look and act like plants in certain ways.

2 Heterotrophic protists that spend most of their lives as unicellular organisms.

Learning Modality

Tactile and Kinesthetic Learning Have students make a large version of Figure 18–2 using textured materials such as fabrics, different grades of sandpaper, and various types of papers for the horizontal bands and the arrows on the diagram, with the labels printed in black marking pen. In addition to being helpful to the students making the diagram, the large version also could serve as a study aid for visually impaired students.

Ancillary Support

The resources below can be used to support your teaching strategy for these two pages.

LM Examining an Algal Bloom, #36
TR Explore: Life by the Drop

SECTION 18–2

Fungi

Performance Objectives

- Identify the four phyla into which fungi are classified.
- Describe the life cycles of fungi.

Mini Lab Skill: Predicting

1 ENGAGE

Ideas Through Images

Have students examine Figure 18–7, read the caption, and answer the following questions.

- **Have you ever seen organisms like these? If so, where?** (Students will most likely identify damp, shaded spots as the places where they have seen fungi.)
- **How are these organisms similar to plants?** (Students will most likely mention the mushrooms' "stems.")
- **How are they different from plants?** (Accept all reasonable responses, including the absence of green coloration.)

2 EXPLORE

Investigate

Cooperative Learning Ask students whether they have ever eaten mushrooms and, if so, to describe how they were prepared and how they tasted. Then have students work in cooperative groups of three, with one student researching a simple recipe, the second student preparing it in class using mushrooms you have purchased in a supermarket, and the third student writing a brief review of the dish. (If the recipe involves cooking, provide a hotplate and a pan for students to use.) Let groups share their recipes and reviews.

SECTION

18–2 Fungi

GUIDE FOR READING

- Classify fungi into four phyla.
- **Explain** how fungi reproduce.

MINI LAB

- **Predict** the conditions that are needed for the growth of mold.

TO MOST PEOPLE, THE WORD fungus means death and decay. Molds spoil food, mildew ruins books and clothes, and mushrooms sprout from rotting logs. Although some fungi are harmful, causing serious diseases in humans and plants, other fungi are beneficial. Fungi help trees and many other seed plants extract nutrients from the soil. Without them, many of the great evergreen forests of North America would wither away and die. Other fungi are used to make bread and many cheeses. And the first antibiotics, as well as many other drugs, have been processed from fungi.

What Is a Fungus?

Fungi are heterotrophic eukaryotes that have cell walls. Some fungi—such as yeast—are single-celled and microscopic. Most fungi, however, are multicellular. Some fungi are parasites that live on plants or animals, causing them harm. Other fungi obtain food by digesting the dead remains of other organisms. And still other fungi live in a mutual relationship with other organisms—ranging from bacteria to animals.

Although many fungi look like plants, several characteristics show that they are more closely related to animals. Similar to plants, fungi have cell walls. But the cell walls of fungi do not contain cellulose. Instead, they are reinforced with **chitin** (KIGH-tihn), a complex carbohydrate that is also found in insect skeletons. Also, many fungi can store energy in the form of glycogen—something that animals do all the time, but that plants cannot.

Checkpoint What is chitin? 1

Figure 18–7 Fungi are a diverse group of organisms. (a) These bracket fungi are growing on a dead tree. Other types of fungi, such as these (b) fly agaric mushrooms and (c) Amanita fulva mushrooms, are poisonous and if eaten could be fatal.

TEACHER SUPPORT

Activity

COLLECTING FUNGI

Take the class on a field trip to collect fungi under your direct supervision. Provide small, self-sealing plastic bags for collection. Also supply plastic forks so students can pry up mushrooms with their hyphae and mycelium intact. **CAUTION:** *Warn students not to touch any fungi with their bare hands.* Have them turn a bag inside-out, place it over one hand to form a "glove," then pick the fungus, and invert the bag again and seal it.

In the classroom, let groups examine the bagged fungi with hand lenses. Provide field guides so students can try to identify the fungi they have collected. Encourage them to label each bag with the fungus's type and its scientific name. If students have collected any poisonous fungi, or any they suspect may be poisonous, properly dispose of them. Have students display the fungi.

Living Fungi

Not much is known about the evolution of fungi, but researchers agree that they have been around since at least the Silurian Period (about 430 million years ago). It seems likely that fungi began evolving on land probably when the first plants appeared.

All fungi, as you can see in *Figure 18–8* have the same basic structures. The most basic structure in a fungus is a threadlike filament called a **hypha** (HIGH-fuh; plural: hyphae). Oddly enough, the cells in the hyphae may have a single nucleus, two nuclei, or many nuclei. In most common types of fungi, hyphae grow down into whatever the fungus is feeding on, forming a cottony mass called a **mycelium** (migh-SEE-lee-uhm). Most of the mycelium grows into and through the food source, secreting enzymes that break it down into compounds that can be absorbed into the fungus's cells. When the conditions are right, parts of a mycelium may become organized into the fruiting bodies you would recognize as a mushroom. **The living fungi are divided into four phyla according to their life cycles—Zygomycota** (zigh-goh-migh-KOHT-uh), **Ascomycota** (as-kuh-migh-KOHT-uh), **Basidiomycota** (buh-sihd-ee-uh-migh-KOHT-uh), **and Deuteromycota** (doo-ter-uh-migh-KOHT-uh).

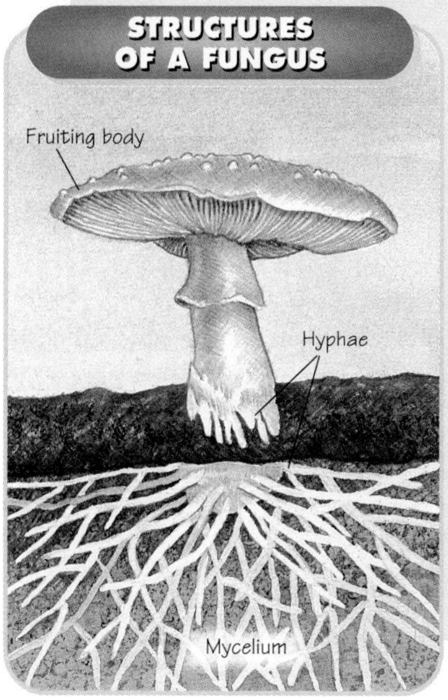

Figure 18–8 Like most fungi, mushrooms have the same basic structures—a fruiting body, hyphae, and mycelium.

Checkpoint What is a mycelium? 2

Zygomycetes

Fungi that belong to the phylum Zygomycota are called zygomycetes. These fungi are often called bread molds because this group includes the black mold that is sometimes found on bread.

CLASSIFICATION OF FUNGI

Phylum	Examples
Zygomycota (Common mold)	*Rhizopus* (Black bread mold)
Ascomycota (Sac fungi)	Yeasts, morels, truffles, *Neurospora* (Red bread mold)
Basidiomycota (Club fungi)	Mushrooms, puffballs, bracket fungi, rusts, jelly fungi, toadstools
Deuteromycota (Imperfect fungi)	*Penicillium*, *Aspergillus*, ringworm and athlete's foot fungus, black spot on roses fungus, tomato blight fungus, cucumber scab fungus

Figure 18–9 Fungi are classified according to how they reproduce. Some of the most common fungi are shown in their respective phyla.

3 TEACH

Ideas Through Images

Have students examine Figure 18–8 and read the caption and the descriptions of hyphae and mycelium in the student text. Then have each group examine the fungi they collected in the Activity on page 420 (or provide students with mushrooms from a supermarket), looking for each of the parts identified in the diagram. Make sure students leave the fungi in the sealed bags while examining them. Have students answer the following questions.

- **Which part of the fungus you are examining is the fruiting body?** (On a supermarket mushroom, it is the round cap.)
- **Are hyphae and mycelia visible? Why or why not?** (Probably not, because the hyphae are left behind when the fungus is picked.)

Checkpoints

1 A complex carbohydrate found in the cell walls of fungi and in insect skeletons.

2 The cottony mass of hyphae that grows into and through a fungus's food source and breaks it down into compounds that can be absorbed by the fungus's cells.

TEACHER SUPPORT

Background Information

A Health Problem Fungal outbreaks in hospitals are a growing problem as microorganisms evolve to become resistant to drugs. In August 1996, British doctors reported that a fungus living on wooden tongue depressors may endanger hospitalized newborns. An outbreak of fungal infection at a London hospital had killed three babies and necessitated the amputation of a fourth baby's arm. In the latter case, the infection's source was traced to wooden splints used to support tubes attached to the infant's arm. The warm, humid conditions in neonatal incubators seemed to promote fungal skin infections.

A Positive Development After decades of trials, USDA researchers have established two new varieties of American elm that resist Dutch elm disease, which is caused by a fungus. The resistant varieties, named New Harmony and Valley Forge, are now being grown in nurseries and should be ready for sale to the public by the year 2000.

Ancillary Support

The resources below can be used to support your teaching strategy for these two pages.

LM Classifying Fungi, #35
BL Inquiry Activity: Fungus Among Us

Problem Solving

Interpreting Information

The Fruit Detective

State The problem is to determine the type of microorganism growing on spoiling fruit.

Solve Students should first separately list the characteristics of protists, fungi, and plants, and then list the characteristics of the organisms pictured on this page. When students compare the lists, they should be able to identify fungi as the fruit-spoiling culprits.

Test To test their conclusions, students may let some fruit spoil and then observe the organisms with a hand lens and, possibly, a microscope. From their observations of bread mold in Figure 18–10 and in the MINI LAB on page 423, students should recognize the fruit-spoiling organisms as mold.

Communicate Ask one student from each group to present the results of the group's analysis. If you have a projection microscope, students can project the image of the organism growing on the fruit and point out the structures that helped them identify it as a mold.

Answers to Think About It

1. Fungi, specifically mold. (See Solve step above.)
2. Warmth, high humidity.
3. Refrigerate the fruit because mold grows best in warm conditions. Make sure the fruit is thoroughly dried after washing it because mold grows best in damp conditions.

Problem Solving

INTERPRETING INFORMATION

The Fruit Detective

It is summer, and you are faced with a dilemma. Whenever you leave tomatoes, blueberries, or strawberries on the kitchen counter, they spoil within a few days—often before you can eat and enjoy them. Although oranges eventually spoil, they stay fresh somewhat longer than the others.

Your friend was visiting one day, and you explained the problem to her. Your friend needed a science project for her summer school class and decided to use your spoiling fruit problem as her project. She knew that the decomposition of food—its spoiling—is caused by the growth of microorganisms. She was determined to find out which type of microorganism was growing on the fruit. She gathered up the spoiled fruit and headed for the school lab.

To find out which type of organism was spoiling the fruit, your friend observed the spoiled areas of the fruit with a magnifying lens. She observed black and blue-green fuzzy growths on the fruit. She then made some wet-mount slides of the visible growth from the fruit and observed them under a microscope. The photographs illustrate what she observed.

• THINK ABOUT IT •

1. **Compare** the characteristics of the organisms shown in the photograph with those organisms described in the chapter. Which type of organism is spoiling the fruit? How do you know?
2. What conditions favoring the growth of these organisms might be present in the summertime?
3. What could you do to keep the fruit fresh longer? **Explain** your answer.

TEACHER SUPPORT

Background Information

The mold growing on the orange in the photographs on this page is *Penicillium,* the most famous Deuteromycete. It is the fungus from which the antibiotic penicillin is made.

Penicillin was discovered in 1928 when Sir Alexander Fleming, a British microbiologist, observed that the *Staphylococcus* bacteria that he was culturing was being killed off by a mold that was growing on the same plate. Fleming isolated the substance that the mold produced to kill the bacteria.

Penicillin became the first antibiotic and is still used to treat bacterial infections such as strep throat, staph, and pneumonia. The availability of penicillin and other antibiotics has increased human life expectancy by eliminating the fatal effects of numerous diseases.

Ascomycetes

The sac fungi, or the fungi that belong to the phylum Ascomycota, include as many as 30,000 recognized species of mildews, molds, and yeasts. This is the largest phylum in the kingdom Fungi. Other members of this phylum are edible—the rare and expensive delicacies known as morels and truffles.

Basidiomycetes

Members of the phylum Basidiomycota include the fungi whose fruiting bodies form mushrooms. Although many mushrooms are good to eat, some can be poisonous. Unfortunately, the difference between the delicious ones and the deadly ones may be difficult to detect. Therefore, never gather your own mushrooms for dinner! Other members of this phylum include puffballs, bracket fungi, rusts, and smuts.

Deuteromycetes

The phylum Deuteromycota is sometimes called *fungi imperfecti*, or "imperfect" fungi. These fungi are called

MINI LAB .... Predicting

Fuzzy Food

PROBLEM *How can you* ***predict*** *the conditions that are needed to grow mold?*

PROCEDURE

1. Line the bottoms of three plastic containers with damp paper towels.
2. Place a slice of bread into each of the three containers.
3. Place the containers in three different places—such as a refrigerator, a windowsill, and in a desk drawer—where they will remain undisturbed for four days.
4. Based on where you put the containers, predict in which containers mold will grow.
5. On the fifth day, use a hand lens to observe the changes in each container. Draw a diagram of what you observe.

ANALYZE AND CONCLUDE

1. In which, if any, containers did mold grow?
2. Were your predictions correct?
3. What conditions were needed for mold to grow?

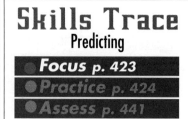

Figure 18–10
Some representative fungi from the different phyla include (a) Rhizopus stolonifer, *the black bread mold, a member of the phylum Zygomycota;* (b) *black truffles, a rare and expensive delicacy, a member of the phylum Ascomycota; and* (c) *honey mushrooms, a member of the phylum Basidiomycota.*

MINI LAB Predicting

Teacher Notes

• For time required and materials needed, see page 414b.

• **Caution:** *Make sure that students who are allergic to molds are not exposed to them during this activity.*

Answers to Analyze and Conclude

1. Containers placed in a refrigerator or on a sunny windowsill will probably show no mold growth. Those placed in warm (at least room temperature) and dark or shaded locations should show mold growth.
2. Answers will depend on students' specific predictions.
3. Moisture, warmth, and no prolonged periods of direct sunlight.

Skills Trace
Predicting

- **Focus** p. 423
- **Practice** p. 424
- **Assess** p. 441

Discussion

Have groups reexamine each of the fungi they collected earlier and try to classify it into one of the four major phyla discussed in the student text. (Most likely, all the collected fungi will be Basidiomycota.) Also remind students of the unidentified material that produced foam in a sugarwater solution (Chapter Discovery Learning Activity, page 414.) Explain that the material was dry yeast. Ask students to identify the phylum to which yeast belong. (Ascomycota.)

TEACHER SUPPORT — Background Information

One example of the complexity of fungi life cycles is in the Basidiomycetes. The hyphae are haploid, and of two mating types, simply called plus and minus. After these hyphae grow for a time, some of their filaments fuse together and grow into a secondary mycelium. The nuclei from the two mating types do not fuse but remain separate inside the secondary mycelium. This mycelium is described as dikaryotic, which means that it has two separate haploid nuclei.

The secondary mycelium may live for many years before sending up the familiarly shaped fruiting body. As the fruiting body matures, it produces club-shaped structures called basidia, from which the phylum gets its name. Inside the basidia, the two types of haploid nuclei fuse and immediately undergo meiosis, producing haploid spores. When released, the spores germinate and develop into hyphae once again.

4 ASSESS

Quick Check

Have each student draw a simple sketch of a mushroom and label its three basic structures from memory. You may want to write the terms hyphae and mycelium on the board as a reference for correct spelling.

Section Review 18-2

1. Zygomycota, Ascomycota, Basidiomycota, Deuteromycota.
2. Fungi reproduce both sexually and asexually. (Students may explain each method in greater detail, as described on this student page.)
3. Many fungi look like plants, and fungi have cell walls, as do plants.
4. Moisture, warmth, and no prolonged periods of direct sunlight.

Skills Trace
Predicting
- Focus p. 423
- Practice p. 424
- Assess p. 441

Learning Modality

Visual and Tactile Learning Have each student make a simple model of a mushroom out of clay and attach paper labels identifying its three basic parts, using Figure 18–8 as a guide. When the clay has dried, let students paint their model mushrooms to simulate those shown in the section's photographs or actual mushrooms they collected in the Activity on page 420.

Figure 18–11
One type of asexual reproduction in fungi involves the production of spores. In puffballs, spores can be dispersed by the slightest touch—in this case, falling raindrops. Once released, these lightweight spores can be carried great distances by the wind.

imperfect because researchers have never been able to identify their sexual stages. One member of this phylum is *Penicillium*, the source of the antibiotic penicillin. Other members of this phylum produce plant and animal diseases, such as tomato blight and athlete's foot, respectively.

Lichens

Lichens—familiar to anyone who hikes or walks in the woods—are the colorful scalelike patches on tree trunks or rocks. But to many people's surprise, lichens are not a single organism. They are a symbiotic partnership between a fungus and a photosynthetic organism, such as a cyanobacterium or a green alga. The alga carries out photosynthesis, providing the fungus with a source of organic substances. The fungus, in turn, provides the alga with water and minerals that it has collected from the surfaces on which it grows. Because both partners benefit from this relationship, lichens are able to survive in some of the world's harshest environments, where neither partner could survive alone.

☑ **Checkpoint** What are lichens? 1

How Do Fungi Reproduce?

Life cycles of most fungi are extremely complicated and vary from phylum to phylum. **Fungi can reproduce both sexually and asexually.** Asexual reproduction occurs either by the production of spores or by the fragmentation of the hyphae. The spores produced in many fungi are small and lightweight. When they are released, the spores are carried by the wind. If they land in suitable places, they germinate and grow into hyphae again.

Sexual reproduction involves two mating types. When the hyphae of opposite mating types meet, some of their filaments fuse together. The nuclei from the two mating types fuse and immediately undergo the process of meiosis to produce tiny spores.

Section Review 18–2

1. **Classify** fungi into four phyla.
2. **Explain** how fungi reproduce.
3. **Critical Thinking—Applying Concepts** Why do you think fungi were once classified as plants?
4. **MINI LAB** **Predict** the conditions that are needed to grow mold.

TEACHER SUPPORT

Activity

MAKING SPORE PRINTS
For the following activity, students should use fresh store-bought mushrooms.

1. Break off the mushroom cap and discard the stem.
2. Place the cap right-side up (gills down) on a sheet of white paper. (If any students are using white-spored fungi, have them use black paper for contrast.)
3. Invert a clear plastic cup over the mushroom cap and leave the setup undisturbed for 24–48 hours.
4. Carefully remove the cup and the mushroom cap, and examine the spore print with your bare eyes and with a hand lens. (The spores will form a radial design. Students should be able to see the individual spores with the hand lens.)

Multicellular Plants

SECTION 18-3

GUIDE FOR READING

- **Classify** plants into two major groups.
- **Describe** the structures that enabled plants to live on land.
- **Explain** how plants reproduce.

THE PLANT KINGDOM INCLUDES some of the most beautiful and important organisms on Earth. Because members of the plant kingdom are the only primary producers that live entirely on land, the food they provide makes terrestrial life possible for humans and other members of the animal kingdom. Plants are not only used for food, they are used for clothing, shelter, medicines, and even gifts. Researchers are learning that plants have powerful effects in shaping global environments. And because plants have a long evolutionary history, they have developed hundreds of relationships with members of other kingdoms. Life as we know it couldn't exist without them.

What Is a Plant?

Plants vary remarkably in shape, size, and habitat. Some mosses and orchids are so small that an adult plant could fit on the tip of a pencil eraser! Other plants—such as the giant redwoods—are the tallest organisms that have ever lived. Some plants live in the freezing Arctic, and others inhabit Earth's hottest areas.

What characteristics tie all these different organisms into a single kingdom? All plants are multicellular, photosynthetic eukaryotes whose cells are enclosed and supported by cell walls made of cellulose. The vast majority of plants reproduce sexually and have life cycles that involve alternation of generations. In addition, many plants can reproduce asexually.

☑ **Checkpoint** What do all plants have in common? 2

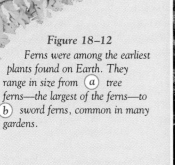

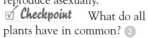

Figure 18–12
Ferns were among the earliest plants found on Earth. They range in size from (a) tree ferns—the largest of the ferns—to (b) sword ferns, common in many gardens.

SECTION 18-3

Multicellular Plants

Performance Objectives

- Identify the two phyla into which plants are classified.
- Describe plant adaptations for life on land.
- Describe the life cycles of plants.

Laboratory Investigation Skill: Predicting

1 ENGAGE

Inquiry Activity

Giving an Example

Identifying Uses of Plants

Ask students how many different ways people use plants. Tell students they will have one minute to list as many uses as they can think of. When time is up, call on each student in turn to identify one use. Continue until students can add no more uses to a common class list.

☑ Checkpoints

1 A symbiotic partnership between a fungus and a photosynthetic organism, such as a cyanobacterium or a green alga.

2 All plants are multicellular, photosynthetic eukaryotes whose cells are enclosed and supported by cell walls made of cellulose.

TEACHER SUPPORT

Managing Classroom Diversity

EDUCATIONAL EQUITY/ TECH PREP STUDENTS

Encourage students who are interested in careers in business to find out about entrepreneur Sally Fox, who developed the first cotton plants to produce naturally colored cotton fibers with commercial value.

In 1982, Fox found a bag of unique cotton seeds that yielded naturally brown and green cotton. An accomplished hand-spinner and weaver, Fox thought other hobbyists might be interested in undyed colored cotton, but the fibers were too short to be spun easily. Fox eventually increased the fiber length through selective breeding. From its beginnings as a small mail-order business in 1986, Fox's company now supplies naturally colored cotton to manufacturers and retailers.

An account of Fox's accomplishments can be found in the article "Seeds of Success" in the August 15, 1994, issue of *Forbes* magazine.

Ancillary Support

The resource below can be used to support your teaching strategy for these two pages.

TR Explore: Frankly, It's Fungi

2 EXPLORE

Inquiry Activity

Making Inferences

Developing a Definition of Plant

Ask students what characteristics differentiate plants from other organisms. Have students work in pairs to write a definition of the word plant. Let students share their definitions in a class discussion, but do not correct any misconceptions at this time. Tell students to save their definitions and refer to them again at the conclusion of this section.

3 TEACH

Ideas Through Images

Have students examine Figure 18–13 and read the caption. Make sure students understand that the illustrations show ancient plants that are extinct today. Then have students answer the following questions.

- **In what ways are these plants similar to plants living today?** (Accept all reasonable responses, including that they have stems or trunks, have leaflike and needlelike structures, and are rooted in soil.)
- **In what ways are they different from plants today?** (Accept all reasonable responses, including that many of the leaflike structures are very different from leaves on modern plants.)

Discussion

Emphasize that the wording used in the text to describe plant evolution—"plants had to adapt," "needed to develop," and "had to evolve," for example—does not mean that plants evolved certain structures or processes in order to live on land. Rather, naturally occurring genetic changes (mutations) made some plants better adapted than others to live on land, and those plants were able to survive and reproduce in drier locations.

Figure 18–13 *(a) The first forests were dominated by ferns and other plants without seeds. (b) Some of the earliest vascular plants did not have leaves and were very primitive.*

As with many other forms of life, plants evolved in water. Water provides an environment that supports the plant body and surrounds the plant with nutrients. During their evolutionary history, plants had to adapt to a series of changes in order to survive in a dry, nonsupporting environment.

Evolution of Plants

The first ancestors of living plants started leaving traces in the fossil record during the late Ordovician Period, about 450 million years ago. At that time, continental drift and changes in global climate set the stage for the evolution of modern organisms. At the beginning of the Silurian Period, about 430 million years ago, a global cold spell ended and continental drift began moving large landmasses from the South Pole closer to the equator. Together, these changes created many warm, swampy habitats that served as ideal places for the evolution of terrestrial life.

Challenges of Life on Land

Plants are most closely related to the green algae. Researchers know this because algae and plants share many molecular similarities and cell structures. The photosynthetic process of plants also resembles that of green algae.

Environment

The first challenge in adapting to life on land was the dry environment. All cells need a constant supply of water. In order for plants to survive out of water, they needed to develop a way to prevent water loss.

Structures

Another adaptation plants had to make was the development of rigid structures to support the plant on land. This support enabled plants to hold their photosynthetic leaves up to the sun.

Plants also needed to develop structures that would anchor them in place and absorb water and nutrients from the soil. Once the water and nutrients were absorbed, they needed to be transported to the leaves, where photosynthesis takes place. To meet this need, plants had to develop an internal transport system.

Reproduction

Finally, plants also had to evolve new methods of reproduction. The life cycles

TEACHER SUPPORT

Background Information

Biologists generally agree that plants evolved from green algae because of their many homologous features. For example, both green algae and plants have chloroplasts, a particular combination of photosynthetic pigments, and cell walls made of cellulose. Both also store carbohydrates in the form of starch. During cell division, both form a cell plate that divides the cytoplasm.

Scientists cannot determine which green algae gave rise to plants, because the soft bodies of algae have left few fossils. The algal ancestors of plants may have lived on the moist edges of lakes or coastal salt marshes during a time when the continents were relatively flat and subject to periodic flooding and draining. Under these conditions, natural selection would have favored algae that could survive periods when they were not submerged. In time, some of the algae species may have acquired adap-tations that enabled them to live permanently above the water line.

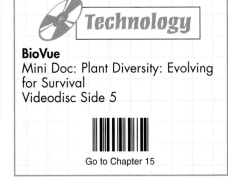

Figure 18–14
Bryophytes were the earliest plants. (a) Hornworts, (b) mosses, and (c) liverworts are three groups of modern bryophytes.

of algae require water in which gametes can swim or young plants can float. Before plants could survive in any but the wettest habitats on land, they had to evolve new ways of transporting sperm to eggs that did not require water. All these requirements were met as plants became fully adapted to life on land.

The Evolution of Two Groups

Early on, the ancestors of plants branched into two groups. The first group was the bryophytes (BRIGH-oh-fights), **which resemble algae in many ways.** Bryophytes evolved only partial solutions to the environmental challenges of living on land. **The second group, the tracheophytes** (TRAY-kee-oh-fights), **developed specialized tissue as a way of adapting to these challenges.**

Bryophytes

The bryophyte group includes mosses, liverworts, and hornworts. Bryophytes are well-equipped to survive in wet places, where they may grow in great numbers. Bryophytes evolved rapidly during the Devonian and Carboniferous periods (about 286 to 408 million years ago), when many land environments were wetter and more humid than they are today.

Modern bryophytes never grow more than a few centimeters tall. Some species, such as *Sphagnum*, or peat moss, grow almost completely submerged in water. Others grow well on wet tree trunks, rocks, and soil. Bryophytes can grow and reproduce only when wet, so they can survive only in places where, for at least part of the year, plenty of water is available. Some moss species can survive dry periods, but in order to do so they must stop growing.

Checkpoint What are bryophytes? 1

Tracheophytes

Although bryophytes live on land, they still depend upon water to survive. The tracheophytes were the first "true" land plants because they evolved ways of decreasing this dependence on the constant presence of standing water and humid conditions. Tracheophytes have **vascular tissues** that transport water and nutrients throughout the plant. As a result, tracheophytes can grow much larger and can live in a wider range of habitats than bryophytes can.

Ferns

Ferns and several extinct relatives were the first tracheophytes. Ferns have vascular tissue in addition to roots, strong

Investigate

Long-Term Project Students are probably unfamiliar with bryophytes other than mosses, and even mosses may be unfamiliar to them if they live in a dry area. Set up (or ask volunteers to set up) a terrarium with several examples of bryophytes that you (or the volunteers) have collected from outdoors or obtained from a greenhouse. You may also want to include a few ferns, since they require similar conditions. Provide a variety of books on plant care, and ask the class to find out what conditions these plants need in order to remain healthy. Let small groups take turns caring for the plants for a week at a time.

Ideas Through Images

Have students examine Figure 18–14 and read the caption. Point out the text statement "Modern bryophytes never grow more than a few centimeters tall," and direct students' attention to the size of the bryophytes in the terrarium that you or volunteers set up in the Investigate activity above. Then have students answer the following questions.

- **Are the hornworts and liverworts in these photographs shown at their actual sizes?** (No, the real plants are smaller.)
- **Why are bryophytes so small?** (They do not have vascular tissue to carry water and nutrients up and down long stems.)

Checkpoint

1 Plants that can grow and reproduce only in places where water is plentiful for at least part of the year.

TEACHER SUPPORT

Background Information

Because bryophytes lack vascular tissue, biologists do not use the terms root, stem, or leaf to describe their parts. The bryophyte's rootlike structures, which anchor the plant and absorb water and nutrients, are called rhizoids. A moss's short main axis does not have the strength of a plant stem and therefore mosses grow very close together holding one another upright. A moss's leaflike structures are no more than two cells thick, lacking the complex tissues found in vascular plants' leaves.

Technology

BioVue
Mini Doc: Plant Diversity: Evolving for Survival
Videodisc Side 5

Go to Chapter 15

Investigate

Research Ask students to consult field guides and other sources to find pictures of cycads and ginkgoes. Have them compare the visible characteristics of these trees with those of pine trees or other conifers common in their area. Also remind students of their Bio Journal entries about living fossils that they wrote earlier (Chapter 17, page 386). Ask them whether cycads and ginkgoes could be considered living fossils. (Yes, they could.)

INTEGRATING EARTH SCIENCE

Ancient dead plants that fell into stagnant swamps did not completely decay but formed thick deposits of organic material called peat. The swamps were later submerged by seawater, and marine sediments built up over the peat. As layers of sediment accumulated over millions of years, heat and pressure gradually converted the peat to coal.

Discussion

Ask students to use a dictionary to find out the derivations and literal meanings of the terms gymnosperm and angiosperm. (*Gymno* from the Greek *gymnos*, meaning naked; *angio* from the Greek *angeion*, meaning vessel; *sperm* from the Greek *sperma*, meaning seed. Thus, the literal meaning of gymnosperm is naked seed and that of angiosperm is vessel seed.) Explain that angiosperm seeds are contained inside a flower part called the ovary. Thus, a vessel seed is an enclosed seed.

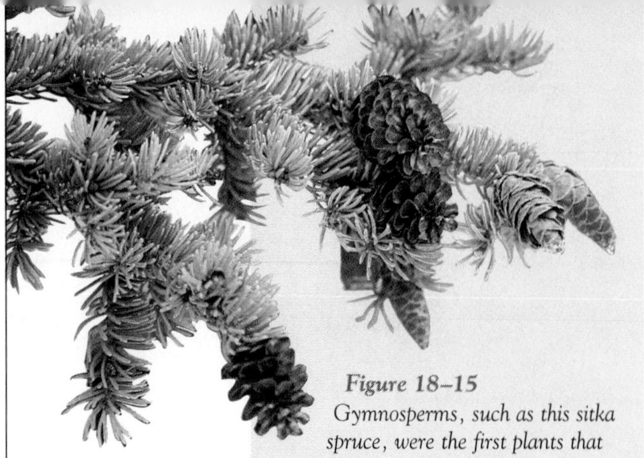

Figure 18–15
Gymnosperms, such as this sitka spruce, were the first plants that did not require standing water in order to reproduce.

stems, and leaves. Ferns and club mosses grew into dense forests that covered huge areas during the Devonian and Carboniferous periods. Some of them grew as much as 30 to 40 meters tall! The partially decomposed and compressed remains of these dense forests formed the great coal deposits that gave the Carboniferous Period its name.

INTEGRATING EARTH SCIENCE
How is coal formed from ferns and other plants? Research the topic and write a brief summary.

Today, most ferns that live in areas with changing seasons die back to the ground each year. In tropical rain forests, some ferns grow into tall, graceful trees. Some ferns can survive long droughts as adult plants. Yet because all ferns have life cycles that require wet conditions, they are rare or absent in many dry terrestrial habitats.

☑ ***Checkpoint*** What is vascular tissue? 1

Gymnosperms

The next major adaptation to terrestrial life was the evolution of a life cycle that freed plants from the need for standing water in order to reproduce. The first seed-bearing tracheophytes that evolved were the **gymnosperms,** which include cycads, ginkgoes, and conifers. Gymnosperms carry their seeds exposed to the air, usually in a cone-shaped structure. A **seed** is a reproductive structure that includes a developing plant and a food reserve enclosed in a resistant outer covering.

Many gymnosperms appeared in the fossil record about 360 to 408 million years ago, during the Devonian Period, when mosses and ferns were prevalent. Millions of years later, continental drift and climate change caused many terrestrial environments to become much drier. That gave gymnosperms an advantage over earlier plants, and by the time dinosaurs walked the Earth, forests were filled with gymnosperms. The Petrified Forest in Arizona contains the fossilized trunks of ancient conifers that were not very different from their modern descendants.

Today, the most common gymnosperms are the conifers, known for their distinctive cones and needlelike leaves. The cones produce and carry seeds. Although conifers are often called evergreens, their leaves don't last forever. The leaves—which normally remain on the plants for 2 to 14 years—exhibit several adaptations that help these plants survive the cold, dark winters and short growing seasons of the northern regions where many conifers live.

☑ ***Checkpoint*** What are gymnosperms? 2

Angiosperms

Angiosperms are the plants whose beautiful flowers are enjoyed as gifts and decorations in all cultures throughout the world. But more importantly, angiosperms are food sources for humans and other animals. These fully terrestrial plants are latecomers to the history of life. Their first fossils didn't appear in the fossil record until about 65 to 144 million years ago, during the Cretaceous Period. But once they appeared, angiosperms rapidly evolved and spread over the Earth.

TEACHER SUPPORT

Ecology Note

A broad band of coniferous forest covers much of northern Eurasia and North America. About 90 million acres in the United States—mostly in the western states and Alaska—are designated National Forest lands. Some of these forested areas are set aside as wilderness, but most are managed by the U.S. Forest Service for multiple uses, including lumbering.

Coniferous forests provide much of our lumber and are also harvested for wood pulp to make paper. By the year 2000, the demand for forest products in the United States is expected to be double what it was in the 1970s. The demand is so great that hundreds of thousands of acres of coniferous forests are cut each year. Some areas are replanted, but the rate of cutting far exceeds the rate of regrowth. Debate continues between those who depend on the commercial use of timber and those who fear that we are doing irreparable damage to our forests.

DIFFERENCES AMONG MONOCOTS AND DICOTS

Structure	Monocots	Dicots
Seeds	One cotyledon 	Two cotyledons 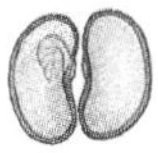
Flowers	Flower parts in threes or multiples of three 	Flower parts in fours or fives or multiples of four or five 
Leaves	Veins in leaves are parallel to each other 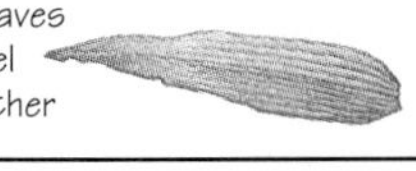	Veins in leaves form a branching network 
Stems	Vascular bundles scattered throughout the stem 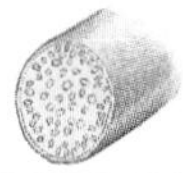	Vascular bundles arranged in a ring around the stem 

Figure 18–16
The distinguishing traits of monocots and dicots are illustrated in this chart. Notice the differences among the seeds, flowers, leaves, and stems.

The key to their success involved the evolution of flowers and seeds. Both adaptations enabled angiosperms to reproduce and grow to maturity more quickly than gymnosperms. Once dinosaurs, insects, and mammals appeared and began eating plants, this rapid reproduction may have been a selective advantage.

Angiosperms are divided into two main groups—the **monocots** and **dicots.** Within the seeds of angiosperms are structures that contain food for the developing plant. These structures are called cotyledons (kaht-uh-LEED-'nz). Monocots—such as rice, wheat, corn, lilies, orchids, tulips, and palms—have one cotyledon. Dicots—such as tomatoes, roses, maples, and the daisylike plants, including sunflowers—have two cotyledons. Both groups evolved an astonishing variety of sizes, leaf shapes, and flower patterns, as shown in ***Figure 18–16.***

Checkpoint What are angiosperms? 3

Adapting to Land

Some of the structures that have allowed plants to thrive on land include roots, leaves, vascular tissue, and stems. Let's take a look at these structures and their functions.

Roots

Roots anchor plants in place in the soil and keep them from being blown away by strong winds. They also absorb water and dissolved inorganic nutrients from the soil. Roots can perform both these tasks because they branch as they grow into the soil, making a dense network.

Leaves

Leaves provide the surface area over which the plant can capture sunlight for photosynthesis. The broader and flatter a leaf is, the more sunlight it can capture. But there's a tough functional tradeoff here. The greater the leaf area, the more tissue surface that is exposed to dry air, and the more water the plant

Figure 18–17
Angiosperms, which are the flowering plants, are the most complex and advanced tracheophytes. Angiosperms are characterized by their flowers, as shown by this cherry tree in full bloom.

Discussion

Students may think that the distinction between monocots and dicots is of little practical use in everyday life. Point out that this distinction accounts for the effectiveness of lawn herbicides that kill weeds without harming the grass. Explain that most lawn weeds are dicots with broad leaves, whereas grass plants are monocots with narrow leaves. Because of this and other differences between monocots and dicots, herbicides can be specifically formulated to kill only the unwanted weeds and not the grass.

Investigate

Research Have students do research to find out where photosynthesis occurs in a leaf. (Most occurs in the palisade tissue, near the leaf's surface but below the epidermis, the thin outer layer.) Ask students to explain why the photosynthetic layer is located near but not on the leaf's surface. (It must be exposed to light but also protected against water loss.)

Checkpoints

1 A tissue that transports water and nutrients throughout a plant.

2 Plants that carry their seeds exposed to the air, usually in a cone-shaped structure.

3 Plants that produce flowers as reproductive structures.

TEACHER SUPPORT

Activity

CLASSIFYING MONOCOTS AND DICOTS
Provide hand lenses and the following in numbered plastic bags. Bag 1, corn kernels; 2, bean seeds; 3, several acorns; 4, a tulip; 5, an oak leaf; 6, a bean leaf; 7, a tulip leaf; 8, a corn leaf; 9, a section of bean stem; 10, a section of corn stem; 11, a section of tulip stem; and 12, a section of a small oak branch.

Have students work in small groups to classify each specimen as a monocot or a dicot. (Monocots: bags 1, 4, 7, 8, 10, 11. Dicots: bags 2, 3, 5, 6, 9, 12.) Also encourage students to try to determine which bags contain specimens from the same plant. (Corn: bags 1, 8, 10. Bean: bags 2, 6, 9. Oak: bags 3, 5, 12. Tulip: bags 4, 7, 11.)

Ancillary Support

The resources below can be used to support your teaching strategy for these two pages.

BL Inquiry Activity: The Seeds of Life
TB Differences Among Monocots and Dicots, #24

Laboratory Investigation

The Laboratory Investigation, Vascular Plant Tissues, on pages 436–437 is appropriate to use at this point in the chapter.

Investigate

Long-Term Project Direct students' attention to the bryophyte terrarium that you or volunteers set up earlier (Investigate, page 427). Ask students whether they have observed any sporophytes on the moss plants and, if so, to describe the structures. If ferns were included in the terrarium, also ask students to describe any spores they may have observed.

Discussion

Have students examine a ripe, unhusked ear of fresh corn. Ask what they think the strands of cornsilk might be, and accept all responses. Tell students to peel off the husks to expose the cob, leaving the cornsilk still attached, and notice that each cornsilk strand is attached to a different kernel. Again ask what the strands might be. If students are still unsure, tell them that the strands are pollen tubes. As explained on page 431 of the student text, each tube grew from a pollen grain in the corn plant's flowers down to an egg in the undeveloped cob. Once an egg was fertilized, it developed into a complete, ripe kernel.

Investigate

Cooperative Learning Have students review their definitions of plant (Explore, page 426) and revise them as needed based on what they have learned in this section. Follow up with a class discussion in which students present their revised definitions. Guide students to agree on one accurate, complete definition, stated in their own words. To resolve any disagreements about the definition, have students consult the student text.

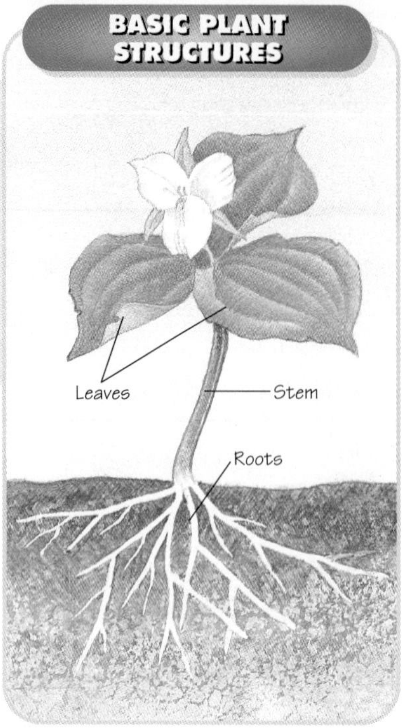

Figure 18–18 *All multicellular green plants, including this trillium, have the same basic structures—leaves, stems, and roots.*

can lose by evaporation. For that reason, the leaves of most land plants are covered with a waxy, waterproof covering called a cuticle.

On the other hand, a totally waterproof barrier presents another problem. Leaves must exchange oxygen and carbon dioxide with the air around them in order to carry out photosynthesis and respiration. A barrier that is waterproof usually doesn't let gases in and out either. That's why cuticles are dotted with tiny openings called **stomata** (singular: stoma) that can open and close as needed to allow for gas exchange and to prevent the loss of too much water.

☑ ***Checkpoint*** What is a cuticle? ①

Vascular Tissues

As plants evolved from the size of mosses to large sunflowers and maple trees, they faced a serious challenge. They had to transport water efficiently from roots to leaves, while moving the products of photosynthesis from leaves to other parts of the plant. The solution was the evolution of two types of specialized vascular tissue, called **xylem** (ZIGH-luhm) and **phloem** (FLOH-ehm).

Xylem carries water and dissolved inorganic nutrients from roots to branches and leaves. Cellulose-reinforced cell walls of xylem tissue are thick and strong, so they are also a major source of strength in woody plants such as trees.

Phloem carries the products of photosynthesis and certain other substances from one part of a plant to another. Depending on the time of day, season, and condition of the plant, phloem may transport these substances upward or downward.

☑ ***Checkpoint*** What are two types of vascular tissue? ②

Stems

Stems hold leaves up to the sun and position leaf surfaces to capture as much light as possible. Stems also conduct water, nutrients, products of photosynthesis, and other materials through the plant by means of their vascular tissues.

How Do Plants Reproduce?

Many changes in plants over time have been adaptations to drier habitats, and life cycles are no exception. **All plant life cycles involve alternation of generations between sporophyte and gametophyte.** But in different plants, the relationship between gametophyte and sporophyte changes. In mosses, the gametophyte is the longest part of the cycle. In flowering plants, the sporophyte part of the cycle is much longer.

Gametes and Spores

What you recognize as moss is the gametophyte generation of the moss life

TEACHER SUPPORT

Activity

CALCULATING WATER LOSS

Students can calculate the daily volume of water lost by a leaf per cm² of surface area.

1. On centimeter graph paper, trace around one average-size leaf on a twig. Count the squares inside the outline. Multiply that count by 2 to determine the total area of the leaf's upper and lower surfaces.

2. Fill a graduated cylinder with water to the 150-mL mark. Add a thin layer of cooking oil. Put the twig in the cylinder so the cut end is in the water. Place the cylinder in a sunny location for as many days as needed for the water level to decrease. Note the new water level.

3. Calculate the amount of water lost.

4. Divide the water loss (step 3) by the number of leaves on the twig.

5. Divide the water loss per leaf (step 4) by the number of days that elapsed.

6. Divide the daily per-leaf water loss (step 5) by the average leaf's total surface area (step 1).

cycle. These gametophytes are either male or female and produce either sperm or eggs. For reproduction to be successful, the plants must be close enough to water so that the sperm can swim to fertilize an egg. The zygote produced by fertilization grows into the sporophyte, a slender stalk with a spore capsule on the end. Inside this capsule, meiosis produces spores. The spores are dispersed and produce gametophyte plants.

Ferns show a slightly different pattern. The gametophytes produce sperm and eggs. Water must be present so the sperm can swim to the eggs for fertilization. But in this case, the zygote grows into an independent sporophyte that is much larger than the gametophyte and can live on its own for years. This sporophyte is what you recognize as a fern. The fern sporophyte produces spores, usually in clusters on the undersides of its leaves.

Pollen and Seeds

Seed plants have gone still further in freeing themselves from the need for water. The plants you see are all members of the dominant sporophyte generation of seed plant life cycles. Where are the gametophytes? They have been reduced to small clusters of a few cells that grow inside structures called cones in gymnosperms and flowers in angiosperms.

The entire male gametophyte is contained in a tiny structure called a pollen grain. A pollen grain produces sperm that do not have to swim because the pollen is carried to the eggs by wind, insects, beetles, birds, or bats. This process is called **pollination.** Once the pollen lands on the female part, a long tube containing the sperm begins to grow down inside the flower until it reaches the egg.

After fertilization, the egg grows into a tiny plant called an embryo, which grows for a short time before becoming dormant inside the seed. The seed itself is supplied with food and a tough outer covering. Protected this way, the seeds of many flowering plants can survive heat, drought, and bitter cold—sometimes for years—before germinating when conditions are right. This adaptability allows angiosperms to grow in many habitats where mosses and ferns cannot.

Figure 18–19
CAREER TRACK
Nursery operation technicians work in greenhouses, garden centers, or botanical gardens. They are responsible for the care and maintenance of plants. In this photograph, a nursery operation technician is growing rare wildflowers.

Section Review 18–3

1. **Classify** plants into two major groups.
2. **Describe** the structures that enabled plants to live on land.
3. **Explain** how plants reproduce.
4. **Critical Thinking—Applying Concepts** Why are tracheophytes able to grow larger than bryophytes?

4 ASSESS

Quick Check

Have each student sketch a typical plant and label its three basic structures, and then write a brief description of each structure's function.

Section Review 18–3

1. The two major groups of plants are bryophytes and tracheophytes.

2. Roots: to anchor plants in soil and absorb water and nutrients. Leaves: covered with a cuticle to reduce water loss and containing stomata for gas exchange. Vascular tissues (xylem and phloem): to transport water, nutrients, and products of photosynthesis. Stems: to position leaves in sunlight for photosynthesis.

3. Students' answers should summarize the information presented in the student text, focusing on the alternation of generations between sporophyte and gametophyte.

4. Tracheophytes have vascular tissue that transports water, nutrients, products of photosynthesis, and other substances up and down their stems and branches.

Checkpoints

1 A waxy, waterproof covering on the leaves of most land plants.

2 Xylem and phloem.

Learning Modality

Visual Learning Have each pair of students create a table summarizing the major characteristics of and differences between bryophytes, ferns, gymnosperms, and angiosperms. Encourage students to work from memory as much as possible, but let them check their tables against the student text for accuracy and completeness.

Ancillary Support

The resources below can be used to support your teaching strategy for these two pages.

TR Writing in Biology: Making Myths
Apply: What a Re-leaf

Section 18-4

The Coevolution of Plants and Animals

Performance Objective
• Explain the meaning of the term coevolution.

Mini Lab Skill: Experimenting

1 ENGAGE

Inquiry Activity
Observing

Observing Insect Pollinators
Ask students what types of insects obtain food from flowers; accept all responses without comment. Then take the class outdoors to observe flowering plants being visited by insects. (Note: You do not have to use decorative plants with showy flowers. Students could observe crops such as corn and alfalfa or even common weeds such as dandelions, clover, and goldenrod.) Have each group select one plant or a small group of plants to observe for a period of time. Ask students to list all the different types of insects they see visiting the flowers. In a follow-up class discussion, have students compare these lists with their original ideas.

2 EXPLORE

Investigate
Research Provide a variety of flowers heavy with pollen and flowers that have gone to seed. (You may want to ask volunteers to collect the flowers.) Have students gently tap each flower over a sheet of paper (black paper for pollen, white paper for seeds) and examine the pollen grains and seeds with a hand lens. Discuss the characteristics of the pollen grains and seeds. (**CAUTION:** *Make sure students who are allergic to pollen examine seeds only.*)

18–4 The Coevolution of Plants and Animals

GUIDE FOR READING

- Define coevolution.

MINI LAB

- **Design an experiment** to see how maple seeds are adapted for dispersal.

NO QUESTION ABOUT IT—*spring is one of the most wonderful times of the year. From Florida to Washington and from California to Maine, the sight and fragrance of flowers in bloom are sources of delight. But flowers are only part of the story of springtime. Sit quietly for a few minutes near an apple tree in bloom or by a lawn where yellow daisies have poked their way into the sunlight. You'll notice that a lot of work is going on. Bees are drifting among the trees, and hummingbirds may be winging their way from flower to flower. What are they doing? And why are they attracted to the flowers?*

Pollination

The answers to these questions may explain why angiosperms have been so successful. In order to carry out two of the most important steps in their life cycle—pollination and seed dispersal—many angiosperms rely on the help of animals.

Why is pollination so important to plants? It is usually best for a species if sexual reproduction occurs between different individuals. Insects and other pollinators help plants reproduce sexually with other plants of the same species. Pollination, therefore, helps to maintain genetic diversity—the variety of different genes present in a population.

Pollination by Wind

Gymnosperms rely on the wind to carry pollen from male to female flowers. Pollen grains are small and light, and they can be scattered for many kilometers in a strong breeze. Gymnosperms

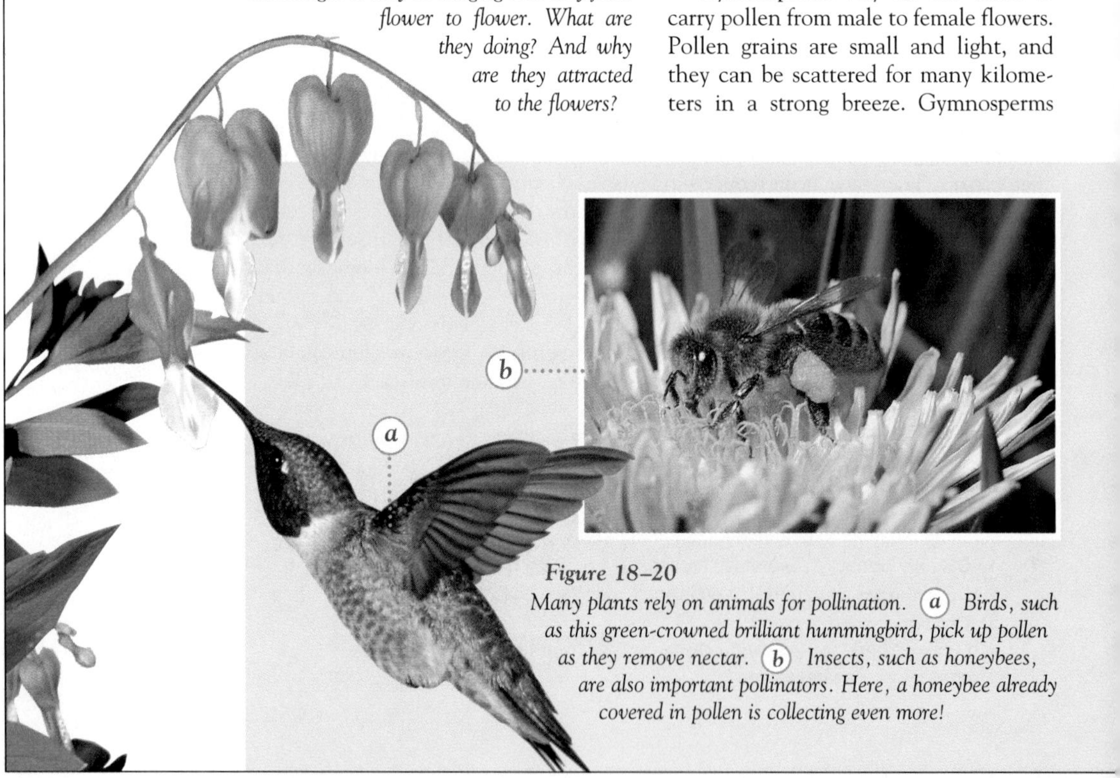

Figure 18–20
Many plants rely on animals for pollination. (a) Birds, such as this green-crowned brilliant hummingbird, pick up pollen as they remove nectar. (b) Insects, such as honeybees, are also important pollinators. Here, a honeybee already covered in pollen is collecting even more!

TEACHER SUPPORT

Activity

WHAT ATTRACTS INSECTS TO FLOWERS?
In the following activity, students test the role of color, honey guides, and nectar in attracting insects to flowers.

1. Cut five flower shapes from stiff white paper.
2. Add color, honey guides, and a central glob of honey to some flowers, as listed below. (Tell students that honey guides are lines that radiate outward from a flower's center.)
1: pink flower, red honey guides, honey
2: pink flower, red honey guides, no honey
3: pink flower, no honey guides, no honey
4: white flower, no honey guides, honey
5: white flower, black honey guides, no honey
3. Put all five flowers in the same location outdoors. Count the number of insects that land on each one.
4. Which factor—color, honey guides, or nectar—seems to be most important in attracting insects to flowers?

must produce and release enormous amounts of pollen to make sure that this hit-or-miss strategy works. You may have seen entire lakes and ponds covered with bright-yellow dust in the spring and early summer. This dust is actually pollen from pines and other conifers.

Pollination by Insects

Many angiosperms, on the other hand, are pollinated by insects that visit one flower after another. Bees, for example, will visit flowers that produce sweet secretions called nectar. As a bee feeds on the nectar, pollen is dusted onto its body. When the bee leaves one flower, it will carry that pollen directly to another nectar-containing flower, transferring the pollen as it moves. How does the bee find flowers with nectar? That's where the scent and color of the flower come in. They serve as signals that help bees find a particular kind of flower.

The spread of pollen from one plant to another by an animal is called **vector pollination.** Vector pollination is much more efficient than pollination by the wind because the insect or other animal takes the pollen directly from one flower to the next. This relationship, called **coevolution,** is beneficial to both organisms. **Coevolution is the evolution of structures and behaviors in two different organisms in response to changes in each organism over time.** Natural selection has favored flower structures and markings that are bright and colorful, making it easier for the bees to locate those flowers. Flowers that are pollinated by night-flying moths are often white and have a strong fragrance that attracts insects that hunt using their sense of smell.

☑ **Checkpoint** What is coevolution? 1

Pollination by Birds and Mammals

Bees and other insects are not the only animals involved in pollination. Many birds, especially hummingbirds, sip liquid nectar from deep within flowers. As they visit one flower after another, they spread pollen from one to another. Other birds that pollinate flowers include the honeycreepers of Hawaii and the brush-tongued parrots of Australia.

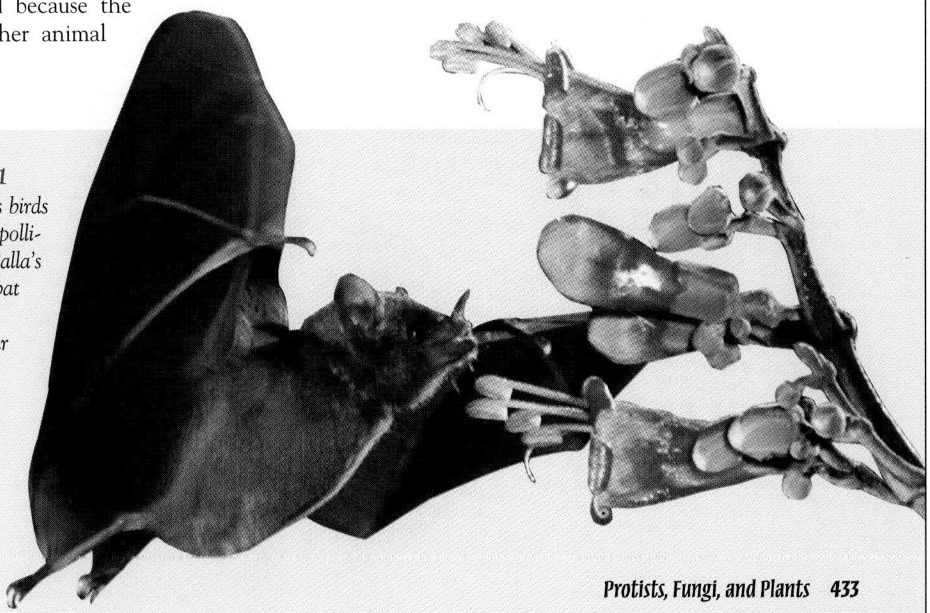

Figure 18–21
Bats as well as birds are important pollinators. This Palla's long-tongued bat feeds off some tropical tubular flowers.

3 TEACH

Discussion

Students may be unfamiliar with the word vector in the term vector pollination. Explain (or ask students to use a dictionary to determine) that a vector is an organism that carries something from one organism to another. Harmful vectors carry diseases. For example, some mosquitoes transmit malaria and equine encephalitis. Insects and other animals that carry pollen from one plant to another are helpful vectors.

☑ Checkpoint

1 The evolution of structures and behaviors in two different organisms in response to changes in each organism over time.

Technology

BioVue
Mini Doc: Pollination and Coevolution
Videodisc Side 5

Go to Chapter 10

TEACHER SUPPORT

Managing Classroom Diversity

TECH PREP STUDENTS

Students who are considering careers in agriculture-related businesses might like to find out about beekeeping and apiculture management. Apiculturists work in a variety of settings, including state and county agricultural agencies and private businesses. Beekeepers derive income from the sale of queen bees, packaged bees, honey, and other bee products.

The rental of bee colonies to crop-growers is also a large and profitable industry. Managing a successful bee-rental company requires not only knowledge of bee behavior, needs, and diseases but also understanding of sound business practices—contractual requirements, accounting, and price-estimating.

A good source of information is *Beekeeping in the United States* (U.S. Department of Agriculture, Agricultural Handbook No. 335).

Ancillary Support

The resources below can be used to support your teaching strategy for these two pages.

TR Enrich: Abuzz With Orchids
BL Inquiry Activity: Which Came First?

MINI LAB Experimenting

Teacher Notes

- For time required and materials needed, see page 414b.
- Students' examination of the maple fruit should lead them to hypothesize that the fruit is adapted for dispersal by wind rather than by clinging to or being eaten by animals. Their experimental designs should be based on this hypothesis.

Answers to Analyze and Conclude

1. They are dispersed by wind.
2. The two lightweight "wings" on either side of the heavier seed function like helicopter blades to carry the fruit away from the tree. Students can determine this by dropping the fruit from a height.

Skills Trace
Experimenting
Focus p. 434
Practice p. 435
Assess p. 441

Discussion

Ask students to describe the characteristics of the seeds they examined in the Explore activity, page 432. Which seeds had winglike structures or were lightweight and feathery for dispersal by wind? Which had hooks, barbs, or other structures that would cause them to cling to animals' fur or people's clothing? Take the class on a walk through a field or vacant lot where plants are going to seed, and have them examine their clothing afterward for clinging seeds.

MINI LAB ····· Experimenting ·····

Traveling Seeds

PROBLEM *How is a maple fruit adapted for seed dispersal? **Design an experiment** to find out.*

PROCEDURE

1. Obtain three to four maple fruits.
2. Carefully observe a seed and note its characteristics.
3. Formulate a hypothesis to explain how the fruit is adapted for seed dispersal.
4. Design an experiment to test your hypothesis.

ANALYZE AND CONCLUDE

1. By which method of seed dispersal do you think maple fruits are dispersed?
2. Which characteristics of the maple fruit help in the dispersal of the seed? How do you know?

A few flowers are pollinated by small pollen-eating bats. The poor vision of bats requires that these flowers be strongly scented to attract the animals, which come out only at night. Flower-feeding bats may lack teeth and have long brushlike tongues that quickly gather nectar and pollen. Bananas, as well as the saguaro cactus of Arizona, are pollinated by bats.

☑ ***Checkpoint*** What are four ways in which pollen is spread from flower to flower? (1)

Seed Dispersal

Pollination is only one part of the reproductive battle for plants. Once the seeds are fertilized and ready to sprout, it is a great advantage for them to travel some distance from the parent plant before germinating. What is the advantage of seeds traveling? If all the seeds landed at the foot of their parent plants, they would all be competing with their relatives for water, nutrients, and sunlight! Seed dispersal makes it possible for a species to move into new environments where conditions may be more favorable.

Dispersal by Wind

Many angiosperm seeds are dispersed by the wind. Some of these seeds are encased in a winglike structure that helps them to glide or spin as they fall to the Earth. Others, such as milkweed and dandelions, are lightweight and have feathery attachments that allow them to float and drift on the slightest breeze.

Figure 18–22
The fruits of this red maple have winglike structures that help in the dispersal of the fruits by wind.

TEACHER SUPPORT

Background Information

Many species of grass have other kinds of organisms living inside them. Biologists believe that some of these symbiotic relationships are examples of coevolution.

One example is tall fescue, a widely grown pasture grass in the central and eastern United States. Many of the qualities that make tall fescue highly desirable for farmers and park groundskeepers can be attributed to a fungus that lives inside the plant. The identical grass without fungus infection is not as resistant to drought or pests and cannot grow in as many soil conditions.

The fungus also helps the plant by making it unpalatable to grazing animals. It also creates a toxicity that causes declining health in livestock. While the relationship between the fungus and the grass has evolved to their mutual benefit, it adds up to a billion-dollar problem for the U.S. livestock industry.

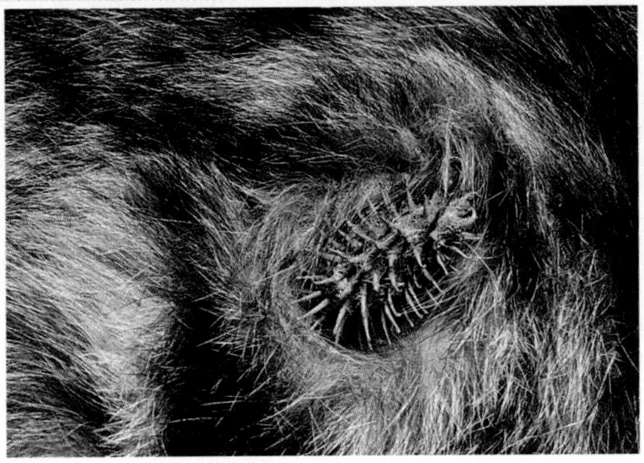

Figure 18–23
Some plants rely on animals for seed dispersal. Notice the small hooks on this cocklebur, which keep it securely attached to a cat's fur.

Dispersal by Animals

Many angiosperms have coevolved with animals in ways that help to spread their seeds. For example, some fruits have tiny hooks or barbs that enable them to catch a ride on the fur of a passing animal. By the time the seeds are finally removed, the animal may have carried them for many kilometers, giving them a free ride to a new location.

Other plants have evolved a very different strategy. Have you ever wondered why plants produce such brightly colored, sweet-tasting nutritious fruits? It is because those fruits attract a wide range of animals—from birds to monkeys—that eat them. The seeds inside these fruits are usually very strong and tough. For that reason, some of them survive being chewed and passed through the animals' digestive tract. As the animal walks or flies or grazes, the seeds may be carried great distances. They may then be deposited far from the parent plant, right in the middle of a handy batch of natural fertilizer!

Figure 18–24
To spread their seeds, plants have enlisted the help of animals. The bright-red color of these berries, along with their sweet taste, will attract animals, such as this cedar waxwing, that eat the berries and then deposit the seeds some distance from the parent plant.

Section Review 18–4

1. **Define** coevolution.
2. **MINI LAB** How would you **design an experiment** to find out how maple seeds are adapted for seed dispersal?
3. **BRANCHING OUT ACTIVITY** Farmers sometimes rely on wind pollination for their corn crops. Find out how farmers plant their crops to take full advantage of wind pollination. **Summarize** your findings in a brief report.

4 ASSESS

Quick Check

Have each student list the methods of pollination and seed dispersal described in the text and give an example of each.

Section Review 18-4

1. The evolution of structures and behaviors in two different organisms in response to changes in each organism over time.

2. Answers should describe methods for testing dispersal by wind.

Skills Trace
Experimenting
- Focus p. 434
- Practice p. 435
- Assess p. 441

3. Students' reports will probably mention locating large numbers of plants in close proximity to allow effective pollination by wind.

Learning Modality

Visual Learning As students study this section, have them draw a concept map of the pollination and seed-dispersal methods described.

Checkpoint

1 By wind, insects, birds, and mammals.

TEACHER SUPPORT

Background Information

As students may realize from their own experience, many unripe fruits are green and have a bitter taste. These characteristics serve an evolutionary purpose in seed dispersal: unripe fruits contain immature seeds that are not capable of sprouting and growing.

The green color of unripe fruits makes them more difficult to see among a plant's leaves. In addition, plants produce bitter-tasting chemical compounds that are incorporated into the developing fruits. These characteristics help to discourage and prevent animals from eating the unripe fruits.

As the seeds mature, the bitter-tasting chemical compounds break down, and the fruits become laden with sugars. While this process occurs, the fruits also change color from green to red, orange, black, or whatever indicates ripeness in that species. These colors are more easily seen by animals, and the fruits' sweet taste reinforces the eating response.

Chapter 18

Laboratory Investigation

Vascular Plant Tissues

Before the Lab

1. Obtain enough fresh celery to provide one leafy stalk for each group of students.
2. If you do not have enough microscopes to provide one for every group, set up as many as you can in learning stations, and let groups take turns using them.

Pre-Lab Discussion

Have students read the entire procedure for this investigation. Then ask students the following questions.

What is the purpose of this investigation? (To determine the role of the vascular system in a plant.)

Why do you think you have to cut off a little of the base before you put the stalk in the solution? (To expose fresh material. The base may have dried out somewhat after the celery was picked.)

Why is blue food coloring added to the water? (To color the xylem tubes so they show up clearly.)

Skills Development

Students will use these skills while completing the laboratory investigation: making predictions, interpreting data, and applying concepts.

Teaching Strategies

1. Help any students who have difficulty slicing their sections of the celery, positioning the slice properly under the microscope, and focusing the lens so the slice can be seen clearly.
2. Make sure students understand what they are to look for when they view the celery slice with the microscope: blue dots indicating cross sections of the xylem tubes.

Laboratory Investigation

Vascular Plant Tissues

The vascular system is the system of tubes that carries water and minerals throughout a plant. The vascular system is made up of two types of tissues—xylem and phloem. In this investigation, you will discover the role of the xylem and phloem.

Problem

Can you **predict** the role of a vascular system in a plant?

Materials (per group)

celery stalk
blue food coloring
metric ruler
clear plastic container
scalpel
microscope

Procedure

1. **Fill the plastic container halfway with water. Add several drops of blue food coloring to make the solution a deep shade of blue.**
2. **Using the scalpel, cut off about 1 cm of the base of the celery stalk. CAUTION: *Be careful when using a scalpel—it is very sharp.***

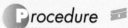

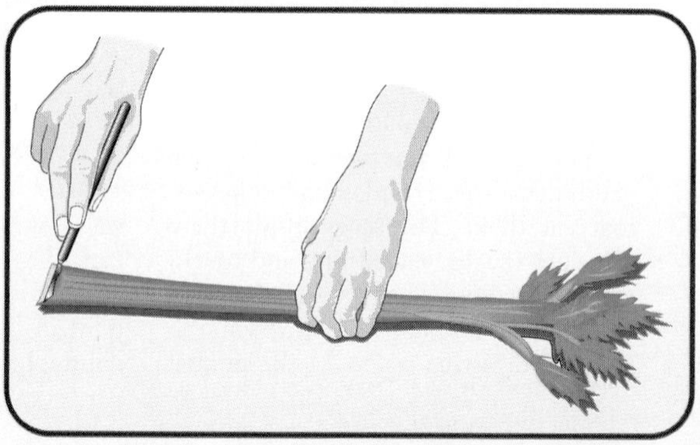

3. **Place the celery into the food-coloring solution, being sure the freshly cut base is in the solution.**
4. **Construct a data table similar to the one shown.**

DATA TABLE

Time	*Height (in millimeters)*
5 minutes	
10 minutes	
15 minutes	
20 minutes	
24 hours	

Safety Tip

Remind students to use extreme caution when using or carrying the scalpels to avoid cuts. Have students notify you immediately of any injury.

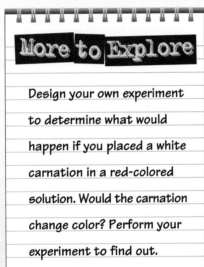

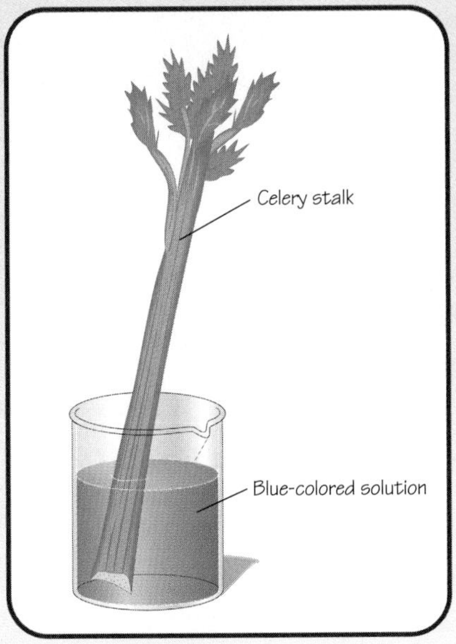

5. **After 5 minutes, measure the height in millimeters of the food coloring in the celery. Record your measurement.**
6. **Measure the height of the food coloring in the celery after 10, 15, and 20 minutes. Record each of your measurements.**
7. **What do you predict will happen to the food coloring in the celery after 24 hours? Write your prediction on a sheet of paper.**
8. **After 24 hours, measure the height of the food coloring in the celery.**
9. **Using the scalpel, cut off a thin slice about 2 to 3 mm from the base of the celery stalk. CAUTION:** ***Be careful when using a scalpel—it is very sharp.***
10. **Observe the cross section of the celery under a microscope. Identify the xylem and make an illustration of what you see.**

Observations

1. What happens to the food coloring in the celery stalk?
2. What tissue is responsible for transporting the food coloring?
3. Does the vascular system of the celery stalk extend throughout its entire length? How do you know?
4. Does the movement of the liquid occur quickly or slowly? Support your answer using your data.

Analysis and Conclusions

1. What was your prediction? Was it correct?
2. What adaptation to life on land does this activity illustrate?
3. Why is a plant's vascular system important?

More to Explore

Design your own experiment to determine what would happen if you placed a white carnation in a red-colored solution. Would the carnation change color? Perform your experiment to find out.

Answers to Observations

1. The coloring rises up the stalk and stains the vascular tissue (xylem).
2. Xylem. (If students mention phloem, refer them back to the descriptions of xylem and phloem on page 430, and emphasize that it is xylem, not phloem, that carries water upward from the roots to the rest of the plant.)
3. Yes. The entire stalk (and perhaps even the leaves) are tinted blue.
4. Accept either response. Compared with liquid's being sucked up a drinking straw, the movement is fairly slow.

Answers to Analysis and Conclusions

1. Students' precise predictions may vary, but all should realize that the coloring will continue to move up the stalk.
2. Vascular tissue; the ability to transport water efficiently from roots to leaves.
3. The vascular system transports materials upward and downward throughout the plant, thus enabling tracheophytes to grow larger than bryophytes can grow.

More to Explore

Students will undoubtedly think of using the same procedure with carnations that they used with the celery. Encourage students to try the procedure with other plants as well, to see if they absorb water and turn color as the celery and carnations did and, if so, whether the rate of color change is similar, faster, or slower.

Study Guide

Review Strategy

Divide the class into five groups. Have each group prepare a set of index cards listing the major characteristics (one per card) of one of the following kingdoms or phyla: algae, protozoans, fungi, bryophytes, tracheophytes. Tell students to write the name of the kingdom or phylum on the back of each card. Let students use the cards as study and self-check aids by shuffling them, sorting them into three kingdoms (protists, fungi, and plants), then sorting the protist cards into algae and protozoans and the plant cards into bryophytes and tracheophytes.

Study Guide

Summarizing Key Concepts

The key concepts in each section of this chapter are listed below to help you review the chapter content. Make sure you understand each concept and its relationship to other concepts and to the theme of this chapter.

18–1 Protists

- Protists are eukaryotic organisms that do not share a unique set of characteristics.
- Algae are photosynthetic autotrophs that look and act like plants in certain ways.
- All protozoans spend some of their lives as unicellular organisms. Some species, however, gather into groups at some time during their life cycles.
- Life cycles among protists are enormously varied.

18–2 Fungi

- Living fungi are divided into four phyla according to their life cycles—Zygomycota, Ascomycota, Basidiomycota, and Deuteromycota.
- Fungi can reproduce both sexually and asexually.

18–3 Multicellular Plants

- During their evolutionary history, plants had to adapt to a series of changes in order to survive in a dry, nonsupporting environment.
- Early on, ancestors of plants branched into two group—bryophytes and tracheophytes.
- All plant life cycles involve alternation of generations between sporophyte and gametophyte.

18–4 The Coevolution of Plants and Animals

- Coevolution is the evolution of structures and behaviors in two different organisms in response to changes in each organism over time.

Reviewing Key Terms

Review the following vocabulary terms and their meaning. Then use each term in a complete sentence.

18–1 Protists

protist
spore
symbiosis
alternation of generations

18–2 Fungi

chitin
mycelium
hypha

18–3 Multicellular Plants

vascular tissue
angiosperm
gymnosperm
monocot
seed
dicot
root
phloem
leaf
stem
stoma
pollination
xylem

18–4 The Coevolution of Plants and Animals

vector pollination
coevolution

Inquiry-Based Strategy

Remind students of the activity in which they tried to classify the life forms produced by unidentified materials as plant, animal, or "other" (Chapter Discovery Learning Activity, page 414). Tell students that each group is to devise a similar problem for another group to solve. The other group will have to differentiate among three unknown materials based on the kingdom or phylum characteristics presented in this chapter. For example, they could use fern spores, mushroom spores, and similar-looking seeds. Explain that one of the three materials could be a nonliving material. Also emphasize that all three materials must be absolutely safe to handle and investigate.

Monitor each group's experimental design to make sure the materials are safe and that students have considered the ways in which the three materials could be tested to reveal their scientific classification. Let students exchange their mystery materials, perform their tests, and report their findings.

CHAPTER 18

Recalling Main Ideas

Choose the letter of the answer that best completes the statement or answers the question.

1. To which kingdom do algae belong?
   a. protist **c.** plant
   b. fungi **d.** animal

2. The process of alternation of generations first appeared in
   a. algae. **c.** plants.
   b. protozoans. **d.** fungi.

3. Yeast is an example of a
   a. protist. **c.** fungus.
   b. plant. **d.** bryophyte.

4. In which structure can cells have a single nucleus, two nuclei, or many nuclei?
   a. mycelium **c.** hypha
   b. chitin **d.** phloem

5. An example of vascular tissue is
   a. xylem. **c.** stoma.
   b. cuticle. **d.** hypha.

6. Which of the following groups of plants lack vascular tissue?
   a. bryophytes **c.** tracheophytes
   b. monocots **d.** dicots

7. The waxy, waterproof covering of plants is a
   a. stoma. **c.** seed.
   b. cuticle. **d.** mycelium.

8. The evolution of structures and behaviors in different organisms in response to evolutionary changes in the other is called
   a. symbiosis. **c.** coevolution.
   b. pollination. **d.** vector pollination.

Putting It All Together

Using the information on pages xxx to xxxi, complete the following concept map.

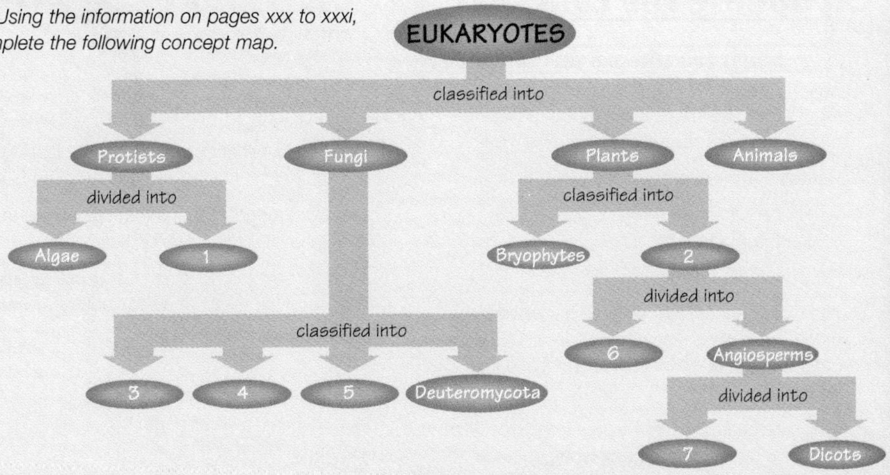

Putting It All Together

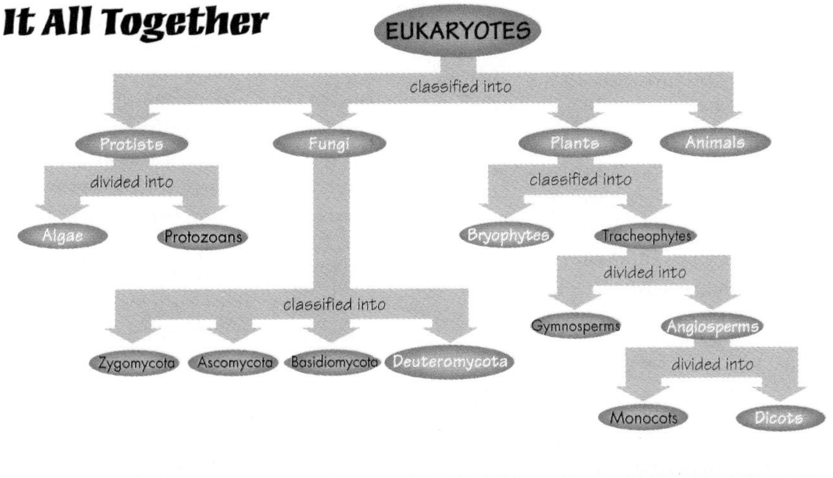

Recalling Main Ideas

1. a	5. a
2. a	6. a
3. c	7. b
4. c	8. c

Assessment

Reviewing What You Learned

1. All are eukaryotes.
2. A close relationship between two species.
3. The process of one species giving rise to many new species in a short period of time.
4. Algae.
5. Chitin.
6. Threadlike filaments that grow down into whatever the fungus is feeding on.
7. Zygomycota, Ascomycota, Basidiomycota, and Deuteromycota.
8. Mushrooms: Basidiomycota. Bread mold: Zygomycota.
9. All are called "imperfect" fungi because researchers have never been able to identify their sexual stages.
10. All plants are multicellular, photosynthetic eukaryotes whose cells are enclosed and supported by cell walls made of cellulose.
11. Mosses need water for sexual reproduction—to allow the sperm to swim to fertilize an egg.
12. They lack vascular tissue.
13. Tissue that transports water, dissolved inorganic nutrients, products of photosynthesis, and other substances from one part of a plant to another.
14. Ferns have vascular tissue, roots, strong stems, and leaves.
15. See Figure 18–16, page 429.

Expanding the Concepts

1. Sexual reproduction increases genetic variation, which provides more raw material for natural selection to operate. This promotes adaptive radiation.
2. Algae are photosynthetic autotrophs that look and act like plants in certain ways. Protozoans are heterotrophs; most are active and move around a great deal.
3. They reproduce only asexually.

4. Spores are haploid cells that grow into haploid male and female gametophytes. Gametophytes produce gametes—eggs and sperm that fuse to produce diploid cells (zygotes).

5. In alternation of generations, diploid and haploid cells switch back and forth. Diploid cells have the normal number of chromosomes for that species. Haploid cells have half the normal number of chromosomes. The diploid generation, or sporophyte, undergoes meiosis to produce haploid spores that grow into haploid male and female cells called gametophytes. Gametophytes produce eggs and sperm. When they fuse, they produce a diploid cell called a zygote, which grows into a sporophyte again.

6. Zygomycetes are often called bread mold. Ascomycetes, or sac fungi, include mildews, molds, yeasts, morels, and truffles. Basidiomycetes include the fungi whose fruiting bodies form mushrooms. Deuteromycetes, or "imperfect" fungi, include *Penicillium* and fungi that cause plant and animal diseases.

7. Fungi and some types of protists are heterotrophs. Fungi look like plants, and both have cell walls. All three are eukaryotes.

8. The first ancestors of plants started leaving traces in the fossil record about 450 million years ago. Algae and plants share many molecular similarities and cell structures, and their photosynthetic processes are similar.

9. Plants needed to develop ways to prevent water loss (protected leaves); rigid structures (stems) to support them; structures (roots) to anchor them in place and absorb water and nutrients from the soil; vascular tissue to transport materials throughout the plant; and methods of reproduction (including pollination) that did not require water to carry sperm to eggs.

10. Seeds contain food for the embryo inside and are protected against heat, drought, and cold by a tough outer covering. Thus seeds further freed plants from the need for water.

11. They evolved flowers and seeds that enable them to reproduce and grow to maturity more quickly than gymnosperms. Angiosperms do not rely exclusively on wind for pollination.

12. Roots anchor plants in the soil and absorb water and dissolved inorganic nutrients from it. Leaves provide the surface area over which the plant can capture sunlight for photosynthesis. Vascular tissues transport water and nutrients from roots to branches and leaves (xylem) and carry the products of photosynthesis and other substances from one part of a plant to another (phloem). Stems and other rigid structures hold the photosynthetic leaves up to the sun.

Extending Your Thinking

1. Students' answers should show evidence of an understanding of the importance of such interactions to the continuing existence of life on Earth.

2. Both bryophytes and angiosperms undergo alternation of generations. However, the gametophytes in angiosperms grow entirely inside flowers. Unlike bryophyte gametes, which need water for fertilization to occur, angiosperm pollen can be carried to the pistil by various agents, including wind, insects, and animals.

Assessment

Reviewing What You Learned

Answer each of the following in a complete sentence.

1. What is one characteristic that all protists share?
2. Define symbiosis.
3. What is adaptive radiation?
4. Which group of protists exhibits alternation of generations?
5. What substance makes up the cell walls of fungi?
6. What are hyphae?
7. List the four phyla of fungi.
8. To which phylum do mushrooms belong? Bread mold?
9. What characteristic do all species of the phylum Deuteromycota share?
10. What characteristics do all plants share?
11. Why do mosses need water?
12. Why have the bryophytes been limited in their evolutionary pathway?
13. What is vascular tissue?
14. What advantages do ferns have over mosses?
15. Compare a monocot and a dicot.

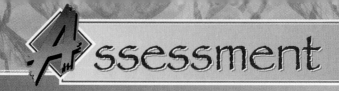

Expanding the Concepts

Discuss each of the following in a brief paragraph.

1. What effect did the development of sexual reproduction have on the evolution of organisms?
2. Compare algae and protozoans.
3. What characteristics make euglenophytes different from other protists?
4. How do spores differ from gametes?
5. Alternation of generations is a characteristic of the green algae known as *Ulva,* as well as of most mosses and ferns. Describe this unusual life cycle.
6. Fungi are characterized by their life cycles. List some examples of the major types of fungi.
7. How are fungi similar to protists? To plants?
8. What early evidence indicates that plants are probably most closely related to green algae?
9. Discuss four adaptations that plants had to make in order to survive on land.
10. Discuss how the development of seeds helped to extend the evolutionary advantages of plants.
11. What advantages do angiosperms have over gymnosperms?
12. List the four structures that allowed plants to thrive on land. Give the function of each structure.

Extending Your Thinking

Use the skills you have developed in this chapter to answer the following.

1. **Using the writing process** There are many exceptional "partnerships in nature." Write an essay that describes how the relationship between animals and plants is important to the overall existence of life on this planet.
2. **Comparing** Describe the similarities and differences between reproduction and development in bryophytes and angiosperms.
3. **Predicting** Why would you expect to find more fungi growing in a forest than in a field?
4. **Predicting** A conifer releases thousands of seeds. Each of these seeds has the potential to grow into a new conifer. Why do you think an organism such as a conifer produces so many seeds?
5. **Designing an experiment** You notice that the plants in the principal's office are dying even though they are being watered and are getting enough sunlight. Upon closer examination, you discover lots of dust on their leaves. Design an experiment to find out and explain what is happening to the plants.

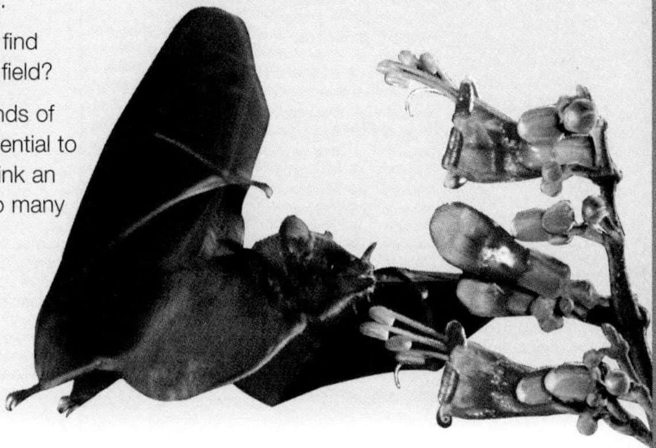

Applying Your Skills

Living Together

Use your knowledge of symbiotic relationships to create a new organism. Your new organism does not have to be real, but the two organisms that compose it should already exist. Your new organism will live in one of the following environments: on the top of a mountain above the tree line; in the deep trenches of the Pacific Ocean; in the back of a cave where no light can penetrate; or in an area that reaches −10°C in the winter and 40°C in the summer.

1. Design a new organism that is composed of two organisms—each from a different kingdom. Draw your new organism and label its parts.
2. Describe the adaptations this organism has made in order to survive in its environment.
3. What is the symbiotic relationship between the two organisms?

• GOING FURTHER •

4. What would happen to your new organism if its environment suddenly changed? What additional adaptations would your organism have to make?

5. Students may suggest an experiment in which a dusty plant and a clean plant are given the same amount of water and sunlight to determine the effects of the dust.

Skills Trace
Experimenting
Focus p. 434
Practice p. 435
Assess p. 441

Applying Your Skills

Teacher Notes

- Provide resource materials or access to a library so students can learn more about the specific conditions of the various suggested environments.
- Suggest that students make a table to compare the specific conditions of the environment they choose to the characteristics of the organisms they have studied.

Answers

Students' answers will vary but should show mastery of the concepts of symbiosis and adaptation.

Scoring Rubric

4 Response is thorough, accurate, and creative; shows an in-depth understanding of science skills, procedures, and concepts.

3 Response is complete, mostly accurate, and original; shows a satisfactory understanding of science skills, procedures, and concepts.

2 Response is mostly complete but includes some inaccuracies; shows an adequate understanding of science skills, procedures, and concepts.

1 Response is only partially complete and has many inaccuracies; shows an incomplete understanding of science skills, procedures, and concepts.

0 Response is mostly incomplete and/or inaccurate; shows a lack of understanding of science skills, procedures, and concepts.

3. Forests tend to be damper and shadier than fields, and these conditions are more supportive of fungal growth.

Skills Trace
Predicting
Focus p. 423
Practice p. 424
Assess p. 441

4. As gymnosperms, conifers rely on wind to carry pollen, which develops from spores, from one plant to another. This is a "hit-or-miss" procedure, with much of the pollen landing in places other than on female flowers. Thus, a great deal of pollen must be released to ensure that female flowers will be pollinated.

Chapter 19 Animals: Invertebrates

Content Management	Student Edition Activities
■ Section 19–1 Evolution of Multicellular Animals, pp. 443–445 The Earliest Known Animals Body Plans	
■ Section 19–2 A Survey of Living Invertebrates, pp. 446–451 Trends in Invertebrate Evolution; The Movement Onto Land; Sponges; Cnidarians; Platyhelminthes; Nematodes; Mollusks; Annelids; Echinoderms; Arthropods; Invertebrate Chordates	MINI LAB: Which End Is Up?, p. 449
■ Section 19–3 Form and Function in Invertebrates, pp. 452–459 Support and Movement; Feeding and Digestion; Internal Transport; Respiration; Excretion; Response; Reproduction	MINI LAB: To Catch a Worm, p. 456 **Laboratory Investigation:** Comparing Nervous Systems, pp. 462–463
◆ BRANCHING OUT • In Depth Section 19–4 Specialized Reproductive Cycles, pp. 460–461 Asexual Reproduction Hermaphrodites External and Internal Fertilization	

■ These sections cover all the necessary content and concepts for a basic course in biology.
◆ This section covers content and concepts that are either applications or extensions of the basic material.

Integration Strategies

SE Language Arts, p. 450

Assessment Strategies

SE Chapter Review, pp. 464–467
TR Section Reviews
Chapter Test
BL Chapter Review
Practice Test
CTB Chapter 19 Test

Tech Prep

Teaching strategies appropriate for students who are in technical/vocational programs or who are considering post-secondary technical education can be found on **TE** page 449.

Meeting the Standards

Sections 19–1 through 19–4 cover one of the six content standards under **The Cell,** all five of the content standards under **Biological Evolution,** one of the six content standards under **Matter, Energy, and Organization in Living Systems,** and three of the four content standards under **The Behavior of Organisms** as described on pages 184–187 of The National Science Education Standards.

Chapter Planning Guide

Teacher's Edition Activities	Other Activities	Media and Technology
Chapter Discovery Learning Activity, p.442 **Investigate:** Model Building, p. 444	**TR** **Writing in Biology:** We're Going to the Invertebrate Zoo! **Enrich:** The Bustling Burgess Shale **BL** **Inquiry Activity:** Inquiring Minds Want to Know	
Activity: Organizing Information on a Family Tree, p. 446 **Investigate:** Research, p. 447 **Inquiry Activity:** Identifying Symmetrical Objects, p. 448 **Investigate:** Research, p. 448 **Investigate:** Long-Term Project, p. 450	**LM** Identifying Invertebrates, #37 Classifying Invertebrates, #38 **TR** **Apply:** Crusty Crustaceans **BL** **Inquiry Activity:** Making the Cut	**TB** Evolution of a Body Cavity, #25
Activity: Investigating the Function of Setae, p. 452 **Inquiry Activity:** The Structure and Function of Tools, p. 453 **Investigate:** Model Building, p. 454 **Investigate:** Model Building, p. 455 **Investigate:** Research, p. 458 **Activity:** Investigating Earthworms' Response to Light, p. 458	**TR** **Explore:** Creature Feature **BL** **Inquiry Activity:** What's the Hold Up?	
Activity: Observing Hydras, p. 460	**TR** **Explore:** More or Less **BL** **Inquiry Activity:** Inside, Outside	

KEY: **SE** Student Edition **TE** Teacher's Edition **LM** Laboratory Manual **TR** Teaching Resources **BL** BioLog **TB** Transparency Box **CTB** Computer Test Bank

Materials List

TE **Chapter Discovery Learning Activity,** p. 442 (15–20 minutes to set up culture, short periods for subsequent observations and investigations); plastic bucket or bin with lid; potting soil; leaves, grass clippings, or shredded newspaper; earthworms; small pieces of fruit and vegetable food scraps; celery leaves, cabbage leaves, carrot tops.

TE **Investigate:** Model Building, p. 444 (30 minutes and 10-minute observation period the next day); plaster of Paris, clam.

TE **Investigate: Research,** p. 447 (20 minutes); natural sponge, coral, mollusk shell, and part of a crab, crayfish, or lobster shell; field guides and other references.

TE **Inquiry Activity: Identifying Symmetrical Objects,** p. 448 (30 minutes); small rectangular mirror, objects in classroom, pictures of animals, plants and plant parts, and other organisms.

SE **MINI LAB: Which End Is Up?,** p. 449 (20 minutes); planarians.

TE **Investigate: Long-Term Project,** p. 450 (10 minutes to set up culture, short periods for subsequent observations), meal worm larvae; plastic container; dry oatmeal, cornmeal, or bran flakes; netting or lid; calendar.

TE **Activity: Investigating the Function of Setae,** p. 452 (20–30 minutes); earthworm, hand lens, aluminum foil, damp paper towel.

TE **Investigate: Model Building,** p. 454 (5 minutes); long sock with its toe cut off.

SE **MINI LAB: To Catch a Worm,** p. 456 (30 minutes); earthworm, lab tray, pencil with eraser.

TE **Activity: Investigating Earthworms' Response to Light,** p. 458 (30 minutes); sheet of clear acetate, tape, dark paper, several earthworms, paper towels.

TE **Activity: Observing Hydras,** p. 460 (15–20 minutes for each observation); hydra culture, medicine dropper or pipette, microscope and slide.

Animals: Invertebrates

Introducing the Chapter

. . . In Pictures

Coral exists in a wide variety of shapes, sizes, and colors. Have students examine the photograph, read the caption, and answer the following questions.

- **Have you ever seen actual living coral? If so, what did it look like?** (Some students may have seen living coral in an aquarium or while visiting tropical regions. Encourage students to describe their observations.)
- **In what ways do corals resemble plants?** (Students will probably mention the large and small "branches" of the fan coral.)
- **How are corals like animals?** (Accept all reasonable responses, including that corals are multicellular heterotrophs.)

Teaching Strategy

The first section of this chapter discusses the evolution of animals, the Cambrian explosion, and the body functions that all animals must perform. In the second section, students learn about invertebrate evolution and the phyla of living invertebrates. The third section discusses the body systems of invertebrates. Invertebrate reproduction is the focus of the BRANCHING OUT section.

CHAPTER 19

Animals: Invertebrates

FOCUSING THE CHAPTER
THEME: *Unity and Diversity*

19–1 Evolution of Multicellular Animals
- Describe some of the adaptations animals made to life on land.

19–2 A Survey of Living Invertebrates
- Describe the different phyla of living invertebrates.

19–3 Form and Function in Invertebrates
- Compare the body systems of the living invertebrates.

BRANCHING OUT *In Depth*

19–4 Specialized Reproductive Cycles
- Describe some of the specialized reproductive cycles of invertebrates.

LABORATORY INVESTIGATION
- Compare the nervous systems of a hydra and a planarian.

Biology and Your World

BIO JOURNAL

Does the organism in this photograph look like a plant or an animal? In your journal, make a list of the characteristics of both plants and animals. When you have completed the chapter, look at your lists and see if you can identify the organism as a plant or an animal.

Coral in the Solomon Islands

BIO JOURNAL

Make sure students focus on the visible characteristics, not on suppositions about characteristics that cannot be determined from the photograph alone. Before students list the characteristics of plants and animals, you may want to review the plant characteristics they studied in Chapter 18. Instruct students to keep their entries in their portfolios.

TEACHER SUPPORT

Chapter Discovery Learning Activity

Have students set up a classroom culture of earthworms to provide subjects for observation and investigation in this chapter. Students could collect the earthworms outdoors, or you could purchase them from a biological supply house or commercial earthworm farm. Any plastic bucket or bin with a lid will make a suitable culture container.

1. Fill the container two thirds full of soil. Mix in some leaves, grass clippings, or shredded newspaper.
2. Dampen the soil, and add the earthworms.
3. Periodically add small pieces of fruit or vegetable scraps to the container, either burying them or laying them on the soil surface.
4. Investigate earthworms' food preferences. For example, do they prefer celery leaves, cabbage leaves, or carrot tops? (Most earthworms will eat cabbage leaves if no other food is available, but will prefer celery leaves if both foods are available and carrot tops if given a choice of all three.)

Evolution of Multicellular Animals

SECTION 19–1

GUIDE FOR READING

- **Explain** the relationship between evolution and animal complexity.
- **Describe** the characteristics of animals.

FOR MORE THAN 80 PERCENT of Earth's history, our planet was inhabited by bacteria, single-celled eukaryotes, and algae. Then, about 550 million years ago, at the beginning of the Cambrian Period, multicellular animals appeared, it seemed, quite suddenly. An incredible assortment of complex animals were produced by a great burst of evolutionary change called, appropriately, the Cambrian explosion. How and why did so many different kinds of animals appear so quickly? Could they have come from even earlier multicellular animals? If so, what were they like? To find out the answers to these questions, read on.

The Earliest Known Animals

When fossils from the Cambrian Period were first discovered, they posed a major puzzle. Scientists could not find any evidence of older, simpler multicellular animal life from which these animals might have evolved. Yet the odd creatures of this era were too complex to have evolved directly from single-celled eukaryotes. Who had their ancestors been, and what happened to them?

The End of an Era

Between 650 and 600 million years ago, the Earth saw many changes. Landmasses that had once been joined together broke up and moved apart. A series of ice ages chilled the globe. The entire Earth was gripped in a deep freeze.

Figure 19–1
(a) *The Burgess Shale is an area in the Rocky Mountains of British Columbia, Canada, that has large deposits of shale.* (b) *The Burgess Shale, which contains fossils of trilobites, is formed from small particles of mud and clay and can often be broken into flat pieces, as shown here.* (c) *This close-up of a Burgess Shale trilobite provides a better view as to what these animals looked like when they were a dominant group during the Cambrian Period.*

SECTION 19–1

Evolution of Multicellular Animals

Performance Objectives
- Describe how evolution has led to animal complexity.
- Identify the characteristics common to all animals.

1 ENGAGE

Ideas Through Images

Have students examine Figure 19–1, read the caption, and answer the following questions.

- **Can you identify the organisms that formed the fossils shown in the photographs?** (Some students may be able to identify trilobites.)
- **Are these organisms like any organisms living today?** (Trilobites are not exactly like any living organisms, but they resemble some arthropods, such as sow bugs.)
- **What do you think happened that caused ancient organisms like these to disappear?** (Students may suggest that the organisms became extinct for various reasons or they evolved to different forms.)

Explain that the Burgess Shale has been extremely important to scientists studying early forms of life and evolution.

TEACHER SUPPORT

Background Information

A coral reef results from the activities of only two of the many types of organisms that inhabit it—the coral animals and coralline algae (a type of red algae). These reef builders occupy only the outer surface of the reef.

Coral animals secrete a layer of limestone for skeletal support. The cell walls of coralline algae contain limestone that accumulates on the reef surface when the algae die. Generation after generation, layers of limestone gradually build up, and the reef grows.

Coral animals feed by trapping fine organic particles suspended in the seawater. They also obtain some food from photosynthetic dinoflagellates that live in their tissues. The dinoflagellates in turn make use of some of the coral animals' waste products, such as carbon dioxide and nitrogen compounds. Without dinoflagellates, coral animals can survive but cannot produce enough limestone to form reefs.

Ancillary Support

The resource below can be used to support your teaching strategy for these two pages.

TR Enrich: The Bustling Burgess Shale

2 EXPLORE

Investigate

Model Building Have students repeat the Activity, Making Model Fossils, on page 389 of Chapter 17, but this time have each student or group use both a hard specimen (such as a clamshell) and a soft specimen (such as the clam body) and compare the fossils that the two specimens produce. Remind students that a fossil is formed over a long period of time. Ask what would happen to a soft specimen during the fossil-formation process. (It would probably decay.)

3 TEACH

Ideas Through Images

Have students reexamine the geologic time scale in Chapter 17, Figure 17–6 on pages 390–391, and the diagram of evolutionary biodiversity in Figure 17–12 on pages 396–397. Ask students to locate the Cambrian Period in each illustration and note the increase in species types during that period. Also have them locate the Ediacaran Period at the end of the Precambrian Era.

Discussion

Write the following on the chalkboard: cells → tissues → organs → systems. Ask students to give examples of tissues, organs, and systems in the human body. Let students cite the examples either in order of increasing complexity (e.g., cardiac muscle → heart → circulatory system), or in order of decreasing complexity (circulatory system → heart → cardiac muscle). As needed, help students differentiate between tissues and organs.

Scientists have discovered that at about this time, fossils of early photosynthetic organisms became rare. They also noticed that fossils of free-swimming single-celled eukaryotes disappeared too. What had happened? In addition to the cold, something—or several things—might have appeared and eaten the earlier forms of life. But who might those hungry new animals have been?

New Information From Australia

The first clear answers came from discoveries made in the Ediacaran Hills of Australia. There, fossils that dated from about 580 to 560 million years ago revealed a strange collection of animals. Some researchers think that these animals belong to such living groups as jellyfishes and worms. Others feel that these fossils belong to other animal groups that quickly became extinct. In either case, these fossils prove that simple multicellular animals had begun to evolve before the Cambrian Period. These findings were so important that paleontologists added what they call the Ediacaran Period to the end of the Precambrian Era.

Another discovery from the same period is even more intriguing. Researchers looked closely at rocks from the Ediacaran Hills and concluded that many other animals must have lived at that time—even though their bodies were never preserved. Studies have revealed a whole series of burrows and tracks in the mud that could have been made by several types of soft-bodied organisms. This discovery provides further evidence that multicellular animals evolved long before the Cambrian explosion, even though few fossils have survived.

Figure 19–2 *This fossil of a polychaete worm was found in the Ediacaran Hills in Australia. It lived during the Precambrian Era and is estimated to be 600 million years old.*

The Cambrian Explosion

By the beginning of the Cambrian Period, the number of different kinds of animals found in the fossil record was increasing with astonishing speed. These animals were unbelievably diverse in size and shape. The ancestors of almost all major living animal groups appeared in the fossil record for the first time. But there were also many animals that do not resemble animals living today.

There are a few reasons why the number of organisms found in the fossil record was increasing. One reason was that new animal groups were evolving quickly. Another reason was that more and more groups of these animals were evolving larger bodies, skeletons, and hard body parts, such as shells.

Hard skeletons and other hard body parts were among the most important evolutionary trends of this time. Skeletons gave animals the support they needed for arms, legs, wings, and flippers. Shells and other hard body parts offered protection from the elements and from predators.

By this time, these animals had also evolved specialized cells. Specialized cells are different groups of cells that evolved over time into different functions and shapes in ways that enable them to perform certain tasks more efficiently than generalized cells could.

TEACHER SUPPORT

Background Information

The first primitive animals probably evolved from heterotrophic protists that lived as colonies of hundreds of cells. These colonies may have been hollow spheres that ingested organic particles suspended in the water. Eventually, the cells may have undergone a division of labor, with some cells adapting for reproduction and the others having functions such as locomotion and feeding.

Cell layers may have developed as the cells on one side of the hollow colony folded inward, forming a temporary cavity with cells specialized for feeding. Eventually, this infolding may have eliminated the original hollow space, producing an organism with two cell layers and allowing further specialization among the cells. The outer cells could have provided locomotion and protection, while the inner cells became specialized for reproduction or feeding. With specialized cells and a simple digestive cavity, such animals could have fed on organic matter on the ocean floor.

As the animals evolved, they became increasingly more complex. For example, specialized cells organized into tissues, which are groups of similar cells that work together. Groups of tissues assembled to form organs—collections of tissues that work together to perform a specific function. And groups of organs that perform related functions evolved into organ systems.

☑ *Checkpoint* What are specialized cells? ①

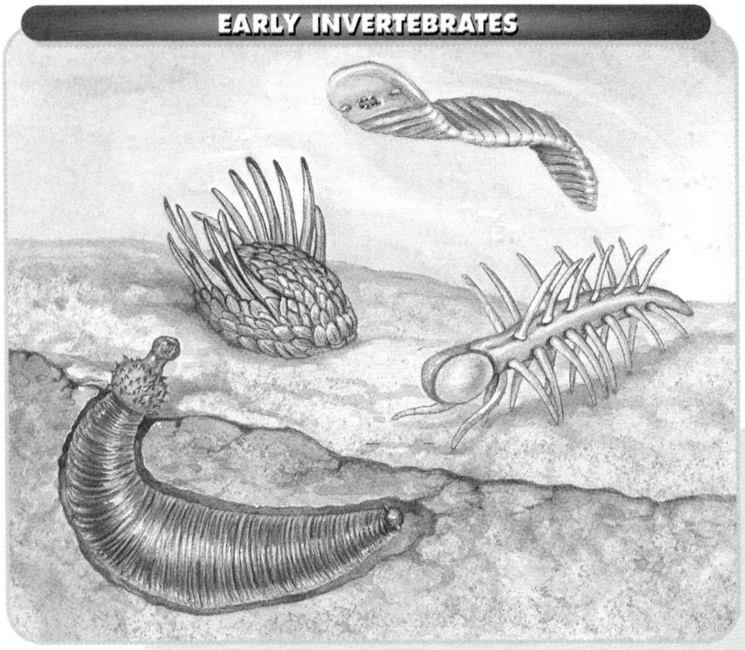

Figure 19–3
During the Cambrian explosion, the number of organisms increased dramatically. This artist's drawing shows some of the invertebrates from this time. In a clockwise direction from the top, these animals are Odontogriphus, Hallucinogenia, Wiwaxia, *and* Ottoia.

Body Plans

Cambrian fossils are fascinating because they show different ways in which tissues and organs can be assembled to produce animals. What does that mean? **To survive, all animals must perform the same functions: body support and movement, feeding and digestion, respiration, excretion, internal transport, and response to the environment.** But if all animals do the same things, why don't we all look alike? Because each major group of animals evolved its own ways of performing these functions.

Over evolutionary time, each phylum combined a particular type of breathing device, a certain type of body support system, and its own variations on other bodily functions. The result is a unique body plan for each phylum. Living phyla represent one set of body plans that work successfully. But Cambrian animals tried out a wide range of body parts and combinations that are no longer found in living species. Thus, animals of the Cambrian Period enabled researchers to study strategies for multicellular life as they were first being evolved.

Section Review 19-1

1. **Explain** the relationship between evolution and animal complexity.
2. **Describe** the characteristics of animals.
3. **Critical Thinking—Inferring** Why are fossils of animals with hard body parts found more frequently than those of soft-bodied animals?

4 ASSESS

Quick Check

Ask students to explain why the number of different kinds of animals found in the fossil record increased so dramatically during the Cambrian Period.

Section Review 19-1

1. As animals evolved, they became increasingly more complex.
2. All animals perform the same functions: body support and movement, feeding and digestion, respiration, excretion, internal transport, and response to the environment. (Students might also mention reproduction.)
3. Soft body parts generally decay before they can be fossilized.

Learning Modality

Visual Learning In conjunction with the Discussion activity on the previous page, have students provide examples of the cell → tissue → organ → system body organization by making labeled drawings in addition to identifying examples orally.

☑ Checkpoint

① Different groups of cells that have evolved into different shapes and functions in ways that enable them to perform certain tasks more efficiently than generalized cells.

TEACHER SUPPORT

Background Information

In addition to the evolutionary advantages of hard body parts to the organisms that developed them, the skeletons and shells were a bonanza for paleontologists. Hard body parts fossilize much more readily and more often than soft body parts and the rather sudden evolution of shells and other hard parts at the beginning of the Cambrian helps explain some of the "explosion" of new species. The Ediacaran fauna and other early metazoa were all soft-bodied. As a result, their fossils are both rare and hard to see, even though these animals were quite common. Then, at the beginning of the Cambrian, there is a sudden appearance of shells of all shapes and sizes. This change helped to create the perception that an enormous variety of animals had suddenly appeared out of nowhere.

Ancillary Support

The resources below can be used to support your teaching strategy for these two pages.

TR Writing in Biology: We're Going to the Invertebrate Zoo!
BL Inquiry Activity: Inquiring Minds Want to Know

Section 19–2

A Survey of Living Invertebrates

Performance Objectives

- Identify cell layers, a body cavity, and segmentation as three important evolutionary trends in invertebrates.
- Name the phyla into which living invertebrates are classified.

Mini Lab Skill: Observing

1 ENGAGE

Ideas Through Images

Have students examine Figure 19–4, read the caption, and answer the following questions.

- **How are all of these organisms alike?** (They all have a head or head area, legs, and eyes, move about on their own, and consume other organisms. All have soft bodies, with the mantis's and scorpion's bodies being encased in a hard outer covering.)
- **How are they different?** (In the number of legs, the organisms' habitats, and their coloration.)
- **How are these animals different from other animals you know, such as fishes, birds, and dogs?** (These animals are invertebrates and, therefore, do not have vertebrae.)

SECTION

19–2 A Survey of Living Invertebrates

GUIDE FOR READING

- **Identify** three important trends in invertebrate evolution.
- **Classify** living invertebrates into different phyla.

MINI LAB

- **Observe** a planarian and identify its head and tail.

ABOUT 97 PERCENT OF ALL THE animal species on Earth belong to one category of animals. They range in size from microscopic dust mites to sponges large enough for humans to hide in. They can be found in the air and at the bottom of the sea. What is this group of animals?

These animals are invertebrates—animals without vertebrae. Invertebrates don't have the sort of bony backbone, or vertebral column, that other animals, including humans, have. The name invertebrate defines a lot of very different animals in an odd way—by describing a characteristic that they don't have, rather than one that they all share.

Trends in Invertebrate Evolution

Because there are so many invertebrate phyla that evolved over millions of years, it is helpful to point out important trends that occurred in their evolutionary history. **The common ancestors of nearly all multicellular animals had evolved two distinct cell layers separated by a jellylike middle layer.** The outer cell layer, or **ectoderm,** develops into skin and other body coverings and also gives rise to the nervous system. The inner cell layer, or **endoderm,** grows into the tissues and organs of the digestive tract.

Jellyfishes are some of the few living animals that retain a primitive jellylike layer between the ectoderm and the endoderm. All other animals have a third tissue layer. This middle layer,

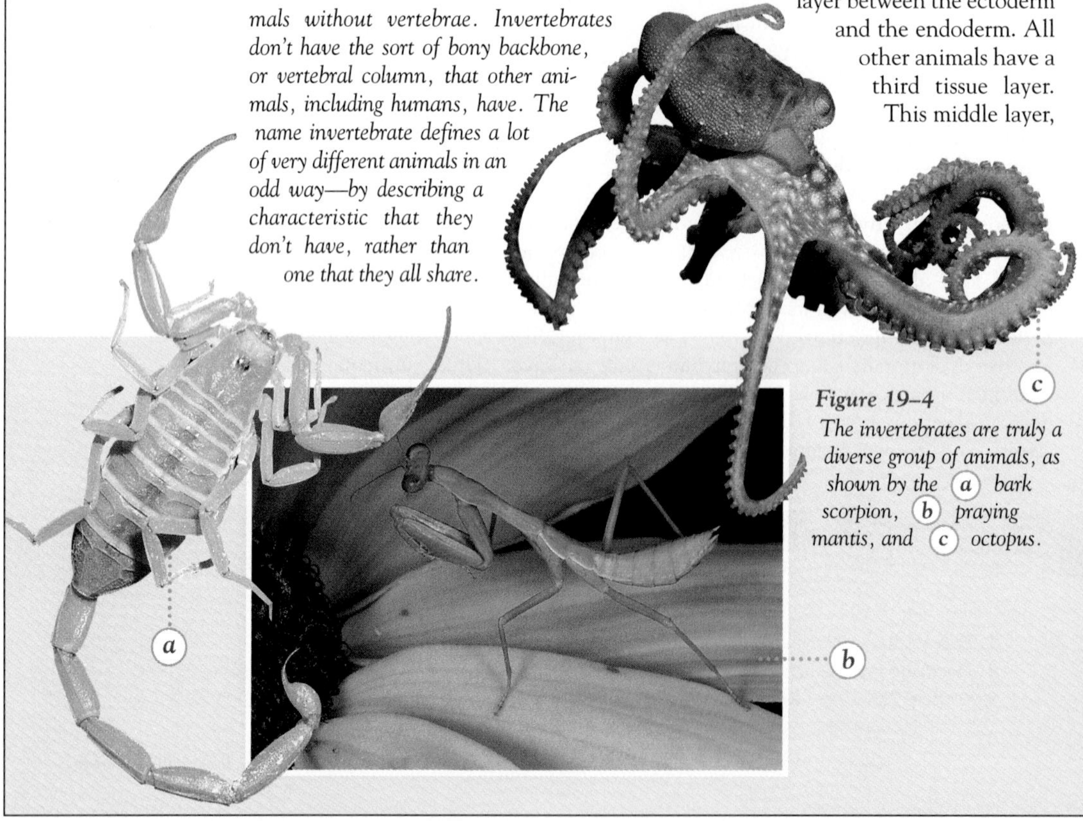

Figure 19–4 The invertebrates are truly a diverse group of animals, as shown by the (a) bark scorpion, (b) praying mantis, and (c) octopus.

TEACHER SUPPORT

Activity

ORGANIZING INFORMATION ON A FAMILY TREE

Before begining this section, ask each student to draw his or her family tree. Show them how to write the names of one set of grandparents near the bottom of the page as the trunk of a tree. Next, show them how to draw a branch for each child of this set of grandparents. From each branch draw additional branches for each grandchild, writing the name of each family member.

Discuss how the evolutionary relationships between animals can be visualized as a family, or phylogenetic, tree, in which the trunk of the tree represents a common ancestor of all the other groups on the tree. Point out that on a phylogenetic tree of the animal kingdom, porifera (sponges) and cnidarians are on the lowest branches, meaning that these groups evolved the longest time ago.

EVOLUTION OF A BODY CAVITY

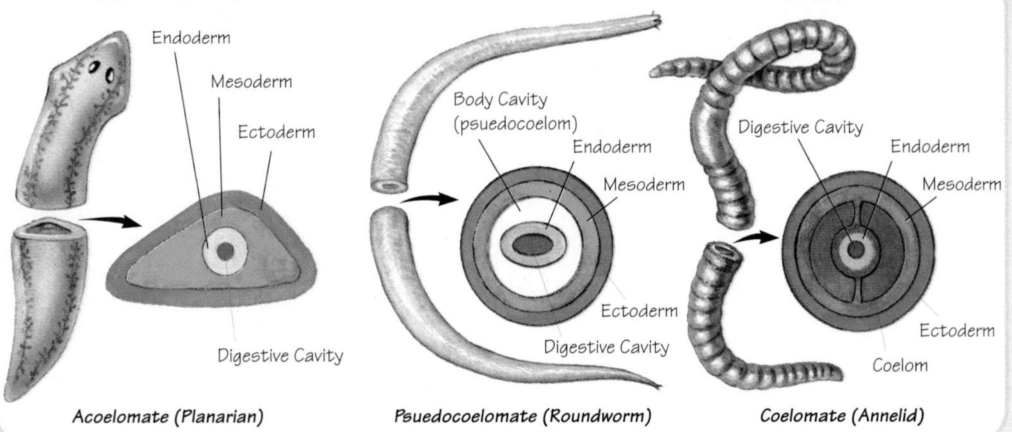

or **mesoderm,** develops into the body's skeleton and muscles.

A second important evolutionary trend in invertebrates is the existence of a mesoderm-lined cavity. This body cavity is called a **coelom** (SEE-lohm). Why should that be important? A body cavity provides an open space inside the body within which organs can grow and function without being squeezed or twisted by body movements. The fluid in some coeloms also plays a role in carrying food, wastes, or dissolved gases from one part of the body to another. Animals that have a body cavity are called coelomates (SEE-loh-mayts).

Figure 19–5
The evolution of a coelom was an important trend in the evolution of invertebrates. Some invertebrates have no coelom and are therefore referred to as acoelomates. Others have a body cavity between the mesoderm and the endoderm that resembles a coelom and are called pseudocoelomates. Still others, called coelomates, have a true coelom that houses the digestive tract and other internal organs. Mollusks were the first phylum to have a true coelom.

A third important evolutionary trend in invertebrates is the evolution of a body plan that is built up from several body compartments. These body compartments are called **segments.** The presence of segments allows an animal to increase in body size with a minimum of new genetic material because certain structures are repeated in each segment. In addition, as animals become more complex, different segments become specialized for specific functions.

Checkpoint What is a coelom? 1

Figure 19–6
An arthropod, such as this lobster, has a body plan that is built up from several compartments.

2 EXPLORE

Investigate

Research Display a natural sponge, a piece of coral, a mollusk shell, and part of a crab, crayfish, or lobster shell for students to examine. Explain that each object was produced by a living animal. Ask students to hypothesize what type of animal each object represents, what the object is made of, and its function. Have students use field guides and other sources to verify or correct their hypotheses.

3 TEACH

Ideas Through Images

Have students examine Figure 19–5, read the caption and the text description of body cavities, and answer the following questions.

- **Which cell layers are common to all three animals?** (All three layers—ectoderm, mesoderm, and endoderm.)
- **What is the major difference between the body structure of a hydra and that of a roundworm?** (A hydra does not have a body cavity, but a roundworm does.)
- **What does the prefix *pseudo-* in the word pseudocoelom mean?** (False.)
- **Which of these animals has a true coelom?** (The annelid does.)

Checkpoint

1 A mesoderm-lined body cavity.

TEACHER SUPPORT

Background Information

There are many advantages to having a body cavity. The coelom makes an animal more flexible and better able to crawl and burrow. It also allows the internal organs to grow and move independently of the outer body wall. The fluid within the coelom cushions the internal organs, which helps prevent internal injury when the animal receives a sharp blow or is pinched. In animals with a hard skeleton, particularly internal bones, even mild exercise could harm internal organs if it were not for the coelom and its cushioning fluid.

In soft-bodied animals such as earthworms, fluid in the coelom functions as a watery skeleton against which muscles in the body wall can exert force to move the body (see pages 452–453). The fluid helps circulate nutrients and oxygen throughout the body and assists in waste disposal. Amoeboid cells in the fluid also assist with these functions.

Ancillary Support

The resource below can be used to support your teaching strategy for these two pages.

TB Evolution of a Body Cavity, #25

Inquiry Activity

Classifying

Identifying Symmetrical Objects

Ask students how they might be able to use a mirror to determine whether an object is symmetrical and, if it is, whether the symmetry is radial or bilateral. Give each group a small rectangular mirror, and let students investigate freely to discover the answer to your question. Explain that they can test photographs of animals, plants and plant parts such as leaves and flowers, and other organisms as well as actual objects in the classroom. Tell them to keep a list of the symmetrical objects they found and the type of symmetry each has. Let students share their discoveries in a class discussion.

Investigate

Research The names of the invertebrate phyla may seem meaningless to students and may also be difficult for them to remember. Emphasize that phyla names are based on Latin and Greek words, and remind students of the text's explanation of genus and species names (Chapter 17, page 394). Have students use a dictionary to find the literal meaning of each phylum name, as listed below. Ask students to explain why each term is an appropriate name for the phylum. (Note: Different dictionaries may give slightly different derivations.)

Porifera (sponges): From Latin *porifer*, meaning bearing pores.
Cnidaria: Phylum is named for specialized cells called *cnidocytes*, meaning stinger cells.
Platyhelminthes: From Greek *platus*, flat, and *helminth*, parasitic worm.
Nematoda: From Greek *nema*, thread, and Latin *ode*, like.
Mollusca: From Latin *mollis*, soft.
Annelida: From Latin *annellus*, small ring.
Echinodermata: From Greek *echinos* for sea urchin, thus spiny, and *derma*, skin.
Arthropoda: From Greek *arthro*, joint, and *pod*, foot.
Chordata: From Latin *chorda*, cord.

The Movement Onto Land

Animals that moved from sea to land faced adaptive challenges similar to those that faced plants making the same evolutionary journey. To live on land, animals, like plants, had to evolve ways to perform essential survival tasks without losing too much water in the process.

It is important to remember, however, that land animals are not necessarily any more advanced than their aquatic cousins. Some successful animal groups live their entire lives in the water. Other groups live entirely on land, and still others live in both environments.

Figure 19–7
Sponges, such as this pink vase sponge, come in a variety of shapes, sizes, and colors. They are the simplest of all invertebrates.

Sponges

Sponges—the most primitive of all living multicellular animals—make up the phylum Porifera (por-IHF-er-ah). Sponge cells are relatively independent, and they live together for mutual benefit. Most sponges live almost entirely in the sea, although a few species are found in fresh water.

Cnidarians

Jellyfishes, corals, sea anemones, and hydras belong to the phylum Cnidaria (nigh-DAIR-ee-ah). Cnidarians are mostly marine, although a few species, such as

Figure 19–8
As invertebrates evolved, they moved from having no symmetry to having radial symmetry and finally to having bilateral symmetry. Animals that show bilateral symmetry have a definite head end and tail end, as well as a front and a back.

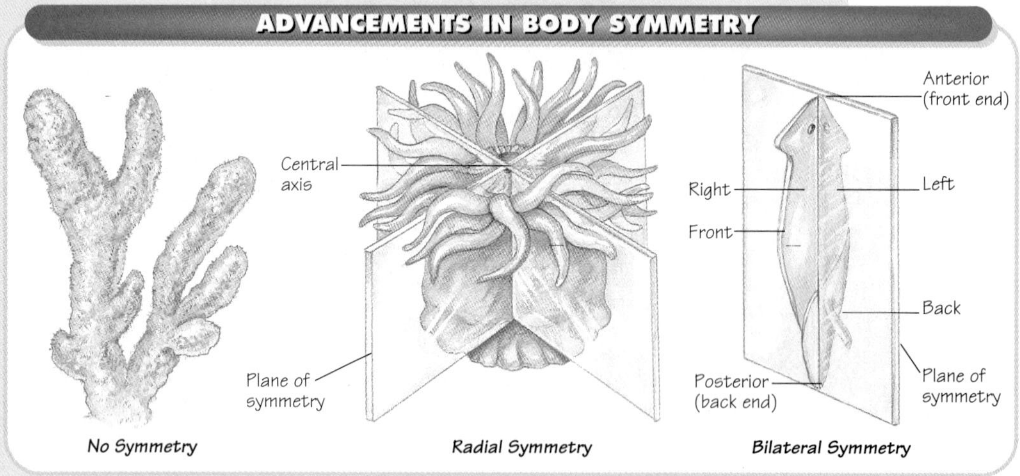

TEACHER SUPPORT

Historical Perspective

The phylum Porifera is an example of the problems taxonomists face in attempting to separate and classify animals. Sponges were considered to be plants until the eighteenth century, when some researchers began to cast doubt on that belief. Only in the nineteenth century did scientists begin to agree that sponges were more properly classified among the animals.

Sponges are difficult animals to study. They cannot be completely understood by examining their individual cells under a microscope or by dissecting them. Sponges act very much like colonies of protozoans that have developed an organized method of working together. (See Background Information, page 444.) There is no evidence that sponges are even remotely related to any other group of animals. In fact, some experts believe that sponges are so different from both protozoans and animals that they should be placed in a separate animal subkingdom, Parazoa.

Figure 19–9
Cnidarians, including this coral, are the first invertebrates to show radial symmetry.

the hydras, live in fresh water. Cnidarians have **radial symmetry.** Animals with radial symmetry have body parts that repeat around an imaginary line drawn through the center of their body, as shown in ***Figure 19–9.*** Cnidarians are some of the most colorful and beautiful of all invertebrates.

☑ **Checkpoint** What is radial symmetry? ❶

Platyhelminthes

Flatworms make up the phylum Platyhelminthes (pla-tee-hehl-MIHN-theez). They are the simplest animals that show **bilateral symmetry.** Animals with bilateral symmetry have left and right sides that are mirror images if you were to draw an imaginary line through their center. They also have specialized front and back ends as well as upper and lower sides. Most flatworms also show **cephalization** (sehf-uh-lih-ZAY-shun), which means they have a front end that is developed enough to merit being called a head.

☑ **Checkpoint** What is bilateral symmetry? ❷

MINI LAB ·········· Observing ··········

Which End Is Up?

PROBLEM *What can you* ***observe*** *about the shape and structure of a planarian to help identify the head end from the tail end?*

PROCEDURE

1. Observe a planarian and then sketch it on a sheet of paper. Label one end anterior and the other end posterior.
2. Using an arrow, indicate the direction of movement of the planarian through the environment.

ANALYZE AND CONCLUDE

1. What things about the shape and structure of the planarian helped you label the anterior and the posterior ends?
2. As an organism moves through the environment, what are the advantages of having sense organs at the anterior end?

Nematodes

Roundworms, or nematodes, make up the phylum Nematoda (nehm-uh-TOHD-uh). Roundworms were among the first animals to evolve a tubelike digestive system, with a mouth at one end and an anus at the other. Some roundworms are microscopic, while others grow to more than a meter long.

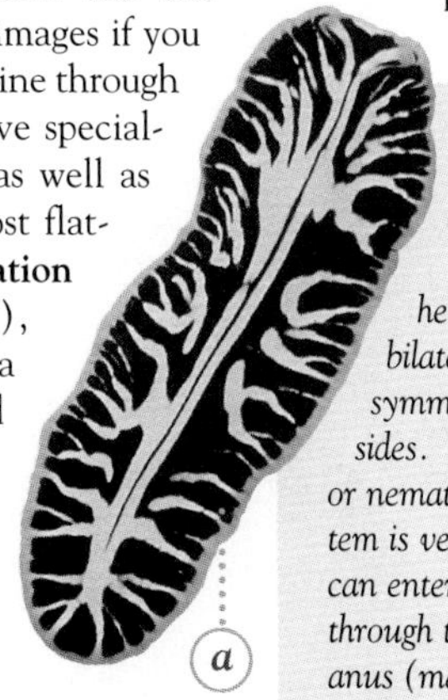

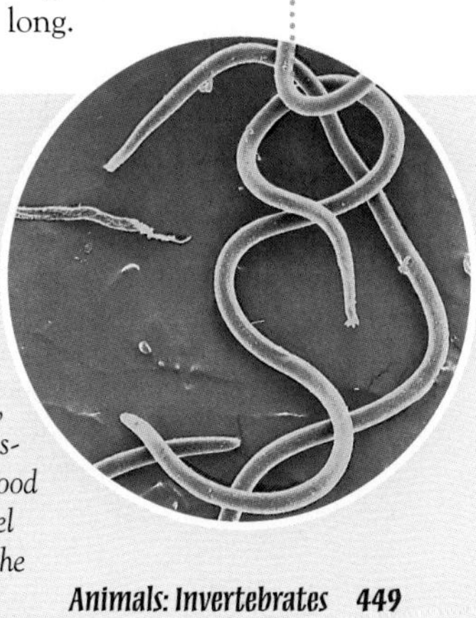

Figure 19–10
(a) This flatworm, a platyhelminth, shows bilateral symmetry—symmetric left and right sides. (b) In roundworms, or nematodes, the digestive system is very efficient because food can enter the mouth and travel through the digestive tract to the anus (magnification: 57X).

MINI LAB Observing

Teacher Note

- For time required and materials needed, see p. 442b.

Answers to Analyze and Conclude

1. Students should mention the eyespots in the head area, the streamlined body shape, and the tapered tail.
2. The organism can sense things in the environment as it moves toward them and can adjust its movement accordingly—to avoid risk or obtain food, for example.

Skills Trace

Observing

Focus p. 449
Practice p. 451
Assess p. 466

☑ Checkpoint

❶ A body plan in which body parts repeat around an imaginary line drawn through the center of the body.

❷ A body plan in which left and right halves are identical on both sides of an imaginary line drawn through the center.

TEACHER SUPPORT

Managing Classroom Diversity

TECH PREP STUDENTS

Encourage students who are interested in agriculture-related businesses to find out about commercial earthworm farming—where it is done, how the worms are raised, and the purposes for which they are sold. Also suggest that students research some of the newer uses of farmed earthworms. For example, some lumber companies are investigating whether the addition of earthworms to the soil can speed up the growth of new trees in areas that have been logged and replanted.

Students who are interested in veterinary medicine, kennel management, or human health care could find out about the ways in which hosts become infested with parasitic worms, the treatments that are available, and preventive measures. *Ascaris,* a roundworm, is estimated to infest one fourth of the human population. Heartworms infest not only dogs but also swine and poultry.

Ancillary Support

The resources below can be used to support your teaching strategy for these two pages.

LM Identifying Invertebrates, #37
BL Inquiry Activity: Making the Cut

Investigate

Long-Term Project Point out that many organisms commonly referred to as worms are not worms at all but the larva stage of insects. (See Applying Your Skills, page 467.) Mealworms, for example, are the larvae of a certain species of beetle. Ask volunteers to set up a class mealworm culture so students can observe the changes from larvae to pupae to adult beetles. Mealworm larvae are usually sold in pet supply stores as food for reptiles and amphibians. Have the volunteers put about two dozen larvae in a plastic container partly filled with dry oatmeal, cornmeal, or bran flakes, and cover the container with netting or a lid with holes punched in it. Keep the culture in a warm, dark location, and let students check it at intervals to look for pupae and, later, adult beetles. Post a calendar near the culture so students can record these changes as they occur. Let students continue to maintain the culture so they can observe the new generation of larvae that hatch from the eggs laid by the adult beetles. Emphasize that true worms—platyhelminthes, nematodes, and annelids—do not change body form as they go through their life cycles.

INTEGRATING LANGUAGE ARTS

Echinos is the Greek word for sea urchin and means spiny; *dermis* is Greek for skin. Thus echinoderm means spiny skin.

Discussion

To help students differentiate among the invertebrate phyla, create a class master chart as students describe each phylum's characteristics. Emphasize the characteristics that are different from one phylum to the next—for example, the third tissue layer in most cnidarians compared with the jellylike layer in sponges and the bilateral symmetry of flatworms compared with cnidarians' radial symmetry.

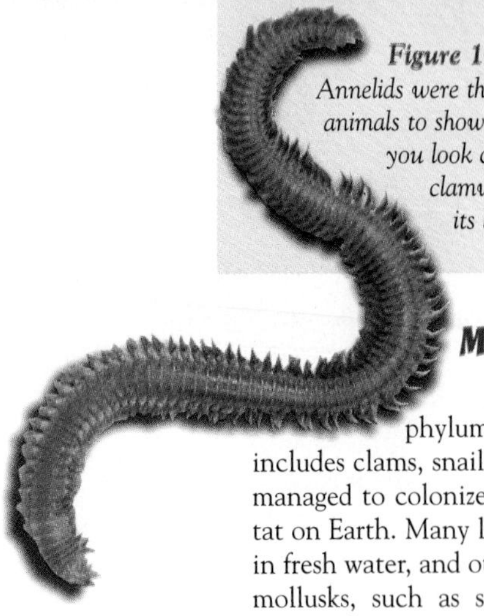

Figure 19–11
Annelids were the first phylum of animals to show segmentation. If you look carefully at this clamworm, you can see its body segments.

Mollusks

Members of the phylum Mollusca—which includes clams, snails, and squids—have managed to colonize almost every habitat on Earth. Many live in the sea, some in fresh water, and others on land. Some mollusks, such as snails, protect their body with a shell. Others, such as sea slugs, avoid predation by literally leaving a bad taste in the predator's mouth. Clams, mussels, oysters, and scallops have two shells connected by a flexible hinge. When they are in danger, they clamp their shells closed. Octopuses and squids can emit clouds of dark-colored ink to confuse predators, allowing the squid or octopus to escape.

Annelids

Segmented worms, or annelids, belong to the phylum Annelida (an-uh-LIHD-uh). This phylum includes a wide range of fascinating animals—from common earthworms to exotic marine worms with feathery rainbow-colored gills. Earthworms and their relatives recycle enormous amounts of decaying organic matter in the soil.

Echinoderms

INTEGRATING LANGUAGE ARTS

What does the word echinoderm mean? Use a dictionary to look up the word parts echino- and -dermis.

Starfishes, sea urchins, and sea lilies all belong to the phylum Echinodermata (ee-kigh-noh-DER-muh-tuh). Like some other invertebrates, echinoderms live their lives entirely in the water. They can be recognized by their spiny skin and by their five-part radial symmetry. Some echinoderms, such as starfishes, are found on nearly every rocky coast around the world. Others, such as the beautiful sea lilies, are found mostly on coral reefs and in the deep sea.

Arthropods

The jointed-leg animals—arthropods—that make up the phylum Arthropoda (AHR-throh-pahd-uh) are by far the largest and most diverse of all the animal phyla. Some experts estimate that there may be as many as 10 million species of arthropods! Their most important characteristics are an external skeleton and jointed legs. The three largest groups of arthropods are the chelicerates (kuh-LIHS-er-ayts), the crustaceans (kruhs-TAY-shuhnz), and the insects.

Spiders and scorpions are part of an ancient group named after their mouthparts—their chelicerae (kuh-LIHS-er-ee), hence, the subphylum Chelicerata. Most chelicerates are carnivorous, and a few, such as the black widow spider, have a

Figure 19–12
As a group, echinoderms have evolved a great variety of forms. However, all echinoderms, such as this sea cucumber, must live in water.

TEACHER SUPPORT

Background Information

Although their basic nervous system and lack of a brain appear to place echinoderms among the very simple animals, they have structures more typical of complex animals—including a unique internal skeleton. Hard nodules of calcium carbonate called ossicles are embedded in the body walls and surrounded by living tissues, providing the strength and protection of a mollusk shell.

Many experts wonder if these animals should really be classified with the invertebrates. Although they do not have vertebrae, their larvae appear to have much in common with a wormlike ancestor of the vertebrates. Also the ossicles of the brittle star fit together much like the vertebrae of a backbone. There are far fewer echinoderm species living today than exist in the fossil record, which may indicate that this phylum is left over from a branch of animal evolution that did not prove to be particularly successful.

Figure 19–13
The three largest groups of arthropods are the chelicerates, the crustaceans, and the insects. (a) The sally light-foot crab is a crustacean, while (b) the leaf-cutter ants are one of the more than 900,000 types of insects.

poisonous bite that can be dangerous to a human. But these animals attack only by accident or when threatened.

Lobsters, shrimps, and crabs make up the class Crustacea. Crustaceans live primarily in the water. They range in size from tiny water fleas to Alaskan king crabs, whose legs can stretch more than two meters across.

At least half of all living animal species belong to the class Insecta. Insects are so diverse in form and habits that it is difficult to pick one that truly represents the entire group.

Invertebrate Chordates

Invertebrate chordates are peculiar animals that show a link between terrestrial animals with backbones and ancient ancestors in the sea. These animals are members of our own phylum, Chordata (kor-DAYT-uh). Chordates have an endoskeleton with a stiff rod, called a notochord, to which muscles are attached. They are found in marine environments throughout the world.

Figure 19–14
Sea squirts are tunicates, which are examples of invertebrate chordates. Sea squirts get their name from the fact that many species will shoot water at their attackers when touched.

Section Review 19–2

1. **Identify** three important trends in invertebrate evolution.
2. **Classify** the living invertebrates into the different phyla.
3. **Critical Thinking—Recognizing Relationships** What type of symmetry do humans have?
4. **MINI LAB** What can you **observe** about a planarian that helps to identify its head and tail?

TEACHER SUPPORT

Background Information

In addition to tunicates, small fishlike animals called lancelets are also invertebrate chordates. Among all adult chordates (vertebrate and invertebrate), lancelets display most clearly the three characteristics of this phylum: a notochord, a hollow dorsal nerve cord, and pharyngeal slits.

Lancelets live half-buried in the sand on the shallow beds of tropical oceans. They feed by trapping tiny food particles as water passes through the pharynx.

4 ASSESS

Quick Check

Ask students to list the names of the invertebrate phyla in a horizontal row, and then below each name list one major characteristic of that phylum and one or more representative organisms.

Section Review 19–2

1. Tissue layers, mesoderm-lined body cavity (coelom), and body plans built up from segments.
2. Porifera, Cnidaria, Platyhelminthes, Nematoda, Molluska, Annelida, Echinodermata, Arthropoda, Chordata.
3. Bilateral.
4. The placement of its eyes in relation to its direction of movement, the tapered tail.

Skills Trace

Observing

- Focus p. 449
- Practice p. 451
- Assess p. 466

Learning Modality

Visual and Kinesthetic Learning

To support the Discussion activity on the previous page, have students write each characteristic on a separate index card as you create the master chart. Also have them write the name of the phylum on the back of each card. With the master chart out of view, have students shuffle the cards and arrange them into chart format below a row of cards with the phyla names.

Ancillary Support

The resources below can be used to support your teaching strategy for these two pages.

LM Classifying Invertebrates, #38
TR Apply: Crusty Crustaceans

Section 19–3

Form and Function in Invertebrates

Performance Objective

• Compare and contrast the body structures and body systems of invertebrates.

Mini Lab Skill: Experimenting
Laboratory Investigation Skill: Comparing

1 ENGAGE

Ideas Through Images

Have students examine Figure 19–15, read the caption, and answer the following questions.

• **What function do you think the starfish's arm serves?** (Student responses may include movement.)

• **What do you think the flowerlike structures on the feather duster worms are?** (Students might suggest that they are clusters of tentacles or feathery gills.)

• **What might be the function of those structures?** (Responses may include obtaining food by filtering small organisms from the water, or respiration.)

• **How would you relate the form of these structures to their function?** (The starfish's arm is flexible, enabling it to move and grasp its prey. The feather duster worm's feathery structures form a net to capture prey and absorb oxygen as water passes through them.)

SECTION 19–3

Form and Function in Invertebrates

GUIDE FOR READING

- List the three different kinds of skeletons.
- Compare open and closed circulatory systems.

MINI LAB

- **Design an experiment** to observe the movements of an earthworm.

THE VARIOUS INVERTEBRATE groups have evolved an astonishing variety of shapes and body structures that perform the essential functions of life. You can think of these different collections of body parts as "tool kits" for survival. Over time, each phylum has evolved its own variation of body parts that serve its own functions. The result is a body plan unique to each phylum. Some body systems are simple, and others are quite complex. Some are efficient, while others appear to be inefficient.

Support and Movement

Almost all multicellular animals use some kind of musclelike tissue to move around and perform other functions. All muscles and musclelike tissues work by contracting, or getting shorter. This is the only way that muscle tissue can generate force to perform useful work.

When it comes to helping animals move around, muscles by themselves don't operate very well. That's why most multicellular animals that move rapidly combine a muscle system with some sort of skeleton that provides firm support. **The three types of skeletons found in the animal kingdom are hydrostatic skeletons, exoskeletons, and endoskeletons.**

Hydrostatic Skeletons

In some animals, the muscles surround and are supported by a water-filled body cavity. This type of skeleton is called a **hydrostatic** (high-droh-STAT-ihk) **skeleton.** Hydrostatic skeletons do not contain hard structures for muscles to pull against. Instead, when the muscles contract, they push against the water in the

a

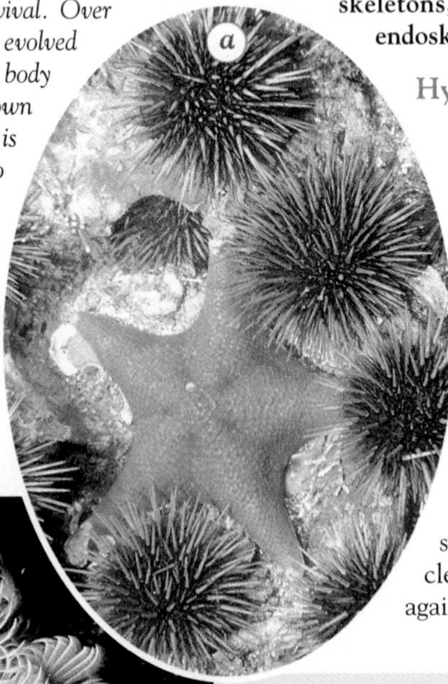

b

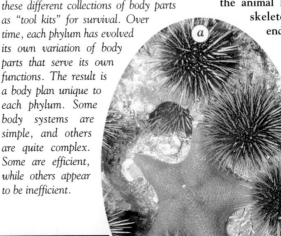

Figure 19–15
Invertebrates have evolved adaptations for survival. (a) Although starfishes move slowly through the water, they are carnivorous predators. (b) Feather duster worms, on the other hand, are annelid worms that use their feathery structures for feeding and respiration.

TEACHER SUPPORT

Activity

INVESTIGATING THE FUNCTION OF SETAE

The setae on earthworms' skin enable them to grip surfaces as they move. The following activity will enable students to observe these structures and investigate their function.

1. Rub a finger very lightly along an earthworm's sides and describe what you feel.
2. Examine the worm with a hand lens and describe what you see.
3. Formulate a hypothesis to explain the function of the structures you felt and saw.
4. Place the earthworm on a smooth surface, such as a glass dish or the shiny side of a piece of aluminum foil, and on a rough surface, such as a damp paper towel. Compare the worm's movements on the two surfaces.
5. What is the function of the structures you observed?

Figure 19–16
A hydrostatic skeleton is basically a fluid-filled tube with soft walls that contain two layers of muscle. Circular muscle forms a band around the circumference of the tube. Longitudinal muscles run lengthwise to the tube. When the longitudinal muscles contract, the sea anemone becomes short and fat. When the circular muscles contract, it becomes long and thin.

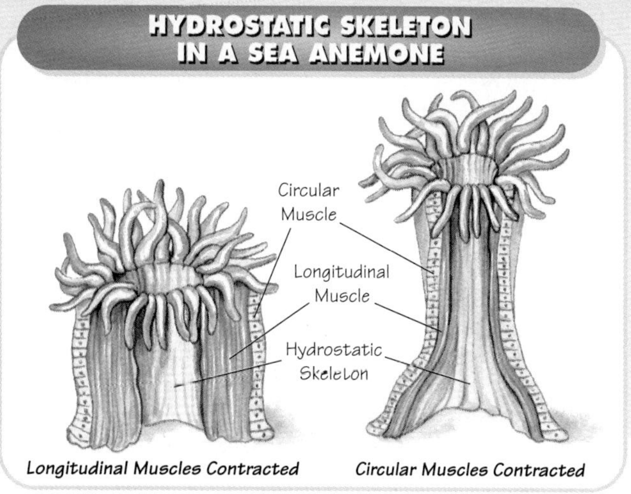

body cavity, as shown in *Figure 19–16.* Obviously, hydrostatic skeletons do not allow an animal to move very fast.

☑ **Checkpoint** What is a hydrostatic skeleton? ❶

Exoskeletons

An external skeleton is called an **exoskeleton.** Arthropods are the best examples of organisms with exoskeletons. In arthropods, the exoskeleton is made of a tough carbohydrate called **chitin** (KIGH-tihn). Muscles are attached to the inside of the exoskeleton. All exoskeletons are thin and flexible at the joints, allowing the skeleton to bend and flex.

The arthropod exoskeleton is adaptable and successful, but it has two major drawbacks. One drawback is that in order to grow, the animal must shed the skeleton and grow a new one! The other drawback is that an exoskeleton is heavy for the amount of support it provides. For this reason, animals with exoskeletons cannot grow very large.

Endoskeletons

A skeleton that is located within the body is called an **endoskeleton.** Sponges and some echinoderms have endoskeletons, but the best examples are found among the vertebrates.

☑ **Checkpoint** What is an endoskeleton? ❷

Feeding and Digestion

Because all animals, including humans, are heterotrophs, we all must eat in order to survive. As animals become more complex, their digestive systems become more specialized. Invertebrates have evolved many different ways of digesting their food.

Digestion Inside Cells

Sponges, the simplest multicellular animals, filter tiny particles of food from the water. Food is digested inside these cells, and the resulting nutrients are distributed among other cells within the sponge. Because this type of digestion takes place inside cells, it is known as **intracellular digestion.**

In many cnidarians and flatworms, larger food particles are taken into a **gastrovascular cavity.** A gastrovascular cavity is a digestive sac with only a single opening to the outside. Food enters through this opening, and indigestible solid wastes leave through the same opening. The food particles are broken down into smaller and smaller particles. Ultimately, the smallest particles are taken up by cells lining the cavity, and digestion is completed within the cells.

☑ **Checkpoint** What is a gastrovascular cavity? ❸

2 EXPLORE

Inquiry Activity

Making Inferences

The Structure and Function of Tools

Give each group of students a different, familiar tool—for example, a screwdriver or a staple remover. Let each group examine and use its tool. Then ask students to describe how the tool's design, or structure, fits its use, or function. Next, give each group a tool with which they are most likely unfamiliar—for example, a pentagraph (used by artists to copy drawings) or a bodkin (used in sewing to thread elastic or ribbon through a casing). Have students explain what they think the tool's function is and the reasons for that conclusion.

3 TEACH

Ideas Through Images

Have students examine Figure 19–16, read the caption, and answer the following questions.

- **The fluid inside the anemone's body cannot be made more compact. Why do you think this is so?** (Students may know that water and other fluids cannot be compacted by pressure.)
- **What other common invertebrate animal crawls by making its body shorter and fatter, then longer and thinner, over and over again?** (An earthworm.)

☑ Checkpoint

❶ A skeleton in which muscles surround and are supported by a water-filled body cavity.

❷ A skeleton that is located within the body.

❸ A digestive sac with only a single opening to the outside.

TEACHER SUPPORT

Managing Classroom Diversity

LEP/AT-RISK STUDENTS

To help make the scientific terms in this section more meaningful to students, have them use a dictionary to find the meanings of any unfamiliar prefixes and roots, as listed here, and then derive each term's literal meaning. Also ask students to suggest other, familiar words and terms with the same prefixes—for example, hydroelectric power, intramural sports, and extracurricular activities.

Hydrostatic: *hydro-*, water; *static*, unchanging.
Exoskeleton: *exo-*, outside.
Endoskeleton: *endo-*, inside.
Intracellular: *intra-*, within, inside of.
Extracellular: *extra-*, outside of.
Gastrovascular: *gastro-*, stomach; *vascular*, containing vessels.

Ideas Through Images

Have students examine Figure 19–17, read the caption, and answer the following questions.

- **Why do you think a digestive system with two openings is considered more advanced than a digestive system with only one opening?** (In a digestive system with two openings, food moves in only one direction, so the system can be more specialized and food is more thoroughly digested.)
- **Which animals have a digestive tract with two openings?** (The earthworm and the grasshopper.)
- **Which of those digestive tracts is more complex, and why?** (The grasshopper's, because it has more specialized digestive organs. You may want to point out that the earthworm also has some specialized digestive organs: an esophagus, a crop that stores food, a gizzard that grinds the food into pieces, and an intestine that completes digestion and absorbs nutrients.)

Investigate

Model Building To help students visualize a digestive tract inside a body wall, give each student or group a long sock with its toe cut off, and tell students to turn the sock halfway inside out to form a tube-within-a-tube. Explain that the inner layer of the sock represents the digestive tract and the outer layer represents the body wall.

Discussion

Ask students to identify other organisms they learned about earlier in this book that also have an internal transport system for carrying nutrients and other substances. Students should identify tracheophytes (Chapter 18). If they do not recall this information, let them refer to page 427. Have students compare the internal transport systems of plants to those of animals.

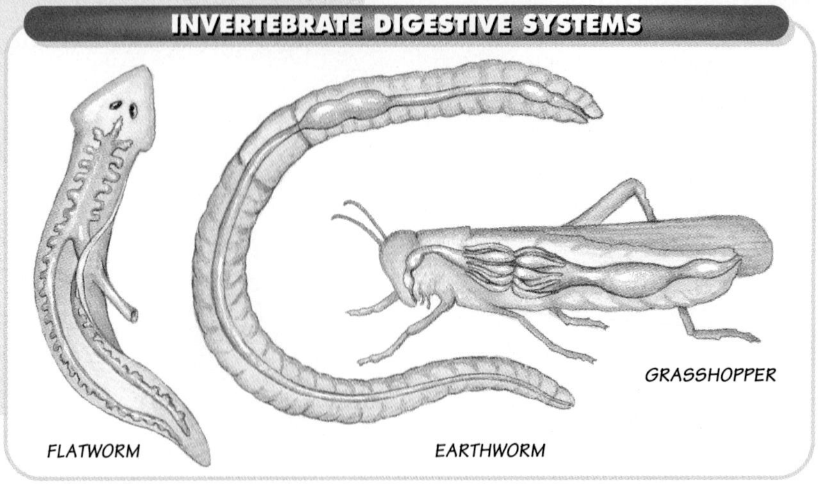

Figure 19–17 *As invertebrates became more complex, their digestive systems developed from one that had one opening to a digestive system with two openings. At the same time, the organs of this digestive system became more specialized.*

Digestion Outside Cells

More highly evolved digestive systems—such as those in annelids, mollusks, arthropods, and chordates—have two openings. Food enters through a mouth and leaves through an anus. Because the digestive tract in such animals forms a tube inside the body wall, this digestive tract is known as a "tube-within-a-tube" body plan.

Almost all the food—except for certain fats—is digested within the digestive cavity. Because this digestion takes place outside the cells, it is called **extracellular digestion.** The final products of digestion are absorbed into blood vessels that line the gastrovascular cavity.

Internal Transport

Living cells of multicellular animals require a constant supply of oxygen and nutrients, as well as a way to eliminate carbon dioxide and poisonous wastes. Small, thin soft-bodied animals may provide for these needs by simple diffusion through the body surface. But more complex multicellular animals have evolved some sort of circulatory system—a collection of one or more pumps and tubes that move important substances around within the body. The pumping part of such systems is called the heart. The fluid being pumped around the body is called blood, and the tubes that carry it are called blood vessels. In invertebrates,

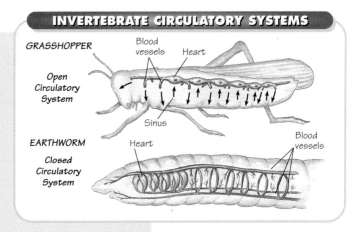

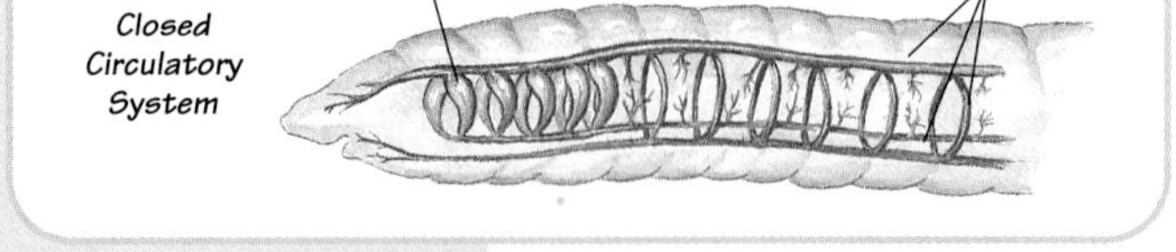

Figure 19–18 *In an open circulatory system, the blood leaves blood vessels and comes in direct contact with the surrounding tissues. Here, it collects in the body sinuses before making its way back to the heart. In a closed circulatory system, the blood is completely contained within a network of blood vessels.*

TEACHER SUPPORT

Ecology Note

Insects have evolved a wide array of mouth structures and digestive systems that enable them to feed on virtually any plant in existence. Insect mouths are highly specialized to exploit the specific food source favored by each species. For example, an aphid's drill-like mouth structures pierce stems and suck out plant juices. Their specialized mouth parts and feeding habits make insects the most successful and destructive plant pests worldwide.

Relying on insecticides to control insect pests is often counterproductive. Increasingly, agriculturists are turning to biological controls, such as introducing carnivorous insects to devour the herbivorous insect pests, releasing species-specific insect diseases or parasites, and using chemical lures or hormones to reduce a population's reproduction rate. Encourage students to research such biological controls.

there are two main types of circulatory systems—open circulatory systems and closed circulatory systems.

Open Circulatory System

Open circulatory systems are systems in which blood from the heart is not entirely contained in blood vessels. Instead, the blood from the heart is pumped through a series of vessels that carry the blood and release it directly onto body tissues. The blood flows through tissues and collects in openings called sinuses. These sinuses connect with a larger sinus around the heart, which takes in the blood once again.

Closed Circulatory System

Closed circulatory systems keep blood contained in a system of closed vessels that pass through various parts of the body and return the blood back to the heart. In such systems, blood does not come into direct contact with tissues. Instead, oxygen, carbon dioxide, and other substances diffuse in and out of the blood through very thin walls of tiny blood vessels. This system provides a more rapid and efficient control of blood flow through the body.

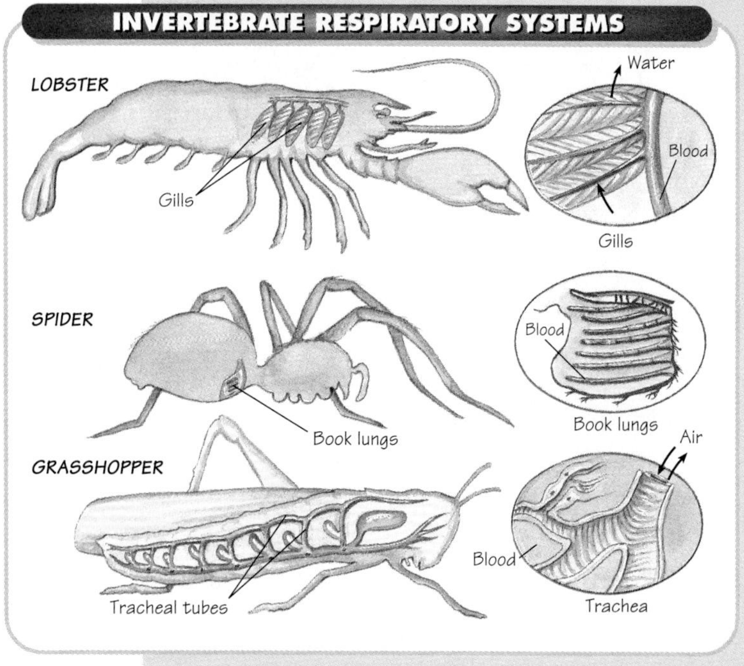

Figure 19–19
The respiratory structures of invertebrates vary. Water-dwelling invertebrates such as lobsters have gills, while some land-dwelling invertebrates such as spiders have book lungs that resemble internal gills. Grasshoppers, which are insects, have tracheal tubes.

Respiration

Small soft-bodied animals may be able to exchange oxygen and carbon dioxide with their environment simply by diffusion through their body surfaces. But once animals get large enough to require a circulatory system, they often also require a specialized organ for respiration.

Regardless of where an animal lives, its respiratory system must deal with two facts of life. First, the respiratory system must have a large surface area that is in contact with the environment, so that gas exchange by diffusion is adequate to support the demands of the organism. Second, all respiratory organs must keep their gas exchange surfaces wet, because diffusion can take place only across moist membranes. If an animal's respiratory surface dries out, gas exchange would stop and the animal would suffocate.

Animals that live in water have no problem with the requirements you have just read about because their environment keeps respiratory surfaces wet.

Ideas Through Images

Have students examine Figure 19–19, read the caption and the text descriptions of respiratory systems on this page and the next, and answer the following questions.

- **Which type of respiratory organ—gills, book lungs, or tracheal tubes—is the most complex, and why?** (Students will probably disagree. Point out that all of these organs are complex. Emphasize that each is a specific adaptation to the particular environment in which the organism lives.)
- **What other animals that you know of have gills?** (Students will probably mention fish, and some may mention the larval stage of amphibians—for example, frog tadpoles.)

Investigate

Model Building The following activity demonstrates that book lungs provide a large surface area for gas exchange. First have students calculate the total surface area of the front and back covers of a book. Then have them divide the book into 10 sections of pages, holding them together with clips, and calculate the total surface area of the book with the page surfaces exposed. Students will find that the total surface area of the divided book is 10 times that of the closed book.

TEACHER SUPPORT

Background Information

In the entire living world, there has never appeared any kind of active transport system that can grab onto oxygen, carbon dioxide, or water, drag it across a membrane, and release it on the other other side. As a result of this fundamental deficiency in living systems, respiratory and excretory systems have had to evolve ways to maximize facilitated diffusion of these substances into and out of various body fluids and cells. The intricate designs of respiratory organs and the mammalian kidney can be seen as the only resort to this difficult situation.

Ancillary Support

The resources below can be used to support your teaching strategy for these two pages.

TR Explore: Creature Feature
BL Inquiry Activity: What's the Hold Up?

MINI LAB Experimenting

Teacher Notes

- For time required and materials needed, see p. 442b.
- Review students' experimental designs to make sure they do not harm the earthworm.

Answers to Analyze and Conclude

1. Students' hypotheses should relate to an earthworm's movement and should be phrased as a testable statement.
2. Answers will depend on the specific hypotheses.
3. Hydrostatic.

Skills Trace
Experimenting

Focus p. 456
Practice p. 459
Assess p. 466

Ideas Through Images

Have students examine Figure 19–20, read the caption and the text on this page and page 458, and answer the following questions.

- **Why is the excretory system important?** (It helps animals maintain proper water balance within their bodies.)
- **What is the function of the excretory pores in flatworms and earthworms?** (To release water and wastes from the animal's body.)
- **What structures in grasshoppers remove wastes?** (Malpighian tubules.)

MINI LAB ···· Experimenting ····

To Catch a Worm

PROBLEM *How does an earthworm move through its environment?* ***Design an experiment*** *to answer this question.*

SUGGESTED PROCEDURE

1. Formulate a hypothesis that you want to test.
2. Obtain an earthworm and a lab tray from your teacher.
3. Observe the movements of the earthworm.
4. Carefully touch the earthworm and observe its reactions.

ANALYZE AND CONCLUDE

1. What was your hypothesis?
2. How did the results of the experiment support your hypothesis?
3. Based on your observations, what type of skeleton do you think an earthworm has?

Many of the worms and cnidarians simply respire through body surfaces. Others—such as annelid worms, mollusks, and crustaceans—have respiratory organs called gills. Gills are feathery structures that expose a large surface area to the environment. Gills are rich in blood vessels that bring blood close to the surface for gas exchange.

Terrestrial invertebrates have evolved several different types of organs for breathing air. Spiders and their relatives have structures called book lungs, which are sheetlike layers of thin tissue that contain blood vessels. Insects have a series of air-filled tubes called trachea that bring air to each body cell. Trachea branch extensively and reach deep into most of their body tissues.

Excretion

For most animals, excretion—the process of eliminating toxic waste products—is closely tied with maintaining proper water balance within the body. Cells that break down amino acids produce a highly toxic water-soluble waste product—ammonia. The ammonia is carried through the body dissolved in blood and body fluids. As a result, getting rid of ammonia usually also involves getting rid of water.

INVERTEBRATE EXCRETORY SYSTEMS

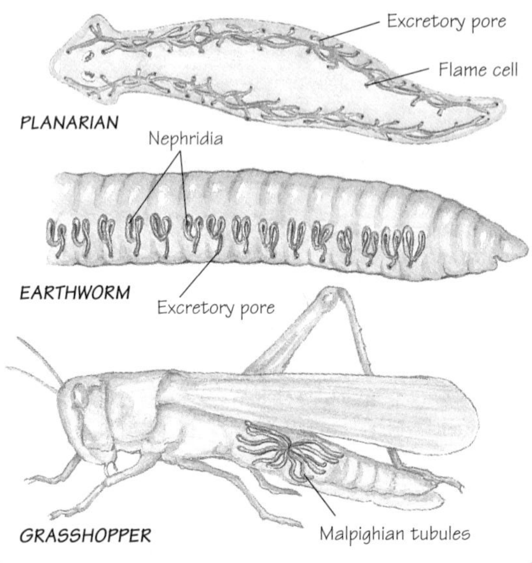

Figure 19–20
Excretory systems help invertebrates control the amount of water in their tissues. Some flatworms, such as planarians, rely on flame cells to remove excess water and ammonia from the body. Other invertebrates, such as earthworms, have nephridia that remove the wastes in the form of urea. In grasshoppers, Malpighian tubules remove the wastes in the form of uric acid.

TEACHER SUPPORT — Background Information

Instead of obtaining oxygen by absorbing it directly through the skin—as flatworms, roundworms, and cnidarians do—mollusks use a more efficient system that makes possible a greater body mass.

Terrestrial mollusks (land snails and slugs) have lungs. Aquatic mollusks have gills that absorb oxygen directly from the water and channel it into the blood system. In bivalves such as clams and oysters, the gills fill a large portion of the mantle cavity.

Cephalopods, such as the squid and octopus, have evolved the most efficient gill systems. Because their gills absorb a greater amount of oxygen, cephalopods are capable of leading far more active lives than other mollusks. In addition, a cephalopod can contract its mantle to speed the flow of water and dissolved oxygen into the mantle cavity and over the gills. Its closed circulatory system includes vast networks of capillaries where gas exchange occurs.

Bio FRONTIER Connections

Starfishes or Coral Reefs?

One of the most beautiful coral reefs in the world—the Great Barrier Reef—is located off the coast of Australia. This reef stretches for kilometers, and sea life of all kinds live around it and in it. Colorful fishes, sea anemones, snails, and eels make it one of the most interesting areas on Earth.

Coral is a cnidarian that feeds off microscopic animals and plants that float by in the water. The coral has tentacles that catch and push food into its mouth. Because coral is a simple soft-bodied creature, it needs special protection. The animal itself secretes the hard outer skeleton, which is made of calcium carbonate. Millions of coral animals create a coral reef.

A Coral's Enemies

But the protection is not perfect, because the coral has enemies. One of these enemies is the crown of thorns starfish.

Oceanographers who study reefs began to notice a change in the Great Barrier Reef in the 1980s. Areas of the reef were beginning to die. When the damage to the Great Barrier Reef was first noticed, scientists also noticed that the crown of thorns starfish was increasing in numbers. The crown of thorns is a brown starfish with poisonous spines, which can cause serious injury to humans. It is known to eat up to 50 square centimeters of coral each year. A number of outbreaks of this starfish have occurred in the past—one in the 1960s and another in the 1980s. Scientists who are seeing an increase in the population of crown of thorns are worried. The starfishes are a threat not only to the Great Barrier Reef, but to reefs throughout the South Pacific and elsewhere.

Crown of thorns starfish devouring coral

Outbreaks of Starfish

Scientists have studied past outbreaks of this starfish by taking core samples of the coral. When the scientists drilled into the coral, they retrieved samples of coral that were hundreds of years old. This is because new coral always forms on top of the old coral. The cores showed fossils of crown of thorns at many levels, some as old as 7000 years!

Some scientists who have studied the problem think that humans are responsible for the outbreak of this starfish. The natural enemies of this starfish are being killed off by overfishing and, therefore, more starfishes are around to eat the coral. Other scientists say that this isn't the case because reefs in other areas of the Pacific show an increase in starfish numbers as well.

Making the Connection

In the 1980s, Australian divers went onto the reef with poison needles and killed the starfishes by injecting them with disease-causing organisms. Do you think this was a good idea? Why or why not? Tourists also are harming the reef by using boats and leaving garbage. Should tourists be banned from the reef or from other natural sites?

Connections

In a single night, an adult crown-of-thorns starfish can clear a coral head that has taken 50 years to grow. Stripped of living polyps, the reef is exposed to small marine animals that bore into and weaken its structure. Regeneration is difficult because the reef soon becomes covered with algae that prevent new coral growth.

No single theory adequately explains the crown-of-thorns plague. Some scientists attribute the starfish's population explosion to the decimation of its chief predator, a large marine snail (the Pacific triton), by shell collectors. However, lack of shell collecting in remote but equally infested areas indicates that other causes may be operating as well. For example, humans destroy living coral when they blast shipping channels. Normally, most of the starfish's larvae are eaten by coral polyps, thus keeping the starfish in check. When human activity kills coral, the larvae mature in safety, and then go on to destroy more coral nearby.

A first-person account of the crown-of-thorns problem, "Starfish Threaten Pacific Reefs" by James A. Sugar, can be found in the March 1970 issue of *National Geographic.*

Answers to Making the Connection

Some students may say that poisons might harm other organisms, while others would accept the use of species-specific diseases. Most students will probably agree that tourists should be banned from fragile reef areas.

TEACHER SUPPORT — Background Information

The Australian government estimated in 1996 that tourism related to the Great Barrier Reef was a $1 billion (Australian) per year business. For this reason alone, Australians are eager to preserve the world's largest coral reef habitat.

While a case can be made for banning tourists from the reef, some environmentalists point out that tourists who snorkel or scuba dive on the reef cannot help becoming aware of the beauty and fragility of the reef ecosystem. Such tourists are likely to speak out in favor of measures that protect the Great Barrier Reef.

Ideas Through Images

Have students examine Figure 19–21, read the caption and the accompanying text, and answer the following questions.

• **Which of the animals in Figure 19–21 show cephalization of the nervous system? How can you tell?** (All three. Nerves are concentrated in the head.)

• **Which animal has the most highly developed brain? How can you tell?** (The octopus. Its brain is larger and more complex than that of the grasshopper.)

Discussion

Show students a video or CD-ROM segment of the noted experiment in which an octopus learned, through trial and error, how to unscrew the lid on a glass jar to reach (and eat) a crab inside. In a follow-up discussion, ask students to describe the observable evidence that the octopus was acting intelligently in its attempts to reach the crab. Also ask them whether they are surprised that such a seemingly simple animal has intelligence.

Investigate

Research Ask students to research insects' sensory organs, particularly their compound eyes. (See Background Information on the next page.) Encourage students to find pictures illustrating insect-eye views of scenes to compare with the views they see with their own eyes.

Laboratory Investigation

The Laboratory Investigation, Comparing Nervous Systems, on pages 462–463 is appropriate to use at this point in the chapter.

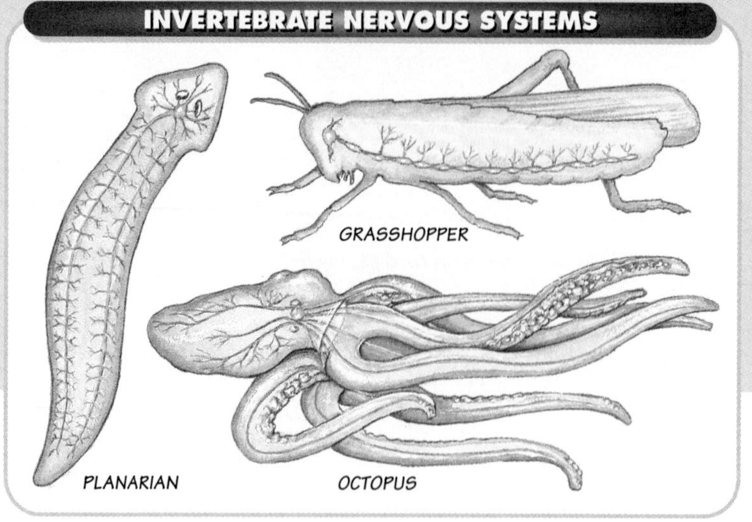

Figure 19–21 *A nervous system allows an animal to respond to its environment. Notice how the nervous system of invertebrates contains a greater concentration of nerve cells in the head region as they become more complex.*

Excretion in Water

Many marine invertebrates—cnidarians, for example—are thin-bodied and surrounded by water. Ammonia leaves the body of these animals by diffusion through body surfaces or through thin gill membranes.

Some freshwater flatworms have excretory systems containing **flame cells** that remove water and some water-soluble wastes such as ammonia at the same time. The flame cells form a network that empties water and wastes through tiny openings in the animal's skin. Many of the wastes, however, still leave the body through diffusion.

Other groups—such as annelids, mollusks, and invertebrate chordates—have evolved structures called **nephridia** (neh-FRIHD-ee-uh; singular: nephridium). Nephridia take the bodily fluids, remove the wastes, and return water and other important solutes to the body. Waste products are eliminated from the body in the form of urine.

☑ ***Checkpoint*** What are flame cells? ❶

Excretion on Land

Terrestrial invertebrates have a different problem. They must get rid of body wastes while conserving water. Some groups convert ammonia into urea, which is soluble in water and is much less toxic than ammonia. Urea can be concentrated and stored in a smaller amount of water than an equivalent amount of ammonia. This waste-containing liquid, called urine, is collected and expelled from the body. Other groups, such as insects and some spiders and scorpions, convert wastes into uric acid, which is removed from the body by structures called **Malpighian** (mal-PIHG-ee-uhn) **tubules.** Much of the uric acid precipitates out of solution, forming a paste that is added to the insects' other solid wastes. Thus, their excretion process loses little water.

☑ ***Checkpoint*** What are Malpighian tubules? ❷

Response

All animals that respond rapidly to their environment do so because of a collection of organs called the nervous system. Amazingly, the basic operations of individual nerve cells are virtually identical—from the most primitive to the most complex animals. The pattern in which nerve cells are arranged, however, changes dramatically from phylum to phylum.

TEACHER SUPPORT

Activity

INVESTIGATING EARTHWORMS' RESPONSE TO LIGHT

In the following activity, students observe earthworms' movement away from light and infer the function of that adaptation.

1. Roll a sheet of clear acetate into a tube with a diameter of about 5 cm and tape the edge. The tube should be at least 30 cm long.
2. Cover one half of the tube with dark paper.
3. Place several earthworms into the uncovered half.
4. Close both ends of the tube with a crumpled paper towel.
5. Leave the tube undisturbed for about 15 minutes; then examine it to see where the earthworms are located. (Most likely, in the darkened half of the tube.)
6. What function does this response serve in earthworm survival? (It causes them to burrow into soil or crawl under leaves to escape predators and to avoid exposure to the drying effects of sunlight and air.)

Centralization

The most primitive invertebrates, including such cnidarians as hydras, have a loose, netlike arrangement of nerve cells. This nerve net spreads throughout their body. Other cnidarians, however, show the beginnings of **centralization,** in which the nerve cells are more concentrated and form nerve cords or nerve rings around the mouth. Nerve cords or nerve rings more efficiently send messages from one body part to another.

Cephalization

As animals began traveling in a head-first direction, nerve cells and sensory cells that gather information from the environment began to concentrate in the head. In primitive flatworms, this does not amount to much more than a few clumps of nerve cells called ganglia (GAN-glee-uh) in the head region. But in insects and some mollusks, ganglia grow larger and become organized into structures that can be called brains. From these brains, collections of nerve cells called nerve cords carry information to and from other parts of the body.

Along with the development of brains, invertebrates began to evolve more and more specialized sensory cells. Flatworms, for example, have simple eyespots that detect the presence or absence of light. Insects, on the other hand, have well-developed eyes that detect complex patterns and colors.

Figure 19–22
CAREER TRACK
Ocean technicians study invertebrates as well as vertebrates that live in the sea. They record data and chart the movements of many animals, studying their behaviors and habitats.

Reproduction

Although nearly every form of reproduction is found among the invertebrates, they are all capable of sexual reproduction. Sexual reproduction helps create and maintain genetic diversity. For that reason, life cycles that involve sexual reproduction are believed to improve a species' ability to survive and cope with environmental change. Many invertebrates, including most of those that reproduce asexually at times, engage in sexual reproduction that involves males that produce sperm and females that produce eggs.

Section Review 19-3

1. **List** the three kinds of skeletons found in invertebrates.
2. **Compare** open and closed circulatory systems.
3. **Critical Thinking—Sequencing** Explain how the nervous system has evolved from cnidarians through invertebrate chordates.
4. **MINI LAB** What can you observe about an earthworm's movements? **Design an experiment** to answer this question.

4 ASSESS

Quick Check

Ask students to list the seven body systems discussed in this section and, for each system, to identify the major types of organs found in different invertebrates.

Section Review 19-3

1. Hydrostatic skeleton, exoskeleton, endoskeleton.
2. Open: Blood is not entirely contained in blood vessels but is released directly into body tissues. Closed: Blood is contained in closed vessels and does not come into direct contact with body tissues.
3. Students' answers should focus on the increasing complexity of invertebrates' nervous systems.
4. Students' experimental designs will vary but should focus on the movement produced by the earthworm's hydrostatic skeleton.

Skills Trace
Experimenting
- Focus p. 456
- Practice p. 459
- Assess p. 466

Learning Modality

Visual Learning Ask students to outline this section, with the seven body systems as major headings, the types of organs as subheads, and supporting details listed below each subhead.

Checkpoint

1. Cells that remove water and some water-soluble wastes for excretion.
2. Structures that remove uric acid from the body.

TEACHER SUPPORT

Background Information

A large measure of insects' survival ability is due to the development of their senses. In addition to their antennae, the bodies of most insects are covered with hairs that are sensitive to touch and can detect chemicals through smell and taste as well. These hairs are concentrated on the head and the lower legs, where they are most likely to come in contact with objects and materials in the insects' environment.

Insects have compound eyes consisting of many lenses—up to 30,000 in some dragonflies. These large multi-lensed eyes give insects the ability to scan a wide area at one time, allowing them to detect the motion of predators or prey.

Some insects rely heavily on hearing. Mosquitoes, for example, can detect sounds with their antennae. Crickets, grasshoppers, and other insects have a membrane called a tympanum on the abdomen or legs. These structures function much like the human eardrum in sensing sound vibrations.

SECTION 19–4

Specialized Reproductive Cycles

Performance Objectives

- Identify an advantage of hermaphroditism.
- Explain the processes of external and internal fertilization.

1 ENGAGE

Ideas Through Images

Have students examine Figure 19–23 and read the caption. Then ask them to recall another organism they observed reproducing by budding. If necessary, remind them of their observations of yeast (Chapter 18, Chapter Discovery Learning Activity on page 414 and Discussion on page 423). Then have students answer the following questions.

- **Is budding an example of sexual or asexual reproduction, and why?** (Asexual, because no genetic material is exchanged; the offspring are genetically identical to the parent.)
- **What is the result of sexual reproduction?** (Offspring with new combinations of genetic material.)

2 EXPLORE

Discussion

Ask students to recall and describe the advantages to a species of sexual reproduction. (It increases genetic diversity, which improves a species' ability to survive and cope with environmental change.) If necessary, have students refer to page 459 to find the answer.

SECTION 19–4 BRANCHING OUT In Depth

Specialized Reproductive Cycles

GUIDE FOR READING

- **Describe** an advantage of hermaphrodites.
- **Compare** external and internal fertilization.

THE ABILITY TO REPRODUCE IS essential to the survival of any species. As a result, life cycles of invertebrates are important—both to the animals and to humans who may be interested in either breeding them or getting rid of them. Interestingly, there is not a single general trend in reproductive style that stretches across the invertebrates. Particular styles of reproduction vary in various phyla, but even the most highly evolved invertebrates use a wide range of strategies for perpetuating their kind.

Asexual Reproduction

Some animals—such as sponges, certain cnidarians, and some echinoderms—can regrow lost body parts. This is a simple form of asexual reproduction, known as regeneration. A planarian, for example, can be cut into several pieces, each of which will grow into a complete worm.

Other invertebrates, such as sponges and cnidarians, also reproduce asexually in a process called budding. Budding is a form of reproduction in which a parent organism grows a bud that becomes an identical individual. It then becomes larger and usually breaks free.

Hermaphrodites

In many species of mollusks, annelids, and echinoderms, individuals have both male and female reproductive structures. These individuals are **hermaphrodites** (her-MAF-ruh-dights). A hermaphrodite has both male and female reproductive organs and produces both sperm and eggs. Usually, though, two individuals

Figure 19–23
Invertebrates show a variety of reproductive techniques. (a) These nudibranchs are hermaphrodites and exchange sperm during mating. (b) Hydras reproduce asexually by budding. Notice the large bud forming on the right side of the hydra.

TEACHER SUPPORT

Activity

OBSERVING HYDRAS

Provide living hydras that students can examine with a microscope, as described below. The pond water that you or students collected earlier to obtain protists for examination (Chapter 18, Activity on page 418) may contain hydras. Hydras also may be present in a classroom aquarium—usually near food that has sunk to the bottom of the tank. Use a medicine dropper or pipette to remove several hydras from the protist culture or aquarium. Place them in a separate container with some of the pond or aquarium water so students can access them easily.

1. Place a drop of water from the hydra culture on a slide and examine it with a microscope. If you do not find a hydra, examine another drop from the culture.
2. Draw the hydra's structure.
3. Examine hydras periodically until you find one that is in the process of budding. Draw the budding hydra.

mate by exchanging sperm, rather than by self-fertilization. If you think about it, you can see how this strategy has advantages in small populations or when individuals are widely scattered. **If any two sexually mature hermaphrodites meet, they can mate with one another, producing two groups of offspring.** In species with separate sexes, individuals must be of different sexes to mate, and they produce only one group of offspring per mating.

☑ **Checkpoint** How do hermaphrodites reproduce? (1)

Figure 19–24 *Notice the brown eggs being released as this* Acorpora *coral is spawning. Spawning is an example of external fertilization.*

External and Internal Fertilization

External fertilization and **internal fertilization** are two basic ways in which sperm cells and egg cells are brought together in sexual reproduction. **External fertilization occurs when eggs and sperm meet outside the organism's body.** This process is called spawning. Generally, the eggs give off a chemical attractant that causes sperm to swim toward them and fertilize them in water. Fertilized eggs typically develop into larvae (singular: larva) that move and drift about in the current. A larva is the immature stage of an organism and is unlike the adult form in appearance. This style of reproduction is simple, but it has some disadvantages. For one thing, it is not very efficient because many eggs and sperm never meet. Therefore, animals that reproduce this way release large quantities of eggs and sperm when they spawn. In addition, this sort of fertilization can work only underwater or in very wet places.

The other option, of course, is internal fertilization. **During internal fertilization, the eggs and sperm meet inside the body of the egg-producing individual.** In more complex invertebrates, this meeting is arranged by mating, in which the male deposits sperm inside the female's reproductive tract. Fertilization takes place within the body of the female, which may then either care for the eggs in some way or deposit them on a rock or other convenient place.

Section Review 19–4

1. **Describe** one advantage of hermaphrodites.
2. **Compare** internal and external fertilization.
3. **BRANCHING OUT ACTIVITY** **Construct a chart** in which you compare the body systems of all living invertebrate phyla, including the method of reproduction. Add artwork or photographs to illustrate the different phyla. Display your chart in the classroom.

TEACHER SUPPORT

Background Information

In addition to asexual reproduction by budding, hydras can also reproduce sexually by producing sperm and eggs. In most species, the individuals are either male or female. A few hydra species, however, are hermaphroditic.

3 TEACH

Discussion

Tell students that starfishes are capable of regenerating lost body parts. Explain that some shellfish harvesters have tried to control starfish predation by cutting them up and throwing the pieces back into the sea. Ask students to explain why this practice is counterproductive.

4 ASSESS

Quick Check

Have students list and describe each type of reproduction discussed in this section.

Section Review 19-4

1. Each mating pair produces two sets of offspring.
2. Internal: Eggs and sperm meet inside the female's body. External: Eggs and sperm meet outside the organism's body.
3. Charts should include the nine phyla introduced in Section 19–2 and seven body systems: skeletal, digestive, circulatory, respiratory, excretory, nervous, and reproductive.

Learning Modality

Visual Learning Have students draw sketches to describe each form of reproduction discussed in this section.

☑ Checkpoint

(1) When two sexually mature hermaphrodites mate, they exchange sperm, and each individual produces offspring.

Ancillary Support

The resources below can be used to support your teaching strategy for these two pages.

TR Explore: More or Less
BL Inquiry Activity: Inside, Outside

Laboratory Investigation

Comparing Nervous Systems

Before the Lab

1. Set up separate planaria and hydra cultures. Planaria can be obtained from pond water or a hay infusion (see Chapter 18, Activity on page 418). Hydras may also be available in a hay infusion or could be obtained from a classroom aquarium (see Activity on page 460 of this chapter).
2. If you purchase planaria and hydra cultures from a biological supply house, make sure you order them well in advance for delivery by the date on which students will need them.

Pre-Lab Discussion

Have students read the entire procedure. Then ask students the following questions.

What is the purpose of this investigation? (To compare the response to stimuli in a hydra and a planarian and make inferences about the complexity of their nervous systems.)

Which types of invertebrates—cnidarians or flatworms—have more complex body systems in general? (Flatworms.)

Which do you expect will evidence a more advanced nervous system? (Flatworms.)

How do you think you will be able to tell which organism's nervous system is more advanced? (Its responses to stimuli will be more complicated and specific, less generalized.)

Laboratory Investigation

Comparing Nervous Systems

As the animal phyla move from simple to complex, the phyla develop more specialized features. In this investigation, you will compare the nervous systems of a cnidarian (hydra) and a platyhelminthe (planarian) to determine which phylum has a more advanced nervous system.

Problem

How can you **compare** the response to stimuli in a hydra and a planarian?

Materials (per group)

- culture of live hydras
- culture of live planarians
- Petri dish or small clear container
- dissecting probe or straight pin
- microscope
- medicine dropper

Procedure

1. **Use a medicine dropper to transfer one hydra to the center of the Petri dish. The hydras can be seen if you hold the culture up to the light.**
2. **Place the Petri dish on the microscope stage. Use the low-power objective of the microscope to focus on the hydra and observe its movements for 5 minutes.**
3. **After some time the hydra will stretch and lengthen. With the dissecting probe, gently touch the extended tentacle. Allow the hydra to recover from the stimulus, then touch the dissecting probe to another part of the organism. Record your observations.**

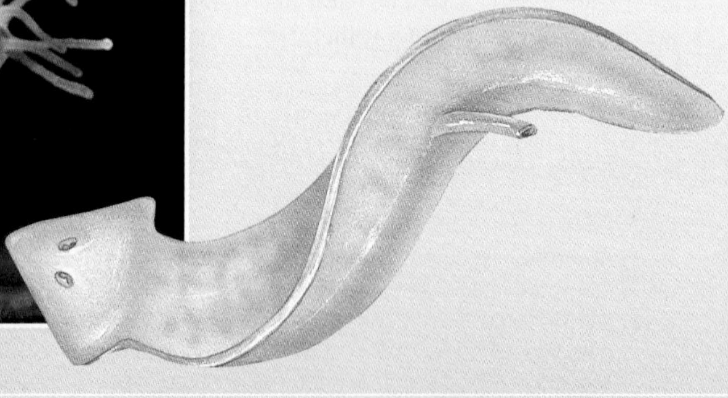

Safety Tips

- Caution students to handle the probe or pin carefully.
- Remind students to clean up any spills immediately.
- Have students wash their hands when they have finished the procedure.

4. Place the hydra back in the culture and rinse out the Petri dish.

5. Use the medicine dropper to transfer a planarian from the culture to the center of the Petri dish.

6. Use the medicine dropper to give the planarian more water (one dropper full should be enough).

7. Place the Petri dish on the microscope stage and use the low-power objective of the microscope to focus on the planarian.

8. After some time—when the planarian is extended and moving smoothly across the dish—gently touch the head area with the dissecting probe. Allow the planarian to recover from the stimulus, then touch different parts of its body. Observe how the planarian reacts to each probe. Record your observations.

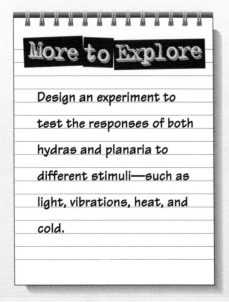

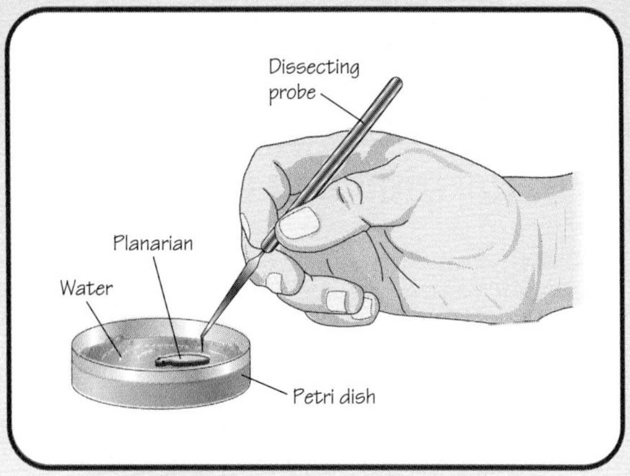

Observations

1. How did the hydra react to each probe? Indicate the body part touched and the response.
2. How did the planarian react to each probe? Indicate the body part touched and the response.
3. Did the planarian react differently when you touched its head and its tail?

Analysis and Conclusions

1. Did the animals respond differently from each other when probed? Describe each animal's reaction to being touched by the stimulus.
2. Which of the two animals do you think has a more advanced nervous system?
3. Which of the two animals you observed showed cephalization? Give examples to prove your point.

More to Explore

Design an experiment to test the responses of both hydras and planaria to different stimuli—such as light, vibrations, heat, and cold.

Answers to Observations

1. The entire hydra contracts into a ball shape. Its reactions are identical regardless of where it is touched.
2. When touched on or near the head, the planarian pulls its head back or moves it in the opposite direction from the stimulus. When touched on the tail end, it pulls its tail away from the stimulus.
3. Yes. (See answer 2.)

Answers to Analysis and Conclusions

1. Yes. (See Observations answers 1 and 2.)
2. The planarian, because its responses were more specific to the stimuli.
3. The planarian. Sample: The hydra's responses are generalized—its entire body reacts to the stimulus. The planarian's responses are specific—it moves only the body area that has been touched. This indicates that the planarian has some type of central nerve area that interprets the impulse before the animal reacts.

More to Explore

Monitor students' experimental designs to make sure that they do not harm the animals, that they test specific, observable responses to each type of stimulus, and that they test only one type of stimulus at a time. Provide materials such as flashlights, warm and cold water, and ice cubes for students' experiments.

Skills Development

Students will use these skills while completing the laboratory investigation: observing, comparing, interpreting data, and making inferences.

Teaching Strategies

1. Help any students who have difficulty positioning the specimens properly under the microscope and focusing the lens so the specimens can be seen clearly.
2. Emphasize that the planarian's and hydra's soft bodies are extremely sensitive to touch, so students need only gentle touches with the probe to elicit a response.

CHAPTER 19

Study Guide

Review Strategy

Divide the class into eight groups, and assign each group one of the invertebrate phyla covered in this chapter (excluding invertebrate chordates). Explain that students in each group are to become the class experts on the group's assigned phylum. Give students some time to review the text material; then have each group give a brief presentation on the group's phylum, explaining its major characteristics, outlining the similarities and differences between its phylum and the others, and giving examples of organisms in that phylum. Encourage other groups to ask the experts questions.

Study Guide

Summarizing Key Concepts

The key concepts in each section of this chapter are listed below to help you review the chapter content. Make sure you understand each concept and its relationship to other concepts and to the theme of this chapter.

19–1 Evolution of Multicellular Animals

- As animals evolved, they became increasingly more complex.
- All animals must perform the same functions: body support and movement, feeding and digestion, respiration, excretion, internal transport, and response to the environment.

19–2 A Survey of Living Invertebrates

- The common ancestors of all multicellular animals had already evolved two distinct cell layers separated by a jellylike middle layer.
- Another important evolutionary trend is the existence of a coelom, or mesoderm-lined cavity.
- The evolution of body plans that are built up from several body compartments is another important evolutionary trend.

19–3 Form and Function in Invertebrates

- The three main types of skeletons found in the animal kingdom are hydrostatic skeletons, exoskeletons, and endoskeletons.
- In some invertebrates, digestion takes place inside the cells. In others, digestion takes place outside the cells.
- Open circulatory systems are systems in which blood from the heart is not contained in blood vessels. Closed circulatory systems keep blood contained in a system of closed vessels that pass through various parts of the body and return blood back to the heart.

19–4 Specialized Reproductive Cycles

- Hermaphrodites are organisms that have both male and female reproductive organs and produce both eggs and sperm.
- External fertilization occurs when eggs and sperm meet outside the organism's body.
- During internal fertilization, the eggs and sperm meet inside the body of the egg-producing individual.

Reviewing Key Terms

Review the following vocabulary terms and their meaning. Then use each term in a complete sentence.

19–2 A Survey of Living Invertebrates

ectoderm
endoderm
mesoderm
coelom
segment
radial symmetry
bilateral symmetry
cephalization

19–3 Form and Function in Invertebrates

hydrostatic skeleton
exoskeleton
chitin
endoskeleton
intracellular digestion
gastrovascular cavity
extracellular digestion
flame cell
nephridium
Malpighian tubule
centralization

19–4 Specialized Reproductive Cycles

hermaphrodite
external fertilization
internal fertilization

Inquiry-Based Strategy

Using earthworms from the classroom culture set up in the Chapter Discovery Learning Activity, students could design and carry out experiments to test earthworms' responses to various stimuli, such as vibrations, heat, cold, varying amounts of moisture in the soil, and so forth. Students also could investigate the complexity of the earthworm's nervous system by repeating the procedure used with the planarian and hydra in the Laboratory Investigation, pages 462–463. Make sure students' experiments do not harm the earthworms. Also, for each investigation, have students explain how the specific response to a particular stimulus helps the earthworm survive in its environment.

Recalling Main Ideas

Choose the letter of the answer that best completes the statement or answers the question.

1. Which is not a characteristic of animals?

a. eukaryotic **c.** heterotrophic
b. autotrophic **d.** multicellular

2. Tissues that develop from the endoderm form the

a. skeletal system. **c.** skin.
b. nervous system. **d.** digestive system.

3. The mesoderm-lined body cavity found in some invertebrates is called a

a. segment. **c.** coelom.
b. nephridium. **d.** mesoderm.

4. The first animals to show bilateral symmetry were the

a. flatworms. **c.** sponges.
b. annelids. **d.** mollusks.

5. The largest animal phylum contains the

a. echinoderms. **c.** arthropods.
b. nematodes. **d.** platyhelminthes.

6. An external skeleton is a(an)

a. hydrostatic skeleton. **c.** endoskeleton.
b. exoskeleton. **d.** coelom.

7. Excretory structures in flatworms are known as

a. flame cells. **c.** nephridia.
b. Malpighian tubules. **d.** trachea.

8. Which animals have both male and female reproductive organs?

a. pseudocoelomates **c.** hermaphrodites
b. acoelomates **d.** coelomates

Putting It All Together

Using the information on pages xxx to xxxi, complete the following concept map.

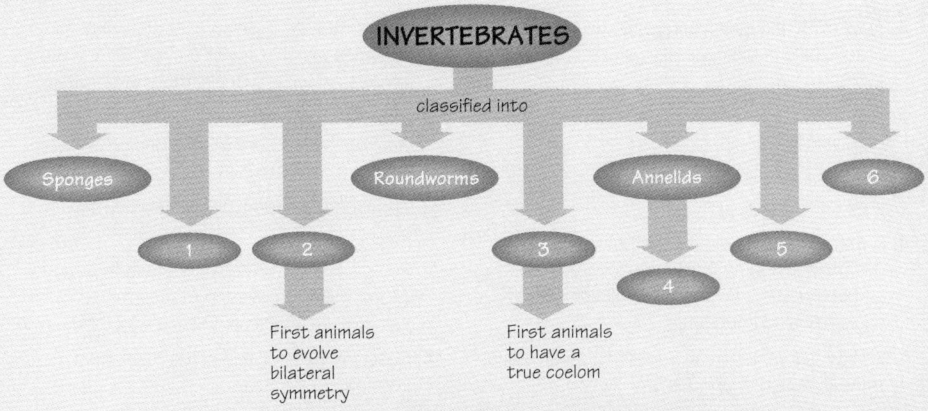

Putting It All Together

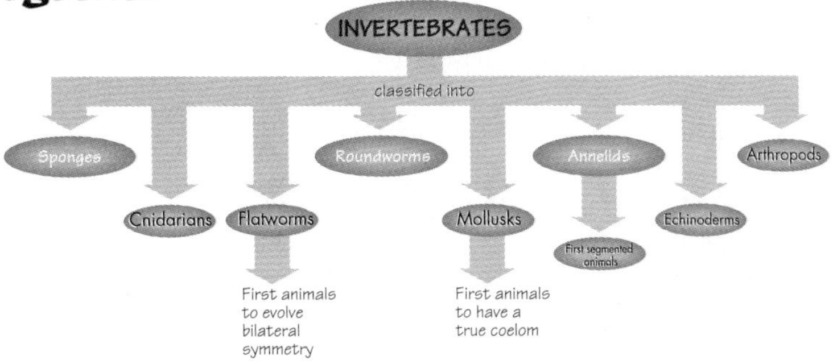

Recalling Main Ideas

1. b
2. d
3. c
4. a
5. c
6. b
7. a
8. c

Assessment

Reviewing What You Learned

1. About 600 million years ago.
2. A great burst of evolutionary change that produced a great variety of complex animals.
3. Body support and movement, feeding and digestion, respiration, excretion, internal transport, response to the environment, and reproduction.
4. An ectoderm is the outer cell layer. An endoderm is the inner cell layer. A mesoderm is the middle cell layer.
5. Mollusca.
6. Sponges make up the phylum Porifera.
7. Starfishes, sea urchins, and sea lilies are examples of echinoderms.
8. Chelicerates, crustaceans, and insects are the three largest groups.
9. Invertebrate chordates have an endoskeleton with a stiff rod (notochord) to which muscles are attached.
10. In animals with radial symmetry, body parts repeat around an imaginary line drawn through the center of the body. In animals with bilateral symmetry, body parts are identical on both sides of an imaginary line drawn through the center.

Skills Trace

Observing

- Focus p. 449
- Practice p. 451
- Assess p. 466

Assessment (continued)

11. In an open circulatory system, blood from the heart is not entirely contained in blood vessels but is released directly onto body tissues. In a closed circulatory system, blood is contained in vessels that pass through various parts of the body and return it to the heart without direct contact with tissues.
12. The concentration of nerve cells and sensory cells in the head.
13. Intracellular digestion takes place inside body cells. Extracellular digestion takes place outside body cells.
14. Nephridia are structures that remove nitrogenous wastes from bodily fluids and return water and other important solutes to the body. Flame cells remove water and some water-soluble wastes such as ammonia from the body. Malpighian tubules remove uric acid from the body.
15. In internal fertilization, eggs and sperm meet inside the body of the egg-producing individual. In external fertilization, eggs and sperm meet outside the organism's body.

Expanding the Concepts

1. Tissues made of specialized cells enabled animals to perform certain tasks more efficiently than generalized cells could.
2. To live on land, animals had to evolve ways to perform essential survival tasks without losing too much water in the process.
3. The mesoderm developed into the body's skeleton and muscles.
4. A coelom provides an open space inside the body within which organs can grow and function without being squeezed or twisted by body movements. The fluid in some coeloms also plays a role in carrying food, wastes, or dissolved gases from one part of the body to another.
5. Segments allow an animal to increase in body size with a minimum of new genetic material because certain structures are repeated in each segment. In addition, as animals become more complex, different segments become specialized for specific functions.

Assessment

Reviewing What You Learned

Answer each of the following in a complete sentence.

1. When did the earliest known animals appear on Earth?
2. What is the Cambrian explosion?
3. What characteristics do all animals share?
4. What is an ectoderm? An endoderm? A mesoderm?
5. In which phylum did a true coelom first appear?
6. What type of organisms make up the phylum Porifera?
7. What are some examples of echinoderms?
8. Name the three largest groups of arthropods.
9. What characteristic does the phylum Chordata have that no other invertebrate phyla have?
10. What can you **observe** in an animal with radial symmetry? Bilateral symmetry?
11. How do an open circulatory system and a closed circulatory system compare?
12. Define cephalization.
13. Distinguish between intracellular and extracellular digestion.
14. What are nephridia? Flame cells? Malpighian tubules?
15. Compare internal fertilization and external fertilization.

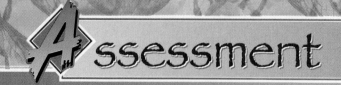

Expanding the Concepts

Discuss each of the following in a brief paragraph.

1. How might the development of specialized tissues help in the rapid explosion of animal forms?
2. What problems did animals face as they moved onto land?
3. Why was the development of the mesoderm so important?
4. A major structural division of the animal kingdom is the acoelomates, psuedocoelomates, and coelomates. Why is the evolution of coelomates so important?
5. Why is segmentation an important development in the evolution of animals?
6. How might the development of jointed appendages give rise to the largest and most diverse group of animals, the arthropods?
7. How would you **design an experiment** to illustrate how a hydrostatic skeleton helps an organism to move?
8. Describe the three types of invertebrate skeletons.
9. A complete digestive system (mouth to anus) allows better processing of food materials for extracellular digestion. Explain why this is true.
10. Describe the evolution of the respiratory system from gills to trachea.

6. Students may infer that jointed appendages provide greater mobility and flexibility.

7. Students may cite the experiment they designed for the MINI LAB on page 456 or another experiment.

Skills Trace
Experimenting
- Focus p. 456
- Practice p. 459
- Assess p. 466

8. Hydrostatic skeleton: Muscles surround and are supported by a water-filled body cavity. When the muscles contract, they push against the water. Exoskeleton: An external skeleton with muscles attached to its inside surface and with thin, flexible joints. Endoskeleton: A skeleton located within the body.
9. Sample answer: Food moves through the digestive system in only one way, so different stages of digestion can occur in specific areas or specialized organs along the digestive track.
10. Because gills would dry out quickly away from water, terrestrial animals evolved other respiratory structures, such as tracheal tubes.

Extending Your Thinking

Use the skills you have developed in this chapter to answer the following.

1. **Hypothesizing** How can crabs, which have a rigid nonliving exoskeleton, grow larger while being restricted by this exoskeleton? Endocrinologists have demonstrated that two hormones may be involved—one that increases the production of urine and one that decreases the production of urine. Develop a hypothesis to explain how they might work.
2. **Using the writing process** Write a one-page summary of the various adaptations that have occurred in the respiratory system of organisms that migrated from life in water to life on land. Start with single cells and moist membranes.
3. **Analyzing** Maintaining a proper water balance for organisms is crucial, no matter where they live. Combining the problem of water balance with toxic products produced by an organism causes an extremely dangerous situation to develop. How have organisms been able to solve this difficult situation, especially as they move to terrestrial environments?
4. **Hypothesizing** The fossil record indicates extreme diversity of the invertebrate form. Today, only a few invertebrates, such as the common cockroach, have survived the test of time, while other organisms, such as the trilobites, have disappeared. Develop a hypothesis to explain this situation.
5. **Problem solving** One group of people demonstrated that almost 85 percent of all blindness throughout the world is preventable. Much of the blindness is caused by various invertebrates (especially certain worms), protists, or the lack of certain vitamins. How would you set out to improve this situation, keeping in mind the necessity of maintaining the balance of nature?

Applying Your Skills

Worm or Beetle?

Is a mealworm really a worm? A mealworm may look like a worm, but it is really the larval stage of the Tenebria *beetle.*

1. Working in a group, observe three or four mealworms for five minutes, using a magnifying glass.
2. Identify as many physical characteristics of the mealworm as you can, then record these in your journal.
3. Draw a picture of your mealworm, identifying the various body parts.
4. Gently touch the mealworm with a pencil eraser. Record its response.
5. Place an object in front of the mealworm. How does the mealworm react? Does it go around, over, or under the object?

• GOING FURTHER •

6. From the chapter, select at least six invertebrate organisms and describe their method of locomotion. Does each have "feet"?
7. What are the common characteristics of the invertebrates you selected? Differences?

Extending Your Thinking

1. Students should recall that in order to grow larger, animals with exoskeletons must shed the skeleton and grow a new one. Accept all hypotheses that relate an increase or decrease in urine production to the shedding process.
2. Single unprotected cells cannot survive in a dry environment. Small, soft-bodied invertebrates can accomplish gas exchange simply by diffusion through their body surfaces. With aquatic invertebrates, gills expose a large surface area to the water. Terrestrial invertebrates have specialized organs for breathing air.
3. Aquatic invertebrates rid their bodies of nitrogenous wastes by diffusion through body surfaces or through thin gill membranes or through flame cells; these processes retain essential water and maintain proper water balance in the animal's body. Some terrestrial invertebrates convert ammonia to concentrated urea and expel it with a small amount of water as urine. Other terrestrial invertebrates have Malpighian tubules, which rid the body of wastes while conserving essential water.
4. Students may suggest that many species evolved structures and systems that proved to be poorly adapted to environmental changes that occurred over time.
5. Students should recognize the value of using natural biological controls to reduce populations of disease-causing organisms, establishing and maintaining adequate nutrition and proper sanitary conditions, and educating people about the causes of blindness so they can alter their behavior appropriately.

Applying Your Skills

Teacher Notes

- If you had students do the Investigate activity on page 450, you already have a supply of mealworms for this activity. If not, you can obtain mealworms from a pet supply store.
- Provide students with mealworms, lab trays, and magnifying glasses.
- Remind students not to harm the mealworms.

Answers

4. It will recoil.
5. The mealworm goes around the object.
6. Only mollusks, some annelids and echinoderms, and arthropods have some form of "feet."
7. Answers will depend on the invertebrates selected.

Scoring Rubric

4 Response is thorough, accurate, and creative; shows an in-depth understanding of science skills, procedures, and concepts.

3 Response is complete, mostly accurate, and original; shows a satisfactory understanding of science skills, procedures, and concepts.

2 Response is mostly complete but includes some inaccuracies; shows an adequate understanding of science skills, procedures, and concepts.

1 Response is only partially complete and has many inaccuracies; shows an incomplete understanding of science skills, procedures, and concepts.

0 Response is mostly incomplete and/or inaccurate; shows a lack of understanding of science skills, procedures, and concepts.

Chapter 20 Animals: Vertebrates

Content Management	Student Edition Activities
■ Section 20–1 Evolution of Vertebrates, pp. 469–474 The Vertebrate Family Tree What Is a Vertebrate? Fishes—Early Vertebrates Challenges of Life on Land The Mesozoic Era The Age of Mammals	
■ Section 20–2 A Survey of Living Vertebrates, pp. 475–478 Classification of Vertebrates Jawless Fishes Cartilaginous Fishes Bony Fishes Amphibians Reptiles Birds Mammals	MINI LAB: A Fishy Story, p. 477
■ Section 20–3 Form and Function in Vertebrates, pp. 479–485 Support and Movement Feeding and Digestion Respiration Internal Transport Temperature Control Excretion Response Reproduction	Laboratory Investigation: Vertebrate Circulatory Systems, pp. 488–489 MINI LAB: How to Keep Warm, p. 484
◆ BRANCHING OUT • In Depth Section 20–4 Reproductive Adaptations to Life on Land, pp. 486–487 Development of the Amniotic Egg Methods of Reproduction	

■ These sections cover all the necessary content and concepts for a basic course in biology.
◆ This section covers content and concepts that are either applications or extensions of the basic material.

Integration Strategies

SE Careers, p. 473
Social Studies, p. 473

Assessment Strategies

SE Chapter Review, pp. 490–493
Section Reviews
Chapter Test
BL Chapter Review
Practice Test
CTB Chapter 20 Test

Tech Prep

Teaching strategies appropriate for students who are in technical/vocational programs or who are considering post-secondary technical education can be found on the following **TE** pages: 479 and 485.

Meeting the Standards

Sections 20–1 through 20–4 cover all five of the content standards under **Biological Evolution** and three of the four content standards under **The Behavior of Organisms** as described on pages 185 and 187 of The National Science Education Standards.

Chapter Planning Guide

Teacher's Edition Activities	Other Activities	Media and Technology
Chapter Discovery Learning Activity, p. 468 Inquiry Activity: Modeling a Vertebral Column, p. 470 Investigate: Model Building, p. 470 Investigate: Research, p. 471 Investigate: Research, p. 473 Activity: Modeling Adaptive Radiation, p. 474	**TR** Writing in Biology: Creature Feature Enrich: From Gills to Ears **BL** Inquiry Activity: Show a Little Backbone	**TB** The Evolution of Four-Limbed Vertebrates, #26
Investigate: Long-Term Project, p. 476 Investigate: Observing Vertebrates, p. 476	**TR** Apply: Two of a Kind **BL** Inquiry Activity: Creature Comforts	
Inquiry Activity: Examining a Human Skeleton, p. 479 Inquiry Activity: Modeling Skeletal Motion, p. 480 Activity: Modeling Heart Function, p. 481 Investigate: Model Building, p. 481 Investigate: Cooperative Learning, p. 484	**LM** Observing Vertebrate Skeletons, #39 Examining Primate Hands, #40 **TR** Explore: We Love to Fly and It Shows **BL** Inquiry Activity: Movin' On Up	
Inquiry Activity: Examining a Bird's Egg, p. 486	**TR** Apply: Egging You On **BL** Inquiry Activity: The Yolk's on You	

KEY: SE Student Edition **TE** Teacher's Edition **LM** Laboratory Manual **TR** Teaching Resources
BL BioLog **TB** Transparency Box **CTB** Computer Test Bank

Materials List

TE Chapter Discovery Learning Activity, p. 468 (45 minutes for setup, 5–10 minutes for each observation); materials to set up two aquariums, one with freshwater fishes and the other with frog eggs or young tadpoles; calendar.

TE Inquiry Activity: **Modeling a Vertebral Column,** p. 470 (30 minutes); materials of students' choice, such as drinking straws and tape.

TE Investigate: **Model Building,** p. 470 (20 minutes); drawing materials and the materials used in the Inquiry Activity on page 470.

TE Activity: **Modeling Adaptive Radiation,** p. 474 (30 minutes); copy of world map, scissors, colored marker or pencil.

TE Investigate: **Long-Term Project,** p. 476 (30 minutes); poster board, art supplies, two aquariums set up in the Chapter Discovery Learning Activity.

TE Investigate: **Observing Vertebrates,** p. 476 (20 minutes); live salamander, newt, lizard, and snake; clear-plastic carrying cases; or, videos or CD-ROM programs about these animals.

SE MINI LAB: **A Fishy Story,** p. 477 (30–45 minutes); aquarium with fish, large beaker, aquarium water, net, clock with second hand.

TE Inquiry Activity: **Examining a Human Skeleton,** p. 479 (30 minutes); life-size laboratory model or small plastic model of human skeleton.

TE Inquiry Activity: **Modeling Skeletal Motion,** p. 480 (45 minutes); variety of materials for creating models of bones and joints, balloons, rubber bands.

TE Activity: **Modeling Heart Function,** p. 481 (15–20 minutes); white and colored index cards, marker.

TE Investigate: **Model Building,** p. 481 (30 minutes for the initial investigation, 5 minutes for the following day); well-cooked beef or chicken, mortar and pestle, green twig from a tree, meat tenderizer, 2 jars.

SE MINI LAB: **How to Keep Warm,** p. 484 (30–45 minutes); different-size containers, thermometer, water, timer, feathers, pieces of fur.

TE Inquiry Activity: **Examining a Bird's Egg,** p. 486 (20 minutes); hard-boiled chicken egg, knife.

Animals: Vertebrates

Introducing the Chapter

. . . In Pictures

Breaching is a behavior of many types of whales, including this humpback. Have students examine the photograph, read the caption, and answer the following questions.

- **What do you think breaching means?** (Leaping out of the water.)
- **In what ways does the whale's body resemble a fish's body?** (Students should cite visible characteristics, such as the whale's streamlined shape, paired side fins, and tail fin.)
- **How does its body differ from that of a fish?** (Students may notice that the whale's tail fin is horizontal to its body, whereas fishes' tail fins are vertical. They may also mention the apparent lack of gill covers. Some students may know that whales have lungs.)

Teaching Strategy

The first section of this chapter describes vertebrate evolution. The classes of living vertebrates and their specific adaptations for performing life functions are discussed in the second and third sections. The BRANCHING OUT section focuses on the reproductive adaptations that have made life on land possible.

CHAPTER 20

Animals: Vertebrates

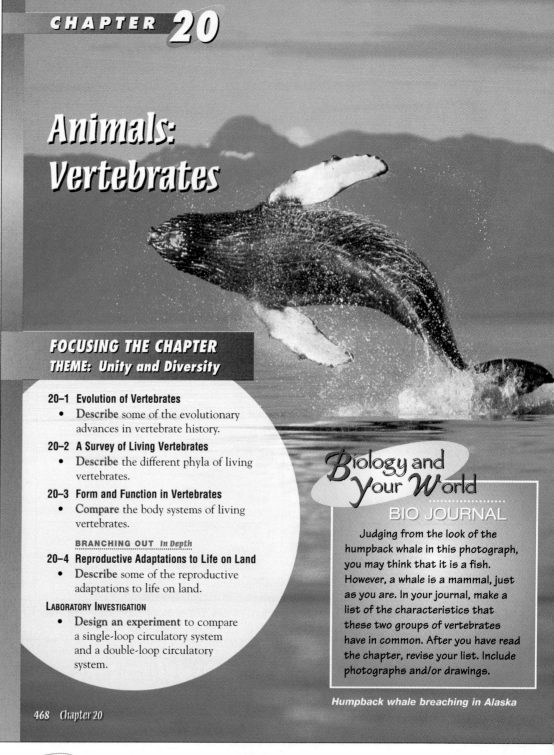

FOCUSING THE CHAPTER
THEME: Unity and Diversity

Biology and Your World

BIO JOURNAL

Judging from the look of the humpback whale in this photograph, you may think that it is a fish. However, a whale is a mammal, just as you are. In your journal, make a list of the characteristics that these two groups of vertebrates have in common. After you have read the chapter, revise your list. Include photographs and/or drawings.

Humpback whale breaching in Alaska

468 Chapter 20

BIO JOURNAL

In addition to the visible characteristics they cited in response to the second question above, students may mention physical and behavioral characteristics, such as an internal skeleton, a protective outer body covering, complex systems for digestion and other life functions, and mobility in water. Instruct students to keep their entries in their portfolios.

TEACHER SUPPORT

Chapter Discovery Learning Activity

Give students an opportunity to observe the differences between fishes and amphibians by having them set up two aquariums, one with freshwater fishes and the other with frog eggs or young tadpoles. If the season is appropriate, students could collect the eggs or tadpoles outdoors. Frog eggs also can be purchased from a biological supply house. Make sure the frog aquarium provides both ample water depth for eggs and young tadpoles and an above-water surface.

Post a calendar near the frog aquarium so students can record the physical changes that occur in the tadpoles: development of the hind legs first, then the front legs; disappearance of the gills and development of the nostrils (indicating the internal development of lungs); and gradual shortening (resorption) of the tail. Also make sure students note changes in the tadpoles' and young frogs' behavior.

Evolution of Vertebrates

SECTION 20-1

GUIDE FOR READING

- **Classify** vertebrates as a subphylum of chordates.
- **Identify** some of the trends in vertebrate evolution.

MORE THAN 99 PERCENT OF *all chordates are vertebrates. Their skeletons and other hard body structures have left behind an excellent fossil record. As a result, we know a great deal about their evolutionary history. As you climb the vertebrate family tree from past to present, you will learn about the important evolutionary steps our vertebrate ancestors have made.*

The Vertebrate Family Tree

Our family tree is rooted in the far distant past. The variety of fossilized organisms preserved in the Burgess Shale during the Cambrian Period included a peculiar creature that was different from all the others. This creature, *Pikaia,* was first thought to be a kind of worm. But researchers who took a closer look decided that it was actually the first known member of the phylum Chordata.

Why did scientists choose to place *Pikaia* in the chordate phylum, rather than among the worms it seems to resemble? The presence of a **notochord,** a flexible supporting structure along its back, provides the reason. A notochord is a characteristic unique to chordates.

☑ **Checkpoint** What is a notochord? 1

What Is a Vertebrate?

Humans, fishes, amphibians, birds, and reptiles are classified differently from *Pikaia* and the other invertebrate chordates by being placed in the chordate subphylum Vertebrata. Why are all these organisms in a separate subphylum? Because unlike their invertebrate chordate counterparts, vertebrates possess a notochord only during their early stages of development. As the vertebrate develops, the notochord is then replaced by a stronger supporting structure called

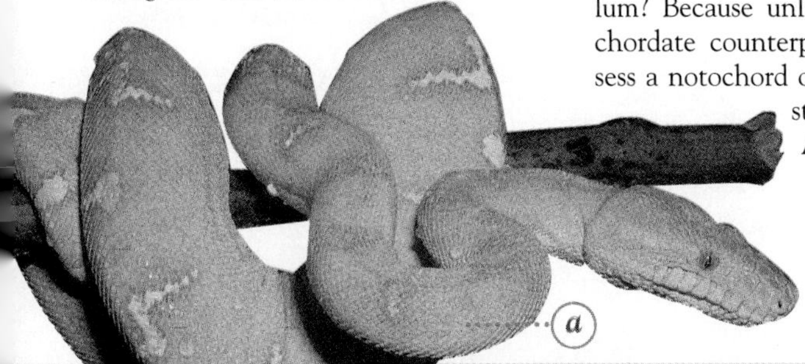
(a)

(b)

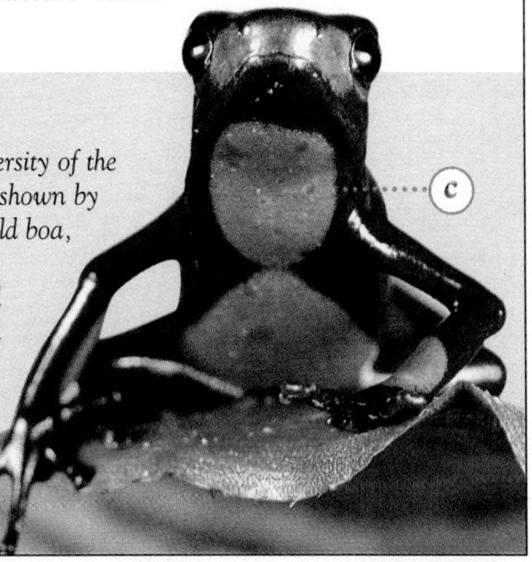
(c)

Figure 20–1 *The great diversity of the vertebrates is shown by (a) the emerald boa, (b) the regal angelfish, and (c) the poison arrow frog.*

TEACHER SUPPORT

Managing Classroom Diversity

LEP STUDENTS
Students may be confused by the terms fish and fishes. Explain that the text uses the convention accepted by ichthyologists: Fish (both singular and plural) refers to individuals of the same species. Fishes (plural) refers to individuals of different species.

GIFTED STUDENTS
In conjunction with the Investigate activity suggested on page 473, in which students research the discoveries that have prompted scientists to change their thinking about the nature of dinosaurs, encourage your more capable students to read the novel *Raptor Red* by Robert T. Bakker (1995)—a fictional account of the daily life of a young adult female Utahraptor. A noted paleontologist regarded as a rebel in his field, Bakker was the first to propose that dinosaurs were active, social, endothermic animals.

SECTION 20-1

Evolution of Vertebrates

Performance Objectives
- Identify Vertebrata as the subphylum to which all vertebrates belong.
- Identify the development of jaws, paired limb girdles and limbs, and an internal skeleton of cartilage or bone as major trends in vertebrate evolution.

1 ENGAGE

Ideas Through Images

Have students examine Figure 20–1, read the caption, and answer the following questions.

- **What similarities do you see in these animals?** (All are brightly colored and have a well-defined head with eyes. Both the snake and the fish have scales. Accept other reasonable responses.)
- **What differences do you see?** (Students should focus on visible differences, such as the fish's fins, the snake's lack of limbs, and the frog's four limbs.)
- **In what other ways do fishes, snakes, and frogs differ?** (Responses will vary depending on students' prior learning. They may know that fishes breathe through gills, snakes breathe with lungs, and frogs breathe through gills when they are tadpoles and with lungs when they are adults.)

☑ **Checkpoint**

1 A flexible supporting structure along an animal's back.

2 EXPLORE

Inquiry Activity

Inferring

Modeling a Vertebral Column Ask students what they think an animal's backbone looks like. Have students work in small groups to make drawings or simple models to show their ideas. For example, students could cut drinking straws into sections and tape them in a stacked column to represent vertebrae. Students who do not realize that a backbone is made of many small segments might show only a few, long bones. Do not comment on the accuracy of students' drawings and models at this time. (See Investigate below.)

3 TEACH

Investigate

Model Building After students have read the text section What Is a Vertebrate? on pages 469–470, have them compare the drawings and models they made in the Explore activity above with an anatomically correct illustration of a vertebral column (for example, the human spinal column as pictured in a health text). Let students adjust or redo their drawings and models so they accurately represent a vertebral column.

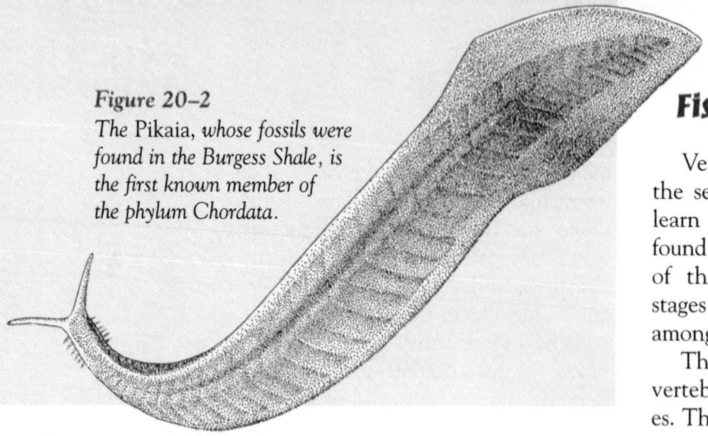

Figure 20–2
The Pikaia, whose fossils were found in the Burgess Shale, is the first known member of the phylum Chordata.

a backbone, or vertebral column. The backbone is made up of individual segments of bone called **vertebrae** (singular: vertebra). The backbone is the central part of the vertebrate endoskeleton because it provides a place for the bones of the skull, arms, and legs to attach. It also provides a means of attachment for muscles and protects the nerve cord.

Checkpoint What are vertebrae? 1

Fishes—Early Vertebrates

Vertebrates evolved for a long time in the sea, so it shouldn't surprise you to learn that our common ancestors are found among the fishes. In fact, several of the most important evolutionary stages in vertebrate evolution occurred among ancient fishes.

The earliest and most primitive fossil vertebrates are often called jawless fishes. These animals didn't lack mouths, of course. All of us have to eat! But their mouths weren't very helpful, because without real jaws they could have no teeth and couldn't bite. They could only suck in water containing food particles, like ocean-going vacuum cleaners.

The first notable trend in vertebrate evolution was the development of true bony jaws. These support structures made it possible for muscles to create a hard bite and provided a place for teeth

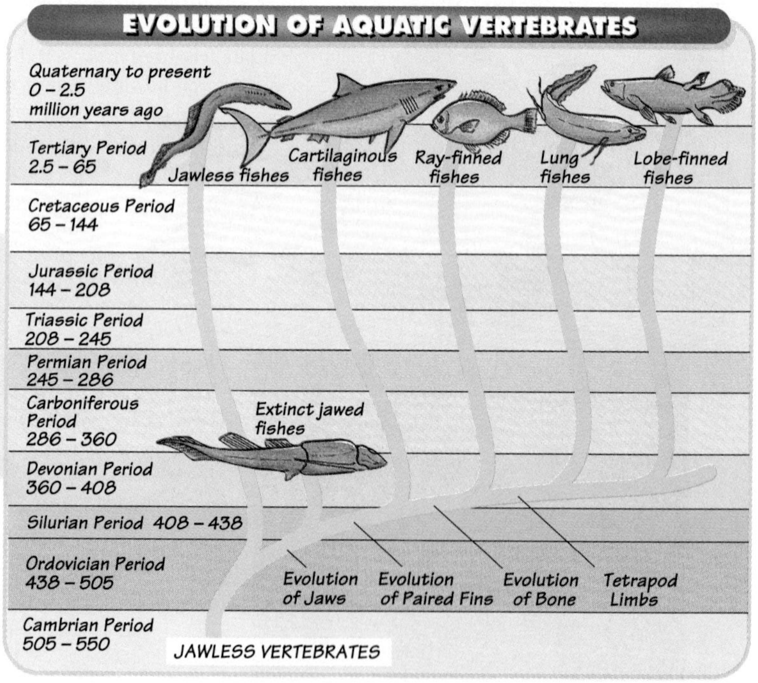

Figure 20–3
This evolutionary tree of aquatic vertebrates shows how fishes evolved over time. The emergence of tetrapod limbs led to the evolution of land vertebrates.

TEACHER SUPPORT

Historical Perspective

As shown in Figure 20–2, *Pikaia* resembled modern lancelets (amphioxus), an odd, living member of the subphylum Cephalochordata. As Stephen Jay Gould has observed, the apparently tenuous existence of this ancient ancestor provides a rare opportunity to observe the importance of chance—or, as Gould prefers to call it, contingency—in the history of life.

Pikaia was by no means a numerous, prominent, or even significant member of the Cambrian fauna; yet, as far as scientists can determine, it may well have been the common ancestor of all other chordates. *Pikaia* and its descendants survived the mass extinctions of ancient times and continued to evolve—fortunately for us because, as Gould writes, "Wind the tape of life back to Burgess times, and let it play again. If *Pikaia* does not survive in the replay, we are wiped out of future history—all of us, from shark to robin to orangutan."

to attach. Jaws thus transformed a simple opening into an adaptable, useful feeding tool.

The next evolutionary trend was the development of paired pectoral and pelvic limb girdles. Limb girdles connect limbs with the backbone in a way that enables muscles to work efficiently. The pectoral girdle connects the backbone to the front limbs (or arms), and the pelvic girdle connects the backbone with the rear limbs (or legs). Fishes didn't have arms or legs, but limb girdles enabled them to evolve complex and useful fins.

Figure 20–4
This Pacific hagfish is an example of a modern jawless fish. Jawless fishes are the ancestors of modern vertebrates.

One group of vertebrates evolved a skeleton made of a strong, resilient material called **cartilage.** Other vertebrates evolved skeletons made of true bone.

One group of vertebrates, the lobe-finned fishes, evolved fins that were different from those of other fishes in an important way. **The bones in the fleshy fins of the lobe-finned fishes evolved into bones that support arms, legs, wings, and flippers in all higher vertebrates.** Because most vertebrates have a body plan that includes four limbs, we are all called **tetrapods,** which means "four-legged."

Amphibians

The first animals to climb onto land probably resembled fishes with legs. These early tetrapods were adapted to life in very wet terrestrial habitats. In fact, the name amphibian, which means "double life," emphasizes that these animals live their lives both in water and on land.

As amphibians moved from water to land, they evolved two adaptations. The first was the tetrapod limbs. The second was a set of lungs and breathing tubes that enabled them to breathe air.

The descendants of amphibians evolved many adaptations that served them well in wet environments. Amphibians were very common in the warm, swampy fern forests of the Carboniferous Period, about 260 million years ago. These animals gave rise to the ancestors of living amphibians and the ancestors of vertebrates who live completely on land.

Challenges of Life on Land

Animals able to live on land didn't appear overnight. Adapting to terrestrial life involved more than just evolving legs and clambering out of the water! Vertebrates colonizing terrestrial habitats faced the same challenges that had to be overcome by terrestrial plants and invertebrates. They had to breathe air, protect themselves from drying out, support themselves against the pull of gravity, and reproduce without the help of standing water.

Figure 20–5
The coelacanth is the surviving species of the lobe-finned fishes—the ancestors of all tetrapods.

Ideas Through Images

Have students examine Figure 20–3, read the caption and the text description of evolutionary trends on this page, and answer the following questions.

- **At what point in the evolution of vertebrates did cartilaginous fishes appear?** (After the evolution of jaws and paired fins but before the evolution of bone.)
- **When did bony fishes first appear?** (After the evolution of paired fins, about 425 million years ago.)
- **Which types of fishes have tetrapod limbs?** (Lungfishes and lobe-finned fishes.)

Discussion

After students have read the first paragraph under Challenges of Life on Land, ask them to describe the specific structural adaptations that enabled plants to survive successfully on land. If students have difficulty recalling this information, let them refer back to pages 429–431 in Chapter 18.

Investigate

Research Tell students that coelacanths were thought to be extinct until the first living specimen was discovered off the South African coast in 1938. Encourage students to research and report on this discovery and its impact on the scientific study of primitive organisms.

☑ Checkpoint

1 Vertebrae are individual segments of bone that make up the backbone, or vertebral column.

TEACHER SUPPORT

Background Information

One group of fishes with bony skeletons evolved into tens of thousands of ray-finned fish species, the most diverse of all vertebrate groups today. These fishes all have fins that connect to pelvic and pectoral girdles through bony struts at their bases. In contrast, the lobe-finned fishes had a fleshy central area, containing some very interesting bones, that connects the fins to the limb girdles. The fossil record contains many transitional forms in the evolution from lobe-finned fishes to early amphibians, making it difficult for paleontologists to agree where one ends and the other begins.

Ancillary Support

The resources below can be used to support your teaching strategy for these two pages.

TR Writing in Biology: Creature Feature
Enrich: From Gills to Ears

BL Inquiry Activity: Show a Little Backbone

Section 20–1 (continued)

Ideas Through Images

Have students examine Figure 20–6 and read the caption. Make sure students understand that the line connecting amphibians to early reptiles does not imply that amphibians "gave way" to reptiles. Point out the text statement that Carboniferous Period amphibians "gave rise to the ancestors of living amphibians" as well as reptiles and other land vertebrates. Then have students answer the following questions.

- **What are lizards?** (If students do not know, explain that lizards are similar to snakes but have two sets of paired limbs.)
- **What is the difference between turtles and tortoises?** (If students do not know, explain that turtles live in aquatic habitats, whereas tortoises live on land.)
- **From what group of reptiles did birds evolve?** (Students can see on the evolutionary tree that birds evolved from dinosaurs.)

Discussion

Point out that evolution rarely (if ever) stops completely. Although no amphibians have ever evolved reptilelike or mammallike reproductive strategies that produce eggs independently of water, some have evolved remarkable reproductive methods that do not rely on large bodies of surface water. For example, some species of very small tree frogs in tropical rain forests lay their eggs in tiny pockets of water that collect in the leaves of bromeliads. Other amphibians incubate their eggs in moist mucus on their backs. Encourage students to find out more about such reproductive strategies.

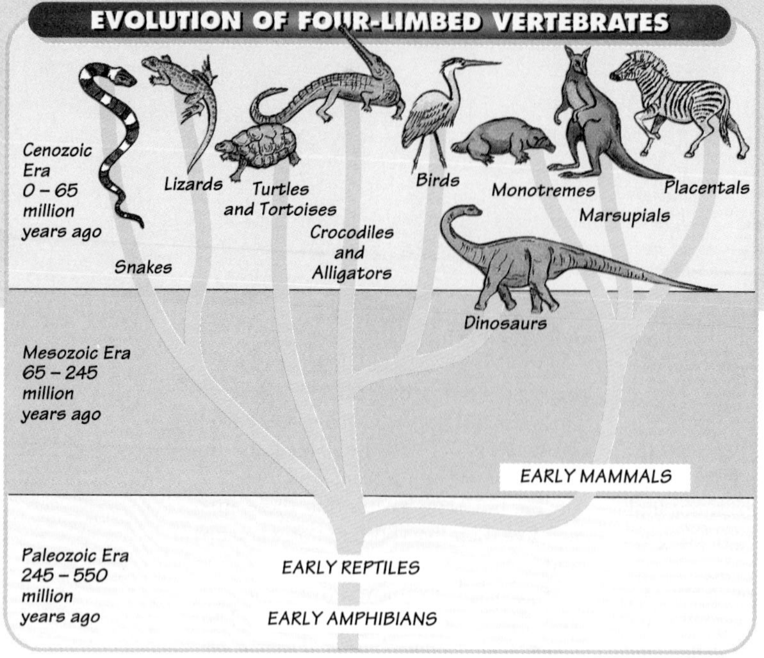

Figure 20–6 All modern reptiles, birds, and mammals evolved from amphibians, early reptiles, and early mammals. This evolutionary tree shows how all the vertebrates are related to one another.

As a group, amphibians need to keep their bodies moist and must prevent the rapid loss of water through their skin. In addition, amphibians must return to water to reproduce.

The First Reptiles

To colonize permanently dry habitats, animals needed a way to reproduce that didn't require water. The first animals to evolve this adaptation were the reptiles.

Unlike amphibians, reptiles reproduce by internal fertilization. Their fertilized eggs don't need water to develop because they are surrounded by a protective shell and several layers of membranes that protect the embryo.

As the Carboniferous Period drew to a close, terrestrial habitats changed. As the Permian Period began, the climate became drier. Many lakes and swamps disappeared. Under these drier conditions, reptiles evolved and diversified rapidly. By the end of the Permian Period, a great variety of reptiles had become widespread.

The Great Permian Extinction

The Permian Period ended about 245 million years ago in the most devastating mass extinction in the entire history of life on Earth. Almost 95 percent of all species of marine animals disappeared. This change in life on Earth was so extraordinary that paleontologists have declared this time not just the end of the Permian Period, but the end of the entire Paleozoic Era—the era of ancient life.

☑ ***Checkpoint*** Why did the end of the Permian Period also mark the end of the Paleozoic Era? ①

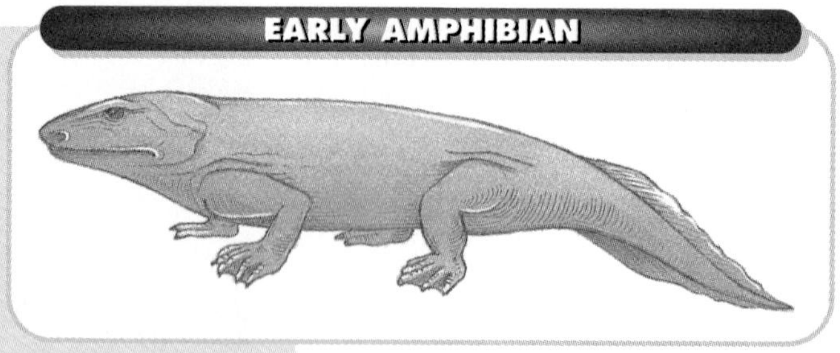

Figure 20–7 Amphibians were the first vertebrates to develop tetrapod limbs and lungs. Early amphibians from the Carboniferous Period may have resembled this artist's drawing.

TEACHER SUPPORT

Historical Perspective

An interesting example from the history of paleontology shows that the scientific view of life is constantly open to question and change. For many years, the oldest known reptiles were found in deposits dating back to the late Carboniferous Period. As a result, no one thought that these more fully terrestrial terapods had existed for very long before starting their great adaptive radiation in the later Permian Period.

Then, in 1988, a new fossil discovered in Scotland turned that view on its head. This great find, named in 1991 and identified as unequivocally reptilian, dates from the very early Carboniferous, about 350 million years ago. This example shows that even today, a lucky discovery can challenge established views and require paleontologists to rewrite their calendars.

The Mesozoic Era

The end of the Paleozoic Era cleared the stage for the next era in the history of life. The Mesozoic, or middle life, Era—the age of the ruling reptiles—could now begin.

Dinosaurs—The Ruling Reptiles

Few animals have captured human imagination as much as the dinosaurs and the other great reptiles of the Mesozoic Era have. Two separate groups of large aquatic reptiles prowled the seas. Ancestors of modern turtles, crocodiles, lizards, and snakes populated many terrestrial habitats. And dinosaurs, the great and terrible lizards, were everywhere.

Until about 30 years ago, paleontologists thought of dinosaurs as giant versions of living snakes and lizards. ● Recent research has revealed how interesting many of these animals actually were. Some dinosaurs traveled in great herds. Others lived in small family groups, caring for their eggs and young in carefully constructed nests. New and interesting information about dinosaurs is discovered every day!

Birds

If you, like many people, wish you could have seen a live dinosaur, you might have to go no farther than your window or the nearest pet store. Research has shown that modern birds evolved from a group of small flesh-eating dinosaurs! The most important piece in this puzzle is shown in **Figure 20–8.** *Archaeopteryx,* a 150-million-year-old fossil, is classified by researchers as the first known bird. If you remove the fossilized feathers, the bones of this animal could pass for those of a small running dinosaur.

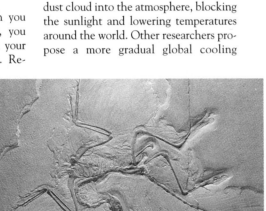

Figure 20–8
Archaeopteryx, *which lived during the late Jurassic Period, is the first known bird.*

The First Mammals

Our mammalian ancestors evolved over a long period of time. The first to appear over 300 million years ago were the odd mammallike reptiles. These animals and their descendants left behind many fossils with characteristics that changed slowly from those of reptiles to those of primitive mammals. That's one reason it is difficult to say exactly when true mammals appeared.

The Great Cretaceous Extinction

At the end of the Cretaceous (krih-TAY-shuhs) Period, 65 million years ago, a mass extinction ended the reign of the dinosaurs. Despite a great deal of research, geologists and paleontologists still do not agree on what caused this mass extinction. Many believe that a huge asteroid smashed into what is now Mexico's Yucatan Peninsula. ● That impact would have blasted a large dust cloud into the atmosphere, blocking the sunlight and lowering temperatures around the world. Other researchers propose a more gradual global cooling

INTEGRATING CAREERS

What are some of the career options open to paleontologists? What kinds of courses must they take?

INTEGRATING SOCIAL STUDIES

Use a map of Mexico to find the Yucatan Peninsula. In which part of the country is it located?

INTEGRATING CAREERS

Paleontologists are employed as university teachers, stratigraphers and petrographers in the oil and gas industry, museum curators, and analysts in state and federal geological surveys. A career in paleontology requires a broad background in the physical and biological sciences that becomes increasingly focused on a subspecialty discipline, such as vertebrate or invertebrate paleontology, paleoanthropology, or paleobotany.

INTEGRATING SOCIAL STUDIES

The Yucatan Peninsula is Mexico's easternmost land area, projecting into the southern Gulf of Mexico.

Investigate

Research The scientific view of dinosaurs has changed dramatically from that of sluggish, lumbering, dim-witted, ectothermic beasts, to agile, behaviorally complex, endothermic creatures. Encourage students to find out about the discoveries that precipitated this change in viewpoint, particularly the contributions of notable researchers such as Robert Bakker (see Managing Classroom Diversity on page 469) and John R. Horner, the discoverer of *Maiasaura,* duckbilled dinosaurs that nested in colonies.

Checkpoint

1 The most devastating mass extinction in the entire history of life on Earth occurred at the end of the Permian Period. This mass extinction so changed life on Earth that paleontologists have declared this time as the end of the era of ancient life.

TEACHER SUPPORT

Background Information

Based on the eight fossil specimens of *Archaeopteryx* that have been found, scientists have identified the features of this animal that support the argument that birds evolved from dinosaurs. *Archaeopteryx's* avian features (those not found in dinosaurs) include feathers, an opposable big toe, and a wishbone formed by two clavicles fused at the midline. Among *Archaeopteryx's* reptilian (nonavian) features are the absence of a bill, trunk vertebrae that are free (they are fused in birds), the absence of air sacs, a skull and brain shaped like those of reptiles, a long tail containing many free vertebrae (birds have short tails with fused vertebrae), teeth, slender ribs, and a pelvic girdle/femur joint that is dinosaurlike rather than avian. So, while *Archaeopteryx* is classified as a bird, mainly because it has feathers, it has numerous characteristics in common with ancient dinosaurs.

Ancillary Support

The resource below can be used to support your teaching strategy for these two pages.

TB The Evolution of Four-Limbed Vertebrates, #26

4 ASSESS

Quick Check

Have students draw a diagram showing the evolution of tetrapod vertebrates.

Section Review 20-1

1. Vertebrates are classified in the chordate subphylum Vertebrata because their notochord is replaced by a vertebral column as they develop.

2. Students should cite the four major trends described on pages 470–471, and they may also mention the development of lungs and breathing tubes in amphibians and reproduction through internal fertilization in reptiles, described on page 472.

3. Both land vertebrates and land plants evolved adaptations to protect their bodies from drying out, support their bodies against the pull of gravity, and reproduce without the help of standing water.

Learning Modality

Visual and Tactile Learning Let students make an enlarged version of Figure 20–6 using textured materials, such as fabrics or various grades of sandpaper as the backgrounds for the vertebrate groups, pictures they have drawn or illustrations cut from magazines to show the types of animals in the groups, and yarn or heavy cord for the lines connecting the groups.

caused by increased volcanic activity. Many volcanic eruptions could have created the same sort of dust cloud.

Whatever the cause, dinosaurs and the other ruling reptiles were wiped out, leaving a clean slate for the evolution of animals that were larger than insects and birds.

The Age of Mammals

The Earth that the mammals inherited was a changing patchwork of environments. During the late Mesozoic Era, the continents began to drift apart. First, two great landmasses separated into a northern continent and a southern continent. These landmasses isolated groups of ancient mammals that began to evolve along different paths. By the end of the Cretaceous Period, most modern continents, except for Antarctica and Australia, had separated. This caused some mammals to flourish in the southern continents, while other mammals evolved in the northern continents.

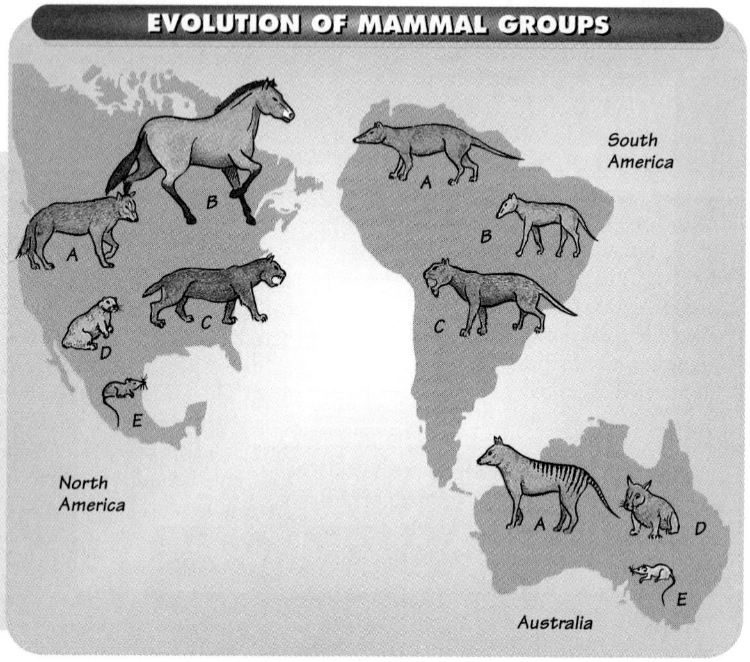

Figure 20–9
As the continents moved apart early in the Cenozoic Era, ancestors of different mammal groups were isolated from one another. In adapting to similar environments, some of these unrelated animals evolved similar appearances and behaviors. Species labeled with the same letter have similar adaptations, although they are unrelated to each other.

Section Review 20–1

1. **Classify** vertebrates as a subphylum of chordates.
2. **Identify** some of the trends in vertebrate evolution.
3. **Critical Thinking—Making Comparisons** In what ways are the vertebrate adaptations to life on land similar to plant adaptations to life on land?

TEACHER SUPPORT

Activity

MODELING ADAPTIVE RADIATION

Remind students of the model they made earlier showing continental drift and its effect on the distribution of organisms throughout the world (Chapter 17, Chapter Discovery Learning Activity on page 386). If students did not do that activity earlier, have them do it now. Then challenge students to adapt the model to show the sequence of geological events and evolutionary changes culminating in the diversity of animals pictured in Figure 20–9.

Students' models should indicate that a particular ancestral mammal—a mouselike or wolflike ancestor, for example—was widely distributed over the undivided land mass (as lungfishes were in step 2 of the earlier activity), and then evolved into increasing divergent descendent species after the continents separated and became isolated.

A Survey of Living Vertebrates

GUIDE FOR READING

- **Describe** the characteristics of living vertebrates.

MINI LAB

- **Design an experiment** to find out what factors affect the breathing rate of a fish.

THEY RANGE IN SIZE FROM TINY fishes a few centimeters long to blue whales, the largest animals ever to live on Earth. They walk, crawl, run, hop, slither, burrow, swim, and fly. They soar over mountains, roam ocean canyons, ride on Arctic ice floes, plod across trackless deserts, and call through the night in tropical rain forests. They are not the most numerous animals, and they are by no means the most diverse. They are the organisms most of us think of when we think of animals. They—or, more accurately, we—are the vertebrates.

Classification of Vertebrates

As you may recall, all vertebrates have a vertebral column, or backbone. What other characteristics do the vertebrates have in common? **Besides a backbone, most vertebrates have two sets of appendages (arms and legs), a closed circulatory system with a ventral heart, and either gills or lungs for breathing.**

Jawless Fishes

Lampreys and hagfishes are the only living vertebrates without jaws. They are not living fossils but specialized parasites and scavengers. Lampreys attach themselves to fishes or other aquatic animals and rasp at their flesh to feed on their blood and body fluids. Hagfishes feed on dead and decaying carcasses.

Cartilaginous Fishes

Sharks, skates, and rays make up the class of cartilaginous fishes called Chondrichthyes

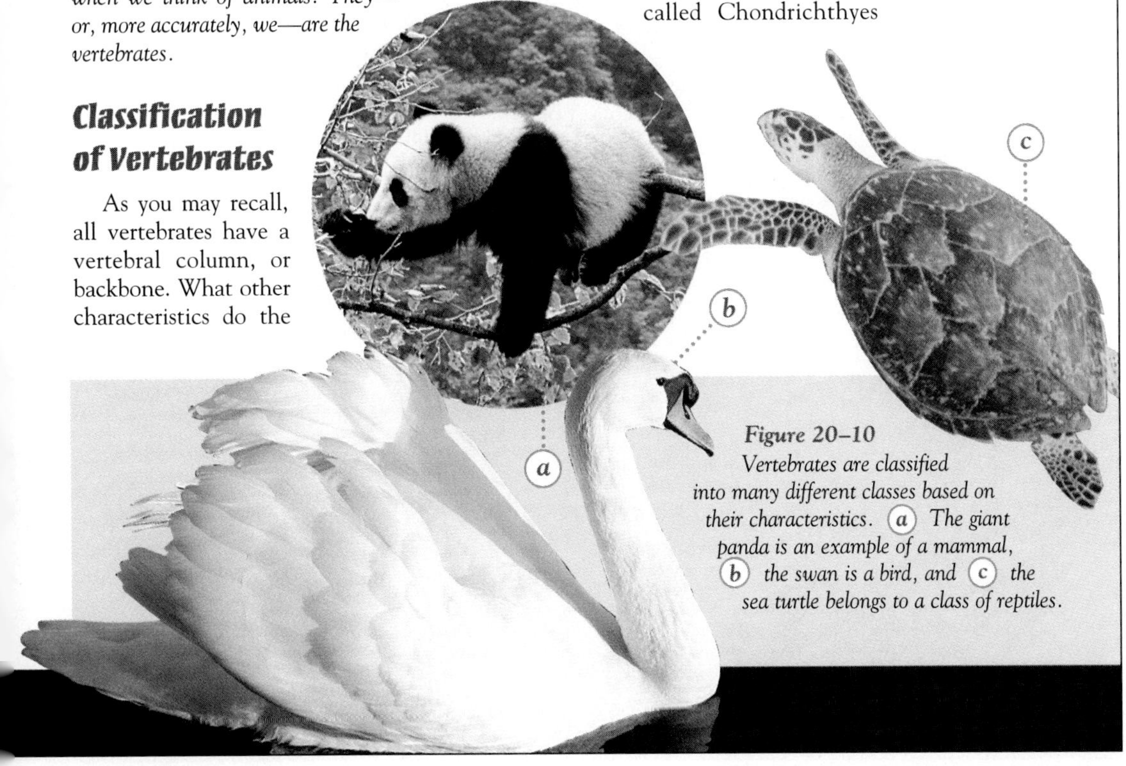

Figure 20–10
Vertebrates are classified into many different classes based on their characteristics. (a) The giant panda is an example of a mammal, (b) the swan is a bird, and (c) the sea turtle belongs to a class of reptiles.

SECTION 20–2

A Survey of Living Vertebrates

Performance Objective

- Describe the scientific classification of living vertebrates.

Mini Lab Skill: Experimenting

1 ENGAGE

Ideas Through Images

Have students examine Figure 20–10, read the caption, and answer the following questions.

- **What are some characteristics that these three animals share?** (Students may mention that all have a vertebral column, four limbs [though the feet of the swan do not show in the photograph], and other traits based on their prior knowledge of the animals shown.)
- **Why do you think each animal is classified in a different class of vertebrates?** (Students may mention body covering [fur for the panda, feathers for the swan, and scales for the sea turtle] and forelimbs [paws for the panda, wings for the swan, and flippers for the sea turtle], as well as other characteristics not visible in the photographs.)

TEACHER SUPPORT

Background Information

Fishes have many other adaptations not discussed in the text. For example, in addition to a keen sense of smell, a shark has sensors on its head that detect minute electrical fields produced by muscle contractions in nearby animals. A shark also has a lateral line system, consisting of rows of sensory organs along its sides, which enables it to detect minor vibrations in the water. Such adaptations make sharks skillful predators.

Bony fishes also have lateral line systems and keen senses of smell, as well as swim bladders, which are specialized organs that help maintain buoyancy. In some species, the swim bladder and the digestive tract are connected, enabling the fish to gulp air and extract oxygen from it when the level of dissolved oxygen in the water becomes too low. This ability played a significant role in the invasion of land by vertebrates.

2 EXPLORE

Investigate

Long-Term Project Have students describe the changes they observe as the tadpoles in the aquarium they set up in the Chapter Discovery Learning Activity develop into adult frogs. Encourage them to create posters or a bulletin board display showing each stage in the complete tadpole-to-mature-frog developmental sequence.

3 TEACH

Discussion

Challenge students to classify each species of fish in their aquarium into one of the three classes described in the student text. (All species will undoubtedly belong to the class Osteichthyes, bony fishes, and the subclass of ray-finned fishes.) Also have students identify the order to which the frogs in the other aquarium belong (Anura).

Investigate

Observing Vertebrates If possible, provide a captive salamander or newt, lizard, and snake for students to examine and compare their visible characteristics. Students who keep these animals for pets may be willing to bring them in for a one-day observation. Provide several portable, clear-plastic cases for carrying the specimens to school. If live specimens are not available, obtain videos or CD-ROM programs so students can observe the physical and behavior similarities and differences among these vertebrates.

Figure 20–11
Fishes and amphibians are two diverse classes of vertebrates. (a) The orange sea horse is one of many bony fishes. (b) As an adult, the yellow-eyed salamander, a member of the order Urodela, lives in moist woods.

(cahn-DRIHK-theez), whose skeletons are made up of cartilage. Some, such as the great white shark, are fearsome predators. Despite their bad reputation, only a few species attack humans—and then only rarely. Many other species eat small fishes, mollusks, or plankton.

Bony Fishes

This enormous and diverse class of fishes, the Osteichthyes (ahs-tee-IHK-theez), contains more than half of all living vertebrate species. They inhabit nearly every aquatic habitat imaginable—from tropical streams to the sea beneath Arctic ice. There are two subclasses of bony fishes—ray-finned fishes and lobe-finned fishes.

The ray-finned fishes consist of more than 20,000 species and include nearly every fish. Ray-finned fishes have a well-developed system of bones, and many have specialized jaws and teeth that enable them to eat a variety of foods.

Although few species of lobe-finned fishes are alive today, they are of great evolutionary importance because they are the ancestors of all tetrapods.

Amphibians

The class Amphibia, or amphibians, have never fully recovered from the great Permian extinction. Only about 2500 species survive, and many of these species have been endangered or threatened. Amphibians lay their eggs in water, where they spend at least part of their life. As adults, amphibians live on land and breathe through lungs. Most have moist skin and cannot tolerate long periods of dryness.

Newts and salamanders, members of the order Urodela, are amphibians with tails. They lay their eggs in water, where they hatch into young that resemble the adult form. The larvae have gills that disappear and are replaced by lungs as they develop into adults.

Frogs and toads make up the order Anura. They do not have tails as adults. Their eggs hatch in water into larvae called tadpoles, which look completely

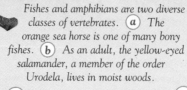

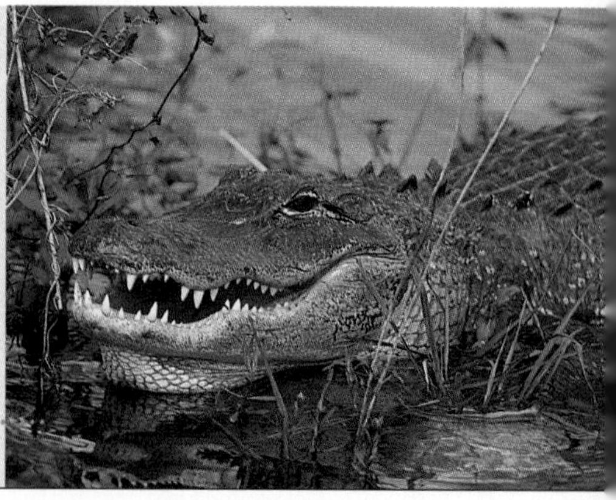

Figure 20–12
Reptiles are classified into three orders. (a) The Jackson's chameleon is a member of the order Squamata, which includes lizards and snakes. (b) This alligator, found in the Florida Everglades, is a member of the class Crocodilia.

TEACHER SUPPORT

Ecology Note

Many amphibians live on land most of the time but return to a pond to mate and lay eggs, following the same route to the same pond at the same time every year. Occasionally these migrating animals must cross roads to reach the pond, thus risking being run over by passing automobiles.

For many years, the Massachusetts town of Amherst closed a road to auto traffic every spring to protect migrating salamanders. Then, in the late 1980s, in cooperation with the state Audubon Society, the town built a tunnel so the salamanders could cross under the road rather than over it. The first night of the migration was cold, and few salamanders appeared. But on the next rainy night, they began to migrate in large numbers, crawling to the roadway, entering the tunnel, and emerging safely from the other side.

Encourage students to research and report on this and other successful salamander and toad tunnels.

different from the adults. Tadpoles live in water until they develop into adult frogs.

☑ **Checkpoint** What are the two orders of amphibians? ❶

Reptiles

Reptiles, members of the class Reptilia, were the first fully terrestrial vertebrates. They reproduce by internal fertilization and produce leathery-shelled eggs that prevent water loss. They also have dry, scaly skin that retains water inside the body. Reptiles breathe air by means of developed lungs.

Tortoises and turtles belong to the order Chelonia (kuh-LOH-nee-uh). These animals, which have a very long fossil record, are encased in a protective shell of bony plates. Some live in fresh water, others in the sea, and still others in habitats as dry as deserts.

Crocodiles, alligators, and caimans make up the order Crocodilia. This order also has a long fossil record. These animals are now mostly in tropical and subtropical regions along fresh- or saltwater coastlines, swamps, and marshes.

The order of lizards and snakes—Squamata (skwah-MAH-tuh)—is the most abundant group of living reptiles. There are more than 2500 species that live in habitats ranging from oceans to deserts. Lizards and snakes look quite different but are actually closely related.

☑ **Checkpoint** What are the three orders of reptiles? ❷

Birds

The class Aves, or birds, are defined by a unique feature—feathers. Feathers are used not only for flight, but also to conserve body heat. This is a large and diverse class, containing 8600 species in 27 different orders.

MINI LAB Experimenting

A Fishy Story

PROBLEM *What factors affect the breathing rate of a fish? **Design an experiment** to answer the question.*

SUGGESTED PROCEDURE

1. Fill a large beaker about halfway with water from an aquarium. Use a net to move one fish from the aquarium to the beaker. Let the fish adjust to its new environment for at least 5 minutes.
2. Observe how the fish moves. Look at its fins and general body shape.
3. Using a clock with a second hand, count how many times the fish opens its mouth per minute. Observe any movement of the gill covers (operculum) during the same time period. Record your data. Return the fish to the aquarium.
4. Using a similar procedure, design an experiment to determine what effect the presence of another fish has on the first fish's breathing rate.
5. Write out your hypothesis and, with your teacher's approval, carry out your experiment.

ANALYZE AND CONCLUDE

1. How many times did the fish open its mouth per minute?
2. Did you observe any coordinated movement of the gill covers with the opening and closing of the mouth?
3. What effect did the presence of another fish have on the first fish? Give evidence to support your answer.

Figure 20–13 *Birds, such as these bee-eaters, are the only class of vertebrates that have feathers.*

MINI LAB Experimenting

Teacher Notes

- For time required and materials needed, see page 468b.
- You may want to allow students to use fishes from the class aquarium they set up in the Chapter Discovery Learning Activity. If those fishes are small, however, large goldfish make better subjects.
- Before students begin, discuss general guidelines for handling live animals. Monitor each group's experimental design to ensure that the fishes are not subjected to stress.

Answers to Analyze and Conclude

1. A number over 100 is not unusual.
2. Yes. When the mouth is opened (to take in water), the gill covers close. When the mouth is closed (to force water over the gills), the covers open.
3. Students will probably find that the presence of another fish increases the breathing rate of the first fish.

Skills Trace
Experimenting
- Focus p. 477
- Practice p. 478
- Assess p. 492

☑ Checkpoints

❶ The two orders of amphibians are Urodela and Anura.

❷ The three orders of reptiles are Chelonia, Crocodilia, and Squamata.

Ancillary Support

The resources below can be used to support your teaching strategy for these two pages.

TR Apply: Two of a Kind
BL Inquiry Activity: Creature Comforts

TEACHER SUPPORT Background Information

As noted in the student text, monotremes show a curious blend of mammalian and reptilian characteristics. Another trait—the one for which the group was named—is that their digestive and urogenital tracts share a single common opening, as in reptiles, not as in other mammals. Monotremes also do not have clearly developed nipples but secrete milk from pores in the abdominal wall.

At birth, marsupials are tiny, hairless, and blind, but they do have a keen sense of smell and strong forelimbs, which they use to locate and crawl to a nipple in the mother's pouch. In Australia, marsupials fill niches occupied by placental mammals on other continents.

The relative success of placental mammals strongly supports the hypothesis that placental development offers survival advantages. The fetus enjoys a more protected environment, a longer period of prenatal development, and a greater supply of maternal nourishment than do monotreme and marsupial young.

4 ASSESS

Quick Check

Have students work in small groups to create a table summarizing the characteristics of the vertebrate classes, orders, and groups discussed in this section.

Section Review 20–2

1. Jawless fishes; cartilaginous fishes (class Chondrichthyes); bony fishes (class Osteichthyes) with two subclasses: ray-finned fishes and lobe-finned fishes; amphibians (class Amphibia) with two orders: Urodela (newts and salamanders) and Anura (frogs and toads); reptiles (class Reptilia) with three orders: Chelonia (tortoises and turtles), Crocodilia (crocodiles, alligators, and caimans), and Squamata (lizards and snakes); birds (class Aves); mammals (class Mammalia) with three main groups: monotremes, marsupials, and placental mammals.

2. Aves (birds) and Mammalia (mammals).

3. Students' experiments may vary, but all should involve subjecting the fish to specific conditions and observing the movements of its mouth and gill covers in response to each condition.

Skills Trace
Experimenting

- Focus p. 477
- Practice p. 478
- Assess p. 492

Learning Modality

Visual and Kinesthetic Learning

As students study this section, have them write each characteristic of the vertebrate classes, orders, and groups on a separate index card, with the name of the class, order, or group on the back of the card. Students can then use the cards to create a summary table as described in the Quick Check above.

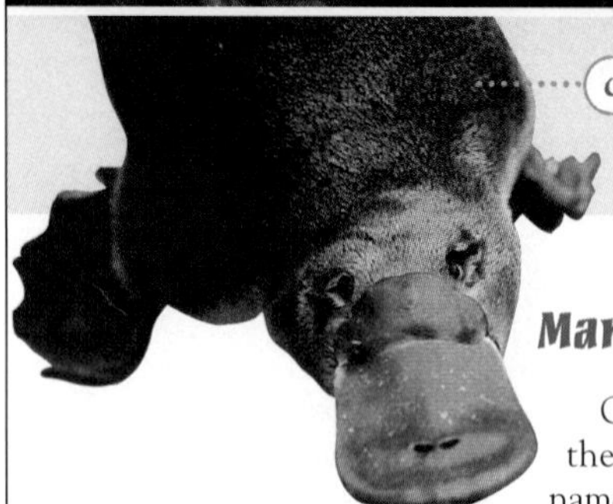

Figure 20–14 *Mammals are divided into three groups based on the way their young develop. (a) The orangutans are placental mammals, (b) the gray kangaroo with its joey is an example of a marsupial, and (c) the duckbilled platypus is an example of a monotreme.*

Mammals

Our class of vertebrates—the class Mammalia—is named for the presence of **mammary glands,** which enable females to nourish their young with milk. Mammals are also characterized by the presence of hair, whose primary function is to help retain body heat. There are three main groups of living mammals: monotremes, marsupials, and placental mammals.

Monotremes, or egg-laying mammals, are very rare. The duckbill platypus and two species of spiny anteaters are the only monotremes in existence today. Monotremes show a curious mix of features. Like reptiles, they lay leathery eggs. But like all mammals, monotremes have body hair and, once their eggs hatch, they nourish their young with milk.

Marsupials, like most other mammals, bear their young alive. Marsupials are born incredibly early, sometimes only eight days after fertilization, while they are little more than embryos. The embryos crawl to a pouch called the marsupium (mahr-SOO-pee-uhm), where they receive nourishment from their mother and complete their development. Such living marsupials as koalas and kangaroos live in Australia, but a few, such as the opossum, live in North, South, and Central America.

The largest group of living mammals—placental mammals—get their name from the **placenta,** an organ that connects the mother with her developing embryo. Nutrients, oxygen, wastes, and carbon dioxide are exchanged through the placenta. There are about 4500 living mammals that are divided into 16 different orders.

Section Review 20–2

1. **Classify** the living vertebrates into different classes and orders.
2. **Critical Thinking—Summarizing** Which classes of vertebrates rely on outer coverings to conserve body heat?
3. **MINI LAB** How could you **design an experiment** to determine what factors affect the breathing rate of a fish?

TEACHER SUPPORT

Background Information

Taxonomy, the science of classification, is as subject to change when new information becomes available as any other branch of science. At one time, living tree shrews were classified as primates, the mammalian order to which humans belong. Primates are closely related to ancient insectivores. Some primatologists now believe that tree shrews belong with other shrews and moles in order Insectivora. Other biologists place these animals in a separate order, Scandentia.

Form and Function in Vertebrates

Guide for Reading

- **Describe** a single-loop circulatory system and a double-loop circulatory system.
- **Compare** the two techniques of body temperature control in vertebrates.

MINI LAB

- **Design an experiment** to find out how animals maintain their internal body temperature.

VERTEBRATES HAVE EVOLVED a series of adaptations to terrestrial life and to a wide range of habitats. Some adaptations involve hard body parts that can be traced in the fossil record. Others involve soft tissue structures and functions that can be compared only among living animals. Moving from the oldest fishes up to primates, most body systems became more complex as vertebrates adapted to different environments.

Support and Movement

Vertebrates have an endoskeleton with bones that are surrounded by muscles and skin. The central element of that skeleton is the vertebral column, or backbone. This series of connected vertebrae, along with muscles and ligaments that attach to them, help support body mass and make it possible to control body movements.

As vertebrates adapted to terrestrial life, the position of both pairs of limbs changed. Early amphibians had limbs that stuck out almost horizontally from the body. These animals walked by bending from side to side, much as fishes swim. But as animals grew larger and heavier, horizontal limbs couldn't offer enough support. It isn't surprising, then, that many reptiles, including dinosaurs, evolved limbs that grew vertically. Vertical limbs could support mass more efficiently. Many mammals also have vertical limbs, allowing them to stand erect with their legs straight under them.

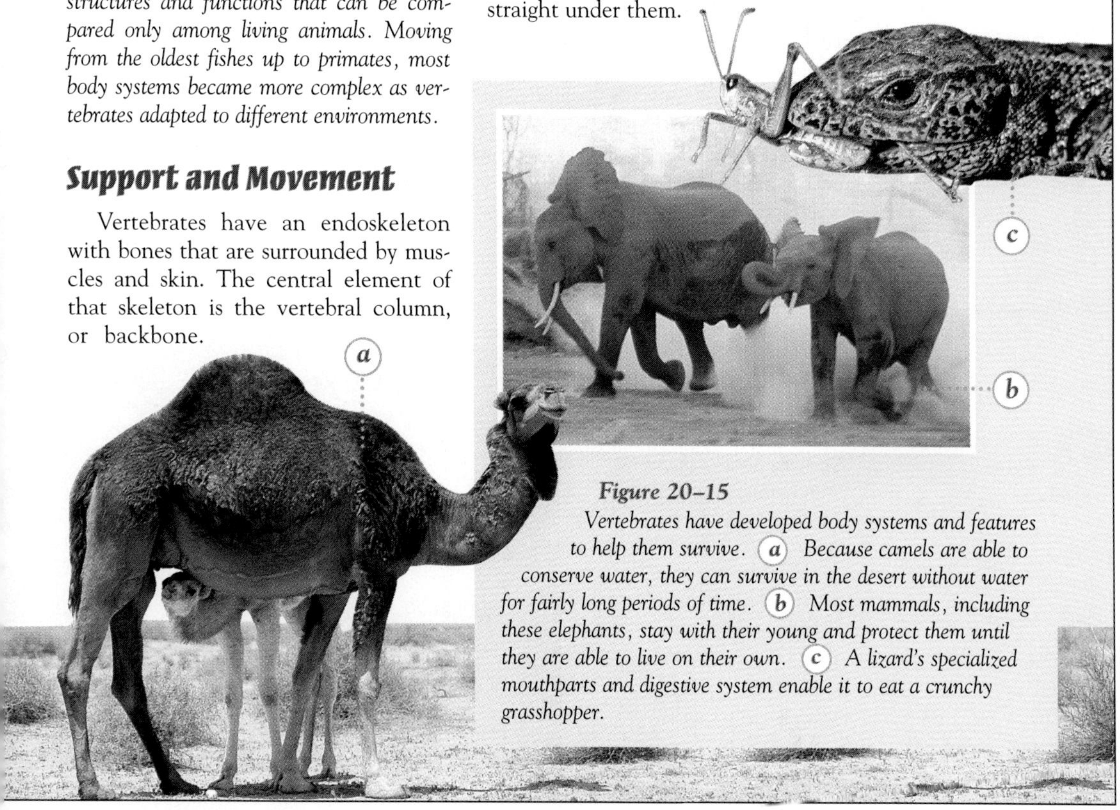

Figure 20–15
Vertebrates have developed body systems and features to help them survive. (a) Because camels are able to conserve water, they can survive in the desert without water for fairly long periods of time. (b) Most mammals, including these elephants, stay with their young and protect them until they are able to live on their own. (c) A lizard's specialized mouthparts and digestive system enable it to eat a crunchy grasshopper.

SECTION 20-3

Form and Function in Vertebrates

Performance Objectives

- Compare how single-loop and double-loop circulatory systems work.
- Differentiate between ectotherms and endotherms.

Laboratory Investigation Skill: Experimenting
Mini Lab Skill: Experimenting

1 ENGAGE

Inquiry Activity
Inferring

Examining a Human Skeleton
Ask students how the structure of their own skeletons enables them to move in specific ways and provides protection for their internal organs. Obtain a life-size laboratory model of a human skeleton or, if one is not available, use a small, reasonably accurate plastic model. Let groups take turns freely examining the model. As they do so, have them write a brief description of the movements possible at various joints, and the ways in which the sizes and shapes of different bones are adapted to perform specific functions.

TEACHER SUPPORT

Managing Classroom Diversity

TECH PREP STUDENTS
Point out to students that all of the technical illustrations in this textbook, as well as in other science books they may have used, were created by graphic artists who specialize in scientific artwork. Encourage students who enjoy the sciences and who also have artistic skill to find out about careers as medical and scientific illustrators. If you or your school's career-counseling office can locate a local medical/scientific illustrator, ask the artist to meet with interested students to discuss this field.

All graphic artists must possess natural artistic ability; be able to think of new ways to present ideas; and be trained in the techniques of applied art. Medical/scientific illustrators also must have training in biology and the physical sciences, to ensure the accuracy of their illustrations. Their work is in demand for use in textbooks, medical journals, lecture presentations, and medical advertising.

Ancillary Support

The resources below can be used to support your teaching strategy for these two pages.

LM Observing Vertebrate Skeletons, #39
BL Inquiry Activity: Movin' On Up

2 EXPLORE

Inquiry Activity

Developing Models

Modeling Skeletal Motion

Challenge small groups of students to design and build a working model of one body section—the shoulder and arm, the hip and leg, or the skull and spinal column, for example—of the human skeleton they examined in the Engage activity, or build a model of an analogous section of another vertebrate animal. Provide a variety of materials that students could use to create their models, such as wooden dowels, narrow cardboard tubes, balloons, and rubber bands, but also encourage students to use other materials of their own choice. Give each group an opportunity to demonstrate and explain its model to the rest of the class, focusing on the relationship between the model's structure and the functions that the body section performs.

3 TEACH

Discussion

Ask students to recall the seven essential life functions identified for invertebrates in Chapter 19 (pages 452–459). As students study those life functions in this section, have them compare the body systems and structures of vertebrates with those of invertebrates.

Discussion

After students have examined Figure 20–17 and read its caption and accompanying text, remind them of what they discovered when they calculated the surface area of a closed book and a divided book modeling book lungs (Chapter 19, Investigate on page 455). Point out that the same principle applies to the respiratory systems of vertebrates: The feathery surfaces of gills provide a large surface area for gas exchange; greater numbers of alveoli provide more surface area for gas exchange in lungs.

Feeding and Digestion

As part of the adaptive radiations of vertebrates, different species evolved ways of life that depend on nearly every kind of food in nature. But each potential food poses its own set of challenges. Meat is easy to digest, but it must first be caught and cut up for swallowing. Plant food is often tough and must be pulverized and shredded before being swallowed. Plant parts such as leaves and stems are also full of hard-to-digest cellulose.

Every group of vertebrates has evolved adaptations that enable them to capture and digest different foods. Some of these adaptations occur in the teeth of mammals. After food is swallowed, the way it is handled also depends on its chemical makeup. Meat is easily digested and can be passed quickly through a short gastrovascular cavity. So carnivores have short digestive tracts that secrete enzymes that break down meat proteins.

Because leaves and other plant parts are the toughest to handle, herbivores such as cows spend a great deal of time chewing and rechewing their food. They also have stomachs with colonies of bacteria that help to digest cellulose.

Respiration

Exchanging oxygen and carbon dioxide with the environment is a universal requirement of living things. Vertebrates have evolved many strategies that help them adapt to different environments.

Fishes and Amphibians

Fully aquatic vertebrates such as fishes rely almost entirely on gills for respiration. Amphibians, however, show a transitional pattern between water breathing and air breathing. Tadpoles have gills, whereas adult amphibians have lungs that are not well developed. Amphibians also do not have muscles that can inflate and deflate lungs. Most adults, therefore, depend on the exchange of gases through their thin, wet skin.

Reptiles

Reptiles—fully adapted to dry environments—could not breathe through their dry skin, so their lungs became more efficient. The inside of the reptilian lung is divided into many small chambers. These chambers greatly increase the amount of surface area available for gas exchange. In addition, reptiles evolved muscles that help inflate and deflate lungs to pump air in and out.

Figure 20–16
CAREER TRACK
Animal physiologists study animals and their habits. In some parts of the world, rhinoceroses are killed for their horns. In this photograph, two animal physiologists prepare to remove the rhinoceros's horn in order to protect it from being hunted.

TEACHER SUPPORT

Background Information

Most plant-eating mammals host symbiotic microorganisms in their digestive systems that aid in the digestion of cellulose. The relationship between bacteria and herbivores is most complicated in mammals called ruminants, including sheep, cattle, and deer. Ruminants have an enlarged esophagus and stomach modified to act as fermentation chambers. These chambers house anaerobic bacteria and protozoans that make fatty acids available to the host. In addition, symbiotic microorganisms produce amino acids and vitamins for use by the host.

EVOLUTION OF THE RESPIRATORY SYSTEM

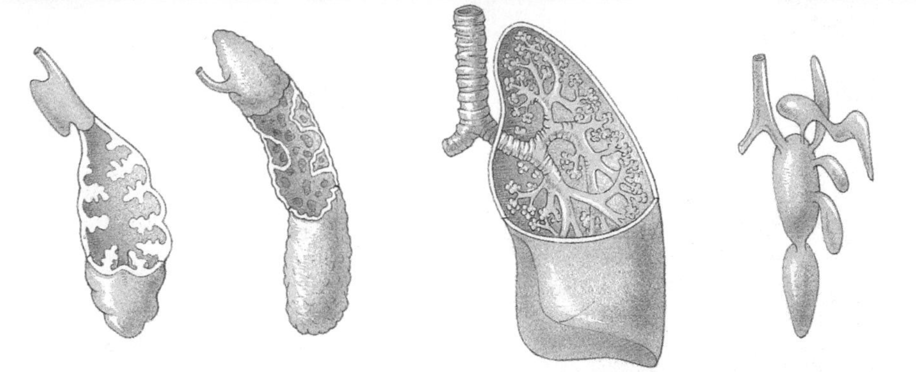

Figure 20–17
As vertebrates evolved, their respiratory structures became more specialized. Notice that the branching of the air tubes increases as you move from amphibians to mammals. Birds have the most advanced respiratory structures, which provide a continuous flow of fresh air into their lungs.

Mammals

Mammals require a higher rate of gas exchange because they have a higher metabolic rate—the rate at which they use food and oxygen. As a result, mammalian lungs have evolved in ways that have made them even more efficient. Air tubes called **bronchi** (BRAHN-kigh; singular: bronchus) enter the lungs and then branch extensively. They end in bubblelike structures called **alveoli** (al-VEE-uh-ligh; singular: alveolus) that are richly supplied with tiny capillaries. This allows for efficient gas exchange. However, the structure of the lungs is somewhat inefficient. Because air must move in and out of the same passageways, there is always some stale air that remains in the lungs after each breath.

Birds

Birds have the highest requirements for lung efficiency of any vertebrate group. Why? Bird flight is an intense long-term exercise that requires a large, steady oxygen supply. As a result, bird lungs have branched bronchi and alveoli similar to mammalian lungs but with an important difference. Air passageways in bird lungs connect to large air sacs in certain bones. Air is pumped through the lungs in a one-way flow. As a result, the gas-exchange surfaces constantly come in contact with fresh, oxygenated air.

Internal Transport

Circulatory systems in vertebrates have come a long way from the simple structures in ray-finned fishes. Typical fishes have a single-loop circulatory system. **In a single-loop circulatory system, blood is pumped from the heart to the gills and flows from gills to the rest of the body tissues before returning to the heart.** The heart itself consists of two chambers—an atrium that receives blood and a ventricle that pumps it out again.

Vertebrates with lungs for respiration have a double-loop circulatory system. **In a double-loop circulatory system, the first loop carries blood between the heart and the lungs. The second loop carries blood between the heart and the rest of the body.**

Investigate

Model Building The following activity will demonstrate to students that meat is generally easier to process and digest than plant material.

1. Use a mortar and pestle to grind a small piece of well-cooked beef or chicken into bits, counting how many times you had to grind it in order to break it apart well.
2. Put the ground-up meat in a small jar. Wash the mortar and pestle.
3. Repeat step 1 with several short lengths of a green twig cut from a bush or young tree. Which material had to be ground more times in order to break it into small bits? (The twig.)
4. Put the ground-up twig in another jar.
5. Moisten the ground-up meat and twig with a bit of water, and sprinkle each with some meat tenderizer. (Explain that meat tenderizer contains an enzyme—papain, derived from unripe papaya fruit—that digests protein in a way similar to carnivore digestive enzymes.)
6. Cover both jars and leave them in a warm place for a few hours or overnight.
7. Examine the jars' contents. Which material has been "digested" even further? (The meat.)

Laboratory Investigation

The Laboratory Investigation, Vertebrate Circulatory Systems, on pages 488–489 is appropriate to use at this point in the chapter.

TEACHER SUPPORT

Activity

MODELING HEART FUNCTION

Use the following activity to help students understand the function of a four-chambered heart. Have them adapt the model to represent two- and three-chambered hearts.

1. Four students should stand in a rough square shape to represent the four chambers of the heart, holding cards labeled with the names of the chambers.
2. Two other students should stand on either side of the model heart—one representing the lungs, and the other representing the rest of the body. These students also should hold labeled cards identifying themselves.
3. Another student should walk through the blood's pathway, starting at any point and continuing through both loops back to the starting point. (You may want to have the students representing blood, lungs, and body exchange colored index cards representing oxygen and carbon dioxide.)

Ancillary Support

The resources below can be used to support your teaching strategy for these two pages.

LM Examining Primate Hands, #40
TR Explore: We Love to Fly and It Shows

Problem Solving
Interpreting Diagrams
My, What Big Teeth You Have!

In this problem-solving activity, students will identify what type of consumer an unknown skull belongs to.

State The problem is to compare the dentition of a known carnivore and a known herbivore to that of an unknown skull in order to classify the unknown animal as a carnivore, a herbivore, or an omnivore.

Solve One major clue is that the unknown skull does not have large canine teeth in the upper jaw, a characteristic of carnivores. However, both its upper and lower incisors are very large, indicating that the animal must do a great deal of biting. The molars are flat, like those of the deer. The unidentified animal is a beaver, a herbivore that feeds on the fresh green bark and wood of trees.

Test Students could determine the unknown animal's identity by using field guides.

Communicate By a show of hands, determine how many students think the unknown animal is a herbivore, how many a carnivore, and how many an omnivore. Choose one student holding each opinion to present his or her rationale to the rest of the class.

Answers to Think About It

1. Flat, for grinding and crushing.

2. Sharp, wedge-shaped, and large, for biting and cutting.

3. The deer has incisors only in the lower jaw. They are curved and narrow but sharp, and are used to cut leaves and twigs from plants. The wolf's canines and incisors are pointed for puncturing prey, whereas the deer's are chisel-shaped for tearing vegetation.

4. A herbivore. (see Solve.)

Problem Solving
INTERPRETING DIAGRAMS

My, What Big Teeth You Have!

You can tell a lot about an animal by its teeth. The back teeth, or premolars and molars, are jagged in carnivores and flat in herbivores, which allows the animal to grind and shred its food. The canines, or eye teeth, are extremely long and pointed. That's how the animal stabs its prey and holds on to it. The front teeth, the incisors, are sharp and wedge-shaped, like a chisel blade, to allow the animal to bite and cut its food.

In the drawings below are three vertebrate skulls. One of the known skulls belongs to a carnivore, a wolf. Another skull belongs to a herbivore, a deer.

Based on the information presented here and the drawings, determine whether the unknown skull belongs to a carnivore, a herbivore, or an omnivore. Then answer the questions below.

VERTEBRATE SKULLS

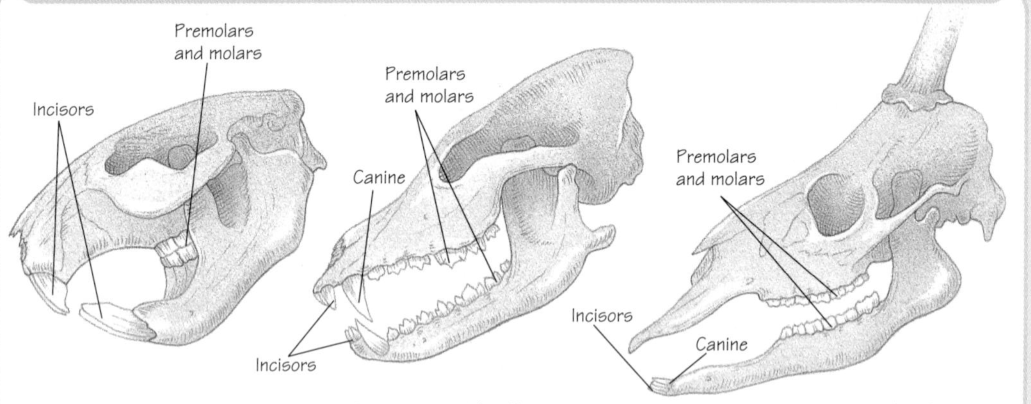

Unknown Skull — *Carnivore Skull (wolf)* — *Herbivore Skull (deer)*

THINK ABOUT IT

1. In the unknown skull, is the shape of the molars flat or jagged? Based on their shape, predict the function of the teeth.
2. What is the size of the incisors in the unknown skull? Based on their shape, predict the function of these teeth.
3. Compare the positions of the teeth in the jaws of the wolf and the deer in both form and function.
4. Identify the unknown skull as that of a herbivore, a carnivore, or an omnivore. Give reasons to support your answer.

482 Chapter 20

TEACHER SUPPORT

Facts and Figures

The gap between incisors and molars (also called "cheek teeth") in many herbivores creates extra space in the mouth when the animal is chewing bulky plant material.

Figure 20–18
The vertebrate circulatory system becomes more complex as you move from fishes to mammals. Fishes have a single-loop circulatory system with a two-chambered heart. After the appearance of lungs, vertebrates evolved a double-loop circulatory system. Amphibians and most reptiles have a three-chambered heart, including two atria and one ventricle. Mammals and birds have the most advanced circulatory systems. Their hearts have four chambers—two atria and two ventricles—eliminating the possibility of mixing oxygen-rich blood with oxygen-poor blood.

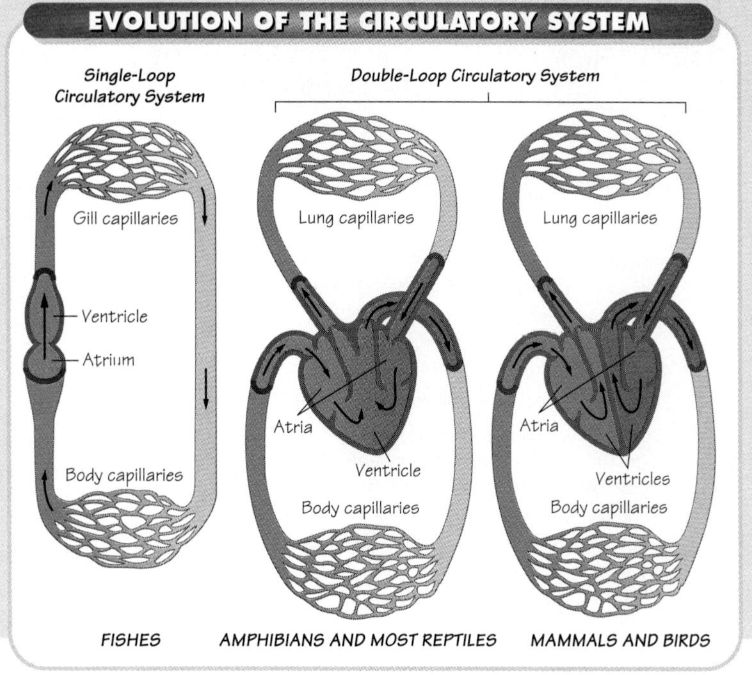

Temperature Control

The ability to control body temperature is an enormous asset. Many chemical reactions, including those important to living things, operate differently at various temperatures. Vertebrates use a variety of techniques to control temperature. All include a source of heat for the body, a method of conserving that heat, and a method of eliminating excess heat when necessary.

Most fishes, amphibians, and reptiles rely on interactions with their environment to help them control body temperature. These animals may bask in the sun to warm up or find shelter in the shade or in underground burrows to cool down. Such animals are known as **ectotherms,** which means "heat from the outside." Although they are often called coldblooded, the term is not accurate.

Mammals and birds generate heat in body tissues through chemical reactions in the body. In addition, mammals and birds have layers of fat and either fur or feathers to keep that heat from leaving the body. When these animals are cold, they shiver to cause muscles to generate more heat. When they are hot, they either pant, as dogs do, or sweat, as humans do, to cool the skin. These animals, often called warmblooded, are more properly called **endotherms,** which means "heat from within."

Excretion

You may recall that the need to eliminate nitrogen-containing wastes is tied in with the need to maintain water balance within the body. As with invertebrates, vertebrate wastes are produced in the form of ammonia. Aquatic vertebrates often get rid of ammonia through diffusion. Fishes lose a great deal across gill membranes, while amphibians lose some through their skin. But these animals also have the beginnings of a **kidney,** the organ used to excrete

Ideas Through Images

Have students examine Figure 20–18 and read the caption. Then have them trace the full pathway of blood flow in each system, beginning with blood returning from the body and entering the atrium (the right atrium in the second and third illustrations). To make sure students trace the flow accurately, you could also do this yourself with an overhead transparency made from the diagram. Ask students to identify the point in each system where oxygen-rich and oxygen-poor blood can mix together. (In fishes, at all points in the system; in amphibians and reptiles, in the single ventricle; in mammals and birds, at no point in the system.)

Discussion

As part of the discussion comparing the body systems of vertebrates with those of invertebrates, ask students to recall which types of invertebrates have nephridia, the structures that serve the same function as the kidneys found in vertebrates. (Earthworms and other annelids, mollusks, and invertebrate chordates.) Which invertebrates excrete nitrogenous wastes as a semisolid paste, as birds and reptiles do? (Insects and some spiders and scorpions.)

TEACHER SUPPORT

Background Information

For a time, the terms homeothermic (meaning steady temperature) and poikilothermic (varying temperature) were used interchangeably with the terms warm-blooded and cold-blooded. All four terms, however, are inaccurate descriptions of vertebrates' temperature-regulation processes.

Ectotherms' blood is not cold. By basking in sunlight, sheltering in shade, and controlling their level of activity, ectotherms actually manage to do a remarkable job of regulating body temperature through behavioral rather than physiological means. Quite a few generally ectothermic animals, ranging from honey bees to tuna fish, have evolved combinations of behavior and physiology that enable them to regulate body temperature with surprising effectiveness.

Endotherms' body temperature is not unvarying. For example, many mammals enter periods of hibernation during which their body temperature drops significantly.

MINI LAB Experimenting

Teacher Notes

- For time required and materials needed, see page 468b.
- Each group's hypothesis should be in the form of a statement that can be verified or rejected on the basis of observable data.
- Make sure each group's experiment involves changing only one variable (the manipulated variable) while holding all other variables constant.

Answers to Analyze and Conclude

1. Answers will vary depending on each group's hypothesis and experimental design.
2. Both feathers and fur serve as insulators, helping to retain body heat. Students may know that feathers and fur provide tiny spaces that trap air heated by the body and prevent the heat from escaping.
3. During the summer, insulation keeps warmer air away from the body.

Skills Trace

Experimenting

- **Focus** p. 484
- **Practice** p. 485
- **Assess** p. 492

Investigate

Cooperative Learning Students are often intrigued by the unusual sensory abilities of other animals compared with those of humans. Divide the class into groups of five, and have the students in each group research and report on one example of a highly developed sensory ability in each of the five major vertebrate groups (fishes, amphibians, reptiles, birds, and mammals), with each student being responsible for a different vertebrate group. Let each group report the examples in an oral presentation or visual display.

MINI LAB .... Experimenting ...

How to Keep Warm

PROBLEM *How do fur and feathers help animals maintain their internal body temperature? **Design an experiment** to answer the question.*

PROCEDURE

1. Formulate a hypothesis that you want to test.
2. Using different-sized containers, a thermometer, water, timer, feathers, and pieces of fur, design an experiment that will allow for the collection of data (changes in temperature). Construct a table for your data.
3. Include a control and prepare a list of numbered directions.
4. After your teacher checks your proposed experiment, carry it out.

ANALYZE AND CONCLUDE

1. Does your data support or reject your hypothesis? Explain your answer.
2. What can you conclude about the insulating properties of feathers? Fur?
3. Is insulation of any benefit during the summer? Explain your answer.

nitrogen and other nonsolid wastes. Kidneys became more complex as vertebrates adapted to drier and drier habitats. The mammalian kidney is the most complex.

Like many invertebrates, some vertebrates convert ammonia into less-toxic compounds to make it easier to concentrate and eliminate. Mammals, some adult amphibians, and some cartilaginous fishes convert ammonia to urea, a less-toxic substance. The urea is excreted from the body as urine. Birds and reptiles convert nitrogenous wastes into a semisolid paste—uric acid. Uric acid is also less toxic than ammonia and requires less water to flush it out of the body.

Response

All vertebrates—from jawless fishes to humans—show a great deal of cephalization, the concentration of nerves and sense organs in the head. Even in simple vertebrates, the bundle of nerves and neural connections in the head is large enough to be called a **brain.** From the brain, a long, thick collection of nerves called the **spinal cord** runs down the

Figure 20–19
Because amphibians and reptiles, such as (a) the common collared lizard sunning itself on a rock, rely on the environment to maintain their body temperature, they are called ectotherms. Birds and mammals, such as (b) these sled dogs cuddled up in straw to help keep their bodies warm, can maintain their body temperature internally and are called endotherms.

TEACHER SUPPORT — Background Information

The vertebrate brain evolved from a set of three bulges at the anterior end of the spinal cord. These three regions—the forebrain, midbrain, and hindbrain—still can be found during embryonic development.

As the brain evolved, three major trends altered these ancestral regions. First, the size of the brain increased relative to the size of the body in certain evolutionary lineages. Birds and mammals have larger brains relative to body size than do fishes, amphibians, and reptiles. A second trend was the division of the original three regions into subregions that assumed specific control and perceptual functions. The third trend was the increasing integrative power of the cerebrum, the dominant part of the forebrain. The cerebrums of birds and mammals are much larger relative to the other parts of the brain than the cerebrums of other vertebrates. The larger cerebrum is directly correlated with the more sophisticated behavior of birds and mammals.

EVOLUTION OF THE BRAIN

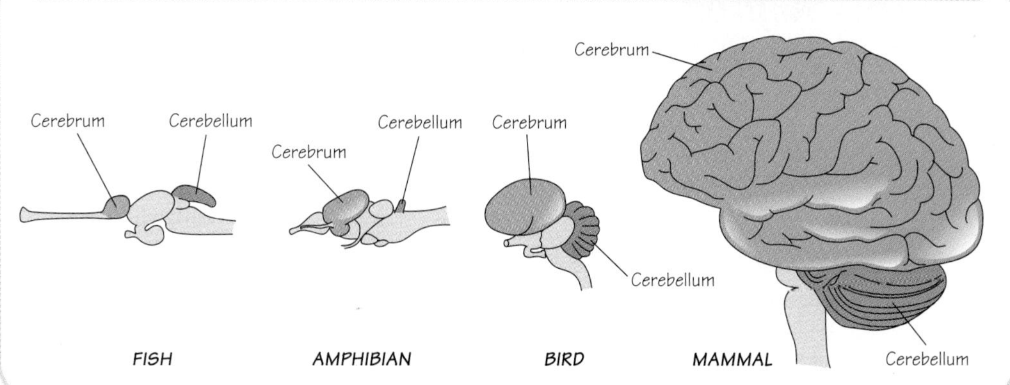

Figure 20–20
Although all vertebrate brains have a cerebrum and a cerebellum, the sizes of each varies. In mammals, the cerebrum, the part of the brain responsible for processing and interpreting information, is the most prominent.

back, protected by the vertebral column. At each joint between the vertebrae, pairs of nerves run in and out of the spinal cord to connect to muscles, organs, and sensory receptors in the skin and throughout the body.

Accompanying their larger brains, vertebrates developed increasingly complex behaviors, and different parts of the brain grew proportionately larger in different groups. The cerebrum, where most thinking takes place, grew steadily from fishes to humans. The cerebellum, the part of the brain largely responsible for coordinating balance and movement, is best developed in birds and mammals.

Reproduction

Almost all vertebrates reproduce sexually. There are, however, a few species of lizards, fishes, and amphibians that develop from unfertilized eggs. In some vertebrates, such as codfish and frogs, fertilization is external. In others—reptiles, birds, mammals, cartilaginous fishes, and certain amphibians—fertilization occurs inside the body of the female. As you move through the vertebrate classes from fishes to mammals, there is a trend from external fertilization to internal fertilization, with some exceptions, of course.

Section Review 20–3

1. **Describe** a single-loop circulatory system and a double-loop circulatory system.
2. **Compare** the two techniques of body temperature control in vertebrates.
3. **Critical Thinking—Drawing Conclusions** Are humans carnivores, herbivores, or omnivores? Give evidence to support your answer.
4. **MINI LAB** How would you **design an experiment** to find out how animals maintain their body temperature?

4 ASSESS

Quick Check

Ask students to list the eight life functions discussed in this section and, for each, to identify the major types of systems and/or organs found in different vertebrate groups.

Section Review 20–3

1. Single-loop system: Blood flows from the heart to the gills and from the gills to the rest of the body before returning to the heart. Double-loop system: The first loop carries blood between the heart and lungs, and the second loop carries blood between the heart and the rest of the body.
2. Ectotherms rely on interactions with their environment to control their body temperature. Endotherms generate heat in body tissues through chemical reactions in the body.
3. Students should conclude that humans generally are omnivores, since most eat both meat and plants. As evidence, students should describe the types and shapes of teeth humans have.
4. Answers will vary. Students' experiments should involve using a control, changing only one variable, and basing conclusions on observable effects of the variable.

Skills Trace
Experimenting

- Focus p. 484
- Practice p. 485
- Assess p. 492

TEACHER SUPPORT

Managing Classroom Diversity

TECH PREP STUDENTS
Ask students who are interested in careers as veterinary technicians which group of vertebrates most interests them. Then have these students research the essential life functions, including support and movement, feeding and digestion, respiration, internal transport, temperature control, excretion and water balance, response, and reproduction, for that group. Have students who have researched different groups compare their findings to see how their respective vertebrate groups are alike and different.

Learning Modality

Kinesthetic Learning The Activity, Modeling Heart Function, on page 481 would provide an excellent experience for students who learn best through kinesthetic means.

Section 20-4

Reproductive Adaptations to Life on Land

Performance Objective

- Explain the importance of amniotic eggs to the survival of terrestrial vertebrates.

1 ENGAGE

Ideas Through Images

Have students examine Figure 20–21 and read the caption. Make sure they notice the mass of egg-filled foam beneath the frogs. Have them answer the following questions.

- **What might be the advantage of many frogs laying their eggs together?** (Accept reasonable responses, such as a large foam nest can retain moisture better than a small one.)
- **How do frog eggs differ from reptile and bird eggs?** (Frog eggs are not enclosed in a shell.)
- **What advantages might a shell provide for the developing young?** (Accept all reasonable responses, including protection from predators and retaining moisture.)

2 EXPLORE

Inquiry Activity

Observing

Examinin ; a Bird's Egg

Ask studen1s what structures they think are contained in a chicken's egg. Give each pair or group of students a hard-boiled egg, and have them remove the shell in as few pieces as possible, remove the thin tissue (membrane) enclosing the inner egg, and then slice the egg in half vertically to reveal the yolk. Ask students to draw a cross section of the egg to show all the structures they found.

SECTION 20–4 BRANCHING OUT **In Depth**

Reproductive Adaptations to Life on Land

GUIDE FOR READING

- Discuss the importance of the amniotic egg.

FISHES AND FROGS RELY ON water for reproduction. However, similar to land plants, the more advanced and successful groups had to evolve reproductive strategies that did not depend on water for either fertilization or egg development. That's why one of the most important adaptations in all of terrestrial vertebrate evolution was the amniotic egg.

Development of the Amniotic Egg

Most fishes and nearly all living amphibians reproduce by external fertilization. When adults mate, males deposit sperm and females deposit eggs in water, where external fertilization takes place. The eggs must develop and hatch in water, where they produce larvae that live entirely in water. In amphibians, larvae feed and grow in the water until they develop into adults. These eggs are relatively simple and easy for females to produce, so the females often lay hundreds, or even thousands, at a time.

Beginning with reptiles, however, reproduction followed a different pattern. Reptiles reproduce by internal fertilization, in which males deposit sperm inside the body of the female. Fertilized eggs develop for a time inside the female's body, where the eggs are provided with a food

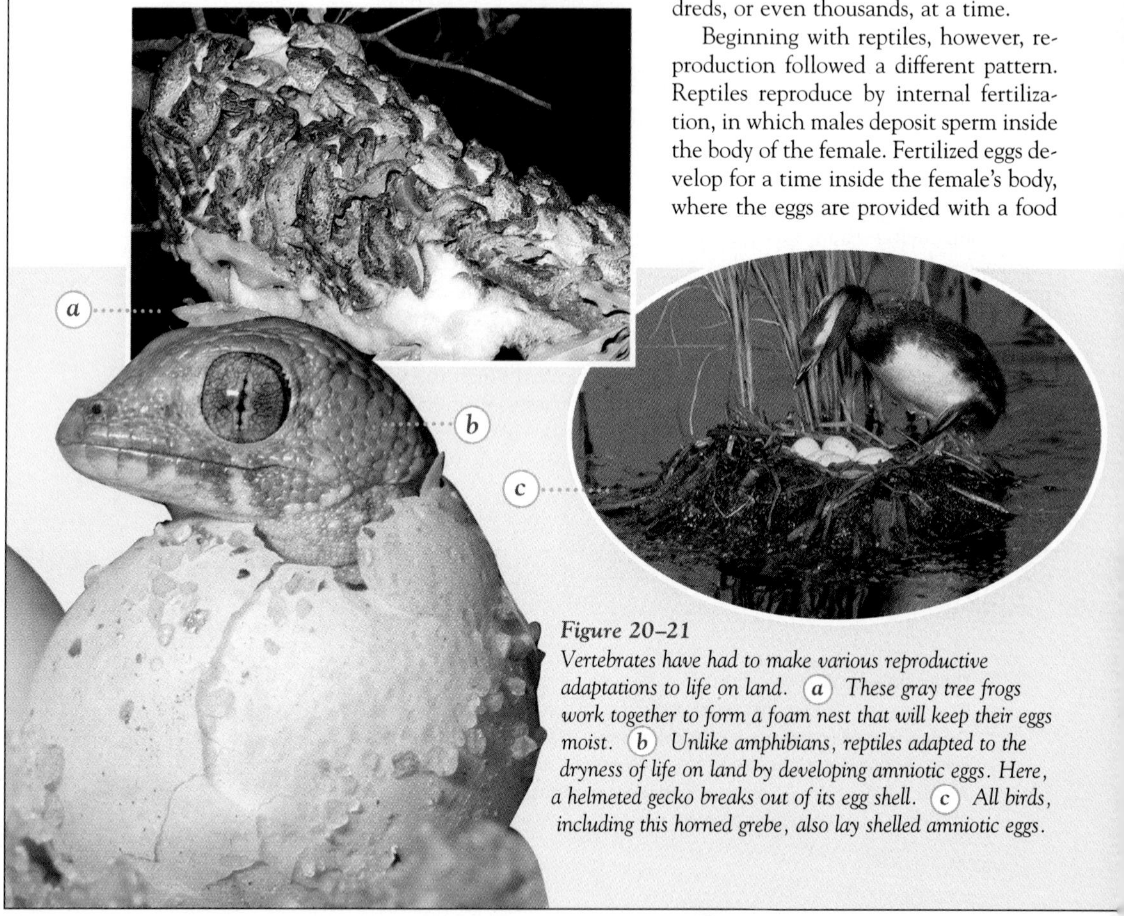

Figure 20–21
Vertebrates have had to make various reproductive adaptations to life on land. (a) These gray tree frogs work together to form a foam nest that will keep their eggs moist. (b) Unlike amphibians, reptiles adapted to the dryness of life on land by developing amniotic eggs. Here, a helmeted gecko breaks out of its egg shell. (c) All birds, including this horned grebe, also lay shelled amniotic eggs.

TEACHER SUPPORT

Ecology Note

Since ancient times, humans have relied on reptile and bird eggs as an important source of protein in the diet. Although the eggs sold in industrialized nations' supermarkets today come from commercial egg farms, many people throughout the world still collect bird and reptile eggs from wild sources. In various parts of the world, populations of indigenous birds or reptiles have been drastically reduced or entirely eliminated due to overcollection of their eggs. Wild predators also destroy the eggs of many species, including those of endangered sea turtles.

Encourage interested students to research specific examples of bird and reptile species that are threatened or that have been eradicated through destruction of their eggs by humans and/or wild predators.

AMNIOTIC EGG

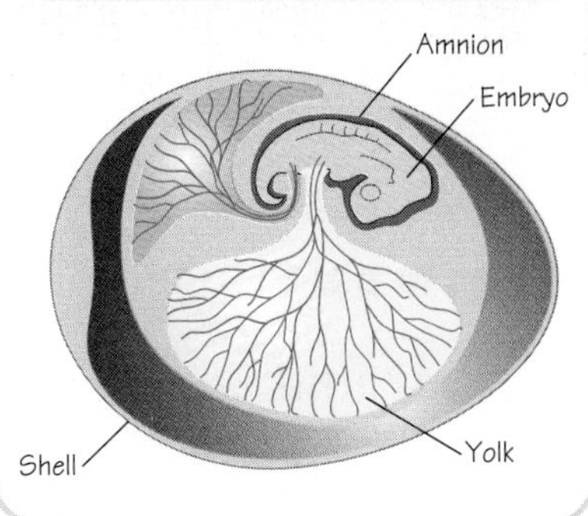

Figure 20–22
The development of the amniotic egg was an important trend in vertebrate evolution. In addition to a shell, amnion, and other membranes, the amniotic egg contains yolk, which is rich in nutrients. The yolk is used by the developing embryo until it is ready to hatch.

supply—the yolk—and are wrapped in several membranes. One of those membranes is the **amnion,** hence the name **amniotic** (am-nee-AHT-ihk) **egg.** The internal membranes bathe the developing embryo in liquid and receive and store its wastes. The entire structure is encased by a shell that allows the exchange of oxygen and carbon dioxide but keeps water inside. Eggs constructed in this way do not need to develop in water. As a rule, fewer of these eggs are laid, and either males or females or both take care of them until they hatch.

Amniotic eggs were an important adaptation to the survival of land animals. This adaptation was passed on from the early reptiles to modern reptiles, birds, and mammals.

☑ ***Checkpoint*** What is an amniotic egg? ❶

Methods of Reproduction

As important as the amniotic egg has been in vertebrate evolution, it was not the only strategy evolved by vertebrates nor was it the final one. Aquatic and terrestrial vertebrates have also evolved various styles of handling both aquatic and amniotic eggs.

The simplest way to handle eggs, in the water or out, is the one you would usually think of—to lay them. In this strategy, eggs complete their development and hatch outside the female's body. Such animals are described as being **oviparous** (oh-VIHP-uh-ruhs).

Some sharks and bony fishes produce eggs but retain those eggs inside the female until the eggs hatch. In most cases, the embryos receive food stored in the yolk sac. Thus, they receive no further nutrients directly from the mother during development. These animals are described as being **ovoviviparous** (oh-voh-vigh-VIHP-uh-ruhs).

Still other animals, including all mammals except monotremes, retain developing embryos inside the body of the female for long periods. Generally, such eggs do not contain a yolk, or they may contain a small amount of yolk that is used up early in development. Thus, the females must provide additional nutrients during embryonic growth and development. Such animals are **viviparous** (vigh-VIHP-ah-ruhs).

Section Review 20–4

1. **Discuss** the importance of the amniotic egg.
2. **BRANCHING OUT ACTIVITY** **Construct a chart** in which you compare the body systems of all the different classes of vertebrates. Add artwork or photographs to illustrate the different classes. Display your chart in the classroom.

3 TEACH

Discussion

Write the terms for the reproduction methods on the board, with the word parts separated by slash marks: ovi/parous, ovo/vivi/parous, and vivi/parous. Have students use a dictionary to find the meaning of each word part. (*Ovo* and *ovi*, egg; *vi* and *vivi*, alive; *parous*, giving birth.) Then relate the meaning of each word to the corresponding method of reproduction.

4 ASSESS

Quick Check

Have students write brief definitions of oviparous, ovoviviparous, and viviparous in their own words.

Section Review 20–4

1. An amniotic egg's internal membranes bathe the embryo in liquid that is kept inside by the shell, so the egg does not need to develop in water—an important adaptation for life on land.

☑ Checkpoint

❶ In an amniotic egg, internal membranes bathe the developing embryo in liquid and receive and store its wastes, and the entire structure is encased by a shell that allows for gas exchange but keeps water in.

2. Students may wish to work on poster-size paper. Have them include the seven vertebrate classes described in Section 20–2 and the body systems described in Sections 20–3 and 20–4.

Learning Modality

Auditory Learning Write each of these terms on a separate index card: amniotic egg, oviparous, ovoviviparous, and viviparous. Have students take turns drawing a card, pronouncing the term, telling what the term means, and explaining how it relates to an adaptation to life on land.

Ancillary Support

The resources below can be used to support your teaching strategy for these two pages.

TR Apply: Egging You On
BL Inquiry Activity: The Yolk's on You

CHAPTER 20

Laboratory Investigation

Vertebrate Circulatory Systems

Before the Lab

1. Well in advance, ask students to collect the plastic bottles they will need for this investigation. You may want to have each group collect more than four so extras will be available if students make mistakes in cutting the bottles.
2. Purchase yarn that is thick enough to be unraveled easily.

Pre-Lab Discussion

Have students read the entire procedure for this investigation. Then ask students the following questions.

What is the purpose of this investigation? (To compare a double-loop circulatory system and a single-loop circulatory system.)

In the single-loop model, why are both the atrium and the ventricle shown with blue paper? (Both contain oxygen-poor blood.)

Why is this so? (After the blood picks up oxygen in the gills, it goes directly to the rest of the body rather than going back to the heart first.)

What happens to the blood in a double-loop circulatory system after it goes to the lungs? (The blood returns from the lungs to the heart, and then it is pumped to the rest of the body.)

Skills Development

Students will use these skills while completing the laboratory investigation: designing an experiment, developing a model, and making comparisons.

Laboratory Investigation

DESIGNING AN EXPERIMENT

Vertebrate Circulatory Systems

The heart is a part of the transport system that pumps blood throughout the body. In this investigation, you will compare a two-chambered, single-loop circulatory system in fishes to a four-chambered, double-loop circulatory system in birds and mammals.

Problem

How do a double-loop circulatory system and a single-loop circulatory system compare? **Design an experiment** to answer the question.

Suggested Materials

- 4 8-oz plastic bottles
- 1 sheet each of red and blue construction paper
- red and blue yarn
- scissors
- scalpel
- clear mailing tape

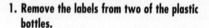

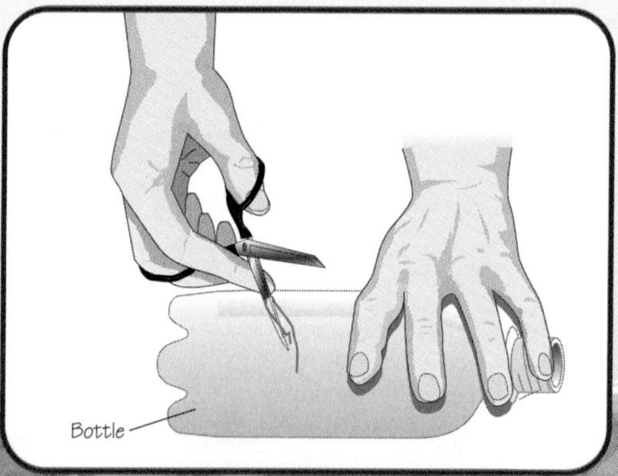

Suggested Procedure

1. **Remove the labels from two of the plastic bottles.**
2. **Using a scalpel, pierce a hole in one of the bottles where it tapers to form the bottom of the bottle. Place the point of a scissors in the hole and cut around the bottle until the bottom of the bottle is removed. CAUTION: *Be careful when using sharp instruments.***
3. **Cut a sheet of blue construction paper just large enough to fit inside the uncut bottle. You will have to roll the paper tightly so that it can be inserted into the bottle. Remove the cap and insert the rolled paper into the bottle. This bottle represents the atrium filled with oxygen-poor blood.**
4. **Insert the remainder of the blue construction paper into the cut bottle. This represents the ventricle filled with oxygen-poor blood.**
5. **Insert the bottle representing the atrium into the bottle representing the ventricle. They should fit snugly together. Tape them together if necessary.**

Safety Tip

Caution students to handle the scalpel and scissors carefully.

6. **Remove the bottle cap from the "ventricle" and insert a 15- to 20-cm length of blue yarn into the neck of the bottle. Secure one end of the yarn by placing the bottle cap back on. This piece of yarn represents the blood vessel leading to the gills.**
7. **Unravel the free end of the blue yarn.**
8. **Unravel both ends of a 15- to 20-cm length of red yarn.**
9. **Tie the unraveled free ends of the blue yarn to one of the unraveled free ends of the red yarn to represent a capillary network in the gills.**
10. **Using another 15- to 20-cm length of blue yarn, unravel one end. Tie these unraveled ends to the remaining unraveled free ends of the red yarn. This will represent a capillary network of the body cells.**
11. **Tape the remaining free end of the blue yarn to the "atrium." This completes the two-chambered, single-loop model.**
12. **Using a procedure similar to the one given in steps 1 to 11, determine how you would construct a model of a four-chambered, double-loop circulatory system.**

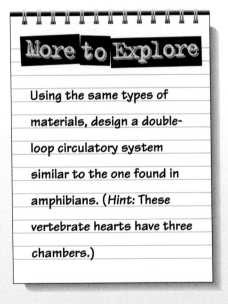

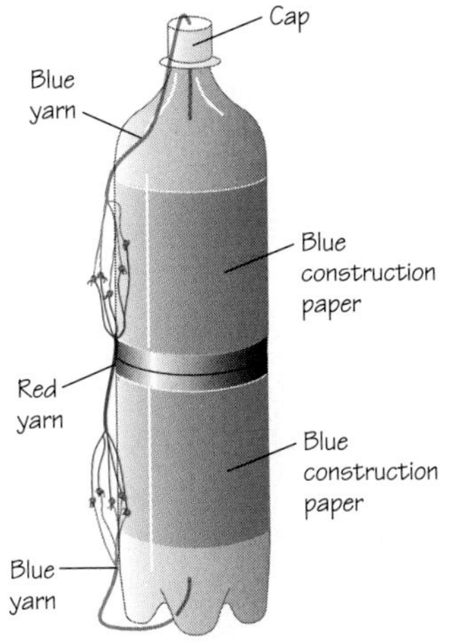

Observations

1. What modifications did you have to make to your single-loop system in order to construct your double-loop system?
2. In the double-loop system, what does the red construction paper symbolize?

Analysis and Conclusions

1. In the single-loop system, where did the blood go after leaving the ventricle? Where did the blood go after leaving the ventricle in the double-loop system?
2. In the single-loop system, where did the blood go after leaving the atrium? Where did the blood go after leaving the atrium in the double-loop system?
3. Why were the red and blue yarns unraveled and joined?
4. Compare the similarities and differences between the two systems you constructed.

More to Explore

Using the same types of materials, design a double-loop circulatory system similar to the one found in amphibians. (*Hint:* These vertebrate hearts have three chambers.)

Teaching Strategies

1. The written directions for building the model are rather complex. Tell students to pay close attention to the diagrams as they build the single-loop system.
2. When students model the four-chambered heart, they should construct each side as they did the single atrium and ventricle in the single-loop system, using blue paper for both right chambers and red paper for both left chambers.

Answers to Observations

1. See Teaching Strategy 2.
2. Red paper indicates that the heart chambers contain oxygen-rich blood.

Answers to Analysis and Conclusions

1. Single-loop system: To the gills, then directly to body cells. Double-loop system (four-chambered heart): Blood from the right ventricle went to the lungs; blood from the left ventricle went to body cells.
2. Single-loop system: To the ventricle. Double-loop system (four-chambered heart): Blood from the right atrium went to the right ventricle; blood from the left atrium went to the left ventricle.
3. To represent the capillaries where gas exchange occurs.
4. Similarities: Atria receive blood from the body and pump it to ventricles; ventricles pump blood away from the heart. Both systems include capillary networks where gas exchange occurs. Differences: Students should mention the different numbers of chambers, the different pathways through which blood flows, and that oxygen-rich and oxygen-poor blood do not mix in the double-loop system.

More to Explore

Constructing a three-chambered heart is more difficult. The two bottles representing the atria will not fit snugly into the one bottle representing the ventricle and must be secured with tape. To represent the mixture of oxygen-poor and oxygen-rich blood, students must put both red and blue paper into the single ventricle and use both red and blue yarn for the vessel exiting the ventricle. However, blood returning to the left atrium from the lungs should be shown with red yarn only, and blood returning to the right atrium from the rest of the body should be shown with blue yarn only. The completed pathway should be right atrium (blue)→ ventricle (blue and red)→ lungs (blue yarn to red yarn) → left atrium (red)→ ventricle (blue and red)→ body cells (blue and red yarn to blue yarn only)→ right atrium (blue).

CHAPTER 20

Study Guide

Review Strategy

Divide the class into five groups, one for each class of vertebrates discussed in this chapter, but with all three classes of fishes assigned to one student group. Have each group create a table summarizing the major characteristics and the body systems of each vertebrate class. Then let the groups photocopy their tables and exchange them so they can be used by other groups as self-check study guides.

Study Guide

Summarizing Key Concepts

The key concepts in each section of this chapter are listed below to help you review the chapter content. Make sure you understand each concept and its relationship to other concepts and to the theme of this chapter.

20–1 Evolution of Vertebrates

- Mammals, fishes, amphibians, birds, and reptiles are classified in the chordate subphylum Vertebrata.
- The notable trends in vertebrate evolution were the development of true bony jaws, the development of paired pectoral and pelvic limb girdles, and the development of bones.

20–2 A Survey of Living Vertebrates

- Besides a backbone, most vertebrates have two sets of appendages, a closed circulatory system with a ventral heart, and either gills or lungs for breathing.

20–3 Form and Function in Vertebrates

- Primitive vertebrates had limbs that stuck out almost horizontally from the body. Reptiles evolved limbs that grew vertically and could support body mass more efficiently.
- Vertebrates have evolved a variety of jaw structures suited to the foods they eat.
- Fishes have a single-loop circulatory system. Amphibians, reptiles, birds, and mammals have a double-loop circulatory system.
- Most fishes, amphibians, and reptiles are ectotherms. Mammals and birds are endotherms.
- Most fishes and aquatic vertebrates excrete nitrogenous wastes in the form of ammonia. Mammals and some cartilaginous fishes excrete urea. Birds and reptiles excrete uric acid.

20–4 Reproductive Adaptations to Life on Land

- Amniotic eggs were an important adaptation to the survival of land animals.
- Vertebrates are either oviparous, ovoviviparous, or viviparous.

Reviewing Key Terms

Review the following vocabulary terms and their meaning. Then use each term in a complete sentence.

20–1 Evolution of Vertebrates

notochord, cartilage, vertebra, tetrapod

20–2 A Survey of Living Vertebrates

mammary gland, placenta

20–3 Form and Function in Vertebrates

bronchus, ectotherm, alveolus, endotherm, kidney, spinal cord, brain

20–4 Reproductive Adaptations to Life on Land

amnion, ovoviviparous, amniotic egg, viviparous, oviparous

Inquiry-Based Strategy

Challenge individual students or small groups to design a new vertebrate animal. To guide students' work, provide a list of questions and issues for them to address, such as those suggested below, and discuss the list before they begin. Give each student or group an opportunity to present and describe its creation to the rest of the class.

1. Describe the animal's habitat—the climate and the abiotic and biotic factors in the environment.
2. Describe each of the animal's body systems (skeletal, digestive, respiratory, circulatory, temperature-control, excretory, and nervous systems) and its method of reproduction.
3. How does each system enable the animal to survive successfully in its environment?
4. To which class of vertebrates does the animal belong?
5. Draw a picture of your animal in its habitat.

Recalling Main Ideas

Choose the letter of the answer that best completes the statement or answers the question.

1. The first vertebrates that did not need water for reproduction were the
   a. reptiles. **c.** birds.
   b. mammals. **d.** amphibians.
2. Which was not a trend in vertebrate evolution?
   a. development of bony jaws
   b. development of gills
   c. development of paired limb girdles
   d. beginnings of arms and legs
3. The largest group of fishes is the
   a. jawless fishes. **c.** cartilaginous fishes.
   b. bony fishes. **d.** lobe-finned fishes.
4. Which animal does not belong with the others?
   a. newt **c.** toad
   b. salamander **d.** tortoise
5. Which is not a group of mammals?
   a. monotremes **c.** placentals
   b. lampreys **d.** marsupials
6. Which vertebrate group has the most advanced respiratory system?
   a. amphibians **c.** reptiles
   b. birds **d.** mammals
7. Ectotherms obtain the heat they need from
   a. the environment. **c.** food.
   b. the body. **d.** chemical reactions.
8. The cerebellum is best developed in
   a. fishes and amphibians.
   b. amphibians and reptiles.
   c. birds and mammals.
   d. reptiles and mammals.
9. An animal whose eggs develop and hatch outside the female's body is called
   a. oviparous. **c.** ovoviviparous.
   b. viviparous. **d.** amniotic.

Putting It All Together

Using the information on pages xxx to xxxi, complete the following concept map.

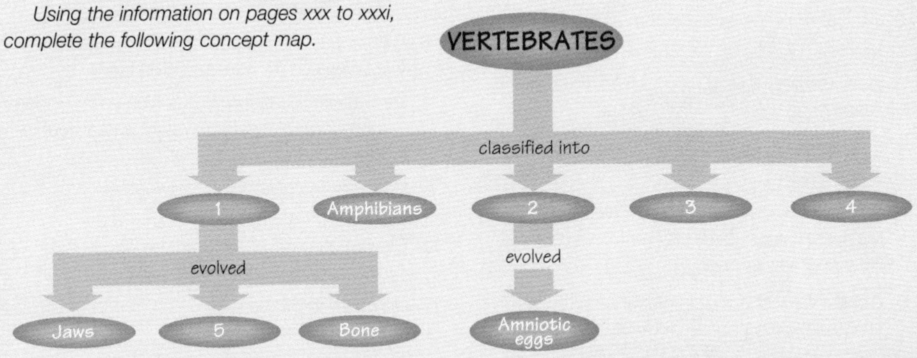

Putting It All Together

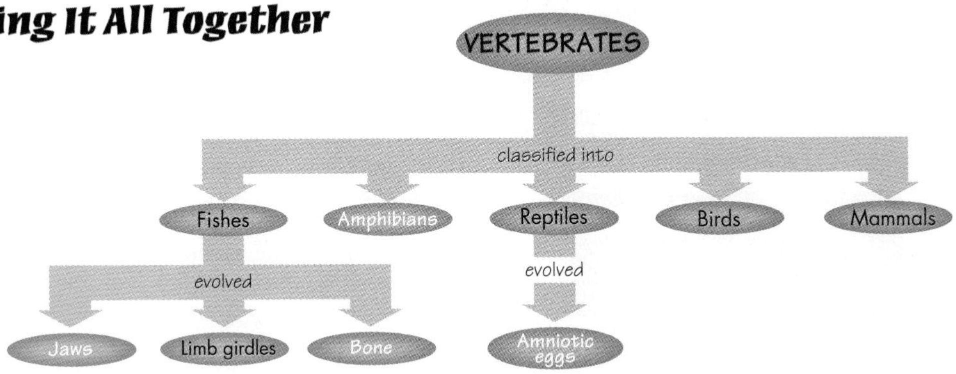

Recalling Main Ideas

1. a	6. b
2. b	7. a
3. b	8. c
4. d	9. a
5. b	

Assessment

Reviewing What You Learned

1. A notochord is a flexible supporting structure along an animal's back.
2. Vertebrates are a subphylum of chordates. The phylum Chordata also includes animals that are invertebrate chordates.
3. A strong, resilient material that makes up the skeleton on some vertebrates.
4. A tetrapod is a vertebrate with four limbs.
5. Amphibians: moist skin, breathe through gills when young and with lungs when adult, and lay eggs without shells. Reptiles: dry, scaly skin, breathe through lungs, and eggs have leathery shells.
6. The age of ruling reptiles, derived from the great success of dinosaurs during that age.
7. The separating of land masses isolated groups of ancient mammals, so they began to evolve along different paths.
8. The order Urodela includes newts and salamanders. The order Anura includes frogs and toads.
9. Chelonia, Crocodilia, and Squamata.
10. They have body hair and nourish their young with milk.
11. Monotremes, marsupials, and placental mammals.
12. The organ that connects the mother with her developing embryo.
13. One of the membranes enclosing the developing embryo.

Expanding the Concepts

1. The development of true jaws transformed the mouth from a simple opening into a useful feeding tool.
2. Limb girdles connect limbs with the backbone in a way that enables muscles to work efficiently.

Assessment (continued)

3. Amphibians have fully developed limbs, lungs as adults so they can live out of water, and a three-chambered heart in a double-loop circulatory system that keeps oxygen-rich and oxygen-poor blood more separated than does the single-loop system of fishes.
4. Reptiles can live entirely out of water, have scaly skin that reduces water loss, reproduce through internal fertilization, and produce eggs with shells.
5. Birds are endothermic, have feathers that retain body heat, have a more advanced respiratory system, have a double-loop circulatory system with a four-chambered heart that keeps oxygen-rich and oxygen-poor blood from mixing, have a more highly developed brain, and produce hard-shelled eggs. Both birds and reptiles have a vertebral column, are tetrapods, are capable of living entirely on land, and reproduce through internal fertilization.
6. As continents began to drift apart in the late Mesozoic Era, groups of ancient mammals were isolated and began to evolve along different paths. Some mammals evolved to flourish in the southern continents, while others evolved in northern continents.

7. Students' experimental designs should include a testable hypothesis, variables, and a control.

Skills Trace
Experimenting
- Focus p. 477
- Practice p. 478
- Assess p. 492

8. First, vertebrates had to evolve limb girdles and well-developed arms and legs. Early amphibians had limbs that stuck out almost horizontally from the body, limiting their range of motion. As vertebrates adapted to terrestrial life, the limbs became more vertical to support body mass more efficiently and allow greater mobility.

Assessment

Reviewing What You Learned

Answer each of the following in a complete sentence.

1. What is a notochord?
2. How are chordates different from vertebrates?
3. What is cartilage?
4. What is a tetrapod?
5. How can you distinguish a reptile from an amphibian?
6. What is another name for the Mesozoic Era? Why did it get this name?
7. Discuss the changes that led to the rapid and diverse adaptive radiation of the mammals.
8. List the orders of amphibians. Give an example of each.
9. Name three orders of reptiles.
10. How are mammals different from other vertebrates?
11. Name the three groups of living mammals.
12. What is a placenta?
13. What is the amnion?

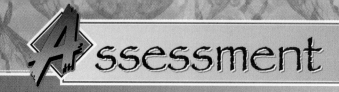

Expanding the Concepts

Discuss each of the following in a brief paragraph.

1. What was the importance of the evolution of jaws?
2. Explain the importance of the evolution of limb girdles.
3. How are amphibians more advanced than fishes?
4. In what ways are reptiles more advanced than amphibians?
5. Scientists believe that birds evolved from reptiles. How are birds different from reptiles? How are they similar?
6. Discuss how changes in global geography affected the distribution of mammals.
7. **Design an experiment** in which you compare the respiratory system of an amphibian with that of a mammal.
8. Describe the types of skeletal changes that were required for movement on land.
9. **Design an experiment** in which you compare a single-loop circulatory system and a double-loop circulatory system.
10. Describe the differences between endotherms and ectotherms.
11. Discuss the role of the amniotic egg in the evolution of reproduction on land.
12. Compare the three methods of reproduction among vertebrates.

9. Students may describe the models they made in the Laboratory Investigation on pages 488–489, or another type of model of their own design.

Skills Trace
Experimenting
- Focus p. 484
- Practice p. 485
- Assess p. 492

10. Ectotherms rely on interactions with their environment to help them control body temperature. They may bask in the sun to warm up or find shelter in the shade or underground to cool down. Endotherms generate heat in body tissues through chemical reactions in the body. They also have layers of fat and either feathers or fur to retain body heat. When they are cold, they shiver to generate heat. When they are hot, they pant or sweat to disperse heat.
11. The amniotic egg has internal membranes that bathe the developing embryo in liquid and receive and store its wastes. The entire structure is encased by a shell that allows gas exchange but keeps water inside.
12. Oviparous: lay eggs that develop and hatch outside the female's body. Ovoviviparous: retain

Extending Your Thinking

Use the skills you have developed in this chapter to answer the following.

1. **Analyzing** The kidney and its ability to maintain the internal water balance of vertebrates can be directly related to the organism's habitat. Discuss the structure and function of the excretory system, primarily the kidney, as vertebrates moved from water to land.
2. **Analyzing** At the end of the Pleistocene Era, there was a mass extinction of large animals, such as the mammoth, the mastodon, and the giant sloth in North America. There are two theories concerning this mass extinction. One theory states that many of the animals could not make the broad environmental adjustments they needed in order to survive. The second theory states that as the population of humans grew and moved into the many new habitats, these animals were killed off by humans. Do you agree with either of these theories, a combination, or some other explanation? Defend your answer.
3. **Using the writing process** The Age of Reptiles lasted approximately 150 million years. Its demise was considered the end of the Cretaceous Period. Compared with the reptiles, humans have existed on Earth for a very short time. Do you think humans will exist on Earth for at least as long as reptiles? Write a one-page response to defend your answer.
4. **Drawing conclusions** Groups of animals that have evolved later are often referred to as advanced. Does this mean that they are better animals? Explain your answer.

Applying Your Skills

Vertebrate Census

Scientists need to keep accurate data of both the kinds and numbers of animals that currently exist on Earth. Vertebrates live all over the world. If you observe and record carefully, you may be surprised at the diversity of vertebrates in your own area.

1. For a two-week time period, keep a list of all the vertebrates you observe in your area.
2. Identify the vertebrates by both their common name and their scientific name.
3. Record the number of each organism you see every day during this time period.

• GOING FURTHER •

4. What do you notice about the vertebrates in your area? How are they similar? Different?
5. If you lived in a different part of the country, would you expect your list to be different? If so, how?

eggs inside the female's body until they hatch. Viviparous: retain developing embryos inside the female's body for long periods, during which they receive nutrients from the mother.

Extending Your Thinking

1. Answers should include the following major points: Aquatic vertebrates often get rid of ammonia through diffusion and also have a simple kidney to excrete nitrogen and other nonsolid wastes. Kidneys became increasingly more complex as vertebrates adapted to drier habitats, with mammalian kidneys being the most complex. A number of vertebrates convert ammonia into less toxic compounds to make it easier to concentrate and eliminate.
2. Accept a variety of responses so long as students defend their answers with well-reasoned explanations.
3. Many students may contend that humans are changing the environment too rapidly and in too many negative ways to be successful for as long a period as the dinosaurs. Other students may believe that humans will learn to take better care of the environment and will persist through the wise use of technology.
4. Students should realize that later-evolving animals are "better" only in the sense that their body systems are generally more complex than those of their earlier ancestors. Any animal (or other organism) that survived for long periods had to be well adapted to its environment. Dinosaurs are a prime example.

Applying Your Skills

Teacher Notes

- Instruct students to pay particular attention to the smaller, less obvious vertebrates in their area such as small toads and frogs.
- Encourage students also to list vertebrates they have not observed directly but for which they have seen trace evidence—for example, a shed snakeskin, a frog's call, deer tracks, or mouse droppings.
- Provide field guides so students can research the scientific names of the vertebrates they have observed.

Answers

4. Students should identify some of the similarities and differences discussed in this chapter.
5. Students should realize that different environmental conditions (climate factors, effect of human activity, and the like) would affect the type and number of vertebrates in an area. Accept all reasonable answers about how their list would be different.

Scoring Rubric

4 Response is thorough, accurate, and creative; shows an in-depth understanding of science skills, procedures, and concepts.

3 Response is complete, mostly accurate, and original; shows a satisfactory understanding of science skills, procedures, and concepts.

2 Response is mostly complete but includes some inaccuracies; shows an adequate understanding of science skills, procedures, and concepts.

1 Response is only partially complete and has many inaccuracies; shows an incomplete understanding of science skills, procedures, and concepts.

0 Response is mostly incomplete and/or inaccurate; shows a lack of understanding of science skills, procedures, and concepts.

Chapter 21 Human History

Content Management	Student Edition Activities
■ Section 21–1 The Origins of *Homo sapiens*, pp. 495–501 The Primates The Primate Family Tree Hominid Origins Prehistoric Migrations	
◆ BRANCHING OUT • In Depth Section 21–2 Coevolution of Humans and Parasites, pp. 502–505 Shaping History Impact on Medicine	MINI LAB: A Breath of Fresh Air, p. 503 Laboratory Investigation: The Spread of Disease, pp. 506–507

■ This section covers all the necessary content and concepts for a basic course in biology.
◆ This section covers content and concepts that are either applications or extensions of the basic material.

Integration Strategies

SE History, p. 501
Biology and Society, p. 503

Assessment Strategies

SE Chapter Review, pp. 508–511
TR Section Reviews
Chapter Test
BL Chapter Review
Practice Test
CTB Chapter 21 Test

Tech Prep

Teaching strategies appropriate for students who are in technical/vocational programs or who are considering post-secondary technical education can be found on the following **TE** pages: 496 and 503.

Meeting the Standards

Sections 21–1 and 21–2 cover one of the three content standards under **The Molecular Basis of Heredity,** four of the five content standards under **Biological Evolution,** and two of the five content standards under **The Interdependence of Organisms** as described on pages 185–186 of The National Science Education Standards.

Chapter Planning Guide

Teacher's Edition Activities	Other Activities	Media and Technology
Chapter Discovery Learning Activity, p. 494 **Inquiry Activity:** Change Through Time, p. 495 **Inquiry Activity:** All Eyes Forward, p. 496 **Investigate:** Cooperative Learning, p. 500	**TR** Writing in Biology: Musing on Museums **Explore:** Brain Brawn **BL** **Inquiry Activity:** Fossil Evidence	**TB** Visualizing *Homo sapiens* Origins, #27
Inquiry Activity: A Curious Development, p. 502	**LM** Investigating Parasites, #41 Observing the Effects of Temperature and Chemicals on the Growth of Bacteria, #42 **TR** **Enrich:** The Black Death **BL** **Inquiry Activity:** One Flu Over the Cuckoo's Nest	**BioVue Animation:** Antibiotic Resistance, Videodisc Side 5 **BioVue Plus CD-ROMs:** Antibiotic Resistance

KEY: **SE** Student Edition **TE** Teacher's Edition **LM** Laboratory Manual **TR** Teaching Resources **BL** BioLog **TB** Transparency Box **CTB** Computer Test Bank

Materials List

TE **Chapter Discovery Learning Activity,** p. 494 (20 minutes); graph paper, ruler.
TE **Inquiry Activity: Change Through Time,** p. 495 (20 minutes); copies of illustrations of hominids and hominoids.
TE **Inquiry Activity: All Eyes Forward,** p. 496 (15 minutes); notebook paper, tape.
TE **Investigate: Cooperative Learning,** p. 500 (3–4 hours for planning and execution); butcher block paper, colored pencils or markers or water colors.
SE **MINI LAB: A Breath of Fresh Air,** p. 503 (30 minutes); sterile nutrient broth, flasks, flask covers, microscope, slides and cover slips, medicine dropper.

CHAPTER 21

Human History

Introducing the Chapter

. . . In Pictures

At the height of the Incan civilization, Machu Picchu included palaces, temples, and fortresses. Machu Picchu, probably an outpost of the centrally administered Incan empire, was abandoned after the Spanish conquest in the 1530s. As students examine these ruins, ask the following question.

- **The peoples of the Americas first came from Asia. Where do you think the Asian people came from? Where do you think the human species first evolved?** (Some students may know that humans evolved on the African continent.)

Tell students that in this chapter they will learn about the evolution of *Homo sapiens*.

Teaching Strategy

In the first section of this chapter, students will learn about the evolution of hominids, including *Homo sapiens*. The BRANCHING OUT section discusses bacterial diseases and antibiotics.

BIO JOURNAL

The Bio Journal topic can be used to stimulate classroom discussion about how humans have been able to populate almost every environment on Earth. Emphasize that the complex human brain has allowed this species to adapt to other environments, even high mountains and extremely cold areas. Instruct students to keep their entries in their portfolios.

CHAPTER 21

Human History

FOCUSING THE CHAPTER
THEME: Evolution

21–1 The Origins of *Homo sapiens*
- Discuss the evidence and various hypotheses to explain how humans evolved.
- Describe the effects of Native American isolation on the history of the Americas.

BRANCHING OUT *In Depth*

21–2 Coevolution of Humans and Parasites
- Explain how antibiotic-resistant bacteria can develop.

LABORATORY INVESTIGATION
- Construct a model to simulate the spread of an infectious disease.

Biology and Your World
BIO JOURNAL

The Incas thrived in inhospitable environments such as the desert coasts and the high mountains of South America. In your journal, describe how an Incan community living at an elevation of 3000 meters, such as the one shown here, might go about meeting its fundamental needs of food, clothing, and shelter all year round.

Incan ruins high in the Andes Mountains at Machu Picchu, Peru

TEACHER SUPPORT

Chapter Discovery Learning Activity

TIME LINES

Divide students into pairs, and give each pair a sheet of graph paper. You may want to briefly review the elements of a time line, emphasizing that spaces between entries on the line should accurately represent relative spans of time. Then give them this list of entries: (1) *Australopithecus*, 4 million years ago; (2) *Homo*, 1.8 million years ago; (3) humans in Africa, 100,000 years ago; (4) humans arrive in North America, 35,000 years ago; (5) Europeans arrive in Americas, 1492; (6) present day. Give each pair time to complete a time line that includes the dates above. Suggest that they turn the graph paper and work horizontally, and advise them to use a ruler to make the time line as accurate as possible. Once all pairs have completed their work, discuss as a class the relative lengths of time involved.

The Origins of Homo sapiens

SECTION 21–1

GUIDE FOR READING

- **List** the characteristics that primates share.
- **Discuss** the origins of *Homo sapiens*.
- **Explain** why people in the Americas lacked resistance to infectious diseases that were common in Europe and Asia.

IN 1924, RAYMOND DART, A South African anatomist, was given a piece of rock from a limestone quarry in Taung, South Africa, that had been loosened in an explosion. After weeks of carefully chipping away at the surrounding limestone, Dart saw a skull—later identified as a child's skull—emerge. It had humanlike features in the shape and relative size of the brain and teeth. Although Dart reported his find in a British journal, it did not receive much attention from the scientific community for more than twenty years.

Since then, other fossils have been uncovered that support Dart's finding. Today, the species to which this "Taung child" belonged is considered to be one of the closest relatives of modern humans. But let's begin the story of the evolution of humans with the primates, an order within the class Mammalia.

The Primates

When Carolus Linnaeus imposed order on life's diversity, he gave special attention to the group of mammals that included humans. He named our order Primata, which means "the first" in Latin. Just what are we "first" in? Linnaeus emphasized the primates' intelligence. Yet some living primates and many fossil species could safely be described as below average in intelligence for mammals. When the first primates appeared, in fact, there was little to distinguish them from other mammals besides an increased ability to coordinate the function of the eyes and the front limbs to perform certain tasks.

a

b

c

Figure 21–1
In the late Paleolithic Period, about 35,000 to 10,000 years ago, prehistoric people drew paintings such as (a) and (b) that showed the type of animal life that existed at that time. These cave paintings were found at Lascaux, France. In addition, prehistoric people produced a variety of sophisticated tools, such as (c) this "laurel leaf" blade used as the point of a spear.

SECTION 21–1

The Origins of Homo sapiens

Performance Objectives

- Describe the characteristics that distinguish primates.
- Cite current scientific thinking on the origins of *Homo sapiens*.
- Discuss the introduction of infectious diseases from Europe and Asia to the Americas.

1 ENGAGE

Inquiry Activity

Sequencing

Change Through Time

Divide the class into small groups, and give each group copies of illustrations of various ancestral primates, labeled but in random order. (Such illustrations can be readily found in library books on human evolution.) These pictures should include *Australopithecus afarensis*, *Paranthropus robustus*, *Homo habilis*, *Homo erectus*, *Homo neanderthalus*, and an early *Homo sapiens*. Also include various examples of early hominoids. Ask each group to place the pictures in a logical sequence that might represent a possible line of evolution. For each step in this sequence, students should write down one or more reasons why one example seems more modern than the previous example, such as head shape, stance, and so on. Once all groups have sequenced the pictures, have groups compare their sequences and reasons in a class discussion.

TEACHER SUPPORT

Ecology Note

About 7 million years ago, the ecology of Africa began to change as the region became drier. Forests receded, and grasslands expanded. The primates of that time were forest animals, adapted to climbing. As the environment changed, some primates evolved. The earliest hominid, *Australopithecus afarensis*, was a product of that evolution, and its most striking adaptation was bipedalism. In a relatively open scrubland ecosystem, upright walking had several advantages—among them the ability to see over the tops of grass and bushes and the ability to carry food or offspring in their arms. Another advantage involved cooling the body in the heat of the tropical sun. An upright stance receives less of the sun's direct rays and catches cool breezes above the ground. Cooling probably also explains the gradual loss of body hair.

Ancillary Support

The resource below can be used to support your teaching strategy for these two pages.

TR Writing in Biology: Musing on Museums

2 EXPLORE

Inquiry Activity

Observing

All Eyes Forward

Ask students to consider what advantage our species has in having both eyes pointing forward. Then have students follow these steps.

1. Take two pieces of notebook paper and roll each into a cylinder with a diameter of about 2.5 cm. Secure these cylinders with tape.

2. Hold the cylinders to your eyes, pointing straight ahead. Focus on an object across the room, such as a chart or model.

3. Note what each eye sees. Then slowly move the cylinders together, until only one image forms.

4. Close the right eye and note what the left eye sees; then close the left eye and note what the right eye sees.

Have students discuss what they have seen. Guide them to an understanding that binocular vision, with the interpretation provided by the brain, provides depth perception and a three-dimensional image.

3 TEACH

Ideas Through Images

Have students examine Figures 21–2 and 21–3, read the captions, and answer the following questions.

• **What differences can you observe between the tree shrew and the tarsier that mark the latter as a more evolved primate?** (The tarsier has a larger head, flatter face, and eyes that face forward, giving it binocular vision.)

• **What is the difference between prosimians and anthropoids?** (Prosimians are primates that do not look like monkeys or apes, whereas the anthropoids include all the primates that do.)

Figure 21–2
(a) The earliest primates probably resembled animals such as this modern tree shrew, whose five-digited paws can be seen grasping food. (b) The tarsier, a tiny prosimian living entirely in trees, has enlarged skin pads on its hands and feet that help it to grasp and leap from branch to branch. Notice the tarsier's large eyes, which enable it to see more clearly at night.

As primates evolved, some achieved the highest intelligence of any animals on Earth. **As a group, primates evolved several distinctive characteristics—a flatter face, flexible fingers, and a well-developed cerebrum.** Primates typically have a flat face, so both eyes face forward with widely overlapping fields of view. This feature gives primates excellent **binocular vision.** That means we can see a clear three-dimensional image of the world.

Primates also have flexible fingers that can grasp, hold, and manipulate objects. That ability is combined in many species with arms that join to the body at a flexible shoulder joint. Because primate arms can swing in broad circles around the shoulder, monkeys and apes can run along branches and swing from tree to tree. Many primates also have a large and well-developed cerebrum that makes complex behaviors possible.

The Primate Family Tree

Living primates include a wide variety of animals. Members of two groups, collectively called **prosimians** (proh-SIHM-ee-uhnz), don't look much like what most of us think of as monkeys or apes. Those that do are called higher primates, and they belong to the group called **anthropoids** (AN-thruh-poydz).

Early in their history, ancestors of living anthropoids were separated by continental drift into two main groups. One group, the New World monkeys, evolved in the Americas. These animals have long, prehensile tails that can coil up to grasp branches, like a fifth hand, when

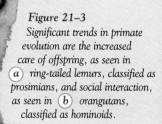

Figure 21–3
Significant trends in primate evolution are the increased care of offspring, as seen in (a) ring-tailed lemurs, classified as prosimians, and social interaction, as seen in (b) orangutans, classified as hominoids.

TEACHER SUPPORT

Managing Classroom Diversity

EDUCATIONAL EQUITY

Ask interested students to prepare a report about Mary Leakey (1913–1996). Though never trained as a scientist, this remarkable woman became known worldwide for her fossil discoveries in East Africa, where she worked alongside her husband, Louis Leakey. Perhaps her greatest find occurred in 1978, when she discovered fossil footprints in volcanic ash at Laetoli, Tanzania, the first evidence that *Australopithecus* walked upright.

TECH PREP STUDENTS

Have students who plan careers working with technology to prepare a presentation about the technologies and procedures used to date the fossil hominids discussed in this section. Ask them to concentrate on radiocarbon dating, which is used for organic materials. Their short presentations to the class could be useful in helping students understand the evidence for the evolution of hominids.

Figure 21–4
Although there is still a debate among scientists as to which group of prosimians is the probable ancestor of anthropoids, this primate family tree shows the tentative sequence of evolutionary steps that led to the evolution of hominids.

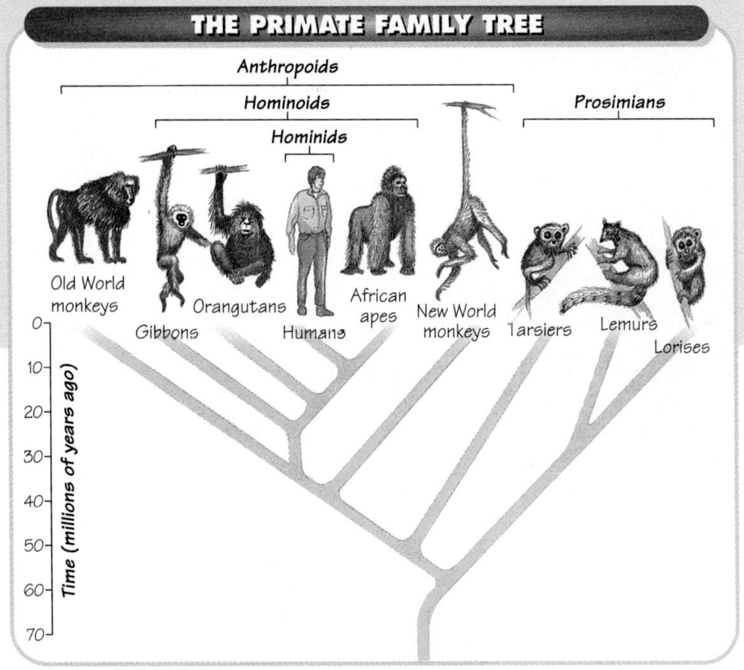

swinging through trees. The second group, which evolved into the Old World monkeys and great apes, arose in Africa, the Middle East, and Asia. Old World monkeys, such as baboons and macaques (muh-KAHKS), often lack tails, but when they do have tails, they are not prehensile. From this second group evolved the **hominoids,** which include gorillas, chimpanzees, and *Homo sapiens*. As ***Figure 21–4*** shows, the hominoid line gave rise to a small group known as the **hominids.** Although the early hominids were not yet human, they did show several evolutionary trends that set them apart from other hominoids.

The history described thus far is supported by an enormous volume of scientific data of several types that virtually all scientists interpret in the same way. The fossil record clearly documents links among many living and extinct primates. Studies in molecular biology shed additional light on relationships between humans and other living great apes.

☑ ***Checkpoint*** What are the two main groups within the primate family? ❶

Hominid Origins

When we look closely at the branch of the primate family tree that ultimately produced humans, things get more interesting, more complicated, and more controversial for several reasons. First, fossil evidence suggests that the ancient hominid line evolved with incredible speed. Changes in some of our ancestors' features—teeth, skull, and legs—are seen in the fossil record. But uniquely human features—intelligence, memory, speech, and language—leave no fossil remains.

In addition to paleontologists, anthropologists also have research interests in human origins. They bring to the hunt a different set of tools, techniques, and strategies for interpreting data. As a result, the study of human origins is a changing and controversial field. Still, we know much more about our past today than we did twenty years ago, and new pieces of the puzzle fall into place every day.

Australopithecines

Most researchers now agree that the first hominids belonged to the genus *Australopithecus* (aw-stray-loh-PIHTH-uh-kuhs), meaning "southern ape." This

Ideas Through Images

Have students examine Figure 21–4, read the caption, and answer the following questions.

- **What is a main difference between the anthropoids known as Old World monkeys and New World monkeys?** (The New World monkeys have prehensile tails, whereas the Old World monkeys have no tails or tails that are not prehensile.)
- **What accounts for that difference in similar anthropoids?** (They have common ancestors but they evolved on different continents, separated by oceans.)
- **From which group did the hominoids evolve?** (From the Old World monkeys.)
- **Did the hominids evolve from the African apes or the orangutans?** (The hominids evolved from neither of those hominoids, though all have common ancestors.)

Discussion

Begin a discussion of hominid origins by asking volunteers to explain how fossils form. Emphasize that fossils form only under certain conditions, and they are found only if erosion or digging brings them to the surface. Then discuss the difficulty in interpreting the fossil record when only the hard parts of an organism become fossilized.

☑ Checkpoint

❶ The prosimians and the anthropoids.

TEACHER SUPPORT

Background Information

Harvard professor Stephen Jay Gould once wrote that when the time comes each year to teach hominid evolution, he grabs last year's folder and dumps the contents into the wastebasket. This field has been revolutionized in the past two decades, both because of new fossil finds and evidence from DNA studies. The increased knowledge has led to an unexpected loss of clarity, which has led to many competing hypotheses about what occurred. Actually, this conforms with the modern view of evolution. The idea of gradualism, in which species slowly evolve into other species, is now not widely accepted. In contrast, the current model holds that species evolve rapidly during times of change, exist for a period, and then disappear, replaced by other species better adapted to new conditions. Exactly how species arise is still little understood.

Ancillary Support

The resource below can be used to support your teaching strategy for these two pages.

BL Inquiry Activity: Fossil Evidence

Ideas Through Images

Have students examine Figure 21–5, read the caption, and answer the following questions.

- **What is an australopithecine, and what does that term mean?** (An australopithecine is a member of the genus *Australopithecus*, one of the first hominids; the term means southern ape.)
- **When and where did Lucy live?** (She lived sometime between 4 and 1.4 million years ago in the area of East Africa now known as Hadar, Ethiopia.)
- **What differences can you observe between Lucy's pelvis and the chimpanzee's pelvis, and what is the significance of those differences?** (Lucy's pelvis is smaller and flatter, and the holes for the leg bones are oriented in a way that would place the legs on the same plane instead of at a right angle, as in the chimpanzee pelvis. The significance is that Lucy walked upright.)
- **What do anthropologists study?** (Anthropologists study the origin, physical characteristics, and social customs of humans.)

Discussion

Begin a discussion of Neanderthals by asking students to relate anything they know about these extinct hominids. A typical notion of a Neanderthal is that it was big, stupid, and apelike. Point out that Neanderthals were actually intelligent tool users that evolved from *Homo erectus*, just as *Homo sapiens* did. Explain that scientists disagree about what became of the Neanderthals. One theory is that they interbred with the Cro-Magnons; another is that they were defeated by those early humans.

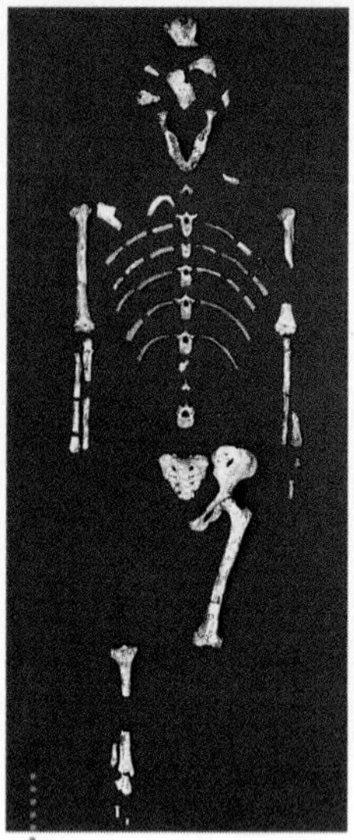

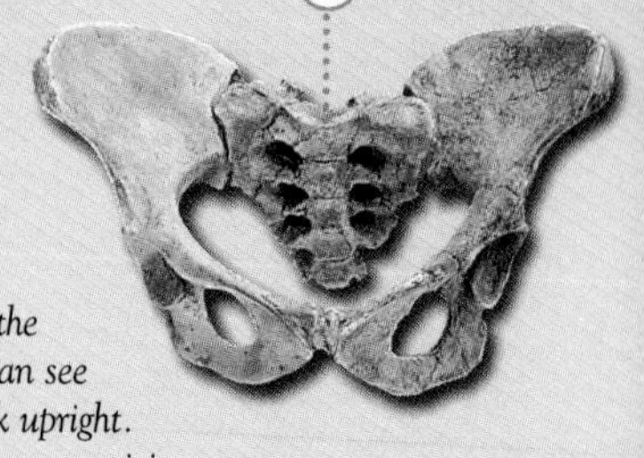

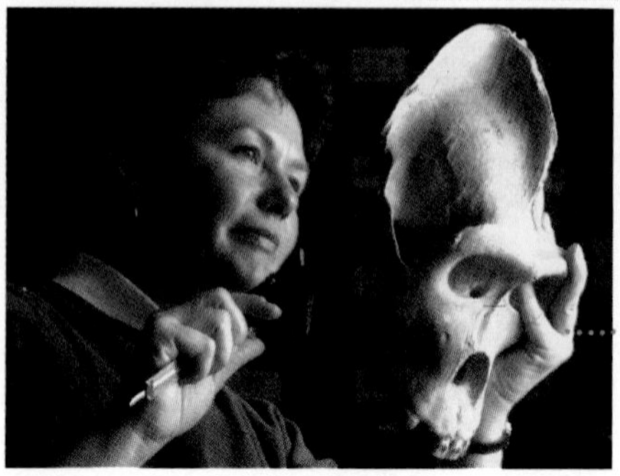

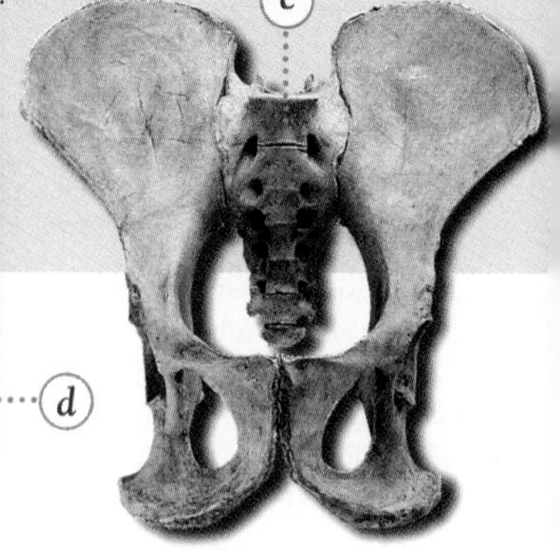

Figure 21–5
(a) In 1974, a research team led by Donald Johansen discovered Lucy—the name given to this skeleton—along with a collection of other fossils in Hadar, Ethiopia. Lucy is considered to be the most complete and oldest australopithecine fossil found to date. By comparing (b) the reconstructed pelvis of the hominid Lucy with (c) that of a chimpanzee, you can see the structural difference that permits hominids to walk upright.
(d) CAREER TRACK As part of her study of human origins, this anthropologist closely examines a primitive skull.

was the genus into which Raymond Dart placed the fossil of the child's skull uncovered in South Africa. Since then, a large number of australopithecine fossils have been found. In particular, a fairly complete *Australopithecus* skeleton was discovered by American anthropologist Donald Johansen in 1974, shown in ***Figure 21–5.***

Based on the fossil evidence gathered so far, scientists estimate that various species of *Australopithecus* lived from nearly 4 million years ago to about 1.4 million years ago. It also seems clear that our own genus, *Homo*, emerged in Africa about 1.8 million years ago. But beyond these basics, questions greatly outnumber answers, as illustrated in the figure on page 499. It now seems as though at least nine hominid species—of the genera *Australopithecus*, *Paranthropus*, and *Homo*—have come and gone over the last 4 million years.

The story line becomes only slightly clearer with the emergence of *Homo erectus* in Africa. It seems that at least 1 million years ago, groups of this remarkable species left Africa and traveled as far away as what are now China and Indonesia. Various populations used stone tools, hunted animals for food, and lived in groups. In some areas, they sought shelter in caves. Although remains of *H. erectus* have been found in many places in the Eastern Hemisphere, the species ultimately disappeared—either evolving into another species or replaced by a new competitor.

By this time, Europe and other northern regions were being chilled by an ice age. The first human ancestors to adapt to these difficult conditions were the rather intelligent hominids known as Neanderthals. Now usually classified as *Homo neanderthalensis*, they lived between 200 and 35 thousand years ago in the Middle East, western Asia, and Europe. Gradually, they were replaced by the first true modern humans, *Homo sapiens*, about 30,000 years ago.

498 Chapter 21

TEACHER SUPPORT

Background Information

The Neanderthals were a relatively large hominid species. A typical male was about 1.7 m tall and a muscular 70 kg. Their heads were distinctly different from the modern human head. A low braincase protruded in the back, there was little forehead or chin, and large arching brow ridges marked the front of the face. Their brains, though, were about the same size as those of *Homo sapiens*. Scientists disagree on how they disappeared. One possibility is that they could have mixed with the modern humans that spread into Europe about 33,000 years ago, though many scientists doubt the two species could have interbred successfully. More likely, the Cro-Magnons outcompeted and eventually eliminated the Neanderthals. A typical Cro-Magnon male was about 1.8 m and 70 kg, but less muscular than a Neanderthal. The advantages the Cro-Magnons had were in intelligence and tool making.

many people—including the Incan leader and his son. By the time Francisco Pizarro arrived in Peru in 1532, the Incan empire was falling apart because of disease. Thus, had it not been for the different prehistories of Europe and the Americas, history might have taken a different turn.

Impact on Medicine

Recently, the ongoing battle between humans and disease has taken a new and disturbing turn, as disease-causing bacteria have evolved in response to changes that humans have made in their environment. One of the most important of those changes is the widespread use of **antibiotics**—compounds that kill bacteria without harming the body cells of humans or other animals.

When antibiotics were first introduced, they did such a superb job of controlling bacterial diseases that they earned the name "wonder drugs." Within a few decades, antibiotics were in widespread use. In hospitals, patients are bombarded with antibiotics to prevent infections. On farms where animals are raised in crowded conditions, antibiotics are added to food to prevent illness and the growth of harmful bacteria. And in the general population, people use antibiotics to treat even minor infections. All this antibiotic use, however, makes sense only in the short term.

In the long term, can you see what this means from the perspective of bacteria? **As antibiotics become a permanent part of their environment, bacteria begin to evolve antibiotic resistance in response to this new and powerful form of natural selection.** What is the result? Today, patients are being infected by "super bugs"—strains of bacteria immune to the effects of five or more antibiotics. These **drug-resistant bacteria** are appearing everywhere, and they present a growing threat to human health that may someday surpass AIDS.

Antibiotic Resistance

When prescribed antibiotics are used properly, the drugs kill enough bacteria to help the body's natural defenses destroy the rest. If the drug therapy and the body's defenses together destroy all the bacteria, there's no problem.

But a few individual bacteria in nearly every population carry mutant genes that make them resistant to one antibiotic or another. If antibiotics are used improperly, enough of the antibiotic-resistant bacteria may survive to multiply and begin a new strain in which most individuals will be antibiotic resistant.

INTEGRATING BIOLOGY AND SOCIETY

Who discovered the first antibiotic? How did that discovery change human society?

MINI LAB ... Experimenting ...

A Breath of Fresh Air

PROBLEM *What locations in your neighborhood would have the greatest number of microorganisms? **Design an experiment** to answer this question.*

SUGGESTED PROCEDURE

1. Using sterile flasks of nutrient broth—a liquid growth medium used by scientists to culture microorganisms—design an experiment that will allow you to compare the presence of microorganisms in the air at various locations. Choose a variety of locations, such as enclosed, crowded areas and open fields. Include a control in your procedure.
2. Predict which location will have the greatest number and which will have the least number of microorganisms.
3. Have your teacher approve your experimental procedure.

ANALYZE AND CONCLUDE

1. How did the growth of microorganisms vary with location?
2. How did the results compare with your predictions?
3. Did your control work effectively? If not, why not?

2 EXPLORE

MINI LAB Experimenting

Teacher Notes

- For time required and materials needed, see page 494b.
- Prepare a sterile nutrient broth by bringing canned beef broth to boil, sealing it in sterile flasks, and refrigerating the flasks until time for the lab.

Answers to Analyze and Conclude

1. In general, students should find that the growth of microorganisms is greatest at an enclosed location that has many people or animals.
2. Students' responses will depend on their predictions.
3. Answers will vary based on how carefully students handled their controls.

Skills Trace
Experimenting

Focus p. 503
Practice p. 505
Assess p. 511

Technology

BioVue
Animation: Antibiotic Resistance
Videodisc Side 5

Go to Chapter 20

Ancillary Support

The resources below can be used to support your teaching strategy for these two pages.

LM Investigating Parasites, #41
BL Inquiry Activity: One Flu Over the Cuckoo's Nest

TEACHER SUPPORT

Managing Classroom Diversity

TECH PREP STUDENTS
Have students interested in careers in agriculture research and prepare a debate about the use of antibiotics in livestock. The use of antibiotics for prevention of disease is widespread in agriculture and may be essential for the production of meat and dairy foods at a scale and price Americans are used to. You could arbitrarily assign students to take one side or the other on this issue, and then have them debate it in front of the class.

GIFTED STUDENTS
Ask students to research the epidemics that occurred in Native American peoples within the boundaries of the United States during the colonial period and thereafter. You could have students prepare a brief presentation to the class, giving basic information both about specific diseases and about how those diseases affected the native peoples.

3 TEACH

Problem Solving

Interpreting Data

Comparing Antibiotic Resistance

Students will draw on their understanding of antibiotics and drug-resistant bacteria, as well as their skills in measuring and interpreting data, to solve the problem.

State The problem is to determine if either of two hospitals might be in danger of developing an antibiotic-resistant strain of bacteria.

Solve To solve this problem, students must measure the zones of inhibition for each antibiotic from each hospital and then compare their measurements with the data in the table provided. In that way, they can determine whether the bacterial strain from each hospital has become resistant to any of the six antibiotics tested. A drug-resistant strain is one that is immune to the effects of five or more antibiotics.

Test To test their measurements of the zones of inhibition, students can compare data with one another.

Communicate Create a table on an overhead transparency that includes columns for the names of antibiotics, measurements of the zones, and evaluation of susceptibility. Then complete the table by asking students to discuss their measurements and conclusions.

Answers to THINK ABOUT IT

1. Hospital A: Erythromcin, Penicillin G, Streptomycin, and Tetracycline; Hospital B: Erythromycin.

2. Hospital B is in danger of developing an antibiotic-resistant strain because the strain from that hospital tested resistant to three antibiotics and intermediate to two others.

Problem Solving

INTERPRETING DATA

Comparing Antibiotic Resistance

Your friend is assisting the head laboratory technician at the state microbiology laboratory, who is working on a problem occurring in area hospitals. A few types of bacteria are becoming resistant to commonly used antibiotics. Two hospitals have sent her cultures to conduct antibiotic-sensitivity tests to determine which bacteria are resistant to the antibiotics.

After adding agar, a solid nutrient material, to two Petri dishes labeled A and B, the technician swabs the surface of the agar in dish A with the bacterial culture from hospital A, then swabs dish B with the culture from hospital B. On each dish she places six discs, each containing a different antibiotic. She covers and incubates the dishes at 35°C for 18 hours. The zones of inhibition—regions of no bacterial growth that surround each disc—are illustrated below. Also listed are the diameters of the zones of inhibition that correspond to bacterial resistance or susceptibility to the antibiotic.

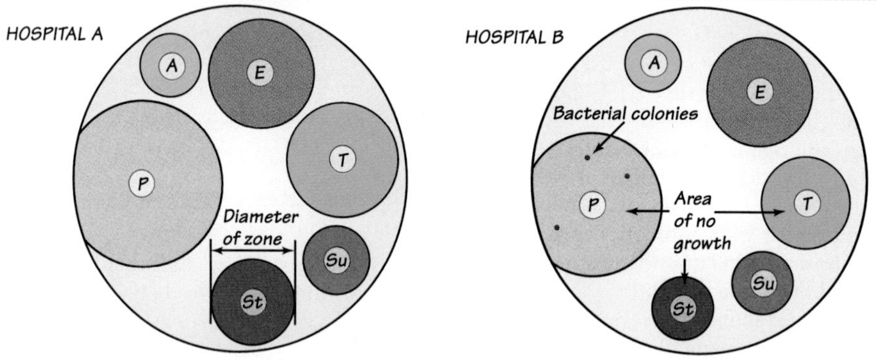

Antibiotic	R	I	S	Antibiotic	R	I	S
Ampicillin (A)	≤ 11	12–13	≥ 14	Erythromycin (E)	≤ 13	14–17	≥ 18
Penicillin G (P)	≤ 20	21–28	≥ 29	Streptomycin (St)	≤ 11	12–14	≥ 15
Sulfonamides (Su)	≤ 12	13–16	≥ 17	Tetracycline (T)	≤ 14	15–18	≥ 19

Key (All numbers represent diameter in millimeters.)

- R Resistant, unlikely that the bacterium will be killed by the antibiotic
- I Intermediate, uncertain whether the bacterium will be killed by the antibiotic
- S Susceptible, likely that the bacterium will be killed by the antibiotic

THINK ABOUT IT

1. Determine the antibiotics to which bacteria from hospital A are susceptible. Determine the antibiotics to which bacteria from hospital B are susceptible.
2. Which hospital might be in danger of developing an antibiotic-resistant strain of bacteria? Explain your answer.

504

TEACHER SUPPORT

Background Information

Resistance genes in bacteria did not originate with the development of antibiotics. After all, antibiotics are produced from naturally occurring substances, and thus resistance genes are a natural bacterial defense. This explains why bacteria can so quickly become resistant once an antibiotic is used—genes are already present in the population. These genes are most often found in plasmids, circular pieces of DNA that are separate from bacterial chromosomes. These plasmids can be exchanged between bacterial cells during conjugation, a type of reproduction, and that is how resistance can spread through a population of bacteria. Researchers have discovered that plasmids containing resistance genes can also be transferred from one type of bacteria to another—such as from a harmless bacteria in the stomach to an invading harmful pathogen.

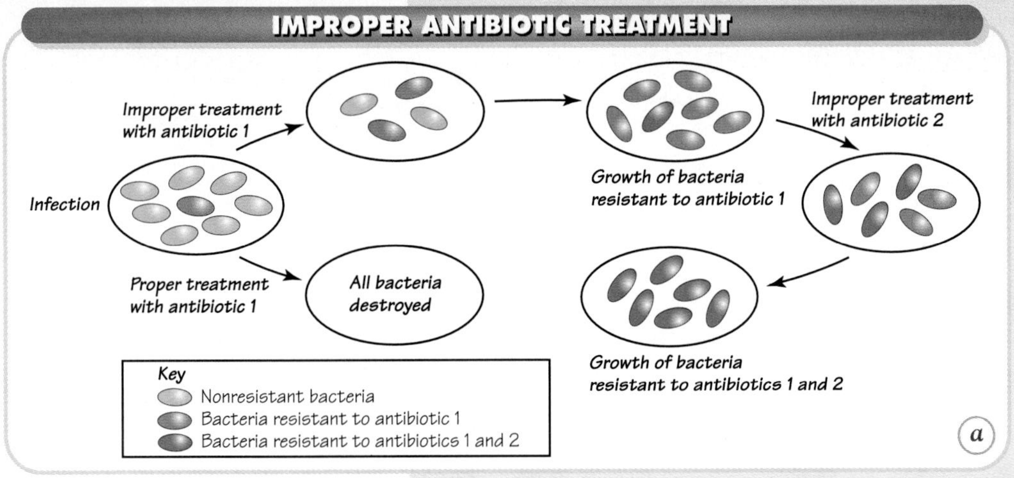

For a time, this new strain may still be susceptible to other antibiotics. But if those drugs are used improperly, new strains of bacteria can emerge that will be resistant to several drugs at once.

☑ **Checkpoint** What are drug-resistant bacteria? (1)

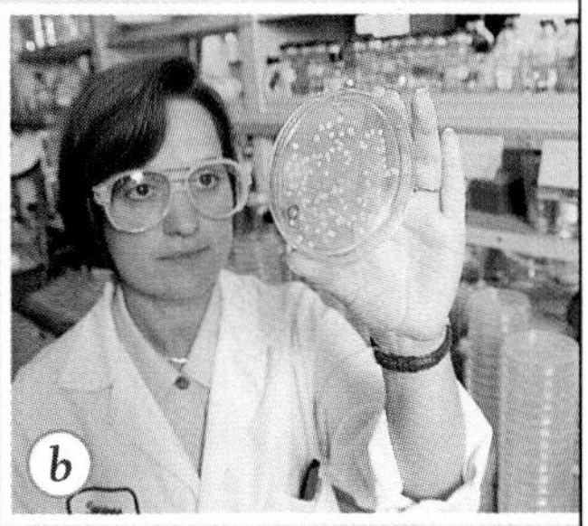

Figure 21–9
(a) This illustration shows how the improper use of antibiotics can give rise to the evolution of drug-resistant bacteria. (b) By developing new antibiotics, a pharmacologist, shown here inspecting a culture of disease-causing bacteria, helps to prevent this potentially serious situation.

Medicine Versus Natural Selection

Problems with drug-resistant bacteria have not yet caused a crisis, but a half dozen common disease-causing bacteria have already evolved antibiotic resistance. Nearly one third of the strains of *Salmonella*—bacteria that cause severe and sometimes fatal diarrhea—are resistant to several antibiotics. Tuberculosis, which was under control in the United States for decades, is increasing because several strains of tuberculosis-causing bacteria are resistant to every antibiotic currently in use.

What can be done? Physicians and researchers are racing to battle the power of evolutionary change in the microbial world. New drugs are being developed. And new treatment strategies—aimed at slowing down evolution of drug-resistant bacteria—are being used to help patients.

Section Review 21–2

1. **Describe** how bacteria become resistant to antibiotics.
2. **MINI LAB** What effect does a specific location have on the number of microorganisms present? **Design an experiment** to answer the question.
3. **BRANCHING OUT ACTIVITY** Interview some health care professionals to find out the bacterial diseases that are difficult to treat with antibiotics because of the evolution of antibiotic-resistant bacteria. **Explain** how this has arisen.

Laboratory Investigation

The Laboratory Investigation, The Spread of Disease, on pages 506–507 is appropriate to use at this point in the chapter.

Ideas Through Images

Have students examine Figure 21–9, read the caption, and answer the following questions.

- **What are some examples of improper uses of antibiotics?** (Animals on farms are given antibiotics to prevent disease and people use antibiotics to treat minor illnesses or infections.)
- **Can bacteria be resistant to more than one antibiotic?** (Yes, if the antibiotics are used improperly.)

4 ASSESS

Quick Check

Have students make a flowchart that describes how improper antibiotic treatment can cause the development of antibiotic-resistant bacteria.

Section Review 21–2

1. As antibiotics become a permanent part of the environment of bacteria, they begin to evolve antibiotic resistance.

2. A typical design will suggest using flasks of sterile nutrient broth at several locations to collect the microorganisms from the air and then comparing the growth that occurs in each flask.

3. Through interviews, students should determine that a variety of bacterial diseases, including tuberculosis, food poisoning, and sexually transmitted diseases, have become more difficult to treat with antibiotics.

Skills Trace

Experimenting

- Focus p. 503
- Practice p. 505
- Assess p. 511

Learning Modality

Auditory Learning Ask students to think about a doctor who is asked by a parent to prescribe an antibiotic for a child in order to prevent colds this winter. Then ask students to explain how the doctor should respond to that parent.

☑ Checkpoint

(1) Strains of bacteria that are immune to the effects of five or more antibiotics.

Ancillary Support

The resources below can be used to support your teaching strategy for these two pages.

LM Observing the Effects of Temperature and Chemicals on the Growth of Bacteria, #42
TR Enrich: The Black Death

Laboratory Investigation

The Spread of Disease

Before the Lab

1. For each group, you need to prepare one "infected" stock solution that will test positive with an indicator and a stock solution for each of the other group members that will test negative. For the "infected" solution, add 10 mL vinegar to 90 mL distilled water. This vinegar solution should be placed in one test tube; fill the other test tubes with distilled water. Use bromthymol blue as the indicator—it will turn yellow in the presence of vinegar. Because students may smell the one vinegar stock solution, swab the outside of all test tubes with vinegar.
2. As an alternative "infected" solution, add 10 mL glucose to 90 mL distilled water. Glucose test strips can be used for the indicator.
3. Make sure you label each test tube and record for yourself whether or not it contains a vinegar or glucose solution.

Pre-Lab Discussion

Have students read the entire procedure for this investigation. Then ask students the following questions.

What is the purpose of this investigation? (To construct a model for a simulation of the spread of an infectious disease through a community.)

What does the exchange of droppersful of solution represent? (The spread of pathogens between people in a community.)

What is the purpose of recording the information about contacts in the data tables? (Recording that information provides a way to trace the spread of the disease, and thus find out who was the original carrier.)

CHAPTER 21

Laboratory Investigation

The Spread of Disease

The way in which a disease spreads through a population demands the careful collection and analysis of data. When an outbreak of a serious infectious disease occurs, scientists must track down the disease and determine its origin. In this investigation, you will simulate the spread of an infectious disease and determine the original carrier of the disease.

Problem

How can you simulate the spread of a disease in a community? **Construct a model** for the simulation.

Materials (per group)

- large test tube of stock solution
- clean test tube
- large pipette
- medicine dropper

Procedure

1. Select one stock solution from a numbered set of stock solutions provided by your teacher. Record the number in your data table.
2. Carefully fill the pipette with the stock solution and transfer it to the clean test tube.
3. At your teacher's signal, begin circulating among your classmates until the teacher tells you to stop. Using the medicine dropper, exchange a dropperful of your solution with the person closest to you. Make the exchange by putting a dropperful of the solution from your clean test tube into the clean test tube of the contact. You should also receive a dropperful of the solution from your contact's test tube. Record the name of that person as Contact 1 in a data table similar to Data Table 1.
4. Repeat step 3 and record the name of this person as Contact 2.
5. Repeat step 3 and record the name of this person as Contact 3.
6. Your teacher will now add several drops of an indicator to your test tube to determine whether you have been infected.
7. After performing the indicator test for the presence of infection for all the students in the class, your teacher will record the names and contacts of the infected individuals. Record this information in a data table similar to Data Table 2.

Safety Tips

- Caution students not to taste any of the solutions or place their fingers in their mouths after handling the test tubes or pipettes.
- Remind students to be careful when handling the glass equipment and to notify you of any breakage.
- Instruct students to wash their hands when they have completed the procedure.

DATA TABLE 1

Your Stock Number	Contact 1	Contact 2	Contact 3

DATA TABLE 2

Infected Person	Contact 1	Contact 2	Contact 3

Observations

1. How many individuals were infected by the end of the simulation? How many were not infected?
2. How many infected individuals were there at the end of the first round of contacts?

Analysis and Conclusions

1. Using the class data, eliminate the names of those who were not infected. From this, try to find the original source of the infection by examining the remaining sequence of contacts.
2. Were you able to identify correctly the original carrier of the disease? If not, specify what information or test is required to identify the original source.
3. Make a diagram of the transmission route.
4. Suppose you came into contact with as many people as possible during a specified period of time. What effect would this have on the outcome of this simulation?

More to Explore

Suppose that the simulation you performed represents the exchange of plasmids among bacteria. Why is it possible for a single mutation in a plasmid of one bacterial cell to appear rapidly in other bacteria?

Answers to Observations

1. The number of students infected may vary. After the first round, two students will be infected, the one with the infected stock solution and the one who received a dropperful from that student. After the second round, a maximum of four could be infected; after the third round, a maximum of eight could be infected. Fewer than the maximum could be infected if one or more students are infected more than once.
2. There should be only two students infected at the end of the first round.

Answers to Analysis and Conclusions

1. Working backward, students may be able to identify the original source as one of the first two students to be infected.
2. The only way the original source can be identified for certain is if the stock solutions of the first two infected students are tested.
3. Students' diagrams should reflect the data recorded in Data Table 2.
4. More students would have been infected, since more droppersful of solution would have been exchanged.

More to Explore

Some students might suggest that plasmids could be exchanged during conjugation, thus spreading the mutation. Binary fission thereafter could increase the number of bacterial cells with the mutation.

Skills Development

Students will use these skills while completing the laboratory investigation: constructing a model, observing, communicating, interpreting data, sequencing, and drawing conclusions.

Teaching Strategies

1. This laboratory investigation can be done as a whole-class activity. An alternative is to divide students into a few large groups.
2. Provide the class with the same number of test tubes containing stock solution as students in the class, with only one containing the "infected" solution. This ensures that the "infected" solution will be chosen.
3. Demonstrate how to fill a pipette with stock solution to transfer the solution to a clean test tube. Also demonstrate how students are to exchange a dropperful of solution when you say stop.
4. Tell students that when you loudly say stop during each round, all should exchange solutions at once.
5. Tell students that as they circulate during a round, they should always keep moving until you say stop. Emphasize that all students must record their contacts immediately after each exchange of solutions.
6. After the third round, you will use the indicator to check each student's test tube. A positive test means the student has been infected.

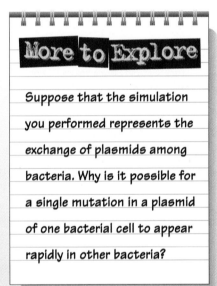

CHAPTER 21

Study Guide

Review Strategy

Have pairs of students work together to create a word puzzle in which vocabulary terms and names of primates are contained in a large square of letters. The names may be arranged vertically, horizontally, or diagonally, and either backward or forward. For each term or name included in the puzzle, students should write a question or clue. Require that at least 20 words be included in each puzzle. Students can make these puzzles on lined notebook paper or graph paper. Once pairs have completed their puzzles, photocopy and distribute them to other pairs to be completed by circling the words in the square of letters.

Study Guide

Summarizing Key Concepts

The key concepts in each section of this chapter are listed below to help you review the chapter content. Make sure you understand each concept and its relationship to other concepts and to the theme of this chapter.

21–1 The Origins of *Homo sapiens*

- Primates share a combination of distinctive characteristics, such as a flatter face, flexible fingers, and a well-developed cerebrum.
- The sequence of the evolution of humans within the order Primata is primates, anthropoids, hominoids, hominids, then humans.
- Researchers agree that the first hominids belong to the genus *Australopithecus*. It has been estimated that various species of this genus lived from nearly 4 million years ago to about 1.4 million years ago.
- Scientists propose different hypotheses to explain the process of evolution of *Homo sapiens* from the *Australopithecus* species.
- After studying a wide range of fossil and genetic evidence, many biologists believe that all living *Homo sapiens* originated in Africa.
- Native Americans, having arrived 30,000 years ago from Siberia, remained isolated from the people in Africa, Europe, and Asia.

21–2 Coevolution of Humans and Parasites

- When Europeans arrived in the Americas in the sixteenth century, they brought diseases to which they had evolved a substantial degree of immunity. Because Native Americans had not evolved any immunity to these diseases, a large percentage of the Native American population perished from epidemics of European diseases.
- Antibiotics—drugs that kill disease-causing bacteria—are becoming a permanent part of the environments in which bacteria live. So bacteria are under powerful pressure from natural selection to evolve drug resistance.
- The consequences of the evolution of drug-resistant bacteria are potentially serious.

Reviewing Key Terms

Review the following vocabulary terms and their meaning. Then use each term in a complete sentence.

21–1 The Origins of *Homo sapiens*

binocular vision
prosimian
anthropoid
hominoid
hominid
epidemic

21–2 Coevolution of Humans and Parasites

antibiotic
drug-resistant bacterium

Inquiry-Based Strategy

An epidemic of tuberculosis has broken out in the local area. Doctors report that this strain does not react to any antibiotic available. Ask groups of students to suppose they work for the city, county, or state health department and have been asked to create a newspaper advertisement or television commercial that explains the causes, dangers, and probable outcome of this epidemic. Since this project is aimed at informing the public, it should also include any steps people should take to prevent getting this strain of TB. Students should determine what research is necessary to complete this project. They may approach it through library research, by interviewing local health officials, or a combination of the two. Tell students a newspaper advertisement should include words and illustrations. A television commercial should include a script and illustrations of visuals that could be used.

Recalling Main Ideas

Choose the letter of the answer that best completes the statement or answers the question.

1. Which animals have long, prehensile tails?

a. prosimians **c.** Old World monkeys
b. hominoids **d.** New World monkeys

2. Which are not anthropoids?

a. apes **c.** humans
b. lemurs **d.** orangutans

3. The first hominids are believed to belong to the genus

a. *Australopithecus.* **c.** *Paranthropus.*
b. *Homo.* **d.** *Dryopithecus.*

4. Which of the following species was probably the first to evolve?

a. *Homo erectus* **c.** *Homo habilis*
b. *Homo sapiens* **d.** *Homo neanderthalensis*

5. Cro-Magnons were intelligent people who lived

a. more than 4 million years ago.
b. 1.8 million years ago.
c. more than 100,000 years ago.
d. less than 100,000 years ago.

6. Infectious diseases killed large numbers of Native Americans because

a. the Native Americans were immune to European diseases.
b. Europeans were immune to Native American diseases.
c. the Native Americans had no immunity to European diseases.
d. Europeans had no immunity to Native American diseases.

7. Antibiotics are drugs that

a. destroy microorganisms.
b. kill bacteria.
c. destroy viruses.
d. prevent infection.

8. Drug-resistant bacteria are

a. immune to all antibiotics.
b. susceptible to all antibiotics.
c. present only in the United States.
d. immune to one or more antibiotics.

Putting It All Together

Using the information on pages xxx to xxxi, complete the following concept map.

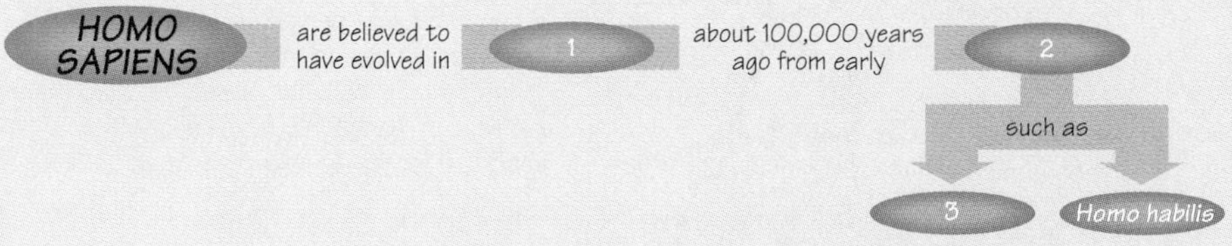

Recalling Main Ideas

1. d
2. b
3. a
4. c
5. d
6. c
7. b
8. d

Assessment

Reviewing What You Learned

1. A flatter face, binocular vision, flexible fingers, and a well-developed cerebrum.
2. The genus *Australopithecus*; it was given a name meaning "southern ape" after the fossil skull that was discovered in South Africa.
3. A hominid skull in a piece of limestone. He placed the skull in the genus *Australopithecus*.
4. Prosimians are living primates that do not look like monkeys or apes, whereas anthropoids are living primates that do.
5. New World monkeys evolved in the Americas and have long, prehensile tails, whereas Old World monkeys evolved in Africa, the Middle East, and Asia and either have tails that are not prehensile or lack tails altogether.
6. The Neanderthals lived between 200,000 and 35,000 years ago in the Middle East, western Asia, and Europe.
7. The Cro-Magnons lived about 40,000 years ago in Europe. Their bones, tools, and cave paintings are evidence that they were intelligent.
8. Both epidemics of diseases and the conquest of Spanish conquistadors contributed to the fall of the Incan empire.
9. The parasites that cause serious diseases coevolved with species in the Eastern Hemisphere, and as a consequence humans in the Western Hemisphere had no natural defenses against the parasites when Europeans brought them to the Americas.
10. An antibiotic is a compound that kills bacteria without harming the body cells of humans or other animals.

Putting It All Together

Assessment (continued)

11. A "super bug" can evolve in response to an environment of which antibiotics are a permanent part. In a hospital, patients are bombarded with antibiotics to prevent infections, which causes bacteria to evolve antibiotic resistance.
12. A sudden rapid spread of a disease through a population.

Expanding the Concepts

1. Fossil evidence suggests that the ancient hominid line evolved with incredible speed. Also, changes in only some features—such as teeth, skull, and legs—are preserved in the fossil record. In addition, paleontologists and anthropologists interpret the data in different ways.
2. A typical response might mention the fossil remains of the australopithecines, *Homo erectus*, the Neanderthals, and *Homo sapiens*.
3. Students should discuss each of the three hypotheses illustrated on page 499. Although these discussions may vary, none of the hypotheses shows a direct line from *Australopithecus* species to *Homo erectus* or *Homo sapiens*.
4. Evidence includes their use of tools and their production of cave paintings.
5. A typical response might suggest that epidemics tend to affect the weak and unhealthy members of a species more than the strong and healthy. Thus, they could be considered a natural mechanism that influences the direction in which a species evolves.
6. Major trade routes were where humans from the Eastern and Western hemispheres had the greatest contact, and thus it was there that pathogens would have first spread quickly among Western Hemisphere humans.
7. Antibiotics are our main weapon against bacteria. When drug-resistant strains evolve, there may be little that can be done to help a person infected with such bacteria.
8. Some students might suggest that all the medicine must be taken to make sure all the harmful bacteria are destroyed, since a portion of the bacterial population might be resistant to the initial effects of the antibiotic.

Extending Your Thinking

1. A typical hypothesis might suggest that the whalers carried to the islands birds that were infected with pathogens, and that these birds spread the pathogens to native birds, which had no immunity.

2. A typical design will suggest using open flasks of sterile nutrient broth to test for microorganisms at these various locations and then comparing the growth that occurs in each flask.

Skills Trace
Experimenting
- Focus p. 503
- Practice p. 505
- Assess p. 511

Assessment

Reviewing What You Learned

Answer each of the following in a complete sentence.

1. List the characteristics that primates share.
2. Which genus marks the emergence of the hominids? How did its name arise?
3. What did Raymond Dart find?
4. What are prosimians? Anthropoids?
5. Compare Old World monkeys and New World monkeys.
6. Based on fossil evidence, when and where did the Neanderthals live?
7. Who were the Cro-Magnons? Describe some of their characteristics.
8. What factors contributed to the fall of the Incan empire?
9. How did the early separation of Eastern Hemisphere and Western Hemisphere *H. sapiens* lead to serious consequences when they came together?
10. What is an antibiotic?
11. How could a "super bug" develop in a hospital that is designed to be disease free?
12. What is an epidemic?

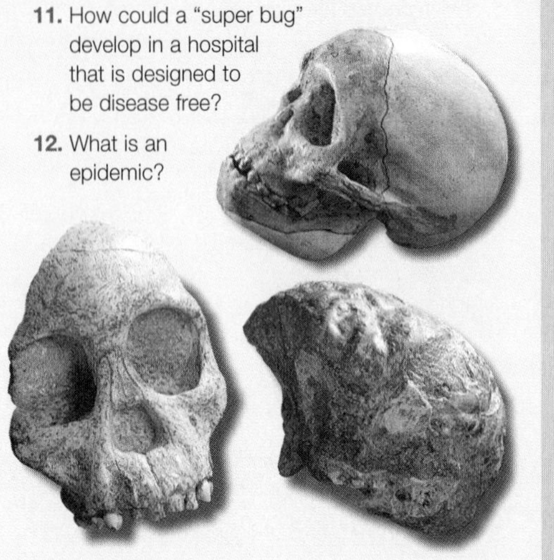

Expanding the Concepts

Discuss each of the following in a brief paragraph.

1. Why is the study of human origins a constantly changing and controversial field?
2. Describe the evidence that has led to the current view of hominid evolution.
3. Compare the hypotheses outlining the sequence of evolutionary steps leading up to *Homo sapiens.*
4. What evidence supports the theory that Cro-Magnons were an intelligent people?
5. What role can epidemics play in influencing the process of evolution?
6. How can you explain the fact that epidemics generally broke out along major trade routes?
7. Why is the evolution of drug-resistant strains of bacteria potentially very serious?
8. When the doctor prescribes an antibiotic medication for a bacterial infection, you often begin to feel better even before you have taken all the medication. Although you feel better, why is it important for you to take all the medication?

Extending Your Thinking

Use the skills you have developed in this chapter to answer the following.

1. **Hypothesizing** In ancient Hawaii, the native bird population thrived. These birds evolved in isolation and had few predators or diseases. After whalers began frequenting these islands, the native bird population from the seashore up to an elevation of 600 meters above sea level began to die. Formulate a hypothesis to explain this catastrophe.

2. **Experimenting** How does the number of microorganisms vary with location—such as city, farm, country, mountain, or seashore? Design an experiment to answer this question.

3. **Communicating** Write an essay to defend this statement: Humans have increased the evolution rate of many domestic and disease-causing organisms.

4. **Evaluating** Do you think there is a need for a worldwide organization to track diseases that affect plants, animals, and humans? Suppose this organization costs billions of dollars each year to maintain. Do you still think it is needed? Give reasons for your answer.

5. **Evaluating** Do you think that the extensive use of antibiotics in domesticated food animals is a problem for humans? Explain your answer.

Applying Your Skills

Antibiotics: The Wonder Drugs?

Before the 1940s, there were few known treatments for bacterial diseases. Today, penicillin is an antibiotic commonly used against certain strains of bacteria.

1. Research how penicillin was discovered. Write a brief essay on the role penicillin has played in human society since it was first discovered.

2. In a small group, discuss what might happen if all the bacteria in the world were destroyed.

> **• GOING FURTHER •**
>
> 3. Tuberculosis (TB), thought by health officials to have been eradicated, is on the rise in the United States. As a group, conduct research to find out more about the cause of this occurrence.

Applying Your Skills

Teacher Note

• Have each student do research independently and produce an essay of a few paragraphs on penicillin. Then divide the class into small groups for discussion.

Answers

1. Students should find that Alexander Fleming discovered penicillin in 1928. This antibiotic was widely used during World War II and in the years following, and it gave rise to many more such drugs. Today, penicillin is not widely prescribed, because most bacteria are resistant to its effects.

2. Students should remember that not all bacteria are harmful. Some bacteria are important to humans in food-making processes, and bacteria play a vital role in decomposing organic matter and recycling nutrients.

3. Students should discover that the recent increase in outbreaks of TB is partly due to the spread of AIDS. Also, as with other bacterial diseases, drug-resistant strains of the tubercle bacterium have evolved.

Scoring Rubric

4 Response is thorough, accurate, and creative; shows an in-depth understanding of science skills, procedures, and concepts.

3 Response is complete, mostly accurate, and original; shows a satisfactory understanding of science skills, procedures, and concepts.

2 Response is mostly complete but includes some inaccuracies; shows an adequate understanding of science skills, procedures, and concepts.

1 Response is only partially complete and has many inaccuracies; shows an incomplete understanding of science skills, procedures, and concepts.

0 Response is mostly incomplete and/or inaccurate; shows a lack of understanding of science skills, procedures, and concepts.

3. A typical response might suggest that the widespread use of antibiotics has caused bacteria to evolve rapidly into drug-resistant strains.

4. A typical response might suggest that such an organization is needed to protect both human lives and the food supply, no matter what the cost. Some students might argue that an international organization would not be needed if world governments would cooperate in the exchange of information.

5. A typical response might suggest that such use may be a problem, since drug-resistant bacteria evolve when antibiotics are a permanent part of their environment, and this use increases bacteria's exposure to antibiotics, especially since humans injest antibiotics when they eat meat from treated animals. If these bacteria then infect humans, antibiotics would be ineffective in treating the resulting diseases.

UNIT 6

From Bacteria to Plants

Introducing the Unit

. . . In Words

Stephen Jay Gould has done much to make science understandable to nonscientists, and in the process he has become somewhat of a celebrity. In addition to being a professor of geology, biology, and the history of science at Harvard University, Gould is a prolific science writer, particularly on the topic of evolution. His essays appear regularly in several popular journals and have been collected in award-winning books.

In the early 1970s, Gould and fellow paleontologist Niles Eldredge introduced the theory of punctuated equilibrium, which suggests that evolution occurs in rapid, irregular spurts instead of as a gradual and continuous process. The quotation reflects Gould's position that evolution is neither orderly nor progressive.

- **What do you think were the first life forms on Earth?** (Lead students to conclude that the first life forms were single-celled organisms similar to modern bacteria.)
- **Where are bacteria found on Earth today?** (Bacteria are found virtually everywhere on Earth, even on the bottom of oceans, on glaciers, and in volcanic hot springs.)
- **Can you think of other organisms that have survived on Earth as long or have adapted to so many environments as bacteria?** (No other organisms can compare to bacteria on either count.)

UNIT 6

From Bacteria to Plants

CHAPTERS

"On any possible, reasonable, or fair criterion, bacteria are—and always have been—the dominant forms of life on Earth."

— Stephen Jay Gould

TEACHER SUPPORT

Unit Discovery Learning Activity

MORE OR LESS?

Help students appreciate the structure and organization of organisms by observing and comparing a unicellular organism, a colonial organism, and a multicellular organism. This exercise will help students understand that though cells are the basic units of life, they can differentiate to form complex multicellular organisms. Follow these steps to carry out this activity.

1. Provide each group of students with a euglena culture, a *Spirogyra* culture, a small potted plant such as a geranium, a microscope, slides and coverslips, medicine dropper, and prepared slides of a leaf, stem, and root cross section.

2. Have students prepare a slide of euglena and observe it under the microscope. They should draw and describe what they observe.

CAREER TRACK

As you explore the topics in this unit, you will discover many different types of careers associated with biology. Here are a few of these careers:

- Virologist
- Microbiologist Technician
- Phycologist
- Agricultural Technician
- Plant Propagator

A giant kelp forest off Santa Barbara Island in California

. . . In Pictures

Giant kelp is a type of brown alga that can grow up to 100 meters long. It forms underwater forests that rival tropical rain forests for diversity and abundance of life. More than 750 species of fishes and invertebrates find food and shelter in giant kelp forests.

- **What kind of organism is the giant kelp?** (To students who may think that it is a plant, explain that it is a multicellular alga.)
- **What role do you think giant kelps play in their environment?** (Lead students to conclude that giant kelps are producers that provide both food and shelter to many consumers.)

CAREER TRACK

Throughout this unit, you will find a broad range of biology-related careers that vary in educational and training requirements. You may wish to have your students find out more about the following careers:

- Virologist, p. 521
- Microbiologist Technician, p. 547
- Phycologist, p. 569
- Agricultural Technician, p. 591
- Plant Propagator, p. 617

Technology

BioVue
Researching the Forest Canopy
Videodisc Side 6

Go to Chapter 2

3. Next have students examine the *Spirogyra* culture and then make a slide and observe it under the microscope. Again, they should draw and describe what they observe.
4. Finally, have students examine the potted plant and observe the leaf, stem, and root cross sections under the microscope. Have them draw and describe what they observe.
5. Ask students within each group to compare the structure and organization of the three organisms. Challenge students to make inferences about how an organism's structure and organization affect its role.
6. In a class discussion, have groups share their observations and inferences. Emphasize that cells are the basic units of all living organisms, though cells can differentiate to form specialized cells, tissues, and organs that make up complex multicellular organisms.

By observing and comparing unicellular, colonial, and multicellular organisms, students should be able to identify and explain examples of the key concepts of **scale and structure** and **unity and diversity,** two themes that are developed in this unit.

Ancillary Support

The resource below can be used to support your teaching strategy for these two pages.

BL Integrating the Media
Unit Discovery Learning Activity

Chapter 22 Bacteria and Viruses

Content Management	Student Edition Activities
■ Section 22–1 Bacteria, pp. 515–519 Bacterial Structure Classifying Bacteria Bacterial Reproduction and Growth Bacteria and Disease	MINI LAB: Not Exactly Bean Soup, p. 518
■ Section 22–2 Viruses, pp. 520–524 The Discovery of Viruses What Is a Virus? How Viruses Infect Cells Viruses and Disease	Laboratory Investigation: Observing the Effects of the Tobacco Mosaic Virus, pp. 528–529
◆ BRANCHING OUT • In Action Section 22–3 Bacteria in Our World, pp. 525–527 Bacteria in Nature Bacteria and Humans Bacteria and Health	MINI LAB: "Did You Wash Your Hands?", p. 526

■ These sections cover all the necessary content and concepts for an enriched course in biology.
◆ This section covers content and concepts that are either applications or extensions of the enriched material.

Integration Strategies

SE Math, pp. 515, 518
Chemistry, pp. 517, 527
Health, p. 519
BL Investigating Careers
Involving the Community
Science Through Art

Assessment Strategies

SE Chapter Review, pp. 530–533
TR Section Reviews
Chapter Test
Performance-Based Assessment
BL Investigating Further
Chapter Review
Practice Test
CTB Chapter 22 Test

Tech Prep

Teaching strategies appropriate for students who are in technical/vocational programs or who are considering post-secondary technical education can be found on the following **TE** pages: 518, 522, and 524.

Meeting the Standards

Sections 22–1 through 22–3 cover three of the six content standards under **The Cell,** three of the five content standards under **Biological Evolution,** and three of the five content standards under **The Interdependence of Organisms** as described on pages 184–186 of The National Science Education Standards.

Chapter Planning Guide

Teacher's Edition Activities	Other Activities	Media and Technology
Chapter Discovery Learning Activity, p. 514 Inquiry Activity: They're Even in Your Food, p. 515 Inquiry Activity: Is Frozen Dirt Alive?, p. 516 Investigate: Research, p. 516	**LM** Controlling Bacterial Growth, #44 **TR** Apply: Splitting Cells **BL** Inquiry Activity: The Shape of Things to Come	CD-ROM: Viruses & Bacteria
Inquiry Activity: Attach, Attack!, p. 520 Investigate: Research, p. 520	**TR** Writing in Biology: Microbes as Action Figures Enrich: Halting HIV **BL** Inquiry Activity: Where Did It All Begin?	BioVue Animation: The Life Cycle of a Virus, Videodisc Side 6 BioVue Plus CD-ROMs: Life Cycle of a Virus **TB** Visualizing a Viral Infection, #28
Investigate: Research, p. 525 Activity: Where Are There More of Them?, p. 526	**LM** Observing Starch-Digesting Bacteria, #43 **TR** Explore: Bacterial Benefactors **BL** Inquiry Activity: Bacterial Scavenger Hunt	

KEY: **SE** Student Edition **TE** Teacher's Edition **LM** Laboratory Manual **TR** Teaching Resources **BL** BioLog **TB** Transparency Box **CTB** Computer Test Bank

Materials List

TE Chapter Discovery Learning Activity, p. 514 (20 minutes); photographs of bacteria and viruses from old textbooks.

TE Inquiry Activity: They're Even in Your Food, p. 515 (30 minutes); glass, raw sauerkraut juice, plain yogurt, slides and coverslips, dropper, microscope.

TE Inquiry Activity: Is Frozen Dirt Alive?, p. 516 (5 minutes the first day, 10 minutes the second day, and 5 minutes the third day); soil, self-sealing plastic bag, Petri dishes containing sterile nutrient agar.

SE MINI LAB: Not Exactly Bean Soup, p. 518 (20 minutes); canned beans, plastic container, water, dropper, slide and coverslip, microscope.

TE Inquiry Activity: Attach, Attack!, p. 520 (20 minutes); photograph of a virus attached to a cell.

SE MINI LAB: "Did You Wash Your Hands?", p. 526 (20 minutes the first day, 10 minutes the second day); Petri dish containing sterile nutrient agar, marking pencil, clear tape.

TE Activity: Where Are There More of Them? p. 526 (20 minutes the first day, 10 minutes two days later); Petri dishes containing sterile nutrient agar, sterile cotton swabs, masking tape, marking pen.

CHAPTER 22

Bacteria and Viruses

Introducing the Chapter

. . . In Pictures

This color-enhanced micrograph of particles of human immunodeficiency virus shows an outer coat (yellow-brown) that surrounds the RNA and other material of this retrovirus. After students have examined the photograph and read the caption, ask the following questions.

- **What is this virus commonly called, and what disease does it cause?** (It is commonly called HIV, and causes AIDS, or acquired immune deficiency syndrome.)
- **How does this virus affect cells in the body?** (Students' responses will vary. Some students may know that HIV destroys certain cells of the immune system.)

Teaching Strategy

In the first two sections of this chapter, students will learn about the basics of bacteria and viruses, including structure, classification, reproduction or replication, and disease implications. The BRANCHING OUT section provides greater detail on the ubiquitous nature of bacteria, as well as their usefulness for, and impact on, human society.

BIO JOURNAL

The Bio Journal topic can be used to stimulate classroom discussion about the effect that bacteria and viruses have on humans and human society. Ask students to think of common infectious diseases. Then ask which they think are viral diseases and which are bacterial. After they have classified several diseases, ask whether they can think of any way that bacteria are beneficial to humans. Instruct students to keep their entries in their portfolios.

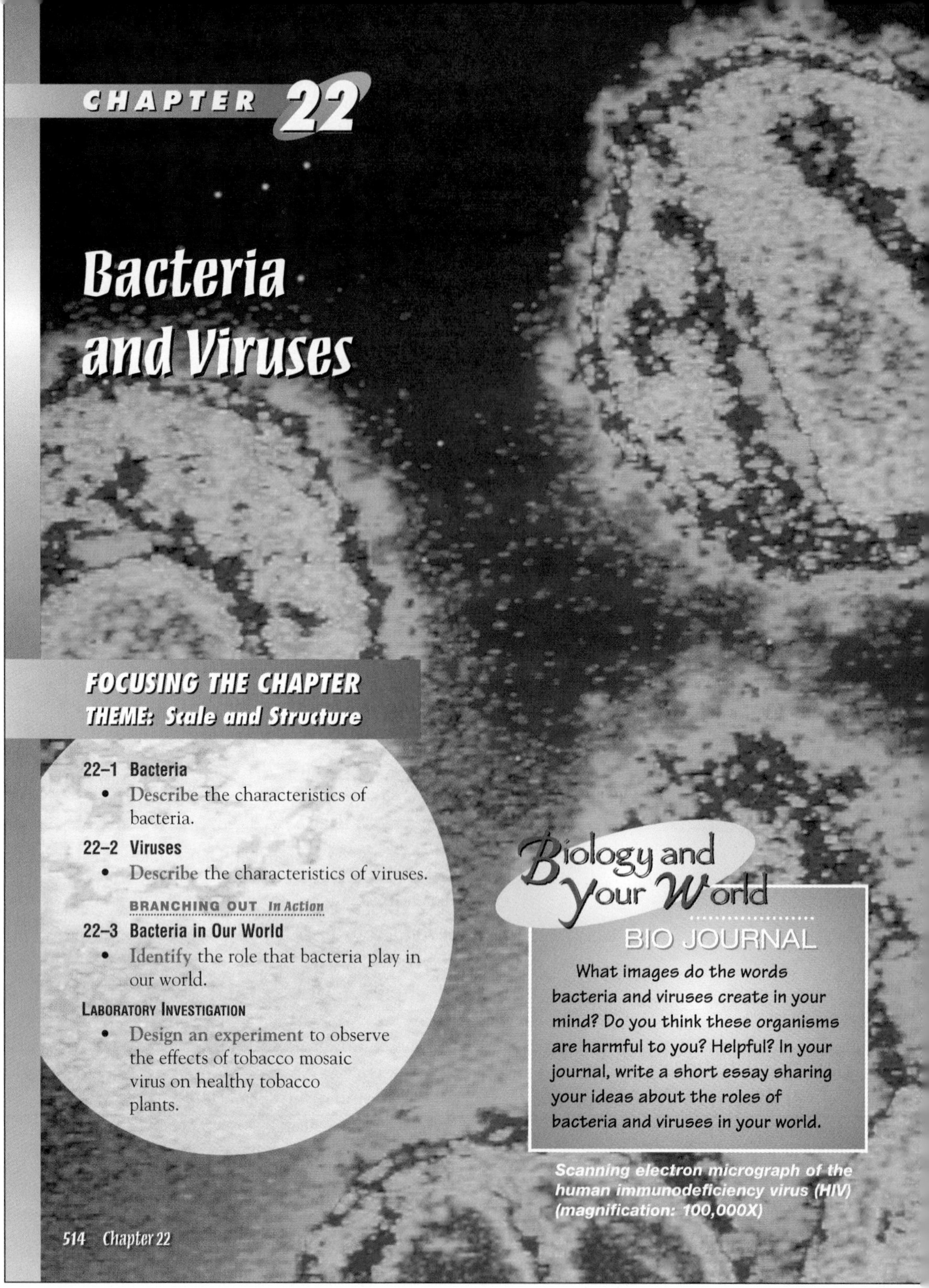

CHAPTER 22

Bacteria and Viruses

FOCUSING THE CHAPTER
THEME: Scale and Structure

22–1 Bacteria
- Describe the characteristics of bacteria.

22–2 Viruses
- Describe the characteristics of viruses.

BRANCHING OUT *In Action*

22–3 Bacteria in Our World
- Identify the role that bacteria play in our world.

LABORATORY INVESTIGATION
- Design an experiment to observe the effects of tobacco mosaic virus on healthy tobacco plants.

Biology and Your World

BIO JOURNAL

What images do the words bacteria and viruses create in your mind? Do you think these organisms are harmful to you? Helpful? In your journal, write a short essay sharing your ideas about the roles of bacteria and viruses in your world.

Scanning electron micrograph of the human immunodeficiency virus (HIV) (magnification: 100,000X)

TEACHER SUPPORT

Chapter Discovery Learning Activity

Display a variety of photographs of bacteria and viruses taken from old microbiology and biology texts, as well as from science journals. You could bring the display to life by using a microprojector or videocamera to show slides of the major shapes of bacteria and several shapes of viruses. Tell students that some of these photographs are of bacteria and some are of viruses. Have groups of students meet to divide a pile of photographs into two groups. Without being specifically told that bacteria are cellular and viruses are noncellular, students should be able to differentiate between images of bacteria and those of viruses.

Bacteria

SECTION 22–1

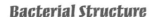

GUIDE FOR READING

- **Describe** the structure of bacterial cells.
- **Classify** bacteria.
- **Explain** how bacteria reproduce and grow.

MINI LAB

- **Observe** some characteristics of bacterial cells through the microscope.

IF YOU WERE ASKED TO POINT out a single living thing from the world around you, what organism would come to mind first? Would it be a tree outside your school? A bird flying overhead? A squirrel gathering food? Any of these would be good choices, of course, but it is likely that you would pick something large enough for everyone to see. It's only natural to think first of the organisms that you see every day. However, there is another world around us that we generally don't think about or see, a world that contains the most abundant and most successful forms of life on the Earth—bacteria.

Bacterial Structure

Bacteria are found everywhere—from mountaintops to sulfur springs to the depths of great oceans. Bacteria are so small that there may be millions of them in a pinch of soil. Billions of bacteria even live inside your own body, residents of your digestive system.

Bacteria get their name from a Greek word meaning "little stick." As ***Figure 22–2*** on page 516 shows, the name fits. Bacteria are **prokaryotes**—cells without nuclei. Most bacteria are much smaller than eukaryotic cells—cells with nuclei. The length of a typical bacterial cell ranges from 1 to 10 micrometers. The length of a eukaryotic cell ranges from 10 to 100 micrometers.

Bacterial cells have a relatively simple structure. **Genetic information in bacterial cells is found on a single circular DNA molecule—or chromosome—in the cytoplasm. The cytoplasm is surrounded by a cell membrane made up of lipids and proteins.**

INTEGRATING MATH

How many bacterial cells of typical length can line up across the width of a coin that is 1 cm in diameter?

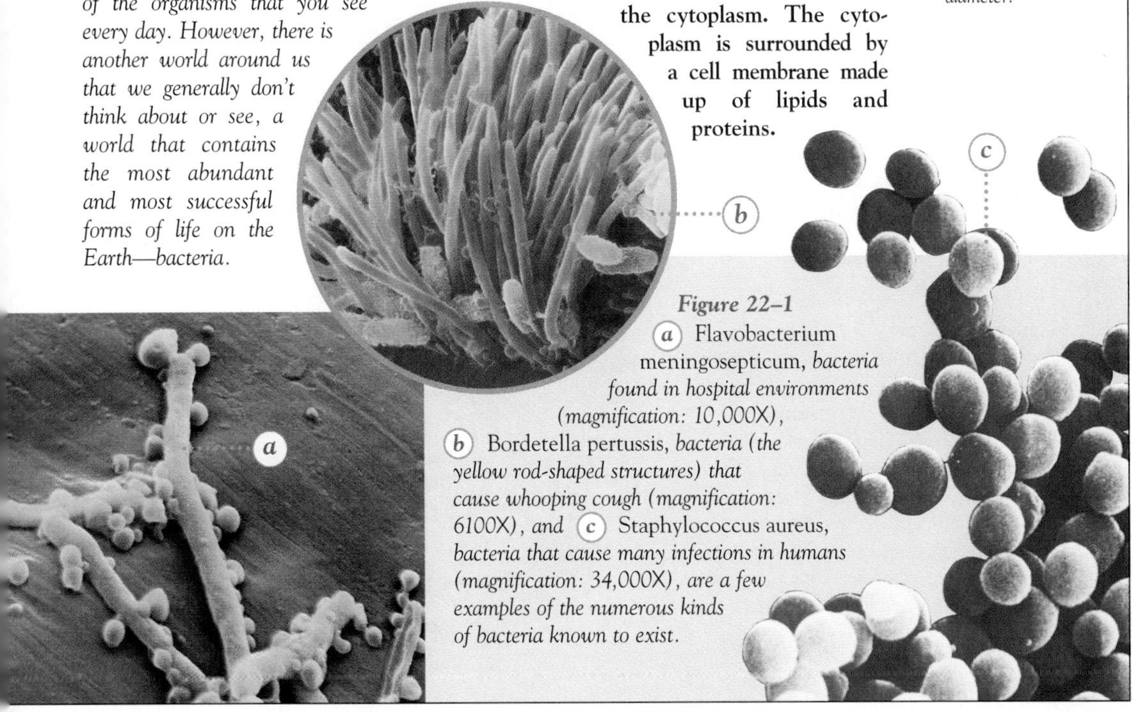

Figure 22–1
(a) Flavobacterium meningosepticum, *bacteria found in hospital environments (magnification: 10,000X),* (b) Bordetella pertussis, *bacteria (the yellow rod-shaped structures) that cause whooping cough (magnification: 6100X), and* (c) Staphylococcus aureus, *bacteria that cause many infections in humans (magnification: 34,000X), are a few examples of the numerous kinds of bacteria known to exist.*

TEACHER SUPPORT

Ecology Note

Earth's environment depends on a cycling of substances through the world ecosystem. These substances include water, carbon, nitrogen, sulfur, phosphorus, sodium, potassium, and other materials. Their cycles are sometimes called biogeochemical cycles, since they involve both biological and geologic parts of the ecosystem. Bacteria are an essential part of all these cycles. For instance, the cyanobacteria are a primary component of the carbon cycle, for through their photosynthesis they contribute much of the oxygen to the atmosphere that is used in cellular respiration. The nitrogen-fixing bacteria, such as *Rhizobium*, are central to the nitrogen cycle. The many bacteria that decompose dead organisms contribute to all the cycles. Each cycle, then, depends on bacteria to keep the system flowing.

SECTION 22–1

Bacteria

Performance Objectives

- Discuss the structure of bacterial cells.
- Describe the classifications of bacteria.
- Describe bacterial reproduction and growth.

Mini Lab Skill: Observing

1 ENGAGE

Inquiry Activity

Observing

They're Even in Your Food

Ask students whether they think there are any organisms living in the food they eat. Then have students perform the following steps.

- Place a drop of raw sauerkraut juice on a microscope slide and add a coverslip. Examine under high power. Look for tiny specks, some of which may be moving. Most of these specks are bacteria.
- Mix a teaspoonful of plain yogurt with half a glass of water. Place a drop of this mixture on another microscope slide and add a coverslip. Examine under high power. Look for tiny rod-shaped organisms.

Students should observe bacilli in both food mixtures. They should also realize that these bacteria do not cause illness in humans.

INTEGRATING MATH

A micrometer (1 µ) equals 1/1,000,000 m, or 1/10,000 cm. Since a typical bacteria cell ranges from 1 µ to 10 µ, the number of such cells that could line up across a coin of 1 cm in diameter would be 1000 to 10,000.

Ancillary Support

The resource below can be used to support your teaching strategy for these two pages.

BL Inquiry Activity: The Shape of Things to Come

2 EXPLORE

Inquiry Activity

Experimenting

Is Frozen Dirt Alive?
Ask students whether they think bacteria can live through freezing temperatures. Provide students with a bucket of soil. During class, have each student place a small amount of soil in a plastic container, and then place those containers in the freezer. The next day, provide each student or small group with two Petri dishes of agar. On one dish of agar, students should sprinkle some soil from the bucket. On the other, they should sprinkle some of the soil frozen overnight. The dishes should then be covered and left overnight. The next day, students should observe that both dishes show evidence of bacterial colonies growing on the agar.

Investigate

Research Have individual students or pairs of students research one of the well-known bacterial diseases. These include diphtheria, tuberculosis, bubonic plague, gonorrhea, syphilis, strep throat, tetanus, typhoid fever, cholera, Lyme disease, Legionnaires' disease, whooping cough, leprosy, anthrax, and food poisoning (*Salmonella* and *E. coli*). Ask students to prepare a report on the disease that includes detailed information on the type of bacterium that causes the disease, as well as the symptoms, spread, and treatment of the disease.

3 TEACH

Ideas Through Images

Have students examine Figure 22–4, read the caption, and answer the following questions.

- **What are the three main shapes of bacteria?** (Rod-shaped, spherical-shaped, and spiral-shaped bacteria.)

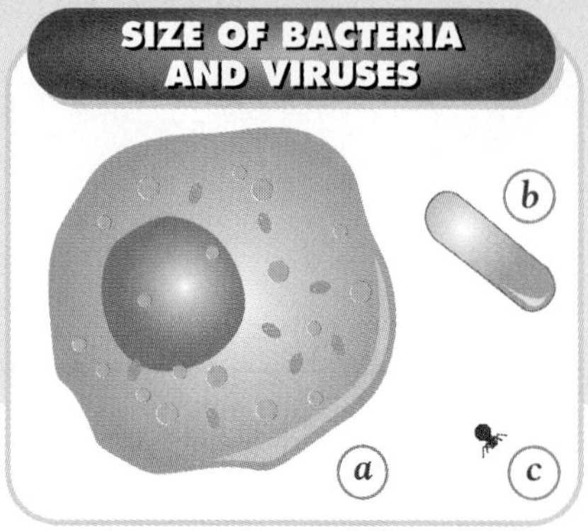

Figure 22–2 *This diagram illustrates the relative size of a typical (a) eukaryotic cell, (b) bacterium, and (c) virus.*

The Bacterial Cell Wall

The cell membrane of a bacterium is surrounded by a cell wall composed of complex carbohydrates. The cell wall protects the bacterium from injury and helps to regulate the movements of molecules into and out of the cell.

Because the cell wall is so important, bacteria are often identified according to the type of cell wall they have. Biologists determine the type of cell wall by using a technique known as Gram staining, named after its inventor, Hans Christian Gram, a Danish physician. Bacteria that take up Gram's purple stain are known as gram-positive. Those that do not take up the stain are said to be gram-negative. What do these categories mean? Gram-negative bacteria have an extra lipid-containing layer around their cell walls. This layer not only keeps out the stain, it enables the gram-negative bacteria to resist many drugs used to fight bacterial infections. For this reason, an infection with gram-negative bacteria is usually very serious.

☑ **Checkpoint** Explain the function of the bacterial cell wall. ❶

Cell Shape and Movement

Bacteria are often described according to their shape. Rod-shaped bacteria are called **bacilli** (buh-SIHL-igh; singular: bacillus). Spherical-shaped bacteria are known as **cocci** (KAHK-sigh; singular: coccus). And spiral-shaped bacteria are called **spirilla** (spigh-RIHL-uh; singular: spirillum).

Bacteria may also be described by how they move. Only a very small number of bacteria have no means of movement. Most can move, and some move very quickly. Some can change their shape to wriggle forward—almost like snakes—and others glide slowly along the surfaces of solid objects. Many bacteria have whiplike flagella that propel them through liquids with amazing speed.

Classifying Bacteria

Biologists have struggled for years to find the best way to classify different types of bacteria. It hasn't been easy. Many bacteria that look similar are actually very different in other respects, and there is no

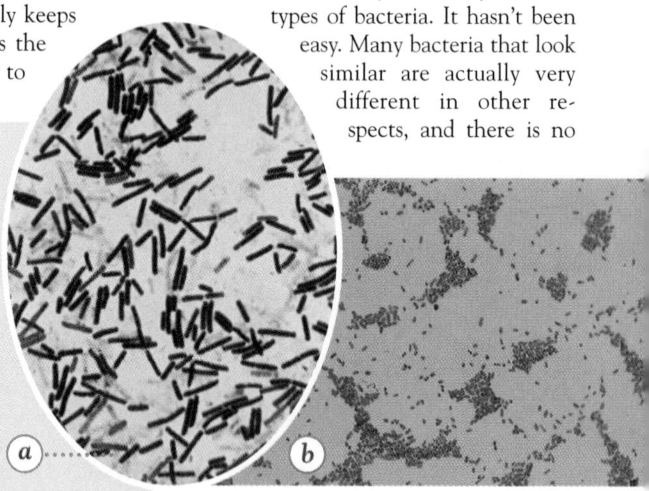

Figure 22–3 *Because (a)* Clostridium botulinum *take up the purple stain in a Gram-staining test, they are known to be gram-positive (magnification: 600X). (b)* Haemophilus influenzae, *on the other hand, do not and are considered gram-negative (magnification: 625X). Gram-negative bacteria have an extra lipid layer around their cell wall that keeps the purple stain out, along with other foreign substances, such as antibacterial drugs.*

TEACHER SUPPORT

Background Information

What ever happened to kingdom Monera? Many textbooks include it as one of the five kingdoms of living things. Typically, the kingdom encompasses all prokaryotic organisms, but in this textbook the term is not used at all. The reason is that recent research has indicated fundamental differences between Archaebacteria and Eubacteria, including cell membrane composition, DNA sequence, and ribosome structure. In fact, on a purely molecular level the Archaebacteria are as different from Eubacteria as *E. coli* are from human cells. For that reason, in this book the two types of prokaryotes are placed in separate kingdoms—just another example of how the study of life is the study of change.

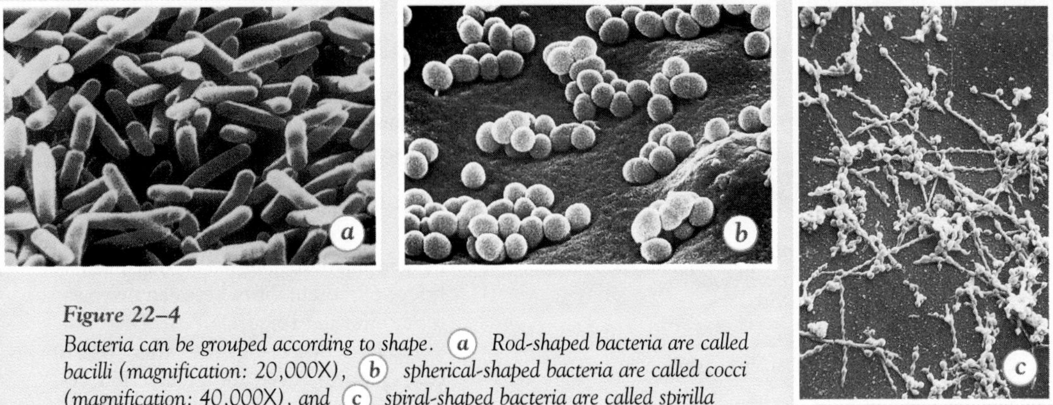

Figure 22–4
Bacteria can be grouped according to shape. (a) *Rod-shaped bacteria are called bacilli (magnification: 20,000X),* (b) *spherical-shaped bacteria are called cocci (magnification: 40,000X), and* (c) *spiral-shaped bacteria are called spirilla (magnification: 45,000X).*

simple way to decide which characteristics are most important. In recent years, however, it has become possible to compare the DNA sequences of bacteria, and scientists have been able to determine in this way which groups of bacteria are most closely related.

This has led to a startling discovery—one group of bacteria differs almost as much from another group of bacteria as prokaryotic cells do from eukaryotic cells! **As a result, the bacteria are now divided into two separate kingdoms—the Archaebacteria and the Eubacteria.**

Archaebacteria

The Archaebacteria are sometimes called "ancient" bacteria because they resemble the first known prokaryotes. The prefix *archae-* comes from a Greek word meaning "ancient." Although they resemble other bacteria, the Archaebacteria display striking differences in their cell membranes, biochemical pathways, and ribosomes. Archaebacteria include organisms that live in very harsh environments. For example, one group lives in oxygen-poor environments, such as thick mud and the digestive tracts of animals. These Archaebacteria are called methanogens because they produce methane gas.

Eubacteria

Eubacteria, or the "true" bacteria, are the largest and most diverse group of bacteria. They are literally found everywhere on the planet, and they practice just about every possible means of "making a biological living."

Many Eubacteria are photosynthetic, meaning that they capture and use the energy from sunlight. Other Eubacteria capture chemical energy from their surroundings—including even inorganic molecules such as hydrogen sulfide, sulfur, and iron—and use it for their needs.

INTEGRATING CHEMISTRY
What is chemical energy?

☑ **Checkpoint** How do Archaebacteria and Eubacteria differ? 2

Figure 22–5
Some Archaebacteria thrive in very hot environments, such as the Chromatic Spring of the Upper Geyser Basin, Yellowstone National Park, which owes its brilliant colors to various species of the bacteria.

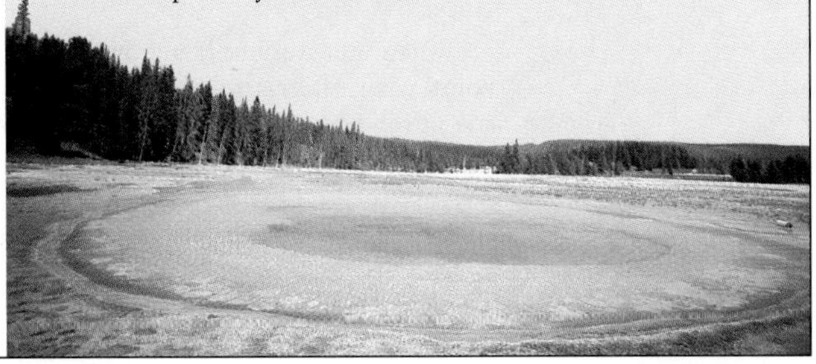

TEACHER SUPPORT

Ecology Note

Archaebacteria include exotic bacteria that live in such extreme environments as deep ocean vents and hot sulfur springs. The kingdom also includes common bacteria called methanogens that live in the digestive tracts of all animals, especially in the rumen of cows and other grazing beasts. These bacteria use hydrogen and carbon to produce methane (CH_4), and most of the methane in the atmosphere is the result of this process. In fact, cows have been called "40-gallon methane tanks on four legs." In the atmosphere, the methane reacts with oxygen to produce CO_2. If it were not for methanogens, Earth would be much different. Carbon would pile up in huge deposits in the ground, and oxygen would make up a much greater percentage of the atmosphere.

- **If biologists identified a bacterium as a type of cocci, what shape would that bacterium have?** (Spherical.)
- **If you observed that certain bacteria were rod-shaped, what kind of bacteria would they be?** (Bacilli.)
- **How could you represent spirilla bacteria in a model?** (Students might suggest using a spring to represent a spiral shape.)

Discussion

Initiate a discussion about the classification of bacteria by asking students to name the two kingdoms that encompass bacteria and explain the differences between the two groups. Through this discussion, emphasize the following points.

- Archaebacteria are different from Eubacteria in their cell membranes, biochemical pathways, and ribosomes. They are similar in that bacteria of neither have nuclei, and thus they are all prokaryotes.
- Placing these bacteria into two separate kingdoms is a fairly recent development, and microbiologists are still discovering characteristics that differentiate the two groups.
- Eubacteria do include organisms that cause disease or illness, such as *Salmonella*. But Eubacteria also include many types that cause no harm to humans.

INTEGRATING CHEMISTRY

The energy of the chemical bonds that hold atoms or ions together in chemical compounds.

☑ Checkpoints

1 The bacterial cell wall protects the bacterium from injury and helps to regulate the movements of molecules into and out of the cell.

2 They differ in their cell membranes, biochemical pathways, and ribosomes.

MINI LAB Observing

Teacher Notes

• For time required and materials needed, see page 514b.
• Prepare a bacterial culture by slightly mashing 6–10 canned beans, placing them in a container, and covering with water. A cloudy liquid, indicating the presence of bacteria, will result in about 48 hours.
• If bright light is used, the bacteria will not be visible.
• Bean culture will most likely contain harmless bacteria; nevertheless, caution students to handle it carefully and wash their hands when finished.

Answers to Analyze and Conclude

1. The culture appears cloudy and has a putrid odor. Students should infer that the cloudiness is caused by bacterial growth and that the odor results from the bacteria decomposing the beans.
2. Students should see all three bacterial shapes.
3. Students should see some of the cells moving through the liquid with a weaving motion or by means of flagella.

Skills Trace
Observing

- **Focus** p. 518
- **Practice** p. 519
- **Assess** p. 532

INTEGRATING MATH

An example might be human population growth.

MINI LAB .... Observing ....

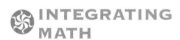

Not Exactly Bean Soup

PROBLEM *How can you **observe** some characteristics of bacterial cells through the microscope?*

PROCEDURE

1. Obtain a small amount of bacterial culture prepared by your teacher.
2. Place a drop of the culture on a microscope slide and observe under high power using a low light setting.
3. Look for bacterial cells of different shapes and for bacteria that are moving.
4. Record your observations.

ANALYZE AND CONCLUDE

1. What is the appearance of the bacterial culture? Does it have an odor? How can you account for the odor and appearance?
2. What cell shapes did you observe?
3. Are any of the cells moving?

Bacterial Reproduction and Growth

Under the proper conditions, bacteria can grow at astonishing rates. Some can completely reproduce themselves in as little as 20 minutes. This means that in the course of a single day, one cell can go through 72 generations—or 3 generations every hour. A single cell reproducing that quickly for a full day would give rise to more than 4 billion cells!

INTEGRATING MATH

Bacterial growth is an exponential growth. Give an example of another exponential growth process.

Binary Fission

When a bacterium has grown to the point where it has roughly doubled in size, it replicates its chromosome and divides in half, producing two identical daughter cells. This is known as **binary fission,** a type of reproduction. **Because binary fission does not involve the exchange of genetic information, it is an asexual form of reproduction.**

Conjugation

A few bacteria are able to reproduce by **conjugation.** During conjugation, a bridge of protein forms between two bacteria, allowing some DNA to be transferred from one cell to the other. When conjugation is over, the connection between the cells is broken. As a result of conjugation, some bacterial cells receive new genetic information and have a different set of genes than before. **Biologists consider conjugation to be a form of sexual reproduction because it results in new combinations of genes.** These new combinations may be useful to the bacteria. They help ensure that even if the environment changes, at least a few bacteria will have the combinations of genes needed to survive.

Spore Formation

"When the going gets tough, the tough get going." That may be the motto of spore-forming bacteria. When faced with difficult conditions, many bacteria form tough structures called **spores.** One type of spore, an **endospore,** is formed inside a bacterial cell. The endospore develops a thick wall that encloses part of the cytoplasm and a DNA molecule.

Endospores are resistant to heat, drying, radiation, and even to chemical disinfectants. **The endospores of some bacteria can survive for years, and when conditions are right, they can become activated and begin to grow.** Endospores enable bacteria to survive harsh conditions that might otherwise kill them. They make it difficult to completely eliminate bacteria.

☑ ***Checkpoint*** Which is an asexual form of reproduction—binary fission or conjugation? 1

TEACHER SUPPORT

Managing Classroom Diversity

TECH PREP STUDENTS

Students who plan careers in health care or food service should understand the growth of bacterial populations in much more detail than is presented in this text. Have these students prepare a report on the stages of bacterial population growth and what is done in their career field to prevent that growth.

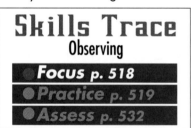

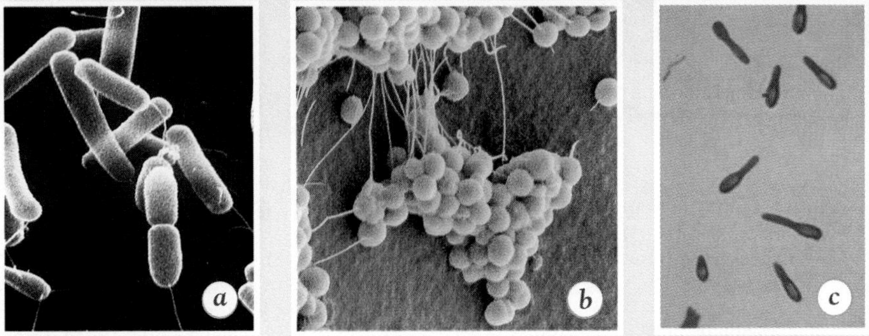

Figure 22–6
The scanning electron micrographs show (a) *binary fission in* Escherichia coli *(magnification: 20,000X),* (b) *conjugation in* Staphylococcus epidemidis *(magnification: 3145X), and* (c) *endospores in* Clostridium tetani *(magnification: 1000X).*

Bacteria and Disease

The French chemist and bacteriologist Louis Pasteur was the first person to show convincingly that certain bacteria cause disease. Pasteur established what has come to be known as the germ theory of disease when he showed that bacteria were responsible for a number of animal and plant diseases.

You may have encountered one of the most widespread disease-causing bacteria, *Streptococcus pyrogenes*, responsible for the severe sore throat called strep throat. Other diseases caused by bacteria include diphtheria, tuberculosis, typhoid fever, tetanus, syphilis, gonorrhea, cholera, Lyme disease, and bubonic plague.

Bacteria cause these diseases in one of two general ways. They may attack the cells and tissues of the body directly, breaking them down and using their materials for nourishment. Or they may release toxins (poisons) that travel throughout the body, interfering with the normal functions of the body.

For example, *Salmonella* is a bacterium that grows in foods such as meat, poultry, and eggs. If these foods are not properly cooked, *Salmonella* may get to the dinner table before you do, releasing poisons into the food. The symptoms of food poisoning range from a mild stomach upset to vomiting and diarrhea.

One of the best ways to fight bacterial diseases is by the use of vaccines, which help prevent an infection from getting started. If an infection does develop, drugs that can destroy bacteria—known as **antibiotics**—are powerful weapons that can treat most bacterial diseases. ●

INTEGRATING HEALTH

How do physicians treat bacterial diseases? Are there any reasons to be cautious with the use of such treatment?

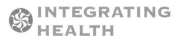

Section Review 22-1

1. **Describe** the structure of bacterial cells.
2. **Classify** bacteria.
3. **Explain** how bacteria reproduce and grow.
4. **Critical Thinking—Relating** What is the relationship between the bacterial cell wall and bacterial resistance to antibiotics?
5. **MINI LAB** What characteristics of bacterial cells did you **observe** through a microscope?

INTEGRATING HEALTH

Physicians usually treat bacterial diseases with antibiotics. Overuse of antibiotics can lead to the evolution of new strains of bacteria that are resistant to them.

4 ASSESS

Quick Check

Have students make three concept maps—one that focuses on the ability to take up stain, another on differentiating bacteria by their shape, and a third on the classification of bacteria.

Section Review 22-1

1. They have a single circular DNA molecule in cytoplasm that is surrounded by a cell membrane, which is enclosed in a cell wall.
2. Into two kingdoms, Archaebacteria and Eubacteria.
3. Through binary fission, conjugation, and spore formation.
4. Bacteria having an extra lipid-containing layer around their cell walls—known as gram-negative bacteria—are able to resist many of the drugs used to fight bacterial infections.
5. Students should have observed that bacteria are unicellular organisms with cell walls.

Checkpoint

1 Binary fission.

Skills Trace

Observing

- Focus p. 518
- Practice p. 519
- Assess p. 532

Learning Modality

Visual Learning Have students make two labeled drawings: one of a typical eukaryotic cell and the other of a typical prokaryotic cell.

Ancillary Support

The resources below can be used to support your teaching strategy for these two pages.

LM Controlling Bacterial Growth, #44
TR Apply: Splitting Cells

SECTION 22–2

Viruses

Performance Objectives

• Discuss the structure of a typical virus.

• Describe the way in which viruses infect cells.

Laboratory Investigation Skill: Designing an experiment

1 ENGAGE

Inquiry Activity

Predicting

Attach, Attack!

Give each student a copy of an electron micrograph that shows a virus particle attaching to a cell membrane. Give a simple description of what the image shows, and then ask students what they think will happen to the virus and the cell. Have students consider this question by making a prediction about what events will occur next and how the virus will ultimately affect the cell.

2 EXPLORE

Investigate

Research Have individual students or pairs of students research one of the well-known viral diseases. These include AIDS, the common cold, influenza, hepatitis, smallpox, yellow fever, encephalitis, rabies, herpes, chickenpox, measles, mumps, and polio. Ask students to prepare a report on the disease and to include information about the virus that causes the disease, as well as the symptoms, spread, and treatment of the disease.

SECTION

22–2 Viruses

GUIDE FOR READING

• **Describe** the structure of a virus.

• **Explain** how viruses infect cells.

THE YEAR IS 1892. DIMITRI Ivanovsky, a 28-year-old biologist in Russia, has been asked by the Czarist government to help solve a major problem. In the early 1800s, tens of thousands of hectares of land in the Ukraine were planted with tobacco, a crop imported from America. By the time Ivanovsky had graduated from college, farmers throughout this region of Russia depended upon the crop for their existence. But something was going wrong. Every year, more and more of the crop was being lost to a strange disease. Ivanovsky's investigation into the cause of the tobacco disease is a fascinating story. It tells about the discovery of another interesting segment in the spectrum of life's diversity—the viruses.

(a)

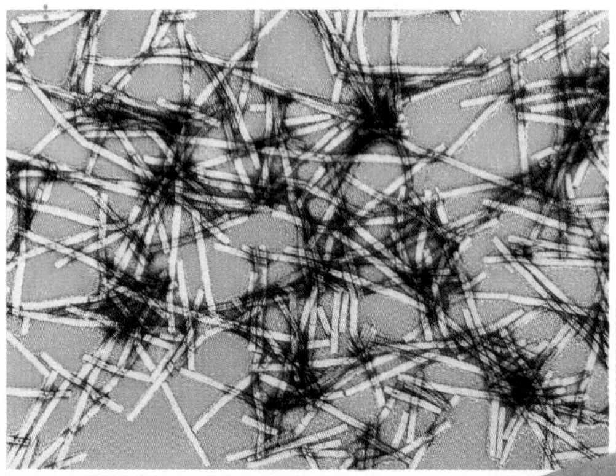

(b)

Figure 22–7
(a) Tobacco mosaic virus (magnification: 34,000X), which was discovered by Dimitri Ivanovsky, causes (b) the leaves of tobacco plants to develop a pattern of spots.

The Discovery of Viruses

Ivanovsky observed once-healthy tobacco leaves develop yellow spots. He watched the entire plant wither and die. Ivanovsky suspected a disease, and he performed a simple experiment to test his idea. He crushed some leaves from a diseased plant and collected the juice. Then he placed a few drops of juice on the leaves of a healthy plant. In a few days, yellow spots appeared on the leaves precisely where the drops had been placed. Ivanovsky had proven that tobacco mosaic disease—as it is now known—could be passed from one plant to the next.

Ivanovsky thought that a bacterium might be causing the disease, so he examined the juice under a microscope. To his surprise, there were no bacteria in the juice. In fact, there were no cells in the juice at all. The young scientist concluded correctly that the infected plants must contain an invisible infectious particle.

What Is a Virus?

A few years later, Dutch scientist Martinus Beijerinck confirmed Ivanovsky's experiments. He showed that not only were these particles invisible under a microscope, they were so small they could pass through the pores of the finest filters.

TEACHER SUPPORT

Background Information

Because viruses are not living things, they are not part of any kingdom, and they are not identified as species. Classification of viruses depends on the chemical and physical properties of the virus. The major division focuses on their genetic material; thus, there are DNA and RNA viruses. Viruses are then further divided by the shape of their protein coats and the size of their particles. For example, this scheme results in a major group called the picornaviruses, which are small RNA viruses with a polyhedral shape. Both poliovirus and the rhinoviruses (which cause the common cold) are subgroups of the picornaviruses.

Another way of grouping viruses is by the type of host a virus infects. Thus, animal viruses infect animals, plant viruses infect plants, and bacterial viruses or bacteriophages infect bacteria.

Bio Frontier Connections

Eliminating Viruses

At one time, smallpox was a dreaded disease that affected people all over the world, killing about 40 percent of its victims. Those who didn't succumb to the disease were seriously disfigured. Smallpox begins with fever and vomiting, followed by a skin rash that quickly spreads over the entire body. The rash forms itchy blisters, which result in unsightly scars when the victim scratches them.

Today, thanks to an intensive, worldwide vaccination campaign by the World Health Organization (WHO), smallpox has been eliminated as a disease. Vaccination for smallpox has been unnecessary since 1977. In 1980, WHO was able to announce that smallpox had been eradicated.

The Virus Lives On

Although smallpox is no longer an immediate threat to human health, the virus that causes it—called variola—still exists. Two samples of smallpox virus are preserved for research purposes in special Level 4 containment laboratories. One of these Level 4 labs is located at the Centers for Disease Control and Prevention in Atlanta, Georgia. The other is in the Russian State Research Center of Virology and Biotechnology in Koltsovo. Level 4 labs, which contain the most dangerous viruses, are floodproof and fireproof. As an added precaution, the viruses are kept in airtight spaces between floors to prevent their escape.

By 1994, scientists studying the virus had completely identified the virus's genetic code. Little reason remained to continue stockpiling the virus. So in 1996, the 190 member nations of WHO decided to destroy all remaining samples of smallpox virus on June 30, 1999. But even after the virus is destroyed, WHO plans to keep some smallpox vaccine on hand . . . just in case.

The Future of Laboratory Viruses

Smallpox isn't the only dangerous virus being studied in containment labs. Ebola virus, which is named after a small river in Zaire where it first appeared, is one of the deadliest viruses on Earth. It is also being studied, as is HIV, the virus that causes AIDS. But scientists differ as to what the future of these and other laboratory viruses should be.

Some scientists think that all deadly viruses should be destroyed. Others fear that in an attempt to destroy them, some viruses might escape from their confinement. Still others think that the scientific value of these viruses, especially in the event of future outbreaks, outweighs the risks of keeping them. As you see, scientists often hold differing—even strongly opposing—viewpoints.

CAREER TRACK *This virologist is working in a Level 4 containment laboratory at the Centers for Disease Control in Atlanta, Georgia. The steel laboratory is equipped with air locks and decontamination alarms to minimize the chance of highly infectious organisms from escaping.*

Making the Connection

Should samples of viruses—such as the smallpox virus—that are only kept in containment labs be destroyed? Why or why not? What information could scientists gain from studying these viruses?

3 TEACH

Connections

The smallpox virus is one of a group called poxviruses. These DNA viruses are also responsible for such animal diseases as cowpox, monkeypox, and mousepox.

The smallpox virus is spread through close contact with infected persons, as well as with contaminated towels, clothing, and similar articles. The virus normally enters the body through the mucous membrane of the upper respiratory system, and then moves through the body in the lymph and circulatory systems.

The World Health Organization (WHO), an agency of the United Nations, is headquartered in Geneva, Switzerland. The WHO began its smallpox-eradication campaign in 1967 with an aggressive plan to immunize much of the world's population with a vaccine made from the poxvirus that causes vaccinia, a disease similar to cowpox. The last known smallpox infection occurred in Somalia in 1977.

Answers to Making the Connection

Students' opinions will differ. Some might suggest that scientists should keep samples in order to further investigate how the viruses infect cells and cause disease. Others might suggest that the risk of keeping such viruses is too great because a mistake could be made and the viruses could escape into the general population.

TEACHER SUPPORT — Historical Perspective

The smallpox virus was the cause of many terrible epidemics throughout human history in Europe and Asia, and as recently as 1967 it caused 2 million deaths worldwide. The introduction of the virus into the Americas by Europeans caused particularly savage epidemics among Native Americans because none had any immunity to the infection. In both Europe and Asia, people had long recognized that someone who had contracted the less severe form of smallpox was forever immunized to the more severe form. In the late 1700s, English physician Edward Jenner noticed that milkmaids who contracted cowpox also gained immunity from smallpox. From that observation and subsequent experimentation, Jenner developed the first vaccine, a term he named from the Latin word for cow, *vacca*, because it was made from the cowpox virus.

Ancillary Support

The resources below can be used to support your teaching strategy for these two pages.

TR Writing in Biology: Microbes as Action Figures

BL Inquiry Activity: Where Did It All Begin?

Visualizing a Viral Infection

Viruses that infect a cell and destroy it through a lytic infection are often called virulent viruses. Viruses that integrate their genetic material into the host cell's DNA through a lysogenic infection are often called temperate viruses.

This visual essay shows a bacterium cell that is entered by a virus. When a temperate virus enters a bacterium, the prokaryotic cell continues undisturbed through binary fission, maybe for many generations, despite the presence of the viral genetic material. The virus accomplishes this by producing a repressor protein that prevents the production of viral enzymes that would cause lysis, or the destruction of the bacterial cell. If a change in the environment causes a change in that repressor protein, the virus enters the lytic stage, and the cell is destroyed.

As students study this visual essay, make sure they understand that a lytic infection is shown by the sequence of steps 1, 2, 3, and 4. The lysogenic infection also begins with step 1 but then continues directly to steps 5 and 6. Only when the provirus state ends does the lysogenic cycle move into steps 7 and 8, which is essentially the same as the lytic infection.

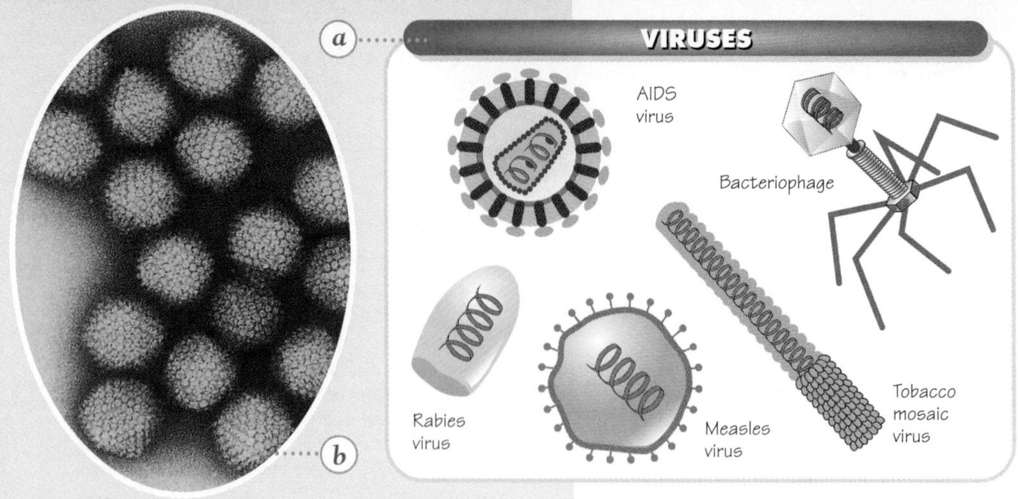

Figure 22–8
(a) The shapes of viruses vary greatly and are determined by their protein coats. (b) The electron micrograph shows Adenovirus—one of many viruses that cause the common cold in humans (magnification: 160,000X).

Knowing that the Latin word for poison was *virus*, Beijerinck wrote that the tobacco mosaic disease was caused by a filterable virus. Today, we refer to these particles as viruses.

A **virus** is a nonliving particle that contains DNA or RNA and that can infect a living cell. Viruses are much smaller than cells, as shown in ***Figure 22–2*** on page 516. Are viruses just smaller forms of living cells? Not at all. **Viruses consist only of genetic information—in the form of DNA or RNA—surrounded by a protein coat.** Although some viruses also contain other materials, such as lipid membranes and enzymes, the viruses cannot live outside a living cell.

☑ **Checkpoint** What is a virus? 1

How Viruses Infect Cells

However lifeless it may seem outside a living cell, once it makes contact with a cell that it can infect, a virus goes to work. **A virus infects a bacterial cell by attaching to the membrane of the cell. It then penetrates or fuses with the cell's membrane, releasing its own genetic material into the cell's cytoplasm.**

As the illustration on the next page shows, once inside the host cell, viruses express their genes in a way that enables them to use the host to reproduce. The host cell makes copies of the virus that can ultimately infect other cells!

Some viruses take over and destroy the host cell. They produce enzymes that cut the host cell's DNA into pieces, grab control of its ribosomes to make viral proteins, and then use up all the cell's resources to make more viruses. This process is known as a **lytic infection.**

Other viruses are more subtle. In a **lysogenic infection,** viruses insert their genetic material right into the DNA of a host. The viral genes then go about making mRNA, like the genes of the host cell. However, these viral mRNAs will direct the synthesis of viral proteins, gradually converting the cell into a living factory for making new viruses.

An example of a lysogenic infection is the lambda virus, a **bacteriophage**—a virus that infects bacteria (the name means "bacteria eater"). When lambda infects a host cell, the virus inserts its double-stranded DNA molecule into the bacterium. In most cases, this DNA is then inserted into the host cell DNA,

TEACHER SUPPORT

Managing Classroom Diversity

TECH PREP STUDENTS
Students who plan careers in health care will have to know how viral diseases are treated differently from bacterial diseases. Have these students prepare a poster or pamphlet explaining why antibiotics do not affect viruses and describing in general terms what kinds of measures are available to fight viral diseases.

Visualizing a Viral Infection

Two ways in which a virus infects a bacterial cell are lytic infection and lysogenic infection.

Lytic Infection

1 Virus attaches to bacterium, and viral DNA or RNA enters host's cytoplasm.

Virus

Nucleic acid

Bacterial DNA

Bacterium

2a Bacterium's DNA is destroyed, and viral proteins and nucleic acids are made.

3a New viruses are assembled.

4a Viral enzymes break open bacterium's cell wall, releasing the new viruses.

Lysogenic Infection

2b Viral DNA is inserted into host cell's DNA. The viral DNA is now called provirus.

Provirus

Provirus

2c This provirus may replicate with the host cell for many generations.

3b Conditions cause provirus to separate and destroy host DNA.

4b New viruses are assembled and released as the cell wall breaks open.

Bacteria and Viruses **523**

Background Information

Each different virus is spread from organism to organism in a specific way. For example, the smallpox virus is spread through contact, the cold virus is spread through the air, and the yellow fever virus is spread through mosquitoes. Once the virus enters the body, it infects only certain cells because of the shape and composition of the virus particle. A cell membrane contains protein molecules that act as receptors. A virus particle of a certain shape may match a certain receptor; in a sense, it fools the cell membrane into thinking it is something else. Once the virus particle attaches to a receptor, it can enter the cell and take over the cell's apparatus. Thus, a cold virus infects cells of the throat and nose, and the hepatitis virus infects cells of the liver.

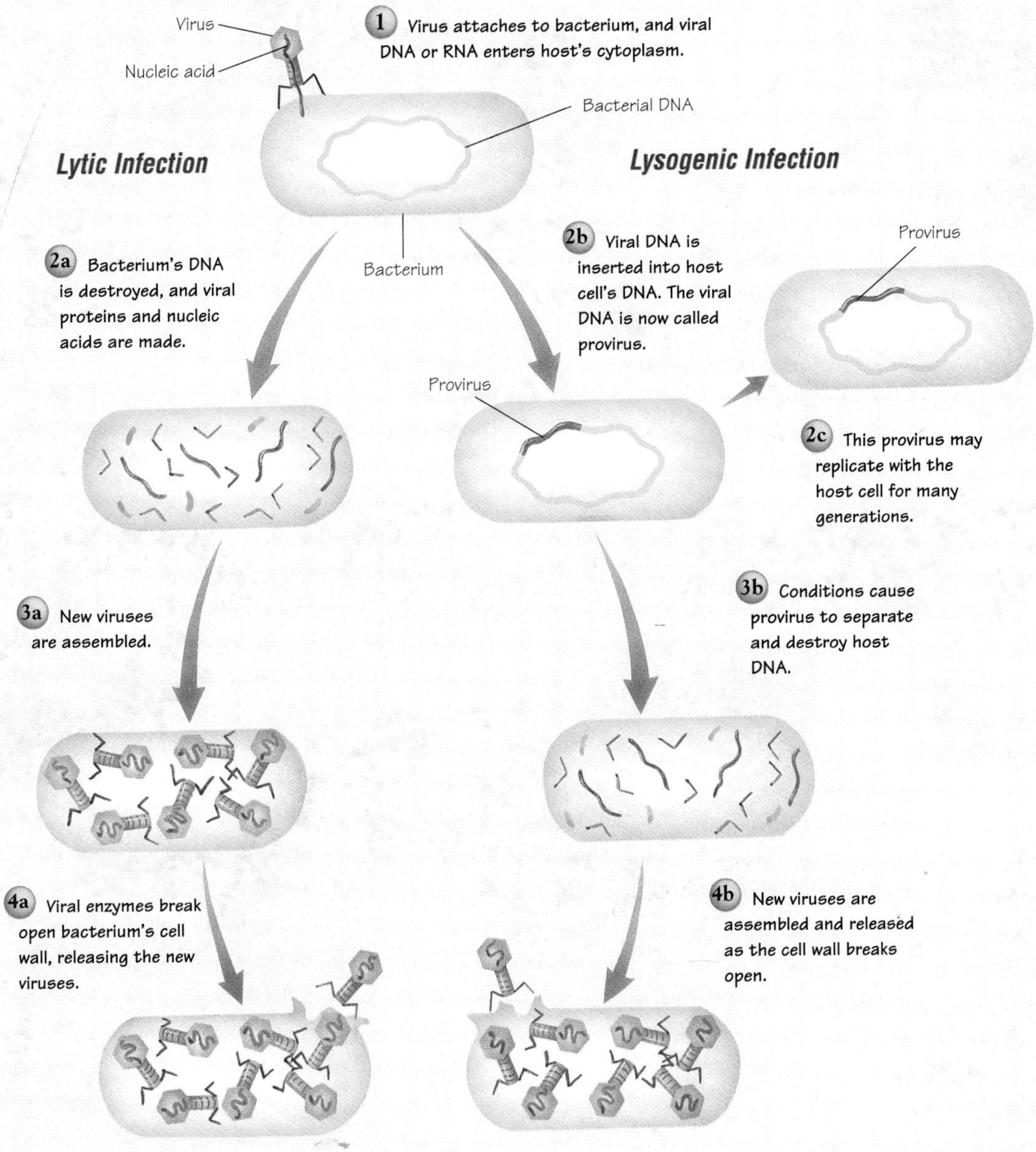

Discussion

After students have read the definition of a virus, have them consider whether viruses have any one of the five characteristics of living things. Help them understand that viruses have no cellular structures or organelles to obtain energy, to respond to the environment, or to grow and develop. Point out that viruses cannot reproduce on their own, and for that reason scientists often talk about "replication" or "multiplication" rather than "reproduction" when referring to the production of more virus particles.

Discussion

Point out to students that viruses vary in size from about 20 to 400 nanometers. Explain that a nanometer is one billionth of a meter. The tobacco mosaic virus is about 300 nanometers long, whereas the polio virus is about 20 nanometers in diameter.

Also, emphasize that specific viruses will infect specific organisms. For example, a plant virus cannot infect an animal nor can an animal virus infect a plant. Mention that there are some viruses that infect only humans.

☑ Checkpoint

1 A nonliving particle that contains DNA or RNA and that can infect a living cell.

BioVue
Animation: The Life Cycle of a Virus
Videodisc Side 6

Go to Chapter 20

Ancillary Support

The resource below can be used to support your teaching strategy for these two pages.

TB Visualizing a Viral Infection, #28

Laboratory Investigation

The Laboratory Investigation, Observing the Effects of the Tobacco Mosaic Virus, on pages 528–529 is appropriate to use at this point in the chapter.

4 ASSESS

Quick Check

Have students make two flow charts, one for a lytic infection and the other for a lysogenic infection.

Section Review 22-2

1. A virus consists of genetic material, either DNA or RNA, surrounded by a protein coat.
2. A virus infects a cell by attaching to the membrane of the cell, penetrating or fusing with that membrane, and releasing its own genetic material into the cell's cytoplasm.
3. In a lytic infection, a virus produces enzymes that cut the cell's DNA into pieces, grabs control of the cell's ribosomes to make viral proteins, and uses all the cell's resources to make more viruses. In a lysogenic infection, a virus inserts its genetic material into the cell's DNA and converts the host cell into a living factory for making new viruses.

Learning Modality

Visual Learning Ask students to make labeled drawings of several kinds of viruses. Each type of virus should show the protein coat surrounding genetic material, with the appropriate labels for each part.

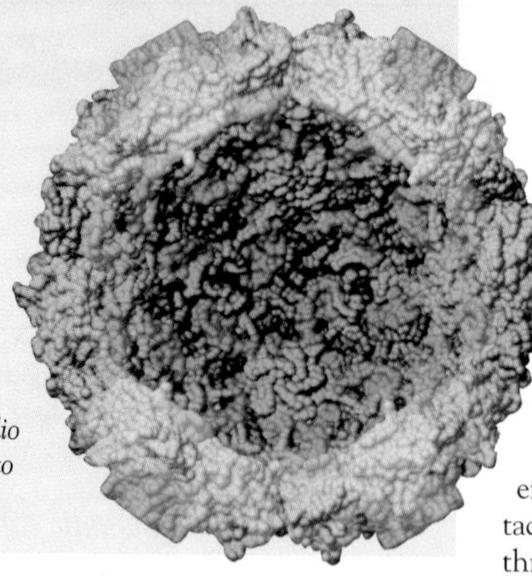

Figure 22–9 *Polio virus, one of the smallest viruses, is only 28 nanometers in diameter. Research in the area of three-dimensional structures of large molecules produced this computer-generated image of the protein coat of type I polio virus. Such studies aim to develop antiviral drugs.*

characteristic of a lysogenic infection. The viral genes—now part of the bacterium's own chromosome—are known as a **provirus.** The provirus may remain part of the cell's own DNA for many generations, passed on from one cell to the next.

The provirus state is not permanent. Any one of a number of factors, including radiation or chemicals that damage DNA, may cause lambda to activate genes that suddenly produce viral coat proteins. Lambda DNA then emerges from the host chromosome, produces copies of viral DNA, assembles scores of new viruses, and destroys the host cell.

☑ **Checkpoint** What is a provirus? 1

Viruses and Disease

All viruses are parasites. A parasite depends entirely upon another living organism for its existence in a way that harms that organism. Because viruses infect living cells, they often harm those cells, producing sickness and disease.

Polio Virus

Polio virus, an example of one of the smaller animal viruses, contains a single RNA strand, roughly 7500 nitrogen bases in length. Polio virus RNA is enclosed in a protein coat that has a highly regular structure resembling the surface of a soccer ball. When a polio virus enters the human body, it usually attaches to the surface of a cell in the throat or nose. Sometimes the virus travels throughout the body and attacks cells in the nervous system. When this happens, the nerve cells that control muscles are destroyed, producing paralysis and sometimes even impairing the ability to breathe.

Polio was once a serious infectious disease that killed or paralyzed thousands of people in the United States each year. Fortunately, highly effective vaccines now given to young children have almost completely eliminated this disease.

Retroviruses

The **retroviruses** are a class of viruses that, like polio virus, contain RNA as their genetic material. Retroviruses received their name from the fact that their genetic information is copied backwards—from RNA into DNA, instead of from DNA to RNA. The prefix *retro-* means backward. Retroviruses are responsible for some types of cancer in humans and animals. One type of retrovirus produces the disease known as AIDS.

Section Review 22-2

1. **Describe** the structure of a virus.
2. **Explain** how viruses infect cells.
3. **Critical Thinking—Comparing** Identify the main differences between lytic and lysogenic viral infections.

TEACHER SUPPORT

Managing Classroom Diversity

TECH PREP STUDENTS

Students who plan careers in agribusiness, food service, health care, or forestry may need to take measures to ensure that viruses and bacteria are not spread. Have these students research their chosen career field to find out what measures they will have to take to prevent the spread of infectious diseases.

MULTICULTURAL STRATEGY

Some students may have firsthand knowledge of bacterial and viral diseases that are more common in their countries of origin than in the United States. Have these students give a short presentation to the class about such diseases and how they are treated in other parts of the world.

Bacteria in Our World

GUIDE FOR READING

- **Describe** the role of bacteria in nature.

MINI LAB

- **Formulate a hypothesis** about the effect on bacteria of washing hands with soap and water.

BACTERIA HAVE BEEN ON OUR *planet longer than any other form of life. Fossils indicate that bacteria first appeared more than 3 billion years ago. It should not be surprising, therefore, that during those 3 billion years bacteria have found ways to live in just about every corner of the Earth. They have carved out a niche for themselves in habitats as varied as the barren tundra, the dark ocean depths, and thick boiling mud.*

Bacteria in Nature

Careful estimates of the numbers of bacteria found in the soil, the ocean, and deep within the Earth suggest that the mass of living bacteria is greater than that of all other organisms combined! Given their tremendous numbers, what roles do bacteria play in the natural world? **In nature, bacteria do a little of everything—from photosynthesis to nutrient recycling.**

Decomposers and Recyclers

From the moment a plant or animal dies, thousands of bacteria attack and digest the dead tissue, breaking it down for nourishment and energy. Gradually the body tissues of the organism fall apart and crumble into the soil, as these armies of bacteria do their work. The raw materials are returned to the Earth, and the cycle of life can begin again. Although the bacteria are not the only organisms involved in this process, they are one of the most significant.

Checkpoint How are nutrients recycled by bacteria? ②

Figure 22–10 Throughout the biosphere—in (a) animals and (b) plants, as well as (c) in the rushing waters of this mountain stream, often completely unnoticed—bacteria are present in huge numbers.

Section 22-3

Bacteria in Our World

Performance Objectives

- Discuss the various roles of bacteria in the natural world.
- Describe the ways in which bacteria are useful to humans.

Mini Lab Skill: Hypothesizing

1 ENGAGE

Ideas Through Images

Have students examine Figure 22–10, read the caption, and answer the following question.

- **Where can bacteria be found in the biosphere?** (They can be found practically everywhere—on and in plants and animals and throughout the environment.)

2 EXPLORE

Investigate

Research Have students schedule a visit to a local wastewater treatment plant to find out how bacteria are utilized in purifying sewage. Ask that they prepare for the visit by doing research in a library.

Checkpoints

① A provirus is the DNA molecule of a virus that has become part of a host cell's own chromosomes.

② By breaking down dead organisms and returning the raw materials to the earth.

TEACHER SUPPORT

Facts and Figures

Here are a few facts and figures about bacteria.

- A spoonful of soil contains about 10 trillion bacteria.
- A bacterium such as *E. coli* can decompose over 1000 times its weight in glucose in 1 hour at 37°C.
- The bacterium *Corynebacterium acne* is responsible for the swollen gland that eventually becomes an inflamed pimple on the skin.
- In the stomach of a person on a normal diet, there are approximately 1000 to 100,000 bacteria per gram of stomach contents, and that figure increases after a large meal.
- In the large intestine or colon, there are about 10 billion bacteria per gram of contents.

Ancillary Support

The resource below can be used to support your teaching strategy for these two pages.

TR Enrich: Halting HIV

3 TEACH

MINI LAB Hypothesizing

Teacher Notes

- For time required and materials needed, see page 514b.
- Prepare the nutrient agar according to instructions on the package. If you have no equipment to sterilize the agar, you could bring the agar solution to boiling on a hot plate or in a microwave oven.
- If no incubator is available, place the dishes in a warm spot in the classroom.
- Caution students not to open the dishes when examining microbial growth after 24–48 hours.
- Having students use different kinds of soaps or having some simply rinse their hands in water will allow for the comparison of the effectiveness of the various methods in eliminating microorganisms.

Answers to Analyze and Conclude

1. The results will support those students whose hypotheses held that washing hands with soap inhibits bacterial growth.
2. Students should observe that there is more growth on the side of the dish they touched with an unwashed finger.
3. Students should conclude that it is advisable because washing your hands eliminates some bacteria that may be harmful if ingested with food.

Skills Trace

Hypothesizing

- Focus p. 526
- Practice p. 527
- Assess p. 533

MINI LAB ······· Hypothesizing ····

"Did You Wash Your Hands?"

PROBLEM *What effect does washing hands with soap have on bacteria? **Formulate a hypothesis.***

PROCEDURE

1. Obtain a Petri dish containing nutrient agar.
2. With a marking pencil, draw a line across the bottom of the Petri dish to divide it into two halves, marked A and B.
3. Open the dish and gently draw a finger across the agar on side A of the dividing mark. Quickly close the dish.
4. Wash your hands with soap and water, then dry them. Open the dish and draw a washed finger across the agar on side B of the dividing mark.
5. Tape the dish closed and give it to your teacher to be incubated. Do you think there will be a difference in the number of microorganisms in sides A and B? Record your hypothesis.
6. When you get your dish back, examine it for any changes and record your observations.

ANALYZE AND CONCLUDE

1. Did the experiment support your hypothesis?
2. Is the amount of bacterial growth on the two sides of the dish different? If so, explain why.
3. Is it advisable to wash your hands before preparing or eating food?

Symbiotic Relationships

You might not like to dwell on it, but your intestines are inhabited by large numbers of bacteria. Safely tucked away inside your digestive system, these bacteria are provided with a warm, safe place, plenty of nourishment, and even free transportation. What do you get in return? These bacteria help you to digest your food. They even make a number of vitamins that you cannot make yourself. This kind of relationship, one in which both organisms benefit, is known as **mutualism.** Most animals have mutualistic relationships with bacteria in their digestive tracts.

Natural Fertilizers

Nearly all organisms require a supply of nitrogen in order to survive. Although the Earth's atmosphere contains plenty of nitrogen gas, plants and other organisms cannot use nitrogen gas directly. Fortunately, many bacteria can carry out a process called nitrogen fixation, in which they take nitrogen gas and convert it to a chemical form that plants can use, producing a natural fertilizer.

☑ *Checkpoint* What is mutualism? 1

Bacteria and Humans

People have used bacteria, often without knowing it, for thousands of years. As you might expect, we have exploited the very things that bacteria do best—breaking down material for nourishment.

Food Processing

Bacteria are used to prepare a wide variety of foods. Some cheeses, sour cream, buttermilk, and yogurt are made by allowing certain types of bacteria to grow in milk products. Other forms of bacteria are used to make pickles, sauerkraut, and vinegar.

Sewage Treatment

Sewage water contains human wastes, discarded foods, and even chemical wastes. Because bacteria can break down each of these materials naturally, tons of bacteria are added to sewage at water-treatment plants. As they grow, these bacteria break down compounds in the wastes into simpler materials. Carefully used, bacterial sewage treatment produces purified water, nitrogen, and carbon dioxide, leaving a sludge that can be used as crop fertilizer.

TEACHER SUPPORT Activity

WHERE ARE THERE MORE OF THEM?

Ask students whether the skin on their faces has more bacteria than the skin at other places on the body. To answer that question, have students perform the following.

1. Prepare 6 Petri dishes of sterile nutrient agar.
2. Use separate sterile cotton swabs to rub a 2-cm area at 6 different places on the body: forehead, side of nose, chin, cheek, back of hand, and calf. For each rubbing, roll the cotton swab over the agar in one of the dishes and throw the cotton swab away.
3. Cover the dishes, label them, and place them in an incubator or a warm spot in the room for 48 hours.
4. Observe and compare the growth on each of the dishes.

Figure 22–11 (a) *The Duffin Creek Water Pollution Control Plant in Picarin, Ontario, Canada, relies on bacteria to break down the organic as well as the chemical wastes in wastewater.* (b) *Most yogurt- and cheese-making processes are dependent on the action of bacteria. In this photograph, a worker examines the curds that will be processed to make Gouda cheese.*

Bacteria in Mining

Believe it or not, bacteria play a major role in the mining industry. Most of the copper ore in the United States is a relatively low grade, which means that it contains only a small amount of copper. Extracting that copper would be a difficult job without *Thiobacillus ferrooxidans*. This bacterium grows naturally in copper-containing ore, producing sulfuric acid, which reacts with copper to form copper sulfate. Copper sulfate is water soluble, so miners simply allow this bacterium to grow in the ore, wash the copper sulfate out as it forms, and later retrieve the copper from the copper sulfate solution. ●

☑ ***Checkpoint*** How are bacteria used by humans? (2)

Bacteria and Health

Although most bacteria are not harmful, the fact that some of them can cause disease is reason enough to try to control the growth of bacteria in certain situations. Sterilization—the killing of bacteria with heat or chemicals—is the simplest way to control bacteria. Most bacteria cannot survive high temperatures, so hospital instruments are sterilized with high-pressure steam. Of course, a hospital room cannot be dropped into boiling water, but it can still be sterilized by the use of disinfectants—chemicals that kill bacteria.

The control of dangerous bacteria is of particular importance while handling and processing food. The growth of bacteria can be slowed down by low temperatures. This is how refrigerators make food last longer. Food can be sterilized by cooking it at high temperatures, and many foods—particularly meats—should not be eaten without thorough cooking to kill harmful bacteria.

INTEGRATING CHEMISTRY

What chemical changes does the copper in copper ore undergo before it is produced as copper metal?

Section Review 22–3

1. **Describe** the role of bacteria in nature.
2. **MINI LAB** What effect does washing hands with soap and water have on bacteria? **Formulate a hypothesis.**
3. **BRANCHING OUT ACTIVITY** Conduct library research to find different methods used to preserve foods. In a brief report, **describe** one of these methods and **explain** how it works.

INTEGRATING CHEMISTRY

Most copper ores occur as the minerals CuS and $CuFeS_2$, which contain only 1% to 2% copper. The first step in the recovery of copper from these ores is a process called froth flotation, which results in an enriched ore that may contain as much as 30% copper. This ore is then subjected to chemical processes that separate the copper from the sulfur (or the sulfur and iron).

4 ASSESS

Quick Check

Have students write a letter to a younger brother, sister, or cousin explaining why he or she should always wash hands before eating a meal.

Section Review 22–3

1. Bacteria do a little of everything, from photosynthesis to nutrient recycling.

2. Washing hands with soap and water reduces the number of bacteria on the hands.

3. Among the methods used to preserve foods are: refrigeration and freezing, drying, freeze drying, canning, vacuum packaging, irradiation, and chemical preservatives. Students' reports should describe one method and explain how it prevents or inhibits growth of bacteria.

Checkpoints

(1) Mutualism is a kind of relationship between two organisms in which both benefit.

(2) Bacteria are used by humans in many ways, including in food processing, treatment of sewage water, and the mining of copper.

Skills Trace

Hypothesizing

- Focus p. 526
- **Practice p. 527**
- Assess p. 533

Learning Modality

Auditory Learning Have students respond orally to questions about the beneficial uses of bacteria. Ask how bacteria are used in agriculture, food processing, sewage treatment, and mining.

Ancillary Support

The resources below can be used to support your teaching strategy for these two pages.

LM Observing Starch-Digesting Bacteria, #43
TR Explore: Bacterial Benefactors
BL Inquiry Activity: Bacterial Scavenger Hunt

CHAPTER 22

Laboratory Investigation

Observing the Effects of the Tobacco Mosaic Virus

Before the Lab

1. To grow the tobacco plants, obtain seeds from a biological supply house and start the plants two or three weeks before needed. Because tomato plants are also susceptible to TMV, they can be used as a substitute.
2. Use tobacco from commercial cigarettes for the tobacco sample. Field-grown tobacco is commonly infected with TMV; using a mixture of tobacco from various brands increases the likelihood of getting infected tobacco.
3. Prepare the dibasic potassium phosphate solution by mixing 6.8 g KH_2PO_4 with 500 mL distilled water.
4. Dispose of the tobacco plants at the end of the observation period in the same manner as you would dispose of pathogenic bacteria.

Pre-Lab Discussion

Have students read the entire procedure for this investigation. Ask students the following questions.

What is the purpose of this investigation? (To design an experiment that focuses on the effect a virus has on a healthy plant.)

What is the purpose of the carborundum powder? (The powder makes an abrasion on the surface of the plant leaf, giving the virus an easy way into the plant.)

The tobacco sample is a mixture of tobacco from several common commercial cigarettes. What does that tell you about TMV and commercial tobacco? (Students should infer that TMV is a widespread virus and can commonly be found in commercial cigarette tobacco.)

CHAPTER 22

Laboratory Investigation

DESIGNING AN EXPERIMENT

Observing the Effects of the Tobacco Mosaic Virus

The tobacco mosaic virus (TMV) studied by Dimitri Ivanovsky still commonly infects field-grown tobacco today. Even though the virus cannot be seen, the symptoms caused by the virus can easily be observed. In this investigation, you will make an extract of TMV and then place it on the leaves of some healthy tobacco plants. The presence of spots on the healthy plants indicates that they have been infected with TMV.

Problem

What effect does the tobacco mosaic virus have on healthy tobacco plants? **Design an experiment** to answer this question.

Suggested Materials

young tobacco plants in pots with soil
tobacco sample
spatula
carborundum powder
dibasic potassium phosphate solution
small beakers
mortar and pestle
cotton swabs
marking pencil
small cards

Suggested Procedure

1. **Formulate a hypothesis that you want to test.**
2. **Divide the dibasic potassium phosphate solution between two beakers. CAUTION: *Be careful when using this solution.* Dip a cotton swab into one of the beakers to moisten it.**
3. **With a spatula, sprinkle the swab with a small amount of carborundum powder. Gently stroke some of the leaves of one plant with the swab. The carborundum is an abrasive and will make microscopic scratches on the surface of the leaf. Try not to rub too hard or you will destroy the leaf entirely. Put this plant aside for now.**
4. **Place the tobacco sample into a mortar, slowly add the dibasic potassium phosphate solution from the other beaker to the sample, and grind the mixture with the pestle. Allow the solid particles to settle. The extract contains the virus. Dampen a cotton swab with a small amount of the liquid in the mortar. Repeat step 3 using another tobacco plant.**

Safety Tip

Students cannot be infected by tobacco mosaic virus, but they could carry the virus to other plants, such as tomato plants. It is important that they wash all the lab equipment they use and also thoroughly wash their hands after completing the lab.

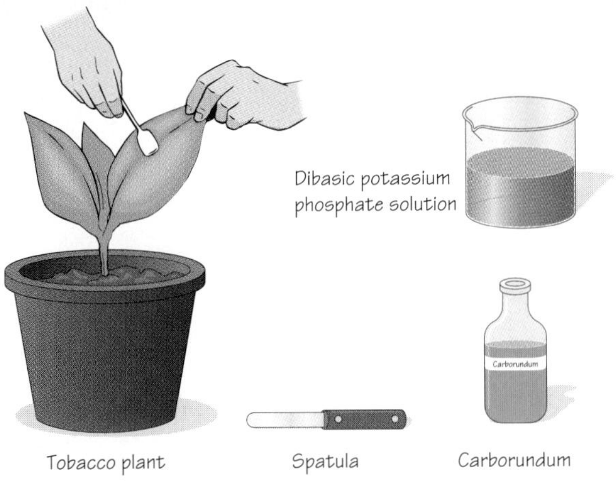

Applying Material to Leaves

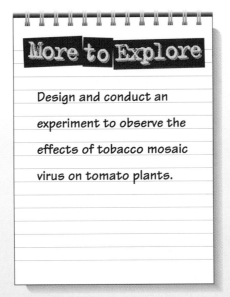

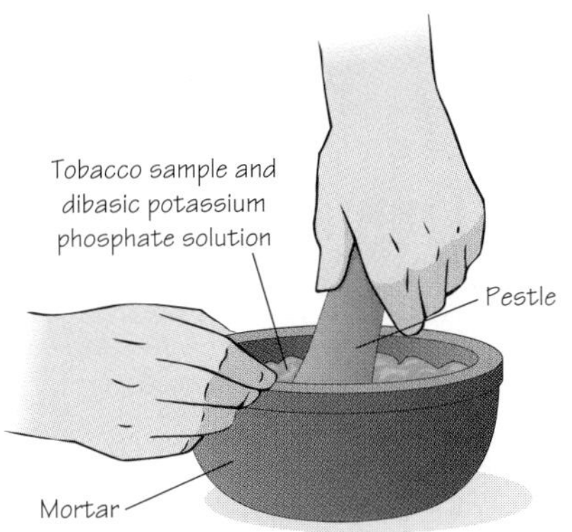

Grinding Mixture

5. Plan to observe the plants for a two-week period. Make sure that the plants get sufficient water and light during that time. You may want to indicate on a small card which plant was swabbed with the virus extract and which one was not. Discard the cotton swabs, as directed by your teacher, and wash all equipment used with soap and water. Be sure to wash your hands with soap and water too.

Observations

1. What changes did your group see in each plant in the first 5 days? Over the next 5 days?
2. Did your group notice whether any changes were confined to one spot, or did they spread throughout the entire plant?

Analysis and Conclusions

1. What was your group's hypothesis for this investigation?
2. Did the result of the experiment support your hypothesis? Can you think of other hypotheses that the results also support?
3. What was the purpose of the plant that was not swabbed with the virus extract? Why was it prepared first?
4. What is the relationship between the treatment of the leaves with carborundum powder and what happens when you scrape a knee or an elbow in a fall?
5. Many plant growers do not allow any tobacco products near plants in their greenhouses. What reason can you give for this?

More to Explore

Design and conduct an experiment to observe the effects of tobacco mosaic virus on tomato plants.

Skills Development

Students will use these skills in the completion of this laboratory investigation: developing hypotheses, designing an experiment, observing, making inferences, and drawing conclusions.

Teaching Strategies

1. Have students read through the lab and then discuss within groups a hypothesis each wants to test. Group members should come to a consensus and then write down the agreed-upon hypothesis.
2. Remind students that it is important to use each swab only once so as not to cross-contaminate the plants. You could have a receptacle containing household bleach into which students can place used swabs.

Answers to Observations

1. Few changes will be visible during the first 5 days. Over the next 5 days, students should observe a mottling and discoloration of the leaves on the plant swabbed with the tobacco virus.
2. Students should observe that the mottling and discoloration gradually spread throughout the plant.

Answers to Analysis and Conclusions

1. One hypothesis might assert that a healthy tobacco plant infected with TMV will show signs of disease within a certain period of time.
2. Answers will depend on the hypotheses made. Students might suggest that the results would support a hypothesis that TMV can infect an entire plant no matter where on the plant it enters.
3. The purpose of the unswabbed plant was as a control. It was prepared first to make sure that it was not accidentally contaminated with the virus.
4. Treating the leaves with carborundum powder removes some of the protective coating of the leaf, allowing harmful bacteria and viruses to enter, just as scraping a knee removes the protective coating of skin, also allowing harmful bacteria and viruses to enter.
5. Tobacco products may contain TMV, which could infect a grower's plants when workers or customers handle those plants.

More to Explore

Students' designs will vary. A typical design might focus on how susceptible a tomato plant is to TMV, such as whether a plant becomes infected if the swabbing is done without using abrasive powder to give the virus an easy way into the plant. A good design will clearly indicate the variable being tested and also establish a control.

Study Guide

Review Strategy

Have students work in small groups to prepare a list of safety precautions that would be appropriate for work in a microbiology laboratory. Students could do some research, but mostly they should be able to develop a list of safety measures through group discussion. Ask that each precaution be accompanied by a rationale for why that precaution is necessary.

Study Guide

Summarizing Key Concepts

The key concepts in each section of this chapter are listed below to help you review the chapter content. Make sure you understand each concept and its relationship to other concepts and to the theme of this chapter.

22–1 Bacteria

- Bacteria are prokaryotes, which are cells without nuclei.
- Genetic information in bacterial cells is found on a single circular DNA molecule, or chromosome, in the cytoplasm. The cytoplasm is surrounded by a cell membrane composed of lipids and proteins.
- The basic shapes of bacteria are rodlike, spherical, and spiral.
- Bacteria are divided into two phyla—the Archaebacteria and the Eubacteria.
- Reproduction in bacteria occurs by binary fission and conjugation.

22–2 Viruses

- A virus is a nonliving particle that contains DNA or RNA and that can infect a living cell.
- Viruses contain genetic information—in the form of DNA or RNA—surrounded by a protein coat.
- A virus infects a cell by first attaching itself to the cell's membrane. It then penetrates or fuses with that membrane, releasing its own genetic material into the cytoplasm. Inside the cell, the virus expresses its genes in ways that produce new copies of the virus particle. These ultimately infect other cells.

22–3 Bacteria in Our World

- In nature, bacteria fix nitrogen, decompose and recycle dead matter, and help animals to digest food.
- Humans use bacteria to prepare foods, process sewage, and mine copper.

Reviewing Key Terms

Review the following vocabulary terms and their meaning. Then use each term in a complete sentence.

22–1 Bacteria

prokaryote
bacillus
coccus
spirillum
binary fission
conjugation
spore
endospore
antibiotic

22–2 Viruses

virus
lytic infection
lysogenic infection
bacteriophage
provirus
retrovirus

22–3 Bacteria in Our World

mutualism

Inquiry-Based Strategy

An unknown disease occurs in a small population somewhere in the world. How can the cause of the disease be found? What measures should be taken to protect the rest of the world from this disease? How long might it take for a cure to be found? Have students find a disease that has appeared suddenly in recent times. Examples include Legionnaires' disease, AIDS, and Ebola. Have them try to answer such questions as those above by finding out how these diseases were confronted when they first appeared.

Recalling Main Ideas

Choose the letter of the answer that best completes the statement or answers the question.

1. Bacteria are cells without nuclei, or
   - a. eukaryotes.
   - b. chromosomes.
   - c. prokaryotes.
   - d. endospores.
2. Where are Eubacteria found?
   - a. in very harsh environments
   - b. in bodies of water only
   - c. on land only
   - d. almost everywhere on the planet
3. In binary fission, a
   - a. bacterium replicates its chromosome and divides in half.
   - b. bacterium forms a thick wall that encloses part of its cytoplasm and a DNA molecule.
   - c. bridge of protein forms from one bacterium to another.
   - d. bacterium captures chemical energy from its surroundings.
4. Drugs that destroy bacteria are called
   - a. vitamins.
   - b. bacilli.
   - c. antibiotics.
   - d. vaccines.
5. A virus is a
   - a. living particle that contains DNA or RNA and that can infect a living cell.
   - b. nonliving particle that contains only DNA and that can infect a living cell.
   - c. nonliving particle that contains DNA or RNA and that can infect a living cell.
   - d. living particle that contains only RNA and that can infect a living cell.
6. When a virus infects a cell, what does it release into the cell's cytoplasm?
   - a. its own poisonous cells
   - b. its own genetic material
   - c. bacteria
   - d. a provirus
7. Which is not an example of the benefit of bacteria to humans?
   - a. Bacteria help humans to fight disease.
   - b. Bacteria help humans to digest food.
   - c. Bacteria help humans to make vitamins.
   - d. Bacteria prevent food poisoning.

Putting It All Together

Using the information on pages xxx to xxxi, complete the following concept map.

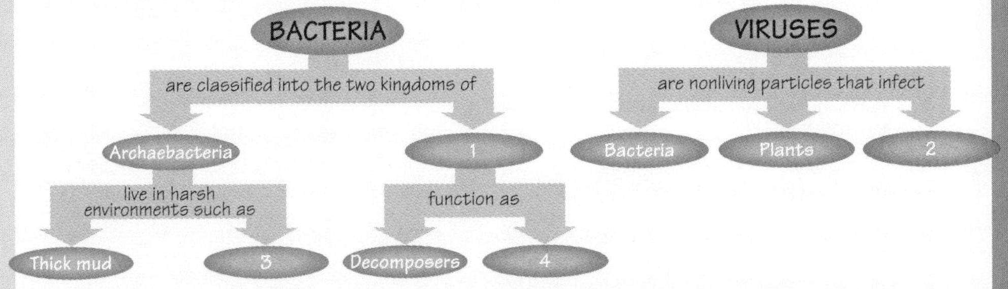

Putting It All Together

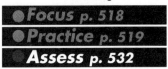

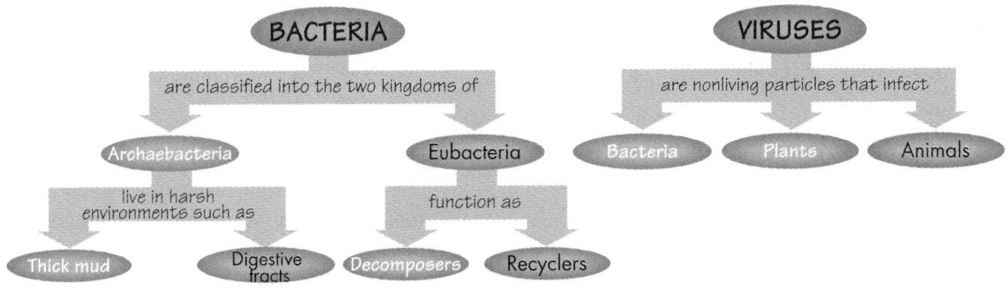

Recalling Main Ideas

1. c
2. d
3. a
4. c
5. c
6. b
7. d

Assessment

Reviewing What You Learned

1. Bacteria differ from other organisms because they are cells without nuclei.
2. Gram-positive bacteria take up Gram's purple stain, whereas gram-negative bacteria do not. Gram-negative bacteria have an extra lipid-containing layer around their cell walls.
3. Bacteria can be rod-shaped, spherical-shaped, or spiral-shaped.

Skills Trace
Observing
- Focus p. 518
- Practice p. 519
- Assess p. 532

4. In their cell membranes, biochemical pathways, and ribosomes.
5. Endospores are resistant to heat, drying, radiation, and chemical disinfectants, which allows the endospores of some bacteria to live for years until conditions are again right for growth.
6. The idea that certain bacteria cause disease in plants and animals.
7. Examples: strep throat, diphtheria, tuberculosis, typhoid fever, tetanus, syphilis, gonorrhea, cholera, Lyme disease, and bubonic plague.
8. A nonliving particle that contains DNA or RNA and that can infect a living cell.
9. The DNA molecule of a virus that has become part of a host cell's own chromosomes.
10. In a lytic infection a virus takes over and destroys the host cell, whereas in a lysogenic infection a virus inserts its genetic material into the cell's DNA, where it may remain dormant for many generations.

Assessment (continued)

11. A virus that contains RNA and an enzyme called transcriptase, which copies its genetic information from RNA into DNA.
12. Bacteria decompose dead organisms and recycle their nutrients, help digestion of food in animal digestive systems, and convert nitrogen gas to a form that plants can use.
13. Humans use bacteria in food processing, sewage treatment, and copper mining.

Expanding the Concepts

1. Gram-negative bacteria have an extra lipid-containing layer around their cell walls, which allows them to resist many of the drugs used to fight bacterial infections.
2. The number of bacteria doubles every 30 minutes, or 21 times in 10½ hours. Thus, the number of bacteria after that period equals 2^{21}, or 2,097,152.
3. Ivanovsky followed the four steps that make up the scientific method: First, he observed a problem, namely, the yellow spots on the tobacco leaves. He then formulated the hypothesis that the spots were the result of a disease that could be passed from plant to plant. He next carried out an experiment to test his hypothesis. Finally, he drew the conclusion that a disease was the cause of the spots on the leaves.
4. Viruses do not exhibit the characteristics of living things. They are not made of cells, do not grow and develop, do not obtain and use energy, do not respond to their environment, and can reproduce only inside a living cell.
5. Students should describe the steps of lytic infection and lysogenic infection as shown in the visual essay on page 523.
6. A parasite depends entirely upon another living organism for its existence in a way that harms that organism. All viruses live off organisms in ways that harm or destroy cells, and therefore, are parasites.
7. The virus is most likely to enter the body by attaching to the surface of a cell in the throat or nose. From there it travels to other body cells and uses them to assemble more viruses.

Assessment

Reviewing What You Learned

Answer each of the following in a complete sentence.

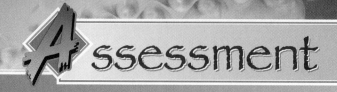

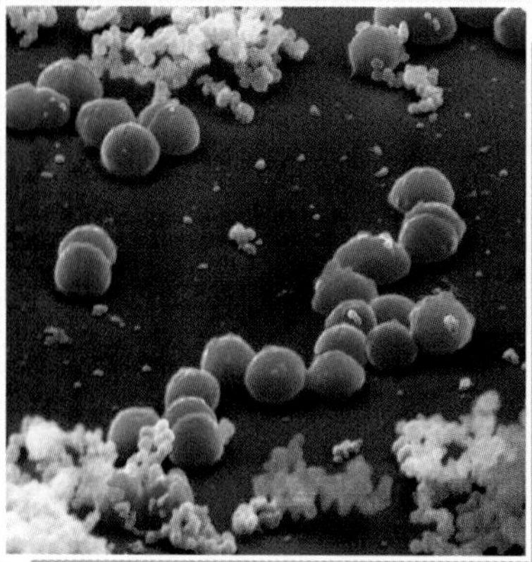

1. Bacteria are considered prokaryotes. How do they differ from other organisms?
2. What distinguishes a gram-positive bacterium from a gram-negative bacterium?
3. Identification of bacteria often begins with their shape. What are the commonly **observed** shapes of bacteria?
4. How do Archaebacteria differ from Eubacteria?
5. How can endospores enable bacteria to withstand long periods of unfavorable conditions?
6. What is the germ theory of disease?
7. What are some human diseases caused by bacteria?
8. What is a virus?
9. What is a provirus?
10. How do lytic and lysogenic infections differ?
11. What is a retrovirus?
12. Identify some roles bacteria play in the natural world.
13. How do humans use bacteria?

Expanding the Concepts

Discuss each of the following in a brief paragraph.

1. Why are the gram-negative bacteria potentially more difficult to treat than the gram-positive bacteria?
2. Some bacteria, under proper conditions, can reproduce very quickly, even as fast as 20 minutes per reproductive cycle. If you were infected with a single bacterium and it began to reproduce at a rate of once every 30 minutes, how many bacteria would exist in you after $10\frac{1}{2}$ hours?
3. How did the work of Dimitri Ivanovsky demonstrate the scientific method of investigation?
4. Why are viruses not considered alive by most scientists?
5. Describe what happens when a virus enters another cell, such as a bacterial cell.
6. Give evidence to support this statement: "All viruses are parasites."
7. How does the polio virus enter and use the human body?
8. The roles of bacteria on Earth are astounding. Discuss at least three of these roles.
9. Discuss how binary fission in bacteria increases the number of bacterial cells but does little to increase the variety of these cells. Compare binary fission with conjugation as another form of reproduction.

8. Students might discuss bacteria's role in photosynthesis, decomposing dead organisms, recycling of nutrients, digestion of foods in animals, nitrogen fixation, food processing, sewage treatment, or copper mining.
9. In binary fission, a bacterial cell simply replicates its genetic material and divides. Thus, there is no new combination of genes that might increase variety among cells. In conjugation, though, some DNA is transferred from one cell to another, resulting in new combinations, and thereby increasing variety.

Extending Your Thinking

1. A typical design might focus on the tracking of individual genes through a careful analysis of the results of each instance of conjugation.
2. A typical response might mention that some bacteria are resistant to antibiotics and that many viral infections cannot be cured. Students might also suggest that a growing world population and a lack of effective medical treatment in much of the world may set the stage for such a spread of terrible diseases.

Extending Your Thinking

Use the skills you have developed in this chapter to answer the following.

1. **Designing an experiment** Bacterial conjugation is a form of sexual reproduction employed by many bacteria. How might conjugation be used to determine the sequence of DNA for a particular strain of bacteria?
2. **Evaluating** Recently, publications and motion pictures have presented frightening scenarios in which highly infectious bacteria or viruses are spread through the biosphere. The potential disaster they imply is disturbing. Do you believe this potential truly exists? Defend your answer.
3. **Evaluating** The use of genetic engineering has intensified the evolutionary potential of organisms. Many of these transformed organisms have been developed to benefit humans in various areas. One such organism is a bacterium that has the ability to digest crude oil. These bacteria help deal with oil spills, particularly in the cleanup of coastal zones. Do you consider the manipulation of organisms to benefit humans or the environment a proper and responsible use of scientific knowledge?
4. **Using the writing process** Bacteriological warfare is potentially so detrimental that it was outlawed during World War I. Numerous meetings between nations were convened to write up a set of rules so that such methods would never be used again. But today all major nations conduct research and develop new organisms to be used "if necessary." Write an essay expressing your views on this subject, discussing actions that must be taken to safeguard our planet from this potential danger.
5. **Hypothesizing** Do you think humans will or can completely control all infectious organisms? Formulate a hypothesis to answer this question.

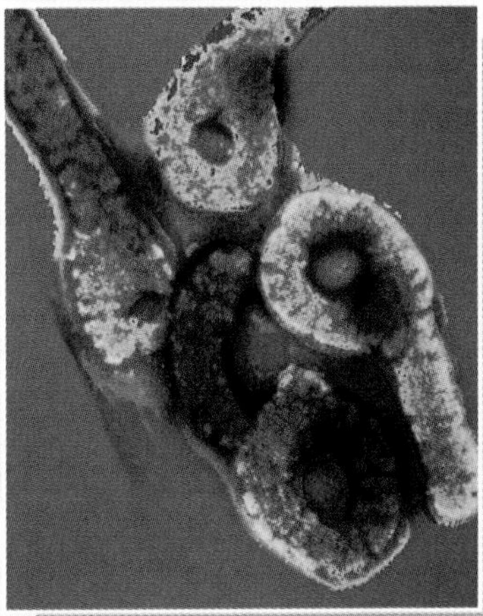

Applying Your Skills

Modeling Viruses and Bacteria

Even though bacteria and viruses are microscopic, both play a very important role in our everyday lives. To better understand how something functions, scientists often make a model of the object or process of interest.

1. Working with a partner, using simple, readily available materials, make a model of a bacterium and a virus, keeping their relative sizes in mind.

• GOING FURTHER •

2. Include important parts of viruses and bacteria and explain the functions of these parts.

3. Some students may suggest that such manipulation of organisms is a logical extension of modern science and technology and can prove only beneficial. Others may suggest that such manipulation is dangerous, since the potential for unseen harmful effects is high.

4. Some students may suggest that such research is prudent in light of threats from around the world, and that part of such research should focus on finding effective countermeasures to bacteriological attacks. Other students may argue that such research is too dangerous and that treaties should be negotiated to end all such development.

5. Some students may optimistically suggest that scientists will eventually be able to control all infectious organisms in the future through widespread vaccination and use of various medicines. Most students will suggest that infectious organisms are continually evolving and adapting to control measures, and thus fighting such organisms will be a never-ending battle.

Skills Trace
Hypothesizing

Focus p. 526
Practice p. 527
Assess p. 533

Applying Your Skills

Teacher Notes

- Provide students with various materials for their models, including string, plastic wrap, and toothpicks. These models could also be made with all edible materials, such as gelatin, spaghetti, pretzels, and other foods.
- Have students do library research before they begin their models to find various representations of bacteria and viruses in biology and microbiology books.
- Have each pair of students make sketches of their models before they begin actual construction.

Scoring Rubric

4 Response is thorough, accurate, and creative; shows an in-depth understanding of science skills, procedures, and concepts.

3 Response is complete, mostly accurate, and original; shows a satisfactory understanding of science skills, procedures, and concepts.

2 Response is mostly complete but includes some inaccuracies; shows an adequate understanding of science skills, procedures, and concepts.

1 Response is only partially complete and has many inaccuracies; shows an incomplete understanding of science skills, procedures, and concepts.

0 Response is mostly incomplete and/or inaccurate; shows a lack of understanding of science skills, procedures, and concepts.

Chapter 23 Protists and Fungi

Content Management	Student Edition Activities
■ Section 23–1 Protists, pp. 535–542 Kingdom Protista Animallike Protists Plantlike Protists Funguslike Protists	MINI LAB: Protists in the Grass, p. 541 Laboratory Investigation: Observing a Paramecium, pp. 550–551
■ Section 23–2 Fungi, pp. 543–546 Kingdom Fungi Classifying Fungi	MINI LAB: Sealed With Tape, p. 546
◆ BRANCHING OUT • In Depth Section 23–3 Protist and Fungal Diseases, pp. 547–549 Protist Diseases Fungal Diseases	

■ These sections cover all the necessary content and concepts for an enriched course in biology.
◆ This section covers content and concepts that are either applications or extensions of the enriched material.

Integration Strategies

SE Health, p. 549

Assessment Strategies

SE Chapter Review, pp. 552–555
TR Section Reviews
Chapter Test
BL Chapter Review
Practice Test
CTB Chapter 23 Test

Tech Prep

Teaching strategies appropriate for students who are in technical/vocational programs or who are considering post-secondary technical education can be found on the following **TE** pages: 544 and 547.

Meeting the Standards

Sections 23–1 through 23–3 cover three of the six content standards under **The Cell,** one of the five content standards under **Biological Evolution,** and one of the five content standards under **The Interdependence of Organisms** as described on pages 184–186 of The National Science Education Standards.

Chapter Planning Guide

Teacher's Edition Activities	Other Activities	Media and Technology
Chapter Discovery Learning Activity, p. 534 Inquiry Activity: What's in That Water?, p. 535 Inquiry Activity: Diatoms, p. 536 Inquiry Activity: What's That Protist?, p. 537	**LM** Investigating the Diversity of Protists, #45 **TR** Explore: Forams for You **BL** Inquiry Activity: Pondering Protists	BioVue Mini Doc: Life in a Drop of Water, Videodisc Side 6 CD-ROM: Protista **TB** Ameba and Paramecium, #29
Inquiry Activity: Looking at Mushrooms, p. 543 Inquiry Activity: A Culture of Yeast, p. 544 Investigate: Research, p. 544	**LM** Comparing the Characteristics of Molds, #46 **TR** Writing in Biology: Letter-Writing Eukaryotes Explore: Fungi Fermentation **BL** Inquiry Activity: Would You Share a Meal With a Fungus?	BioVue Mini Doc: Fungi, Videodisc Side 6 CD-ROM: Fungi **TB** Life Cycle of a Basidiomycete, #30
Investigate: Research, p. 547	**TR** Enrich: Warming Up to Diseases **BL** Inquiry Activity: Gettin' Funky With Fungi and Protists	

KEY: **SE** Student Edition **TE** Teacher's Edition **LM** Laboratory Manual **TR** Teaching Resources **BL** BioLog **TB** Transparency Box **CTB** Computer Test Bank

Materials List

TE Chapter Discovery Learning Activity, p. 534 (20 minutes); photographs and slides of various kinds of protists.

TE Inquiry Activity: What's in That Water?, p. 535 (30 minutes for observations); jars of pond water, dropper, slides and coverslips, microscope.

TE Inquiry Activity: Diatoms, p. 536 (30 minutes after 1-2 days); rock, twig, or shell containing diatoms, jar, water, scalpel, slide, coverslip, microscope.

TE Inquiry Activity: What's That Protist?, p. 537 (30–40 minutes); prepared slides of protists, microscope.

SE MINI LAB: Protists in the Grass, p. 541 (10 minutes for setup, 20–30 minutes for observation); dried grass, glass jar with lid, water, dropper, slide and coverslip, microscope.

TE Inquiry Activity: Looking at Mushrooms, p. 543 (20–30 minutes); supermarket mushrooms, scalpel, paper towels, hand lens.

TE Inquiry Activity: A Culture of Yeast, p. 544 (20–30 minutes); package of dried yeast, molasses, water, beaker, dropper, slide and coverslip, microscope.

SE MINI LAB: Sealed With Tape, p. 546 (20 minutes); bread mold culture, slide, clear cellophane tape, microscope.

Chapter 23

Protists and Fungi

Introducing the Chapter

. . . In Pictures

These examples of cup fungi, types of ascomycetes, grow in rotting wood on the forest floor, and in so doing help break down the dead plant material into basic compounds that can be reused by other organisms.

- **If you saw these organisms in the woods, what would you call them?** (Most students will suggest calling them a type of mushroom.)
- **Are mushrooms plants? Why or why not?** (Some students might suggest they are a primitive kind of plant. Other students might suggest that they do not have green leaves that photosynthesize, and thus are not plants.)
- **How do you think these organisms obtain the nutrients they need for their life processes?** (From rotting material.)

Teaching Strategy

In the first two sections, students will learn about the different kinds of protists and fungi and study the reproduction and life cycles of each. The BRANCHING OUT section at the end of the chapter gives students an introduction to how some protists and fungi can cause diseases in other organisms, including humans.

BIO JOURNAL

The Bio Journal topic can be used to stimulate classroom discussion about life forms students have seen that are not plants or animals. Ask if any students have ever seen mushrooms in the woods or algae in ponds, lakes, or oceans. Discuss students' observations of these organisms, and ask how such life forms should be classified. Instruct students to keep their entries in their portfolios.

CHAPTER 23

Protists and Fungi

FOCUSING THE CHAPTER THEME: Unity and Diversity

23–1 Protists
- Classify the protists.

23–2 Fungi
- Identify the four phyla of fungi.

BRANCHING OUT *In Depth*

23–3 Protist and Fungal Diseases
- Describe different diseases that protists and fungi cause.

Laboratory Investigation
- **Design an experiment** to observe the structure of a paramecium and its response to different stimuli.

Biology and Your World

BIO JOURNAL

In your journal, describe the organisms shown in the photographs on this page and the next. Where have you encountered similar organisms?

Cup fungus on a forest floor in Peru

TEACHER SUPPORT

Chapter Discovery Learning Activity

Display a variety of photographs of protists taken from old microbiology and biology texts and science journals. Make sure you include some images of animallike, plantlike, and funguslike protists. Use a microprojector or videocamera to show slides of various organisms, such as an ameba, a euglena, a paramecium, a diatom, and a cellular slime mold. Have students work in groups to brainstorm for lists of similarities and differences that exist among the protists they observe. Ask these groups to work out a tentative classification system. Discuss group lists and systems as a class.

GUIDE FOR READING

- **Classify** the protists.
- **Describe** the animallike, plantlike, and funguslike protists.

MINI LAB

- **Design an experiment** to observe protists.

A NIGHT OF HEAVY RAIN HAS soaked the thick mat of dead leaves and branches on the forest floor. As mist rises in the morning sunlight, something seems to have come alive on this carpet of debris. A thin yellow coating has appeared on a few of the branches. In a few days, it will grow and concentrate into a thick living mass.

The organisms that make up this yellow mass serve an important role in the forest—they break down dead plant matter, recycling it into usable components. Let's explore these organisms more closely.

Kingdom Protista

The organisms shown in *Figure 23–1* are members of the kingdom Protista. Traditionally, Protista is considered to be the first eukaryotic kingdom. Indeed, the organisms in this kingdom are known as protists—meaning "the very first" in Greek. Most protists are single-celled organisms, although quite a few consist of hundreds or thousands of cells.

The kingdom Protista may contain as many as 200,000 species—ranging from microscopic organisms to those large enough to be seen with the unaided eye. Although some protists live their lives in ways you never notice, others produce the oxygen you breathe, and some cause especially deadly diseases. Altogether, protists affect us all in ways that cannot be ignored.

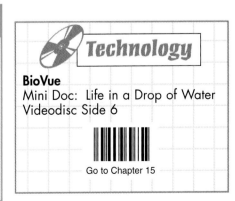

Figure 23–1 *The protists include some especially interesting and beautiful organisms—and some bothersome ones as well.* (a) *Colonies of* Synura *can contaminate water supplies, giving the water a fishy, oily taste (magnification 400X).* (b) *Because of its trumpetlike body, this protist was named* Stentor, *after a loud-voiced hero of the Trojan War (magnification: 125X).* (c) *A diatom is surrounded by an intricate, glasslike shell (magnification: 4600X).*

SECTION 23–1
Protists

Performance Objectives

- Describe the classifications of protists.
- Differentiate among animallike, plantlike, and funguslike protists.

Laboratory Investigation Skill: Experimenting
Mini Lab Skill: Experimenting

1 ENGAGE

Inquiry Activity
Observing
What's in That Water?

Several days before students begin this chapter, collect samples of pond water in several jars. In each jar, include some mud and algae from the pond's bottom. Show students the jars of water and ask whether they think there are any living organisms in these jars of dirty water. Then have students make slides of samples from the water and observe them through a microscope. Ask students to make drawings of at least two or three of the organisms they observe. Advise them to pay special attention to how the organisms move. Keep the pond water samples available as students study this section, and encourage them to make slides periodically to look for organisms they have learned about, such as amebas, paramecia, and euglenas.

TEACHER SUPPORT

Historical Perspective

In the nineteenth century, microscopes were refined to the point where biologists began to describe many different kinds of single-celled organisms. Some scientists, including the German naturalist Ernst Haeckel (1834–1919), proposed that a new kingdom needed to be created to include all these organisms, which were not really plants or animals. But not until the 1960s, with the advent of more powerful microscopic technology, did most biologists recognize the gross inadequacy of the two-kingdom, animal/plant system. By the 1970s, the term protist, which means first organism, came to be used for single-celled, nucleated organisms and their derivatives. Some biologists use another term, protoctist, to encompass the same organisms because protist has too often been used as a synonym for protozoan.

Technology

BioVue
Mini Doc: Life in a Drop of Water
Videodisc Side 6

Go to Chapter 15

2 EXPLORE

Inquiry Activity

Observing

Diatoms

Ask students how they think they could collect diatoms to observe like the one shown in Figure 23–1. Suggest that they look for brownish-yellow, crusty coatings on rocks, twigs, or shells in shallow ocean, lake, or pond water. Have students follow these steps to collect diatoms.

1. Place a coated rock, twig, or shell and some of the water in a jar.
2. In the lab, drain off most of the water, and then float a clean glass coverslip in the remaining water. If left for 1–2 days, diatoms will attach to the coverslip.
3. Scrape the coverslip with a scalpel and spread the material on a slide and observe with a microscope.

3 TEACH

Ideas Through Images

Have students examine Figure 23–2, read the caption, and answer the following questions.

- **In which protozoan phylum is *Trichonympha*?** (Zoomastigina.)
- **Since *Trichonympha* is a zoomastigan, how does it move?** (Zoomastigans are flagellates, and thus it uses a flagellum to move.)
- **How does this flagellate help termites?** (*Trichonympha* breaks down wood particles inside a termite's digestive tract.)

Ideas Through Images

Have students examine Figures 23–3 and 23–4, read the captions, and answer the following questions.

- **Which protozoan phylum includes the ameba?** (Sarcodina.)

Single-Celled Eukaryotes

Biologists have argued for years over the best way to classify single-celled eukaryotes, and this issue may never be settled. Why the disagreement? Many of these organisms have more in common with one or two of the multicellular kingdoms—fungi, plants, and animals—than they do with each other. However, they do not develop the specialized multicellular structures that are found in each of the other three eukaryotic kingdoms. These facts make many single-celled eukaryotes extremely difficult to classify.

Classifying Protists

Currently, the kingdom Protista is defined in terms of what it is not! **Any eukaryote that is not classified as a fungus, a plant, or an animal is classified as a protist.** As you will see, the protists are an extremely diverse group—they solve the problems associated with being alive in remarkably different ways.

Biologists often describe a protist by first noting to which of the three multicellular kingdoms it is most similar. This is exactly the strategy that we will follow.

☑ **Checkpoint** What is a protist? 1

Animallike Protists

The animallike protists are also called protozoans, a name that means "first animals." There are four phyla of animallike protists—Zoomastigina (zoh-oh-mas-tuh-JIGH-nuh), Sarcodina (sar-koh-DIGH-nuh), Ciliophora (sihl-ee-AHF-uh-ruh), and Sporozoa (spor-oh-ZOH-uh). As you will see, protists are categorized into these phyla based on the way they move.

Flagellates

Organisms in the phylum Zoomastigina move through water using whiplike structures called **flagella** (singular: flagellum.) For this reason, the zoomastiginans are sometimes called flagellates.

Flagellates absorb food directly through their cell membranes. Some flagellates live in ponds and streams, where they live off dead and decaying organic matter. Others, however, live within the bodies of living animals.

Termites, for example, harbor large numbers of different flagellates in their digestive system. These flagellates help to digest the cellulose fibers in wood—something very useful to the termite. This relationship is an example of mutualism, a relationship between two organisms that benefits both organisms.

Other flagellates are parasites—organisms that harm animals in which they live. A parasitic flagellate

Figure 23–2 (a) *A termite is able to digest wood because of* Trichonympha, *a flagellate that lives inside the termite's digestive tract.* (b) *This* Trichonympha *is breaking down some wood particles, shown as colored streaks in the wide end of its body (magnification: 133X).*

TEACHER SUPPORT — Background Information

Amebas are the bloblike protists that have no permanent form. One species, *Entamoeba histolytica,* causes a dangerous form of dysentery, but the vast majority of these sarcodines are harmless to humans. They feed on bacteria, algae, and tiny multicellular organisms.

In the laboratory, amebas have been used in a great many studies of the relationship between the nucleus and the cytoplasm. Biologists have found that amebas can be cut into pieces or even have their nuclei removed and still continue to live. In some studies, scientists have actually done microsurgery to transplant a nucleus from one ameba to another, usually without harming the organisms.

Figure 23–3
(a) An ameba is a shape-shifting, bloblike protist. (b) Amebas take in a food particle by extending a pseudopod around it (magnification: 31X).

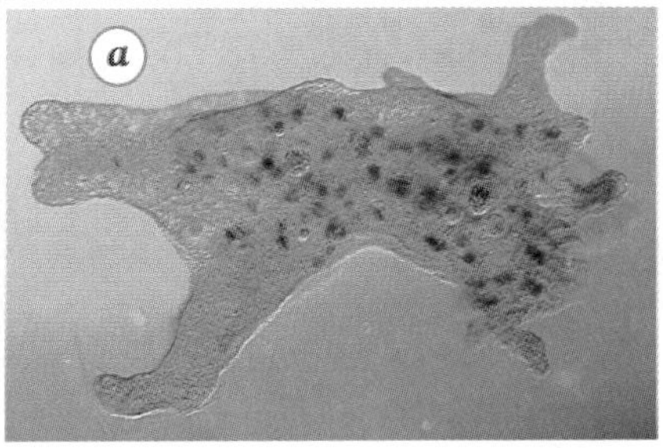

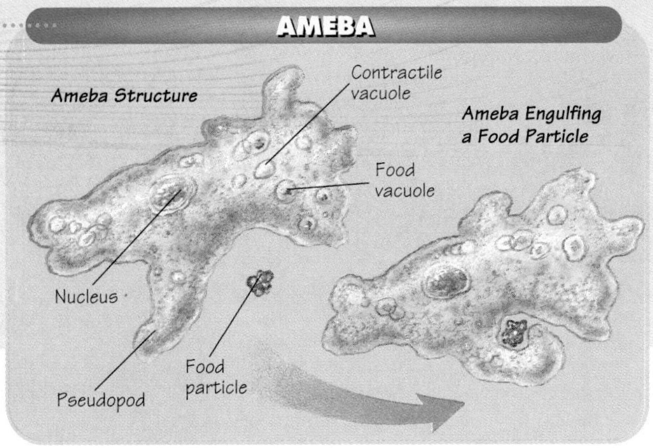

called a trypanosome lives in the human bloodstream and causes African sleeping sickness.

Flagellates reproduce asexually by cell division. However, many have a sexual phase to their life cycle.

☑ **Checkpoint** What is a flagellate? 2

Sarcodines

Protists in the phylum Sarcodina move by pushing out temporary projections of cytoplasm. These projections are called **pseudopods** (SOO-doh-pahdz), meaning "false feet."

The best-known sarcodines are the amebas. Amebas have neither cilia, nor flagella, nor cell walls, and they even lack a definite cell shape. In fact, the word ameba comes from a Greek word that means "change."

An ameba moves by extending its pseudopod, as shown in ***Figure 23–3.*** Cytoplasm streams into the pseudopod, and the rest of the cell follows. Amebas also use pseudopods to capture and take in food particles.

Although there are thousands of different species of amebas, they are greatly outnumbered by another class of sarcodines called the Foraminifera (fuh-ram-uh-NIHF-er-uh). Foraminifers are so common that they have produced huge deposits of microscopic shells on the warmer regions of the ocean floor.

The sarcodines also include a stunning group of organisms known as the heliozoans—meaning "sun animals." Heliozoans produce thin shells of silica (SiO_2), the substance used to form glass.

☑ **Checkpoint** What is a sarcodine? 3

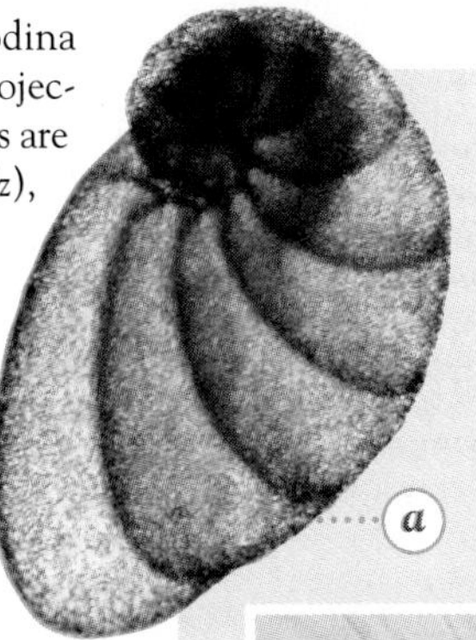

Figure 23–4
(a) Foraminifers and other sarcodines produce thin shells of calcium carbonate, which they extract from sea water (magnification: 63X). (b) A heliozoan projects microtubules that support thin spikes of cytoplasm, making it look like a microscopic pin cushion (magnification: 310X).

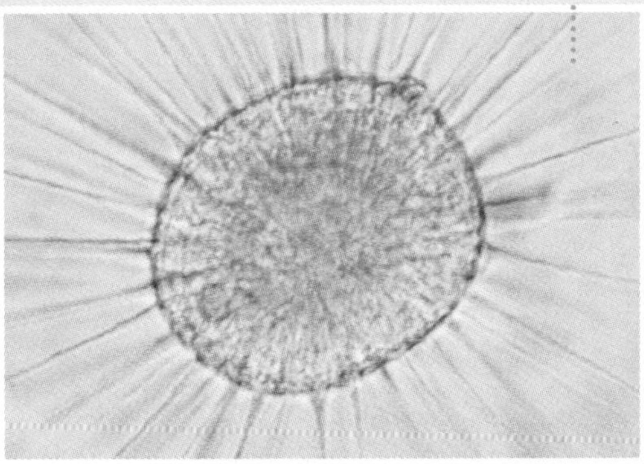

- **Why is an ameba described as shape-shifting?** (It has no permanent shape. It changes its shape as it pushes out projections called pseudopods.)
- **What phylum includes foraminifers?** (Sarcodina.)
- **What do foraminifers produce that gives them a permanent shape?** (They produce thin shells of calcium carbonate.)

Inquiry Activity
Identifying
What's That Protist?

Ask students whether they think they could identify various examples of protists. Provide 15–20 prepared slides of protists, including a flagellate, an ameba, a paramecium, a euglena, a diatom, and so on. Make sure the names on these slides are removed or covered. Number each slide, and ask students to identify each one by writing a term, such as a kind of organism or a phylum name, next to a number on a piece of paper. You could have pairs or small groups of students work together in this identification process. Once every student or group has had a chance to complete the list, go over the identification of all the slides in a class discussion, pointing out the characteristics of each organism that would distinguish it from other organisms.

☑ Checkpoints

1. Any eukaryote that is not classified as a fungus, a plant, or an animal.
2. A zoomastiginan, which is an organism that moves through the water using a flagellum.
3. A protist in the phylum Sarcodina that moves by pushing out temporary projections of its cytoplasm.

TEACHER SUPPORT

Background Information

Students often wonder what the real difference is between a cilium and a flagellum. Some might suspect that there must be a subtle difference in internal structure about which their textbook or teacher is not telling them. The truth is that there is no difference—a cilium and a flagellum are the same organelle. The difference in terminology is derived from the days of the light microscope, when biologists thought that the many fine hairs surrounding some cells might well turn out to be different from the few long whips that move other cells. With the advent of the electron microscope, however, it became clear that the structure and biochemistry of both organelles are identical, at least in protists. There is a real difference, however, between the flagella of prokaryotes and those of protists.

Ancillary Support

The resource below can be used to support your teaching strategy for these two pages.

TR Explore: Forams for You

Discussion

Initiate a discussion of sporozoans by emphasizing that they are unlike other protozoans in that they have no specialized structures for movement. Then ask students to recall the definition of parasite. Emphasize that all sporozoans are parasites. Tell students that they will learn about the sporozoan that causes malaria in the final section of this chapter. Then discuss how sporozoans pass an infection from one host to another through the production of spores.

Ideas Through Images

Have students examine Figures 23–5 and 23–6, read the captions, and answer the following questions.

- **Which protozoan phylum includes the paramecia?** (Ciliophora.)
- **What structures do paramecia use for movement?** (They use short, hairlike projections called cilia.)
- **What are some other structures in a paramecium cell?** (A contractile vacuole, a gullet, an anal pore, and two nuclei—a macronucleus, and a micronucleus.)
- **What are two ways in which paramecia can reproduce?** (Through binary fission or through conjugation.)
- **What is the advantage of conjugation for a paramecium species?** (Conjugation provides new combinations of genes, which could help the species adapt to changes in its environment.)

Laboratory Investigation

The Laboratory Investigation, Observing a Paramecium, on pages 550–551 is appropriate to use at this point in the chapter.

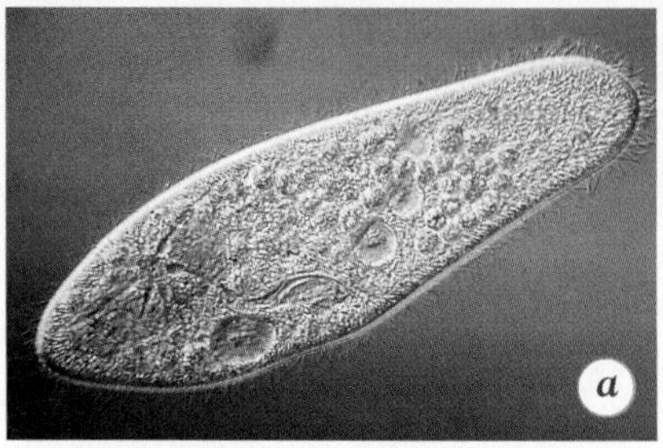

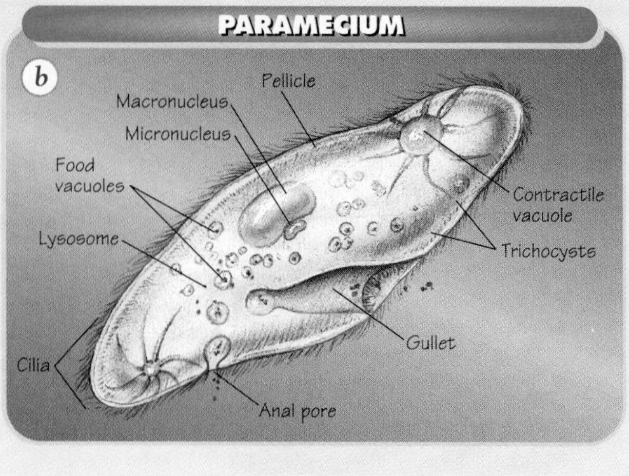

Figure 23–5
(a) A paramecium may contain only one cell, but that cell is extraordinarily complex and organized (magnification: 100X). (b) Each structure performs a specialized task.

Sporozoans

The members of the phylum Sporozoa do not have structures specialized for movement. All sporozoans are parasites, and they reproduce by forming small, single-celled structures called **spores**—the structures that give the phylum its name. Through spores, sporozoans can pass from one host to the next.

Sporozoans can infect fishes, worms, insects, birds, and humans. In fact, a sporozoan causes malaria—one of the most serious infectious diseases on Earth.

Sporozoans often have complex life cycles involving more than one host. The sporozoan that causes malaria, for example, lives part of its life in a mosquito.

Checkpoint How do sporozoans reproduce? 1

Ciliates

The members of the phylum Ciliophora are the protists with **cilia**—short, hairlike projections that are similar to flagella. For this reason, these protists are often called ciliates. The coordinated beating of cilia pulls the ciliate quickly through the water, just as the rowing of hundreds of oars pulled boats in ancient times.

One especially complex and interesting ciliate is the paramecium, an organism common in freshwater ponds. As shown in ***Figure 23–5,*** a paramecium contains a variety of different structures that perform different tasks. For example, the **contractile vacuole** expels the water that diffuses into the paramecium by osmosis.

A paramecium has a **gullet** for taking in food particles that are processed into food vacuoles. Waste products are discharged when a used-up food vacuole fuses with the cell membrane at a region known as the **anal pore.** And embedded in the cell membrane are tiny bottle-shaped structures called **trichocysts.** Trichocysts are discharged when the cell is damaged or shocked, and they produce barbed projections that can damage predators.

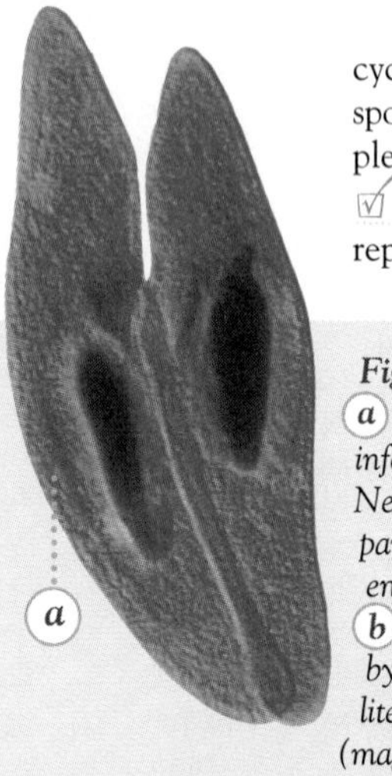

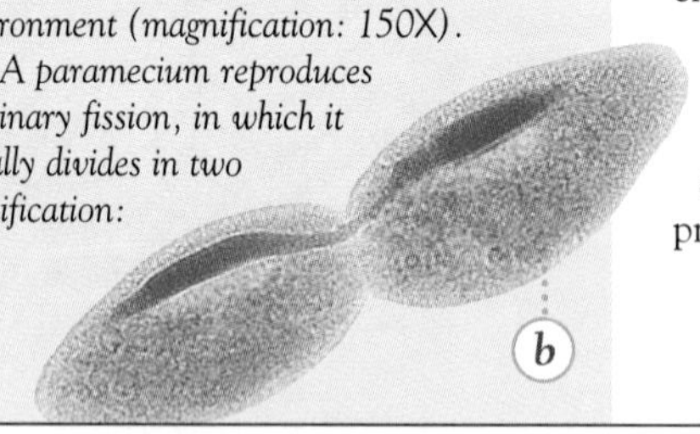

Figure 23–6
(a) Two paramecia exchange genetic information in a process called conjugation. New combinations of genes might help a paramecium to adapt to changes in its environment (magnification: 150X). (b) A paramecium reproduces by binary fission, in which it literally divides in two (magnification: 80X).

538 Chapter 23

TEACHER SUPPORT

Facts and Figures

- Estimates of the number of protist species range from 60,000 to 200,000. Most biologists agree that many species remain undiscovered and thus undescribed.
- There are over 10,000 species of diatoms.
- Some kinds of ciliates, including paramecia, have about 15,000 cilia per cell, which gives the cell the ability to move at the rate of 1 mm/sec.
- A bloom of some species of marine dinoflagellates can produce what is known as a red tide, which can cause death in humans who eat shellfish contaminated with the dinoflagellate toxin. In such a bloom, there may be as many as 10^8 cells per liter of water.
- An acellular slime mold looks like a giant ameba; in a favorable environment, it can grow to 45 cm in length.

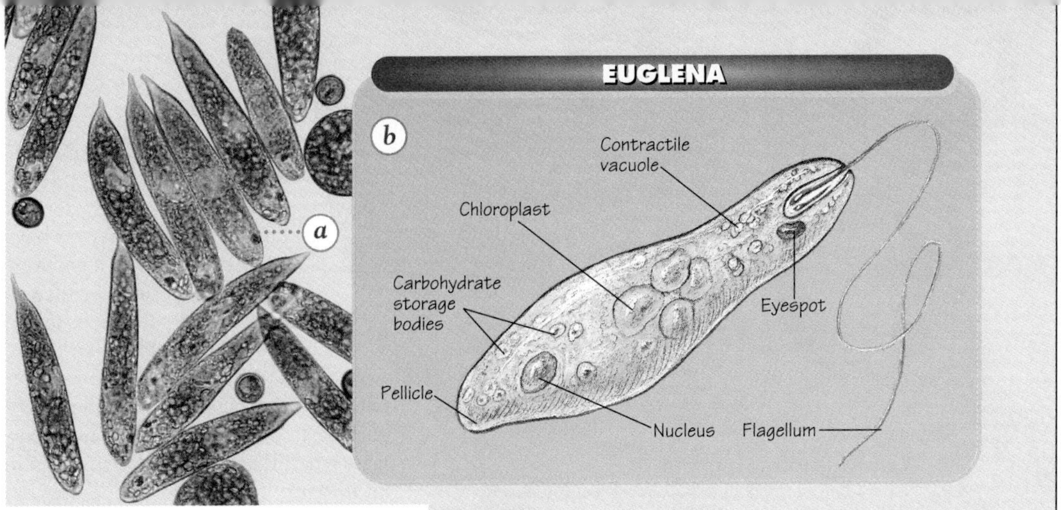

Figure 23–7
Euglenas are plantlike protists. (a) *They get their green color from pigments in their chloroplasts—the structures where photosynthesis occurs (magnification: 200X).* (b) *In other respects, euglenas are similar to animallike protists.*

One of the most remarkable features of ciliates is that they have two kinds of nuclei—a small **micronucleus** and a much larger **macronucleus.** Why does a ciliate need two nuclei? Evidence indicates that it uses the macronucleus as a "working library" of genetic information—a site for keeping multiple copies of the genes that it uses every day. The micronucleus, by contrast, contains backup copies of all the cell's genes.

Using the paramecium as an example, let's see how the two nuclei function in the ciliate's life cycle. Most of the time, a paramecium reproduces by binary fission. First, both the macronucleus and micronucleus are replicated. Then the cell splits in two, leaving each daughter cell with a single micronucleus and a single macronucleus.

Paramecia reproduce differently under stress, however, such as at extremes of temperature or when food is limited. At these times, they engage in a form of sexual reproduction known as **conjugation.** In conjugation, two paramecia exchange genetic information from their micronuclei. The result is two paramecia that are genetically identical but different from the way they were before the process began. Conjugation may provide the genetic diversity that paramecia need to meet environmental challenges.

☑ ***Checkpoint*** What is conjugation? 2

Plantlike Protists

The plantlike protists contain the green pigment chlorophyll and are capable of photosynthesis. Although most of these protists can move from place to place, they are described as plantlike because they are capable of photosynthesis. We will discuss three phyla of plantlike protists—Euglenophyta (yoo-glee-nuh-FIGHT-uh), Pyrrophyta (pigh-roh-FIGHT-uh), and Chrysophyta (krihs-uh-FIGHT-uh).

The plantlike protists are also examples of **algae,** a general term that describes all single-celled photosynthetic organisms. Most biologists include three other phyla of algae—red algae, brown algae, and green algae—among the plantlike protists. However, these algae are so similar to green plants that we will present them in another chapter.

Ideas Through Images

Have students examine Figure 23–7, read the caption, and answer the following questions.

- **Which plantlike protist phylum includes the euglenas?** (Euglenophyta.)
- **What kind of animallike protist is a euglena most like?** (A euglena cell has two flagella, so it is most like a flagellate.)
- **Why are the euglenas classified as plantlike protists?** (They have chloroplasts that carry out photosynthesis.)
- **What does the eyespot on a euglena give it an ability to do?** (It gives it the ability to sense light, and euglenas typically move toward light.)

☑ Checkpoints

1 By forming small, single-celled structures called spores.

2 In conjugation, two paramecia exchange genetic information from the micronuclei.

TEACHER SUPPORT

Background Information

Classifying euglenas has always proved challenging to biologists. When scientists classified all organisms into two kingdoms, plants and animals, the euglenas seemed to straddle the dividing line—they acted like animals but photosynthesized like plants. In fact, only their chloroplasts distinguish them from the protozoan *Astasia.* At high water temperatures, Euglena cells lose their chloroplasts. If the temperature is kept high in the laboratory, the cells eventually lose the chloroplasts permanently. At that point, only an expert can distinguish between Euglena cells and *Astasia* cells.

Ancillary Support

The resources below can be used to support your teaching strategy for these two pages.

BL Inquiry Activity: Pondering Protists
TB Ameba and Paramecium, #29

Correcting Misconceptions

Many students will have had some experience with algae, either observing some sort of algae on the beach or using algae in foods. Point out that the term includes those kinds of organisms, and they will be discussed in the next chapter. Emphasize that the term algae also encompasses organisms that are radically different from the image in most people's minds, including euglenas, dinoflagellates, and diatoms.

Ideas Through Images

Have students examine Figure 23–8, read the caption, and answer the following questions.

- **Which plantlike phylum includes the dinoflagellates?** (Pyrrophyta.)
- **What is a bioluminescent organism?** (An organism that produces light.)
- **Which phylum includes diatoms?** (Chrysophyta.)
- **What is the shell of a diatom made of?** (Silica.)

Discussion

Initiate a discussion of chrysophytes by directing students' attention back to the photograph of a diatom in Figure 23–1 on page 535. Emphasize that this organism has a glassy shell made of silica, the main ingredient in glass. Point out that diatoms are a prominent part of the phytoplankton that float on the surface of the oceans and are responsible for much of the photosynthesis that occurs on Earth. Tell students that these organisms are found in a seemingly endless variety of shapes.

Figure 23–8
(a) *The dinoflagellate* Pyrocystis *is one example of a bioluminescent organism—or an organism that produces light (magnification: 125X).*
(b) *This false-color photograph shows the beautiful and intricate shell of a diatom (magnification: 3500X).*

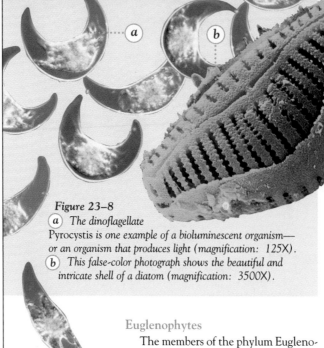

Euglenophytes

The members of the phylum Euglenophyta are remarkably similar to the flagellates. In fact, the only real difference between some species is the presence or absence of chloroplasts.

The phylum gets its name from the genus *Euglena*. A typical euglena is about 50 micrometers in length and has two flagella, as shown in ***Figure 23–7*** on page 539. The longer of the two flagella spins in a way that pulls the cell rapidly through water, making euglenas excellent swimmers.

Most euglenas are found in ponds and lakes, although a few saltwater species have been discovered. Euglenas reproduce asexually through binary fission.

Euglenas contain 10 to 20 oval-shaped chloroplasts that carry out photosynthesis. They also have a light-sensing structure called an eyespot—a cluster of red pigment near the flagella. With the aid of the eyespot, euglenas typically move rapidly to the brightest parts of their habitat. When light is not available, they can absorb food from the water around them, in much the same way that the animallike flagellates do.

While euglenas do not have cell walls, they do have an intricate cell membrane that is sometimes called a pellicle. The pellicle is folded into a series of ribbonlike ridges, each supported by microtubules. It also is tough and flexible, allowing a euglena to squirm and crawl along surfaces when there is not enough water to let it swim.

☑ ***Checkpoint*** What is the eyespot? What is the pellicle? (1)

Dinoflagellates

Members of the phylum Pyrrophyta are often called the dinoflagellates (digh-noh-FLAJ-uh-lihts). Like the euglenophytes, most dinoflagellates are photosynthetic, although a few species seem to have lost their chloroplasts and live as heterotrophs. Most dinoflagellates are found in oceans, but a few live in lakes and ponds.

When agitated by a sudden movement in the water, many dinoflagellates undergo a chemical reaction that produces light. In the ocean on a dark night, this light is a remarkable, eerie sight. The light also gives the phylum its name—Pyrrophyta means "fire plants."

Chrysophytes

The chrysophytes include species commonly known as yellow-green algae, golden algae, and diatoms. The chloroplasts of these organisms contain bright-yellow pigments that give the phylum its name—Chrysophyta means "golden plants."

Like plants, chrysophytes contain cell walls. However, the chrysophytes' cell walls contain the carbohydrate pectin rather than cellulose.

TEACHER SUPPORT

Ecology Note

Oceans cover about three fourths of Earth. In the deep ocean, relatively few species live on the bottom, or even much below a few meters. But much life can be found at and near the ocean's surface in a collection of floating organisms know as plankton. In fact, most of Earth's biomass can be found drifting with ocean currents. The zooplankton includes various protozoa, larvae and eggs, and tiny invertebrates. The phytoplankton, the photosynthesizing portion of the plankton, consists of plantlike protists, or algae, including dinoflagellates, diatoms, and many other forms. These producers capture the energy of sunlight, and in so doing provide the basis of the food web in the marine ecosystem. The zooplankton depend on the phytoplankton for food, and the other organisms in the sea gain their sustenance from the zooplankton.

The most abundant of the chrysophytes are the diatoms. In fact, diatoms are among the most abundant organisms on the Earth. You can see evidence of this fact on regions of the ocean floor that are littered with huge deposits of diatom remains.

Diatoms produce thin, delicate shells made of silica—the main ingredient in glass. The typical diatom shell contains two parts that fit together snugly, a bit like the two halves of a Petri dish. Some of these shells are etched with fine lines and markings that give diatoms a jewellike brilliance. If you look at a few diatom samples under a microscope, you may come to the same conclusion that we have—diatoms are among the most beautiful organisms on Earth!

Checkpoint What is a diatom? 2

Funguslike Protists

Some of the most interesting protists lack chlorophyll and absorb food through their cell walls. Because these characteristics also apply to fungi, these protists are known as the funguslike protists. The funguslike protists include the cellular slime molds, acellular slime molds, and water molds.

A few funguslike protists were once classified as fungi. However, fungi have cell walls made of chitin, which these organisms do not. And like other protists, funguslike protists contain centrioles, which true fungi lack.

Cellular Slime Molds

Members of the phylum Acrasiomycota (uh-kras-ee-oh-migh-KOH-tuh) are commonly called cellular slime molds. These organisms begin their life cycles as individual amebalike cells. In fact, they look so much like amebas that only an expert can tell them apart! As the slime mold grows, however, the resemblance ends very quickly.

When an individual cell begins to run out of moisture or food, it sends out chemical signals that attract other cells of the same species. Within a few days, thousands of cells will aggregate into a large sluglike mass, as shown in ***Figure 23–9*** on page 542.

This mass migrates for several centimeters, then stops and forms a **fruiting body**—a reproductive structure that produces spores. When the spores are scattered, each can give rise to a single amebalike cell that starts the cycle all over again.

How do individual, free-living cells signal each other first to aggregate, then to form a specialized structure like the

MINI LAB Experimenting

Protists in the Grass

PROBLEM *Under which conditions do protists grow best? Design an experiment to find out.*

SUGGESTED PROCEDURE

1. Place a handful of grass in each of two clean glass jars. Add water until each jar is 3/4 full. Seal the jars tightly with lids.
2. Design an experiment to see whether protist growth in the jars is affected by temperature, motion, or sunlight.
3. With your teacher's permission, perform your experiment. After 3 days, open the jars in a well-ventilated area and gently stir their contents. Study drops of water from each jar under the compound microscope.

ANALYZE AND CONCLUDE

1. Did you observe protists in the water from either jar? If so, describe their appearance.
2. What conclusions can you draw from your experiment? Explain your answer.

MINI LAB Experimenting

Teacher Notes

- For time required and materials needed, see page 534b.
- Pick the grass and dry it on a flat tray for at least 1 day before the activity. A window sill is a good place for the grass to dry.
- A well-ventilated room is necessary to keep the pungent smell of the mixture from filling the work area. An exhaust hood would be ideal.

Answers to Analyze and Conclude

1. Typically, students may observe several different types of protists, such as paramecia and amebas.

2. A typical hypothesis might suggest that protists need a moist environment to live and thrive.

Skills Trace

Experimenting

- Focus p. 541
- Practice p. 542
- Assess p. 555

Checkpoints

1 The eyespot is a light-sensing structure near the flagella of a euglena. The pellicle is a tough, flexible membrane that is folded into a series of ribbonlike ridges.

2 A chrysophyte that produces a thin, delicate shell made of silica.

TEACHER SUPPORT Background Information

The chrysophytes, known as golden algae, include some amebalike organisms. But the vast majority of the 10,000 or so chrysophyte species are diatoms, which constitute an important part of the phytoplankton. Diatoms can be found floating on the ocean and on fresh water. They occur primarily as single cells, but some form colonies. The shell walls of diatoms are called frustules and consist of two halves, called valves, that fit together like parts of a pillbox. These shells are formed as the organism absorbs silicates from the water. The shells consist of minute passageways that connect the internal cytoplasm with the external environment. The remains of these shells, so-called diatomaceous earth, are used in filters, commercial abrasives, the manufacture of dynamite, and rubber and plastic products.

Ancillary Support

The resource below can be used to support your teaching strategy for these two pages.

LM Investigating the Diversity of Protists, #45

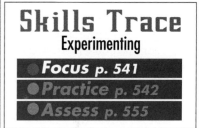

Ideas Through Images

Have students examine Figure 23–9, read the caption, and answer the following questions.

- **Which funguslike protist phylum includes the organism growing on the dead log?** (Myxomycota.)
- **What do the structures shown on the log produce?** (Those structures are fruiting bodies, and they produce spores.)
- **What is the structure of an acellular slime mold?** (It is actually a single cell with multiple nuclei.)
- **Which phylum includes the water mold shown?** (Oomycota.)

4 ASSESS

Quick Check

Have students make three tables to organize the information in this section, one each for animallike protists, plantlike protists, and funguslike protists. The tables should include the phyla names, characteristics, and examples of specific organisms.

Section Review 23–1

1. Biologists classify any eukaryote that is not a fungus, a plant, or an animal as a protist.

2. Animallike protists are single-celled eukaryotes that are most like animals. Plantlike protists contain the green pigment chlorophyll and are capable of photosynthesis. Funguslike protists lack chlorophyll and absorb food through their cell walls.

3. To classify such an organism, an observer would need to know more about its life cycle to make sure it is not a type of slime mold.

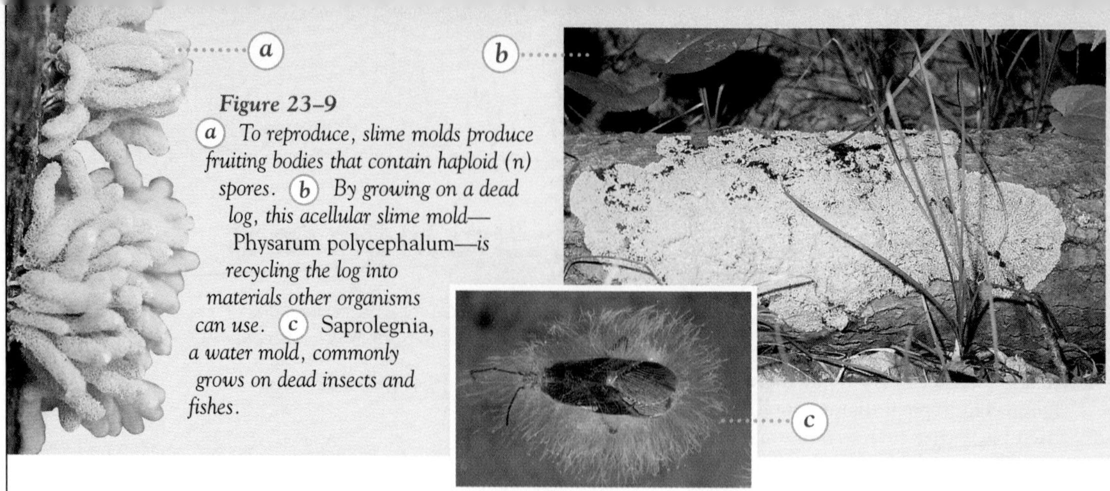

Figure 23–9 (a) *To reproduce, slime molds produce fruiting bodies that contain haploid (n) spores.* (b) *By growing on a dead log, this acellular slime mold—* Physarum polycephalum*—is recycling the log into materials other organisms can use.* (c) Saprolegnia, *a water mold, commonly grows on dead insects and fishes.*

fruiting body? That's a question that biologists are still asking! For decades, biologists around the world have been investigating these and other questions about the cellular slime molds. The answers may hold clues to how multicellular organisms are organized.

Acellular Slime Molds

Members of the phylum Myxomycota (mihks-uh-migh-KOH-tuh) are called the acellular slime molds. Just like the cellular slime molds, the acellular slime molds begin their life cycles as amebalike cells that grow into large masses. In the acellular slime molds, however, the mass is actually a single cell with thousands of nuclei.

Acellular slime molds stream across leaves and twigs, gobbling up bacteria and other organic matter along the way. Eventually, they form fruiting bodies that form haploid (n) spores. When the spores contact moist soil, they germinate to produce flagellated cells. These cells fuse to produce diploid (2n) amebalike cells. In this manner, the cycle starts all over again.

Checkpoint What is an acellular slime mold? 1

Water Molds

Have you ever seen a thin whitish fuzz growing on a dead fish or other marine animal? If so, you have seen a water mold—a member of the phylum Oomycota (oh-uh-migh-KOHT-uh). Like fungi, water molds thrive on dead or decaying matter. However, they have cell walls made of cellulose and produce spores that swim rapidly—two characteristics that fungi do not share.

Most water molds live in water, but a few made their way onto land. These include parasites of such crops as grapes, avocados, and potatoes.

Section Review 23–1

1. How do biologists **classify** protists?
2. **Describe** the animallike, plantlike, and funguslike protists.
3. **Critical Thinking—Analyzing** Suppose that you have identified an amebalike organism under the compound microscope. What further information would help you to classify it?
4. **MINI LAB** How can you **design an experiment** to observe protists?

4. Students' designs should include the usual elements of a controlled experiment, such as a testable hypothesis and a control.

Skills Trace
Experimenting
- Focus p. 541
- Practice p. 542
- Assess p. 555

Learning Modality

Tactile Learning Have different groups of students make a model of an ameba, a paramecium, a euglena, and a diatom. Students could either use the illustrations in the section as their reference or find similar illustrations in other sources.

Fungi

SECTION 23–2

GUIDE FOR READING

- **Describe** how fungi take in food.
- **Identify** the four phyla of fungi.

MINI LAB

- **Identify** the reproductive structures in bread mold.

WHEN YOU HEAR THE WORD fungus, what comes to mind? Chances are, it isn't anything pretty. To put it mildly, fungi have a bad reputation. Some spoil our food, others rot our lumber or destroy trees, while still others can make us sick. The fungi have a well-deserved reputation as pests and destroyers.

Do fungi have any value at all? In fact, the fungi fill a very important role in nature—they are the world's champions of decomposition! Without fungi breaking down organic matter, the raw materials that go into each season of life would be lost forever—and the Earth would be a barren place.

Kingdom Fungi

The kingdom Fungi (FUHN-jigh) includes a wide variety of organisms with different structures and different life cycles. However, all fungi (singular: fungus) have certain features in common.

Fungi are heterotrophs, and they obtain food by extracellular digestion and absorption. This means that they produce enzymes that break down food particles outside their bodies, then absorb the digested molecules. This process separates fungi from animals and plants, which obtain their energy in other ways.

Except for yeasts, which are unicellular, the cells of a fungus are organized into filaments called **hyphae** (HIGH-fee; singular: hypha). And the hyphae form a tangled mass called a **mycelium** (migh-SEE-lee-uhm). In most fungi, individual cells are separated by perforated cross walls. The holes in these cross walls join the cytoplasm of adjacent cells, and this allows nutrients to move quickly through the hyphae.

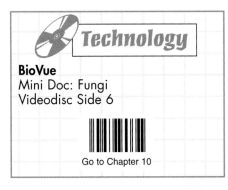

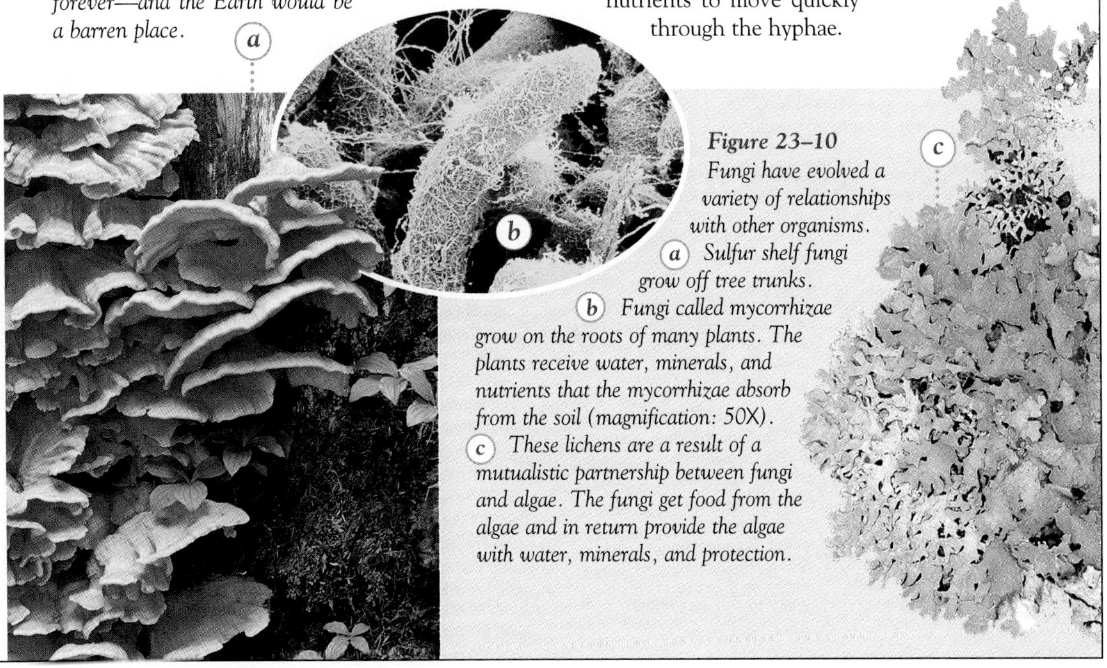

Figure 23–10 Fungi have evolved a variety of relationships with other organisms. (a) Sulfur shelf fungi grow off tree trunks. (b) Fungi called mycorrhizae grow on the roots of many plants. The plants receive water, minerals, and nutrients that the mycorrhizae absorb from the soil (magnification: 50X). (c) These lichens are a result of a mutualistic partnership between fungi and algae. The fungi get food from the algae and in return provide the algae with water, minerals, and protection.

SECTION 23-2
Fungi

Performance Objectives
- Discuss how fungi obtain nourishment.
- Describe the four fungi phyla.

Mini Lab Skill: Identifying

1 ENGAGE

Inquiry Activity
Observing

Looking at Mushrooms

Give each student a whole mushroom, a scalpel, and a hand lens. Ask students to investigate the mushroom's structure by carefully cutting it apart. Tell them to pay special attention to the underside of the mushroom cap. Have them make drawings of what they see.

Ideas Through Images
Have students examine Figure 23–10, read the caption, and answer the following questions.

- **What do the fungi in these photographs have in common?** (They have evolved to have a relationship with some other type of organism.)
- **What makes up a lichen?** (Fungus and alga.)

Checkpoint

1 A member of the phylum Myxomycota that begins as an amebalike cell and grows into a large, single cell with thousands of nuclei.

TEACHER SUPPORT

Background Information

The term yeast is not a taxonomic name; rather, it is used to refer to any single-celled fungus. The yeast that is most familiar, baker's yeast or *Saccharomyces cerevisiae,* is an ascomycete. But other yeasts belong to other phyla. For example, the yeasts involved in vaginal and urinary-tract infections are deuteromycetes.

Likewise, the term mold is not a taxonomic name. It is a term that is used to refer to multicellular fungi that produce branching hyphae—all fungi that are not yeasts. Thus, the distinction between yeasts and molds is one of morphology. This distinction becomes clear when considering certain fungi that are yeasts under some environmental conditions and molds under others.

Technology

BioVue
Mini Doc: Fungi
Videodisc Side 6

Go to Chapter 10

2 EXPLORE

Inquiry Activity

Experimenting

A Culture of Yeast

Two days before students do this activity, prepare a yeast culture by making a mixture that includes 25 mL of molasses, 150 mL of water, and about one fourth of a package of yeast powder. Cover the beaker and leave it in a warm place. Ask students what they think baker's yeast, or *Saccharomyces cerevisiae*, consists of. Have them prepare slides by spreading a drop of the yeast culture on a slide and then examining the slides through a microscope. Ask students to draw what they see.

3 TEACH

Ideas Through Images

Have students examine Figure 23–11, read the caption, and answer the following questions.

- **What is a collection of hyphae called?** (A mycelium.)
- **To which phylum does bread mold belong?** (Zygomycota.)
- **What do zygomycetes produce in their sporangia?** (Spores.)
- **What are zygomycete spores called, and how are they produced?** (Zygospores; they are produced by the fusion of haploid nuclei of opposite mating types.)

Investigate

Research Have students investigate what kinds of fungi are used for food. Ask that they make a table that includes information about common mushrooms, morels, truffles, and others. In this table they should include information about phyla, species, environments, and other appropriate descriptive material.

All fungi can reproduce asexually. They do so when cells or hyphae break off and begin to grow on their own. Some fungi also produce spores that can scatter a great distance away.

In addition, many fungi have a sexual phase to their life cycles. Typically, these fungi have hyphae of two mating types, called + (plus) and – (minus). When a + hypha fuses with a – hypha, the two nuclei come together in one cell. The two nuclei fuse to form a diploid (2n) nucleus, which eventually undergoes meiosis to produce haploid (n) spores.

Classifying Fungi

There are four phyla of fungi—Zygomycota (zigh-goh-migh-KOHT-uh), **Ascomycota** (as-koh-migh-KOHT-uh), **Basidiomycota** (buh-sihd-ee-oh-migh-KOHT-uh), **and Deuteromycota** (doo-ter-oh-migh-KOHT-uh). Let's take a close look at each of these phyla.

Zygomycetes

The zygomycetes—members of the phylum Zygomycota—are named for a thick-walled diploid spore called a zygospore. A zygospore is small, light enough to drift in the wind, and amazingly resistant to damage. Zygomycotes also produce spores asexually, which can help them to grow rapidly.

One common zygomycete is *Rhizopus stolonifer*. When a zygospore of this species settles on a piece of bread, the diploid nucleus undergoes meiosis. Haploid hyphae break through the spore wall and quickly grow through the porous bread, producing enzymes that break down the bread into absorbable nutrients.

Ascomycetes

The phylum Ascomycota is named for the ascus, a tough sac that contains the spores produced by sexual reproduction. These spores are called ascospores, and

Figure 23–11
(a) The bread mold Rhizopus stolonifer *is one common zygomycete. (b) To reproduce asexually, a zygomycete produces spore-bearing structures called sporangia. In the sexual phase of its life cycle, hyphae of opposite mating types (+ and –) fuse to form structures called gametangia. The gametangia produce diploid (2n) zygospores, which undergo meiosis to produce haploid (n) spores.*

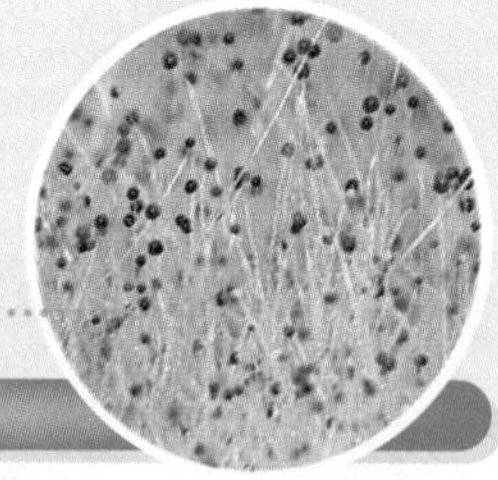
(a)

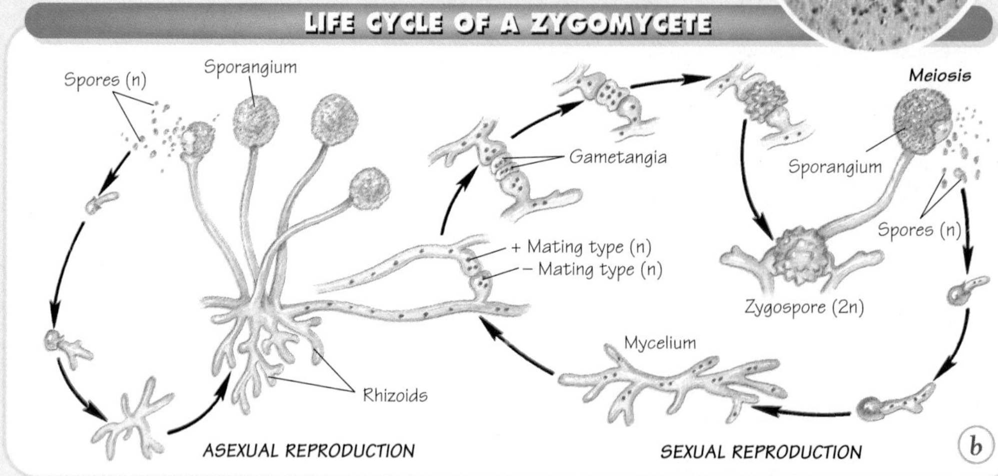

(b)

TEACHER SUPPORT

Managing Classroom Diversity

LEP STUDENTS

Have students use a dictionary to look up the prefix *myc-* or *myco-*. Also ask them to look up the word mycology. Then help students understand the formation of the names of the four fungi phyla. For example, point out that zygomycete translates to fungus organism that produces zygospores.

TECH PREP STUDENTS

Ask students who plan careers in biotechnology and health care to research the ways in which fungi are cultured in a laboratory, as well as the reasons why fungi are cultured for medical purposes.

LIFE CYCLE OF AN ASCOMYCETE

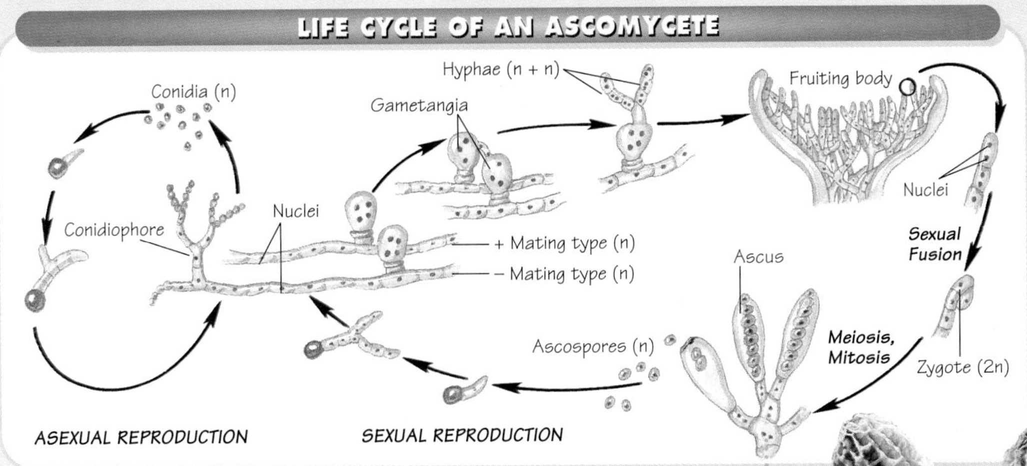

Figure 23–12
(a) *To reproduce asexually, an ascomycete produces specialized hyphae called conidiophores, which in turn produce spores called conidia. The sexual phase of its life cycle involves a fruiting body and a spore-containing structure called an ascus.* (b) *Gourmets prize the rich, nutty taste of the ascomycete* Morchella, *commonly called the morel.*

they are produced by hyphae of opposite mating types. First, haploid nuclei from different hyphae fuse together, eventually forming a diploid nucleus. Then, the diploid nucleus quickly enters meiosis and gives rise to 4 new haploid nuclei. In most ascomycetes, one or two rounds of mitosis follow meiosis, producing either 8 or 16 haploid ascospores.

Like the slime molds, ascomycetes form spores in a structure called a fruiting body. In many ascomycetes, such as common bakers' yeast, the fruiting body is small and insignificant. However, it is quite spectacular in other organisms, such as the morel shown in ***Figure 23–12.***

Basidiomycetes

Members of the phylum Basidiomycota are sometimes called the "club fungi," and they include nearly all the organisms commonly called mushrooms.

LIFE CYCLE OF A BASIDIOMYCETE

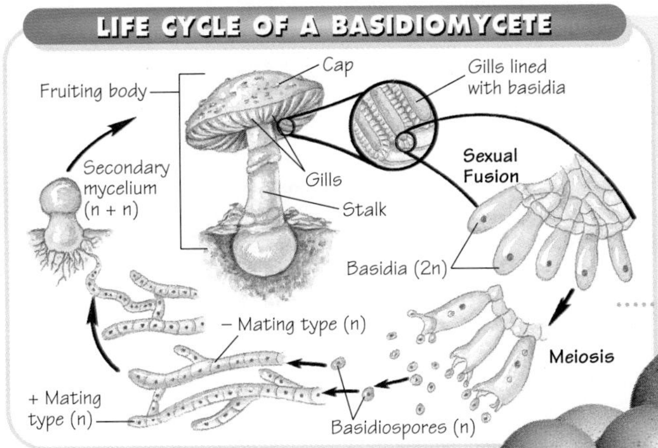

Figure 23–13
(a) *Most mushrooms, including these puffballs, are the fruiting bodies of basidiomycetes.* (b) *A single mushroom may contain millions of basidia—diploid (2n) cells that undergo meiosis to produce haploid (n) basidiospores.*

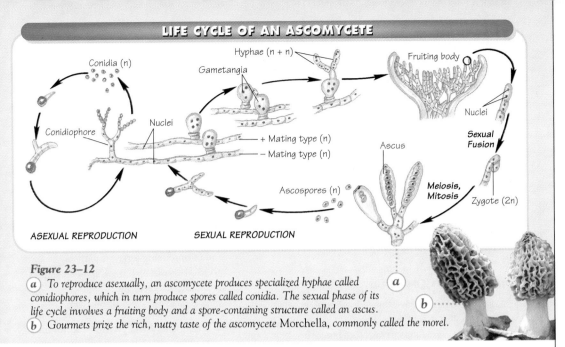

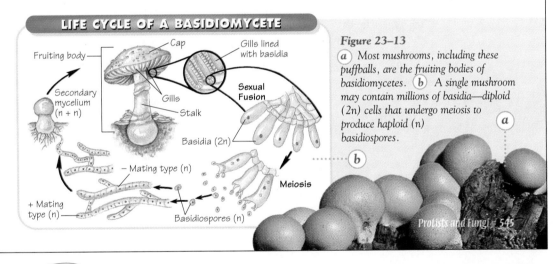

Ideas Through Images

Have students examine Figure 23–12, read the caption, and answer the following questions.

- **When an ascomycete reproduces asexually, what structures produce the spores?** (The conidiophores.)
- **What structure of an ascomycete contains the spores produced by sexual reproduction, and what are those spores called?** (The ascus contains the spores, called ascospores.)
- **In the photograph of the morels, what is the structure that can be seen above ground?** (The fruiting bodies.)

Ideas Through Images

Have students examine Figure 23–13, read the caption, and answer the following questions.

- **What are two other names for basidiomycetes?** (Club fungi and mushrooms.)
- **In basidiomycete reproduction, what structures produce the secondary mycelium?** (The opposite mating types donate nuclei to produce the secondary mycelium.)
- **What parts of basidiomycetes are eaten as mushrooms?** (The fruiting bodies.)

TEACHER SUPPORT

Facts and Figures

- Fungi were most likely the first organisms to live on land, probably about 450 million years ago.
- The antibiotic penicillin is made today from the fungus *Penicillium chrysogenum.* There are over 100 species of *Penicillium,* each of which produces spores with a brush-like border. The name is derived from a Latin word for "little brush."
- In 1992, an individual example of the basidiomycete *Armallaria ostoyae,* commonly known as a honey fungus, was discovered in Washington State. Its underground network of hyphae covered some 600 hectares (1,480 acres), which makes it the world's largest living thing. Scientists estimated the fungus to be 500–1000 years old.

Ancillary Support

The resources below can be used to support your teaching strategy for these two pages.

LM Comparing the Characteristics of Molds, #46
TR Writing in Biology: Letter-Writing Eukaryotes
Explore: Fungi Fermentation
BL Inquiry Activity: Would You Share a Meal With a Fungus?
TB Life Cycle of a Basidiomycete, #30

MINI LAB Identifying

Teacher Notes

- For time required and materials needed, see page 534b.
- Make the bread mold by exposing a piece of bread to the air for a few hours, adding a few drops of water to the bread, and then sealing it in a Petri dish. Leave the bread undisturbed in a dark, warm place for 2 or 3 days.

Answers to Analyze and Conclude

1. Students should identify the tiny black spheres at the end of the hyphae as the sporangia, which contain spores.

2. In producing multiple sporangia, the bread mold produces many spores that will drift in the air. Only some of the spores will eventually land on a suitable growth medium.

Skills Trace
Identifying
- Focus p. 546
- Practice p. 546
- Assess p. 555

4 ASSESS

Quick Check

Have students make flowcharts for the way the fungi in each of the phyla reproduce.

MINI LAB .... Identifying ......

Sealed With Tape

PROBLEM *How can you **identify** reproductive structures in bread mold?*

PROCEDURE

1. Touch the sticky side of a 2-cm piece of cellophane tape to the black "fuzzy" area of a bread mold culture.
2. Gently stick the tape to a glass slide. Observe the slide under the compound microscope. Draw a diagram of your observations.

ANALYZE AND CONCLUDE

1. Describe the reproductive structures of bread mold. What structures do they contain?
2. Why does a single bread mold culture produce a large number of reproductive structures?

The phylum also includes puffballs, toadstools, and the bracket fungi that appear on the trunks of trees.

The above-ground structure of a basidiomycete is actually just its fruiting body. Beneath the soil is a mycelium that has slowly digested its way through organic matter to reach the surface.

Just like the ascomycetes, the basidiomycetes have hyphae of opposite mating types. In basidiomycetes, however, the + and − hyphae donate nuclei to produce a structure called a secondary mycelium. A secondary mycelium can grow beneath the soil for many years. Some reach enormous sizes, often many meters in diameter. When conditions are right, the secondary mycelium produces a fruiting body—a mushroom—that forces its way upward through the soil.

Within the mushroom, haploid nuclei fuse and undergo meiosis, producing clusters of haploid spores called basidiospores. These spores appear in "gills" on the underside of the mushroom. A single mushroom can produce as many as a million spores—each with the potential of producing a new organism.

☑ *Checkpoint* What are some examples of basidiomycetes? 1

Deuteromycetes

Members of the phylum Deuteromycota are commonly called the imperfect fungi because they are believed to reproduce only through asexual spores. The deuteromycetes include a number of well-known organisms. Both athlete's foot and ringworm are produced by deuteromycetes, as is the mold from which we harvest the antibiotic penicillin.

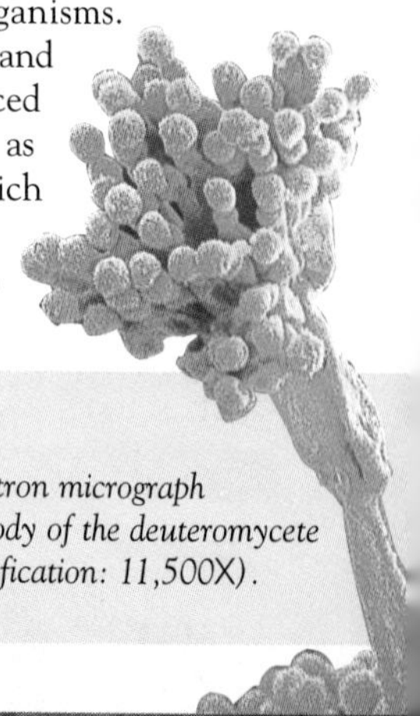

Figure 23–14
This false-color electron micrograph shows the fruiting body of the deuteromycete Penicillium *(magnification: 11,500X).*

Section Review 23–2

1. **Describe** how fungi take in food.
2. **Identify** the four phyla of fungi.
3. **Critical Thinking—Comparing** How do the four different phyla of fungi compare?
4. **MINI LAB** How can you **identify** reproductive structures in bread mold?

Section Review 23–2

1. Fungi take in food by extracellular digestion and absorption.

2. Zygomycota, Ascomycota, Basidiomycota, Deuteromycota.

3. See pages 544–546.

4. Identifying reproductive structures on bread mold involves finding the spore-bearing sporangia, which are the tiny black spheres at the end of the hyphae.

Skills Trace
Identifying
- Focus p. 546
- Practice p. 546
- Assess p. 555

Learning Modality

Visual Learning Have groups of students make posters for each of the fungi phyla. A poster should include basic information for a phylum, as well as illustrations of specific members and a diagram of the life cycle.

Protist and Fungal Diseases

GUIDE FOR READING

- **Describe** diseases caused by protists and fungi.

MAKE NO MISTAKE ABOUT IT: *Our world would grind to a halt without protists and fungi. These organisms fill all sorts of vital roles—from producing oxygen to decomposing dead organic matter. However, while many protists and fungi are some of nature's most useful organisms, others are some of its most damaging . . . and deadly!*

Protist Diseases

Protists are so diverse that you should expect at least a few of them to have evolved into disease-causing parasites. For better or for worse, that is exactly the case.

African Sleeping Sickness

In central Africa, flagellates of the genus *Trypanosoma* cause a disease called African sleeping sickness. These protists are passed from person to person through the bite of the tsetse fly.

Trypanosomes destroy blood cells, producing fever, chills, and rashes. Even worse, however, is the damage they can cause to the nervous system. Affected individuals may lose consciousness and lapse into a deep, sometimes fatal sleep—the sleep that gives the disease its name.

Checkpoint What is African sleeping sickness? 2

Intestinal Diseases

Several protists infect the human digestive system, gaining entry through contaminated water. These protists include *Entamoeba* and *Giardia*, both of which attack the wall of the intestine. An *Entamoeba* infection produces a disease called amebic dysentery, and a *Giardia* infection causes a disease called giardiasis. Both infections cause diarrhea and severe abdominal pain.

Amebic dysentery is most common in areas with poor sanitation, but even crystal-clear mountain streams may be contaminated with *Giardia*. This organism produces tough microscopic cysts that can be killed only by thoroughly boiling the water that contains them.

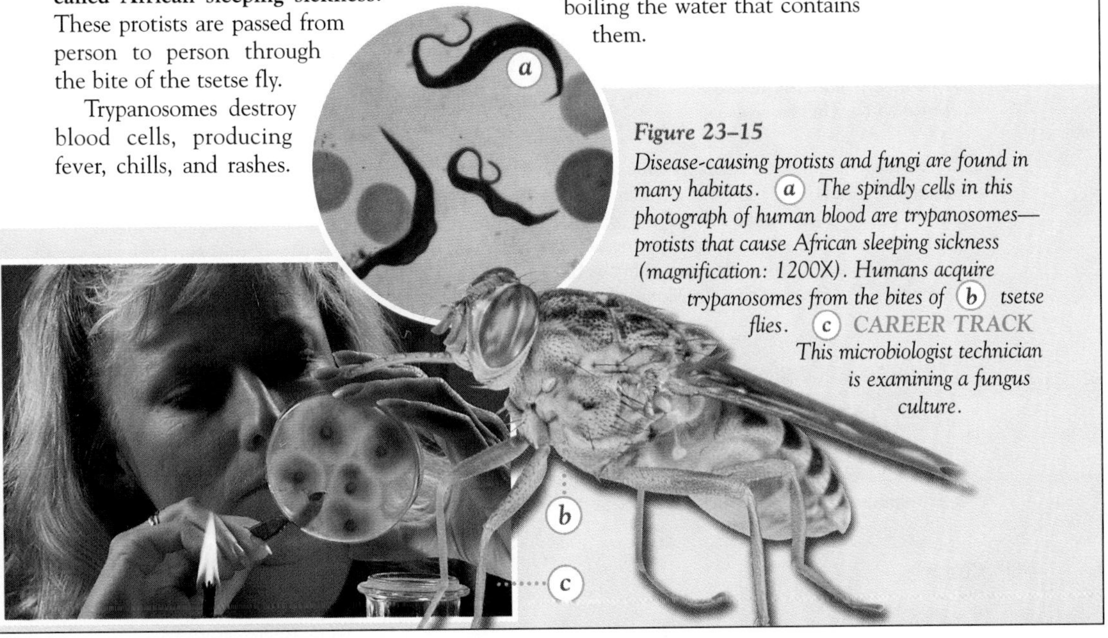

Figure 23–15
Disease-causing protists and fungi are found in many habitats. (a) The spindly cells in this photograph of human blood are trypanosomes—protists that cause African sleeping sickness (magnification: 1200X). Humans acquire trypanosomes from the bites of (b) tsetse flies. (c) CAREER TRACK *This microbiologist technician is examining a fungus culture.*

TEACHER SUPPORT

Managing Classroom Diversity

MULTICULTURAL STUDENTS
Sickle cell disease (or anemia) is an inherited condition that especially strikes people of African heritage. Have students investigate the connection between that disease and the protist-caused disease malaria. Ask them to explain the connection in terms of the life cycle of *Plasmodium*.

TECH PREP STUDENTS
Students who plan careers in food production and services, as well as health care, need to know what measures to take to prevent the spread of dysentery. Have them research what measures are taken in communities to prevent dysentery caused by *Entamoeba* and *Giardia* and report their findings to the class.

SECTION 23–3

Protist and Fungal Diseases

Performance Objective
- Discuss disease-causing protists and fungi and related diseases.

1 ENGAGE

Ideas Through Images

Have students examine Figure 23–15, read the caption, and answer the following questions.

- **What causes African sleeping sickness?** (Flagellate protists called trypanosomes cause the disease.)
- **How are people infected with trypanosomes?** (The protists infect people through bites of tsetse flies.)
- **What organism found in water can cause an intestinal disease?** (A protist called *Giardia* can cause an intestinal disease.)

2 EXPLORE

Investigate

Research Have small groups of students create a pamphlet that would inform readers about one of the diseases discussed in the text, including African sleeping sickness, amebic dysentery, malaria, and ringworm/athlete's foot. Each pamphlet should explain how a person gets the disease, how it is treated, and how it can be prevented. Ask that all pamphlets include illustrations.

Checkpoints

1 Puffballs, toadstools, bracket fungi.

2 African sleeping sickness is a protist disease caused by flagellates of the genus *Trypanosoma*.

3 TEACH

Connections

The Great Potato Famine was devastating to Ireland, whose population was reduced by 20 percent due to death and emigration. Wet and cool weather in the 1840s provided just the environment for the growth of the fungus, commonly known as potato blight. Destruction of the potato crop meant a lack of needed food.

Whirling trout disease was first detected in the United States in 1958. Its likely source was the importation of trout fillets from Denmark. It is now a major problem in Western rivers; between 1990 and 1996, for example, an estimated half-million fish were killed by the disease in just a 90-km stretch of Montana's Madison River.

Answers to Making the Connection

Starvation and widespread evictions from the land caused many Irish people to leave their country, and nearly 2 million of them emigrated to the United States. The result was the establishment of large Irish enclaves in many American big cities, notably New York and Boston. Since the 1840s, the influence of Irish Americans has been felt throughout much of the United States in culture, and politics.

Protist diseases affecting both plants and animals are of great concern to those who work in agriculture, forestry, and wildlife management. An example is a fungus, the ascomycete *Ceratocystis ulmi*, which has practically wiped out the stately American elm tree. Despite decades of research, scientists have not yet found a way to prevent the destruction caused by this fungal infection, commonly known as Dutch elm disease.

Biology AND YOU Connections

Potatoes, Trout, and People

Have protists and fungi evolved into parasites of plants and animals? Not surprisingly, the answer is yes. In fact, these organisms have devastated many plant and animal species over the years—and their attacks continue today.

The Great Potato Famine

By 1845, the potato was the major food crop of Ireland. Unfortunately, the summer that year was unusually wet and cool—ideal conditions for the water mold *Phytophthora infestans*. The threadlike hyphae of this mold invade the roots, stems, and leaves of the potato plant, eventually killing it entirely.

Phytophthora destroyed almost 60 percent of Ireland's potato crop in 1845, and the damage was even worse the following year. Over a million people died from the Great Potato Famine, as the event has become known. It also led to the emigration of at least 2 million people from Ireland to the United States.

Phytophthora infestans destroying a potato plant

Damage to Other Crops

Although the Great Potato Famine was especially devastating, it is hardly the only example of protists or fungi destroying crops. In 1935, for example, wheat rust destroyed more than 25 percent of the grain harvest in the United States. And even today, millions of dollars are lost each year to protists and fungi that attack fruits, grains, vegetables, and other crops.

Whirling Trout Disease

Fans of both fishing and dining value the rainbow trout, a colorful fish native to the northwestern United States. In the last few years, however, many rainbow trout have been seen swimming in circles and chasing their own tail—and dying soon thereafter. This strange behavior was named whirling trout disease.

As biologists discovered, the disease is caused by *Myxobolus cerebralis*, an animallike protist that infects both the rainbow trout and the worms they eat. In trout, the protist attacks cartilage and the nervous system.

Hope for the rainbow trout may lie with another fish, the brown trout, which lives in the same streams as rainbow trout but is resistant to *Myxobolus*. The brown trout is native to Europe, where *Myxobolus* is common. It is thus believed to have evolved into a resistant strain. Wildlife biologists hope that the rainbow trout can do the same.

Rainbow trout are susceptible to infections from an animallike protist, Myxobolus cerebralis.

Making the Connection

How did the Great Potato Famine in Ireland affect life in the United States? Aside from potatoes and rainbow trout, what other plants and animals are affected by protist parasites?

TEACHER SUPPORT

Background Information

The basidiomycete *Puccinia graminis* causes wheat rust, or stem rust of wheat. The name of the disease derives from its reddish color, and it has been a problem since ancient times.

The life cycle of this fungus is quite complex. Thick-walled spores of the protist overwinter on wheat debris. In the spring, they germinate and develop into another type of spore, which requires the leaves of barberry plants to germinate. More spores are produced on the barberry leaf, and when those reach wheat plants they penetrate the stem or leaf through the stoma. As the fungus grows, it damages the plant with its developing mycelium and reduces photosynthesis, destroying the plant. More spores are produced that infect more plants. Finally, the thick-walled spores are produced as winter approaches.

Figure 23–16
(a) *Bites from the* Anopheles *mosquito transmit* Plasmodium, *the protist that causes malaria.* (b) Plasmodium *has a complex life cycle that involves human liver cells and blood cells.*

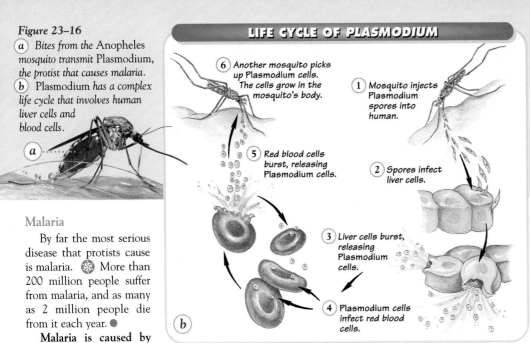

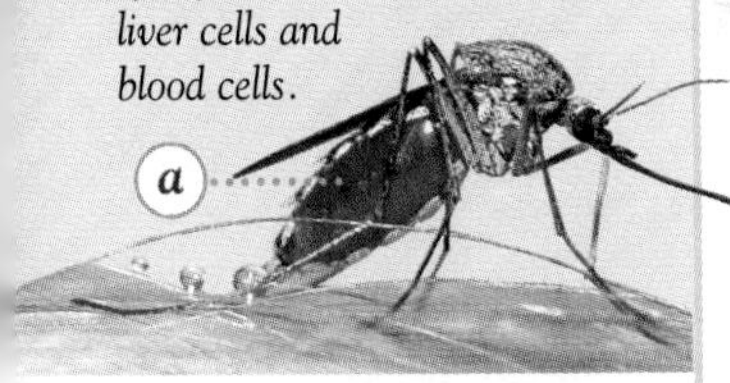

a

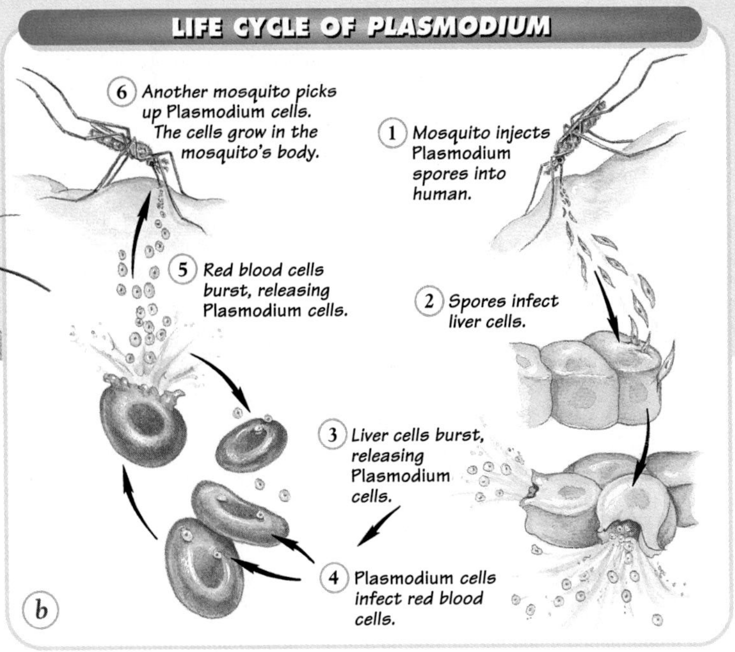

LIFE CYCLE OF PLASMODIUM
6 Another mosquito picks up Plasmodium cells. The cells grow in the mosquito's body.
1 Mosquito injects Plasmodium spores into human.
5 Red blood cells burst, releasing Plasmodium cells.
2 Spores infect liver cells.
3 Liver cells burst, releasing Plasmodium cells.
4 Plasmodium cells infect red blood cells.
b

Malaria

By far the most serious disease that protists cause is malaria. More than 200 million people suffer from malaria, and as many as 2 million people die from it each year. ●

Malaria is caused by *Plasmodium*, a sporozoan that is transmitted to humans through the bite of the *Anopheles* mosquito. *Plasmodium* enters the bloodstream through the mosquito's saliva, then infects liver cells and red blood cells. In a 48- to 72-hour cycle, infected cells burst open, dumping waste products and toxins into the bloodstream. This produces fever and chills—the characteristic symptoms of malaria.

Medical scientists have developed a number of vaccines that seem to block the growth of the parasite. Unfortunately, these vaccines are only partly effective. For the immediate future, the best means of controlling malaria is controlling the mosquitoes that carry it.

Fungal Diseases

Although fungi cause a few serious diseases, many common fungal diseases are relatively harmless and easy to treat. A deuteromycete of the genus *Tinea*, for example, attacks human skin but does not invade the body any farther. **A *Tinea* infection of the scalp causes a disease called ringworm, and a *Tinea* infection between the toes causes athlete's foot.** In both diseases, *Tinea* spores produce hyphae that penetrate the skin's outer layers, causing a red, inflamed sore. Fortunately, *Tinea* infections can be cured by applying antifungal medicines to the infected area.

INTEGRATING HEALTH

Where is malaria most common? How can it be treated?

Section Review 23-3

1. **Describe** diseases caused by protists and fungi.
2. **Explain** how malaria is transmitted.
3. **BRANCHING OUT ACTIVITY** **Research** other diseases that protists or fungi cause. Are any of these diseases common where you live?

INTEGRATING HEALTH

Malaria is common in tropical and subtropical regions of the world, including Africa, Southeast Asia, and Central and South America. The classic treatment of malaria was with quinine, a medicine derived from the bark of the cinchona tree. Stronger, synthetic forms of that drug are used today. Eradicating the mosquito vectors and their breeding areas is an important preventive measure against malaria.

4 ASSESS

Quick Check

Ask students to write a fanciful "life story" of a *Plasmodium* protist in two or three paragraphs, using Figure 23–16 as their resource.

Section Review 23-3

1. Students should describe the cause and symptoms of African sleeping sickness, amebic dysentery, giardiasis, malaria, ringworm, and athlete's foot.

2. Malaria is transmitted to humans through the bite of the *Anopheles* mosquito, which carries the sporozoan *Plasmodium* that causes the disease.

3. Students can find information about protist and fungal diseases in microbiology texts, health books, and encyclopedias. Protist diseases they might research include trichomoniasis (trich), balantidiasis, Chagas' disease, and toxoplasmosis. Fungal diseases they might research include coccidioidomycosis (valley fever or San Joaquin fever), histoplasmosis, North American blastomycosis (Gilchrist's disease), and candidiasis, including oral thrush and vaginitis.

Learning Modality

Auditory Learning Have students respond orally to questions about the life cycle of *Plasmodium*. Briefly describe a specific stage of the cycle, and then ask individual students to describe what happens next.

Ancillary Support

The resources below can be used to support your teaching strategy for these two pages.

TR Enrich: Warming Up to Diseases

BL Inquiry Activity: Gettin' Funky With Fungi and Protists

CHAPTER 23

Laboratory Investigation

Observing a Paramecium

Before the Lab

1. Order cultures of *Paramecium caudatum* from a biological supply house; one culture is usually adequate for a class of 24.
2. Prepare a 0.5 percent salt solution by adding 0.5 g of table salt to 100 mL of water and mixing well.
3. Prepare the acetic acid solution by mixing 1 mL of the concentrated acid with 20 mL water.
4. Prepare a colored culture of yeast by placing 5 mL of yeast, 5 mL of sugar, and 230 mL of warm water in a flask. Add 5–10 drops of crystal violet for stain. Let stand overnight to allow yeast to grow.

Pre-Lab Discussion

Have students read the entire procedure for this investigation. Then ask students the following questions.

What is the purpose of this investigation? (The purpose is to investigate how a paramecium reacts to various stimuli.)

What structures on a paramecium might you expect to see when you magnify the organism with a microscope? (Paramecium structures include cilia, a contractile vacuole, food vacuoles, a gullet, an anal pore, and two nuclei, a micronucleus and a macronucleus.)

How do you predict a paramecium will respond to light and a dilute acid solution? (Students' predictions will vary; accept all reasonable responses.)

What kind of stimulus is the yeast, and how do you predict a paramecium will react to it? (Yeast is a food for paramecia, and a paramecium will ingest the yeast.)

Laboratory Investigation

DESIGNING AN EXPERIMENT

Observing a Paramecium

A paramecium may be a single-celled organism, but it is hardly simple or primitive. In fact, it reacts to stimuli—changes in its environment—in a variety of different ways. In this investigation, you will observe a paramecium under the microscope and see how it responds to different stimuli.

Problem

How does a paramecium respond to different stimuli? **Design an experiment** to answer this question.

Suggested Materials

- paramecium culture
- medicine dropper
- compound microscope
- microscope slide with depression
- coverslip
- methyl cellulose
- 0.5-percent salt solution
- penlight or flashlight
- dilute acetic acid
- colored yeast culture

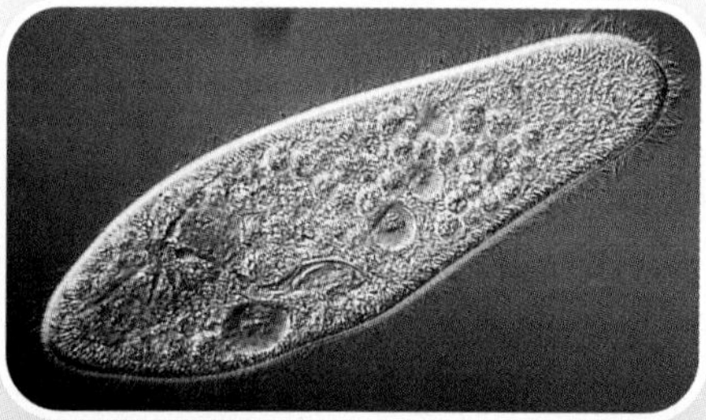

Suggested Procedure

1. Use the medicine dropper to transfer a drop of the paramecium culture to the microscope slide.

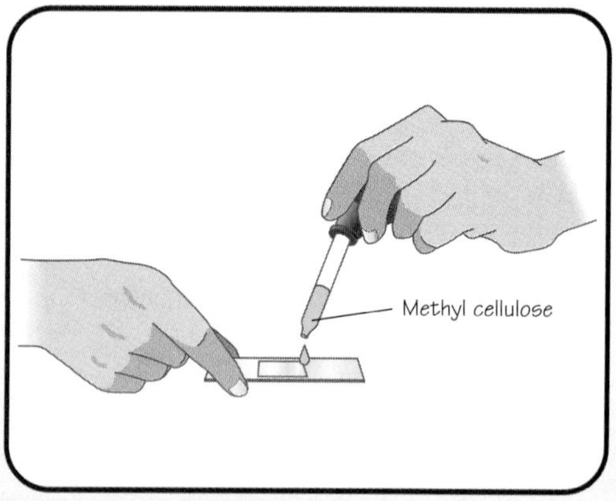

2. Add a drop of methyl cellulose to the slide. Methyl celluose slows down a paramecium's movement.

Safety Tips

- Remind students to use caution when handling the acid solution. They should immediately flush any area of skin that has come into contact with the acid under running water.
- Ask students to clean up any spills immediately.

3. Place a coverslip on the slide. Use the low-power objective to locate a paramecium on the slide, then switch to the high-power objective to observe its structure. Draw a detailed diagram of the paramecium.

4. While observing the paramecium under the high-power objective, count the number of times the contractile vacuole fills and empties in 30 seconds.

5. Place a drop of 0.5-percent salt solution at one edge of the coverslip. Count the number of times the contractile vacuole fills and empties in 30 seconds.

6. Flush out the salt solution by adding several drops of water at one edge of the coverslip.

7. Using a similar procedure, design an experiment to determine how a paramecium responds to the following stimuli:

- **light**
- **dilute acid solution**
- **yeast**

8. With your teacher's approval, perform the experiment you designed. CAUTION: *Be careful when using an acid. It may burn your skin.*

Observations

1. In your drawing of the paramecium, label any structures that you can identify.
2. Describe any changes in the activity of the contractile vacuole when the 0.5-percent salt solution was added.
3. Describe the paramecium's response to the dilute acid solution.
4. How did the paramecium respond to light?
5. How did the paramecium respond to the yeast culture?

Analysis and Conclusions

1. Why is a paramecium classified as an animal-like protist and not a plantlike protist or a funguslike protist?
2. How does a paramecium move from place to place?
3. Why does a paramecium need a contractile vacuole? Use the data collected in this investigation to support your answer.
4. How does a paramecium respond to light? Why might such a response be useful?
5. Describe the paramecium's activity in the presence of the yeast culture. What purpose does this activity serve?

More to Explore

Design an experiment to determine the ideal temperature, pH, or food supply for a paramecium's growth.

3. Students should have observed an increase in the rate of filling and emptying when the dilute acid solution was added.
4. Paramecia generally show a positive response by moving toward a lighted area.
5. Students should have observed the formation of food vacuoles at the base of the gullet. This can easily be seen by the colored yeast that is ingested.

Answers to
Analysis and Conclusions

1. A paramecium is classified as an animallike protist because it does not have chloroplasts to perform photosynthesis and does not absorb food through a cell wall.
2. A paramecium moves from place to place through the coordinated beating of its cilia.
3. A paramecium needs a contractile vacuole to expel water that diffuses into the cell by osmosis. The decrease in the rate when the salt solution is added confirms that notion because less water would enter the paramecium if the environment inside the cell has a lower salt concentration than the environment outside the cell.
4. A paramecium responds to light by moving toward a lighted area. This response might be useful in a natural environment because an area lighted by sunlight would be likely to contain a greater amount of food than an area of darkness.
5. In the presence of the yeast culture, a paramecium takes in food through the gullet and forms food vacuoles, where the food is digested. This activity provides the organism with the nutrients needed to carry out cell processes.

Skills Development
Students will use these skills while completing the laboratory investigation: designing an experiment, measuring, observing, making inferences, and drawing conclusions.

Teaching Strategies
1. Demonstrate how to use the pipette to transfer a drop of paramecium culture to a slide.
2. Have groups of students collaborate in designing experiments using light, a dilute acid solution, and a yeast culture. Check these designs before groups proceed with their experiments.

Answers to
Observations

1. Students' drawings should be similar to the one in Figure 23–5 on page 538. Most students should be able to label the cilia, contractile vacuole, food vacuoles, gullet, macronucleus, and micronucleus.
2. Students should have observed a decrease in the rate of filling and emptying when the salt solution was added. A typical decrease would be from about 5 cycles (filling/emptying) per 30 seconds to 2–3 cycles per 30 seconds.

More to Explore

Students' designs will vary. A typical design will use the same general procedure as the laboratory investigation. Students should clearly designate a variable, such as temperature or pH of the water or the type or amount of food, and also establish a control for comparison.

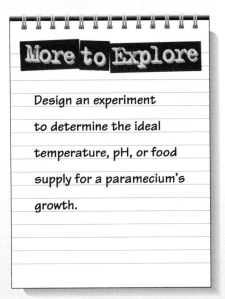

CHAPTER 23

Study Guide

Review Strategy

Divide students into small groups, and have each group design a board game based on the life cycle of an organism described in the chapter or some other aspect of protists and fungi. Group members should collaborate on the design of the board, the goal of the game, the way in which pieces move, and method of asking and answering questions. For example, questions could be on the board itself or on cards drawn by players. Make sure no two groups focus on the same material as the basis for a game. Have groups trade their completed games and test them.

Recalling Main Ideas

1. b
2. a
3. c
4. a
5. d
6. a
7. a
8. c
9. c
10. c

Assessment

Reviewing What You Learned

1. The four major phyla of animallike protists are Zoomastigina, Sarcodina, Ciliophora, and Sporozoa.
2. Amebas take in food by extending a pseudopod around food.
3. Ciliates move with a coordinated beating of cilia that pulls the organism quickly through the water.
4. At times of stress, paramecia reproduce through conjugation, in which two paramecia exchange genetic information from their micronuclei.
5. Algae are the single-celled photosynthetic organisms.
6. Three phyla of plantlike protists are Euglenophyta, Pyrrophyta, and Chrysophyta.

Study Guide

Summarizing Key Concepts

The key concepts in each section of this chapter are listed below to help you review the chapter content. Make sure you understand each concept and its relationship to other concepts and to the theme of this chapter.

23–1 Protists

- A eukaryote that is not a fungus, plant, or animal is classified as a protist.
- Animallike protists are classified into phyla by the way they move. Flagellates propel their bodies with whiplike flagella. Sarcodines move with "false feet" called pseudopods. Ciliates move through the beating of hairlike cilia. Sporozoans are parasites that have no special structures for movement.
- Plantlike protists are capable of photosynthesis. They include the euglenophytes, which resemble flagellates; dinoflagellates, many of which can produce light; and chrysophytes, which include the diatoms.
- Funguslike protists lack chlorophyll and absorb food through their cell walls. They include the slime molds and water molds.

23–2 Fungi

- Fungi are heterotrophs, and they obtain food by extracellular digestion and absorption.
- The cells of fungi are organized into filaments called hyphae. Hyphae form a tangled mass called a mycelium.
- The four phyla of fungi are Zygomycota, Ascomycota, Basidiomycota, and Deuteromycota. The structure commonly called a mushroom is typically the fruiting body of a basidiomycete.

23–3 Protist and Fungal Diseases

- Protists cause African sleeping sickness and intestinal diseases. Malaria is caused by *Plasmodium,* a sporozoan that is transmitted to humans through the *Anopheles* mosquito.
- A species of the genus *Tinea,* a deuteromycete, causes ringworm and athlete's foot.

Reviewing Key Terms

Review the following vocabulary terms and their meaning. Then use each term in a complete sentence.

23–1 Protists

flagellum
pseudopod
spore
cilium
contractile vacuole
gullet
anal pore
trichocyst
micronucleus
macronucleus
conjugation
alga
fruiting body

23–2 Fungi

hypha
mycelium
ascus

Inquiry-Based Strategy

Tell students that several cases of amebic dysentery have occurred in a community. Have students research what steps must be taken to prevent more cases by asking the following questions: How is amebic dysentery spread? How can it be prevented? Allow students to determine what research is needed to answer these questions and what would need to be done in such a community.

Students may find that health books will provide them with the answers they need. Some students may also want to talk to government health authorities in their own community.

CHAPTER 23

Recalling Main Ideas

Choose the letter of the answer that best completes the statement or answers the question.

1. Animallike protists are classified into phyla by the way they
   a. reproduce. c. take in food.
   b. move. d. produce shells.
2. A flagellum functions as a
   a. whiplike motor. c. glasslike shell.
   b. spore. d. nucleus.
3. An ameba moves by extending its
   a. cilia. c. pseudopod.
   b. flagella. d. nucleus.
4. A paramecium expels water through its
   a. contractile vacuoles. c. trichocysts.
   b. gullet. d nucleus.
5. Which of these phyla contain only parasites?
   a. flagellates c. ciliates
   b. sarcodines d. sporozoans
6. Unlike a paramecium, a euglena contains
   a. chloroplasts. c. cilia.
   b. mitochondria. d. flagella.
7. Which is a funguslike protist?
   a. water mold c. heliozoan
   b. sporozoan d. club fungus
8. In many fungi, spores are produced in structures called
   a. hyphae. c. fruiting bodies.
   b. mycelia. d. nuclei.
9. Mushrooms, including toadstools and bracket fungi, are examples of
   a. water molds. c. basidiomycetes.
   b. ascomycetes. d. deuteromycetes.
10. The *Anopheles* mosquito transmits the protist that causes
    a. African sleeping sickness.
    b. amebic dysentery.
    c. malaria.
    d. ringworm.

Putting It All Together

Using the information on pages xxx to xxxi, complete the following concept map.

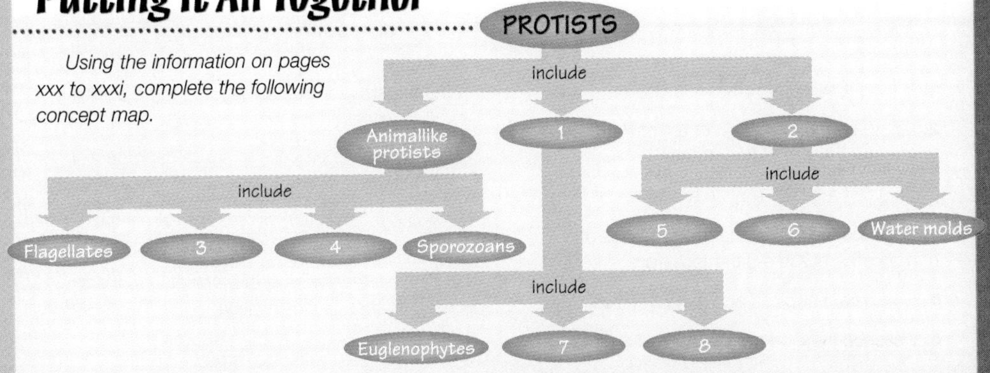

Putting It All Together

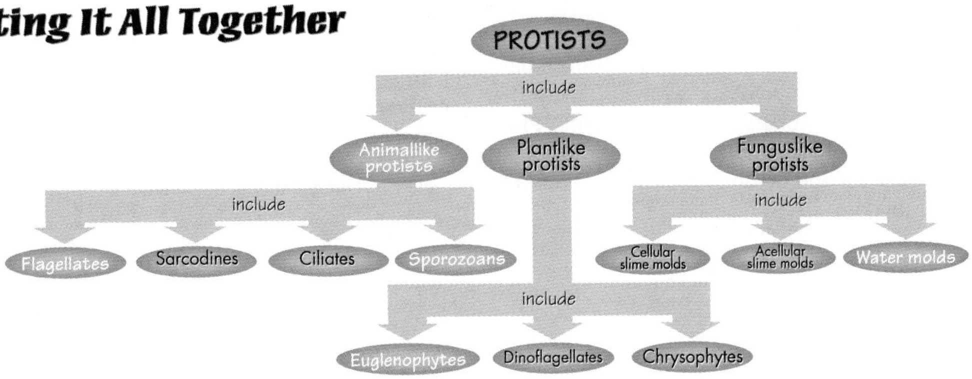

7. The chrysophytes, a phylum of plantlike protists, include species commonly known as yellow-green algae, golden algae, and diatoms.
8. When a paramecium is damaged or shocked, its trichocysts are discharged and produce barbed projections that can damage predators.
9. Three phyla of funguslike protists are Acrasiomycota, Myxomycota, and Oomycota.
10. The main role of fungi in nature is to break down, or decompose, dead organic matter and return the raw materials to Earth.
11. Nutrients pass through fungus cells by moving through the holes in the cross walls that join the cytoplasm of adjacent cells.
12. An ascus is a tough sac in an ascomycete that contains the spores produced by sexual reproduction.
13. A secondary mycelium is a structure that is produced by the donation of nuclei from opposite mating types of a basidiomycete and that grows beneath the soil, sometimes reaching enormous size.
14. Students should list three diseases; these may include the protist diseases African sleeping sickness, amebic dysentery, giardiasis, and malaria, and the fungal diseases ringworm and athlete's foot.

Expanding the Concepts

1. It is difficult to classify protists because the kingdom consists of such an extremely diverse group of organisms, including any eukaryote that is not classified as a fungus, a plant, or an animal.
2. Students might mention any important feature or example of the four phyla in their answers. All students should mention that zoomatiginans move with flagella, sarcodines move with pseudopods, sporozoans are parasites and do not have specialized structures for movement, and ciliates move with cilia.
3. A mutualistic relationship exists between termites and the flagellate *Trichonympha,* which lives in the termites' digestive system and helps digest the cellulose fibers in wood.
4. In a paramecium, the macronucleus is a "working library" of genetic information, while the micronucleus contains backup copies of all the cell's genes. During times of stress, the micronucleus also performs a role in conjugation.

Assessment (continued)

5. A euglena and a paramecium are remarkably similar in structure. The main difference is that a euglena contains chloroplasts to carry out photosynthesis and a light-sensing structure called an eyespot that a paramecium does not have.

6. A diatom is a chrysophyte. Its chloroplasts contain bright yellow pigments, and its cell wall contains pectin. A diatom also has a delicate, glasslike shell made of silica that fits together in two parts.

7. Both a cellular slime mold and an acellular slime mold begin life as an amebalike cell. As a cellular slime mold grows, it aggregates with other cells of the same species to form a large sluglike mass. As an acellular slime mold grows, it also becomes a large mass, but that mass is actually a single cell with thousands of nuclei.

8. In the sexual phase of a fungus life cycle, hyphae of two opposite mating types (+ and –) fuse, bringing two nuclei together in the same cell. The two nuclei fuse to form a diploid nucleus, which undergoes meiosis to produce haploid spores.

9. The structure commonly called a mushroom in a basidiomycete is actually a fruiting body produced by the secondary mycelium that forces its way upward through the soil when conditions are right.

10. An *Anopheles* mosquito picks up *Plasmodium* when it bites a person infected with malaria. Inside the mosquito, the *Plasmodium* grows and produces spores that are passed to a person bitten by the mosquito. The spores then infect liver cells, which burst and release *Plasmodium* cells that infect red blood cells. Mosquitoes pick up the infected red blood cells when biting the person, and the life cycle continues.

11. Both ringworm and athlete's foot are caused when *Tinea* spores germinate on damp skin and produce hyphae that penetrate the skin's outer layers. On the scalp, such an infection is called ringworm, while between the toes it is called athlete's foot.

Assessment

Reviewing What You Learned

Answer each of the following in a complete sentence.

1. What are the four major phyla of animallike protists?
2. How do amebas take in food?
3. What type of movement categorizes the ciliates?
4. Describe the role of conjugation in paramecia.
5. What are algae?
6. Identify three phyla of plantlike protists.
7. What are the chrysophytes?
8. How does a paramecium use its trichocysts?
9. Identify three phyla of funguslike protists.
10. Describe the main role of fungi in nature.
11. How do nutrients pass through the cells of a fungus?
12. What is an ascus?
13. What is a secondary mycelium?
14. Identify three diseases that protists or fungi can cause.

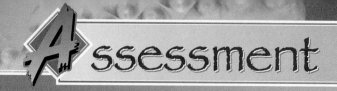

Expanding the Concepts

Discuss each of the following in a brief paragraph.

1. Why is it difficult to classify protists?
2. Compare the four phyla of animallike protists.
3. Give an example of a mutualistic relationship between a protist and an animal.
4. Describe the role of the micronucleus and macronucleus in a paramecium.
5. Compare a euglena and a paramecium.
6. Describe the external structure of a diatom.
7. Compare a cellular slime mold to an acellular slime mold.
8. Describe the process of sexual reproduction in fungi.
9. In basidiomycetes, what is the role of the structure commonly called a mushroom?
10. Discuss the life cycle of *Plasmodium,* the protist that causes malaria.
11. Compare ringworm and athlete's foot.

Extending Your Thinking

1. Protists include any eukaryote that is not classified as an animal, a plant, or a fungus. But protists are animallike, plantlike, or funguslike. The diagram accurately represents this similarity between protists and organisms of the three multicellular kingdoms.

2. This organism belongs to the phylum Basidiomycota. The structure that can be observed is the fruiting body of the organism, formed by the secondary mycelium. The spores of the fruiting body appear in "gills" located on the underside of the mushroom.

Skills Trace
Identifying

Focus p. 546
Practice p. 546
Assess p. 555

Extending Your Thinking

Use the skills you have developed in this chapter to answer the following.

1. **Interpreting diagrams** The diagram shown below illustrates the six kingdoms of organisms. In what ways does the diagram accurately represent protists?

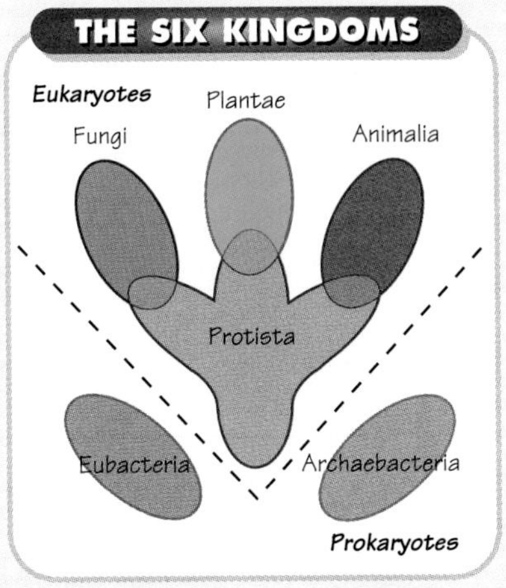

2. **Identifying** What structures can you identify in the mushroom shown on the opposite page? To what phylum does this organism belong? Explain your answer.
3. **Giving an example** Many protists and fungi can reproduce sexually or asexually. Give a specific example of each type of reproduction and describe the advantages it offers the protist or fungus.
4. **Designing an experiment** An orchid grower thought that fungi and protists in the soil could damage an orchid. So he sterilized the soil by heating it to 100°C. To his alarm, the orchid withered and eventually died. Develop a hypothesis to explain this result. Then, design an experiment to test your hypothesis.
5. **Using the writing process** Write a short story or play about a world that does not have protists or fungi. Your story should predict the problems this world would face and suggest some possible solutions.

Applying Your Skills

From the "Mouths" of Protists and Fungi

Some protists and fungi have relatively simple life cycles, while the lives of others are far more complex. If protists and fungi could talk about their lives, what would they say?

1. Your teacher will assign you a specific protist or fungi. Research the life cycle of this organism. Identify its methods of reproduction, movement, and energy production, as well as its role in nature.
2. Write a short story, poem, or play in which the narrator or main character is your assigned organism. Your work should include all the relevant information that you researched.

• GOING FURTHER •

3. Read your work to your classmates. You may use props or other visual aids to enhance your presentation.
4. Work with a classmate to present a comparison of two different protists or fungi.

3. Students' examples will vary. Binary fission in a paramecium or the production of spores in zygomycetes are examples of asexual reproduction. Advantages of asexual reproduction are its simplicity and its helpfulness in rapid growth of a population. Conjugation in paramecia or the production of spores through the fusing of opposite mating types in fungi are examples of sexual reproduction. The advantage of sexual reproduction is its production of organisms with new combinations of genes, which can help organisms meet environmental challenges.

4. Some students may hypothesize that the orchids need a certain kind of fungus in the soil, such as mycorrhizae, in order to help them absorb water, minerals, and nutrients. Their experimental designs should include use of a control and variables.

Skills Trace
Experimenting
- Focus p. 541
- Practice p. 542
- Assess p. 555

5. Some students might focus on beneficial uses of protists and fungi, such as the yeast used in bread making. Others might focus on the loss of organisms at the bottom of the global food pyramid or a disruption of the world food web.

Applying Your Skills

Teacher Notes

- Make a list of all the specific organisms students read about, researched, or observed in studying this chapter. Then either assign each student a specific organism or allow students to choose one.
- Microbiology texts are good resources for students to use to find out about the life cycle of and other pertinent information on their assigned organism.
- Once students have finished a rough draft of a short story, poem, or play, discuss with each what props or visual aids might be helpful in a presentation to the class.
- Have two students who worked on different phyla of protists or fungi present their works in the same period, and then orally ask them questions that would highlight differences in the organisms.

Scoring Rubric

4 Response is thorough, accurate, and creative; shows an in-depth understanding of science skills, procedures, and concepts.

3 Response is complete, mostly accurate, and original; shows a satisfactory understanding of science skills, procedures, and concepts.

2 Response is mostly complete but includes some inaccuracies; shows an adequate understanding of science skills, procedures, and concepts.

1 Response is only partially complete and has many inaccuracies; shows an incomplete understanding of science skills, procedures, and concepts.

0 Response is mostly incomplete and/or inaccurate; shows a lack of understanding of science skills, procedures, and concepts.

Chapter 24 Multicellular Algae, Mosses, and Ferns

Content Management	Student Edition Activities
■ Section 24–1 Multicellular Algae, pp. 557–561 Algae—Protists or Plants? Reproduction in Algae	Laboratory Investigation: Diversity of Green Algae, pp. 570–571
■ Section 24–2 Bryophytes, pp. 562–564 Adaptations of the Bryophytes Mosses Hornworts and Liverworts	MINI LAB: Male or Female?, p. 563
■ Section 24–3 Seedless Vascular Plants, pp. 565–567 Origins of Vascular Plants Club Mosses and Horsetails Ferns	MINI LAB: Spores in a Sorus, p. 566
◆ BRANCHING OUT • In Action Section 24–4 Algae in Our World, pp. 568–569 Shaping the Environment Benefit to Humans	

■ These sections cover all the necessary content and concepts for an enriched course in biology.
◆ This section covers content and concepts that are either applications or extensions of the enriched material.

Integration Strategies

SE Physics, p. 558

Assessment Strategies

SE Chapter Review, pp. 572–575
TR Section Reviews
Chapter Test
BL Chapter Review
Practice Test
CTB Chapter 24 Test

Tech Prep

Teaching strategies appropriate for students who are in technical/vocational programs or who are considering post-secondary technical education can be found on the following **TE** pages: 559 and 565.

Meeting the Standards

Sections 24–1 through 24–4 cover two of the six content standards under **The Cell** and all five of the content standards under **Biological Evolution** as described on pages 184–185 of The National Science Education Standards.

Chapter Planning Guide

Teacher's Edition Activities	Other Activities	Media and Technology
Chapter Discovery Learning Activity, p. 556 **Inquiry Activity:** The Green Stuff in Pond Water, p. 557 **Investigate:** Research, p. 558	**LM** Observing the Characteristics of Multicellular Algae, #47 **TR** **Enrich:** The Awful Algae **BL** **Inquiry Activity:** Plant or Animal?	
Inquiry Activity: What's So Good About Peat Moss?, p. 562	**LM** Comparing Multicellular Algae, Ferns, and Mosses, #48 **TR** **Explore:** Brilliant Bryophytes **BL** **Inquiry Activity:** The Great Cover-Up	
Inquiry Activity: Fun With Ferns, p. 565 **Activity:** An Alternation of Generations, p. 566	**TR** **Writing in Biology:** Interior Design **Apply:** Fern Facts **BL** **Inquiry Activity:** Water When You Need It	**TB** Life Cycle of a Fern, #31
Investigate: Cooperative Learning, p. 568	**TR** **Explore:** Algae for Everyone **BL** **Inquiry Activity:** Algae All Around	

KEY: **SE** Student Edition **TE** Teacher's Edition **LM** Laboratory Manual **TR** Teaching Resources **BL** BioLog **TB** Transparency Box **CTB** Computer Test Bank

Materials List

TE Chapter Discovery Learning Activity, p. 556 (20–30 minutes); an example of brown algae, a moss, a fern.

TE Inquiry Activity: The Green Stuff in Pond Water, p. 557 (20 minutes); pond water with algae, slide, coverslip, microscope, dissecting needle.

TE Inquiry Activity: What's So Good About Peat Moss? p. 562 (30 minutes); peat moss (Sphagnum spp.), soil, beakers of various sizes, water.

SE MINI LAB: Male or Female? p. 563 (20–30 minutes); moss plant or prepared slides, microscope slides, coverslips, water, microscope.

TE Inquiry Activity: Fun With Ferns, p. 565 (20–30 minutes); mature fern frond with spores, metric ruler, scissors, slide, coverslip, water, microscope.

SE MINI LAB: Spores in a Sorus, p. 566 (30 minutes); mature fern frond with sori, dissecting needle, slide, coverslip, water, microscope.

TE Activity: An Alternation of Generations, p. 566 (30 minutes for initial setup, 5–10 minutes for each observation); mature fern frond, peat moss, sand, flower pot, saucer, water, plastic wrap.

TE Investigate: Cooperative Learning, p. 568 (15 minutes); algae recipe.

CHAPTER 24

Multicellular Algae, Mosses, and Ferns

Introducing the Chapter

. . . In Pictures

Ferns vary in size from tiny floating ferns of less than 1 cm in diameter to tropical tree ferns that can be as tall as 25 m. These tree ferns in an eastern Australian park are evidence that Australia is not all dry and desertlike, for almost all ferns need a wet environment to complete their life cycle. As students study the photograph, ask the following questions.

- **Unlike algae, which are protists, ferns are considered true plants. What do you think makes them plants?** (They have leaves, roots, and branches.)
- **In order to reproduce, these fern trees require a wet environment. Why do you think that is?** (Some students might speculate that the reproductive cells of ferns need water to move together or fuse.)

Teaching Strategy

In the first three sections of this chapter, students will learn about multicellular algae, bryophytes, and seedless vascular plants. The BRANCHING OUT section provides students with information on the importance of algae in the natural world, as well as the uses of algae in modern society.

CHAPTER 24

Multicellular Algae, Mosses, and Ferns

FOCUSING THE CHAPTER
THEME: Unity and Diversity

24–1 Multicellular Algae
- **Classify** algae.
- **Describe** reproduction in green algae.

24–2 Bryophytes
- **List** some of the adaptations bryophytes need to live on land.
- **Identify** the main stages in the life cycle of bryophytes.

24–3 Seedless Vascular Plants
- **Discuss** the significance of vascular tissue.
- **Describe** the life cycle of a fern.

BRANCHING OUT *In Action*

24–4 Algae in Our World
- **Discuss** the role of algae in nature.
- **List** ways in which humans use algae.

LABORATORY INVESTIGATION
- **Compare** the characteristics of different types of green algae.

Biology and Your World

BIO JOURNAL

Have you ever looked carefully at the plant life in or near a pond, lake, or rocky seashore? How do you think these plants are suited to their aquatic environment? Based on your observations, make a list in your journal of the ways in which aquatic plants and terrestrial plants differ.

Tree ferns in Border Ranges National Park, South Queensland, Australia

BIO JOURNAL

Ask students what terrestrial plants need to do that aquatic plants do not. Point out that aquatic plants would dry out if suddenly transported to dry land. Have students speculate about what terrestrial plants have that prevents drying out. Instruct students to keep their entries in their portfolios.

TEACHER SUPPORT

Chapter Discovery Learning Activity

Divide students into groups of three or four, and give each group several examples of the organisms they will study in this chapter, including a type of brown algae such as kelp, some kind of moss, and a small fern. Ask them to examine these organisms and make drawings with labels for whatever characteristics they can identify. Ask them also to speculate about the environment to which each organism is adapted. Have each group discuss which of the examples could be considered a plant and which could not be. Then have several groups present their findings to the class. Challenge groups to give reasons why they classified some organisms as plants but not others.

Multicellular Algae

SECTION 24–1

GUIDE FOR READING

- **Compare** the characteristics of multicellular algae and plants.
- **Explain** what is meant by alternation of generations.

AT HIGH TIDE ON A WINTER'S day, the Maine coastline seems like a cold and barren place. Icy water crashes against gray rock, and there is hardly a hint of anything alive. Just six hours later, at low tide, the scene is different. As the pull of the moon's gravity drops the waterline, it reveals a damp forest of green and brown clinging to the rocks. Even as waves toss them violently, these hardy underwater seaweeds hang on, bringing life to the cold salt water and providing food and shelter for scores of animals. These seaweeds are dramatic reminders of the way in which plant life has found its way into every corner of the planet—and the way in which plants continue to transform the world in which we live.

Algae—Protists or Plants?

The seaweeds you have just read about are **algae**—photosynthetic aquatic organisms that are classified as protists. Although most algae are unicellular, some are multicellular, such as the seaweeds that are seen on rocky seashores at low tide. We have already discussed three of the algae phyla—*Euglenophyta*, *Pyrrophyta*, and *Chrysophyta*—along with other protists. Remember that the algae in these phyla are unicellular. Because many of the algae in the remaining phyla, like plants, are multicellular, they have been included along with plants in this chapter. These algae also have reproductive cycles that are very similar to those in plants. Therefore, even though the multicellular algae are protists, you might think of them as "honorary" plants.

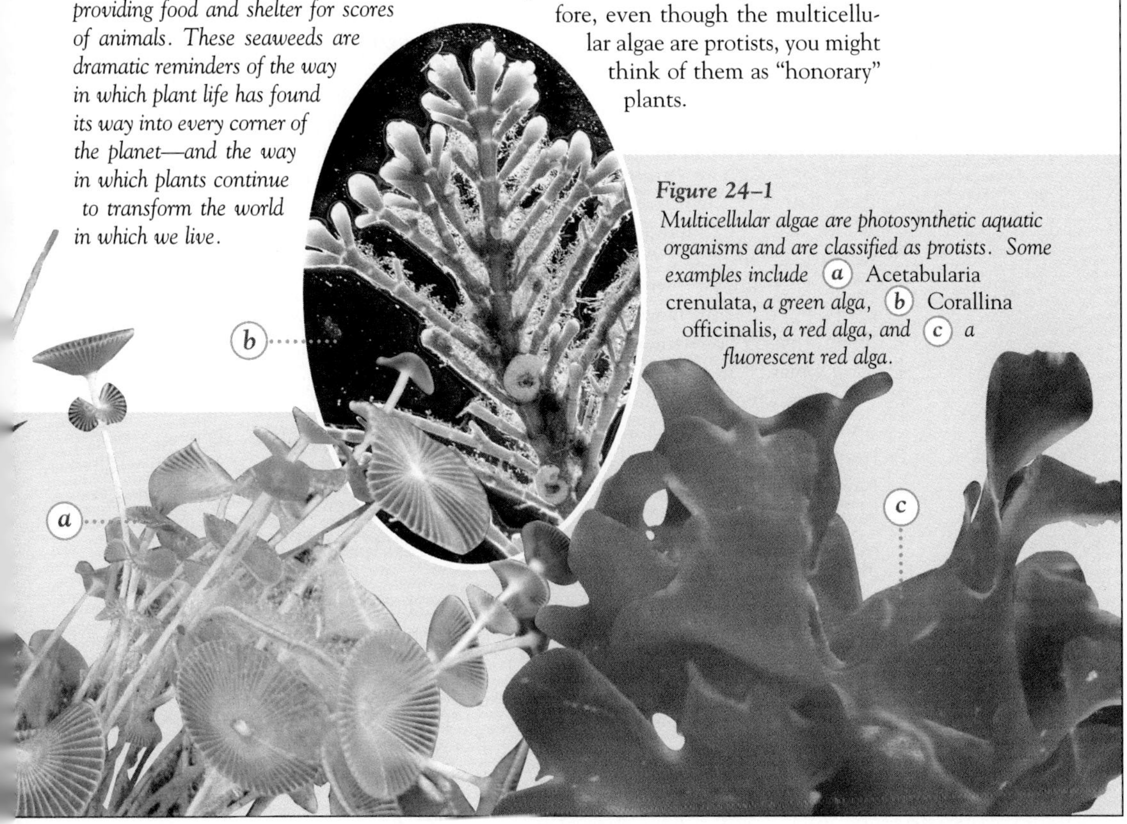

Figure 24–1
Multicellular algae are photosynthetic aquatic organisms and are classified as protists. Some examples include (a) Acetabularia crenulata, *a green alga,* (b) Corallina officinalis, *a red alga, and* (c) *a fluorescent red alga.*

TEACHER SUPPORT

Historical Perspective

While crossing the Atlantic Ocean in 1492, Christopher Columbus noticed a large expanse of brown seaweed in an area now known as the Sargasso Sea. To Columbus, the seaweed suggested that land was near. But for centuries afterward, ships' captains avoided the Sargasso Sea for fear of the seaweed entangling them. In fact, it was weak winds, not confining seaweeds, that were the cause of ships' difficulties.

The seaweed is a brown alga of the genus *Sargassum*, which floats by means of small, berry-shaped bladders. It dominates the surface of the Sargasso Sea, an area near Bermuda, where it is a food source in a unique marine ecosystem.

SECTION 24–1

Multicellular Algae

Performance Objectives

- Discuss similarities and differences between multicellular algae and plants.
- Explain the sequence of steps in the reproductive cycles of green algae.

Laboratory Investigation Skill: Comparing

1 ENGAGE

Inquiry Activity

Observing

The Green Stuff in Pond Water

Ask students to list the characteristics of the plantlike material growing in pond water. Have students use dissecting needles to make slides of any green plantlike material in the pond water. Ask them to examine this material through the microscope and make drawings of what they see.

Ideas Through Images

Have students examine Figure 24–1, read the caption, and answer the following questions.

- **Are these the only photosynthetic aquatic organisms on Earth?** (No. Students should remember that some bacteria are also photosynthetic aquatic organisms.)
- **What differences are evident in the three types of algae shown?** (The three each have a much different shape. One is green, while two are red.)

Ancillary Support

The resource below can be used to support your teaching strategy for these two pages.

BL Inquiry Activity: Plant or Animal?

2 EXPLORE

Investigate

Research Have pairs of students prepare brief reports with text and illustrations on specific kinds of algae. Ask that they do preliminary research to find types of green, red, or brown algae on which to concentrate. Have each pair choose one species, and make sure no two pairs research the same species. Ask that the final report include information about the algae's characteristics, environment, and any uses by humans.

3 TEACH

Ideas Through Images

Have students examine Figure 24–2, read the caption, and answer the following questions.

- **How would you describe the main differences between the two algae shown?** (The most obvious difference is that the bull kelp is a brown color, and the coralline alga is red. The bull kelp is floating on top of the water, while the coralline alga is anchored. The shapes of the two algae are much different.)
- **In what type of environment do most red and brown algae live?** (Most red and brown algae live in saltwater environments.)

INTEGRATING PHYSICS

The color of an object depends on which colors of the visible spectrum of light are absorbed and which are reflected. Different pigments in the different kinds of algae absorb some colors and reflect others. The pigments in green algae, for example, reflect green light and absorb other colors, especially violet and red.

(a) **Figure 24–2**
Most brown and red algae are saltwater organisms. Many of the brown algae, such as (a) bull kelp, form stalks with leaflike blades and hollow bladders that fill with gas to help the alga stay afloat. Red algae are especially abundant in the warm waters of the tropics, and many, such as (b) the red coralline algae, are involved in the building of coral reefs. (b)

INTEGRATING PHYSICS

How does the color of algae depend upon the pigments present in the algae?

Brown Algae

The brown algae contain carotenoids, or yellow-orange pigments, called xanthophylls (ZAN-thuh-fihlz) and fucoxanthins (fyoo-koh-ZAN-thihnz), that help them gather sunlight for photosynthesis. When these pigments are combined with the green pigment chlorophyll, the result is a dingy-brown color that explains the name of their phylum, Phaeophyta (fee-oh-FIGHT-uh), which means "dusky plants" in Greek.

All brown algae are multicellular, and some of them are so large you might have trouble believing they are protists. The brown algae known as giant kelps can be as long as 100 meters. One of the most common forms is *Fucus*, which is found almost everywhere on the eastern coast of the United States and is sometimes known as rockweed for the way in which it attaches itself to rocks.

☑ **Checkpoint** What is the source of the color of brown algae? 1

Red Algae

Red algae get their name from phycoerythrin (figh-koh-uh-RIHTH-rihn), a bright-red pigment used to supplement chlorophyll in photosynthesis. They belong to the phylum Rhodophyta (roh-dah-FIGHT-uh), which means "red plants" in Greek. Despite this name, many red algae are green, purple, or reddish-black, depending on the particular combination of additional pigments they contain. These extra pigments make it possible for many red algae to live at great depths, where little sunlight penetrates.

Green Algae

While most brown and red algae are found in salt water, most green algae live in fresh water. Green algae are remarkably similar to green plants and are placed in the phylum Chlorophyta (klawr-uh-FIGHT-uh), which means "green plants" in Greek. **Like plants, green algae have cell walls made of cellulose, the green pigments chlorophyll *a* and *b*, and they store food in the form of starch.** Although most green algae are aquatic, a few of them are found on land in wet soil or growing on moist tree trunks.

Many green algae, such as *Chlamydomonas* (klam-uh-DAH-muh-nuhs), live all or most of their lives as single cells. Some, however, form multicellular structures. *Spirogyra* (spigh-roh-JIGH-ruh) consists of long filaments that produce tangles of greenish fuzz in lakes and ponds. And *Ulva* (UHL-vuh), found along the shoreline, has large bright-green leaflike sheets that help to explain its common name—sea lettuce.

TEACHER SUPPORT

Background Information

In the Endosymbiont Hypothesis, biologist Lynn Margulis proposed that eukaryotic cells arose through symbiotic relationships between prokaryotic cells. In *Garden of Microbial Delights,* she and her coauthor, Dorion Sagan, suggest that red algae were created when some translucent, funguslike cells ate but failed to digest cyanobacteria, the photosynthetic blue-green bacteria. The cyanobacteria then reproduced independently inside the host cells. After some period of time, the bacteria became the red algae chloroplasts. Among the evidence supporting this hypothesis is that both red algae and some cyanobacteria contain the pigment phycocyanin and that the RNA in the chloroplasts of red algae are extremely similar to the RNA in some cyanobacteria.

Problem Solving
INTERPRETING GRAPHS

Marveling at Multicellular Algae

One of your friends recently visited a public aquarium for a behind-the-scenes tour. She had the opportunity to see several of the hundreds of species of multicellular algae housed in the aquarium. A scientist who worked there told her that green plants evolved long ago from green algae. He gave your friend a chart and asked her to compare the characteristics of multicellular algae with those of plants.

Your friend was also given a graph that showed the action spectrum for photosynthesis and the absorption spectra of some pigments—namely, chlorophyll *a* and *b* and the carotenoids. The absorption spectra showed the wavelengths of light absorbed by each pigment. The action spectrum showed the wavelength of light at which photosynthesis takes place.

If green algae and green plants both contain chlorophyll *a*, why doesn't the graph show the peak for chlorophyll *a* in the (green) 560-nanometer range? The brown algae contain chlorophyll *c*, which is not shown on the graph. Is it reasonable to think that chlorophyll *c* might absorb light in the green range? Why or why not?

MULTICELLULAR ALGAE AND GREEN PLANTS

	Photosynthetic Pigments	Stored Product From Photosynthesis	Major Component of Cell Wall
Brown Algae	Chlorophyll *a* Chlorophyll *c* Carotenoids	Lamarin Mannitol	Cellulose
Red Algae	Chlorophyll *a* Chlorophyll *d* Carotenoids	Floridean starch Mannitol	Cellulose
Green Algae	Chlorophyll *a* Chlorophyll *b* Carotenoids	Starch	Polysaccharides Cellulose in many
Green Plants	Chlorophyll *a* Chlorophyll *b* Carotenoids	Starch	Cellulose

ABSORPTION SPECTRA

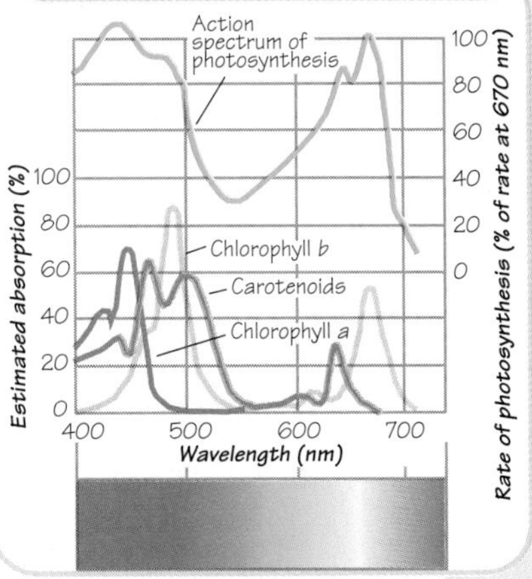

THINK ABOUT IT

1. What can you **conclude** about the evolution of green plants from a comparison of the characteristics of the three types of multicellular algae and green plants?
2. How might differences in the types of pigments present in the green, red, and brown algae account for the differences in their color? **Explain** the significance of these differences.
3. Using information from this chapter, **list** at least one other similarity between green plants and multicellular algae.

TEACHER SUPPORT

Managing Classroom Diversity

TECH PREP STUDENTS
Have students who plan to work in biological or medical laboratories prepare a report about the use and preparation of agar-agar for culturing bacteria. Ask that they explain where the material originates, what its function is in a culture, and how such cultures are prepared.

MULTICULTURAL STRATEGY
Have interested students visit an Asian restaurant to interview a chef about the uses of algae in the foods. Ask other students to visit a store that sells Asian foods or health foods to find out what products contain some kind of algae.

Problem Solving
Interpreting Graphs
Marveling at Multicellular Algae

Students will draw on their understanding of the differences between the three phyla of multicellular algae, and of the role of pigments in photosynthesis.

State Students must compare the characteristics of multicellular algae and green plants, as well as the action and absorption spectra for photosynthesis.

Solve Members of all three algae phyla contain chlorophyll *a* and carotenoids, but only green algae contain chlorophyll *b*. Plants also contain chlorophyll *a*, chlorophyll *b*, and carotenoids, so it is likely that plants evolved from green algae.

Chlorophyll *a* reflects green light, which explains why the graph of its absorption spectrum does not peak in the green range. Students can use the action spectrum to conclude that chlorophyll *c* does not absorb any or much green light.

Test Have students research the evolution of green plants and the characteristics of their pigments.

Communicate Ask several students to explain how they interpreted the graph to reach their conclusions.

Answers to THINK ABOUT IT

1. Because the photosynthetic pigments of green plants and green algae are the same, green plants probably evolved from green algae.

2. Differences in types of pigments may account for differences in color because different algae can carry out photosynthesis in different kinds of light.

3. The reproductive patterns of some green algae are similar to those in green plants.

☑ Checkpoint

❶ The combination of the pigments it contains.

Laboratory Investigation

The Laboratory Investigation, Diversity of Green Algae, on pages 570–571, is appropriate to use at this point in the chapter.

Ideas Through Images

Have students examine Figure 24–3, read the caption, and answer the following questions.

- **What is the process that produces the next generation of *Chlamydomonas* when it reproduces asexually?** (In asexual reproduction, haploid cells divide by the process of mitosis to produce the next generation.)
- **In sexual reproduction of *Chlamydomonas,* what does the fusion of gametes produce?** (The fusion of gametes produces a zygote.)
- **How many sets of chromosomes does each gamete have? How many does a zygote have?** (Each gamete has one set, which is to say it is haploid. A zygote has two sets, which is to say it is diploid.)
- **What is the process by which the zygote produces haploid cells?** (Meiosis.)

Correcting Misconceptions

The idea of alternation of generations may confuse some students. They might conclude that every other generation of an organism is radically different. Point out that this use of the term generation has a different meaning from what it might have in another context. Synonyms for this context include phase and stage.

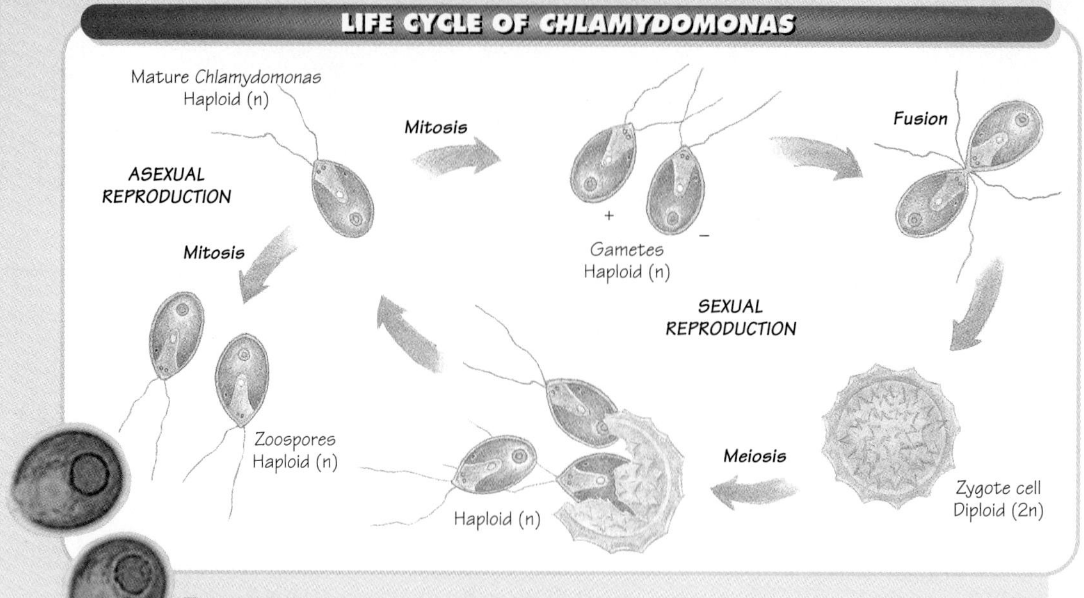

Figure 24–3
The life cycle of Chlamydomonas, *a unicellular green alga, involves asexual as well as sexual reproduction. In asexual reproduction, haploid (n) cells divide by mitosis to produce the next generation of haploid cells. In sexual reproduction, haploid (n) gametes are produced that fuse to form a diploid (2n) zygote. The zygote produces four haploid cells by meiosis.*

Reproduction in Algae

Most green algae have life cycles that involve both sexual and asexual stages. Their reproductive patterns are remarkably similar to plants, and therefore we will look at them in detail. Let's start with *Chlamydomonas*.

Reproduction in *Chlamydomonas*

Chlamydomonas cells have a single set of chromosomes, which is to say they are haploid (n). Under ordinary conditions, *Chlamydomonas* undergoes asexual reproduction, as illustrated in ***Figure 24–3.*** Notice that mature cells divide by mitosis to produce haploid cells, which are called **zoospores.** A zoospore (ZOH-oh-spor) is a reproductive cell that can produce a new individual simply by cell division.

If conditions are unfavorable, especially when the cells are starved for nitrogen, *Chlamydomonas* enters a sexual phase of its life cycle. The cells divide to produce haploid (n) **gametes** of two different mating types. A gamete is a reproductive cell that can produce a new individual only after fusing with a gamete of the opposing mating type.

The zygote grows a thick, protective wall that enables it to survive extremely harsh conditions—something it has to do when a pond dries up or freezes over. When favorable conditions return, the zygote goes through meiosis and produces four haploid cells that break out of the protective wall and swim away. These cells begin the life cycle all over again.

☑ **Checkpoint** What is a zoospore? A gamete? 1

Reproduction in *Ulva*

In some ways, the life cycle of *Ulva* is similar to that of *Chlamydomonas*, but

TEACHER SUPPORT

Background Information

The basic plan of alternation of generations is a life cycle in which diploid (2n) and haploid (n) phases alternate. Use of the term generations can be confusing, since these are phases in one complete life cycle of an organism rather than the production of offspring. The following are generalizations that apply to an alternation of generations in any organism, from algae to vascular plants.

- Any cell of the sporophyte generation is usually diploid (2n).
- Any cell of the gametophyte generation is usually haploid (n).
- The change from sporophyte to gametophyte occurs as the result of meiosis.
- The change from gametophyte to sporophyte occurs as a result of fertilization, or the fusion of gametes.

LIFE CYCLE OF ULVA

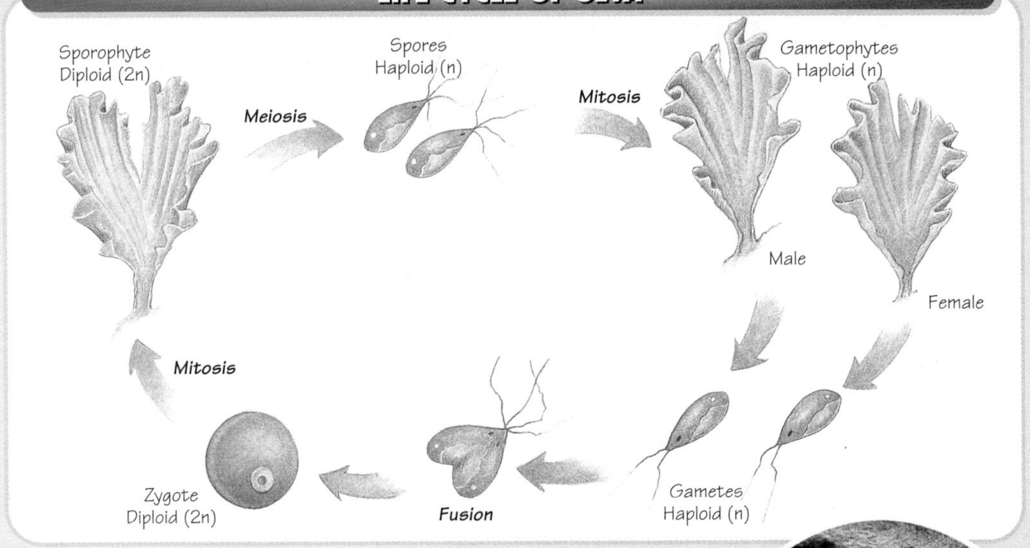

Figure 24–4
Ulva, *a multicellular green alga, has a life cycle that displays the pattern of alternation of generations. Sporophyte plants are diploid (2n) and produce haploid (n) spores by meiosis. The spores germinate to produce male and female gametophytes, which produce haploid (n) gametes. Fertilization of the gametes forms a dipoid (2n) zygote, which gives rise to the diploid sporophyte.*

there are some important differences. As you can see in ***Figure 24–4,*** the diploid and haploid phases of *Ulva's* life cycle are both multicellular. Even though the "plants" of these two stages look almost identical, they produce completely different kinds of reproductive cells.

The life cycle of *Ulva* contains the first hint of a pattern that you will see over and over in plants. Notice that the cycle contains two separate generations—the **sporophyte** (spore plant) and the **gametophyte** (gamete plant). **Because the organism always alternates between sporophyte and gametophyte phases, this pattern of reproduction is called the alternation of generations.** Nearly all plants follow the pattern of **alternation of generations** in their life cycles.

Section Review 24–1

1. **Compare** the characteristics of multicellular algae and plants.
2. **Explain** what is meant by alternation of generations.
3. **Critical Thinking—Comparing** How is reproduction in *Chlamydomonas* similar to that in *Ulva?* How is it different?

Ideas Through Images

Have students examine Figure 24–4, read the caption, and answer the following questions.

- **What is the pattern called by which *Ulva* reproduces?** (Alternation of generations.)
- **Which generation, or phase, produces haploid spores?** (The sporophyte generation.)
- **What process is involved in producing those spores?** (Meiosis.)
- **Which generation produces gametes?** (Gametophyte.)
- **What does the fusion of the gametes produce?** (A zygote.)
- **What does the zygote grow to become?** (The sporophyte generation.)

4 ASSESS

Quick Check

Ask students to make a table that contains information about the three phyla of multicellular algae. This table should include the names, characteristics, and examples of each phylum.

Checkpoint

1 A zoospore is a reproductive cell that can produce a new individual simply by cell division. A gamete is a reproductive cell that can produce a new individual only after fusing with a gamete of the opposing mating type.

Section Review 24–1

1. Both plants and multicellular algae contain pigments used in photosynthesis, and the reproductive patterns of many multicellular algae are very similar to those of plants. But multicellular algae do not have many structures that plants have.

2. A pattern in which an organism alternates between a sporophyte generation and a gametophyte generation.

3. In both *Chlamydomonas* and *Ulva*, haploid gametes fuse to produce a diploid zygote. In *Chlamydomonas*, this process occurs only when environmental conditions become unfavorable. Otherwise, that alga undergoes asexual reproduction. In *Ulva*, this process occurs in the normal alternation of generations when the alga is in the gametophyte phase.

Learning Modality

Auditory Learning Ask a student to describe orally any step in the life cycle of *Ulva*. Stop the student at any point and ask another student to continue. Keep going around the class until all students have contributed, thus describing many complete cycles of the alternation of generations.

Ancillary Support

The resources below can be used to support your teaching strategy for these two pages.

LM Observing the Characteristics of Multicellular Algae, #47
TR Enrich: The Awful Algae

Section 24–2

Bryophytes

Performance Objectives

- Describe some of the adaptations of bryophytes for life on land.
- Identify the stages in the life cycle of a moss.

Mini Lab Skill: Comparing

1 ENGAGE

Inquiry Activity

Designing an Experiment

What's So Good About Peat Moss?

Ask students why they think people use peat moss for growing plants in pots and gardens. Then provide groups with peat moss (*Sphagnum* spp.), as well as soil, beakers of various sizes, and a supply of water. Ask each group to design an experiment that will demonstrate a characteristic of peat moss that would be useful to a gardener. Most students will infer that peat moss absorbs water, and they will design an experiment to show superior water-absorbing ability when compared with soil.

Ideas Through Images

Have students examine Figure 24–5, read the caption, and answer the following questions.

- **What are the three types of bryophytes?** (Mosses, liverworts, and hornworts.)
- **Because bryophytes are on the boundary between aquatic and terrestrial plants, in what kinds of environments would you expect them to be found?** (In wet environments, often near bodies of water.)
- **The bug-on-a-stick moss gets its name from the stalk and capsule on its sporophyte. What does this imply about reproduction in bryophytes?** (A sporophyte is one phase in an alternation of generations. This implies that bryophytes reproduce sexually with an alternation of generations.)

Section 24–2 Bryophytes

Guide for Reading

- Identify some of the adaptations bryophytes needed to live on land.
- Describe the life cycle of a moss.

MINI LAB

- Compare the male and female structures of a moss plant.

LIVING ON LAND IS A TOUGH business. To thrive on land, a plant at the very least must be able to resist drying out by drawing enough water from the soil when water is not directly available. In addition, because the buoyant effect of water is absent, a land plant must develop structures to support itself against gravity. Although a few algae do manage to survive on land, their thin walls and lack of specialized tissues make it difficult for them to thrive in dry environments.

Adaptations of the Bryophytes

How have plants responded to the challenges posed by land? The first land plants were most likely close relatives of the green algae that could live out of water at least part of the time. About 400 million years ago, two important groups of multicellular plants evolved from these pioneering algae—bryophytes and tracheophytes.

Bryophytes, meaning "moss plants," are only partially adapted to life away from water. **Bryophytes have waxy coverings that protect them against water loss. In addition, special structures enclose their reproductive cells to prevent them from becoming dry.** Bryophytes display a distinct alternation of generations. And in most species, the sporophyte develops as an embryo inside the female gametophyte, which also helps to protect it from drying out.

Figure 24–5 Bryophytes are marginally adapted to life on land and can be considered to be on the boundary between aquatic and terrestrial plants. Bryophytes include (a) the bug-on-a-stick moss, Boxbaumia aphylla, *which gets its name from the shape of the stalk and the capsule of its sporophyte, (b) hornworts, such as* Ceratophyllum demersum, *and (c) liverworts, such as* Lunularia.

TEACHER SUPPORT

Background Information

The transition to land by photosynthesizers probably began before the end of the Ordovician Period, about 438 million years ago, as green algae adapted to freshwater rivers, lakes, and ponds. This adaptation entailed the development of toughened cell walls to limit the exchange of water between the inner cell and the outer fresh water. The next step was to populate seasonal ponds, spring seeps, and other areas that were wet some of the time. The first land plants, which appear in the fossil record during the Silurian Period, were probably bryophytes, or bryophytelike ancestors of both bryophytes and vascular plants. These early bryophytes lived along shady water margins, since their gametes still required damp conditions to travel. Because of such algaelike characteristics, bryophytes have been less successful on land than vascular plants.

To a limited extent, bryophytes are able to gather water from moist soil and pass it from cell to cell. These plants are anchored to the soil by **rhizoids** (RIGH-zoidz), thin filaments that absorb water and nutrients from the soil. However, bryophytes do not have special fluid-conducting tissue, which is one of the reasons why they have remained small. In fact, the tallest known bryophytes are only about 20 centimeters tall!

☑ *Checkpoint* What are rhizoids? (1)

Mosses

The most widespread bryophytes are the mosses. They are found throughout the world in damp locations, and for some animals they prove to be an important source of food. **Like all bryophytes, mosses have a life cycle that involves alternation of generations between a haploid gametophyte and a diploid sporophyte.**

When a moss spore lands on wet soil, it germinates and grows into a tangle of thin filaments known as a **protonema** (proht-oh-NEE-muh). As the protonema gets larger, its filaments become more organized. Eventually, it grows upward, producing a leafy moss plant. These green moss plants are the gametophyte stage of the moss life cycle.

Gamete Formation and Fertilization

Mosses produce gametes—sperm and eggs—in special structures at the tips of the gametophyte plants. Some species produce both sperm and eggs on the same plant, whereas in other species the two sexes are on separate plants.

Although the gametes are protected against drying out, there is only one way for the flagellated sperm to get to the egg cells—that is, by swimming to them. This means that mosses cannot reproduce unless they are soaked with water. If there is enough water around for the sperm to swim to the eggs, sperm and egg fuse to form a diploid zygote that grows into a sporophyte. In mosses, the sporophyte grows right out of the body of the gametophyte and is dependent on the gametophyte for food and moisture.

Spore Formation

As the sporophyte matures, it develops a capsule at the top of a stalk. In the capsule, cells from the sporophyte undergo meiosis to produce haploid spores. Upon maturing, the capsule breaks open and the spores are scattered by the wind.

☑ *Checkpoint* What are the stages in the life cycle of a moss? (2)

MINI LAB .... Comparing

Male or Female?

PROBLEM *How do the male and female structures of a moss plant compare?*

PROCEDURE

1. Obtain a set of moss samples from your teacher.
2. To observe the samples under a microscope, prepare a wet-mount slide of each sample by adding a drop of water and then covering with a coverslip.
3. Observe under the low-power objective of a microscope and make a drawing of your observations.
4. Identify each moss sample as male or female by using ***Figure 24–6*** on page 564.

ANALYZE AND CONCLUDE

1. What is the function of each of the structures you observed?
2. What is the relationship between the shape of the structure and its function?
3. From which structure will the new sporophyte grow after fertilization?
4. Which stage in the moss's life cycle do these plants represent?

2 EXPLORE

MINI LAB Comparing

Teacher Notes

- For time required and materials needed, see page 556b.
- Obtain moss plants in damp, shady areas or through a biological supply house.

Answers to Analyze and Conclude

1. The function of the male structure is to produce sperm. The function of the female structure is to produce eggs and to house the fertilized egg that grows into the new sporophyte.
2. The male structure is bud-shaped and enclosed, which is necessary to hold and protect the sperm until they are released into water. The female structure is vase-shaped and open at the top, which allows for the entry of the sperm needed for fertilization.
3. The new sporophyte will grow from the female structure.
4. These structures represent the gametophyte stage of the moss's life cycle.

Skills Trace
Comparing
- Focus p. 563
- Practice p. 564
- Assess p. 574

☑ Checkpoints

(1) Thin filaments that absorb water and nutrients from the soil.

(2) The gametophyte stage, during which gametes are produced; and the sporophyte stage, during which spores are produced by meiosis.

TEACHER SUPPORT

Managing Classroom Diversity

EDUCATIONAL EQUITY
Have students investigate the work of Winona Hazel Welch (1896–1991), a professor at DePauw University from 1939 to 1961. After she received her doctorate from Indiana University in 1928, she did research in bacteriology and plant pathology before concentrating her efforts on the study of mosses. Her efforts culminated in the user-friendly *Mosses of Indiana* and the scholarly *Fontinalaceae*, a detailed examination of a little-known moss group.

GIFTED STUDENTS
Ask students to investigate hornworts and liverworts and make a presentation to the class about these bryophytes. Help them find visual aids that would enhance their presentation, such as pictures or slides that could be used in a microprojector.

3 TEACH

Ideas Through Images

Have students examine Figure 24–6, read the caption, and answer the following questions.

- **Which generation of moss is the form of the plant with which you are most familiar?** (The gametophyte.)
- **What reproductive cells do gametophytes produce?** (The gametophytes produce the gametes, sperm, and eggs.)
- **The fusion of the gametes results in what generation of the organism?** (The sporophyte.)
- **When a spore germinates, it produces a protonema. What does that look like?** (Algae.)

4 ASSESS

Quick Check

Have students make an outline of the subsection entitled Mosses. Then ask them to compare their finished outlines with the life cycle shown in Figure 24–6.

Section Review 24–2

1. Bryophyte adaptations include waxy coverings that protect them against water loss, special structures that prevent their reproductive cells from becoming dry, and rhizoids that absorb water and nutrients from the soil.

2. Students' responses should mention the gametophyte stage and the sporophyte stage and reflect the details shown in Figure 24–6.

3. Students should hypothesize that bryophytes evolved from green algae for two reasons: Bryophytes have the same green pigments as the green algae, and the reproduction of bryophytes is quite similar to that of green algae.

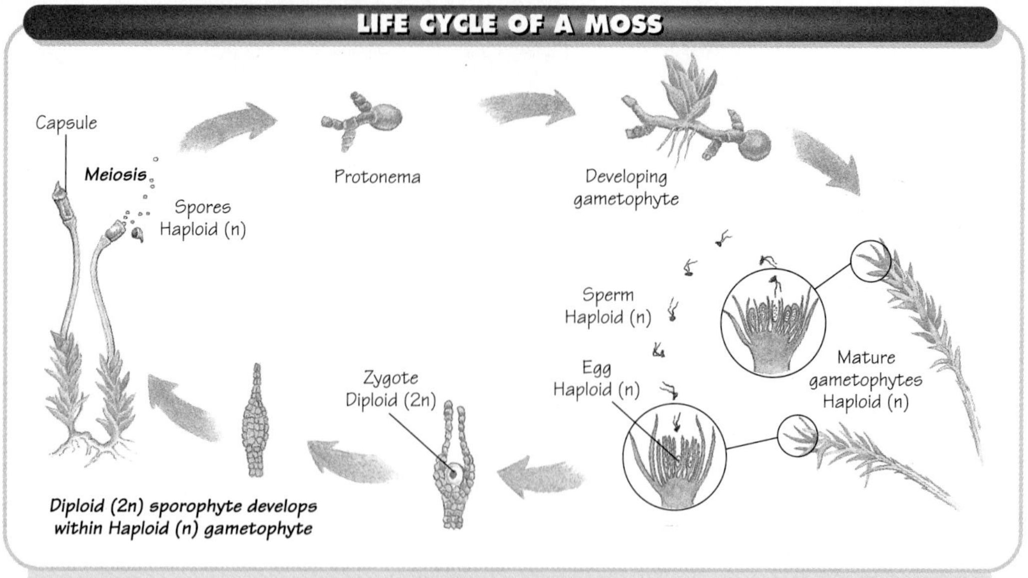

Figure 24–6
Reproduction in mosses involves alternating generations of diploid (2n) sporophytes and haploid (n) gametophytes. The leafy moss plants are the gametophytes that produce the sperm and the eggs. Upon fertilization, which requires standing water, the diploid (2n) sporophyte emerges within the gametophyte plant. The mature sporophyte develops a capsule in which haploid (n) spores are produced by meiosis. The spores then germinate and grow into gametophytes.

Hornworts and Liverworts

Hornworts and liverworts, which are also bryophytes, are similar to the mosses in many ways. The name liverwort comes from the way in which the lobes of liverwort gametophytes resemble the lobes of a liver.

Hornworts and liverworts are particularly dependent upon water and are generally found in places that remain damp year-round. They are covered with a waxy cuticle to protect against water loss, they have rhizoids that attach them to the soil, and they show an alternation of generations in their life cycles.

Section Review 24–2

1. **Identify** some of the adaptations bryophytes needed to live on land.
2. **Describe** the life cycle of a moss.
3. **Critical Thinking—Hypothesizing** From which algal group—brown, red, or green—do you think bryophytes evolved? Give evidence to support your hypothesis.
4. **MINI LAB** How do the male and female structures of a moss plant compare?

564 Chapter 24

4. The male structure of a moss plant is enclosed and bud-shaped, whereas the female structure is open and vase-shaped.

Skills Trace
Comparing
- Focus p. 563
- Practice p. 564
- Assess p. 574

Learning Modality

Visual Learning Have pairs of students create a flip book of the life cycle of a moss that begins and ends with a drawing of a gametophyte.

Seedless Vascular Plants

GUIDE FOR READING

- **Explain** the main characteristic of vascular plants.
- **Describe** the life cycle of a fern.

MINI LAB

- **Calculate** the number of spores produced by a mature fern frond.

FOSSILS INDICATE THAT THE very first land plants appeared roughly 450 million years ago. For a while, these plants were quite small, not unlike today's bryophytes. Vast land areas were still unoccupied because they were too dry for the survival of the bryophytes. Then, about 420 million years ago, something happened, and a sudden explosion of plant diversity took place. Much larger plants appeared—some of which were the size of small trees. These new plants were not only bigger, they were also able to invade land that was too dry to support bryophytes or algae.

Origins of Vascular Plants

How did the new plants manage to survive on much drier land? Fossils show that the plants had an evolutionary novelty, a type of cell that was specialized to conduct water. These cells, which are called **tracheids** (TRAY-kee-ihdz), are hollow, have thick cell walls to resist pressure, and are connected end to end like a series of drinking straws. Plants with tracheids, called **vascular plants,** can draw water from the ground and transport that water through the tracheids to reach the higher parts of the plants.

Vascular plants, or tracheophytes—which means "plants with tracheids"—developed vascular systems that draw water from deep in the ground and carry it to great heights. The development of a vascular system made it possible

Figure 24–7 Plants with vascular tissues are able to draw water from land. Among these are (a) club mosses, such as Lycopodium, *(b) horsetails, such as* Equisetum arvense, *used in colonial times as scouring pads to clean pots and pans, and (c) brachen ferns. (d) These structures, called fiddleheads, are unfurling fern fronds, which are eaten as a delicacy at this tender stage.*

SECTION 24–3

Seedless Vascular Plants

Performance Objectives

- Describe the function of the tracheid.
- Identify the stages in the life cycle of a fern.

Mini Lab Skill: Calculating

1 ENGAGE

Inquiry Activity

Observing

Fun With Ferns

Ask students if they have ever closely examined a fern frond. Give each student a frond from a fern plant. Also provide rulers, scissors, slides, and microscopes. Ask students to write the best description of the frond that they can, including such characteristics as size, color, structure, and so on. Students should also make diagrams of what they see, both with the naked eye and under the microscope. Once everyone has completed the activity, have volunteers present their findings.

TEACHER SUPPORT

Managing Classroom Diversity

MULTICULTURAL STRATEGY

Have students investigate the many uses of ferns and fern fronds in cultures around the world. Some students could concentrate on the uses of ferns in folk medicine; others could investigate the use of fern fronds in the construction of thatch houses in Asia and the South Pacific. Still others could find out how ferns are used in the exquisitely beautiful gardens of Japan.

TECH PREP STUDENTS

Ask students who plan careers in forestry to find out what kinds of club mosses, horsetails, and ferns are indigenous to your area. Most libraries have books in the reference section on local flora, and these can be used to identify ferns that students might find in a local park or woodland area.

Ancillary Support

The resources below can be used to support your teaching strategy for these two pages.

LM Comparing Multicellular Algae, Ferns, and Mosses, #48
TR Explore: Brilliant Bryophytes
BL Inquiry Activity: The Great Cover-Up

2 EXPLORE

MINI LAB Calculating

Teacher Notes

- For time required and materials needed, see page 556b.
- Obtain mature fern fronds from a garden store or florist. Be certain to obtain a species that has the brown sori on the underside of the frond. Ferns can also be found in damp, wooded areas.

Answers to Analyze and Conclude

1. Answers will depend on the species of fern, as well as the individual frond.
2. The number of sori will vary depending on the species and the individual frond.
3. Most students should reason that not all spores fall on an area where there is enough moisture or nutrients to support growth and development.

Skills Trace
Calculating

- Focus p. 566
- Practice p. 567
- Assess p. 575

3 TEACH

Ideas Through Images

Have students examine Figure 24–8, read the caption, and answer the following questions.

- **Which generation in the life cycle of the fern is the large, leafy plant we all know?** (The sporophyte.)
- **How is the gametophyte produced? What does it produce?** (The sporophyte produces spores. Under the right conditions, a spore will grow into the gametophyte, which produces the gametes.)

MINI LAB .... Calculating ......

Spores in a Sorus

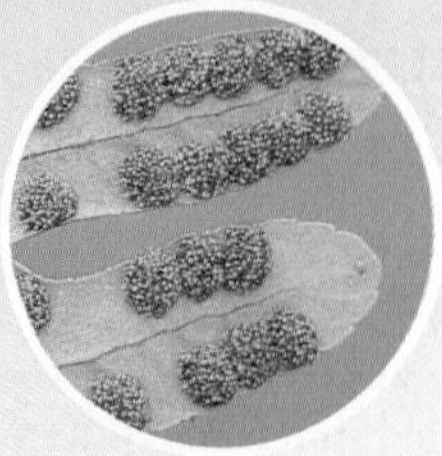

PROBLEM *How can you **calculate** the number of spores produced by a mature fern frond?*

PROCEDURE

1. Obtain a fern frond. Draw and label the frond, identifying the sori.
2. Using a dissecting needle, gently scrape some sori from a frond onto a microscope slide. **Caution:** *Be careful using a dissecting needle.* Add a drop of water and cover with a coverslip.
3. Observe the slide under the low-power objective of a microscope, then make a drawing of what you see.
4. Calculate the number of spores in a single sorus.

ANALYZE AND CONCLUDE

1. How many leaflets are on your fern frond?
2. What is the average number of sori on each leaflet? From your estimated number of spores, calculate the number of spores produced by a mature fern frond.
3. Why aren't there as many fern plants growing on Earth as the number of fern spores produced?

for these plants to develop true roots, stems, and leaves. From forests to grasslands to deserts, these plants now dominate Earth's landscapes. Because they are such a diverse lot, the tracheophytes are further classified into several divisions. In this chapter, we will consider only those tracheophytes that do not form seeds—the seedless vascular plants.

Checkpoint What are vascular plants? 1

Club Mosses and Horsetails

Not long after the first vascular plants appeared on Earth, two groups rapidly diversified and gave rise to an astonishing variety of species. Some, including the club mosses, were placed in the Division Lycophyta (ligh-koh-FIGHT-uh), and others, such as the horsetails, were placed in the Division Sphenophyta (sfee-noh-FIGHT-uh). Plants from these two groups formed the Earth's first great forests, and for more than 100 million years were the largest of the land plants.

Many of these species grew to heights of up to 40 meters. That's as tall as a 12-story building! Today these plants are represented by just a few species, most of which grow in damp, well-shaded places in the forest. These plants have large, independent sporophytes. It's usually the sporophytes that we notice, because the gametophytes are much smaller and grow along the forest floor.

Checkpoint How are club mosses and horsetails classified? 2

Ferns

Ferns are found throughout the world and are some of the most popular houseplants among plant enthusiasts. The Division Pterophyta (ter-oh-FIGHT-uh), in which ferns are placed, includes about 12,000 species, most of which grow in warmer regions. Ferns have an excellent vascular system, well-developed underground stems called **rhizomes,** and large leaves known as **fronds.**

Checkpoint What are rhizomes? Fronds? 3

Sporophyte

The large, visible fern plant that you are probably familiar with is the sporophyte in the fern's life cycle. **Like the life cycle of other plants, the life cycle of the fern involves alternation of generations.** Fern sporophytes are diploid and produce haploid spores by meiosis. Spores form on the undersides of

TEACHER SUPPORT — Activity

AN ALTERNATION OF GENERATIONS

Ask students if they can describe what grows from fern spores. After students have responded, ask them to test their predictions by actually planting fern spores. Divide the class into groups, and have each group follow these steps.

1. Prepare a pot of soil by filling the pot with soil and peat moss and adding a layer of sand on top. To eliminate bacteria in the soil, pour boiling water into the pot, letting the water drain through the bottom. Let the soil cool.
2. Take a fern frond that has spores on its underside and tap it over a sheet of paper. Then sprinkle the spores onto the sand in the pot.
3. Cover the pot with plastic wrap and place it on a saucer of water. Let it stand for several weeks and observe what grows.

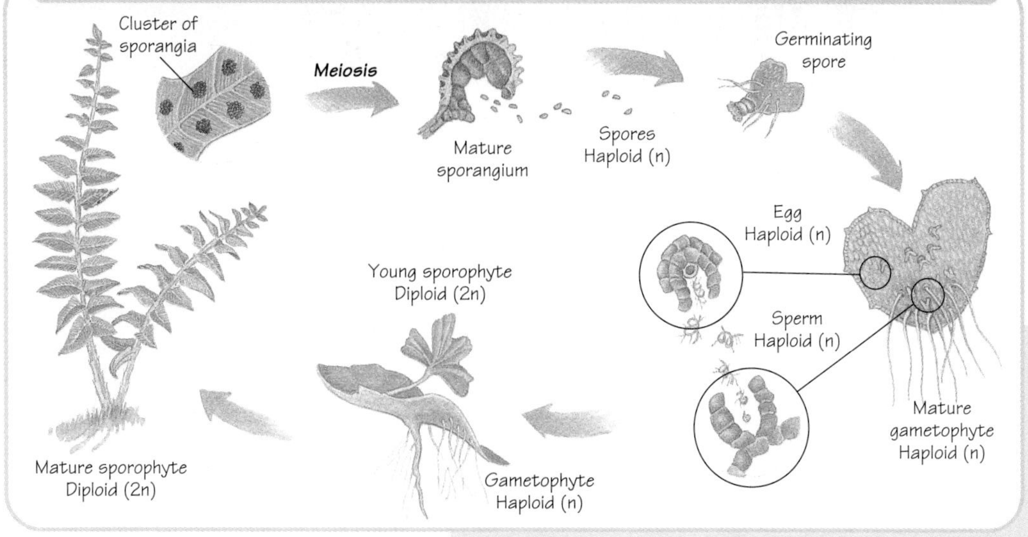

the fronds in little chambers known as **sori** (singular: sorus). When the spores mature, these chambers burst open, releasing the tiny spores that may be scattered by wind or water. When a spore settles on rich, damp soil, it germinates and begins to grow into a tiny plant.

Figure 24–8
The fern life cycle displays the characteristic pattern of alternation of generations of diploid (2n) sporophytes and haploid (n) gametophytes. The gametophytes are tiny and grow from germinating spores on the forest floor. Fertilization of the haploid (n) gametes requires watery conditions and results in the formation of a diploid (2n) zygote. The zygote develops into the mature sporophyte, the large fern plant with fronds and sori.

Gametophyte

The plants that develop from spores are independent haploid gametophytes. Fern gametophytes are small heart-shaped plants just one cell thick. Most are no more than a centimeter or two across. On the underside of the gametophyte, sperm and eggs develop in tiny reproductive organs. When the ground is moist enough, the flagellated sperm cells emerge from the underside of the plant and swim into the open chambers containing eggs. The fertilized zygote that results from the fusion of sperm and egg is a diploid cell that develops into an embryo. That embryo grows right out of the gametophyte and becomes the large, independent sporophyte.

Section Review 24–3

1. **Explain** the main characteristics of vascular plants.
2. **Describe** the life cycle of a fern.
3. **Critical Thinking—Hypothesizing** What advantage might there be for a plant's life cycle to undergo alternation of generations?
4. **MINI LAB** How can you **calculate** the number of spores produced by a mature fern frond?

4 ASSESS

Quick Check

Ask students to make a flowchart that describes the steps in the life cycle of a fern from sporophyte to sporophyte. They may use information both from the text and from Figure 24–8.

Section Review 24–3

1. The presence of tracheids, cells that conduct water through a plant.
2. See Figure 24–8.
3. Some students might suggest that each of the two generations requires different environmental conditions, and thus an alternation of generations is an adaptation to an environment in which the amount of water available varies through the year.
4. By multiplying an estimate of the number of spores in a sorus by the number of sori on a leaflet by the number of leaflets on a frond.

Checkpoints

1. Plants that have a vascular system that can draw water from the ground and carry it to great heights.
2. Club mosses make up the class Lycophyta, and horsetails make up the class Sphenophyta.
3. Rhizomes are the well-developed underground stems of ferns, and fronds are the large leaves of ferns.

Skills Trace

Calculating

- Focus p. 566
- Practice p. 567
- Assess p. 575

Learning Modality

Visual Learning Have students refer to Figure 24–8 as you hold up to the class fern parts or pictures of fern parts. Ask student volunteers to describe the corresponding step in the fern life cycle.

Ancillary Support

The resources below can be used to support your teaching strategy for these two pages.

TR Writing in Biology: Interior Design
Apply: Fern Facts
BL Inquiry Activity: Water When You Need It
TB Life Cycle of a Fern, #31

SECTION 24–4

Algae in Our World

Performance Objectives

- Describe the role that algae play in nature.
- Identify ways in which humans use algae.

1 ENGAGE

Ideas Through Images

Have students examine Figure 24–9, read the caption, and answer the following questions.

- **Why is the sea otter wrapped in algae?** (To keep from being washed away by the waves.)
- **Where is the alga found in the sushi?** (It is the wrapping around the rice, which contains small pieces of fish or vegetables.)
- **Why do you think a substance derived from seaweed is placed in ice cream?** (Students' answers may vary.)

2 EXPLORE

Investigate

Cooperative Learning Ask cooperative groups to find a recipe that includes some kind of alga as an ingredient, and then prepare that food for the class. Point out that many recipes, especially Asian, Pacific Island, and vegetarian dishes, include some form of seaweed or sea vegetable as an ingredient. Ask that when groups find such a recipe, they make an attempt to classify the type of alga used, at least by phylum.

24–4 Algae in Our World

GUIDE FOR READING

- **Explain** the role of algae in nature.
- **List** ways in which algae benefit humans.

AS YOU HAVE SEEN, THE multicellular algae, bryophytes, and seedless vascular plants are three extremely diverse groups of organisms. Each has a long fossil history, and each has helped to shape the patterns of life on Earth for many millions of years. What roles do these organisms play in the natural world, and how do humans use them? In this section, we will examine the role of algae in our world.

Shaping the Environment

All the photosynthetic organisms have had major roles in shaping Earth's environment. They are at the base of the food chain in local habitats throughout the biosphere. Algae and photosynthetic prokaryotes, for example, are food for most of the life in the ocean, and without them animal life underwater would not be possible. **The algae produce an enormous share of atmospheric oxygen. They also provide the oxygen dissolved in fresh and salt water that makes aquatic animal life possible.**

Algae, along with mosses, are among the few organisms that can grow on rocks and gravel. Their actions help to break down minerals and mix them with organic matter to form soil, making it possible for other plants to follow them.

Checkpoint How do photosynthetic algae contribute to the biosphere? (1)

Benefit to Humans

Many algae are used by humans around the world. **Algae are used in the processing of foods, chemicals, and even wastewater.**

Figure 24–9 Algae are widely used by a variety of organisms. (a) This otter wraps itself in strands of brown kelp to keep from being swept away by waves. Many people enjoy eating foods such as (b) ice cream and (c) sushi, which are made using types of red and brown algae.

TEACHER SUPPORT

Historical Perspective

The ability to study bacteria outside a living body is crucial to combatting diseases they cause. Robert Koch (1843–1910), a German bacteriologist, was the first to perfect a method for doing so. The growth medium he used first was beef broth. The addition of the protein gelatin to the broth solidified the medium, but a problem remained. Many bacteria could digest the gelatin, and the result was the formation of little puddles in the medium, making it difficult to study the bacteria. The solution came in 1881 from the wife of one of Koch's co-workers, who told Koch about the agar-agar she used in cooking as a solidifying agent. Koch found that this substance, produced by the red alga *Gelidium*, could not be digested by bacteria, and agar (the current term for agar-agar) has been used in laboratories as a culture medium ever since.

Sources of Food

Have you ever eaten algae? Whether or not you knew it, the answer is almost certainly yes. Large, thin sheets of the red alga *Porphyra* are dried and used as a food wrapping, called *nori* in Japanese. Small pieces of fish or vegetables are placed on a bed of rice and wrapped in *nori* to produce the dish called sushi.

You've never eaten sushi? Well, chances are you've had ice cream, marshmallows, or a candy bar. Nearly all brands of these foods contain *algin*, a carbohydrate produced by brown algae and used as a thickening agent. Carrageenan (kar-uh-GEEN-uhn) is a carbohydrate produced by red algae and is used to stabilize pie fillings, puddings, and even toothpaste. Many algae are also rich sources of vitamin C and iron, and they are used to enrich other foods.

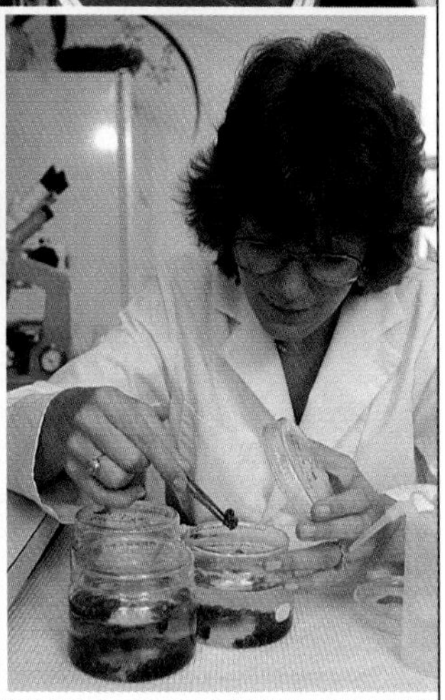

Figure 24–10
The chemical industry has found many uses for algae and their products, such as in (a) *the manufacture of paints.*
(b) CAREER TRACK *The diverse uses of algae by humans is the result of the research performed by phycologists. Phycologists study the structures and functions of algae.*

Uses in Industry

The range of chemical compounds produced by algae makes them especially useful to industry. Chemicals from algae are used to make plastics, waxes, transistors, deodorants, paints, lubricants, and even artificial wood. Algae have important uses in scientific laboratories. The compound agar-agar, extracted from certain red algae, is used to make the nutrient mixtures in which biologists grow bacteria and other organisms.

Wastewater Treatment

Wastewater is usually high in nutrients. These nutrients can upset the balance of life in freshwater streams and lakes if released into these waters. Many wastewater treatment plants use large, shallow holding ponds stocked with algae that absorb the nutrients. The treated water, with a smaller concentration of nutrients, can be safely released into the environment—thanks to the algae.

Section Review 24–4

1. **Explain** the role of algae in nature.
2. **List** several uses of algae that benefit humans.
3. **BRANCHING OUT ACTIVITY** Visit a pet shop that sells fishes and aquariums for household setups. Find out how an aquarium is designed to manage the growth of algae. In a brief report, **describe** what you learned.

3 TEACH

Discussion

Begin a discussion of how algae are beneficial to humans by showing students a food label that lists algin. Ask students familiar with Japanese foods to describe the seaweeds, or algae, used in those foods. Then review the various uses of algae in industry and wastewater treatment. Emphasize the important role the algae product agar has in the culturing of bacteria.

4 ASSESS

Quick Check

Have students make two lists, one of the ways in which algae are important in shaping the environment and the other of the ways algae and algae products are used by humans.

Section Review 24–4

1. Algae are among the photosynthetic organisms that form the base of food chains throughout the biosphere. Algae produce an enormous share of atmospheric oxygen, and they also provide the oxygen dissolved in fresh and salt water. They grow on rocks and gravel and break down minerals that mix with organic matter to form soil.

2. Humans use algae as sources of food, in chemical compounds in various industrial products, in scientific laboratories, and in wastewater treatment.

3. Students might discover various strategies for managing algae growth in an aquarium. These include keeping the aquarium out of direct sunlight, adding algae-eating snails to the environment, and using an algae scraper to keep the sides of the aquarium clean.

Learning Modality

Auditory Learning Question students orally about how algae shape the environment and how algae are of benefit to humans.

☑ Checkpoint

1. Photosynthetic algae contribute to the environment by producing an enormous share of atmospheric oxygen and providing the oxygen dissolved in fresh and salt water that makes aquatic animal life possible.

Ancillary Support

The resources below can be used to support your teaching strategy for these two pages.

TR Explore: Algae for Everyone
BL Inquiry Activity: Algae All Around

CHAPTER 24

Laboratory Investigation

Diversity of Green Algae

Before the Lab

1. Obtain living cultures of the different forms of green algae from a biological supply house.
2. Place each of the four forms at separate stations around the laboratory.

Pre-Lab Discussion

Have students read the entire procedure for this investigation. Then ask students the following questions.

What is the purpose of this investigation? (To compare different forms of algae within the phylum Chlorophyta.)

Why do these forms of algae appear green? (They each contain the green pigments chlorophyll *a* and *b*, which reflect green light.)

What is the purpose of making drawings of what you see under the microscope? (To create a detailed record of what has been observed that can be used later for study and comparison.)

Skills Development

Students will use these skills while completing the laboratory investigation: observing, communicating, comparing, and drawing conclusions.

Teaching Strategies

1. Demonstrate for students how to prepare a wet-mount slide, if necessary.
2. Demonstrate how to separate a strand of *Spirogyra* into a 2-cm segment with a dissecting needle. Tell students that this measurement need not be exact. The purpose is only to prepare a sample that will fit on the slide.
3. Make sure students make their drawings as they observe the different forms rather than later from memory.

Laboratory Investigation

Diversity of Green Algae

Green algae are members of the phylum Chlorophyta. All organisms within this phylum contain chlorophyll and are able to perform photosynthesis. In this investigation, you will observe several samples of green algae and compare their characteristics.

Problem

How do the different multicellular forms of green algae **compare?**

Materials (per group)

- living cultures of *Chlamydomonas, Spirogyra, Volvox,* and *Ulva*
- microscope slides
- medicine dropper
- coverslips
- dissecting needle
- microscope

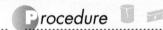

Procedure

1. **Using a medicine dropper, place one drop of the *Chlamydomonas* culture on a microscope slide. Cover with a coverslip as shown in the diagram. Observe under the low-power objective of a microscope. Draw a diagram of what you see and label the cell wall, nucleus, chloroplast, and cytoplasm.**
2. **Obtain a strand of *Spirogyra* and place it on a slide. Separate the strand into a 2-cm segment using a dissecting needle. CAUTION: *Be careful when using a dissecting needle.* Add a drop of water if necessary and cover with a coverslip. Focus the image under the low-power objective and then switch to the high-power objective. Observe the shape and draw a diagram of at least two cells of the filamentous alga. Label the cell wall, nucleus, chloroplast, and cytoplasm.**
3. **Place one drop of the *Volvox* culture on a microscope slide and cover with a coverslip. Again, observe the organism under the low-power objective and then switch to the high-power objective. Observe the structure of the organism and observe any movement that occurs. Draw a diagram of *Volvox* and label a chloroplast and flagellum.**

Safety Tip

Remind students to use caution when handling the dissecting needles.

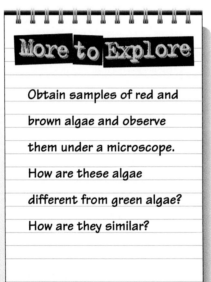

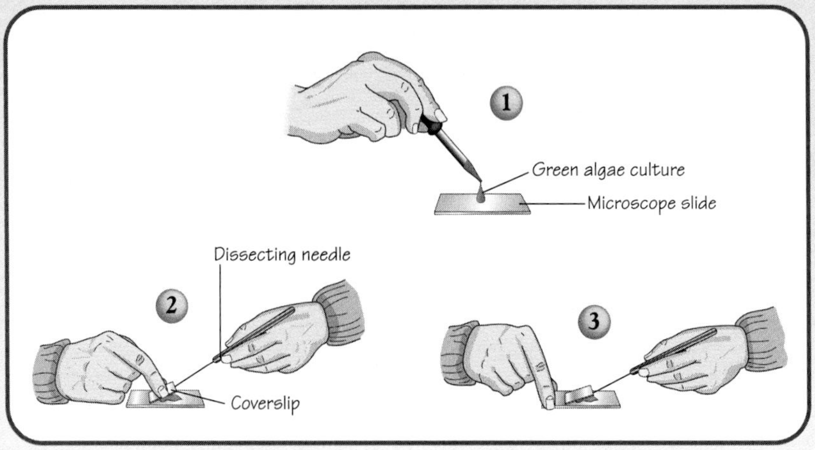

4. Separate a small piece of the *Ulva* from the specimen sample. Add a drop of water and then cover with a coverslip. As before, focus the image under the low-power objective of a microscope and then switch to high power. Determine the number of cells in the field of view. Draw a diagram of at least three cells, then label the nucleus, cell wall, chloroplast, and cytoplasm.

Observations

1. Describe the structure of each of the green algae you observed.
2. What features or characteristics do the green algae share?
3. Describe the motion of the *Volvox* you observed under the microscope.

Analysis and Conclusions

1. Compare the characteristics of the green algae you observed. Discuss their shape, structure, and motility. Construct a table to illustrate your answer.
2. Compare the arrangement of the chloroplasts among the specimens you observed. Why are they arranged in this way?
3. Why is there so much diversity within such a small classification of organisms? Explain your answer.

More to Explore

Obtain samples of red and brown algae and observe them under a microscope. How are these algae different from green algae? How are they similar?

Answers to Analysis and Conclusions

1. Students' tables should contain the general characteristics of each of the forms of algae. In comparing the different forms, students should note that all but *Chlamydomonas* are multicellular and that only *Chlamydomonas* and *Volvox* are motile.
2. The chloroplasts vary in size and shape among the different forms. In *Chlamydomonas*, each cell contains one cup-shaped chloroplast. In *Spirogyra*, ribbonlike chloroplasts are spirally arranged in each cell. In *Volvox*, each cell contains two starlike chloroplasts. In *Ulva*, chloroplasts are extremely small and ill-defined. The arrangement of chloroplasts is related to adaptations each form made as it evolved in a specific environment.
3. Great diversity exists within the phylum because of how each form adapted to the conditions of the environment in which it evolved.

More to Explore

Students might obtain samples of red and brown algae by collecting them from natural environments, or they could use samples or prepared slides from school. These algae vary widely, but in each case students should note the differences in the pigments when compared with green algae. They are similar in the structure of their cells.

Answers to Observations

1. Students' descriptions should include the general characteristics of each form of green algae. *Chlamydomonas* is a single-celled form whose oval cells move with a pair of flagella. *Spirogyra* is a multicellular alga whose cylindrical cells form unbranched filaments, or threads of watersilk, its common name. *Volvox* is a colonial form whose rounded cells live in spherical colonies. *Ulva*, or sea lettuce, is a multicellular form with a structure similar to a crinkly edged, flattened leaf.
2. They consist of green cells that contain chloroplasts, a nucleus, a cell wall, and cytoplasm.
3. A *Volvox* colony moves in a rolling or tumbling fashion, caused by the beating of flagella on the perimeter of the colony.

CHAPTER 24

Study Guide

Review Strategy

Ask small groups of students to prepare flashcards that contain the details of one of the life cycles described in this chapter, including, *Chlamydomonas*, *Ulva*, a moss, and a fern. Then have groups working on different life cycles meet to quiz one another using the flashcards. Ask that after initial use, groups revise their cards, either to clarify illustrations or to increase or decrease the difficulty.

Study Guide

Summarizing Key Concepts

The key concepts in each section of this chapter are listed below to help you review the chapter content. Make sure you understand each concept and its relationship to other concepts and to the theme of this chapter.

24–1 Multicellular Algae

- Algae are photosynthetic aquatic organisms that are classified as protists.
- Brown and red algae are multicellular marine organisms. Most green algae are unicellular freshwater organisms.
- Reproductive patterns in green algae are similar to those in plants. Haploid (n) *Chlamydomonas* cells divide by mitosis to produce haploid zoospores. Under unfavorable conditions, *Chlamydomonas* cells divide to produce gametes that fuse to form a diploid (2n) zygote. The zygote later undergoes meiosis to produce haploid cells.
- The multicellular green alga *Ulva* alternates between generations of diploid (2n) sporophytes and haploid (n) gametophytes.

24–2 Bryophytes

- Bryophytes—such as mosses, hornworts, and liverworts—have waxy coverings, which protect them against water loss, and special structures that enclose their reproductive cells to keep them from becoming dry.
- Like all bryophytes, mosses have a life cycle that involves alternation of generations between a haploid (n) gametophyte and a diploid (2n) sporophyte.

24–3 Seedless Vascular Plants

- Tracheophytes, such as club mosses, horsetails, and ferns, are vascular plants—plants with fluid-conducting tissue.
- The life cycle of a fern alternates between the generations of sporophyte and gametophyte.

24–4 Algae in Our World

- Algae produce an enormous amount of atmospheric oxygen and much of the oxygen dissolved in fresh and salt water that makes aquatic life possible. Algae and photosynthetic prokaryotes are food for most of the life in the ocean.
- Many algae are used by humans around the world. Algae are used in the processing of foods, chemicals, and wastewater.

Reviewing Key Terms

Review the following vocabulary terms and their meaning. Then use each term in a complete sentence.

24–1 Multicellular Algae
alga
zoospore
gamete
sporophyte
gametophyte
alternation of generations

24–2 Bryophytes
rhizoid
protonema

24–3 Seedless Vascular Plants
tracheid
vascular tissue
rhizome
frond

Inquiry-Based Strategy

Have students investigate when plants arose on land and what plants were prominent in ancient environments by asking them the following questions: When did plants first live on land? How long did it take for vascular plants to dominate the land? What did a typical land environment look like during specific periods of the Paleozoic and Mesozoic eras?

Ask groups of students to investigate these questions and prepare a report, including some kind of visual presentation, for the class. Students might approach this task by making detailed illustrations tied to specific points on a geologic time scale. They could find such information in the library by examining books on Earth history, paleontology, and evolution.

Recalling Main Ideas

Choose the letter of the answer that best completes the statement or answers the question.

1. Why are multicellular algae considered plants?
   - **a.** They live on land.
   - **b.** They are protists.
   - **c.** Their reproductive cycles are similar to those of plants.
   - **d.** They are multicellular organisms.
2. The algae that live at great ocean depths are
   - **a.** red algae.
   - **b.** brown algae.
   - **c.** unicellular algae.
   - **d.** multicelluar algae.
3. Which is not a green alga?
   - **a.** *Ulva*
   - **b.** *Fucus*
   - **c.** *Volvox*
   - **d.** *Spirogyra*
4. What enables bryophytes to absorb water and nutrients from the soil?
   - **a.** vascular tissue
   - **b.** tracheids
   - **c.** ribosomes
   - **d.** rhizoids
5. Moss sperm and eggs form a zygote that grows into a
   - **a.** capsule.
   - **b.** zoospore.
   - **c.** gametophyte.
   - **d.** sporophyte.
6. In asexual reproduction, *Chlamydomonas* cells produce
   - **a.** haploid gametes by mitosis.
   - **b.** haploid gametes by meiosis.
   - **c.** diploid zoospores by meiosis.
   - **d.** haploid zoospores by mitosis.
7. In reproduction in *Ulva,* diploid plants produce
   - **a.** haploid spores by meiosis.
   - **b.** haploid spores by mitosis.
   - **c.** diploid spores by meiosis.
   - **d.** diploid spores by mitosis.
8. Large ferns used as decorative houseplants represent which stage in the fern's life cycle?
   - **a.** gametophyte
   - **b.** sporophyte
   - **c.** zygote
   - **d.** zoospore
9. Which functions do algae perform in nature?
   - **a.** provide food for sea animals
   - **b.** produce atmospheric oxygen
   - **c.** provide oxygen to fresh and salt water
   - **d.** all of the above

Putting It All Together

Using the information on pages xxx to xxxi, complete the following concept map.

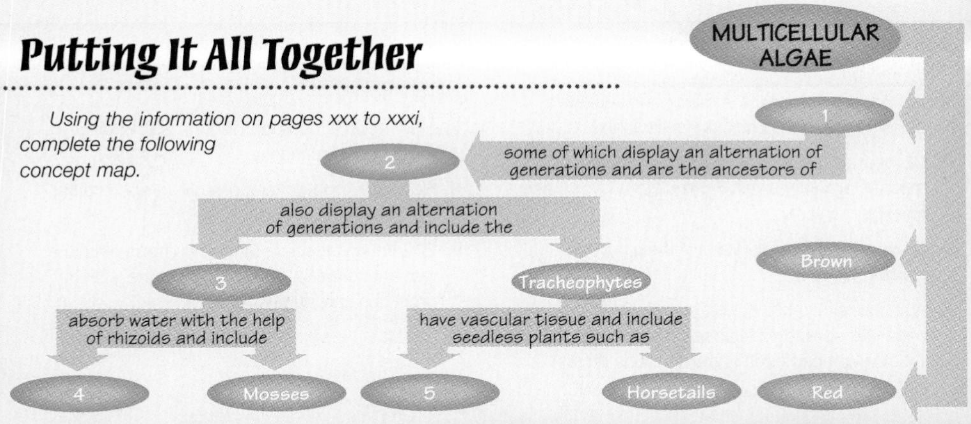

Putting It All Together

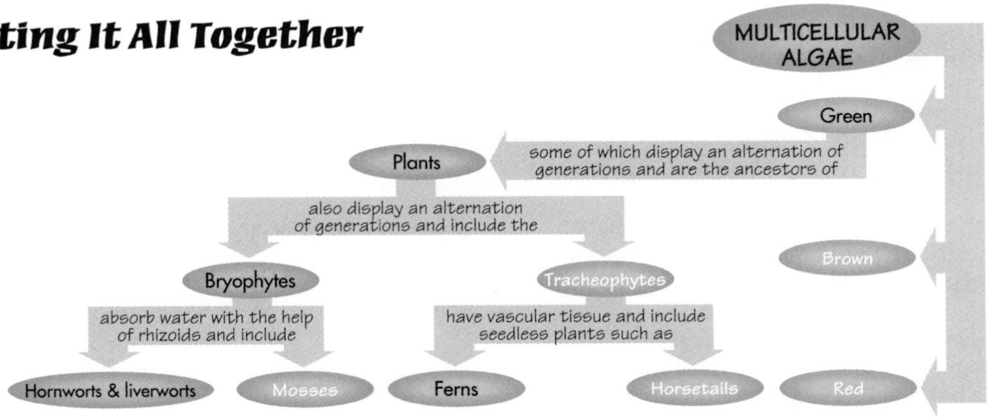

Recalling Main Ideas

1. c
2. a
3. b
4. d
5. d
6. d
7. a
8. b
9. d

Assessment

Reviewing What You Learned

1. Photosynthetic aquatic organisms that are classified as protists.
2. All algae are similar to plants in that they have pigments that carry out photosynthesis. Some algae have reproductive cycles that are very similar to those in plants. Algae are different from plants in that they have no adaptations that allow life out of water.
3. Multicellular algae that contain both yellow-orange pigments and the green pigment chlorophyll.
4. Red algae are green, purple, or reddish-black multicellular algae that contain a bright red pigment, the green pigment chlorophyll, and additional pigments.
5. Green algae are different from red and brown algae in the pigments they contain. Also, most green algae live in fresh water and are remarkably similar to green plants.
6. A reproductive cell that can produce a new individual only after fusing with a gamete of the opposing mating type. A reproductive cell that can produce a new individual simply by cell division.
7. A pattern in which an organism alternates between a sporophyte generation and a gametophyte generation.
8. Bryophytes were able to live on land through adaptations that included a waxy covering, special structures enclosing their reproductive cells, and rhizoids.
9. See Figure 24–6.
10. A tracheid is a type of cell that is specialized to conduct water.
11. A sorus is a chamber on the underside of a fern frond where spores are formed.
12. Ferns have excellent vascular systems, whereas mosses have no vascular tissue.
13. Algae are used in some foods, in numerous industrial products, in scientific laboratories, and in wastewater treatment.

Assessment

Reviewing What You Learned

Answer each of the following in a complete sentence.

1. What are algae? How are they classified?
2. List ways in which algae are similar to plants. How are they different from plants?
3. Describe the characteristics of brown algae.
4. Describe the characteristics of red algae.
5. How are green algae different from red and brown algae?
6. What is a gamete? A zoospore?
7. Define alternation of generations.
8. How were the bryophytes able to live on land?
9. Sequence the steps in the life cycle of a moss.
10. What is a tracheid?
11. What is a sorus?
12. Why can ferns survive in more extreme conditions than can mosses?
13. How do humans use algae?

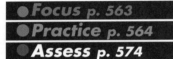

Expanding the Concepts

Discuss each of the following in a brief paragraph.

1. **Compare** the reproductive cycle of *Ulva* with that of *Chlamydomonas.*
2. What were some of the major adaptations plants evolved in order to live on land?
3. Compared to the size of most land plants, mosses are very small. Formulate a hypothesis to explain this fact.
4. Draw and label a diagram of the life cycle of a moss.
5. Approximately 420 million years ago, plants began to spread to all areas of the Earth. What might explain this tremendous increase in land plants?
6. Which group of algae are the most likely ancestors of land plants? Give reasons to support your answer.
7. How does alternation of generations differ in ferns and in mosses?
8. How does the development of a spore differ from that of a zygote?
9. Why must mosses—and even ferns—have a wet environment at least part of the year in order to reproduce?
10. Discuss the significance of the role of algae in nature.

Assessment (continued)

Expanding the Concepts

1. In both *Chlamydomonas* and *Ulva,* haploid gametes fuse to produce a diploid zygote. In *Chlamydomonas,* this process occurs only when environmental conditions become unfavorable. In *Ulva,* this process occurs in an alternation of generations when the alga is in the gametophyte phase.

Skills Trace

Comparing

Focus p. 563

Practice p. 564

Assess p. 574

2. Major adaptations that allowed plants to live on land included waxy coverings, special structures to prevent reproductive cells from becoming dry, rhizoids that absorbed water and nutrients from the soil, and tracheids and other vascular tissue.
3. Students' hypotheses should relate that mosses are very small because they have no vascular system to transport water to great heights, which is necessary in a large plant.
4. See Figure 24–6.
5. A tremendous increase in the population of a certain type of organism depends on the development of an adaptation to environmental conditions. For plants, that adaptation was a vascular system, which made it possible for plants to develop true roots, stems, and leaves. This adaptation explains the increase.
6. Green algae are the most likely ancestors of land plants. Like plants, they have cell walls made of cellulose and the green pigments chlorophyll *a* and *b,* and they store food in the form of starch. Their reproductive patterns are remarkably similar to those of plants.
7. In mosses, the familiar, larger plants are the gametophytes; the sporophytes grow out of the body of gametophyte plants and are dependent on them for food and moisture. Ferns differ in that the large, visible fern plants are the sporophytes. The gametophytes that develop from the spores released by the sporophytes are small, independent plants.
8. A spore develops through meiosis, and thus is haploid (n). A zygote results from the fusion of two gametes, and thus is diploid (2n).
9. Both mosses and ferns produce flagellated sperm cells. The only way these gametes can reach egg cells for fertilization is to swim, and that requires a wet environment.
10. Algae, as photosynthetic organisms, are at the base of food chains in local habitats throughout the biosphere. In addition, they produce an enormous share of atmospheric oxygen and provide the oxygen dissolved in fresh and salt water that makes aquatic life possible. Algae also grow on rocks and gravel, thereby breaking down minerals and mixing them with organic matter to form soil.

Extending Your Thinking

1. See Figures 24–4, 24–6, and 24–8. Title of diagram: Alternation of Generations.

Extending Your Thinking

Use the skills you have developed in this chapter to answer the following.

1. **Synthesizing** Examine the life cycles of *Ulva,* mosses, and ferns. Draw a generalized, labeled diagram that represents the main elements shared by the cycles. What would be the title of this diagram?
2. **Calculating** Choose a flowering plant in or around your home. Select a segment of that plant and count the number of blossoms on the selected segment. From this number, estimate the total number of flower blossoms on the entire plant.
3. **Relating** In the early stages of space exploration, scientists considered sending single-celled algae into space with astronauts to provide many of the astronauts' needs. Identify what these needs are and predict how the algae would meet them.
4. **Inferring** Some people who tire of taking care of their pet fishes get rid of them by releasing them into lakes and streams. Many of these fishes die because they are placed in environments with which they are incompatible. Hawaii, for example, has lost a number of native fish species because of the release of algae-eating fishes into native streams. Explain why the native species might have died.
5. **Predicting** Green algae have fewer accessory pigments—pigments other than chlorophyll that absorb light energy and pass it to chlorophyll—than do red or brown algae. Based on this information, would you expect to find green algae in shallow or deep water? Where would you expect to find red algae? Brown algae?

Applying Your Skills

Have You Eaten Your Algae Today?

Algae are used in the manufacture and processing of several foods. In this activity, you will read food labels and ingredient lists in order to identify the use of algae.

1. For one week, keep a record of the food products you eat that contain algae. Be sure to look at the labels of foods such as cereals, milk, and ice cream.
2. At the end of the week, prepare a list of the forms of algae or algae extracts that were used. Which type of algae is used most often in the food products you researched?
3. Share your list with other students and prepare a combined list for your class.

• GOING FURTHER •

4. Write an essay about the role of algae in your life.

2. Responses will depend on the plant each student chooses. In making their calculation, students should count the number of blossoms on the segment and multiply that number by an estimated number of how many such segments would make up the whole plant.

Skills Trace
Calculating

- Focus p. 566
- Practice p. 567
- Assess p. 575

3. Students should identify the astronauts' basic needs as food, oxygen, and water. They might predict that algae could meet the food need. Algae might meet the oxygen need if light was provided so they could carry out photosynthesis. Algae could also help to meet the water need through their use in treatment of waste water.

4. Algae are at the base of the food chain in habitats throughout the biosphere. If an algae-eating fish were introduced into a stream, it could change the food chain by consuming the base. This could eliminate the food source required by native species, resulting in their death.

5. Some students might predict that the accessory pigments in red and brown algae would allow them to live at greater depths than green algae, which would more likely be found in shallow water. This reasoning holds true for red algae, which contain pigments that allow them to use the blue-green light that extends deep into ocean water. Both brown and green algae lack such pigments, and thus can live only near the surface.

Applying Your Skills

Teacher Notes

- Review with students where to look on a package for a list of ingredients.
- Tell students they should look for terms such as algin, alginates, and carrageenan. Algin or alginates can be found in such foods as ice cream and pudding. Carrageenan is often used as a stabilizer in chocolate milk.
- After students have completed their lists, initiate a class discussion about the algae and algae extracts that were found most often. Also discuss ethnic foods that utilize algae. Then have students write their essays.

Scoring Rubric

4 Response is thorough, accurate, and creative; shows an in-depth understanding of science skills, procedures, and concepts.

3 Response is complete, mostly accurate, and original; shows a satisfactory understanding of science skills, procedures, and concepts.

2 Response is mostly complete but includes some inaccuracies; shows an adequate understanding of science skills, procedures, and concepts.

1 Response is only partially complete and has many inaccuracies; shows an incomplete understanding of science skills, procedures, and concepts.

0 Response is mostly incomplete and/or inaccurate; shows a lack of understanding of science skills, procedures, and concepts.

Chapter 25 Plants With Seeds

Content Management	Student Edition Activities
■ Section 25–1 Seed-Bearing Plants, pp. 577–579 Seeds Reproduction	MINI LAB: Peanut With a Purpose, p. 578
■ Section 25–2 Gymnosperms, pp. 580–583 Divisions of Gymnosperms Reproduction in Conifers	MINI LAB: Cones and More Cones, p. 583
■ Section 25–3 Angiosperms, pp. 584–589 From Gymnosperms to Angiosperms The Flower Reproduction in Angiosperms Seed Formation Monocots and Dicots	MINI LAB: Flower Power, p. 585
◆ BRANCHING OUT • In Depth Section 25–4 What's in a Fruit?, pp. 590–593 Types of Fruits Fruits and Seed Dispersal	Laboratory Investigation: Structure of a Pea Pod, pp. 594–595

■ These sections cover all the necessary content and concepts for an enriched course in biology.
◆ This section covers content and concepts that are either applications or extensions of the enriched material.

Integration Strategies

SE Earth Science, p. 584

Assessment Strategies

SE Chapter Review, pp. 596–599
TR Section Reviews
Chapter Test
BL Practice Test
Chapter Review
CTB Chapter 25 Test

Tech Prep

Teaching strategies appropriate for students who are in technical/vocational programs or who are considering post-secondary technical education can be found on the following **TE** pages: 581, 586, and 590.

Meeting the Standards

Sections 25–1 through 25–4 cover one of the six content standards under **The Cell,** all five of the content standards under **Biological Evolution,** and one of the five content standards under **The Interdependence of Organisms** as described on pages 184–186 of The National Science Education Standards.

Chapter Planning Guide

Teacher's Edition Activities	Other Activities	Media and Technology
Chapter Discovery Learning Activity, p. 576 **Inquiry Activity:** How Long Do Seeds Last?, p. 577	**TR** Writing in Biology: Garden Design Explore: Sproutin' Around **BL** Inquiry Activity: How Does Your Garden Grow?	
Inquiry Activity: Characteristic Gymnosperms, p. 580 **Investigate:** Cooperative Learning, p. 581	**TR** Enrich: Flourishing Fossils **BL** Inquiry Activity: Evergreen or Only Sometimes Green?	**TB** Visualizing the Life Cycle of a Gymnosperm, #32
Inquiry Activity: Characteristic Angiosperms, p. 584 **Inquiry Activity:** A Bloom of Another Kind, p. 586	**LM** Identifying Seed-Bearing Plant Tissues, #49 Comparing Monocots and Dicots, #50 **TR** Apply: Leaf Language **BL** Inquiry Activity: Fruit or Vegetable?	BioVue Plus CD-ROMs: Researching the Forest Canopy **TB** Visualizing the Life Cycle of an Angiosperm, #33
Inquiry Activity: Are There Types of Fruits? p. 590 **Investigate:** Cooperative Learning, p. 591 **Inquiry Activity:** Hitchhiking on You, p. 593	**TR** Explore: The Seedy Side of Fruit **BL** Inquiry Activity: Sailing Seeds	

KEY: **SE** Student Edition **TE** Teacher's Edition **LM** Laboratory Manual **TR** Teaching Resources **BL** BioLog **TB** Transparency Box **CTB** Computer Test Bank

Materials List

TE **Chapter Discovery Learning Activity,** p. 576 (20–30 minutes); apple, knife or scalpel.
SE **MINI LAB: Peanut With a Purpose,** p. 578 (20–30 minutes); peanuts in the shell, hand lens or dissecting microscope.
TE **Inquiry Activity: Characteristic Gymnosperms,** p. 580 (15–20 minutes); photographs or slides of different kinds of gymnosperms.
SE **MINI LAB: Cones and More Cones,** p. 583 (30 minutes); pine branch with female and male cones, hand lens, slide, coverslip, microscope.
TE **Inquiry Activity: Characteristic Angiosperms,** p. 584 (15–20 minutes); photographs or slides of different kinds of angiosperms.
SE **MINI LAB: Flower Power,** p. 585 (30–45 minutes); simple flower (such as a tulip), forceps, scalpel or razor blade, hand lens or dissecting microscope.
TE **Inquiry Activity: A Bloom of Another Kind,** p. 586 (30 minutes); daisy or other composite flower, forceps, scalpel or razor blade, hand lens or dissecting microscope.
TE **Inquiry Activity: Are There Types of Fruits?,** p. 590 (15–20 minutes); a variety of fruits, including various nuts, berries, legumes, drupes, grains, and pomes; masking tape; marking pen.
TE **Inquiry Activity: Hitchhiking on You,** p. 593 (5–10 minutes for walk, 15 minutes to examine seeds); plastic sandwich bags, hand lens.

CHAPTER 25

Plants With Seeds

Introducing the Chapter

. . . In Pictures

These fruits, some of the more popular in our diet, all share this in common: Each is the combination of the seed and ovary of the plant to which it belongs. Have students examine the photograph, read the caption, and answer the following questions.

- **What fruits can you see in this photograph?** (A banana, apple, orange, lemon, peach, pear, pineapple, strawberry, grapefruit, cherry, coconut, and papaya.)
- **What role do you think a fruit, such as an apple, plays in the life cycle of a plant?** (Students will most likely mention the seeds present in the apple and infer that the fruit contains, protects, and nourishes the seeds.)

Teaching Strategy

In the first three sections of this chapter, students are introduced to the seed-bearing plants, gymnosperms, and angiosperms. The focus in this chapter is on the structures and processes involved in reproduction of these plants. The BRANCHING OUT section gives students an in-depth understanding of the role fruits play in the dispersal of seeds.

BIO JOURNAL

The Bio Journal topic can be used to stimulate classroom discussion about the evolutionary advantage a big, fleshy, good-tasting fruit would have for some plants. Ask students to think of ways in which such a structure would help in the dispersal of the plant. Encourage students to formulate hypotheses. Instruct students to keep their entries in their portfolios.

CHAPTER 25

Plants With Seeds

FOCUSING THE CHAPTER
THEME: Patterns of Change

25–1 Seed-Bearing Plants
- Describe the features of seed-bearing plants.

25–2 Gymnosperms
- Identify the characteristics of gymnosperms.
- Sequence the steps in the life cycle of a gymnosperm.

25–3 Angiosperms
- Identify the characteristics of angiosperms.
- Describe the parts of a flower.
- Sequence the steps in the life cycle of an angiosperm.

BRANCHING OUT *In Depth*

25–4 What's in a Fruit?
- Examine the connection between the type of fruit and its role in seed dispersal.

LABORATORY INVESTIGATION
- Observe a pea pod to relate the structures of a fruit to its function.

Biology and Your World
BIO JOURNAL

What characteristics do you think all fruits share? A sweet or tart taste, perhaps? Or soft, juicy centers? In your journal, list the names of some fruits you like or dislike and note any characteristics they have in common. Revisit the list and evaluate your notes after you have read the chapter.

An appetizing variety of fruits

TEACHER SUPPORT

Chapter Discovery Learning Activity

Give each pair of students a ripe apple and a scalpel or paring knife. Ask students to write a description of the outside of the apple before cutting into it. Then instruct them to cut the apple in half and closely examine the inside. **CAUTION:** *Warn students to be careful when handling the scalpel or knife.*

Ask students to write descriptions of the inside of the apple and make drawings of the apple's core. Also ask them to count whatever objects are inside the apple. As a final task, have students formulate a hypothesis about the role the apple plays in the life cycle of an apple tree.

Seed-Bearing Plants

SECTION 25–1

GUIDE FOR READING

- **Define** seed.
- **Explain** why seed-bearing plants are able to live everywhere on Earth.

MINI LAB

- **Observe** the structures of a seed.

DURING THE CARBONIFEROUS Period, most of the Earth was warm and humid. Great forests of seedless plants covered the damp landscape. Then, about 290 million years ago, the Earth's climate changed. The next 50 million years, known as the Permian Period, were marked by the spread of glaciers and widespread drought. In these dry climates, plants that depended on standing water found it more and more difficult to reproduce. By contrast, any plant that was less dependent on water was immediately favored by natural selection.

These conditions affected animals as well as plants. It was during this period that the reptiles, which lay eggs with shells that can survive on dry land, first began to dominate the water-dependent amphibians. Not surprisingly, at the same time, the seed-bearing plants began to out-compete their seedless neighbors.

Seeds

As you know, algae, mosses, and ferns are still present on the Earth, but these plants form only a tiny fraction of the world's great forests and grasslands. The plants that grow everywhere today and the plants that you know from lawns and gardens and fields and farms are quite different from mosses and ferns. These familiar plants have one very important feature in common with each other that makes them different from the plants we examined in the last chapter—their ability to form **seeds.**

The single most important group of plants on land are the seed-bearing plants. These plants all belong to the subphylum Spermopsida (sper-MOP-sih-duh). Why is the ability to form seeds so important? The best way to answer that question is to see exactly how a seed is put together.

Figure 25–1 Plants such as (a) pine, (b) water lilies, and (c) scarlet plume ensure their future generations by the production of seeds.

TEACHER SUPPORT — Historical Perspective

In 1879, a botany professor at Michigan Agricultural College (now Michigan State University) designed a long-term experiment to investigate the survivability of common weed seeds. Dr. W. J. Beal gathered 50 freshly grown seeds from each of 23 different types of plants, including common mallow and common mullein. He then prepared 20 sets of seeds by mixing each set in moist sand that filled a pint bottle. He buried those bottles in a row on a sandy knoll, with the tops left uncovered and the bottles slanting down so that they would not fill with water. Since then, one of Beal's bottles has been dug up every five or ten years to see if any of the seeds in it would germinate. Some of the seeds of three species in the bottle dug up in 1980—after 100 years—still germinated when placed in good growing conditions.

SECTION 25–1

Seed-Bearing Plants

Performance Objectives

- Describe what a seed is.
- Discuss why seed-bearing plants can live anywhere on Earth.

Mini Lab Skill: Observing

1 ENGAGE

Ideas Through Images

Have students examine Figure 25–1, read the caption, and answer the following questions.

- **How are these plants similar to the club mosses, horsetails, and ferns that you studied in Chapter 24?** (They all carry out photosynthesis and have vascular tissue.)
- **How are they different?** (Club mosses, horsetails, and ferns are seedless, while these plants have seeds.)

2 EXPLORE

Inquiry Activity

Designing an Experiment

How Long Do Seeds Last?

Ask students how long they think a seed for a common garden plant could be kept out of soil and still grow if planted in proper conditions. Have them work in pairs to design an experiment that would test the survivability of a certain kind of seed kept away from soil and under a variety of conditions.

Ancillary Support

The resource below can be used to support your teaching strategy for these two pages.

TR Writing in Biology: Garden Design

3 TEACH

MINI LAB Observing

Teacher Notes

- For time required and materials needed, see page 576b.
- If possible, use raw peanuts, which are usually available in health food stores.
- Have students plant several of the raw peanuts and watch them grow. Once a seed sprouts, transfer it to a large container, where it will bloom and produce fruit.
- Have students review and revise their answers to the questions after they have studied Sections 25–3 and 25–4.

Answers to Analyze and Conclude

1. Students might suggest that the entire peanut represents the reproductive package of the peanut plant and that the embryo can be found within the papery covering of each peanut. After completing the chapter, students should conclude that the entire peanut is the fruit. The embryo is found inside the "nut," or seed.

2. Students might suggest that the parts inside the covering are the stored food for the developing plant. After completing the chapter, students should recognize the two parts as cotyledons. The stored food inside the cotyledons is used by humans for food.

Skills Trace
Observing

- Focus p. 578
- Practice p. 579
- Assess p. 598

MINI LAB .... Observing ....

Peanut With a Purpose

PROBLEM *How can you observe the various structures of a seed?*

PROCEDURE

1. Obtain a peanut in its shell. Describe the shell covering.
2. Carefully break open the shell and remove the contents.
3. Select one of the peanuts (the seed) and remove its papery red covering. Then gently separate the two halves of the peanut.
4. Examine the two halves with a hand lens or dissecting microscope. Sketch and label what you see.

ANALYZE AND CONCLUDE

1. What does the entire peanut, including the shell, represent? Where did you find the embryo?
2. What are the names of the two parts found inside the red covering? What is their function? How does their function relate to the importance of peanuts to humans?

A seed is a reproductive package that contains a plant embryo and a supply of stored food inside a protective coating. Seeds are resistant to drying, and most seeds can survive even the most extreme conditions of drought and heat for several years. By producing seeds, a plant seals its next generation into protective packages that can endure the worst that nature may subject them to and then spring to life when conditions are just right.

How are seeds different from the spores that are produced by other land plants? Most seeds are tougher and more resistant to drying than are spores. Seeds contain a fully formed plant embryo, rather than the single cell that is usually found in most spores. Seeds contain stored food—often enormous amounts of it—which spores lack. And many seeds have special tissues or structures that aid in their distribution, making it possible for seeds to find new places to grow far from their parent plants.

The very first seed-bearing plants appeared right alongside the great seedless vascular plants of the Carboniferous Period. As they diversified over millions of years, the seed-bearing plants gradually took over one part of the Earth after another. What has made these plants so successful? It is their independence from water! **The seed-bearing plants, unlike all other plants, do not require standing water for reproduction. This means that they can grow just about anywhere and reproduce at times of the year that are much too dry for ferns or mosses to reproduce.**

☑ *Checkpoint* What is a seed? ❶

Reproduction

Seed-bearing plants, like other plants, display alternation of generations. In ferns, as you may recall, the most visible stage of the cycle is the sporophyte, a large diploid (2n) plant. The fern gametophyte is a tiny independent haploid (n) plant that produces male and female gametes. These gametes require standing water for fertilization, and that is why ferns, despite their vascular tissues, are still dependent upon damp conditions.

The common large plants you see around you are the diploid (2n) sporophytes of seed-bearing plants. Where are their gametophytes? The answer may surprise you. Their gametophytes live inside the sporophyte!

Cones and Flowers

The tiny gametophytes of the seed-bearing plants do not have an independent life of their own. Instead, they live inside special parts of the sporophyte

TEACHER SUPPORT — Background Information

In an attempt to simplify, teachers often refer to pollen grains as gametes. It's important, though, to be clear about exactly what is a gamete and what is a spore. Recall that a gamete is a cell that must fuse with another gamete to form a new individual. Pollen grains, therefore, are not gametes; they are spores because they grow by mitosis into a new individual—the gametophyte. In angiosperms, the true male gametes are the two sperm nuclei that appear in the pollen tube. The true female gametes are the egg cell and the polar nuclei that fuse with the sperm nuclei to form the embryo and endosperm, respectively.

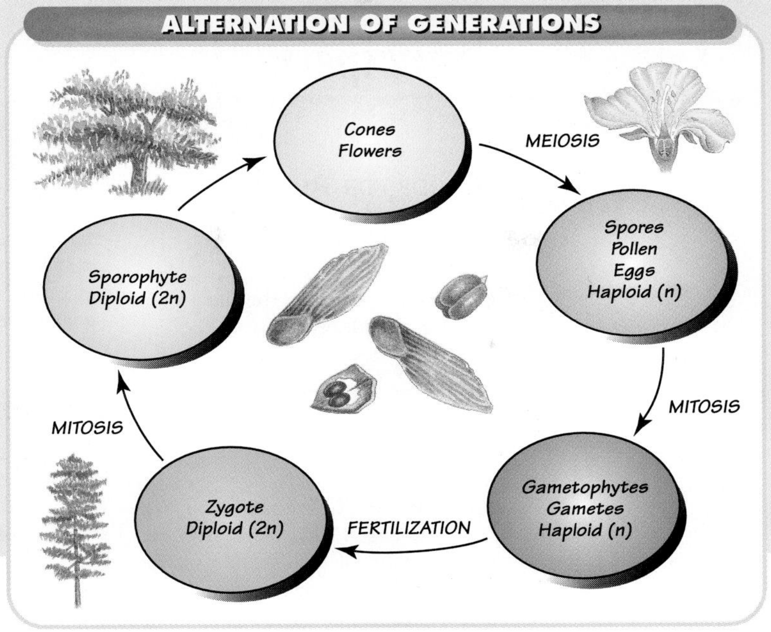

Figure 25–2
Reproduction in seed plants is characterized by the alternation of generations. The mature plant, a diploid (2n) sporophyte, produces reproductive structures known as cones and flowers. The haploid (n) gametes are produced within these structures, and upon fertilization, give rise to the diploid (2n) zygote. The zygote develops into the seed, which is capable of growing into a sporophyte.

plant—parts known as cones and flowers. Pine cones and flowers are home to the gametophyte generation.

Spores

In plants that you have read about so far, the sporophytes produce haploid spores that grow to produce the gametophyte generation. Does this happen in the seed-bearing plants? Yes, but the spores produced by seed plants come in two very different forms—a tiny spore, called **pollen,** and a much larger spore, known as the **egg.**

As you will see, each of these spores grows into a tiny gametophyte that is contained within the much larger body of the sporophyte. Although we will examine the details of this process a bit later, one point is worth emphasizing right now. The fact that the sporophyte contains the gametophyte means that seed plants do not need standing water for reproduction. Millions of years of evolution have produced a kind of plant that, in effect, creates its own little microenvironment for its gametophyte generation. If seed-bearing plants have one unique ability that allowed them to spread to every corner of the planet, this is it—the ability to reproduce without water.

Section Review 25–1

1. **Define** seed.
2. **Explain** why seed-bearing plants are able to live everywhere on Earth.
3. **Critical Thinking—Comparing** How do spores and seeds differ?
4. **MINI LAB** What structures of a seed can you **observe** by examining a peanut?

4 ASSESS

Quick Check

Have students compare the alternation of generations shown in Figure 25–2 with that shown for a moss in Figure 24–6 on page 564.

Section Review 25–1

1. A seed is a reproductive package that contains a plant embryo and a supply of stored food inside a protective coating.

2. The seed-bearing plants do not require standing water for reproduction. This characteristic means that they can reproduce at places and times of the year that are much too dry for other kinds of plants to reproduce.

3. A seed is resistant to drying out and contains a fully formed plant embryo, stored food, and special structures that aid in its distribution. In contrast, a spore is not as resistant to drying out, contains only a single cell of the plant, and has no stored food or special structures for distribution.

4. Structures of a seed that can be observed by examining a peanut include the seed coat, the plant embryo, and the cotyledons containing stored food.

Checkpoint

1 A seed is a reproductive package that contains a plant embryo and a supply of stored food inside a protective coating.

Skills Trace

Observing

- Focus p. 578
- Practice p. 579
- Assess p. 598

Learning Modality

Auditory Learning Ask students to differentiate between seeds and spores by stating a characteristic of one or the other and having another student respond by identifying it with either a spore or a seed.

Ancillary Support

The resources below can be used to support your teaching strategy for these two pages.

TR Explore: Sproutin' Around
BL Inquiry Activity: How Does Your Garden Grow?

SECTION 25–2
Gymnosperms

Performance Objectives
• Identify the main characteristics of gymnosperms.
• Describe the stages in the life of a gymnosperm.

Mini Lab Skill: Relating

1 ENGAGE

Inquiry Activity
Observing

Characteristic Gymnosperms
Display a variety of photographs of examples of gymnosperms taken from old botany books, nature magazines, or personal photographs. You might also show commercial slides of conifers and other gymnosperms on a slide projector. Then have students work in groups to brainstorm for a list of characteristics they think all gymnosperms would exhibit.

Discussion
Initiate a discussion of students' knowledge and experience with evergreens, including common shrubs such as taxus and junipers and common pine and spruce trees. Ask students to compare evergreens with leafy trees, such as maples and oaks. In this comparison, students should mention needles and pine cones, and their staying green throughout the year. Then ask them to recall the life cycles they learned about in the last chapter, such as the cycles of mosses and ferns. Have students speculate about the life cycle of evergreens.

SECTION 25–2 **Gymnosperms**

GUIDE FOR READING
- **Describe** the characteristics of gymnosperms.
- **Outline** the stages in the life cycle of a gymnosperm.

MINI LAB
- **Relate** the structures of male and female cones to their function.

DID YOU KNOW THAT THE world's tallest, largest, and oldest trees all belong to a group of seed-bearing plants called conifers? In California, a coastal redwood has been measured at 114 meters in height. The General Sherman sequoia in Sequoia National Park, also in California, is 11 meters in diameter and has an estimated mass of 2,040 metric tons. And a living bristlecone pine of the western Great Basin has been estimated to be 4900 years old! In this section, you will not only examine the conifers, but also three other groups of seed-bearing plants.

Divisions of Gymnosperms
Today, there are five divisions of living seed-bearing plants. **Four of the divisions, collectively known as gymnosperms, consist of plants that bear their seeds on the surfaces of reproductive structures called scales.** The **scales** are usually grouped into clusters familiarly known as cones. Because their seeds are exposed on the surfaces of the scales, these plants are called **gymnosperms,** which means "naked seeds."

Seed Ferns
The first seed-bearing plants were known as seed ferns. These seed-bearing plants had leaves that were similar to those of ferns. The seed ferns are known only because of the fossils they formed. As far as we know, not a single seed fern exists today.

Figure 25–3 *(a) A closeup of a ginkgo tree shows the "naked" seeds that are characteristic of gymnosperms. (b) The Ginkgo tree, the only living member of the Division Ginkgophyta, is often planted in cities to provide shade and to beautify the area. (c) Although it may look like a palm tree,* Cycas revoluta *is a member of the Division Cycadophyta.*

TEACHER SUPPORT
Background Information
The conifers make up the largest division of gymnosperms, and the largest genus of conifers is *Pinus*, which includes 100 species of pine trees. Pines make up much of the coniferous forests, or taiga, of the Northern Hemisphere. Only one species of pine occurs naturally in the Southern Hemisphere. The pines also claim the oldest living organisms, the bristlecone pines. A bristlecone pine cut down in 1964 was estimated to be 4900 years old.

In North America, the wood of the eastern white pine, *Pinus strobus*, has long been used in furniture making and flooring. It was valued so greatly for use in the masts of sailing ships that in colonial days large trees were marked for use by the English Crown only. American colonists were allowed to use these trees only if they fell on their own, and that is the origin of the term windfall.

Figure 25–4
(a) *Welwitschia mirabilis, one of the rare group of plants classified as gnetophytes, grows in the Namib Desert in southern Africa. The plant shown here is a female plant with mature seed cones.* (b) *Conifers, such as this bristlecone pine, are some of the oldest living organisms. Forests of conifers provide homes for other plants and countless animals—from insects to birds.*

Cycads

Cycads, which are members of the Division Cycadophyta (sigh-KAD-oh-fight-uh) are palmlike plants that first appeared more than 225 million years ago. Cycads were especially common in the forests that were home to the great dinosaurs of the Triassic Period. Cycads are not palm trees, but they are often confused with them. The confusion is easy to understand, especially because one of the most common cycads is called the sago "palm." These beautiful plants are still common in tropical regions of Mexico, Australia, the West Indies, and Florida.

Ginkgoes

Remarkable trees that make up the Division Ginkgophyta (GIHNK-goh-fight-uh) are called ginkgoes. These plants were common in fossils that are dated to be more than 200 million years old. European scientists thought that these organisms were extinct until they discovered that the Chinese have carefully cultivated them as ornamental trees for centuries. The only living species in this class, commonly known as the ginkgo tree, *Ginkgo biloba*, is so similar to its fossil relatives that it may be the oldest living species of seed-bearing plants.

Gnetophytes

Gnetophytes—members of the Division Gnetophyta (NEE-toh-fight-uh)—are rare plants with many characteristics that remind scientists of flowering plants. In fact, some recent evidence suggests that the first plants with true flowers may have evolved from a gnetophyte.

Conifers

Conifers, which make up the Division Coniferophyta (koh-NIHF-er-oh-fight-uh), are sometimes called evergreens. The members of this class include some of the most important of all land plants—spruce, pine, cedar, redwood, fir, and yew trees. Forests of conifers cover vast areas of North America, China, Europe, and Australia.

The leaves of conifers are long and thin—you probably know them as needles. These thin leaves are coated with a tough, waxy substance. Conifer leaves are well adapted to prevent water loss, and most will remain on the plant for years. This, of course, is where the name evergreen comes from, although a few conifers—notably the bald cypress—lose their leaves each year.

☑ **Checkpoint** What are the four living divisions of gymnosperms? (1)

2 EXPLORE

Investigate

Cooperative Learning Have each cooperative learning group make a survey of gymnosperms in a specific area near the school, such as a park, a small neighborhood, or a farm. Ask groups to find a field guide in a library that will help them identify specific trees and shrubs. Their product should be a table that lists identified gymnosperms, cites locations, and gives descriptions.

3 TEACH

Ideas Through Images

Have students examine Figures 25–3 and 25–4, read the captions, and answer the following questions.

- **Together, what do the photographs in these two figures represent?** (They represent the four divisions of gymnosperms.)
- **What's so special about ginkgoes, such as the one shown in Figure 25–3?** (It may be the oldest living species of seed-bearing plants.)
- **Which photograph represents the division of gymnosperms that we often call evergreens?** (The photograph of the bristlecone pine.)

☑ Checkpoint

(1) Cycadophyta, Ginkgophyta, Gnetophyta, and Coniferophyta.

TEACHER SUPPORT

Managing Classroom Diversity

LEP STUDENTS
Give special attention to pronouncing the names for the four divisions of gymnosperms. Point out that the initial letter in cycad and conifer is the same but stands for different sounds because of the vowel that follows each. Make sure students understand that the *g* in gnetophyte is silent.

TECH PREP STUDENTS
Have students who plan careers in forestry or carpentry investigate the types of wood used for construction. Encourage them to do some library research and then to visit a local lumber yard to interview the manager about types of wood sold there.

Ancillary Support

The resources below can be used to support your teaching strategy for these two pages.

TR Enrich: Flourishing Fossils
BL Inquiry Activity: Evergreen or Only Sometimes Green?

Visualizing the Life Cycle of a Gymnosperm

The life cycle of a pine tree is chosen as representative of gymnosperms because conifers make up the majority of gymnosperms and pine trees make up the majority of conifers. Point out to students that members of the other divisions of gymnosperms, and even other members of Coniferophyta, may have variations in their life cycles.

After students have had a chance to look over the visual essay, orally walk through the essay for the class, step by step. In doing so, emphasize the following points.

- A pine tree produces two different types of cones—male cones and female cones. The male cones produce pollen, whereas the female cones produce eggs.
- The pollen grain, which contains sperm cells, will become the male gametophyte once it lands on the female cone. The ovule contains the female gametophyte, which contains an egg.
- When a pollen grain lands on the sticky female cone, it produces a structure called the pollen tube, which very slowly grows through the layer of tissue around the female gametophyte.
- The time between step 5 and step 6—from the landing of the pollen grain to the fusion of gametes—is about 15 months.
- Only one of the sperm cells carried by the pollen grain fuses with the egg cell. The other sperm cell disintegrates.
- Since both sperm and egg cells are haploid, the result of their fusion is a diploid zygote, which will eventually become the diploid sporophyte, or pine tree.

Visualizing the Life Cycle of a Gymnosperm

The pine tree, a gymnosperm, bears cones that produce gametophytes—pollen and eggs. Fertilization leads to the formation of a seed that germinates and grows into a new sporophyte.

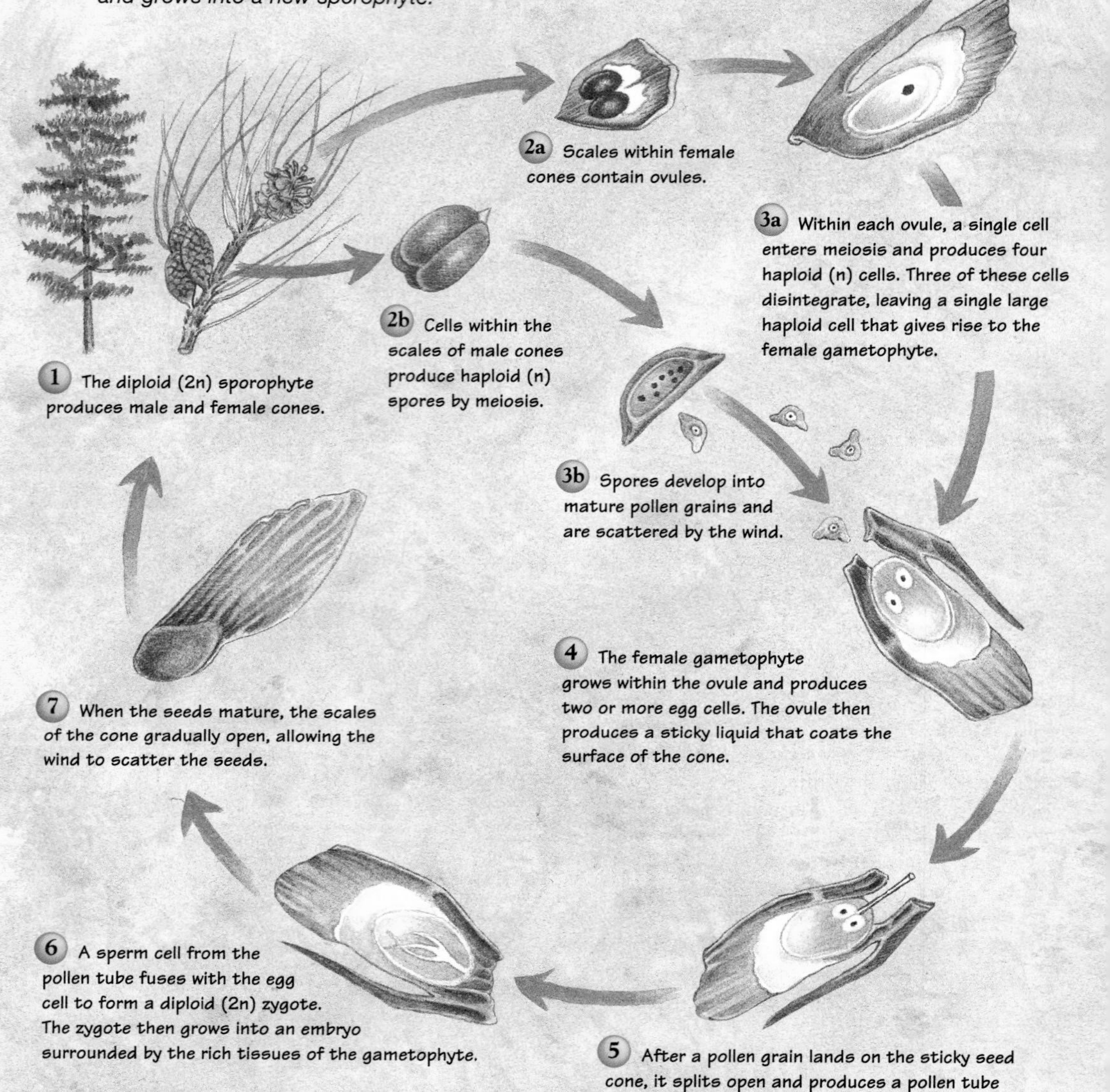

2a Scales within female cones contain ovules.
3a Within each ovule, a single cell enters meiosis and produces four haploid (n) cells. Three of these cells disintegrate, leaving a single large haploid cell that gives rise to the female gametophyte.
1 The diploid (2n) sporophyte produces male and female cones.
2b Cells within the scales of male cones produce haploid (n) spores by meiosis.
3b Spores develop into mature pollen grains and are scattered by the wind.
4 The female gametophyte grows within the ovule and produces two or more egg cells. The ovule then produces a sticky liquid that coats the surface of the cone.
7 When the seeds mature, the scales of the cone gradually open, allowing the wind to scatter the seeds.
6 A sperm cell from the pollen tube fuses with the egg cell to form a diploid (2n) zygote. The zygote then grows into an embryo surrounded by the rich tissues of the gametophyte.
5 After a pollen grain lands on the sticky seed cone, it splits open and produces a pollen tube that penetrates the female gametophyte.

TEACHER SUPPORT

Facts and Figures

- In the life cycle of a pine tree, the pollen tube takes about 15 months after pollination before its contents are discharged and sperm unites with egg.
- There are about 745 known species of gymnosperms, of which some 575 are conifers.
- The amount of wood in the General Sherman sequoia in California is equivalent to the wood in 75 five-room houses or 20 billion toothpicks.
- Although ginkgoes once were widely distributed, as shown by the fossil record, no ginkgoes exist in the wild today. All ginkgoes alive today have been cultivated by humans.
- The gnetophyte shown in Figure 25–4, *Welwitschia*, grows only in the deserts of southern Africa, where average rainfall is 2.5 cm a year. The plant survives on the moisture of fog and dew absorbed through its leaves.

Reproduction in Conifers

As you might expect, the life cycle of a gymnosperm displays alternation of generations—generations of sporophytes and gametophytes that develop within the sporophytes. Most gymnosperms have two kinds of cones. The **male cones** produce pollen, and the **female cones** produce eggs. Because the female cones eventually contain mature seeds, they are sometimes called **seed cones.** Refer to the illustration showing the life cycle of a gymnosperm on page 582.

In a typical gymnosperm, such as a pine tree, the process of fertilization and seed formation may take as long as a year. Female seed cones that appear in one growing season will be fertilized the same year, but they will not be ready to release their seeds until the following season.

Now think for a moment about the way in which the conifer seed is put together. Botanists like to point out that the seed is a product of and contains tissues from three alternating generations! The embryo itself is a diploid sporophyte. It is surrounded by the food-storing tissues of the haploid gametophyte that produced the egg cell. And the whole structure is enclosed in a seed coat formed from the sporophyte generation that produced the seed.

MINI LAB ········ Relating ········

Cones and More Cones

PROBLEM *How do the various structures found on male and female pine cones **relate** to their function?*

PROCEDURE

1. Obtain a pine tree branch with pine cones.
2. Examine a pollen cone. Dust some of the pollen grains on a microscope slide, prepare a wet-mount slide, and observe through the low-power objective of a microscope. Sketch a pollen grain.
3. Look at a seed cone. Observe the scales and note their arrangement. Gently shake the cone. Observe what happens.
4. Remove one of the scales and examine its base. Even if the seeds have been shed, an impression of the seed still remains.
5. Examine a seed cone that has been soaked in water.

ANALYZE AND CONCLUDE

1. How is the structure of the pollen grain related to its function?
2. How is the structure of a seed related to its function?
3. What function do the scales of a seed cone serve? How do the scales on a soaked cone compare with a dry one?

Section Review 25–2

1. **Describe** the main characteristics of gymnosperms.
2. **Outline** the stages in the life cycle of a gymnosperm.
3. **Critical Thinking—Inferring** Why do the male cones of conifers, such as pine, produce large quantities of pollen?
4. **MINI LAB** How do the structures of a male and a female cone **relate** to their functions?

MINI LAB Relating

Teacher Note

- For time required and materials needed, see p. 576b.

Answers to Analyze and Conclude

1. A pollen grain has two tiny wings on either side of its rounded center that aid in its dispersal by wind.
2. The seed coat has a wing that aids in dispersal by wind.
3. The scales cover and protect the seeds. The scales on a soaked cone are closed.

Skills Trace
Relating
- Focus p. 583
- Practice p. 583
- Assess p. 599

4 ASSESS

Quick Check

Have students make a table of the four divisions of gymnosperms that includes the name of each division, general characteristics, and examples.

Section Review 25–2

1. Gymnosperms bear their seeds on the surfaces of reproductive structures called scales, which are usually grouped into clusters known as cones. Gymnosperms reproduce through an alternation of generations, with the gametophytes developing within the sporophytes.
2. See page 582.
3. The pollen of pines is scattered by the wind, so the more pollen grains produced, the more chances that fertilization will occur.
4. The cones are clusters of scales that hold and protect the spores, ovules, or seeds. Cones have reproductive functions.

Skills Trace
Relating
- Focus p. 583
- Practice p. 583
- Assess p. 599

Learning Modality

Visual Learning Have students make a flip book of the life cycle of a gymnosperm, using the visual essay on page 582 for reference.

Ancillary Support

The resource below can be used to support your teaching strategy for these two pages.

TB Visualizing the Life Cycle of a Gymnosperm, #32

SECTION 25–3
Angiosperms

Performance Objectives
- Discuss the main characteristics of angiosperms.
- Describe the parts of a flower.
- Identify the sequence of stages in an angiosperm life cycle.

Mini Lab Skill: Experimenting

1 ENGAGE

Inquiry Activity
Observing

Characteristic Angiosperms
Display a variety of photographs of examples of angiosperms taken from old botany books, nature magazines, or personal photographs. You might also show commercial slides of angiosperms on a slide projector. Make sure many of the photographs or slides show the plants in bloom. Then have students brainstorm for a list of characteristics they think all angiosperms would exhibit.

Ideas Through Images
Have students examine Figure 25–5, read the caption, and answer the following questions.

- **What characteristic shown in the photographs distinguishes angiosperms from gymnosperms?** (Angiosperms produce flowers; gymnosperms do not.)
- **How might the relationship between the ambush bug and goldenrod be beneficial for both organisms?** (The bug receives nourishment from the flower. Some students may know that the bug aids the plant in pollination.)

INTEGRATING EARTH SCIENCE
By examining the fossils, scientists learn about the structure of the plants that grew in earlier periods. From those structures, scientists make inferences about the evolution and environments of those plants.

SECTION 25–3 **Angiosperms**

Guide for Reading
- **Describe** the main characteristics of angiosperms.
- **Identify** the parts of a flower.
- **Outline** the stages in the life cycle of an angiosperm.

MINI LAB
- **Design an experiment** to show how the structures of a flower are related to its function.

THE DOMINANT FORM OF plant life on land today is a class of seed plants known as angiosperms, or flowering plants. They are believed to have evolved from gymnosperms that began a mutually beneficial interaction with animal species such as insects. As the insects benefited by feeding on protein-rich pollen, the plants benefited by gaining a more reliable means of pollination and seed dispersal. In this section, you will read about adaptations in structure and function that led to the overwhelming success of flowering plants.

INTEGRATING EARTH SCIENCE
How do scientists use fossils to determine the nature of plants and animals that lived millions of years ago?

From Gymnosperms to Angiosperms
How are **angiosperms,** members of the Division Anthophyta different from gymnosperms? **Unlike the exposed seeds of gymnosperms, angiosperms produce seeds encased in a protective tissue of the sporophyte known as the ovary.** The combination of seed and **ovary** is known as a **fruit.** The angiosperms have one other distinguishing feature—a specialized reproductive structure known as a **flower.** Hence, the name "flowering plants."

Angiosperms are so common on Earth that you might think they have been around since land plants first appeared. That is not the case, however. They are actually the youngest of all the major groups of plants. The oldest fossils of flowering plants appeared in the

Figure 25–5 Flowering plants such as (a) the blue passion in the rain forest of Central America and (b) the magnificent Gul-Mohur tree in India owe their success to a mutually beneficial relationship they have evolved with insects and other animals for pollination and seed dispersal. An example of such a relationship is (c) the goldenrod plant and the ambush bug sitting on it.

TEACHER SUPPORT
Ecology Note
The oldest angiosperm fossils are fossils of grains of pollen found in southern England that date from the early Cretaceous Period. By the middle of that geologic period, flowering plants had spread and diversified and become very successful. There are a number of reasons for their success, including protecting their seeds inside ovaries. Some biologists also point to the relative quickness with which angiosperms set their seed and grow. During this same period, the giant dinosaurs that had ruled Earth during the Jurassic Period were disappearing. They were replaced by much smaller, low-feeding species. If a plant could not gain a foothold and grow quickly, it would be snatched up by the smaller dinosaurs. In this, the slow-growing gymnosperms were at a disadvantage as opposed to the quick-growing angiosperms.

Visualizing the Life Cycle of an Angiosperm

A mature flowering plant is a diploid sporophyte that produces haploid gametophytes inside the flowers. Fertilization leads to the formation of a seed that germinates and grows into a sporophyte.

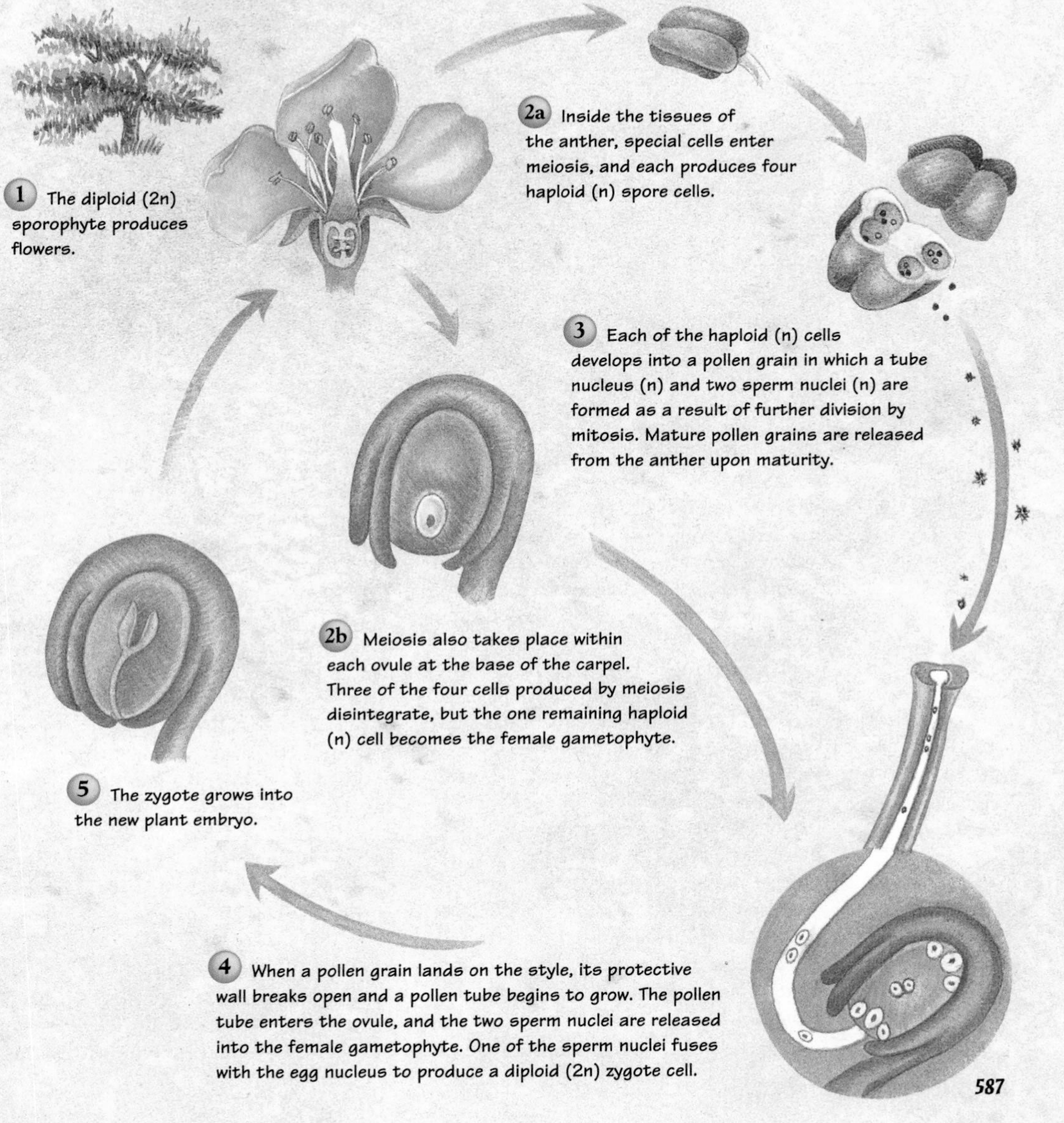

1 The diploid (2n) sporophyte produces flowers.
2a Inside the tissues of the anther, special cells enter meiosis, and each produces four haploid (n) spore cells.
3 Each of the haploid (n) cells develops into a pollen grain in which a tube nucleus (n) and two sperm nuclei (n) are formed as a result of further division by mitosis. Mature pollen grains are released from the anther upon maturity.
2b Meiosis also takes place within each ovule at the base of the carpel. Three of the four cells produced by meiosis disintegrate, but the one remaining haploid (n) cell becomes the female gametophyte.
5 The zygote grows into the new plant embryo.
4 When a pollen grain lands on the style, its protective wall breaks open and a pollen tube begins to grow. The pollen tube enters the ovule, and the two sperm nuclei are released into the female gametophyte. One of the sperm nuclei fuses with the egg nucleus to produce a diploid (2n) zygote cell.

Visualizing the Life Cycle of an Angiosperm

This visual essay is a generalized life cycle of an angiosperm. Point out to students that different angiosperm species may have variations in their reproductive cycles.

After students have had a chance to look over the visual essay, orally walk through the essay for the class, step by step. In doing so, emphasize the following points.

- The mature angiosperm plants with which we are all familiar are diploid sporophytes. In these plants, haploid gametes are produced through meiosis in their flowers.
- The male gametophyte develops when the pollen grain lands on the stigma and the pollen tube begins to grow.
- The female gametophyte in an angiosperm is wholly enclosed by the sporophyte; that is, it consists of a few cells inside the ovary of the sporophyte's flower.
- Pollination consists simply of the pollen landing on the stigma; fertilization occurs when the gametes fuse.
- In the angiosperm, the pollen tube grows down through the cells of the stigma and style, and thus reaches the ovary much more quickly than a pollen tube in the gymnosperm life cycle.
- The pollen grain contains two sperm nuclei, one of which fuses with the egg nucleus to form the diploid zygote. The other sperm nucleus (not shown in this visual essay) fuses with two haploid nuclei in the embryo sac to produce the endosperm.

TEACHER SUPPORT

Facts and Figures

- The range of time for completion of the angiosperm life cycle is tremendous. Some plants complete the cycle in less than a month, while others may take as long as 150 years.
- In corn, the pollen tube may be as long as 50 cm, though in most plants the length of the pollen tube is much less.
- A pollen tube may complete its growth in less than 24 hours. The average time is less than two days. In some plants, pollen tube growth takes over a year.
- The smallest flowers are those of the tiny duckweed *Wolffia columbiana*. The body of the plant is only about 0.7 mm wide; its flowers are only about 0.1 mm long.
- The largest flowers are those of the *Rafflesia* plant, indigenous to Indonesia. These huge blooms can grow to 1 m in diameter with a mass of 9 kg.
- There are about 250,000 known species of angiosperms.

Ancillary Support

The resources below can be used to support your teaching strategy for these two pages.

LM Identifying Seed-Bearing Plant Tissues, #49

TB Visualizing the Life Cycle of an Angiosperm, #33

Discussion

Begin a discussion of double fertilization by asking a student to review the basic steps leading up to fertilization. Point out that a pollen grain is not the gamete itself. Rather, it contains two male gametes that move down through the pollen tube and into the ovary. Explain that in most species, the ovule contains eight haploid nuclei, one of which is the egg. Two of the other seven are used in the second fertilization process, which results in the endosperm. Emphasize the advantage of this double fertilization for the angiosperm—the process is more energy efficient than reproduction in gymnosperms.

Ideas Through Images

Have students examine Figure 25–8, read the caption, and answer the following questions.

- **What indicates that the annatto in the photograph is a fruit?** (Seeds can be seen inside the structure, and the outer wall probably is the thickened ovary joined with other parts of the flower stem.)
- **What would you expect to find within the thornless blackberries? Why?** (You would expect to find seeds because the berries are fruit, and a fruit is the combination of seed and ovary.)
- **From what part of the plant did each of the peppers originate?** (Each originated in the ovary of a flower.)

Ideas Through Images

Have students examine Figure 25–9, read the caption, and answer the following questions.

- **What is the difference shown in the cross sections of these two stems?** (The difference is in the distribution of vascular bundles. In the monocot stem, the bundles are scattered. In the dicot stem, the bundles are arranged in a circle around the stem.)

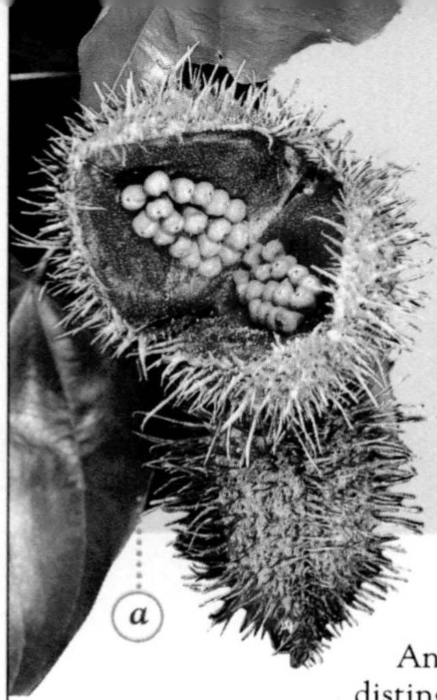

Figure 25–8 *(a) Annatto, (b) peppers, and (c) thornless blackberries are examples of fruits—the mature, ripened ovaries of angiosperms within which angiosperm seeds are formed and nourished until they are dispersed.*

An important feature distinguishes the life cycle of an angiosperm from the life cycle of a gymnosperm. In angiosperms, a second fertilization event takes place, in which another sperm nucleus fuses with two of the haploid nuclei in the embryo sac to produce a triploid (3n) cell. This cell grows and divides quickly to form a food-rich tissue known as an **endosperm,** which surrounds the embryo. The endosperm serves to nourish the growing plant after the seed sprouts, until the new plant is self-sufficient. Because two fertilization events take place inside each embryo sac, the whole process is called **double fertilization.**

Double fertilization may be a prime reason why angiosperms have been so successful. As you may remember, gymnosperms also build up a reserve of stored food for the seed. However, in gymnosperms this reserve is produced by the gametophyte before fertilization takes place. As a result, if an ovule is not fertilized, all those resources are wasted. In angiosperms, the resources are never wasted. If an ovule fails to be fertilized, the endosperm does not form either, and food is not prepared for a zygote that never forms.

☑ ***Checkpoint*** What is an endosperm? (1)

Seed Formation

As you have just seen, fertilization causes the formation of a diploid (2n) plant embryo and a layer of triploid (3n) endosperm tissue. Fertilization sets in motion a number of other events as well. The wall of the ovule toughens and forms a seed coat that protects the developing seed. In many plants, the petals and stamens fall away, leaving the carpel, which contains the developing seeds.

The Fruit

As nutrients pour into the flower, many of them are taken up by the growing endosperm tissue inside the seed. However, in most plants, nutrients also flow into the wall of the ovary, which surrounds the seeds. Gradually, the wall of the ovary thickens and joins with other parts of the flower stem to form a fruit. This is the characteristic for which angiosperms are named—the way in which they form seeds enclosed inside the walls of the ovary.

Fruits and Vegetables

It's important to realize that a fruit in plant reproduction simply refers to an ovary and the seeds it contains. By this

TEACHER SUPPORT

Background Information

As a flower is developing in the bud, a diploid cell becomes differentiated from the other cells in the ovule. This cell, called the megaspore, or megaspore mother cell, undergoes meiosis to produce four haploid nuclei. As the cell grows larger, those four nuclei divide again, producing a total of eight haploid nuclei. One of those eight becomes the egg. Two of those eight, called the polar nuclei, fuse with a sperm nucleus to form the endosperm.

In some plants, the endosperm remains an extensive part of the seed. This is especially true for grains and other monocots. A kernel of corn, for instance, consists in large part of the endosperm. In most dicots, though, the endosperm is digested as the zygote develops into an embryo. In the common bean, for example, the endosperm has been completely used by the time the seed is mature.

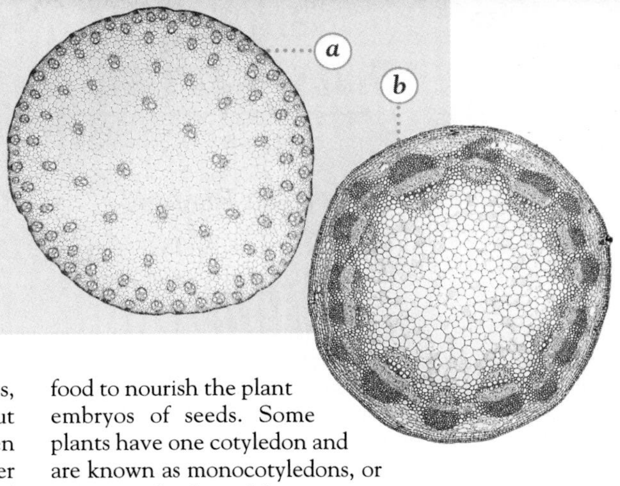

Figure 25–9
One way in which monocots and dicots differ is in the arrangement of vascular tissue. (a) A cross section of a corn stem, a monocot, reveals a scattered distribution of vascular bundles (magnification: 7X). (b) In the stem of a sunflower, a dicot, vascular bundles are arranged in a circle (magnification: 8X).

definition, fruits include not only apples, grapes, bananas, and watermelon, but also tomatoes, peas, corn, and even beans and rice! Just remember, whether or not it tastes sweet, if it contains a seed enclosed inside the ovary wall, it's a fruit.

☑ **Checkpoint** What is a fruit? ❷

Speed of Reproduction

Another reason for the success of angiosperms is the speed of their reproductive cycle. The small number of cells in the gametophyte stages of angiosperm reproduction means that most flowering plants can reproduce much more quickly than most gymnosperms can.

Monocots and Dicots

The diverse plants that make up the angiosperms are further classified into two groups based on the number of **cotyledons** (kaht-uh-LEED-'nz)—the large seed leaves that contain stored food to nourish the plant embryos of seeds. Some plants have one cotyledon and are known as monocotyledons, or **monocots** for short. Monocots constitute the Class Monocotyledonae, which includes grasses, irises, and cattails. Other plants have two cotyledons and are known as dicotyledons, or **dicots.** The dicots constitute the Class Dicotyledonae, which includes roses, clover, tomatoes, oaks, and daisies. The flowering trees—such as maple, oak, elm, apple, and dogwood—are all dicots.

Although the primary distinction between monocots and dicots is the number of seed leaves, it is not the only one. Veins in monocot leaves usually lie parallel to each other, whereas veins in dicot leaves usually form a branching network. While monocot flowers usually have floral parts in multiples of three, dicot flowers usually show multiples of four or five.

Section Review 25–3

1. **Describe** the main characteristics of angiosperms.
2. **Identify** the parts of a flower.
3. **Outline** the stages in the life cycle of an angiosperm.
4. **Critical Thinking—Relating** What adaptations have led to the dominance of angiosperms on Earth?
5. **MINI LAB** How would you **design an experiment** to determine the relationship between flower structures and their function?

• **What other differences are there between monocots and dicots?** (Monocots have only one cotyledon, parallel veins in their leaves, and floral parts in multiples of three. Dicots have two cotyledons, a branching network of veins in their leaves, and floral parts in multiples of four or five.)

4 ASSESS

Quick Check

Ask students to make a flowchart that begins with the growth of a flower and ends with the growth of a fruit.

Section Review 25–3

1. They produce seeds encased in a protective tissue of the sporophyte known as the ovary, have a specialized reproductive structure known as a flower, and reproduce through an alternation of generations.
2. See Figure 25–7 on page 586.
3. See page 587.
4. These include the development of the flower and the process known as double fertilization, through which only fertilized ovules are nourished and no resources are wasted.
5. A typical design might suggest closely observing a flower over a period of time and identifying the ways in which the various structures contribute to plant reproduction.

☑ Checkpoints

❶ The food-rich tissue that surrounds the plant embryo.

❷ The combination of the plant ovary and the seeds it contains after the walls of the ovary have thickened and joined with other parts of the flower stem.

Skills Trace

Experimenting

- Focus p. 585
- Practice p. 589
- Assess p. 599

Learning Modality

Tactile Learning Ask groups of students to build a model of a typical flower, using Figure 25–7 for reference. Allow groups to use whatever materials they find around the classroom or at home.

Ancillary Support

The resources below can be used to support your teaching strategy for these two pages.

LM Comparing Monocots and Dicots, #50
TR Apply: Leaf Language
BL Inquiry Activity: Fruit or Vegetable?

SECTION 25-4

What's in a Fruit?

Performance Objective

- Describe how fruits are important to the survival of plants.

Laboratory Investigation Skill: Observing

1 ENGAGE

Inquiry Activity

Classifying

Are There Types of Fruits?
Make a display of different kinds of fruits, including various nuts, berries, legumes, drupes, grains, and pomes (simple fleshy fruits such as apples and pears). Place a number written on a piece of tape next to each fruit. Tell students that biologists group fruits into several general types. Ask students how they think the fruits on display could be grouped. Allow students to handle the various fruits but not to cut them up or break them apart. After time for examination, have each student classify the fruits into several groups by writing the numbers in lists on a piece of paper. Discuss students' groupings.

Ideas Through Images

Have students examine Figure 25–10, read the caption, and answer the following questions.

- **What is a fruit?** (A fruit is the combination of seed and ovary.)
- **The papaya fruit has a thick wall. Is that only the thickened ovary?** (No. As the wall of the ovary thickens, it gradually joins with other parts of the flower stem to form the fruit.)
- **Why do you think many angiosperms have evolved to produce fruit that animals find so good to eat?** (Some students might suggest that in eating the fruit, animals help to distribute, or disperse, the plant's seeds.)

SECTION 25–4 BRANCHING OUT In Depth

What's in a Fruit?

GUIDE FOR READING

- **Explain** the role that fruits play in the survival strategy of plants.

WHAT'S IN A FRUIT? HAVING just read the previous section, the answer might seem simple. Fruits are mature ovaries that contain seeds. And within each seed is an embryo along with enough stored food to support that embryo's early growth. The fruits that a plant produces are home to the plant's next generation, its chances to be part of the future. This means that a fruit is more than just a reproductive structure—it is a key to the survival strategy of a whole species.

Perhaps you have marveled at the amazing variety of fruits found in nature. This section offers an opportunity for you to make the connection between the different types of fruit and the dispersal strategy they support.

Types of Fruits

As you have read, the double fertilization that takes place in flowering plants produces two distinct cells. One is the diploid zygote that forms the embryo. The other is the triploid endosperm. The embryo and endosperm are surrounded by a protective seed coat.

In flowering plants, all of this occurs inside the ovary, which contained the female gametophyte before fertilization took place. When a seed is formed, the ovary doesn't just disappear. Not only are the seeds of flowering plants enclosed within the ovary, but in many plants the ovary wall undergoes dramatic changes as the seeds develop. For many plants, these changes in the ovary are the key to survival in a difficult world.

The simplest fruits are those that consist of a single seed enclosed by a single ovary wall. Grains, such as wheat and corn, fit this description. In most grains, the wall of the ovary is so thin that it actually fuses to the seed coat. Each kernel of corn, therefore, is not just a seed but an ovary as well.

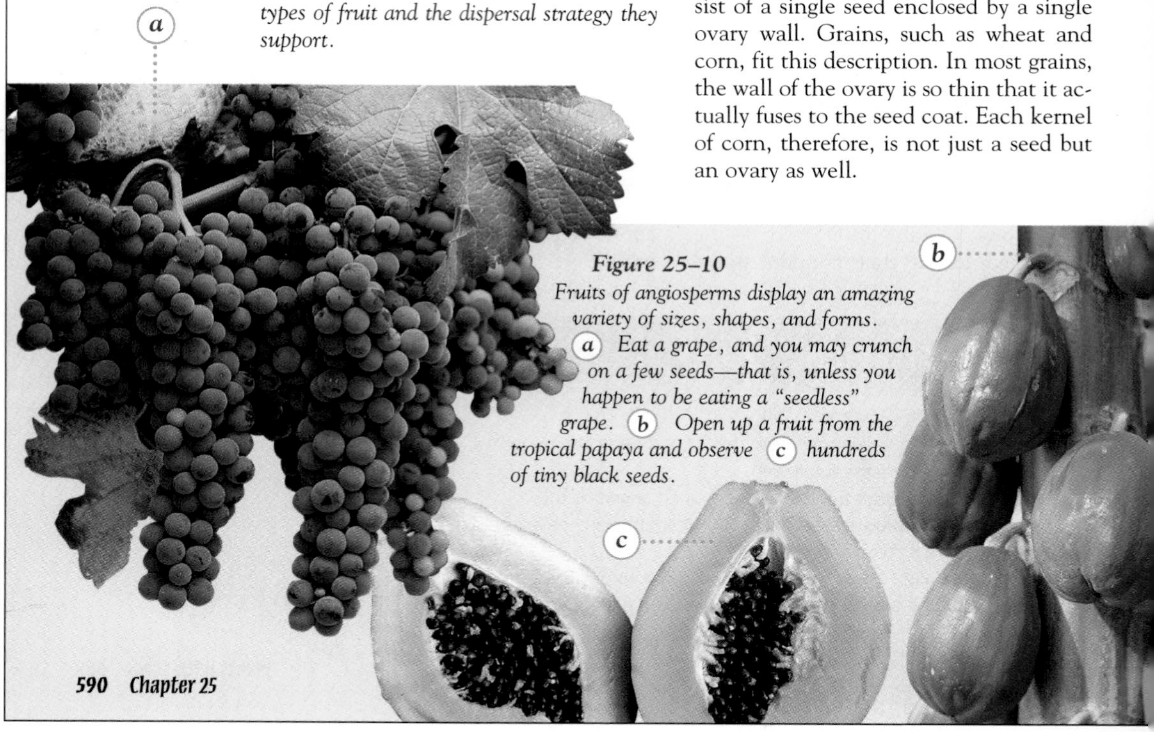

Figure 25–10 *Fruits of angiosperms display an amazing variety of sizes, shapes, and forms. (a) Eat a grape, and you may crunch on a few seeds—that is, unless you happen to be eating a "seedless" grape. (b) Open up a fruit from the tropical papaya and observe (c) hundreds of tiny black seeds.*

590 Chapter 25

TEACHER SUPPORT — Managing Classroom Diversity

LEP STUDENTS
Explain that the term annual is derived from the Latin word *annus,* which means year. Thus, an annual lives only one year, or one growing season. The word perennial is derived from the Latin words *per,* which means throughout, and *annus,* or year. Thus, a perennial lives throughout the year, surviving from one season to the next.

TECH PREP STUDENTS
Ask students who plan careers in agriculture to investigate the importance of honeybees and other insects in the pollination of the major food crops. Have them write a short report on the significance of bees in pollination and predict what would happen if bee populations were suddenly eliminated.

In acorns and chestnuts, the ovary wall hardens and forms a protective shell around the seed. Fruits such as these are called **nuts.** Instead of a tough casing, the ovary walls of peaches and cherries are soft and fleshy. The flesh of these fruits—which are known as **drupes**—encloses a single tough, stony seed.

There's no rule that says an ovary must contain just one seed. Many plants produce dozens or even hundreds of seeds in a single ovary. This is the case with **berries,** in which the soft ovary wall usually encloses many seeds. Examples of berries include the grape and, believe it or not, the tomato.

Legumes produce seeds within a pod that splits open on two sides. Peas and beans are legumes. Do you remember the last time you ate peanuts from the shell? Peanut seeds too are produced in a pod that splits open along a two-sided seam. And that means that peanuts are not nuts at all, but legumes!

Some of the fruits we prize most highly are more complex than they seem. Apples, for example, do contain seeds surrounded by an ovary wall. But most of the fruit is actually formed by the stem surrounding the ovary. If you slice an apple or pear open crosswise, the boundary between the ovary and the surrounding tissue will be apparent.

☑ **Checkpoint** What are some of the different types of fruits found in nature? 1

Fruits and Seed Dispersal

Why should fruits come in such a bewildering variety of shapes, sizes, and styles? Why should some be sweet and edible and others be little more than a protective sac around the seed? We can find the answers by watching what happens to the fruit after it is produced by the plant.

Some of the simplest fruits, such as those of grasses and grains, are formed in species where seeds simply fall to the ground at the base of the parent plant. Most of these species are **annuals,** meaning that they live for just one growing season. Therefore, if seeds are dropped to the ground, they have a good chance of finding good growing conditions next year, when the generation that produced them has died.

This is not the case with **perennials**—the plants that live for many growing seasons. These plants need to disperse their seeds to give the new seedlings a chance to grow far enough away from their parent plant so they do not compete for sunlight, water, and nutrients. This is where fruits come in. **Because plants cannot move, they have to depend on other forces to scatter their seeds about. Fruits have evolved many ways to ensure that the seeds within them get the best possible chance to sprout under suitable conditions.**

Figure 25–11
(a) *A pineapple, which is formed as a result of the fusing of the ovaries of a cluster of flowers, is called a multiple fruit.* (b) *A tomato is classified as a berry because it contains an ovary that encloses many seeds.* (c) CAREER TRACK *This agricultural technician monitors wheat, grown with salt water irrigation in Ashalim, Negev Desert, Israel. Wheat is a simple fruit that has a single seed enclosed by a single ovary wall.*

2 EXPLORE

Investigate

Cooperative Learning Have each group survey the fruits they can find in a specific area near the school, such as a portion of a park, a small neighborhood, or a farm. Ask groups to find a field guide in a library that will help them identify specific trees and shrubs and the fruits they produce. Students' final products should be a table that lists identified plants and fruits, cites locations, and gives descriptions.

3 TEACH

Ideas Through Images

Have students examine Figure 25–11, read the caption, and answer the following questions.

- **What is a multiple fruit?** (A multiple fruit is a fruit that is formed as a result of the fusing of the ovaries of a cluster of flowers.)
- **How is a grape like a tomato?** (They are both fruits that contain many seeds and are thus classified as berries.)

Laboratory Investigation

The Laboratory Investigation, Structure of a Pea Pod, on pages 594–595 is appropriate to use at this point in the chapter.

☑ Checkpoint

1 Grains, nuts, drupes, berries, legumes, and fruits formed by the stem surrounding the ovary.

TEACHER SUPPORT

Background Information

What's the difference between a fruit and a vegetable? A fruit is any plant ovary that has developed and matured. A vegetable, by contrast, may consist of leaves (such as lettuce), stems (asparagus), roots (sweet potato), or any other parts of the plant except the fruit. A tomato is definitely a fruit, though most people think of it as a vegetable because it is not sweet. Curiously, the Supreme Court confirmed this misconception in 1893, when the justices ruled in *Nix v. Hedden* that a tomato is legally a vegetable.

Botanists divide the mature ovary around the seed into three regions. The skin of the fruit is called the exocarp. The inner boundary around the seed is the endocarp. Everything in between is the mesocarp. If the mesocarp is at least partly fleshy, botanists classify it as a fleshy fruit, including drupes, berries, and pomes (such as the apple).

Ancillary Support

The resource below can be used to support your teaching strategy for these two pages.

TR Explore: The Seedy Side of Fruit

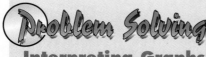

Problem Solving
Interpreting Graphs
Plants and Rodents: Friends or Foes?

Students will draw on their ability to calculate averages to solve this problem.

State The problem is to determine whether Japanese wood mice are effective dispersers of Asian skunk cabbage seeds.

Solve Students can answer the first question by estimating the percentage shown by each bar and multiplying that percentage by 80.

In answering the second question, dispersal distance is the mean value of the bar; thus, a bar that indicates 2–4 m should be interpreted as 3 m.

Test Because the experiment is too complex to replicate, students would be unable to test their conclusions.

Communicate Choose students at random to explain how they interpreted the graphs and made their calculations.

Answers to THINK ABOUT IT

1. Eaten Seeds, left to right: 18, 14, 10, 12, 4, 5, 3, 2, 1. Stored Seeds, left to right: 3, 2, 1, 3, 1, 2.

2. The average distance the eaten seeds were dispersed was about 5.5 m (372 ÷ 68). The average for stored seeds was 9 m (108 m ÷ 12).

3. The mice transport the seeds a longer distance for storage.

4. Seed dispersal is important so that new colonies of skunk cabbage do not compete with already formed colonies. Most students will conclude that the wood mice are effective dispersers, since they move the seeds away from the plants 5.5 m on average if they eat the seeds and 9 m on average if they store the seeds.

5. A typical response might suggest studying berries moved by raccoons or acorns moved by squirrels.

Problem Solving
INTERPRETING GRAPHS
Plants and Rodents: Friends or Foes?

While looking for ideas for a science fair project, you come across a study of the relationship between the Japanese wood mouse and the Asian skunk cabbage. According to this study, the seeds of the cabbage cannot be dispersed by water or wind due to the terrestrial location of the cabbage and the mass of its seeds. The researchers hypothesized that seed-dispersing animals bring the seeds to new locations, away from already formed colonies of skunk cabbage.

The researchers found that Japanese wood mice eat the skunk cabbage seeds and store them for the winter. The eaten seeds that are not well chewed give rise to seedlings after leaving the animal's digestive tract. Other seeds are dropped during the eating process. Many of the seeds stored for the winter never are recovered and survive to produce seedlings also.

The graphs illustrate the distance the mice dispersed the seeds and the quantity of seeds they dispersed.

DISTANCE OF SEED DISPERSAL BY MICE

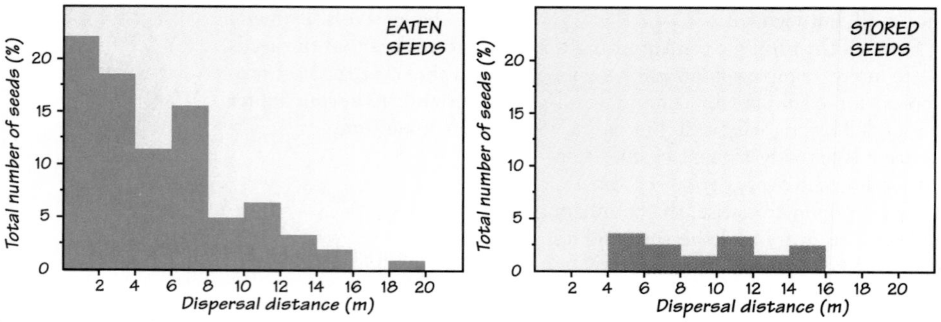

THINK ABOUT IT

1. A total of 80 seeds were dispersed by the mice, 68 of which were eaten and 12 of which were stored. What number of seeds does each bar on each graph represent?
2. Calculate the average distance that eaten seeds and stored seeds were dispersed.
3. On the average, do the mice transport the seeds a longer distance for storage or for immediate consumption?
4. Explain how seed dispersal is important to the survival of the Asian wood cabbage. Do you think Japanese wood mice are effective dispersers of Asian skunk cabbage seeds?
5. If you performed similar research for your science fair project, what combinations of animals and plants might you study?

TEACHER SUPPORT

Ecology Note

It may be hard to believe, but evolution has in effect designed some seeds to be eaten. The seeds of clover plants, for example, do not germinate very well unless they have been scarified. This means that the surface of the seed coat needs to be roughed up a bit in order for the seed to germinate efficiently. Thus, clover seems to be adapted to being eaten by grazing animals. The scarification of the seed may be a signal to the plant embryo that the seed has indeed been eaten, has passed through the digestive system of an animal, and is about to be deposited in a pile of manure. For clover, then, the need for scarification is just a mechanism to ensure that the seed sprouts in the right place and at the right time.

Dispersal by Wind

Many seeds are released directly into the air, depending on the wind to help distribute them. Maple and ash trees have winged fruits that carry their seeds many meters from the parent plant. The fruit of the dandelion has a parasol of tiny filaments, allowing it to drift in the wind over great distances.

Figure 25–12 Fruits and seeds often include special features that help in seed dispersal. Milkweed fruits burst open when mature, releasing seeds that are dispersed by wind—aided substantially by attachments of tufts of silk.

A few plants produce fruits that provide their seeds with jet propulsion to help them find a spot in which to grow. The dwarf mistletoe, a parasitic plant that grows on the branches of pine trees, produces sticky seeds enclosed within a fluid-filled chamber. As the fruit matures, the fluid pressure builds until it's so strong it blows away the end of the fruit, pushing out the seed at speeds as great as 100 kilometers an hour! This live artillery enables the plant to spread quickly.

Dispersal by Water

Plants that live on or near the water often rely on this means of seed transportation. Some of their fruits contain air pockets to keep the seeds afloat until they have germinated. The most spectacular example of a waterborne fruit is the coconut palm. The fruits of this plant are packed with corklike tissue and air spaces, enabling it to float for long periods. Coconuts sprout quickly when washed ashore. They are one of the most successful seaside plants in the world.

Dispersal by Animals

Many flowering plants use animals to distribute their seeds. Some fruits have "bribes" that entice the animals to help disperse them—the edible fleshy parts of fruits like apples, grapes, and blackberries. When an animal eats the fruit, it enjoys the tasty ovary wall. But the tough seeds inside the fruit may pass through the animal's digestive system unharmed. As the animal walks or flies or grazes, the seeds may be carried great distances. Finally, they leave the digestive system and are deposited in a new location, where they may sprout and grow.

As animals ourselves, we may think that plants are at our mercy. But when an animal pulls off a branch, chomps on a flower, or gobbles up a fruit, the plant is also using the animal—to find a home for its offspring.

Section Review 25–4

1. **Explain** the role that fruits play in the survival strategy of plants.
2. **BRANCHING OUT ACTIVITY** Visit a farmers' market or the produce section of your local supermarket. **Identify** the produce items that can be classified as fruits and **formulate a hypothesis** to explain how they may be dispersed.

Inquiry Activity

Experimenting

Hitchhiking on You

Ask students whether they have ever had to pull seeds off their clothing. Then ask small groups of students to find a weed-filled vacant lot or unmowed field to walk through after school. Tell students to wear gloves, long pants and shirts, and heavy socks. Each student should take a plastic sandwich bag in which to place anything that stuck to the clothing during this walk. The next day in class, have those in each group examine their collection of hitchhiking seeds using a hand lens and then draw what they see. Discuss as a class what each group discovered.

Students who are allergic to plants should be given an alternate activity. One such activity involves using Velcro ™ and similar objects that stick to clothing. Students can examine these objects with a hand lens to see what characteristics they possess.

4 ASSESS

Quick Check

Have students make a concept map that shows the various types of fruits and examples of each.

Section Review 25–4

1. Because plants cannot move from place to place, they have to depend on other forces to scatter their seeds about. Fruits, which aid in this dispersal, have evolved in many ways to ensure that the seeds within them get the best possible chance to sprout under suitable conditions.

2. Students might describe any of the great variety of fruits at a farmers' market or in the produce department of a supermarket. You could require that each student identify ten fruits and formulate a hypothesis about dispersal for each one. After individual students have completed their lists, have student recorders compile a class list of all the fruits identified. Discuss with the class any conflicting hypotheses about individual fruits. Then have each student choose a fruit to research in order to confirm or revise the hypothesis about how it is dispersed.

Learning Modality

Visual Learning Ask groups of students to write and illustrate a children's book about the dispersal of a seed by wind, water, or animal.

Ancillary Support

The resource below can be used to support your teaching strategy for these two pages.

BL Inquiry Activity: Sailing Seeds

CHAPTER 25

Laboratory Investigation

Structure of a Pea Pod

Before the Lab

1. If possible, use snow peas or sugar snap peas, which are normally available at greengrocers and large supermarkets. Try to select pods that have sepals remaining. String beans may be used as a substitute, but they will not have sepals. They will, however, have the remainder of the style.

2. Soaked bean seeds can be used instead of soaked peas. Prepare the soaked peas or beans a day ahead of time by immersing them in warm water. Then, just before class, remove them from the water and place on paper towels. Thawed frozen peas may be used.

Pre-Lab Discussion

Have students read the entire procedure for this investigation. Then ask the following questions.

What is the purpose of this investigation? (To observe the structure of a pea pod and infer what parts of it are important to the reproduction of a pea plant.)

Why is a pea pod considered a fruit? (It meets the definition of a fruit, which is the combination of seed and ovary.)

What kind of plant produces seeds within a pod that splits open on two sides? (A legume.)

What do you think is the purpose of examining a soaked pea after first examining the pea pod? (Some students might suggest that a soaked pea will be larger than a pea from the pod, and so its characteristics will be more evident to the observer.)

Laboratory Investigation

Structure of a Pea Pod

After pollination occurs, the ovary of a fruit matures into a fruit containing seeds. A pea pod meets this description, even though it usually is not thought of as a fruit. Peas and their pods usually are consumed before they mature and dry, so people rarely see their natural development. Like all fruits, the pea pod develops from a flower, and parts of the flower can still be identified after pollination. In this investigation, you will observe the features of the pea pod that are flower remnants and study how seeds form.

Problem

What are the parts of a fruit that are important to its reproduction? **Observe** a pea pod to help you answer this question.

Materials (per group)

pea pod (or string bean or lima bean pod)
soaked pea
hand lens
scalpel or razor blade
dissecting needle

Procedure

1. **With a hand lens, examine the external appearance of the pea pod. Record your observations.**
2. **Find the stalk that attaches the pod to the plant. Locate the sepals, which are the remaining parts from the base of the flower. Record the number of sepals.**

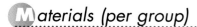

Safety Tips

- Caution students to be extremely careful when using the scalpel or razor blade, as well as the dissecting needle. Advise them to always cut in the direction away from the body or opposite hand.
- Remind students not to place anything from the pea pod or any of the soaked peas or beans in their mouths. These materials have not been cooked and could contain harmful microorganisms.

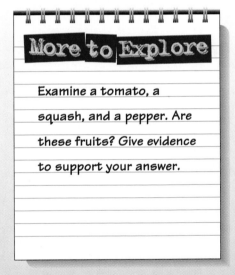

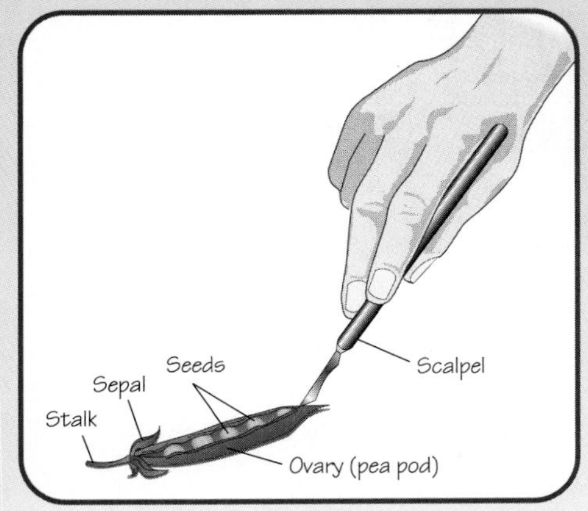

3. **At the opposite end of the pod, find the remains of the style.**
4. **Carefully open the pod along the curved edge using the razor blade or scalpel. CAUTION: *Be very careful when using sharp instruments.***
5. **Count the number of peas in the pod and note their characteristics. Record the number of peas as well as your observations of their appearance.**
6. **Notice the fibers to which the peas are attached by a short stalk. Record the number of fibers you see.**
7. **Obtain a soaked pea and examine it. Locate the scar that shows where the pea was attached to the pod.**
8. **Using the dissecting needle, carefully remove the seed coat from the pea.**
9. **Separate the cotyledons. Use a hand lens to observe the embryo plant.**

Observations

1. Describe the external appearance of the pea pod.
2. How many sepals does the pea pod have?
3. Are all the pea seeds attached to the same side of the pod?
4. Are all the peas alike?
5. Draw a sketch of the embryo plant of the soaked pea and label its parts.

Analysis and Conclusions

1. Based on your observations of the number of sepals and cotyledons present, classify the pea as a monocot or a dicot.
2. How do you explain any differences among the peas?
3. What is the function of the stalk that attaches the pea to the pod?
4. What reproductive structure does the pod represent?
5. Based on the color of the pea pod, can you identify one of the processes it carries out?

More to Explore

Examine a tomato, a squash, and a pepper. Are these fruits? Give evidence to support your answer.

Answers to Observations

1. Students should describe an elongated, closed pouch with one straight edge and one edge that is curved outward. The pod is green and has a waxy covering.
2. The pea pod has five sepals.
3. No. The peas are alternately attached to opposite sides of the pod, attached to one and then the other of the fibers that extend the length of the pea pod.
4. Students should observe that there are slight variations in shape among the peas, though all are similar in appearance.
5. Students' sketches should include the parts of the embryo identified in the MINI LAB on page 578.

Answers to Analysis and Conclusions

1. Because the plant has five sepals and two cotyledons, the pea is classified as a dicot.
2. The differences among the peas are the result of the separate fertilization events that produced each pea. Thus, each pea is genetically distinct from the others. Students also might suggest that some peas may not have been fertilized or may not have received the same amount of nutrients as the other peas.
3. The function of the stalk is to deliver water and nutrients to the developing seed.
4. The pod represents the walls of the ovary.
5. The green color of the pod suggests that it carries out the process of photosynthesis.

Skills Development

Students will use these skills while completing the laboratory investigation: observing, measuring, inferring, communicating, and drawing conclusions.

Teaching Strategies

1. Demonstrate how to use a scalpel or razor blade to cut open the pod along the curved edge.
2. Advise students to keep paper and pencil at hand while examining the pea pod so that they may record their observations immediately.

More to Explore

Students could obtain a tomato, squash, or pepper from a supermarket, and then use much the same procedure as in the Laboratory Investigation. Have students count the seeds in the fruits they examine and then make sketches of what they see.

CHAPTER 25

Study Guide

Review Strategy

Divide the class into groups of three or four, making sure LEP and at-risk students are evenly distributed throughout. Ask each group to make a list of ten questions for each of the sections in this chapter. Advise students that these questions should range from simple recall questions to questions that require some thoughtful analysis. Then have groups trade sets of questions. Allow members of a group to collaborate on the answers to the set of questions it receives from another group. Discuss as a class any question that a group puts forward as particularly difficult or interesting.

Recalling Main Ideas

1. a
2. a
3. b
4. b
5. d
6. a
7. b
8. c
9. b

Assessment

Reviewing What You Learned

1. A seed allows the plant embryo to survive even the most extreme conditions.
2. A seed is resistant to drying out and contains a fully formed plant embryo, stored food for the embryo, and special structures that aid in distribution. A spore is not as resistant to drying out, contains only a single cell of the plant, and has no stored food or special structures.
3. Gymnosperms and angiosperms.
4. The gymnosperms are plants that bear their seeds on the surface of scales and include cycads, ginkgoes, gnetophytes, and conifers.

Study Guide

Summarizing Key Concepts

The key concepts in each section of this chapter are listed below to help you review the chapter content. Make sure you understand each concept and its relationship to other concepts and to the theme of this chapter.

25–1 Seed-Bearing Plants

- A seed is a reproductive package that contains a plant embryo and a supply of stored food inside a protective coating.
- Seed-bearing plants do not require standing water for reproduction.

25–2 Gymnosperms

- There are five classes of living seed-bearing plants. Four are known as the gymnosperms—cycads, ginkgoes, gnetophytes, and conifers.
- The life cycle of a gymnosperm displays alternation of generations of sporophytes and gametophytes within the sporophytes.

25–3 Angiosperms

- Angiosperms produce seeds encased in protective tissue of the sporophyte, the ovary.
- Flowers are the reproductive organs of angiosperms, formed from four types of leaves—sepals, petals, stamens, and carpels.
- Reproduction in angiosperms also follows alternation of generations of sporophytes and gametophytes. Production of gametophytes, fertilization of eggs, and development of seeds take place within the structures of flowers.
- A fruit is a combination of seed and ovary.

25–4 What's in a Fruit?

- Fruits vary as a result of changes that take place in the ovary wall as the seeds develop inside.
- Variation in fruit type is tied to the plant's strategy for producing offspring.

Reviewing Key Terms

Review the following vocabulary terms and their meaning. Then use each term in a complete sentence.

25–1 Seed-Bearing Plants

seed, egg, pollen

25–2 Gymnosperms

scale, female cone, gymnosperm, seed cone, male cone

25–3 Angiosperms

angiosperm, flower, ovary, sepal, fruit, petal, stamen, pistil, filament, endosperm, anther, double fertilization, carpel, cotyledon, ovule, monocot, style, dicot, stigma

25–4 What's in a Fruit?

nut, legume, drupe, annual, berry, perennial

Inquiry-Based Strategy

Each area or region has its own particular mix of vegetation, depending on its latitude, proximity to a large body of water, soil type, climate, and so on. This mix can be altered through urbanization and suburbanization. Ask students to investigate what the mix of natural plant life of their area would look like if human society suddenly disappeared. Point out that some areas are dominated by gymnosperms while others are dominated by angiosperms. Ask that in answering this question, they note what species of plants would be present as well as generalize about the types of plants that would be most common.

Students might approach answering this question by investigating what the area looked like before Europeans settled in this country. They also might find books on the natural vegetation of the area in a local library.

CHAPTER 25

Recalling Main Ideas

Choose the letter of the answer that best completes the statement or answers the question.

1. The sporophyte of seed-bearing plants contains the
   a. gametophyte. **b.** angiosperm. **c.** gymnosperm. **d.** antheridia.
2. Plants that bear their seeds on the surface of reproductive structures are called
   a. gymnosperms. **b.** bryophytes. **c.** angiosperms. **d.** lichens.
3. Scales are grouped into clusters known as
   a. crowns. **b.** cones. **c.** bunches. **d.** plates.
4. Spruce, pine, cedar, redwood, and cypress trees are all examples of
   a. bryophytes. **b.** conifers. **c.** monocots. **d.** flowering plants.
5. The specialized reproductive structure that distinguishes angiosperms from other seed plants is the
   a. egg. **b.** pistil. **c.** root. **d.** flower.
6. The four types of specialized leaves from which flowers are formed are sepals, petals,
   a. stamens, and carpels.
   b. tassels, and anthers.
   c. scales, and tissues.
   d. pollen grains, and ovules.
7. The food-rich tissue that surrounds the embryo is known as the
   a. nutrient cell. **b.** endosperm. **c.** placenta. **d.** female tissue.
8. In plant reproduction, the ovary and the seeds it contains are called the
   a. endosperm. **b.** spore. **c.** fruit. **d.** cone.
9. A fleshy fruit such as an apple is well-adapted for
   a. wind dispersal.
   b. animal dispersal.
   c. water dispersal.
   d. pollination.

Putting It All Together

Using the information on pages xxx to xxxi, complete the following concept map.

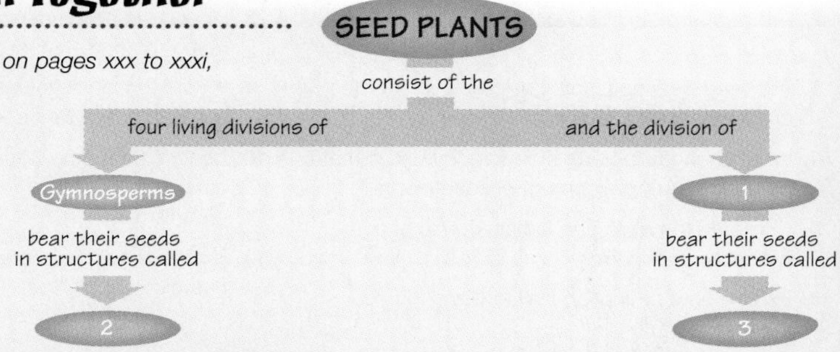

Putting It All Together

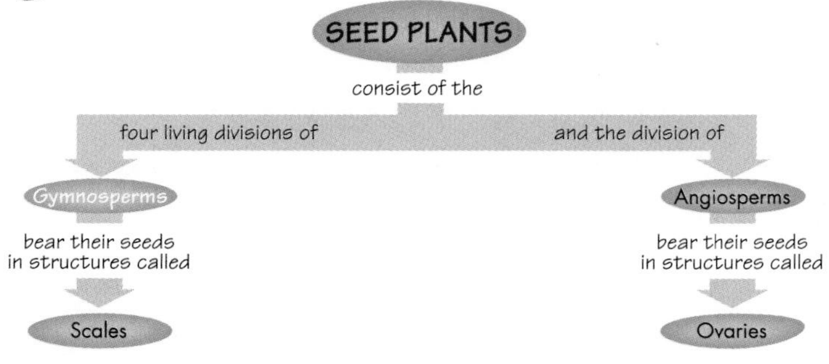

5. The structures that can be seen are sepals, petals, stamens, and carpels.

Skills Trace
Observing
- Focus p. 578
- Practice p. 579
- Assess p. 598

6. The male parts of a flower are the stamens, and the female parts of a flower are the carpels.
7. Double fertilization is the process in angiosperms by which a second sperm nucleus fuses with two of the haploid nuclei in the embryo sac to produce a triploid cell, which grows to form an endosperm.
8. Gymnosperms bear their seeds on the surfaces of reproductive structures called scales, whereas angiosperms bear flowers and produce seeds encased in a protective tissue of the sporophyte.
9. Monocots have only one cotyledon in their embryos, parallel veins in their leaves, and floral parts in multiples of three, whereas dicots have two cotyledons in their embryos, a branching network of veins in their leaves, and floral parts in multiples of four or five.
10. A nut is a type of fruit in which the ovary wall has hardened and formed a protective shell around the seed; a drupe is a fruit in which the ovary wall is soft and fleshy and encloses a single stony seed.
11. A typical response might mention the wind dispersal of winged fruits of maple trees, the dispersal of the waterborne fruit of the coconut palm, and the dispersal of blackberries by a bear or raccoon.

Expanding the Concepts

1. Conifers are unique in that their long and thin leaves, often called needles, are coated with a tough, waxy substance to prevent water loss and remain on the plant for years.
2. Peppers consist of seeds surrounded by mature, ripened ovaries, and thus they can be classified as fruits.
3. Seed-bearing plants are basically sporophytes, since a mature gymnosperm or angiosperm is a diploid sporophyte that produces haploid gametophytes within either its cones or its flowers.

Assessment (continued)

4. The spread of glaciers and widespread drought, conditions that favored plants that were less dependent on water, paralleled the development of seed plants.
5. On a male cone of a typical gymnosperm, cells within the scales produce haploid spores, which develop into mature pollen grains that are scattered by the wind. By contrast, scales within a female cone contain ovules, which give rise to the female gametophytes that produce egg cells.
6. Pollination occurs when pollen from the same plant or another plant of the same species lands on the stigma. Fertilization is the fusing of sperm and egg to produce a diploid zygote. In angiosperms, a second fertilization occurs as well, in which another sperm nucleus fuses with two of the haploid nuclei in the embryo sac to produce a triploid cell, which develops into an endosperm.
7. See pages 585 to 588.
8. When a pollen grain lands on the stigma at the end of the style, the protective wall of the grain breaks open and a pollen tube grows through the style and into the ovule. The sperm nuclei carried by the pollen grain are released through the pollen tube into the ovule, and one of the nuclei fuses with the egg nucleus to produce a diploid zygote cell.
9. Fruits have evolved many ways to ensure that the seeds within them get the best possible chance to sprout under suitable conditions.
10. Dispersal of seeds by animals involves a mutually beneficial relationship because certain plants and animals have evolved structures and behaviors in response to each other.
11. Monocots differ from dicots in several fundamental ways. Monocots have embryos with only one cotyledon, a scattered distribution of vascular bundles, parallel veins in their leaves, and floral parts in multiples of three. Dicots have embryos with two cotyledons, vascular bundles arranged in a circle around the stem, a branching network of veins in their leaves, and floral parts in multiples of four or five.

Assessment

Reviewing What You Learned

Answer each of the following in a complete sentence.

1. What is the importance of a seed?
2. How do spores differ from seeds?
3. What are the two groups of seed-bearing plants called?
4. What are gymnosperms? Give examples of these plants.
5. **Observe** a flower and list the structures you see.
6. What are the male and female parts of a flower?
7. What is double fertilization?
8. Compare gymnosperms and angiosperms.
9. Compare features of monocots and dicots.
10. What is a nut? A drupe?
11. Give examples of the dispersal of seeds by wind, water, and animals.

Expanding the Concepts

Discuss each of the following in a brief paragraph.

1. Why are the cone-bearing plants—the conifers—so unique and successful?
2. Are peppers classified as fruits? Give evidence to support your answer.
3. Are seed-bearing plants basically sporophytes or gametophytes? Explain.
4. What changes in Earth's geography and climate paralleled the development of seed plants?
5. Compare the male and female cones of a typical gymnosperm.
6. Explain how pollination and fertilization occur in angiosperms.
7. Describe the flower in terms of its structure and function.
8. How does pollen deposited on the stigma reach the egg?
9. What function is served by the fruit in terms of survival of the plant species?
10. Describe a method of seed dispersal involving a mutually beneficial relationship between organisms.
11. Explain why monocots and dicots are placed in two different groups.

Extending Your Thinking

1. Students' descriptions should reflect the material in the visual essays on pages 587 and 582, respectively.

2. Wildlife are essential for the dispersal of seeds for many kinds of plants. Even if the dispersal of the seeds of the trees needed for lumber does not depend on animals, other plants in the ecosystem depend on animals for such dispersal.

Skills Trace

Relating

- Focus p. 583
- Practice p. 583
- Assess p. 599

Extending Your Thinking

Use the skills you have developed in this chapter to answer the following.

1. **Sequencing** Describe the events in the life cycles of an angiosperm and a gymnosperm.
2. **Relating** Lumber for home construction and industry essentially comes from gymnosperm forests. Because these forests are considered to be renewable resources, extensive programs have been developed for reforestation. These plans include forest and wildlife management. Why is it essential to include wildlife management in maintaining a healthy environment for trees?
3. **Drawing conclusions** Most conifers in temperate regions on the Earth keep their leaves through the winter, whereas angiosperm trees shed their leaves each autumn. What are the advantages and disadvantages of an evergreen tree? Of a tree shedding and regrowing its leaves?
4. **Designing an experiment** Are fruit-eating animals attracted to the color of a fruit or to its fragrance? Formulate a hypothesis and then design an experiment to find out the answer. Be sure to include a control.
5. **Evaluating** Seed plants have moved into every habitat since their origin. It has been estimated that of the 3 million species of plants, only 20 or 30 major species have been cultivated for food. Considering that only a few species are so important, why do we frequently hear or read about the need to maintain genetic diversity of plants?

Applying Your Skills

Can Seeds Fly?

The survival of plants depends on their ability to reproduce. In seed-bearing plants, the ability to reproduce is enhanced by mechanisms that protect and disperse the seeds and fruits. This allows less competition with the parent plants for nutrients, light, and water. How have some plants adapted to different methods of seed dispersal?

1. Working in a group, choose three seeds from the variety of seeds provided by your teacher.
2. Observe each type of seed. Draw and list the characteristics of each seed.
3. Place one seed on a flat surface and gently blow on the seed. What happens? Repeat this procedure with each of the other seeds.
4. What parts of the seeds are important for their dispersal?

• GOING FURTHER •

5. Construct a classification key using the seeds observed in this activity.

5. Genetic diversity of plants ensures that humans have options in the event of some catastrophe that affects the major cultivated species, such as a disease. Obscure plants might contain natural chemicals that will be useful in the future for fighting human diseases. Also, a healthy natural environment requires a variety of plants.

Applying Your Skills

Teacher Notes

- Collect a variety of different types of seeds.
- Have students work in pairs, matching gifted students with LEP or at-risk students.
- Ask that each pair of students present their findings to the rest of the class.

Answer

4. Answers will vary depending on the kinds of seeds.

Scoring Rubric

4 Response is thorough, accurate, and creative; shows an in-depth understanding of science skills, procedures, and concepts.

3 Response is complete, mostly accurate, and original; shows a satisfactory understanding of science skills, procedures, and concepts.

2 Response is mostly complete but includes some inaccuracies; shows an adequate understanding of science skills, procedures, and concepts.

1 Response is only partially complete and has many inaccuracies; shows an incomplete understanding of science skills, procedures, and concepts.

0 Response is mostly incomplete and/or inaccurate; shows a lack of understanding of science skills, procedures, and concepts.

3. Some students might suggest that shedding leaves each autumn has the advantage of eliminating water loss during the cold and dry time of the year. But angiosperms pay a price for this advantage by having to replace the leaves each spring, and that replacement takes energy. Gymnosperms do not have the advantage of shedding their leaves, but they also do not pay the price in replacing their leaves.

4. Students should first formulate a hypothesis, such as that animals are attracted more by fragrance than by color. A typical experiment might use a common fruit, such as the apple, and a series of attempts to attract animals in a natural environment.

Skills Trace

Experimenting

- Focus p. 585
- Practice p. 589
- Assess p. 599

Chapter 26 Plant Structure, Function, and Growth

Content Management	Student Edition Activities
■ Section 26–1 Plant Structure and Function, pp. 601–610 The Structure of a Plant Roots How Roots Work Stems Leaves Fluid Transport in Plants	**MINI LAB:** Leaf Me Alone, p. 608 **Laboratory Investigation:** Plant Tissues and Their Functions, pp. 620–621
■ Section 26–2 Plant Growth, pp. 611–615 Tropisms Plant Hormones Controlling Plant Life Cycles	**MINI LAB:** Growing My Way?, p. 614
◆ BRANCHING OUT • In Depth Section 26–3 Plant Propagation, pp. 616–619 Vegetative Reproduction The New Technology of Plant Cloning	**MINI LAB:** Growing Plant Parts, p. 619

■ These sections cover all the necessary content and concepts for an enriched course in biology.
◆ This section covers content and concepts that are either applications or extensions of the enriched material.

Integration Strategies

SE Chemistry, p. 604
History, p. 606
Chemistry, p. 608

Assessment Strategies

SE Chapter Review, pp. 622–625
TR Section Reviews
Chapter Test
BL Chapter Review
Practice Test
CTB Chapter 26 Test

Tech Prep

Teaching strategies appropriate for students who are in technical/vocational programs or who are considering post-secondary technical education can be found on the following **TE** pages: 604, 611, and 617.

Meeting the Standards

Sections 26–1 through 26–3 cover four of the six content standards under **The Cell,** two of the five content standards under **The Interdependence of Organisms,** three of the six content standards under **Matter, Energy, and Organization in Living Systems,** and two of the four content standards under **The Behavior of Organisms** as described on pages 184–187 of The National Science Educational Standards.

Chapter Planning Guide

Teacher's Edition Activities	Other Activities	Media and Technology
Chapter Discovery Learning Activity, p. 600 **Inquiry Activity:** Where Did the Drops Come From?, p. 601 **Inquiry Activity:** Which Side Are You On?, p. 602 **Investigate:** Research, p. 603 **Inquiry Activity:** A Record in Wood, p. 606 **Investigate:** Cooperative Learning, p. 607	**LM** Observing Leaf Structures, #51 **TR** **Writing in Biology:** Meditations in Green **Explore:** Holdin' Up Plants **BL** **Inquiry Activity:** What's in a Leaf?	**CD-ROM:** Roots and Stems **CD-ROM:** The Leaf **TB** Structure of a Leaf, #34
Inquiry Activity: Ups and Downs in a Plant's Life, p. 611 **Inquiry Activity:** Do Seedlings Respond to Light?, p. 612 **Inquiry Activity:** A Matter of Hormones, p. 613	**LM** Investigating the Effects of Plant Hormones, #52 **TR** **Apply:** Toward the Light **BL** **Inquiry Activity:** Which Way Will It Grow?	
Inquiry Activity: Itsy, Bitsy Spider, p. 616 **Investigate:** Cooperative Learning, p. 617	**TR** **Enrich:** The Seeds of a Clone **BL** **Inquiry Activity:** To Mate or Not to Mate	

KEY: SE Student Edition **TE** Teacher's Edition **LM** Laboratory Manual **TR** Teaching Resources **BL** BioLog **TB** Transparency Box **CTB** Computer Test Bank

Materials List

TE Chapter Discovery Learning Activity, p. 600 (15 minutes); photographs of three different kinds of plants.

TE Inquiry Activity: Where Did the Drops Come From? p. 601 (10 minutes for setup and 5 minutes for observation after 4 hours); small potted plant, clear plastic sandwich bag, clear plastic tape.

TE Inquiry Activity: Which Side Are You On? p. 602 (15 minutes for setup and brief daily observations over 1 week); small potted plant, jar of petroleum jelly.

TE Inquiry Activity: A Record in Wood, p. 606 (30 minutes); a section of a tree trunk or a photograph of a tree trunk showing annual rings.

SE MINI LAB: Leaf Me Alone, p. 608 (30 minutes); 3 stalks of celery with leaves, food coloring, 3 beakers, single-edge blade, metric ruler.

TE Inquiry Activity: Ups and Downs in a Plant's Life, p. 611 (10 minutes for setup and brief periodic observations over 2 days); small, fast-growing potted plant, such as coleus.

TE Inquiry Activity: Do Seedlings Respond to Light? p. 612 (10 minutes for setup and brief periodic observations over 2 weeks); bean seeds, plastic pots, potting soil, cardboard boxes.

TE Inquiry Activity: A Matter of Hormones, p. 613 (10–20 minutes for setup and brief periodic observations over 1 week); 2 small potted plants, gibberellic acid solution, spray bottle, metric ruler, graph paper.

SE MINI LAB: Growing My Way? p. 614 (20 minutes for initial setup, 10–20 minutes 2–4 days later, and 10 minutes the next day); 6 soaked corn seeds, Petri dish, clear plastic tape, filter paper or paper towels, modeling clay, single-edge blade, metric ruler.

TE Inquiry Activity: Itsy, Bitsy Spider, p. 616 (15 minutes for setup and brief periodic observations over 2 weeks); mature spider plant with several runners, small pots, potting soil.

TE Investigate: Cooperative Learning, p. 617 (several hours for research and then 30 minutes for grafting); 2 rose plants, sharp knife, wide rubber bands or strips of cloth.

SE MINI LAB: Growing Plant Parts, p. 619 (20 minutes for initial setup and brief daily observations over the next 2 weeks); coleus plant, single-edge blade, onion, potato, toothpicks, 3 beakers, water.

CHAPTER 26

Plant Structure, Function, and Growth

Introducing the Chapter

. . . In Pictures

This well-tended grove of peach trees should produce a bounty of fruit for the farmer. The trees are planted in rows, though in such a way that the rows curve to match the contour of the land. Such contour planting is just one method for preventing erosion of the soil. As students examine the photograph, ask the following questions.

- **What structures of these trees anchor them to the ground?** (The roots.)
- **How does the moisture in the ground reach the upper part of the tree?** (Through the vascular tissue in the tree trunk.)
- **What structures provide the tree with energy?** (The leaves, in which photosynthesis takes place.)

Teaching Strategy

In the first two sections of this chapter, students will learn about basic plant structures and their functions, as well as about plant growth. The BRANCHING OUT section provides students with an in-depth understanding of both traditional methods of vegetative reproduction and new methods of genetic engineering and plant cloning.

CHAPTER 26

Plant Structure, Function, and Growth

FOCUSING THE CHAPTER
THEME: Systems and Interactions

26–1 Plant Structure and Function
- **Identify** the main parts of a plant and **explain** their functions.
- **Explain** how water uptake and fluid transport take place in plants.
- **Discuss** some specializations of plant structures that help plants adapt to their environment.

26–2 Plant Growth
- **Describe** plant tropisms.
- **Examine** the role of hormones in plant growth.

BRANCHING OUT *In Depth*

26–3 Plant Propagation
- **Describe** vegetative reproduction in nature and in agriculture.

LABORATORY INVESTIGATION
- **Observe** the water-transport tissues in certain types of vegetables.

Biology and Your World

BIO JOURNAL

Have you ever wondered why the leaves of plants display an amazing variety of sizes and shapes? In your journal, make a note of the leaf types found in and around your home and school. Then formulate hypotheses to explain the connection between shape and function.

A peach orchard in blossom

BIO JOURNAL

The Bio Journal topic can be used to stimulate discussion about the adaptations in structures that allow plants to thrive in almost any environment. Ask students to discuss what advantage a large leaf might have for a plant, as well as any disadvantages such a leaf might have. Instruct students to keep their entries in their portfolios.

TEACHER SUPPORT

Chapter Discovery Learning Activity

Ask students what comes to mind when someone says the word plant. What is a typical plant? What parts do all plants have? Post in a prominent place in the classroom three large photographs of very different plants, such as an oak tree, a flowering shrub, and a small weed or vine. Then ask students to examine all three photographs and make a labeled drawing of a "generic" plant. Tell them they should draw what is both above ground and below ground. In labeling the drawing, they should use the most general terms they know for plant parts. Also ask them to include a brief phrase with each label to describe the function of that part. Once students have completed their drawings, have them meet in groups and exchange ideas. Finally, in a class discussion, have them compare Figure 26–2 with their own drawing.

SECTION 26–1

Plant Structure and Function

GUIDE FOR READING

- **Explain** the functions of roots, stems, and leaves in plants.
- **Describe** the process of fluid transport in xylem and phloem tissues in plants.

MINI LAB

- **Design an experiment** to determine how the number of leaves affects water uptake in a plant.

THE GREAT SAND DUNES OF Cape Cod National Seashore in Massachusetts are battered by storms and laced with saltwater sprays. In the winter, they endure bitter cold and in the summer, blinding heat. Yet, every year, plants poke through the sand to claim a portion of this difficult landscape. Thousands of kilometers to the west, a bristlecone pine ekes out a living on the stony mountainsides of the Sierra Nevada. Neither the lack of soil nor the strong winds of the high country keep these rugged plants from growing.

How do plants manage to live just about anywhere? The best place to start to answer this question is with the plants themselves—their structure and the ways in which they are adapted to their specific environments.

The Structure of a Plant

Plants provide nearly all the food that makes life on land possible. They release the oxygen that animals breathe and even fashion the places in which animals live. They trap the energy of sunlight and convert it into forms that other living things can use. In this section, you will see how the different tissues within

Figure 26–1
Plants manage to thrive in some of the most difficult places imaginable. (a) Joshua trees and (b) birdcage evening primroses growing in the desert soil of southern California and (c) evergreen trees rising up from the nearly vertical rock cliffs of the Oregon coast are just a few examples of these plants.

TEACHER SUPPORT

Ecology Note

Plants are an integral part of all the biochemical cycles, including the carbon cycle, the nitrogen cycle, and the phosphorus cycle. Thus, the destruction of forests, a problem throughout the world, may have many long-term effects. Eliminating plants can have immediate effects, as well. Roots provide a necessary function for the organism, but they also stabilize the environment by holding the soil in place. Cutting down a forest will immediately affect the richness of the soil of an area and also increase sediment pollution in nearby rivers. The local climate will change as well without the gases produced by the forest's greenery. For instance, after a forest was heavily lumbered in a region of India, annual rainfall decreased almost 50 percent.

SECTION 26–1

Plant Structure and Function

Performance Objectives

- Discuss the functions of plant roots, stems, and leaves.
- Explain the process of fluid transport in xylem and phloem tissues in plants.

Mini Lab Skill: Experimenting
Laboratory Investigation Skill: Observing

1 ENGAGE

Inquiry Activity
Predicting

Where Did the Drops Come From?

Ask students if they think leaves release anything into the atmosphere. Then divide students into small groups and give each a small potted plant, such as a coleus plant. Ask each group to follow this procedure.

1. Place a plastic sandwich bag completely around one of the plant's leaves and secure it to the stem with tape.
2. Place the plant in a place where that leaf will get direct sunlight.

Have members of each group discuss what changes they think will occur in their setup over the next few hours. Ask that they come to a consensus and write a prediction. After 2–4 hours, ask groups to observe their plants and see if their predictions were accurate. The inside surface of the plastic bag should have drops of water on it as a result of transpiration.

2 EXPLORE

Inquiry Activity

Comparing

Which Side Are You On?

Help students recall that plants need carbon dioxide to carry out photosynthesis. Ask whether they think the gas enters through the top or the bottom of a leaf. Then divide students into groups and give each group a potted plant, such as a geranium. Also give each group a small jar of petroleum jelly. Instruct students to coat half of the plant's leaves on the top surface and the other half on the bottom surface. Have students place the plants in a sunny place and observe for a week. At the end of a week, groups should meet and compare the leaves on the plants. Students will find that the leaves coated on the underside will have shriveled, whereas the leaves coated on top will have thrived.

3 TEACH

Ideas Through Images

Have students examine Figure 26–2, read the caption, and answer the following questions.

- **What are the two main systems that make up a plant?** (The two main plant systems are the root system and the shoot system.)
- **Which type of tissue makes up most of both the root system and the shoot system?** (Ground tissue.)
- **How do water and nutrients gathered by the root system reach the top of the shoot system?** (Through the plant's vascular tissue.)

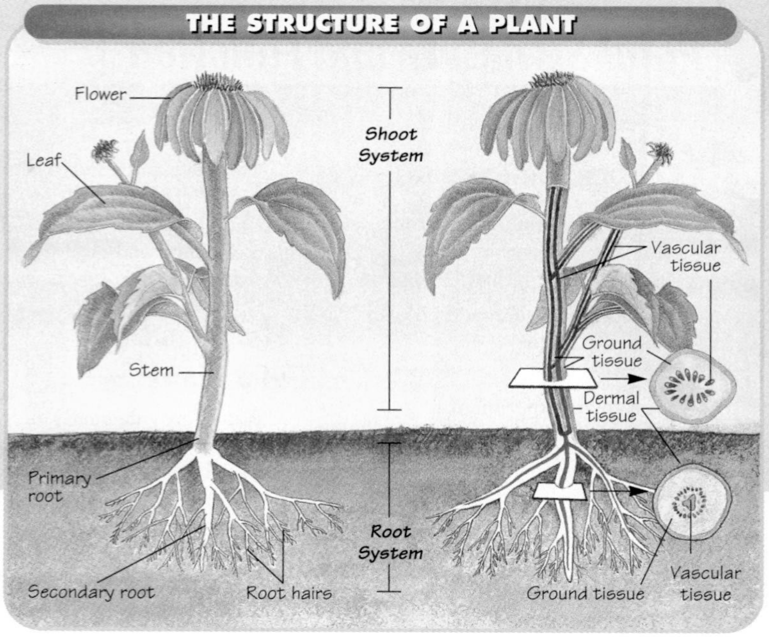

Figure 26–2 A flowering plant consists of a root system below the soil and a shoot system above the soil. Stems, leaves, flowers, and fruits comprise the shoot system, while primary and secondary roots along with root hairs make up the root system. The root system and the shoot system of a flowering plant are made up of three types of tissues: dermal tissue, vascular tissue, and ground tissue.

a plant work together to make these organisms so successful.

Roots, Stems, and Leaves

The body of a plant consists of three distinct regions known as roots, stems, and leaves. What are their primary functions? **Roots** anchor a plant in the ground, drawing water and minerals from the soil. **Stems** typically rise above the ground, support the body of the plant, and carry water and nutrients from one end of the plant to the other. **Leaves** are the main organs of photosynthesis—the process by which plants convert energy from sunlight into chemical energy—so they are usually arranged to capture as much sunlight as possible.

Plant Tissue

Plants generally contain three kinds of tissue. Dermal tissue is the outer covering of the plant. Vascular tissue makes up the fluid-conducting system of the organism. And the rest of the plant is ground tissue, which provides most of a plant's supporting strength and also contains most of the cells that are active in photosynthesis. If you were to compare a plant to a typical mammal, you could say that the dermal tissue is its skin, the vascular tissue is its bloodstream, and ground tissue is everything in between.

☑ ***Checkpoint*** What are the three types of plant tissue? ❶

Plant Cells

The three types of plant tissue contain many cell types specialized to perform certain functions. Dermal tissue, as you might expect, has to protect the plant from its environment while allowing gases such as oxygen and carbon dioxide to flow between the plant and the atmosphere.

In many plants, the ground tissue consists mainly of parenchyma (puh-REHN-kih-muh) cells. These thin-walled cells usually form the bulk of tissue in roots, stems, and leaves. Parenchyma cells in leaves are very active in photosynthesis. The plant roots that we use as

TEACHER SUPPORT

Background Information

Parenchyma cells are found in all the major parts of plants. Although these cells are usually spherical when first produced, their thin walls are easily flattened as they are packed against each other. The majority end up having a shape of 14 sides. The main function of parenchyma cells with chloroplasts is photosynthesis; those without chloroplasts store water or food.

Xylem consists of a combination of different types of cells, including vessel elements, tubelike cells that are usually open at each end. Joined together, the vessel elements form long tubes. Phloem also consists of different types of cells, including sieve-tube members. These are like vessel elements, but they are not open at the end. They do have small pores through which cytoplasm extends from cell to cell.

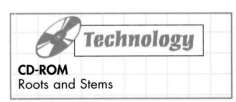

Figure 26–3
(a) *A dandelion's root system shows the thicker primary root and the thinner secondary roots that branch out from the primary roots.* (b) *A young radish seedling's primary root has put out hundreds of tiny root hairs to help it absorb water and other nutrients from its environment.*

food, such as carrots and radishes, are mostly parenchyma cells. The ground tissue may also contain collenchyma (kuh-LEHN-kih-muh) cells and sclerenchyma (sklih-REHN-kuh-muh) cells. The thick walls of these cells provide strong support for the rest of the plant.

The vascular tissues carry fluids from one part of the plant to another. The principal vascular cell types are **xylem** (ZIGH-luhm), which carries water, and **phloem** (FLOH-ehm), which carries sugars and other foods throughout the plant.

Roots

As a plant grows, it sends roots into the soil to collect nutrients and water, and also to help provide support for the portion of the plant that is above ground. A growing seedling first sends a single primary root into the soil. ***Figure 26–3*** shows secondary roots that branch off the primary root as further growth takes place. As the secondary roots grow, their surface area enlarges dramatically. The surface area of the roots, even in a small plant, may be 50 or 100 times the surface area of its leaves!

Epidermis

The **epidermis** is the outer covering of a root. Epidermal cells grow tiny thin-walled projections, known as root hairs, that make direct contact with the soil. These root hairs, which even in a small plant may number in the billions, are responsible for most of the root's surface area. Plants absorb nearly all the water and nutrients directly through root hairs.

☑ *Checkpoint* What are root hairs? 2

Cortex

Just beneath the epidermis is a layer of spongy cells known as the **cortex.** The parenchyma cells of the root cortex are important in moving water from the epidermis to the vascular tissue near the center of the root.

Vascular Cylinder

In most roots, a **vascular cylinder**—a central region of xylem and phloem cells—carries water and nutrients between the roots and the rest of the plant. Water and minerals that have passed through the cortex enter the vascular cylinder, where they are transported upward into the rest of the plant.

How Roots Work

During its growing season, a single corn plant may take as much as 3 liters of water a day from the soil. How does it do

Ideas Through Images

Have students examine Figure 26–3, read the caption, and answer the following questions.

- **What is the difference between a primary root and a secondary root?** (A primary root is thicker and grows generally straight down. Secondary roots are thinner roots and branch out from the primary root.)
- **What function do root hairs serve?** (Root hairs absorb water and nutrients from the soil.)

Investigate

Research Have pairs of students work together to prepare a report on an endangered plant species. Point out that many books in the library discuss endangered plant species. Ask that each report include a description of the plant, an illustration or photograph, a description of its natural environment, and an explanation of why the plant is endangered.

☑ Checkpoints

1 Dermal tissue, vascular tissue, and ground tissue.

2 Tiny thin-walled projections on epidermal cells that make direct contact with the soil.

TEACHER SUPPORT

Ecology Note

The roots of most plants anchor the organism to the ground and collect nutrients and water from the soil. But one fascinating group of plants have roots that never touch the soil. These are the epiphytes of tropical rain forests, which include various orchids, bromeliads, ferns, and mosses. In that environment, the competition is for light, which is blocked by the towering canopy of broadleaf evergreen trees. Epiphytes have adapted by clinging to tree branches high above the ground. They are not parasites; they obtain energy and nutrients through photosynthesis and with specialized roots. Epiphyte roots absorb moisture from the air and obtain nutrients from the organic debris that accumulates at the base of the tree's leaves. In some species of orchid epiphytes, the root is also the only photosynthetic organ.

Technology

CD-ROM
Roots and Stems

INTEGRATING CHEMISTRY

The concentration of a solution determines whether water will flow into or out of that solution through the surrounding membrane. Chemists express solution concentration in various ways, including grams of solute per 100 grams of solvent, molarity, and molality.

Ideas Through Images

Have students examine Figure 26–4, read the caption, and answer the following questions.

- **What prevents water and mineral ions that enter the vascular cylinder from leaving the same way?** (The Casparian strip.)
- **What is the Casparian strip?** (A waxy layer that seals the cells of the endodermis together.)
- **What two kinds of vascular cells are surrounded by the endodermis?** (Xylem and phloem.)

Discussion

Initiate a discussion of active transport by reminding students that in this process a substance moves against a concentration difference. Emphasize that active transport requires an expenditure of energy by the cell, whereas osmosis (an example of passive transport) does not. Ask students to recall that a cell uses ATP molecules for energy, and ATP is made through the process of cellular respiration. Point out that plant cells carry out respiration just as animal cells do.

THE STRUCTURE OF A ROOT

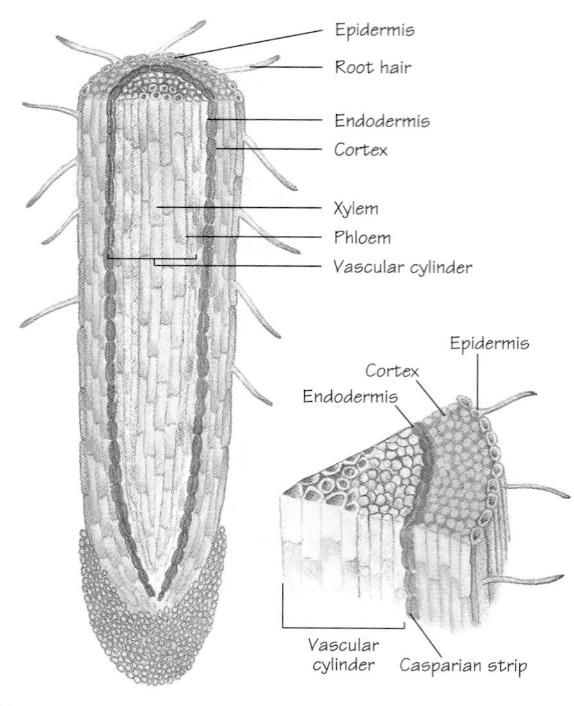

Figure 26–4
A section of a typical dicot root shows concentric layers of epidermis, cortex, and endodermis surrounding the vascular cylinder in the center. The Casparian strip, or endodermis, separates the cortex from the vascular cylinder. Like police officers directing traffic, these cells ensure that water travels into the vascular cylinder and does not leave it.

INTEGRATING CHEMISTRY

What is the significance of the concentration of a solution? What units do chemists use to measure solution concentration?

this? The answer is osmosis. Osmosis is the movement of water across a membrane. If the concentration of dissolved material is higher on one side of a membrane, then water will flow across the membrane toward the side of higher concentration. ● This means that water will move out of damp soil into root hairs, which contain high concentrations of dissolved salts and sugars.

When there is plenty of water in the soil, osmosis rapidly draws water into the root epidermis. As the epidermal cells are diluted by the incoming water, osmosis causes water to move out of the epidermis into the cells of the cortex and then into the cells of the vascular cylinder.

This process will not work if the concentration of dissolved material in the soil is greater than the concentration inside the root cells. Could this happen? It certainly could. When plants are flooded with salty water, osmosis may cause water to flow out of the roots back into the soil. The rapid loss of water from roots, known as "root burn," may weaken or kill a plant. Applying too much fertilizer to the soil can also cause root burn.

☑ **Checkpoint** What is osmosis? 1

Active Transport

Besides water, root hairs must take in minerals that plants need to survive. Unlike water, nearly all the minerals are brought across the cell membrane of the root hair by active transport. Protein molecules in the cell membrane use energy in the form of ATP to "pump" mineral ions across the cell membrane.

Once they enter the root, these ions continue to move by active transport. They are pumped from the epidermis to the cortex and then into the vascular cylinder. By using energy to move mineral ions into the vascular cylinder, the plant also draws water right along with the ions. How does this happen? As mineral ions are moved toward the center of the root, their concentration in these cells increases. Water then moves from the outer cortex toward the center of the root, drawn by osmosis.

The Casparian Strip

In most roots, the inner boundary of the cortex is formed by a layer of cells

TEACHER SUPPORT

Managing Classroom Diversity

TECH PREP STUDENTS

Ask students who plan careers in food service to make a poster that shows what parts of the plant common vegetables are derived from. This may take library research in encyclopedias and books about plants. Review with students their research before they begin to make the poster. Discuss with them how illustrations of food vegetables could be tied to a photograph of a generalized plant.

THE STRUCTURE OF A STEM

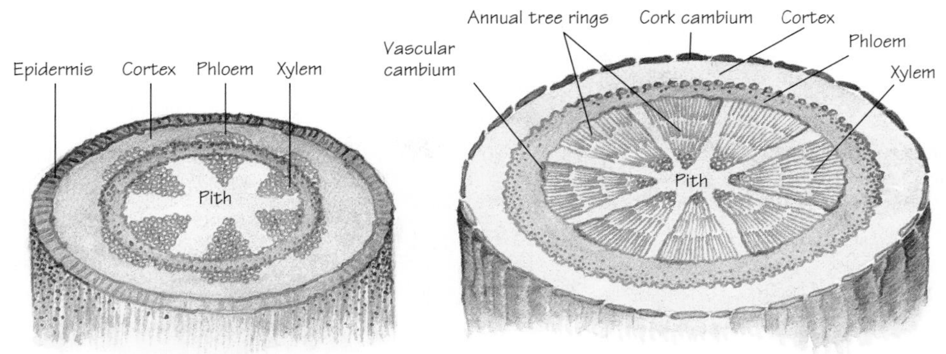

Figure 26–5
This diagram shows the cross sections of a young woody dicot stem (left) and an older woody dicot stem (right). In the older stem, notice the location of the vascular cambium, which, over the years, produces wood and the cork cambium. The cork cambium forms the bark of a tree.

called the **endodermis.** These cells form a tight layer that separates the cortex from the vascular cylinder. In fact, the seal is so tight that each cell in the endodermis is set—almost like a brick in mortar—in a waxy layer known as the Casparian strip. Neither water nor mineral ions can move through this waxy layer. Therefore, the endodermal cells are able to control entry to the vascular cylinder.

✓ **Checkpoint** What is the role of the Casparian strip? ❷

Stems

Stems connect the roots that gather water and nutrients with the leaves that carry out photosynthesis. Stems may be as short as a few centimeters or they may rise tens of meters into the air.

Stems are surrounded by a layer of epidermal cells. Like the roots, they also contain ground tissue and vascular tissue, but these are arranged differently in stems than they are in roots. In monocots, vascular bundles containing xylem and phloem cells are scattered through the ground tissue. In dicots, these vascular bundles are arranged in a ring. The ground tissue inside the ring is known as the **pith.** The ground tissue outside the ring is called the cortex.

Wood

You've probably noticed that the stems of many plants not only get longer as they grow, they also get thicker. Some plants get thicker stems every year by producing a tough material called wood.

Vascular bundles of xylem and phloem surround the pith in the center of the stem. As the stem grows, new cells are produced at the boundary between the xylem and the phloem. These cells push outward, adding more xylem and phloem and increasing the diameter of the stem. This layer of rapidly dividing cells is called the vascular cambium because it produces more and more vascular tissue.

Most of what we call wood is xylem. As more and more xylem tissue is added, the woody stem gets larger and larger. But the phloem tissue, which is outside the vascular cambium, has a problem. As the xylem layer gets larger, the older layers of phloem crack open, leaving gaps between them. To solve this problem,

Ideas Through Images

Have students examine Figure 26–5, read the caption, and answer the following questions.

- **How can you tell that these illustrations represent dicot stems and not monocot stems?** (In a monocot stem, the vascular bundles are scattered through the ground tissue. In a dicot stem, as shown here, the vascular bundles are arranged in rings.)
- **In a young woody dicot stem, what is the outside layer of the stem called?** (The epidermis.)

Correcting Misconceptions

Make sure students understand that the term stem includes both the green stem seen in smaller plants and the bark-covered trunk of a huge tree. Point out that in common usage, stem and trunk would be distinct from each other, but in the science of plants a trunk is just a large stem.

✓ Checkpoints

❶ The movement of water across a membrane.

❷ To control the passage of water and mineral ions into and out of the vascular cylinder of a root.

TEACHER SUPPORT

Facts and Figures

- Root foods include sweet potatoes, yams, cassava, beets, turnips, rutabagas, parsnips, radishes, horseradishes, and carrots.
- Leaf foods include lettuce, cabbage, parsley, celery, spinach, chard, and rhubarb.
- Most wood floats because it usually has a specific gravity less than 1.0, the specific gravity of water. The lightest commercially used wood is balsa, with a specific gravity of 0.12. *Lignum vitae*, a West Indian tree, has a specific gravity of over 1.25; it is so hard that it is used instead of metal in submarine drive shafts.
- About 50 percent of the weight of live wood is due to its water content.
- Leaves range in size from the 1-mm wide duckweed leaves to the 6-m wide leaves of the Seychelles Island palms.

Ancillary Support

The resource below can be used to support your teaching strategy for these two pages.

TR Explore: Holdin' Up Plants

Ideas Through Images

Have students examine Figure 26–6, read the caption, and answer the following questions.

- **Which is older, a ring near the center of a tree or one near the edge?** (The one near the center.)
- **What type of vascular tissue makes up almost all of the plant material shown in this photograph?** (Xylem tissue.)

INTEGRATING HISTORY

The study of growth rings in old trees, as well as in the beams of ancient buildings, can provide historians with evidence about the environmental conditions of an area in each of the specific years a tree was alive. The science of tree-ring dating, called dendrochronology, has been useful in gathering data about the relatively recent past and in calibrating radiocarbon dating, a method used to date organic materials in the thousands of years.

Inquiry Activity

Inferring

A Record in Wood

Ask students what they think they could infer from the annual rings on the trunk of a tree. Divide students into small groups and, if possible, give each group a section from the trunk of a tree that was at least 20 years old when it was cut down. As a substitute, provide each group with a photocopy of a photograph of a tree trunk's annual rings from a botany book. (Sometimes, paper or lumber companies will provide such a photograph.) Ask each group to assume the outermost ring was made this year. Then ask them to make a chronology of the years of this tree's life, inferring from the rings the climate of each year.

Figure 26–6
Found in approximately concentric circles, annual tree rings form due to a seasonal variation in the production of xylem. As a result, this tree trunk provides a record of the weather conditions of years past.

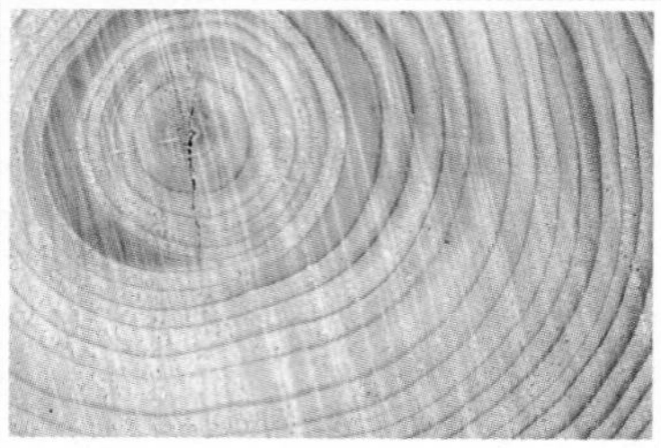

woody plants have another layer of cells, called the cork cambium. This layer produces cork, a tough layer with thick cell walls loaded with waxes and oils that form the bark covering the stem.

The Stem of a Tree

As ***Figure 26–5*** on page 605 shows, nearly all the wood of a tree is actually xylem. In an older tree, the innermost xylem layers no longer conduct water and are known as heartwood. The outer layers, which are active in water transport, are called sapwood. In temperate climates, the cambium produces much more xylem in the summer than it does in the fall and winter. This leads to a seasonal variation in the texture of wood, producing **annual tree rings.** Tree rings often provide important historical information. ● Thick rings indicate that weather conditions were favorable and much new wood was added to the tree. Thin rings may mean that a drought or other problems allowed little growth.

INTEGRATING HISTORY

What historical information has been provided by the study of the growth rings in old trees?

As you have seen, outside the vascular cambium is a thin layer of phloem, which carries nutrients, and then a layer of cork cambium, which produces the bark. This means that trees carry most of their nutrients and do most of their growing in thin layers of cells just under the bark.

These tissues just under the bark are delicate and easily damaged. If a strip of bark is removed from the base of a tree, often these layers will be pulled off with the bark. The loss of cambium and phloem means that the tree will stop growing and will lose the ability to carry nutrients to its roots. Eventually, the roots of the tree may starve and the tree will die.

☑ *Checkpoint* What are annual tree rings? 1

Leaves

Leaves are the main organs in which plants carry out photosynthesis. One way to understand plants is to think of them as organisms that "eat" sunlight. If you consider sunlight as "food" for plants, then the structure of a typical plant makes perfect sense. Most leaves are thin, broad structures that have a lot of surface area with little mass—most leaves aren't heavy. That means they are efficient collectors of solar energy—the primary job of a leaf.

Leaves come in an incredible variety of shapes and sizes, adapted to the environment in which a plant lives, as illustrated by the photographs on page 609. Like roots and stems, leaves have an outer covering of epidermal cells, fluid-carrying vascular tissue, and ground tissue consisting of parenchyma cells. Leaves are attached to stems by a thin structure called a petiole (PEHT-ee-ohl). The petiole is where a leaf separates from the stem when a plant drops its leaves in the fall.

The Epidermis

Leaf epidermal cells are covered with a waxy waterproof layer called the cuticle. This layer protects the leaf against water loss and insect invasion. But leaves cannot be sealed off completely from the air around them. Leaves need to "breathe" just as you do. The reason is photosynthesis. In sunlight, plants take in enormous amounts of carbon dioxide and give off oxygen. How do these gases

TEACHER SUPPORT

Historical Perspective

Some tropical trees produce a uniform wood without annual rings because the cambium makes xylem throughout the year. But most wood shows seasonal variations. For instance, the trees of the American Southwest grow for only a few months a year, when water is available, and thus show distinct rings. In that region, archaeologists have studied the rings of ancient wooden beams found in Native American pueblos. Through careful correlation, they have established an accurate chronology for the region going back to 59 BC. That is, they can now date a specific site by matching the rings of beams at that site with beams at other sites. In Europe, similar efforts have been made throughout the continent, using old trees and beams in German cathedrals and Roman ruins. A chronology has been established going back some 2700 years, or to about 700 BC.

THE STRUCTURE OF A LEAF

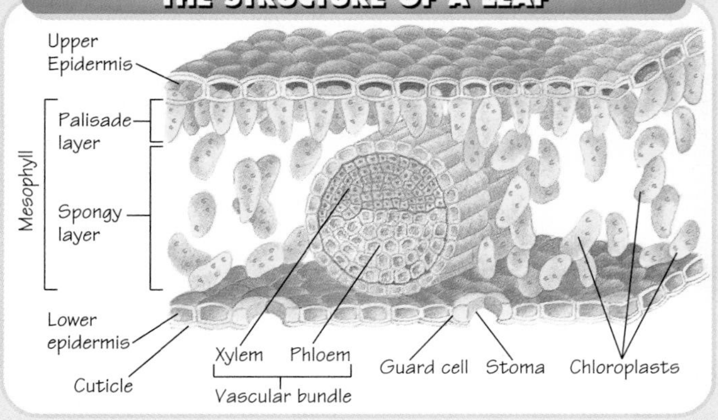

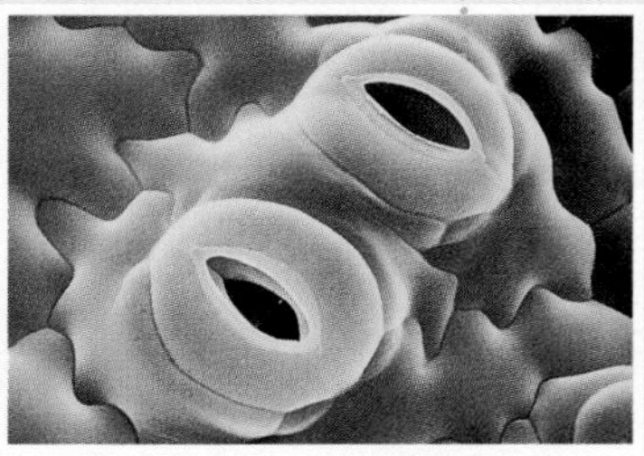

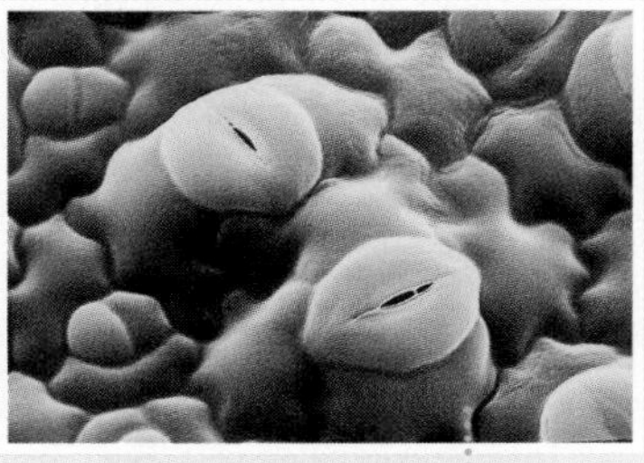

Figure 26–7
(a) In a dicot leaf, a mesophyll layer containing vascular bundles and chloroplasts is sandwiched between the upper epidermis and the lower epidermis. Located in the lower epidermis are stomata. (b) Stomata open (magnification: 257X) and (c) close (magnification: 343X) to allow gases in and out of the leaves.

get in and out of the leaf? The undersides of leaves have small openings known as **stomata** (STOH-muh-tuh; singular: stoma). Each stoma is surrounded by guard cells that control the passage of gases by opening and closing the stomata.

At first glance, it might seem to make sense for a plant to keep its stomata open all the time. But that would lead to a problem. In order for a gas to enter the cells inside a leaf, it must first dissolve in water. That means the cell surfaces inside the leaf must always be kept wet. What happens to a wet surface exposed to air? It dries out. So if a plant always kept its stomata open, it would lose water rapidly.

Plants solve this problem by balancing their need for carbon dioxide against their need to conserve water. Stomata generally open up during periods of rapid photosynthesis. This allows carbon dioxide to enter the leaf. However, if a plant begins to lose too much water, the thick cell walls of the guard cells cause the cells to push together, closing the opening. If more water becomes available, the guard cells swell as they take in fluid, causing them to expand and opening the stomata to allow gas exchange to take place.

☑ **Checkpoint** What are stomata? ❷

Mesophyll Tissue

The ground tissue of most leaves consists of a tissue known as mesophyll. Mesophyll cells are packed with chloroplasts, which are cells that perform most of a plant's photosynthesis. A typical leaf consists of two types of mesophyll—a layer of tall palisade cells just beneath the upper epidermis and a layer of irregularly shaped spongy cells just above the lower epidermis. Spongy mesophyll has plenty of air spaces, and these cells are the ones that carbon dioxide enters first.

Leaf Veins—Vascular Tissue

Leaf tissue needs plenty of water, and the vascular system of a plant makes sure that it gets that water. Xylem cells carry water into the leaf, and osmosis carries the water from cell to cell within the leaf. Phloem tissue carries the products

Ideas Through Images

Have students examine Figure 26–7, read the caption, and answer the following questions.

- **In common terms, what are the upper epidermis and lower epidermis of a leaf?** (The top and bottom, respectively.)
- **Where does the carbon dioxide needed for photosynthesis enter the leaf?** (Through the stomata in the lower epidermis.)

Investigate

Cooperative Learning Ask cooperative learning groups to do research to find out how to preserve leaves for inclusion in a collection. After you have reviewed the method students have found, ask that they make a leaf collection for display of some of the common plants of the area, including large trees such as oak and maple, as well as shrubs often found in landscaped yards.

☑ Checkpoints

❶ The concentric circles in the stem of a tree formed as a result of seasonal variations in the production of xylem.

❷ The small openings on the underside of leaves.

TEACHER SUPPORT — Background Information

During the daytime, stomata are open, allowing in the carbon dioxide that plants use in photosynthesis and releasing the excess oxygen produced during that process. At night, however, when the plant does not carry on photosynthesis, open stomata support respiration. When darkness falls, plants take in oxygen. Actually, cells throughout the plant use oxygen all the time, just as animal cells do. But during the day, the rate of photosynthesis is much greater than the rate of respiration, so the plants' use of oxygen is not apparent. At night, such activities as cell growth, protein synthesis, and active transport require the ATP energy produced by respiration. Therefore, when the forest is dark, those great green trees and other plants take in oxygen and release carbon dioxide, like the animals that live among them.

Technology

CD-ROM
The Leaf

Ancillary Support

The resources below can be used to support your teaching strategy for these two pages.

LM Observing Leaf Structures, #51
BL Inquiry Activity: What's in a Leaf?
TB Structure of a Leaf, #34

MINI LAB **Experimenting**

Teacher Notes

- For time required and materials needed, see page 600b.
- Suggest that students trim the bottom of each stalk before beginning their experiment to ensure the uptake of liquid.

Answers to Analyze and Conclude

1. Students' setups may vary. A typical design will include a stalk in each of three beakers of colored water. One stalk will have its leaves removed completely, another stalk will have only one or two leaves, and a third stalk will have several leaves. After 20–30 minutes, all stalks are removed and cut at regular intervals to find how far up each drew the fluid. The data should show that the stalk with the most leaves drew the fluid up farthest.

2. The more leaves, the greater the water uptake. Students should support that conclusion by citing observations from the three stalks in their experiment.

3. Students should infer that capillary action drew water up the stem of all three celery stalks, even the one with the leaves removed. Since transpiration occurs through leaf stomata, transpirational pull was involved only in the other two celery stalks, both of which drew water up farther than the stalk with no leaves.

Skills Trace

Experimenting

- **Focus** p. 608
- **Practice** p. 610
- **Assess** p. 625

MINI LAB .... Experimenting ...

Leaf Me Alone

PROBLEM *How does the number of leaves affect water uptake in a plant? **Design an experiment** to answer the question.*

SUGGESTED PROCEDURE

1. Using three stalks of celery with all their leaves and three beakers containing red food coloring, design an experiment that will determine the effect the number of leaves on a plant has on its ability to transport water up the stem.
2. Formulate a hypothesis and be sure to include a control. You may want to use a metric ruler to measure your results.
3. Have your teacher approve your experimental design and then perform the investigation. Record your observations in a data table or diagram.

ANALYZE AND CONCLUDE

1. How did the data differ among the three setups? Explain your answer.
2. How did the number of leaves affect the plant's water uptake? Give evidence to support your answer.
3. Explain how transpirational "pull" is involved in your results.

INTEGRATING CHEMISTRY

What are hydrogen bonds? How do they determine the properties of water?

of photosynthesis from the leaf into the rest of the plant. In most plants, xylem and phloem cells are found together in vascular bundles, known as the "veins" of the leaf. In most monocots, the veins run parallel to each other. In dicots, they usually form a branched network.

Checkpoint Why do leaves contain vascular tissue? 1

Fluid Transport in Plants

You have already seen how xylem and phloem form a vascular network that carries water and nutrients throughout a plant. Vascular systems are a bit like the circulatory systems of animals, which carry fluids within the body. However, plants don't have a muscular "heart" to push fluid through their "veins." How, then, are plants able to move fluid from one end of the plant body to the other?

Xylem Transport

Recall that water enters the cells of root tissue by osmosis. But osmosis cannot generate enough force to lift the water more than a few centimeters above the ground. This is one of the reasons why nonvascular plants, such as mosses, are so small. In vascular plants, individual xylem cells are joined end to end—like stiff-walled drinking straws—to form continuous tubes that reach from one end of the plant to the other. Two powerful forces draw water up into these tubes.

Water molecules are strongly attracted to each other, a property known as cohesion. Because of their ability to form hydrogen bonds, water molecules can also be strongly attracted to other substances, a property called adhesion. ● If a thin tube is placed in a bowl of water, these properties will cause the water level to rise inside the tube, a process known as capillary action. Capillary action is one of the forces that draw water upward from the roots into the stems of vascular plants.

A second, and stronger, force is produced by the plant's own use of water. The leaves of a plant use water for photosynthesis, and they lose large amounts of water vapor through their stomata, a process known as **transpiration.** A large tree can lose as much as 100 liters of water a day through transpiration. As leaves lose water, they draw water out of xylem vessels through osmosis. Then, as a locomotive pulls a train hundreds of cars long, the movement of water into the leaves creates an upward "pull" through the xylem. The strong cohesion

TEACHER SUPPORT

Background Information

The shape, size, texture, and organization of leaves are often the best clues in identifying the hundreds of thousands of different kinds of leafy plants. Leaves can be arranged on a stem in a variety of ways. They may make a spiral or alternate pattern along the stem. Two leaves may be attached at the same node, making an opposite arrangement. Three or more leaves attached at the same node create a whorled arrangement. Leaves themselves may be simple, when the blade is undivided, or compound, when the blade is divided into some kind of leaflets. When leaflets are in pairs along a central stalk, they are called pinnately compound. When leaflets are attached at the same point at the top of the petiole, they are called palmately compound.

Visualizing Plant Adaptations

The forces of natural selection affect all organisms, and plants are no exception. Facing some of the most extreme conditions on Earth—from parched deserts to the frozen Arctic—plants have adapted to meet the demands of these environments.

1 Desert Plants
The cactuses have extensive root systems that are able to quickly soak up the rare desert rainfall. Their leaves have been reduced to sharp spines, and they do most of their photosynthesis in thick, water-conserving stems.

2 Water Plants
Water lilies have stomata on the upper surfaces of their leaves. This important adaptation allows them to take carbon dioxide directly from the air, rather than absorbing it from water.

3 Salt-Tolerant Plants
A saltbush is a halophyte, meaning "salt-tolerant plant," that takes up sodium into its roots by active transport, drawing water along with it by osmosis. The extra sodium is then transported to the leaves, where it is pumped into expandable bladder cells on the surface of the leaf. The delicate bladder cell walls eventually burst, and the excess salt is washed away by rain or a high tide.

4 Carnivorous Plants
Carnivorous plants turn the tables on the animal kingdom! Many of these plants are found in nitrogen-poor soil, so capturing small organisms is an important way of meeting their nutritional needs. When an insect lands on a leaf of the Venus flytrap (right), the flytrap's leaves slam together. The insect is digested by enzymes released from the leaves. The annual sundew (left) is a tiny plant with tentacles on its leaves. The tentacles secrete a sticky liquid that attracts insects. When an insect lands on a tentacle, other tentacles bend over to surround the insect, secreting enzymes that digest the insect.

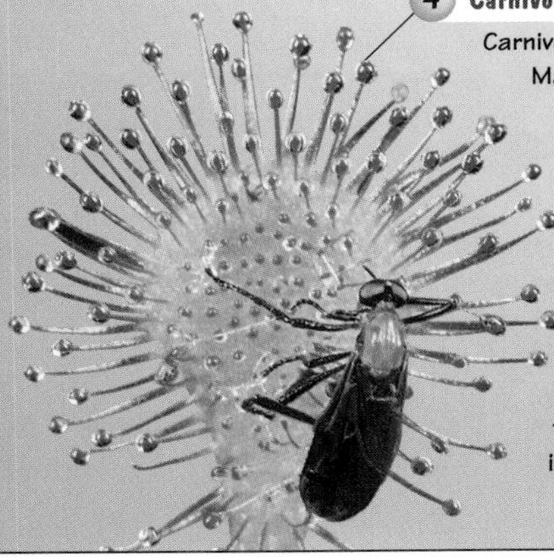

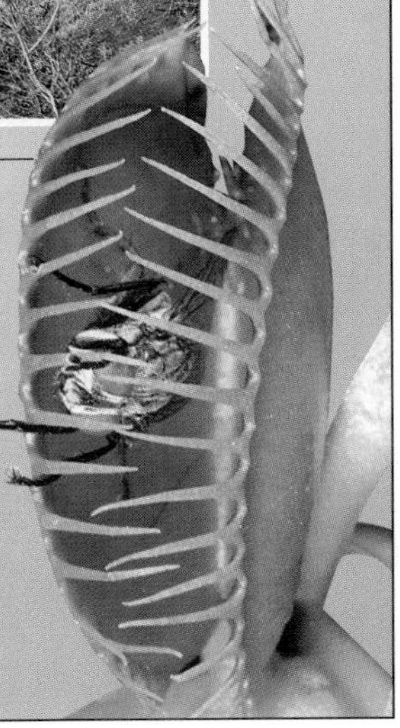

INTEGRATING CHEMISTRY

A hydrogen bond is a force of attraction that holds molecules together. Hydrogen bonds are responsible for many of the properties of water, including its high boiling point and its adhesion to vascular tissue in plants that results in capillary action.

Visualizing Plant Adaptations

These are only four examples of a practically endless list of plant adaptations that could be discussed.

The evolution of carnivorous plants may seem the most remarkable to students. Scientists speculate that initially plants in nutrient-poor soil collected rainwater on depressions in their leaves. An insect landing in that water could have drowned. Once the insect body decomposed, the materials would have been absorbed by the leaf, providing the plant with needed nutrients. Thus, a plant in that environment with a certain shape of leaf would have a reproductive advantage. Eventually, plants such as pitcher plants could have developed. Adaptations such as those of the Venus flytrap or the annual sundew would have developed later.

Ask students to speculate about how adaptations in desert plants, water plants, and salt-tolerant plants might have evolved.

Checkpoint

1 Vascular tissue conducts water and the products of photosynthesis from the leaves to other parts of the plant.

TEACHER SUPPORT

Background Information

Carnivorous plants have adaptations in their leaves that provide the plants with needed nutrients. The tentacle-covered leaves of the sundew are one of several kinds of insect-trapping mechanisms. Another is found in the Venus flytrap. Its leaves are fashioned like a steel trap, with two halves of the blade hinged along a middle rib. Stiff projections along the leaf margins trap an insect when it touches trigger hairs on the leaf surface. Still another mechanism is found in bladderworts, which float in shallow water. These plants have stomach-shaped bladders at the base of their leaves. When an insect touches a trigger hair, a "trapdoor" springs open and water rushes into the bladder, taking the insect in with it. Finally, the leaves of pitcher plants are formed like vases. When an insect ventures to the bottom of the "vase," a pool of liquid and a slippery inner surface make it difficult for the insect to climb out.

Ancillary Support

The resource below can be used to support your teaching strategy for these two pages.

TR Writing in Biology: Meditations in Green

Laboratory Investigation

The Laboratory Investigation, Plant Tissues and Their Functions, on pages 620–621, is appropriate to use at this point in the chapter.

4 ASSESS

Quick Check

Have students make three concept maps, one each for roots, stems, and leaves. Ask that these concept maps include as much information as possible about both the structure and function of these plant parts.

Section Review 26–1

1. Roots collect nutrients and water from the soil and also provide support for the portion of the plant that is above ground. Stems contain vascular tissue that connects the roots with the leaves. Leaves are the main organs in which plants carry out photosynthesis.

2. Xylem cells carry water through the plant to the leaves. Water enters xylem cells by osmosis. Then the forces of capillary action and transpiration draw water up through the plant's xylem tissue. A network of phloem carries sugars and other foods throughout the plant in the form of phloem sap. A combination of active transport and osmosis is believed to transport the sap through the phloem network.

3. Students might mention any adaptations in the roots, stems, or leaves of plants. A typical response will describe the adaptations discussed on page 609.

4. Students should mention that a leaf has an outer layer of epidermal cells that protects against water loss and insect invasion. This layer allows gases to pass into and out of the leaf through stomata. A leaf's vascular tissue, in bundles called veins, provides the leaf with water and carries away the products of photosynthesis. The ground tissue, mostly mesophyll tissue, contains the chloroplasts that perform photosynthesis.

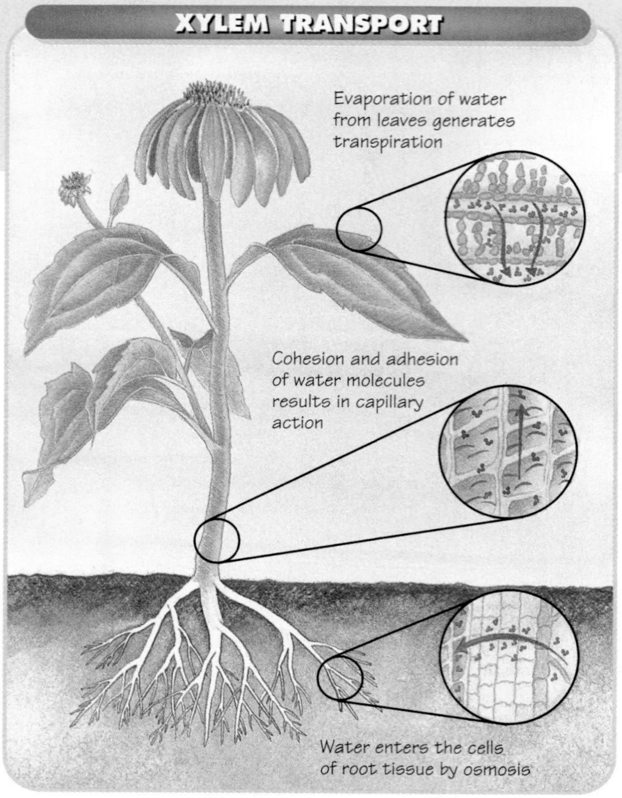
XYLEM TRANSPORT
Evaporation of water from leaves generates transpiration
Cohesion and adhesion of water molecules results in capillary action
Water enters the cells of root tissue by osmosis

Figure 26–8
Xylem tissues are capable of transporting water from the tip of a plant's roots to the tops of its shoots. This action is the result of a combination of factors, illustrated in the diagram.

of water molecules produces a powerful force—called transpiration pull—that draws water upward into the leaves. **The combination of capillary action, osmosis, and transpiration pull is capable of lifting water to the tops of the tallest trees—such as the giant redwoods.**

☑ *Checkpoint* What is transpiration? 1

Phloem Transport

Like xylem, phloem forms a continuous network that reaches from the roots to the leaves. The combination of sugars and other nutrients dissolved in water forms phloem sap. Naturally, phloem sap carries the sugars produced in the leaves by photosynthesis down into the stems and roots of the plant. However, phloem also moves sugars into developing fruits. And if one part of a plant is kept in darkness or shade, phloem will carry nutrients to wherever they are needed.

The mechanism of phloem transport is not completely understood. **A combination of active transport and osmosis, known as the pressure-flow hypothesis, is believed to transport sugars through a plant's phloem tissue.** Suppose that leaf tissue is actively producing sugars and transporting them into the phloem sap. Osmosis will cause a flow of water into the sap at the same point, producing pressure. If sugars are needed at another point, the cells absorb the sugar from the phloem, and osmosis causes water to follow the sugars. The combination of these effects produces a steady flow of phloem sap between the parts of the plant that produce sugars and the parts that use them.

Section Review 26–1

1. **Explain** the functions of roots, stems, and leaves in plants.
2. **Describe** the process of fluid transport in xylem and phloem tissues in plants.
3. **Identify** the adaptations of plants that enable them to thrive in their environment.
4. **Critical Thinking—Relating** Describe the structure and function of a leaf.
5. **MINI LAB** How can you **design an experiment** to find out how the number of leaves affect water uptake in a plant?

5. Students should suggest a design in which water uptake can be measured in several plants of the same species with varying numbers of leaves.

Skills Trace
Experimenting
- Focus p. 608
- Practice p. 610
- Assess p. 625

Learning Modality

Kinesthetic Learning Ask students to develop a role-play situation that represents the pull created by transpiration, by which the exit of students at one end of a chain makes room for the entrance of other students at the opposite end of the chain.

Plant Growth

SECTION 26–2

Guide for Reading

- **Define** tropism.
- **Discuss** the role of auxins in plant growth.
- **Explain** why timing is important in plant life cycles.

MINI LAB

- **Predict** the effect of various factors on root growth.

PLANTS ARE DIFFERENT FROM animals in many ways, but one of the most important is the way in which they grow. Unlike most animals, plants continue to grow and increase in size throughout their lives. Even the oldest plants, including trees in the Pacific Northwest that are thousands of years old, continue to grow and produce new tissue.

Tropisms

Plants grow in response to cues from their environment. These responses are known as tropisms. The term **tropism** is derived from a Greek word that means "to turn." There are several common tropisms, each of which demonstrates the ability of plants to respond to changes in their environment.

Geotropism

Every seedling has the ability to sense and respond to the force of gravity. **Geotropism,** as this response is called, helps seedlings find their way out of the soil and into the sunlight. It affects roots and stems differently. Roots turn toward the force of gravity, while stems grow away from it.

Phototropism

The ability of plants to grow in response to light is known as **phototropism.** When a plant is grown near a window or other source of light, it will generally grow in the direction of the light source. The phototropic response can be so quick that young seedlings turn toward the light in a matter of a few hours!

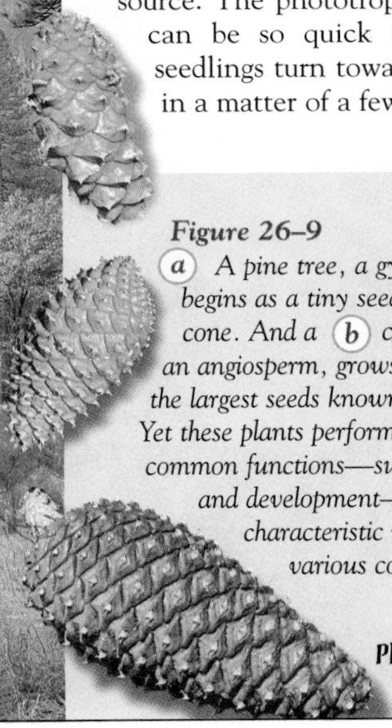

Figure 26–9 (a) *A pine tree, a gymnosperm, begins as a tiny seed from a pine cone. And a* (b) *coconut palm, an angiosperm, grows from one of the largest seeds known, a coconut. Yet these plants perform many common functions—such as growth and development—and exhibit characteristic responses to various conditions.*

Section 26–2
Plant Growth

Performance Objectives

- State the meaning of tropism.
- Describe how auxins affect plant growth.
- Discuss the importance of timing in plant life cycles.

Mini Lab Skill: Predicting

1 ENGAGE

Inquiry Activity
Predicting

Ups and Downs in a Plant's Life

Two days before students are to begin this section, divide the class into small groups and give each group a small, fast-growing potted plant, such as a coleus plant. The activity works best if the plant is in a four-sided plastic pot. Ask each group to write a prediction of how the plant will react if the pot is placed on its side. Once the predictions are made, ask that each group find a location in the room to turn the pot on its side. If the plant is in a round pot, students can prop the pot with books or other objects. After a day or two, students should observe that all the plant stems will have turned upward.

Checkpoint

1 The process by which leaves lose water vapor through their stomata.

TEACHER SUPPORT

Managing Classroom Diversity

GIFTED STUDENTS

Challenge interested students to try to duplicate Darwin's experiment with phototropism, described on page 612. Like Darwin, they could use canary grass, which is fast growing. Aluminum foil could be used for the opaque caps on the grass shoots.

TECH PREP STUDENTS

Ask students who plan careers in agriculture and landscaping to investigate and report on the commercial use of plant hormones in promoting plant growth.

Ancillary Support

The resource below can be used to support your teaching strategy for these two pages.

TR Apply: Toward the Light

2 EXPLORE

Inquiry Activity

Experimenting

Do Seedlings Respond to Light?

Have students plant four bean seeds that have been soaked overnight in each of two plastic pots containing potting soil. Dampen the soil with water and have students water the seedlings whenever the surface of the soil feels dry. Place one pot under a cardboard box with the lid cut off. Place the other pot under a box in which light can enter only through a slit that students have cut in one side of the box. Have students observe the seedlings over the course of a few days, noting that in one setup, the plant stems bend toward the light entering from the side as they grow, while in the other the stems grow straight toward the light from above.

3 TEACH

Ideas Through Images

Have students examine Figures 26–10 and 26–11, read the captions, and answer the following questions.

- **What is a tropism?** (A plant's growth in response to a cue from its environment.)
- **What cue from the environment causes the *Briar leguminosae* to fold its leaves?** (A touch.)
- **Which part of the young plants in Figure 26-IIb changed the most in response to light?** (The top third of the stem bent the most.)

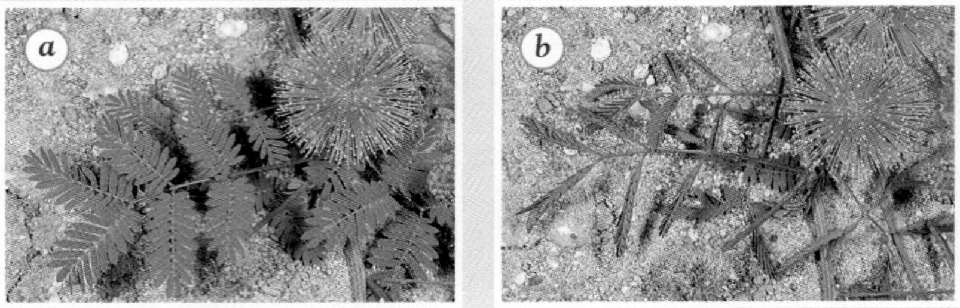
a
b

Figure 26–10 *The sensitive* Briar leguminosae *plant from Texas is shown here with its leaves* (a) *expanded and* (b) *folded to illustrate the plant's response to touch—a response called thigmotropism.*

Thigmotropism

Many plants respond to touch, an ability known as **thigmotropism** (thihg-MAH-truh-pihz-uhm). Climbing plants, such as ivy and pole beans, use thigmotropism to regulate their growth patterns in a way that enables them to wind around solid objects for support.

Plants can respond to other environmental factors, too, including the length of day and the time of year. Some flowers, for example, open only during the daytime. Others, including the cereus cactus of the American Southwest, open only at night.

☑ **Checkpoint** What is phototropism? 1

Plant Hormones

How do plants control their growth to respond to cues such as light and gravity? In many cases they do this by using chemical messengers known as hormones. A hormone is a substance produced in one part of an organism that affects activities in another part. You may know that animals produce hormones, too.

Phototropism was first explored by Charles Darwin and his son Francis in the 1880s. Their simple experiment making use of dark bands around the tips of seedlings is illustrated in ***Figure 26–11.***

Figure 26–11
(a) *Charles and Francis Darwin investigated the effect of covering the tip of a seedling with opaque and clear bands. Their experiments showed that the tip of a seedling releases a substance that causes the plant to bend toward the light.*
(b) *These young plants are growing toward light that is coming from the right.*

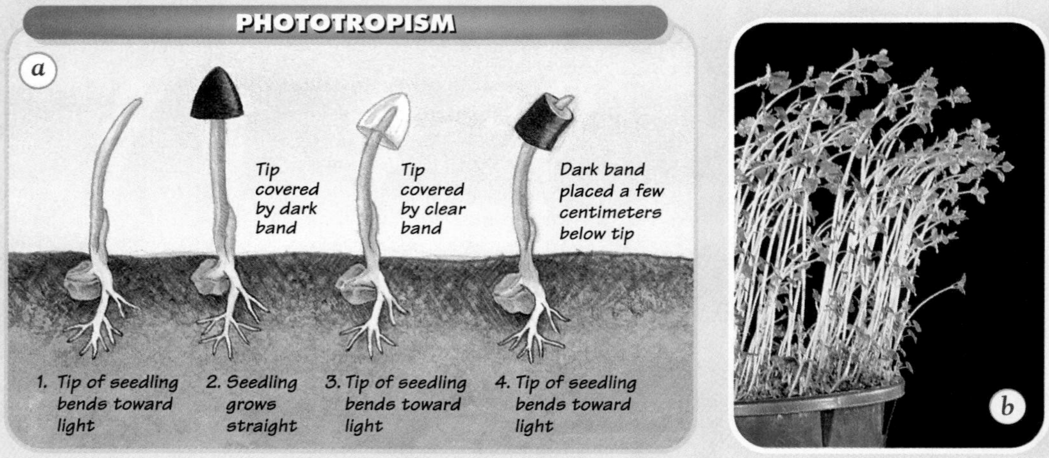
PHOTOTROPISM
a
Tip covered by dark band
Tip covered by clear band
Dark band placed a few centimeters below tip
1. Tip of seedling bends toward light
2. Seedling grows straight
3. Tip of seedling bends toward light
4. Tip of seedling bends toward light
b

TEACHER SUPPORT

Historical Perspective

Charles Darwin is hailed as one of the greatest scientists in history. It is less well known, however, that he had an inauspicious beginning to his career. He failed both at medical school and in an attempt to become a clergyman. His father exclaimed that this son would disgrace the family. It was at Cambridge University that Darwin finally found his calling, under the tutelage of the botanist John Stevens Henslow. Around school, Darwin became known as "the man who walks with Henslow" because he spent many days in the field learning about plants from the kindly professor. A few years later, Henslow wrote Darwin that the HMS *Beagle* needed a naturalist for its next voyage, and the rest is history. Darwin never lost his interest in plants, and late in his life he made great strides in understanding what he called heliotropism.

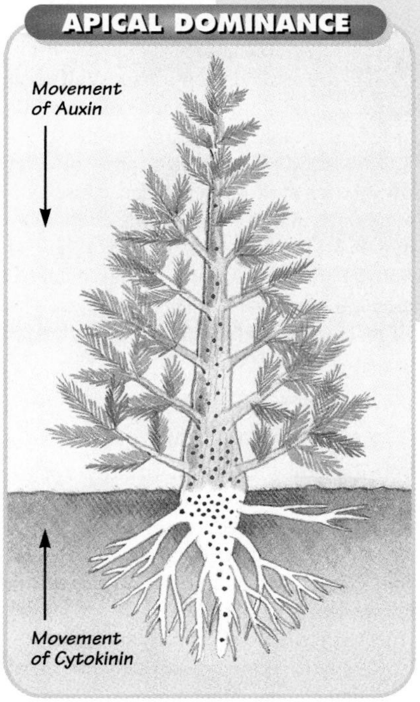

Figure 26–12
As a plant gets larger, side branches sprout from the main body of the plant. These side branches, however, grow more slowly near the tip of the plant than they do near the base, giving many plants their characteristic shapes. This growth pattern, called apical dominance, is the result of an auxin released from the apical meristem. This auxin inhibits the growth of meristems in the side branches closest to the apex.

Auxins

The Darwins suggested that the tip of a growing plant releases a substance that slows down growth on the side of the plant facing the light and speeds up growth on the other side. This, they reasoned, causes the plant to bend. Forty years later, that substance was discovered. It was a compound called indoleacetic (IHN-dohl-uh-seet-ihk) acid, and it was given the name **auxin,** from a Greek word that means "to increase."

Auxins stimulate cell growth and are produced by cells in the apical meristem, which is the rapidly growing region near the tip of a root or stem. Auxin is the hormone that produces phototropism. When light hits just one side of the plant, auxin builds up in the side away from the light, causing an enhanced growth of cells on that side. This causes the plant to bend toward the light. In a similar way, if a tree is knocked on its side by a storm, the production of auxins will cause the tree to begin to grow upward. Released from the meristems (regions of rapid growth), auxins redirect new growth in the direction of sunlight.

An auxin is also responsible for geotropism. By a mechanism that is still not understood, auxins build up on the lower sides of roots and stems. In stem tissue, auxin stimulates cell growth, turning the plant upright. In roots, auxin inhibits growth, causing roots to grow downward.

Cytokinins

Cytokinins (sigh-toh-KIGH-nihnz) are plant hormones that, like auxins, affect the rates of plant growth and cell division. However, many of the effects of cytokinins are opposite those of auxins. For example, auxins inhibit growth in lateral branches, but cytokinins stimulate it. Cytokinins are produced by cells throughout the plant, including those of the root tissue. Chemically, cytokinins are very much like adenine, one of the bases found in DNA and RNA.

Cytokinins seem to act in tandem with auxins. Recent experiments show that the ratio between auxin and cytokinin concentrations determines cell growth, rather than the level of either hormone by itself.

☑ *Checkpoint* What are auxins? Cytokinins? ❷

Ideas Through Images

Have students examine Figure 26–12, read the caption, and answer the following questions.

- **What is apical dominance?** (The growth pattern of plants in which the side branches near the tip grow more slowly than the side branches near the base of the plant.)
- **Where are auxins produced in the plant?** (At the apical meristem.)

Inquiry Activity

Designing an Experiment

A Matter of Hormones

Ask students how they could find out whether the addition of a plant hormone would make a plant grow faster. Provide groups of students with the basic materials for an experiment, including two small potted plants, gibberellic acid solution, and a spray bottle. Then ask each group to design an experiment—one that includes a control and a variable—to find out whether gibberellin can enhance a plant's growth. A typical experiment might compare two plants, one sprayed with the solution and one not. Students can measure and graph the height of the plants over a 1-week period.

☑ Checkpoints

❶ The ability of plants to grow in response to light.

❷ Auxins are plant hormones that stimulate cell growth. Cytokinins are plant hormones that affect the rates of plant growth and cell division, often with effects that are the opposite of those of auxins.

TEACHER SUPPORT

Background Information

A weed is not a special kind of plant. A weed is simply a plant that has no value or overgrows more desirable plants. To farmers and gardeners, weeds can be a serious threat to the productivity of their crops. Not surprisingly, a great deal of effort has been put into finding weed killers, or herbicides, which are chemicals that suppress the growth of weeds and make room for more useful plants. Some of the most powerful weed killers are actually chemical relatives of plant hormones. One of the most effective herbicides, for instance, is called 2,4-D. This product is a chemically modified form of auxin that serves to "trick" the plant. By mimicking the plant's own signaling system, 2,4-D blocks growth, which eventually kills the weed.

Ancillary Support

The resources below can be used to support your teaching strategy for these two pages.

LM Investigating the Effects of Plant Hormones, #52

BL Inquiry Activity: Which Way Will It Grow?

MINI LAB Predicting

Teacher Notes

- For time required and materials needed, see page 600b.
- Soak the corn seeds for 24 hours before the activity begins.
- Tell students that the filter paper or paper towels must only be moist in order for the tape to hold. Students may discover that if the dish is tightly packed with paper, tape is not necessary.
- All seeds may not fully sprout. Tell students they may continue the procedure using the four best seeds, trimming two and leaving two untrimmed.

Answers to Analyze and Conclude

1. Students should find that only the uncut roots grew. The trimmed roots do not grow further because the apical meristem, which produces the auxins necessary for growth, was cut away.
2. The roots of all the seeds at first grew downward toward the lowest edge of the dish. The untrimmed roots, which continued to grow, showed a curve in their growth after the dish was rotated, again growing downward toward the lowest edge.
3. Most students will have predicted that the trimmed roots would not grow and the untrimmed roots would curve downward. Those who did not predict such results may suggest that more information about growth hormones and geotropism would have been helpful.

Skills Trace

Predicting

- Focus p. 614
- Practice p. 615
- Assess p. 625

MINI LAB .... Predicting

Growing My Way?

PROBLEM *How can you **predict** the effect of various factors on root growth?*

PROCEDURE

1. Obtain six corn seeds that have been soaked overnight. Arrange the seeds across the bottom of a Petri dish with their pointed ends facing the same direction. Lay clear plastic tape across the seeds and attach the ends of the tape to the sides of the dish.
2. Cover the seeds with six layers of moistened paper towels trimmed to fit inside the dish. Be sure there is no water collecting in the dish. Cover and tape the dish shut.
3. Stand the dish on its edge in some modeling clay with the pointed ends of the seeds pointing downward. Place the upright dish in a dark place for about two days.
4. When the roots are about 2 cm long, remove the cover of the Petri dish and moistened paper. Using a single-edge blade and a ruler, trim the last 2 mm from the root tips of three seedlings. Record the length of all the roots. Replace the moistened paper and tape the lid back on.
5. Rotate the dish so that the roots are pointing upward, replace it in the clay, and return the dish to a dark spot. Predict what will happen.
6. Examine the dish the following day.

ANALYZE AND CONCLUDE

1. Did all the roots grow during the second part of the experiment? If not, explain why or why not.
2. In which direction did the roots grow?
3. Was your prediction correct? If not, what information would have been helpful?

Gibberellin

Gibberellin is a hormone that was first discovered in rice plants. Japanese rice farmers knew that some of their plants were affected by a disease that caused them to grow so quickly that the plants became tall and spindly. Eventually, this caused the tall, thin plants to fall over and die. The farmers' name for this disorder was "foolish seedling" disease.

Gibberellin regulates the rate at which stems elongate. It can cause dramatic size increases in plants, even causing dwarf varieties to reach the size of normal plants. Certain tissues in seeds release large amounts of gibberellin, which serves as a signal that it is time for the seed to sprout.

Ethylene

When natural gas was first used for lighting and heating in the nineteenth century, people noticed that fruit on indoor plants seemed to ripen quickly in rooms where gas was present. The effect was traced to ethylene, one of the minor components of natural gas. Surprisingly, fruit tissues, in response to an auxin, release small amounts of ethylene that stimulate the ripening process.

Commercial producers of fruit sometimes take advantage of this hormone. Many crops, including lemons and tomatoes, are picked before they ripen so they can be handled more easily. Then, just before they are delivered to market, they are treated with synthetic ethylene to quickly produce a ripe color. Unfortunately, this trick doesn't always produce a ripe flavor—one reason why naturally ripened fruits often taste much better.

☑ **Checkpoint** What is the role of gibberellin in plant growth? 1

Controlling Plant Life Cycles

Some plants, known as **annuals,** live for just a single year. Annuals such as marigolds, corn, and peas grow from seed to maturity, flower, and produce new seeds in just a single growing season. A few plants, including carrots and sugar beets, live for two years and are called

TEACHER SUPPORT Managing Classroom Diversity

MULTICULTURAL STRATEGY

Explain that it was a Japanese scientist, E. Kurosawa, who first discovered the substance that caused the "foolish seedling" effect on rice. Other Japanese scientists were able to purify the substance in the mid-1930s, and they named it gibberellin after the name of the fungus that produced it, *Gibberella fujikuroi.*

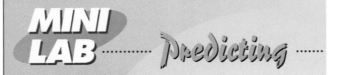

biennials. Biennials usually flower and produce seeds in the second year of their life. Plants that live for more than two years are called **perennials.** Most common trees and shrubs are perennials.

Whether annual or perennial, timing is everything to a plant. **Because plants cannot search for mates as animals do, plants must time their reproductive cycles so their reproductive cells will be ready at the same time as those of other members of their species.** Also, because plants cannot migrate when the weather changes, they must react to seasonal changes—such as storing food for the long winters in temperate regions, preparing to grow again when spring arrives.

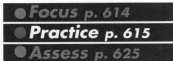

Figure 26–13 *Compare the leaves of* Oxalis stricta, *commonly known as prayer plant, during (a) day and (b) night. The folding and unfolding of the leaves is caused by the action of phytochrome.*

Plants seem to know what time of year it is. In the 1950s, two scientists at the U.S. Department of Agriculture discovered that a red pigment, called **phytochrome,** was used by plants to sense day and night. Phytochrome enables plants to sense the changing seasons by changes in the length of light and dark periods each day. Phytochrome then acts as a master timing switch to coordinate other events in the plant life cycle.

Abscisic acid is a hormone regulated by phytochrome. As the nights become longer and cooler, synthesis of the green pigment chlorophyll stops in many plants. Nutrients are drawn from the leaves into the body of the plant, and, eventually, the leaves fall off.

The appearance of abscisic acid and the drop in auxin production from these leaves has other effects on the plant. The tips of branches grow thick, forming waxy bud scales that will protect the apical meristem from winter weather. Finally, xylem and phloem cells pump salts and organic molecules into the fluids of the plant, producing a thick sap that, like the antifreeze in a car's radiator, will resist cold temperatures.

Section Review 26–2

1. **Define** tropism.
2. **Discuss** the role of auxins in plant growth.
3. **Explain** why timing is important in plant life cycles.
4. **Critical Thinking—Comparing** What features do geotropism, phototropism, and thigmotropism have in common? How do they differ?
5. **MINI LAB** **Predict** the effect that gravity has on the growth of root tips.

5. Students should predict that root tips will grow toward the force of gravity.

Skills Trace

Predicting

- Focus p. 614
- **Practice p. 615**
- Assess p. 625

Learning Modality

Visual Learning Manipulate a potted plant as you explain the processes involved in geotropism, phototropism, and thigmotropism.

Discussion

Begin a discussion of plant life cycles by asking students to think of how long plants live. Students know that some trees can live hundreds of years. Those with some gardening experience may know that some plants last only one season and need to be planted again the next year. Review with students the life cycles of annuals, biennials, and perennials, and ask for examples of each. Then discuss how plants sense the length of night and day and how that ability is involved in the shedding of leaves in the autumn.

4 ASSESS

Quick Check

Ask students to make a table of plant hormones that lists and describes the effects of each one discussed in the section.

Section Review 26–2

1. A growth response of plants to cues from their environment.
2. Auxins stimulate cell growth. An auxin is responsible for phototropism, and an auxin is also responsible for geotropism.
3. Because plants cannot search for mates as animals do, plants must time their reproductive cycles so that their reproductive cells will be ready at the same time as those of other members of their species.
4. The feature that the three tropisms have in common is that the plant grows in response to some kind of cue in the environment. They differ in the type or direction of growth.

☑ Checkpoint

❶ Gibberellin regulates the rate at which stems elongate.

Section 26–3
Plant Propagation

Performance Objective
• Explain what vegetative reproduction is.

Mini Lab Skill: Comparing

1 ENGAGE

Ideas Through Images

Have students examine Figure 26–14, read the caption, and answer the following questions.

• **How is the type of reproduction shown different from the reproduction you learned about in Chapter 25?** (The process described in the last chapter was sexual reproduction, in which sperm and egg fused to create a zygote. The process shown here is asexual reproduction, in which a new plant grows from one parent plant.)

• **Has anyone ever had a spider plant growing at home? Describe the characteristics of that plant.** (Some students should be able to describe the production of runners by spider plants.)

• **Who can describe other plants that reproduce asexually?** (Students might mention African violets, English ivy, potatoes, and others.)

Inquiry Activity
Experimenting
Itsy, Bitsy Spider

Ask students how they think a part of a spider plant could grow into a completely independent plant. Provide students access to a mature spider plant that has several runners with buds. Also provide small pots and potting soil. Challenge student groups to grow a new plant from a part of the spider plant.

Plant Propagation

Guide for Reading

- **Define** the term vegetative reproduction.

MINI LAB
- **Compare** the way vegetative reproduction occurs in different plants.

MANY PLANTS ARE ABLE TO grow from a detached stem or leaf, so with a little care it is possible to grow an entire plant from just a small cutting! Why is it so easy to regenerate a plant from such small pieces? Earlier you explored many of the ways in which various types of plants reproduce sexually. However, one of the most important attributes of plants is their ability to reproduce asexually, and the results are familiar to any gardener.

Vegetative Reproduction

Plants grow from regions known as meristems, which contain actively dividing cells capable of producing any cell type in the mature plant. This means that the meristematic cells in even a small cutting are capable of replacing any of the cell types that were present in the original organism from which the cutting was taken. **The propagation of plants by asexual reproduction, in which offspring are produced from the division of cells of the parent plant, is known as vegetative reproduction.**

Vegetative Reproduction in Nature

A well-known example of **vegetative reproduction** occurs in the spider plant, *Chlorophytum*, shown in ***Figure 26–14.*** This plant produces slender lateral shoots, called runners, that can produce buds of their own. If they find soil, these new buds can put down roots

Figure 26–14 *In addition to reproducing sexually, many plants are capable of reproducing asexually, through vegetative reproduction. In one type of vegetative reproduction, a small part of the plant—such as a stem or a leaf—gives rise to a completely new plant. Examples of plants that commonly reproduce in this manner are the (a) strawberry, (b) spider plant, and (c) Japanese iris.*

TEACHER SUPPORT

Historical Perspective

There is evidence that the Chinese understood grafting as early as 1000 BC. The Greek botanist Theophrastus (*c* 371–*c* 286 BC), sometimes called the founder of botany, wrote about grafting and other forms of vegetative reproduction in his book *Causes of Plants.*

The history of the common navel orange provides an example of the benefits of careful grafting. In about 1820, a farmer near Bahia, Brazil, noticed that the fruit on one branch of one of his trees—probably a natural mutant—was superior to all his other fruit. Through grafting, he multiplied that form of the fruit. Some 50 years later, a missionary sent a dozen of the orange trees to Washington, DC, and two of those were sent to a farm near Riverside, California. From those two trees sprang almost the entire navel orange industry the world over.

Figure 26–15
(a) In silverweed plants, vegetative reproduction occurs when horizontal stems, called runners, grow over the ground surface and develop new plants at the tips. (b) In lily-of-the-valley plants, vegetative reproduction occurs when horizontal stems, called rhizomes, grow at or below the ground's surface and produce new shoots and roots at the nodes.

and grow into completely independent plants. Strawberries grow in much the same way, and gardeners know that a thick bed of delicious fruit can be produced from just a few plants by allowing the runners to spread out and take root.

Incidentally, the new plants that are produced in this way are genetically identical to their "parent" plants. This means that a group of such plants is a **clone,** a group of organisms produced by cell division from a single cell. In this case, that single cell was the fertilized zygote from which the original plant was first produced. Vegetative reproduction is an important method of propagation for many plants, such as those shown in **Figure 26–15.**

☑ **Checkpoint** What is vegetative reproduction? (1)

Vegetative Reproduction in Agriculture

Not surprisingly, humans have taken advantage of vegetative reproduction for thousands of years. Many common houseplants, including African violets, can be propagated from cuttings.

Grafting is sometimes used by farmers who wish to combine the best characteristics of two different plants. A bud or stem from one plant is carefully sliced off and inserted onto the stem of another plant. To minimize injury, this is usually done when the plants are dormant.

Nearly all the wine grapes grown in the world are the product of careful grafting. In the late nineteenth century, a series of diseases all but wiped out grape vines across Europe. Luckily, the Concord grape, a native of North America, was resistant to these diseases.

Figure 26–16
Humans have put their understanding of vegetative reproduction to use, as in (a) grafting to produce desirable characteristics in an orange tree. (b) CAREER TRACK This plant propagator is carefully transferring pine shoots to Petri dishes to monitor their early growth.

2 EXPLORE

Investigate

Cooperative Learning Ask student groups to do research to find a method they could use to graft part of one rose plant onto another rose plant. Such a method will most likely involve removing a bud graft from one plant, making a T-shaped cut in the stem of another plant, placing the graft into that cut, and fastening with cloth or rubber bands. Once group members feel confident that their method will work, have them proceed to make one or several grafts.

3 TEACH

Ideas Through Images

Have students examine Figure 26–15, read the caption, and answer the following questions.

- **What part of the silverweed plant grows into a new plant?** (New buds produced on the runners put out by the plant put down roots and grow into new plants.)
- **What is a runner?** (A runner is a horizontal stem that grows over the ground surface.)
- **What is a rhizome?** (A rhizome is a horizontal stem that grows on or below the ground and can produce shoots and roots at its nodes.)

☑ Checkpoint

(1) The process of asexual reproduction in which offspring are produced from the division of cells of the parent plant.

TEACHER SUPPORT

Managing Classroom Diversity

TECH PREP STUDENTS
Ask interested students to find out the qualifications technicians need in order to work in laboratories that carry out genetic engineering in plants and do experiments in plant cloning. Ask these students to outline an educational path they might follow to work in such a laboratory.

Ancillary Support

The resources below can be used to support your teaching strategy for these two pages.

TR Enrich: The Seeds of a Clone
BL Inquiry Activity: To Mate or Not to Mate

Connections

The process of genetic engineering generally involves the use of bacteria or viruses to introduce desirable genes into some type of living organism, including plants.

A genetically engineered tomato similar to the one described in the Connections feature has been marketed in some parts of the United States. Only one gene was changed in the laboratory, and that gene delayed the ripening process by slowing the production of an enzyme that causes spoilage. Thus, the tomato stays harder and looks better longer.

Answers to Making the Connection

A typical student response might mention that a tomato with a longer shelf life is an advantage to the owner. Most students will probably say that the owner has an ethical obligation to inform the consumers about this product because its long-term effects are unknown.

MINI LAB Comparing

Teacher Note

- For time required and materials needed, see page 600b.

Answers to Analyze and Conclude

1. Coleus stem—roots. Onion—roots and a shoot. Potato—shoots and roots.

2. Students should find that the coleus stem cutting will quickly produce roots. Other developments may vary.

Skills Trace

Comparing

- Focus p. 619
- Practice p. 619
- Assess p. 624

Bio Frontier Connections

Genetically Engineered Food

Recently, the owner of a small chain of grocery stores in a midwestern state was approached by a vegetable distributor who had a new tomato he wanted to sell. As the result of genetic engineering, this tomato can stay on the vine much longer before it softens, allowing it to ripen more fully on the vine. This means that the tomato will have a better flavor than many other tomatoes and yet will still be firm enough to withstand the trip from farm to market.

Engineering a Better Tomato

Until now, farmers have relied on selective breeding to take advantage of the natural mutations that occur in their crops. With selective breeding, it may take 10 to 15 years to create a successful new tomato variety. Using genetic engineering, in which scientists isolate individual genes from one kind of organism and transfer them into a different kind of organism, it is possible to create a new variety in a matter of months.

So What's the Problem?

The U.S. Food and Drug Administration (FDA) expects more than 100 genetically engineered foods to appear in supermarkets in the next few years. Some people are concerned about the potential dangers of genetically engineered foods. In some cases, the gene transfer might cause allergic reactions in people who are allergic to the organism from which the gene came. Other genetic-engineering methods involve creating plants that produce their own natural insecticides. These chemicals might be harmful to insects that farmers find beneficial.

If animal genes are placed in plants, then vegetarians, who don't eat animal products, might accidentally ingest them. For example, in one experiment, the "antifreeze" gene from arctic flounder, a fish, was placed into strawberries to prevent them from freezing on cold nights.

Vine-ripened tomatoes

Getting back to the new tomato, the FDA has said it is as safe as traditionally bred tomatoes and does not require special labels to alert consumers that it is genetically altered. Yet the food-chain owner is concerned because she has heard that a number of organizations have complained that genetically engineered foods are not safe. On the other hand, the grower will sell the tomatoes to her at a very reasonable price because she will be one of the first to try the new tomato.

Making the Connection

Although the food-chain owner and her company are fictitious, the situation is real. What should she do? What reasons does she have to buy the tomato? What are some reasons not to buy it? Should the owner inform her customers that the tomatoes are genetically altered? Why or why not?

TEACHER SUPPORT Ecology Note

Genetic engineering of plants holds the promise of great advances. Gene-altered crops could mean much greater yields and less use of fertilizers and pesticides. Some scientists even look forward to the day when people could receive vaccines by eating a genetically engineered "vaccine plant." But environmentalists foresee great risks in using this technology. Genetically engineered plants could naturally crossbreed with related plants, and the new gene could escape into the environment. A weed with a new disease-resistance or hardiness gene could suddenly take over an ecosystem, eliminating many other natural species. Even more ominous is the prospect of an altered bacterium or virus producing unintended consequences, such as forever changing the nutritional value of a food or causing harmful mutations in a variety of organisms.

The fruit of the Concord grape, however, does not make a very good wine. So vintners grafted European wine stems onto American roots. The result was successful, and even today the best wine grapes of Europe are grown on American roots.

Checkpoint What is grafting? (1)

The New Technology of Plant Cloning

For years, plant biologists worked to find ways to take a single cell from one plant and stimulate it to grow into a complete organism. Today, for many species of plants, that dream is a reality.

Isolated cells from many plants can be grown in laboratory culture in nutrient-rich broths. Under the right conditions, these cells can be kept as protoplasts—cells that do not grow cell walls. Why would anyone want to grow protoplasts? These cells can be very useful in genetic engineering. DNA from other sources can be injected into protoplasts, and in some cases that DNA finds its way into the cell nucleus and becomes part of the plant cell genome.

Using a carefully controlled mix of hormones, protoplasts will begin to make cell walls and will gradually form a small clump of cells known as a callus. Each callus is transferred to a sterile dish or tube, where it grows into a small plantlet. As the plant increases in size, it can be planted in ordinary soil and grown to maturity.

The ability to grow and manipulate plant cells in this way gives biologists a new opportunity to study the genetics of plants and to produce more productive varieties for agriculture.

MINI LAB .... Comparing

Growing Plant Parts

PROBLEM *How does vegetative reproduction in various plants compare?*

PROCEDURE

1. From a coleus plant, cut a stem that has several leaves above the cut. Place the cutting in a container of water.
2. Partially insert four toothpicks around the middle of an onion bulb. Place the onion, base down, in a container of water so the toothpicks sit on the edge of the container and allow only the bottom of the onion to touch the water.
3. Wash a potato and, using toothpicks, suspend it in a container of water.
4. Observe and compare the growth of each plant.

ANALYZE AND CONCLUDE

1. How did the three plants compare in terms of the structures that grew?
2. How did they compare in terms of time, length, or other factors you observed?

Section Review 26-3

1. **Define** vegetative reproduction.
2. **Describe** ways in which growers take advantage of vegetative reproduction.
3. **MINI LAB** How does vegetative reproduction in different plants **compare?**
4. **BRANCHING OUT ACTIVITY** Visit a plant nursery and **identify** the plants that are grown by vegetative reproduction. Consult a plant grower if necessary.

Learning Modality

Auditory Learning Ask student volunteers to describe orally the processes by which vegetative reproduction occurs in nature and in agriculture.

4 ASSESS

Quick Check

Have students make a flowchart of the process by which laboratory technicians use a single cell to make a new organism.

Section Review 26-3

1. Vegetative reproduction is the process of asexual reproduction in which offspring are produced from the division of cells of the parent plant.

2. Vegetative reproduction is a fast and easy way to propagate many plants. Grafting is used to combine the best characteristics of two different plants.

3. Students should describe the results of their experiment with a coleus cutting, an onion, and a potato, comparing ways in which growth occurred in the three plants. For example, they could mention that the cutting produced roots, while both the onion and potato produced roots and shoots.

Skills Trace

Comparing

- Focus p. 619
- Practice p. 619
- Assess p. 624

4. Students should discover that a variety of plants are grown at nurseries by vegetative reproduction. For instance, many common trees and shrubs are grown from stem cuttings. Houseplants such as African violets and begonias are often grown from leaf cuttings. Ask students to identify at least ten examples, with a brief description of how each is accomplished.

Checkpoint

(1) A type of vegetative reproduction in which a bud or stem from one plant is sliced off and inserted onto the stem of another plant.

CHAPTER 26

Laboratory Investigation

Plant Tissues and Their Functions

Before the Lab

1. Start the radish seedlings 3–4 days before the lab is to be done. Put moistened filter papers or paper towels into the bottom of a Petri dish, sprinkle a few radish seeds onto the paper, and put the top on the dish. Keep in a dark place until needed.
2. Secondary root growth can be encouraged by keeping the whole carrots in moistened paper toweling inside a plastic bag in the refrigerator. The vascular cylinder is easier to remove in aged specimens. Use a large, old carrot as the source for the carrot slices. Soaking the slices in water before class will facilitate punching out the vascular cylinder.
3. The outer leaves of lettuce should be used; romaine lettuce is particularly good. Soak the lower surface of the leaves in distilled water to make them turgid, which facilitates the peeling of the lower surface.

Pre-Lab Discussion

Have students read the entire procedure for this investigation. Then ask students the following questions.

What is the purpose of this investigation? (To observe plant tissues, especially water-transport tissues, in several kinds of plants.)

What are the main parts of a root? (Students should describe the epidermis, cortex, and vascular cylinder.)

What would you expect to find on the underside of a leaf? (Students should mention stomata and their guard cells.)

Skills Development

Students will use these skills while completing the laboratory investigation: observing, communicating, and drawing conclusions.

CHAPTER 26

Laboratory Investigation

Plant Tissues and Their Functions

A plant, like an animal, must transport water, minerals, and nutrients through its body. It must also transport the products of photosynthesis—such as sugars—to all parts of its body. In this investigation, you will examine tissues and organs that transport water through a plant.

Problem

What water-transport tissues can you **observe** in certain types of vegetables?

Materials (per group)

- Petri dish with radish seedlings
- hand lens
- whole carrot
- scalpel or single-edged razor blade
- round slice of carrot
- lettuce leaf
- microscope slide
- coverslip
- medicine dropper
- distilled water
- dissecting needle
- compound microscope
- forceps

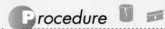

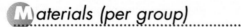

Procedure

1. **Using a hand lens, examine the radish seedlings in the Petri dish. Sketch and label one seedling.**
2. **Obtain a whole carrot and use the scalpel to cut it in half lengthwise. Make a second cut along the length of one of the carrot halves so that you have a very thin long slice. CAUTION:** ***Be careful when using sharp instruments.***
3. **Hold the thin slice up to the light and examine it. Sketch and label this lengthwise section.**
4. **Using the hand lens, observe the round carrot slice. Sketch and label what you observe.**
5. **Force the inner core out of the round carrot slice by pushing it firmly. Examine the surface of the core.**
6. **Obtain a lettuce leaf that has had its lower surface soaking in distilled water. Bend the leaf so that it breaks and peels away the lower surface.**

Safety Tips

- Caution students to be extremely careful when using the scalpel or razor blade and the dissecting needle. Instruct them to report any cuts immediately.
- Remind students not to put any of these materials in their mouths. Point out that the radishes, carrots, and lettuce have not been kept under conditions that would prevent growth of microorganisms, and thus eating these foods could be dangerous.

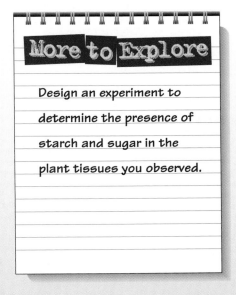

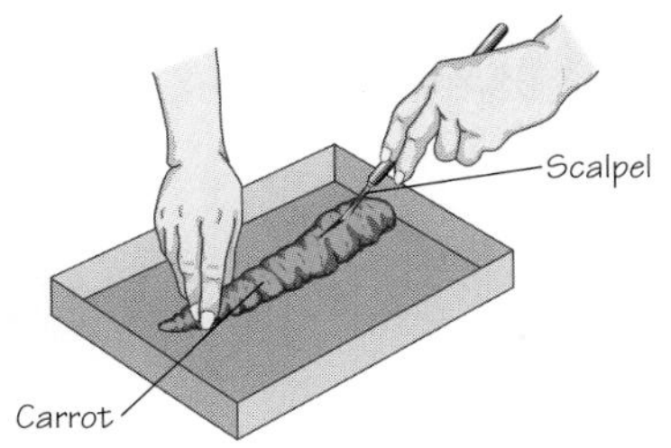

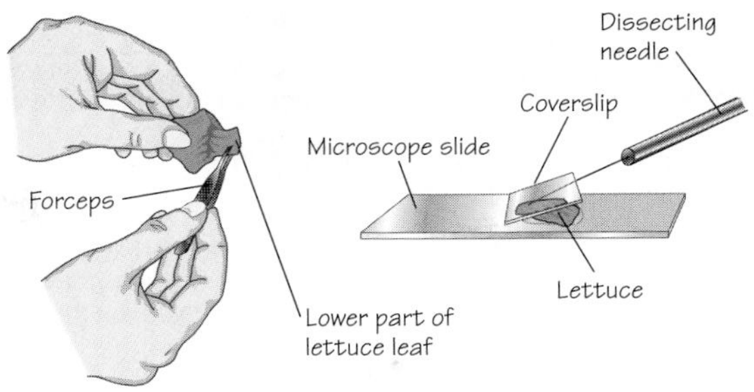

7. With the forceps, peel off a small piece of the leaf tissue. Put this piece of tissue on a microscope slide. Using a medicine dropper, add a drop of water to the slide. With a dissecting needle, slowly lower one edge of the coverslip and then the other onto the lettuce leaf.

8. Observe the leaf tissue under the low-power objective of the microscope. Then switch to the high-power objective. Look for jigsaw-puzzle-shaped cells and pairs of rounded cells.

Observations

1. Describe the outer surface of the radish seedling root. What structures did you observe? Did the entire surface of the root have the same appearance?
2. What was the shape of the inner core of the carrot?
3. Can you find extensions growing from the surface of the carrot core? What are they?
4. What did you observe on the lettuce leaf between the two rounded cells in each pair?

Analysis and Conclusions

1. Are there root hairs at the tip of the radish root? Explain your answer.
2. What kind of tissue is found in the center of the carrot root? What is its function?
3. What kind of tissue makes up the thick, outer part of the carrot? What is its function?
4. What kind of tissue did you peel from the the lettuce?
5. What are the rounded cells? What is their function?

More to Explore

Design an experiment to determine the presence of starch and sugar in the plant tissues you observed.

Teaching Strategies

1. Demonstrate for students how to cut the whole carrot in half lengthwise. Also demonstrate how to force the inner core out of the carrot slice.
2. Demonstrate how to bend the lettuce leaf and peel away the lower surface. Then demonstrate how to prepare a piece of lettuce tissue for examination under the microscope.

Answers to Observations

1. The surface of the root has thin, fuzzy threads, or root hairs, growing from it. The entire surface is not the same. The root hairs do not cover the root tip but start growing above it.
2. The shape of the inner core of the carrot is a cylinder.
3. Students should observe extensions growing from the surface of the carrot core; those extensions are secondary roots.
4. Students should observe an opening, or stoma, between the two rounded guard cells in each pair.

Answers to Analysis and Conclusions

1. A typical response might suggest that there are no root hairs at the tip of the radish, because the cells at the tip are newly formed and only the mature cells above the tip have root hairs.
2. Vascular tissue in the form of the vascular cylinder is found in the center of the carrot root. The function of that tissue is to conduct water and nutrients through the plant.
3. Dermal tissue makes up the thick, outer part of the carrot. In a root, this dermal tissue is called the epidermis. This tissue protects the root. It also contains the root hairs, which absorb water and nutrients from the soil.
4. The cuticle, the waxy layer on the leaf's epidermis, was the tissue peeled away.
5. The rounded cells are the guard cells. They control the passage of gases into and out of the leaf by opening and closing the stomata.

More to Explore

A typical design might suggest using indicators for starch and sugar to test the various plant tissues. Students should incorporate into their designs a control, such as using an indicator on a substance known to contain sugar or starch in order to establish a basis for comparison.

Chapter 26

Study Guide

Review Strategy

Divide the class into several small groups, making sure that each group contains a good mix of gifted students and LEP students. Then assign a part of a section to each group. Ask groups to prepare a review of their assigned parts for a presentation to the whole class. The members of each group should examine the material, develop a list of main points, brainstorm for a series of review questions, and pinpoint any difficult passages or hard-to-understand concepts. Then give each group 10 minutes for a class presentation.

Recalling Main Ideas

1. c
2. a
3. d
4. c
5. a
6. b
7. b
8. d
9. a

Assessment

Reviewing What You Learned

1. Dermal tissue, vascular tissue, and ground tissue.
2. Guard cells control the passage of gases by opening and closing the stomata; they also close the stomata if a plant loses too much water.
3. A primary root is a thicker root that a seedling first sends into the soil, while a secondary root is a thinner root that branches out from a primary root.
4. Osmosis causes water to move from the soil into the root epidermis, and then causes water to move out of the epidermis into the cells of the cortex and the cells of the vascular cylinder.

Study Guide

Summarizing Key Concepts

The key concepts in each section of this chapter are listed below to help you review the chapter content. Make sure you understand each concept and its relationship to other concepts and to the theme of this chapter.

26–1 Plant Structure and Function

- The body of a plant consists of three distinct regions known as roots, stems, and leaves.
- Roots anchor a plant in the ground, drawing water and minerals from the soil. They consist of the epidermis, the cortex, the endodermis, and the vascular cylinder. Roots take up water and minerals from soil by osmosis and active transport.
- Stems rise above the ground, support the body of the plant, and carry water and nutrients from one end of the plant to the other. They consist of the epidermis, the cortex, the pith, and vascular bundles.
- Leaves, the organs of photosynthesis, have an epidermis, fluid-carrying vascular tissue, and ground tissue. The undersides of leaves have small openings known as stomata through which gases enter and exit.
- A combination of capillary action, osmosis, and transpiration pull enables water to rise to the tops of trees in xylem tissue. A combination of active transport and osmosis is probably responsible for phloem transport.

26–2 Plant Growth

- A plant's response to its environment is known as a tropism. Geotropism is a response to gravity, phototropism is a response to light, and thigmotropism is a response to touch.
- Auxins stimulate cell growth and are produced by cells in the apical meristem.

26–3 Plant Propagation

- The process of asexual reproduction, in which offspring are produced from the division of cells of the parent plant, is known as vegetative reproduction.
- A clone is an organism produced by the division of a single cell.

Reviewing Key Terms

Review the following vocabulary terms and their meaning. Then use each term in a complete sentence.

26–1 Plant Structure and Function

root, stem, leaf, xylem, phloem, epidermis, cortex, vascular cylinder, endodermis, pith, annual tree ring, stoma, transpiration

26–2 Plant Growth

tropism, geotropism, phototropism, thigmotropism, auxin, annual, biennial, perennial, phytochrome

26–3 Plant Propagation

vegetative reproduction, clone, grafting

Inquiry-Based Strategy

People grow a variety of plants indoors, with mixed success. Some seem to kill every plant that enters the house, while others seem to be able to grow anything. Have students investigate the best methods for growing indoor plants by asking them to answer the following questions: What are some basic recommendations for keeping plants in the home? Do different plants require different conditions?

Allow students to determine what research is necessary to answer the questions. Then each group of students should prepare a guide for growing plants indoors that includes general recommendations, specific recommendations for specific plants, explanations for why various plants grow best in certain conditions, and photographs or drawings that illustrate plants and methods.

Recalling Main Ideas

Choose the letter of the answer that best completes the statement or answers the question.

1. In plants, the main organs of photosynthesis are the
   - **a.** roots.
   - **b.** stems.
   - **c.** leaves.
   - **d.** petioles.
2. The function of a plant's ground tissue is to
   - **a.** support and carry out photosynthesis.
   - **b.** protect the plant.
   - **c.** conduct fluids through the plant.
   - **d.** prevent water evaporation.
3. Plants take in almost all their water and nutrients through structures called
   - **a.** guard cells.
   - **b.** vascular cylinders.
   - **c.** osmosis.
   - **d.** root hairs.
4. Most of the wood in a tree is made up of
   - **a.** cork cambium cells.
   - **b.** phloem tissue.
   - **c.** xylem tissue.
   - **d.** bark cells.
5. Phototropism results in
   - **a.** seedling stems growing toward the light.
   - **b.** seedling stems growing away from the light.
   - **c.** seedling roots growing toward the light.
   - **d.** seedling roots growing toward the force of gravity.
6. The Darwins' hypothesis about the cause of phototropism was confirmed when
   - **a.** geotropism was discovered.
   - **b.** auxin was discovered.
   - **c.** gibberellin was discovered.
   - **d.** ethylene was discovered.
7. What determines whether a plant is classified as an annual or a perennial?
   - **a.** the kind of flowers it has
   - **b.** its age
   - **c.** whether or not it will produce fruit
   - **d.** its ability to sense day and night
8. Vegetative reproduction results in offspring that
   - **a.** are grafts of two plants.
   - **b.** inherit genetic traits from both parent plants.
   - **c.** have some traits unlike the parent plant.
   - **d.** are genetically identical to the parent plant.
9. Farmers use the technique called grafting to
   - **a.** combine the best characteristics of two different plants.
   - **b.** produce protoplasts.
   - **c.** grow new kinds of potatoes.
   - **d.** produce genetically identical plants.

Putting It All Together

Using the information on pages xxx to xxxi, complete the following concept map.

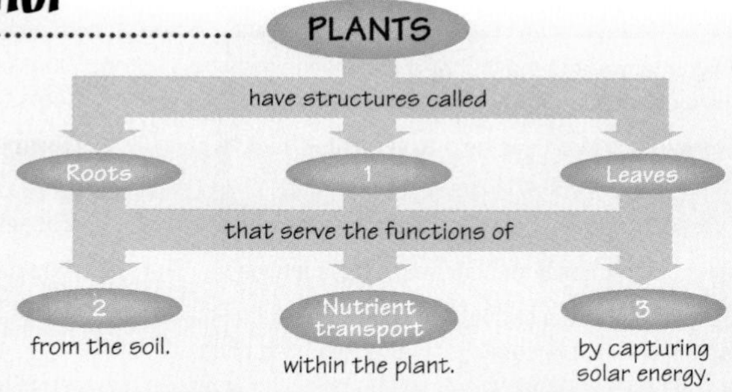

Putting It All Together

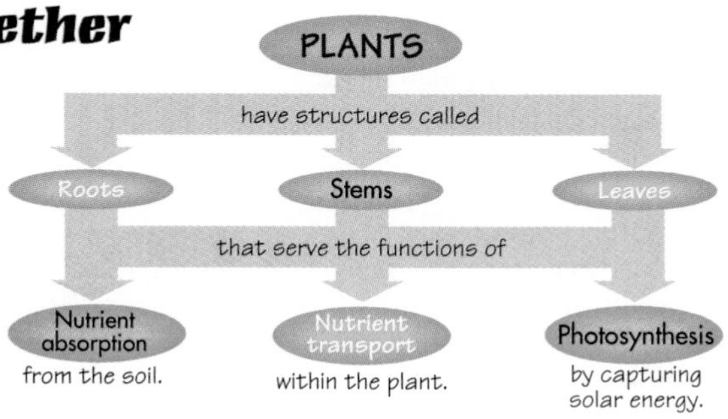

5. In the stem of a tree, the innermost xylem layers that no longer conduct water are the heartwood, while the outer layers of xylem, which are active in water transport, are the sapwood.
6. Carnivorous plants gain needed nutrients, including nitrogen, when they digest trapped insects.
7. Stomata are small openings on the undersides of leaves.
8. Roots grow toward the force of gravity, while stems grow away from the force of gravity.
9. A hormone is a substance produced in one part of an organism that affects activities in another part of that organism.
10. Ethylene stimulates the ripening process in fruits.
11. Phytochrome enables a plant to sense night and day, and thereby sense the changing seasons; it also regulates the hormone abscisic acid.
12. The meristematic cells in a cutting are capable of replacing any of the cell types that were present in the original organism.
13. A clone is a group of organisms produced by cell division from a single cell.
14. Spider plants and strawberry plants can reproduce by producing slender lateral stems called runners, which have buds that can put down roots and eventually grow into independent plants.
15. Protoplasts are useful in genetic engineering because they do not have cell walls, and DNA from other sources can be injected into them.

Expanding the Concepts

1. A plant uses the energy produced by photosynthesis in any cell process that requires energy, including active transport, cell division and growth, and protein synthesis.
2. During periods of rapid photosynthesis, guard cells allow the stomata to open, allowing for the passage of gases into and out of the leaf.
3. As a woody stem of a tree grows, the vascular cambium, which lies between the phloem and xylem, produces new cells of both these vascular tissues. The accumulation of xylem over the years forms most of what we call wood.

Assessment (continued)

4. In some desert plants, leaves have been reduced to sharp spines because the water loss from a typical leaf would be too much for a plant to sustain in the dry environment. Thus, the lack of leaves is an adaptation to the conditions of the environment.

5. A climbing plant exhibits geotropism by sending its roots toward the force of gravity and its stems away from that force. It exhibits phototropism by stems growing toward the light. And it exhibits thigmotropism by stems winding around a solid object, using it for support.

6. Paving the ground around a tree's trunk might drastically reduce the amount of water in the soil around the tree, and thus harm the tree by limiting its water supply. Paving might also prevent the tree trunk from increasing in size. Since the tissues just under the trunk are easily damaged, close paving could damage the tissue and cause the tree to die.

7. Osmosis is the movement of water across a membrane and requires no energy from the organism. Active transport involves the movement of ions across a membrane, and this process does require the use of energy in the form of ATP.

Skills Trace
Comparing
- Focus p. 619
- Practice p. 619
- Assess p. 624

8. The study of tree rings can help archaeologists date human artifacts. It can also provide a record of weather conditions in years past. By knowing about the weather in an ancient period, archaeologists can infer how the people of the period lived.

9. If a container is not turned, phototropism causes the plant to grow in the direction of the light coming through the window and appear lopsided. Turning a container periodically compensates for any bending the plant made in the previous position.

Assessment

Reviewing What You Learned

Answer each of the following in a complete sentence.

1. What are the three main kinds of plant tissue?
2. Explain the two functions of the guard cells on the underside of most plant leaves.
3. What is the difference between a primary root and a secondary root?
4. Describe the role that osmosis plays in root cells.
5. What is the difference between heartwood and sapwood?
6. What do carnivorous plants gain from the insects they trap?
7. What are stomata?
8. How are roots and stems affected by geotropism?
9. What is a hormone?
10. Explain the effect ethylene has on plants.
11. What roles does phytochrome play in plants?
12. Which characteristic of meristematic cells enables cuttings to develop into complete plants?
13. What is the definition of a clone?
14. How do spider plants or strawberry plants reproduce vegetatively?
15. How are protoplasts useful in genetic engineering?

Expanding the Concepts

Discuss each of the following in a brief paragraph.

1. What are some ways that a plant uses the energy produced by photosynthesis?
2. How do guard cells help to regulate the rate of photosynthesis?
3. Describe how wood is produced in a tree stem.
4. Why don't some desert plants have leaves?
5. Describe how a single plant can exhibit geotropism, phototropism, and thigmotropism.
6. What effect would paving the ground around a tree's trunk have on the tree?
7. **Compare** osmosis and active transport.
8. What information about ancient people can archaeologists infer from tree rings?
9. Why do people turn the containers of plants grown on windowsills?

Extending Your Thinking

1. A typical design might designate the size of the tubes as the variable. The control could be a tube with a medium-size diameter. The setup, then, would include three tubes of different diameters standing in shallow water. Measurements could be made of the height the water rises in each tube. Conclusions would involve a comparison of those measurements. Students' labeled diagrams, then, might show three tubes of varying diameters in a basin of water.

Skills Trace
Experimenting
- Focus p. 608
- Practice p. 610
- Assess p. 625

Extending Your Thinking

Use the skills you have developed in this chapter to answer the following.

1. **Designing an experiment** How does capillary action vary with the diameter of a tube? Design an experiment to answer the question. Make sure that your experiment has only one variable. Plan a control, too. Draw a labeled diagram to explain your design. Have your teacher check your proposed experiment.
2. **Predicting** In the early 1700s, Stephen Hales experimented with plants. In one experiment, he attached a tube of water to the root of a tree and measured the amount of water pulled up the tube into the tree. Based on what you have learned, predict the conditions under which the tree will exert the strongest pull: a sunny day, a cloudy day, or at night. Explain your choice.
3. **Observing** Find two logs or tree stumps that display the cross sections of two tree trunks. Describe the differences you see in the annual tree rings.
4. **Hypothesizing** When digging up and transplanting a tree from one site to another, the branches must be cut back severely. Form a hypothesis to explain why this is necessary to help the plant become established in its new location.

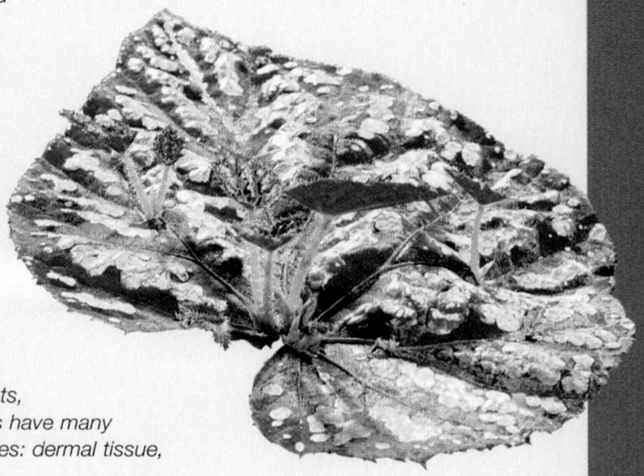

Applying Your Skills

Modeling Plant Parts in 3-D

A plant has three major kinds of organs—roots, stems, and leaves. Even though these structures have many differences, they share three common tissue types: dermal tissue, vascular tissue, and ground tissue.

1. Working in groups of three, have each member of a group choose a different plant organ: root, stem, or leaf.
2. Discuss the materials your group will use to build three-dimensional models of these plant organs. Then collect the materials.
3. Establishing a common scale, build a model of each plant organ. Include in each model a representation of the tissues or cells.
4. Write labels for your model that will demonstrate your understanding of the relationship between structures and functions.

• GOING FURTHER •

5. With members of your group, propose a plan to show how you could use easily available materials to make a working model of a plant.

2. Students should predict that the strongest pull would be exerted on a sunny day, for that is when photosynthesis would occur most rapidly in the plant's leaves. During such periods, the guard cells open up the stomata, allowing water vapor to escape. That transpiration in the leaves creates an upward pull through the plant's xylem. On a cloudy day or at night such a strong pull would not be created.

Skills Trace
Predicting

Focus p. 614
Practice p. 615
Assess p. 625

3. Students' descriptions will vary depending on the trunks they examine. Differences in the rings might include their number, the width of some of the rings, and the contrast between the light and dark sections of rings.
4. Some students might suggest that in transplanting the tree, the roots would probably be damaged or partially lost. With a root system not as extensive as before, the tree would not receive as much water or nutrients. Cutting back the branches reduces the size of the tree, and thus reduces the amount of water and nutrients it needs from the roots.

Applying Your Skills

Teacher Notes

- A list of specific parts of each organ could be given to the students prior to the building of models, or students could be told to use the figures in this chapter or in other textbooks for reference.
- Suggest, as an example, that a pliable straw could be used to represent xylem or phloem in a model. Then allow groups to brainstorm and collect other materials.
- Students should be assessed only for the work on their own models. But they could also be held responsible for the names and functions of all parts on the two types of models they did not participate in building.

Scoring Rubric

4 Response is thorough, accurate, and creative; shows an in-depth understanding of science skills, procedures, and concepts.

3 Response is complete, mostly accurate, and original; shows a satisfactory understanding of science skills, procedures, and concepts.

2 Response is mostly complete but includes some inaccuracies; shows an adequate understanding of science skills, procedures, and concepts.

1 Response is only partially complete and has many inaccuracies; shows an incomplete understanding of science skills, procedures, and concepts.

0 Response is mostly incomplete and/or inaccurate; shows a lack of understanding of science skills, procedures, and concepts.

UNIT 7

Animals

Introducing the Unit

. . . In Words

Edward O. Wilson is an entomologist whose research on ants has had a broad influence on many areas of science. As a leader for environmental protection to minimize species extinction, he calls for increased protection of the environment. Wilson warns that current extinctions due to rain forest destruction may rival those that marked the end of the age of dinosaurs. He promotes sustainable development and restoration of damaged lands and urges that Earth's species be surveyed and used wisely.

- **What do you think biological diversity means?** (Lead students to conclude that biological diversity is the variety of living organisms, genetic information, and biological communities.)
- **Why is biological diversity important?** (It sustains many species and different ecosystems.)

. . . In Pictures

The peacock (*Pavo cristatus*) pictured here is native to India and Sri Lanka. During courting, the peacock spreads its long tail feathers into a spectacular fan as it struts in front of the female. In ancient times, peacocks were treasured and often bestowed on important dignitaries. Today peafowl can be found in zoos and parks around the world.

UNIT 7

Animals

CHAPTERS

"Biological diversity is the key to the maintenance of the world as we know it."
— Edward O. Wilson

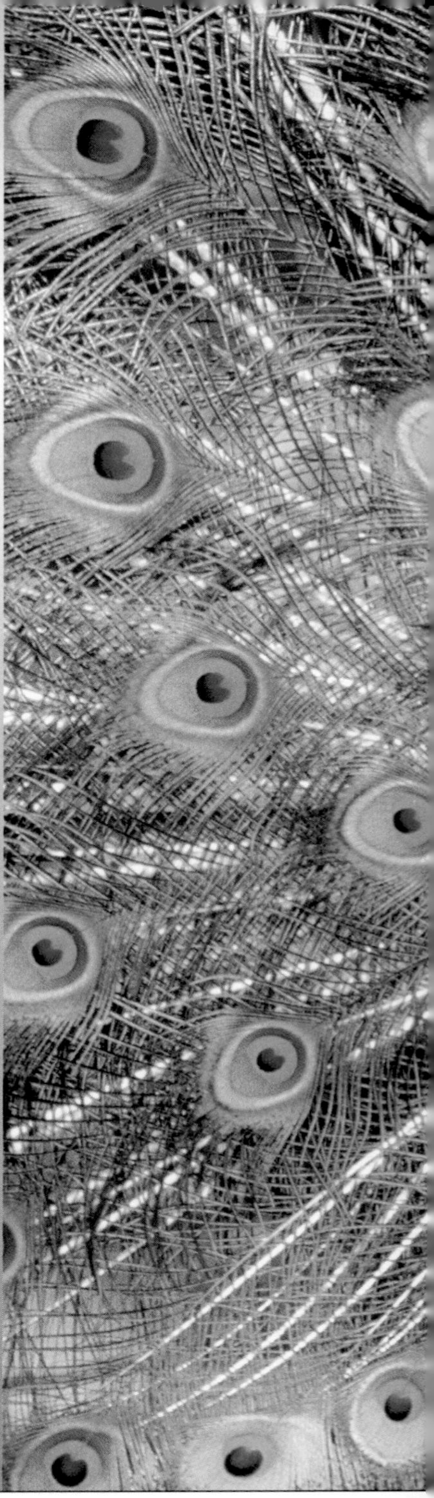

TEACHER SUPPORT

Unit Discovery Learning Activity

FIELD WORK

Most students are undoubtedly somewhat aware of the other animals they share their environment with, at least the conspicuous mammals and birds. But probably few students have taken the time to actually observe the animals around them. This activity encourages students to study carefully the animals whose paths they cross every day. Follow these steps to carry out the activity.

1. Ask each student to select a spot, such as a park, backyard, or corner of the school grounds, where they can be undisturbed for one hour to observe the animals around them. Students should take with them only a pen or pencil and a notebook.

2. Once at their sites, students should write a description of the area and the weather, and note the time of day.

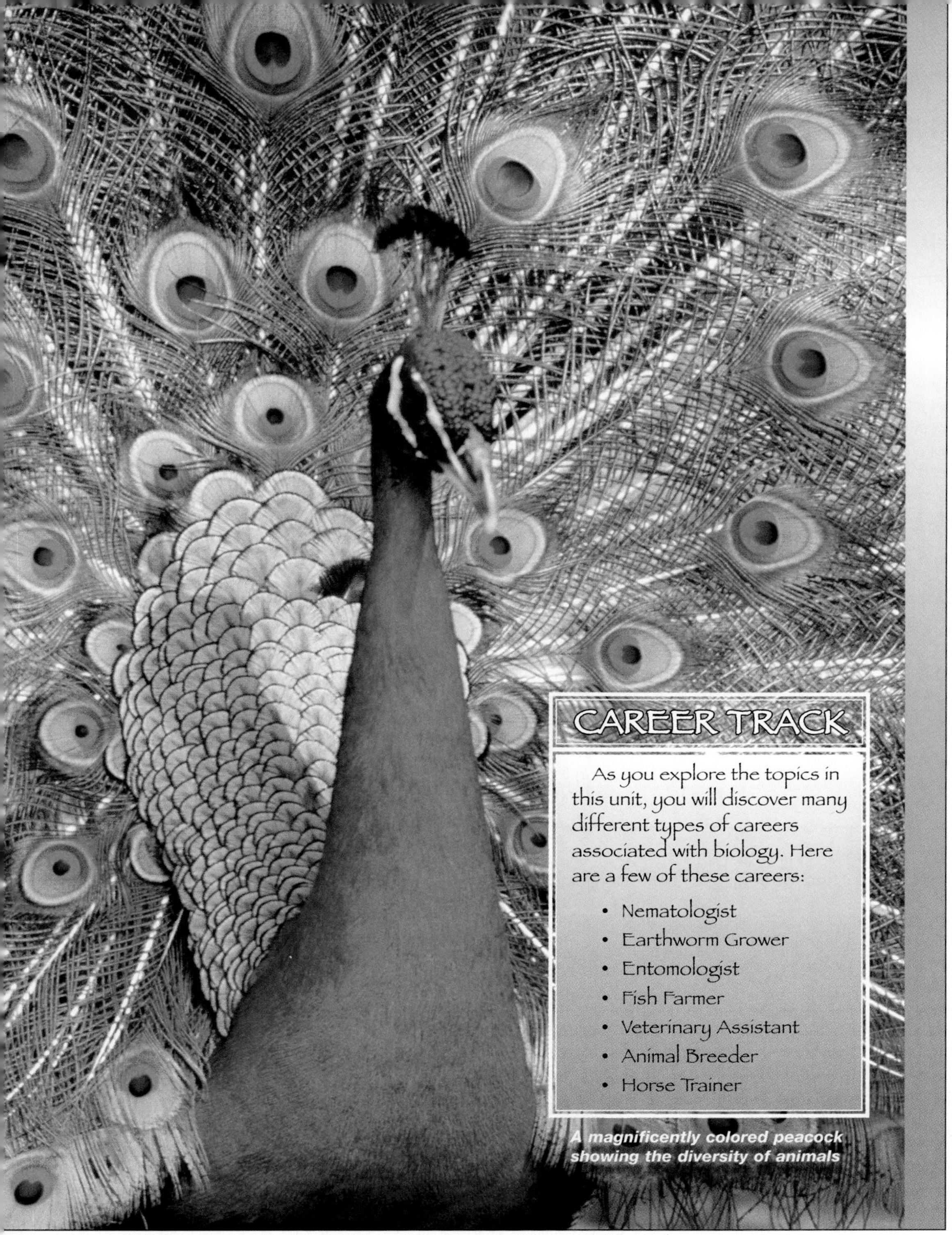

CAREER TRACK

As you explore the topics in this unit, you will discover many different types of careers associated with biology. Here are a few of these careers:

- Nematologist
- Earthworm Grower
- Entomologist
- Fish Farmer
- Veterinary Assistant
- Animal Breeder
- Horse Trainer

A magnificently colored peacock showing the diversity of animals

- **What purpose do you think the peacock's spectacular coloring and fan serve?** (Its coloring probably had protective value in its original habitat, and its fan is used for attracting a mate.)
- **How is a peacock a good example of biological diversity?** (Students might suggest that it is unique among birds and it carries distinct genetic information.)

CAREER TRACK

Throughout this unit, you will find a broad range of biology-related careers that vary in educational and training requirements. You may wish to have your students find out more about the following careers:

- Nematologist, p. 640
- Earthworm Grower, p. 656
- Entomologist, p. 679
- Fish Farmer, p. 700
- Veterinary Assistant, p. 719
- Animal Breeder, p. 737
- Horse Trainer, p. 751

3. Next, instruct students to begin a list of all the animals they observe. Remind students to look on the ground, in shrubs and trees, and in the air.
4. Ask students to describe the physical characteristics of the animals, as well as their behaviors and interactions with other animals. Encourage students also to make sketches of the animals.
5. After students have completed their field work, have them compare their observations with their classmates' observations. Ask students to make a class list of local animals.
6. Challenge small groups of students to classify the animals on the class list. Then have groups compare and defend their classification systems.

By observing, comparing, and classifying animals from the local environment, students should be able to identify and explain examples of the key concepts of **unity and diversity,** a theme that is developed in this unit.

Technology

BioVue
Diversity at the Zoo
Videodisc Side 7

Go to Chapter 2

Ancillary Support

The resource below can be used to support your teaching strategy for these two pages.

BL Integrating the Media
Unit Discovery Learning Activity

Chapter 27 Sponges, Cnidarians, and Unsegmented Worms

Content Management	Student Edition Activities
■ Section 27–1 Sponges and Cnidarians, pp. 629–635 Sponges Cnidarians	MINI LAB: Spongy Skeletons, p. 631
■ Section 27–2 Unsegmented Worms, pp. 636–639 Classifying Worms Platyhelminths Nematodes	MINI LAB: Tapering Tapeworms, p. 638 Laboratory Investigation: Observing a Hydra and a Planarian, pp. 642–643
◆ BRANCHING OUT • In Depth Section 27–3 Nematodes—A Help or a Hindrance?, pp. 640–641 Parasitic Nematodes *Caenorhabditis elegans*	

■ These sections cover all the necessary content and concepts for an enriched course in biology.
◆ This section covers content and concepts that are either applications or extensions of the enriched material.

Integration Strategies

SE Chemistry, p. 630
Health, p. 637
BL Investigating Careers
Involving the Community
Science Through Art

Assessment Strategies

SE Chapter Review, pp. 644–647
TR Section Reviews
Chapter Test
Performance-Based Assessment
BL Investigating Further
Chapter Review
Practice Test
CTB Chapter 27 Test

Tech Prep

Teaching strategies appropriate for students who are in technical/vocational programs or who are considering post-secondary technical education can be found on the following **TE** pages: 633 and 637.

Meeting the Standards

Sections 27–1 through 27–3 cover two of the six content standards under **The Cell,** one of the five content standards under **Biological Evolution,** one of the five content standards under **The Interdependence of Organisms,** one of the six content standards under **Matter, Energy, and Organization in Living Systems,** and two of the four content standards under **The Behavior of Organisms** as described on pages 184–187 of The National Science Education Standards.

Chapter Planning Guide

Teacher's Edition Activities	Other Activities	Media and Technology
Chapter Discovery Learning Activity, p. 628 **Inquiry Activity:** Modeling Jellyfish Locomotion, p. 629 **Investigate:** Research, p. 630 **Activity:** Observing Sponge Reaggregation, p. 630 **Investigate:** Research, p. 632 **Inquiry Activity:** The Acrobatic Hydra, p. 634	**LM** Observing Sponges and Hydras, #53 **TR** **Writing in Biology:** Let Me Introduce You! **Apply:** Spunky Sponges **BL** **Inquiry Activity:** Sponges	**TB** Life Cycle of a Hydrozoan, #35
Inquiry Activity: Observing Flatworms and Roundworms, p. 636 **Investigate:** Research, p. 636 **Activity:** Comparing True Worms With Wormlike Insect Larvae, p. 636	**TR** **Explore:** Plainly Planarians **BL** **Inquiry Activity:** Worms: Flat or Round?	
Inquiry Activity: Observing Parasitic Nematodes, p. 640 **Investigate:** Research, p. 640	**LM** Investigating Nematodes, #54 **TR** **Explore:** Nifty Nematodes **BL** **Inquiry Activity:** The Host With the Most	

KEY: **SE** Student Edition **TE** Teacher's Edition **LM** Laboratory Manual **TR** Teaching Resources **BL** BioLog **TB** Transparency Box **CTB** Computer Test Bank

Materials List

TE Chapter Discovery Learning Activity, p. 628 (20–30 minutes); dried natural sponges (both hard and soft types), coral, hand lens, vinegar, medicine dropper, knife or scissors.

TE Inquiry Activity: Modeling Jellyfish Locomotion, p. 629 (15 minutes); umbrella.

TE Activity: Observing Sponge Reaggregation, p. 630 (20 minutes for initial setup, brief follow-up observations over several weeks); small bowl, fresh seawater or prepared saltwater-aquarium solution, small piece of living sponge, piece of nylon stocking material, aquarium pump.

TE Investigate: Research, p. 632 (30 minutes); world map, sources describing sponges and cnidarians, map pins.

SE MINI LAB: Spongy Skeletons, p. 631 (30–45 minutes); Grantia, Spongilla, and Hexactinellida sponges (available from biological supply companies), bleach, microscope slide, medicine dropper, compound microscope.

TE The Acrobatic Hydra, p. 634 (15–20 minutes); living hydras, microscope, slide, medicine dropper.

TE Inquiry Activity: Observing Flatworms and Roundworms, p. 636 (30–45 minutes); microscope, prepared slides of flatworms and roundworms.

TE Investigate: Research, p. 636 (30–45 minutes); sources describing flatworms and roundworms.

TE Activity: Comparing True Worms With Wormlike Insect Larvae, p. 636 (20–30 minutes for initial setup of cultures, brief follow-up observations); mealworm culture, insect larvae, calendar.

SE MINI LAB: Tapering Tapeworms, p. 638 (20–25 minutes); microscope, prepared slide of tapeworm.

TE Inquiry Activity: Observing Parasitic Nematodes, p. 640 (20–30 minutes); microscope, prepared slides of parasitic nematodes, including encysted Trichinella.

CHAPTER 27

Sponges, Cnidarians, and Unsegmented Worms

Introducing the Chapter

. . . In Pictures

Both the coral and the sea fan are cnidarians in the class *Anthozoa*, which exist only as polyps and lack the medusa stage characteristic of some cnidarians. Have students examine the photograph, read the caption, and answer the following questions.

• **Is coral a plant, an animal, a protist, or some other type of organism?** (An animal.)

• **Why do you think the sea fan, which is also an animal, is sometimes mistaken for a plant?** (It appears to be growing on and attached to the coral, similar to the way plants grow on the ground. Students may also mention that the branched structure of the sea fan is somewhat plantlike.)

Teaching Strategy

The characteristics and life cycles of sponges and cnidarians are presented in the first section of this chapter, and those of flatworms and roundworms in the second section. The BRANCHING OUT section focuses on parasitic roundworms.

CHAPTER 27

Sponges, Cnidarians, and Unsegmented Worms

FOCUSING THE CHAPTER
THEME: Unity and Diversity

Biology and Your World

BIO JOURNAL

In your journal, describe the organisms shown in the photographs on this page and the next. Have you ever seen these organisms before? If so, where have you encountered them?

Sea fan on a coral reef

BIO JOURNAL

Encourage students to make their descriptions as detailed as they can to convey the organisms' diversity and complexity. Make sure students focus on visible characteristics. Students may have seen organisms like these in aquarium displays; some may have seen live or dead jellyfish at a beach. Instruct students to keep their entries in their portfolios.

TEACHER SUPPORT

Chapter Discovery Learning Activity

Provide a variety of dried natural sponges and corals for students to examine and investigate. Include both hard sponges (made of spicules) and soft, flexible sponges (made of spongin). Guide their investigations with questions and prompts such as those given below.

• **Examine each object with a hand lens. Describe and/or draw what you see.**
• **Put a drop of vinegar on each object. What happens?** (The coral will fizz.)
• **Dip each object in water. What happens?** (Soft sponges will absorb and hold water. Hard sponges and coral will allow water to drain out.)
• **What does the inside of each object look like?** (Let students cut the sponges and break off pieces of the coral to see their interior.)
• **What do you think was the source of each object?** (Have students return to this question at the conclusion of Section 27–1.)

Sponges and Cnidarians

GUIDE FOR READING

- **Explain** how sponges differ from other animals.
- **Describe** the organization of tissues in cnidarians.

MINI LAB

- **Compare** different sponges.

THE SEA IS HOME TO AN incredibly diverse set of animals, some of which are shown on this page. Jellyfishes are nearly transparent, and they drift and swim with the currents in the open sea. Corals can be as hard as rocks, and they are the only animals—other than humans—that create entire ecosystems. Many sea anemones are among both the most beautiful and the most harmless animals, while others carry venom powerful enough to kill a human. And sponges are some of the most unusual animals of all.

Let's take a look at each of these fascinating groups of organisms. You may never look at sea life the same way again!

Sponges

Adult sponges are sessile, which means they live attached to one spot. For this reason, early naturalists thought sponges were unusual aquatic plants. However, sponges are animals, not plants. In fact, they are among the most ancient of the multicellular animals, although they have less in common with the rest of us than any other phylum!

Classifying Sponges

Sponges are members of the phylum Porifera, meaning "pore bearing." Tiny pores, or openings, penetrate a sponge's body, allowing sponges to filter food from the water that passes through these pores.

Why are sponges classified as animals and not as plants? First, sponge cells lack cell walls—the tough outer boundaries that surround plant cells. And second, sponges are heterotrophic, which means they obtain energy from the food they take in. Plants

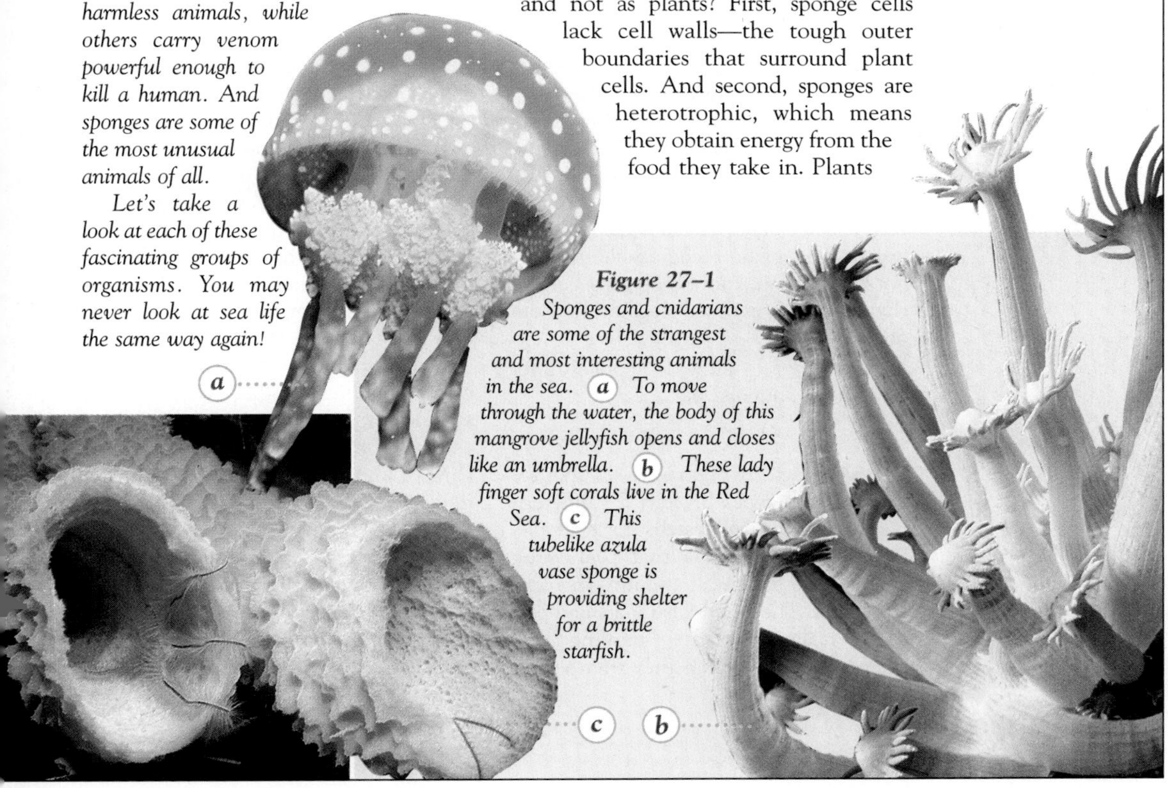

Figure 27–1 *Sponges and cnidarians are some of the strangest and most interesting animals in the sea. (a) To move through the water, the body of this mangrove jellyfish opens and closes like an umbrella. (b) These lady finger soft corals live in the Red Sea. (c) This tubelike azula vase sponge is providing shelter for a brittle starfish.*

SECTION 27–1

Sponges and Cnidarians

Performance Objectives

- Explain the differences between sponges and other animals.
- Describe the three specialized tissue layers of cnidarians.

Mini Lab Skill: Comparing

1 ENGAGE

Inquiry Activity

Inferring

Modeling Jellyfish Locomotion

Draw students' attention to the description of the jellyfish's locomotion method in the caption for Figure 27–1. Have students open and close an umbrella several times to simulate this motion, and tell them to imagine the effect if the umbrella were being held under water. Ask students to describe how this open-and-close movement would propel a jellyfish through the water. (Like the inner surface of an umbrella being closed under water, the jellyfish's inner surface pushes against the water, propelling it upward for a distance. As the jellyfish opens again, it hovers in the water. Repeating its open-and-close motion moves the jellyfish through the water in short bursts.) Point out to students that they may have experienced this same effect doing the breast stroke while swimming.

TEACHER SUPPORT

Background Information

The phylum Porifera includes an estimated 5000 to 10,000 species. Sponges are aquatic animals; most are marine. Because they cannot survive for even a short period out of water, sponges are usually not found along shores where low tides would leave them exposed to the air. Sponges have been found at depths of up to 8600 meters, but most thrive in warm, shallow seas. Only two families of sponges live in fresh water.

Cnidarians include about 10,000 species. Although cnidarians are not related to sponges, they are usually listed next in the sequence of animals because their simple, multicellular form includes features not found in sponges, including a gastrovascular cavity with cells organized to play a more active role in digestion. Unlike sponges, cnidarians actively move through their watery environment.

Ancillary Support

The resources below can be used to support your teaching strategy for these two pages.

TR Apply: Spunky Sponges
BL Inquiry Activity: Sponges

2 EXPLORE

Investigate

Research Post a large world map in the classroom, and provide students with field guides and other sources describing sponges and cnidarians. Ask students to research various examples of these invertebrates, find out where they normally live, and mark those locations with pins on the map. Students will discover that most of these organisms live in warm-water environments. Most are also marine animals, although some freshwater sponges can be found in lakes and ponds.

3 TEACH

Ideas Through Images

Have students examine Figure 27–2 and read the caption. To explain the water flow, compare a sponge to an underwater building in which water enters through windows (the sponge's pores), travels through rooms and hallways (the body wall), and exits through a chimney (the central cavity with the osculum at the top).

INTEGRATING CHEMISTRY

Calcium carbonate ($CaCO_3$) is a solid compound composed of atoms of calcium, carbon, and oxygen in the ratio of 1:1:3. Limestone consists of calcium carbonate, which foams in the presence of acid. Silica (silicon dioxide, SiO_2) is a solid compound composed of atoms of silicon and oxygen in the ratio of 1:2. The mineral quartz is a pure crystalline form of silica. Both sand and sandstone are composed of small particles of quartz.

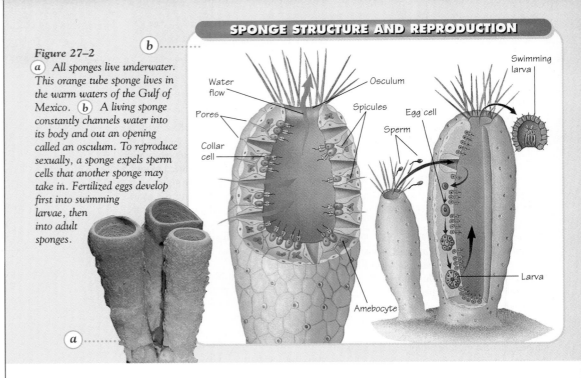

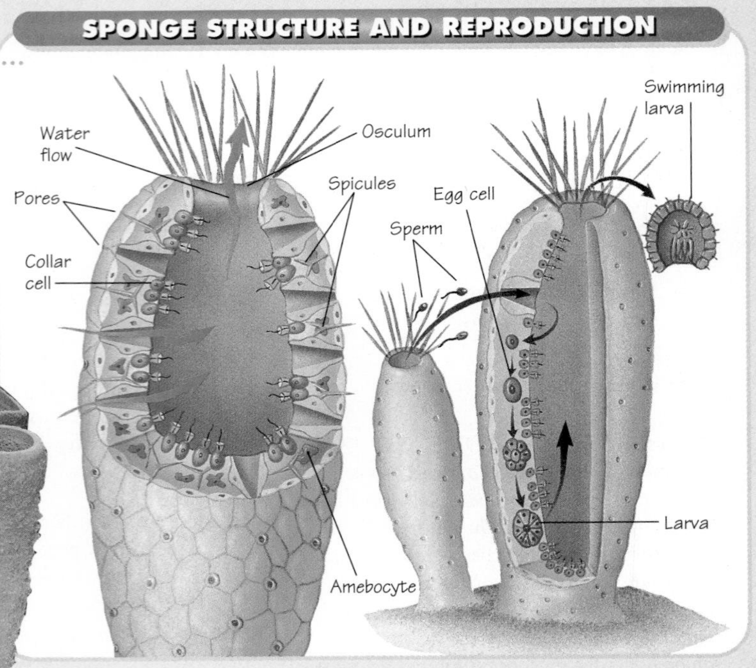

Figure 27–2 *(a) All sponges live underwater. This orange tube sponge lives in the warm waters of the Gulf of Mexico. (b) A living sponge constantly channels water into its body and out an opening called an osculum. To reproduce sexually, a sponge expels sperm cells that another sponge may take in. Fertilized eggs develop first into swimming larvae, then into adult sponges.*

are autotrophic, meaning they manufacture their own food from raw materials.

The differences between sponges and other animals are even greater than you might expect by looking at them. **Unlike the cells of other animals, a sponge's cells are not organized into recognizable organs—or even recognizable tissues.** For this reason, most biologists believe that sponges evolved separately from other animals.

Checkpoint How do sponges differ from other animals? 1

INTEGRATING CHEMISTRY

What are the physical and chemical properties of calcium carbonate and silica?

Sponge Structure

As shown in ***Figure 27–2,*** sponges use different types of cells for different purposes. Their **collar cells,** for example, have whiplike flagella that beat water through the body wall and into the central cavity. These cells also snag food particles from the water moving past them—particles which they then engulf and digest. Sponges also use wandering cells called **amebocytes** (uh-MEE-boh-sights) to digest and distribute food, as well as to produce components of the sponge skeleton.

The sponge's body plan allows it to perform many different tasks efficiently. Respiration, feeding, and the elimination of wastes are each accomplished by exchanging materials with the water that flows through the sponge's body.

Some sponges support their bodies with small crystallike spikes called **spicules.** Spicules are made of either calcium carbonate ($CaCO_3$) or silica (SiO_2), and they can interlock to form rigid yet delicate networks, as shown in ***Figure 27–3.*** ●

Sponges also support their body with a protein called **spongin.** The skeletons of sponges that contain this protein are soft, flexible, and elastic—qualities that give them a "spongy" texture.

TEACHER SUPPORT

Activity

OBSERVING SPONGE REAGGREGATION

Damaged sponges will sometimes regrow through a process called reaggregation. The following activity will allow students to observe this process.

1. Half-fill a small bowl with fresh seawater or prepared saltwater-aquarium solution.
2. Wrap a small piece of living sponge in a piece of nylon stocking material.
3. Squeeze the sponge through the nylon material and into the bowl. This will destroy the sponge's structure but will not kill its individual cells.
4. Use an aquarium pump to aerate the seawater. Add more seawater as needed to maintain its original level.
5. Observe the sponge cells regularly. (Over a period of several weeks, the cells may clump together, or reaggregate, and grow into a new sponge.)

Sponge Life Cycles

Sponges reproduce sexually by producing sperm and eggs, as shown in ***Figure 27–2***. However, like many animals, sponges can reproduce asexually, too. One way sponges do this is by producing ball-shaped structures called **gemmules** (JEHM-yoolz). Gemmules are clusters of amebocytes that are protected by a tough outer covering of spicules. This allows gemmules to survive long periods of harsh conditions that would kill adult sponges. When conditions improve, gemmules grow into complete sponges.

A process called **budding** is another way in which sponges reproduce asexually. In budding, a piece of the sponge falls off and grows into a new sponge.

✓ *Checkpoint* What are gemmules? ❷

Cnidarians

The phylum Cnidaria (nigh-DEHR-ee-uh) contains the corals, jellyfishes, and sea anemones. All cnidarians live underwater, and nearly all live in the sea.

Cnidarians represent an important step up the evolutionary ladder of complexity. Why? **Unlike sponges, the cnidarians have layers of differentiated cells that are organized into three specialized layers of tissues.** The innermost tissue layer is called the **endoderm,** and the outermost layer is called the **ectoderm.** In between these layers is a poorly developed jellylike layer called the **mesoglea** (mehs-oh-GLEE-uh).

✓ *Checkpoint* What are the cnidarians? ❸

Cnidarian Structure

A cnidarian's body plan is radially symmetric, meaning that its body parts are arranged in circles around a central mouth. For this reason, you could say that cnidarians have a top and a bottom but no front or back.

MINI LAB ············ Comparing ····

Spongy Skeletons

PROBLEM *How do different sponges compare?*

PROCEDURE

1. Add a few drops of bleach to a microscope slide. **CAUTION:** *Avoid direct contact with bleach.*
2. Place a small piece of a *Grantia* sponge on the slide. The sponge's cells will deteriorate in the bleach, but the spicules will not be affected.
3. Add two drops of water, place a coverslip on the slide, and study the sponge under the low-power objective of a compound microscope.
4. Repeat steps 1 to 3 for a *Spongilla* sponge and a *Hexactinellida* sponge.

ANALYZE AND CONCLUDE

1. Describe the sponge structures you observed.
2. What is the role of spicules in a living sponge?
3. Compare the different sponges you studied. How do living sponges compare with artificial sponges used for cleaning?

Figure 27–3
The skeleton of a Venus' flower basket sponge consists of an intricate network of spicules.

MINI LAB Comparing

Teacher Notes
- For time required and materials needed, see page 628b.
- Sponges are available from biological supply companies.

Answers to Analyze and Conclude
1. Before adding the bleach, students should observe spongin. After adding bleach, students should observe spicules of calcium carbonate in *Grantia* and six-rayed siliceous spicules in *Hexactinellida* and *Spongilla.*
2. Provide support in sponges.
3. *Grantia* have needlelike spicules of calcium carbonate, while *Hexactinellida* and *Spongilla* have six-sided silicon spicules. Living sponges contain spongin and spicules, but artificial sponges do not.

Skills Trace
Comparing
- Focus p. 631
- Practice p. 635
- Assess p. 646

✓ Checkpoints

❶ Sponges' cells are not organized into recognizable organs or tissues as other animals' cells are.

❷ Clusters of amebocytes (wandering cells) that are protected by a tough outer covering of spicules.

❸ Cnidarians are aquatic invertebrates that have three specialized layers of tissues.

TEACHER SUPPORT

Managing Classroom Diversity

EDUCATIONAL EQUITY
Provide several books with top-view photographs of cnidarians so students can observe these invertebrates' characteristic radial symmetry. One excellent book with several such views, as well as many other beautiful and dramatic color photographs, is *Sea Jellies: Rainbows in the Sea (A New England Aquarium Book)* by Elizabeth Tayntor Gowell.

A biologist with a special interest in marine biology and conservation, Gowell has been an instructor at an environmental study school, has worked for the New England Aquarium and the Massachusetts Institute of Technology, and is now an environmental consultant for coastal projects and a science writer. Gowell co-authored *Dive to the Coral Reefs,* which is also richly illustrated but written at a lower reading level.

Ancillary Support

The resource below can be used to support your teaching strategy for these two pages.

TR Writing in Biology: Let Me Introduce You!

Ideas Through Images

Have students examine Figure 27–4, read the caption, compare this figure with Figure 27–2 on page 630, and answer the following questions.

- **What major difference do you see between a sponge's body structure and a cnidarian's body structure?** (A sponge does not have tissue layers; a cnidarian polyp or medusa has three tissue layers.)
- **Both sponges and cnidarians have an inner body cavity. What is the difference between the two cavities?** (A sponge's body cavity does not digest food, but a cnidarian's body cavity does.)
- **In the drawings of the cnidarian polyp and medusa, why is the opening of the body cavity labeled as both the mouth and the anus?** (Food enters the cavity and wastes leave it through that single opening.)

Discussion

Have students use a dictionary to find the meaning of the phylum name Cnidaria. (The phylum is named for specialized cells called cnidocytes, meaning "stinger cells.") Ask students to explain why the name is appropriate for these animals. Also use this procedure with the phylum names Platyhelminthes and Nematoda in Section 27–2. (Platyhelminthes is from Greek *platus*, "flat," and *helminth*, "parasitic worm." Nematoda is from Greek *nema*, "thread," and Latin *ode*, "like.")

Investigate

Research Explain that although only a few cnidarians are harmful to people, those that are can deliver extremely powerful stings. The sea wasp mentioned in the text, for example, contains one of the most deadly poisons known. Even when diluted 10,000 times, it can kill a laboratory animal in seconds. Encourage students to find out more about stinging cnidarians.

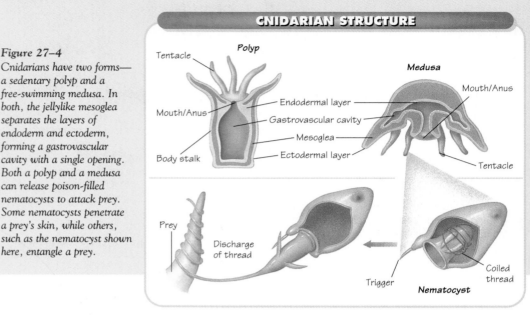

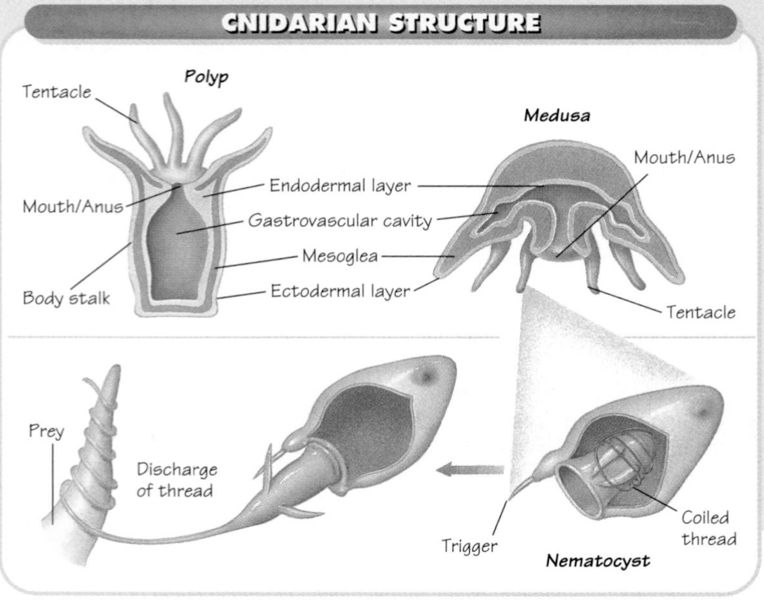

Figure 27–4 *Cnidarians have two forms—a sedentary polyp and a free-swimming medusa. In both, the jellylike mesoglea separates the layers of endoderm and ectoderm, forming a gastrovascular cavity with a single opening. Both a polyp and a medusa can release poison-filled nematocysts to attack prey. Some nematocysts penetrate a prey's skin, while others, such as the nematocyst shown here, entangle a prey.*

To send information around its body, a cnidarian uses a simple nervous system called a nerve net. The nerve net shows no centralization or cephalization—meaning "located in a head"—so a cnidarian has nothing that you could describe as a brain. Some species, however, have specialized nerve cells that function as sensory organs. Organs called **ocelli** (oh-SEHL-igh; singular: ocellus) are simple eyespots that detect the presence or absence of light. And organs called **statocysts** provide information on which way is up, helping the cnidarian to balance itself.

Although cnidarians do not have recognizable muscle tissue, they do have musclelike cells that contract when stimulated by the nerve net. These cells help cnidarians to move and to feed.

Cnidarians also have specialized structures called **nematocysts,** which are used for defense and for catching prey. A nematocyst is a sac containing poison and a tiny springlike harpoon. When triggered, the spring uncoils, flinging the poison-tipped harpoon toward the cnidarian's prey. Once the prey is paralyzed, the cnidarian uses its tentacles to push the prey through its mouth and into the **gastrovascular cavity,** where most digestion takes place.

The nematocysts of most cnidarians threaten only fishes and other small animals. But some species, such as the tiny sea wasp, carry powerful stings that can seriously injure—or even kill—a human.

Cnidarian Life Cycles

Typically, cnidarians alternate between two stages: a free-swimming stage called a **medusa** and a sessile stage called a **polyp.** In some groups, such as jellyfishes, the cnidarian spends most of its life as a medusa. In other groups, the dominant stage is the polyp. And in still other groups, such as corals, the medusa stage is left out altogether. In addition, many cnidarians also alternate between sexual and asexual reproduction.

☑ ***Checkpoint*** What is a polyp? A medusa? ❶

TEACHER SUPPORT

Managing Classroom Diversity

AT-RISK STUDENTS

To make the term medusa more meaningful to students, explain that Medusa was the name of a monster in Greek mythology. She and her two hideous sisters, Stheno and Euryale, were known as the Gorgons. They had fangs for teeth and snakes growing from their heads in place of hair—thus the use of the term medusa for the tentacled, free-swimming cnidarian stage. According to Greek myth, anyone who looked directly into Medusa's eyes was turned to stone. The hero Perseus was able to slay Medusa by looking at her reflection in his shield as he cut off her head.

Students may be familiar with the myth of Medusa through a motion picture, released several years ago, that combined live actors and an animated figure of Medusa. Encourage students to read age-appropriate versions of the myth.

Problem Solving

INTERPRETING GRAPHS

The Hydra Test

Like all organisms that live in water, hydras are affected by the concentration of many substances in the water surrounding them. The following experiment was designed to show how two substances—sodium ions (Na^+) and potassium ions (K^+)—affect the growth of a hydra's tentacles.

Hypothesis: The growth of a hydra's tentacles is equally affected by Na^+ and K^+.

Five solutions of growth medium were prepared, with different combinations of sodium and potassium ions added to each. Hydras were placed in each solution, then the lengths of their tentacles were measured each day for six days. The trends in the data and the contents of the five solutions are presented in the diagram below.

A polyp of *Hydra*, with a small bud at its side (magnification: 10X)

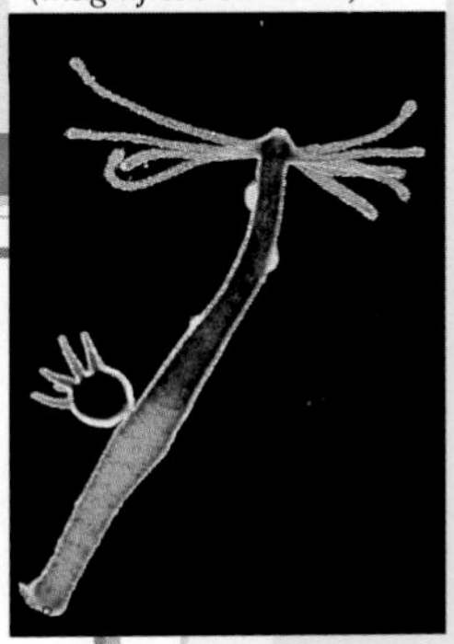

HYDRAS' TENTACLE LENGTH IN FIVE SOLUTIONS

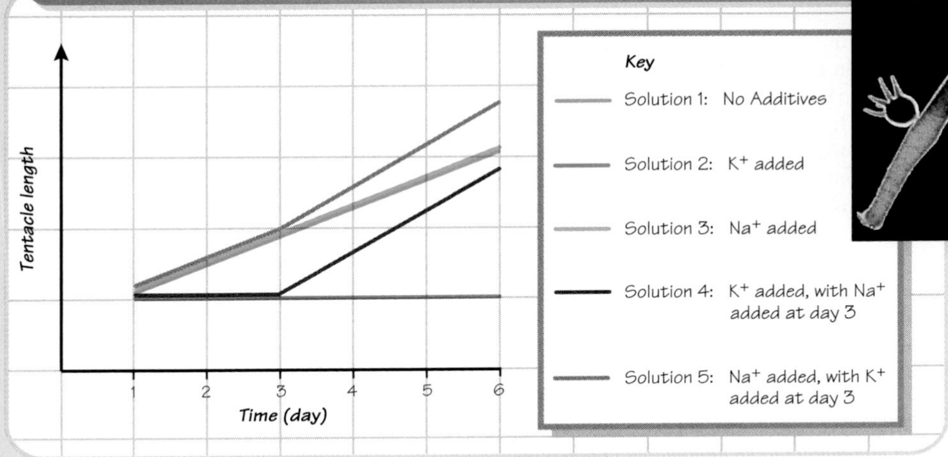

THINK ABOUT IT

1. Identify the control group and the variables in this experiment.
2. Describe the growth of the hydras' tentacles in each of the five solutions. In which solution did the tentacles grow the most? The least?
3. Did the results of the experiment support or contradict the hypothesis? Explain your answer.
4. What can you conclude about the growth of a hydra's tentacles from this experiment? Identify any assumptions that you used to reach this conclusion.

TEACHER SUPPORT

Managing Classroom Diversity

TECH PREP STUDENTS

Students who are considering careers in the health-care field could research the physiological responses, sometimes life-threatening, that occur in the human body as the result of being stung by a sea wasp, Portuguese man-of-war, or other dangerous cnidarian. Encourage students to research the symptoms of such a sting, the specific effects of the toxin, any treatments that are available, and ways to avoid being stung.

GIFTED STUDENTS

Suggest that students read what is perhaps the most famous literary account of deadly contact between humans and jellyfish: "The Adventure of the Lion's Mane" by Sir Arthur Conan Doyle. A man's body is found cast up on a beach with long, angry welts across his back and chest, as though he had been severely whipped. Sherlock Holmes exposes the culprit as a lion's mane jellyfish, *Cyanea capillata*.

Problem Solving

Interpreting Graphs

The Hydra Test

Students use their ability to interpret graphs and their understanding of how to conduct a scientific experiment.

State To determine what effects sodium ions and potassium ions have on the lengthwise growth of a hydra's tentacles.

Solve Group 1 is the control. Data from groups 2 and 3 show that potassium ions inhibit tentacle growth (graph 2), sodium ions do not interfere with normal growth rate (graph 3). Data from groups 4 and 5 show the effects of both sodium and potassium ions. Graph 4 shows that potassium ions inhibit tentacle growth, but growth is stimulated when sodium ions are added. Graph 5 shows that sodium ions allow normal growth, but growth is stimulated when potassium ions are added. Potassium ions inhibit tentacle growth when present alone, while sodium ions do not inhibit growth. When potassium and sodium ions are combined, tentacle growth is stimulated beyond the normal rate.

Test Students could perform the experiment, collect their own data, and determine whether their data match those here.

Communicate Read the conclusion stated above to the class.

Answers to THINK ABOUT IT

1. and **2.** See Solve.
3. No. K^+ inhibits growth and Na^+ does not interfere with normal growth. The presence of both ions increases the rate of growth beyond the normal rate.
4. See Solve.

Checkpoint

1 The sessile stage of a cnidarian; a free-swimming stage of a cnidarian.

Inquiry Activity

Observing

The Acrobatic Hydra

Ask students how they think hydras move from place to place. Then provide living hydras for students to observe with a microscope. Have students draw a series of pictures showing a hydra's unusual somersaulting method of locomotion. Students might enjoy doing the pictures as a flipbook.

Ideas Through Images

Have students examine Figure 27–6, read the caption, and answer the following questions.

- **Besides hydrozoans, what other organisms that you know of can reproduce by budding?** (Sponges, corals, sea anemones. Students may also mention other organisms, such as yeasts, that they have studied.)
- **What is a zygote?** (If students do not recall this information, remind them that a zygote is the fertilized cell that results from the union of egg and sperm.)

Discussion

If you have not already done so, you may want to share with students the information on coral reefs, coralline algae, and reef-dwelling dinoflagellates.

Figure 27–5
These hydrozoans live in the Gulf of Mexico. (a) The Portuguese man-of-war is a floating hydrozoan colony that contains several different polyps. (b) Beware the fire coral if you encounter it—its stings are painful!

Hydrozoans

There are several important classes of cnidarians, one of which is the class Hydrozoa (high-droh-ZOH-uh). The hydrozoans spend most of their lives as polyps, although many species have a brief medusa stage. Most hydrozoans grow as branching collections of polyps called colonies. As shown in ***Figure 27–6***, a colony can range in width from a centimeter to more than a meter.

In many cases, the polyps in a colony are specialized to perform different tasks, including feeding and defense. The colony can also contain reproductive polyps, which produce small free-swimming medusae. The medusae mature rapidly, reproduce sexually by producing sperm and eggs, and then die.

The best-known hydrozoans are members of the genus *Hydra*—which just happen to be among the least typical members of the group! Unlike most hydrozoans, hydra live in fresh water, lack a medusa stage, and spend most of their lives as solitary polyps. Hydras also move from place to place with a peculiar somersaulting motion.

Jellyfishes

True jellyfishes are members of the class Scyphozoa (sigh-fuh-ZOH-uh). In most respects, these animals have typical

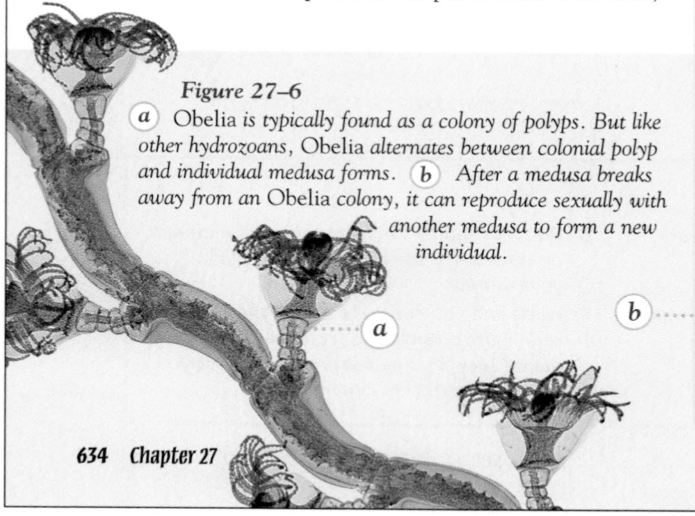

Figure 27–6
(a) Obelia is typically found as a colony of polyps. But like other hydrozoans, Obelia alternates between colonial polyp and individual medusa forms. (b) After a medusa breaks away from an Obelia colony, it can reproduce sexually with another medusa to form a new individual.

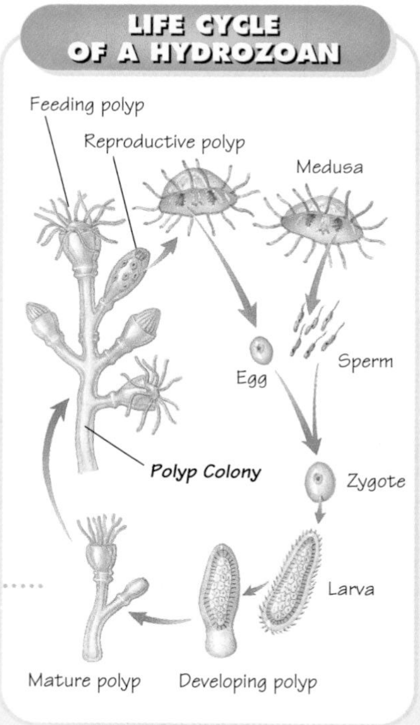

TEACHER SUPPORT

Ecology Note

Coral provides both benefits and hazards to humans. Coral polyps, like several other invertebrates, can produce some important medicines. A soft coral called *Plexaurella* has been found to be a source of medicines that are important in the treatment of cardiovascular diseases. Another coral, *Alcyonium digitatum* (commonly known as dead man's finger) is used to treat goiter. Unfortunately, this coral can also cause skin irritation, which North Sea fishers call Dogger Bank itch.

Coral reefs can present a problem in harbor areas when they block the harbor entrance as they grow and put an end to commerce. One example occurred about 100 years ago in the city of Suakin on the Red Sea. Once a flourishing seaport, Suakin today is a ghost town, its harbor choked by a growing coral reef and its ship traffic ended. Dynamiting reefs to clear shipping lanes is not always successful and is also, of course, ecologically destructive.

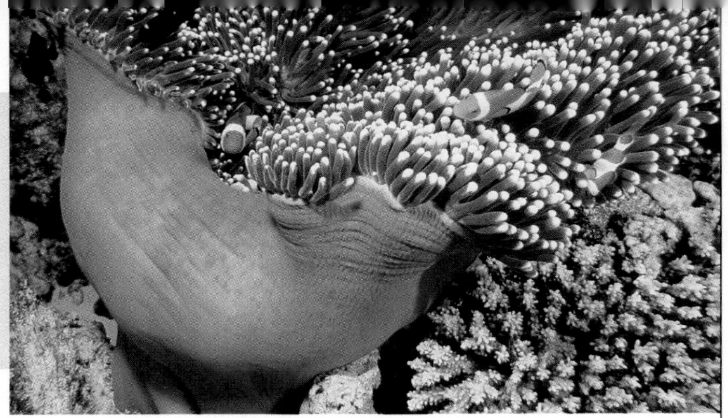

Figure 27–7
This large sea anemone has nematocysts on its tentacles that can paralyze fishes. However, it dines not on the small clownfish shown here, but on larger fishes that the clownfish attract.

cnidarian life cycles. The polyp stage is small and usually short-lived, however, while the medusa stage can grow to more than 3 meters in diameter and live a long time.

Most jellyfishes are harmless to humans, but several have stings that can cause allergic reactions in some people. A few species that live mostly in the South Pacific have venom powerful enough to kill a human in minutes.

Corals and Sea Anemones

The corals and sea anemones—members of the class Anthozoa (an-thuh-ZOH-uh)—include many of the most beautiful animals in the sea, as well as some of the most ecologically important. These animals grow either as solitary or colonial polyps and have no medusa stage.

Corals and sea anemones reproduce sexually when mature polyps produce eggs and sperm. Fertilization produces free-swimming larvae that attach themselves to rocks and grow into polyps. In addition, many anthozoans reproduce asexually by budding. And pieces of coral that break off colonies often survive and begin new colonies.

Coral Reefs

Hard corals, soft corals, and sea anemones are the best-known inhabitants of coral reefs, which are large living structures found near the coastlines in many tropical regions. As shown in the photograph on page 628, coral reefs can be as intricate as an Oriental carpet.

How do coral reefs form? With the help of the algae living inside them, hard coral colonies form layers of skeleton made of calcium carbonate. Over thousands of years, this calcium carbonate—together with carbonate rocks produced by algae—create the reef's foundation.

Section Review 27–1

1. **Explain** how sponges differ from other animals.
2. **Describe** the organization of tissues in cnidarians.
3. **Describe** the two stages of a cnidarian's life cycle.
4. **Critical Thinking—Analyzing** All sponges and cnidarians live underwater. Why are they ill-equipped to live on land?
5. **MINI LAB** How do living sponges **compare** with artificial household sponges?

4 ASSESS

Quick Check

Have each student draw simple sketches to show the body structures of a sponge and a cnidarian polyp and medusa, and label the major parts.

Section Review 27–1

1. Sponges' cells are not organized into recognizable organs or tissues as other animals' cells are.
2. Cnidarians have three specialized tissue layers: the innermost endoderm, the outermost ectoderm, and the jellylike mesoglea between those two layers.
3. Cnidarians alternate between two stages: a free-swimming stage called a medusa and a sessile (stationary) stage called a polyp.
4. Both sponges and cnidarians must take in water to obtain food and release water to rid their bodies of wastes. They also lack a protective body covering to prevent water loss in dry environments. Accept other reasonable explanations.
5. Living sponges contain spongin and spicules, but artificial sponges do not.

Skills Trace
Comparing

- Focus p. 631
- **Practice p. 635**
- Assess p. 646

Learning Modality

Visual and Tactile Learning Have students use modeling clay to make three-dimensional models of the body structures of a sponge and a cnidarian polyp and medusa, and then attach tags to label the major parts.

Ancillary Support

The resources below can be used to support your teaching strategy for these two pages.

LM Observing Sponges and Hydras, #53
TB Life Cycle of a Hydrozoan, #35

Section 27–2

Unsegmented Worms

Performance Objective
• Identify the characteristics of flatworms and roundworms.

Laboratory Investigation Skill: Designing an experiment
Mini Lab Skill: Identifying

1 ENGAGE

Inquiry Activity

Comparing

Observing Flatworms and Roundworms

Ask students what they think flatworms and roundworms look like, and have them sketch an example of each. Set up learning stations with microscopes and a number of prepared slides of various types of flatworms and roundworms, and let students take turns observing the organisms. (Note: You may want to exclude the tapeworm from this activity, since it is used in the MINI LAB on page 638.) Ask students to sketch each specimen, label each drawing with the organism's name, and label any body parts they think they can identify, such as the head end or the eyespots of a planarian. Have students compare the features of the two types of worms and also compare their original sketches with the sketches they made based on actual observations.

2 EXPLORE

Investigate

Research Provide field guides and other sources so students can research various examples of flatworms and roundworms, the habitat in which each is normally found, and, for parasitic worms, the animals that serve as hosts. Have students summarize their findings in a table.

SECTION 27–2

Unsegmented Worms

Guide for Reading

- **Describe** the characteristics of flatworms and nematodes.

MINI LAB

- **Identify** the structures of a tapeworm.

When you hear the word worm, do you think only of earthworms—the long, squirmy creatures that crawl out of the ground after it rains? If so, look at the worms shown on this page. In fact, worms come in different colors, shapes, and sizes. They are found in soil and in water. And they fill many different roles in nature—including the roles of pests and parasites. As you can see, there is more to worms than meets the eye!

Classifying Worms

In everyday language, the word worm applies to a wide range of animals. In fact, many of the animals called worms, such as inchworms, are not true worms but insects!

To classify the real worms, biologists first look at a worm's body plan. Worms that have bodies divided into parts are called the segmented worms, and worms that are not divided in this way are called the unsegmented worms. There are two phyla of unsegmented worms, and we'll present both phyla in this section. Segmented worms will be discussed in the next chapter.

Platyhelminths

The members of phylum Platyhelminthes (plat-ih-hehl-MIHN-theez) are called platyhelminths or, more commonly, flatworms. **Flatworms are the simplest worms. They are also the simplest animals to show bilateral symmetry—meaning they have symmetric sides that can be identified as left and right.**

The name flatworm is appropriate because these worms are flat from top to bottom. Although flatworms can be several meters long, they are usually no more than a few millimeters thick. Otherwise, the flatworms are an enormously

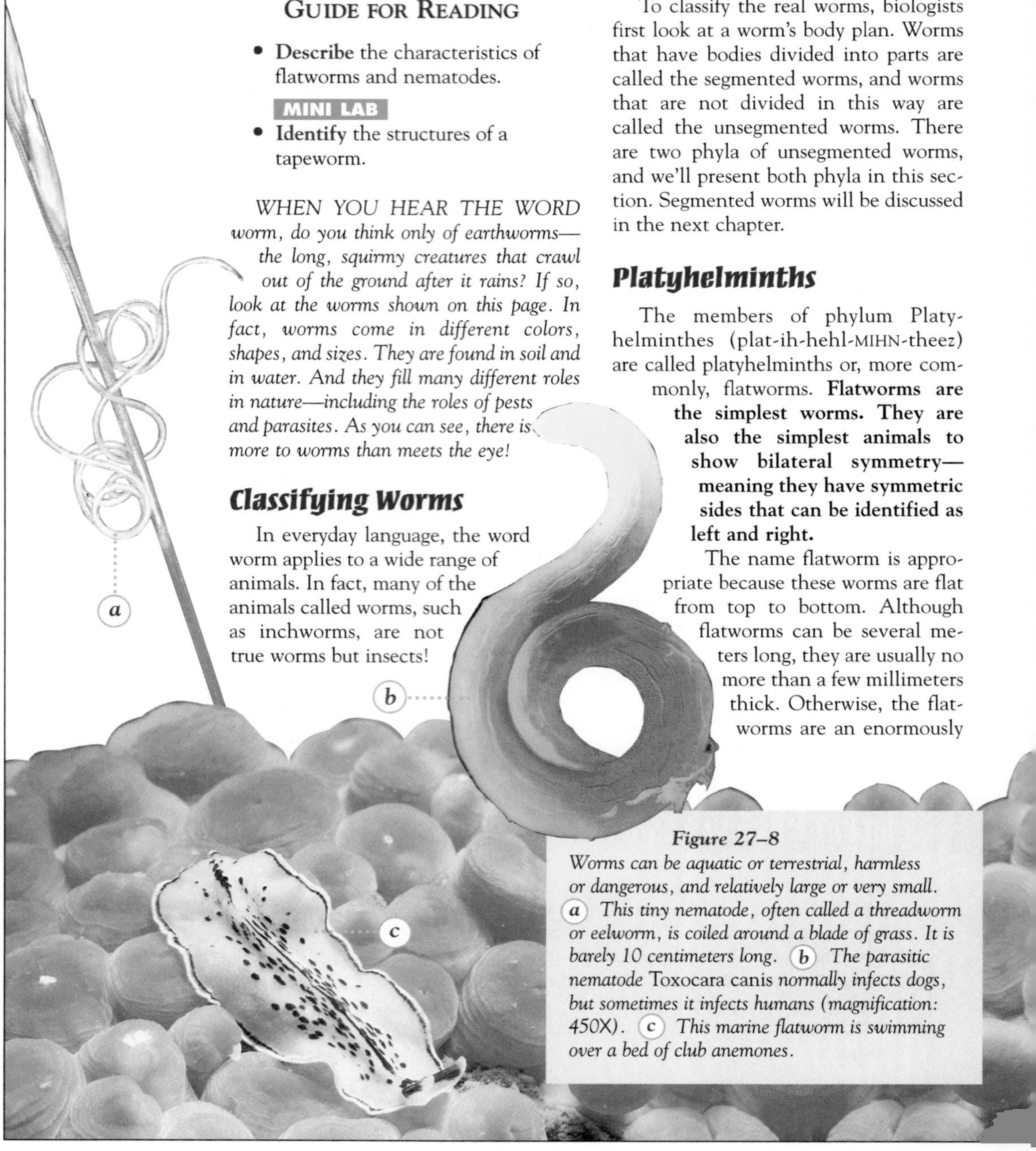

Figure 27–8
Worms can be aquatic or terrestrial, harmless or dangerous, and relatively large or very small. (a) This tiny nematode, often called a threadworm or eelworm, is coiled around a blade of grass. It is barely 10 centimeters long. (b) The parasitic nematode Toxocara canis *normally infects dogs, but sometimes it infects humans (magnification: 450X). (c) This marine flatworm is swimming over a bed of club anemones.*

TEACHER SUPPORT

Activity

COMPARING TRUE WORMS WITH WORMLIKE INSECT LARVAE

To emphasize the differences between true worms and the wormlike larval stage of insects, have students set up classroom cultures of insect larvae and compare these organisms with the flatworms and roundworms described in this section.

An easy-to-maintain larval culture can be prepared using mealworms purchased from a pet supply store. Students could also collect insect larvae (caterpillars) from outdoors if the season is appropriate. Tell students also to collect some of the leaves or other material on which the larvae were feeding when they were found. If the season is not appropriate for collecting larvae, you can purchase different types from a biological supply company. Have students record metamorphic changes on a calendar.

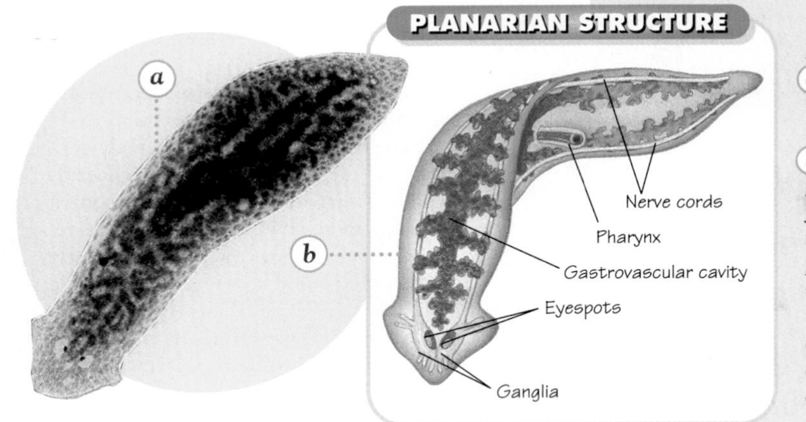

Figure 27–9
(a) *Planarians are common in lakes, ponds, and streams (magnification: 10X).*
(b) *To take in food, a planarian secretes digestive juices on a prey, then sucks in food particles through its pharynx. The planarian's nervous system contains two eyespots connected to collections of nerve cells called ganglia. The ganglia act as a very simple brain.*

diverse group. For example, some flatworms are harmless and free-living, while others are destructive parasites of plants, animals, and humans.

Along with bilateral symmetry, most flatworms have a few basic features in common. Typically, a flatworm's nervous and sensory systems show enough cephalization to reasonably label one end as a head. And because their bodies are so thin, they do not need respiratory or circulatory systems. Beyond these features, however, free-living and parasitic flatworms have very different anatomies and body plans. Let's take a closer look at three examples of free-living and parasitic flatworms.

Checkpoint What is a flatworm? (1)

Planarians

The free-living flatworms include the members of the class Turbellaria, commonly called planarians. Most planarians are either carnivores that feed on much smaller aquatic animals or scavengers that feed on dead or decaying organic matter.

Planarians are common throughout the world. Many species live in lakes, streams, and oceans, while other species live on land in wet parts of the tropics. In the United States, the most common planarians live in fresh water.

Flukes

The members of the class Trematoda (trehm-uh-TOH-duh) are called flukes. Flukes are parasites that live in the blood and tissues of various hosts.

Although flukes are usually less than a centimeter long, their actions as parasites cause serious, painful, and even life-threatening damage to millions of humans and countless other animals around the world. Some of the most destructive fluke parasites are native to Africa and Asia, and many were spread to South America and Central America during the 1800s, where they are now well-established. Flukes of the genus *Schistosoma* (shihs-tuh-SOHM-uh) infect about 200 million people around the world. ●

Few of the flukes that cause serious human diseases are common in the United States, so most Americans know little about them. However, some species of *Schistosoma* are parasites of freshwater fishes and water birds, and they occasionally infect humans. These flukes are not adapted to be human parasites, however, so they don't live long. Instead, they produce a short-lived rash known as "swimmer's itch" before the body's defense mechanisms eliminate them.

INTEGRATING HEALTH

What are the symptoms of a Schistosoma *infection? How can it be treated?*

3 TEACH

Ideas Through Images

Have students examine Figure 27–9, read the caption, and answer the following questions.

- **Which organs are part of the planarian's nervous system? Its digestive system?** (Nervous system: ganglia, eyespots, and nerve cords. Digestive system: pharynx and gastrovascular cavity.)
- **How does a planarian show cephalization?** (It has ganglia and eyespots located in a head region.)

INTEGRATING HEALTH

Symptoms of a *Schistosoma* infection include rash, fever, cough, and body pains in the early stages; dysentery, emaciation, and weakness in later stages. Treatment with drugs is possible but of little use if the patient is exposed to reinfection.

Laboratory Investigation

The Laboratory Investigation, Observing a Hydra and a Planarian, on pages 642–643, is appropriate to use at this point in the chapter.

Checkpoint

(1) A flatworm is the simplest type of worm, with bilateral symmetry, cephalization, and no respiratory or circulatory system. Some flatworms are free-living; others are parasitic.

TEACHER SUPPORT

Managing Classroom Diversity

TECH PREP STUDENTS

Students who are considering careers in public health could research the continuing problem of *Schistosoma* infection worldwide.

As a world health problem, schistosomiasis is second only to malaria. Control measures involve sanitary disposal of human feces and education to reduce human contact with infested water. Unfortunately, these measures are beyond the limited means of most countries in which the disease is widespread. In addition, the use of human feces as agricultural fertilizer is an important part of the traditional economy in many infected areas.

Where infection is limited to small areas, poisoning or draining snail habitats can help reduce intermediate-host populations. In many developing nations, however, the building of new dams and irrigation systems has actually increased the snail population and, in turn, the incidence of schistosomiasis.

Ancillary Support

The resource below can be used to support your teaching strategy for these two pages.

TR Explore: Plainly Planarians

MINI LAB Indentifying

Teacher Notes
- For time required and materials needed, see page 628b.
- To help students identify the tapeworm's scolex, refer them to Figure 27–10.

Answers to Analyze and Conclude
1. The scolex contains several suckers and a ring of hooks. The role of the scolex is to attach the tapeworm to its host's intestinal wall.
2. Most of a tapeworm's body consists of proglottids. They are important because they are the reproductive organs for the tapeworm.
3. The tapeworm's food has already been digested by its host's enzymes.

Skills Trace
Identifying
- Focus p. 638
- Practice p. 639
- Assess p. 646

Discussion

Emphasize that some parasitic flatworms live an immature life stage in one type of animal and an adult, reproductive stage in another type of animal. Explain that the animal harboring the immature stage is called the intermediate host, and the animal harboring the sexually mature stage is called the final host. With blood flukes, for example, snails are the intermediate hosts and humans the final hosts.

MINI LAB Identifying

Tapering Tapeworms

PROBLEM *How can you **identify** the structures of a tapeworm?*

PROCEDURE

1. Study a slide of a tapeworm under the low-power and high-power objectives of a compound microscope.
2. Sketch the tapeworm's body. Label the structures that you can identify.

ANALYZE AND CONCLUDE

1. What structures does the scolex contain? What is the role of the scolex?
2. How much of the tapeworm's body consists of proglottids? Why are proglottids important for the tapeworm?
3. Why does a tapeworm lack elaborate systems for digestion and elimination?

Tapeworms

The members of the class Cestoda (sehs-TOHD-uh)—the tapeworms—are another class of parasitic flatworms. Tapeworms live in the intestines of their hosts. With this arrangement, the tapeworms' food is not only collected for them, it is also digested by the host's enzymes! For this reason, tapeworms have no gut or mouth of their own, and they have no use for a nervous system or sense organs.

As shown in ***Figure 27–10,*** the front end of a tapeworm contains several suckers and a ring of hooks that attach to the intestinal wall of the host. Because the front end is not really a proper head, it is called a **scolex** (SKOH-lehks). A tapeworm hangs in the intestine from its scolex, absorbing digested food as it passes by.

The rest of the tapeworm's body consists of segments called **proglottids** (proh-GLAHT-ihdz). Proglottids consist of little more than male and female reproductive organs, which constantly produce eggs and sperm. One proglottid can contain more than 100,000 eggs, and a single tapeworm can produce as many as half a billion eggs in a single year!

Tapeworms rarely cause death directly. But because they "steal" a lot of food, they can cause their hosts to lose weight and become weak.

Flatworm Life Cycles

Like their body plans, the life cycles of flatworms vary enormously between free-living and parasitic species. The free-living flatworms usually have simple life cycles. However, many have the unusual feature of being simultaneous hermaphrodites, which means that they carry functioning male and female reproductive organs at the same time. These flatworms almost never fertilize their own eggs, however. Instead, they pair with another member of their species and the two cross-fertilize each other.

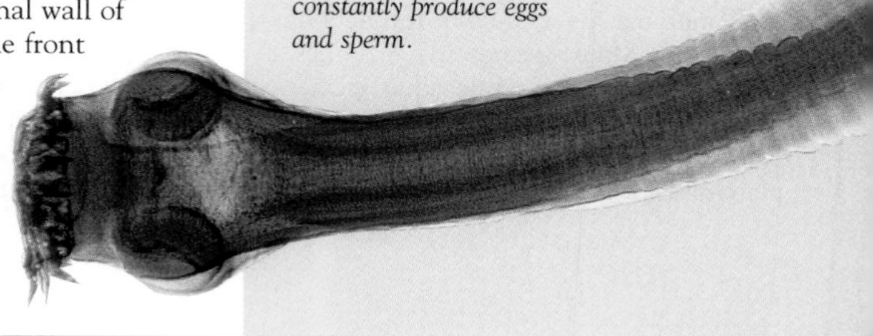

Figure 27–10 *The scolex—the front end of a tapeworm—contains hooks and suckers that attach to a host's intestines. The rest of a tapeworm's body consists of segments called proglottids, each of which constantly produce eggs and sperm.*

TEACHER SUPPORT

Ecology Note

The importance of nematodes as plant parasites was not understood until fairly recently, partly because they are smaller and less visibly destructive than well-recognized pests such as insects, snails, and slugs. Every year, nematodes reduce crop yields by an estimated 10 percent in the United States and prompt the use of more than 50 million kilograms of pesticides. Practices such as crop rotation, cultivation, addition of organic matter, and control of soil moisture and acidity help control nematode populations. Ironically, nematodes also benefit agriculture because they are parasites of many insect pests. For example, one nematode species attacks both the larvae and adults of a woodwasp that damages pine trees. Other parasitic nematodes enter the body cavity of insect hosts and introduce species-specific bacteria. Still other nematodes are being investigated for use against snails that harbor schistosomes.

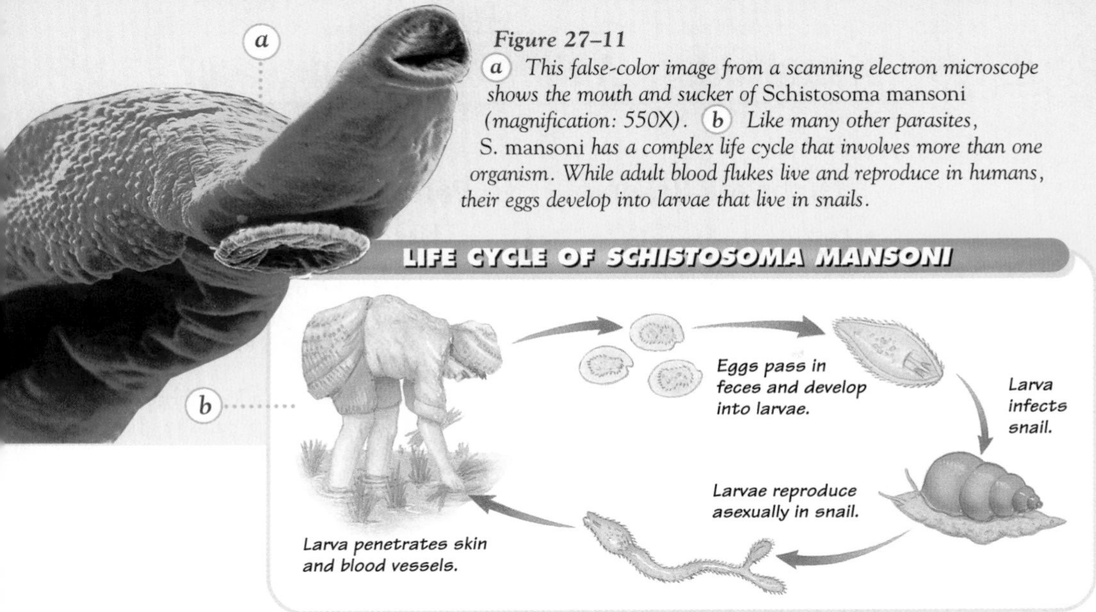
a
b
LIFE CYCLE OF SCHISTOSOMA MANSONI
Eggs pass in feces and develop into larvae.
Larva infects snail.
Larvae reproduce asexually in snail.
Larva penetrates skin and blood vessels.

Figure 27–11
ⓐ *This false-color image from a scanning electron microscope shows the mouth and sucker of* Schistosoma mansoni *(magnification: 550X).* ⓑ *Like many other parasites,* S. mansoni *has a complex life cycle that involves more than one organism. While adult blood flukes live and reproduce in humans, their eggs develop into larvae that live in snails.*

Many parasitic flatworms have complicated life cycles, often involving two host species or even three or more. Blood flukes, for example, have several stages in a life cycle that involves two separate hosts—humans and snails. Tapeworms also switch back and forth between two different hosts.

Nematodes

The members of the phylum Nematoda—the nematodes—are also called roundworms. You may never have heard of these worms, but they play important roles in the biosphere—and in the study of biology. **The nematodes are the simplest animals with a digestive tract similar to a human's, with a mouth at one end and an anus at the other.** Although most nematodes are free-living, others are parasites of humans, other animals, and plants. In fact, nematodes are parasites of almost every kind of plant and animal.

Nematodes range in length from 1 millimeter to more than 1 meter. Although nematodes are often inconspicuous, they may be the most numerous of all multicellular animals. The free-living nematodes live in soil, water, sand, and on or around the bodies of other organisms. Just one rotting apple may contain nearly 100,000 of them!

Section Review 27–2

1. **Describe** the characteristics of flatworms and nematodes.
2. **Critical Thinking—Comparing** Compare the life cycles and body structures of a planarian and a tapeworm. Why does a tapeworm produce a far greater number of eggs than a planarian produces?
3. **MINI LAB** How can you **identify** the structures of a tapeworm?

Ideas Through Images

Have students examine Figure 27–11, read the caption, and answer the following questions.

- **What is the intermediate host of *Schistosoma mansoni* (blood fluke)?** (A snail.)
- **How do the snails become infected?** (From contact with infested human feces.)
- **What is the final host?** (Humans.)
- **Based on this life cycle, how could infection by blood flukes be controlled?** (It could be controlled through proper disposal of human feces, eradication of host snails, and/or avoiding contact with infested water.)

4 ASSESS

Quick Check

Ask students to create a two-column chart comparing the characteristics and life cycles of flatworms and roundworms.

Section Review 27–2

1. Flatworms: have bilateral symmetry, cephalization, and no respiratory or circulatory systems. Nematodes: have a digestive tract with a mouth and an anus. For other characteristics of both groups, see pages 636–639.
2. See pages 636–639.
3. The front end of a tapeworm, the scolex, contains suckers and hooks. The rest of the body consists of proglottids, the reproductive segments.

Skills Trace
Identifying

- Focus p. 638
- Practice p. 639
- Assess p. 646

Learning Modality

Auditory Learning Ask volunteers to tape-record the information in the chart they created in the Quick Check above. Let students who learn best through auditory means use the tape as a study guide and self-check resource.

Ancillary Support

The resource below can be used to support your teaching strategy for these two pages.

BL Inquiry Activity: Worms: Flat or Round?

Section 27–3

Nematodes—A Help or a Hindrance?

Performance Objectives

- Describe the life cycles of parasitic nematodes.
- Explain the importance of *Caenorhabditis elegans* in genetic research.

1 ENGAGE

Inquiry Activity

Comparing

Observing Parasitic Nematodes

Set up learning stations with slides of parasitic nematodes only. Include several examples of encysted *Trichinella* larvae. Have students compare the slides with the photograph in Figure 27–12.

2 EXPLORE

Investigate

Research Ask students whether they have ever heard of heartworms, and let them relate what they know. Suggest that students do library research or talk with a veterinarian or veterinary assistant to find out how heartworms are transmitted, the types of animals that serve as the intermediate and final hosts, and the specific effects on their final hosts.

3 TEACH

Discussion

Tell students that adult *Ascaris* worms are quite large—up to 40 cm long—and can cause serious damage or even death if they migrate from the small intestine to other vital organs, such as the liver. Emphasize that the best protection against ascarid infection is proper sanitation.

27–3 Nematodes—A Help or a Hindrance?

GUIDE FOR READING

- **Describe** the life cycles of parasitic nematodes.
- **Explain** why researchers study *Caenorhabditis elegans*.

IN OUR MODERN, INDUSTRIAL society, it is often easy to ignore animals that are too small to see or that live in natural habitats that we don't often visit. But that doesn't mean these animals are unimportant.

Nematodes arrived on the Earth hundreds of millions of years ago and have been evolving relationships with other organisms ever since. Unfortunately, this process has produced worms that cause a great deal of human pain and suffering. But not all nematodes are harmful to humans. In fact, one nematode species just might hold the key to some very useful information about all life on Earth.

Parasitic Nematodes

Like the parasitic flatworms, parasitic nematodes typically have life cycles that are quite complex, often involving more than one host. In addition, some of these life cycles can be quite gruesome!

For example, consider the nematode *Ascaris lumbricoides*, a parasite that infects millions of humans every year. Like the eggs of flukes, the eggs of *A. lumbricoides* are carried in feces, and they can spread by improper disposal of human wastes. If those eggs are eaten on food that has not been properly washed and cooked, the life cycle shown in **Figure 27–13** could be the result.

Trichinella, another parasitic nematode, causes a terrible disease called trichinosis. Although adult *Trichinella* worms live in the intestines, much of the damage of trichinosis comes from the worms' larval forms. The larvae travel through the bloodstream and burrow into muscles and other organs, which is extremely painful.

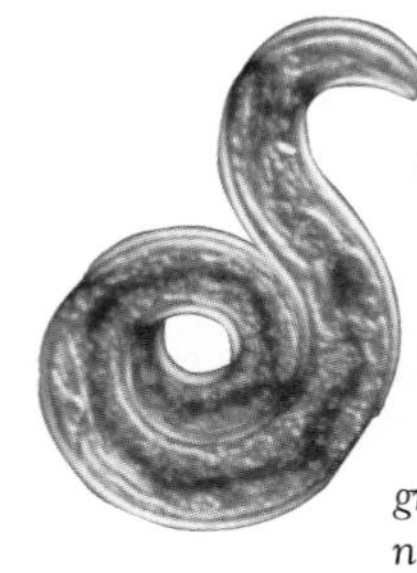

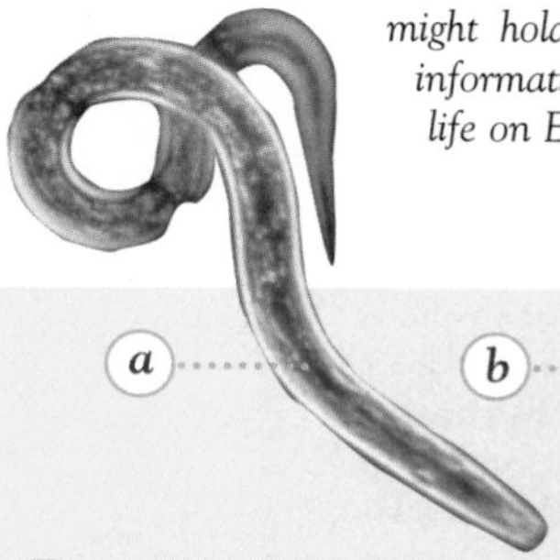

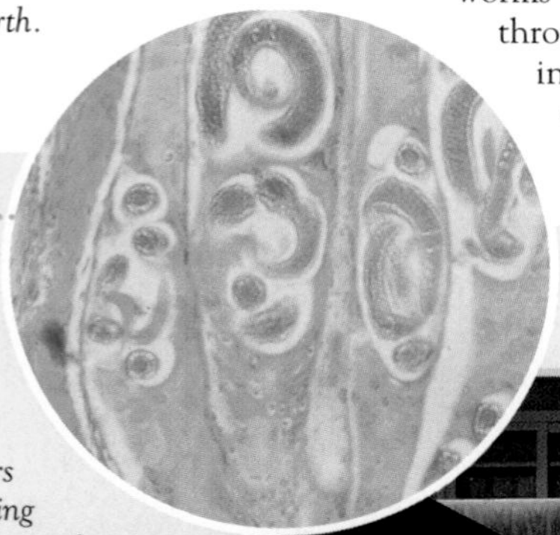

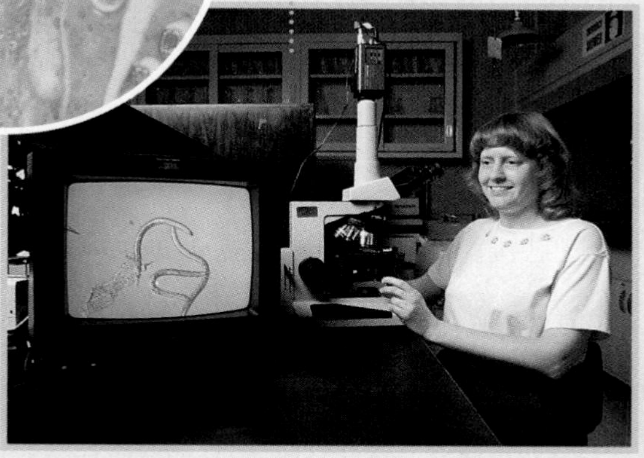

Figure 27–12 *Although many nematodes cause a great deal of human suffering, others are beneficial—and in some surprising ways.* (a) Caenorhabditis elegans, *a free-living nematode, has proved valuable in genetic research (magnification: 32X).* (b) *Larvae of the nematode* Trichinella *can wall themselves inside human muscle cells, a condition that is both painful and difficult to treat (magnification: 35X).* (c) CAREER TRACK *Nematologists work to protect plants and animals from nematode pests.*

TEACHER SUPPORT

Background Information

More serious than ascarids are the tiny hookworms that infect almost one fourth of the world's population in tropical and subtropical regions. In the United States, hookworm disease is largely confined to rural areas of the Southeast. Symptoms are diarrhea, anemia, lack of energy, and retardation. Treatment with drugs is effective, but it is also necessary to prevent reinfection through proper disposal of human waste and by avoiding skin contact with contaminated soil.

Filarial nematodes differ from other parasitic nematodes in that their life cycles require an arthropod intermediate host. Several kinds of filarial diseases are widespread, particularly in tropical regions. Some of the most notorious filarias are *Wuchereria bancrofti*, which causes elephantiasis and is spread by mosquitoes; *Onchocerca volvulus*, which causes river blindness and is spread by blackflies; and *Loa loa*, the eye worm, which is spread by deer flies.

Like other nematode parasites, *Trichinella* has a complex life cycle that involves more than one host. Almost always, humans acquire trichinosis by eating undercooked pork that contains *Trichinella* cysts.

Checkpoint What causes the disease trichinosis? 1

Caenorhabditis elegans

Caenorhabditis elegans, a tiny nematode, is providing incredibly important information to a wide variety of different researchers. **Because *Caenorhabditis elegans* is such a simple animal, it contains relatively few genetic instructions. This means that researchers have a chance to identify and study its entire genome.** What's more, these animals are easy to culture, and they grow to maturity in only three-and-a-half days. This means that their characteristics can be tracked quickly.

C. elegans has another unusual feature. Curiously, every adult worm of this species has exactly 959 cells. And because the worms are transparent, researchers can watch each cell develop. As a result, scientists now know the precise location and complete history of each *C. elegans* cell from the moment the egg is fertilized! This information helps researchers to study how genes direct growth and development.

Research on *C. elegans* is yielding clues to all sorts of mysteries, such as why animals age. Recently, researchers uncovered several genes that enable a worm to live as long as two months, which is five times longer than its usual life span. It may take years to determine just how these genes work, but the results may provide clues to determining why all animals—including humans—live to the ages that they do.

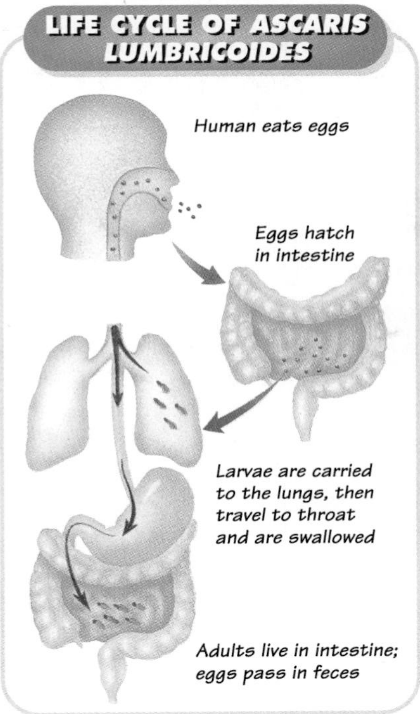

LIFE CYCLE OF ASCARIS LUMBRICOIDES
Human eats eggs
Eggs hatch in intestine
Larvae are carried to the lungs, then travel to throat and are swallowed
Adults live in intestine; eggs pass in feces

Figure 27–13 Ascaris lumbricoides *has an unusually complex life cycle that involves a human's digestive tract, bloodstream, and lungs. Although most* Ascaris *infections are not serious, severe infections can block a segment of the gut or spread to the appendix or other organs.*

Section Review 27–3

1. **Describe** the life cycles of parasitic nematodes.
2. **Explain** why researchers study *Caenorhabditis elegans*.
3. **BRANCHING OUT ACTIVITY** Nematodes are found all over the Earth. **Research** different nematodes and the roles they fill.

4 ASSESS

Quick Check

Have each student list the sequence of stages in the life cycle of *Ascaris lumbricoides* or *Trichinella*.

Section Review 27–3

1. Parasitic nematodes typically have life cycles that are quite complex, often involving more than one host. Students might also describe the *Ascaris* life cycle shown in Figure 27–13.
2. *Caenorhabditis elegans* is a simple animal with few genetic instructions, so researchers can identify and study its entire genome. It matures quickly, so its characteristics can be tracked through several generations in a short period of time. Also, it is transparent, so researchers can watch each cell develop.
3. Answers will vary depending on the specific nematodes that students research.

Learning Modality

Visual Learning Students could do the Quick Check activity above by drawing the life cycle and numbering the stages in their correct sequence.

Checkpoint

1 Trichinosis is a disease caused by the parasitic nematode *Trichinella* that affects the host's muscles and other organs.

TEACHER SUPPORT

Facts and Figures

Caenorhabditis elegans has become such a well-established laboratory animal that more is known about its genetic and developmental biology than that of almost any other organism. Because it is only 1 mm long when mature, *C. elegans* can be raised in small laboratory dishes. It takes only 12 hours from fertilization of the egg to hatching of the juvenile worm. In that time, successive cell divisions produce 671 cells, of which 113 are programmed to die, leaving 558 in the worm that hatches. This "programmed-to-die" characteristic is valuable to researchers studying the aging process.

The precise number of 959 cells in the mature worm is adequate for studying the development of complex organ systems, but not so many that it is impossible to track the divisions of each cell. The pattern and number of cell divisions in *C. elegans* are unvarying, making it possible to investigate the effects of local damage or a single genetic mutation.

Ancillary Support

The resources below can be used to support your teaching strategy for these two pages.

LM Investigating Nematodes, #54
TR Explore: Nifty Nematodes
BL Inquiry Activity: The Host With the Most

Laboratory Investigation

Observing a Hydra and a Planarian

Before the Lab

1. Set up separate planarian and hydra cultures. Planarians can be obtained from pond water or a hay infusion. Hydras may also be available in a hay infusion or could be obtained from a classroom aquarium.
2. If you purchase planarian and hydra cultures from a biological supply company, make sure you order them well in advance for delivery by the date on which students will need them. Do not feed the animals for 24 hours before the investigation.
3. Live brine shrimp can be purchased at many pet stores, or you can order dried brine shrimp eggs from a biological supply company. (Hatching of the eggs takes a few days, so start them early.) About an hour before the lab, add a suspension of red carmine powder to the shrimp culture to color the shrimp.
4. Prepare the dilute acid solution by mixing one part acetic acid (vinegar) with ten parts water.

Pre-Lab Discussion

Have students read the entire procedure for this investigation. Then ask students the following questions.

What is the purpose of this investigation? (To determine through experiments how a hydra and a planarian respond to different stimuli.)

How do you think the hydra will react to brine shrimp? (Students may know that brine shrimp are used as food for tropical fish and are eaten by many other aquatic animals. Thus, they will probably predict that the hydra will move toward the brine shrimp, seize them, and eat them.)

Laboratory Investigation

DESIGNING AN EXPERIMENT

Observing a Hydra and a Planarian

Like all living things, hydras and planarians respond to stimuli, or changes in their environment. In hydras and planarians, these responses depend on a nervous system. The hydra's nervous system consists of a nerve net, whereas the planarian's nervous system has a small brain, eyespot, and nerve cord. In this investigation, you will observe a hydra and a planarian and see how they respond to different stimuli.

Problem

How do a hydra and a planarian respond to different stimuli? **Design an experiment** to answer this question.

Suggested Materials

- hydra culture
- planarian culture
- medicine droppers
- culture dishes
- colored brine shrimp
- compound microscope
- toothpicks
- stereomicroscope
- blunt metal probe
- coverslips
- petroleum jelly
- depression slides
- dilute acid solution

Suggested Procedure

1. **Using a medicine dropper, transfer a hydra to a small culture dish half filled with water.**
2. **Observe the hydra under the stereomicroscope. Sketch and label its structures.**
3. **Add a few brine shrimp to the culture dish. Use the stereomicroscope to observe how the hydra reacts to brine shrimp.**
4. **To observe the hydra under the compound microscope, prepare a "hanging drop." First, use a toothpick to dab a small amount of petroleum jelly on the corners of the upper side of a coverslip.**

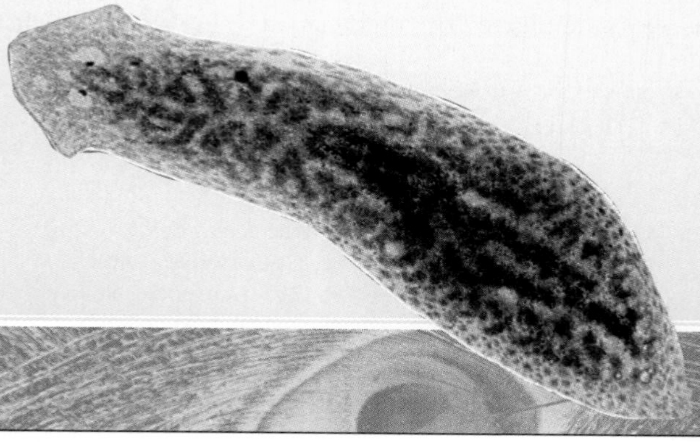

Safety Tips

- Caution students to handle the probe and other equipment carefully.
- If you use a strong acid instead of vinegar (as suggested in Before the Lab), warn students to avoid direct contact with the acid solution. If acid does splash onto their skin, have them flush the area under running water.
- Ask students to clean up any spills of water or acid solution immediately.
- Remind students to wash their hands when they have completed the procedure.

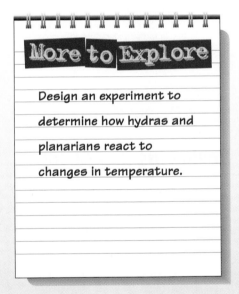

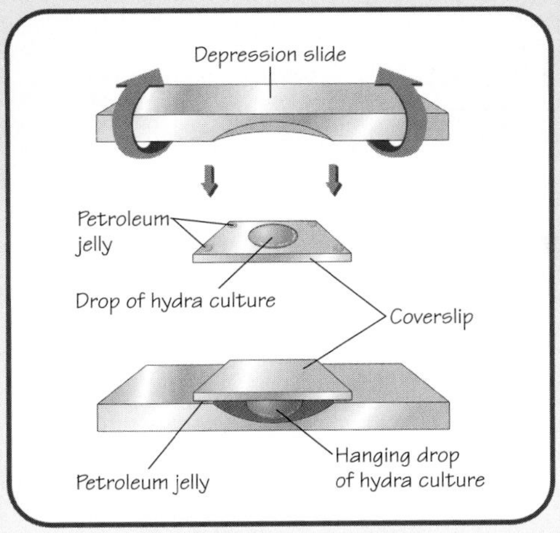

5. Use a medicine dropper to transfer the hydra to the middle of the coverslip. Hold a depression slide over the coverslip, depression side down, and lower it onto the coverslip, as shown in the illustration. Turn the slide over so the coverslip faces up.

6. Using the low-power objective of a compound microscope, observe the hydra and brine shrimp. Record your observations. When you have finished, return the hydra to your teacher.

7. Using a similar procedure, design an experiment to determine how a hydra responds to the following stimuli:
- **light touch from a toothpick**
- **dilute acid solution**

8. Using steps 1 to 3, design an experiment to determine how a planarian responds to the following stimuli:
- **light touch from a metal probe**
- **brine shrimp**

9. Write your hypotheses. With your teacher's approval, carry out the experiments you designed. Record your observations.

Observations

1. Draw and label the parts of the hydra and the planarian.
2. Describe the hydra's responses to brine shrimp, touch, and the dilute acid solution.
3. Describe the planarian's responses to touch and the brine shrimp.

Analysis and Conclusions

1. Did the hydra detect the shrimp at a distance or by physical contact?
2. What reaction did the hydra have to touch? To the dilute acid solution? Why might such reactions be useful?
3. Based on your observations, how does the planarian respond to brine shrimp? What can you infer about the structures in the planarian that are involved in this response?

More to Explore

Design an experiment to determine how hydras and planarians react to changes in temperature.

Answers to
Observations

1. Hydra drawings should resemble the photograph of a polyp of *Hydra* on page 633. Planarian drawings should resemble Figure 27–9 on page 637.
2. Brine shrimp: The hydra begins waving its tentacles around when a brine shrimp is present (if it is hungry). The tentacles sting and paralyze the shrimp and bring it to the hydra's mouth, which opens and surrounds the shrimp. Touch: The entire hydra contracts into a ball, regardless of where it is touched, though it generally responds more rapidly to stimulation of its tentacles. Acid solution: The hydra responds to the acid solution by discharging its nematocysts.
3. Touch: When the planarian is touched on or near the head, it pulls its head back or moves it in the opposite direction from the stimulus. When touched on the tail end, it pulls its tail away from the stimulus. Brine shrimp: The planarian moves its head from side to side and in a circular pattern and moves toward the brine shrimp. When it reaches the shrimp, it extends its pharynx and ingests the food.

Answers to
Analysis and Conclusions

1. The hydra should detect the shrimp at a distance.
2. See Answers to Observations 2 above.
3. The planarian moves its head around and moves toward the brine shrimp. Based on these observations, it could be inferred that the planarian has special receptor cells for detecting food concentrated in its head.

How do you think the hydra and planarian will react to being touched? (Students will probably anticipate some type of avoidance response.)

How do you think the hydra will respond to the acid solution? (Again, students will probably mention an avoidance response.)

Skills Development

Students will use these skills while completing the laboratory investigation: designing an experiment, observing, comparing, making inferences, and drawing conclusions.

Teaching Strategies

1. Help any students who have difficulty positioning the specimens properly under the microscopes and focusing the lens so they can be seen clearly. If necessary, demonstrate how to prepare a hanging-drop mount.
2. Emphasize that the planarian's and hydra's soft bodies are extremely sensitive to touch, so students need only gentle touches to elicit a response.

More to Explore

Monitor students' experimental designs to make sure that they do not cause undue stress to the animals and that they test specific, observable responses to changes in temperature. Provide materials such as flashlights, warm and cold water, and ice cubes for students to use in their experiments.

Chapter 27

Study Guide

Review Strategy

Have small groups prepare sets of cards, each with a question about a specific type of organism presented in this chapter on one side and the answer to the question on the other side. Then challenge each group to create an original board game that incorporates the cards. Let groups exchange and play one another's games.

Recalling Main Ideas

1. a
2. a
3. b
4. c
5. b
6. b
7. a
8. d
9. d

Assessment

Reviewing What You Learned

1. Sponges' cells are not organized into recognizable organs or tissues, as other animals' cells are.
2. A sponge supports its body with small, crystallike spikes called spicules or a protein called spongin.
3. Collar cells are cells with whiplike flagella that beat water through the sponge's body wall and into its central cavity.
4. Ocelli are simple eyespots that enable cnidarians to detect the presence or absence of light.
5. Budding is an asexual method of reproduction in which a piece of the organism falls off and develops into a new individual.
6. An inner cavity that has a single opening and in which digestion occurs. Hydra, jellyfishes, corals, and sea anemones all have a gastrovascular cavity.
7. *Hydra*, *Obelia*, and the Portuguese man-of-war.
8. Planarians are free-living flatworms. Flukes and tapeworms are parasitic flatworms.

Study Guide

Summarizing Key Concepts

The key concepts in each section of this chapter are listed below to help you review the chapter content. Make sure you understand each concept and its relationship to other concepts and to the theme of this chapter.

27–1 Sponges and Cnidarians

- Unlike the cells of other animals, a sponge's cells are not organized into recognizable organs or tissues.
- Sponges can reproduce sexually with sperm and egg cells. They can also reproduce asexually by making ball-shaped structures called gemmules or through a process called budding.
- Cnidarians are the corals, jellyfishes, and sea anemones. All cnidarians live underwater.
- Unlike sponges, cnidarians have layers of differentiated cells that are organized into three specialized layers of tissues.
- Cnidarians alternate between two stages—a free-living stage called a medusa and a sessile (attached) stage called a polyp. Many cnidarians also alternate between sexual and asexual reproduction.

27–2 Unsegmented Worms

- Flatworms are the simplest worms. They are also the simplest animals to show bilateral symmetry—identifiable left and right sides.
- Planarians are common free-living flatworms. Parasitic flatworms include flukes, which live in blood and other tissues, and tapeworms, which live in intestines.
- Nematodes are the simplest animals with a digestive tract similar to a human's, with a mouth at one end and an anus at the other.
- Free-living nematodes include carnivores, herbivores, and detritus feeders such as *Caenorhabditis elegans*.

27–3 Nematodes—A Help or a Hindrance?

- Like the parasitic flatworms, parasitic nematodes typically have life cycles that are quite complex, often involving more than one host. Nematodes cause trichinosis and other diseases.
- *Caenorhabditis elegans* contains few genetic instructions, allowing researchers the chance to identify and study all of them.

Reviewing Key Terms

Review the following vocabulary terms and their meaning. Then use each term in a complete sentence.

27–1 Sponges and Cnidarians

collar cell
amebocyte
spicule
spongin
gemmule
budding
endoderm
ectoderm
mesoglea
ocellus
statocyst
nematocyst
gastrovascular cavity
medusa
polyp

27–2 Unsegmented Worms

scolex
proglottid

Inquiry-Based Strategy

Ask small groups each to design an experiment involving one of the organisms they have explored in a hands-on activity in this chapter. Do not allow students to investigate any potentially harmful organisms. Let students adapt one of the chapter's investigations or design an original experiment.

Encourage each group to focus on one of the three life functions investigated in the chapter: feeding and digestion, reproduction, and response to stimuli. Provide each group with a small plastic aquarium and any other materials they will need to carry out the experiment, such as various foods or stimuli.

Check each group's experimental design to make sure students have a clear objective in mind and that organisms will not be subjected to injury or undue stress. Give each group an opportunity to share its experimental design, observations, results, and conclusions with the rest of the class.

CHAPTER 27

Recalling Main Ideas

Choose the letter of the answer that best completes the statement or answers the question.

1. Which animal group has the least in common with the other three?

a. sponges **c.** flatworms
b. cnidarians **d.** roundworms

2. Sponges produce ball-shaped structures called gemmules for

a. asexual reproduction.
b. sexual reproduction.
c. food digestion.
d. structural support.

3. In cnidarians, the endoderm, ectoderm, and mesoglea are the names of

a. reproductive cells. **c.** nerve cells.
b. tissue layers. **d.** sensory organs.

4. Cnidarians balance themselves with information from

a. ocelli. **c.** statocysts.
b. collar cells. **d.** amebocytes.

5. A typical jellyfish spends most of its life as a

a. sessile organism. **c.** solitary polyp.
b. medusa. **d.** colonial polyp.

6. Flatworms are the simplest animals to have

a. radial symmetry. **c.** a mouth and anus.
b. bilateral symmetry. **d.** a respiratory tract.

7. Which are free-living flatworms?

a. planarians **c.** tapeworms
b. flukes **d.** nematodes

8. Nematodes are parasites of

a. humans only.
b. dogs and cats only.
c. plants only.
d. many animals and plants.

9. *Ascaris lumbricoides* is an example of a

a. free-living flatworm. **c.** free-living nematode.
b. parasitic flatworm. **d.** parasitic nematode.

Putting It All Together

Using the information on pages xxx to xxxi, complete the following concept map.

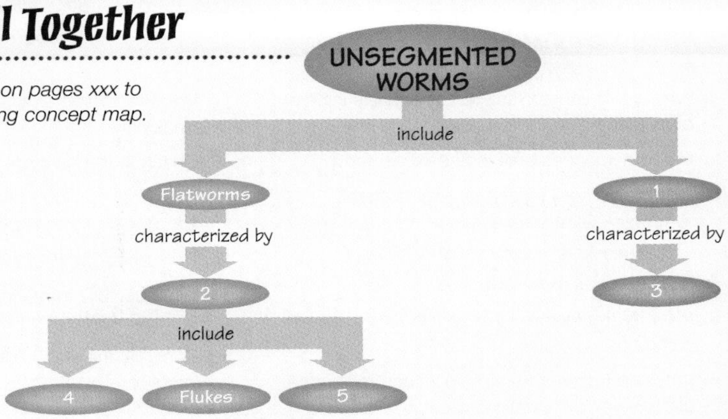

Putting It All Together

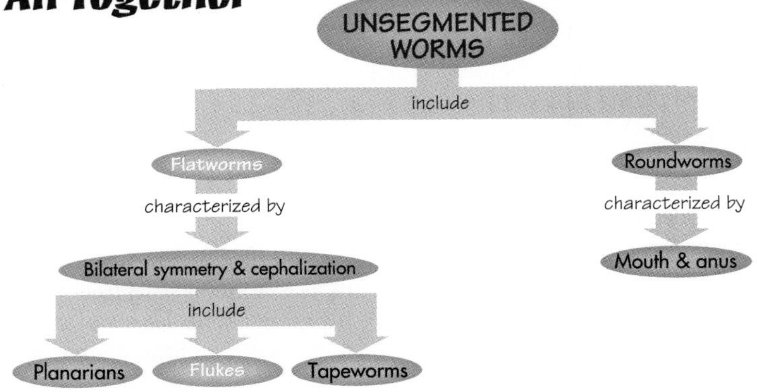

9. A tapeworm attaches itself to its host's intestines with the suckers and hooks on its scolex.
10. Proglottids are the segments of a tapeworm's body that contain male and female reproductive organs.
11. A simultaneous hermaphrodite is an organism that has functioning male and female reproductive organs at the same time.
12. A nematode's digestive tract has two openings—a mouth at one end and an anus at the other end.
13. Trichinosis is a disease caused by the parasitic nematode *Trichinella*, which affects the host's muscles and other organs.
14. Two nematode species are *Ascaris lumbricoides* and *Caenorhabditis elegans*.

Expanding the Concepts

1. Sponges lack cell walls—the tough outer boundaries that surround plant cells. Sponges are heterotrophs that must take in food to obtain energy, whereas plants are autotrophs that manufacture their own food from raw materials.
2. Sponges' collar cells move water through the body wall and into the central cavity. They snag food particles from the water moving past them, engulf the particles, and digest them. Wandering cells called amebocytes also digest and distribute food within the sponge.
3. In animals with radial symmetry, body parts are arranged in circles around a central mouth. Cnidarians (corals, jellyfishes, sea anemones, and hydrozoans) have radial symmetry. In animals with bilateral symmetry, the right and left sides of the body are identical. Flatworms (planarians, flukes, and tapeworms) and roundworms (*Trichinella*, *Ascaris lumbricoides*, and *Caenorhabditis elegans*) have bilateral symmetry.

Skills Trace
Comparing

Focus p. 631
Practice p. 635
Assess p. 646

Chapter 27

Assessment (continued)

4. Coral reefs form when hard coral colonies, with the help of the algae living inside them, lay down layers of skeleton made of calcium carbonate. Over thousands of years, this calcium carbonate and the carbonate rocks produced by the algae create the reef's foundation.

5. All flatworms have bilateral symmetry, cephalization, and no respiratory or circulatory systems.

Skills Trace
Identifying

- Focus p. 638
- Practice p. 639
- Assess p. 646

6. Tapeworms do not need digestive systems, because they absorb food that has been digested by the host's enzymes. They do not need circulatory systems, because their bodies are so thin.
7. Swimmer's itch is a short-lived rash that is produced by parasitic blood flukes before the body's defense mechanisms eliminate them.
8. Blood flukes have several stages in a life cycle that involves two separate hosts—snails and humans. Students should describe the life cycle as shown in Figure 27–11.
9. Flatworms that are simultaneous hermaphrodites carry functioning male and female reproductive organs at the same time. Usually they pair with another member of their species, and the two cross-fertilize each other.
10. In most cases, *Trichinella* infects humans when they eat undercooked pork containing cysts with the worms' larvae. The larvae travel through the bloodstream and burrow into muscles and other organs.
11. Information about *C. elegans* is useful for researchers studying how genes direct growth and development. Such studies may provide clues to help researchers determine why all animals, including humans, live to the ages they do.
12. Students should describe the life cycle of *Ascaris lumbricoides* as shown in Figure 27–13.

Assessment

Reviewing What You Learned

Answer each of the following in a complete sentence.

1. How do sponges differ from other animals?
2. How does a sponge support its body?
3. What are collar cells?
4. What are ocelli?
5. What is budding?
6. What is a gastrovascular cavity? Name two organisms that have a gastrovascular cavity.
7. Identify three different hydrozoans.
8. Which flatworms are free-living? Which are parasites?
9. How does a tapeworm attach to its host's intestines?
10. What are proglottids?
11. What is a simultaneous hermaphrodite?
12. How is a nematode's digestive tract similar to a human's?
13. What is trichinosis?
14. List the names of two nematode species.

Expanding the Concepts

Discuss each of the following in a brief paragraph.

1. Why are sponges classified as animals instead of as plants?
2. How do sponges take in and digest food?
3. **Compare** radial symmetry with bilateral symmetry. Give an example of an organism that displays each type of symmetry.
4. How do coral reefs form?
5. **Identify** the features that all flatworms have in common.
6. Why can tapeworms survive without elaborate digestive and circulatory systems?
7. What is "swimmer's itch"? How is it transmitted?
8. Describe the life cycle of a blood fluke.
9. Describe reproduction in flatworms that are simultaneous hermaphrodites.
10. How does *Trichinella* infect humans?
11. What useful information has been provided by studies of *Caenorhabditis elegans*?
12. Describe the stages of an *Ascaris lumbricoides* infection.

Extending Your Thinking

1. Students' experimental designs should involve comparing one or more tomato plants that are infected with one or more plants (the control group) that are not infected. All other variables—the amount of light and water that the plants receive, whether or not they are fertilized, and so forth—should be held constant.
2. Students should suggest asking questions about the symptoms that the patient is experiencing, how long the symptoms have been apparent, whether the patient has visited an area where sanitation is poor or has eaten suspect foods that may have contained parasitic organisms, and the like.
3. A sample hypothesis might state that the prevailing winds cause the water to carry nutrients that the corals need to grow.
4. Sample answer: In the free-swimming medusa stage, cnidarians can obtain food that otherwise might not reach them; they also can encounter other individuals of the same species for sexual reproduction. In the sessile polyp stage, cnidarians are less vulnerable to free-swimming predators; polyps that form large colonies are not dependent on chance encounters for sexual reproduction.

Extending Your Thinking

Use the skills you have developed in this chapter to answer the following.

1. **Designing an experiment** Suppose that while transplanting a tomato plant, you discover several small white worms attached to the plant's roots. Design an experiment to determine whether these worms damage tomato plants.
2. **Problem solving** A medical student suspects that a patient has contracted an intestinal disease caused by flatworms or nematodes. To make an accurate diagnosis, what questions should the medical student ask the patient?
3. **Hypothesizing** On a certain tropical island, the wind typically blows in one direction only. Offshore from the island, coral reefs grow on the side that faces the wind but not on the side away from the wind. Formulate a hypothesis to explain why coral reefs would grow in this way.
4. **Analyzing data** In its medusa stage, a cnidarian moves freely in the water. In its polyp stage, it is sessile—attached to a rock or other structure. What advantages does this two-stage life cycle provide?
5. **Constructing a model** Construct a model of a sponge, planarian, tapeworm, or other organism presented in this chapter. Label the organism's important structures.

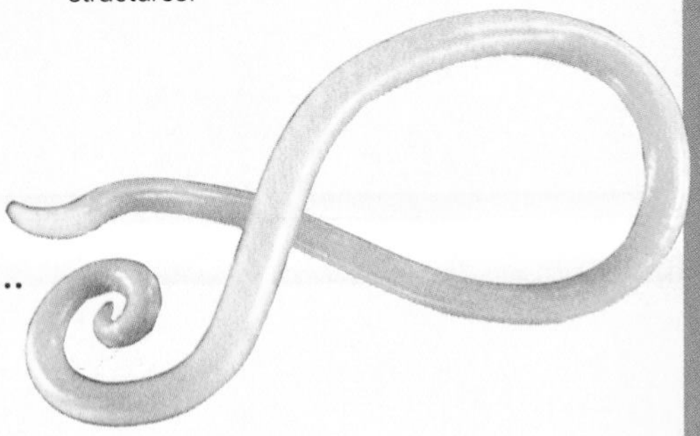

Applying Your Skills

How Are They Alike?

In this chapter, you studied a wide variety of animals. Although these animals are quite different from one another, they are similar in several basic ways.

1. Working in groups, observe a piece of coral. Record the structures you observe, then label the structures you can identify.
2. Compare the coral's anatomy with the anatomies of a hydra and a planarian. How do these organisms obtain food? How do they reproduce? Why are they classified as animals?
3. Compare corals, hydras, and planarians with other animals you have studied in this chapter, such as sponges, jellyfishes, flukes, tapeworms, and nematodes. Describe their different feeding and reproductive strategies.

• GOING FURTHER •

4. Construct a chart that presents the important information about these animals.
5. Research one of the diseases caused by unsegmented worms. Prepare a report on your findings.

Answers

2. A coral's anatomy is very similar to that of a hydra; both have tentacles arranged in circles around a central mouth on top of a tubelike body. A planarian has a long, flat body with bilateral symmetry and cephalization. Corals and hydras reproduce sexually and asexually by budding. Planarians are hermaphrodites that reproduce sexually. All of these organisms are classified as animals because they are multicellular heterotrophs.

3. Students should describe the various feeding strategies of the free-living and parasitic animals discussed in the chapter and the different reproductive strategies, including gemmules, budding, and simultaneous hermaphroditism.

Scoring Rubric

4 Response is thorough, accurate, and creative; shows an in-depth understanding of science skills, procedures, and concepts.

3 Response is complete, mostly accurate, and original; shows a satisfactory understanding of science skills, procedures, and concepts.

2 Response is mostly complete but includes some inaccuracies; shows an adequate understanding of science skills, procedures, and concepts.

1 Response is only partially complete and has many inaccuracies; shows an incomplete understanding of science skills, procedures, and concepts.

0 Response is mostly incomplete and/or inaccurate; shows a lack of understanding of science skills, procedures, and concepts.

5. Some students may include in their models only those structures shown and labeled in Figures 27–2, 27–4, 27–6, and 27–9. Other students may include additional structures they have researched in other sources. Let students use a wide variety of materials of their own choice to construct their models.

Applying Your Skills

Teacher Notes

• Provide students with various types of coral and hand lenses.

• To compile the information and construct the chart, students will need to consult various pages throughout the chapter, as well as other sources. Encourage them to evaluate the information they find, select the major points, and restate those points succinctly.

Chapter 28 Mollusks, Annelids, and Echinoderms

Content Management	Student Edition Activities
■ Section 28–1 Mollusks, pp. 649–653 Mollusk Structures Mollusk Life Cycles Classifying Mollusks	MINI LAB: Seashells by the Seashore, p. 653
■ Section 28–2 Annelids, pp. 654–656 Annelid Body Plan Classifying Annelids	Laboratory Investigation: How Earthworms Respond to Stimuli, pp. 662–663
■ Section 28–3 Echinoderms, pp. 657–659 Echinoderm Structures Classifying Echinoderms	MINI LAB: Starfish Hunt, p. 659
◆ BRANCHING OUT • In Depth Section 28–4 Adaptations of Cephalopods, pp. 660–661 The Nervous System Other Adaptations	

■ These sections cover all the necessary content and concepts for an enriched course in biology.
◆ This section covers content and concepts that are either applications or extensions of the enriched material.

Assessment Strategies

SE Chapter Review, pp. 664–667
TR Section Reviews
Chapter Test
BL Chapter Review
Practice Test
CTB Chapter 28 Test

Tech Prep

Teaching strategies appropriate for students who are in technical/vocational programs or who are considering post-secondary technical education can be found on the following **TE** pages: 654 and 660.

Meeting the Standards

Sections 28–1 through 28–4 cover one of the six content standards under **The Cell,** three of the five content standards under **Biological Evolution,** two of the six content standards under **Matter, Energy, and Organization in Living Systems,** and three of the four content standards under **The Behavior of Organisms** as described on pages 184–187 of The National Science Education Standards.

Chapter Planning Guide

Teacher's Edition Activities	Other Activities	Media and Technology
Chapter Discovery Learning Activity, p. 648 **Inquiry Activity:** Examining a Cuttlebone, p. 649 **Investigate:** Observing Snail Structures, p. 650 **Activity:** Observing Feeding Behavior, p. 650 **Investigate:** Research, p. 651	**LM** Observing the Structure of the Squid, #55 **TR** **Explore:** Galloping Gastropods **BL** **Inquiry Activity:** Slimy Snail Trails	
Inquiry Activity: Investigating Earthworm Cephalization, p. 654	**LM** Observing the Structure of the Earthworm, #56 **TR** **Apply:** Get a Grip **BL** **Inquiry Activity:** Wigglin' Worms	**TB** Visualizing an Earthworm, #36
Inquiry Activity: Examining Echinoderms, p. 657 **Inquiry Activity:** Investigating Suction, p. 658 **Investigate:** Research, p. 659	**TR** **Writing in Biology:** Composite Creatures **Explore:** Flowers of the Sea **BL** **Inquiry Activity:** Spiny-Skinned Animals	
Inquiry Activity: Modeling Jet Propulsion, p. 660	**TR** **Enrich:** Coming Out of Their Shells **BL** **Inquiry Activity:** Big-Headed Mollusks	

KEY: **SE** Student Edition **TE** Teacher's Edition **LM** Laboratory Manual **TR** Teaching Resources **BL** BioLog **TB** Transparency Box **CTB** Computer Test Bank

Materials List

TE Chapter Discovery Learning Activity, p. 648 (45 minutes for initial setup of habitats); mollusks, annelids, and echinoderms, plastic containers and/or aquariums with lids or screen covers, appropriate habitat materials and foods, field guides.

TE Inquiry Activity: Examining a Cuttlebone, p. 649 (20–30 minutes); cuttlebone, hand lens, probe, medicine dropper, weak acid solution.

TE Investigate: Observing Snail Structures, p. 650 (10–15 minutes); large aquatic snail in an aquarium.

TE Activity: Observing Feeding Behavior, p. 650 (20 minutes); several specimens of *Nassarius obsoletus* (mud snails), pan of seawater, piece of raw fish, hand lens.

SE MINI LAB: Seashells by the Seashore, p. 653 (30 minutes); variety of shells.

TE Inquiry Activity: Investigating Earthworm Cephalization, p. 654 (20–30 minutes); earthworm, lab tray; *optional*: food, probe, or other stimulus item of students' choice.

TE Inquiry Activity: Examining Echinoderms, p. 657 (30 minutes); living echinoderms (from Chapter Discovery Learning Activity), preserved echinoderm specimens, small mirror.

TE Inquiry Activity: Investigating Suction, p. 658 (15–20 minutes); small suction cup.

SE MINI LAB: Starfish Hunt, p. 659 (30 minutes); live starfish in pan of seawater or dried starfish specimen, hand lens.

TE Inquiry Activity: Modeling Jet Propulsion, p. 660 (20–30 minutes); marking pen, basin of water, small balloons, drinking straws, plastic tubing.

CHAPTER 28

Mollusks, Annelids, and Echinoderms

Introducing the Chapter

. . . In Pictures

As shown in this photograph, many starfishes are brightly colored. Have students examine the photograph, read the caption, and answer the following questions.

- **Have you ever seen a living starfish? If so, what did it look like?** (Answers will depend on students' experience. Some students may have seen a starfish in an aquarium, and others may have observed starfishes in or along the ocean.)
- **What type of symmetry does a starfish have?** (Radial symmetry. Students should recall the description of radial symmetry in Chapter 27 on page 631.)

Teaching Strategy

The first three sections of this chapter present the characteristic structures, body plans, and life cycles of mollusks, annelids, and echinoderms and describe the classes in each phylum. Specific adaptations of cephalopods are described in the BRANCHING OUT section.

BIO JOURNAL

Encourage students to focus on the starfish's visible characteristics—its color, textured skin, and flexible arms. Students may also know that starfishes cling to rocks and other objects with small suckers, or tube feet. Among other similarities and differences, students should mention that starfishes are radially symmetrical—like cnidarians—but unlike the other invertebrate animals they have studied so far in this text. Instruct students to keep their entries in their portfolios.

CHAPTER 28

Mollusks, Annelids, and Echinoderms

FOCUSING THE CHAPTER
THEME: *Unity and Diversity*

28–1 Mollusks
- **Compare** the different classes of mollusks.

28–2 Annelids
- **Identify** the main characteristics of annelids.

28–3 Echinoderms
- **Describe** the features of echinoderms.

BRANCHING OUT *In Depth*
28–4 Adaptations of Cephalopods
- **Explain** why some cephalopods grow larger than other mollusks.

LABORATORY INVESTIGATION
- **Design an experiment** to discover how earthworms respond to stimuli.

Biology and Your World

BIO JOURNAL

In your journal, describe the starfish shown on this page. How is it similar to other organisms you have studied? How is it different?

Red sunstar—a ten-armed echinoderm

TEACHER SUPPORT

Chapter Discovery Learning Activity

OBSERVING INVERTEBRATES

Have students set up containers housing various types of mollusks, annelids, and echinoderms. Provide field guides so students can research the habitat and food requirements of each organism.

Mollusks Make sure students include at least one large aquatic snail, as it will make an excellent subject for observing the structure and function of a radula.

Annelids Have students establish an earthworm culture. They could also set up an aquarium with tubiflex worms (available in pet shops) and/or leeches.

Echinoderms A marine habitat requires a delicate balance of factors that may be difficult for students to maintain in the classroom. However, if you or your students have experience with saltwater aquariums, provide echinoderm specimens as well.

GUIDE FOR READING

- **Identify** the characteristics of mollusks.
- **Describe** the different classes of mollusks.

MINI LAB

- **Classify** a collection of mollusk shells.

THEY CLIMB TREES IN TROPICAL rain forests and float over coral reefs. They crawl through garbage cans, eat their way through farm crops, and speed through the deep ocean. Some are so small that you can hardly see them with the unaided eye, while others are 20 meters long! They are the mollusks—one of the oldest and most diverse animal phyla.

Mollusks come in so many sizes, shapes, and forms that you might wonder why they are classified in the same phylum. To learn the answer, read on.

Mollusk Structures

All mollusks have similar body plans that typically include a foot, gut, mantle, and shell. They also pass through similar stages in their early development. The **foot** is a soft, muscular structure that usually contains the mouth of the mollusk. The mouth typically contains other feeding structures, such as a structure called the **radula** (RAJ-oo-luh). The mollusk's body contains its digestive tract—its **gut**—and other internal organs. The **mantle** is a thin, delicate layer of tissue that surrounds the mollusk's body, much like a cloak. Glands in the mantle secrete calcium carbonate, which forms the mollusk's **shell.** Although not all mollusks have shells, those that do not are thought to have evolved from shelled ancestors.

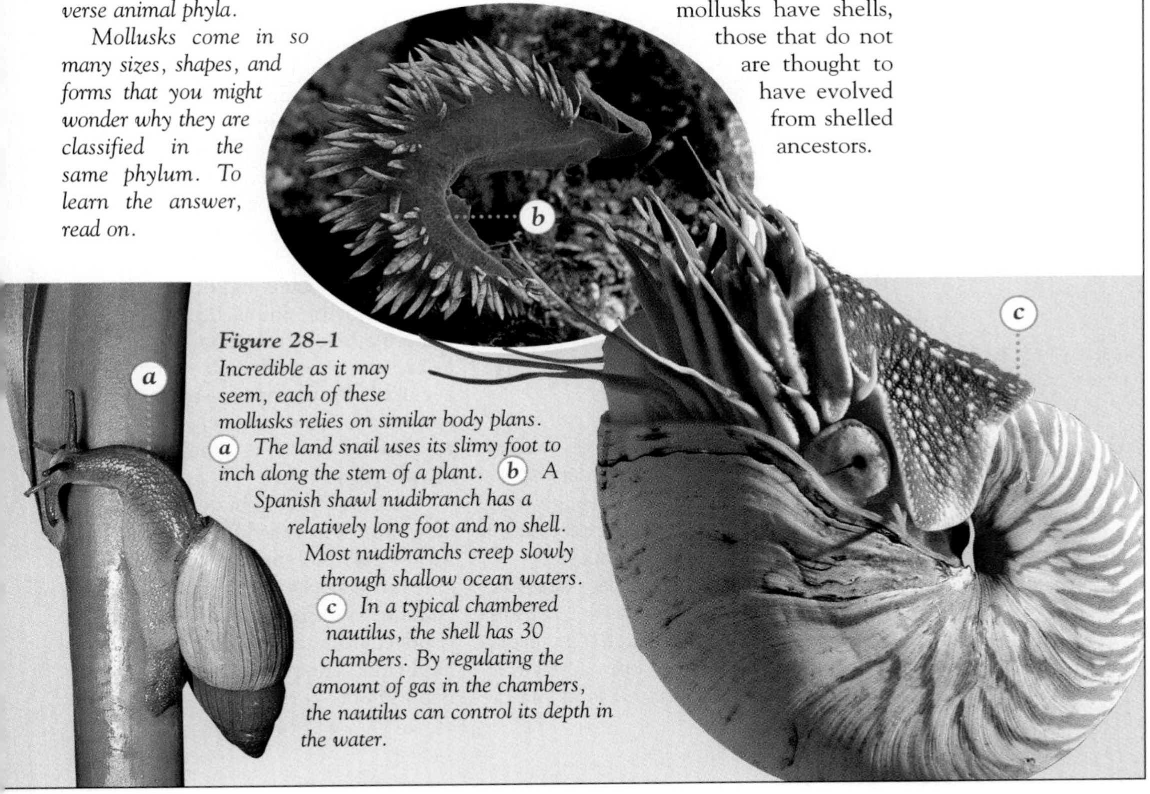

Figure 28–1 Incredible as it may seem, each of these mollusks relies on similar body plans. (a) The land snail uses its slimy foot to inch along the stem of a plant. (b) A Spanish shawl nudibranch has a relatively long foot and no shell. Most nudibranchs creep slowly through shallow ocean waters. (c) In a typical chambered nautilus, the shell has 30 chambers. By regulating the amount of gas in the chambers, the nautilus can control its depth in the water.

TEACHER SUPPORT

Background Information

Shells occur in such a variety of shapes and sizes that they serve as the main means of identifying many mollusk species. The obvious advantage of a hard exterior shell is the protection it provides for the animal's soft body.

Like the exoskeletons of arthropods, exterior shells have one major disadvantage: Because shells do not consist of living, dividing cells, mollusks outgrow them as they develop. Many mollusks, however, have evolved shell designs that allow them to build onto the shell to accommodate their increased body size. The shell is not continuously added on to but is expanded periodically as needed.

Another disadvantage of exterior shells is that they reduce mobility. Except for mollusks with greatly reduced shells—such as squids, octopuses, and cuttlefish—most mollusks, such as snails, lumber along under the load of their heavy shells or, like clams, remain fairly stationary throughout their adult lives.

SECTION 28–1
Mollusks

Performance Objectives

- Identify the structures, body systems, and life cycles typical of mollusks.
- Describe the characteristics of gastropods, bivalves, and cephalopods.

Mini Lab Skill: Classifying

1 ENGAGE

Inquiry Activity

Inferring

Examining a Cuttlebone

Give each group a cuttlebone (available in pet shops), and ask students to try to determine what the object is made of and its source. Encourage them to examine the object with a hand lens, scratch it with a probe, place a few drops of weak acid solution on it to see if it reacts (cuttlebone consists of calcium carbonate, which will fizz), and make brief notes about their observations. In a follow-up discussion, have groups share the results of their investigations and their ideas about what the object is made of and where it came from. (Students who have pet birds may know that the object is a cuttlebone, but they probably will not know its composition or source.)

2 EXPLORE

Ideas Through Images

Have students examine Figure 28–1, read the caption, and answer the following questions.

- **To which group does each of these animals belong?** (They are all mollusks.)
- **What similarities do you see among these animals?** (Soft bodies with some protective structure; all have some sort of tentacles.)

3 TEACH

Ideas Through Images

Have students examine Figure 28–2 and read the caption. Ask them to compare the features of the clam or mussel they examined in the Explore activity on page 649 with the bivalve body plan shown in the illustration. Then have students answer the following questions.

- **Where is the foot on the clam?** (It is the wide, flat structure that sometimes extends out of the shell.)
- **What is the function of the foot?** (It is used for locomotion and also contains the mouth.)
- **How does the foot vary in these mollusks?** (It varies in its location, shape, and size.)

Investigate

Observing Snail Structures Encourage students to watch a large aquatic snail as it moves along the side of an aquarium, noting the opening and closing motion of its mouth and the action of its radula. Ask students to suggest what the snail might be feeding on. (Algae growing on the aquarium's side.) Ask students to locate the snail's foot. (It is the long, muscular structure with which it moves.) Point out that the mantle is under the snail's shell and is difficult to observe.

MOLLUSK BODY PLANS

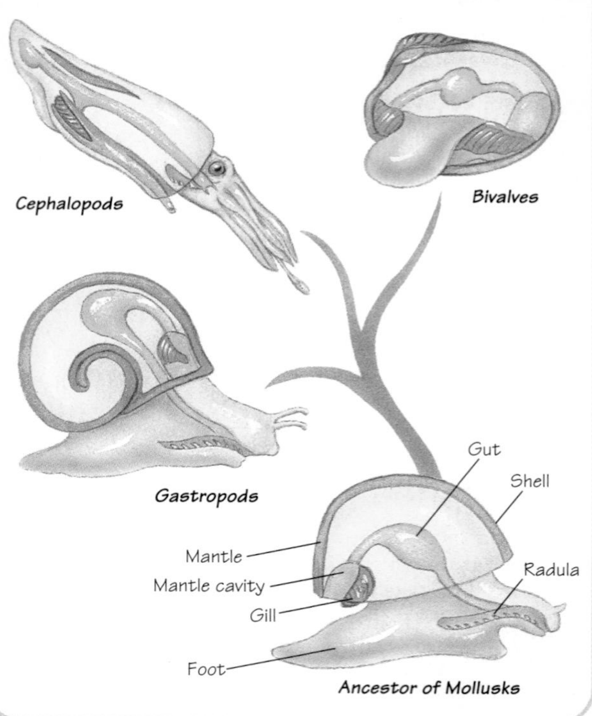

Figure 28–2
The first mollusks lived in water and were protected by a hard external shell. As they evolved, their body parts changed and adapted for different purposes, producing the diversity of mollusks that live today.

Over the past 600 million years, the members of the phylum Mollusca have evolved to live in nearly every habitat and to eat almost anything. You can think of the mollusk's basic parts as a "tool kit" that adapted for different uses by changing shape, size, and position.

☑ **Checkpoint** What is a mollusk? ❶

Feeding and Respiration

Mollusks may be carnivores, herbivores, filter feeders, detritus feeders, scavengers, or parasites. Not surprisingly, the mollusks' feeding structures are found in a wide variety of sizes and shapes.

Most aquatic mollusks breathe through gills located inside the mantle cavity, and they also exchange gases through exposed, wet skin. Terrestrial mollusks, such as slugs and land snails, usually breathe through a specially adapted mantle cavity. This mantle is well supplied with blood vessels and is folded to increase its surface area.

The mantle of terrestrial mollusks regularly loses moisture to dry air, so it must be kept moist. That's one reason why most terrestrial mollusks prefer to move around at night, during rainstorms, and in places where the air is moist.

Internal Transport and Excretion

Internal transport in mollusks is managed by a circulatory system with a simple heart. In sessile and slow-moving mollusks, blood is pumped from the heart through open spaces called sinuses. The blood then enters vessels that pass through gills and, eventually, return to the heart. This type of circulatory system is called an **open circulatory system.** While this system is not especially efficient, it suffices for "stick-in-the-mud" mollusks like clams and oysters.

Fast-moving animals, however, need a more efficient transport system. Mollusks such as squids and octopuses use a **closed circulatory system,** which is more like our own. In a closed circulatory system, blood is pumped through blood vessels only.

Like many invertebrates, mollusks excrete wastes in two different ways. Solid wastes pass out through the end of the gut, known as the anus. Nitrogen-containing wastes, such as ammonia, are removed from the blood by organs called **nephridia** (nee-FRIHD-ee-uh; singular: nephridium).

TEACHER SUPPORT

Activity

Observing Feeding Behavior Provide groups with the small marine gastropod *Nassarius obsoletus,* or mud snails.

1. Place the snails in a pan of seawater.
2. Drop a piece of raw fish into the water, and observe the snails' response. (The snails will turn and head directly toward the fish.)
3. Examine a snail with a hand lens as it moves toward the food, noting its structures and behavior. (The snail's siphon pulls water over its gills and osphradium, a chemically sensitive structure that can detect odors in water. By moving its siphon, the snail can determine the food's location and adjust its path.)
4. Continue to observe the snail as it feeds, noting its structures and behavior. (When the snail reaches the food, it extends its long proboscis, which has a mouth at the tip.)

Response

Mollusks have almost as many different kinds of nervous systems as they have habitats. Clams and their close relatives have a few ganglia and nerve cords, as well as scattered sensory organs used for balance, touch, taste, and detection of light. Other mollusks evolved more advanced nervous systems. Octopuses and their kin have well-developed brains, excellent vision, and sophisticated senses of touch and taste.

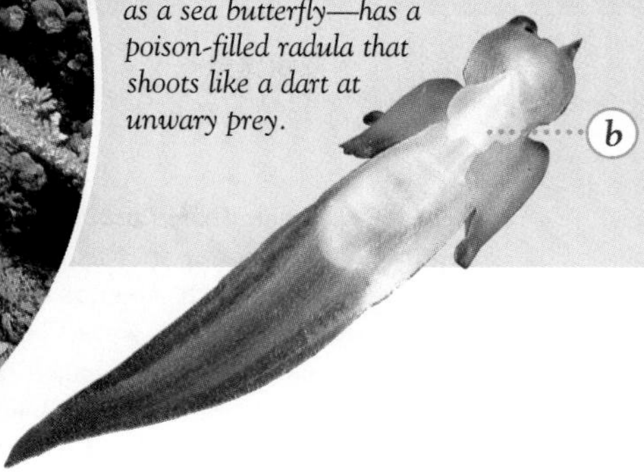

Figure 28–3
(a) Like other bivalves, this giant clam filters small food particles from the water. (b) A pteropod—also known as a sea butterfly—has a poison-filled radula that shoots like a dart at unwary prey.

Mollusk Life Cycles

Most mollusks have straightforward life cycles that involve separate males and females. In almost all species, the fertilized egg develops into a type of free-swimming larva called a **trochophore** (TRAHK-oh-for). Eventually, this free-swimming larva transforms into a miniature adult, which in some species settles down and becomes sessile and in other species continues swimming.

Many aquatic mollusks release sperm and egg cells into the open water, where external fertilization occurs more or less by chance. Other species, such as octopuses and squids, reproduce with internal fertilization, in which the male uses a tentacle to deliver sperm to the female.

Quite a number of mollusks are hermaphrodites—animals that have both male and female reproductive organs. Certain hermaphroditic snails often pair together and fertilize each other's eggs. Sometimes they line up in long chains, each fertilizing the individual in front while being fertilized by the one behind.

☑ Checkpoint What is a trochophore? 2

Classifying Mollusks

As you can see, there is more to mollusks than meets the eye! Let's take a closer look at the different classes in this fascinating phylum of animals.

Gastropods

The members of the class Gastropoda (gas-TRAHP-oh-duh) include the familiar snails and slugs found across North America and elsewhere. The gastropods also include such exotic and brilliantly colored species as abalones, nudibranchs, and sea hares.

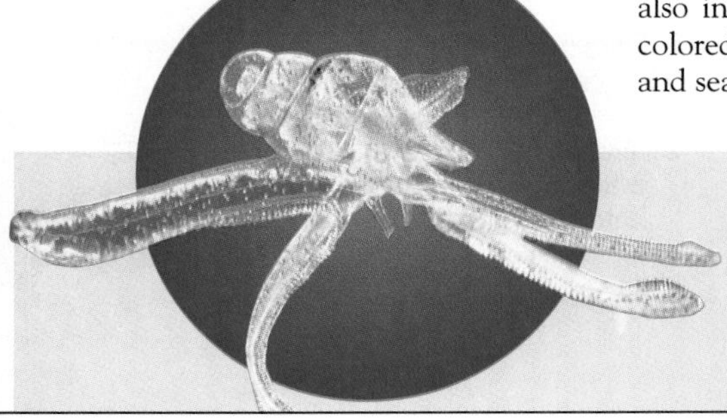

Figure 28–4
This photograph shows a marine snail in an advanced larval stage. The snail's transparent shell reveals its stomach, liver, heart, and other internal organs.

Discussion

After students read about the trochophore stage of mollusks, ask them to suggest the advantages to a species that has a relatively stationary adult stage of having free-swimming larvae. (The young can move to new areas where competition for food and other resources may be less acute and predators less prevalent.)

Investigate

Research Have students use a dictionary to find the literal meanings of the terms gastropod (stomach-footed) and cephalopod (head-footed). Ask students to explain why each term is an appropriate name for that class of mollusks. Also point out, if necessary, that the prefix *bi-* in bivalve means two.

Discussion

After students have read the statement on text page 653 that some gastropods have only small internal shells, remind them of the object they investigated in the Inquiry Activity on page 649. Tell them that the object was a cuttlebone, and explain that cuttlebone is the internal shell of a type of mollusk called a cuttlefish, which is shown in Figure 28–10 on page 660.

☑ Checkpoints

1 An invertebrate animal whose body plan typically includes a foot, gut, mantle, and shell.

2 The free-swimming larva of a mollusk.

TEACHER SUPPORT

Managing Classroom Diversity

MULTICULTURAL STRATEGY
All sorts of mollusks have long been diet staples and delicacies in many cultures worldwide. Ask students to research recipes for preparing various types of mollusks and each recipe's country or culture of origin. Encourage students to include dishes that may be part of their own families' traditional culture. Also suggest that they check local stores to see what types of fresh and canned mollusks are available.

Give students an opportunity to describe the recipes they have found. If possible, let each student or group prepare one dish to share with the rest of the class. **CAUTION:** *Make sure the recipes do not include raw clams, mussels, or other bivalves that could be contaminated with red tide toxins.* If preparing the recipes in class is not feasible, suggest that students bring in samples of dishes that were prepared at home.

Ancillary Support

The resources below can be used to support your teaching strategy for these two pages.

LM Observing the Structure of the Squid #55
TR Explore: Galloping Gastropods
BL Inquiry Activity: Slimy Snail Trails

Problem Solving

Interpreting Graphs

The Invasion of the Zebra Mussels

Students will use their ability to interpret graphs to draw some conclusions about the effectiveness of ducks in controlling the population of the zebra mussel.

State The problem is to determine whether ducks could significantly reduce the zebra mussel population in Lake Erie.

Solve The best way for students to solve the problem is to answer the Think About It questions in the order given.

Test Students could use the information in the article: D.J. Hamilton, C.D. Ankney, and R.C. Bailey, "Predation of zebra mussels by diving ducks: an exclosure study," *Ecology*, 75(2), 1994, pp. 521–531 to evaluate their answers.

Communicate Have students share their answers to the questions.

Answers to THINK ABOUT IT

1. The bottom graph shows the differences in biomass between the mussels on cage-covered rocks and those on uncovered rocks. The top graph shows that the mussel biomass lost on the uncovered rocks correlates well with the biomass of mussel shells found in the ducks.

2. To prevent ducks from eating the zebra mussels to establish a control for the experiment.

3. The correlation between the lost zebra mussel biomass and the biomass of ingested shells indicates that the ducks do eat a significant quantity of zebra mussels. Students may reasonably conclude that the ducks will control the zebra mussel population. However, no data are provided about the proportion of zebra mussels eaten to the entire zebra mussel population, so students cannot tell whether the reduction in zebra mussel biomass is significant.

Problem Solving

INTERPRETING GRAPHS

The Invasion of the Zebra Mussels

In 1986, a ship from Europe emptied its ballast water in the Great Lakes region of North America. Unfortunately, the ballast water contained a type of mollusk called a zebra mussel. Zebra mussels have been a nuisance in the Great Lakes ever since!

Zebra mussels attach to almost anything underwater, then reproduce in great numbers. In the Great Lakes, dense mats of zebra mussel shells are clogging water intake pipes and other structures. The zebra mussels also consume huge quantities of plankton, a food source for many other marine organisms.

Biologists hope that ducks that live on the Great Lakes will start eating more zebra mussels. In one experiment that took place in Lake Erie, researchers monitored several rocks on which zebra mussels were growing. On half the rocks, they placed cages that ducks could not penetrate. After a few weeks, they captured several ducks and measured the mass of zebra mussel shells inside them. The results are shown in the graphs.

RESULTS OF ZEBRA MUSSEL EXPERIMENT

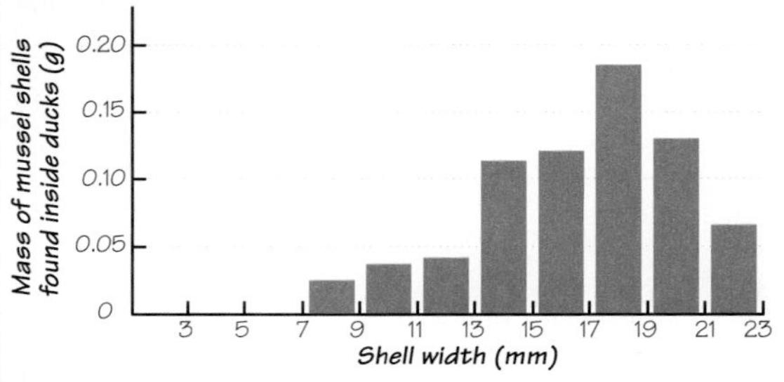

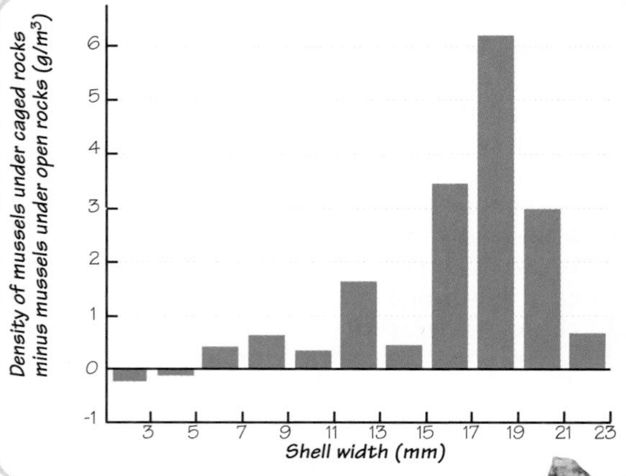

THINK ABOUT IT

1. **Interpret** the data presented in the graphs.
2. **Explain** why the researchers placed cages on half the rocks they monitored.
3. From the information presented, what can you **conclude** about the ducks' ability to control the zebra mussel population of Lake Erie?

TEACHER SUPPORT

Facts and Figures

Giant Mollusks

- The largest bivalve is the giant clam (*Tridacna*) found on coral reefs in the East Indies and Australia. The shells can be more than 1.2 meters across and have a mass of 230 kilograms.
- The largest octopus is the common Pacific octopus (*Octopus hongkongensis*), which can measure up to 9.7 meters from the tip of one tentacle to the tip of the opposite one.
- The largest squid is the giant squid (*Architeuthis*), which can have a body 4 meters long with tentacles over 9 meters long.

Most gastropods have a one-piece shell into which they can withdraw for defense. Others have only small internal shells, while still others have lost their shells altogether. Many shell-less species protect themselves by producing powerful poisons or by having a bad taste to predators.

Bivalves

You may have dined on members of the class Bivalvia, which include clams, oysters, mussels, and scallops. Most bivalves live in shallow waters near the shore. They typically are filter feeders, which means they feed by filtering organisms from huge volumes of water.

Bivalves have two shells that are hinged at the back and held together by strong muscles. The mantle of the bivalve secretes the shell that encloses the organism, as well as a substance called nacre (NAY-ker), which provides the shell with a smooth, shiny inner coating.

Nacre also produces a highly valued product of oysters and other bivalves. Because a bivalve opens its valves so often, it sometimes takes in a pebble or a sand grain. The mantle responds by coating such objects with nacre, which over many years creates a pearl. For this reason, nacre is also called mother-of-pearl.

☑ *Checkpoint* What is a bivalve? ❶

Cephalopods

The members of the class Cephalopoda (sehf-uh-LAHP-oh-duh) are the largest, most active, and most intelligent mollusks. **Most living cephalopods have shells that are either small, internal, or missing altogether.** The only living cephalopod with a large external shell is the chambered nautilus, shown in *Figure 28–1* on page 649. The chambered nautilus resembles the cephalopods from the beginning of the Cambrian Period, more than 500 million years ago.

Most cephalopods have long tentacles armed with sucker disks. These tentacles can grab and handle prey ranging from other mollusks to crabs, shrimps, and fishes.

MINI LAB — Classifying

Seashells by the Seashore

PROBLEM *How can you **classify** different mollusks?*

PROCEDURE

1. Obtain a sample of mollusk shells from your teacher. Study the outer and inner surfaces of the shells.
2. Group the shells according to their similarities.

ANALYZE AND CONCLUDE

1. Compare the outer and inner surfaces of the shells.
2. Explain how you classified the shells into groups. Discuss any alternative classification scheme you considered.
3. From studying these shells, what can you infer about the organisms that produced them?

Section Review 28–1

1. **Identify** the main characteristics of mollusks.
2. **Describe** the different classes of mollusks.
3. **Critical Thinking—Analyzing** Why can bivalves live without an elaborate brain and nervous system, such as those found in cephalopods?
4. **MINI LAB** How can you **classify** mollusk shells?

MINI LAB Classifying

Teacher Note

• For time required and materials needed, see page 648b.

Answers to Analyze and Conclude

1. Answers will depend on the particular shells used. The outer surfaces may be rough or smooth, solid-colored or multicolored. Generally the inner surfaces are smooth and pearly.
2. The initial grouping characteristic should be the number of pieces (valves) in each shell. For subsequent divisions, students may use shape, color, texture, and other properties.
3. The animals have a soft body.

Skills Trace
Classifying
- Focus p. 653
- Practice p. 653
- Assess p. 667

4 ASSESS

Quick Check

Have students describe each major mollusk structure and compare them between the different mollusk classes.

☑ Checkpoint

❶ A bivalve is a mollusk with two shells that are hinged at the back

Section Review 28–1

1. See pages 649–651.

2. See pages 651 to 653.

3. Bivalves are sessile filter feeders as adults, so they do not need the elaborate brain and nervous system found in cephalopods.

4. By the number of shells and other physical characteristics.

Skills Trace
Classifying
- Focus p. 653
- Practice p. 653
- Assess p. 667

Learning Modality

Visual and Tactile Learning Let students use clay to make three-dimensional models of the gastropod and bivalve body plans shown in Figure 28–2 on page 650.

SECTION 28-2

Annelids

Performance Objectives

- Describe annelids' specialized structures.
- Identify the characteristics of oligochaetes, polychaetes, and leeches.

Laboratory Investigation Skill: Designing an experiment

1 ENGAGE

Ideas Through Images

Have students examine Figure 28–5, read the caption, and answer the following questions.

- **To which group of animals do these three organisms belong?** (They are all annelids, or members of the phylum Annelida.)
- **What do you think is the major difference between setae and legs, such as those of a centipede or millipede?** (Based on the caption's description of setae as spikelike, students can infer that setae are not jointed and cannot move independently, as legs can.)

2 EXPLORE

Inquiry Activity

Designing an Experiment

Investigating Earthworm Cephalization

Ask students if they think an earthworm has a head end. Challenge groups to design an experiment to determine the answer. Students could simply observe an earthworm's natural movement (always head-end first) or could stimulate responses by providing food or touching the worm. Review the groups' designs, and then have them carry out their experiments, using earthworms from the class culture. Have groups compare results and describe which end of the earthworm is the head.

SECTION 28–2 Annelids

GUIDE FOR READING

- **Describe** the annelids.
- **Identify** the three classes of annelids.

YOU PROBABLY ARE FAMILIAR with one annelid—the common earthworm. But annelids include a huge number of species, including those pictured on this page.

Annelids live in many different habitats—including oceans, fresh water, and land. Some are less than a millimeter long, while others grow to 3 meters. Some are herbivores, others are harmless filter feeders, while still others are fearsome predators—at least for their size!

Annelid Body Plan

Segmented worms are members of the phylum Annelida. **All annelids have bodies that are divided into individual segments.** The segments are filled with fluid and are tightly sealed by body walls called **septa.**

Because of its fluid-filled segments and muscle organization, an annelid moves in an interesting way. Running up and down the annelid are **longitudinal muscles.** When these muscles contract, they shorten the segments. Surrounding these longitudinal muscles are ring-shaped **circular muscles.** When these muscles contract, they lengthen the segments. By coordinating these two sets of muscles, the annelid can move—albeit slowly—in almost any direction.

One common annelid is the earthworm. To learn more about earthworms, study the illustration on the next page.

Classifying Annelids

The annelids are very numerous and live in all sorts of habitats on Earth. **Annelids are divided into these three classes: the Oligochaeta, the Polychaeta, and the Hirudinea.**

(b)

(a)

(c)

Figure 28–5 Different annelids evolved different uses for their setae, or bristles. (a) This bristleworm uses its setae to swim, as well as to sting potential predators. (b) In plume worms, the setae are adapted for filtering food from the water surrounding them. This plume worm lives in the ocean off the coast of Florida. (c) Sandworms use spikelike setae to move through desert sands.

TEACHER SUPPORT

Managing Classroom Diversity

TECH PREP STUDENTS

Encourage students who would like to manage their own agriculture-related business to find out about commercial earthworm farming. Another aspect of earthworm farming that students could investigate is raising a particular species called Red Wigglers, which have been specifically bred for composting purposes. Red Wigglers will eat small scraps and peelings from almost all fruits and vegetables, as well as coffee grounds, tea bags, eggshells (crushed), corn on the cob (but not the cob itself), and even, in time, banana peels. They do not seem to care for potatoes, perhaps because of the high starch content, and also will not eat seeds.

Visualizing an Earthworm

Most segments of an earthworm are nearly identical—both on the inside and on the outside. A few segments, however, contain specialized structures for such functions as digestion, circulation, and control of the nervous system.

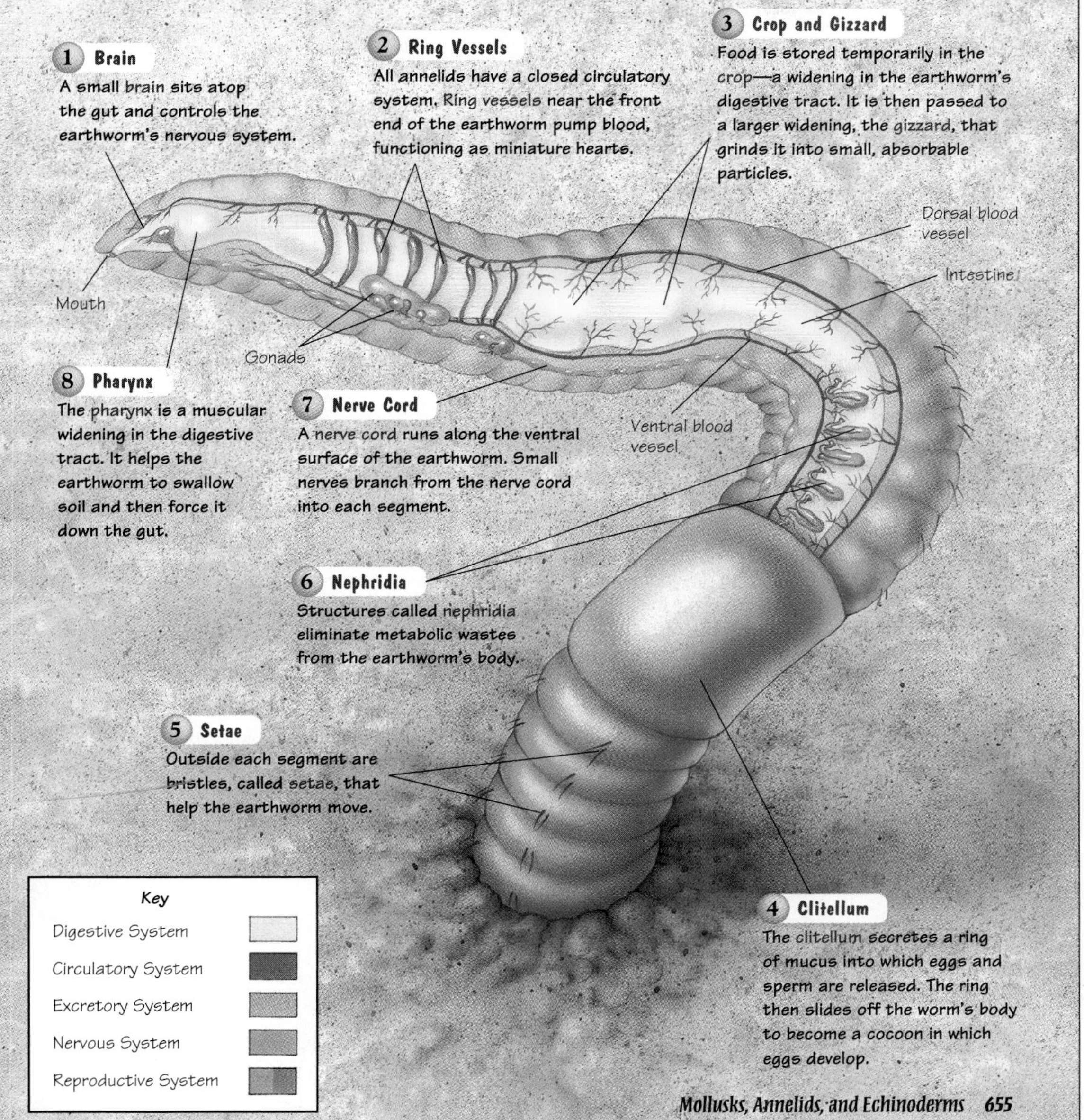

1 Brain
A small brain sits atop the gut and controls the earthworm's nervous system.
2 Ring Vessels
All annelids have a closed circulatory system. Ring vessels near the front end of the earthworm pump blood, functioning as miniature hearts.
3 Crop and Gizzard
Food is stored temporarily in the crop—a widening in the earthworm's digestive tract. It is then passed to a larger widening, the gizzard, that grinds it into small, absorbable particles.
Dorsal blood vessel
Intestine
Mouth
Gonads
8 Pharynx
The pharynx is a muscular widening in the digestive tract. It helps the earthworm to swallow soil and then force it down the gut.
7 Nerve Cord
A nerve cord runs along the ventral surface of the earthworm. Small nerves branch from the nerve cord into each segment.
Ventral blood vessel
6 Nephridia
Structures called nephridia eliminate metabolic wastes from the earthworm's body.
5 Setae
Outside each segment are bristles, called setae, that help the earthworm move.
4 Clitellum
The clitellum secretes a ring of mucus into which eggs and sperm are released. The ring then slides off the worm's body to become a cocoon in which eggs develop.
Key
Digestive System
Circulatory System
Excretory System
Nervous System
Reproductive System

3 TEACH

Visualizing an Earthworm

Have students examine the drawing of the earthworm and read about the different structures described. Then have students answer the following questions.

- **How can you group the structures described here under the body systems listed in the key?** (Digestive system: crop and gizzard, pharynx; circulatory system: ring vessels, blood vessels; excretory system: nephridia; nervous system: brain, nerve cord; reproductive system: clitellum.)
- **How does the earthworm display cephalization?** (It has a small brain that controls the nervous system and is located in the head.)

A typical earthworm has 100 to 180 segments. Regardless of the total number of segments, specific organs are always located in particular segments. By counting the segments, students can locate these organs.

Segment 1: Mouth.
Segment 3: Brain.
Segments 7–9: Hearts (five pairs).
Segments 17 and 18: Gizzard.
Segment 19 through end: Intestine.
Segments 31–37 (clitellum): Reproductive organs.

TEACHER SUPPORT

Historical Perspective

For centuries, the medicinal leech *Hirudo medicinalis* was used for bloodletting—a treatment thought to cure a wide range of illnesses. Shortly after the Civil War, more than 1.5 million leeches per year were used in the United States alone.

When in contact with a host, the leech attaches itself and then draws out blood by a pumping action. At the same time, the leech's salivary glands secrete hirudin, a substance that dilates the host's blood vessels, prevents blood from clotting, and acts as an anesthetic. A leech may eat up to five times its own body mass in blood before it drops off and may not need to feed again for 30 weeks.

Once common throughout Europe, the leech is now scarce due to overcollecting and habitat destruction. However, it is still in demand for hirudin, which is used as an anticoagulant for some heart patients and in some surgical procedures.

Ancillary Support

The resources below can be used to support your teaching strategy for these two pages.

LM Observing the Structure of the Earthworm, #56
TR Apply: Get a Grip
BL Inquiry Activity: Wigglin' Worms
TB Visualizing an Earthworm, #36

Laboratory Investigation

The Laboratory Investigation, How Earthworms Respond to Stimuli, on pages 662–663 is appropriate to use at this point in the chapter.

Discussion

Ask students whether they have ever seen the motion picture *The African Queen* and, if so, to describe the scene in which Humphrey Bogart's character emerges from murky water to find that he is covered with leeches. If students are not familiar with this movie, obtain it on videocassette and play the scene for them. Ask them to describe the character's—and their own—reaction to the leeches. Also ask them to explain why rubbing leeches with salt (as Katharine Hepburn's character does in the movie) might make them drop off. Suggest that they find out whether this measure is actually effective or whether other methods are recommended.

4 ASSESS

Quick Check

Have each student write a brief description of how an annelid uses its muscles and setae to move.

Section Review 28–2

1. All annelids have bodies that are divided into individual segments and filled with fluid, against which muscles work to cause movement.
2. Oligochaetes, polychaetes, leeches.
3. Students may mention tapeworms (although tapeworm segments are strictly reproductive in function and are not true body segments), as well as insects, crayfish, and other arthropods. Some students may say that the human body is not segmented, while others may contend that the head, trunk, upper limbs, and lower limbs are different "segments" of the human body.

Figure 28–6
(a) Earthworms are hermaphrodites. These two earthworms are exchanging sperm, which eventually will be used to fertilize egg cells. (b) Leeches produce a chemical that prevents blood from clotting. This helps them to tap the blood supply of their hosts. (c) CAREER TRACK *These researchers at the U.S. Department of Agriculture are studying earthworms.*

Oligochaetes

The name Oligochaeta (ahl-ih-goh-KEE-tuh) means "few bristles," and an oligochaete—such as an earthworm—has a few short bristles on its body. These bristles, called setae, are arranged in rows along the worm's underside. As the earthworm moves, these bristles dig into the soil, providing traction.

Although oligochaetes may not be beautiful or attention grabbing, some are ecologically important. As the English naturalist Charles Darwin noted, earthworms swallow and grind up incredible amounts of soil and organic matter. This action aerates soil and recycles many nutrients, including nitrogen.

☑ **Checkpoint** How do earthworms use their bristles? (1)

Polychaetes

The class Polychaeta (pahl-ih-KEE-tuh) includes the worms shown in ***Figure 28–5*** on page 654. These worms swarm throughout the world's oceans—from the polar regions to the tropics.

The name Polychaeta means "many bristles." Typically, each body segment of a polychaete includes a pair of paddlelike structures tipped with bristles. These structures are short and barely visible in some polychaetes but are long and brightly colored in others.

Leeches

The class Hirudinea (hir-yoo-DIHN-ee-uh) contains the leeches, a group of familiar but not-so-popular animals. Many leeches are blood-drinking parasites of aquatic animals, and some will feed on humans if given the chance. Most leech species live in the tropics, including leeches so large and powerful they can penetrate human skin. In temperate climates, leeches that usually feed on fishes or other aquatic animals will sometimes attach themselves to swimmers.

Section Review 28–2

1. **Describe** the body plan of annelids.
2. **Identify** the three classes of annelids.
3. **Critical Thinking—Comparing** Besides the annelids, what other animals show segmentation? Do humans show segmentation of any kind?

Learning Modality

Auditory Learning Ask a volunteer to tape-record the labels in the earthworm illustration on page 655, and let other students use the tape as they study the figure.

Echinoderms

GUIDE FOR READING

- **Describe** the characteristics of echinoderms.

MINI LAB

- **Observe** the structures of a starfish.

SOME OF THE ECHINODERMS are delicate, brightly colored, feathery armed creatures. Others look like mud-brown half-rotten cucumbers! Echinoderms live only in the sea, where they seldom affect humans. But their body plans and life history combine some unique features found in no other animals—living or extinct. For this reason alone, echinoderms are well worth studying.

Echinoderm Structures

Each of the animals shown in ***Figure 28–7*** is a member of the phylum Echinodermata (ee-kigh-noh-DER-muh-tuh), meaning "spiny skin." **Echinoderms have radial symmetry, an internal skeleton, spiny skin, and a network of tubes and appendages known as a water vascular system.**

Echinoderms are radially symmetric, meaning their bodies include units repeated around a central axis. Their internal skeleton, called an endoskeleton, is made of stiff plates of calcium carbonate that may be hinged to one another or fused together into a solid casing.

However, the most unusual feature of echinoderms is their **water vascular system.** Physically, the water vascular system contains a network of fluid-filled canals connected to countless **tube feet,** each of which looks like a medicine dropper attached to a suction cup. In many species, the water vascular system is tied to all sorts of life functions, including feeding, movement, internal transport, respiration, and excretion.

Figure 28–7
Echinoderms include the unusual organisms shown here. (a) Sphere-shaped sea urchins are protected by sharp spikes, which in many species contain poison. This photograph shows small white sea urchins surrounding a larger sea urchin. (b) Some sea cucumbers look like warty pickles. What do you think this specimen looks like? (c) This starfish is attacking a bivalve. After it pries open the shell, it will extend its stomach and secrete digestive enzymes into the bivalve's body.

SECTION 28–3
Echinoderms

Performance Objective
- Describe the structures, body systems, and life cycles typical of echinoderms.

Mini Lab Skill: Observing

1 ENGAGE

Inquiry Activity
Comparing

Examining Echinoderms
Ask students how they can tell whether an animal is an echinoderm. Draw students' attention to the living echinoderms in the marine habitat they created in the Chapter Discovery Learning Activity on page 648, or provide preserved specimens for them to examine. Have students compare the specimens with one another and with the photographs in Figure 28–7. Ask students to identify the similarities among all the animals. (All have radial symmetry and spines of some type.) Also ask how they could test each animal to verify that it does have radial symmetry. (By holding a mirror upright on its top surface, with the mirror's center aligned with the animal's central point, and then rotating the mirror and observing the reflections.) Let students try this with several different specimens.

Checkpoint
1 To provide traction as they move.

TEACHER SUPPORT — Background Information

The symmetry of an adult starfish is called secondary radial symmetry because it develops secondarily from a bilaterally symmetrical larva. The earliest known fossil echinoderms also were not radially symmetrical, but neither were they bilaterally symmetrical. Rather, they possessed odd, asymmetrical shapes.

Bilateral symmetry seems to best suit the needs of active animals, and radial symmetry the needs of sessile or sedentary animals. For this reason, many biologists consider it likely that ancestral echinoderms were bilateral animals that became radial as they adopted a more sedentary, filter-feeding way of life. Modern free-living echinoderms, such as starfishes, evolved from these sedentary ancestors, whose adult radial symmetry they still retain.

Ancillary Support
The resource below can be used to support your teaching strategy for these two pages.

BL Inquiry Activity: Spiny-Skinned Animals

2 EXPLORE

Inquiry Activity

Hypothesizing

Investigating Suction

Give each group a small suction cup, and challenge students to make it adhere to a vertical surface for at least one minute. (Through trial and error, students will discover that the surface must be smooth and that the cup will stay in place longer if it is first moistened.) Ask groups to share their findings.

3 TEACH

MINI LAB Observing

Teacher Note

• For time required and materials needed, see page 648b.

Answers to Analyze and Conclude

1. The top of the starfish is covered with spiny skin, while the bottom has rows of tube feet and a mouth in the central disc. It attacks and eats its prey with the bottom, or oral, side.

2. The tube feet are thin, hollow, flexible, and have a small suckerlike structure on the ends. They grasp objects, and are used for movement.

3. They have no respiratory system for breathing air. Nor do they have an excretory system.

Skills Trace
Observing

- Focus p. 659
- Practice p. 659
- Assess p. 667

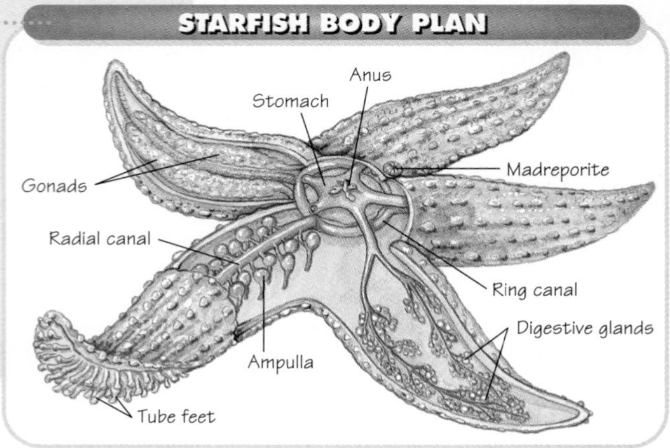

Figure 28–8 (a) *Starfishes are able to regenerate lost arms. This starfish seems to be growing several arms at once!* (b) *A starfish's skin is lined with spines. Inside its body, the water vascular system consists of radial canals down each arm, joined by a central ring canal. The system opens to the outside through a hole called a madreporite.*

Like cnidarians, echinoderms have no front or back end, no head, and no brain. They do have top and bottom sides, however. The bottom side is called the oral surface because it contains the mouth, whereas the top side is called the aboral surface.

Checkpoint What is an echinoderm? 1

Feeding, Respiration, and Elimination

Starfishes are predators of clams, oysters, and other bivalves. Other echinoderms are filter feeders, using individual tube feet to snag passing plankton. And still others use tube feet to pick up a mixture of sand and detritus, which they then shove into their mouth. Once the food is inside, digestive glands distributed throughout the body process it further.

Thanks to their water vascular system, many echinoderms have an enormous surface area exposed to the surrounding water. As a result, the echinoderm's cells can exchange gases directly with the water, as well as eliminate wastes into it. Because the water vascular system so efficiently handles these tasks, echinoderms do not need specialized respiratory, elimination, or circulatory systems. However, some species have feathery tufts called skin gills that aid in gas exchange.

Response, Movement, and Reproduction

Like cnidarians, echinoderms lack any structure that even resembles a brain. However, echinoderms do have a few specialized nerve cells. Sensory cells provide an adequate sense of taste and smell. Some species have eyespots that can distinguish light from dark, although they cannot detect objects. And some

Figure 28–9 (a) *Disk-shaped sand dollars often settle on the ocean floor.* (b) *Crinoids use their feathery arms to filter plankton from the passing water.*

TEACHER SUPPORT Background Information

Echinoderms that spawn are faced with a problem: Eggs and sperm, being single cells, cannot survive long in seawater. Thus, if only one individual spawns, its eggs or sperm will die before fertilization can occur. Echinoderms have evolved a variety of mechanisms to synchronize their reproductive activities. One such mechanism—detecting eggs and sperm released by another member of the same species and spawning in response—is described in the student text. For this mechanism to be effective, however, all individuals must be full of mature eggs and sperm and therefore ready to spawn at any time.

Many starfish species possess an internal calendar that controls the timing of their egg and sperm production. Experiments have shown that these animals "set their calendar" by detecting seasonal changes in daylength. In fact, they can be induced to produce eggs and sperm at any time simply by placing them on an appropriate schedule of daylengths.

echinoderms have **statocysts,** specialized structures that tell which way is up.

An echinoderm moves with its tube feet. However, an echinoderm has thousands of these appendages, yet only a simple nervous system. How it coordinates its movement remains a mystery!

Most echinoderms have separate sexes that release eggs and sperm into the water. This is less of a hit-or-miss process than it might seem, however, because an echinoderm can detect the egg and sperm cells of its species in the water and then releases its own reproductive cells in response. Once fertilized, echinoderm larvae swim in the open water before changing to the adult form.

Classifying Echinoderms

Starfishes are members of the class Asteroidea. Although the most familiar starfishes have five arms, other species grow many more. Most starfishes are carnivores that feed on bivalve mollusks, corals, and other sedentary prey.

Brittle stars belong to the class Ophiuroidea (ahf-ih-yoo-ROI-dee-uh). These animals look like starfishes whose arms have been stretched until they are long, thin, and flexible. Typically, they hide during the daylight hours, wandering about only under cover of darkness.

Sand dollars and sea urchins are members of the class Echinoidea (ehk-ih-NOI-dee-uh). Most sea urchins will wedge themselves into cracks and crevices by day, coming out only after dusk.

Sea cucumbers are members of the class Holothuroidea (hahl-oh-thoo-ROI-dee-uh). Most sea cucumbers are detritus feeders, picking up the food they encounter as they bulldoze their way across the sandy ocean bottom.

Members of the class Crinoidea (krigh-NOI-dee-uh) include sea lilies and feather stars. These delicate-looking animals may be the most ancient members of their phylum.

MINI LAB Observing

Starfish Hunt

PROBLEM *What structures can you **observe** in a starfish?*

PROCEDURE

1. Obtain a starfish specimen from your teacher.
2. Sketch the starfish, including both its top and bottom sides. Label the structures you can identify.

ANALYZE AND CONCLUDE

1. Compare the two sides of the starfish. With which side does it attack and eat prey?
2. Describe the tube feet of the starfish. What is the purpose of these structures?
3. Why can starfishes live only in water?

Section Review 28–3

1. **Describe** the characteristics of echinoderms.
2. For each of the five classes of echinoderms, **give an example** of an organism in that class and **describe** its characteristics.
3. **Critical Thinking—Comparing** How do the feeding strategies of different echinoderms compare?
4. **MINI LAB** What structures can you **observe** in a starfish?

4. Students should identify the exterior structures labeled in Figure 28–8.

Skills Trace
Observing
- Focus p. 659
- Practice p. 659
- Assess p. 667

Learning Modality

Visual Learning Have students draw a series of pictures showing how a starfish pries open and eats a bivalve.

Ideas Through Images

Have students examine Figure 28–8, read the caption, and answer the following questions.

- **What body systems does a starfish have?** (A digestive, reproductive, water vascular system, and a primitive nervous system.)
- **What structures are part of the water vascular system?** (The madreporite, ring canal, radial canals, and tube feet.)

Investigate

Research Have students consult other sources to find photographs of starfishes' top and bottom sides. Have them compare the photographs with the drawing in Figure 28–8.

4 ASSESS

Quick Check

Ask students to describe the physical characteristics of echinoderms' water vascular system and give one example of how the system is used.

Section Review 28–3

1. They have radial symmetry, an internal skeleton, spiny skin, and a water vascular system.
2. See page 659.
3. Starfishes are predators; other echinoderms are filter-feeders.

Checkpoint

❶ An invertebrate animal with radial symmetry, an internal skeleton, spiny skin, and a network of tubes called a water vascular system.

Ancillary Support

The resource below can be used to support your teaching strategy for these two pages.

TR Writing in Biology: Composite Creatures
Explore: Flowers of the Sea

Section 28–4

Adaptations of Cephalopods

Performance Objective

• Describe cephalopods' unique nervous system.

1 ENGAGE

Ideas Through Images

Have students examine Figure 28–10, read the caption, and answer the following questions.

• **How do these animals differ from other mollusks without external shells, such as slugs?** (They have tentacles, the head is much larger in proportion to the body, and they have prominent eyes.)

• **What does an octopus use its tentacles for?** (Moving across rocks and sand, catching prey, feeling objects.)

2 EXPLORE

Inquiry Activity

Developing Models

Modeling Jet Propulsion

Challenge groups to figure out a way to move a marking pen from one end of a water-filled basin to the other without touching it. Also provide a variety of items they could use, such as plastic tubing, drinking straws, and (most important) small balloons. Let groups investigate freely, then have them share their solutions. (The most successful solution would be to attach an inflated balloon to the pen, then release its end so the air escapes.) Ask groups to explain how their devices worked.

Adaptations of Cephalopods

GUIDE FOR READING

- **Explain** how squids and octopuses increase the speed of nervous transmissions.

EARTHWORMS, CLAMS, SNAILS, and starfishes move from place to place fairly slowly, if they move at all. And they are small creatures, typically growing no longer than about 30 centimeters. But cephalopods are different. Octopuses and squids travel with speed and agility, and some grow to incredible sizes. Including its tentacles, a giant squid can grow over 16 meters in length—longer than 8 humans placed end to end!

Why can cephalopods move so quickly and grow to such huge sizes? The answers to these questions begin with a very important body system—the nervous system.

Figure 28–10 Few invertebrates show the sophisticated adaptations of cephalopods. (a) This deep-sea octopus uses a well-developed nervous system to control its long, flexible tentacles. (b) To surprise a prey, a cuttlefish can change color to blend into the background. When the unsuspecting prey is within reach, the cuttlefish quickly extends its tentacles to seize it. (c) Cephalopods evolved unusually wide nerves, including the squid giant axon shown between tweezers in this photograph. Wide nerves transmit impulses faster than narrow nerves do.

The Nervous System

Usually, humans take their nervous system for granted. When you decide to wiggle your big toes, for example, your nervous system takes only a few milliseconds to transmit a message from your brain to muscles in your foot.

How do messages travel so quickly through nerves? In part, the answer lies with a white fatty substance called **myelin.** Myelin surrounds many nerve cells, and it acts like the insulation around an electrical wire. With myelin, nerves can carry transmissions as fast as 200 meters per second!

Living Without Myelin

Humans and other vertebrates—animals with backbones—all make myelin to increase the speed of nervous transmissions. But invertebrates are not able to make myelin. And without myelin, a small nerve can transmit impulses at a rate of only a few millimeters per

TEACHER SUPPORT

Managing Classroom Diversity

TECH PREP STUDENTS

Research laboratories employ a wide variety of professionals—not only research scientists with advanced degrees but also research assistants, laboratory technicians, animal care specialists, computer programmers and technicians, and data analysts. Encourage students who are considering science careers to find out about job opportunities in the research field.

With the assistance of your school guidance office, interested students may be able to identify and contact someone working in a nearby diagnostic or research laboratory. Suggest that students interview the person—on-site, if possible—to learn about his or her background, training, and job responsibilities and about other laboratory-related professions.

second—too slow to coordinate distant body parts. As a result, most invertebrates have small, compact bodies.

Cephalopods, however, evolved a different way to increase the speed and efficiency of nervous transmissions. It turns out that wide nerve cells carry transmissions faster than narrow nerve cells. **Squids and octopuses evolved unusually wide nerve cells, thus increasing the speed of their nervous transmissions without the use of myelin.** In a nerve called the squid giant axon, the cells are over a millimeter in diameter—a significant width for a single cell of any kind.

Squids and octopuses can grow to large sizes because wide nerves allow their brain to communicate quickly with distant body parts. Without such communication, octopuses and squids could not grow to the sizes they are today.

☑ *Checkpoint* What is myelin? 1

Research on Nerves

Aside from their size, the nerves of cephalopods are very similar to the nerves of other animals, including humans. And in a laboratory experiment, large, wide nerves are much easier to handle and manipulate than small, narrow nerves. For these reasons, researchers investigating nerve function typically study the squid giant axon and other nerves of cephalopods. In fact, much of what scientists have learned about nerves has come from these studies.

Figure 28–11 *An octopus may discharge a cloud of ink in response to a threatening presence—in this case, a deep-sea diver.*

Other Adaptations

The nervous system is only one of the fascinating features of cephalopods. For example, these animals can move by a very unusual method—jet propulsion! Cephalopods typically draw water into their flexible mantle cavity, then rapidly force out the water through a tube called a **siphon.** Most cephalopods have several movable siphons, allowing for quick movements in different directions.

To protect themselves, many cephalopods release a cloud of dark-colored, strong-tasting ink just before they make their retreat. And some use specialized cells called **chromatophores** to change color, allowing the cephalopod to blend into its background. Cephalopods are also very intelligent. In fact, an octopus can learn to perform simple tasks, such as unscrewing a lid from a jar to reach food inside it.

Section Review 28–4

1. **Explain** how squids and octopuses increased the speed of nervous transmissions without the use of myelin.
2. **Identify** some adaptations in cephalopods.
3. **BRANCHING OUT ACTIVITY** Investigate the research performed on the large nerves of cephalopods. **Describe** how messages are transmitted through nerves.

3 TEACH

Discussion

Show students a video or CD-ROM segment demonstrating gastropod intelligence—for example, an octopus using its tentacles to explore a diver's equipment. Ask students to describe the observable evidence that shows that the gastropod was acting intelligently.

Correcting Misconceptions

Emphasize that the wording used to describe the evolution of wide nerve cells (boldface type, page 661) does not mean that squids and octopuses purposefully developed such cells. Rather, genetic changes resulted in wider nerve cells in some individuals, and those animals were able to survive and reproduce more successfully than others. If necessary, review the basic concepts of natural selection.

4 ASSESS

Quick Check

Have students describe, in their own words, how cephalopods' nervous systems are able to transmit messages without myelin.

☑ Checkpoint

1 Myelin is a white, fatty substance that surrounds nerve cells in vertebrates and acts like the insulation around an

Section Review 28–4

1. They evolved unusually wide nerve cells, which carry transmissions faster than narrow nerve cells.

2. Cephalopods have wide nerve cells, movement through jet propulsion, production of ink, ability to change color, and high intelligence.

3. In general, a message is transmitted through nerves in the following way: A stimulus is picked up by one of the sense organs and takes the form of an electrical signal, known as an impulse, that travels through sensory neurons to the brain. The brain then sends an impulse through motor neurons to different parts of the body to produce a response.

Learning Modality

Visual and Kinesthetic Learning Have students find colored photographs of cephalopods blending in with their backgrounds, then place an acetate sheet over each photograph and trace the animal's outline.

Ancillary Support

The resources below can be used to support your teaching strategy for these two pages.

TR Enrich: Coming Out of Their Shells

BL Inquiry Activity: Big-Headed Mollusks

CHAPTER 28

Laboratory Investigation

How Earthworms Respond to Stimuli

Before the Lab

1. Students can use earthworms from the culture they set up in the Chapter Discovery Learning Activity for this chapter (page 648). If you purchase earthworms from a worm farm or biological supply company, make sure you order them well in advance to ensure delivery by the date that students will need them.

2. To prepare the 5-percent acetic acid solution that students will need for the More to Explore investigation, mix 1 mL of distilled vinegar with 19 mL of distilled water.

Pre-Lab Discussion

Have students read the entire procedure for this investigation. Then ask students the following questions.

What is the purpose of this investigation? (To observe how an earthworm responds to different stimuli and make inferences about how these responses help earthworms to survive in their environment.)

Which external features will you be able to see on the earthworm? (Its head end, setae, clitellum, and segments.)

In step 5, why should you leave the earthworm undisturbed for five minutes? (To give the earthworm time to sense the damp and dry surfaces and move to the one it prefers.)

Skills Development

Students will use these skills while completing the laboratory investigation: observing, hypothesizing, designing an experiment, making inferences.

CHAPTER 28

Laboratory Investigation

DESIGNING AN EXPERIMENT

How Earthworms Respond to Stimuli

As earthworms burrow their way through the soil, they respond to stimuli. Their responses to certain stimuli affect their chances of survival in their environment. To detect stimuli, the earthworm uses sensory cells in its skin rather than specialized sense organs such as eyes. In this investigation, you will observe an earthworm and see how it responds to different stimuli.

Problem

How does an earthworm respond to different stimuli? **Design an experiment** to answer this question.

Suggested Materials

live earthworm in a storage container
tray
paper towels
medicine dropper
hand lens
lamp
cold water

Suggested Procedure

1. **With a hand lens, observe the skin, mouth, setae, and segments of the earthworm. CAUTION: *Be careful not to harm the earthworm when handling it.* Make a sketch of the earthworm and label its external features.**

2. **Fill the medicine dropper with water and use it to wet the earthworm. Make sure you keep the earthworm moist. It will die if its skin dries out.**

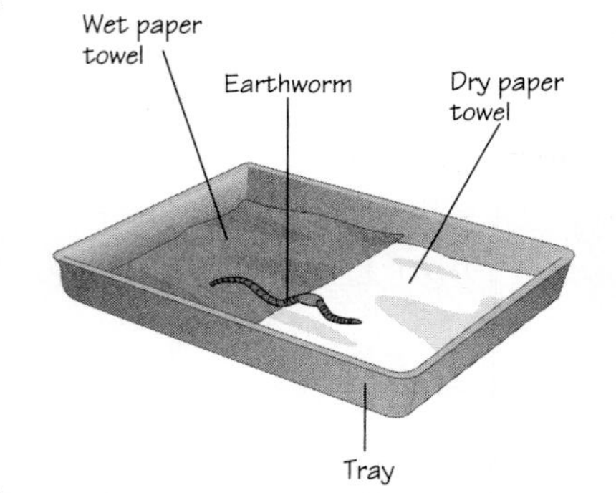

Safety Tips

- Make sure students handle the earthworms gently and do not cause them stress.
- Remind students to be careful when handling glass items and to report any breakage immediately.
- Have students wash their hands as soon as they have completed the procedure.

3. **Fold a dry paper towel in half and place it on one side of your tray. Fold a dampened paper towel in half and place it on the other side of the tray. See the diagram.**
4. **Place the earthworm in the center of the tray, between the dry paper towel and the moist paper towel.**
5. **Place the tray in an area where the earthworm will remain undisturbed for 5 minutes.**
6. **After 5 minutes, observe the location of the earthworm. Record your observations.**
7. **Using a similar procedure, design an experiment to determine how earthworms respond to the following stimuli:**
   - **light**
   - **cold**
8. **Write your hypotheses. With your teacher's approval, carry out the experiments you designed. Record your results.**
9. **When you have completed your experiments, return the earthworm to your teacher.**

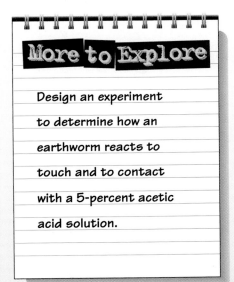

Observations

1. Describe the earthworm's external features, including color and texture.
2. How did the earthworm respond when placed between the moist and dry environments?
3. What was the earthworm's response to light? To cold?

Analysis and Conclusions

1. How is an earthworm's body adapted for movement into and through soil?
2. What is the function of the earthworm's slimy skin?
3. How does an earthworm's response to moisture help it to survive?
4. Do an earthworm's responses to light and cold have any protective value? Explain your answer.
5. Would you expect to find earthworms in hard soil? Explain your answer.

More to Explore

Design an experiment to determine how an earthworm reacts to touch and to contact with a 5-percent acetic acid solution.

Teaching Strategies

1. Make sure students label only the earthworm's external features and do not simply copy the diagram and labels in Visualizing an Earthworm on page 655.
2. If necessary, remind students to place additional drops of water on the earthworm occasionally to keep it moist.
3. Check students' hypotheses (step 8) to make sure they are in the form of testable statements. Also check their experimental designs to make sure the earthworm will not be injured.

Answers to Observations

1. Students should mention that the worm is divided into ringed segments and has identifiable head and tail ends, an enlarged section (the clitellum) partway down its body, and tiny bristles on its underside. Descriptions of color may vary somewhat, depending on the species used; accept all reasonable responses. The texture of an earthworm is smooth and slimy, except for the bristly setae.
2. It moved to the moist towel.
3. It moved away from the light. It became sluggish or stopped moving when exposed to cold temperatures.

Answers to Analysis and Conclusions

1. It is long and thin, its head end is more pointed, its surface is smooth and moist, and its setae help grip the soil.
2. The slimy skin allows the worm to slide smoothly through soil and on other objects. Students also may mention that earthworms breathe through their skin, which must be kept moist for gas exchange to occur.
3. Its preference for moist environments helps keep its skin from drying out, which would kill it.
4. An earthworm's avoidance of light helps to keep it sheltered below ground or under leaf litter, where the environment is more moist and where it is protected from most predators. An earthworm's lack of activity in a cold environment reduces its energy requirements, thus helping it survive during cold weather or seasons.
5. You would probably not find earthworms in hard soil. Hard (compacted) soil generally has little organic material to support earthworms. Also, with their soft bodies, it would be difficult for them to penetrate hard soil.

More to Explore

Students can test an earthworm's response to touch by simply touching its head end gently with a blunt probe or toothpick or by placing an obstacle in its path as it moves. To test the earthworm's response to the weak acid solution, students should present only a small amount of the solution, perhaps by touching the worm with one end of a moistened cotton-tipped swab or by placing a few drops in its path as it moves across a damp paper towel.

CHAPTER 28

Study Guide

Review Strategy

Have each group prepare a set of cards, each with a question about a specific type of organism presented in this chapter on one side and the answer to the question on the other side. Also have students assign dollar values to the questions based on their level of difficulty. Have groups exchange cards and then use them to play a game in the style of Jeopardy, with one student playing the role of game host. You could also do this as a class activity with three students as the contestants, the rest of the class as the audience members (who supply the correct question if all three contestants fail to do so), and yourself as game host.

Recalling Main Ideas

1. a	6. a
2. b	7. a
3. c	8. c
4. a	9. c
5. d	10. a

Assessment

Reviewing What You Learned

1. Mollusks may be carnivores, herbivores, filter feeders, detritus feeders, scavengers, or parasites.
2. The foot, gut, mantle, and shell.
3. To remove nitrogen-containing wastes from the blood of mollusks.
4. The free-swimming larva of a mollusk.
5. Many shell-less gastropods protect themselves by producing powerful poisons or by having a bad taste to predators.
6. A smooth, shiny substance that coats the inner surface of a shell.
7. Cephalopods are a class of mollusks. Most have shells that are small, internal, or missing altogether (except in the chambered nautilus, which has a large external shell); are large, active, and intelligent; and have tentacles with sucker disks.

Study Guide

Summarizing Key Concepts

The key concepts in each section of this chapter are listed below to help you review the chapter content. Make sure you understand each concept and its relationship to other concepts and to the theme of this chapter.

28–1 Mollusks

- All mollusks have similar body plans that typically include a foot, gut, mantle, and shell. They also pass through similar stages in their early development.
- Gastropods include snails and slugs. Bivalves include clams and oysters, which have two shells joined at a hinge. The largest mollusks are the cephalopods, including octopuses and squids.

28–2 Annelids

- All annelids have a body divided into segments separated by walls called septa.
- Annelids have a tube-within-a-tube digestive tract, a small brain, and a closed circulatory system. Nephridia remove metabolic wastes.
- Earthworms are oligochaetes. Sandworms and bloodworms are polychaetes. Leeches are hirudineans.

28–3 Echinoderms

- Echinoderms have radial symmetry, an internal skeleton, spiny skin, and a water vascular system—a network of tubes and appendages used for many purposes.
- Echinoderms include starfishes, brittle stars, sand urchins, sea urchins, sea cucumbers, sea lilies, and feather stars.

28–4 Adaptations of Cephalopods

- To increase the speed of their nervous transmissions without myelin, squids and octopuses evolved wide nerve cells.

Reviewing Key Terms

Review the following vocabulary terms and their meaning. Then use each term in a complete sentence.

28–1 Mollusks

foot
radula
gut
mantle
shell
open circulatory system
closed circulatory system
nephridium
trochophore

28–2 Annelids

septum
longitudinal muscle
circular muscle
brain
ring vessel
crop
gizzard
clitellum
seta
nephridium
nerve cord
pharynx

28–3 Echinoderms

water vascular system
tube foot
statocyst

28–4 Adaptations of Cephalopods

myelin
siphon
chromatophore

Inquiry-Based Strategy

Ask each group to design an experiment involving one of the organisms included in the habitats they set up in the Chapter Discovery Learning Activity or another organism they have obtained expressly for this purpose. Let students either adapt one of the chapter's investigations or design an original experiment.

Encourage each group to focus on one of the easily observed life functions covered in the chapter: feeding, movement, respiration, reproduction, and response to stimuli. Provide each group with a small plastic aquarium and any other materials they will need to carry out the experiment, such as various foods or stimulus items.

Check each group's experimental design to make sure students have a clear objective in mind and that organisms will not be subjected to injury or stress. Give each group an opportunity to share its experimental design, observations, results, and conclusions with the rest of the class.

Recalling Main Ideas

Choose the letter of the answer that best completes the statement or answers the question.

1. The shell of a mollusk is secreted by glands in the
   a. mantle. c. gut.
   b. foot. d. radula.

2. Mollusks excrete nitrogen-containing wastes through organs called
   a. gills. c. trochophores.
   b. nephridia. d. radulas.

3. The circulatory system of a clam or an oyster is described as
   a. hermaphroditic. c. open.
   b. water vascular. d. closed.

4. Snails and slugs are members of the class
   a. Gastropoda. c. Cephalopoda.
   b. Bivalvia. d. Hirudinea.

5. The segments of an annelid are divided by body walls called
   a. trochophores. c. nephridia.
   b. ring vessels. d. septa.

6. Earthworms are members of the class
   a. Oligochaeta. c. Hirudinea.
   b. Polychaeta. d. Echinoidea.

7. Which type of body plan do echinoderms have?
   a. radial symmetry c. spherical symmetry
   b. bilateral symmetry d. no symmetry

8. The name echinoderm means
   a. segmented body. c. spiny skin.
   b. large brain. d. one-piece shell.

9. For feeding, respiration, excretion, and other life functions, an echinoderm uses its
   a. nephridia.
   b. gills.
   c. water vascular system.
   d. closed circulatory system.

10. The fatty substance that insulates many nerve cells in vertebrates is
    a. myelin. c. chromatophore.
    b. nacre. d. radula.

Putting It All Together

Using the information on pages xxx to xxxi, complete the following concept map.

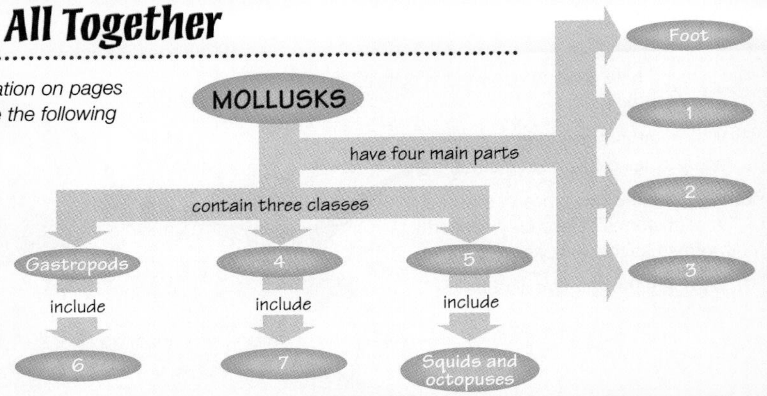

Putting It All Together

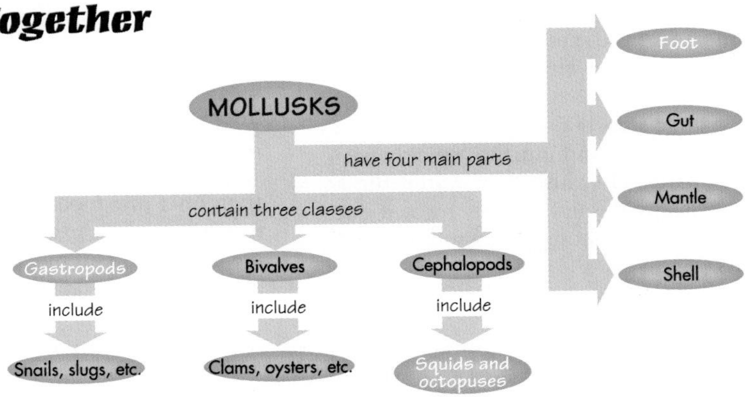

8. An annelid's digestive tract includes the pharynx, a muscular widening that helps the worm swallow soil and force it down the gut; the crop, a widening that stores the food temporarily; and the gizzard, a larger widening that grinds the food into small, absorbable particles. These particles pass into the intestine, where they are absorbed into the bloodstream.
9. Earthworms swallow and grind up large amounts of soil and organic matter, a process that aerates soil and recycles many nutrients, including nitrogen.
10. As an earthworm moves, its bristles dig into the soil, providing traction.
11. The clitellum secretes a ring of mucus into which eggs and sperm are released. The ring then slides off the worm's body to become a cocoon in which eggs develop.
12. Radial symmetry, an internal skeleton, spiny skin, and a network of tubes and appendages called a water vascular system.
13. Starfishes are predators of clams, oysters, and other bivalves. Other echinoderms are filter-feeders, using individual tube feet to snag passing plankton. Still others use tube feet to pick up a mixture of sand and detritus, which they then shove into their mouths.
14. Most invertebrates have small, compact bodies because they cannot make myelin. Without myelin, small nerves transmit impulses too slowly to coordinate distant body parts.

Expanding the Concepts

1. The foot is a soft, muscular structure that usually contains the mouth. The gut is the digestive tract. The mantle is a thin, delicate layer of tissue that surrounds the mollusk's body and secretes calcium carbonate, which forms the shell. The shell protects the mollusk's soft body.
2. In an open circulatory system, blood is pumped from the heart through open spaces called sinuses. The blood then enters vessels that pass through gills and eventually return to the heart. In a closed circulatory system, blood is pumped through blood vessels only. Clams and oysters have an open circulatory system. Squids and octopuses have a closed circulatory system.

3. Most aquatic mollusks release sperm and egg cells into the open water, where external fertilization occurs more or less by chance. Other mollusks, such as squids and octopuses, reproduce with internal fertilization, in which the male uses a tentacle to deliver sperm to the female. Many mollusks are hermaphrodites that pair together and fertilize each other's eggs.
4. When a bivalve takes in a pebble or a sand grain, its mantle responds by coating the object with nacre, which over many years turns the object into a pearl.
5. Mollusks and annelids breathe through their skin, which must be moist in order for gas exchange to occur.
6. An earthworm has longitudinal muscles that run up and down its body and ring-shaped circular muscles that surround the longitudinal muscles. When the longitudinal muscles contract, they shorten the worm's segments. When the circular muscles contract, they lengthen the segments. The earthworm moves by coordinating these two sets of muscles.
7. Oligochaetes have a few short bristles on their bodies. Polychaetes typically have a pair of paddlelike structures tipped with bristles on each body segment. Leeches are blood-drinking parasites.
8. The water vascular system contains a network of fluid-filled canals connected to numerous tube feet, each of which looks like a medicine dropper attached to a suction cup. Echinoderms use their tube feet in movement and in feeding to pry open bivalves, catch passing plankton, or pick up material and put it in their mouths. The vascular system also exposes an enormous surface area to the surrounding water so that the echinoderm can exchange gases with it and release wastes into it, thus eliminating the need for specialized respiratory, circulatory, or excretory systems.
9. A starfish uses its tube feet to pry open the bivalve's two shells. It then extends its stomach inside the bivalve's soft body and secretes enzymes that digest it.

Assessment

Reviewing What You Learned

Answer each of the following in a complete sentence.

1. Describe the different ways in which mollusks obtain food.
2. List the basic body parts found in almost all mollusks.
3. What is the purpose of nephridia?
4. What is a trochophore?
5. Some gastropods lack shells. How do they protect themselves?
6. What is nacre?
7. What are cephalopods? Describe the characteristics they have in common.
8. Describe an annelid's digestive tract.
9. Why are earthworms important for fertile soil?
10. How do earthworms use the bristles on their ventral surface?
11. What is the function of the clitellum in earthworms?
12. What are the characteristics of echinoderms?
13. Describe the different ways in which echinoderms feed.
14. Why do most invertebrates have small, compact bodies?

Expanding the Concepts

Discuss each of the following in a brief paragraph.

1. Describe the roles of the four basic parts of a mollusk.
2. Compare an open circulatory system with a closed circulatory system. Give examples of organisms that use each.
3. Discuss the different reproductive strategies in mollusks.
4. Describe how pearls are formed in oysters and other bivalves.
5. Why must mollusks and annelids keep their skin moist?
6. What are the two types of muscles in earthworms? Describe how earthworms use these muscles to move.
7. Compare the different classes of annelids.
8. Describe the structure and function of the water vascular system in echinoderms.
9. How do starfishes feed on clams, oysters, and other bivalves?
10. Discuss the adaptations that allow cephalopods to move faster and grow larger than other mollusks.

10. Cephalopods evolved unusually wide nerve cells that increased the speed of their nerve impulses without the use of myelin, which they and all other invertebrates lack. As a result, cephalopods can grow to large sizes because their wide nerves allow their brains to communicate quickly with distant body parts. They also draw water into their flexible mantle cavities and rapidly force it out again through their siphons, which allows quick movements.

Extending Your Thinking

1. Leeches feed by sucking blood from their hosts. The chemical keeps the blood flowing freely while a leech feeds.
2. Students' experimental designs should involve offering earthworms various food choices rather than only one food at a time. If you allow students to perform their experiments, make sure the foods are cut into small pieces. **CAUTION:** *Do not allow students to handle raw meat or poultry.*

Extending Your Thinking

Use the skills you have developed in this chapter to answer the following.

1. **Analyzing** Researchers have identified a chemical in leeches that suppresses blood clotting. Why is this chemical important in leeches?
2. **Designing an experiment** Which foods can earthworms eat? Design an experiment to discover whether earthworms will eat bread, vegetables, meat, or other foods. Conduct the experiment only with the permission of your teacher.
3. **Observing** Suppose that you are asked to make daily observations of an octopus that lives in an aquarium. What characteristics or behaviors might indicate the intelligence of the octopus?
4. **Classifying** Describe the characteristics of the animal shown in the photograph on page 666. Based only on the photograph, into which phylum and class does the animal belong? What further information would help you classify the animal? Explain your answer.
5. **Predicting events** Suppose that pollutants contaminated a patch of farmland and killed the earthworm population in the soil. Predict how this would affect the farmland.

Applying Your Skills

The Great Snail Pull

Land snails are famous for moving slowly. But because of their muscular foot, these animals are unusually strong for their size. Perform this activity to find out how strong snails actually are.

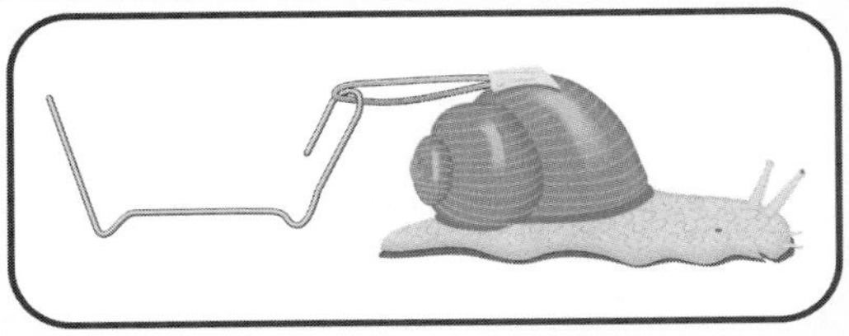

1. Obtain a land snail from your teacher. On a piece of paper, sketch its body and label the parts you can identify.
2. Gently tape a loop of thread to the snail's back. Bend open a paper clip and link it to the loop of thread, as shown in the illustration. Make sure you do not damage the snail's shell or harm the snail in any way.
3. Add washers or other weights to the paper clip until the snail can no longer move forward.
4. Measure the mass of the snail and the mass of the weights it was able to pull, then return the snail to your teacher. How many times its own mass did the snail pull?
5. Describe the way in which a snail moves. How is the snail able to pull the added weight?

• GOING FURTHER •

6. Design an experiment to determine how water, light, aromas, or other factors influence a snail's behavior.

3. Students may mention the behaviors they observed in the video segment (Discussion on page 661) or other behaviors that involve exploring objects, making choices, solving problems, and the like.

Skills Trace
Observing
- Focus p. 659
- Practice p. 659
- Assess p. 667

4. Characteristics: Exterior shell; soft body with foot, head end, and eye-tipped antennae; moist surface. Phylum: Mollusca. Class: Gastropoda.

Skills Trace
Classifying
- Focus p. 653
- Practice p. 653
- Assess p. 667

5. Answers should demonstrate an understanding of earthworms' essential role in helping to decompose organic material, recycle nutrients, and aerate soil.

Applying Your Skills

Teacher Notes

- Remind students to handle the snails gently.
- Caution students to begin with a light load and increase it gradually.
- Provide spring scales or equal-arm balances for measuring the masses of the snail and weights.

Answers

1. Students should label at least the foot and shell. They may also be able to detect and label the mantle.
4. Answers will vary.
5. A snail moves by means of its broad, muscular foot. The snail is able to pull the extra weight because its broad foot covers a large surface area in relation to its body size, so it can produce a lot of force to move the weights.
6. Check students' experimental designs to make sure they do not involve materials or procedures that would harm the snail. You may want to let students carry out their experiments and share their results.

Scoring Rubric

4 Response is thorough, accurate, and creative; shows an in-depth understanding of science skills, procedures, and concepts.

3 Response is complete, mostly accurate, and original; shows a satisfactory understanding of science skills, procedures, and concepts.

2 Response is mostly complete but includes some inaccuracies; shows an adequate understanding of science skills, procedures, and concepts.

1 Response is only partially complete and has many inaccuracies; shows an incomplete understanding of science skills, procedures, and concepts.

0 Response is mostly incomplete and/or inaccurate; shows a lack of understanding of science skills, procedures, and concepts.

Chapter 29 Arthropods

Content Management	Student Edition Activities
■ Section 29–1 Arthropod Form and Function, pp. 669–673 Arthropod Body Plan Arthropod Structures Arthropod Growth and Development	MINI LAB: Flying to the Light, p. 670
■ Section 29–2 A Tour of the Arthropods, pp. 674–676 Chelicerates Crustaceans Uniramians	MINI LAB: What's a Shrimp?, p. 676
◆ BRANCHING OUT • In Depth Section 29–3 The Importance of Arthropods, pp. 677–679 Arthropod Interactions The Pollination Crisis	Laboratory Investigation: Feeding Fly Larvae, pp. 680–681

■ These sections cover all the necessary content and concepts for an enriched course in biology.
◆ This section covers content and concepts that are either applications or extensions of the enriched material.

Integration Strategies

SE Agriculture, p. 679

Assessment Strategies

SE Chapter Review, pp. 682–685
TR Section Reviews
Chapter Test
BL Chapter Review
Practice Test
CTB Chapter 29 Test

Tech Prep

Teaching strategies appropriate for students who are in technical/vocational programs or who are considering post-secondary technical education can be found on the following **TE** pages: 669 and 677.

Meeting the Standards

Sections 29–1 through 29–3 cover two of the five content standards under **Biological Evolution,** two of the five content standards under **The Interdependence of Organisms,** one of the six content standards under **Matter, Energy, and Organization in Living Systems,** and three of the four content standards under **The Behavior of Organisms** as described on pages 185–187 of The National Science Education Standards.

Chapter Planning Guide

Teacher's Edition Activities	Other Activities	Media and Technology
Chapter Discovery Learning Activity, p. 668 **Inquiry Activity:** Examining Arthropods, p. 669 **Investigate:** Research, p. 669 **Investigate:** Research, p. 672 **Investigate:** Long-Term Project, p. 672 **Activity:** How Do Ants Communicate?, p. 672	**LM** Observing the Structure of the Grasshoppper, #57 **TR** **Writing in Biology:** Who Am I? **Explore:** A Breath of Fresh Water **BL** **Inquiry Activity:** A Bug in Shining Armor	**TB** Visualizing a Grasshopper, #37
Inquiry Activity: Grouping Arthropods, p. 674 **Investigate:** Research, p. 675 **Investigate:** Research, p. 675 **Activity:** Modeling an Arthropod's Exoskeleton, p. 675	**LM** Investigating Isopod Environments, #58 **TR** **Apply:** Great Balls o' Isopods! **BL** **Inquiry Activity:** The Wide, Wide World of Arthropods	**BioVue Mini Doc:** Insects Are High Society, Videodisc Side 7
Inquiry Activity: Identifying Arthropods in Soil, p. 677 **Investigate:** Cooperative Learning, p. 677	**TR** **Enrich:** On the March! **BL** **Inquiry Activity:** People and Pollinators	

KEY: **SE** Student Edition **TE** Teacher's Edition **LM** Laboratory Manual **TR** Teaching Resources
BL BioLog **TB** Transparency Box **CTB** Computer Test Bank

Materials List

TE Chapter Discovery Learning Activity, p. 668 (45 minutes for initial setup of habitats); arthropods (including tarantula, crabs, crayfishes, hermit crabs, mealworms, and crickets) collected outdoors or purchased from biological supply companies or pet shops, plastic containers with lids or screen covers, appropriate habitat materials and foods, field guides and other sources for researching animals' needs.

TE Inquiry Activity: Examining Arthropods, p. 669 (20–30 minutes); arthropods from Chapter Discovery Learning Activity.

SE MINI LAB: Flying to the Light, p. 670 (35–45 minutes); fruit fly culture, light source, metric ruler or meterstick.

TE Investigate: Long-Term Project, p. 672 (5–10 minutes for setup and then brief observations over several weeks); hermit crabs housed in plastic container or terrarium, empty gastropod shells of various sizes.

TE Activity: How Do Ants Communicate?, p. 672 (30–40 minutes); outdoor anthill, spoon, honey, sheet of paper.

TE Inquiry Activity: Grouping Arthropods, p. 674 (20–30 minutes); list of arthropod features (from Visualizing a Grasshopper on page 671) or examples of the various types of arthropods.

TE Activity: Modeling an Arthropod's Exoskeleton, p. 675 (45 minutes); wide-diameter cardboard tubes, manilla folders, sheets of lightweight flexible cardboard, scissors, tape.

SE MINI LAB: What's a Shrimp?, p. 676 (20–25 minutes); whole unshelled, raw shrimp; hand lens.

TE Inquiry Activity: Identifying Arthropods in Soil, p. 677 (45 minutes); outdoor soil plot (obtain permission to dig), trowel or small shovel, field guide.

CHAPTER 29

Arthropods

Introducing the Chapter

. . . In Pictures

This unusual-looking lobster is a good example of an arthropod in that it has a segmented body, jointed appendages, and a tough exoskeleton. Have students examine the photograph, read the caption, and answer the following questions.

To which phylum of the animal kingdom does the lobster belong? (Arthropoda; it is an arthropod.)

What other animals belong to this phylum? (Students might mention shrimp, insects, spiders, and others.)

What are some characteristics that you think all arthropods share? (Students may recall that all arthropods have segmented bodies, jointed appendages, and a tough exoskeleton.)

Teaching Strategy

The first section of this chapter introduces the typical body plan of arthropods and their specialized structures for carrying out various life processes. The second section presents the three subphyla of arthropods, with examples and characteristics of each. The BRANCHING OUT section discusses the importance of arthropods to humans.

BIO JOURNAL

Students' responses most likely will vary from appreciation of the complexity, widespread success, and—in some cases—physical beauty of arthropods, to highly negative opinions based on the potential dangers or distasteful habits of some arthropods, such as cockroaches, ticks, and houseflies. Encourage students to discuss their opinions and the reasons for them. Instruct students to keep their entries in their portfolios.

CHAPTER 29

Arthropods

FOCUSING THE CHAPTER
THEME: Unity and Diversity

29–1 Arthropod Form and Function
- Describe an arthropod's structure and life cycle.

29–2 A Tour of the Arthropods
- Identify the subphyla of arthropods.

BRANCHING OUT *In Depth*

29–3 The Importance of Arthropods
- Discuss the importance of arthropods to humans.

LABORATORY INVESTIGATION
- Design an experiment to determine the foods that fruit fly larvae prefer.

Biology and Your World

BIO JOURNAL

Do you think that arthropods are interesting? Beautiful? Bothersome? In your journal, describe your thoughts and feelings about arthropods.

Lobster in the Indian Ocean

TEACHER SUPPORT

Chapter Discovery Learning Activity

COLLECTING ARTHROPODS

Have students set up containers with various types of arthropods that have been purchased from a biological supply company. Provide field guides and other sources so students can research the habitat and food requirements of each organism. **CAUTION:** Do not allow students to touch potentially dangerous arthropods.

Crustaceans Crabs and crayfishes make good subjects for investigating feeding behavior and locomotion. Also provide at least one hermit crab.

Chelicerates Include a tarantula if possible, as its large size will make it easy to observe its body segments and mouth parts.

Uniramians Include a mealworm culture for observing an example of complete metamorphosis, and crickets for observing an example of incomplete metamorphosis.

Arthropod Form and Function

Guide for Reading

- **Describe** an arthropod's body.
- **Explain** the purpose of molting.

MINI LAB

- **Design an experiment** to determine how fruit flies respond to light.

IF YOU HAVE EVER ADMIRED A lady bug, been chased from a picnic by wasps, or enjoyed eating a shrimp dinner, then you've had close encounters with arthropods. From mites so small that they ride on dust particles to king crabs that scuttle on meter-long legs, arthropods are the most successful animals on Earth. There may be more than 15 million species of insects alone. What's more, insects outnumber humans by about 200 million to 1!

What are these animals? Why are they so successful? Let's explore the answers to these questions.

Arthropod Body Plan

Arthropods have segmented bodies, jointed appendages, and are surrounded by a tough exoskeleton. You can think of the arthropods' original design as a biological version of the first mass-produced automobiles. The first automobiles had an internal-combustion engine, gas tank, steering wheel, transmission, and other familiar parts. Over time, however, automobiles changed. Engineers designed electric starters to replace hand cranks, fuel injectors to replace carburetors, and body shapes that range from small sports cars to large semitrailers. But the changes have been little more than variations on the original theme.

Like automobiles, the arthropods' original body plan and basic parts remained the same, while their size, shape, and complexity evolved along different paths.

Checkpoint What is an arthropod? ①

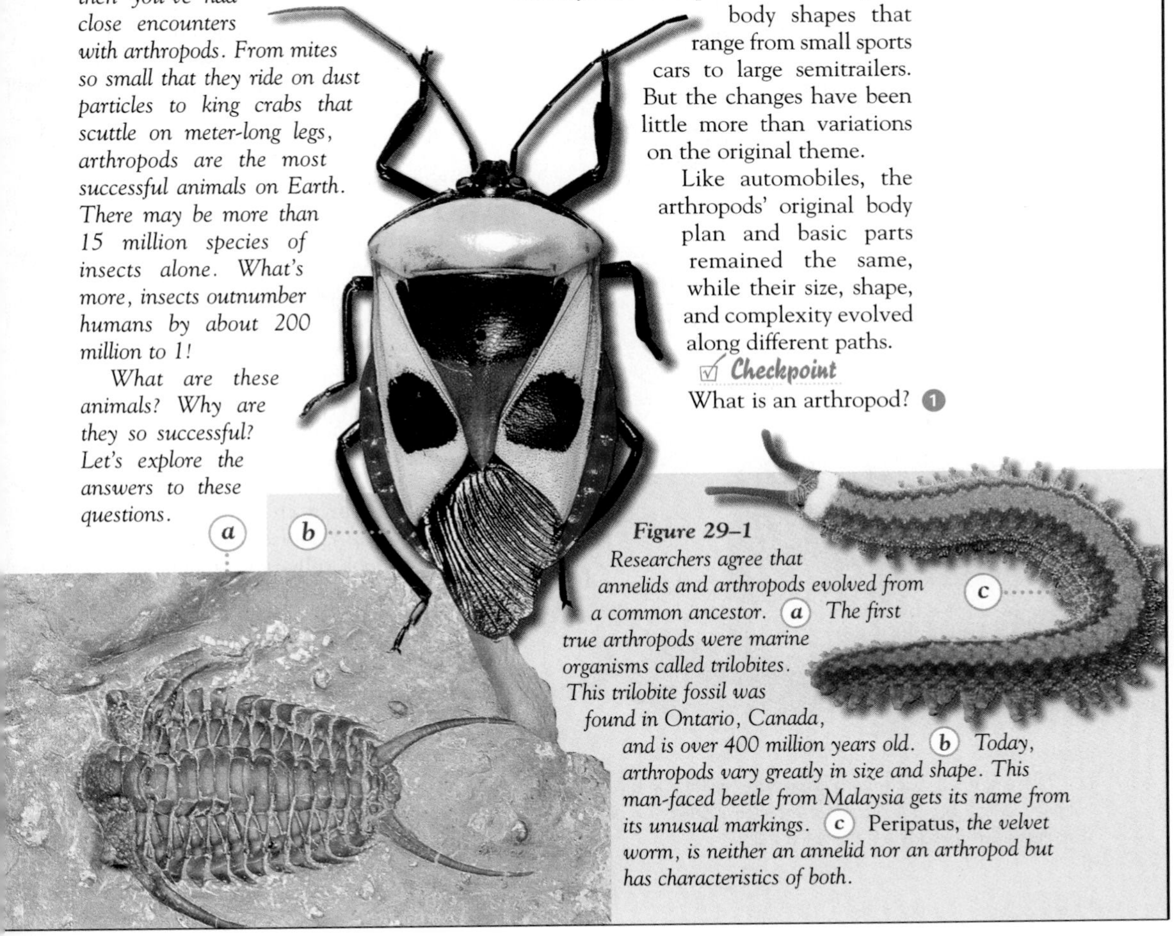

Figure 29–1 *Researchers agree that annelids and arthropods evolved from a common ancestor.* (a) *The first true arthropods were marine organisms called trilobites. This trilobite fossil was found in Ontario, Canada, and is over 400 million years old.* (b) *Today, arthropods vary greatly in size and shape. This man-faced beetle from Malaysia gets its name from its unusual markings.* (c) Peripatus, *the velvet worm, is neither an annelid nor an arthropod but has characteristics of both.*

Section 29–1

Arthropod Form and Function

Performance Objectives

- Describe the typical body plan of arthropods.
- Discuss why arthropods molt.

Mini Lab Skill: Experimenting

1 ENGAGE

Inquiry Activity

Comparing

Examining Arthropods

Have students compare the living arthropods in the habitats they created in the Chapter Discovery Learning Activity with one another and with the photographs in Figure 29–1. Ask students to identify the physical similarities among all the animals. (Students should observe that all arthropods have a segmented body, jointed appendages, and a tough exoskeleton.)

2 EXPLORE

Investigate

Research Suggest that students research the world's largest insects. One source, *The Big Bug Book* by Margery Facklam, includes illustrations showing insect "giants" at their actual size.

Checkpoint

① An arthropod is an invertebrate animal with a segmented body, jointed appendages, and a tough exoskeleton.

TEACHER SUPPORT

Managing Classroom Diversity

TECH PREP STUDENTS

Encourage students who are interested in automobile mechanics to research the ways in which automobile parts and systems have changed in the past 75 years. Avenues of investigation include fuel injection systems, ignition systems, steering mechanisms (including power steering), braking systems (including power brakes and antilock braking systems), and safety devices such as seat belts and airbags. This research could be done as a cooperative learning activity, with each student in the group researching a different part or system.

You may want to ask students to share their findings with the rest of the class in oral presentations or bulletin board displays. Encourage students to bring in actual parts, if possible, for demonstrating the differences between older and newer mechanisms and to support their explanations with diagrams they have drawn or photocopied.

3 TEACH

MINI LAB Experimenting

Teacher Notes
- For time required and materials needed, see page 668b.
- One culture tube of fruit flies from a biological supply company should provide enough flies for the class.
- Transfer ten adult flies to a separate vial for each group.

Answers to Analyze and Conclude

1. Fruit flies become more active in the presence of light and will move toward it as long as it is close enough for the flies to detect.
2. Light intensity, temperature (will vary inversely with distance and may be affected by handling of the tube).
3. Students should put colored filters over the light at the same distance from the tube.

Skills Trace
Experimenting
- Focus p. 670
- Practice p. 673
- Assess p. 685

Discussion

Compare and contrast arthropods' three types of respiratory structures, emphasizing the following points.
- Many aquatic arthropods have feathery gills that absorb oxygen from a steady stream of water that moves over them because of movement of the appendages.
- Book gills and book lungs are similar, though book gills are found in aquatic arthropods and book lungs are in terrestrial arthropods. The many layers of tissue in these structures increase the surface area for gas exchange.
- In arthropods with tracheal tubes, the movement of muscles pumps air in and out of the spiracles and through the network of tubes.

MINI LAB ···· Experimenting ···

Flying to the Light

PROBLEM *How does a fly react to light? **Design an experiment** to answer this question.*

SUGGESTED PROCEDURE

1. Obtain a light source and a culture tube containing fruit flies.
2. Position the culture tube at different distances in front of the light source. Observe the behavior of the fruit flies at each position.
3. Formulate a hypothesis and design an experiment to find the farthest distance at which the light affects the behavior of the fruit flies. Check with your teacher before beginning the experiment.

ANALYZE AND CONCLUDE

1. What conclusion can you draw from your results? Explain how the data you collected support this conclusion.
2. What other variables might have affected your experiment? Explain.
3. Design an experiment to determine how the color of light affects the behavior of fruit flies.

Arthropod Structures

Arthropods have a tough exoskeleton made mostly of a carbohydrate called **chitin** (KIGH-tihn). Some exoskeletons, like those of caterpillars, are firm yet leathery. Others, especially those of ticks and some crabs, are so tough and hard that they are almost impossible to crush by hand. In many terrestrial arthropods, the exoskeleton has a waxy covering that helps prevent loss of body fluids.

In addition, an arthropod's body is divided into segments. Centipedes and millipedes can have dozens of segments, while other arthropods—such as ants—have only three. Because the exoskeleton is rigid, it contains joints between segments and parts of appendages. The joints enable body parts to flex and extend. To learn more about arthropods, study the illustration on the next page.

Feeding and Respiration

Feeding in arthropods is very diverse. The arthropods include run-of-the-mill herbivores and carnivores, as well as filter feeders, detritus feeders, bloodsuckers, and a host of specialized parasites.

To breathe, arthropods use a variety of different structures. Many aquatic species—such as lobsters and crabs—breathe through **gills,** which are featherlike organs located in a chamber beneath the exoskeleton. Horseshoe crabs breathe through **book gills,** and spiders breathe through **book lungs**—both of which are made of layers of respiratory tissue that resemble the pages in a book.

Most terrestrial arthropods, however, breathe through a branching, air-filled network of structures called **tracheal** (TRAY-kee-uhl) **tubes.** Tracheal tubes connect the arthropod's tissues with the atmosphere, and oxygen passes through the tracheal tubes by diffusion.

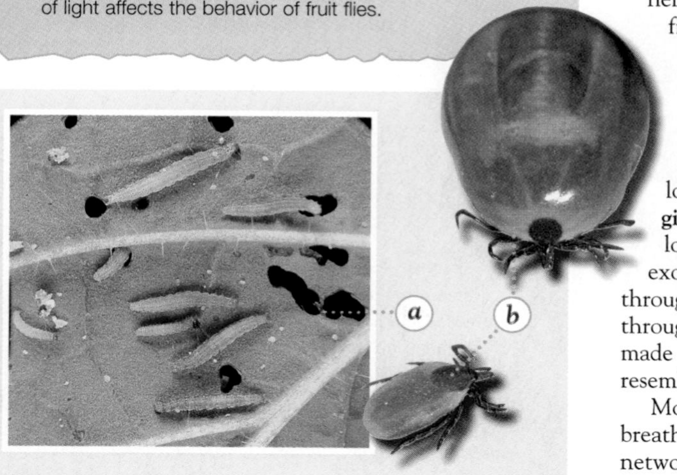

Figure 29–2
(a) These diamondback moth larvae are feeding on a cabbage leaf. (b) The larger of these two Eastern wood ticks has filled its body with a blood meal.

TEACHER SUPPORT — Background Information

The chitin that forms arthropod exoskeletons is more flexible than the calcium carbonate of which mollusk shells are made. Chitin can be molded into a variety of shapes and is less cumbersome to carry around. The chitinous exoskeleton provides the same support as a mollusk shell but does not restrict the animal's mobility. To get these advantages, however, arthropods have had to sacrifice a measure of safety: While mollusks are able to add on to their existing shells, arthropods can retain their flexibility only by molting and growing a new exoskeleton. They must do this several times during their growth and are vulnerable each time as the new exoskeleton hardens.

Insects can travel great distances quickly, regardless of the terrain, because of their wings—a feature found in no other invertebrates. Insect wings are not adaptations of legs but are separate appendages made of thin sheets of chitin held together by hollow veins.

Visualizing a Grasshopper

The bodies of all insects have three distinct parts—head, thorax, and abdomen. Most insects, including grasshoppers, have three pairs of legs.

1 Antennae
A grasshopper has one pair of antennae, which it uses as sense organs. Tiny hairs that cover the antennae can sense vibrations, molecules of food, and other stimuli.

2 Gonads
The male grasshopper produces sperm in testes, and the female, shown here, produces eggs in an ovary. After the eggs are fertilized, the female digs a hole in the ground and buries the eggs inside it.

3 Wings
Like most insects, a grasshopper has two pairs of wings. Grasshoppers not only fly with their wings but communicate with the sounds of their wings beating.

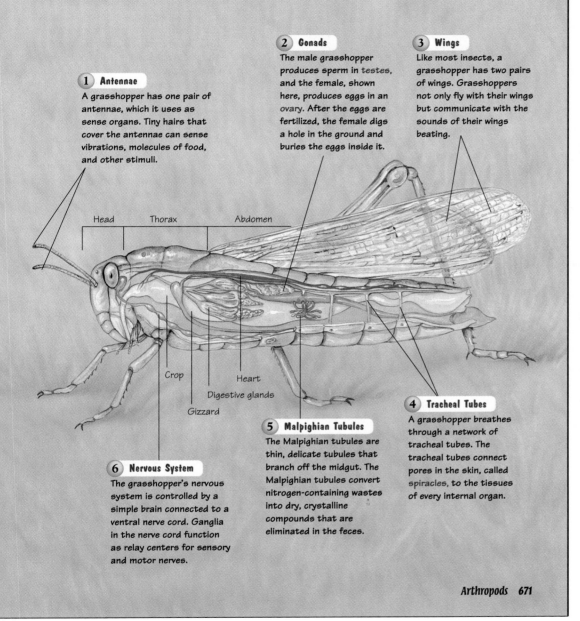

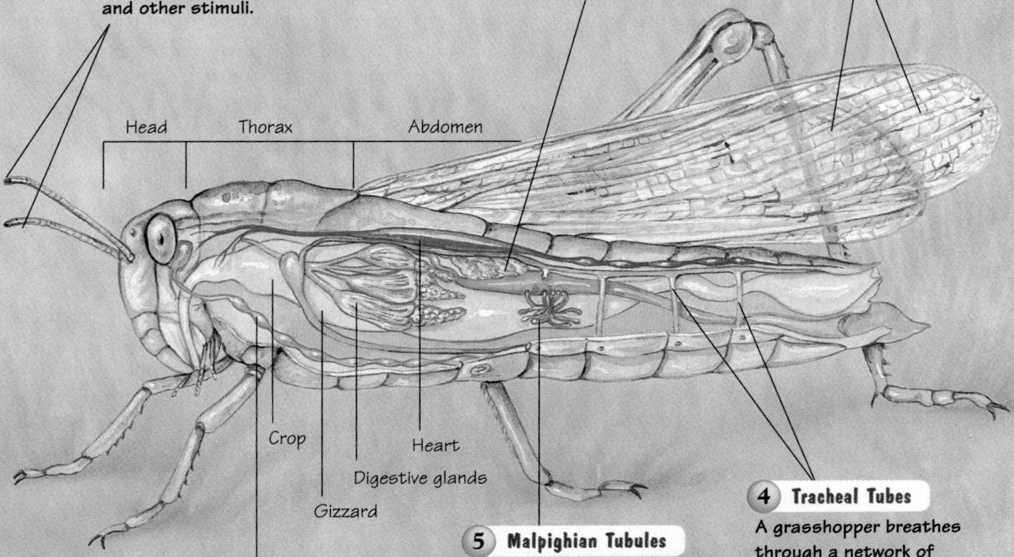

4 Tracheal Tubes
A grasshopper breathes through a network of tracheal tubes. The tracheal tubes connect pores in the skin, called spiracles, to the tissues of every internal organ.

5 Malpighian Tubules
The Malpighian tubules are thin, delicate tubules that branch off the midgut. The Malpighian tubules convert nitrogen-containing wastes into dry, crystalline compounds that are eliminated in the feces.

6 Nervous System
The grasshopper's nervous system is controlled by a simple brain connected to a ventral nerve cord. Ganglia in the nerve cord function as relay centers for sensory and motor nerves.

Visualizing a Grasshopper

Have students read the caption and the labels. Then challenge students to identify which structures are located in or on each of the three body parts. (Head: eyes, antennae, brain, mouth; thorax: wings, legs, nerve cord, digestive tract, tracheal tube, first pair of legs; abdomen: spiracles, gonads, Malpighian tubules, tracheal tubes, heart, digestive tract, nerve cord.) Make sure students understand that the grasshopper's body plan is typical of insects but not of other types of arthropods, such as spiders, crabs, crayfishes, and centipedes.

Have students compare the illustration with living grasshoppers or crickets in the habitats they set up in the Chapter Discovery Learning Activity and note any exterior features they can identify. Students should be able to locate the antennae and wings without difficulty. They may also be able to see the spiracles with a hand lens.

Also have students examine the other living arthropods in the class habitats and try to determine whether they are insects or other types of arthropods. As preparation for Section 29–2, ask students to list the features they observe as they examine the arthropods, particularly the number of body segments, pairs of legs, and antennae each organism has.

TEACHER SUPPORT

Background Information

Insects' spiracles are guarded by fine, hairlike bristles that keep out dirt and have valves that can be opened or closed to regulate airflow. A grasshopper has ten pairs of spiracles. The first four pairs open only at inspiration, and the remaining six pairs open only at expiration. Closing the valves also helps to decrease the evaporation of water.

From the system of main longitudinal and transverse tracheal tubes, smaller branches connect to all parts of the insect's body, eventually becoming so small that groups of the smallest ones (tracheoles) are formed by single cells. In some places, larger tubes widen to form air sacs. Muscular breathing movements aid in air circulation by alternately compressing the air sacs and then allowing them to expand. In the smallest branches, oxygen moves by diffusion alone—first along the tubes, then into the surrounding blood spaces and tissues. Carbon dioxide leaves by the reverse route.

Ancillary Support

The resources below can be used to support your teaching strategy for these two pages.

LM Observing the Structure of the Grasshopper, #57
TR Explore: A Breath of Fresh Water
TB Visualizing a Grasshopper, #37

Ideas Through Images

Have students examine Figure 29–3 and read the caption. Point out that each image-forming unit, called an ommatidium, is at a slightly different angle, which allows the animal to see multiple images from slightly different viewpoints at the same time. With such eyes, insects can detect slight movements and respond quickly to predators and prey. Discuss how this is an advantageous adaptation.

Investigate

Research Point out the text statement under the subhead Response and Movement that insects' ears are located in odd places. Have students find out where insects' ears are placed. For example, some have ears (i.e., vibration-sensing tympanums) on their abdomens or legs.

Discussion

Ask students to suggest why the molting period is a dangerous time for an arthropod. (When the animal sheds its old exoskeleton and its new one has not yet hardened, it is vulnerable to predators.) Also explain that some arthropods can regrow lost appendages during the molting process. If, for example, a crab's leg is seized by a predator, the leg may break off at a joint, allowing the crab to escape. A new leg begins to form at the crab's next molt and grows further with subsequent molts.

Investigate

Long-Term Project Hermit crabs do not molt as they grow. The head, thorax, legs, and claws of a hermit crab have a hard covering, but the soft abdomen is unprotected, requiring the crab to find shelter inside empty gastropod shells. When the crab outgrows its shell, it must abandon it and find a larger one. If students keep a hermit crab, provide a few empty gastropod shells larger than the crab's present one so that they may observe the crab moving from its old shell into a new one.

Figure 29–3
This image from a scanning electron microscope shows the head of a housefly (magnification: 24X). Each compound eye contains about 4000 separate image-forming units.

Transport and Excretion

Like clams and other mollusks, arthropods have an open circulatory system. A well-developed heart pumps blood through arteries into smaller vessels, from which it flows into spaces called sinuses. There, muscles slosh the blood to bathe body tissues. Eventually, the blood collects in a large sinus surrounding the heart. It then re-enters the heart and begins its journey again.

Arthropods may excrete nitrogen-containing wastes in several ways. In most terrestrial species, these wastes are excreted by dead-end sacs called **Malpighian** (mal-PIHG-ee-uhn) **tubules.** Malpighian tubules extract nitrogenous wastes from blood in body sinuses. The tubules concentrate those wastes and add them to feces moving through the gut.

Most aquatic arthropods excrete nitrogenous wastes by allowing ammonia to diffuse across gill surfaces. Marine species may also have a pair of antennal glands that control the balance of water and solutes in body fluids.

☑ ***Checkpoint*** What are Malpighian tubules? ❶

Response and Movement

Did you ever try to sneak up on a fly? Flies and most other arthropods have a well-developed nervous system and sense organs. Large compound eyes detect color and movement. Many arthropods "smell" with their feathery antennae and "taste" with sensory hairs on their legs. And although insects' ears are located in what we would consider to be odd places, they can often detect sounds far above the range that humans can hear.

Arthropods move using their well-developed muscular system, which works well with the exoskeleton. Muscles are arranged around each body joint so that some muscles flex the joint while others extend it, allowing arthropods to walk, jump, swim, or fly.

Arthropod Growth and Development

Suppose that you lived inside a suit of armor. In fact, suppose this armor enclosed every part of your body, was tailored exactly to your measurements, and was actually a part of your skin. What would happen? In a few months you would be in bad shape, because the suit of armor couldn't stretch to accommodate your growing body!

Arthropods are faced with exactly this problem because an exoskeleton is just like a suit of armor. Thus, arthropods evolved a process called **molting**—a complex, dangerous, and physiologically expensive process in which the arthropod literally changes its skin. **In molting, an arthropod sheds its entire exoskeleton and manufactures a larger one, thus allowing its body to grow.**

Molting involves many steps. As the time for molting approaches, skin glands digest the inner part of the exoskeleton. Meanwhile, other glands secrete a new

TEACHER SUPPORT

Activity

HOW DO ANTS COMMUNICATE?
The following activity will allow students to observe communication among ants.
CAUTION: *Warn students not to touch the ants.*

1. Locate an active anthill outdoors. Put a spoonful of honey on the ground about 1 meter away from it.
2. Put a sheet of paper between the honey and the anthill, and observe the ants. (Scouts will find the honey and establish a chemical trail directly back to the anthill.)
3. When ants are traveling back and forth on the trail regularly, quickly turn the paper one-quarter turn. Watch the ants closely. (The ants will seem confused as they search for the old trail.)
4. How do the ants' movements change over time? (Some will discover the honey's new location and establish a new chemical trail.)

Figure 29–4
(a) *Molting allows arthropods to grow and develop. This photograph shows a* Libellula depressa *dragonfly emerging from its old exoskeleton.*
(b) *Arthropods that undergo incomplete metamorphosis do not change as drastically as those that undergo complete metamorphosis. While a grasshopper retains the same body plan throughout its life, a butterfly changes from a wormlike larva to a winged adult.*

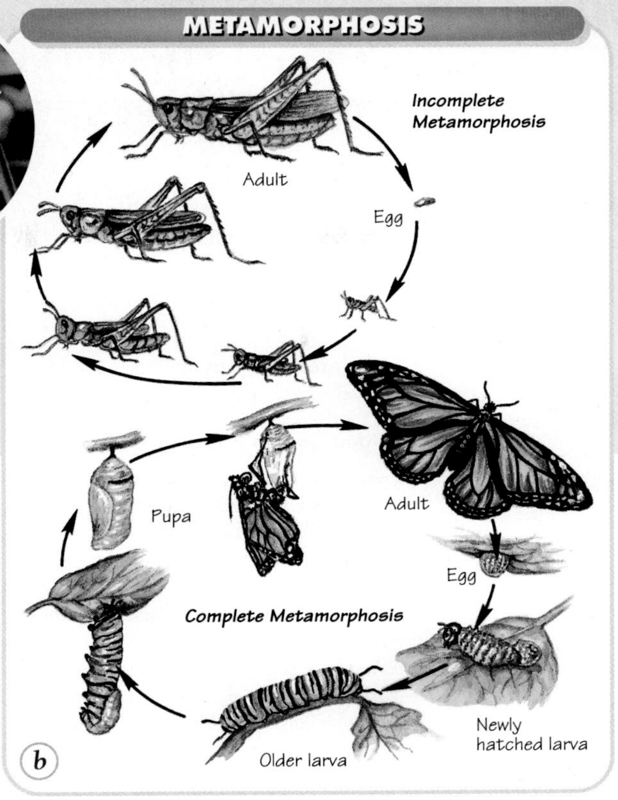

skeleton, which at first is quite soft. When the arthropod is ready, it pulls itself out of what remains of the original skeleton—a process so difficult that it can take several hours. As soon as the arthropod is free, it usually eats its old skin, thus recycling chitin and minerals.

Before the new exoskeleton hardens, the arthropod pumps itself with air or fluids to enlarge itself. This makes the new exoskeleton as large as possible before molting is necessary again.

Molting not only allows arthropods to change size, it allows them to change their form and shape, a process called **metamorphosis.** As shown in ***Figure 29–4,*** some arthropods undergo incomplete metamorphosis, which involves minimal changes. Others undergo complete metamorphosis, which produces distinct larval, pupal, and adult stages.

You probably know all about caterpillars turning into butterflies. But that familiarity should not hide the wonder of this change. Just try to imagine a baby mouse changing into an adult bird. Even in aquatic arthropods that don't have a pupal stage, metamorphosis could be compared to a mouse changing into a guinea pig that grows into an elephant!

Section Review 29–1

1. **Describe** an arthropod's body.
2. **Explain** the purpose of molting.
3. **Critical Thinking—Analyzing Events** The first arthropods—the trilobites—lived in the sea. Describe the features that help terrestrial arthropods adapt to life on land.
4. **MINI LAB** How can you **design an experiment** to determine a fly's response to light?

4 ASSESS

Quick Check

Have students sketch a grasshopper (or other typical insect) and label its three main body sections and major external features.

Section Review 29–1

1. The body is segmented, has jointed appendages, and is surrounded by a tough exoskeleton.

2. Molting allows the arthropod's body to grow.

3. Book lungs or tracheal tubes enable arthropods to breathe the surrounding air; Malpighian tubules enable them to excrete nitrogen-containing wastes; wings allow some arthropods to fly; a waxy covering on the exoskeleton helps prevent loss of body fluids.

4. By holding a fly culture at various distances from a light source or by using colored filters over the light.

Skills Trace
Experimenting

- Focus p. 670
- **Practice p. 673**
- Assess p. 685

Checkpoint

1 Malpighian tubules are dead-end sacs that extract nitrogenous wastes from blood in body sinuses, concentrate the wastes, and add them to feces moving through the gut.

Learning Modality

Visual and Tactile Learning Let students use materials of their own choice to make a simple two- or three-dimensional model of a typical insect's body plan, then attach tags labeling the three main body sections and major exterior structures such as antennae.

Ancillary Support

The resources below can be used to support your teaching strategy for these two pages.

TR Writing in Biology: Who Am I?
BL Inquiry Activity: A Bug in Shining Armor

Section 29–2

A Tour of the Arthropods

Performance Objectives

- Identify the three arthropod subphyla and the major characteristics of each.
- Describe the body structures that differentiate insects from other arthropods.

Mini Lab Skill: Inferring

1 ENGAGE

Ideas Through Images

Have students examine Figure 29–5, read the caption, and answer the following questions.

- **In what ways are these arthropods alike?** (All have an exoskeleton and a segmented body.)
- **In what ways are they different?** (Answers may include differences in the number of walking legs—five pairs in the horseshoe crab, four pairs in the scorpion, and three pairs in the bedbug—and differences in the number of body segments.)

2 EXPLORE

Inquiry Activity

Comparing

Grouping Arthropods

Have students review the lists they made when they examined the phylum of arthropods to determine which were insects (see Visualizing a Grasshopper on page 671). Ask them to list the arthropods' names in separate columns so the animals are grouped according to common features—for example, one, two, or three body parts; three, four, or more than four pairs of walking legs; and one pair, two pairs, or no antennae.

SECTION 29–2

A Tour of the Arthropods

Guide for Reading

- **Describe** each subphylum of arthropods.
- **Identify** the structure of insects.

MINI LAB

- **Infer** how crustaceans move by studying a shrimp.

YOU COULD SPEND A LIFETIME touring the arthropods—the largest phylum of the animal kingdom. Millions of species live all over the Earth, and their ways of making a living are diverse enough to boggle the imagination.

Living arthropods are divided into three groups called subphyla, each of which contains several classes. One of these classes—insects—includes more species than any other class of multicellular organisms.

Chelicerates

Spiders are the most familiar members of the subphylum Chelicerata (kuh-lihs-er-AT-uh), which also includes mites, scorpions, and horseshoe crabs. **A chelicerate has a body that is divided into two parts—a cephalothorax and an abdomen.** The **cephalothorax** includes the head and carries the legs. The **abdomen** contains most internal organs.

Chelicerates also have two pairs of unique, specialized mouthparts. The first pair are called **chelicerae** (kuh-LIHS-er-ee), from which the subphylum gets its name. The second pair are known as **pedipalps.** Chelicerae and pedipalps serve different purposes in different species.

☑ **Checkpoint** What are the chelicerates? ❶

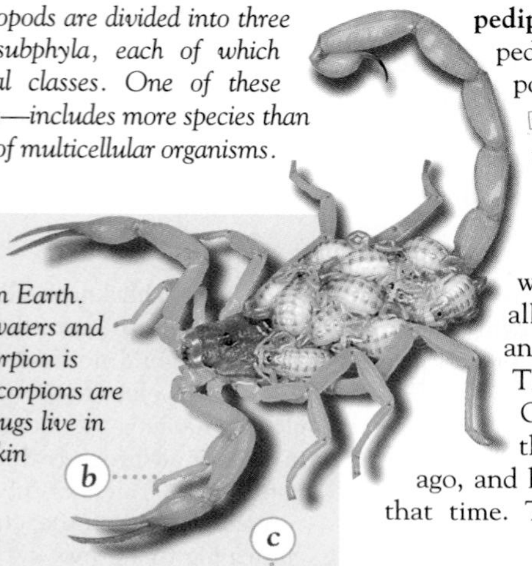

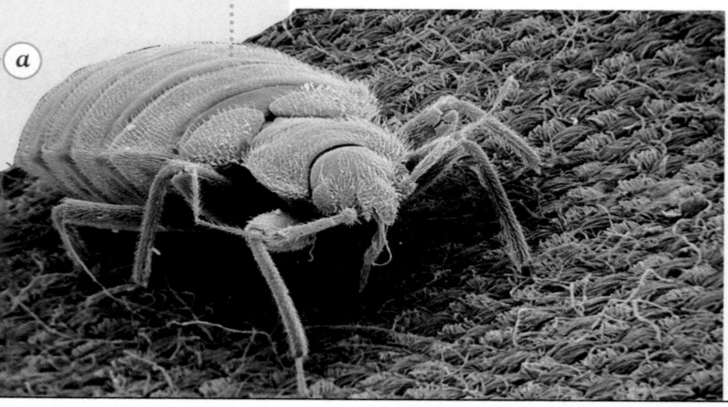

Figure 29–5 Arthropods live almost everywhere on Earth. (a) Horseshoe crabs live in shallow waters and sandy beaches. (b) This female scorpion is carrying her offspring on her back. Scorpions are common in deserts. (c) Tiny bedbugs live in bedsheets, where they feed on dead skin cells (magnification: 10X).

Horseshoe Crabs

The horseshoe crabs—which aren't true crabs at all—are among the most ancient living arthropods. They first appeared in the Ordovician Period, more than 430 million years ago, and have changed little since that time. The larvae of horseshoe

TEACHER SUPPORT

Ecology Note

Some of the largest animals on Earth, whales, eat some of the smallest animals on Earth, krill. Krill are shrimplike crustaceans that swarm in countless numbers throughout the oceans, particularly in cold arctic waters. Although only about 5 cm long, krill are the main food of many large whales, including the great blue whale—the largest animal that ever lived.

Whales that eat krill do not have teeth but have large, fringed plates of baleen hanging from the roof of the mouth. The whale feeds by swimming through a mass of krill with its mouth open. The whale then uses its tongue to squeeze the water back out through the baleen, leaving the krill behind to be swallowed.

Other large animals—including the world's largest fishes, basking sharks and whale sharks—also eat krill. These fishes filter krill from the water with structures projecting from their gills. Some seabirds and seals also eat these crustaceans.

crabs resemble even more ancient arthropods—so much so that they are called trilobite larvae.

Arachnids

Spiders, mites, ticks, and scorpions are grouped in the class Arachnida (uh-RAK-nih-duh). All arachnids have four pairs of walking legs attached to their cephalothorax.

Spiders are predators, usually of other arthropods. Some spiders lie in ambush and pounce on their prey. But more commonly, spiders spin intricate webs, such as the one shown in ***Figure 29–6.***

Mites and ticks, which usually live as parasites of plants and animals, are the only arachnids that typically target humans and domesticated plants and animals. Their chelicerae and pedipalps are specialized for digging into host tissues and sucking out blood or plant fluids.

In scorpions, the pedipalps evolved into large claws, while their elongated abdomens carry a venomous stinger. Although a scorpion's sting is painful to humans—and occasionally fatal—its normal prey are insects or other small invertebrates.

Figure 29–6 (a) *This spider,* Argiope aurantia, *builds round webs in open areas. The silk of a spider web is incredibly strong and thin.* (b) *Although crustaceans are very diverse, the crayfish is a good representative. As in an arachnid, the head and thorax of a crayfish are fused into a rigid cephalothorax, which carries mouthparts, claws, and walking legs.*

Crustaceans

The subphylum Crustacea (kruhs-TAY-shee-uh) includes crabs, shrimps, and crayfishes. Although most of the 35,000 crustacean species live in the ocean, some live in fresh water and a few live in moist places on land. Crustaceans range in size from *Daphnia,* a tiny water flea, to spider crabs that have a mass of up to 20 kilograms.

Nearly all crustaceans have two pairs of antennae, several pairs of mouthparts, and appendages with two branches. One specialized pair of mouthparts is the **mandibles,** which in different crustaceans are adapted for a variety of uses. The appendages typically contain a leg, claw, or mouthpart on the outer branch and a gill on the inner branch. In addition, crustaceans often incorporate calcium carbonate into their exoskeleton, making it especially strong.

☑ **Checkpoint** What are crustaceans? ❷

Uniramians

Centipedes, millipedes, and insects belong to the subphylum Uniramia (yoo-nih-RAH-mee-uh). **All uniramians have a single pair of antennae and appendages with only a single branch.** The uniramians are by far the most diverse, widespread, and successful of the three arthropod subphyla.

3 TEACH

Investigate

Research Point out the text statement in the second paragraph under the subhead Chelicerates that chelicerae and pedipalps serve different purposes in different chelicerate species. Encourage interested students to do research to find out what these various functions are and then report their findings to the class.

Investigate

Research Ask students to consult other sources to find diagrams of a spider's and a crayfish's body plan to compare with the insect body plan pictured on page 671.

☑ Checkpoints

❶ Arthropods with a body divided into two parts and with two pairs of specialized mouthparts.

❷ Arthropods with two pairs of antennae, several pairs of mouthparts, and appendages with two branches.

Technology

BioVue
Mini Doc: Insects Are High Society
Videodisc Side 7

Go to Chapter 15

TEACHER SUPPORT

Activity

MODELING AN ARTHROPOD'S EXOSKELETON

Ask students to bring in wide-diameter cardboard tubes. Also provide manilla folders and sheets of lightweight, flexible cardboard. Challenge groups to construct an arachnid, crustacean, or insect exoskeleton that will fit one student in the group.

Tell students to make the exoskeletons as accurate as they can, using the diagram on page 671, the photographs throughout the chapter, and the text descriptions as guidelines. Also caution them to make sure that the arthropod's soft, inner tissues are not exposed when its body segments or appendages are bent at a joint. (Students will have to overlap skeletal plates at joints.) Let students add antennae, eyes, and other structures.

Have each group demonstrate its model to the rest of the class and explain its parts. Also ask the student wearing the exoskeleton to describe how it feels as he or she moves.

Ancillary Support

The resources below can be used to support your teaching strategy for these two pages.

LM Investigating Isopod Environments, #58
TR Apply: Great Balls o' Isopods!
BL Inquiry Activity: The Wide, Wide World of Arthropods

MINI LAB Inferring

Teacher Notes
- For time required and materials needed, see page 668b.
- Remind students to wash their hands after they have finished the procedure.

Answers to Analyze and Conclude

1. It contracts its ventral muscles and spreads its fanlike sections, so that it jerks backward in the water. It also walks and swims with its legs.
2. Ventral side, because it is not completely covered with exoskeleton.

Skills Trace
Inferring
- Focus p. 676
- Practice p. 676
- Assess p. 685

4 ASSESS

Quick Check

Have each student summarize the major characteristics of chelicerates, crustaceans, and insects in a three-column chart.

Section Review 29–2

1. Chelicerates: body divided into two parts, two pairs of mouthparts. Crustaceans: two pairs of antennae, several pairs of mouthparts, appendages with two branches. Uniramians: one pair of antennae, appendages with one branch.

2. Three-part body (head, thorax, abdomen); three pairs of legs.

3. The sticky silk snags and holds prey that strikes the web. The spider walks on the nonsticky silk.

4. They contract their muscles to bend their bodies at the joints; most use their legs for walking and the muscles in their abdomens for swimming.

Skills Trace
Inferring
- Focus p. 676
- Practice p. 676
- Assess p. 685

MINI LAB .... Inferring ....

What's a Shrimp?

PROBLEM *What can you **infer** about the way in which crustaceans move by studying a shrimp?*

PROCEDURE

1. Obtain a shrimp from your teacher. Sketch the shrimp's body, and note any appendages. Label the parts of the shrimp that you can identify.
2. Open and close each joint in the shrimp's exoskeleton. In your sketch, identify the locations of the joints.
3. Compare the dorsal (top) and ventral (bottom) sides of the shrimp.

ANALYZE AND CONCLUDE

1. From your data, what can you infer about a shrimp's range of motion and the way it moves from place to place? Explain your answer.
2. Do you suspect that a shrimp is more easily attacked from its dorsal or its ventral side? Explain.

Centipedes and Millipedes

Because the exoskeletons of centipedes and millipedes lack a waterproof covering, these uniramians live in moist places. Centipedes are typically carnivores that eat other arthropods, earthworms, small amphibians, or even small snakes and mice. All body segments except the first and last carry a single pair of legs. Millipedes feed on dead and decaying plant material, and they carry two pairs of legs on each segment.

Insects

Estimates of the total number of insect species vary by several million! Despite their diversity, members of the class Insecta have certain features in common. **All insects have a three-part body consisting of head, thorax, and abdomen, and three pairs of legs.** Many insects also have two pairs of wings attached to the thorax and a single pair of antennae.

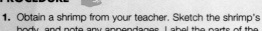

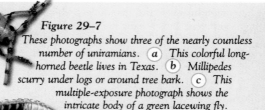

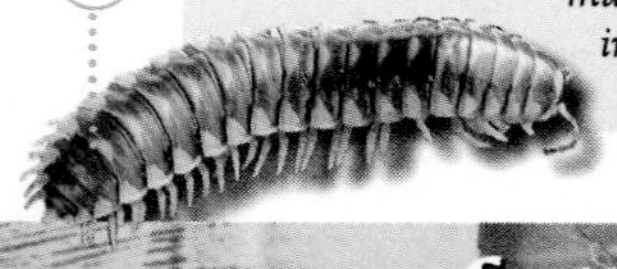

Figure 29–7
These photographs show three of the nearly countless number of uniramians. (a) This colorful long-horned beetle lives in Texas. (b) Millipedes scurry under logs or around tree bark. (c) This multiple-exposure photograph shows the intricate body of a green lacewing fly.

Section Review 29–2

1. **Describe** the characteristics of chelicerates, crustaceans, and uniramians.
2. **Identify** the structure of insects.
3. **Critical Thinking—Inferring** Spiders use two kinds of silk in their web—one that is sticky and one that is not. Infer why they need both types of silk.
4. **MINI LAB** What can you **infer** about how crustaceans move by studying a shrimp?

Learning Modality

Visual and Kinesthetic Learning Obtain picture cards (preferably photographs) showing a variety of arthropods, and have students sort them into groups representing the three arthropod subphyla.

The Importance of Arthropods

GUIDE FOR READING

- Discuss the importance of arthropods.

WHAT ANIMALS MAKE THE world go round? You could make a case for the Earth's tiny armor-plated creatures—arthropods. From bees that flit from flower to flower to insect pests that feed on crops, arthropods seem to be everywhere—influencing life on Earth in all sorts of ways. To get an idea of the arthropods' impact, consider this astonishing fact: In the Amazon basin, the total mass of living ants and termites alone accounts for nearly one third of all animal biomass there!

Arthropod Interactions

Because arthropods are so varied and numerous, their roles in food webs, nutrient cycles, and partnerships with other animals are enormously important in nearly every habitat. Arthropods eat plants, animals, decomposing organic matter—and each other. In the process, they form a variety of symbiotic relationships with other organisms. Some are mutualistic partnerships, such as the partnership between bees and flowers, as illustrated in ***Figure 29–8***.

However, other arthropods live in relationships that are not so pleasant. Several arthropods sting or bite humans—as you probably already know! Bees and wasps typically sting to defend themselves, and some arthropods bite as part of their life cycle. A female mosquito, for example, needs a blood meal from a human or other animal to develop her eggs. Although bites from arthropods are usually only irritating, they can transmit organisms that cause serious diseases, such as malaria, encephalitis, and Lyme disease.

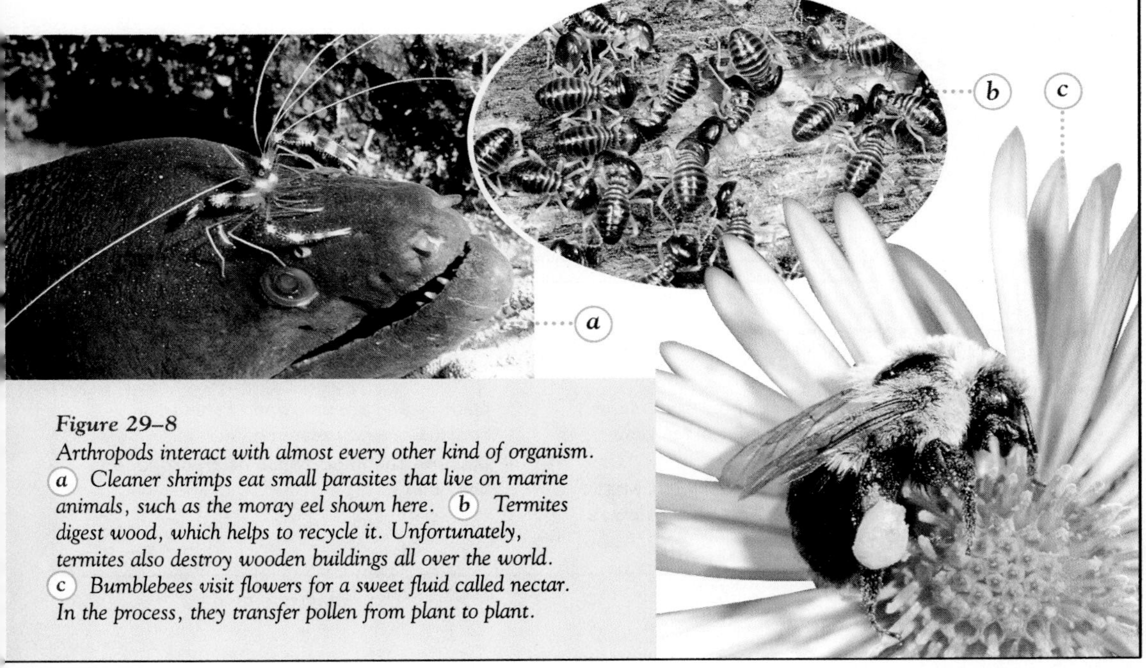

Figure 29–8
Arthropods interact with almost every other kind of organism. (a) Cleaner shrimps eat small parasites that live on marine animals, such as the moray eel shown here. (b) Termites digest wood, which helps to recycle it. Unfortunately, termites also destroy wooden buildings all over the world. (c) Bumblebees visit flowers for a sweet fluid called nectar. In the process, they transfer pollen from plant to plant.

TEACHER SUPPORT

Managing Classroom Diversity

TECH PREP STUDENTS

Encourage students who are planning careers in public health or health care to research diseases that are transmitted by insects and other arthropods and dangerous conditions that are caused by them. An excellent source of such information is *Dangerous Insects* by Missy Allen and Michel Peissel. For each of the 25 arthropods included, the book presents a description of the organism's physical characteristics and behavior, a color-coded world map showing where it is found, the infection or injury it causes, the symptoms of a bite or sting, treatments for the injury it causes, and ways to prevent exposure.

Also ask students to research the condition known as anaphylactic shock, a life-threatening reaction that occurs in a person who is highly allergic to a specific substance. For some individuals, the substance may be peanuts or eggs, and for some it may be the toxin in the bite or sting of a wasp, hornet, or bee.

SECTION 29–3

The Importance of Arthropods

Performance Objective

- Describe how arthropods are important.

Laboratory Investigation Skill: Experimenting

1 ENGAGE

Inquiry Activity

Observing

Identifying Arthropods in Soil

Ask students what types of arthropods live in soil. Take the class outdoors to a field, vacant lot, or wooded area, and have each group mark a 0.5-m^2 area on the ground. Let students dig up the soil to a depth of 8–10 cm and examine it for living arthropods, pupae, and molted exoskeletons. Have them identify as many of the arthropods as they can on their own and using field guides.

2 EXPLORE

Investigate

Cooperative Learning Have each group of four students list as many arthropods as they can, with the first student listing arthropods that are harmful to plants, the second student listing arthropods that are harmful to humans, the third listing arthropods that are harmful to other animals, and the fourth listing arthropods that are beneficial in any way. Let groups share their lists in a class discussion.

3 TEACH

Problem Solving
Interpreting Graphs
Do Pesticides Kill Soil-Dwelling Arthropods?

State The problem is to analyze the data in the graph and draw conclusions about the effects of three pesticides on arthropods in the soil.
Solve Students should compare the data for the pesticides to the data for the control. Control: The population of soil-dwelling arthropods remained fairly constant over time. Pesticide A: Soon after the pesticide was sprayed, the population decreased significantly and remained below the population of the control. Pesticide B: The population decreased slightly at first but then recovered and increased dramatically, surpassing the population of the control. Pesticide C: The population varied slightly but overall remained fairly constant and similar to the population of the control. Conclusion: Pesticide C had the least effect on soil-dwelling arthropods.
Test Student groups can conduct this experiment themselves outdoors, which will give them practice in collecting, graphing, and analyzing data, and drawing conclusions.
Communicate Students should describe the data on the graph, explain what the data mean, and draw conclusions. Students may reach consensus or may decide that multiple alternate conclusions exist for one or more of the data sets.

Answers to THINK ABOUT IT
1. They varied slightly.
2. See **Solve** above.
3. Answers will vary.
4. Arthropods help decompose organic matter and aerate soil. They also harm crops.

Problem Solving
INTERPRETING GRAPHS

Do Pesticides Kill Soil-Dwelling Arthropods?

Suppose you are trying to grow zucchini in your garden but have been discouraged because insects are gobbling up your plants. Your neighbor loans you three pesticide sprays—each deadly to a certain arthropod species. However, you are concerned that after a pesticide is applied, it could find its way into the soil and harm arthropods there, too.

To compare the pesticides, you test them on three small plots of soil. You also monitor a fourth plot of soil as a control.

In your experiment, you first collect a ten-liter sample of soil from the center of each plot and count the number of individual arthropods living in the sample. Then you apply a different pesticide to three of the plots but apply no pesticide to the fourth plot. Every day for the next three weeks, you collect ten-liter samples of soil from each plot and count the arthropods in the samples. The graph shows the results of this experiment.

RESULTS OF TESTS ON THREE PESTICIDES

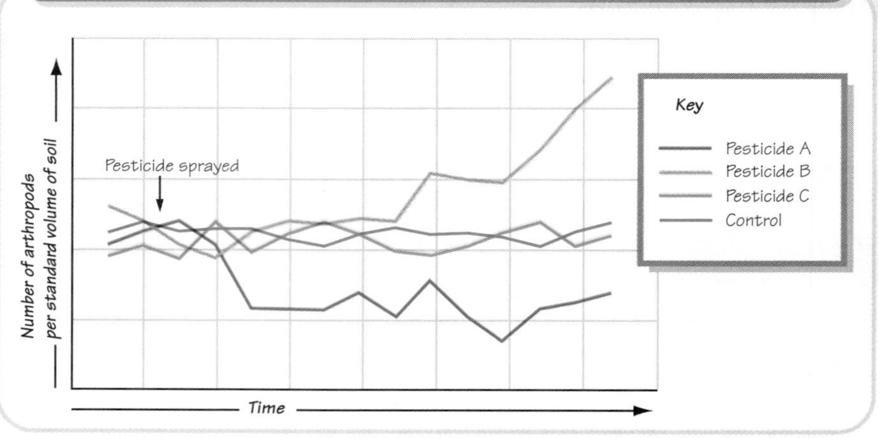

THINK ABOUT IT

1. **Compare** the number of arthropods in each plot before the pesticides were applied.
2. For each of the three pesticides, what can you **conclude** about the pesticide's effects?
3. **Identify** any assumptions behind the conclusions you reached.
4. **Discuss** the importance of arthropods in the soil.

TEACHER SUPPORT

Ecology Note

Soil, though only a few centimeters to a few meters in depth, is a dynamic biome teeming with life representing all five kingdoms of living organisms. These organisms help to form and enrich soil as they live and die. Arthropods are well represented among soil-dwelling organisms, and they play important roles. Ants, for example, are second only to earthworms as the soil's prime movers, creating porosity for air and water to enter, as well as adding and mixing organic matter in the soil. Insect larvae, various beetles, crickets, mites, and springtails are all found in the soil and are vital to soil food webs. These and other soil-dwelling arthropods also help supply soil with organic matter, which decays to form humus. Humus gives soil nutrients, good texture, and water-holding ability.

Not surprisingly, arthropods inflict damage on plants and plant products, too. Insects are common pests of nearly every agricultural crop, and farmers spend huge amounts of time and money trying to kill or control them.

The Pollination Crisis

To reproduce, most flowering plants depend on pollination—the transfer of pollen from one flower to another. Plants have evolved all sorts of mechanisms for pollination, but by far the most significant rely on animals. In fact, out of every three mouthfuls of food you eat, one mouthful depends on plants pollinated by animals!

Most people think only of honeybees and bumblebees as pollinators. But mosquitoes pollinate orchids in peat bogs, scarab beetles pollinate Amazonian water lilies, and there are many other examples. Biologists estimate that animal pollinators include between 130,000 and 200,000 animal species—most of which are insects.

Unfortunately, pollinators in the United States are in trouble. Their problems began almost 400 years ago, when colonists in Jamestown, Virginia, introduced European honeybees to North America. These bees spread into every habitat in the continent, competing with native pollinators and reducing their numbers. Native pollinators suffered another blow in the 1950s, when the widespread use of pesticides cut their population by more than 20 percent. As a result, many plants in the United States now rely on European honeybees as their principal pollinators.

Figure 29–9
CAREER TRACK
Entomologists study insects and the ways in which insects affect life on Earth.

This might not be so bad—except now honeybees are also in trouble! In the past 15 years, mites and other parasites have infected honeybee colonies, in some cases killing up to half the members of a hive. In addition, honeybees in South America have interbred with aggressive African bees. These Africanized honeybees reached Texas in 1990, and they are sure to spread farther in the years ahead. These bees carry diseases and attack humans.

Researchers estimate that if the pollinators' problems continue, up to a third of the United States alfalfa crop could be lost, and damage to other crops could cost more than $1.25 billion. Researchers have just begun to study this growing problem. Its solution is vital for both agriculture and conservation.

INTEGRATING AGRICULTURE

Which insects are pests of the crops raised in your state? How do farmers control these pests?

Section Review 29–3

1. **Discuss** the importance of arthropods.
2. **BRANCHING OUT ACTIVITY** Select a flowering plant species that is common where you live. **Design an experiment** to determine whether insects pollinate this species. Conduct the experiment only with your teacher's supervision.

Laboratory Investigation

The Laboratory Investigation, Feeding Fly Larvae, on pages 680–681 is appropriate to use at this point in the chapter.

INTEGRATING AGRICULTURE

Encourage students to contact your state or county agricultural agency or to interview local farmers.

Discussion

Discuss the role of bees and other insects as pollinators. Introduce the concept of coevolution and explain how some plants and animals have evolved structures and behaviors in response to changes in one another over time. For example, some plants have evolved bright-colored flowers, strong fragrances, or sweet nectar as adaptations to attract pollinating animals.

4 ASSESS

Quick Check

Have each student list three examples of the benefits of arthropods and three examples of the damage or diseases they may cause.

Section Review 29–3

1. Arthropods eat plants, animals, decomposing organic matter, and one another. In the process, they form a variety of symbiotic relationships with other organisms, including the mutualistic partnership of pollination. Arthropods can transmit organisms that cause serious diseases. They also inflict damage on plants and plant products.

2. Experiments should involve close observation to identify insect pollinators. Provide field guides so students can identify any unfamiliar insect species.

Learning Modality

Visual Learning Have students classify each arthropod activity shown in Figure 29–8 as beneficial or harmful to humans and other organisms.

Ancillary Support

The resources below can be used to support your teaching strategy for these two pages.

TR Enrich: On the March!
BL Inquiry Activity: People and Pollinators

Chapter 29

Laboratory Investigation

Feeding Fly Larvae

Before the Lab

1. Students could use larvae from the fruit fly culture used for the MINI LAB, Flying to the Light, on page 670. If you purchase larvae from a biological supply company, make sure you order them well in advance for delivery by the date on which students will need them.
2. Gather various samples of food, including cooked oatmeal, canned pumpkin, and ripe fruit, or ask students to bring samples of food from home.
3. For the experiment they design in More to Explore, students can use arthropods from the class habitats they set up in the Chapter Discovery Learning Activity or others they have collected expressly for the experiment.

Pre-Lab Discussion

Have students read the entire procedure for this investigation. Then ask students the following questions.

What is the purpose of this investigation? (To observe the behavior of fruit fly larvae and determine which foods they prefer.)

In step 3, what would be the control setup? (One section of the circle—or a separate circle—that does not contain any food.)

Why should you include a control setup? (The larvae's behavior might be the result of other factors besides the types of food offered. By comparing the control and experimental setups, students can determine which behaviors are responses to the foods only.)

Laboratory Investigation

DESIGNING AN EXPERIMENT

Feeding Fly Larvae

Fruit fly larvae are particularly fond of yeast and other microorganisms present in overripe, fermenting fruit. In this investigation, you will determine which foods fruit fly larvae prefer.

Problem

Which foods do fruit fly larvae prefer? **Design an experiment** to answer this question.

Suggested Materials

- drawing paper
- pencil
- drawing compass
- metric ruler
- various foods
- yeast
- water
- fruit fly larvae

Suggested Procedure

1. **Using a compass, draw a circle with a diameter of 10 cm on a sheet of paper. You may also want to use the pencil and ruler to draw more lines at any time during the investigation.**
2. **Working with a partner, choose four different food samples you will test to find which one the fruit fly larvae prefer. You might try cooked oatmeal, canned pumpkin, or pieces of crushed ripe fruit.**

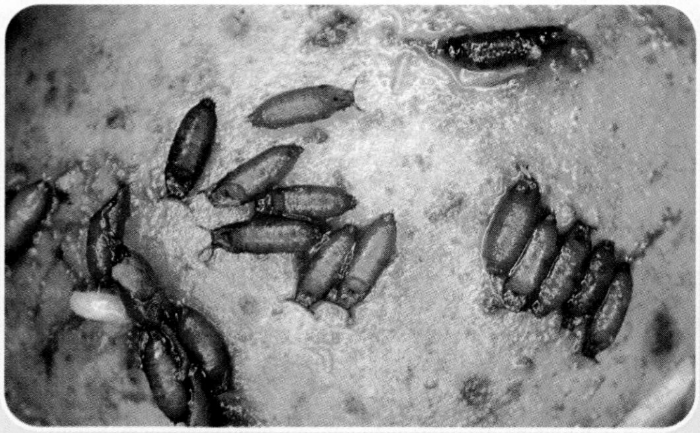

Safety Tips

- Make sure students handle the organisms gently so as not to cause them harm.
- Remind students not to eat any of the food samples.
- Have students wash their hands when they have finished the procedure.

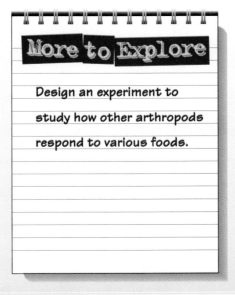

3. **Decide how to arrange the food and larvae on the paper circle. Remember to include a control setup and to verify your experiment by repeating it.**
4. **Discuss with your partner what behaviors you will look for during each test.**
5. **Check with your teacher before carrying out the experiment. Make sure you keep a record of your procedure and observations at each step.**

Observations

1. Prepare a data table to record the types of food and the reactions of the fruit fly larvae.
2. Describe the behavior of the larvae during each part of your experiment.

Analysis and Conclusions

1. Which of the four foods did the fruit fly larvae prefer? What evidence in your data table supports your conclusion?
2. How do you think fruit fly larvae sense food?
3. What sources of error could be present in your experiment?
4. How would you improve your experiment if you were to do it again?
5. Examine the laboratory investigations done by other pairs of students. What did you learn that gave you ideas about how you might change your own investigation?

More to Explore

Design an experiment to study how other arthropods respond to various foods.

Answers to Observations

1. Students should record the behaviors they observe, as well as the number of larvae that feed on each type of food.
2. Accept a variety of responses, such as waving the head end around as though sensing the foods, moving toward one or more foods, remaining on one type of food to feed, leaving one food to move to another, and the like. Make sure students describe observable behavior, not such subjective evaluations as "They liked the crushed banana."

Answers to Analysis and Conclusions

1. Answers will depend on the types of foods used, but in general the larvae will prefer overripe fresh fruits over unripe or canned fruits and other types of foods. Students should cite evidence such as the number of larvae that remained to feed on a particular food.
2. Students might suggest tactile hairs or olfactory organs that sense odors.
3. If students presented foods that were too similar (e.g., three types of overripe fruits), larvae may cluster on one by chance, not because it is a preferred food. Putting the four foods at different distances from the larvae could also skew the results.
4. Accept all reasonable responses.
5. Answers will depend on the various experimental designs of students.

More to Explore

Students could put various foods in the class arthropod habitats, repeat the laboratory investigation procedure with other arthropods, or design an original experiment. (**CAUTION:** Warn students not to include raw meat or poultry among the foods. If they opt to put foods in the habitats, instruct them to remove and discard any uneaten foods at the end of the day to prevent spoilage.)

Skills Development

Students will use these skills while completing the laboratory investigation: designing an experiment, observing, communicating, inferring, and drawing conclusions.

Teaching Strategies

1. In step 1, students may want to draw lines to divide the circle into four equal sections, then place a different food in each section in step 2.
2. If students have difficulty deciding how to arrange the food and larvae in step 3, suggest that they put the foods at the circle's perimeter and all of the larvae in the center.
3. Have students dispose of the food samples when they have completed the procedure.

Study Guide

Review Strategy

Ask each small group of students to choose one type of arthropod described in this chapter and, in chart form, to identify its scientific classification and describe its physical features, behavior, and benefits and/or dangers to humans and other organisms. Then have groups combine their charts to make a class chart. Let students use this class chart to quiz one another about arthropods.

Study Guide

Summarizing Key Concepts

The key concepts in each section of this chapter are listed below to help you review the chapter content. Make sure you understand each concept and its relationship to other concepts and to the theme of this chapter.

29–1 Arthropod Form and Function

- Arthropods have segmented bodies, jointed appendages, and are surrounded by a tough exoskeleton.
- Most terrestrial arthropods breathe through a network of tracheal tubes. Nitrogen-containing wastes are eliminated by Malpighian tubules.
- In molting, an arthropod sheds its entire exoskeleton and manufactures a larger one, thus allowing the arthropod's body to grow.
- Some arthropods—such as grasshoppers—undergo incomplete metamorphosis, in which they grow larger but do not change drastically as they molt. Other arthropods—such as butterflies—undergo complete metamorphosis, involving distinct larval and pupal stages.

29–2 A Tour of the Arthropods

- A chelicerate has a body that is divided into two parts—a cephalothorax and an abdomen. The chelicerates include horseshoe crabs, spiders, mites, ticks, and scorpions.
- Nearly all crustaceans have two pairs of antennae, a pair of specialized mouthparts, and appendages with two branches. The crustaceans include crabs, shrimps, and crayfishes.
- Uniramians have a single pair of antennae and appendages with only a single branch. Uniramians include centipedes, millipedes, and insects.
- All insects have a three-part body consisting of head, thorax, and abdomen, and three pairs of legs.

29–3 The Importance of Arthropods

- Because arthropods are so varied and numerous, their roles in food webs, nutrient cycles, and partnerships with other animals are important in nearly every habitat.
- The United States is facing a pollination crisis because of threats to bees and to native pollinators.

Reviewing Key Terms

Review the following vocabulary terms and their meaning. Then use each term in a complete sentence.

29–1 Arthropod Form and Function

chitin
gill
book gill
book lung
tracheal tube
testis
ovary
spiracle
Malpighian tubule
molting
metamorphosis

29–2 A Tour of the Arthropods

cephalothorax
abdomen
chelicera
pedipalp
mandible

Inquiry-Based Strategy

Have each group design an experiment as described in the Inquiry-Based Strategy for Chapter 28 (page 664), focusing on one easily observed life function such as feeding, movement, response to stimuli, or reproduction—including complete and incomplete metamorphosis. Some questions that students might like to investigate are suggested below.

- What behaviors does a web-building spider evidence when a prey insect strikes its web?
- How long is each stage and the entire cycle of metamorphosis for [a specific type of insect]? How does temperature affect the cycle?
- How do the larvae and/or adults of [a specific type of arthropod] respond to touch? What is the survival benefit of this response?
- Do [larvae or adults of a specific arthropod] prefer light or dark environments? What is the survival benefit of this behavior?
- Are male crickets territorial?

Recalling Main Ideas

Choose the letter of the answer that best completes the statement or answers the question.

1. The first arthropods to appear in the fossil record are the
   - **a.** mosquitoes.
   - **b.** trilobites.
   - **c.** velvet worms.
   - **d.** annelid worms.
2. An arthropod's exoskeleton is made mostly of
   - **a.** calcium carbonate.
   - **b.** protein.
   - **c.** chitin.
   - **d.** wax.
3. Lobsters, crabs, and other aquatic arthropods breathe through
   - **a.** gills.
   - **b.** tracheal tubes.
   - **c.** book lungs.
   - **d.** Malpighian tubules.
4. Because grasshoppers do not change their body shape drastically as they molt, their pattern of growth is called
   - **a.** exoskeleton growth.
   - **b.** pupal growth.
   - **c.** complete metamorphosis.
   - **d.** incomplete metamorphosis.
5. Which of these organisms is an arachnid?
   - **a.** centipede
   - **b.** spider
   - **c.** grasshopper
   - **d.** horseshoe crab
6. Water fleas, spider crabs, and crayfishes are members of the subphylum
   - **a.** Chelicerata.
   - **b.** Uniramia.
   - **c.** Crustacea.
   - **d.** *Macrotermes.*
7. The exoskeletons of centipedes and millipedes lack
   - **a.** a waterproof covering.
   - **b.** body segments.
   - **c.** spiracles.
   - **d.** chitin.
8. Termites are significant to humans because they
   - **a.** feed on dead skin cells.
   - **b.** cause allergies.
   - **c.** spread disease among livestock.
   - **d.** destroy wood and wooden structures.
9. Biologists estimate that animal pollinators include
   - **a.** about 10 different species.
   - **b.** about 1000 different species.
   - **c.** over 130,000 different species.
   - **d.** only honeybees and bumblebees.

Putting It All Together

Using the information on pages xxx to xxxi, complete the following concept map.

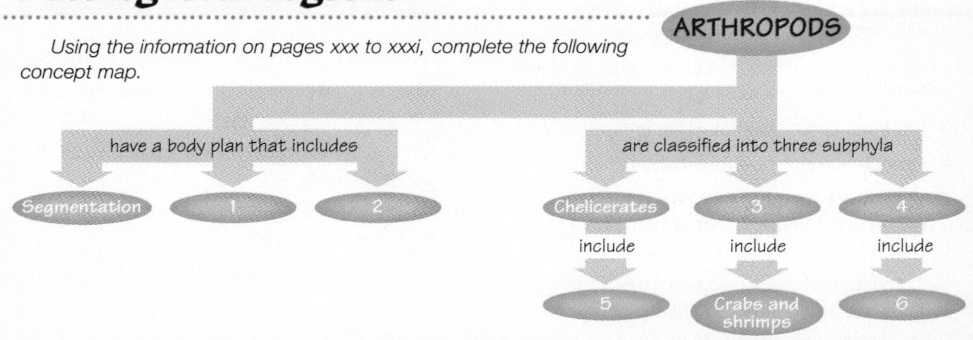

Putting It All Together

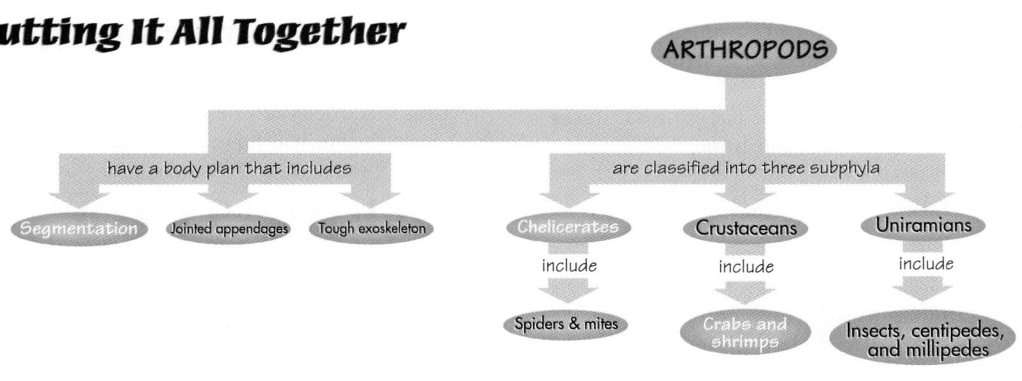

Recalling Main Ideas

1. b
2. c
3. a
4. d
5. b
6. c
7. a
8. d
9. c

Assessment

Reviewing What You Learned

1. Arthropods have segmented bodies, jointed appendages, and a tough exoskeleton.
2. An ancient marine organism and the first true arthropod.
3. It helps prevent loss of body fluids in many terrestrial arthropods.
4. Tracheal tubes.
5. Dead-end sacs that extract nitrogenous wastes from blood in body sinuses, concentrate the wastes, and add them to feces moving through the gut.
6. A process by which an arthropod sheds its entire exoskeleton and manufactures a larger one in order to grow.
7. In incomplete metamorphosis, the arthropod retains the same body plan throughout its life and undergoes only minimal changes. In complete metamorphosis, the arthropod experiences larval, pupal, and adult stages with different body plans.
8. Most spiders spin intricate webs with sticky silk that traps prey.
9. Mites and ticks are parasites that feed by digging into host tissues and sucking out blood or plant fluids.
10. Both centipedes and millipedes have a single pair of antennae and appendages with only a single branch; they lack a waterproof body covering. Centipedes are typically carnivores. All their body segments except the first and last have a single pair of legs. Millipedes feed on dead and decaying plant material. They have two pairs of legs on each body segment.
11. A three-part body consisting of a head, thorax, and abdomen, and three pairs of legs.
12. They are responsible for most of the pollination on which flowering plants depend for their reproduction.
13. Africanized bees carry disease and attack humans.

Assessment (continued)

Expanding the Concepts

1. Students should cite the subphyla and classes of arthropods discussed in the chapter and their varying characteristics, including physical features, behavior, and habitats.
2. Chelicerates have a body divided into two parts and two pairs of specialized mouthparts. Crustaceans have two pairs of antennae, several pairs of mouthparts, and appendages with two branches. Uniramians have one pair of antennae and appendages with only a single branch.
3. Arthropods are herbivores, carnivores, filter feeders, detritus feeders, bloodsuckers, and specialized parasites.
4. Arthropods have an open circulatory system. A well-developed heart pumps blood through arteries into smaller vessels, from which it flows into spaces called sinuses. Muscles move the blood around the sinuses, bathing body tissues with blood. Eventually, the blood collects in a large sinus surrounding the heart, then reenters the heart and begins its circuit again.
5. Because an exoskeleton is hard and cannot be enlarged, arthropods must molt as their soft inner bodies grow. This process exposes the vulnerable arthropod to predators before its new exoskeleton hardens; it uses energy and requires the arthropod to use minerals to build its new exoskeleton.
6. Terrestrial arthropods typically breathe through a branching, air-filled network of tracheal tubes. These tubes connect the arthropod's tissues with the atmosphere, and oxygen passes through the tubes by diffusion. Aquatic arthropods typically breathe through gills, which absorb oxygen from the water.
7. Advantage: the protection that the exoskeleton affords; disadvantage: the arthropod's need to molt in order to grow.
8. Chelicerates have a body divided into two parts (a cephalothorax and an abdomen) and two pairs of specialized mouthparts (chelicerae and pedipalps). Uniramians have more diverse body plans, but all have one pair of antennae and appendages with only a single branch.
9. Human diseases caused or transmitted by insects, and their damage to and destruction of crops.
10. Since their introduction to the United States almost 400 years ago, European honeybees have competed with native pollinators and reduced their numbers. In the 1950s, widespread use of pesticides further reduced the population of native pollinators. In the past 15 years, mites and other parasites have infected European honeybee colonies, killing up to half the members of the hive in some cases. Africanized honeybees, which attack humans and domesticated animals, have spread into the United States.

Assessment

Reviewing What You Learned

Answer each of the following in a complete sentence.

1. What are the characteristics of arthropods?
2. What is a trilobite?
3. What is the function of the waxy covering on the exoskeleton of some arthropods?
4. Which structures do most land-dwelling arthropods use for breathing?
5. What are Malpighian tubules?
6. What is molting?
7. Compare incomplete metamorphosis and complete metamorphosis.
8. How do most spiders capture prey?
9. How do mites and ticks feed?
10. Describe the characteristics of a centipede and a millipede.
11. What characteristics do all insects have in common?
12. Why are insects important to many flowering plants?
13. Describe the threat that Africanized bees pose in the United States.

Expanding the Concepts

Discuss each of the following in a brief paragraph.

1. Describe the diversity of arthropods.
2. What characteristics do biologists use to divide arthropods into three subphyla?
3. List the different ways in which arthropods feed.
4. Describe an arthropod's circulatory system.
5. Why do arthropods molt? Why is molting a dangerous and physiologically expensive process for arthropods?
6. Compare the structures used for breathing in terrestrial arthropods and aquatic arthropods.
7. Describe the advantages and disadvantages that a hard exoskeleton provides an arthropod.
8. Compare the body plans of a chelicerate and a uniramian.
9. Discuss some of the problems that insects cause humans.
10. Describe the pollination crisis in the United States and identify its causes.

684 Chapter 29

Extending Your Thinking

1. Students' experimental designs should involve subjecting specimens of one species of larva of the same age to different temperatures and tracking the length of each group's larval stage.

Skills Trace

Experimenting

- Focus p. 670
- Practice p. 673
- Assess p. 685

Extending Your Thinking

Use the skills you have developed in this chapter to answer the following.

1. **Designing an experiment** Many factors can influence an insect's molting cycle. Design an experiment to determine whether atmospheric temperature influences when a butterfly larva—a caterpillar—forms a cocoon and enters the pupa stage.
2. **Inferring** Arthropods are rarely found in sizes longer than half a meter, and most are less than a few centimeters in length. From your knowledge of the arthropod body plan, infer which structures limit an arthropod's growth.
3. **Evaluating arguments** Your friend argues that the pollination crisis in the United States is not a serious problem because new species of pollinators will evolve to replace those that are in decline. Do you agree with this assertion? Explain your answer.
4. **Making judgments** Arthropods are often the subjects of scientific research, and they sometimes die during the course of an experiment. Prepare a list of arguments both for and against the use of arthropods in research. How do you feel about this issue?
5. **Formulating hypotheses** At a park, you notice a red can and a green can resting at opposite ends of a picnic table. Several bees are swarming around the red can, but they seem to be avoiding the green can. Formulate a hypothesis to explain this observation.

Applying Your Skills

Creating a Dichotomous Key

To classify organisms, biologists use a type of flowchart called a dichotomous key. A dichotomous key is an ordered series of yes-or-no questions and direction arrows. Each question is followed by two direction arrows—one for yes and one for no—that lead to the next questions in the series or to the name of the organism.

1. Obtain a collection of eight photographs of different arthropods from your teacher. Research the characteristics of these arthropods and how they are classified.
2. Write a dichotomous key that can be used to classify the eight arthropods.
3. Exhange the eight photographs and your dichotomous key with another group of classmates. Follow the dichotomous key that the other group prepared to classify the organisms that they were given.
4. With the members of the other group, discuss the strengths and weaknesses of the dichotomous keys that your groups prepared.

• GOING FURTHER •

5. Prepare a poster to illustrate the way in which arthropods are classified.

5. Hypotheses may involve either the cans' color or their contents and should be phrased as testable statements.

Applying Your Skills

Teacher Notes

- Try to provide at least two representatives of each subphylum in the collection of photographs that students will use.
- Provide field guides and other sources for students to use in their research (step 1).
- Emphasize that there is no one right key for this activity and that many different keys are possible.

Answers

2. Make sure students do not start their keys with the three subphyla of arthropods, as doing so would violate the yes-no nature of a dichotomous key. Students may, however, start with one subphylum or a major characteristic of one subphylum or class.
4. Students should realize that the best keys begin with a major dichotomy and conclude with the most detailed differences between organisms.

Scoring Rubric

4 Response is thorough, accurate, and creative; shows an in-depth understanding of science skills, procedures, and concepts.

3 Response is complete, mostly accurate, and original; shows a satisfactory understanding of science skills, procedures, and concepts.

2 Response is mostly complete but includes some inaccuracies; shows an adequate understanding of science skills, procedures, and concepts.

1 Response is only partially complete and has many inaccuracies; shows an incomplete understanding of science skills, procedures, and concepts.

0 Response is mostly incomplete and/or inaccurate; shows a lack of understanding of science skills, procedures, and concepts.

2. The nonexpandable, relatively heavy and inflexible exoskeleton is a major limiting factor influencing arthropod growth, as is the comparative inefficiency of arthropods' respiratory and circulatory systems.

Skills Trace
Inferring

- Focus p. 676
- Practice p. 676
- Assess p. 685

3. Students should realize that the evolution of new species may take far too long to be a possible solution to the country's pollination crisis. Students may, however, suggest that human-manipulated evolution—selective breeding—might be a partial solution, particularly in addressing the problems created by Africanized bees.
4. For: The information gained from scientific research is far more valuable than the lives of these "lowly" animals. Against: Humans do not have the right to destroy even the "lowliest" of organisms.

Chapter 30 Fishes and Amphibians

Content Management	Student Edition Activities
■ Section 30–1 Fishes, pp. 687–694 The First Chordates Fish Form and Function Classifying Fishes	MINI LAB: Is That a Fish on Your Pizza?, p. 694
■ Section 30–2 Amphibians, pp. 695–698 Amphibian Form and Function Classifying Amphibians	MINI LAB: Frogs in Cold Water, p. 698 Laboratory Investigation: Raising Tadpoles, pp. 702–703
◆ BRANCHING OUT • In Depth Section 30–3 The World of Fishes, pp. 699–701 Fishes in Ecosystems Fishes as Food Fishes in the Rain Forest	

■ These sections cover all the necessary content and concepts for an enriched course in biology.
◆ This section covers content and concepts that are either applications or extensions of the enriched material.

Integration Strategies

SE Agriculture, p. 701

Assessment Strategies

SE Chapter Review, pp. 704–707
TR Section Reviews
Chapter Test
BL Chapter Review
Practice Test
CTB Chapter 30 Test

Tech Prep

Teaching strategies appropriate for students who are in technical/vocational programs or who are considering post-secondary technical education can be found on the following **TE** pages: 695 and 700.

Meeting the Standards

Sections 30–1 through 30–3 cover three of the five content standards under **Biological Evolution,** two of the five content standards under **The Interdependence of Organisms,** one of the six content standards under **Matter, Energy, and Organization in Living Systems,** and three of the four content standards under **The Behavior of Organisms** as described on pages 185–187 of The National Science Education Standards.

Chapter Planning Guide

Teacher's Edition Activities	Other Activities	Media and Technology
Chapter Discovery Learning Activity, p. 686 **Inquiry Activity:** What's a Fish?, p. 687 **Inquiry Activity:** A Fish Tail, p. 688 **Investigate:** Model Building, p. 691	**LM** Observing the Structure of the Fish, #59 **TR** **Explore:** Sink or Float **BL** **Inquiry Activity:** Gone Fishing	**TB** Visualizing a Fish, #38
Inquiry Activity: A Bridge From Water to Land, p. 695 **Investigate:** Cooperative Learning, p. 695 **Investigate:** Research, p. 697	**LM** Observing the Structure of the Frog, #60 **TR** **Writing in Biology:** Shaping Poetry **Apply:** Neat Newts **BL** **Inquiry Activity:** Leaving Home	**CD-ROM:** The Digital Frog **TB** Visualizing a Frog, #39
Investigate: Cooperative Learning, p. 699	**TR** **Enrich:** Monsters of the Deep **BL** **Inquiry Activity:** Fishy Situations	**BioVue Mini Doc:** Animals of the Flooded Forest, Videodisc Side 7

KEY: **SE** Student Edition **TE** Teacher's Edition **LM** Laboratory Manual **TR** Teaching Resources **BL** BioLog **TB** Transparency Box **CTB** Computer Test Bank

Materials List

TE Chapter Discovery Learning Activity, p. 686 (30 minutes); aquarium, dechlorinated water, aerator, water plants, clean gravel, fish, fish food.
TE Inquiry Activity: What's a Fish?, p. 687 (20 minutes); set of photographs of about ten different kinds of fishes.
TE Inquiry Activity: A Fish Tail, p. 688 (20 minutes); goldfish, aquarium net, saucer, cotton, water from aquarium, dropper, glass slide, microscope.
TE Investigate: Model Building, p. 691 (1 hour for research and planning, and then several hours over 2 days for building the model); cardboard, clay, papier-mâché, paints, paintbrushes.
SE MINI LAB: Is That a Fish on Your Pizza?, p. 694 (30 minutes); fresh anchovies (often available at bait-and-tackle stores), scalpel.
TE Inquiry Activity: A Bridge From Water to Land, p. 695 (20 minutes); photographs or slides of a variety of amphibians.
TE Investigate: Research, p. 697 (1–2 hours); map of the local area.
SE MINI LAB: Frogs in Cold Water, p. 698 (30 minutes); frog, jar, pond water at room temperature, large beaker, ice water, thermometer, watch or clock with second hand.
TE Investigate: Cooperative Learning, p. 699 (5 hours for research and planning, and then half a day for completion of a mural section); large poster board or butcher block paper, colored pencils, water paints, paintbrushes.

CHAPTER 30

Fish and Amphibians

Introducing the Chapter

. . . In Pictures

These snappers are patrolling the world's largest coral reef in search of food. They are carnivorous fish, one-half to one meter in length, with strong jaws and sharp teeth. In this shallow environment, snappers are near the top of the food chain, but not at the very top. As students examine this photograph, ask the following questions.

- **What is an important characteristic by which fishes can be distinguished from animals such as mollusks and arthropods?** (Students are likely to say that fishes have an internal skeleton, including a backbone.)
- **What are other kinds of animals that also have a backbone?** (Students may mention amphibians, reptiles, birds, and mammals.)

Teaching Strategy

In the first section of this chapter, students are introduced to the basic characteristics of fishes. In the second section they are introduced to the basic characteristics of amphibians. The BRANCHING OUT section provides an in-depth look at fishes in their natural environment, as well as their importance in the human diet.

BIO JOURNAL

The Bio Journal topic can be used to stimulate classroom discussion about the general characteristics of fishes. Ask students to brainstorm for features that all fishes have, such as a mouth, eyes, and fins. Some students may mention internal structures, such as gills and a skeleton. This will prepare students to begin thinking about some of the characteristics introduced in Section 30–1. Instruct students to keep their entries in their portfolios.

CHAPTER 30

Fishes and Amphibians

FOCUSING THE CHAPTER
THEME: Unity and Diversity

30–1 Fishes
- Describe the body plan of fishes.

30–2 Amphibians
- Explain how amphibians are adapted to live in water and on land.

BRANCHING OUT *In Depth*

30–3 The World of Fishes
- Discuss the importance of fishes in ecosystems.

LABORATORY INVESTIGATION
- Design an experiment to determine the effect of colored light on tadpoles.

Biology and Your World

BIO JOURNAL

In your journal, list the external features of a fish using the photograph on this page. How are fishes different from other animals you have encountered? How are they similar?

School of snappers near the Great Barrier Reef, Australia

TEACHER SUPPORT

Chapter Discovery Learning Activity

Have groups set up aquariums so that they can examine the form and function of fishes as they progress through the chapter. You may want to have each group do some initial investigation about how to take care of fish in an aquarium. Students should discover that the basics for an aquarium include dechlorinated water, gravel, and plants. If the aquarium is large, some kind of aerator must be added to make sure the water contains enough oxygen. Once the aquariums are set up, students could make drawings of the various kinds of fishes in each and observe the behavior of fishes under various conditions, including in different intensities of light. Make sure each group devises some system to ensure that the fishes are fed each day and the aquarium water is changed periodically.

GUIDE FOR READING

- **Describe** the chordates.
- **Discuss** the characteristics of fishes.
- **Identify** the three classes of living fishes.

MINI LAB
- **Classify** a fish.

FROM FRESHWATER SPRINGS to salty seas and from sunlit mountain streams to dark, frigid ocean depths, fishes are the masters of the underwater world. Some fish species have changed little since the dinosaurs prowled the Earth, while scores of other species have evolved in just the last few thousand years. Some are beautiful, some are frightening, but all are fascinating.

To biologists, fishes are important for another reason: They provide clues about the development of the vertebrates—animals with backbones. Indeed, certain fishes may be the closest living examples of the common ancestor of all vertebrates.

The First Chordates

Fishes, frogs, birds, reptiles, and humans—all are members of the phylum Chordata. You will learn a great deal about the chordates as you read this chapter and the following chapters.

At some stage of its life, a chordate has a notochord, a hollow dorsal nerve cord, and pharyngeal slits. A structure called the **notochord** is a long, flexible rod that typically develops in the embryonic stage. In fishes and most other chordates, the notochord is replaced by a vertebral column—a backbone. The **hollow dorsal nerve cord** lies next to the notochord. Typically, it develops into the main nerve pathway from the body to the brain. And the **pharyngeal** (fuh-RIHN-jee-uhl) **slits** are slits in the **pharynx,** or throat region of the body. In fishes, these structures develop into featherlike structures called **gills,** which are used for breathing.

Figure 30–1
(a) Although this tunicate may look like an underwater flower, it is one of the few examples of an invertebrate chordate. (b) Fishes, such as these brook trout, are true vertebrates—animals with backbones. The vertebral column helps support a fish's body and is flexible enough to allow a variety of movements. (c) Different fishes evolved a variety of adaptations to help them survive. The unusual shape and coloring of this frogfish help it to blend into its surroundings.

TEACHER SUPPORT

Historical Perspective

Perhaps the greatest American naturalist of the nineteenth century was Louis Agassiz (1807–1873), who from 1848 until his death was a professor of zoology at Harvard University. Agassiz was born in Switzerland, and his earliest scientific work was the classification of fish specimens brought to Europe from Brazil. He won worldwide attention in the 1830s for his study of fossil fishes. That fame led to a course of lectures in the United States in the 1840s. Agassiz made many contributions to science, perhaps the greatest being his revelation that Earth had Ice Ages in the past. But fishes remained an interest throughout his life. According to legend, he would lock a new student into a room for a day with only one object, a dead fish. At day's end, the student faced an unenviable task: reporting to the professor all that had been learned by looking at that fish.

SECTION 30–1
Fishes

Performance Objectives
- Discuss characteristics of chordates.
- Describe the characteristics of fishes.
- Describe jawless fishes, cartilaginous fishes, and bony fishes.

Mini Lab Skill: Classifying

1 ENGAGE

Inquiry Activity
Comparing
What's a Fish?
Divide students into small groups and give each group a set of photographs of about ten different fishes. These fishes should include both typical fishes, such as bass and rainbow trout, and fishes that exhibit variations on the basic body shape, such as flounder, scorpionfish, shark, and catfish. Have the members of a group compare the examples provided, discuss what features all have in common, and collaboratively draw their own "basic" fish.

2 EXPLORE

Ideas Through Images
Have students examine Figure 30–1, read the caption, and answer the following questions.

- **Because this tunicate is classified as a chordate, what characteristics do you know it has?** (At some stage in its life, it must have a notochord, a hollow dorsal nerve cord, and pharyngeal slits.)
- **What is a significant difference between the tunicate and the two fishes shown?** (The tunicate is an invertebrate; it has no backbone. Both the brook trout and the frogfish are vertebrates; they do have backbones.)

Inquiry Activity
Observing
A Fish Tail

Ask students whether a fish has a circulatory system similar to ours. Then have pairs of students carry out the following procedure.

1. Soak a wad of cotton with water from an aquarium. Then use an aquarium net to catch a goldfish. While the goldfish is still in the net, wrap it with the wet cotton, leaving the tail uncovered.
2. Place the goldfish in a shallow saucer. Use the dropper to wet the tail with aquarium water. Then cover the tail with a glass slide. Be gentle.
3. Place the dish on a microscope stage with the tail under the lens. Then observe the tail with low power. Make a drawing and write a description of what you see.

Students should be able to observe blood flowing through vessels in the tail.

3 TEACH

Ideas Through Images

Have students examine Figure 30–2, read the caption, and answer the following questions.

- **Where on a fish's body are the gill slits located?** (In the pharynx, or the throat section of the body.)
- **How many gills do most fishes have?** (One pair.)
- **Why do fishes need gills for gas exchange?** (Fishes, like most other organisms, must take in oxygen and eliminate carbon dioxide. The gills make this exchange.)

Figure 30–2
(a) This whale shark has several gill slits on each side of its head. Aside from sharks and lampreys, most other fishes—such as the golden trevally swimming next to the shark—have only one pair of gills. (b) Some fishes breathe in unusual ways. These kissing gouramis exchange gases with air bubbles they pick up during trips to the surface.

A few chordates are invertebrates, meaning they lack a backbone. The invertebrate chordates include lancelets and the tunicates shown in ***Figure 30–1*** on page 687. However, the vast majority of chordates—including the fishes—do have backbones. These chordates are the vertebrates.

☑ ***Checkpoint*** What are chordates? Vertebrates? ❶

Fish Form and Function

All fishes have fins, and almost all fishes breathe through gills and have scales. In other respects, fishes are incredibly diverse. However, most fishes have the basic characteristics shown in the illustration on the next page.

Respiration

To breathe, most fishes use gills to exchange gases with the surrounding water. Gills provide a great amount of surface area for gas exchange and are richly supplied with blood vessels. In many fishes, gills are protected by a bony structure called an **operculum,** which also forms a single gill slit on each side of the head.

How does water reach the gills? The answer lies with the coordinated movements of the mouth and pharynx, which together act as a two-stage water pump. First, the gill slits close, the mouth opens, and the fish's "cheeks" are pulled sideways. This action increases the volume of the mouth and pharynx, and water is sucked in. Next, the gill slits open, the mouth closes, and the volume of the mouth decreases. This pushes the water over the gills and out through the gill slits.

☑ ***Checkpoint*** How do fishes breathe through gills? ❷

Feeding

No other vertebrates come close to fishes in variety of feeding strategies. In part, this is because a fish's head is made of many bones, joints, and muscles. In different groups of fishes, these structures evolved in various ways, producing different mouth sizes and shapes, as well as a great variety in size, shape, and number of teeth. As a result, different fishes have evolved ways to eat almost every conceivable food.

Part of the bony fishes' success comes from an interesting link between eating and breathing. By combining their ability to suck in water with their specialized mouthparts, many fishes can literally suck in their prey.

TEACHER SUPPORT

Background Information

Fish biologists, or ichthyologists, have identified a variety of different fish body shapes, each an adaptation to the lifestyle of the fish. For example, rover-predators are smooth and streamlined, with a pointed head and a forked tail. Examples of fishes with this common shape are tuna, bass, sharks, and minnows. These fishes are adapted for cruising, and then suddenly capturing prey with a burst of speed. Surface-oriented fishes have upward-pointing mouths, flattened heads, and large eyes, all adaptations for capturing insects on the surface. Guppies are an example. In contrast, bottom fishes are quite flattened in one of several ways. Examples are flounders, rays, and darters. Students might want to investigate these and other basic shapes and learn how different fishes are adapted to different environments.

Visualizing a Fish

The body plan of fishes has allowed them to thrive in waters throughout the Earth.

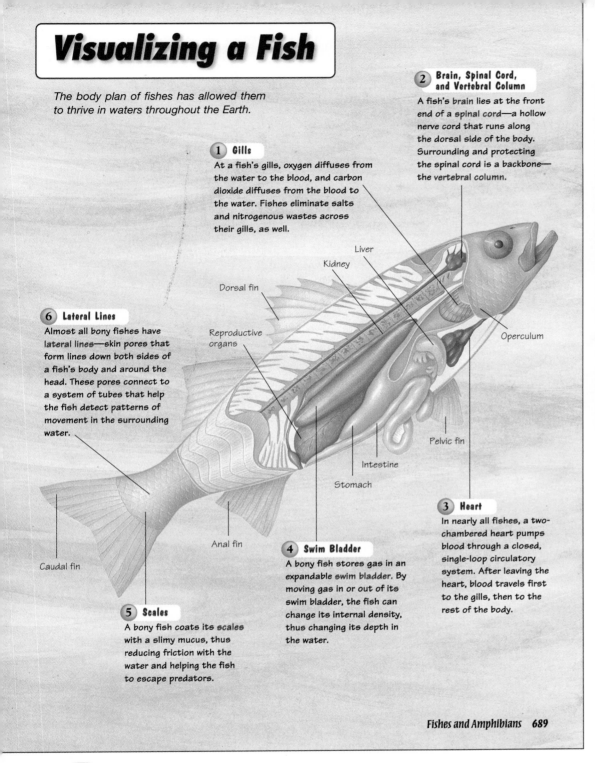

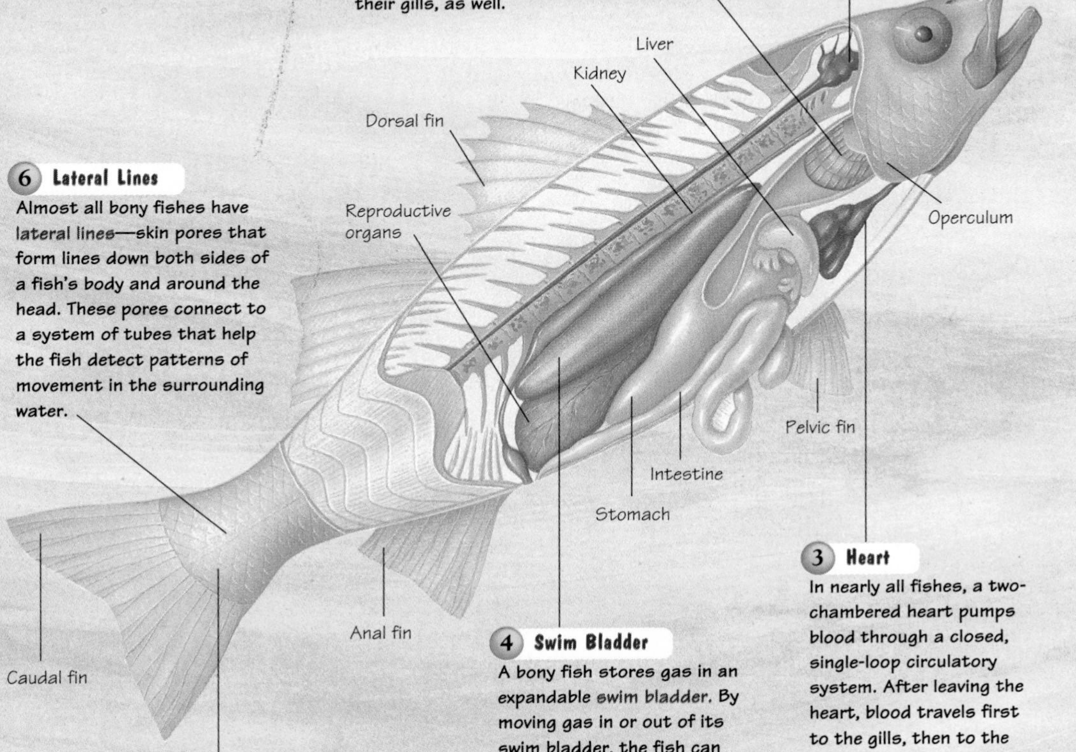

1 Gills
At a fish's gills, oxygen diffuses from the water to the blood, and carbon dioxide diffuses from the blood to the water. Fishes eliminate salts and nitrogenous wastes across their gills, as well.

2 Brain, Spinal Cord, and Vertebral Column
A fish's brain lies at the front end of a spinal cord—a hollow nerve cord that runs along the dorsal side of the body. Surrounding and protecting the spinal cord is a backbone—the vertebral column.

3 Heart
In nearly all fishes, a two-chambered heart pumps blood through a closed, single-loop circulatory system. After leaving the heart, blood travels first to the gills, then to the rest of the body.

4 Swim Bladder
A bony fish stores gas in an expandable swim bladder. By moving gas in or out of its swim bladder, the fish can change its internal density, thus changing its depth in the water.

5 Scales
A bony fish coats its scales with a slimy mucus, thus reducing friction with the water and helping the fish to escape predators.

6 Lateral Lines
Almost all bony fishes have lateral lines—skin pores that form lines down both sides of a fish's body and around the head. These pores connect to a system of tubes that help the fish detect patterns of movement in the surrounding water.

Visualizing a Fish

This generalized fish essentially has the body shape of a rover-predator—a sleek shape exemplified by many common fishes, including bass, tuna, swordfish, and minnows. Point out to students that some fishes have radically different shapes, though all have the basic internal and external structures shown here. Have students read the caption and labels. Then discuss this body plan, emphasizing the following points.

- A fish fits the definition of chordate because it has a vertebral column, or backbone, a dorsal nerve cord, and gills, which develop from pharyngeal slits.
- The swim bladder is an outgrowth of the fish intestine that controls buoyancy.
- The fins of this fish are arrayed in a definite pattern that can be seen on all fishes, though with some variations.

Checkpoints

1 Chordates are organisms that have a notochord, a hollow dorsal nerve cord, and pharyngeal slits at some stage in their lives. Vertebrates are chordates that have backbones.

2 Fishes breathe through gills by pushing water over the gills and out through the gill slits. The gills exchange gases with the water.

TEACHER SUPPORT

Background Information

The basic body plan of fishes includes several fins. Along the sides, near the underside of the fish, are two sets of fins that correspond to the limbs of land animals. These are the pectoral fins (analogous to arms) and the pelvic fins (analogous to legs). On the top of the fish is a dorsal fin. Most fishes have one dorsal fin, though it may be divided into two or three parts, as in the case, for instance, of snappers. Sharks actually have two separate dorsal fins. Most bony fishes have an anal fin, which is on the underside toward the back, just behind the anus. Finally, the fin at a fish's tail is the caudal fin, which in most fishes has an upper and lower lobe of the same size. Although anglers measure a fish from the snout to the end of the tail—the total length—biologists prefer the standard length, measured from the snout to the end of the vertebral column.

Ancillary Support

The resources below can be used to support your teaching strategy for these two pages.

LM Observing the Structure of the Fish, #59
BL Inquiry Activity: Gone Fishing
TB Visualizing a Fish, #38

Ideas Through Images

Have students examine Figure 30–3, read the caption, and answer the following questions.

- **How is a fish able to pull prey and water into its mouth?** (The mouth and pharynx act as a two-stage water pump. First, the gill slits in the pharynx close, the mouth opens, and the "cheeks" are pulled sideways. This pulls water in. Then the gill slits open, the mouth closes, and the water leaves through the gill slits.)
- **How does the second step of this process benefit the fish?** (As the water flows over the gills on its way out of the gill slits, the gills exchange gases with the water. The fish receives needed oxygen and eliminates wastes, including carbon dioxide.)

Ideas Through Images

Have students examine Figure 30–4, read the caption, and answer the following questions.

- **What are the chambers of a fish's heart?** (The atrium and the ventricle.)
- **Describe a fish's single-loop circulatory system.** (The heart pumps blood through the aorta to the gills, where gas exchange occurs. Then the blood travels throughout the body and back to the heart.)
- **How does the function of a fish cerebrum differ from the function of a cerebrum in a human brain?** (In a human brain, the cerebrum is where thinking occurs. In a fish brain, the cerebrum is mostly involved in the sense of smell and basic behaviors.)
- **How do messages from the fish brain reach other parts of the body?** (Through the spinal cord and spinal nerves.)

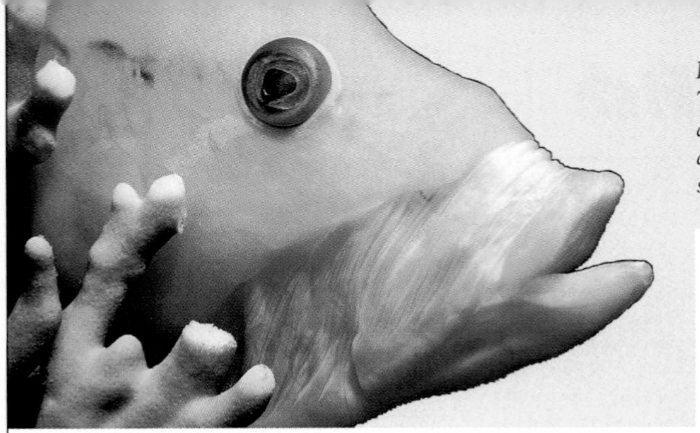

Figure 30–3
The mouth of this slingjaw wrasse expands like a telescope. Together, its mouth and pharynx act as a powerful aquatic vacuum cleaner to suck in prey.

Excretion

Many fishes get rid of much of their nitrogenous wastes in the same way that many other aquatic animals do—by allowing ammonia to diffuse across their gills and into the water. Fishes also use a simple **kidney** to filter nitrogenous wastes from the blood. In addition, fishes can actively pump salts in or out of their body fluids by using specialized cells in their gills.

Do you think that fishes drink a lot of water? In fact, freshwater fishes don't swallow water at all! Why? The blood and body fluids of freshwater fishes contain more dissolved substances than the water around them. As a result, water constantly enters the body through osmosis. The fishes eliminate this water by passing lots of dilute urine through their kidneys.

Saltwater fishes, on the other hand, constantly lose water through osmosis. These fishes do drink continuously, but they produce very little urine.

☑ ***Checkpoint*** How do fishes get rid of nitrogenous wastes? 1

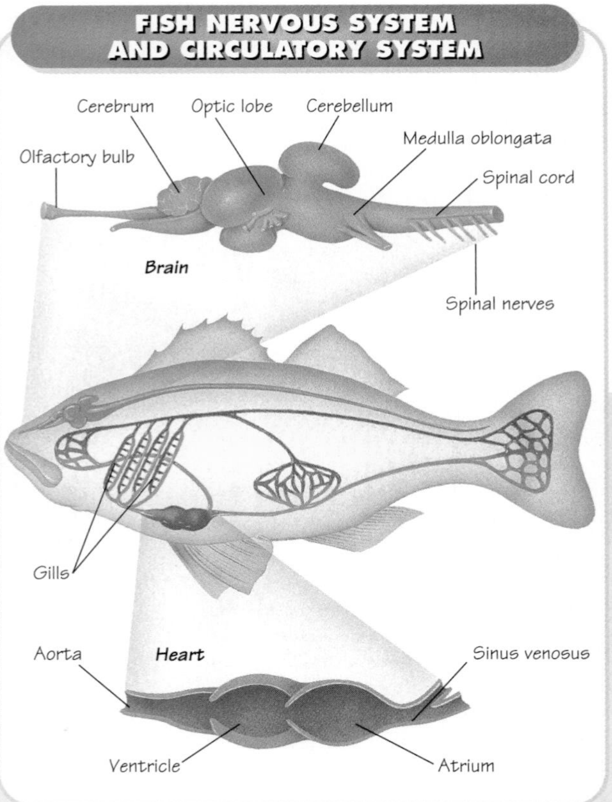

Figure 30–4
Like other vertebrates, a fish has a heart located near its respiratory organs and a brain located at the front of the spinal cord. The heart has two chambers—an atrium and a ventricle. Blood travels from the heart first to the gills, then to the rest of the body. The brain contains many of the same parts as the brains of other vertebrates, including the cerebrum, cerebellum, and medulla oblongata.

TEACHER SUPPORT

Facts and Figures

- About 41 percent of all fish species are found exclusively in fresh water, despite the fact that fresh water makes up less than .01 percent of the world's water. The reason that freshwater species are so numerous is that they can be easily isolated from other species.
- Over 30 percent of fish species are associated with tropical coral reefs.
- Bony fishes usually have about the same number of scales throughout their lives. But like a tree trunk, the scales have rings to indicate a season of growth. Thus, the number of rings equals the age of the fish in years.
- Most fish eggs measure 3 mm or less in diameter. A stickleback egg is about 2 mm in diameter and takes 5–12 days to hatch.
- A female cod can scatter as many as 9 million eggs in the water. Some will be fertilized, but most will be eaten by other organisms.

Nervous System

Although the nervous system in fishes is far simpler than in humans, it is set up in much the same way. Up front are **olfactory bulbs,** which are specialized for the sense of smell. The olfactory bulbs are directly connected to the two lobes of the **cerebrum.** In humans, the cerebrum is where thinking occurs. But in many fishes, the cerebrum seems to be mostly involved with the sense of smell and basic behaviors. Next come the **optic lobes,** which process visual information. Then comes the **cerebellum,** where body movements are coordinated. Finally, connecting the brain with the spinal cord, is the **medulla oblongata,** which regulates the function of many internal organs and helps maintain balance.

Sense Organs

As different species of fishes evolved in different environments, their sensory abilities adapted to provide them with information about their surroundings. Fishes that live in clear water and are active in the daytime, for example, have well-developed eyes and color vision. In some cases, this vision is better than our own. On the other hand, species that are active at night have enormous eyes that see only in black and white but function well in what to us is pitch darkness.

Many fishes, especially those that live in murky water, carry large numbers of chemical receptors—in what we might think are strange places. Some fishes can "smell" with their lips and "taste" with their barbels—a kind of whiskers. These chemical receptors can be very sensitive. Some predatory sharks respond to a single drop of blood in 115 liters of water!

Some fishes have other senses that humans can only imagine. Sharks, for example, have specialized cells that detect tiny electric currents. Why might this sense be useful?

Figure 30–5
(a) The large, lively eyes of these longspine squirrelfish help them to prowl for food at night, when light is scarce. (b) This polka-dot catfish is able to "taste" with chemical receptors along its barbels, or whiskers. (c) Electric eels have the amazing ability to generate an electric current, which they use mainly to shock would-be predators.

a
b
c

Ideas Through Images

Have students examine Figure 30–5, read the caption, and answer the following questions.

- **Would these longspine squirrelfish probably have color vision? Why or why not?** (They probably would not. Because they prowl for food at night, these fish probably have eyes that see extremely well but only in black and white.)
- **Why would a catfish have evolved taste ability?** (A catfish lives in murky waters, where sight is difficult. Having the ability to "taste" with its barbels would help it catch food.)

Investigate

Model Building Divide the class into small groups and ask each group to build a model of a specific kind of fish. Give groups a chance to do some initial research to choose a specific type of fish, such as a shark, swordfish, catfish, anglefish, or clownfish. Make sure no two groups are building a model of the same type of fish. This model should be three-dimensional, with a cutaway portion that shows some internal structures. Provide students with some basic materials, such as a cardboard platform and clay or papier-mâché, but encourage groups to find other materials at home or around the classroom.

Checkpoint

1 In fishes, ammonia diffuses across their gills and into the water. Fishes also have a simple kidney that filters nitrogenous wastes from the blood.

TEACHER SUPPORT

Ecology Note

Students may wonder why fishes are so varied in color, and why some fishes are spectacularly colorful and others are dull-colored. The answers to these questions have to do with the environment in which a fish lives. Whether predator or prey, a fish functions best if it blends in with its surroundings. Near a colorful coral reef, the fishes tend to be colorful, though in ways that might distract potential predators. An example is a fish with a false eyespot near its tail—a predator lunging for the "head" may miss as the prey quickly swishes the other way. In contrast to the colorful fishes near a coral reef are the fishes of the open ocean, where color is a liability. Such fishes are often darker on the back and lighter on the belly. Light from the surface brightens the back and darkens the belly, and, in a sense, the fishes can disappear from sight.

Ancillary Support

The resource below can be used to support your teaching strategy for these two pages.

TR Explore: Sink or Float

Discussion

Begin a discussion of fish reproduction by noting that all fishes reproduce through sexual reproduction, with the production of gametes through meiosis and the fertilization of an egg by a sperm cell. The differences among fishes involve where fertilization occurs and whether the resulting embryo is cared for by the parent. Point out that most fishes are oviparous. In fact, the great majority of fishes release their eggs and sperm into the water, and fertilization occurs when a sperm cell comes into contact with an egg, a process called spawning. A few types of fishes are ovoviparous; these include guppies and many kinds of sharks. The hammerhead shark is an example of a viviparous fish; the connection between embryo and mother is quite elaborate.

Correcting Misconceptions

Students may have heard the term shellfish, especially in the context of food production by the fishing industry. Point out that mollusks and crustaceans are sometimes called shellfish and are even included in the statistics of the fish caught by fishing boats, but these invertebrates are not fishes.

Ideas Through Images

Have students examine Figure 30–7, read the caption, and answer the following questions.

- **In what phylum and superclass are jawless fishes included?** (The phylum Chordata and the superclass Pisces.)
- **What are two examples of jawless fishes?** (Lampreys and hagfishes.)
- **In what way are these fishes parasites?** (They are both organisms that feed off other organisms, and in so doing harm those other organisms.)

Figure 30–6
Most fishes spend all of their lives either as males or females. But there are exceptions! This clownfish was born male, then changed into a female as it got older. Fishes of other species can change from female to male.

Whenever any animal moves, its nerves and muscle cells produce electric currents. By detecting these currents, sharks can find prey that are otherwise hidden. Sharks also seem to use their electric sense to "zero in" on prey in the final moments before a strike.

Certain fishes not only detect electric currents but produce their own. Several species from the murky waters of the Amazon basin are known to navigate and communicate with one another using this electric sense.

Reproduction

Fishes reproduce in several different ways. Many are **oviparous,** meaning they lay eggs just before or soon after the eggs are fertilized. These species may or may not take care of the eggs. In either case, the developing embryos are nourished by a yolk sac attached to their gut.

Other species are **ovoviviparous** (oh-voh-vigh-VIHP-uh-ruhs), meaning the female holds eggs inside its body while the eggs grow into free-swimming babies. However, the embryos are nourished entirely by the original yolk. Still other fishes are **viviparous** (vigh-VIHP-er-uhs), meaning that the female provides additional nourishment to developing young inside its body. Oviparous species may have either internal or external fertilization, while ovoviviparous and viviparous forms have internal fertilization.

Although most fishes are either male or female, a few have the interesting ability to change genders, as illustrated in ***Figure 30–6.*** And fishes of a few species may be both male and female at the same time.

Classifying Fishes

We lump together all sorts of aquatic vertebrates under the name fishes. However, fishes are classified not in a single class but in three classes of the superclass Pisces. **The three classes of living fishes are jawless fishes, cartilaginous fishes, and bony fishes.**

Figure 30–7
Hagfishes and lampreys are the only living jawless fishes, a class once very common and diverse. (a) *Adult lampreys are eellike fishes that live as parasites of other aquatic animals. These two lampreys are living off a carp.* (b) *A lamprey attaches to its host with the aid of strong teeth around its mouth.*

TEACHER SUPPORT — Managing Classroom Diversity

LEP STUDENTS
Students may have difficulty understanding which is the proper plural, fish or fishes. In common usage, fish can be either singular or plural in almost any situation. But biologists are more exacting. The rule is that a single organism of a single species is a fish. Many organisms of a single species can also be referred to as fish. But many organisms from more than one species should be referred to as fishes.

EDUCATIONAL EQUITY
Have interested students investigate the story of the discovery of a living coelacanth in 1938 at the mouth of the Chalumna River in South Africa. Central to that discovery, which made news around the world, was the young ichthyology curator of the East London, South Africa, Natural History Museum, Marjorie Courtenay-Latimer. That living fossil was named *Latimeria chalumnea* to honor the discoverer and the location.

Figure 30–8
The teeth of this sand tiger shark can rip and tear almost any prey. Unlike most vertebrates, a shark regularly replaces its teeth throughout its lifetime.

Jawless Fishes

For millions of years, jawless fishes ruled the sea. However, the jawless fishes of today—hagfishes and lampreys—bear little resemblance to their ancient ancestors or to any other fishes! Unlike other vertebrates, these animals have lost their bony skeletons. They also have no scales.

Lampreys spend the first seven years of their life buried in sand, where they live as filter-feeding larvae. Eventually, they mature into parasitic adults.

Hagfishes are even more peculiar. These parasitic fishes have six hearts, use an open circulatory system, and produce huge amounts of slime, which helps them to escape predators. Their bodies are so flexible that they can literally tie themselves in knots!

Cartilaginous Fishes

Members of the class Chondrichthyes (kahn-DRIHK-theez) are called cartilaginous fishes. They include sharks, rays, and skates. This ancient and successful group of fishes lives predominantly in the sea. Only a few species adapted to fresh water.

Although bones had evolved in their ancestors, living cartilaginous fishes have a skeleton made entirely of cartilage, as their name implies. The body is covered with platelike scales, each armed with toothlike structures that make the scales rough to the touch. In addition, scales around the mouth have evolved into teeth.

There are only about 750 living species of cartilaginous fishes. However, they are diverse and important in marine ecosystems. Most are carnivores, but their diets range from small worms and mussels to large fast-swimming fishes, marine mammals—and an occasional human. Other species are harmless filter feeders that feed on plankton.

☑ **Checkpoint** What are the cartilaginous fishes? ❶

Figure 30–9
Bony fishes have evolved unique adaptations. (a) Archerfish shoot water at unwary prey—here, an insect on a reed. When the insect falls in the water, the archerfish eats it. (b) When threatened, a puffer expands its body like a balloon. If it expands rapidly while in a predator's mouth, the predator could suffocate.

Ideas Through Images

Have students examine Figure 30–8, read the caption, and answer the following questions.

- **What are the scientific and common names for the class to which sharks belong?** (They belong to the class Chondrichthyes, or the cartilaginous fishes.)
- **What fishes other than sharks also belong to this class?** (Rays and skates.)
- **How do the skeletons of these fishes differ from those of most other fishes?** (Cartilaginous fishes have a skeleton made entirely of cartilage.)
- **Are all cartilaginous fishes carnivores?** (No. Most are, but some feed on plankton.)

Ideas Through Images

Have students examine Figure 30–9, read the caption, and answer the following questions.

- **What is the scientific name for the bony fishes?** (Bony fishes are members of the class Osteichthyes.)
- **What are the two subclasses of bony fishes?** (Ray-finned fishes and fleshy-finned fishes.)
- **What are some examples of ray-finned fishes?** (Students might mention almost any fish studied, including archerfish, puffers, guppies, groupers, bluefish, flounders, anchovies, eels, and salmon.)
- **What are the characteristics of ray-finned fishes?** (Ray-finned fishes have a bony skeleton and ray fins.)

TEACHER SUPPORT

Background Information

The ray-finned fishes are the dominant fishes of our time, both in terms of species and numbers of individuals. They are named after the rods that support and anchor their fins. These fin rays hold in place the fin web, much as the thin rods in a handheld fan hold together the webbing of the fan. With these pliable structures, fishes are able to power and steer their way through the water.

In contrast to the ray fins are the lobe fins of many of the fleshy-finned fishes, including the coelacanth. A lobe fin is like a limb of a land animal, with more substantial support bones and a musculature that allows the fish to "stand" on its pelvic and pectoral fins. In fact, the coelacanth rests on its lobe fins on the ocean floor, waiting for prey to come near. Presumably, coelacanths evolved in tropical swamps and perhaps were the precursors of land animals.

☑ Checkpoint

❶ The cartilaginous fishes are fishes that have a skeleton made entirely of cartilage.

MINI LAB .... Classifying ....

Is That a Fish on Your Pizza?

PROBLEM *How can you **classify** a fish?*

PROCEDURE

1. Obtain an anchovy from your teacher. Sketch the anchovy, including close-ups of a dorsal fin, a pectoral fin, and the tail (caudal fin).
2. Count the number of scales along the lateral line, which runs from the gill slit to the caudal fin.
3. Using a scalpel, cut open the underside of the fish. Describe the structures you observe.

ANALYZE AND CONCLUDE

1. Why are anchovies included in the class Osteichthyes?
2. How can you further classify this fish based on the shape of its fins?
3. How does the number of scales you counted compare with the numbers counted by your classmates? How is this significant?

Bony Fishes

The members of the class Osteichthyes (AHS-tuh-ihk-theez)—the bony fishes—have skeletons made of strong, lightweight bone. Biologists have identified more than 30,000 species of bony fishes, and more species remain to be discovered. While some bony fishes are rare, others are quite abundant. For example, researchers estimate that there are as many as a billion billion individuals of various species of herring!

Biologists divide the bony fishes into two subclasses. Ray-finned fishes include nearly every bony fish you can think of. These fishes range from guppies to groupers, from bluefish to flounders, and from anchovies to eels and salmon. Many perform feats you would never dream fishes could manage. Archerfish can use their mouth like a water pistol, as shown in ***Figure 30–9*** on page 693. Flying fish leap out of the water and use large pectoral fins to glide through the air. And some species of catfish can actually climb a tree!

The other subclass of bony fishes are fleshy-finned fishes, which include lungfishes and lobe-finned fishes. Lungfishes have retained their ancestors' primitive lung, which is an air-filled sac connected to the gut. A lungfish fills its lung by swallowing air and empties it by belching.

Lobe-finned fishes were common in the Devonian Era. But today, the only living species is *Latimeria*, also known as a coelacanth (SEE-luh-kanth). Coelacanths live in the deep sea, far from the shallow freshwater swamps of their ancestors. Still, they offer a fascinating look at ancient fishes. Of all living animals, they are among the closest to the common ancestor of all four-limbed vertebrates.

Section Review 30–1

1. **Describe** the chordates.
2. **Discuss** the characteristics of fishes.
3. **Identify** the three classes of living fishes.
4. **Critical Thinking—Explaining Facts** For fishes to survive in an aquarium, the water must be kept clean and well-ventilated. Explain why water quality is so important to a fish's survival.
5. **MINI LAB** How can you **classify** a fish?

MINI LAB Classifying

Teacher Note
- For time required and materials needed, see page 686b.

Answers to Analyze and Conclude

1. Because they have a bony skeleton.
2. The fins of the anchovy are in the shape of rays. Therefore, it can be classified in the subclass of ray-finned fishes.
3. The number of scales will be the same for each fish in the same species. Students may infer that each species has a certain number of scales from the gill slit to the caudal fin.

Skills Trace
Classifying
- Focus p. 694
- Practice p. 694
- Assess p. 707

4 ASSESS

Quick Check

Ask students to make a table that contains the names, characteristics, and examples of the three classes of fishes.

Section Review 30–1

1. A chordate is an organism that has a notochord, a hollow dorsal nerve cord, and pharyngeal slits at some stage of its life.
2. All fishes have fins, and almost all breathe through gills and have scales. Students might also mention any of the structures described on page 689.
3. Jawless fishes, cartilaginous fishes, and bony fishes.
4. Water quality is important to a fish's survival because fishes breathe by pushing water over their gills and exchanging gases with the water. If the water contains harmful substances or not enough oxygen, the fish will suffer or die.
5. By the presence or absence of a jaw, the material that composes its skeleton, and the structure of its fins.

Skills Trace
Classifying
- Focus p. 694
- Practice p. 694
- Assess p. 707

Learning Modality

Auditory Learning Have pairs of students ask each other oral questions using the material from this section. For each subsection, they could switch roles, from questioner to responder.

GUIDE FOR READING

- **Describe** the characteristics of amphibians.
- **Identify** two orders of amphibians.

MINI LAB

- **Design an experiment** to find out how temperature affects frogs.

AMPHIBIANS HAVE SURVIVED for millions of years, typically in places where fresh water is plentiful. Amphibians also provide a link to the past. The 2500 species of living amphibians are the only surviving descendants of an ancient group that gave rise to all other land vertebrates.

Amphibian Form and Function

The name amphibian means "double life," emphasizing that these animals live both in water and on land. **With some exceptions, amphibians lay eggs in water, live in water as larvae and on land as adults, and have moist skin that lacks scales.**

Although the class Amphibia is relatively small, it is diverse enough to make it difficult to identify a typical species. Even so, frogs are good representatives. To learn more about the anatomy of frogs, study the illustration on the next page.

Checkpoint What is an amphibian? (1)

Feeding and Respiration

The double life of amphibians is reflected in their feeding habits. Amphibian larvae—commonly called tadpoles—are typically filter feeders or herbivores that graze on algae. Like other herbivores, tadpoles eat almost constantly, and their long, coiled intestines are usually filled with food. However, when tadpoles change into adults, their feeding apparatus and digestive tract are transformed to a strictly meat-eating design, complete with a much shorter intestine.

In most larval amphibians, gas exchange occurs through both skin and gills. Lungs typically replace gills when an amphibian becomes an adult, although some gas exchange continues across the skin.

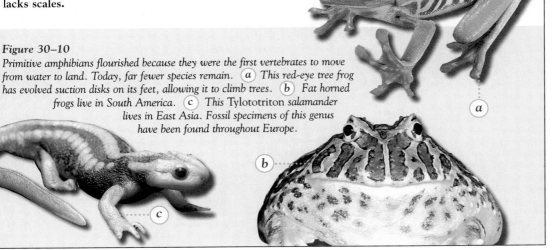

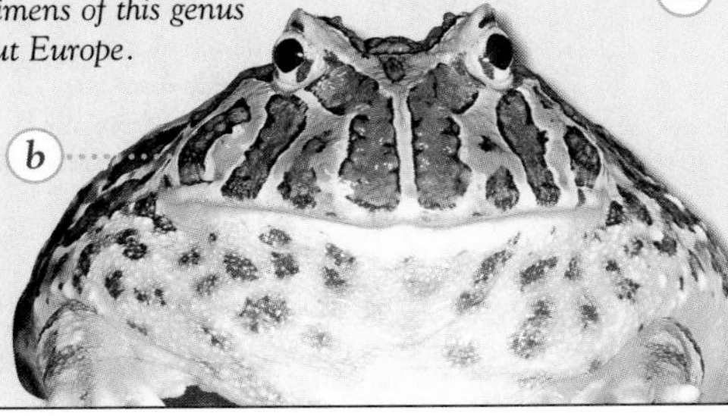

Figure 30–10
Primitive amphibians flourished because they were the first vertebrates to move from water to land. Today, far fewer species remain. (a) This red-eye tree frog has evolved suction disks on its feet, allowing it to climb trees. (b) Fat horned frogs live in South America. (c) This Tylototriton salamander lives in East Asia. Fossil specimens of this genus have been found throughout Europe.

TEACHER SUPPORT

Managing Classroom Diversity

TECH PREP STUDENTS
Many scientists point to the destruction of Earth's ozone layer as the primary cause in the decline of amphibian populations. Ask students who plan careers in heating and refrigeration and the automobile industry to investigate how the fluids traditionally used in refrigerators and air conditioners have contributed to this problem. Also ask that they find out what corrective measures are being taken or will be taken to change such technology.

MULTICULTURAL STRATEGY
Have students search for myths and folk tales from around the world that include references to frogs and toads. These include, perhaps most famously, several tales by the brothers Grimm, including "The Three Feathers." Students should also be able to find tales from other parts of the world, including China and Africa. Encourage students to investigate, in books on myth interpretation, why frogs and toads are common in folk tales.

SECTION 30–2
Amphibians

Performance Objectives
- Discuss the characteristics of amphibians.
- Identify Urodela and Anura as two orders of amphibians.

Mini Lab Skill: Experimenting
Laboratory Investigation Skill: Experimenting

1 ENGAGE

Inquiry Activity
Observing

A Bridge From Water to Land
Display a variety of photographs of different kinds of frogs, toads, salamanders, and newts. Make sure these pictures show amphibians in a variety of environments. Discuss with the class the uniqueness of amphibians, the organisms that gave rise to all land animals.

2 EXPLORE

Investigate
Cooperative Learning Assign to each cooperative learning group a topic related to amphibians. Such topics could include: (1) sight, smell and hearing; (2) typical habitats; (3) movement on land and in water; (4) reproduction and metamorphosis; (5) predator and prey; (6) circulation and respiration; and (7) declining populations. Ask that each group do research and then put together a presentation to teach the rest of the class about its topic.

Checkpoint

(1) A vertebrate that lays eggs in water, lives in water as a larva and on land as an adult, and has moist skin that lacks scales.

Technology

CD-ROM
The Digital Frog

3 TEACH

Visualizing a Frog

The amphibians called frogs and toads make up the order Anura. True frogs, of which this is a representation, make up the family Ranidae, members of which are distributed throughout the world. In the United States, there are more than 20 kinds of true frogs, including the bullfrog, green frog, wood frog, and northern leopard frog. The bullfrog, *Rana catesbeiana*, is the largest American frog, sometimes growing to a length of 20 cm. The African Goliath frog, the world's largest, can be as long as 40 cm.

In discussing this visual essay with students, first contrast the general body plan with that of fishes, as shown on page 689. Note the limbs in place of a fish's fins, as well as the lack of a tail. Call upon students' experiences with fishes and amphibians to point out that a fish lacks a neck. A fish moves its body from side to side, whereas a frog can turn its head. Also emphasize the following points.

- Unlike a fish, a frog has lungs. But unlike other vertebrates, a frog lacks the muscles to draw air into the lungs. To make up for this poor function, a frog exchanges gas through its moist skin.
- A fish has no problem with drying eyes—it's never out of water. An amphibian must have an adaptation to protect its eyes. These include the nictitating membrane, as well as upper and lower eyelids. Amphibians also produce tears.
- The exchange of gases necessary for respiration is accomplished by the lungs and through the skin. In addition, the inner walls of a frog's mouth are rich in blood vessels, and an enormous amount of gas is exchanged there.

Visualizing a Frog

Frogs and other amphibians represent an important link in the evolution of terrestrial vertebrates. While a larval frog lives only in water, an adult frog has adaptations for life on land.

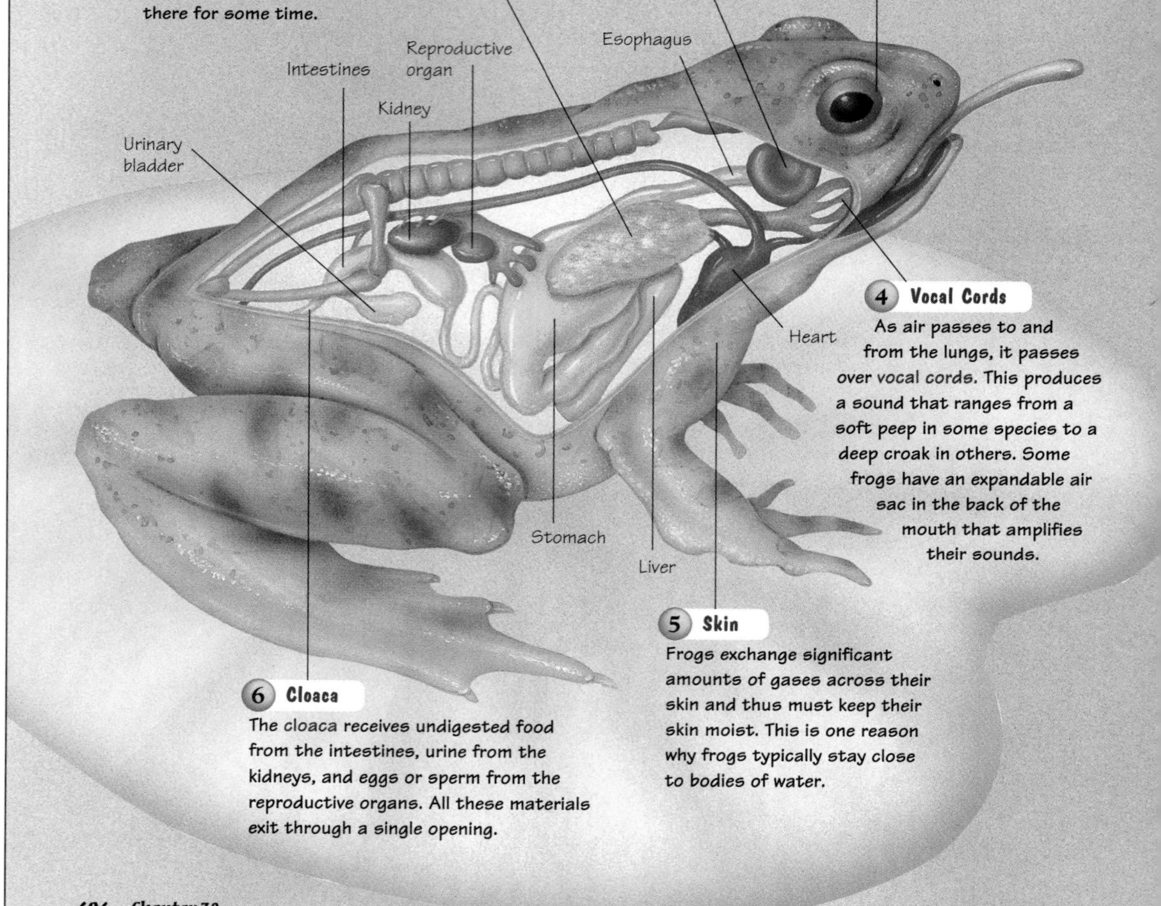

1 Lungs
Although a frog has functional lungs, it lacks the specialized chest and stomach muscles that other vertebrates use to move air in and out of their lungs. Instead, a frog fills its mouth with air, forces air into the lungs, and holds it there for some time.

2 Tympanic Membrane
As in a human ear, a frog's tympanic membrane vibrates in response to sound—the first step in the process of hearing. Some frogs hear well both on land and in water.

3 Eyes
A frog's eyes are specially "tuned" to detect objects resembling flying insects, the frog's main prey. In addition, transparent eyelids called nictitating membranes protect the eyes underwater and keep them moist in air.

4 Vocal Cords
As air passes to and from the lungs, it passes over vocal cords. This produces a sound that ranges from a soft peep in some species to a deep croak in others. Some frogs have an expandable air sac in the back of the mouth that amplifies their sounds.

5 Skin
Frogs exchange significant amounts of gases across their skin and thus must keep their skin moist. This is one reason why frogs typically stay close to bodies of water.

6 Cloaca
The cloaca receives undigested food from the intestines, urine from the kidneys, and eggs or sperm from the reproductive organs. All these materials exit through a single opening.

696 Chapter 30

TEACHER SUPPORT

Background Information

The class Amphibia includes three orders: Apoda, Urodela, and Anura. The apodes, mostly found in tropical regions, have wormlike bodies and no limbs. The most important characteristic of the urodeles is that adults have tails—in fact, Urodela means "with tails." A tail of a newt or salamander has several functions, though none more important than breathing. The exchange of gases through the skin of the tail, which is rich in blood vessels, makes the lung relatively unimportant.

The anurans include both frogs and toads. In general, frogs have webbed feet, and smoother skin and longer hind legs than toads. They tend to live near water and are more active. Toads have warty skin, little webbing, and shorter legs than frogs. They tend to live on land and are less active than frogs. But frogs and toads are so similar that scientists often use the term frogs for all anurans.

Figure 30–11
An amphibian typically begins its life in water, then moves to land. (a) *Frog eggs hatch into aquatic larvae called tadpoles. Like most fishes, a tadpole has gills, fins, and a two-chambered heart. As a tadpole changes into a terrestrial adult, gills and fins shrink away as lungs, heart, and legs develop.* (b) *This midwife toad is protecting a long string of eggs around its hind feet.*

(a)

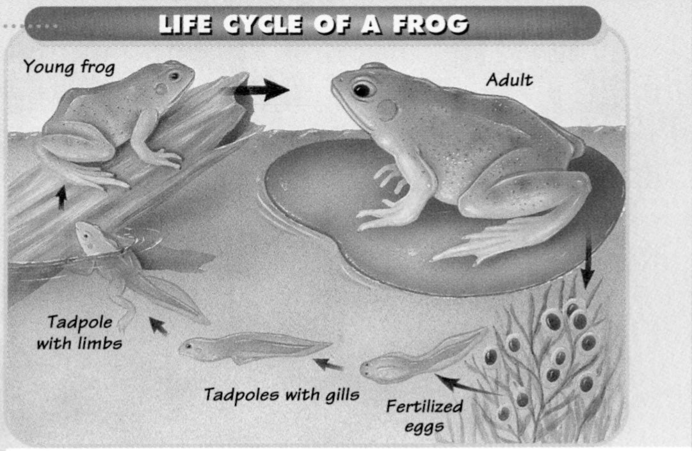

(b)

Internal Transport and Excretion

In the heart of an adult amphibian, oxygenated and deoxygenated blood are received separately in two chambers called atria, then mix together in a single pumping chamber called a ventricle. Although this mixing would cause all sorts of problems for a reptile or mammal, an amphibian compensates for this problem by exchanging significant amounts of gases through its skin.

Like fishes, amphibians have little problem excreting nitrogenous wastes. Some wastes diffuse across the skin, while others are removed from the bloodstream by kidneys. Amphibians need kidneys because they constantly gain water through osmosis, just as freshwater fishes do. To get rid of all that water, amphibians produce large amounts of dilute urine.

☑ ***Checkpoint*** How do amphibians eliminate wastes? ❶

Movement

Although most adult amphibians possess the same four limbs found in most terrestrial vertebrates, they use these limbs differently. As shown in ***Figure 30–12*** on page 698, an amphibian's limbs stick out sideways from its body, making it difficult for it to walk on four limbs as mammals do.

Instead, amphibians move in other ways. Many salamanders throw their body into an s-shaped curve, then use their legs to push themselves along the ground. Land-dwelling frogs and toads use strong hind legs to hop from place to place. And tree frogs have small "suction cups" on the ends of their fingers and toes that help them to climb.

Reproduction

In most species of amphibians, the female lays eggs in water, then the male fertilizes them externally. In a few species, including salamanders, eggs are fertilized internally. These species may be oviparous, ovoviviparous, or even viviparous. Most amphibians abandon eggs after they lay them, but some take great care of both eggs and young.

Classifying Amphibians

Newts and salamanders belong to the order Urodela (yoor-oh-DEE-luh). Although the ancestors of these amphibians grew up to 3 meters long, living salamanders rarely grow longer than about

Ideas Through Images

Have students examine Figure 30–11, read the caption, and answer the following questions.

- **In most species of amphibians, where does fertilization occur?** (In most species, the female lays eggs in water, and then the male fertilizes them externally.)
- **What does a tadpole have that an adult frog does not have?** (A tadpole has a tail, gills, and fins, which become lungs and limbs in the adult.)

Investigate

Research Ask students to find out what amphibian species are common to their region and to identify specific local habitats where amphibians can be found. They might use library resources, check with local or state agencies that oversee wildlife, interview naturalists, and call the biology department at a local college. Students can then key a map of the area to where various amphibians are found.

Laboratory Investigation

The Laboratory Investigation, Raising Tadpoles, on pages 702–703, is appropriate to use at this point in the chapter.

☑ Checkpoint

❶ Some wastes diffuse across the skin, and others are removed by the kidneys. Amphibians eliminate excess water by producing large amounts of dilute urine.

TEACHER SUPPORT

Ecology Note

Since the late 1980s, biologists have been reporting an alarming phenomenon—the decline of amphibian populations throughout the world. Some species in specific areas have actually disappeared. These reports have originated in such diverse places as Australia, Europe, Central and South America, and the United States. For instance, some frogs and toads were once so abundant in California that backpackers had to be careful to avoid stepping on them, but now those same anurans have virtually vanished. Scientists are not sure of the cause. Hypotheses include loss of habitat due to development, the introduction of new species in areas, water and air pollution, acid rain, the greenhouse effect, and the ozone hole in the atmosphere. Some believe that this decline is an indicator of a degraded global environment that will eventually affect all organisms, including humans.

Ancillary Support

The resources below can be used to support your teaching strategy for these two pages.

LM Observing the Structure of the Frog, #60
TR Writing in Biology: Shaping Poetry
Apply: Neat Newts
BL Inquiry Activity: Leaving Home
TB Visualizing a Frog, #39

MINI LAB Experimenting

Teacher Notes

- For time required and materials needed, see page 686b.
- Frogs can be obtained from a biological supply house. For care and feeding of frogs, see the suggestions under Teaching Strategies starting on **TE** page 702.
- An experiment to compare frog breathing rates would be to place the jar containing the frog into a container of ice water. Once the water in the frog's container has changed by 5–10 degrees, remove the jar from the container of ice water and check the breathing rate.
- Follow the safety tips described on page 702.

Answers to Analyze and Conclude

1. As the water temperature decreases, the frog's breathing rate also decreases, a process that conserves energy in a stressful environment.

2. A typical hypothesis might suggest that a lower environmental temperature reduces the rate of breathing.

Skills Trace
Experimenting
- Focus p. 698
- Practice p. 698
- Assess p. 707

MINI LAB Experimenting

Frogs in Cold Water

PROBLEM *How does temperature affect a frog? Design an experiment to find out.*

PROCEDURE

1. Obtain from your teacher a frog in a small jar containing water.
2. Count the number of times the frog breathes in 1 minute by watching the movements of its throat. Record this information.
3. Design an experiment to determine how water temperature affects a frog's breathing rate. Be sure to include a control. Have your teacher approve your procedure before you begin the experiment. Your experiment must not harm the frog in any way. Return the frog to your teacher.

ANALYZE AND CONCLUDE

1. How did water temperature affect the frog's breathing rate? How is this an advantage to the frog?
2. Formulate a hypothesis to explain your results.

15 centimeters. Their larvae are usually fully aquatic, having gills and a tail. Although most adults lose their gills as they move to live in moist woods, not all species develop lungs. And some species, such as the axolotl (AK-suh-laht-'l) and mud puppy, keep their gills as adults and live in water throughout their lives. Still other species switch back and forth between water and land.

Frogs and toads are members of the order Anura (uh-NOOR-uh). These amphibians live in many regions of the world and are common throughout the continental United States. One difference between frogs and toads is that frogs are more closely tied to water as adults. In fact, some toads have developed remarkable ways to adapt to environments with little or no surface water. These toads dig burrows deep into moist soil, from which they absorb water through their skin.

a

b

Figure 30–12
Amphibians are not especially numerous, but they are diverse. (a) *Newts thrive in a variety of habitats. This alpine newt lives in western Europe.* (b) *To moisten its skin, this eastern spadefoot toad is burying itself in wet mud.*

Section Review 30–2

1. **Describe** the characteristics of amphibians.
2. **Identify** two orders of amphibians.
3. **Critical Thinking—Formulating Hypotheses** Suppose that you discover the population of frogs and toads at a small lake is down by 25 percent from a year ago. Formulate a hypothesis to explain this observation.
4. **MINI LAB** How can you **design an experiment** to find out how temperature affects frogs?

4 ASSESS

Quick Check

Ask students to write a comparison of a typical fish and a typical amphibian.

Section Review 30–2

1. Most amphibians lay eggs in water, live in water as larvae and on land as adults, and have moist skin that lacks scales.

2. Urodela and Anura.

3. A typical hypothesis might mention an environmental change that does not favor frogs and toads.

4. A typical design will include comparisons of frogs' breathing rates at different temperatures.

Skills Trace
Experimenting
- Focus p. 698
- Practice p. 698
- Assess p. 707

Learning Modality

Visual Learning Have pairs of students work together to make a labeled sketch of a frog from a live frog in the classroom.

The World of Fishes

Guide for Reading

- **Explain** the importance of fishes in ecosystems.

Water covers nearly 70 percent of Earth's surface, so most of our planet is home turf for fishes. In fact, fishes are Earth's most numerous vertebrates and can be found in all kinds of water. You shouldn't be surprised to discover that your life is affected by all these fishes—from the largest sharks to the smallest herring and anchovies.

Fishes in Ecosystems

Fishes live in almost every aquatic habitat on Earth, where they fill many different roles in natural ecosystems. Why are fishes so numerous and diverse? First, the fish body plan has proved successful in fishes of many different sizes, ranging from guppies and minnows—which are less than a centimeter long—to giant whale sharks that span over 15 meters. Second, fishes feed on nearly every type of food you could imagine, including some substances that you probably would never consider as fish food! Thus, fishes are part of many different food webs in a wide range of ecosystems.

In addition, many fish eggs and larvae are much smaller than adult forms. Thus, many species fit into different places of food webs at different times in their life cycle. The larvae of some fishes, for example, may be eaten by the same animals that are prey for the adults!

Fishes as Food

When you think of a good fish to eat, you probably think of a large fish, such as a salmon, trout, or tuna. But in nature, arguably the most important food fishes are small fishes, such as the herring shown in *Figure 30–13.*

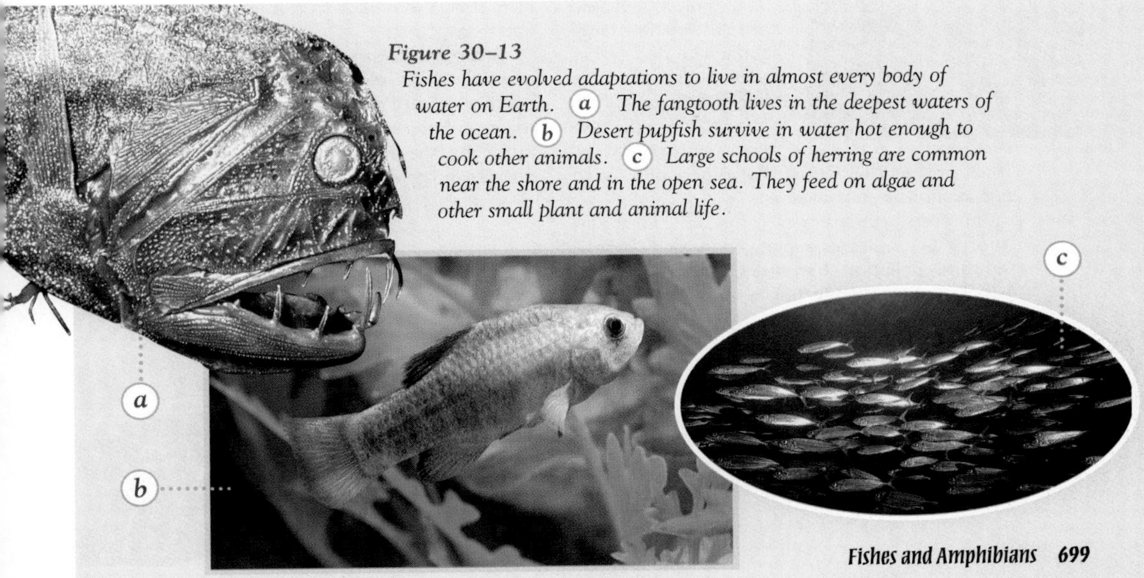

Figure 30–13
Fishes have evolved adaptations to live in almost every body of water on Earth. (a) The fangtooth lives in the deepest waters of the ocean. (b) Desert pupfish survive in water hot enough to cook other animals. (c) Large schools of herring are common near the shore and in the open sea. They feed on algae and other small plant and animal life.

Section 30–3

The World of Fishes

Performance Objective

- Describe how fishes are important in natural ecosystems.

1 ENGAGE

Ideas Through Images

Have students examine Figure 30–13, read the caption, and answer the following question.

- **How might overfishing affect the marine ecosystem?** (Since herring are part of marine food webs, other organisms could be affected in various ways. Those that herring use as food might increase in population, whereas those that use herring as food might decrease.)

2 EXPLORE

Investigate

Cooperative Learning Have student groups make a mural that shows a variety of environments in which fishes live. Each group would concentrate on a specific environment. These environments might include coral reef, deep ocean, freshwater lake, river or stream, rain forest, and saltwater to fresh water migration. Allow each group to decide what fish species, other organisms, and labels to include.

TEACHER SUPPORT

Facts and Figures

- An area where fishes are caught, or harvested, is known as a fishery. Both the areas where commercial fishing occurs and the fishing industries themselves are known as fisheries.
- About 70 million metric tons of fishes are harvested from the ocean every year.
- Approximately 20 kg of fishes are caught and consumed per year for each person in the world.
- Sardines are first on the list of fishes caught, with almost 9 million metric tons harvested each year. They are followed by anchovies, pollock, jack mackerel, and tuna.
- The leading fishing countries are, in order of importance, China, Japan, Peru, Chile, Russia, the United States, and India.
- Pacific Ocean fisheries account for more than half of the world's fish catch.

Ancillary Support

The resources below can be used to support your teaching strategy for these two pages.

TR Enrich: Monsters of the Deep
BL Inquiry Activity: Fishy Situations

3 TEACH

Connections

Fish farming is also called aquaculture, and marine aquaculture is sometimes called mariculture. These terms encompass cultivation of both fish species and shellfish. Aquaculture now accounts for about 10 percent of the global commercial fish harvest each year.

In the United States, commercial salmon farming was first established in Oregon. On a typical salmon ranch, about 30 million eggs are harvested each year from some 11,000 female coho salmon. Those eggs are incubated in 10°C water; after hatching, the fry are raised in 12°C water, warmer than natural waters. In these conditions, the fry reach maturity in about half the normal time. After 7 to 8 months, the smolt are transferred to near-shore ponds for a two-week stay, and it is hoped the salmon will return to those ponds. Once released, few actually do return—often less than 1 percent. The ranch operators need about a 2 percent return rate in order for the operation to be profitable.

Answers to Making the Connection

A typical response might suggest that the advantages include a stable production of fish products and a diminished impact on natural fish populations. Disadvantages might include the cost of this kind of farming and the loss of genetic diversity in natural fish populations.

Biology AND YOU .... Connections

Fish Farming

For many years, the commercial fishing industry has used huge nets to harvest fishes from oceans and large lakes. However, fishes can also be raised on aquatic farms—just as cows and pigs are raised on land.

Fish farming is not a new idea—humans have been raising and breeding fishes for thousands of years. People in China, Japan, and Thailand have a long tradition of raising and breeding fishes as pets. These fishes include goldfish, koi, and Siamese fighting fish. Today, the best koi sell for more than $10,000 per fish!

Koi fish are valued for their gracefulness and color.

Fish Farming in the United States

Fish farming is common in many countries. However, there are relatively few large commercial fish farms in the United States. Many of these farms raise catfish, a popular food. Unfortunately, most of the other fishes that Americans like to eat cannot be cultivated easily.

In recent years, however, the U.S. fishing industry has undergone many changes. Overfishing and pollution has been threatening the populations of many fish species in the wild, making these fishes more expensive to catch and bring to market. As a result, biologists are working to develop better and more economical techniques for raising popular fishes on farms.

Techniques of Fish Farming

Some species, such as catfish, grow well in crowded conditions, so they can be raised in shallow ponds. Other species, such as trout, require steady supplies of clean, cool, running water. These fishes may be farmed in streams, natural ponds, or cages set out in open water.

To raise salmon—a very popular food—fish farmers take advantage of the salmon's unusual life cycle. A salmon begins its life in a freshwater stream. It then migrates to the sea, grows to adulthood, and returns to the place it hatched in order to spawn. So, in a technique called salmon ranching, salmon eggs are placed in an aquaculture facility that is set apart from a stream. The salmon hatch and swim downstream to the sea. When they mature, they instinctively swim back to the facility, where they can be captured.

Although salmon ranching has proved successful, it is also controversial. Some researchers fear that mass releases of artificially raised salmon will reduce the genetic diversity—and thus the evolutionary fitness—of salmon species in the wild.

Making the Connection

What are the advantages and disadvantages of fish farming? Do you think that fishing is adequately regulated in the bodies of water near your community?

CAREER TRACK *This fish farmer is testing the water quality of a fish tank.*

TEACHER SUPPORT — Managing Classroom Diversity

TECH PREP STUDENTS

The problems the fishing industry faces today are the result of a lack of foresight in the use of resources. Ask students interested in careers in various environmental fields to investigate similar instances of a lack of foresight that has caused trouble in those fields. Examples include the clear-cutting of forests, the strip mining of coal, soil erosion in agriculture, and the production of gas-guzzling cars.

GIFTED STUDENTS

Ask students to investigate the commercial fishing industry around the world. Each student could concentrate on one aspect of commercial fisheries, including equipment and techniques, important fishery locations, problems of overfishing, and attempts to regulate fishing, both by the United States and through world treaties.

Figure 30–14
Fishes are a vital part of the ecosystem of the Amazon basin—and not just the part underwater. When the river floods, fishes wander into the surrounding rain forest.

In the ocean, huge schools of herrings, anchovies, and other small fishes provide food for predators ranging from larger fishes to squids, sea birds, sea lions, dolphins, whales—and humans. You may or may not eat small fishes, but they are an important part of the food supply in many countries. What's more, enormous quantities of fish meal are used to supplement livestock feed in the United States and in Europe. ●

Unfortunately, several stocks of small fishes have been overharvested. More than 30 years ago, overfishing nearly wiped out the enormous anchovy schools off the coast of South America. Almost overnight, flocks of sea birds and schools of dolphins and porpoises also disappeared. Why? Because these carnivores depend heavily on anchovies for food.

People in the fishing industry have been slow to learn the lessons of overharvesting. In fact, many delicious fishes that once were very common—including cod, halibut, and several other species—have been overfished almost to extinction. Hope for fishes may lie with laws that protect their spawning grounds and nurseries, as well as a new emphasis on fish farming, which is described on the opposite page.

Checkpoint Why are anchovies and other small fishes important? ❶

Fishes in the Rain Forest

Fishes also play important roles in places you might normally consider to be terrestrial ecosystems. In the rain forest of the Amazon basin, for example, each year's rainy season brings torrential downpours that can raise river levels as much as 11 meters. When this happens, the rivers overflow into thousands of square kilometers of rain forest, creating what Brazilians call *varzea*, or flooded forest, as shown in ***Figure 30–14.***

During the rainy season, many fishes wander from the riverbed into the flooded forest. There, they feed on ants and other insects that fall into the water, as well as fruits and seeds of rain forest trees. In fact, fish that are relatives of the ferocious piranhas use their huge teeth and strong jaws to crack open Brazil nuts and other hard-shelled seeds. Biologists suspect that certain rain forest plants depend on these types of fishes, rather than birds or mammals, to spread their seeds.

The vital interactions between the fishes and the forest offer another reason to preserve tropical forests. If the *varzea* disappears, so too will the river fishes that depend on the flooded forest for food and breeding places.

INTEGRATING AGRICULTURE

Why do ranchers feed ground-up fish to livestock?

Section Review 30–3

1. **Explain** the importance of fishes.
2. **BRANCHING OUT ACTIVITY** Conduct a survey to determine which fishes are popular foods with your classmates. **Research** how these fishes are raised or harvested.

Ideas Through Images

Have students examine Figure 30–14, read the caption, and answer the following questions.

- **What occurs in a rain forest that causes fishes to swim beyond the banks of a river?** (The river overflows and floods the forest.)
- **How does such an event help to preserve the forest?** (The fishes eat the fruit and spread the seeds of the plants in the forest.)

INTEGRATING AGRICULTURE

Ranchers feed ground-up fish to livestock because fish products are a relatively inexpensive form of protein.

4 ASSESS

Quick Check

Have students make an outline of the section, using the section subheadings as the primary divisions in the outline.

Checkpoint

❶ They provide food for many predators; they also are part of the human food supply.

Section Review 30–3

1. Fishes are important in food webs, in the fishing industry, and in their interactions in rain forests.

2. Have each student write his or her favorite fish food on a slip of paper, and then have two volunteers make a list that ranks the foods in order of most to least mentioned. Students can find how fishes are harvested by using the library.

Learning Modality

Auditory Learning Have students respond orally to questions about fishes in their natural environments, as well as about their role in the food industry.

Technology

BioVue
Mini Doc: Animals of the Flooded Forest
Videodisc Side 7

Go to Chapter 10

CHAPTER 30

Laboratory Investigation

Raising Tadpoles

Before the Lab

1. Purchase frog eggs or tadpoles from a biological supply house.
2. Keep the eggs in a cool place in buckets of pond water. Every few days, rinse the eggs and remove any dead eggs that float to the surface.
3. Tadpoles are ready for use in the lab when they develop hind buds.

Pre-Lab Discussion

Have students read the entire procedure for this investigation. Then ask students the following questions.

What is the purpose of this investigation? (To determine the effect of colored light on the development of tadpoles.)

What could cause the color of light in a tadpole's natural environment to be other than white light? (In natural waters, some colors of light might normally be filtered out. A heavy canopy of leaves might also filter out some colors of light.)

What changes do you expect to occur in a tadpole as it develops into an adult? (Students should mention loss of tail and gills, development of legs and lungs, and changes in color, size, and shape.)

Skills Development

Students will use these skills while completing the laboratory investigation: designing an experiment, observing, measuring, communicating, comparing, drawing conclusions, and hypothesizing.

Teaching Strategies

1. Help groups with their experimental designs. A typical design will include three aquariums with four tadpoles each. The control aquarium should be covered with clear cellophane, and the other two with different-colored cellophane. All three aquariums should be placed where they receive bright light.

Laboratory Investigation

DESIGNING AN EXPERIMENT

Raising Tadpoles

Frogs lay their eggs in a variety of watery habitats—from woodland ponds shaded by the leaves of overhanging trees to the edges of lakes in the full sun. In this investigation, you will determine whether tadpoles are affected by different kinds of light.

Problem

How can you determine the effect of colored light on tadpoles? **Design an experiment** to answer this question.

Suggested Materials

- 3 large plastic containers
- pond water or dechlorinated tap water
- 12 tadpoles of the same species and age
- tadpole food
- sheets of cellophane, in two colors
- tape

Suggested Procedure

1. Use the large plastic containers to create three identical aquariums. Fill each aquarium with water from the same source—either pond water or dechlorinated tap water. You may choose to add clean rocks or other decorations to the aquariums. Place 4 tadpoles in each aquarium.

2. Design a procedure to determine how colored light affects tadpoles. To expose the tadpoles to colored light, tape sheets of colored cellophane

Safety Tips

- Remind students to handle the tadpoles gently and not to cause them any harm.
- Ask students to clean up any spills immediately.
- Have students wash their hands after they have completed the procedure.

around all sides of the aquariums. Do not tape cellophane directly to a light source. Be sure that your experiment includes a control group.

3. **With your teacher's permission, carry out the experiment you designed. Prepare a data table to record the observations you will be making.**
4. **During the course of your experiment, follow your teacher's instructions for the care and upkeep of tadpoles. As a general rule, tadpoles should be fed twice a week. The water in the aquariums should be changed every 3 days and be kept at a temperature near 20°C. Avoid handling the tadpoles directly, which can affect their health.**
5. **Observe the tadpoles every day for 2 months. Note their appearance, general behavior, and feeding habits. Record all observations in your data table. CAUTION:** ***Always wash your hands after handling tadpoles, their food, or the aquariums.*** **At the end of the experiment, return the tadpoles to your teacher.**

Observations

1. How did the tadpoles change over the course of the experiment?
2. Compare the development of the three groups of tadpoles. How did they develop similarly? Differently?
3. In each aquarium, did the living conditions remain the same throughout the experiment? If not, describe any differences that you observed.

Analysis and Conclusions

1. How does the color of light that a tadpole receives affect its development? Use the data you collected to support your answer.
2. Identify any assumptions you made in your answer to question 1. How could you change the design of your experiment to account for these assumptions?
3. Suppose that tadpoles were submitted to colored light in their natural environment. Do you think they would develop as they did in your experiment? Explain.
4. Formulate a hypothesis to explain the tadpoles' response to colored light. Discuss how you could test this hypothesis.

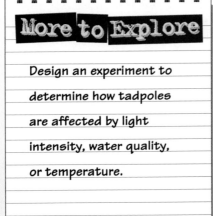

More to Explore

Design an experiment to determine how tadpoles are affected by light intensity, water quality, or temperature.

2. Students should feed the tadpoles at least twice a week with 1 mL of food per aquarium. Tadpole food includes boiled spinach, boiled lettuce, and boiled egg yolk. One day after food is added, students should remove uneaten food from the aquarium.
3. Students' data tables might include columns for length, limb development, and general characteristics, such as eye shape and size, pigmentation, and loss of gills and tail.
4. Students may want to measure tadpoles periodically. One way to accomplish this is to remove a tadpole with an aquarium net and place it in a Petri dish that is sitting over a piece of graph paper. Students might measure all tadpoles in an aquarium and then find the average for the group.

Answers to Observations

1. In general, students should have observed the metamorphosis of the tadpoles from larval stage to adult, including increase in body size, growth of limbs, loss of gills and tail, increase in eye size, and change of color.
2. All tadpoles should have grown and developed in the same ways and at about the same rate. The difference students should have observed is that the control tadpoles have lighter pigmentation than those raised under colored light. Students may, or may not, be able to observe differences between the tadpoles raised under the two colors of cellophane.
3. In general, conditions in the three aquariums should have remained much the same throughout the experiment, though students may have noticed that algae grew faster in the control aquarium because the light intensity was higher.

Answers to Analysis and Conclusions

1. Most students will probably conclude that tadpoles raised under colored light have darker pigmentation because the tadpoles raised in the two experimental aquariums were darker in color than those raised in the control aquarium. Some students may correctly conclude that it is light intensity, not light color, that affects the pigmentation of tadpoles.
2. Some students may identify the assumption that light intensity rather than light color affects pigmentation in tadpoles. To test this, they could design an experiment in which tadpoles are raised under different intensities of light.
3. Most students will assert that the data collected suggest that tadpoles would develop in natural conditions the same way they developed in this experiment.
4. Students should formulate a hypothesis that conforms with their observations in the experiment. They might suggest testing this hypothesis with a larger experiment that includes more specimens and more exacting ways of measuring tadpole development.

More to Explore

A typical design will suggest setting up two or more aquariums to test one of the given variables. Each experiment should include a control. For example, in an experiment that tests temperature, the control would be an aquarium whose water was kept at room temperature. Other setups would keep the water at somewhat lower or higher temperatures.

CHAPTER 30

Study Guide

Review Strategy

Group students in twos or threes, and ask each group to make a word puzzle using vocabulary terms from the chapter. This puzzle should contain the terms in a large square of letters, with the terms arrayed forward, backward, horizontally, vertically, and diagonally. Distractor letters should be used to fill out all the slots within the large square. Give each group a piece of graph paper on which to make this puzzle. Accompanying the word puzzle should be a list of questions whose answers are the terms in the puzzle. Once all groups have completed the task, use a copy machine to duplicate the puzzles and have students do one or two of the puzzles that they did not help construct.

Recalling Main Ideas

1. d
2. c
3. b
4. c
5. d
6. b
7. d
8. a
9. d

Assessment

Reviewing What You Learned

1. A notochord, a hollow dorsal nerve cord, and pharyngeal slits.
2. A bony structure in many fishes that protects the gills.
3. An atrium and a ventricle.
4. The olfactory bulbs, which are directly connected to the cerebrum, are a part of the fish's nervous system specialized for the sense of smell.
5. The coelacanth is the only living species of lobe-finned fishes, and it is among the closest to the common ancestor of all four-limbed vertebrates.
6. The three classes of fishes are jawless fishes, cartilaginous fishes, and bony fishes, which include most of the world's fishes.
7. It helps a fish detect patterns of movement in the surrounding water.

Study Guide

Summarizing Key Concepts

The key concepts in each section of this chapter are listed below to help you review the chapter content. Make sure you understand each concept and its relationship to other concepts and to the theme of this chapter.

30–1 Fishes

- At some stage of its life, a chordate has a notochord, a hollow dorsal nerve cord, and pharyngeal slits. Invertebrate chordates lack a backbone. Most chordates are vertebrates.
- All fishes have fins, and almost all fishes breathe through gills and have scales. In other respects, fishes are very diverse.
- A fish has a much simpler nervous system than a human has, but it is organized in a similar way. In addition, most fishes have a closed, single-loop circulatory system, a kidney to eliminate wastes, and well-developed sense organs.
- Fishes reproduce in several different ways and may be oviparous, ovoviviparous, or viviparous. Individuals of some species can change gender under certain conditions.
- The three classes of fishes are jawless fishes, cartilaginous fishes, and bony fishes. The bony fishes include two subclasses: ray-finned fishes and fleshy-finned fishes.

30–2 Amphibians

- With a few exceptions, amphibians lay eggs in water, live in water as larvae and on land as adults, and have moist skin that lacks scales.
- Frogs have a well-developed nervous system and sense organs. A frog's eyes are specially "tuned" to detect objects resembling flying insects, the frog's main prey.
- Newts and salamanders are members of the order Urodela. Frogs and toads are members of the order Anura.

30–3 The World of Fishes

- Fishes live in almost every aquatic habitat on Earth, where they fill many different roles in natural ecosystems.
- Herrings, anchovies, and other small fishes are important foods for larger animals—including sea birds and dolphins. Overharvesting these fishes can decrease the populations of their predators.

Reviewing Key Terms

Review the following vocabulary terms and their meaning. Then use each term in a complete sentence.

30–1 Fishes

notochord
hollow dorsal nerve cord
pharyngeal slit
pharynx
gill
operculum
spinal cord
vertebral column
swim bladder
scale
lateral line
kidney
olfactory bulb
cerebrum
optic lobe
cerebellum
medulla oblongata
oviparous
ovoviviparous
viviparous

30–2 Amphibians

tympanic membrane
nictitating membrane
vocal cord
cloaca

Inquiry-Based Strategy

Boats from a small fishing town once returned from sea loaded with fishes. Now they return almost empty. What has caused this change? What can be done to reestablish the fish population in this area? Ask students to research the answers to these questions. Direct them to the library, and give them wide latitude in finding specific instances of similar situations that have occurred in the past few decades, especially in the New England area. Students might find such information in library books and periodicals. Some may discover a case in which overfishing caused the problem; others may focus on water pollution and acid rain. Solutions to the problem might include limits on fishing, regulations on fishing techniques, and cleaning up the environment.

CHAPTER 30

Recalling Main Ideas

Choose the letter of the answer that best completes the statement or answers the question.

1. The vertebrate chordates include
   - a. arthropods.
   - b. tunicates.
   - c. lancelets.
   - d. amphibians.
2. Gills are located in the area of a fish's body called the
   - a. lungs.
   - b. sinus venosus.
   - c. pharynx.
   - d. cerebrum.
3. To move up and down in the water, a fish moves gas in and out of its
   - a. kidney.
   - b. swim bladder.
   - c. pharynx
   - d. gills.
4. Some fishes lay eggs just before or soon after the eggs are fertilized. This type of reproduction is described as
   - a. ovoviviparous.
   - b. external fertilization.
   - c. oviparous.
   - d. viviparous.
5. Which of these organisms is a cartilaginous fish?
   - a. coelacanth
   - b. herring
   - c. dolphin
   - d. shark
6. Frogs eggs typically develop into larvae
   - a. on land.
   - b. in water.
   - c. inside the female's body.
   - d. inside the male's body.
7. In adult amphibians, gas exchange occurs through
   - a. lungs only.
   - b. gills only.
   - c. skin only.
   - d. lungs and skin.
8. Nictitating membranes cover and protect a frog's
   - a. eyes.
   - b. gills.
   - c. lungs.
   - d. kidneys.
9. In natural ecosystems, fishes feed on
   - a. plants only.
   - b. other fishes only.
   - c. plants and small animals only.
   - d. many different foods.

Putting It All Together

Using the information on pages xxx to xxxi, complete the following concept map.

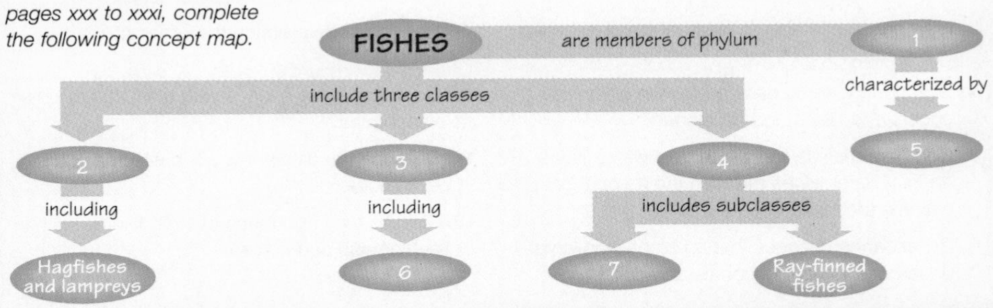

8. Most amphibians lay eggs in water, live in water as larvae and on land as adults, and have moist skin that lacks scales.
9. The amphibian heart has two atria, which receive oxygenated and deoxygenated blood, and a single pumping chamber called a ventricle.
10. Amphibians exchange significant amounts of gases across their skin.
11. As adults, frogs are more closely tied to water than are toads.
12. The order Urodela includes newts and salamanders, and the order Anura includes toads and frogs.
13. When rivers overflow in the rain forest during the rainy season, fishes feed on fruits and seeds, and thus spread the seeds of some plants.

Expanding the Concepts

1. The nervous system in fishes is far simpler than the nervous system in humans, though it is set up in much the same way. The brain of both fishes and humans contains a cerebrum, a cerebellum, and a medulla oblongata. In humans, the cerebrum is where thinking occurs; in fishes, the cerebrum seems to be involved with the sense of smell and basic behaviors.
2. The scales of bony fishes are covered with mucus, thus reducing friction with the water and helping the fish to escape predators. The scales of cartilaginous fishes are platelike, each armed with toothlike structures; and the scales around the mouth have evolved into teeth.
3. Sharks have specialized cells that detect tiny electric currents. Sharks can use this ability to find hidden prey because an animal's nerves and muscle cells produce electric currents when it moves.
4. Oviparous fishes have either internal or external fertilization, and eggs are laid just before or soon after they are fertilized. Both ovoviviparous fishes and viviparous fishes have internal fertilization, and in both the eggs are held inside the body while they grow into free-swimming babies. In ovoviviparous fishes, the eggs are nourished entirely by the yolk. In viviparous fishes, the female provides additional nourishment to the developing young inside its body.

Putting It All Together

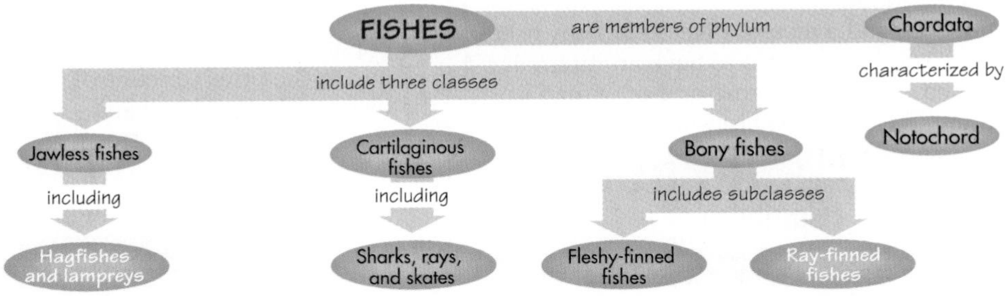

Assessment (continued)

5. Water constantly enters the body of freshwater fishes through osmosis; they eliminate water by producing lots of dilute urine. Saltwater fishes constantly lose water through osmosis; they drink water continuously and produce very little urine.
6. When an amphibian larva becomes an adult, gills and fins shrink away as lungs and legs develop. The larval two-chambered heart becomes a three-chambered heart in the adult. The larval feeding apparatus and digestive tract are transformed into a meat-eating design, complete with a much shorter intestine.
7. At the larval stage, when the organism has fins, gills, and a two-chambered heart, all of which are characteristic of fishes.
8. Jawless fishes have no jaws, no bony skeletons, and no scales. Cartilaginous fishes have a skeleton made of cartilage. Their bodies are covered with platelike scales, and most are carnivores. Bony fishes have bony skeletons.
9. As air passes to and from a frog's lungs, it passes over vocal cords, creating a croaking noise in some frogs or a peeping noise in others. Some frogs have an expandable air sac that amplifies their sound.
10. A frog has functional lungs, but it lacks the specialized chest and stomach muscles that other vertebrates use to move air in and out of their lungs.
11. Many salamanders throw their bodies into an s-shaped curve and then use their legs to push themselves along the ground. Land-dwelling frogs and toads use strong hind legs to hop from place to place. Tree frogs have small "suction cups" on their fingers and toes that help them climb.
12. Small fishes such as herring and anchovies provide food for many predators, including larger fishes, squids, sea birds, sea lions, dolphins, and whales. They also are an important part of the human food supply in many countries and are used in livestock feed in the United States and Europe.

Assessment

Reviewing What You Learned

Answer each of the following in a complete sentence.

1. Identify three structures that all chordates have at some time during their life cycle.
2. In fishes, what is the function of the operculum?
3. Identify the chambers of a fish's heart.
4. What are the olfactory bulbs?
5. What is a coelacanth? Why is it significant?
6. Identify the three classes of fishes. Which class is most numerous?
7. What is the purpose of the lateral line in fishes?
8. List three characteristics common to almost all amphibians.
9. Describe the heart of an adult amphibian.
10. Why must amphibians keep their skin moist?
11. What is the main difference between frogs and toads?
12. Identify the different orders of amphibians.
13. How do fishes help to disperse seeds in the rain forest of the Amazon basin?

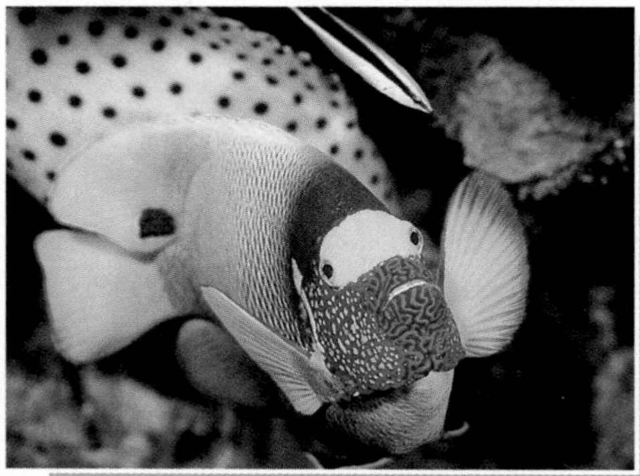

Expanding the Concepts

Discuss each of the following in a brief paragraph.

1. Compare the nervous systems of fishes and humans.
2. Describe the function of scales in bony fishes and cartilaginous fishes.
3. How are sharks able to "zero in" on prey buried in the sand?
4. Describe the three general ways in which fish eggs are fertilized and developed.
5. Compare the ways in which freshwater fishes and saltwater fishes maintain the amount of water in their body.
6. Describe the changes that an amphibian larva undergoes when it becomes an adult.
7. In which stage of an amphibian's life—larva or adult—does it more closely resemble a fish? Explain.
8. Describe the three classes of fishes.
9. How do frogs produce their characteristic sounds?
10. Compare a frog's lungs with the lungs of other vertebrates.
11. Describe the different ways in which amphibians move.
12. Discuss the importance of small fishes, such as herring and anchovies.

706 Chapter 30

Extending Your Thinking

1. Students should identify scales, pectoral fins, a tail fin, eyes, and a mouth. Like other bony fishes, this fish would be expected to have an internal bony skeleton and other structures presented in the feature "Visualizing a Fish," on page 689.

Skills Trace
Classifying
- Focus p. 694
- Practice p. 694
- Assess p. 707

2. A typical design might include studying two frog populations in the laboratory, one living in clean water and one living in polluted water. If the population living in polluted water declines relative to the other, or control, population, then the hypothesis would be valid.

Skills Trace
Experimenting
- Focus p. 698
- Practice p. 698
- Assess p. 707

Extending Your Thinking

Use the skills you have developed in this chapter to answer the following.

1. **Classifying** Examine the bony fish shown in the photograph on the opposite page. What structures can you identify from this photograph? List some other structures you would expect to find in this fish.
2. **Designing an experiment** A biologist hypothesizes that water pollution is causing the frog population to decline at a local lake. Design an experiment to provide evidence for or against this hypothesis.
3. **Analyzing concepts** Discuss the factors that may have contributed to the decline in the number of fishes caught off the coastal waters in many regions of the United States.
4. **Making judgments** Currently, laws in the United States protect endangered animals of any species—including fishes and amphibians. Research an instance in which the government halted a commercial development in order to protect a fish or amphibian species. Do you think that the government's action was appropriate? Discuss both sides of the issue.
5. **Communicating** Research the structure and life cycle of an interesting fish or amphibian, such as a shark, sea horse, or salamander. Present a report on your findings to the class.

Applying Your Skills

An Incredible Journey

A salmon is born in a freshwater stream, migrates to the sea, then returns years later to the same stream where its life began. Although biologists have learned a great deal about salmon, much about a salmon's behavior remains a mystery.

1. Research the structures or processes that allow salmon to survive in both salt water and fresh water.
2. Formulate a hypothesis to explain how a salmon is able to find the stream where it hatched.
3. As a salmon swims up a river to its home stream, it swims against strong currents and overcomes obstacles such as waterfalls. Do salmon have stronger muscles than other fishes? Research the answer to this question.

4. A female salmon lays about 8000 eggs, but only about 1 percent of the eggs survive to adulthood. Discuss the significance of this fact.

• GOING FURTHER •

5. Create a poster to illustrate a salmon's life cycle. You may also include information on salmon fishing, salmon farming, and factors that influence the salmon population in the wild.

3. A typical response might emphasize overfishing of many fish species and the destruction of fish spawning grounds. Also, pollution along the coast could have caused the populations of some fishes to decline, which then caused the decline in fishes that feed on the fishes affected by the pollution.
4. Students may discover instances of the government's halting a commercial development because of the presence of an endangered species—the most famous perhaps being the halting of construction of a dam in the 1970s because of an endangered fish called the snail darter. Arguments for such action are often based on the concept that a danger to one organism indicates a danger to the larger ecosystem. Arguments against such action generally focus on the damage to the economy and society that lack of development will cause.
5. Students might choose any of the great variety of fishes and amphibians mentioned in the text or a library source. Make sure no two students research the same species by reviewing their plans after they do initial research.

Applying Your Skills

Teacher Note

• Have students individually do the initial research that is required to answer the questions. Then have students meet in groups to discuss their answers and to create a poster about a salmon's life cycle.

Answers

2. Most biologists think that salmon navigate the open seas by sensing Earth's magnetic field and by following ocean currents. Finding its native waters or "home" stream probably involves a salmon's sense of smell.
3. Salmon have stronger muscles than some other fish, and they devote all of their physical resources to completing this journey. As a consequence, they often die soon after spawning is complete.
4. The laying of so many eggs is an adaptation to the difficult salmon life cycle, in which chances of survival are slim. Students might also mention that many of those eggs or young salmon are probably important to other species as a food source.

Scoring Rubric

4 Response is thorough, accurate, and creative; shows an in-depth understanding of science skills, procedures, and concepts.

3 Response is complete, mostly accurate, and original; shows a satisfactory understanding of science skills, procedures, and concepts.

2 Response is mostly complete but includes some inaccuracies; shows an adequate understanding of science skills, procedures, and concepts.

1 Response is only partially complete and has many inaccuracies; shows an incomplete understanding of science skills, procedures, and concepts.

0 Response is mostly incomplete and/or inaccurate; shows a lack of understanding of science skills, procedures, and concepts.

Chapter 31 Reptiles and Birds

Content Management	Student Edition Activities
■ Section 31–1 Reptiles, pp. 709–713 The Reptile Body Plan Classifying Reptiles	MINI LAB: Ready to Slither, p. 710 Laboratory Investigation: Adaptation for Survival, pp. 722–723
■ Section 31–2 Birds, pp. 714–719 The Bird Body Plan Birds and Flight	MINI LAB: Fine Feathered Friends, p. 717
◆ BRANCHING OUT • In Depth Section 31–3 Evolution of Birds, pp. 720–721 Birds From Dinosaurs? Did Archaeopteryx Fly?	

■ These sections cover all the necessary content and concepts for an enriched course in biology.
◆ This section covers content and concepts that are either applications or extensions of the enriched material.

Integration Strategies

SE Physics, p. 719

Assessment Strategies

SE Chapter Review, pp. 724–727
TR Section Reviews
Chapter Test
BL Chapter Review
Practice Test
CTB Chapter 31 Test

Tech Prep

Teaching strategies appropriate for students who are in technical/vocational programs or who are considering post-secondary technical education can be found on the following **TE** pages: 709 and 715.

Meeting the Standards

Sections 31–1 through 31–3 cover one of the six content standards under **The Cell,** three of the five content standards under **Biological Evolution,** one of the six content standards under **Matter, Energy, and Organization in Living Systems,** and three of the four content standards under **The Behavior of Organisms** as described on pages 184–187 of The National Science Education Standards.

Chapter Planning Guide

Teacher's Edition Activities	Other Activities	Media and Technology
Chapter Discovery Learning Activity, p. 708 Inquiry Activity: A Reptile Revue, p. 709 Investigate: Cooperative Learning, p. 712	**LM** Classifying Lizards, #61 **TR** Explore: Taking a Look at Turtles **BL** Inquiry Activity: Moving to Higher Ground	
Inquiry Activity: The Sights and Sounds of Birds, p. 714 Investigate: Cooperative Learning, p. 714	**LM** Examining an Unfertilized Chicken Egg, #62 **TR** Writing in Biology: Personalities Apply: Muscle and Bone **BL** Inquiry Activity: Bird Is the Word	CD-ROM: Birds: Characteristics and Adaptations **TB** Visualizing a Bird, #40
Inquiry Activity: Not Much of a Difference, p. 720 Investigate: Research, p. 720	**TR** Enrich: Lords of the Dance **BL** Inquiry Activity: Getting Off the Ground	

KEY: SE Student Edition **TE** Teacher's Edition **LM** Laboratory Manual **TR** Teaching Resources **BL** BioLog **TB** Transparency Box **CTB** Computer Test Bank

Materials List

TE Chapter Discovery Learning Activity, p. 708 (20 minutes); hard-boiled chicken egg, hand lens, knife, small paper plate.

TE Inquiry Activity: A Reptile Revue, p. 709 (20–30 minutes); a turtle, lizard, and snake in separate containers.

SE MINI LAB: Ready to Slither, p. 710 (20–30 minutes); mounted snake skeleton or photograph of skeleton, shed snake skin.

TE Inquiry Activity: The Sights and Sounds of Birds, p. 714 (15–20 minutes); photographs or drawings of local birds, recording of bird songs and sounds, tape or CD player.

TE Investigate: Cooperative Learning, p. 714 (4–5 hours over several days); poster board, colored pencils or markers.

SE MINI LAB: Fine Feathered Friends, p. 717 (30 minutes); contour feather, down feather, hand lens.

TE Inquiry Activity: Not Much of a Difference, p. 720 (15–20 minutes); photographs or drawings of a flightless bird and drawing of a small two-legged dinosaur.

CHAPTER 31

Reptiles and Birds

Introducing the Chapter

. . . In Pictures

This Lanner falcon, indigenous to Africa and the Middle East, is a powerful predator of the skies, and was once highly prized for capture and training by falconers. In the United States, the most common falcons are the peregrine falcon and the American kestrel, sometimes called the sparrow hawk. As students examine this photograph, ask the following questions.

- **What functions do feathers serve for a bird?** (Feathers are integral to flight and insulate and waterproof a bird.)
- **From the shape of this falcon's beak, what might you infer about the food it eats?** (This beak is adapted to piercing and tearing flesh implying that a falcon is a carnivorous predator.

Teaching Strategy

In the first section of this chapter, students learn about the basic characteristics and types of reptiles. In the second section, they learn about the basic characteristics of birds and gain an understanding of flight. The BRANCHING OUT section provides students with an in-depth look at the evolution of birds.

BIO JOURNAL

The Bio Journal topic can be used to stimulate classroom discussion about the reptiles and birds students commonly see or keep as pets. Ask students to describe any turtles, lizards, or snakes they or relatives have kept as pets. Then ask what birds they see in their neighborhood or on their way to school. In discussing these birds, focus on adaptations that different birds have made to their environment. Instruct students to keep their entries in their portfolios.

CHAPTER 31

Reptiles and Birds

FOCUSING THE CHAPTER
THEME: Unity and Diversity

31–1 Reptiles
- **Describe** the characteristics of reptiles.

31–2 Birds
- **Explain** the adaptations that allow birds to fly.

BRANCHING OUT *In Depth*

31–3 Evolution of Birds
- **Discuss** the evolution of birds and flying reptiles.

LABORATORY INVESTIGATION
- **Design an experiment** to show how a chameleon changes color in response to its environment.

Biology and Your World

BIO JOURNAL

Do you have a favorite bird? A favorite reptile? What roles do birds and reptiles play in your life? Answer these questions in your journal.

Lanner falcon of eastern Africa

TEACHER SUPPORT — Chapter Discovery Learning Activity

OBSERVING A CHICKEN EGG

Divide the class into pairs, and give each pair a hard-boiled chicken's egg to examine. Tell them to follow this procedure.

1. Carefully crack and peel off the eggshell.
2. Examine the eggshell with a hand lens. Note the structure of the shell and any membrane attached to it. Make a sketch of the structure of the shell.
3. Lay the shelled egg on a paper plate and cut it in half lengthwise and examine its parts. Make a sketch and write a description of what you see.

Once all groups have finished their examination, discuss as a class what they observed. Each student should have observed a membrane on the inside of the shell. Students also should have noticed the egg yolk and the white around the yolk. Challenge students to infer how this egg is adapted to life on land.

Reptiles

SECTION 31–1

Guide for Reading

- **Describe** the characteristics of reptiles.
- **Explain** why reptiles were able to adapt to land.

MINI LAB

- **Infer** how a snake moves by examining its skeleton and scales.

HUMANS HAVE ALWAYS BEEN fascinated by reptiles—as well as frightened by many of them. Many people fear snakes for their venomous bites or slithery movements. And explorers' encounters with lizards and crocodiles inspired images of dragons in European folk tales.

Yet reptiles are as astonishing as any creatures of human imagination. Dinosaurs grew to incredible sizes on land, and other extinct reptiles conquered sea and air. In fact, birds evolved from one line of small dinosaurs! Although living reptiles are smaller and less powerful than their ancestors, they are wondrous animals all the same.

The Reptile Body Plan

Reptiles are scaly-skinned vertebrates that breathe with lungs and lay eggs that hatch on land. A reptile's scales may be smooth or rough. Folklore to the contrary, reptile skins are never slimy.

The basic reptilian body plan is typical for terrestrial vertebrates, with a well-developed skull, a backbone and tail, two limb girdles, and four limbs. However, two types of reptiles have slightly different body plans: Turtles have a hard shell that is fused to their vertebrae, and snakes have lost both sets of legs.

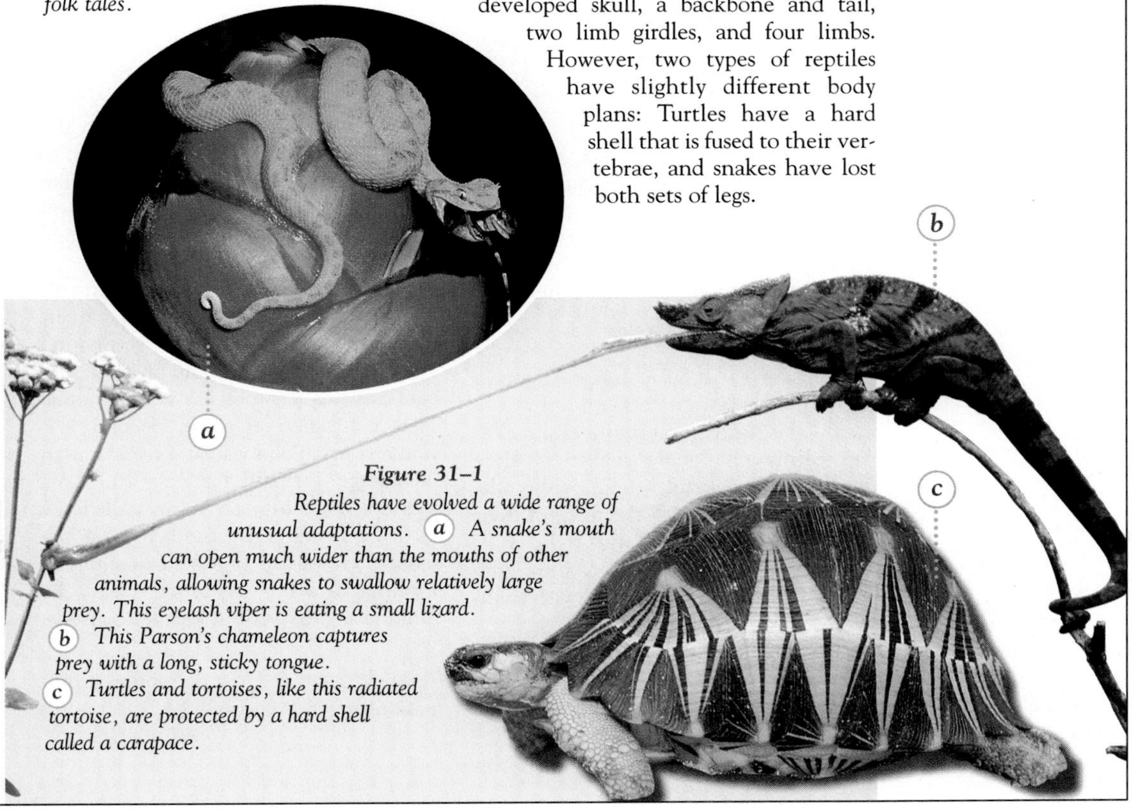

Figure 31–1
Reptiles have evolved a wide range of unusual adaptations. (a) *A snake's mouth can open much wider than the mouths of other animals, allowing snakes to swallow relatively large prey. This eyelash viper is eating a small lizard.* (b) *This Parson's chameleon captures prey with a long, sticky tongue.* (c) *Turtles and tortoises, like this radiated tortoise, are protected by a hard shell called a carapace.*

TEACHER SUPPORT — Managing Classroom Diversity

TECH PREP STUDENTS

In this unit, the different kinds of animals are presented with a basic body plan—a generalized representation that includes the structures shared by all. Ask students to make a "basic body plan" of the sorts of technology they will be using in the future. For example, students might draw and label a "basic" car or a "basic" air conditioner. Students should be able to think of some technology for which they can make a generalized plan.

LEP STUDENTS

Have students use a dictionary to write a definition and pronunciation guide for each of the following words: aerodynamic, alveolus, amnion, cloaca, compass, dorsal, ectotherm, endotherm, excretion, gizzard, metabolism, nitrogenous, paleontologist, precipitate, receptor, terrestrial, toxic, transitional, and ventral. After they have looked up all the words, work with them on the pronunciation of each.

Section 31–1

Reptiles

Performance Objectives

- Discuss the characteristics that distinguish reptiles.
- Describe the adaptations that allow reptiles to live on land.

Mini Lab Skill: Inferring
Laboratory Investigation Skill: Designing an experiment

1 ENGAGE

Inquiry Activity

Comparing

A Reptile Revue

At different locations in the classroom, display three types of reptiles: a lizard, a turtle, and a snake. Ask students what they think are the general characteristics that all reptiles have. Then have students observe the three different reptiles and make a list of shared characteristics. Once individual students have completed their lists, ask that groups form to discuss reptile characteristics and to create a consensus list. Finally, have groups present their lists to the whole class, and ask the class to agree on one list of characteristics.

Ideas Through Images

Have students examine Figure 31–1, read the caption, and answer the following questions.

- **What characteristics do all reptiles have in common?** (They all have scaly skin, breathe with lungs, and lay eggs that hatch on land.)
- **How are the adaptations shown for the snake and for the lizard similar in function?** (Each adaptation provides the organism with a method of catching and consuming prey.)

2 EXPLORE

MINI LAB Inferring

Teacher Notes
- For time required and materials needed, see page 708b.
- Mounted snake skeletons and shed snake skins can be obtained from a biological supply company. Pet shops and snake owners are other sources for snake skins.

Answers to Analyze and Conclude
1. Snakes may have between 100 and 400 vertebrae, each with ribs attached. The large number of vertebrae and ribs allow the snake to move in a wavelike motion.
2. Students should count the same number of belly scales as vertebrae, because most snakes have one ventral scale per vertebra.
3. Students should count many more scales on the skin's dorsal side than on the ventral side, since dorsal scales are small and arranged diagonally. Snakes use the large bandlike scales on the ventral side for traction, thus allowing them to push themselves over a surface.

Skills Trace
Inferring

Focus p. 710
Practice p. 713
Assess p. 727

MINI LAB .... Inferring

Ready to Slither

PROBLEM *What can you **infer** about the movement of snakes by observing their scales and skeletons?*

PROCEDURE

1. From your teacher, obtain a mounted snake skeleton or a photograph of a snake skeleton. Study the skeleton, then count the number of vertebrae and ribs.
2. Obtain the shed skin of a snake. Examine the shed skin, then count the number of belly scales.

ANALYZE AND CONCLUDE

1. How many vertebrae and ribs does the skeleton have? How is it adapted for a snake's type of movement?
2. How many belly scales are on the snake's skin? Compare this number to the number of vertebrae and ribs.
3. Compare the scales on the dorsal and ventral sides of the snake. How does a snake use its scales to move?

Reptiles are **ectotherms,** meaning "heat from the outside." Because a reptile's body does not generate much heat and lacks effective insulation, reptiles need to gain heat from their environment—typically by basking in the sun.

Feeding

Reptiles eat a wide range of foods. Certain iguanas and other reptiles are herbivores, while most lizards and snakes are carnivores. Some snakes paralyze prey with a powerful venom, while others suffocate prey with the force of their body, which they wrap into tight coils. Other reptiles, such as crocodiles, grab prey with powerful jaws filled with sharp teeth.

Interestingly, most reptiles cannot chew very well. Instead, their digestive tracts are specialized for processing large pieces of food. In addition, many reptiles have developed unusual ways of eating, as shown in ***Figure 31–1*** on page 709.

Respiration and Internal Transport

Because gases cannot diffuse across scaly skin, reptiles need well-developed and efficient lungs. Unlike amphibians, reptiles have muscles attached to their rib cage that enable their lungs to inflate and deflate.

Reptiles have a double-loop circulatory system that pumps blood first through the lungs and then through the rest of the body. A few reptiles, including crocodiles and alligators, have a four-chambered heart, similar to the hearts of birds and mammals. However, most reptiles have what might be called a "not-quite-four-chambered" heart, as shown in ***Figure 31–2.***

Excretion

Reptiles that live mostly in water, such as crocodiles and alligators, excrete most of their nitrogenous wastes in the form of ammonia—a compound toxic to most animals. For this reason, crocodiles and alligators drink large amounts of water, which dilutes the ammonia and helps to carry it out of the body.

Terrestrial reptiles, however, don't always live near water. Thus, most convert nitrogenous wastes into a compound called uric acid. As a waste product, uric acid has two advantages over ammonia. First, it is much less toxic. Second, it is not very soluble in water. Why is that an advantage? In many reptiles, urine from kidneys flows into an organ called the cloaca. As water is absorbed from the cloaca, crystals of uric acid precipitate, forming a white, semisolid paste. By eliminating dry wastes, reptiles conserve water.

☑ *Checkpoint* How do reptiles eliminate nitrogenous wastes? ❶

TEACHER SUPPORT — Background Information

All reptiles shed their skin, both to replace worn-out skin and to allow for growth. Lizards often lose their skin in large pieces. Snakes, though, shed their whole skin periodically, essentially by crawling out of it. In general, the snake eats nothing for about two weeks before this molting process begins. During that time, the outer layer of skin begins to separate from the inner layer, and air seeps in between. When the actual molting starts, the skin is first peeled back around the mouth. The snake then rubs against the ground and rocks to peel the skin down its body, all the while twisting and turning, until the skin turns inside out and falls off. This process usually takes 1 to 5 hours. How often molting occurs depends on the species and the age of the snake. A young rattler sheds about seven times a year, whereas an older rattler sheds only a few times.

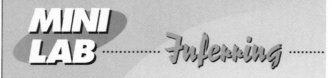

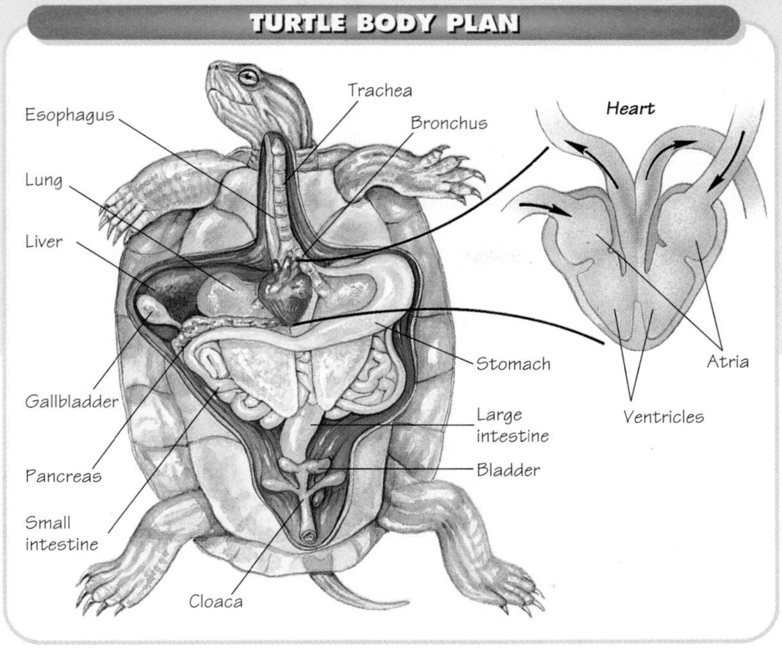

Figure 31–2
Many features of the reptile body plan can be seen in other terrestrial animals, including humans. One unusual structure in a reptile is the heart, in which oxygenated and deoxygenated blood mix slightly as they leave the ventricles.

Nervous System and Sense Organs

Reptile brains are similar to the brains of amphibians, although reptiles have a larger cerebrum and cerebellum. As a group, reptiles are not known for complex behaviors. Many seem to do little more than sit, stalk prey, eat, and sleep.

Reptiles also have well-developed sense organs, some of which they use in unusual ways. For example, have you ever watched a snake flicking its tongue? If so, you have seen it "tasting" its environment. The tips of the tongue pick up molecules from the air, then deposit them on taste receptors in the mouth.

Although reptiles typically do not have a well-developed sense of hearing, many reptiles have excellent vision. In fact, some turtles and snakes probably see more colors than you do.

Several types of sense organs are found only in reptiles. For example, snakes known as pit vipers have an extraordinary ability to detect the body heat of prey, as illustrated in ***Figure 31–3.***

☑ **Checkpoint** How do snakes taste the air? ❷

Movement

Compared to amphibians, most reptiles have larger and stronger legs that support their body weight easily. In different reptiles, legs are adapted for running, swimming, burrowing, or climbing.

Figure 31–3
Reptiles use information from their sense organs in many unusual ways. (a) Like other chameleons, this flap-necked chameleon changes color in response to its environment. (b) Near the eye of this Chinese green tree viper is a depression called a pit organ. The pit organ contains heat receptors, allowing the viper to sense any prey that maintains a high body temperature.

3 TEACH

Ideas Through Images

Have students examine Figure 31–2, read the caption, and answer the following questions.

- **What feature does this body plan have that most reptiles do not have?** (The shell, or carapace.)
- **Why is a reptile's heart sometimes called a "not-quite-four-chambered" heart?** (Because oxygenated and deoxygenated blood mix as they leave the heart ventricles.)
- **In what way are a reptile's lungs improved over an amphibian's lungs?** (A reptile has muscles attached to the ribcage, enabling it to inflate and deflate its lungs. An amphibian lacks such muscles.)

☑ Checkpoints

❶ Some reptiles excrete most of their nitrogenous wastes in the form of ammonia. Most, however, convert nitrogenous wastes into uric acid and eliminate it as a dry paste.

❷ The tips of a snake's tongue pick up molecules from the air, then deposit them on taste receptors in the mouth.

TEACHER SUPPORT

Background Information

Chameleons, such as the flap-necked chameleon in Figure 31–3, do change colors, though not because of a change in background color, which is a common misconception. Rather, a chameleon changes color in response to changes in light, temperature, or mood. Fright, for example, may cause a color change. A chameleon might also change color to display itself as frightening to a potential intruder. This change can occur rapidly, as cells of different colors expand or shrink, thus mixing colors in different proportions. Chameleons are not the only lizards that change color. *Anolis,* the common green anole in the iguana family, is often called the American chameleon because it, too, changes color in response to temperature, light, and mood. But its change is caused by a hormonal response, and thus an anole cannot change color nearly as fast as a true chameleon.

Ancillary Support

The resources below can be used to support your teaching strategy for these two pages.

TR Explore: Taking a Look at Turtles
BL Inquiry Activity: Moving to Higher Ground

Laboratory Investigation

The Laboratory Investigation, Adaptation for Survival, on pages 722–723 is appropriate to use at this point in the chapter.

Ideas Through Images

Have students examine Figure 31–4, read the caption, and answer the following questions.

- **How are the legs of reptiles better adapted to land than the legs of amphibians?** (Reptiles have larger and stronger legs than amphibians, enabling them to support their bodies and move about on land much more easily than amphibians can.)
- **What is an amniotic egg?** (An egg that has a membrane that surrounds and protects the embryo.)
- **Why is the amniotic egg better adapted to land than amphibian eggs?** (Amphibian eggs are not protected by a shell, and thus must be laid in water. An amniotic egg has its own moisture and nourishment, and thus it can be laid on land.)
- **What other adaptations helped reptiles adapt to life on land?** (Their eggs are fertilized internally and typically are cared for after being laid.)

Investigate

Cooperative Learning Have cooperative learning groups prepare presentations to the class about one of the following types of reptiles: tuataras, sea turtles, tortoises, alligators, crocodiles, snakes, and lizards. Ask that in their presentations, the groups strive to teach the class about the important features of the reptiles they have been assigned, with an emphasis on adaptations each has made to specific environments.

Many reptiles can stay absolutely still for a long period of time, then dash away with incredible speed.

The ancestors of snakes lost their legs while adapting to a burrowing existence. In the process, they evolved large bandlike scales on their ventral surface. To move, a snake uses its ventral scales for traction as it pushes its body into long, curving waves.

Reproduction

Early reptiles were the first vertebrates to evolve a life cycle that does not rely on standing water. **Reptiles were able to adapt to terrestrial life because they fertilized eggs internally, developed an amniotic egg, and typically cared for their eggs in some way.**

An **amniotic egg** gets its name from the amnion, a membrane that surrounds and protects the developing embryo. In fact, an amniotic egg contains several membranes and a leathery external shell. Inside, the embryo is bathed in a watery liquid—an environment that in some ways resembles the ocean in which life originally developed. The egg holds ample food in the form of a yolk and provides a place to store wastes until hatching. In addition, the shell and internal membranes "breathe" by allowing oxygen and carbon dioxide to diffuse across them.

Because amniotic eggs are produced and packaged inside the female's reproductive tract, they must be fertilized internally. Almost all male reptiles have an external reproductive organ—a penis—that delivers sperm into the female's cloaca. Lizards and snakes have two such structures, often called hemipenes.

Most reptiles are oviparous, laying eggs that hatch outside the body. Creating these eggs requires a lot of energy, so it is not surprising that many reptiles take special precautions to help their eggs develop. Sea turtles, for example, make a difficult journey to their nesting beaches. There, they bury their eggs at just the right depth and distance from the sea for the eggs to incubate properly.

✓ **Checkpoint** Why were reptiles able to adapt to land? 1

a

b

Figure 31–4 (a) *The basilisk lizard is so quick and agile it can literally walk on water!* (b) *Like other reptiles, these Nile crocodiles developed in an amniotic egg. An amniotic egg nourishes an embryo and protects it from its environment.*

Classifying Reptiles

Almost all ancient reptiles became extinct millions of years ago, but two surviving species still live on small islands near New Zealand. These reptiles are tuataras (too-uh-TAH-ruhz), the last survivors of the order Rhyncocephalia. Tuataras show many features of the ancient reptiles from which they evolved.

TEACHER SUPPORT

Facts and Figures

- The largest reptile is the leatherback, *Dermochelys coriacea*, a sea turtle that can grow to about 2.7 m in length. The biggest on record was 865 kg.
- The longest snake is the reticulated python, *Python reticulatus*, which can grow to about 10 m.
- The largest lizard is the Komodo dragon, *Varanus komodoensis*. It is found on only a few islands in Indonesia. A male can grow to be over 3 m long with a mass of over 160 kg.
- The shell of a pond or red-eared terrapin, *Pseudemys scripta*, is composed of 59–61 bones. This freshwater turtle is a popular pet in the United States.
- The American alligator, *Alligator mississippiensis*, can grow to a maximum length of about 5.8 m.
- The American crocodile, *Crocodylus acutus*, has a maximum length of about 7 m.

Figure 31–5
Although reptiles are not as numerous or diverse as they were millions of years ago, many fascinating species still live today. (a) *The American alligator lives in swampy regions of the southeastern United States.* (b) *Tuataras are found only on islands near New Zealand. This tuatara is poised to eat a tree weta, a large insect.* (c) *Snakes are common in many areas of the world. This anaconda lives in Peru.*

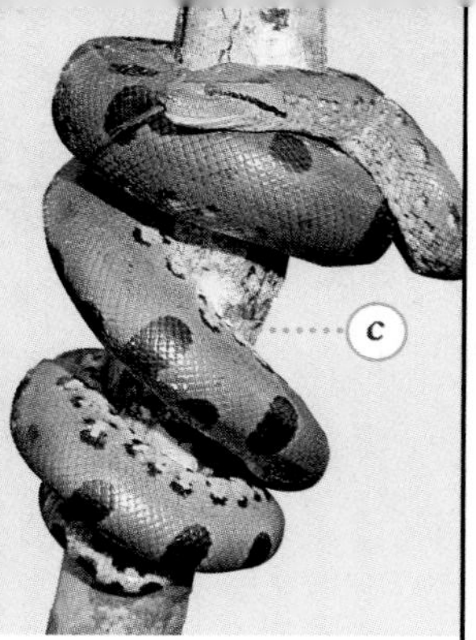

Tortoises and turtles are members of the order Chelonia. The first of these reptiles evolved over 200 million years ago, and they have changed little since then. Turtles usually live in or near freshwater ponds and streams or in the open ocean. Tortoises tend to be more terrestrial, living in dry places such as deserts and the rocky Galapagos Islands.

Members of the order Crocodilia—which includes crocodiles and alligators—are about as old as tortoises and turtles. Crocodilians live only in places that are at least as warm as southern Florida and Mississippi.

What's the difference between an alligator and a crocodile? Alligators live only in fresh water and are found almost exclusively in North America and China. Crocodiles, on the other hand, may live in fresh or salt water and are native to Southeast Asia, India, and Africa. In the United States, an alligator has a shorter, blunter snout and its teeth do not protrude outside its closed mouth.

Lizards, snakes, and most other living reptiles belong to the order Squamata. Lizards range in size from insect-eating geckos, which are only a few centimeters long, to the reptile commonly called the Komodo dragon. A Komodo dragon can grow up to 3 meters in length and can kill animals as large as a full-grown goat!

Different snake species live on land, in water, and even in trees. Poisonous snakes include cobras in India, rattlesnakes in North America, and the deadly fer-de-lance in Central America. Common fears to the contrary, however, poisonous snakes don't normally hunt humans. They usually bite humans only when they feel threatened or cornered.

Section Review 31–1

1. **Describe** the characteristics of reptiles.
2. **Explain** why reptiles were able to adapt to land.
3. **Critical Thinking—Analyzing Concepts** Explain why crocodilians live only in warm, shallow waters.
4. **MINI LAB** By studying the skeleton and scales of a snake, what can you **infer** about how it moves from place to place?

4 ASSESS

Quick Check

Have students make a table that includes information about the four orders of reptiles, including the names of the orders, characteristics, and examples.

Section Review 31–1

1. Reptiles are scaly-skinned vertebrates that breathe with lungs and lay eggs that hatch on land. In addition, reptiles are ectotherms.
2. Reptiles were able to adapt to land because they fertilized eggs internally, developed an amniotic egg, and typically cared for their eggs in some way, such as burying them, warming them, and guarding them. Reptiles also have well-developed lungs and a cloaca.
3. Crocodilians, like all reptiles, are ectotherms; thus, their bodies do not generate much heat and lack effective insulation. Only in warm, shallow waters can crocodilians keep their body temperatures high enough to live.
4. From the many vertebrae and ribs of a snake's skeleton, you can infer that a snake moves in curving waves. From the large bandlike ventral scales, you can infer that it uses its scales for traction as it pushes itself along the ground.

Checkpoint

❶ Reptiles were able to adapt to land because they fertilized their eggs internally, developed an amniotic egg, and typically cared for their eggs in some way.

Skills Trace

Inferring

- Focus p. 710
- Practice p. 713
- Assess p. 727

Learning Modality

Auditory Learning Make a drawing of a lizard on the chalkboard and ask students to direct you orally in adding details and labels to the animal's insides.

Ancillary Support

The resource below can be used to support your teaching strategy for these two pages.

LM Classifying Lizards, #61

Section 31–2
Birds

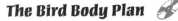

Performance Objectives
- Discuss the characteristics that distinguish birds.
- Describe adaptations that allow a bird to fly.

Mini Lab Skill: Observing

1 ENGAGE

Inquiry Activity
Identifying

The Sights and Sounds of Birds
Choose eight to ten examples of birds that are common in your area. Find photographs or drawings of each in old magazines or bird books and display them in the classroom, labeled with numbers rather than names. Then use a recording from the library of bird songs and sounds to play for students. Ask students to match the names and sounds of the birds with the images by keeping a list on a piece of paper. When all students have completed their lists, discuss students' experiences and observations of these birds. Have students think about the habits and adaptations of each.

2 EXPLORE

Investigate
Cooperative Learning Ask each cooperative learning group to make a poster that focuses on one of the following topics related to birds: mating displays and reproduction, nests and caring for young, sense organs of birds, predator and prey, feathers and the physics of flight, a bird's brain and behavior, and migration. Allow each group to decide, after doing research, how its poster should be designed to best cover its topic. Posters could contain photos from magazines, labeled drawings, or information in paragraph form.

SECTION 31–2 Birds

GUIDE FOR READING
- **Describe** the characteristics of birds.
- **Explain** why a bird can fly.

MINI LAB
- **Observe** the characteristics of a down feather and a contour feather.

WHETHER THEY ARE GREETING the dawn with song or coloring the air with brilliant feathers, birds are among the most prevalent and welcome of all animals. From common house sparrows to the spectacular and rare quetzal of Central America and from tiny hummingbirds to huge ostriches, the approximately 8700 living bird species seem to live everywhere. Not surprisingly, one secret to their success lies in the adaptations that allow them to fly.

The Bird Body Plan

Birds are descendants of small dinosaurs. Thus, you shouldn't be surprised to discover that birds are much like reptiles. Unlike reptiles, however, birds have **feathers**—an adaptation that has allowed them to become very successful. Nothing like feathers is seen elsewhere in the animal kingdom, and no one knows how or why they first evolved.

All birds have feathers. They also have hind limbs that they use for walking, running, or perching, as well as front limbs that are modified into wings. Most birds use their feathers and wings to fly, although many birds—including ostriches and emus—cannot fly. Some flightless birds, such as penguins, use their wings as flippers for swimming.

Compared to reptiles, birds have a high rate of metabolism—the total chemical and physical processes that go on inside the body. In addition, a bird's body is insulated enough to conserve most of its metabolic energy and can thus maintain a constant high body temperature. For this reason, birds are described as **endotherms,** which literally means "heat from within." Some birds keep a body temperature near 40°C even on a cold, winter day.

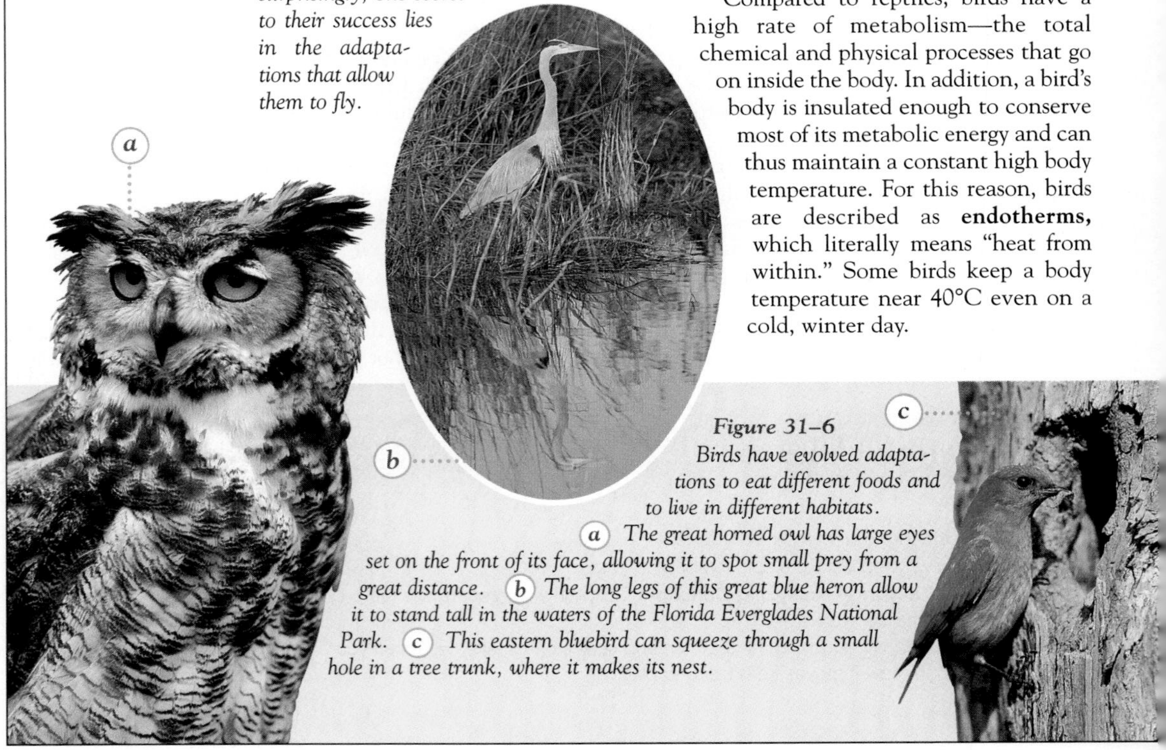

Figure 31–6 Birds have evolved adaptations to eat different foods and to live in different habitats. (a) The great horned owl has large eyes set on the front of its face, allowing it to spot small prey from a great distance. (b) The long legs of this great blue heron allow it to stand tall in the waters of the Florida Everglades National Park. (c) This eastern bluebird can squeeze through a small hole in a tree trunk, where it makes its nest.

TEACHER SUPPORT

Ecology Note

Since the end of World War II, ornithologists have recorded a drastic decline of songbirds in the eastern United States, including vireos, warblers, and flycatchers. Reasons for the decline are complex, but loss of habitat is a primary concern. Where once there were vast forests, now there are cities and suburbs. Thus, as the environment has changed, some kinds of birds have begun to disappear. Yet other kinds have increased dramatically—the "urban birds," including pigeons, house sparrows, and blackbirds. Such birds have adapted to the steel and concrete ecosystems of the city, and even the habits of the people who live there. For instance, a country pigeon usually eats twice a day and digests the food between feeding times. But a city pigeon has adapted to eat whenever food is available, especially the bits of food left behind in parks and playgrounds.

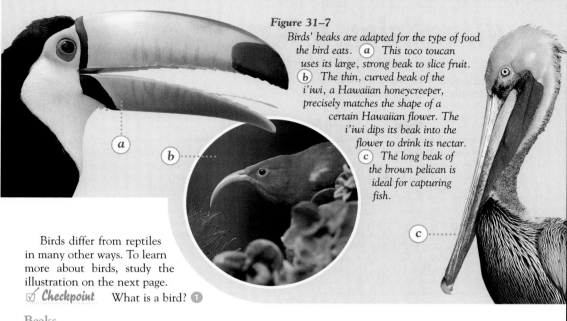

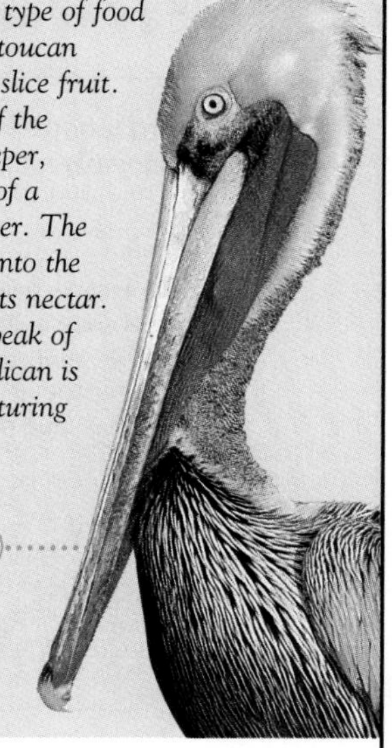

Figure 31–7
Birds' beaks are adapted for the type of food the bird eats. (a) This toco toucan uses its large, strong beak to slice fruit. (b) The thin, curved beak of the i'iwi, a Hawaiian honeycreeper, precisely matches the shape of a certain Hawaiian flower. The i'iwi dips its beak into the flower to drink its nectar. (c) The long beak of the brown pelican is ideal for capturing fish.

Birds differ from reptiles in many other ways. To learn more about birds, study the illustration on the next page.

☑ **Checkpoint** What is a bird? 1

Beaks

You probably know that birds have beaks, but you may not realize the many different ways in which birds use beaks. From flamingoes that strain plankton out of water to eagles that rip small mammals apart, beaks perform scores of different functions. As a result, different birds have beaks of different shapes, sizes, and strengths, as shown in ***Figure 31–7.***

Respiration and Internal Transport

For several good reasons, birds need efficient respiratory and circulatory systems. First, birds must maintain a high rate of metabolism. Second, although birds are so graceful that they make flying look easy, they actually use a great deal of energy to fly. For a human, the equivalent to a bird's flying would be long-distance running, with a slow, steady pace alternating with sprints.

To keep up that pace, birds must take in a steady stream of oxygen and get rid of large amounts of carbon dioxide. Thus, birds have a remarkable respiratory system. When fresh air is inhaled, it bypasses the lungs and enters large air sacs located around them. When air is exhaled, it travels through the lungs in a series of small tubes. These tubes are lined with tiny air sacs called **alveoli** (al-VEE-uh-ligh; singular: alveolus), which is where gas exchange takes place.

This one-way flow means that alveoli are constantly exposed to fresh, oxygen-rich air. At the same time, air lower in oxygen and higher in carbon dioxide is constantly exhaled. This is a much more efficient system than the lungs that operate like inflatable balloons—the type of lungs found in humans and most other vertebrates.

To carry food, oxygen, and wastes, birds have a double-loop circulatory system. The pump is a four-chambered heart consisting of a pair of two-part halves divided by a structure called a **septum.** Because of a bird's generally small body size, high metabolic rate, and high-energy activity, a bird's heart pumps rapidly—at rates that range from 150 to 1000 beats per minute!

☑ **Checkpoint** Why do birds need an efficient respiratory system? 2

3 TEACH

Ideas Through Images

Have students examine Figure 31–7, read the caption, and answer the following questions.

- **Why do different birds have beaks of different shapes, sizes, and strengths?** (Different birds use their beaks in different ways; that is, the beak is adapted to the type of food a bird eats.)
- **Why would the beak of the toco toucan not be useful for catching and eating mice?** (Although the beak is good for eating fruits, the bird would have a hard time following, trapping, and killing a mouse with such a heavy and clumsy structure.)

☑ Checkpoints

1 A bird is a vertebrate with feathers; hind limbs used for walking, running, or perching; front limbs modified into wings; and the ability to maintain a constant body temperature.

2 Because in order to fly they must maintain a high rate of metabolism and they require a great deal of energy.

Technology

CD-ROM
Birds: Characteristics and Adaptations

Ancillary Support

The resource below can be used to support your teaching strategy for these two pages.

TR Apply: Muscle and Bone

TEACHER SUPPORT

Managing Classroom Diversity

MULTICULTURAL STRATEGY
Native American cultures of the northwestern United States and Canada have many myths that involve Raven as the central figure, including creation myths. Ask students to find one of these myths and prepare a dramatic reading or role-play for the class. Other cultures also have ancient myths that involve birds, including the Aztec myth of *Quetzalcoatlus*. Encourage other students to find and present myths that involve birds.

TECH PREP STUDENTS
Have students planning careers in the energy and transportation fields investigate how oil spills affect aquatic birds. You could have them continue the MINI LAB on page 717 by testing the effect that oil has on feathers. Also ask them to prepare a report that describes the technology now available for cleaning up oil spills or reducing chances of future spills.

Visualizing a Bird

As students examine this generalized diagram of a bird, make sure they understand that different types of birds may have different shapes or structures, but that all birds share the same basic internal organization. In a class discussion of this visual essay, emphasize the following points.

- The air sacs serve two functions. First, they provide a way in which the bird can inhale a relatively great amount of air compared to body size, thus providing enough oxygen to sustain the energy exerted in flight. Second, the air sacs extend inside some bones, making the bones lighter and thus minimizing the bird's mass.
- The cloaca also serves more than one function. As in reptiles, the cloaca is involved in the excretion of uric acid. It also is involved in reproduction. Note that birds, like reptiles, have internal fertilization, an adaptation to terrestrial life.
- Both the gizzard and the crop are involved in the digestion of food and are especially useful in birds that eat seeds.
- The heart of birds is more complex than that of fishes, amphibians, or reptiles. A bird's heart functions much like our own, with four separated chambers.

Visualizing a Bird

A bird's body is specially adapted for its remarkable method of movement—flying!

1 Brain
A bird's brain is relatively large and well-developed. It typically coordinates complex mating behaviors, nest building, and flight.

2 Air Sacs and Lungs
When a bird inhales, air collects in large air sacs. The air then travels into the lungs and out of the body. With this regular, one-way air flow, the lungs are constantly exposed to fresh, oxygen-rich air.

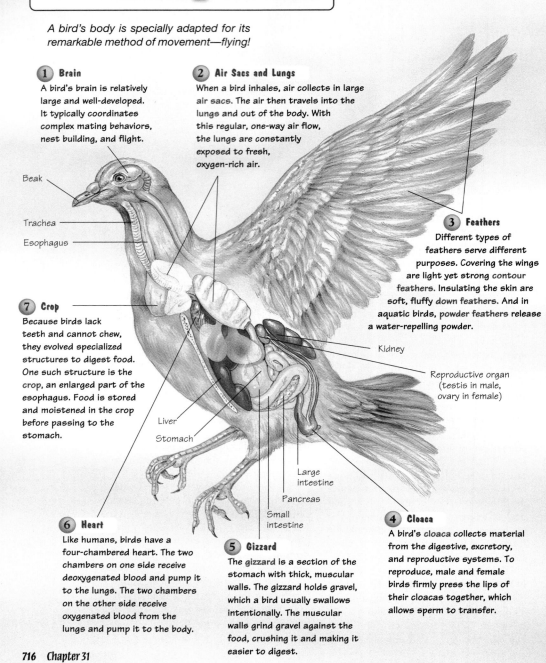

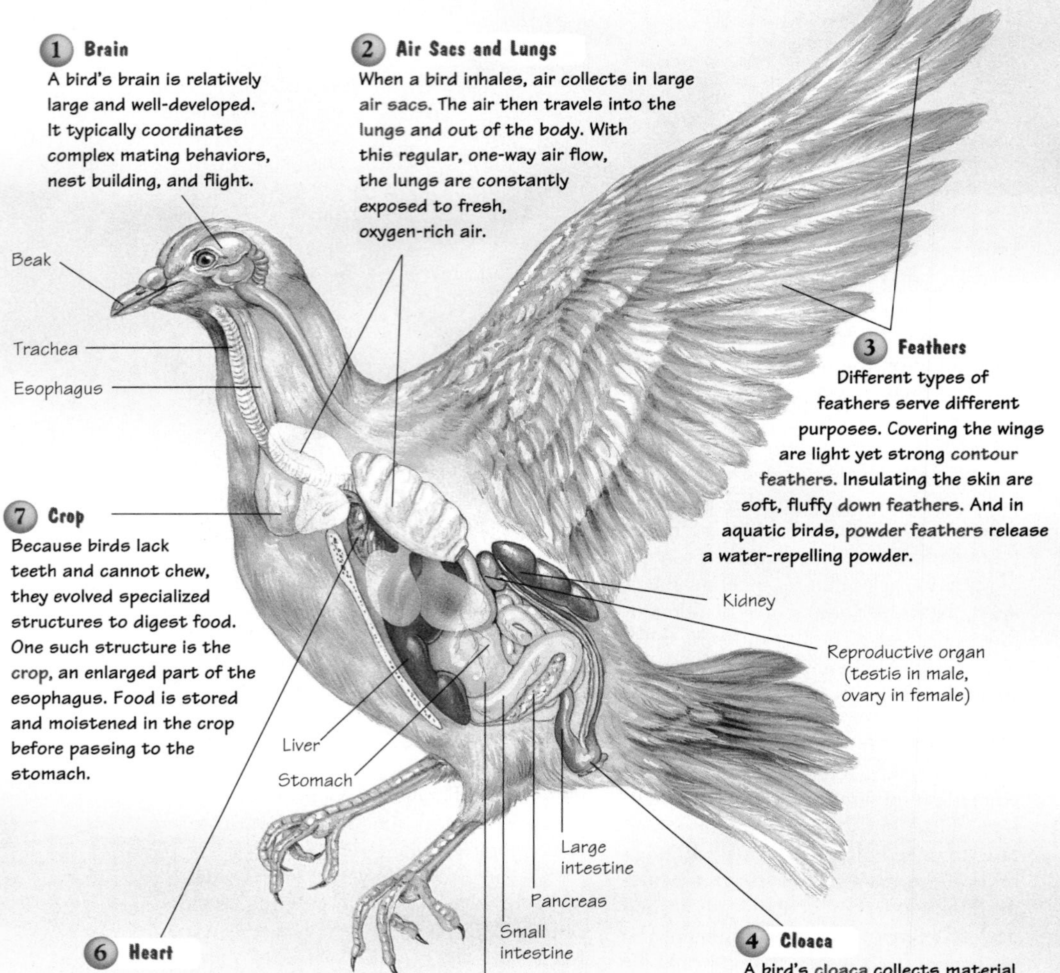

3 Feathers
Different types of feathers serve different purposes. Covering the wings are light yet strong contour feathers. Insulating the skin are soft, fluffy down feathers. And in aquatic birds, powder feathers release a water-repelling powder.

7 Crop
Because birds lack teeth and cannot chew, they evolved specialized structures to digest food. One such structure is the crop, an enlarged part of the esophagus. Food is stored and moistened in the crop before passing to the stomach.

6 Heart
Like humans, birds have a four-chambered heart. The two chambers on one side receive deoxygenated blood and pump it to the lungs. The two chambers on the other side receive oxygenated blood from the lungs and pump it to the body.

5 Gizzard
The gizzard is a section of the stomach with thick, muscular walls. The gizzard holds gravel, which a bird usually swallows intentionally. The muscular walls grind gravel against the food, crushing it and making it easier to digest.

4 Cloaca
A bird's cloaca collects material from the digestive, excretory, and reproductive systems. To reproduce, male and female birds firmly press the lips of their cloacas together, which allows sperm to transfer.

TEACHER SUPPORT

Facts and Figures

- Birds have the highest body temperatures of any endotherms, with a normal temperature of 40–41°C.
- The smallest living bird is the Cuban bee hummingbird, *Mellisuga helenae*, which is about 5 cm in length with a mass of 2.5 g.
- The largest living bird is the flightless North African ostrich, *Struthio camelus*, which can grow to about 2.4 m with a mass of 135 kg.
- The Wandering albatross, *Diomedea exulans*, has the widest wingspan at 3.5 m.
- The world's fastest bird is the peregrine falcon, *Falco peregrinus*, which when diving after prey can reach a speed of 280 km/h.
- The Oldsquaw, or long-tailed duck, *Clangula hyemalis*, a sea duck that winters along the eastern United States coast, has been known to dive to 60 m below the surface and stay under water for as long as 15 minutes.

Excretion

Birds handle wastes in much the same way that reptiles do. Nitrogenous wastes are removed from blood by the kidney, converted to uric acid, and deposited in the cloaca. There, water is reabsorbed, causing uric acid crystals to precipitate and form the whitish, semisolid paste you recognize as bird droppings.

Many birds that live in marine habitats take in more salt than they can keep. Because vertebrate kidneys cannot excrete salt efficiently, these birds have evolved specialized salt glands near the base of the beak. These glands excrete enough concentrated salt solution to enable the bird to maintain a salt and water balance.

Nervous System and Sense Organs

Although you might use the term "bird brain" to refer to someone foolish, birds are in fact relatively intelligent animals. Although a bird's medulla and spinal cord are much like those of its reptilian ancestors, its cerebrum and cerebellum are both large and well-developed.

Would you guess that birds have well-developed sense organs? Before you answer, think about the demands of bird life. Many species fly at high speeds, catch prey from great distances, and migrate thousands of kilometers between summer and winter nesting grounds. All these tasks demand the gathering and processing of large amounts of information from the environment. So it is not surprising that bird senses equal or surpass our own.

Most birds have excellent vision, and birds that stay awake in the daytime often see color far better than humans do. Hawks and their relatives can see incredibly fine detail, which lets them spot small prey on the ground while flying high overhead. Although birds lack external ears, many species have an acute sense of hearing. Owls, for example, from quite a distance can detect mice rustling along the forest floor.

Of the five human senses, only taste and smell are not well-developed in birds. However, many birds have a sense that has long puzzled and amazed humans. This sense is the ability of migratory birds to navigate across continents and oceans. As we now know, some of these birds have a magnetic sense that works like an internal compass. Other birds use a combination of acute eyesight and a built-in clock to navigate by the stars.

☑ *Checkpoint* Why do birds need well-developed senses? (1)

MINI LAB ······ Observing

Fine Feathered Friends

PROBLEM *What characteristics can you* ***observe*** *in a contour feather and a down feather?*

PROCEDURE

1. Use a hand lens to observe a contour feather from a bird's wing or tail. Sketch and label your observations.
2. Observe and sketch a bird's down feather.
3. Dip each feather into water for 2 seconds. Record your observations of how the feathers react to water.

ANALYZE AND CONCLUDE

1. How are the contour feather and down feather different in appearance? How are they similar?
2. What is the function of barbs and hooks on contour feathers?
3. From the feathers' reactions to water, infer how birds respond to rain.

MINI LAB Observing

Teacher Notes

- For time required and materials needed, see page 708b.
- Obtain contour and down feathers from a biological supply company. A local pet or zoo store might be an alternative source.

Answers to Analyze and Conclude

1. Both the contour feather and the down feather have a central shaft. The contour feather is long and stiff, and along its central shaft are parallel side branches that are attached to one another. In contrast, the down feather is small and fluffy, with a loose array of fuzzy side branches along its central shaft.
2. The barbs and hooks hold the side branches together in a definite order, keeping the feather smooth, flat, and regular, which makes it effective for flight.
3. Students should observe that the feathers do not absorb the water and infer that birds are not affected by rain.

Skills Trace
Observing

- Focus p. 717
- Practice p. 719
- Assess p. 727

☑ **Checkpoint**

(1) Because of the tasks they must perform, including flying at high speeds, catching prey from great distances, and migrating thousands of kilometers.

TEACHER SUPPORT

Background Information

Contour feathers begin as pulp inside tubes called feather sheaths. When a feather grows to full size, the sheath splits and drops away. The feather base, or quill of the shaft, remains embedded in a follicle of the skin, attached to muscles that can move the feather into various positions. The outer shaft, called the rachis, supports the feather webbing, or vane. A vane is composed of parallel barbs that extend outward diagonally from the rachis. Each barb has parallel barbules that extend outward diagonally from their shafts, and the barbules are attached to one another by minute hooks and catches. Hooks also attach the barbs to one another, forming a smooth, continuous surface for air to move over. Down feathers, by contrast, lack the interlocking barbules that create the vanes, and thus are fluffier. That fluffiness traps air, and in doing so provides insulation.

Ancillary Support

The resources below can be used to support your teaching strategy for these two pages.

LM Examining an Unfertilized Chicken Egg, #62
TB Visualizing a Bird, #40

Connections

The specific song a songbird sings is a learned behavior, not something determined by genes. Some birds change their song from season to season, and that is the case with canaries. But to accumulate the knowledge of various songs over a lifetime would take more brain matter than would be advantageous for the bird to have, since flying requires a light weight. Thus, this animal has evolved a method of producing brain cells only as needed. Human brains do not have the same ability, because, unlike canaries, humans depend on long memories and the ability to recall events in the distant past. Creating new brain cells for new skills just might disrupt those memories.

Answers to Making the Connection

Some invertebrates are able to regenerate some of their parts. For example, if the top of a *Hydra* is cut off, including the mouth and tentacles, the "head" will grow a new body and the body will grow a new "head." Starfishes are famous for regeneration. Any piece that contains some of the central body portion can regenerate the whole organism.

Generally, human organs cannot regenerate themselves. Skin and bones can repair tears and breaks, though that is not true regeneration. The liver can regenerate to normal size even if three fourths of it has been cut away, as long as the remaining portion is not diseased.

Biology and You Connections

Secrets in a Bird's Brain

Although medical scientists have learned a great deal about the nervous system, many serious diseases and injuries that affect this system remain incurable. As a rule, dead nerve cells do not regenerate in the human brain and spinal cord. Thus, physicians have limited treatments for severe injuries to the nervous system and diseases such as Alzheimer's disease, in which the nerves in the brain are gradually destroyed.

Can human nerves be stimulated to regenerate? Incredibly enough, the answer may come from studies on the brains of another class of vertebrates—birds!

Song Centers

At one time, biologists thought that a vertebrate brain never formed new nerve cells after the brain was fully developed. In fact, they thought that the brain steadily lost nerve cells over time.

However, studies on canaries have provided evidence against this idea. In these studies, researchers concentrated on a part of the canary's brain called the song center—the part used in learning and performing the canary's familiar songs. A canary's song center expands during breeding season—the time when canaries sing frequently. The song center shrinks at other times, when canaries are more quiet.

How do these changes occur? At Rockefeller University in New York, one group of scientists showed that canaries develop new nerves in the song center, and they do so quite regularly. What's more, the scientists discovered that canaries periodically develop new cells throughout the brain! In male canaries, at least some of these changes are triggered by changing levels of sex hormones. However, scientists are still looking for the genes that put these hormones into action.

A canary's brain regularly develops new nerves—a feat that scientists once thought was impossible!

Help for Humans?

Do the genes that cause brain cells to reproduce and grow in birds also exist in humans? If humans have these genes, is there a way to turn them on? If the answers to these questions are yes, then scientists could someday develop treatments to repair human brains damaged by injury or disease.

Research on bird brains may someday help us to understand the human brain.

Making the Connection

Which animals are able to regenerate lost body parts? Which human organs are able to regenerate?

Teacher Support: Background Information

Ornithologists often distinguish between the calls and songs of birds. In general, a call is a short vocalization that serves a specific purpose, such as a danger call or a short communication between members of the same species. These calls are innate, or genetically determined. Some birds, particularly those called songbirds, produce a song, which is a more elaborate series of notes. Songs are learned from adult to offspring, as demonstrated when birds are raised in a soundproof cage. In such an environment, a songbird will never learn its song. Generally, the song is produced by the male bird, though in some species the female also sings. A song serves two basic functions: to warn away other members of the species or to create a territory, and to attract a mate.

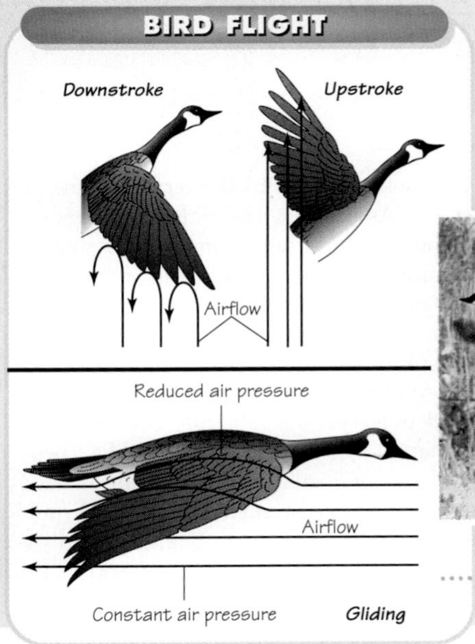

(a) (b) (c)

Figure 31–8
To fly, birds need to coordinate the movements of their feathers and wings. (a) During the downstroke, feathers cover the wings' surface. This pushes air downward and provides lift. During the upstroke, the feathers are spread apart, allowing air to pass through and making the wings easier to lift. Birds can glide because the wings' shape reduces air pressure above the wings. (b) Both downstrokes and upstrokes can be seen in these Canada geese. (c) CAREER TRACK Veterinary assistants help veterinarians treat pets, farm animals, or wildlife.

Birds and Flight

Various birds evolved ways in which to run and swim. However, unlike almost all other vertebrates, most birds can fly. **Birds can fly because of their relatively light bodies, powerful breast muscles, and aerodynamic feathers and wings.**

First, birds are lighter than other vertebrates mainly because of their bones, which have spaces within them. In addition, air sacs used in breathing extend inside several bones, making these bones even lighter. Birds minimize their body mass in other ways, too. Sex organs, for example, are small and light most of the year, then increase to working size during breeding season.

Second, birds have large, strong breast muscles, which they use to flap their wings. These huge muscles provide the force that lifts a bird into the air.

Third, a bird's wings and feathers are shaped in just the right way for flight, as shown in **Figure 31–8**. In fact, birds' wings served as the model for the wings that humans created—the wings of airplanes.

INTEGRATING PHYSICS

How does an airplane fly? How are an airplane's wings similar to a bird's wings?

Section Review 31–2

1. **Describe** the characteristics of birds.
2. **Explain** why a bird can fly.
3. **Critical Thinking—Analyzing Concepts** Explain why crops and gizzards are especially common in birds that eat seeds, while they are less common in carnivorous birds.
4. **MINI LAB** What characteristics can you **observe** in a down feather and a contour feather?

4 ASSESS

Quick Check

Ask students to make flowcharts that describe these processes in birds: respiration, circulation, and excretion.

Section Review 31–2

1. Students might respond with any of the characteristics discussed in the section. All students should mention feathers, wings, flight, and the ability to maintain a constant high body temperature.

2. A bird can fly because of its relatively light body, powerful breast muscles, and aerodynamic feathers and wings.

3. Seeds, with their tough outer coatings, are much more difficult to digest than meat. Thus, moistening in the crop and crushing in the gizzard are important in digesting seeds.

4. The contour feather is long and stiff with a central shaft and parallel side branches that are attached to one another. The down feather is small and fluffy, also with a central shaft but with a loose array of side branches.

INTEGRATING PHYSICS

An airplane is able to fly because as it moves through air the pressure exerted by the air passing under the wings is greater than the air passing over the wings. This difference in air pressure produces what is called lift. The shape of the wing can enhance lift. When the amount of curvature on the top of the wing is greater than that on the bottom, the difference in air pressure is greater as well. This principle of aerodynamics is the same utilized by birds; in fact, airplane wings are essentially copies of birds' wings.

Skills Trace

Observing

- Focus p. 717
- Practice p. 719
- Assess p. 727

Learning Modality

Visual Learning Give pairs of students a copy of an outline of a bird and ask them to add as many labels as they can using what they have learned in the section.

Ancillary Support

The resources below can be used to support your teaching strategy for these two pages.

TR Writing in Biology: Personalities
BL Inquiry Activity: Bird Is the Word

SECTION 31–3
Evolution of Birds

Performance Objective
- Explain what evidence shows that birds evolved from dinosaurs.

1 ENGAGE

Inquiry Activity
Comparing

Not Much of a Difference
Give small groups of students a copy of a photograph or drawing of a flightless bird, such as an ostrich or an emu. Also give them a copy of a drawing of a small two-legged dinosaur, such as a *Compsognathus*. Ask students whether they can see any similarities between the two. Have students examine the two animals and collaborate in making a list of similar features. Then discuss these lists as a whole class.

2 EXPLORE

Investigate
Research Ask students to write a report that places *Archaeopteryx* in the context of its time. In this report, students should identify the geologic period in which this early bird evolved and describe the environment in which it lived, including shape of the continents at the time, the climate, the vegetation, and the other animal life.

3 TEACH

Ideas Through Images
Have students examine Figure 31–10, read the caption, and answer the following questions.

- **In what way was *Archaeopteryx* like a dinosaur?** (It had teeth, a heavy skull, a jointed tail, and a large ribcage.)

Evolution of Birds

GUIDE FOR READING
- **Discuss** the evidence that shows that birds evolved from dinosaurs.

ROUGHLY 150 MILLION YEARS ago, what is now the Solnhofen region of Germany was a very different place from what it is today. Sharks, fishes, and turtles swam in a lagoon. Small dinosaurs and lizards scurried on land. And overhead soared a surprising number of vertebrates. Some were the earliest birds—extinct relatives of the birds that live today.

How do we know that birds flew over the Solnhofen lagoon? Where did they come from? How did they evolve the ability to fly? The fossil record provides answers for each of these questions.

Birds From Dinosaurs?

When a dead animal sank to the bottom of the Solnhofen lagoon, it was eventually covered with a fine mud that isolated its body from oxygen. Over millions of years, the mud turned into fine-grained limestone. As a result, the Solnhofen limestone today contains some of the most beautiful and complete fossils ever discovered. And the star of this collection is one of the first birds—*Archaeopteryx*, meaning "ancient wing."

At first, proper identification of *Archaeopteryx* was difficult because its skeleton looks almost exactly like the skeleton of a small two-legged dinosaur. An *Archaeopteryx* skeleton has teeth, a heavy skull, a jointed tail, and other dinosaurlike features. But the exceptional specimens of the Solnhofen region included structures that almost never fossilize well—feathers!

Because feathers are found only in birds, their presence in the dinosaurlike *Archaeopteryx* provides evidence that birds evolved from dinosaurs. *Archaeopteryx* is a transitional species, a relic of a time when early birds had a combination of dinosaurlike and birdlike characteristics.

Checkpoint What evidence shows that birds evolved from dinosaurs? 1

Figure 31–9 *Quetzalcoatlus, an ancient reptile, had enormous wings and no tail. Could it fly?* (a) *To answer this question, a team of biologists and engineers built a mechanical model.* (b) *To the surprise of many scientists, the model flew!* (c) *Among living birds, ostriches and other ostrichlike birds may most resemble their dinosaur ancestors.*

TEACHER SUPPORT

Background Information

The Solnhofen limestone is in Bavaria, a state in southeastern Germany near Austria. Although today this region is deep within the continent of Europe, during the Jurassic Period it was a tropical lagoon behind coral reefs on the shore of a major sea. The lagoon itself probably contained relatively little life. Paleontologists hypothesize that major storms would sometimes force materials, including dead animals, across the reefs. The animal remains then sunk to the lagoon bottom, where they were immaculately preserved. Six skeletons of *Archaeopteryx* have been found in the Solnhofen. Except for the feathers and somewhat smaller size, these skeletons are almost identical to those of *Dromaeosaurus*. The skeletons of another small dinosaur, *Compsognathus*, are also quite similar.

Did Archaeopteryx Fly?

For many years, researchers debated whether *Archaeopteryx* could fly. Although *Archaeopteryx* had plenty of feathers, it had heavy bones and lacked an enlarged breastbone, the structure to which large flight muscles attach in birds today. These facts suggested that the feathers were important only for insulation and that *Archaeopteryx* moved by running or climbing.

However, the wings and flight feathers of *Archaeopteryx* look a great deal like those of modern species. In addition, the discovery of other flying reptiles has caused researchers to rethink their ideas about what sorts of animals can fly.

In Texas, paleontologists discovered fossils of a very unlikely reptile. As they assembled the bones, they found wings larger than those of any other known animal—living or extinct. Some specimens had wingspans of 12 meters, the width of a small hang glider! What's more, these creatures had extremely large heads and no tail. This unusual species was named *Quetzalcoatlus*, after a feathered serpent deity in Aztec mythology.

At first, scientists questioned whether *Quetzalcoatlus* could ever have gotten off the ground. They argued that its body was too large, that it had no tail to stabilize it, and that its flight muscles could not possibly have been strong enough. But some determined biologists and engineers built a mechanical model of this improbable beast, using its fossils as their guide. To their delight and amazement, the model flew!

Quetzalcoatlus clearly would have spent more time gliding like an albatross than flying like a bluejay. But it could fly! And so, it seems, could other pterosaurs and early birds such as *Archaeopteryx*.

EVOLUTION OF BIRDS

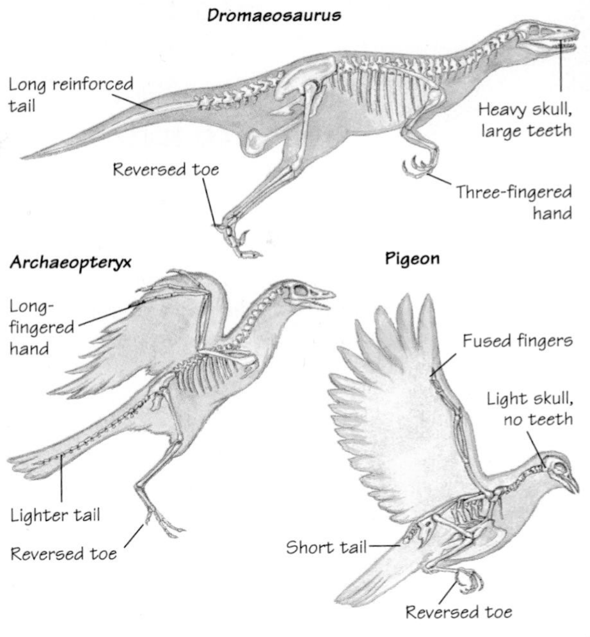

Figure 31–10
The skeleton of Archaeopteryx *has characteristics in common with dinosaurs, such as* Dromaeosaurus, *as well as with modern birds.*

Section Review 31-3

1. **Discuss** the evidence that shows that birds evolved from dinosaurs.
2. **BRANCHING OUT ACTIVITY** Research the body plan of a flying dinosaur or early bird. Under your teacher's supervision, **construct a model** of one of these animals.

- **What did *Archaeopteryx* have in common with modern birds?** (Most importantly, it had feathers. The basic body shape is much the same as well.)
- **Which are the "fingers" of *Archaeopteryx* more like, the dinosaur's or the bird's?** (The bird's "fingers" are fused, whereas the dinosaur's are not. *Archaeopteryx's* "fingers" are more like the dinosaur's.)

4 ASSESS

Quick Check

Have students make a list of ways in which *Archaeopteryx* was more like a dinosaur and ways in which it was more like a modern bird.

Section Review 31-3

1. The fossilized skeleton of an early bird, *Archaeopteryx*, is almost exactly like that of a small two-legged dinosaur, including the presence of teeth, a heavy skull, a jointed tail, and other dinosaurlike features. The only major difference is that feathers are found in the *Archaeopteryx* fossil.

2. Have students or groups do library research to find examples of the body plans of flying dinosaurs or early birds. Pterosaurs, which first appeared in the late Triassic and lasted until the mass extinction at the end of the Cretaceous, include eight genera and thus many variations. Members of the genus *Pterodactylus* were contemporaries of *Archaeopteryx*. There is no complete skeleton of *Quetzalcoatlus*. An interesting early bird is *Hesperornis*, a flightless, diving bird of the Cretaceous.

Checkpoint

1 The fossilized skeleton of *Archaeopteryx*, one of the first birds, is almost exactly like the skeleton of a small two-legged dinosaur, except for the presence of feathers.

Learning Modality

Auditory Learning Ask students to orally compare the features of the skeletons of the dinosaur, the modern bird, and *Archaeopteryx*.

Ancillary Support

The resources below can be used to support your teaching strategy for these two pages.

TR Enrich: Lords of the Dance
BL Inquiry Activity: Getting Off the Ground

Laboratory Investigation

Adaptation for Survival

Before the Lab

1. American chameleons, properly called green anoles, are readily available and relatively inexpensive at pet stores. Chameleon food includes mealworms, crickets, and other live insects. These can also be purchased from pet stores. When purchasing green anoles, ask for any information on how they should be kept in captivity.
2. If you have no screen terrarium lids, make sure construction materials are available, including screening, wood strips, and staples.
3. A flexible-necked desk lamp can be used as both a heat source and a light source. Position the lamp over the terrarium so that it shines through the screen lid. Adjust temperature by using bulbs of different wattage.

Pre-Lab Discussion

Have students read the entire procedure for this investigation. Then ask students the following questions.

What is the purpose of this investigation? (To design an experiment to determine how chameleons change color with changes in their environment.)

What variables can you choose from in designing your experiment? (Background color, temperature, light intensity.)

Which variable do you predict will most clearly cause a change in color of the chameleon? (Most students will predict that background color will most clearly cause a change in the chameleon's color.)

Skills Development

Students will use these skills while completing the laboratory investigation: designing an experiment, observing, comparing, drawing conclusions, and hypothesizing.

Laboratory Investigation

DESIGNING AN EXPERIMENT

Adaptation for Survival

American chameleons, or anoles, are native to the southeastern United States, where they can be seen on fences, trees, and wooden buildings. In this investigation, you will explore an unusual adaptation of chameleons—their ability to change color rapidly.

Problem

How can you **design an experiment** to determine how chameleons change color with their environment?

Suggested Materials

- American chameleon
- 20-gallon terrarium
- screen terrarium lid
- sand or gravel
- dried branches
- rocks
- moistened sponge, with a surface area of about 4 cm × 4 cm
- mealworms or other small live insects
- heat source
- thermometer
- colored pencils
- colored paper
- light source
- watch or clock

Suggested Procedure

1. To create housing for the chameleon, construct a screen top that fits tightly over the 20-gallon terrarium. Cover the bottom of the terrarium with sand or gravel. Add rocks and small branches to create an environment in which the chameleon can climb and hide. Suspend the moistened sponge from the screen to maintain proper humidity.
2. Place the thermometer inside the terrarium. If necessary, use a heat source to maintain the temperature between 22°C and 27°C.
3. Obtain a chameleon from your teacher. **CAUTION:** *Follow your teacher's instructions for handling chameleons. Be especially careful not to grab a chameleon by the tail. This could trigger a response in which the tail falls off!* Place the chameleon in the terrarium. Cover the terrarium with the screen top.

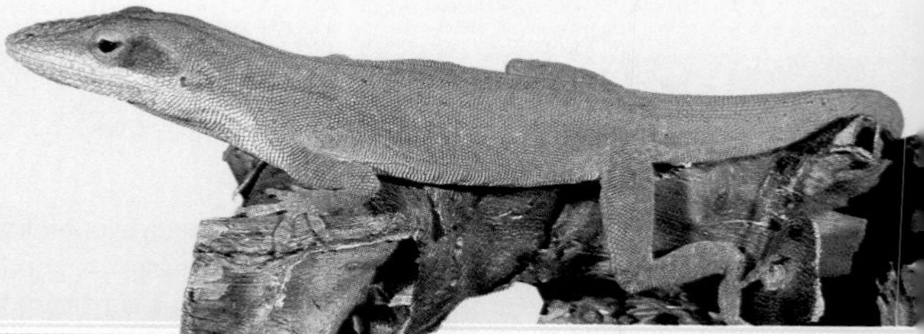

Safety Tips

- Caution students not to play with the anoles and to be extra careful when feeding them the live insects.
- Make sure that the heat source and light source students use are properly set up and maintained.
- Remind students to wash their hands after they have completed the investigation.

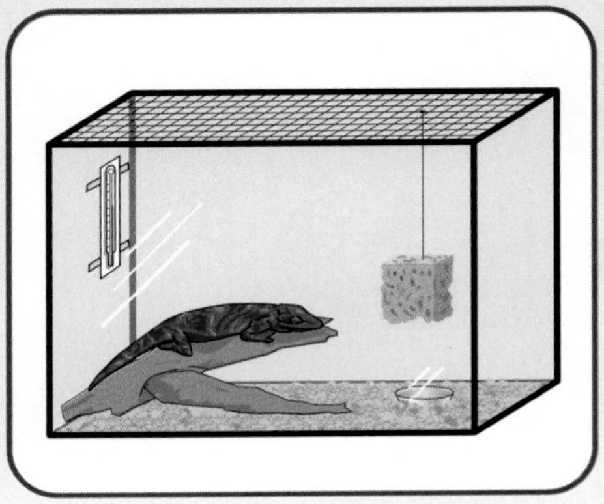

4. **Feed live insects to the chameleon three to four times a week. CAUTION:** ***Always wash your hands after handling live animals.***
5. **Observe the chameleon twice a day. Note its coloration and behavior. Use colored pencils to sketch the chameleon's appearance.**
6. **Design an experiment to test the effect of an environmental factor on color changes in chameleons. Choose one of these variables to investigate:**
   - **background color**
   - **light intensity**
   - **temperature (within 22°C to 27°C)**

   Your experiment should test only one variable and should test the chameleon's long-term and short-term response to its environment. Your experiment should not involve handling the chameleon and should not harm the chameleon in any way.
7. **With your teacher's approval, perform the experiment you designed.**

Observations

1. Describe any color changes you observed in the chameleon.
2. If there was a color change, was it the same on all parts of the chameleon's body?
3. How much time did it take for you to notice a change? For the change to be complete?

Analysis and Conclusions

1. Did the chameleon change color in response to the environmental factor you investigated? Explain.
2. How quickly was the chameleon able to change color? For how long was the chameleon able to maintain a new color?
3. How does the chameleon's ability to change color help it to survive?
4. Formulate a hypothesis to explain how a chameleon is able to change color. How might you test this hypothesis?

More to Explore

Research other animals that are able to change color rapidly. Do these animals use similar mechanisms to change color?

Answers to
Observations

1. Students' responses will depend on the experiment carried out and the health of the anoles. Most students will describe changes between brown and green, though sometimes changes in color will have been too subtle to detect.
2. An anole's color may show some variation over its body.
3. The quickest an anole can change color is about 10 minutes. Answers will vary.

Answers to
Analysis and Conclusions

1. Students' responses will depend on the variable investigated and on the health of the anoles. Anoles tend to be green in high light intensity and brown in low light intensity, and green at higher temperatures and brown at lower temperatures. Background color may not make any difference in the animal's color.
2. Some students might describe a complete change in as few as 10 minutes. The new color may be maintained if the environmental condition, such as a higher temperature, is maintained.
3. Most students will suggest that changing color may help the animal blend into the environment under changing conditions, making it more difficult for predators to detect.
4. A typical hypothesis might suggest that a chameleon has the ability to change the pigment in its skin cells by triggering some kind of chemical response. Testing such a hypothesis would be difficult. Students might suggest microscopic studies and chemical analyses of different colors of chameleon skin. (See Background Information on page 711.)

Teaching Strategies

1. Because anoles are not able to drink water from containers, advise students to mist plants and other surfaces in the terrarium daily.
2. Emphasize to students that they should not handle the anoles during the experiment. If absolutely necessary, they should pick the animals up by grasping the shoulder area.
3. Advise students that anoles will change color if frightened or angry. Thus, students should try to observe the terrariums mostly from a distance.
4. Make sure students feed the animals with live food. Anoles will not eat dead organisms.
5. Make sure students' experimental designs will not in any way harm the animals.

More to Explore

Through library research, students should discover that the animals that have the most amazing ability to change color are the true chameleons, which live mostly in Africa. Other reptiles, as well as squid and some fish, can also change color.

CHAPTER 31

Study Guide

Review Strategy

Divide students into small groups. If possible, place LEP or at-risk students with gifted students who are proficient in English. Have each group construct a crossword puzzle in the shape of some animal studied in the chapter, such as a turtle, a bird, or *Archaeopteryx*. The puzzle may contain any of the vocabulary terms or proper names used in the chapter. To indicate which word is appropriate for a place in the puzzle, groups might write questions or incomplete sentences that contain blanks to fill in. Then have groups trade puzzles and try to solve them.

Recalling Main Ideas

1. d
2. b
3. d
4. c
5. a
6. d
7. b
8. c
9. b

Assessment

Reviewing What You Learned

1. Reptiles regulate their body heat by gaining heat from their environment, whereas birds maintain a constant high body heat by conserving most of their metabolic energy.
2. To "taste" its environment by picking up molecules and depositing them on taste receptors in the mouth.
3. An egg that contains an amnion, a membrane that surrounds and protects the developing embryo.
4. Aquatic reptiles excrete most of their nitrogenous wastes in the form of ammonia, whereas terrestrial reptiles convert nitrogenous wastes into uric acid and eliminate it in the form of a dry paste.
5. Snakes use their ventral scales for traction as they push their bodies into long, curving waves.

Study Guide

Summarizing Key Concepts

The key concepts in each section of this chapter are listed below to help you review the chapter content. Make sure you understand each concept and its relationship to other concepts and to the theme of this chapter.

31–1 Reptiles

- Reptiles are scaly-skinned vertebrates that breathe with lungs and lay eggs that hatch on land. They are also ectotherms, meaning they gain body heat from their environment.
- Reptiles have an efficient respiratory system and a double-loop circulatory system. Crocodiles and alligators excrete ammonia, which they dilute with large amounts of water. Other reptiles convert nitrogenous wastes into a dry paste of uric acid.
- Reptiles were able to adapt to terrestrial life because they fertilized eggs internally, developed an amniotic egg, and typically cared for eggs after the eggs were laid.
- Tortoises and turtles have remained almost unchanged for 200 million years, as have crocodiles and alligators. Other reptiles include snakes and lizards.

31–2 Birds

- All birds have feathers. They also have hind limbs that they use for walking, running, or perching, as well as front limbs that are modified into wings.
- A bird's body is insulated enough to conserve its metabolic energy. Thus, birds are endotherms—meaning "heat from within."
- Birds have an efficient respiratory system in which air is stored in air sacs, then passed through the lungs and out of the body. This one-way flow constantly provides the lungs with fresh, oxygen-rich air.
- Birds use different feathers for different purposes. Contour feathers line and shape the wing. Down feathers line the skin and insulate the bird. And powder feathers help repel water in aquatic birds.
- Birds can fly because of their relatively light bodies, powerful breast muscles, and aerodynamic feathers and wings.

31–3 Evolution of Birds

- Because feathers have been found only in birds, their presence in the dinosaurlike *Archaeopteryx* established that birds evolved from dinosaurs.

Reviewing Key Terms

Review the following vocabulary terms and their meaning. Then use each term in a complete sentence.

31–1 Reptiles

ectotherm
amniotic egg

31–2 Birds

feather
endotherm
alveolus
septum
air sac
lung
contour feather
down feather
powder feather
cloaca
gizzard
crop

Inquiry-Based Strategy

Many bird populations throughout the United States are declining at alarming rates. Have students research what they can do to stop such declines by asking the following question: What steps can be taken at the local level to protect birds?

Have groups of students work on answering this question by doing library research in books and periodicals and also by contacting local conservation organizations. Ask that each group prepare a "how-to" pamphlet that includes specific ways in which people can help protect local bird populations. These ways might include planting particular trees and shrubs, limiting use of pesticides and other chemicals, and building bird houses and feeders. Ask that each pamphlet contain both descriptions and detailed illustrations.

Recalling Main Ideas

Choose the letter of the answer that best completes the statement or answers the question.

1. Which of these animals is an endotherm?
   a. snake **c.** alligator
   b. turtle **d.** hummingbird

2. Snakes and lizards excrete nitrogenous wastes in the form of
   a. carbon dioxide. **c.** toxic venom.
   b. uric acid. **d.** ammonia.

3. In pit vipers, the pit organs sense
   a. taste. **c.** sound.
   b. smell. **d.** heat.

4. In most reptiles, reproduction is
   a. viviparous. **c.** oviparous.
   b. ovoviviparous. **d.** asexual.

5. In birds and reptiles, materials from the reproductive, digestive, and excretory tracts collect in the
   a. cloaca. **c.** kidney.
   b. crop. **d.** gizzard.

6. Which type of feathers enable birds to fly?
   a. down feathers **c.** powder feathers
   b. smooth feathers **d.** contour feathers

7. Birds swallow gravel, which is stored in the
   a. crop. **c.** stomach.
   b. gizzard. **d.** cloaca.

8. Small sex organs, hollow bones, and air sacs are all adaptations in birds for
   a. internal fertilization. **c.** flight.
   b. internal transport. **d.** movement.

9. Although *Archaeopteryx* is classified as a bird, it resembled a
   a. large four-legged dinosaur.
   b. small two-legged dinosaur.
   c. pterosaur.
   d. snake.

Putting It All Together

Using the information on pages xxx to xxxi, complete the following concept map.

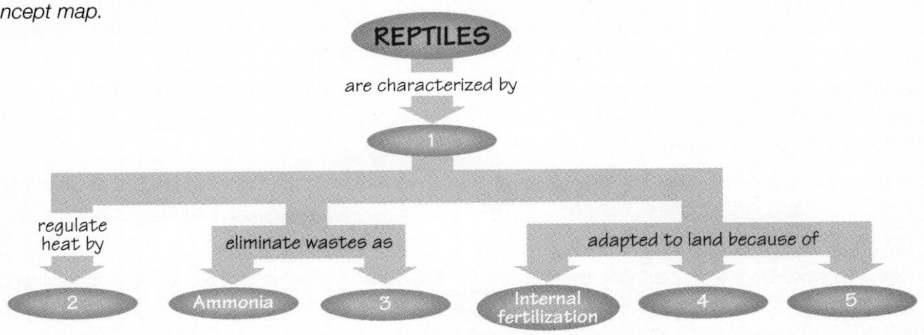

Putting It All Together

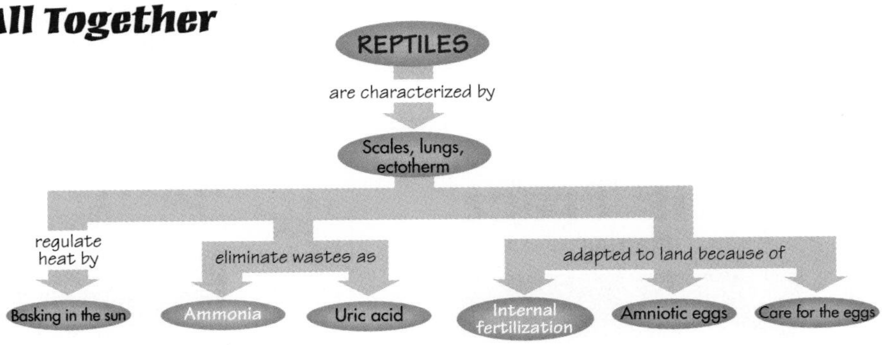

6. (1) Rhyncocephalia, including tuataras; (2) Chelonia, including tortoises and turtles; (3) Crocodilia, including crocodiles and alligators; (4) Squamata, including lizards and snakes.
7. Tiny air sacs in the lungs where gas exchange takes place.
8. Beaks of various sizes and shapes are adapted to the different types of foods that different birds eat.
9. Contour feathers are the light yet strong feathers that provide a large surface area for flight. Down feathers insulate the skin. Powder feathers release a water-repelling powder that prevents aquatic birds from becoming waterlogged.
10. Most reptiles have a "not-quite-four-chambered" heart, whereas birds have true four-chambered hearts. In a reptile's heart, oxygenated and deoxygenated blood mix slightly as they leave the ventricles. In a bird's heart, oxygenated and deoxygenated blood are kept separate.
11. Some birds migrate by using their magnetic sense; others use a combination of acute eyesight and a built-in clock to navigate by the stars.
12. The male and female birds firmly press the lips of their cloacas together, which allows sperm to transfer from male to female.
13. Because it had feathers.
14. An extinct flying reptile that had a wingspan of up to 12 meters.

Expanding the Concepts

1. In a typical response, students might mention scales on reptiles and feathers on birds, the four legs of reptiles and the two legs and wings of birds, and the differences in the hearts of reptiles and birds.
2. In a bird, when fresh air is inhaled, it bypasses the lungs and enters large air sacs. When air is exhaled, it travels through tubes in the lungs that are lined with alveoli, where gas exchange occurs. Birds need a more efficient respiratory system because they must maintain a high rate of metabolism and they expend a great deal of energy to fly.
3. A typical response might mention the development of efficient respiratory and excretory systems, the ability to move about on land or in the air, and the development of internal fertilization, amniotic eggs, and parental care for the eggs.

Assessment (continued)

4. Reptiles are ectotherms, and thus they need a warm climate to keep their body temperature at a high enough level. Birds, though, are endotherms and can maintain their body temperature even in a cold climate.
5. Some lizards have a long, sticky tongue that they use to snare prey. Snakes can paralyze prey with poison or suffocate prey with the force of their bodies. Reptiles such as crocodiles grab prey with powerful jaws filled with sharp teeth.
6. Bones with spaces within them, air sacs that extend inside bones, sex organs that are small except during breeding season, strong breast muscles used to flap their wings, wings shaped to provide lift, and feathers that can push air downward.
7. Most birds have excellent vision, and those that hunt during day can see color better than humans. Many have an acute sense of hearing. They also have senses that help them in migration, such as a magnetic sense and a built-in clock. Taste and smell are not well developed in birds.
8. The Solnhofen region was once a lagoon. When a dead animal sank to the bottom of that lagoon, a fine mud covered it and isolated it from oxygen, which would cause decay. When the mud turned to fine-grained limestone, many well-preserved fossils were the result.
9. The evidence that birds evolved from dinosaurs is that the fossil skeleton of *Archaeopteryx*, which can be identified as an early bird by the presence of feathers, is almost exactly like the fossil skeleton of a small two-legged dinosaur.
10. *Archaeopteryx* could probably fly, even though it had heavy bones and lacked an enlarged breastbone. Evidence includes a mechanical model of *Quetzalcoatlus*, an extinct flying reptile, that could fly despite a large body and the lack of other flight adaptations.

Assessment

Reviewing What You Learned

Answer each of the following in a complete sentence.

1. Compare the ways in which reptiles and birds regulate their body heat.
2. Why does a snake flick its tongue in the air?
3. What is an amniotic egg?
4. How does excretion differ in terrestrial and aquatic reptiles?
5. How do snakes move without legs?
6. Identify four orders of reptiles. Give an example of a reptile in each order.
7. What are alveoli?
8. Why did beaks evolve different sizes and shapes in different bird species?
9. Identify three different types of feathers. Describe the purpose of each type.
10. Compare a bird's heart with a reptile's heart.
11. How are birds able to migrate over great distances?
12. How do birds reproduce?
13. Although *Archaeopteryx* resembled dinosaurs in many ways, why is it classified as a bird?
14. What is *Quetzalcoatlus?*

Expanding the Concepts

Discuss each of the following in a brief paragraph.

1. Compare the basic body plans of reptiles and birds.
2. Describe a bird's respiratory system. Why do birds have a more efficient respiratory system than does an animal that lives only on land?
3. Discuss the adaptations that allow reptiles and birds to live away from bodies of water.
4. Why do most reptiles live in warm or hot climates, while birds are able to live in other climates?
5. Describe the different ways in which reptiles capture prey.
6. What adaptations allow birds to fly?
7. Discuss the different sense organs in birds.
8. Why are well-preserved fossils especially prevalent in the Solnhofen region of Germany?
9. Explain the evidence that birds evolved from dinosaurs.
10. Could *Archaeopteryx* fly? Discuss the evidence that applies to this question.

726 Chapter 31

Extending Your Thinking

1. A large flock could give individuals protection through a system of communication among the birds. In flocks, birds could find mates more easily than if they lived separately.

Skills Trace
Inferring
- Focus p. 710
- Practice p. 713
- Assess p. 727

2. Students should be able to classify the animal as some kind of lizard in the order Squamata. Evidence for this classification includes the animal's four legs, the scales on its body, and the long tongue being used to snare an insect.

Skills Trace
Observing
- Focus p. 717
- Practice p. 719
- Assess p. 727

CHAPTER 31

Extending Your Thinking

Use the skills you have developed in this chapter to answer the following.

1. **Inferring** Some species of birds are highly social and live in huge flocks. Based on what you know about birds, infer the survival advantages of group living.
2. **Observing** Examine the photograph of the animal shown on this page. Describe the characteristics that you observe. How would you classify this animal?
3. **Developing a hypothesis** On average, reptiles that live in water are larger than reptiles that live on land. Formulate a hypothesis to explain this difference.
4. **Applying concepts** As the seasons change, many birds migrate over great distances. What advantages does migration offer birds?
5. **Designing an experiment** Parakeets, parrots, and other birds can mimic the sounds they hear. Design an experiment to determine whether a parakeet or parrot can be trained to repeat a phrase when prompted.
6. **Using the writing process** In reference to penguins, Herman Melville asked, "What outlandish being are these?" Kurt Vonnegut wrote, "They were skinny things underneath their head waiters' costumes." Write a creative description of a penguin or another bird of your choice.

Applying Your Skills

Take a Bird Census

Wildlife biologists use many methods for collecting information about birds. At least one method, called a census, requires your help. A census counts the number of individuals of each species in a particular place and at a particular time.

1. Work in three-member teams. Each team should select a leader, an expert, and a recorder. The leader does the actual counting, the expert consults references to help identify species, and the recorder develops and uses a data sheet.
2. As a team, select an open outdoor plot and assemble in the middle of the plot. For 10 minutes, count the number of birds you see and identify the species of each bird. If you cannot identify a bird, write a description of it.
3. Analyze your data. Include the total number of individuals of each species.
4. Compare your census data with the data from other teams. Prepare a report of the bird population that lives in the regions you surveyed.

• GOING FURTHER •

5. Contact an environmental organization active in your community. Request information on how to participate in bird counts that they sponsor.

• Let students know the method you would like them to use to record the birds they will see. A simple checkoff list can be used, with the names of common birds printed in a list. A more complicated chart or journal might also be developed.
• The Audubon Society sponsors an annual bird census carried out by volunteers. Students might check to find the nearest chapter.

Scoring Rubric

4 Response is thorough, accurate, and creative; shows an in-depth understanding of science skills, procedures, and concepts.

3 Response is complete, mostly accurate, and original; shows a satisfactory understanding of science skills, procedures, and concepts.

2 Response is mostly complete but includes some inaccuracies; shows an adequate understanding of science skills, procedures, and concepts.

1 Response is only partially complete and has many inaccuracies; shows an incomplete understanding of science skills, procedures, and concepts.

0 Response is mostly incomplete and/or inaccurate; shows a lack of understanding of science skills, procedures, and concepts.

3. A typical hypothesis might suggest that water helps support a body's weight, and thus reptiles with relatively greater weight would be more adaptable to living in water than on land.
4. Through migration, a bird could always live in a warm climate, where plants are growing and animal prey is active. Thus, migrating ensures a constant supply of food.
5. A typical design might suggest setting up a procedure to train several different parakeets or parrots to learn different phrases and then determining whether each bird could repeat its specific phrase when prompted.
6. Students might write a creative description of any of the birds mentioned in the chapter or any bird they are familiar with.

Applying Your Skills

Teacher Notes

• Make available several different field guides for students to use. Those written by Roger Tory Peterson are widely used by birders because of the clear pinpointing of marks on the different birds that can be used for identification.

Chapter 32 Mammals

Content Management	Student Edition Activities
■ Section 32–1 Characteristics of Mammals, pp. 729–736 Mammalian Body Plan Classifying Mammals	**MINI LAB:** Step on It!, p. 736 **Laboratory Investigation:** Investigating Mammalian Skulls, pp. 740–741
◆ BRANCHING OUT • In Depth Section 32–2 The Influence of Humans, pp. 737–739 Domestication Changing Life on Earth	

■ This section covers all the necessary content and concepts for an enriched course in biology.
◆ This section covers content and concepts that are either applications or extensions of the enriched material.

Assessment Strategies

SE Chapter Review, pp. 742–745
TR Section Reviews
Chapter Test
BL Chapter Review
Practice Test
CTB Chapter 32 Test

Tech Prep

Teaching strategies appropriate for students who are in technical/vocational programs or who are considering post-secondary technical education can be found on the following **TE** pages: 731 and 738.

Meeting the Standards

Sections 32–1 through 32–2 cover four of the five content standards under **Biological Evolution,** three of the five content standards under **The Interdependence of Organisms,** and three of the four content standards under **The Behavior of Organisms** as described on pages 185–187 of The National Science Education Standards.

Chapter Planning Guide

Teacher's Edition Activities	Other Activities	Media and Technology
Chapter Discovery Learning Activity, p. 728 **Inquiry Activity:** A Hairy Situation, p. 729 **Investigate:** Long-Term Project, p. 730 **Inquiry Activity:** A Colorful Environment?, p. 732 **Investigate:** Research, p. 734	**LM** Observing the Behavior of a Mammal, #63 Comparing the Vision of Predators and Prey, #64 **TR** **Explore:** Hand to Hand **BL** **Inquiry Activity:** Amazing Mammals	**BioVue Plus CD-ROMs:** Diversity at the Zoo **TB** Evolution of Skulls and Teeth, #41
Inquiry Activity: A Mammalian World, p. 738	**TR** **Writing in Biology:** Take Me Home! **Enrich:** Hunted to Extinction? **BL** **Inquiry Activity:** Man's Best Friend	

KEY: **SE** Student Edition **TE** Teacher's Edition **LM** Laboratory Manual **TR** Teaching Resources **BL** BioLog **TB** Transparency Box **CTB** Computer Test Bank

Materials List

TE Chapter Discovery Learning Activity, p. 728 (20–30 minutes); photographs or slides of different mammals from a variety of environments.
TE Inquiry Activity: A Hairy Situation, p. 729 (30 minutes); animal hairs from a variety of sources, microscope, slides, coverslips, pipette.
TE Investigate: Long-Term Project, p. 730 (45 minutes for setup, 5–10 minutes for daily maintenance and observation); gerbils, animal cages, gerbil food, water bottles, food dishes, various objects to enrich the environment such as small boxes, tubes, and balls.
TE Investigate: Research, p. 734 (3–5 hours research and preparation time out of class); copy of real estate sales sheet.
SE MINI LAB: Step on It!, p. 736 (20–30 minutes); photographs of mammal footprints.

CHAPTER 32

Mammals

Introducing the Chapter

. . . In Pictures

This photograph shows two examples of *Oreamnos americanus*. Although their common name is mountain goat, these animals are really goat-like antelopes and not closely related to true goats. These even-toed, hoofed mammals, or artiodactyls, are indigenous to the mountain regions of the northwestern United States, western Canada, and Alaska. They are characteristically whitish with a bearded chin; both sexes permanently wear backward-curving black horns.

- **What external characteristic of these mountain goats have you not seen in organisms studied in previous chapters?** (The hair that covers their bodies.)
- **What is the function of hair on such an animal?** (To keep the animal warm.)

Teaching Strategy

In the first section of this chapter, students will learn about the characteristics and classification of mammals. The BRANCHING OUT section provides students with an in-depth look at the ways in which humans have changed Earth's animal populations.

BIO JOURNAL

The Bio Journal topic can be used to stimulate classroom discussion about the environments in which mammals can be found. Ask students to list examples that live in rain forests, deserts, arctic regions, plains, hardwood forests, and the ocean. Instruct students to keep their entries in their portfolios.

CHAPTER 32

Mammals

FOCUSING THE CHAPTER
THEME: Unity and Diversity

32–1 Characteristics of Mammals
- **Describe** the characteristics of mammals.
- **Identify** different orders of mammals.

BRANCHING OUT *In Depth*

32–2 The Influence of Humans
- **Discuss** the ways in which humans have changed the populations of other mammals.

LABORATORY INVESTIGATION
- **Infer** the characteristics of a mammal by studying its skull.

Biology and Your World

BIO JOURNAL

Study the mountain goats shown on this page. In your journal, describe their characteristics. How do these characteristics help the mountain goats survive in their environment?

Mountain goats in Olympic National Park, Washington

TEACHER SUPPORT — Chapter Discovery Learning Activity

MAMMAL ADAPTATIONS

Show students pictures of different kinds of mammals in a variety of environments. If possible, show slides using a projector. This display might include a mouse, lion, camel, whale, Arctic wolf or bear, duck-billed platypus, kangaroo, cow, and so on. For each image shown, ask students to name an adaptation that would allow the mammal to live in the environment shown. After concluding the display, have students meet in small groups to collaborate on a list of characteristics that would fit all or most of the mammals they have seen. After all groups have made their lists, have a representative of each group read its list to the class.

SECTION 32–1

Characteristics of Mammals

Guide for Reading

- **List** the characteristics of mammals.
- **Explain** how mammals are classified.

MINI LAB

- **Classify** mammals from their footprints.

GROUNDHOGS AND FIELD MICE burrow holes in prairies, apes and lemurs swing from tree to tree in rain forests, and whales and dolphins swim majestically through oceans. What do these animals have in common? All are mammals. As you will discover, mammals evolved all sorts of shapes, sizes, and lifestyles and live in a great variety of habitats. And mammals include humans—a typical mammal species in some ways, but very different in others.

Mammalian Body Plan

Like the bodies of other terrestrial vertebrates, the mammalian body plan evolved from that of ancient reptiles. For this reason, the body parts and internal organs of mammals are similar in appearance and function to those of today's reptiles. Yet several important characteristics set mammals apart. **Mammals are endotherms, have external body hair, and have a layer of fat beneath the skin. Female mammals produce milk to feed their offspring.**

To generate their body heat, all mammals—especially small ones—have a much higher metabolic rate than most other vertebrates. Two other mammalian traits—external body hair and a layer of fat beneath the skin—evolved as insulation to store that important heat.

Mammals have several other characteristics, many of which help paleontologists to identify mammalian bones and fossils. These characteristics include a simpler lower jaw than reptiles, complex teeth that are replaced just once in a lifetime, a unique set of bones in the middle ear, and several features of limb bones, limb girdles, and the vertebral column.

☑ *Checkpoint* What is a mammal? ❶

Figure 32–1 *Mammals live almost everywhere on Earth.* (a) *This tree shrew, which is thought to resemble the first mammals, lives on the island of Borneo. It is eating an insect called a katydid.* (b) *A heavy layer of blubber keeps a walrus warm on land and in the ocean.* (c) *The hooves of bighorn sheep are sharp-edged and elastic, allowing them to roam over rocky terrain.*

Section 32–1

Characteristics of Mammals

Performance Objectives

- Identify several characteristics of mammals.
- Describe how mammals are classified.

Mini Lab Skill: Classifying
Laboratory Investigation Skill: Inferring

1 ENGAGE

Inquiry Activity

Comparing

A Hairy Situation

Provide several samples of animal hair, such as hair from cows, dogs, cats, hamsters, gerbils, goats, horses, sheep, and rabbits. Ask students whether they think hair is the same, no matter what the source. Then have students make wet-mount slides of several samples and examine them under a microscope. For each slide, students should make a sketch of what they see. After examining three or four samples, students should write a comparison of what they have seen, noting similarities and differences.

☑ Checkpoint

❶ A mammal is an endothermic vertebrate that has external body hair and a layer of fat beneath its skin. Female mammals produce milk to feed their offspring.

TEACHER SUPPORT

Background Information

The first true mammals probably appeared in the late Triassic, about 210 million years ago. In contrast to the reptiles that dominated the daylight hours, these early mammals were active at night. A requirement for such night life is internal regulation of a high body temperature, since basking in the sun is not an option. The insulation provided by long, dense body hair is the most important adaptation for this purpose. What paleontologists need to figure out is how hair evolved; long hair would have been of little advantage to an ectothermic reptile, but without long hair an endothermic mammal seems impossible. One theory is that hairs first evolved as sensory projections that gave organisms tactile information about the environment. As hairs multiplied, they provided insulation, and that property of hair eventually became the focus of adaptation.

Ancillary Support

The resource below can be used to support your teaching strategy for these two pages.

BL Inquiry Activity: Amazing Mammals

2 EXPLORE

Investigate

Long-Term Project Ask students how they think an environment affects a mammal's growth and development. Then have groups set up a variety of environments in which to keep gerbils. For example, one group might set up a basic environment, which would include only the bare necessities such as food, water, and bedding in a bare cage. Another group might set up an enriched environment, in which the basics are augmented with various objects and playthings of the students' choosing. Have groups maintain and observe their gerbils over several weeks, taking periodic measurements and noting growth, development, and behavior.

3 TEACH

Ideas Through Images

Have students examine Figure 32–3 on page 731, read the caption, and answer the following questions.

- **What is the advantage of interlocking teeth?** (Interlocking teeth can crush, slice, or tear food more quickly than simple teeth. An organism with interlocking teeth processes and digests food more efficiently.)
- **Why does a mammal need more food than a reptile?** (A mammal is an endotherm and thus needs energy to maintain a high metabolic rate and a constant body temperature.)
- **Why did the teeth of the chimpanzee evolve differently from the teeth of the lion, since both are mammals?** (Each became adapted to eating different food. The chimpanzee's teeth evolved to allow it to eat plants; the lion's teeth are adapted for meat eating.)

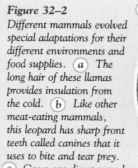

Figure 32–2 *Different mammals evolved special adaptations for their different environments and food supplies.* (a) *The long hair of these llamas provides insulation from the cold.* (b) *Like other meat-eating mammals, this leopard has sharp front teeth called canines that it uses to bite and tear prey.* (c) *Cows can digest grass because of their elaborate digestive tract, which includes a four-chambered stomach.*

complex design of these teeth allows top and bottom teeth to interlock during chewing, like the blades of scissors. Interlocking teeth are important because they can crush, slice, or tear food more quickly than simple teeth can. The more thoroughly food is chewed, the more quickly and efficiently the digestive tract can break it down. And the more efficiently an animal can process and digest its food, the more food it can eat!

The rest of the digestive tract evolved to digest the type of food the mammal eats. Because digestive enzymes can quickly break down meat, carnivores have a relatively short intestine. And because tough plant tissues take much more time to digest, most leaf-eating herbivores have a much longer intestine. Cows and their relatives, which are among the most successful grazing animals, evolved ways to digest plant foods that are nearly useless to other animals.

Feeding

Because of its high metabolic rate, a mammal must eat nearly ten times as much food as a reptile of the same size! As a result, mammals evolved a variety of specialized jaws and teeth, some of which are shown in ***Figure 32–3.*** In mammals, the joint between the skull and lower jaw is simpler, stronger, and more versatile than it is in reptiles. This joint allowed mammals to evolve larger, more powerful jaw muscles and different ways of chewing.

Mammals also evolved specialized teeth called **molars** and **premolars.** The

Internal Transport and Respiration

Like birds, mammals have a double-loop circulatory system powered by a four-chambered heart. Blood travels between the heart and lungs in one loop, then between the heart and the rest of the body in the other loop.

A mammal's lungs inflate in two ways at once. Muscles in the chest lift the rib cage up and outward, increasing the volume of the chest cavity. At the same time, a powerful muscle called the **diaphragm** pulls the bottom of the chest cavity downward, which further increases its volume. As a result, air enters the

TEACHER SUPPORT

Background Information

In a young shark, a tooth lasts seven or eight days before being replaced. But in most mammals, replacement occurs only once, when the deciduous or "milk" teeth are replaced by adult or permanent teeth. The reason for this difference lies in the structure and function of the teeth. In sharks, teeth are uniformly conical, and they are used primarily for tearing. In mammals, there are different kinds of teeth, including the interlocking molars and premolars used for grinding and mashing. If these teeth were replaced often, there would be too much chance that the top and bottom teeth would not fit properly, and thus their function would be diminished. As mammals evolved, there was a selective advantage for those individual organisms that had stronger teeth that needed to be replaced less often.

EVOLUTION OF SKULLS AND TEETH

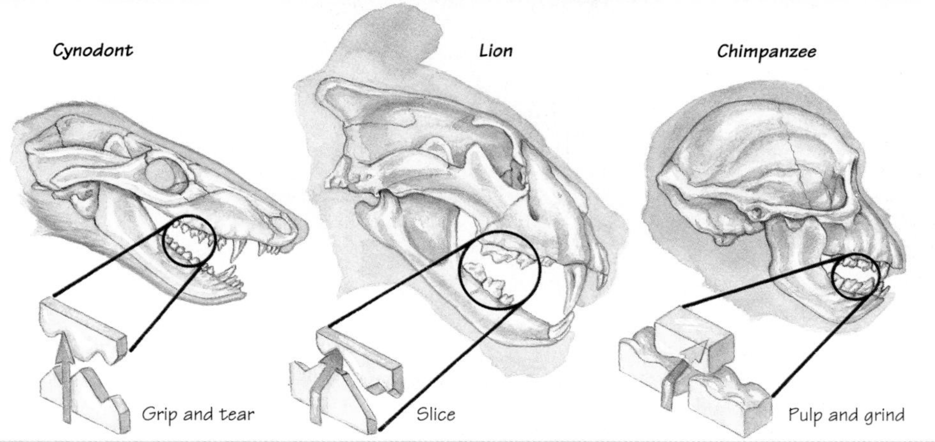

Figure 32–3
An ancient reptile called a cynodont had teeth that did not precisely interlock but could grip and tear food. In true mammals, such as lions, the lower jaw is slightly narrower than the upper jaw. Thus, when the jaws close, the back teeth slice food as they shear past each other. Plant-eating mammals, such as chimpanzees, evolved back teeth that were square and flat, ideal for grinding food.

lungs. When these muscles reverse their activity, air rushes out of the lungs as the chest cavity shrinks.

Even marine mammals, such as seals and whales, breathe air with this type of lungs. However, these animals have evolved both physical and physiological adaptations for life in the water. They are able to store oxygen in their tissues, withstand the buildup of carbon dioxide, and hold their breath during long dives.

☑ **Checkpoint** How do a mammal's lungs inflate? ❶

Excretion

Mammals have a complex, well-developed excretory system. The liver transforms nitrogenous wastes into urea, which the **kidneys** filter from the blood and combine with other waste products to form urine.

Mammalian kidneys not only eliminate wastes, they do an excellent job of conserving important compounds, including water, salts, and sugars. This enables some mammals to inhabit deserts, where water is scarce, and others to live in rain forests, where salt is rare. However, mammalian kidneys cannot excrete salt without eliminating water at the same time. That's why most mammals can't survive by drinking sea water.

Nervous System

As in the brains of other vertebrates, the medulla oblongata of the mammalian brain regulates breathing, heart rate, and other bodily functions not normally under conscious control. The brain also includes a cerebellum, which coordinates movement. In the cerebellum, the conscious intention to move is translated into a series of muscle contractions.

However, a mammal's brain differs from the brains of other animals because of its well-developed cerebral cortex—the center of thinking and other complex behaviors. Some activities, such as reading a textbook, are possible only with the human cerebral cortex. But many other complex behaviors—ranging from social behaviors to the use of tools—may be more widespread among other mammals than was previously thought.

Laboratory Investigation

The Laboratory Investigation, Investigating Mammalian Skulls, on pages 740–741 is appropriate to use at this point in the chapter.

Discussion

Begin a discussion of the mammalian nervous system by asking students to recall the brains of other vertebrates. Point out that the bird's brain, for instance, includes a cerebrum, but it is not large and does not control any complex behaviors. In mammals, the cerebrum is large, and much of it is called the cerebral cortex. Emphasize that the complex behaviors of mammals owe much to the evolution of that portion of the brain. Ask students to speculate about what environmental conditions caused the mammal brain to increase in size and complexity.

☑ Checkpoint

❶ A mammal's lungs inflate when the chest cavity increases in volume; muscles in the chest lift the rib cage up and outward, and a muscle called the diaphragm pulls the bottom of the chest cavity downward.

TEACHER SUPPORT

Managing Classroom Diversity

EDUCATIONAL EQUITY

In recent decades, perhaps no field researchers have gained greater recognition than Dian Fossey and Jane Goodall. Fossey spent many years in East Africa observing the habits of mountain gorillas. Her 1983 book *Gorillas in the Mist* recounts her fascinating life. Goodall did the same kind of work with chimpanzees in Tanzania. In *Through a Window: My Thirty Years With the Chimpanzees of Gombe*, published in 1990, she tells both her own and her subjects' stories. Encourage students to research the work of these two women.

TECH PREP STUDENTS

Many jobs require some observation in the field and then the completion of a form or report of what was observed. Ask students to interview someone about field observation in their future career. Then have students make a list of skills needed to carry out the required tasks.

Ancillary Support

The resources below can be used to support your teaching strategy for these two pages.

LM Observing the Behavior of a Mammal, #63
TB Evolution of Skulls and Teeth, #41

Ideas Through Images

Have students examine Figure 32–4 and Figure 32–5, read the captions, and answer the following questions.

- **What can you infer about the habits of the ancestors of cats from the information in Figure 32–4?** (The ancestors of cats must have been nocturnal animals because cat eyes are adapted to seeing at night rather than in the daylight.)
- **If human eyes are adapted to bright light, what can you infer about whether they are well adapted to distinguishing between colors?** (Being adapted to bright light implies that human ancestors were active during the daylight hours, when colors are bright and being able to see colors is an advantage. Therefore, human eyes are also probably well adapted to distinguishing between colors.)
- **How would you describe the process that accounts for the mole's loss of eyesight?** (As the ancestors of the mole spent more and more time underground, the ability to see came to have no advantage to the animal. Through many generations, the process of natural selection eventually produced a mammal without a sense of sight.)

Inquiry Activity

Designing an Experiment

A Colorful Environment?

Challenge small groups of students to design an experiment that would investigate whether a dog has well-developed color vision. Tell students that in their designs, they should use only easily obtainable materials and include a control. After all groups have designed an experiment, discuss as a class the various designs and their likely outcomes. If one design seems both simple and well done, encourage students to carry out the experiment and report the results to the class.

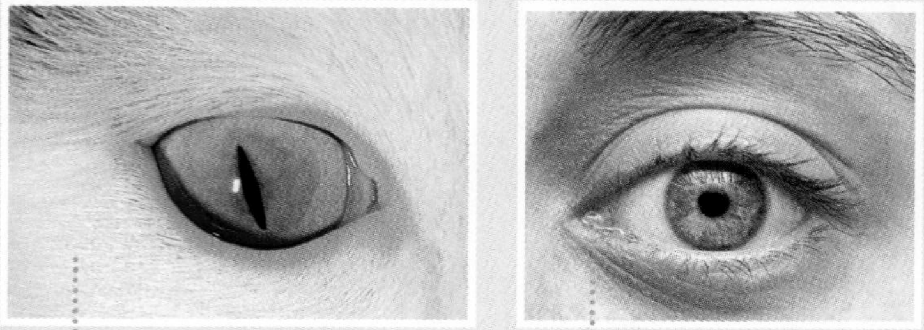

Figure 32–4
(a) Because a cat's eye is adapted for low-intensity light, it can tolerate only small amounts of bright light. Its pupils close into thin slits during the day. (b) A human eye is adapted for bright light. Its round pupil allows a relatively large amount of light into the eye.

a

b

Sense Organs

According to current theory, the first mammals were small and nocturnal, meaning "active at night." If this is true, it helps to explain the range of mammalian senses.

Nocturnal animals must see in dim light, which means their eyes adapted for low-light vision. Like certain black-and-white photographic film, low-light eyes are very sensitive to differences in light intensity but cannot detect differences in color. If the first mammals had this type of eye, it would help to explain why most of their descendants do not see color well.

The ancestors of humans and some other primates, on the other hand, were active during the day. Human ancestors evolved eyes that work more like color film—less sensitive in dim light but able to distinguish color well.

Nocturnal mammals also benefit from sharp senses of smell and taste. This is still the rule among mammals, although humans again are an exception. Although our senses of smell and taste serve us well, they are pitiful in comparison with other mammals. Dogs and cats, for example, can identify individual humans on the basis of subtle differences in body odor that we cannot recognize.

In addition, a sharp sense of hearing is enormously important to nocturnal animals. When ancestral mammals evolved a simplified jaw joint, three bones that were once part of the jaw evolved into the bones of the middle ear. These bones form a delicate mechanism that transfers vibrations from the eardrum to the inner ear. There, sensory cells are stimulated in an organ called the cochlea, allowing the brain to interpret the vibrations as sounds.

Movement

The first mammals evolved several changes in their skeleton, each of which was passed on to their descendants. Among these changes was a backbone that flexed vertically as well as side to side. This flexibility allows mammals to move with a bouncing, leaping stride. Shoulder and pelvic girdles also became more streamlined and flexible, permitting both front and hind limbs to move in a great variety of ways.

Figure 32–5
Unlike most mammals, this mole is blind. Most species of moles lost their eyesight as they adapted to an underground existence. These animals are members of the order Insectivora, meaning "insect-eating."

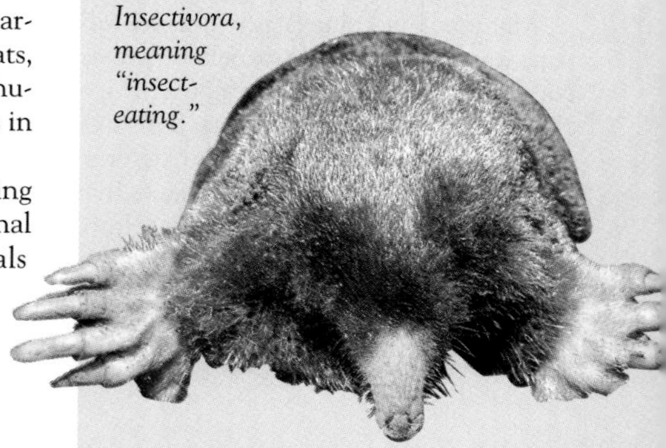

TEACHER SUPPORT

Background Information

According to one theory, the large and complex brain of mammals evolved as a result of the sensory needs of a nocturnal animal. Reptiles and birds are mostly active during the day and depend greatly on vision to find food. Visual information, especially the three-dimensional impressions that result from binocular vision, needs little analysis and thus relatively less brain matter. But a nocturnal animal must also depend on information from scent and sound. As the animal moves, it must compare and integrate perceptions from three senses, a process that requires a relatively more complex brain. Furthermore, an animal that could associate such information with past events—compare past to present—would have a selective advantage. This theory, then, explains why mammals have four to five times the brain size of reptiles and birds.

Reproduction and Development

Compared with other animals, mammals put more energy and effort into nourishing and protecting their young, both before and after birth. Most mammals reproduce in the same way that humans do. The male deposits sperm inside the reproductive tract of the female, where fertilization occurs. Typically, the female carries the developing embryo for a significant length of time.

In many mammals—with humans an important exception—newborn young can stand up and move around on their own a short time after birth. Newborn mammals feed for varying lengths of time on their mother's milk.

Checkpoint How do mammals reproduce? ❶

Figure 32–6 *This female impala is nursing its offspring. Milk is produced in the female's mammary glands—the structures that provide the class Mammalia with its name.*

Classifying Mammals

Compared with other classes of animals, there are fewer species of mammals—even mollusks are more diverse! Nor are there many individual mammals alive today, especially compared with insects. However, mammals have evolved a variety of fascinating physical and behavioral traits. They include some of the Earth's largest and most familiar organisms.

Mammals are classified into three groups based on the way in which they reproduce and develop. These groups are monotremes, marsupials, and placental mammals. To learn more about mammals, study the photographs on the next two pages.

Monotremes

Members of the order Monotremata are descendants of the most primitive mammals and seem to be part reptile and part mammal. They are represented today only by the duck-billed platypus and two species of spiny anteaters, also called echidnas. These living relics live only in Australia and New Guinea.

In monotremes—a name that means "one hole"—both the reproductive system and the urinary system open into a cloaca, like the cloaca of reptiles. Development in monotremes is also very different from development in other mammals. As in reptiles, the female lays leathery-shelled eggs that hatch outside the body. And although newly hatched young are nourished with milk, the young do not suckle at their mother's breast as the young of other mammals do. Instead, milk trickles from pores onto the surface of the mother's abdomen, from which the young lap it up.

Checkpoint What is a monotreme? ❷

Ideas Through Images

Have students examine Figure 32–6, read the caption, and answer the following questions.

- **What are the three groups of mammals?** (Monotremes, marsupials, and placental mammals.)
- **In which major group of mammals can this impala be classified?** (Placental mammals.)
- **How do monotreme females nourish their young?** (Monotreme young lap up milk that is on the surface of the mother's abdomen.)
- **Where are marsupial young when they are nourished with their mother's milk?** (Inside the mother's pouch.)

Checkpoints

❶ Mammals reproduce sexually, when the male deposits sperm inside the female, where fertilization occurs. The female typically carries the developing embryo for a significant length of time.

❷ A monotreme is a member of the order Monotremata, which includes the duck-billed platypus and two species of spiny anteaters. Monotremes have a cloaca, and females lay eggs that hatch outside the body.

TEACHER SUPPORT

Ecology Note

Grasses and herbivorous mammals provide a fascinating example of coevolution. Grasses evolved in the late Miocene, about 10 million years ago. Growing low to the ground, they were easy targets for plant-eating mammals, which evolved long snouts that could snip the plants as close to the ground as possible. In defense, grasses evolved to grow from the base of a leaf, not the tip, and thus can keep growing when a browsing mammal removes the tip. Grasses also evolved to incorporate crystalline silica into their cell walls. The response in mammals was the evolution of strong grinding teeth that are unaffected by the abrasive grasses. In a sense, grasses are even responsible for the evolution of long, strong legs in the herbivores. Exposed to predators on a grassy plain, a browsing mammal needed strong legs to run away fast when necessary.

Ancillary Support

The resources below can be used to support your teaching strategy for these two pages.

LM Comparing the Vision of Predators and Prey, #64
TR Explore: Hand to Hand

Visualizing Mammals

In doing further research, students may discover a more complex classification system for members of the class Mammalia. The subclass Prototheria includes various extinct mammals, while the subclass Theria includes all living mammals. The monotremes make up the infraclass Ornithodelphia, and the marsupials make up the infraclass Metatheria. The many orders of placental mammals are grouped in the infraclass Eutheria.

This scheme need not be introduced to students at this level, though in a discussion of the orders shown in this visual essay, emphasize that members of the orders Monotremata and Marsupalia are distinctly different from each other and from the members of the 12 other orders shown. In addition, another 10 percent of mammals are included in 5 orders not shown. These include relatively obscure animals, such as the aardvark and the pangolins.

Investigate

Research Give each student a copy of a real estate information sheet about a house for sale. Typically, such a sheet has a picture of the house as well as basic information, including dimensions, number of floors and rooms, special features, and so on. Then ask students to prepare a similar sheet, entitled Habitat for Sale, that contains specific information about a habitat for a wild mammal of their choosing. Each student will have to do library research on the mammal, copy or create a picture of the mammal's habitat, and include basic information about that habitat. After students have finished, they should trade sheets and try to guess which mammal would fit each habitat.

Visualizing Mammals

Of the approximately 4500 living species of mammals, approximately 90 percent are classified in the orders discussed on these two pages.

1 Monotremata
Reptilelike monotremes lay eggs, which contain enough yolk to nourish the developing embryo. Monotremes include this spiny, short-beaked echidna.

2 Marsupialia
Marsupial offspring develop in the external pouch of the female. This order includes this kangaroo, as well as wombats and koalas.

5 Edentata
Edentates either lack teeth or have small, simple teeth. They include this anteater, as well as armadillos and sloths.

7 Dermoptera
Often called flying lemurs, mammals of this order are native to Southeast Asia. They do not actually fly but glide on skin stretched between their legs.

8 Primates
Primates include apes and monkeys, such as this mandrill baboon. The most primitive living primates are small tree dwellers called lemurs. The most advanced primates are humans.

12 Chiroptera
This order includes bats. Most bats fly at night and navigate using a sophisticated echolocation system.

13 Lagomorpha
In many ways, rabbits and hares look and act like rodents. They use sharp front teeth to devour a wide range of plants.

TEACHER SUPPORT

Facts and Figures

- Mammals probably evolved from synapsid reptiles, such as *Dimetrodon* and *Cynognathus.*
- The blue whale, the largest animal ever to have lived, can grow to 30 meters in length with a mass of 200 metric tons.
- Generally, heart rate among mammals varies with body weight—the higher the weight, the lower the rate. Normal rates include: elephant, 30–40 beats/minute; man, 75 beats/minute; dog, 90–100 beats/minute; house mouse, 500 beats/minute.
- The gestation period in mammals varies from 16 days in some rodents to 650 days, or about 22 months, in the African elephant.
- Most mammals are colorblind. Primates can distinguish colors, as can most reptiles and birds.
- Both artiodactyls and perissodactyls have hoofs and thus are called ungulates, derived from the Latin word for hoof.

3 Rodentia

Rodents live all over the world and are the most numerous order of mammals. They include this beaver and rats and mice.

4 Carnivora

Carnivores—meaning meat-eaters—include this hyena, as well as dogs, cats, wolves, bears, weasels, and seals.

6 Artiodactyla

The name artiodactyl means "even-toed"—most artiodactyls have two functional toes on each foot. The order includes many grazing animals, such as cows, pigs, camels, antelopes, deer, hippopotamuses, and the giraffe shown here.

10 Cetacea

Cetaceans had terrestrial ancestors that adapted to a totally aquatic existence. This order includes whales and the dolphins shown here.

9 Perissodactyla

Perissodactyls, meaning "odd-toed," have a single functional toe on each foot. In many cases, the toe forms a hoof. The order includes horses, rhinoceroses, tapirs, and these zebras.

11 Sirenia

Sirenians include these manatees, also known as sea cows. These animals live in waters off Africa, South America, and Florida.

14 Proboscidea

Mammals with trunks survive today only in two endangered species, the Indian elephant and this African elephant.

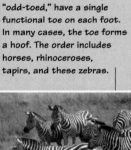

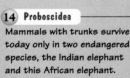

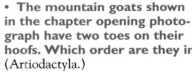

Ideas Through Images

After students have examined the photographs and read the captions in the visual essay, ask the following questions.

- **Which order contains mammals that are most like the earliest mammals? What evidence is there for your response?** (The order Monotremata contains mammals like the earliest mammals. The evidence is that monotremes are like reptiles in several ways, including having a cloaca and laying eggs, and mammals evolved from reptiles.)
- **If your friend said she saw a lagomorph yesterday, what would she be talking about?** (A rabbit or hare.)
- **Which two mammalian orders contain organisms that spend their lives in the ocean?** (Cetacea and Sirenia.)
- **Which two mammalian orders contain animals with hoofs?** (Artiodactyla and Perissodactyla.)
- **If you were told that you had one chance to name the order that includes a mystery mammal, and you were given no hints, which order would you be smart to name, and why?** (The best chance would be to name the order Rodentia because rodents make up the most numerous order of mammals.)
- **The mountain goats shown in the chapter opening photograph have two toes on their hoofs. Which order are they in?** (Artiodactyla.)
- **Which order includes the common opossum of North America?** (Marsupialia.)

TEACHER SUPPORT

Background Information

Mammals evolved on land, and the great majority are terrestrial animals. Exceptions are the aquatic mammals, such as manatees and whales. About 55 million years ago, some mammals returned to the sea. Over time, they adapted to that environment, as limbs became flippers and body hair mostly disappeared. They also gained the ability to dive to great depths and stay under water for long periods. A sperm whale, for instance, can remain submerged for 75 minutes, at a depth of up to 900 meters. A variety of adaptations allow for these dives, including the collapse of the lungs, a decrease of blood flow to some organs so that essential organs receive a uniform blood flow, and a decrease in heart rate. The decrease in heart rate is common in mammals that dive, including beavers, seals, and muskrats. The heart rate of a human whose face is submerged in water for 1 minute will decrease from 75 to 60 beats/minute.

MINI LAB Classifying

Teacher Note
- For time required and materials needed, see page 728b.

Answers to Analyze and Conclude

1. Students' responses will depend on which tracks they examined. Students might suggest that footprints could be useful in identifying the size of mammals.

2. Typically, students might group prints in terms of size, number of toes, or the spread of digits. Size would not be a useful characteristic in classification for biologists, but structure and shape would be.

Skills Trace
Classifying
- Focus p. 736
- Practice p. 736
- Assess p. 745

4 ASSESS

Quick Check

Have students identify the characteristics of the mammalian body plan as you call out each subsection head on pages 730–733.

Section Review 32–1

1. See page 729.
2. Mammals are classified into three groups based on the way in which they reproduce and develop.
3. Mammals that were active during the day evolved eyes that are sensitive to differences in color but are less sensitive in dim light. Mammals that were nocturnal evolved eyes that were sensitive to differences in light intensity, as well as sharp senses of smell, taste, and hearing.
4. A typical response might suggest that classification of mammals could be accomplished by examining the structure and shape of their footprints.

Skills Trace
Classifying
- Focus p. 736
- Practice p. 736
- Assess p. 745

MINI LAB .... Classifying ....

Step on It!

PROBLEM *How can you **classify** mammals from their footprints?*

PROCEDURE

1. Obtain a set of photographs of mammal footprints from your teacher. Study the relative sizes and shapes of the footprints. Record your observations.
2. Devise a classification scheme for the footprints. Infer the characteristics of each category.
3. Obtain a list of the mammals represented in the photographs from your teacher. Revise your classification scheme as necessary. Try to match each mammal with its footprint.

ANALYZE AND CONCLUDE

1. Which mammal was the easiest to identify from its footprint? Which was the most difficult? Discuss the usefulness of footprints in identifying a mammal's characteristics.
2. Compare the classification scheme you devised with the way in which biologists classify these mammals.

Marsupials

Members of the order Marsupialia once roamed in great numbers across what is now South America, Antarctica, Australia, and New Guinea. Today, only one species, the common opossum, survives in North America. The rest of the living marsupials—including kangaroos, wombats, koalas, and a number of other unusual species—live only in Australia and New Guinea. Unfortunately, most are in danger of extinction because of the human introduction of rats, sheep, rabbits, and other animals.

In marsupials, young are born alive, but at an incredibly early stage in development. When they are only a little more advanced than embryos, newborn marsupials crawl across their mother's belly and into a pouch. There, the babies attach to nipples and feed on their mother's milk as they develop.

Placental Mammals

Almost all mammals—including humans—are classified as placental mammals. In these mammals, the developing embryo attaches to the wall of the mother's uterus. There, tissues from both embryo and mother grow into a structure called the **placenta.** The placenta provides an interface for the circulatory systems of embryo and mother. Through it, oxygen and nutrients from the mother are exchanged for carbon dioxide and waste products from the embryo. The developing young are kept inside the mother—attached to the placenta—until they reach an advanced stage of development.

☑ *Checkpoint* What is a placental mammal? ❶

Section Review 32–1

1. **List** the characteristics of mammals.
2. **Explain** how mammals are classified.
3. **Critical Thinking—Making Inferences** Some early mammals were nocturnal, and others were active during the day. Compare the structures and adaptations of these two types of mammals.
4. **MINI LAB** How can you **classify** mammals from their footprints?

Learning Modality

Visual Learning Ask students to draw and label a basic body plan for mammals, similar to the basic body plans they studied in the sections on fishes, reptiles, amphibians, and birds in earlier chapters.

The Influence of Humans

GUIDE FOR READING

- **Identify** the common ancestor of dogs.
- **Discuss** how humans changed the Earth's animal populations.

WILDEBEEST, ANTELOPES, AND zebras once migrated in enormous herds across Africa. Bison roamed the great plains of North America in herds large enough to defy counting. These animals ate some plants and ignored others, churned the ground with their hooves and fertilized it with their dung. Today, however, humans have replaced wild plants with fields of corn, wheat, and other agricultural crops, and they have replaced wild animals with cows, goats, pigs, and sheep.

As human civilization has advanced, it has dramatically altered the populations of nearly every species it has encountered. In the future, decisions you make may further influence the course of life on Earth.

Domestication

As humans evolved, they learned to hunt and capture wild animals for food. Over time, however, they learned techniques of **domestication**—ways to tame, raise, and breed animals for human purposes.

What was the first domesticated animal? Evidence indicates that over 10,000 years ago, humans began interacting with *Canis lupus*, the gray wolf. **Today, descendants of the gray wolf include the many breeds of the first domesticated animal—*Canis familiaris*, the dog.**

Modern dogs look and act not like adult wolves, but like wolf puppies. A dog's head, for example, develops much like the head of a wolf puppy, but it does not change further to resemble an adult wolf. And typical dog activities—such as tail-wagging, face-licking, forming social bonds, and playing games—are all behaviors that juvenile wolves outgrow.

Figure 32–7 *Human actions have changed the population of almost every mammal species on Earth.* (a) *Up to 60 million bison once roamed North America. By 1900, however, bison had been hunted to near extinction!* (b) *The Earth is now home to huge numbers of domesticated animals, such as these pigs.* (c) CAREER TRACK *This animal breeder is holding the reins of a Père David's deer, a species that has been kept alive in captivity.*

TEACHER SUPPORT — Historical Perspective

The domestication of dogs probably first occurred 10,000 to 12,000 years ago. Archaeologists think that the animals attached themselves voluntarily to human encampments, attracted by the same thing that attracts wild animals to camps today—waste food and other refuse. Humans, in turn, found dogs useful for hunting and guarding, and the relationship between the two mammals was born. The next animals to be domesticated were sheep, goats, and cattle. Domestication served the purpose of providing a regular food supply to a growing human population. Domestic animals could also be selected for desirable characteristics, such as milk production in cows and a heavy coat in sheep. In studying ancient sites, archaeologists identify bones as "domestic" by comparing large numbers of remains. If there is little size or other variation, then researchers infer that the animals were bred for certain traits.

SECTION 32–2

The Influence of Humans

Performance Objectives

- Identify the gray wolf as the common ancestor of dogs.
- Describe the effect of human activities on some populations of animals.

1 ENGAGE

Ideas Through Images

Have students examine Figure 32–7, read the caption, and answer the following questions.

- **How is the life of a pig on a farm different from the life of a buffalo on the plains?** (A pig is kept in a pen or fenced field and raised for one purpose—to be butchered. A buffalo roams wherever its instincts take it and is part of the natural ecosystem.)
- **How does an animal breeder try to control the future generations of an animal?** (An animal breeder selects animals that have desirable traits and breeds only those animals. In that way, the breeder controls the traits in future generations of the animal.)

Checkpoint

1. A mammal in which the developing embryo attaches to the wall of the mother's uterus, where tissues from both mother and fetus grow into a structure called a placenta.

2 EXPLORE

Inquiry Activity
Classifying
A Mammalian World

Ask students in small groups to brainstorm for a list of everything they can think of in their lives that is in some way an animal product. Once they have this list, have them classify the entries on the basis of the type of animal it is. Have each group present its list to the class, and then discuss how many foods and other materials are made from mammal products.

3 TEACH

Connections

Distemper includes several infectious viral diseases that can affect dogs, raccoons, and many other species. Most dogs in the United States are vaccinated against this disease in the first few months of life, but populations in the wild serve as a reservoir for the virus.

Lyme disease, caused by the bacterium *Borrelia burgdorferi,* was named after the town of Lyme, Connecticut, where in 1977 the then-mysterious disease spread among the town's school children. A similar problem in the West is the spread of Rocky Mountain spotted fever, a bacterial disease also spread by ticks.

Answers to *Making the Connection*

Students' responses will depend on the area in which they live. In almost every case, humans have radically changed the environment, whether by building cities and suburbs or establishing farms or ranches. Some species have adapted to these changes, while some have disappeared.

Biology AND YOU Connections

Wildlife and Disease

The Masai Mara and Serengeti parks of East Africa are among the world's most spectacular wildlife reserves. But the important goal of these parks—to provide a safe home for endangered wildlife—is not always easy to achieve.

Male lions in the Serengeti National Park in Tanzania

In 1993, for example, many of the lions that lived in these parks became sick, eventually dying in violent convulsions. By the time the epidemic reached its peak, more than 1000 lions were dead.

What killed these lions? Tissues from infected lions revealed an unexpected culprit: canine distemper virus. This virus is most often found in dogs. But it mutated in recent years, adapting to infect other species. At the Masai Mara and Serengeti parks, the virus first infected dogs that lived near the parks. It then spread to wild hyenas that shared food with the dogs, then to the lions that shared food with the hyenas.

To stop this disease, international wildlife experts and veterinarians decided on an interesting course of action—they vaccinated all the domestic dogs in and around the parks. Today, the disease seems to be under control.

Deer, Ticks, and Lyme Disease

While some diseases have spread from domestic animals to wildlife, other diseases have spread in a different direction. In New England, for example, hunting and conservation laws stimulated the recovery of deer populations. But with increased deer came increased numbers of *Ixodes* ticks, parasites of deer. *Ixodes* ticks also bite humans, to whom they sometimes transmit the microorganisms that cause Lyme disease. This infection affects the skin, joints, and nerves.

Complex Relationships

The outbreaks of canine distemper in lions and Lyme disease in humans illustrate the complex relationships that can form among humans, domestic animals, and wildlife. We share the Earth with a huge variety of other forms of life. When we deliberately change one aspect of our relationship with other living things, we can easily change an unforeseen aspect of this relationship as well.

As deer populations have increased, so too have incidents of Lyme disease.

Making the Connection

What changes have humans made to the environment in your community? How has wildlife changed in response to these changes?

738 Chapter 32

TEACHER SUPPORT

Managing Classroom Diversity

TECH PREP STUDENTS

In recent decades, farms have been getting larger and larger, and many farm animals are being raised in conditions never contemplated by traditional farmers. Chickens and hogs, for instance, are being grown in pens where they never touch the ground and never live in a normal way. Ask students who plan careers in agriculture-related fields to investigate this phenomenon and write a paper that discusses the pros and cons of this kind of farming.

MULTICULTURAL STRATEGY

In the United States, one of the most common domesticated animals is the dog. But in some Asian cultures, letting a dog in the house would seem ridiculous. Some cultures even use dogs as food. Ask interested students to investigate what animals are domesticated as pets in different societies around the world.

Researchers hypothesize that dog breeders may have unintentionally selected for mutations in "master control genes." Such genes affect how other genes are switched on and off and thus control how an animal develops. Conceivably, mutations in master control genes could halt an animal's development at some point before adulthood.

Changing Life on Earth

In the centuries that followed the domestication of the dog, humans learned to domesticate goats, sheep, camels, horses, and other familiar animals. Humans also learned to make new and better weapons, thus becoming more efficient at hunting wild animals. These abilities undoubtedly helped human communities and civilizations to develop.

However, the success of humans has dramatically altered the populations of the Earth's animals. **By overhunting and by using huge tracts of land for farming and ranching, humans have greatly reduced the populations of many species of wildlife—including most large mammals.**

In the 1800s, for example, the huge buffalo herds of the Great Plains of the United States were hunted to near extinction. Today, overhunting in many countries is threatening elephants, rhinoceroses, tigers, and many other animals. In addition, humans typically claim large lands for farming or ranching wherever they settle, often by draining swamps, chopping down rain forests, or destroying other natural ecosystems.

To protect wildlife, people in many countries have passed special laws, set aside tracts of land as wildlife reserves, and tried to reintroduce some species into their former habitats. However, humans have made the Earth a far different place from the days when wild animals roamed it freely. Buffaloes, elephants, gazelles, and lions may play roles in nature in the future, but those roles are sure to differ from their roles of the past.

Figure 32–9 (a) *Researchers have identified* Canis lupus, *the gray wolf, as the common ancestor of all dogs.* (b) *Today, breeders have created dogs of all sorts of shapes, sizes, and colors.*

Section Review 32–2

1. **Identify** the common ancestor of dogs.
2. **Discuss** how humans have changed the Earth's ecosystems.
3. **BRANCHING OUT ACTIVITY** In the United States and elsewhere, zoos and wildlife conservation societies run programs to maximize the biodiversity of many species in their care. **Research** the effects of these programs.

Discussion

Begin a discussion of how humans have affected animal populations by asking students to think about what animals populated their area before humans lived there, especially in modern times. Most students will know about the destruction of the buffalo herds in the late nineteenth century. Point out that similar destruction is occurring throughout the world, especially where human populations are growing rapidly and land is being cleared for agricultural use.

4 ASSESS

Quick Check

Ask students to make a flowchart that shows how humans could affect the animal populations of an area.

Section Review 32-2

1. The gray wolf.
2. By overhunting and by using huge tracts of land for farming and ranching, humans have greatly reduced the populations of many species of wildlife, including most large mammals. Humans have also drained swamps, chopped down rain forests, and destroyed other natural ecosystems.
3. Among these efforts are programs such as the introduction of wolves into Montana and the establishment of protected areas in Africa. Encourage students both to use library resources and to contact local conservation organizations for information about any programs in the local region.

Learning Modality

Auditory Learning Ask students to explain orally how animal populations might be affected by the building of a city, the draining of a swamp, the establishment of a farm, or the construction of a housing development.

Ancillary Support

The resources below can be used to support your teaching strategy for these two pages.

TR Writing in Biology: Take Me Home!
Enrich: Hunted to Extinction?
BL Inquiry Activity: Man's Best Friend

Chapter 32

Laboratory Investigation

Investigating Mammalian Skulls

Before the Lab

1. Obtain mammalian skulls from a biological supply company. You could obtain several different kinds of mammalian skulls so that pairs of students can compare findings at the conclusion of the lab.
2. You might want to provide students with a taxonomic key to mammalian skulls, which can be found in a number of books. An excellent source is *Handbook to the Orders and Families of Living Mammals* by Timothy E. Lawlor.
3. Provide some kinds of materials that students can use to cover the openings to the braincase, as indicated in step 5. This might best be done by using tape and plastic wrap.

Pre-Lab Discussion

Have students read the entire procedure for this investigation. Then ask students the following questions.

What is the purpose of this investigation? (To infer characteristics of a mammal by studying its skull.)

What measurements will you be making in this investigation? (Students will make measurements of the skull and the snout, find the mass, and determine the volume.)

What kinds of mammals have large canine teeth? (Carnivores.)

What kinds of mammals have a gap between the incisors and the premolars? (Rodents, horses, deer, and sheep.)

Skills Development

Students will use these skills while completing the laboratory investigation: observing, measuring, communicating, and inferring.

Laboratory Investigation

Investigating Mammalian Skulls

Paleontologists have inferred all sorts of information about ancient animals from the bones they left behind. One of the most useful bones to study is the skull. The skull provides clues about an animal's feeding habits, the way it used its senses, and its relative intelligence. In this investigation, you will explore some of the ways in which this information can be revealed.

Problem

What can you **infer** about a mammal by studying its skull?

Materials (per group)

- mammal skull
- metric ruler
- balance
- uncooked rice
- graduated cylinder

Procedure

1. **Working with a partner, measure the overall dimensions of the skull in centimeters. Use the balance to measure the mass of the skull in grams. Record this information.**
2. **Locate the lower jaw, which is called the mandible. The rest of the skull is called the cranium, and it is formed by several bones fused together. Study the lines on top of the cranium, which indicate where bones joined. The older the animal, the more fused the bones will be.**
3. **Holding the skull on its side, measure the length and width of the snout. Look for any indication of antlers or horns.**
4. **Locate the large opening at the bottom of the skull, which is where the skull attached to the vertebral column. The farther back the opening, the more forward the skull projected from the body. In humans and some primates, the opening is close to the middle of the skull. Thus, a primate's head is balanced when it stands upright. Predict whether your specimen is from a primate.**

Safety Tip

Advise students to be careful when handling the skull. A dropped skull can easily crack or break apart, making a thorough examination impossible.

5. **The brain is stored in the braincase, the large cavity just beneath the top of the skull. Cover all openings to the braincase except the large one at the bottom. Fill the braincase with rice, then empty the rice into a graduated cylinder. Measure and record its volume.**

6. **Study any teeth present in the skull. Identify the incisors, which are sharp, flat teeth located in front of the mouth. Next to the incisors are rounded canine teeth. And in back of the mouth are premolars and molars. Carnivores have large canine teeth, whereas rodents have large incisors. In addition, a gap between the incisors and premolars indicates that it is the skull of a rodent, horse, deer, or sheep. Study the arrangement of teeth in your specimen, then record your observations.**

7. **Study the shape and structure of the molars. Broad, flat molars were used for chewing plant matter, whereas ridges on these teeth indicate they were used for tearing meat. Infer which type of food the animal ate.**

8. **Study the eye sockets of the skull. Determine whether the animal's eyes pointed forward or lay on either side of the head.**

Observations

1. Sketch and describe the general shape of the skull and the shape of the braincase. Include the measurements of the skull on the drawing.
2. Label all the parts of the skull that you can identify.

Analysis and Conclusions

1. From your data and observations, what can you infer about the age of your specimen?
2. What can you infer about the animal's diet?
3. Classify the animal as best you can. Describe the evidence that supports this classification.

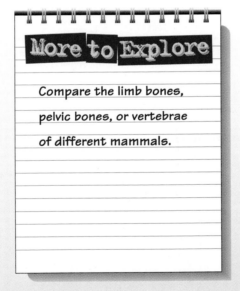

4. Describe any evidence that does not support how you classified the animal. What additional information about the skull would help you to classify it?
5. With your classmates, compare the braincase volumes of the different skulls you investigated. Which skull had the greatest braincase volume? The smallest braincase volume? How useful is braincase volume in predicting the intelligence of an animal?

More to Explore

Compare the limb bones, pelvic bones, or vertebrae of different mammals.

Answers to

Analysis and Conclusions

1. A typical response will mention the lines on the top of the cranium, interpreting the specimen's age by how fused those bones appear.
2. Students should be able to infer something about the diet from the type and number of teeth. A typical response might suggest that the specimen's diet was mostly plants if the skull contains mostly large molars, or that the specimen's diet was mostly meat if the skull contains large canines.
3. Typically, students will base their classification on the size and shape of the skull, the placement of the bottom opening, the kind of teeth present and the shape and organization of those teeth, and the location of the eye sockets.
4. A typical response might mention any specific feature of the skull as not supporting the classification. Additional information that could help in identification might include detailed descriptions of skulls and photographs of different kinds of skulls for comparison.
5. To answer this question, pairs should exchange information about the skull each examined, or pairs could contribute to a master table on the board. Some students might suggest that braincase volume could be useful in predicting intelligence. Others might suggest that, for example, dogs seem more intelligent than cows, and therefore braincase size does not correlate directly with intelligence.

More to Explore

In examining such parts of different mammals, students should make measurements of all parts of a specimen and write detailed descriptions. Then, in comparing bones from different mammals, they should infer what the differences say about the diet and habits of the mammals studied.

Teaching Strategies

1. Advise pairs that before examining the skull they should have a plan for systematically recording data. They might create a table for that purpose or simply make a list of headings on paper for each type of data they will gather.
2. Demonstrate how to cover all the openings of the braincase except the one at the bottom. Emphasize to students that these coverings must be secure, or they will be cleaning up spilled rice.
3. Orally review the kinds of teeth found in a mammalian skull. Use the drawings in Figure 32–3 or some other visual to clarify the definitions of incisors, canine teeth, premolars, and molars.

Answers to

Observations

1. Students' sketches will depend on the skulls they examine. All sketches should include several measurements of the skull and snout.
2. On their sketches, students should include labels for mandible, cranium, snout, braincase, eye sockets, specific types of teeth, and other structures students identify.

CHAPTER 32

Study Guide

Review Strategy

Divide the class into four or five groups, and give each group a list of 10–15 mammals they have studied or discussed in relation to this chapter. Give each group a different list; only the members of a group should know the names on its list. Then challenge groups to write detailed descriptions of the mammals on their lists. Once the descriptions have been completed, have groups compete with one another in a game of Name That Mammal. To begin, have Group 1 read a description. Group 2 has the first chance to answer by naming the correct mammal. If that group answers incorrectly, the next group has a chance. After the question is answered, Group 2 asks Group 3 a question, and so on. When all descriptions have been read, the group with the most correct answers is the winner.

Recalling Main Ideas

1. a
2. c
3. d
4. b
5. b
6. d
7. c
8. d

Study Guide

Summarizing Key Concepts

The key concepts in each section of this chapter are listed below to help you review the chapter content. Make sure you understand each concept and its relationship to other concepts and to the theme of this chapter.

32–1 Characteristics of Mammals

- Mammals are endotherms, have external body hair, and have a layer of fat beneath the skin. Female mammals produce milk to feed their offspring.
- To help them eat great quantities of food, mammals evolved specialized jaws and interlocking teeth. Because digestive enzymes can quickly break down meat, carnivores have a relatively short intestine. Because plant matter takes more time to digest, herbivores have a longer intestine.
- Like birds, mammals have a double-loop circulatory system powered by a four-chambered heart. Mammals use a diaphragm to expand and contract the chest cavity, which forces air in and out of the lungs.
- Unlike the brains of other animals, a mammal's brain has a well-developed cerebral cortex—the center of thinking and other complex behaviors.
- Nocturnal mammals must see in dim light, which means their eyes adapted for low-light vision. They also have well-developed senses of hearing, taste, and smell. Because humans evolved from animals active during the day, they evolved excellent color vision, but other senses are relatively less developed.
- Most mammals reproduce in the same way that humans do. The male deposits sperm inside the reproductive tract of the female, where fertilization occurs.
- Monotremes, such as the duck-billed platypus and echidna, seem to be part reptile and part mammal. Marsupials include kangaroos, wombats, and koalas. Most mammals are placental mammals—a placenta joins developing offspring with the mother.

32–2 The Influence of Humans

- The descendants of the gray wolf include the many breeds of the first domesticated animal—*Canis familiaris,* the dog.
- By overhunting and by using huge tracts of land for farming and ranching, humans have greatly reduced the populations of many species of wildlife—including most large mammals.

Reviewing Key Terms

Review the following vocabulary terms and their meaning. Then use each term in a complete sentence.

32–1 Characteristics of Mammals

molar
premolar
diaphragm
kidney
placenta

32–2 The Influence of Humans

domestication

Inquiry-Based Strategy

Divide the class into groups of two or three and present the following question: What is a typical body plan and a typical environment for a member of each order of mammals? Assign each group one of the orders briefly described in the visual essay on pages 734–735. Have each group answer the question by doing library research and creating a poster that includes a labeled illustration of a representative of its assigned mammalian order and general facts about the order. Tell students that their posters should be informative, factually correct, and artistically pleasing.

Recalling Main Ideas

Choose the letter of the answer that best completes the statement or answers the question.

1. Mammals are classified as endotherms because they
   a. conserve body heat.
   b. lose body heat.
   c. produce milk for offspring.
   d. are ovoviviparous.
2. In mammals, the diaphragm is used to
   a. move from place to place.
   b. encase the heart.
   c. help move air in and out of the lungs.
   d. move food through the digestive tract.
3. Compared with other vertebrate brains, the primate brain contains a proportionately larger
   a. medulla oblongata. c. cerebellum.
   b. hindbrain. d. cerebral cortex.
4. Compared with nocturnal animals, animals that are active during the daytime are more sensitive to
   a. low-intensity light. c. sounds.
   b. colors. d. smells.
5. Mammals that lay eggs and lack a placenta are classified in the order
   a. Dermoptera. c. Edentata.
   b. Monotremata. d. Marsupialia.
6. Kangaroos, wombats, and koalas are members of the order
   a. Chiroptera. c. Rodentia.
   b. Monotremata. d. Marsupialia.
7. Which of these mammal classifications contains the most species?
   a. monotremes c. placental mammals
   b. marsupials d. rodents
8. The first domesticated animals were
   a. sheep. c. horses.
   b. rabbits. d. dogs.

Putting It All Together

Using the information on pages xxx to xxxi, complete the following concept map.

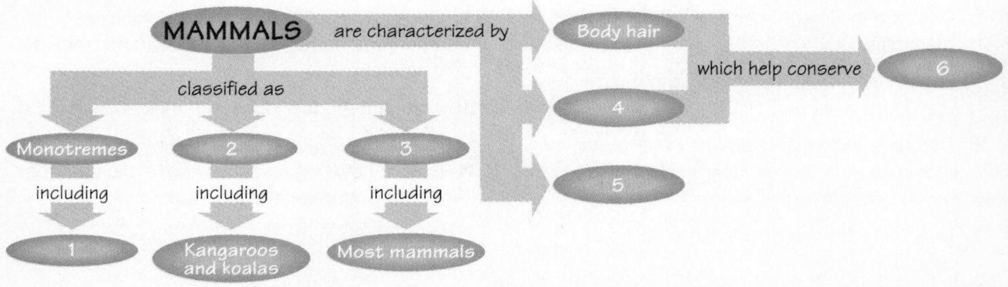

Putting It All Together

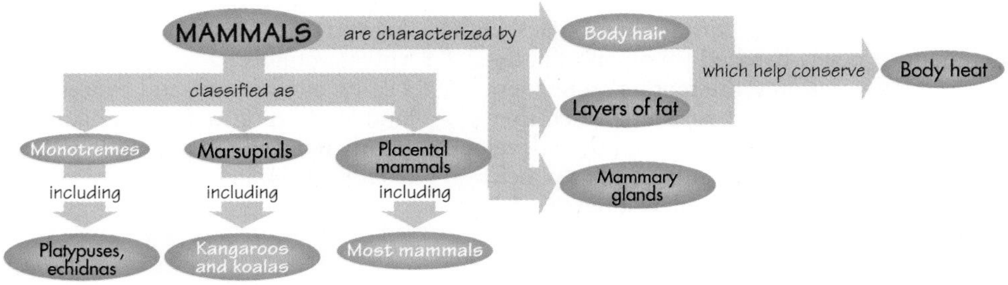

Assessment

Reviewing What You Learned

1. Mammals are endotherms, have external body hair, and have a layer of fat beneath the skin. Female mammals produce milk to feed their offspring.
2. Mammals conserve body heat with external body hair and a layer of fat beneath the skin.
3. Mammals must take in more food because they are endotherms and have a higher metabolic rate than reptiles and amphibians.
4. The diaphragm is a powerful muscle that pulls the bottom of the chest cavity downward, which increases its volume and causes air to enter the lungs.
5. The mammalian kidney's main function is to filter urea from the blood, which it combines with other waste products to form urine.
6. A mammal's brain differs from the brains of other animals because of its well-developed cerebral cortex.
7. The backbone flexes vertically as well as from side to side, allowing for a bouncing, leaping stride; shoulder and pelvic girdles also are streamlined and flexible, permitting both front and hind limbs to move in a great variety of ways.
8. In marsupials, the young are born when they are little more advanced than embryos, and then they develop in the mother's pouch.
9. In monotremes, both the reproductive system and the urinary system open into a cloaca, the female lays eggs outside the body, and the young are nourished on milk that trickles from pores onto the mother's abdomen.
10. Placental mammals are those in which the developing embryo attaches to the wall of the mother's uterus, where tissues from both embryo and mother grow into a placenta.
11. Students might list any three of these orders: Edentata, Dermoptera, Primates, Chiroptera, Lagomorpha, Rodentia, Carnivora, Artiodactyla, Cetacea, Perissodactyla, Sirenia, Proboscidea.
12. Students might list any three common domesticated animals, including dog, cat, cow, pig, sheep, horse, and goat.

Assessment (continued)

13. A typical response might mention whales, buffalos, elephants, rhinoceroses, or tigers.

Expanding the Concepts

1. A typical response will mention changes in the jaw, the backbone, the limbs and limb girdles, the nervous system, the reproductive system, and the circulatory system.
2. These characteristics include a simpler jaw than reptiles', complex teeth, a unique set of bones in the middle ear, and several features of the limb bones, limb girdles, and the vertebral column.
3. With interlocking teeth, mammals can crush, slice, or tear food quickly, thoroughly, and efficiently. This allows for the consumption of more food than an organism could eat with simpler teeth, which is necessary to maintain a high rate of metabolism.
4. Mammalian kidneys cannot excrete salt without eliminating water at the same time. Thus, to eliminate the salt consumed in sea water, a mammal would also have to excrete the water, and it then would not have enough water to stay alive.
5. Sight in nocturnal mammals is adapted to low-light vision and is sensitive to differences in light intensity but not to differences in color, which is more important to mammals that are active during the day. Nocturnal animals also benefit from sharp senses of smell, taste, and hearing.
6. Monotremes resemble reptiles in that both have a cloaca, into which the reproductive and urinary systems open, and both lay eggs that hatch outside the body.
7. The young of most mammals are kept inside the mother—attached to the placenta—until they reach an advanced stage of development. Most newborn young can stand up and move around on their own, but they are protected and nourished with milk from the mother.
8. Inside the mammalian ear, the bones of the middle ear form a delicate mechanism that transfers vibrations from the eardrum to the inner ear. There, sensory cells are stimulated in an organ called the cochlea, allowing the brain to interpret the vibrations as sounds.
9. Monotremes lay eggs outside their bodies, and then nourish newly hatched young on milk that trickles from pores onto the mother's abdomen. Marsupials give birth to their young when they are little more than embryos, which then develop and feed on their mother's milk inside a pouch. Placental mammals keep the developing young inside the mother until they reach an advanced stage of development. After birth, the young feed on milk produced in the female's mammary glands.
10. Modern dogs look and act not like adult wolves, but like wolf puppies. The dog's head remains like the head of a wolf puppy, and typical dog activities are all behaviors that juvenile wolves outgrow.
11. By overhunting and by using huge tracts of land for farming and ranching, humans have greatly reduced the populations of many species of wildlife, including most large mammals.

Assessment

Reviewing What You Learned

Answer each of the following in a complete sentence.

1. How do mammals differ from other vertebrates?
2. How do mammals conserve their body heat?
3. Why must mammals take in and digest a greater amount of food than reptiles or amphibians do?
4. What is the diaphragm?
5. What is the function of a mammal's kidneys?
6. Compare the mammal's brain with the brains of other vertebrates.
7. How did adaptations of the backbone, shoulder, and pelvic girdle affect the way mammals move?
8. What distinguishes marsupials from other mammals?
9. How do monotremes differ from other mammals?
10. What are the placental mammals?
11. List three orders of placental mammals.
12. List three examples of domesticated animals.
13. Give an example of a mammal that humans have overhunted.

Expanding the Concepts

Discuss each of the following in a brief paragraph.

1. Compare a mammal's body plan with the body plans of reptiles.
2. Discuss the characteristics that paleontologists use to identify mammalian bones and fossils.
3. Describe the importance of interlocking teeth to mammals.
4. Explain why most mammals cannot survive by drinking sea water.
5. Compare the sensory organs in nocturnal mammals with those in mammals that are active during the day.
6. Describe the ways in which monotremes resemble reptiles.
7. Mammals typically produce fewer offspring than other vertebrates do. Discuss the adaptations that help mammalian offspring survive.
8. Describe the structure of a mammal's ear.
9. Compare reproduction and development among monotremes, marsupials, and placental mammals.
10. Compare modern dogs with their ancestor, the gray wolf.
11. Explain how human actions have changed the animal populations of the Earth.

744 Chapter 32

Extending Your Thinking

Use the skills you have developed in this chapter to answer the following.

1. **Applying concepts** Mammalian carnivores tend to eat large meals separated by long intervals of time, whereas herbivores tend to eat continuously throughout their waking hours. Describe how these behaviors are supported by the digestive systems of these animals.
2. **Inferring** Small mammals have a greater surface-to-volume ratio than large mammals have. Infer how this difference affects their metabolic rates.
3. **Classifying** Study the mammal shown in the photograph on the opposite page. To which order does this mammal belong? Explain your answer.
4. **Making predictions** In the 1800s, human females typically gave birth to many more offspring than they do today. Many of these babies did not survive infancy. Predict what might happen to the human birth rate in the future.
5. **Using the writing process** Research how the mammal populations where you live have changed over the past few hundred years. Present your findings in a report or incorporate them into a play, short story, or poem.

Applying Your Skills

Mammal Inventory

Mammals can populate almost any habitat, including the one where you live. In this activity, you'll learn more about the roles that mammals play in your community.

1. Select an area the size of a city block or a neighborhood park. Draw a map of this area and describe how the area is used.
2. With a partner, walk through the area you selected. Record the names of any mammals you observe and note their activities. If you cannot identify an animal, draw a rough sketch of it and list its characteristics. Do not approach any of the animals.
3. Repeat step 2 at least two times. Make your walks at different times of the day.
4. If necessary, consult field guides or other references to identify an animal.
5. Prepare a report on the mammals that live in the area you studied. Describe the roles that these mammals play.

• GOING FURTHER •

6. Perform this activity in a different location. Compare the mammal populations in the two areas you studied.

Extending Your Thinking

1. A carnivore's digestive system has a short intestine and can quickly digest its food. The resources of the body, then, are not concentrated on digestion as the carnivore begins to hunt for more food. A herbivore has a long intestine, which takes a long time to digest food. Thus, it is adapted to grazing and staying in one small area all day.
2. A greater surface-to-volume ratio means a relatively greater loss of energy to the environment. Therefore, a small mammal has to have a greater metabolic rate than a large mammal in order to maintain its body temperature.
3. Students should observe that the mammal shown—a leopard—has long, sharp canine teeth, which indicates that it is a meat-eating mammal and a member of Carnivora.

Skills Trace
Classifying

- Focus p. 736
- Practice p. 736
- Assess p. 745

4. Most students will predict that the birth rate will drop in the future as medical practices improve and living standards rise, allowing more babies to survive.
5. Most students should find through their research that there were once more predators in the area than there are now. They also may find that there are more of some kinds of mammals, including deer. Students should reflect these findings in a creative play, short story, or poem.

Applying Your Skills

Teacher Notes

- Provide students access to several mammal or animal guides.
- After pairs of students have observed an area for the first time, review their methods and results. Each pair should have a map of the area described. And each pair should have identified at least five or six mammals, and listed their characteristics.

Scoring Rubric

4 Response is thorough, accurate, and creative; shows an in-depth understanding of science skills, procedures, and concepts.

3 Response is complete, mostly accurate, and original; shows a satisfactory understanding of science skills, procedures, and concepts.

2 Response is mostly complete but includes some inaccuracies; shows an adequate understanding of science skills, procedures, and concepts.

1 Response is only partially complete and has many inaccuracies; shows an incomplete understanding of science skills, procedures, and concepts.

0 Response is mostly incomplete and/or inaccurate; shows a lack of understanding of science skills, procedures, and concepts.

Chapter 33 Animal Behavior

Content Management	Student Edition Activities
■ Section 33–1 Behaviors and Societies, pp. 747–753 Perception and Response Behavior Animal Societies	**MINI LAB:** Pieces of the Puzzle, p. 751 **Laboratory Investigation:** Investigating the Instinctive Behaviors of Planarians, pp. 756–757
◆ BRANCHING OUT • In Depth Section 33–2 Insect and Primate Societies, pp. 754–755 Ant Societies Primate Societies	

■ This section covers all the necessary content and concepts for an enriched course in biology.
◆ This section covers content and concepts that are either applications or extensions of the enriched material.

Integration Strategies

SE Chemistry, p. 748

Assessment Strategies

SE Chapter Review, pp. 758–761
TR Section Reviews
Chapter Test
BL Chapter Review
Practice Test
CTB Chapter 33 Test

Tech Prep

A teaching strategy appropriate for students who are in technical/vocational programs or who are considering post-secondary technical education can be found on the following **TE** page: 749.

Meeting the Standards

Sections 33–1 and 33–2 cover all four of the content standards under **The Behavior of Organisms** as described on page 187 of The National Science Education Standards.

Chapter Planning Guide

Teacher's Edition Activities	Other Activities	Media and Technology
Chapter Discovery Learning Activity, p. 746 **Inquiry Activity:** Singing My Own Special Song, p. 747 **Inquiry Activity:** New to Normal, p. 748 **Investigate:** Cooperative Learning, p. 752	**LM** Observing the Behavior of Fish, #65 Observing the Behavior of Crickets, #66 **TR** **Explore:** What Does Your Nose Know? **BL** **Inquiry Activity:** Time Off for Good Behavior	
Investigate: Long-Term Project, p. 754	**TR** **Writing in Biology:** Communication **Enrich:** Mixed-Up Mammal **BL** **Inquiry Activity:** Not So Secret Societies	

KEY: **SE** Student Edition **TE** Teacher's Edition **LM** Laboratory Manual **TR** Teaching Resources
BL BioLog **TB** Transparency Box **CTB** Computer Test Bank

Materials List

TE Inquiry Activity: New to Normal, p. 748 (10 minutes each day for a week); established aquarium containing fishes, small object such as a marble or piece of metal.
SE MINI LAB: Pieces of the Puzzle, p. 751 (30 minutes); unlined 5x8-inch index card, ruler, scissors.
TE Investigate: Cooperative Learning, p. 752 (several hours over 3 days); poster board and art materials.

TE Investigate: Long-Term Project, p. 754 (2–3 hours for setup and periodic observation thereafter); 2 pieces of plexiglass, wooden base, wooden frame, wood screws, clean soil, garden trowel, jar, honey, ant food.

CHAPTER 33

Animal Behavior

Introducing the Chapter

. . . In Pictures

Meerkats, *Suricata suricata*, are a species of mongoose that live on the semiarid plains of southwestern Africa. These rabbit-sized mammals depend on cooperation within the colony to survive in such a harsh environment. The meerkats shown are watching for predators. These animals are extremely sociable.

- **What do animals that live in groups accomplish that individuals could not accomplish alone?** (A typical response might mention protection from predators or cooperation in obtaining food.)
- **Do you think the behavior shown here by meerkats is determined by their genes or learned from their parents?** (Some students might suggest that most behaviors in animals are genetically determined. Others might argue that such complex behaviors as this must be learned.)

Tell students that in this chapter they will explore both inborn and learned behaviors in animals.

Teaching Strategy

In the first section of this chapter, students will learn about different types of animal behaviors and the purpose of each. The BRANCHING OUT section gives an in-depth look at two kinds of animal societies, ant societies and primate societies.

CHAPTER 33

Animal Behavior

FOCUSING THE CHAPTER
THEME: Systems and Interactions

33–1 Behaviors and Societies
- Discuss different animal behaviors.

BRANCHING OUT *In Depth*
33–2 Insect and Primate Societies
- Compare the societies that insects and primates form.

LABORATORY INVESTIGATION
- Design an experiment to determine the instinctive behaviors of a planarian.

Biology and Your World

BIO JOURNAL

Look at the meerkats shown in the photograph on this page. In your journal, describe the meerkats' behavior. What purpose do you think this behavior serves?

Meerkats emerging from their den

746 Chapter 33

BIO JOURNAL

The Bio Journal topic can be used to stimulate classroom discussion about behaviors that help the group. Ask students to list behaviors that have proved beneficial for groups in which they have been members. Instruct students to keep their entries in their portfolios.

TEACHER SUPPORT — Chapter Discovery Learning Activity

DOG BEHAVIOR

Most students have some familiarity with dogs, and many have raised dogs from puppies. Using this experience, ask small groups to brainstorm for a list of 20 behaviors that are common to dogs, such as barking at a stranger, tail wagging when excited, and so on. Once the list is made, ask group members to discuss the entries, classifying each as either inborn or learned as the dog grows and matures. After groups have classified the entries on their lists, have a member of each group read aloud to the class all behaviors classified as inborn. Then discuss any disagreements among groups. Finally, ask students whether they think some of these behaviors could be a combination of genetics and learning.

Behaviors and Societies

GUIDE FOR READING

- **Explain** the purpose of animal behaviors and **identify** different types of behaviors.
- **Explain** why animals live in societies.

MINI LAB

- **Classify** a learned behavior.

OF THE SIX KINGDOMS OF LIFE on Earth, the animals have evolved the most complex set of behaviors. From earthworms that emerge above ground after rainstorms to peacocks that strut their colorful tail feathers to attract a mate to humans who constantly ask questions to learn about the world around them, animals interact with their environment in an impressive and diverse set of ways. To truly understand animals, you need to understand why they behave in the ways they do.

Perception and Response

Why do animals behave in certain ways? The answers begin with their sense organs, the organs that allow animals to perceive the world around them.

We humans know the world only through our five senses—vision, smell, touch, taste, and feel—each of which operates within certain limits. However, these limits differ in other animals. A fly on your pant leg, for example, can see colors in your clothes that you cannot see, use its legs to taste soda you spilled

Figure 33–1 *Animals perceive and respond to stimuli in vastly different ways—some of which are quite amazing. (a) A spider has a relatively simple brain, yet it is able to build a complex, intricate web. (b) The spotted bowerbird needs no special training to build its unusual nest. (c) In the compound eyes of this black fly, thousands of lenses each form individual images (magnification: 30X). This creates a very different view of the world from the one your eyes provide.*

SECTION 33–1

Behaviors and Societies

Performance Objectives

- Classify animal behaviors and describe the purpose of each.
- Discuss why animals live together in groups.

Mini Lab Skill: Classifying
Laboratory Investigation Skill: Designing an experiment

1 ENGAGE

Inquiry Activity

Designing an Experiment

Singing My Own Special Song

Ask groups of students to collaborate in designing an experiment that would test this hypothesis: Songbirds are not born knowing their unique songs but must learn them as they mature. Tell groups that experiments should include a control and identify a variable being tested. Once groups have designed their experiments, discuss them as a class.

Ideas Through Images

Have students examine Figure 33–1, read the caption, and answer the following questions.

- **Why does a spider build a web?** (To catch insects to eat.)
- **How is building a web an adaptation just like the compound eye of a black fly?** (Both are ways in which an animal has evolved to survive.)

TEACHER SUPPORT

Background Information

The observation of animal behavior is nothing new. Knowing about the habits of animals has been essential to human survival and prosperity. But only relatively recently have scientists systematically studied animal behavior. There are a number of different approaches to such study. Ethologists concentrate on observing the behavior of animals in their natural environments. Konrad Lorenz and Niko Tinbergen were famous ethologists; primate observers Dian Fossey and Jane Goodall could also be called ethologists. Comparative psychologists concentrate on the genetic, hormonal, and neural basis of animal behavior. Behavioral ecologists concentrate on predator-prey interactions, habitat selection, and other behaviors associated with ecology. Sociobiologists concentrate on the study of the evolution of social behavior.

Ancillary Support

The resource below can be used to support your teaching strategy for these two pages.

TR Explore: What Does Your Nose Know?

2 EXPLORE

Inquiry Activity

Observing

New to Normal

Ask students how they think fishes would react to a new object in their environment and how long they would take to get used to that object. Have groups of students use an established classroom aquarium to investigate that question. At the same time each day for a week, they should drop a small object into the aquarium, such as a marble or small piece of metal. Students should then observe and take notes about the behavior of the fishes. After 10 minutes each day, the object should be removed. Students should note both the exploratory behavior at first, and then the habituation to the object after several days.

3 TEACH

Ideas Through Images

Have students examine Figure 33–2, read the caption, and answer the following questions.

- **What stimulus causes a tick to drop onto a passing mammal?** (The odor of butyric acid, a compound that is part of mammalian sweat.)
- **How does a tick learn this behavior?** (It does not learn it. This behavior is an instinct, a genetically programmed behavior.)
- **Do humans have instincts?** (Yes, humans have instincts, but with their complex nervous system they learn most of their behaviors.)

INTEGRATING CHEMISTRY

The chemical formula for butyric acid is C_3H_7COOH. One of the properties of this fatty acid is a strong, disagreeable odor, the odor of rancid butter.

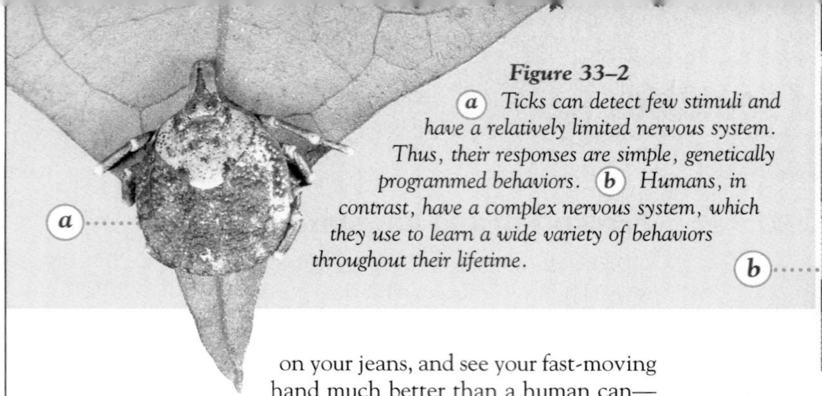

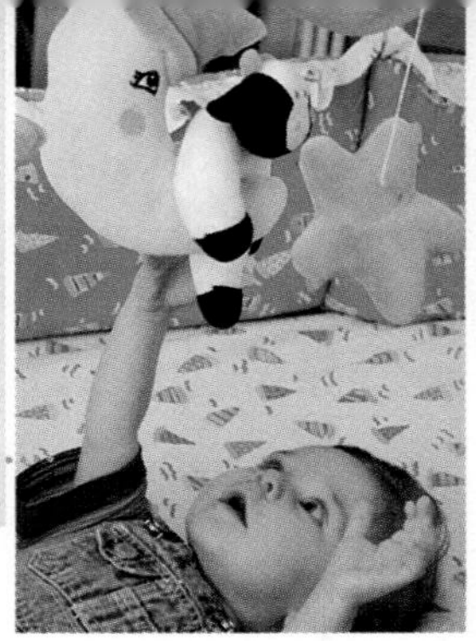

Figure 33–2 *(a) Ticks can detect few stimuli and have a relatively limited nervous system. Thus, their responses are simple, genetically programmed behaviors. (b) Humans, in contrast, have a complex nervous system, which they use to learn a wide variety of behaviors throughout their lifetime.*

on your jeans, and see your fast-moving hand much better than a human can—which is why flies are so hard to swat! Meanwhile, a dog sitting at your feet recognizes you by your smell—even if you've taken a shower—and hears your parents walking down the hall long before you can. On the other hand, the dog probably can't detect the differences in the colors of the pencils on your desk.

Among the animal species, sensory abilities differ in these sorts of ways. Because of these differences, animals respond to their environment in different ways, too.

Behavior

Biologists use the word **behavior** to describe an animal's response to its environment. Obviously, different animal species behave very differently, as shown in ***Figure 33–1*** on page 747.

Despite the enormous differences among the ways in which animals behave, the typical reasons for their behavior are very similar. **All animals have evolved behaviors that help them survive. Some behaviors are instinctive, or inborn in the animal, and others are learned as the animal develops.**

INTEGRATING CHEMISTRY

What is the chemical formula for butyric acid? What are its properties?

Instincts

Some behaviors are genetically programmed into every member of a species. These behaviors are often called innate behaviors, or **instincts.** The simplest instincts are fixed and cannot be changed.

For example, consider a female tick waiting on a blade of grass. This tick may have lived 20 years or longer without ever encountering the odor of butyric acid, a compound that is part of mammalian sweat. When the tick does "smell" this compound, however, it lets go of the grass and—if it's lucky—drops onto a passing mammal, such as a mouse. It then follows temperature cues to a place where blood is near the surface. After sinking its mouthparts into the mouse's skin, the tick drinks the blood until it is full. At that point, it lets go once again, drops to the ground, lays its eggs, and dies.

This sequence of behaviors is genetically programmed into the tick's nervous system. Instincts control most of the behaviors of ticks and most other invertebrates.

☑ *Checkpoint* What are instincts? 1

Advantages of Instincts

Instincts are inflexible behaviors that may often be a drawback for an animal. However, instincts also provide enormous advantages. They permit animals to perform tasks essential to their survival, with no learning period required.

All sorts of animals rely on instinctive behaviors, including large animals with a complex nervous system. A female graylag goose, for example, will instinctively retrieve an egg that rolls out of its nest. Spiders build webs instinctively, birds construct nests without ever having done so before, and newborn mammals—from mice to humans—will instinctively suckle at their mother's breast.

TEACHER SUPPORT

Ecology Note

The inflexibility of instinctive behavior is both its blessing and its curse. The blessing is that a behavior is done perfectly the first time, with no learning required. Such behavior may be complex and is often essential for the survival of the animal. Faced with a certain stimulus, the animal always responds the same way, without thinking about it or having to make a decision. For example, many flying insects instinctively navigate by the sun, the moon, and the stars for reference. But what happens when the environment changes? Everyone has watched insects perish as they batter themselves to death or burn up as they land on an artificial light. Instincts do not allow for change. As humans change the environment, through development and pollution, animals may not be able to adapt to the new conditions.

Problem Solving

INTERPRETING DIAGRAMS

A Fishy Investigation

Many animals have instincts for movement or for orienting their body. For example, when an insect's environment changes suddenly, it typically will move rapidly in a random direction. This type of movement is called kinesis. With an instinct for kinesis, insects increase their chances of avoiding danger.

Another type of instinctive movement is called a taxis (plural: taxes). Taxes are movements toward or away from a stimulus. Examples of taxes include the instinctive movements of moths toward light, earthworms toward moisture, and reptiles toward heat.

To orient their body in water, fishes rely on one taxis that responds to light and another taxis that responds to gravity. In one experiment, researchers removed the gravity-detecting organ from several fishes, then observed their response to light. The results of this experiment are illustrated below.

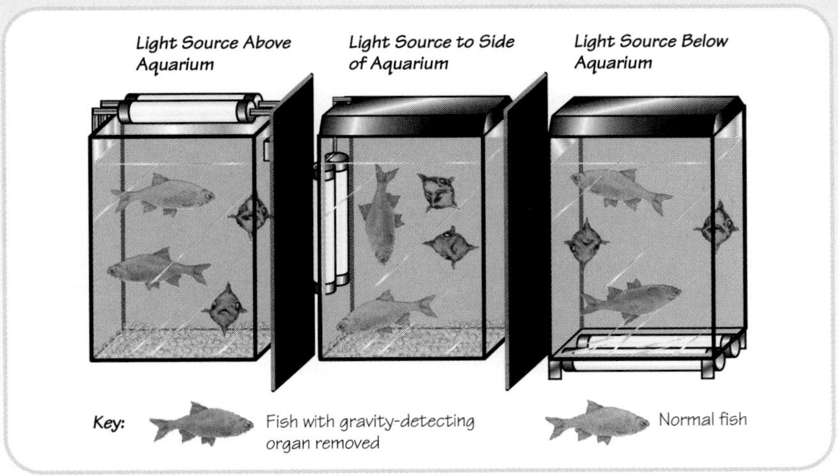

THINK ABOUT IT

1. **Explain** how taxes for gravity and light help fishes to survive.
2. **Describe** the results of the experiment illustrated above.
3. From these results, what can you **conclude** about the taxes toward light and gravity in fishes?
4. Do you suspect that a fish could learn to compensate for the loss of its gravity-detecting organ? **Design an experiment** to answer the question.

Problem Solving

Interpreting Diagrams

A Fishy Investigation

Students will draw on their knowledge of fishes, their understanding of instincts, and their ability to interpret diagrams.

State The problem is to determine how two instincts cause fishes to react to stimuli and which instinct is more powerful when the stimuli conflict.

Solve Students can solve the problem by examining the diagrams and comparing the reactions to the same stimuli of both groups of fishes.

Test Students could test the normal responses of fishes by lighting a classroom aquarium in a variety of ways and observing the fishes' reactions.

Communicate Discuss students' answers to the Think About It questions. Allow debate of any differences of opinion.

Answers to THINK ABOUT IT

1. The taxis for gravity helps a fish to know which way is up. The taxis for light helps a fish camouflage itself in the water.

2. Light source above: All the fishes orient themselves with their dorsal fins pointing up. Light source to the side: The normal fishes orient themselves diagonally, demonstrating a reaction to both taxes, but the "purple" fishes point their dorsal fins directly at the light source. Light source below: The normal fishes are rightside-up, but the "purple" fishes are upside-down.

3. Each taxis is a reaction to a specific stimulus—the force of gravity or the direction of light.

4. A typical experiment might involve the removal of the organ in numerous fishes and then close observation over time.

Checkpoint

❶ Behaviors that are genetically programmed into every member of a species.

TEACHER SUPPORT

Managing Classroom Diversity

GIFTED STUDENTS

Ask interested students to design an experiment in which they explore classical conditioning. First, have them do library research to find out about Pavlov's work with dogs. Then ask that they do similar investigations with animals in the classroom, such as fish or gerbils. For example, they could try to train fish to swim to a certain corner of the aquarium whenever a whistle is blown.

TECH PREP STUDENTS

Have students write a set of instructions that could help someone learn a skill that he or she would need in a future career, such as operating a piece of equipment or preparing a sample. Then have students identify the types of learning embodied in their instructions by labeling each step as one of the types of learning described in the text.

Section 33–1 (continued)

Ideas Through Images

Have students examine Figure 33–3, read the caption, and answer the following questions.

• **What are the four types of learning?** (Habituation, classical conditioning, operant conditioning, and insight learning.)

• **Did the dogs Pavlov worked with learn to expect food through trial and error?** (There was no trial and error involved. Pavlov's dogs learned over time to associate food with the turning on of a light.)

• **What is the difference between a frog and a chimpanzee that accounts for only a chimpanzee's being able to learn through insight?** (The chimpanzee has a much more complex nervous system than a frog, including a larger and more complex brain.)

Correcting Misconceptions

When learning about animal behavior, students have a tendency to attribute human feelings, emotions, and motivations to animals, which is called anthropomorphism. This tendency is also common in fables. For instance, the story of the turtle and the hare, in which the plodding turtle eventually wins the race, may teach a valuable lesson, but it says nothing about the behaviors that allow different kinds of animals to survive; they are simply adapted to their environments in different ways.

Another fallacy operates in the opposite way. Examples of animal behavior are often used to "prove" something about human behavior, such as whether humans are naturally aggressive or family oriented. But the behavior of animals has little or no application to human behavior.

Laboratory Investigation

The Laboratory Investigation, Investigating the Instinctive Behaviors of Planarians, on pages 756–757 is appropriate to use at this point in the chapter.

Figure 33–3
Most animals are capable of one or more types of learning. (a) Ivan Pavlov taught dogs to expect food whenever he turned on a light—an example of classical conditioning. (b) In nature, predators learn that brightly colored animals, such as this tomato frog, are often poisonous. This is an example of operant conditioning. (c) This chimpanzee is signing the word "me"—a skill only a few species can master.

Solid evidence indicates that genes control many instinctive behaviors. However, no one yet understands just how these genetic instructions are carried out. And, as you might expect, efforts to prove genetic control become much more complicated when dealing with complex behaviors, such as those that humans perform.

Learning

While animals often rely on instincts, many species also have the ability to change their behaviors as a result of experience. This is called **learning.** You may be surprised to discover the wide range of animals that learn behaviors of one sort or another. These animals range from humans to insects to cnidarians!

The simplest form of learning is **habituation,** in which an animal decreases or stops its response to a stimulus that neither helps nor harms the animal. If you give pieces of plain paper to a sea anemone, for example, the sea anemone will swallow the paper at first. But after a few trials, the sea anemone learns that paper is neither a food nor a danger and it simply stops responding to it.

In **classical conditioning**—a form of learning also called associative learning—an animal learns to associate a stimulus with either a reward or a punishment. One of the first scientists to study classical conditioning was the Russian biologist Ivan Pavlov, shown in ***Figure 33–3.***

If you have a pet, you may have helped it learn a behavior through classical conditioning. If you always ring a bell or perform a certain kitchen chore before meal time, for example, your pet may run eagerly to its food dish before you even get out the pet food!

In **operant conditioning**—often called trial-and-error learning—animals learn to perform some sort of task in order to get a reward or to avoid punishment. Laboratory rats, for example, can be trained to run through a maze or to push a lever in order to obtain food or to avoid a mild electric shock. In nature, birds and other predators can learn to associate the bright colors of some butterflies and tree frogs with an unpleasant taste.

Insight learning occurs when an animal applies past experiences to a new situation without any trial and error. This kind of learning is the rarest and most complicated kind of learning, and it is

TEACHER SUPPORT

Historical Perspective

Although Pavlov's dogs may be the most famous of all experiments on learning, the scientist's investigations actually began in an attempt to get rid of an annoying behavior. Ivan Pavlov (1849–1936) was a Russian physiologist who worked at his institute in St. Petersburg. There he did pioneering studies of the digestive system, and dogs were his experimental subjects. In this research, he measured the saliva produced when dogs, secured in harnesses, were fed. But after dogs had been in the laboratory for a while, they would begin to salivate as soon as they were put in a harness. This infuriated Pavlov, since it invalidated his measurements. So he began his studies of this behavior in an attempt to eliminate it. These studies proved fascinating, though, when he found he could cause dogs to salivate simply by ringing a bell or turning on a light.

common only in primates. Even otherwise intelligent animals such as dogs and cats rarely show insight learning. The typical dog, for example, will repeatedly wrap its leash around a tree and gain no insight on this behavior—as many dog owners know all too well! Chimpanzees, on the other hand, will use an object as a tool in a new situation, particularly to obtain food.

Checkpoint What is insight learning? 1

Complex Behaviors

Years ago, people studying animal behavior argued to great lengths about whether behavior was instinctive or learned. This debate was sometimes called the "nature versus nurture" controversy.

Today, this debate has largely ended. Why? Because it is clear that many behaviors are produced by a combination of instinct and learning. This combination can be called instinctively guided learning, and it provides many advantages to an animal. Because learned behaviors depend in part on heredity, they evolve over time to adapt the species to its environment. Yet because they are also somewhat flexible, they allow individual animals to adjust to local conditions.

Birds and fishes provide several examples of instinctively guided learning. For example, geese are born with an instinct to follow the first large moving object that they see during a critical time early in their lives. Normally, that object is their mother, whom they follow in search of food or shelter. This phenomenon is known as **imprinting.** Interestingly, if researchers remove eggs from the mother and expose goslings to another moving object—even another kind of animal—the birds will imprint on that object! See ***Figure 33–5*** on page 752.

In a similar way, newly hatched salmon imprint on the particular odor of

MINI LAB ············ Classifying

Pieces of the Puzzle

PROBLEM *How can you **classify** a learned behavior?*

PROCEDURE

1. Working in groups, cut an unlined index card into 5 pieces of various sizes. Make each cut as straight as possible.
2. Shuffle the pieces, then have one member of the group time you as you try to reassemble the pieces.
3. Repeat step 2 three times. Record your time for each trial.

ANALYZE AND CONCLUDE

1. Compare how quickly you reassembled the index card in each of the four trials.
2. Classify the types of learning that you displayed.
3. Compare your ability to reassemble an index card with other behaviors you have learned.

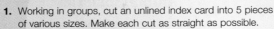

Figure 33–4
CAREER TRACK
A horse trainer applies the different techniques of learning to teach useful behaviors to horses.

MINI LAB Classifying

Teacher Notes
- For time required and materials needed, see page 746b.
- Tell students that they can cut a card in any way, as long as the result is 5 pieces and the cuts are straight.

Answers to Analyze and Conclude

1. Students should find that each successive trial takes less time.
2. Students should classify the first trial as trial-and-error learning because the card has to be reassembled by making and correcting a series of mistakes. The trials thereafter should be classified as insight learning, since the student applied past experience in reassembling the card.
3. A typical response might mention learning a skill in sports, music, dance, or academics.

Skills Trace
Classifying
- Focus p. 751
- Practice p. 753
- Assess p. 761

Checkpoint

1 Insight learning occurs when an animal applies past experiences to a new situation without any trial and error.

TEACHER SUPPORT

Background Information

The scientist who first recognized the behavior known as imprinting was the Austrian Konrad Lorenz (1903–1989), a pioneer in the field of animal behavior. His most famous work was done with young greylag geese, or goslings, as shown in Figure 33–5 on page 752. He found that these goslings became permanently attached to a figure—even Lorenz himself—under certain conditions. Three characteristics make this learning behavior unique: (1) It requires no reinforcement; simple exposure is enough for attachment to occur. (2) It is irreversible; once an imprint is made it cannot be undone. (3) It is limited to a specific phase of development, often lasting only a few hours. For example, imprinting most effectively occurs in mallard ducklings between 12 and 16 hours after hatching, and after 30 hours imprinting cannot occur.

Ancillary Support

The resources below can be used to support your teaching strategy for these two pages.

LM Observing the Behavior of Fish, #65
Observing the Behavior of Crickets, #66

BL Inquiry Activity: Time Off for Good Behavior

Ideas Through Images

Have students examine Figure 33–5, read the caption, and answer the following questions.

- **What was the "nature versus nurture" controversy?** (A debate about whether most behaviors are instinctive or learned.)
- **What is instinctively guided learning, and what advantage does it have for an animal?** (Instinctively guided learning is a combination of instinct and learning. The advantage is that such behaviors depend in part on heredity but are more flexible than simple instincts.)
- **In what way do young geese benefit from instinctively guided learning?** (Young geese instinctively imprint on their mother, and in that way find food and shelter. By following the mother, the young geese also learn how to survive.)

Investigate

Cooperative Learning Have cooperative learning groups investigate one of the following topics associated with the work of a famous scientist: imprinting in greylag geese (Lorenz), classical learning in dogs (Pavlov), the waggle dance of bees (Von Frisch), the mating behavior of stickleback fish (Tinbergen), learning in pigeons (Skinner), and group behavior in chimpanzees (Goodall). Ask that the product of their research be a visual essay on poster board that explains the topic investigated.

the stream in which they hatch. Young salmon head out to sea, where they spend several years feeding and growing. When they mature and prepare to mate, they perform an amazing feat. They remember the odor of their home stream and return there to spawn.

Animal Societies

Any animal that reproduces sexually needs to locate and mate with another of its species—even if the two animals spend no time together afterward. Thus, an animal lives at least part of its life with a member of its own kind. In the broadest sense, an **animal society** is any group of animals living together. **Animal societies help the species to survive and provide benefits for the individual animals.**

☑ *Checkpoint* What is an animal society? ❶

Types of Animal Societies

Animals live in a wide variety of different societies. For example, songbirds and other species live as **mated pairs,** in which a male and a female live together and jointly raise their offspring. As mated pairs, songbirds can defend their home and feed their young more successfully than a single parent could alone.

Other animals live in **family groups,** such as a pride of lions, a herd of elephants, and various groups of apes and monkeys. Family groups use strength in numbers to improve their ability to hunt, to protect their territory from competitors, to guard their young from predators, and to fight with rivals if necessary.

Still other animals rely on highly structured living groups. Ants, termites, and bees live in **social insect colonies,** as shown in ***Figure 33–6.***

Communication

In order for individual animals to form and operate a society—from a mated pair of bluebirds to the largest beehive—they must communicate with one another. In this sense, biologists define **communication** as the passing of information from one animal to another in a way that influences both animals from that point on.

(a)

(b)

Figure 33–5
In imprinting, a stimulus early in an animal's life establishes an irreversible behavior. (a) In a famous series of experiments, baby geese imprinted on biologist Konrad Lorenz. The geese behaved as if Lorenz was their mother! (b) Salmon return to their home stream—often overcoming all sorts of obstacles—because they imprinted on the stream's scent.

TEACHER SUPPORT

Background Information

A honeybee communicates to its hivemates the food source it has just found in a nearby field through a waggle dance. When a bee discovers a good source of nectar and returns to the hive, the other bees can sense the type of flower that has been found by the scent carried by the returning bee. The other bees know the location of the source through a complex series of movements. The returning bee runs a short distance in the direction of the source, waggles its abdomen from side to side, and then walks in a semicircle back to its starting place. The bees can interpret the direction of the source by the direction of the bee's run; they can interpret the distance they will need to fly from the distance or time of the bee's run. A 1-second run means twice the distance of a 0.5-second run. The ability to interpret this waggle dance is instinctive, not learned.

Figure 33–6
Animal societies range from two birds living together in a nest to hundreds of thousands of ants or bees living in a colony. (a) As a mated pair, these adult crimson chats together raise their offspring. (b) These crescent-tail bigeyes live in a large group called a school. Swimming in schools helps to protect fishes from predators. (c) By living in a highly organized colony, these honeybees accomplish tasks that they never could accomplish individually.

Animals communicate to find and select mates, to pass on information about food or danger, to assert dominance, to claim territory, or to threaten to fight. In fact, many of the most intriguing, entertaining, and even frightening activities in the animal kingdom are behaviors used by animals to communicate with one another.

Different species communicate by using one or more of their senses. Birds, for example, have well-developed hearing and vision. Thus, it is not surprising that male birds attract mates with sound signals, such as songs or calls, and visual signals, such as brightly colored feathers.

Animals that have a highly developed sense of smell often use chemical signals to transmit information. Social insects such as ants, for example, often give off a variety of chemical signals known as **pheromones** (FER-uh-mohnz). Pheromones tell nest mates about food, the condition of the nest, or danger. Many mammals use pheromones to mark their territory or to signal that they are ready to mate.

Section Review 33–1

1. **Explain** the purpose of animal behaviors and **identify** different types of behaviors.
2. **Explain** why animals live in societies.
3. **Critical Thinking—Applying Concepts** Do humans learn in each of the different ways described in this section? Give examples to justify your answer.
4. **MINI LAB** How can you **classify** a learned behavior?

4. A learned behavior can be classified by identifying the way in which the behavior was learned.

Skills Trace
Classifying

- Focus p. 751
- Practice p. 753
- Assess p. 761

Learning Modality

Auditory Learning Orally describe the differences between the kinds of learning and have students orally provide examples of each.

Ideas Through Images

Have students examine Figure 33–6, read the caption, and answer the following questions.

- **What advantage would forming a mated pair provide birds?** (A mated pair is better able to provide for and protect its offspring than a single individual.)
- **What do bees do together that they could not accomplish alone?** (They build their hives and defend their food and larvae.)
- **What function does a school serve for fish?** (Protection from predators.)

4 ASSESS

Quick Check

Have students make flowcharts that explain the steps involved in habituation, classical conditioning, operant conditioning, and insight learning.

Section Review 33-1

1. All animals have evolved behaviors that help them survive. Some behaviors are instinctive, or inborn in the animal, and others are learned as the animal develops.
2. Animal societies help a species to survive and provide benefits for the individual animals.
3. Yes. Example: the habituation to a common sight, the classical conditioning of a feeling of hunger when hearing a school bell before lunch, the operant conditioning when learning a new skill, and the insight learning when mastering a new situation by recalling the past.

Checkpoint

1. An animal society is any group of animals living together.

Section 33–2

Insect and Primate Societies

Performance Objectives

• Explain how individual ants compare with the superorganism they form.
• Discuss the characteristics of a nonhuman primate society.

1 ENGAGE

Ideas Through Images

Have students examine Figure 33–7, read the caption, and answer the following questions.

• **How is a large company more than just the sum of the individuals who work there?** (The company has different people do different jobs. Working together, they produce something that none could produce individually.)

• **How is a social insect colony like a large company?** (Each individual insect has a specific role. Working together, they accomplish more than the sum of what they would accomplish individually.)

2 EXPLORE

Investigate

Long-Term Project Have groups build ant farms for classroom observation. Ant farms can be purchased ready-made, or students could find plans in a library book and construct their own. A common design involves using a wooden base, a square wooden frame, and two sheets of plexiglass. The space between the plexiglass sheets is filled with soil. Ant colonies can be purchased from a biological supply company.

Insect and Primate Societies

Guide for Reading

- **Compare** individual ants and the superorganism they form.
- **Describe** the typical nonhuman primate society.

YOU MIGHT THINK THAT ANTS and primates have very little in common. Ants are tiny insects with minuscule collections of nerve cells that can barely be called brains. Primates, on the other hand, are large, intelligent mammals—among them, the most intelligent animals of all.

Yet despite their differences, ants and primates have each developed the most sophisticated societies on Earth. These societies are well worth studying—their secrets may apply to humans in some surprising ways.

Ant Societies

Place up to 100 army ants or leaf-cutter ants on a table, and they will probably walk around in circles until they die. But watch a colony of either of these ants in action, and you will be amazed at what 500,000 ants can do!

Army ants send raiding parties up to 200 meters from the nest, form living bridges of their bodies to cover difficult terrain, and form teams to kill and transport large prey. Leaf-cutter ants cut leaves into small pieces and carry the pieces home. There, they chew the leaves into a pulp, which they use to grow a special fungus that they weed, water, harvest, and eat!

How do ant colonies accomplish such amazing feats? In a colony, ants constantly click and rub each others' antennae. Ants pass information back and forth with these actions. In a way that researchers do not yet understand, this constant communication creates what is called a **superorganism**—a colony that is more than the sum of its parts.

Figure 33–7
In social insect colonies, each individual is born to fill a specific role. (a) This soldier army ant has razor-sharp mouthparts, making it a fierce predator. (b) This queen fire ant is surrounded by smaller workers. In all ant colonies, only the queen bears offspring. (c) Among leaf-cutter ants, worker ants have the job of carrying leaves back to the nest.

TEACHER SUPPORT

Background Information

Students might wonder how the complex societies of ants and some other insects evolved. Most insects do not live long enough to see their offspring—they lay eggs and die, and the next generation does the same. The first step toward a society most likely occurred when some insects began to build nests for their eggs. Then the lifespans of those insects lengthened, and the generations began to overlap. At that point, the exchange of food, called trophallaxis, between adults and larvae may have begun, as the larvae evolved to secrete substances when fed that the adults consumed. A next step probably was the building of the nests of individual insects next to one another. Once the insects were in close proximity, a transition to some kind of division of labor occurred. For example, some individuals may have begun guarding the nest.

Figure 33–8
Primate societies are composed of unique, intelligent individuals that develop close relationships with one another. (a) To learn the rules of their society, young primates—such as this infant olive baboon—typically stay close to their mother. (b) The kneeling Japanese macaque is cleaning the fur of another macaque—an activity called grooming.

Although ants individually are helpless and unintelligent, as a superorganism they are able to process information and accomplish complicated tasks. As a whole, an ant colony "knows" how to build a nest, how to raid territory, how to raise offspring, and how to protect the colony. The colony also can "learn" where to find food and where enemies are located.

Some researchers compare ant colonies to the human brain, which is formed from huge numbers of individual neurons. Like ants, the neurons of the brain are "stupid" individually, but somehow connect and communicate with one another to create intelligence.

Primate Societies

Nonhuman primates don't build much, do not farm crops, and only occasionally use tools. But their societies may offer insights into the evolution of human societies—and human intelligence.

Nonhuman primates typically live in groups of closely related individuals, with females as central members. In many species, most males periodically switch from group to group. Most females, on the other hand, spend their lives with the groups into which they were born.

As researchers have shown, primate social groups are built on a complex web of relationships. Individuals build friendships and make enemies, do favors for one another, and even have been seen to trick or manipulate one another for their own ends. All these factors come into play when primates hunt, travel, or encounter neighboring groups.

Of course, it takes a good memory and lots of intelligence to keep track of all these relationships. Perhaps in part to develop this intelligence, primate infants depend on their parents for relatively long periods of time. Some researchers suggest that the growth of the primate social system was the major reason why intelligence developed to such a great extent in ancestral humans.

Section Review 33–2

1. **Compare** individual ants and the superorganism they form.
2. **Describe** the typical nonhuman primate society.
3. **BRANCHING OUT ACTIVITY** Find an ant colony in your neighborhood and **observe** the colony for 15 minutes. Make a list of all your observations.

3 TEACH

Ideas Through Images

Have students examine Figure 33–8, read the caption, and answer the following questions.

- **How would you describe the composition of a typical primate society?** (Primates live in family groups of closely related individuals.)
- **Which individuals typically are the central members of a primate society?** (The females.)
- **What advantages are gained by living in such a group?** (Primates can better guard their young from predators, defend their territory, fight with rival groups, and find food.)
- **How might intelligence in primates be related to living in groups?** (Primates form complex relationships with groups, and it takes memory and intelligence to keep track of those relationships.)

4 ASSESS

Quick Check

Ask students to make a table that compares the characteristics of an ant society with those of a primate society.

Section Review 33–2

1. Individual ants are helpless and unintelligent. The superorganism they form, though, is able to process information and accomplish complicated tasks.

2. They live in groups of closely related individuals, with females as central members. Within the society, individuals build a web of relationships.

3. Students might search the neighborhood for an ant colony and then report back to the class the location of their find. All students could then have an opportunity to observe the colony at various times. Commonly, an ant colony can be identified by a conical mound of dirt. All students should be able to observe the comings and goings of ants; many will be able to observe the ants working together to carry food back to the colony.

Learning Modality

Tactile and Kinesthetic Learning Ask one student to attempt to pick up and carry away a large table in the classroom. When that student fails to accomplish the task, ask several students to position themselves around the table and pick it up. Point out that all the students in the class could not pick the table up if they tried in succession, but a few working together could accomplish the feat easily.

Ancillary Support

The resources below can be used to support your teaching strategy for these two pages.

TR Writing in Biology: Communication
Enrich: Mixed-Up Mammal
BL Inquiry Activity: Not So Secret Societies

Laboratory Investigation

Investigating the Instinctive Behaviors of Planarians

Before the Lab

1. Planarians may be gathered from streams, ponds, and lakes or obtained from a biological supply company.
2. Purchase beef or chicken liver from a grocery store and keep it refrigerated until the lab begins. Just before the lab, cut the liver into small pieces and place them in a dish at a central location.
3. Prepare a dilute acetic acid solution by mixing 1 part distilled vinegar with 10 parts distilled water.

Pre-Lab Discussion

Have students read the entire procedure for this investigation. Then ask students the following questions.

What is the purpose of this investigation? (To determine the taxes of a planarian.)

What is a planarian? (A free-living, invertebrate flatworm in the phylum Platyhelminthes.)

Where do planarians live and what kind of food do they eat? (Planarians live on the bottoms of lakes and ponds. They feed on small invertebrates and the bodies of larger dead animals.)

How do you think a planarian finds its food? (Students might suggest that planarians can smell or otherwise sense food sources in the environment.)

Skills Development

Students will use these skills while completing the laboratory investigation: measuring, observing, designing an experiment, analyzing, and drawing conclusions.

CHAPTER 33

Laboratory Investigation

DESIGNING AN EXPERIMENT

Investigating the Instinctive Behaviors of Planarians

Many animals rely on simple instincts called taxes (singular: taxis). A taxis is a movement either toward or away from a stimulus, such as light, gravity, or chemical changes in the environment. In this investigation, you will explore the taxes of a planarian, a type of free-living flatworm found in ponds and streams.

Problem

How can you determine the taxes of a planarian? **Design an experiment** to answer the question.

Suggested Materials

- glass-marking pencil
- test tube, with cork or stopper
- planarian
- pond water
- test-tube rack
- Petri dish
- small piece of liver
- index card
- dilute acetic acid
- salt
- forceps

Suggested Procedure

1. **Using the glass-marking pencil, draw a circle around the test tube at its midpoint. The circle divides the test tube into top and bottom halves.**
2. **Obtain a planarian from your teacher. Gently transfer the planarian to the test tube. CAUTION: *Be careful when handling live animals.* Add pond water as necessary to fill the test tube. Seal the test tube with the stopper or cork.**

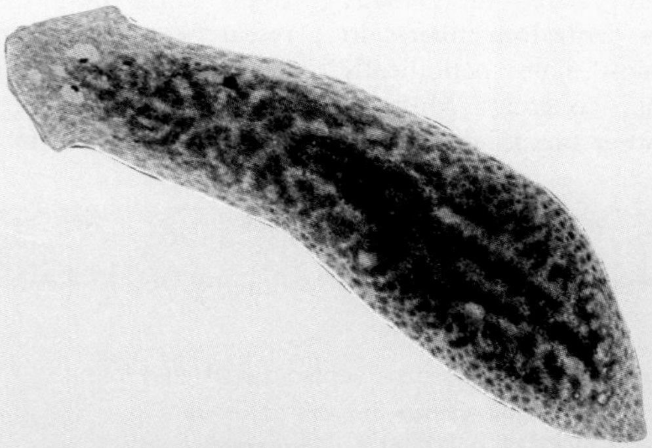

Safety Tips

- Remind students to handle the planarians carefully and not to harm them.
- Warn students to use caution when handling glass and to notify you immediately of any breakage.
- Instruct students not to pick up the liver with their fingers, but to use the forceps.
- Have students wash their hands thoroughly after they have completed the procedure.

3. **Gently move the test tube back and forth until the planarian is in the center of the test tube.**

4. **Place the test tube in a test-tube rack. For 3 minutes, measure the amount of time the planarian spends in the top half of the test tube and the amount of time it spends in the bottom half of the test tube.**

5. **Turn the test tube upside down, then repeat steps 3 and 4.**

6. **Carefully transfer the planarian and pond water to a Petri dish. Add more pond water, if necessary, to cover the bottom of the dish. Using forceps, place a piece of liver in the Petri dish. Observe the planarian's response.**

7. **Design an experiment to determine whether the planarian has a taxis for one of the following stimuli:**
   - **light**
   - **change in pH**
   - **change in salinity**

   Make sure your experiment does not harm the planarian in any way. Your experiment should include a control group.

8. **With your teacher's permission, perform the experiment you designed.**

Observations

1. Compare the time the planarian spent in the top half of the test tube with the time it spent in the bottom half of the test tube.
2. Describe the planarian's response to liver.
3. Describe the planarian's response to the stimulus you tested in your experiment.

Analysis and Conclusions

1. What is a taxis? Why are taxes important to animals with a limited nervous system?
2. Do planarians have a taxis for gravity? Explain your answer.
3. Why was it necessary to turn the test tube upside down in step 5?
4. Can planarians detect food in nearby water, then move toward the food? Or do they encounter food only by chance? Explain your answer.
5. Do planarians have a taxis for the stimulus you tested in your experiment? Use the data you generated to justify your answer.
6. Explain how a planarian's taxes help it to survive in its environment.

More to Explore

Try to train a planarian to navigate through a simple maze.

Answers to Observations

1. The planarian spends most of its time in the bottom half of the test tube.
2. It moves to the liver.
3. Planarians move away from light and from chemicals that might be harmful, such as acid or salt.

Answers to Analysis and Conclusions

1. A taxis is a movement either toward or away from a stimulus. Because the animal cannot make decisions about movement, taxes help it react appropriately.
2. Yes. The planarian spent more time in the bottom half of the test tube than in the top half.
3. To ensure that the planarian is reacting to gravity rather than something else in its environment.
4. Planarians can detect food in nearby water and move toward it, as shown by the movement of the planarian toward the liver.
5. Planarians do have taxes that cause them to move away from light, acid, or salt.
6. A taxis for gravity provides information about where the bottom of a body of water is, for this animal moves best if it is against a surface. The taxis for light helps it avoid places where it might dry out from the sun and also keeps it from being seen by predators. The chemical taxes help the animal locate food and move away from an environment that might be harmful.

Teaching Strategies

1. Demonstrate how to place planarians in test tubes and Petri dishes.
2. Advise students to make sure they seal the test tube with the stopper so that no water escapes. Then demonstrate how to gently move the test tube back and forth to place the planarian at the center line.
3. Review each experimental design before giving students permission to proceed. Make sure the experiments will not cause harm to the animals. However, do allow students to proceed with designs that are flawed, and then discuss the flaws after they make their observations.
4. A typical experiment using light as the stimulus might utilize an index card to cover half of a Petri dish containing pond water and two or more planarians. Students could place the dish in direct sunlight, cover half with the index card, and observe the movements of the planarians.
5. A typical experiment focusing on a change in pH or salinity might involve adding a small amount of dilute acetic acid or salt to one side of a Petri dish containing pond water and planarians, and then observing the movements of the animals. Advise students to remove the planarians quickly once the movements are clear.

More to Explore

Students could construct a simple maze with toothpicks in a Petri dish. The sides of the maze should be high enough to contain the planarian in shallow pond water. The prize could be a piece of liver. Students could time the planarian as it negotiates the maze several times.

CHAPTER 33

Study Guide

Review Strategy

Have students work in pairs to write study questions from the chapter's content, as well as an answer for each question written. Recommend that they write at least two questions for each paragraph in a section. Ask that about half of the questions be simple recall, which could be answered by providing a term or definition. The rest of the questions should require some application of the material learned in the chapter. Once students have completed their questions, have different pairs trade sets of questions and answer them.

Study Guide

Summarizing Key Concepts

The key concepts in each section of this chapter are listed below to help you review the chapter content. Make sure you understand each concept and its relationship to other concepts and to the theme of this chapter.

33–1 Behaviors and Societies

- An animal's sense organs shape the ways in which it perceives and responds to its environment. Because sense organs differ among animals, their behaviors differ as well.
- All animals have evolved behaviors that help them to survive. Some behaviors are instinctive, or inborn in the animal, whereas others are learned as the animal develops.
- Instincts are genetically programmed behaviors. The simplest instincts are fixed and cannot be changed.
- Many animals can change their behavior as a result of experience—a process called learning. The simplest form of learning is habituation, in which an animal decreases or stops its response to a stimulus that is neither harmful nor helpful.
- In classical conditioning, an animal learns to associate a stimulus with either a reward or a punishment. In operant conditioning, an animal learns to perform some sort of task in order to get a reward or to avoid punishment.
- Insight learning occurs when an animal applies past experiences to a new situation without any trial and error. Instinctively guided learning is a combination of instinct and learning.
- An animal society is any group of animals living together. Animal societies help the species to survive and provide benefits for the individual animals.
- Types of animal societies include mated pairs, family groups, and social insect colonies. All animal societies rely on communication among members.

33–2 Insect and Primate Societies

- Although ants individually are helpless and unintelligent, in a social insect colony—a superorganism—they are able to process information and accomplish complicated tasks.
- Nonhuman primates typically live in groups of closely related individuals, with females as central members.

Reviewing Key Terms

Review the following vocabulary terms and their meaning. Then use each term in a complete sentence.

33–1 Behaviors and Societies

behavior
instinct
learning
habituation
classical conditioning
operant conditioning
insight learning
imprinting
animal society
mated pair
family group
social insect colony
communication
pheromone

33–2 Insect and Primate Societies

superorganism

Inquiry-Based Strategy

What human behavior is completely or mostly determined by genetic programming? Ask students to answer this question both through research and by designing an experiment that would prove the behavior in question is not the result of learning. Allow students to find their own sources and choose a behavior to investigate further. Encourage them to design a complex experiment, without regard to whether it could be done. Each design should include a statement of a hypothesis and a description of a test of that hypothesis, including the designation of a control and the identification of a variable. A well-done experimental design will most likely require some illustrations.

Recalling Main Ideas

Choose the letter of the answer that best completes the statement or answers the question.

1. Another name for an innate behavior is a(an)

a. sensory behavior. **c.** learned behavior.
b. instinct. **d.** insight behavior.

2. An animal stops responding to a stimulus that is neither helpful nor harmful. This is called

a. habituation. **c.** classical conditioning.
b. instinctive learning. **d.** operant conditioning.

3. Pavlov trained dogs to expect food whenever he turned on a light. This is an example of

a. habituation. **c.** classical conditioning.
b. instinctive learning. **d.** operant conditioning.

4. Another name for trial-and-error learning is

a. habituation. **c.** classical conditioning.
b. insight learning. **d.** operant conditioning.

5. Insight learning is common only in

a. birds and reptiles. **c.** dogs and cats.
b. primates. **d.** humans.

6. Baby geese follow the first large object they encounter during a critical period in their development. This phenomenon is an example of

a. insight learning. **c.** imprinting.
b. habituation. **d.** operant conditioning.

7. Many animals use pheromones as

a. chemical signals. **c.** sound signals.
b. visual signals. **d.** temperature signals.

8. By clicking and rubbing their antennae together, ants are able to

a. communicate. **c.** mate.
b. attack each other. **d.** groom each other.

9. Unlike male primates, female primates typically

a. build friendships and make enemies.
b. rely on a complex web of relationships.
c. move from group to group.
d. remain in the same group.

Putting It All Together

Using the information on pages xxx to xxxi, complete the following concept map.

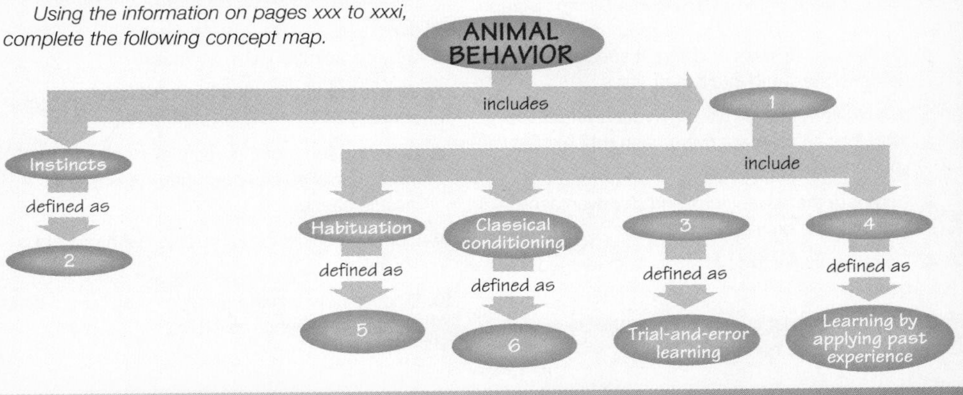

Putting It All Together

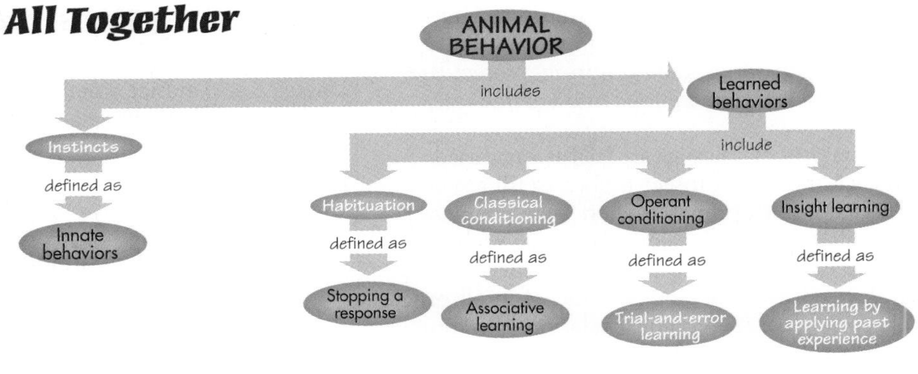

Recalling Main Ideas

1. b
2. a
3. c
4. d
5. b
6. c
7. a
8. a
9. d

Assessment

Reviewing What You Learned

1. An animal's response to its environment.
2. Students might list any three of the instinctive behaviors mentioned in the text.
3. A typical response will mention a newborn instinctively suckling at its mother's breast.
4. A typical response will describe the habituation of a sea anemone to pieces of plain paper.
5. A form of learning that occurs when an animal learns to associate a stimulus with either a reward or a punishment.
6. Operant conditioning occurs when an animal learns to perform some sort of task in order to get a reward or avoid a punishment.
7. The issue involved a debate about whether most behaviors were instinctive—"nature"—or learned—"nurture."
8. A combination of instinct and learning.
9. An example of imprinting is the instinct in geese to follow the first moving object that they see during a critical time early in their lives.
10. A possible answer is that songbirds, including crimson chats, live in mated pairs.
11. A pride of lions, a herd of elephants, a group of apes or monkeys, and a school of fish are examples of family groups of animals.

Assessment (continued)

12. Animals communicate with sound signals, visual signals, and chemical signals.
13. An animal colony that is more than the sum of its parts.
14. In a social insect colony, individuals communicate with one another to create intelligence, like individual neurons in a human brain.
15. Typical behaviors include young primates staying close to their mothers, males periodically switching from group to group, females spending their lives with the groups in which they were born, and group members forming a complex web of relationships.

Expanding the Concepts

1. Animals of different species have different sensory abilities. Thus, each species perceives the world according to the information gathered by its unique combination of senses.
2. Most behaviors are instinctive in animals with primitive nervous systems because such animals do not have complex brains to learn complex behaviors.
3. The advantage of instincts is that they permit animals to perform tasks essential to their survival, with no learning period required. The disadvantage is that instincts are inflexible behaviors and do not provide for the ability to change as a result of experience.
4. Instinctive behaviors are genetically programmed and are thus fixed and cannot be changed. Learned behaviors, in contrast, are not determined by genes but are acquired as a result of some kind of experience.
5. The debate has ended because it is clear that many behaviors are produced by a combination of instinct and learning, a combination called instinctively guided learning.
6. Societies help species to survive and also benefit individuals.
7. Without communication, a society could not form and operate. Animals communicate to find and select mates, to pass on information about food or danger, to assert dominance, to claim territory, or to threaten to fight.
8. Insect societies can kill and transport large prey, transport food, cover rough terrain, build nests, raid territories, raise offspring, protect the colony, and learn where food and enemies are located.
9. Social insect colonies are highly organized, and each individual insect is born to fill a specific role. In contrast, primate societies are composed of closely related but unique individuals who develop complex relationships with one another.
10. It takes good memory and lots of intelligence to keep track of the complex relationships formed within a primate society. Primate intelligence may have evolved in conjunction with the development of such societies.

Extending Your Thinking

1. Answers may include: sound communication—language and music; visual communication—pictures and "body language"; and chemical communication—chemical signals provided by pheromones.

Skills Trace
Classifying

Focus p. 751
Practice p. 753
Assess p. 761

Assessment

Reviewing What You Learned

Answer each of the following in a complete sentence.

1. What is a behavior?
2. List three examples of instinctive behavior.
3. Describe a human behavior controlled by an instinct.
4. Give an example of habituation.
5. What is classical conditioning?
6. Explain operant conditioning.
7. Describe the once-controversial issue of "nature versus nurture."
8. What is instinctively guided learning?
9. Give an example of imprinting.
10. Give an example of an animal that lives in mated pairs.
11. List three family groups of animals.
12. Identify three ways in which animals communicate.
13. What is a superorganism?
14. In what way is a social insect colony similar to the human brain?
15. List three behaviors typical of primate groups.

Expanding the Concepts

Discuss each of the following in a brief paragraph.

1. Explain why animals of different species perceive the world in different ways.
2. In animals with a primitive nervous system, are most behaviors instinctive or learned? Explain your answer.
3. Compare the advantages and disadvantages that instincts provide an animal.
4. Compare instinctive behaviors with learned behaviors.
5. Why has the debate ended over the issue of "nature versus nurture"?
6. Why do animals live in societies?
7. Why is communication essential in any animal society?
8. Describe some of the complex behaviors that insect societies carry out that the individual insects cannot.
9. Compare social insect colonies with primate societies.
10. Discuss how primate societies may have helped primate intelligence to evolve.

Extending Your Thinking

Use the skills you have developed in this chapter to answer the following.

1. **Classifying** Give examples of ways in which humans use sound communication, visual communication, or chemical communication.
2. **Predicting** A salmon imprints on the stream in which it hatches and has an instinct to return there to spawn. Suppose that over the course of a year, a stream becomes polluted with industrial wastes. Predict the effects on the salmon population that hatched in the stream.
3. **Designing an experiment** Young herring gulls peck at a brightly colored spot on their parent's beak whenever the parent returns to the nest. The pecking stimulates the parent to regurgitate food for the young gull to eat. Design an experiment to determine whether the size, shape, or color of the spot affects the pecking response of the young gull.
4. **Analyzing concepts** To what extent do instincts affect human behavior? Explain your answer.
5. **Using the writing process** Write a short story, play, or poem in which a character learns a new behavior. Classify the type of learning that your writing illustrates.

Applying Your Skills

Classifying Animal Behavior

Although some animal behaviors are easy to understand and classify, other behaviors are not so straightforward. In this activity, you will apply what you have learned about animal behavior by studying a real animal.

1. Select an animal to study. The animal may be a pet, a farm animal, or an animal in nature. Observe the animal for about 1 hour. Do not touch or approach the animal. Record all the behaviors that you observe.
2. Infer which behaviors are forms of communication. Classify the communication as sound signals, visual signals, or chemical signals. Record any responses to the communications from other animals.
3. Classify other behaviors that you can identify. Typical behaviors include feeding, courtship, care of young, shelter-seeking, claiming territory, and grooming.
4. Analyze your data and present your conclusions in a report.

• GOING FURTHER •

5. In 1973, biologists Konrad Lorenz, Niko Tinbergen, and Karl von Frisch were awarded a Nobel prize for their studies of animal behavior. Research their work.

Applying Your Skills

Teacher Notes

- You may want to have pairs of students carry out this activity. Review with each individual or pair the animal designated for observation before students begin their study. Encourage observation of animals in nature, such as a bird, insect, or squirrel.
- Have students prepare a record sheet in anticipation of what they will observe and record. This sheet might include spaces for the type of animal, where it was observed, what kinds of behaviors it displayed, and so on.
- Once students have completed their observations, have them meet in groups to discuss their results. These groups could be formed on the basis of similar subjects of study, such as an insect-observation group, a bird-observation group, and so on.

Scoring Rubric

4 Response is thorough, accurate, and creative; shows an in-depth understanding of science skills, procedures, and concepts.

3 Response is complete, mostly accurate, and original; shows a satisfactory understanding of science skills, procedures, and concepts.

2 Response is mostly complete but includes some inaccuracies; shows an adequate understanding of science skills, procedures, and concepts.

1 Response is only partially complete and has many inaccuracies; shows an incomplete understanding of science skills, procedures, and concepts.

0 Response is mostly incomplete and/or inaccurate; shows a lack of understanding of science skills, procedures, and concepts.

2. Hatched salmon imprint on the particular odor of the stream in which they hatch. If industrial wastes were to pollute that stream, the odor would change, and the returning salmon might not be able to recognize it as the stream where they hatched. Students might predict that as a result the salmon would not reproduce and their population would decline.
3. Students' experimental designs will vary. A classic experiment uses a model of a head and beak. The color, shape, and size of the spot are varied, and each variation is presented to young gulls on a nest. The number and strength of pecks at each different kind of spot are recorded and compared. When this experiment has been done in the laboratory, the color red has seemed to provide the greatest stimulus to the young gulls.
4. A typical response might suggest that human behavior is a combination of instinct and learning. Many students will argue that the emphasis is on learning because human behavior is too complex and flexible for instincts to play the dominant role.
5. In a typical short story, play, or poem, the character will learn a new behavior with a combination of trial-and-error learning and insight learning.

Unit 8

The Human Body

Introducing the Unit

. . . In Words

Rachel Carson (1907–1964) was a marine biologist and is considered one of America's finest science and nature writers. When Carson entered college, she planned to become a writer. However, a biology course prompted her to study science. She said to a friend, "Biology has given me something to write about."

After college, Carson worked for the U.S. Fish and Wildlife Service but continued to write. Her best known book is *Silent Spring*, published in 1962. In it she reported on the uncontrolled and often indiscriminate use of pesticides and the irreparable damage caused by these chemicals to the environment. *Silent Spring* created a storm of controversy, but it is credited with launching the U.S. environmental movement. Carson stressed the interrelatedness of all living things and emphasized that human welfare is dependent on natural processes.

- **What do you think Carson meant by "Science is part of the reality of living"?** (Students might suggest that science explains all parts of life.)
- **Is science the what, how, and why for everything in your experience? Explain.** (Students might suggest that science can explain what an experience is, as well as how and why it happened.)

. . . In Pictures

These modern dancers use athletic abilities to perform amazing movements. Their skills are the result of long hours of practice and conditioning. A strong, healthy body with all systems functioning at peak levels is vital to such strenuous and exacting activities.

UNIT 8

The Human Body

CHAPTERS

"Science is part of the reality of living; it is the what, the how, and the why for everything in our experience."

— Rachel Carson

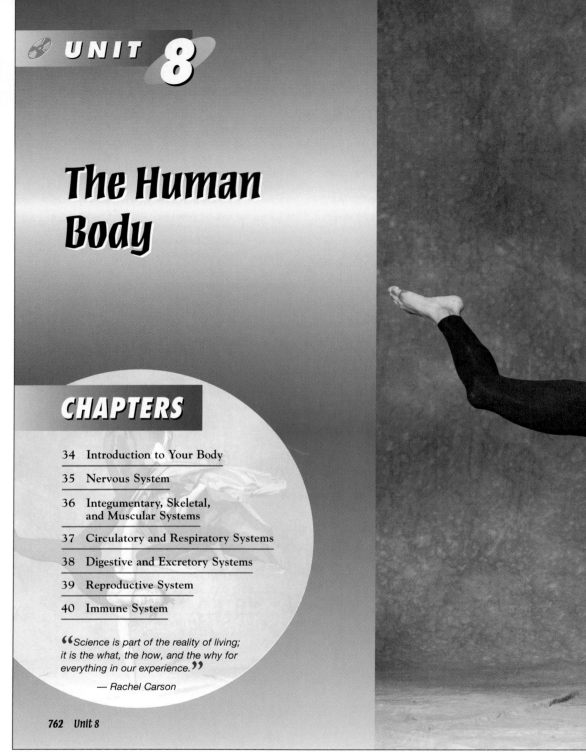

TEACHER SUPPORT

Unit Discovery Learning Activity

AN OUT-OF-BODY EXPERIENCE

This activity is designed to help start students thinking about the human body and how it is organized. Students will draw from their own experience and knowledge to create an anatomical diagram of the human body. Follow these steps to carry out the activity.

1. Have student pairs create a list of all the human body organs that they can think of without using their text.

2. After students have completed their list, ask them to divide the different organs into groups based on similar function. They should identify the function of each group.

3. Give each pair of students a 2-m-long sheet of table paper or butcher paper and a marker. Instruct one student to trace the outline of the other on the paper.

CAREER TRACK

As you explore the topics in this unit, you will discover many different types of careers associated with biology. Here are a few of these careers:

- Biomedical Equipment Technician
- Electroneurodiagnostic Technologist
- Physical Therapist
- Emergency Medical Technician
- Dietician
- Physician Assistant
- Immunologist

Two dancers showing the various ranges of motion possible to the human body

- **Which systems of the body do these dancers depend on to carry out these amazing movements?** (They depend primarily on the skeletal, muscular, nervous, endocrine, circulatory, digestive, and respiratory systems.)
- **Why is it important even for nondancers to have strong, healthy bodies?** (Lead students to conclude that a strong, healthy body in which all systems are working at peak level is important for carrying out all kinds of activities.)

CAREER TRACK

Throughout this unit, you will find a broad range of biology-related careers that vary in educational and training requirements. You may wish to have your students find out more about the following careers:

- Biomedical Equipment Technician, p. 771
- Electroneurodiagnostic Technologist, p. 791
- Physical Therapist, p. 813
- Emergency Medical Technician, p. 838
- Dietician, p. 852
- Physician Assistant, p. 888
- Immunologist, p. 915

Technology

BioVue
The Body Shop: Dancing and Biomechanics
Videodisc Side 8

Go to Chapter 2

4. Next have students try to accurately draw each of the organs on their list in the appropriate position on the body outline. Students should use a different color for each group of organs they identified in step 2. They should also label each organ and key the diagram with the function of each different group of organs.
5. Have student groups compare and discuss their diagrams. Encourage students to reach a consensus on the organ groups and their functions.
6. Have students review and revise their diagrams as they progress through the unit.

By identifying various organs of the human body and considering how they are organized, students should be able to identify and explain examples of the key concepts of **scale and structure,** one of the themes that is developed in this unit.

Ancillary Support

The resource below can be used to support your teaching strategy for these two pages.

BL Integrating the Media
Unit Discovery Learning Activity

Chapter 34 Introduction to Your Body

Content Management	Student Edition Activities
■ Section 34–1 Organization of the Human Body, pp. *765–767* 100 Trillion Cells Levels of Organization	MINI LAB: Bones, Muscles, and Skin—Oh My!, p. *767*
■ Section 34–2 Communication and Control, pp. *768–773* The Nervous System The Endocrine System Endocrine System Control How Do Hormones Work?	Laboratory Investigation: *Daphnia* and Adrenaline, pp. *776–777*
◆ BRANCHING OUT • In Action Section 34–3 Physiology in Action, pp. *774–775* Human Physiology Getting Ready Preparing to Play Time for Action	MINI LAB: Dropping the Ball, p. *775*

■ These sections cover all the necessary content and concepts for an enriched course in biology.
◆ This section covers content and concepts that are either applications or extensions of the enriched material.

Integration Strategies

SE Chemistry, p. 773
BL Investigating Careers
Involving the Community
Science Through Art

Assessment Strategies

SE Chapter Review, pp. 778–781
TR Section Reviews
Chapter Test
Performance-Based Assessment
BL Investigating Further
Chapter Review
Practice Test
CTB Chapter 34 Test

Tech Prep

Teaching strategies appropriate for students who are in technical/vocational programs or who are considering post-secondary technical education can be found on the following **TE** page: 766.

Meeting the Standards

Sections 34–1 through 34–3 cover five of the six content standards under **The Cell** and one of the four content standards under **The Behavior of Organisms** as described on pages 184–185 and 187 of The National Science Education Standards.

Chapter Planning Guide

Teacher's Edition Activities	Other Activities	Media and Technology
Chapter Discovery Learning Activity, p. 764 **Activity:** Relating Organism Size and Cell Number, p. 765	**TR** **Explore:** Hard Cell—Soft Cell **BL** **Inquiry Activity:** Body Machines	**CD-ROM:** The Family Health Book
Investigate: Model Building, p. 769 **Investigate:** Cooperative Learning, p. 771 **Investigate:** Research, p. 771	**LM** Interpreting Information Through the Senses, #67 Observing Skin Sensitivity, #68 **TR** **Writing in Biology:** Biological Jeopardy! **Enrich:** Winter Woe **BL** **Inquiry Activity:** Body Talk	**TB** Hormone Action, #42
Inquiry Activity: Rating the Heart, p. 774 **Activity:** Fueling the Body, p. 774	**TR** **Explore:** Quick! **BL** **Inquiry Activity:** Strollin' Down the Pathways	

KEY: SE Student Edition **TE** Teacher's Edition **LM** Laboratory Manual **TR** Teaching Resources **BL** BioLog **TB** Transparency Box **CTB** Computer Test Bank

Materials List

TE Chapter Discovery Learning Activity, p. 764 (10 minutes); furniture or books in the classroom.

SE MINI LAB: Bones, Muscles, and Skin—Oh My!, p. 767 (10–20 minutes); hand lens, forceps, scalpel, cooked chicken leg with skin.

TE Investigate: Model Building, p. 769 (20 minutes); egg carton, scissors, water, coins or ping-pong balls or students' choice of materials.

TE Activity: Fueling the Body, p. 774 (20–30 minutes); chart of calories expended in different activities, chart of calories contained in foods, calculator.

SE MINI LAB: Dropping the Ball, p. 775 (10–20 minutes); one red ball labeled TRH, one green ball labeled TSH, three yellow balls labeled thyroxine.

CHAPTER 34

Introduction to Your Body

Introducing the Chapter

. . . In Pictures

Running a race uses most of the organ systems of the body, as well as their component cells and tissues. Have students examine the photograph, read the caption, and answer the following questions.

• **What body system will enable each runner to know when to start and stop running?** (The runner will hear a gunshot or command and see the finish line, using his or her senses of sight and hearing, which are parts of the nervous system.)

• **What body system will enable each runner's muscles to get the energy needed to move around the track?** (The blood, which is part of the circulatory system, will carry oxygen and glucose to the muscle cells, where they combine to produce energy.)

Teaching Strategy

In the first section of this chapter, the four basic types of tissues are defined and the major functions of the eleven organ systems are outlined. The next section explains how the nervous and endocrine systems communicate with and regulate the other organ systems. In the BRANCHING OUT section, the integrated functioning of the organ systems is illustrated with an example.

BIO JOURNAL

To help students think of the organ systems they would use in running a race, have them imagine how they would feel after running as fast as they could several times around a track. Then ask them to consider what their bodies would go through between starting the race and crossing the finish line. Instruct students to keep their entries in their portfolios.

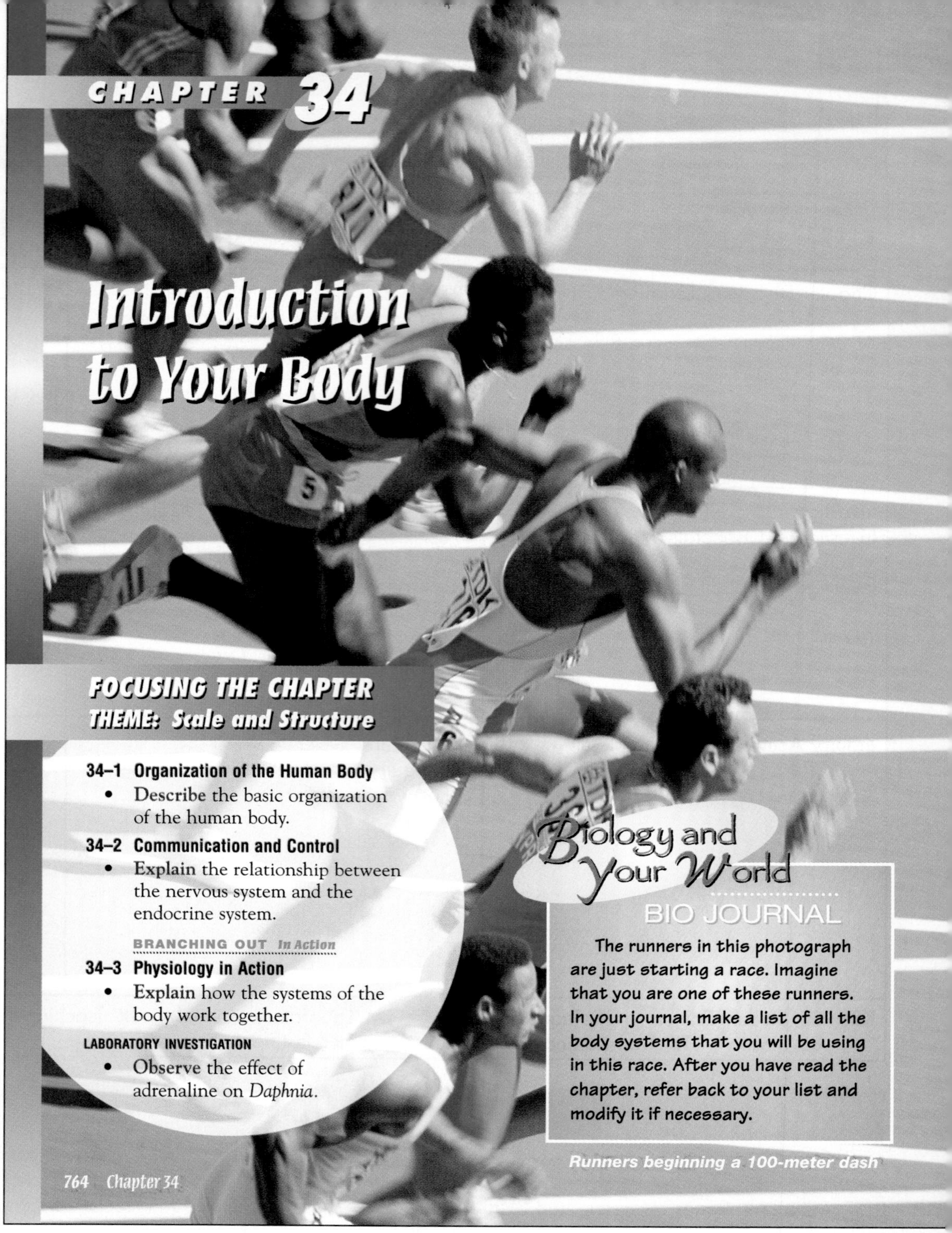

CHAPTER 34

Introduction to Your Body

FOCUSING THE CHAPTER
THEME: Scale and Structure

Biology and Your World

BIO JOURNAL

The runners in this photograph are just starting a race. Imagine that you are one of these runners. In your journal, make a list of all the body systems that you will be using in this race. After you have read the chapter, refer back to your list and modify it if necessary.

Runners beginning a 100-meter dash

TEACHER SUPPORT

Chapter Discovery Learning Activity

COMMUNICATION IN THE BODY

This activity will demonstrate the importance of communication among the organ systems of the body and will help students understand the significance of the nervous and endocrine systems in regulating body functions.

1. Divide the class into two groups, and have each group work to achieve the same simple goal, such as rearranging the furniture in the classroom or the books in a bookcase.

2. Instruct one group to avoid any form of communication and work independently toward the goal.

3. Instruct the other group to communicate freely and work together toward the goal.

Results: The group of students that communicates and works together is likely to achieve its goal quickly and easily; the other group is likely to have less success in achieving the goal.

Organization of the Human Body

SECTION 34–1

GUIDE FOR READING

- **Name** the four basic types of tissues.
- **List** the eleven organ systems of the body and describe their functions.

MINI LAB

- **Design an experiment** to observe the different types of tissue.

IT'S THE LAST INNING AND the score is tied as the batter looks over at her coach. The coach gives a series of signals, one of which is the signal to bunt. The batter's heart beats faster, because she knows that a successful bunt will score the winning run from third base. As the pitcher winds up, the batter takes a shallow breath. Her eyes follow the release of the ball, which becomes a blur as it spins toward the plate. The batter drops the bat to waist level, catches the ball squarely, and bunts it down the base line, just inside fair territory.

She drops the bat and runs toward first base. The runner from third sprints down the base line and slides easily across home plate. The winning run is scored!

100 Trillion Cells

A spectator watching a softball game might see this winning play as a remarkable example of teamwork between batter, base runner, and coach. As impressive as it might be, the real teamwork involves a much larger number of players—the 100 trillion cells that make up the human body. Each of these cells has a purpose of its own, but each is also part of something larger. How can so many individual cells work together? How are their activities controlled and coordinated? And how is the human body organized to use the activities of these cells to handle the everyday business of life? These are some of the questions that we will try to answer in this chapter and in those that follow.

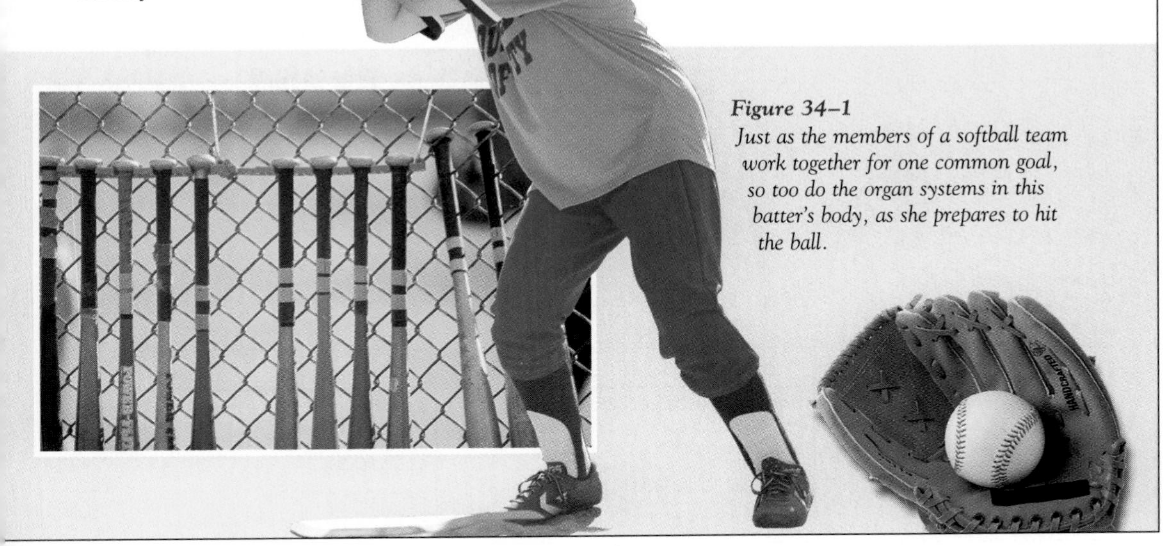

Figure 34–1
Just as the members of a softball team work together for one common goal, so too do the organ systems in this batter's body, as she prepares to hit the ball.

TEACHER SUPPORT

Activity

RELATING ORGANISM SIZE AND CELL NUMBER

Ask the class if they know why humans and other large organisms consist of trillions of cells instead of just a few large cells. Point out that the quantity of nutrients an organism needs and the amount of wastes it produces depend on its volume. However, its ability to take in nutrients and give off wastes depends on its surface area because all materials that enter or leave the body must cross one or more membranes. To show students how volume increases relative to surface area as organisms grow in size, have them calculate volumes and surface areas of increasingly larger cubes or cylinders. Lead them to conclude that large organisms, such as humans, must have trillions of cells in order to have enough surface area to match their metabolic needs.

SECTION 34–1

Organization of the Human Body

Performance Objectives

- Distinguish among epithelial, connective, nerve, and muscle tissues.
- Identify the primary roles of the body's 11 organ systems.

Mini Lab Skill: Experimenting

1 ENGAGE

Ideas Through Images

Have students examine Figure 34–1 and read the caption. Ask them to use what they already know about the body systems to answer the following questions. Doing so will help them appreciate how many different systems are involved in an activity such as the one shown.

- **Which organ systems is the batter using to maintain her stance with the bat?** (Skeletal, muscular, and nervous systems.)
- **Which organ system does the batter rely on to know how and when to hit the ball?** (Nervous system.)
- **Which organ systems will the batter need to help her run the bases?** (Skeletal, muscular, circulatory, respiratory, and nervous systems.)

Technology

CD-ROM
The Family Health Book

Ancillary Support

The resources below can be used to support your teaching strategy for these two pages.

TR Explore: Hard Cell—Soft Cell
BL Inquiry Activity: Body Machines

2 EXPLORE

Ideas Through Images

Have students examine Figure 34–2, read the caption, and answer the following questions.

- **Which body system protects the body from injury, infection, and dehydration?** (The integumentary system.)
- **What do you think is the main organ of the integumentary system?** (The skin.)
- **What is the function of the immune system?** (It fights off invading germs and protects the body from diseases and parasites.)
- **What other system do you think is closely tied to the immune system, and why?** (The circulatory system because specialized cells in blood fight invading germs and help protect the body from disease.)
- **How do you think the circulatory and respiratory systems are related?** (The respiratory system brings oxygen into the body, and the circulatory system carries oxygen to the cells. Students might also mention that carbon dioxide is carried by the circulatory system to the respiratory system [lungs], which rids the body of it.)
- **Of which system is the brain the main organ?** (The nervous system.)

3 TEACH

Discussion

Tell students that organs and organ systems often consist of all four types of tissues. Lead students in a discussion of why organs and organ systems show this diversity, considering a specific organ, such as the stomach. The function of the stomach is digestion; it has muscle tissue that functions to cause the stomach walls to contract; epithelial tissue that lines the stomach and blood vessels; and nerve tissue that coordinates the digestive system.

Figure 34–2
The human body contains eleven major organ systems. This chart lists each of these systems, along with its function.

SOME MAJOR BODY SYSTEMS

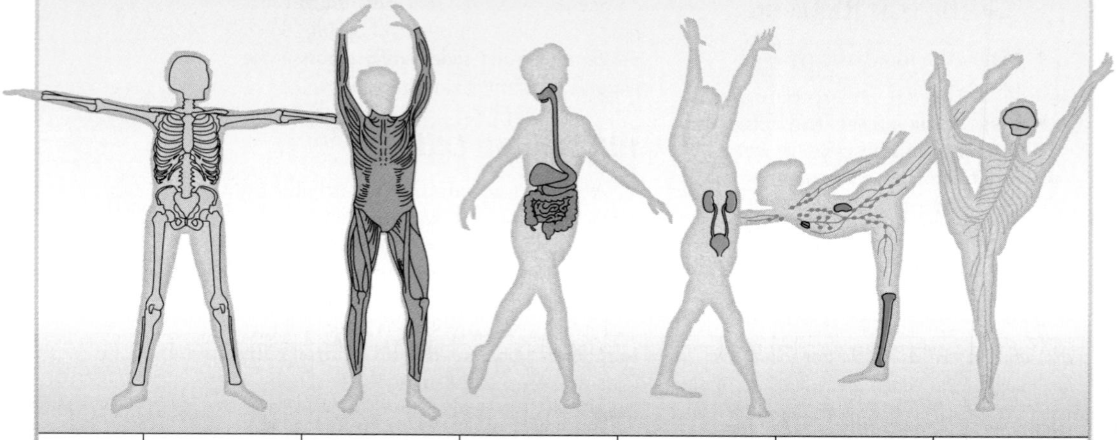

SYSTEM	Skeletal	Muscular	Digestive	Excretory	Immune	Nervous
Function	Supports and protects the body	Gives the body the ability to move	Processes food into a form that the cells of the body can use; absorbs food	Rids the body of wastes	Fights off invading germs; provides protection from diseases and parasites	Retrieves information and relays messages

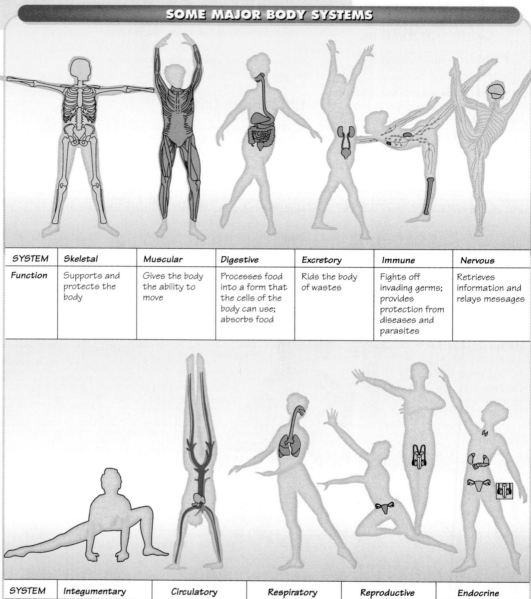

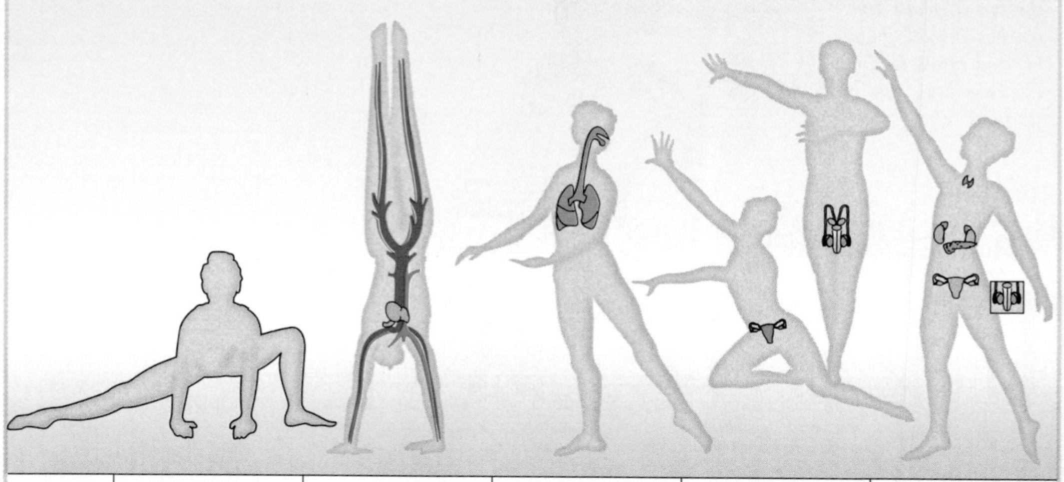

SYSTEM	Integumentary	Circulatory	Respiratory	Reproductive	Endocrine
Function	Protects the body from injury, infection, and dehydration	Brings oxygen, food, and chemical messages to cells	Brings oxygen to the body and rids the body of carbon dioxide	Produces reproductive cells; in females, nurtures and protects developing embryo	Helps to regulate and control the body's functions

TEACHER SUPPORT

Managing Classroom Diversity

TECH PREP STUDENTS

Encourage students who are interested in a career in health care to learn more about how tissues are studied by laboratory technicians for signs of disease, such as cancer. Have them interview a medical laboratory technician about a specific tissue test, such as a pap smear or biopsy. They should ask what tissues are collected, how they are prepared and examined, and what signs indicate the presence of disease. If possible, have students find illustrations of normal and abnormal tissues as they appear under the microscope to share with the rest of the class.

Levels of Organization

In a country with millions of people, every person is an individual. However, people sometimes associate in groups. The most basic of these groups is the family, but there are larger groups as well. Communities, counties, and states are groups of people who work together to organize and choose governments.

Tissues

As in a human society, it's possible to classify the cells of the human body into groups. A group of similar cells that perform a single function is called a **tissue.** Your body contains many tissues. **There are four basic types—epithelial** (ehp-ih-THEE-lee-uhl), **connective, nerve, and muscle tissues.** Epithelial tissue covers interior and exterior body surfaces. Connective tissue provides support for the body and connects all its parts. Nerve tissue transmits nerve impulses through the body. And muscle tissue, along with bones, enables the body to move.

Organs

A group of tissues that work together to perform a single function is called an **organ.** The eye is an organ made up of epithelial tissue, nerve tissue, muscle tissue, and connective tissue. As different as these tissues are, they all work together for a single function—sight.

MINI LAB Experimenting

Bones, Muscles, and Skin—Oh My!

PROBLEM *What types of tissue can you observe in a chicken leg? **Design an experiment** to answer this question.*

SUGGESTED PROCEDURE

1. Using a hand lens, forceps, and scalpel, design an experiment to observe the different types of tissues in a cooked chicken leg with skin.
2. Formulate a hypothesis and have your teacher approve your planned experiment.
3. Carry out your experiment. Identify the different tissues you observed.

ANALYZE AND CONCLUDE

1. From your observations, what tissues are present in the chicken leg?
2. Which tissue seems to be most plentiful? Explain the reason.

Organ Systems

An **organ system** is a group of organs that perform closely related functions. For example, the eye is one of the organs of the nervous system, which gathers information about the outside world and uses it to control many of the body's functions. ***Figure 34–2*** shows the eleven organ systems in the body.

Section Review 34-1

1. **Name** the four basic types of tissues.
2. **List** the eleven organ systems in the body and **describe** their functions.
3. **Critical Thinking—Relating Facts** The eleven systems of the human body are all dependent upon one another. Explain how a virus, which affects the respiratory system, could affect the other systems of the body.
4. **MINI LAB** What different types of tissue can you observe? **Design an experiment** to find out.

MINI LAB Experimenting

Teacher Notes

- For time required and materials needed, see page 764b.
- Warn students to use caution when handling the scalpel.
- Instruct students not to eat the chicken.
- Have students wash their hands immediately after they finish the procedure.

Answers to Analyze and Conclude

1. Epithelial tissue (skin, blood vessels), connective tissue (bone, cartilage, tendon), nerve tissue (nerves), and muscle tissue (muscles).
2. Students probably will say that muscle tissue is most plentiful because the animal needs muscles for moving the leg.

Skills Trace
Experimenting
- Focus p. 767
- Practice p. 767
- Assess p. 781

4 ASSESS

Quick Check

Call on a student to name one of the body's organ systems and describe its function. Continue through all 11 systems.

Section Review 34-1

1. Epithelial, connective, nerve, and muscle.

2. See Figure 34–2.

3. A typical answer might state that the immune system recognizes and destroys the virus; the excretory system removes the waste products; the circulatory system transports immune system cells to the site of infection; and the digestive system provides nutrients for recovery.

4. Accept all reasonable experimental designs. Types of tissues will vary depending on the design.

Skills Trace
Experimenting
- Focus p. 767
- Practice p. 767
- Assess p. 781

Learning Modality

Visual Learning Have students draw a diagram that shows the hierarchical organization of cells, tissues, organs, and organ systems.

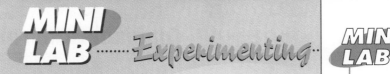

SECTION 34–2
Communication and Control

Performance Objectives
• List the glands that make up the endocrine system and identify their functions.
• Describe how the endocrine system is controlled by negative feedback.

Laboratory Investigation Skill: Experimenting

1 ENGAGE

Ideas Through Images
Have students examine Figure 34–3, read the caption, and answer the following questions. This will help students understand how and why organ systems communicate.

• **What are some other forms of communication among people?** (Television, radio, fax, voice mail.)

• **Which forms of communication are two-way, allowing the speaker to get feedback from the listener?** (Talking in person or on the phone.)

• **Why might different organ systems need to communicate with one another?** (Students may say that different organ systems might need to communicate in order to work together toward a common goal, such as moving a runner around a track.)

• **How might organ systems have two-way communication?** (Students may say that the actions or products of two different organ systems might affect each other.)

SECTION
34–2 Communication and Control

Guide for Reading
- **Describe** the endocrine system.
- **Explain** how negative feedback works.

IN A HUMAN SOCIETY, THERE are many forms of communication. Every day, you communicate with your teacher and with other students by writing or speaking to them. You use this kind of communication to express your thoughts and ideas, to ask questions, and to exchange greetings.

Communication is even more important in a large society. Think of the ways in which newspapers and magazines affect your view of the world. Remember the images that you may have seen on television last night. In many ways, these mass communications bind the people of a society together with common experiences and expose them to a range of diverse ideas. The same principle applies to the cells, tissues, organs, and organ systems of the body. Unless they communicate, they cannot act together.

The Nervous System
Similar to a telephone network that reaches every home and office in a large city, the body contains a cellular network that carries messages from cell to cell. That network is the **nervous system.** The message-carrying cells of the nervous system are called **neurons.** Neurons can relay signals from one end of a cell to the other. They can also pass these impulses from cell to cell.

You can think of neurons as tiny wires in a vast communications network. They gather information from every region of the body and relay it to central locations. Here the information can be analyzed, then instructions and commands can be carried to organs throughout the body.

The center of this network is the brain, where impulses arrive from every part of the body. In the brain they are analyzed and compared, past information is stored and retrieved, and appropriate responses are sent back out through the network.

Figure 34–3 *Communication is an important means of exchanging information. In the body, the nervous system and endocrine system are responsible for communication. (a) Talking with your friends, (b) speaking on the telephone, and (c) reading newspapers are three common ways in which information is passed from person to person.*

TEACHER SUPPORT
Background Information
Both nervous and endocrine systems are important for homeostasis, or the control of body responses to changing internal and external conditions. In both systems, the structure or process being controlled may be located far from the control center. Despite these similarities, there are several important differences between the two types of control. For one, nervous control is found only in animals, whereas chemical control is found in all organisms. In addition, nervous control is usually much more rapid. Several hours or even days may elapse between the release of a chemical messenger by the endocrine system and the response by the cells that are sensitive to the messenger. Nerve impulses, in contrast, typically relay information about events in one part of the body to another in less than a second.

The Endocrine System

If you wanted to send a message to just one or two people, you could call them on the telephone. But if you had to reach thousands of people at the same time, you might broadcast your message on radio or television.

It might not have radio or television, but your body does have a chemical "broadcasting" system that can send messages to millions of cells at the same time. This broadcasting system is the **endocrine system.** ***Figure 34–4*** illustrates the endocrine system. **The endocrine system is made up of a series of glands located throughout the body. Glands are organs that produce and release chemicals, and endocrine glands generally release their chemicals into the bloodstream.**

Hormones

Unlike the organs of the nervous system, the endocrine glands are not connected to one another. The endocrine glands send signals between each other and to other cells in the body.

These signals are produced by the endocrine glands in the form of **hormones**—the chemicals that travel through the bloodstream and affect the behavior of other cells. Only those cells that have **receptors**—specific chemical binding sites—for a particular hormone can respond to it. Cells that have receptors for a particular hormone are called **target cells.** Hormone receptors are similar to radios tuned to just one station. A cell that does not have receptors for a hormone cannot respond to it, just as you would miss an announcement on a jazz station if you were listening to a rock station.

Checkpoint What are hormones? 1

HUMAN ENDOCRINE GLANDS

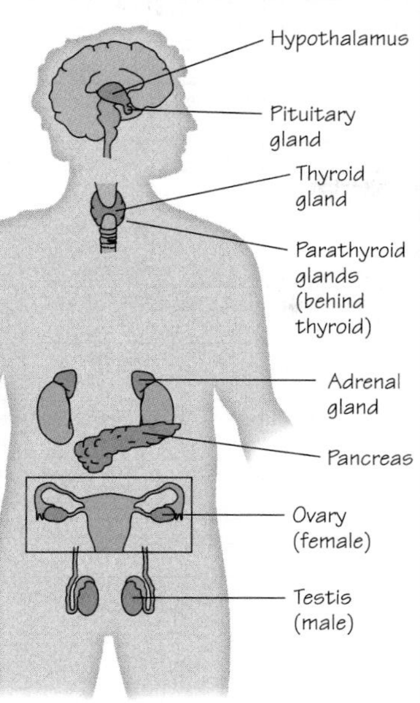

Figure 34–4 *The endocrine system consists of glands located throughout the body. Notice that in females the sex glands are called ovaries and in males they are called testes.*

Pituitary Gland

A network of broadcasting stations usually has a place where the activities of individual stations are coordinated—and the endocrine system is no exception. Its headquarters is a tiny structure at the base of the brain known as the

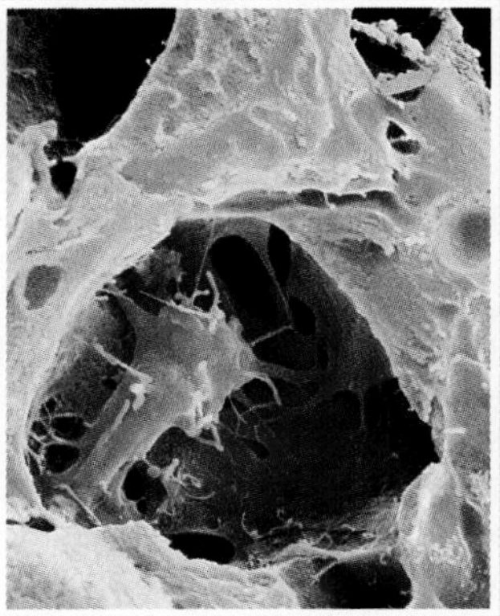

Figure 34–5 *The pituitary gland, located in the brain, is responsible for secreting nine different hormones. In this scanning electron micrograph, the pituitary gland is colored a pale red-brown. The yellow objects in the center and top of the gland are large white blood cells (magnification: 2100X).*

2 EXPLORE

Investigate

Model Building Have students investigate the role of receptor cells in tissues by building a model. Suggest that they use a procedure such as the following.

1. Represent the target tissue with an empty egg carton; represent target cells in the tissue by cutting small holes over a few of the sections of the carton.

2. Pour water over the top of the egg carton in a gentle stream to represent a circulating hormone.

3. Compare the receptor cells with the others. Which ones contain hormone?

Point out to students that receptor cells sometimes respond to chemicals other than hormones in the blood. Chemicals from food, for example, may bind to receptor sites and prohibit hormones from entering the cell. Ask students to think of a way to simulate this action using their model. (One possibility is to use coins, ping-pong balls, or other objects to represent molecules of the chemical and place them over the holes in the egg carton. When water is poured over the carton, the chemicals will keep the hormone from entering the "target cells.")

Checkpoint

1 Hormones are chemicals that travel through the bloodstream and affect the behavior of other cells.

TEACHER SUPPORT

Background Information

Although the endocrine glands serve the crucial role of regulating the functions of the rest of the body, they are surprisingly small. Most human endocrine tissue can fit into the palm of one hand. The pituitary gland is only about the size of a pea.

The hormones that the endocrine glands produce are extremely potent chemicals. Most are effective at very low concentrations, even as low as one part per million parts of blood. Estrogen is a good example. It controls the reproductive system throughout a female's life, yet the average female produces only about a teaspoon of estrogen in her lifetime.

Ancillary Support

The resources below can be used to support your teaching strategy for these two pages.

LM Interpreting Information Through the Senses, #67
Observing Skin Sensitivity, #68

BL Inquiry Activity: Body Talk

3 TEACH

Ideas Through Images

Have students examine Figure 34–6, read the caption, and answer the following questions. Answering the questions will give students a better understanding of how the pituitary gland regulates the rest of the endocrine system.

- **What is the target organ or tissue of each of the following pituitary hormones: FSH, LH, ACTH, PTH, and oxytocin?** (Ovary and testes [FSH and LH], adrenal gland, bone, and uterus, respectively.)
- **Which pituitary hormones control the output of the following hormones produced by other glands: thyroxine, testosterone, adrenaline, and cortisol?** (TSH, LH, and ACTH [adrenaline and cortisol], respectively.)
- **What organ systems are regulated by pituitary hormones?** (Systems include reproductive, circulatory, digestive, excretory, muscular, and skeletal systems.)

Correcting Misconceptions

It is a common misconception that females produce only estrogen and males produce only testosterone. Explain that the adrenal gland in both genders produces small quantities of both estrogen and testosterone. In addition, estrogen and testosterone are very similar chemically and can be readily converted by the body from one to the other. Have students find the chemical composition of both hormones in a chemistry book and try to identify how they differ.

Laboratory Investigation

The Laboratory Investigation, *Daphnia* and Adrenaline, on pages 776–777 is appropriate to use at this point in the chapter.

HORMONES AND THEIR ACTIONS

Gland	Hormone	Action
Thyroid	Thyroxine	Increases metabolic rate and body temperature; regulates growth and development
	Calcitonin	Inhibits release of calcium from bone
Parathyroid	Parathyroid hormone (PTH)	Stimulates release of calcium from bone
Pituitary	Antidiuretic hormone (ADH)	Stimulates reabsorption of water
	Oxytocin	Stimulates uterine contractions and release of milk
	Follicle-stimulating hormone (FSH)	Stimulates follicle maturation in females and sperm production in males
	Luteinizing hormone (LH)	Stimulates ovulation and growth of corpus luteum in females and testosterone secretion in males
	Thyroid-stimulating hormone (TSH)	Stimulates thyroid to release thyroxine
	Adrenocorticotropic hormone (ACTH)	Stimulates adrenal cortex to release hormones
	Growth hormone (GH) or somatropin	Stimulates growth; synthesizes protein; inhibits glucose oxidation
	Prolactin	Stimulates milk production
Adrenal	Aldosterone	Controls salt and water balance
	Cortisol, other corticosteroids	Regulate carbohydrate, protein, and fat metabolism
	Adrenaline and noradrenaline	Initiate the body's response to stress; increase blood glucose level; dilate blood vessels; increase rate and strength of heartbeat; increase metabolic rate
Pancreas	Glucagon	Stimulates conversion of glycogen to glucose, raising the blood glucose level
	Insulin	Stimulates conversion of glucose to glycogen, lowering the blood glucose level
Ovary	Estrogen	Develops and maintains female sex characteristics; initiates buildup of uterine lining
	Progesterone	Promotes continued growth of uterine lining and formation of placenta
Testis	Testosterone	Develops and maintains male sex characteristics; stimulates sperm development

Figure 34–6
Each gland of the endocrine system releases a different hormone. This chart lists the endocrine gland, the hormone or hormones it produces, as well as the action of each hormone.

pituitary gland. The hormones produced by the pituitary gland are important because many of them regulate the other endocrine glands.

Hypothalamus

What controls the pituitary gland? The pituitary gland is attached to a region of the brain known as the **hypothalamus** (high-poh-THAL-uh-muhs). Either directly or indirectly, the hypothalamus controls the release of hormones from the pituitary gland.

Some hormones released from the pituitary gland are actually made in the hypothalamus. Others are made in the pituitary gland, then released into the bloodstream only when chemical signals are received from the hypothalamus.

The link between the hypothalamus and the pituitary gland is important for two reasons. First, it explains how the pituitary gland works, controlling the activities of other endocrine glands in response to signals that it receives from the hypothalamus. Second, it shows that the nervous system and the endocrine system are interconnected. That means that input into the nervous system can influence the endocrine system by way of the connection between the hypothalamus and the pituitary gland.

☑ ***Checkpoint*** Where in the body is the hypothalamus found? 1

770 Chapter 34

TEACHER SUPPORT

Historical Perspective

Because of the important role the hypothalamus plays in regulating most body systems, it is not surprising that disorders of the hypothalamus can wreak havoc on the body. In fact, hypothalamic disorders may even have changed the course of history. Most scholars agree that Napoleon Bonaparte was afflicted with a hypothalamic disorder. The progress of the disease is apparent from accounts of Napoleon's appearance and behavior. In his 20s, he was trim and energetic, sleeping just a few hours each night. By the time he was in his 40s, however, he was chubby and lethargic, slept day and night, and was mentally confused. It is interesting to speculate what course history might have taken had Napoleon's disorder been treatable during his lifetime.

Figure 34–7
CAREER TRACK
A biomedical equipment technician is responsible for the maintenance and repair of medical equipment. In this photograph, a technician is running an annual validation test for temperature and temperature uniformity on a sterilizing oven in a pharmaceutical research facility.

Endocrine System Control

To better understand how the endocrine system works, let's take a look at one of the body's most important hormones, thyroxine. Thyroxine is made by the **thyroid gland.** To make thyroxine, the thyroid gland needs the amino acid tyrosine and a small amount of iodine, which must be obtained from food.

Thyroxine affects nearly all the body's cells, increasing their metabolic rate—the rate at which they use food and oxygen. It also increases the rate at which cells grow.

Too much thyroxine in the bloodstream results in increased blood pressure, nervousness, increased pulse rate, and dangerous weight loss. Too little thyroxine results in a lowered pulse rate, lowered blood pressure, excessive sleepiness, and weight gain. How does the thyroid gland usually manage to get the level of this important hormone just right?

Control in the Hypothalamus

Like most cells in the body, the cells of the hypothalamus also have receptors for thyroxine. When levels of thyroxine drop, most cells slow down their activity, but some cells of the hypothalamus increase their activity. These cells now produce more of a thyroid-releasing hormone (TRH).

Remember how close the hypothalamus is to the pituitary? TRH travels from the hypothalamus to the pituitary gland through a network of tiny blood vessels. It then causes cells in the pituitary gland to release increased amounts of another hormone, thyroid-stimulating hormone (TSH), into the bloodstream. The target cells for TSH are the cells of the thyroid gland itself. TSH causes the thyroid gland to release more thyroxine.

Feedback Regulation

As you can see, the combination of the hypothalamus, pituitary gland, and thyroid gland automatically regulates the level of thyroxine in the bloodstream. When there is too little thyroxine in the blood, the thyroid gland is stimulated by TSH to make more. When there is too much thyroxine, TSH is not released, and the thyroid gland makes less. You could say that the activity of the thyroid gland "feeds back" to the hypothalamus. When the thyroid gland is working too fast, its own product—thyroxine—causes the hypothalamus to signal the thyroid gland to slow down. When it is working too slow, low levels of thyroxine cause the hypothalamus to signal the thyroid gland to speed up.

The relationship between the thyroid gland and the hypothalamus is an example of **negative feedback.** In humans, the release of hormones is regulated through negative feedback. **Through negative feedback, the secretion of a hormone inhibits further production of another hormone.** Negative feedback enables the conditions within the body to remain relatively constant over time.

Investigate

Cooperative Learning Divide the class into two groups, and ask each group to think of as many solutions as possible to a problem, such as how to raise money for a club. Have students in one group work individually on the problem, while students in the other group brainstorm together in another room. After 10 to 15 minutes, reassemble the class and ask the groups to share their ideas. Lead the class in a discussion of how the feedback provided by other members of the brainstorming group stimulated each student to think of more ideas compared with the students who worked alone. Ask whether this is an example of positive or negative feedback, and have students explain the difference. (It is an example of positive feedback. Positive feedback promotes an activity; negative feedback inhibits it.) Finally, have the class discuss how a positive feedback hormonal control system might function.

Investigate

Research Ask students to research the feedback system that controls the output of the pancreatic hormones, insulin and glucagon. Based on what they learn, have them draw a diagram or graph to show the relationship between blood glucose levels and hormone production. Ask volunteers to share their work with the rest of the class.

Checkpoint

1 The hypothalamus is located in the brain.

TEACHER SUPPORT

Historical Perspective

The first evidence that the pancreas is involved in the disease diabetes mellitus goes back to the late 1800s. Two German scientists who were studying the role of the pancreas in digestion removed the pancreas from some dogs, but not from others. By chance, they noticed that the urine of the dogs without a pancreas attracted bees and other insects. That of the normal dogs did not. They concluded that the urine of the dogs without a pancreas contained sugar, as was known to be true of people with diabetes. This led to more research into the connection between the pancreas and diabetes, and ultimately to the discovery of the pancreatic hormone, insulin.

Ancillary Support

The resource below can be used to support your teaching strategy for these two pages.

TR Enrich: Winter Woe

Connections

To put the material in the Connections feature in a broader context, tell students that any time the body does not have enough thyroid hormone, a condition known as hypothyroidism results. Point out that lack of iodine in the diet is just one of many possible causes of hypothyroidism. Have students investigate some of the other causes. (See Background Information below.)

Thyroxine is a small molecule, yet its role in the body is enormous. Because every tissue requires thyroxine for normal growth and development, infants and young children who lack thyroxine are likely to suffer numerous abnormalities and delays in development, including stunted growth and mental retardation. In adults, lack of thyroxine leads to a condition called myxedema, which is characterized by lethargy, puffiness, mental dullness, and numerous other changes.

Lead the class in a discussion of why the effects of iodine deficiency in adults are reversible, whereas in children they are permanent. Point out that when people become iodine deficient, their thyroxine levels do not drop immediately. This is because the thyroid is unique among the endocrine glands in storing large amounts of hormone, which it releases slowly. In fact, there is enough thyroxine in the normal adult thyroid gland to last about 100 days.

Answers to Making the Connection

Other places where people might not be able to get the iodine they need include mountainous inland regions, such as Switzerland, Ecuador, and the Himalayas. Solutions to solve the problem of cost versus health may vary. Possible solutions might include a government subsidy to salt manufacturers to defray the additional cost of iodizing salt.

Biology and You Connections

The Salt Connection

As you have just read, thyroxine is a hormone produced by the thyroid gland and needed by the body for its cells to function properly. Thyroxine not only stimulates nerve cell growth, it is also important for brain development.

In order to produce thyroxine, the thyroid gland requires a small amount of the mineral iodine. Like all minerals, the iodine that is needed to make thyroxine must be obtained from the foods we eat. Because iodine is rarely found in soil, most foods contain very little. Fortunately, seafood is rich in iodine, and eating a small amount of seafood every now and then provides the iodine your body needs.

Iodine Deficiency

What happens if your diet does not contain the small amount of iodine your body needs? The thyroid gland attempts to compensate for the lack of iodine. It does this by increasing in size so that it can absorb as many atoms of iodine as possible. This increase in size produces a noticeable swelling of the thyroid gland, a condition called goiter.

At one time, goiter was common in parts of the midwestern United States, where seafood was hard to get. Today, however, goiter is almost unheard of in the United States. Why have incidences of goiter decreased? Because in many countries, table salt is now iodized. Trace amounts of iodine are added to much of the table salt in the United States and other industrial nations. A few sprinkles of iodized salt can supply enough iodine for the body to make all the thyroxine it needs.

Iodized salt

Severe Problems

For children, the consequences of iodine deficiency are much more severe than for adults. Because the developing brain requires thyroxine to stimulate nerve cell growth, lack of thyroxine can result in mental retardation.

Unfortunately, some parts of the world have been slow to initiate production of iodized salt to supplement the diets of people who live inland and do not eat seafood. One such place is China, and that country is experiencing a major health crisis because the diets of many Chinese people do not contain enough iodine. The Public Health Ministry of China estimates that as many as 10 million Chinese now suffer mental retardation because of iodine deficiencies during childhood.

Recently, public health authorities in China have realized the severity of the health crisis in their country. They're now rushing to ensure that iodized salt becomes available in all parts of China as soon as possible.

Making the Connection

Can you think of places other than inland China where people might not be able to get the iodine they need? Iodized salt is more expensive in China than regular salt. What solutions would you offer to solve the problem of cost versus health?

772 Chapter 34

Teacher Support: Background Information

After iodine deficiency, one of the most common causes of hypothyroidism is Hashimoto's disease, which is far more common in females than males. Hashimoto's disease is believed to be caused by an abnormality of the immune system, which leads to infiltration of the thyroid gland by white blood cells. As a result, the thyroid loses its ability to produce thyroxine. In contrast to hypothyroidism, some people have too much thyroid hormone, a condition called hyperthyroidism, which can also have a variety of causes. Again, females are more likely to be affected. The most common cause of hyperthyroidism is Graves' disease. Signs and symptoms include bulging eyes, enlarged thyroid gland, rapid heart rate, hand tremor, and weight loss. Like Hashimoto's disease, Graves' disease is thought to be an autoimmune disorder.

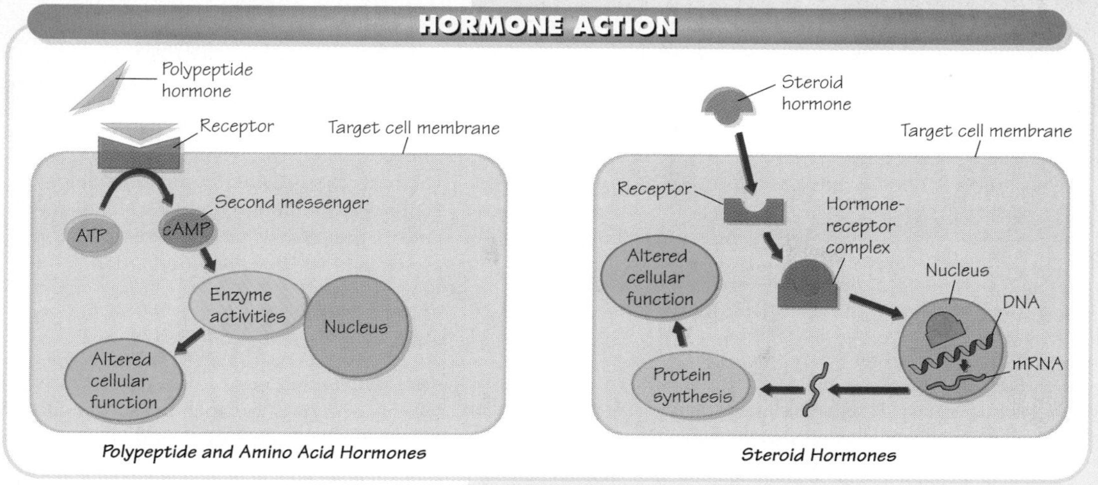

Figure 34–8
Polypeptide and amino acid hormones do not enter the cell, but bind to receptors on the cell membrane where they activate second messengers, such as cAMP. Steroid hormones enter the cell and bind to receptors inside it.

How Do Hormones Work?

Hormones come in many different shapes and sizes. Some are proteins, others are lipids, and still others are chemically modified amino acids. How do hormones affect their target cells?

There are two basic patterns of hormone action. Polypeptide and amino acid hormones bind to receptors on the cell surface. ● As ***Figure 34–8*** shows, when a hormone binds to a receptor on the cell surface, it activates enzymes on the inner side of the cell membrane to produce a large number of second messenger molecules. These second messengers may be ions such as Ca^{2+} or small molecules such as cyclic adenosine monophosphate, cAMP. Once released, these second messengers can activate or inhibit a wide range of other cell activities.

Unlike the polypeptide hormones, steroid hormones easily pass across the cell membrane. Steroid hormones are lipids produced from cholesterol. Target cells for these hormones have protein receptors that tightly bind to a specific steroid hormone. This hormone-receptor complex, as it is called, enters the nucleus, where it binds to a specific DNA sequence. Hormone receptor complexes work as regulators of gene expression—they can turn on or turn off whole sets of genes. Steroid hormones, which directly affect gene expression, can produce dramatic changes in cellular function.

INTEGRATING CHEMISTRY

What are polypeptides? What are amino acids? Use a chemistry textbook to find out.

Section Review 34–2

1. **Describe** the function of the endocrine system.
2. **Explain** how negative feedback works.
3. **Critical Thinking—Comparing** How do polypeptide and steroid hormones compare in terms of hormone action?

INTEGRATING CHEMISTRY

Polypeptides are large molecules containing chains of amino acids. Amino acids are the nitrogen-containing compounds that form polypeptides and proteins.

4 ASSESS

Quick Check

Have students draw a flowchart to show how a low level of thyroxine in the bloodstream results in increased output of this hormone by the thyroid gland.

Section Review 34–2

1. The function of the endocrine system is to regulate the other systems of the body. It does this by releasing hormones that travel to target cells where they activate or inhibit cellular activities.
2. In negative feedback, the secretion of one hormone inhibits further production of another hormone.
3. Polypeptide hormones bind to receptors on the surface of target cells and activate enzymes on the inner side of the cell membrane to produce messenger molecules. Steroid hormones, in comparison, pass across the cell membrane and bind with protein receptors inside the cell.

Learning Modality

Tactile Learning Have students use clay or other materials to demonstrate how hormones pass through or bind to target cell membranes and affect target cell functioning.

TEACHER SUPPORT

Ecology Note

Since 1940, the average human sperm count has dropped by almost half, partly due to a corresponding increase in environmental pollution. Many chemicals—coming from herbicides, plastics, and other sources—enter the body in the food we eat and the water we drink. There they act like estrogen and compete with testosterone in males, passing through cell membranes and binding to receptor proteins. These environmental estrogens have been called "gender benders" because they lead to development problems in male fetuses and low sperm counts in men. Similar problems have also been documented in wild animal populations that have been exposed to high levels of environmental estrogens.

Ancillary Support

The resources below can be used to support your teaching strategy for these two pages.

TR Writing in Biology: Biological Jeopardy
TB Hormone Action, #42

Section 34–3
Physiology in Action

Performance Objective
• Identify the field that studies how the body works.

Mini Lab Skill: Modeling

1 ENGAGE

Inquiry Activity
Designing an Experiment
Rating the Heart

Ask students how different types of activities affect heart rate. For example, does the heart beat faster when someone is swimming or running, playing a video game or talking on the telephone? Have students design an experiment to find out. First, they must decide how they will monitor subjects' heart rates. (By repeatedly taking subjects' pulse or by connecting them to an ECG machine.) Also, they should consider how individual variation in heart rate might affect their results. (People who are fit or trained in the activity are likely to have a lower heart rate.)

2 EXPLORE

Discussion
Ask students to recall the softball player from the first section. How can the anxiety she probably feels as she steps to the plate to bat lead to the production of adrenaline and physical changes (such as faster heart rate and greater blood flow to the muscles)? Guide the discussion by asking what gland produces adrenaline (the adrenal cortex), what hormone stimulates the adrenal cortex (ACTH produced by the pituitary gland), and what stimulates the pituitary to produce ACTH (nervous impulses from the hypothalamus).

SECTION 34–3 BRANCHING OUT *In Action*

Physiology in Action

Guide for Reading

- **Define** human physiology.

MINI LAB
- **Construct a model** of negative feedback in the endocrine system.

AS COMPLICATED AS IT IS, IT sometimes seems remarkable to think that all the cells of the human body are capable of working together for a common purpose. How does this happen? To take a case in point, how did the body of the ballplayer we described at the beginning of the chapter make it possible for her to drive in the winning run?

Human Physiology

When you think about the variety of things your body is capable of doing—including the simple things you take for granted—you realize how incredible the human body is. **The study of how the body works is called human physiology** (fihz-ee-AHL-uh-jee). Let's use the example of the softball player to see how the systems of the body work together.

Getting Ready

Two days ago, this player missed practice because she had chills and a fever. Today she feels better because her immune system fought off a cold virus.

At lunch time, she ate two slices of pizza, a salad, a glass of milk, and an apple. Her digestive system quickly broke down the complex molecules in this food so they could be absorbed into the blood of the circulatory system. The sugars from that meal were carried throughout the body, providing her with energy.

Preparing to Play

As she waited in the on-deck circle, the pressure was on her to bring home the third-base runner. Her nervous

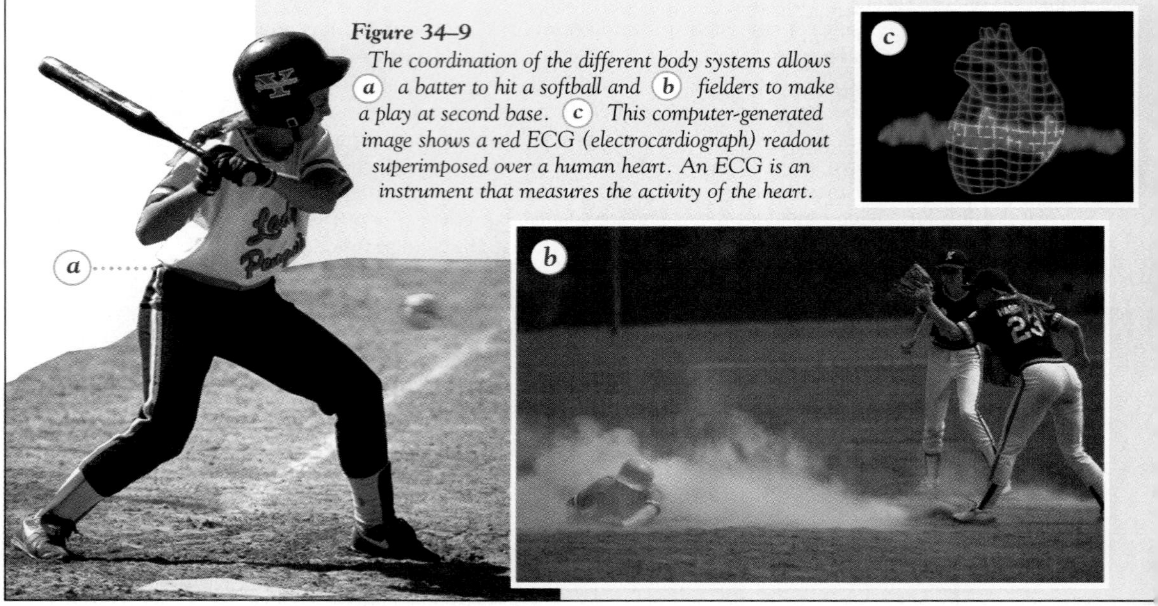

Figure 34–9 The coordination of the different body systems allows (a) a batter to hit a softball and (b) fielders to make a play at second base. (c) This computer-generated image shows a red ECG (electrocardiograph) readout superimposed over a human heart. An ECG is an instrument that measures the activity of the heart.

TEACHER SUPPORT

Activity

FUELING THE BODY

Point out to the class that activities such as sports require more energy than activities such as reading a book or playing a video game. Provide students with a chart that shows the number of calories needed per hour for different activities. Have them estimate how many calories someone would need to play two hours of softball. Ask them to consider what factors influence how much energy an individual needs for a particular activity. Then have students estimate how much energy in calories the batter got from her lunch. Do they think the batter consumed enough calories to give her the energy she needs to play softball for two hours? If the batter had not eaten enough to fuel the entire game, where would the extra energy come from?

system buzzed with anxiety, and that message was passed to the endocrine system. Nerve impulses stimulated the adrenal cortex to release adrenaline into the bloodstream. Within seconds, her heart rate and blood pressure rose, and the blood supply to her muscles increased.

With a few deep breaths, her respiratory system cleared the carbon dioxide from her lungs and filled her blood with the oxygen it needed. As her coach flashed a series of signals, her nervous system searched her stored memory of pre-game plans to recall the signs.

Time for Action

As the pitcher threw the ball to the plate, the batter's eyes watched the ball. Her nervous system took less than three tenths of a second to realize that the ball was headed for the strike zone. Instantly, nerves carried the message to key muscles in her arms and legs.

After she bunted the ball, her nervous system issued a new set of commands to the muscular system. Now muscles in her legs contracted in a pattern that placed tremendous force on the long bones of the skeletal system, enabling her to run.

As she continued to run, her respiratory system provided more oxygen to the bloodstream, and her muscles quickly used the energy stored in them. Finally, as she crossed the base safely, she relaxed.

MINI LAB Modeling

Dropping the Ball

PROBLEM *How can you construct a model of negative feedback in the endocrine system?*

PROCEDURE

1. Working with three other students, stand in a line. The first person in line will be the hypothalamus. The second person will be the pituitary gland, the third person will be the thyroid gland, and the fourth person will be the body.
2. Give the *hypothalamus* a red ball labeled TRH, the *pituitary gland* a green ball labeled TSH, and the *thyroid gland* 3 yellow balls labeled thyroxine, to be held in one hand.
3. At a signal from the *body,* the *hypothalamus* passes the TRH ball to the *pituitary gland.* The *pituitary gland* passes the TSH ball to the *thyroid gland.* The *thyroid gland* passes one thyroxine ball to the right hand of the *body* and a second thyroxine ball to the left hand of the *body.*
4. The *body* is now saturated with thyroxine. In order to accept the last thyroxine, the *body* must pass one thyroxine to the *hypothalamus.* The *body* is now able to accept the third thyroxine.
5. When the *hypothalamus* receives the thyroxine, the *thyroid gland* should drop the TSH ball.

ANALYZE AND CONCLUDE

1. What is the function of TRH? Of TSH?
2. Why did the *body* pass the thyroxine to the *hypothalamus?* What effect did this have?
3. What would happen if the *body* kept accepting thyroxine?

Section Review 34-3

1. **Define** human physiology.
2. **MINI LAB** How did you **construct a model** of negative feedback in the endocrine system?
3. **BRANCHING OUT ACTIVITY** Imagine that you are about to take a final exam. In a one-page essay, **summarize** how the systems of your body will work together to prepare you for this task and to carry it through.

3 TEACH

MINI LAB Modeling

Teacher Note

- For time required and materials needed, see page 764b.

Answers to Analyze and Conclude

1. To stimulate the pituitary gland to produce TSH; to stimulate the thyroid gland to release thyroxine.
2. To indicate the level of the hormone was high enough and the *body* did not need more.
3. The *hypothalamus* would keep signaling the *pituitary* to stimulate *thyroid* production of the hormone.

Skills Trace
Modeling
- Focus p. 775
- Practice p. 775
- Assess p. 780

4 ASSESS

Quick Check

Show students photographs of people involved in a variety of activities. Have them summarize the roles of the major organ systems involved in each activity.

Section Review 34-3

1. The study of how the body works.

2. Students created a model of negative feedback by having the hypothalamus stop stimulating the thyroid gland, via the pituitary, to produce more thyroxine once the level in the body was high enough.

Skills Trace
Modeling
- Focus p. 775
- Practice p. 775
- Assess p. 780

3. Students' essays should show they understand that an activity must be regulated and controlled by the nervous and endocrine systems.

Learning Modality

Kinesthetic Learning Write a list of different organ systems on the chalkboard. Then ask volunteers to demonstrate a variety of indoor activities that use all or most of the organ systems listed.

Ancillary Support

The resources below can be used to support your teaching strategy for these two pages.

TR Explore: Quick!
BL Inquiry Activity: Strollin' Down the Pathways

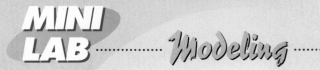

Chapter 34

Laboratory Investigation

Daphnia and Adrenaline

Before the Lab

1. Obtain adrenaline from a biological supply company; obtain *Daphnia* from an aquarium store or biological supply company.
2. Dilute the adrenaline with distilled water to obtain the correct concentration.

Pre-Lab Discussion

Have students read the entire procedure for this investigation. Then ask students the following questions.

What is the purpose of this investigation? (To determine the effect of adrenaline on heart rate.)

What gland produces adrenaline, and what hormone regulates its production? (The adrenal gland produces adrenaline. The pituitary hormone ACTH regulates the production of adrenaline.)

How does adrenaline affect the body? (It increases blood glucose levels, dilates blood vessels, increases rate and strength of heartbeat, and increases metabolic rate.)

Under natural conditions, when does the body increase its production of adrenaline? (During times of stress.)

Skills Development

Students will use these skills while completing the laboratory investigation: hypothesizing, designing an experiment, measuring, communicating, and interpreting data.

Teaching Strategies

1. If students transfer more than one *Daphnia* to the slide, ask them to try to return the extras to the culture or to share them with classmates.
2. To help students locate the heart, point out that it looks like a sac just below the curve of the back.

CHAPTER 34

Laboratory Investigation

DESIGNING AN EXPERIMENT

Daphnia and Adrenaline

Although hormones are very small molecules that are released in minute amounts, they cause very noticeable effects in an organism. Adrenaline is a hormone that prepares the body to deal with stress. It increases the heart rate and the metabolic rate. In this investigation, you will observe the heart of a small crustacean called *Daphnia*, or water flea, and you will determine the effects adrenaline has on its heart.

Problem

What can you observe about the effect adrenaline has on a *Daphnia*? **Design an experiment** to answer this question.

Suggested Materials

Daphnia culture
0.01% adrenaline solution
depression slides
medicine droppers
microscope

DAPHNIA

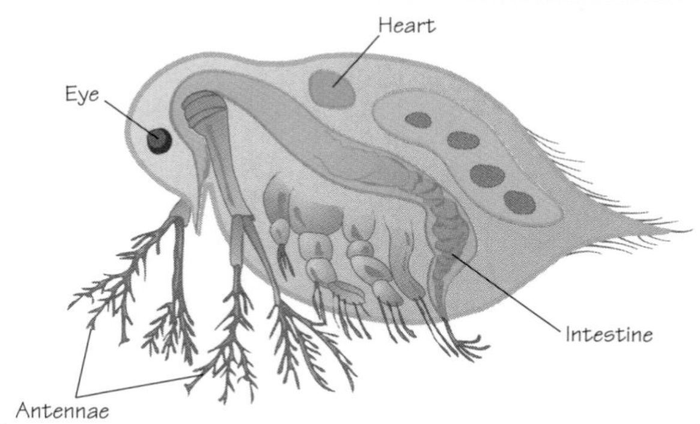

Suggested Procedure

1. **Use the medicine dropper to transfer a single *Daphnia* from the culture to the center of the depression slide. The *Daphnia* will look like a small white dot.**
2. **Place the slide under the low-power objective of a microscope and observe the *Daphnia*. Locate the heart.**
3. **Count the number of times the heart beats in one minute. Record this information in a data table similar to Data Table 1.**
4. **Repeat step 3 two more times. Then average the three measurements. Record your data. Return the *Daphnia* to the culture dish.**
5. **Using a procedure similar to the one given in steps 1 to 4, determine the effect a 0.01% solution of adrenaline has on the *Daphnia*'s heart.**

Safety Tips

- Remind students to be careful when using microscopes.
- Remind students to handle the *Daphnia* carefully and not to harm it.
- Be careful when using microscope slides as they may break.

DATA TABLE 1

Normal Heart Rate	
Count 1	
Count 2	
Count 3	
Average	

DATA TABLE 2

Heart Rate With Adrenaline

Time (minutes)	Heart Rate
1	
3	
5	
7	
9	

6. Formulate a hypothesis. Make sure that you have your teacher's approval for the experiment.

7. Be sure to return the *Daphnia*'s heart beat to its normal rate. To do so, remove some of the adrenaline solution from the slide with a medicine dropper. Using a clean medicine dropper, replace the volume of the liquid with water from the culture. Continue observing and counting the heart rate every other minute until the heart rate returns to normal.

8. Carry out your experiment and record your data in a data table similar to Data Table 2.

Observations

1. Share your observations and measurements with the rest of the class. As a class, find the average number of heartbeats for the *Daphnia* before the adrenaline solution was added and just after it was added.
2. What was the effect on the heart rate when you added the adrenaline solution?
3. How long did it take the *Daphnia* to return to a normal heart rate?

Analysis and Conclusions

1. Formulate a hypothesis to explain the results of your experiment. Could a different hypothesis also explain the results? Discuss this possibility.
2. How do you think the *Daphnia* adjusted its heart rate to the adrenaline solution?
3. Why might it be a good idea to take an average of the class data in this experiment?
4. Why do you think that *Daphnia* are useful organisms in an experiment such as this? Explain your answer.

More to Explore

Design an experiment to determine the effects of various concentrations of adrenaline solution on a *Daphnia.*

3. Because the normal heart rate of *Daphnia* is very rapid (almost 300 beats per minute), students may have difficulty counting the heartbeats. Suggest that they count for 15 seconds and then multiply the count by four to get the count per minute. A stopwatch will make this easier.

Answers to Observations

1. Individual results will vary, but the class averages should show an increase in heartbeats with the addition of adrenaline.
2. Adrenaline caused the heart rate to increase dramatically.
3. It should take the *Daphnia* less than 10 minutes.

Answers to Analysis and Conclusions

1. Students will probably hypothesize that the adrenaline they added to the slide increased the heart rate of the *Daphnia*. Other possible causes of the increased heart rate might include the stress placed on the organism or an increase in the temperature of its environment.
2. Receptors on the heart that are specific to adrenaline recognized the hormone, which stimulated the heart muscle to beat faster.
3. Averaging class data helps produce more accurate results by lessening the effect of any errors in individual measurements.
4. Students may say that *Daphnia* are useful organisms in an experiment such as this because they are convenient to store and handle and it is easy to observe how their heart rates respond.

More to Explore

A quick way to determine the effects of different concentrations of adrenaline is to divide the class into several groups and have each group use a different concentration of the hormone. After the lab is completed, ask the groups to share their results and discuss how and why they differ.

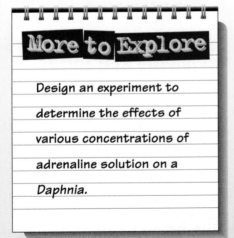

CHAPTER 34

Study Guide

Review Strategy

Students can use the key concepts listed on this page to review the main points of the chapter. Ask students to rewrite each statement listed under the section titles as a question and record it on a separate index card with the answer on the back of the card. Then have students choose partners and use their cards to quiz each other on the key concepts. Urge partners to come to consensus on the correct answer for each question.

Study Guide

Summarizing Key Concepts

The key concepts in each section of this chapter are listed below to help you review the chapter content. Make sure you understand each concept and its relationship to other concepts and to the theme of this chapter.

34–1 Organization of the Human Body

- There are four basic types of tissue—epithelial, connective, nerve, and muscle.
- The eleven systems of the body include the skeletal system, muscular system, digestive system, excretory system, immune system, nervous system, integumentary system, circulatory system, respiratory system, reproductive system, and endocrine system.

34–2 Communication and Control

- The endocrine system is made up of a series of glands located throughout the body. Glands are organs that produce and release chemicals, and endocrine glands generally release their chemicals into the bloodstream.
- Hormones are chemicals that travel through the bloodstream and affect the behavior of other cells.
- During negative feedback, the secretion of a hormone inhibits further production of another hormone.

34–3 Physiology in Action

- The study of how the body works is called human physiology.

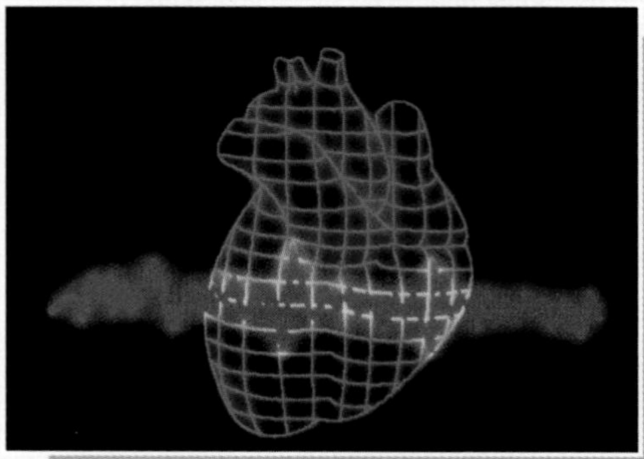

Reviewing Key Terms

Review the following vocabulary terms and their meaning. Then use each term in a complete sentence.

34–1 Organization of the Human Body

tissue
organ
organ system

34–2 Communication and Control

nervous system
neuron
endocrine system
hormone
receptor
target cell
pituitary gland
hypothalamus
thyroid gland
negative feedback

Inquiry-Based Strategy

Ask students to hypothesize what might happen to someone who developed a disorder of the pituitary gland, such as a tumor. After students have had a chance to respond, ask them to design an experiment that would help them find out. Their research designs should address such questions as which organisms would be suitable subjects (those that have a pituitary gland) and how a pituitary gland disorder could be modeled (by removing the pituitary gland or giving the organism high doses of pituitary hormones). Have volunteers share their ideas with the rest of the class, and encourage other class members to provide feedback. Then ask a few volunteers to research pituitary disorders and their effects and share what they learn with the rest of the class. Finally, ask the class to evaluate their original answers.

Recalling Main Ideas

Choose the letter of the answer that best completes the statement or answers the question.

1. A group of similar cells that perform a similar function is called a(an)
a. organism. **c.** tissue.
b. organ. **d.** organ system.

2. Which type of tissue covers interior and exterior surfaces?
a. epithelial **c.** connective
b. muscle **d.** nerve

3. The body system that relays messages from one part of the body to another is the
a. immune system. **c.** excretory system.
b. nervous system. **d.** digestive system.

4. Organs that produce and release substances are called
a. hormones. **c.** glands.
b. receptors. **d.** target cells.

5. What controls the release of hormones from the pituitary gland?
a. hypothalamus **c.** thyroid
b. adrenal glands **d.** pancreas

6. Which endocrine gland produces estrogen?
a. testes **c.** adrenal gland
b. ovaries **d.** pituitary gland

7. Which system is responsible for clearing the blood of carbon dioxide and replacing it with oxygen?
a. circulatory **c.** excretory
b. digestive **d.** respiratory

Putting It All Together

Using the information on pages xxx to xxxi, complete the following concept map.

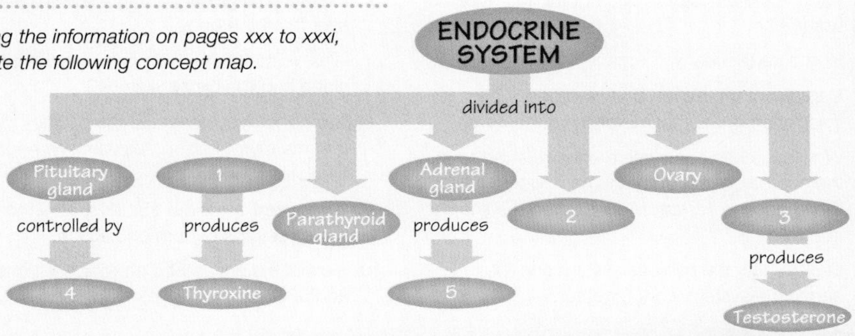

Putting It All Together

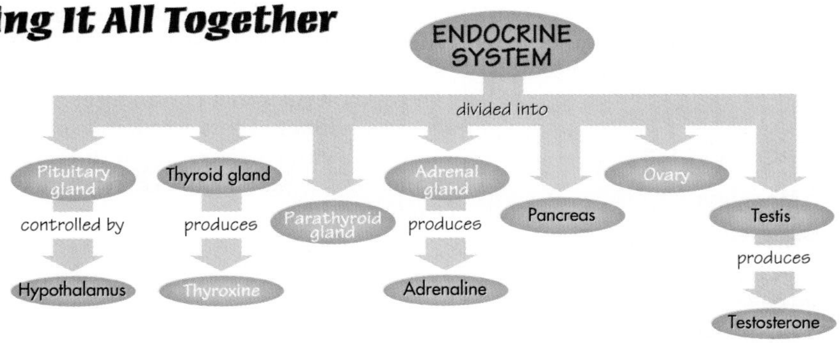

Recalling Main Ideas

1. c
2. a
3. b
4. c
5. a
6. b
7. d

Assessment

Reviewing What You Learned

1. Muscle tissue enables the body to move.
2. A tissue is a group of similar cells that perform a single function.
3. An organ system is a group of organs that perform closely related functions.
4. The function of the excretory system is to rid the body of wastes.
5. Neurons are the message-carrying cells of the nervous system.
6. The endocrine system is made up of a series of glands located throughout the body.
7. Glands are organs that produce and release chemicals.
8. Hormones are chemicals that are produced by the endocrine system, travel through the bloodstream, and affect the behavior of other cells in the body.
9. The integumentary system protects the body from injury, infection, and dehydration.
10. Receptors are specific chemical binding sites for hormones on cells.
11. Target cells are those that have receptors for a particular hormone.
12. The pituitary gland is located at the base of the brain.
13. The hypothalamus is located in the brain above the pituitary gland.
14. The thyroid gland produces thyroxine.
15. Hormones are usually made of proteins, lipids, or amino acids.
16. A second messenger hormone is an ion or small molecule that activates or inhibits cell activities.
17. Negative feedback involves the secretion of a hormone that inhibits further production of another hormone.

Assessment (continued)

Expanding the Concepts

1. Epithelial tissue covers interior and exterior surfaces; connective tissue provides support for the body and connects its parts; nerve tissue transmits nerve impulses through the body; muscle tissue enables the body to move.
2. Tissues are groups of similar cells that perform a single function; organs are groups of tissues that perform a single function.
3. None can work in isolation. All are connected by nervous and endocrine controls.
4. The nervous system is often referred to as the coarse control because its impulses are carried to organs throughout the body. The endocrine system is considered the fine control because its hormones affect only specific cells.
5. The pituitary gland and hypothalamus are part of the brain, and these two glands control the activities of other endocrine glands. This means that input into the nervous system can influence the endocrine system through its connection with the hypothalamus and pituitary gland.
6. Glucagon converts glycogen to glucose, raising the blood glucose level; insulin converts glucose to glycogen, lowering the blood glucose level.
7. The hypothalamus controls the release of hormones from the pituitary gland. Some of these hormones are actually made in the hypothalamus but released from the pituitary gland.
8. With too little thyroxine in the blood, the hypothalamus signals the pituitary to release TSH, stimulating the thyroid to release thyroxine. With enough thyroxine in the blood, the hypothalamus stops signaling the pituitary to release TSH.

Assessment

Reviewing What You Learned

Answer each of the following in a complete sentence.

1. Explain the function of muscle tissue.
2. What is a tissue?
3. What is an organ system?
4. Explain the function of the excretory system.
5. What are neurons?
6. How does the endocrine system work?
7. What are glands?
8. What are hormones? In which system are they produced?
9. How does the integumentary system work?
10. What are receptors?
11. What are target cells?
12. Where is the pituitary gland located?
13. Where is the hypothalamus located?
14. Which gland produces thyroxine?
15. What kinds of chemicals are hormones usually made of?
16. Explain the purpose of the second messenger hormone.
17. Why is negative feedback important?

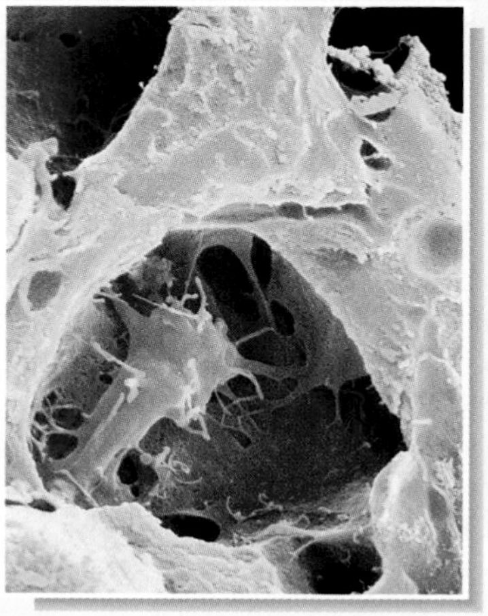

Expanding the Concepts

Discuss each of the following in a brief paragraph.

1. What is the function of each of the four types of tissue?
2. Compare tissues with organs.
3. Can any of the eleven body systems work in isolation of another? Explain your answer.
4. Why is the nervous system often referred to as the coarse control of the human system while the endocrine system is considered the fine control?
5. Explain how the nervous system and the endocrine system work together.
6. Explain how glucagon and insulin have opposite effects on the body.
7. What is the relationship between the pituitary gland and the hypothalamus?
8. Using the hypothalamus, the pituitary gland, and the thyroid gland, explain how negative feedback works.
9. **Construct a model** that illustrates the two basic patterns of hormone action.
10. Explain the action of a polypeptide hormone and a steroid hormone.

9. Models should show how some hormones bind to receptors on the cell membrane and others pass through the cell membrane and bind to receptors inside the cell.

Skills Trace
Modeling

- Focus p. 775
- Practice p. 775
- Assess p. 780

10. Polypeptide hormones bind to receptors on the cell surface and activate enzymes on the inner side of the cell membrane to produce second messenger molecules that control other cell activities. Steroid hormones pass across the cell membrane and bind with receptors inside the cell, and the hormone-receptor complexes regulate gene expression.

Extending Your Thinking

Use the skills you have developed in this chapter to answer the following.

1. **Analyzing** Explain how the negative-feedback mechanism works in a way similar to a thermostat that maintains the temperature of a room.
2. **Making judgments** With the advent of genetic engineering, many techniques have led to bacterially produced hormones. One of these hormones—human growth hormone (GH)—is now readily available. Consider the advantages and disadvantages of administering this hormone over an extended period of time to adjust the size of a patient.
3. **Designing an experiment** A person driving a car is maintaining a constant speed at the speed limit. How could you design an experiment to illustrate how this is an example of negative feedback?
4. **Hypothesizing** You have probably heard stories of people who had incredible strength when placed in an extremely dangerous situation. How might a person be able to summon such strength for a short period of time?
5. **Making judgments** Anabolic steroids are synthetic drugs produced from the hormone testosterone. Although anabolic steroids are used for medical purposes to reduce swelling and promote healing, they are sometimes misused to develop muscle mass and muscle strength. Whatever the case, the long-term effects of steroid use are serious and dangerous. Should anabolic steroids be reclassified as an illegal substance? Why or why not?

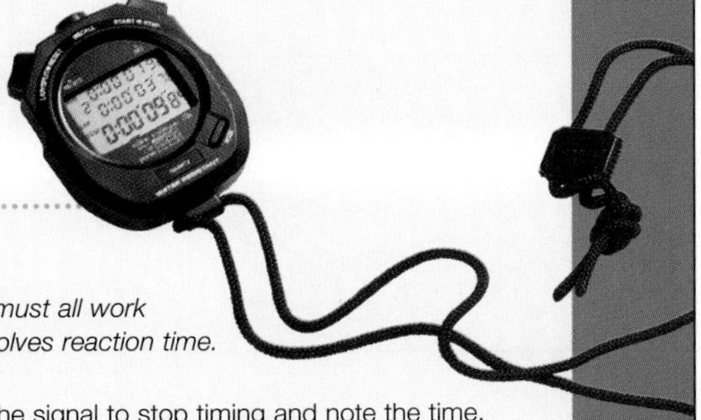

Applying Your Skills

The Squeeze Play

In order to do things effectively, the systems of the body must all work together. As a class, conduct the following activity, which involves reaction time.

1. In groups of 8 to 10 students, stand in line holding hands. Identify the first person in line as the timekeeper. He or she will need a stopwatch or clock with a second hand. All students but the timekeeper should close their eyes.
2. When everyone in the group is ready, the timekeeper begins timing and, at the same time, squeezes his or her neighbor's hand. As soon as the neighbor feels the squeeze, he or she squeezes the hand of the next person. Each person does this in turn. When the last person feels the squeeze, he or she yells "stop." This is the signal to stop timing and note the time. Record your group's reaction time.
3. Repeat steps 1 and 2 two more times, recording your data each time. Calculate a class average for reaction time.

• GOING FURTHER •

4. Do you think you react faster earlier in the day than you do later in the day?
5. Will practice doing this activity decrease your reaction time? Explain your answer.

Extending Your Thinking

1. When the temperature rises, the thermostat shuts off the heat; when the temperature falls, the thermostat turns on the heat. This helps to keep the temperature relatively constant. In a similar way, the level of one hormone is regulated by the presence or absence of another hormone, to keep conditions in the body relatively constant.
2. Student answers should include reference to the following information: Growth hormone helps children who lack the hormone grow to normal size; in normal children it leads to abnormal size and health problems.
3. Students' experimental designs should reflect that if the car speeds up when it drops below the speed limit or slows down when it exceeds the speed limit, it illustrates negative feedback.

Skills Trace
Experimenting

● Focus p. 767
● Practice p. 767
● Assess p. 781

4. Stress leads to secretion of adrenaline, which dilates blood vessels, increases rate and strength of heartbeat, and increases blood glucose levels, all of which help the muscles to work harder.
5. Some students may say that anabolic steroids should be reclassified as illegal substances in order to help control their abuse.

Applying Your Skills

Teacher Notes

- Explain the procedure in advance so that reaction time is not affected by confusion about what to do.
- Suggest that students record all their data in one table so that reaction times can be compared across groups.
- The class average should be calculated using the average time for each group.

Answers

4. Have students do the activity in the morning and then later in the day to see whether reaction time changes.
5. Students might repeat the activity every day for a week and compare the two reaction times.

Scoring Rubric

4 Response is thorough, accurate, and creative; shows an in-depth understanding of science skills, procedures, and concepts.

3 Response is complete, mostly accurate, and original; shows a satisfactory understanding of science skills, procedures, and concepts.

2 Response is mostly complete but includes some inaccuracies; shows an adequate understanding of science skills, procedures, and concepts.

1 Response is only partially complete and has many inaccuracies; shows an incomplete understanding of science skills, procedures, and concepts.

0 Response is mostly incomplete and/or inaccurate; shows a lack of understanding of science skills, procedures, and concepts.

Chapter 35 Nervous System

Content Management	Student Edition Activities
■ Section 35–1 The Human Nervous System, pp. 783–786 Neurons The Nerve Impulse Myelin The Synapse	
■ Section 35–2 Organization of the Nervous System, pp. 787–791 The Central Nervous System The Peripheral Nervous System	Laboratory Investigation: Observing the Structures of the Brain, pp. 800–801
■ Section 35–3 The Senses, pp. 792–795 The Five Senses	MINI LAB: How Tasty Is It?, p. 795
◆ BRANCHING OUT • In Depth Section 35–4 Nerve Impulses and Drugs, pp. 796–799 The Resting Potential The Action Potential Drugs and the Synapse	MINI LAB: Face to Face, p. 798

■ These sections cover all the necessary content and concepts for an enriched course in biology.
◆ This section covers content and concepts that are either applications or extensions of the enriched material.

Integration Strategies

SE Health, p. 787

Assessment Strategies

SE Chapter Review, pp. 802–805
TR Section Reviews
Chapter Test
BL Chapter Review
Practice Test
CTB Chapter 35 Test

Tech Prep

A teaching strategy appropriate for students who are in technical/vocational programs or who are considering post-secondary technical education can be found on the following **TE** page: 790.

Meeting the Standards

Sections 35–1 through 35–4 cover four of the six content standards under **The Cell** and two of the four content standards under **The Behavior of Organisms** as described on pages 184–185 and 187, respectively, of The National Science Education Standards.

Chapter Planning Guide

Teacher's Edition Activities	Other Activities	Media and Technology
Chapter Discovery Learning Activity, p. 782 **Inquiry Activity:** Quick as a Wink, p. 784 **Activity:** Simulating Action Potential, p. 785	**TR Enrich:** Word Games **BL Inquiry Activity:** Making the Connection	
Inquiry Activity: The Effect of Creasing on Surface Area, p. 788 **Activity:** Observing the Pupillary Reflex, p. 789	**LM** Observing Nervous Responses, #69 **TR Explore:** Left Is Right **BL Inquiry Activity:** Don't Forget to Breathe!	
Inquiry Activity: How Do I Know Thee?, p. 792 **Investigate:** Model Building, p. 793 **Inquiry Activity:** Comparing Sound and Light, p. 793 **Activity:** Mapping the Tongue, p. 794	**LM** Investigating the Senses, #70 **TR Writing in Biology:** Thinking About Your Senses **Apply:** Super Sensors **BL Inquiry Activity:** Sense-Ability	**TB** The Eye and The Ear, #43
Inquiry Activity: Modeling the Sodium-Potassium Pump, p. 796 **Investigate:** Long-Term Project, p. 797	**TR Explore:** Measuring Your Potential **BL Inquiry Activity:** Get the Facts	**BioVue Mini Doc:** Drugs and the Brain, Videodisc Side 8

KEY: SE Student Edition **TE** Teacher's Edition **LM** Laboratory Manual **TR** Teaching Resources
BL BioLog **TB** Transparency Box **CTB** Computer Test Bank

Materials List

TE Chapter Discovery Learning Activity, p. 782 (5–10 minutes); stopwatch.
TE Inquiry Activity: Quick as a Wink, p. 784 (15–20 minutes); stopwatch, calculator.
TE Activity: Simulating Action Potential, p. 785 (10–15 minutes); dominoes.
TE Inquiry Activity: The Effect of Creasing on Surface Area, p. 788 (20 minutes); empty cardboard shoe or cereal box, several sheets of newspaper, calculator.
TE Activity: Observing the Pupillary Reflex, p. 789 (10–15 minutes); blindfold, flashlight or other bright light.
TE Inquiry Activity: How Do I Know Thee?, p. 792 (20 minutes); paper cups, orange juice, ginger ale, brown paper bag containing several small familiar objects.
TE Investigate: Model Building, p. 793 (10–15 minutes); large pan of water, pebble.
TE Inquiry Activity: Comparing Sound and Light, p. 793 (20–30 minutes); two brown paper bags.
TE Activity: Mapping the Tongue, p. 794 (15–20 minutes); cotton swabs, mirror, paper cups, tonic water, and solutions of sugar, lemon juice, and salt.
SE MINI LAB: How Tasty Is It?, p. 795 (20–30 minutes for setup, 30 minutes for students to complete the procedure); paper cups containing 5 percent, 0.5 percent, and 0.05 percent sucrose solutions.
TE Inquiry Activity: Modeling the Sodium-Potassium Pump, p. 796 (5–10 minutes); air pump, bicycle tire.
TE Investigate: Long-Term Project, p. 797 (2–3 days for survey, 1–2 hours to make poster); poster board, colored markers or paints.
SE MINI LAB: Face to Face, p. 798 (20 minutes); screen or clear plastic sheet, ball of crumpled paper.

CHAPTER 35

Nervous System

Introducing the Chapter . . . In Pictures

We may think of strength as the most important attribute of a gymnast, such as the one in the photograph, but good balance is important as well. Have students examine the photograph, read the caption, and answer the following questions.

- **What is the main skill this gymnast is demonstrating?** (Balancing her body so that she does not fall to the ground.)
- **What role do you think the nervous system might play in the gymnast's balancing act?** (The nervous system uses sensory feedback to assess the body's position and balance. Then it relays information to the muscles to correct or maintain the body's balance.)

In this chapter, students will learn how the nervous system controls the gymnast's balancing act—and many other complex activities as well.

Teaching Strategy

The first section of this chapter explains nervous transmission at the cellular level. The second section describes the structure and function of the major parts of the nervous system. In the third section, each of the five senses is described. The BRANCHING OUT section describes the sodium-potassium pump and how various drugs affect the nervous system. This section gives students a better understanding of the nervous system at the cellular level.

CHAPTER 35

Nervous System

FOCUSING THE CHAPTER THEME: *Stability*

35–1 The Human Nervous System
- Describe the basic structures of the nervous system.

35–2 Organization of the Nervous System
- Explain how the nervous system is organized.

35–3 The Senses
- Describe each of the five senses.

BRANCHING OUT *In Depth*

35–4 Nerve Impulses and Drugs
- Explain the effects various drugs have on nerve impulses.

Laboratory Investigation
- Identify the parts of a sheep brain.

Biology and Your World

BIO JOURNAL

The gymnast in this photograph relies on her nervous system for balance and coordination. Pick a favorite sport or activity. In your journal, explain how you rely on your nervous system to perform that sport or activity. Remember to include your five senses as well.

Gymnast on balance beam

TEACHER SUPPORT

Chapter Discovery Learning Activity

VISION AND BALANCE

Ask students how they could determine if the sense of vision is important for balance. Guide them in developing an experimental design such as the following. They should work with a partner.

1. Stand on one foot and maintain your balance as long as you can for up to three minutes, while your partner records your time.
2. Repeat step 1 with your eyes closed.
3. Switch places with your partner and repeat steps 1 and 2; then go on to step 4.
4. Compare the two times for each individual, and pool your results with the rest of the class. What if anything can you conclude about the sense of vision and balance from the pooled data?

Results: Although individual results may be erratic, the pooled data should reflect that visual input does not affect balance.

BIO JOURNAL

Tell students that muscle tone and contraction are also important aspects of the nervous regulation of most sports and activities. Instruct students to keep their entries in their portfolios.

The Human Nervous System

GUIDE FOR READING

- **Name** the three parts of a neuron.
- **Describe** the way in which a nerve impulse begins.

A COMPUTER CAN DELIVER A *page of text, graphics, and even a video in a few seconds. However, there is another "machine" less than a meter away from the computer that can perform equally astonishing feats. In a fraction of a second, this machine can take in everything on the computer screen; scan the area around the computer; monitor the sound, light, and heat in the room; and automatically regulate the activities of hundreds of devices running at the same time. What kind of information-processing system can do all this? The answer is inside you—the human nervous system.*

Neurons

To understand a computer, you start with the basics—with electricity, wires, and switches. Gradually, you see how thousands of individual components are wired together to form a functional unit. We can do almost the same thing with the nervous system. The basic units of the nervous system are cells called **neurons.** These cells carry messages in the form of electrical signals known as **impulses.**

Some features of a typical neuron are shown in ***Figure 35–2*** on the next page. **A neuron is made up of a cell body, dendrites, and an axon.** The largest part of the neuron is its **cell body.** Most of the metabolic activity of the cell takes place there. In addition, the cell body collects information from the **dendrites**—small branched extensions that spread out from the cell body. Dendrites carry impulses toward the cell body. And the long

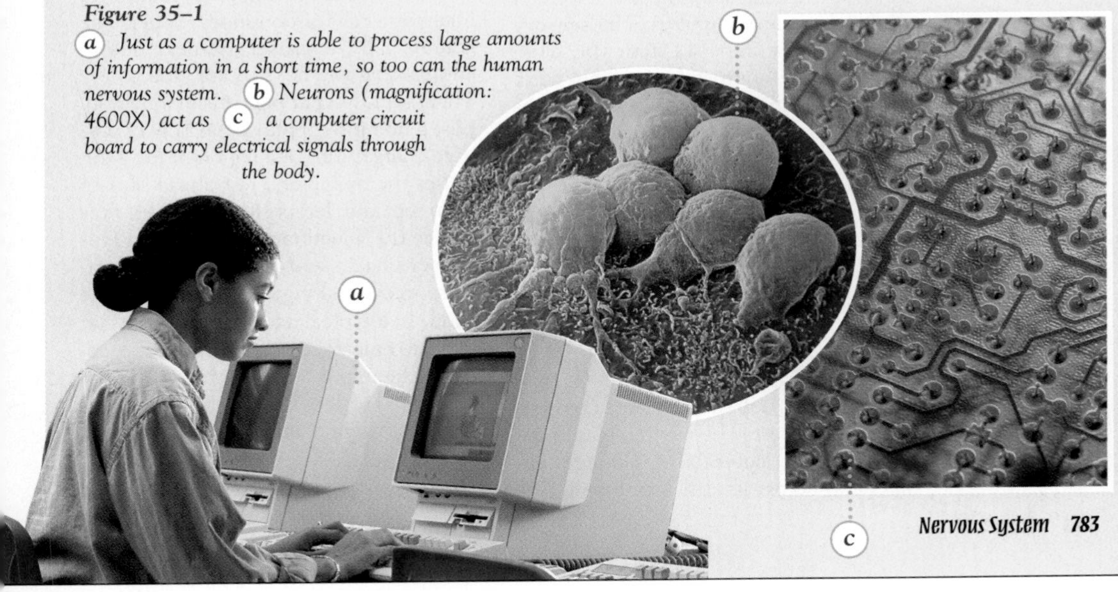

Figure 35–1 (a) *Just as a computer is able to process large amounts of information in a short time, so too can the human nervous system.* (b) *Neurons (magnification: 4600X) act as* (c) *a computer circuit board to carry electrical signals through the body.*

TEACHER SUPPORT

Managing Classroom Diversity

EDUCATIONAL EQUITY

Some students may be less familiar with computers than others. Give them another analogy to help them appreciate the role that neurons play in the human nervous system. For example, have them compare the nervous system with their home's electrical system. Tell them that interconnected neurons carry electrical impulses throughout the body in a way that is analogous to wires inside the walls carrying electricity throughout the house.

LEP STUDENTS

Demonstrate how quickly neurons transmit messages by sliding one coin into another with a shove down a slight incline. For comparison, sprinkle some coarse sand on the incline and trickle a small stream of water down the incline over the sand. Like circulating hormones in the endocrine system, the water takes longer than the coins to travel the same distance.

SECTION 35–1

The Human Nervous System

Performance Objectives

- List the three main structures of a neuron.
- Identify what triggers a nerve impulse.

1 ENGAGE

Ideas Through Images

Have students examine Figure 35–1, read the caption, and answer the following questions. Doing so will help them understand how a computer is analogous to the human nervous system.

- **What parts of a computer perform the same function as human senses?** (Human senses monitor the outside environment and pass the information to the nervous system. The keyboard, mouse, and diskette and CD readers play a similar role in a computer.)
- **What function do both neurons and computer circuit boards perform?** (Both carry electrical signals.)
- **Which do you think is "smarter," a computer or the human nervous system? Why?** (Some students may say a computer is smarter because it can perform mathematical calculations and similar functions in a fraction of the time that the human nervous system can. Others may say the human nervous system is smarter because it can use intuition and creativity to solve complex problems.)

2 EXPLORE

Inquiry Activity

Designing an Experiment

Quick as a Wink

Ask students to think about how quickly a driver steps on the brakes when something darts into the road ahead. How long does it take for the message to travel from the driver's eyes to the brain and then to the foot that steps on the brake? Have students design an experiment to find out. Guide them in developing an experimental design such as the following.

Divide the class into groups of three. Have one member of each group repeat a simple motion, like raising one finger at irregular intervals, as a signal for the second member of the group to move his or her foot. Have the third member of the group use a stopwatch to measure how much time passes between the signal and the movement. If the response is too quick to measure, have them make an estimate, for example, 0.1 or 0.2 seconds.

After students have measured or estimated the response time, ask them how they could calculate the rate at which the nervous message traveled from the eyes to the foot. (By dividing the time the message took to travel from eyes to foot by the distance the message traveled, where distance traveled is approximately the distance from the eyes to the foot via the brain.)

Ideas Through Images

Have students examine Figure 35–2, read the caption, and answer the following questions.

- **What are the three main parts of a neuron?** (Dendrites, cell body, and axon.)

- **How does a nerve impulse move through a neuron?** (Impulses move through the dendrites toward the cell body, and then away from the cell body through the axon.)

Figure 35–2 *The main structures of a typical neuron include the dendrites, the cell body, and the axon.*

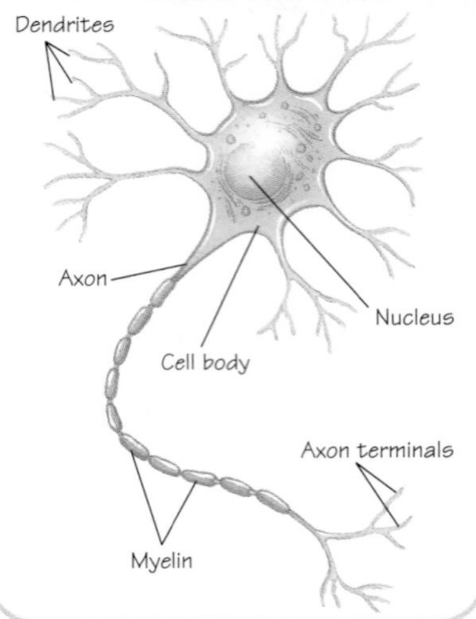

branch that carries impulses away from the cell body is called an **axon.** A neuron may have many dendrites, but it usually has only one axon.

In most animals, neurons are clustered into bundles of fibers called **nerves.** Some nerves contain only a few neurons, but many others have hundreds or even thousands of neurons.

There are three general types of neurons, distinguished by the directions in which they carry impulses. The **sensory neurons** carry impulses from the sense organs to the brain and the spinal cord. **Motor neurons** carry impulses in the opposite direction—from the brain or spinal cord to muscles or other organs. **Interneurons** connect sensory and motor neurons, and carry impulses between them.

☑ *Checkpoint* What are the three types of neurons? ❶

The Nerve Impulse

A neuron not carrying an impulse is said to be at rest. The resting neuron has an electrical potential—a charge difference—across its cell membrane. The inside of the cell is negatively charged and the outside is positively charged.

This difference in electrical charges is called the **resting potential.** Although negative and positive ions are found on both sides of the membrane, there is a net excess of negative charges on the inside of the membrane, and that's what produces the resting potential.

An impulse begins when a neuron is stimulated by another neuron or by the environment. Once it begins, the impulse travels rapidly down the axon away from the cell body. As ***Fig. 35–3*** shows, the impulse is a sudden reversal of the membrane potential. For a few milliseconds, positive ions rush across the cell membrane, reversing the charge difference. For that brief instant, the inside of the membrane is more positive than the outside. In less than 10 milliseconds, the potential reverses itself again, and the resting potential is restored.

This rapid change in voltage on the inside of the axon—negative to positive and back to negative—is called an **action potential.** A nerve impulse is an action potential traveling down an axon.

How does the action potential move? Imagine a row of dominoes. When one domino falls, it causes the next one to fall, causing the next to fall, and so on. That's almost what happens in a neuron. Like a domino toppling, the flow of positive charges into one region of the axon causes the membrane just ahead of it to open up and let positive charges flow across the membrane there, too. This happens again and again, until the impulse moves along the length of the axon. In a typical axon, the impulse can move as quickly as one meter per second. Once the impulse passes, the resting potential is restored, and the neuron is ready to conduct another impulse.

☑ *Checkpoint* What is an action potential? ❷

TEACHER SUPPORT

Facts and Figures

Neurons, the basic structural units of the nervous system, are unusual cells in several respects.
- Neurons are the most highly differentiated of all human cells.
- The axons of neurons may be up to a few meters long.
- The resting potential of a neuron is about 70 millivolts.
- Neurons transmit impulses at a rate of 0.3 to 120 meters per second.

Myelin

As you know, most electrical wires are insulated—that is, they are covered with rubber or plastic to prevent a short circuit. The nervous system has a kind of insulation, too. In some nerve cells, Schwann cells surround the axons of certain neurons. As Schwann cells grow around an axon, they wrap it in layers of their own cell membrane, forming a material known as **myelin** (MIGH-uh-lihn). The Schwann cells that surround a single long axon leave many gaps—called nodes—between themselves where the axon membrane is exposed.

When an impulse moves down an axon covered with myelin, the action potential jumps from one node to the next. This happens because electrical current flows from one node to the next, which greatly speeds up the rate at which the impulse moves. A large axon with myelin can carry messages at speeds as great as 200 meters per second!

☑ **Checkpoint** What are Schwann cells? ❸

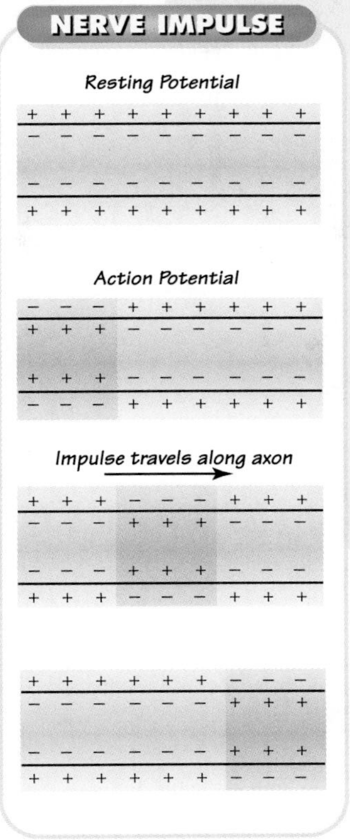

Figure 35–3 *At rest, the outside of the neuron's membrane is more positively charged than is the inside. If a stimulus is applied, causing an impulse, the electrical charges become reversed. The reversal of electrical charges continues as the action potential moves down the axon.*

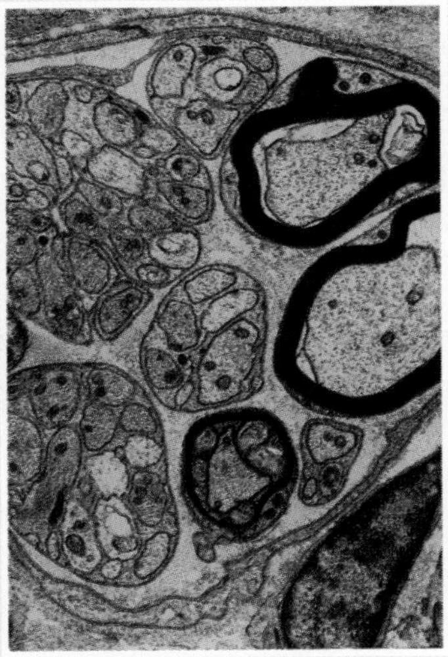

Figure 35–4
(a) This transmission electron micrograph of the cross section of nerve tissue shows both myelinated and unmyelinated axons. The axons that are covered with myelin are those that seem to have black rings around them (magnification: 47,000X). (b) An action potential can move much faster along a myelinated axon because it can jump from node to node, rather than moving continuously along the membrane.

(b)

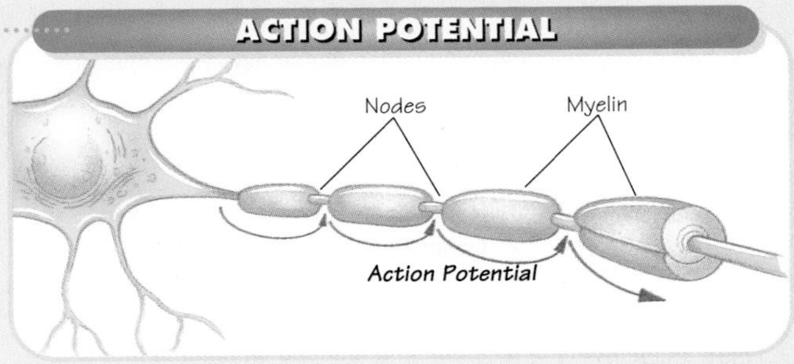

3 TEACH

Ideas Through Images

Have students examine Figure 35–4, read the caption, and answer the following questions.

- **How does an axon with nodes differ from one without nodes?** (An axon with nodes is sheathed with myelin; an axon without nodes is not.)
- **If some of a person's myelin were destroyed, how do you think the person would be affected?** (When myelin is destroyed, the transmission of electrical impulses is impaired. This may cause paralysis, poor coordination, slurred speech, blurred vision, and tremor.)

Discussion

Explain that myelinated axons can conduct impulses as rapidly as 200 meters per second while unmyelinated axons conduct impulses at speeds of only a few millimeters per second. Point out that invertebrates cannot produce myelin. Discuss how myelin is an evolutionary advantage for vertebrates, whose body sizes are generally larger than those of invertebrates.

☑ Checkpoints

❶ Sensory neurons, motor neurons, and interneurons.

❷ The rapid change in voltage on the inside of an axon.

❸ Cells that grow around an axon and wrap it in layers of their own cell membrane, forming myelin.

TEACHER SUPPORT

Activity

SIMULATING ACTION POTENTIAL
Use the domino analogy mentioned in the student text to simulate the movement of an action potential down an axon. Arrange dominoes on end in a row, and then knock the dominoes down by giving the first one a push. Then ask students the following questions.

- **Why did all the dominoes fall when just the first domino was pushed?** (Because kinetic energy was passed from one domino to the next.)
- **What was the source of the kinetic energy that was transmitted down the line of dominoes?** (Some was provided by the push on the first domino, some by the position of the dominoes: Standing on end, they were easily toppled by gravity when gently bumped.)
- **What would you have to do in order to get the dominoes to topple again?** (Return them to the starting position so the dominoes would be able to fall and release kinetic energy again.)

Ancillary Support

The resources below can be used to support your teaching strategy for these two pages.

TR Enrich: Word Games
BL Inquiry Activity: Making the Connection

4 ASSESS

Quick Check

Call on students to summarize the function of each of the following parts of a neuron: dendrite, cell body, axon, myelin, and synapse.

Section Review 35–1

1. Dendrites, cell body, and axon.
2. A nerve impulse begins when a neuron is stimulated by another neuron or by the environment.
3. Answers should reveal students' awareness that hitting a nerve is likely to be painful and can cause a sudden contraction of associated muscles.

Learning Modality

Visual Learning To help visual learners understand the concept of electrical potential, give them examples of other types of energy potential that can be demonstrated in the classroom. For example, kinetic potential can be demonstrated with a depressed spring. Ask students what will happen when the spring is released. (A burst of energy will move the spring back to its resting state.) Illustrate with the spring and ask students if they can think of other examples of kinetic potential. (Possible answers include a child sitting at the top of a slide and a diver ready to dive off the high board.)

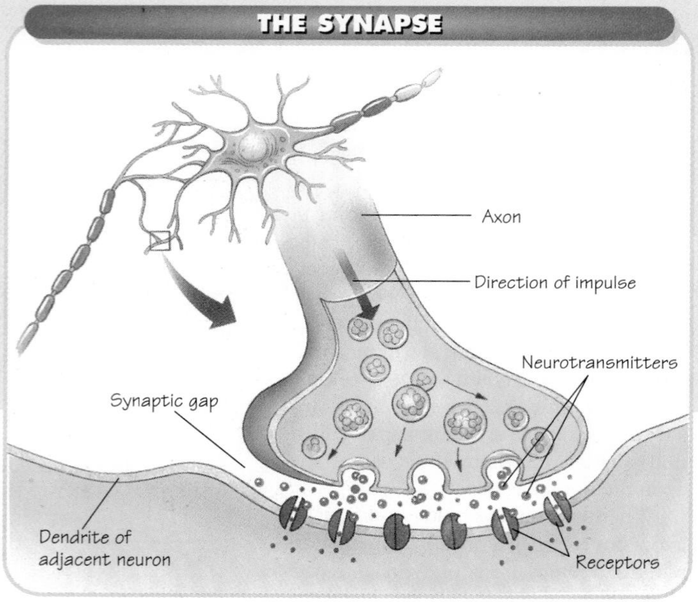

Figure 35–5
When an impulse reaches the end of the axon of one neuron, neurotransmitters are released into the synaptic gap. The neurotransmitters bind to the receptors on the membrane of an adjacent neuron. As a result, the nerve impulse continues to the next neuron.

The Synapse

Even though some neurons are among the longest cells in your body, there comes a point when an impulse reaches the end of an axon. Usually the neuron then makes contact with another cell, and it may even pass the impulse to this cell. Motor neurons, for example, pass their impulses to muscle cells.

The point at which a neuron can transfer an impulse to another cell is called the **synapse** (SIHN-aps). The synapse is a small space between the axon of one neuron and the dendrites of the next neuron. The synapse contains tiny sacs filled with **neurotransmitters** (NOO-roh-trans-miht-erz). Neurotransmitters are chemicals used by one neuron to signal another cell.

When an action potential arrives at the end of an axon, the sacs release the neurotransmitters into the synapse between the two cells. The neurotransmitter molecules attach to receptors on the neighboring cell. This causes positive ions to rush across the cell membrane, stimulating that cell. If the stimulation is great enough, a new impulse begins.

A fraction of a second after binding to their receptor, the neurotransmitter molecules are released from the cell surface. They may then be broken down by enzymes or recycled by the axon.

Section Review 35–1

1. **Name** the three parts of a neuron.
2. **Describe** the way in which a nerve impulse begins.
3. **Critical Thinking—Relating Concepts** Your "funny bone" is actually a nerve in your arm. How does this explain your reaction when you "hit" it?

TEACHER SUPPORT

Background Information

There are many different neurotransmitters, but three of the best known are acetylcholine, norepinephrine, and serotonin. Acetylcholine is important in transmitting impulses across synapses between nerves and muscles. Norepinephrine is important throughout both central and peripheral nervous systems. Serotonin is especially important in the brain. Many pathogens, toxins, and drugs adversely affect the functioning of the nervous system by interfering with the normal synthesis, storage, or activity of these neurotransmitters. Specific examples include the toxin of the bacterium that causes tetanus. Because it blocks inhibitory impulses, the toxin leads to uncontrolled muscle spasms. Tetanus is often called lockjaw because muscles in the jaw are often involved.

Organization of the Nervous System

GUIDE FOR READING

- **Describe** the two major divisions of the nervous system.

THE HUMAN NERVOUS SYSTEM is similar to a complex telephone network in a large city. In a telephone network, telephone lines and wires connect homes, businesses, and schools through a central telephone switching station. The nervous system has connecting wires as well—the neurons. The nervous system itself works like the central switching station of the body. It receives, compares, and analyzes information, then it sends messages and commands to the rest of the body.

The Central Nervous System

The human nervous system is divided into two main parts—the central nervous system and the peripheral nervous system. **The central nervous system consists of the brain and the spinal cord.** The brain and spinal cord share many structural similarities. The brain is protected by the bones of the skull, and the spinal cord is protected by the vertebrae of the backbone. Both are cushioned by three layers of tough, elastic tissue called **meninges** (muh-NIHN-jeez). Between the meninges is a space filled with **cerebrospinal** (ser-uh-broh-SPIGH-nuhl) **fluid,** which cushions the brain and spinal cord. These three means of protection help to prevent many injuries to the central nervous system.

The Brain

The brain contains about 100 billion cells—a far greater number than the number of people in the world! That fact alone should prepare you for how complicated this organ is. Although the brain represents only about 2 percent of the mass of the body, it is so active that it may use as much as 25 percent of the body's energy. To supply the food and oxygen needed to support that activity, the brain has a rich blood supply. If that blood supply is interrupted—even for just a few minutes—the brain may suffer damage serious enough to cause death. ●

INTEGRATING HEALTH

Refer to a health book to find out what causes a stroke.

Figure 35–6 The human nervous system is often compared to a telephone network. Just as (a) these telephone wires connect homes to a central station, these (b) nerves connect the different parts of the nervous system. The individual nerve fibers, which are falsely colored blue, are motor nerves (magnification: 500X). (c) Without a properly functioning nervous sytem, these skaters would not have the ability to coordinate and perform these graceful movements.

TEACHER SUPPORT

Background Information

Normal human brains show a great deal of variation in size, ranging from 1000 to 2000 mL in volume. Most human brains fall between 1350 and 1450 mL. Human ancestors living 2 million years ago had brains close in size to the brains of modern-day primates. Then, between about 1.5 and 0.5 million years ago, human brain size doubled. Many scholars believe this increase in brain size is the single most significant evolutionary change that occurred in the human lineage. Anthropologists believe that the increase in brain size reflects an increasing dependence on culture and learning.

SECTION 35–2

Organization of the Nervous System

Performance Objective

- Distinguish between the central and peripheral nervous systems.

Laboratory Investigation Skill: Identifying

1 ENGAGE

Ideas Through Images

Have students examine Figure 35–6, read the caption, and answer the following questions.

- **For the nerves shown, where do nerve impulses originate and to which cells are the impulses transmitted?** (They originate in the brain and are transmitted to muscle cells.)
- **What activities are the skaters using their muscles to perform?** (They are using their muscles to balance, lift, grip, and move.)
- **How do you think the brain gets the information it needs to regulate these activities?** (From the senses, and from the body, which supplies information about posture, muscle tone, and balance.)

INTEGRATING HEALTH

A stroke is caused by a sudden disruption of blood flow to part of the brain due to blockage of an artery to the brain or the bursting of an artery in the brain.

2 EXPLORE

Inquiry Activity

Designing an Experiment

The Effect of Creasing on Surface Area

Tell students that many tissues in the body, including the surface of the brain, are creased or folded. This gives them more surface area for a given volume, and surface area is important because everything enters and leaves cells across membranes. Ask students how much they think creases can add to the surface area of a tissue. Guide them in designing an experiment such as the following to find out.

First measure the length and width, and then calculate the surface area, of a small box, such as an empty shoe or cereal box. Next, stuff the box with sheets of folded newspaper, keeping track of the number of sheets used. When the box is full, find the surface area of the newspaper (multiply the number of sheets by the area of one sheet), and add it to the surface area of the box. How much has the surface area increased?

3 TEACH

Ideas Through Images

Have students examine Figure 35–8, read the caption, and answer the following questions.

- **What is the difference between the hemispheres and the lobes of the cerebrum?** (The hemispheres are the two sides, left and right, of the cerebrum; the lobes are the four areas of the cerebrum, which are found in both hemispheres.)
- **Which is larger, the cerebrum or cerebellum?** (The cerebrum is the largest part of the human brain.)

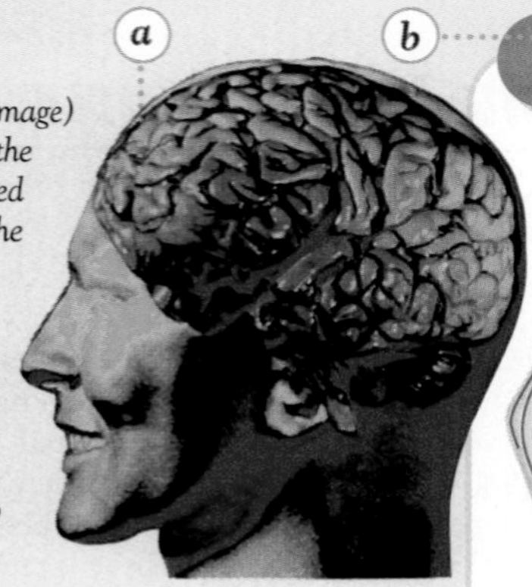

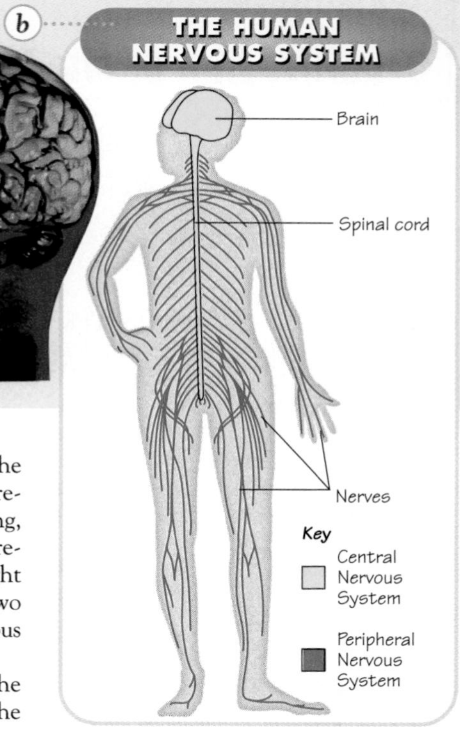

Figure 35–7 *ⓐ An MRI (magnetic resonance image) of the brain—the control center of the human body—has been superimposed over an image of the head. ⓑ The human nervous system consists of two main divisions. The central nervous system, colored yellow, consists of the brain and the spinal cord. The peripheral nervous system, colored red, consists of all the nerves that carry information to and from the spinal cord.*

The **cerebrum** (SER-uh-bruhm) is the largest part of the human brain. It is responsible for functions such as learning, intelligence, and judgment. The cerebrum is divided into a left and a right hemisphere by a deep groove. These two hemispheres are connected at the corpus callosum (KOR-puhs kuh-LOW-suhm).

The surface of the cerebrum, the **cerebral cortex,** is deeply creased. The creasing enlarges its surface area and increases the number of cells that can be packed into this layer. The cerebral cortex processes information from the senses and controls body movements.

The **cerebellum** (ser-uh-BEHL-uhm), the second-largest part of the brain, is located just below the cerebrum at the base of the skull. When the cerebral cortex commands a muscle group to move, that message is routed through the cerebellum. The cerebellum coordinates and balances the actions of muscles so the body moves gracefully and efficiently.

The **brainstem** connects the brain to the spinal cord. The brainstem includes regions called the **medulla oblongata** (mih-DUHL-uh ahb-lahn-GAHT-uh) and the **pons.** Some of the body's most important functions—including blood pressure, heart rate, breathing, and swallowing—are controlled in this part of the brain.

The thalamus is located just beneath the cerebrum. The thalamus receives messages from sense organs, including the eyes and the nose, before they are relayed to the cerebral cortex. Just beneath the thalamus is the hypothalamus, a small region that is linked to the pituitary gland.

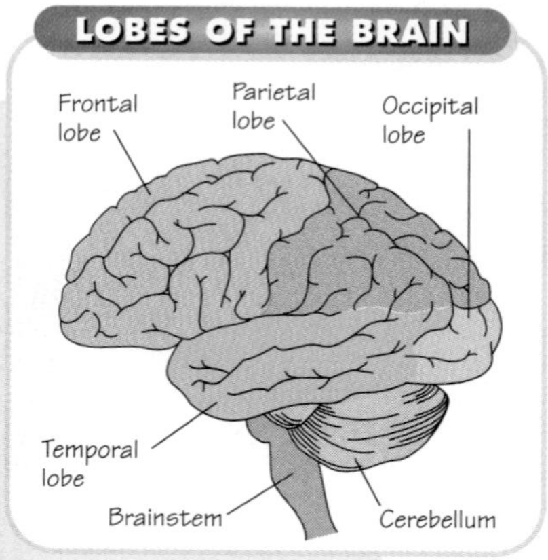

Figure 35–8 *Each hemisphere, or half, of the cerebrum contains the same four lobes—frontal lobe, parietal lobe, occipital lobe, and temporal lobe.*

TEACHER SUPPORT

Historical Perspective

In the middle of the nineteenth century, Paul Broca, a French neurologist, discovered that a small region in the third convolution of the left frontal lobe of the cerebral cortex controls speech. This area is now called Broca's area. Broca made his discovery by studying people with brain damage who had lost the ability to speak. He also studied split-brain patients—people whose hemispheres were no longer connected because they had suffered damage to the corpus callosum. Broca's discovery of the speech area of the brain was important for two reasons. It provided some of the first evidence that the left and right hemispheres of the brain have separate functions, and it was one of the first indicators that particular brain functions are localized in specific regions of the brain.

Figure 35–9
The spinal cord is surrounded by three layers of meninges. In the upper right, the cross section of the spinal cord shows both the gray matter and the white matter. The gray matter gets its color from the color of the cell bodies, of which it is mostly made. The white matter consists mainly of long axons, which get their color from myelin sheaths.

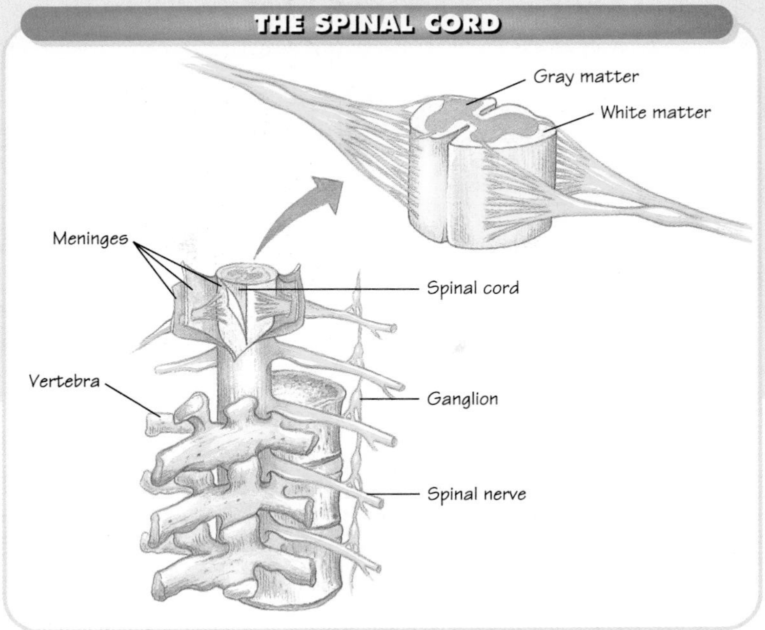

The Spinal Cord

The spinal cord is the primary link between the brain and the rest of the body. Thirty-one pairs of spinal nerves branch out from the spinal cord, connecting the brain to all parts of the body. Certain kinds of information are processed directly in the spinal cord. One example is the well-known knee-jerk reflex. A **reflex** is a quick, automatic response to a stimulus. As shown in ***Figure 35–10,*** a tap on the knee stimulates a reflex. The nerve impulses travel through sensory neurons to the spinal cord. There the impulse synapses with motor neurons, which sends the message back to the leg muscle to contract.

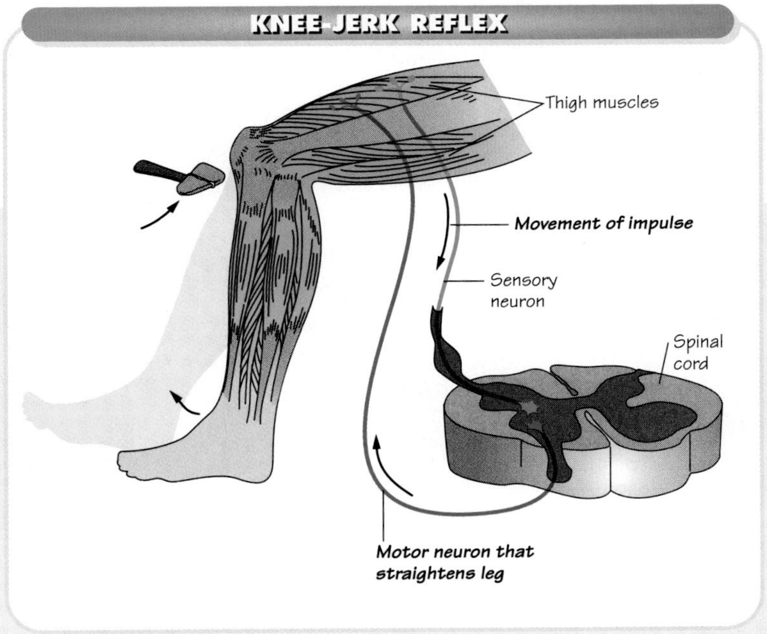

Figure 35–10
The knee-jerk reflex is one of the simplest neural circuits in the body. Tapping the kneecap causes a sensory neuron to send a signal to the spinal cord, where it stimulates an interneuron. The interneuron stimulates a motor neuron, which sends the signal back to the leg "telling" the leg muscles to contract, thereby straightening the leg.

Ideas Through Images

Have students examine Figure 35–9, read the caption, and answer the following questions.

- **What advantage is it for the spinal cord to pass inside each of the vertebrae?** (Passing inside the vertebrae helps protect the spinal cord from injury.)
- **What function do the meninges serve?** (They help cushion and protect the spinal cord, like packing material in a box.)
- **What fills the spaces between the meninges, and what is its role?** (Cerebrospinal fluid fills the spaces; it also cushions the spinal cord.)
- **What does white matter consist of and, what role does it play?** (The white matter is made up of axons; they transmit electrical impulses up and down the spinal cord.)

Laboratory Investigation

The Laboratory Investigation, Observing the Structures of the Brain, on pages 800–801 is appropriate to use at this point in the chapter.

TEACHER SUPPORT

Activity

OBSERVING THE PUPILLARY REFLEX

In the pupillary reflex, the pupil of the eye automatically widens or narrows when the amount of light falling on it changes. Unlike the simpler knee-jerk reflex shown in Figure 35–10, the pupillary reflex involves the brain and does not occur instantaneously. Ask students to recall a time when they went from a bright light into a dark room, for example, from a sunny street into a dark theater. No doubt they will remember being able to see very little for a measurable period of time, perhaps a few seconds. This is the time it takes for the pupil to widen so it can let in the maximum amount of light. Demonstrate the pupillary response by asking one or more volunteers to cover their eyes with a blindfold and keep them shut for a few minutes. Then ask the volunteers to open their eyes. Ask the rest of the students to observe what happens to the width of volunteers' pupils. How long does it take for their pupils to narrow?

Ancillary Support

The resources below can be used to support your teaching strategy for these two pages.

LM Observing Nervous Responses, #69
TR Explore: Left Is Right

Connections

Share the following information about brain tumors with students. It is the type of information one would need in order to make an informed consent decision such as the one discussed.

Many types of brain tumors are fatal, and even benign brain tumors are extremely serious. This is because the hard, bony skull cannot expand outward to accommodate a tumor's growth, so the tumor compresses the softer tissue of the brain. Untreated, a benign tumor can lead to permanent brain damage, and a cancerous tumor can lead to death.

If tumors are treated early, there is a good chance for full recovery, especially if the tumor is benign. Treatment usually involves surgical removal of all or part of the tumor. This is sometimes followed by radiation treatments to kill any remaining tumor cells.

All surgery involves some risk. For brain surgery, the risks include permanent brain damage, especially if the tumor is large. Chemotherapy also has adverse side effects, including nausea and hair loss.

Parents must sign informed consent releases for their minor children. Therefore, high-school students usually do not make such decisions for themselves. Ask students what role they should play in the decision-making process. How much input do they think they should have? How much should they be told by their doctors? What would they want to be told?

Answers to Making the Connection

An informed consent decision should be made by weighing the risks of an operation against the risks of not having the operation. The amount of pain and disability that is likely to occur during recovery and the length of recovery may also influence an informed consent decision.

Bio Frontier Connections

Informed Consent

Whenever Kim came home from work lately, all she wanted to do was lie down and take a nap. At first, she didn't think too much of it, even though she usually liked to go for a run before dinner.

When her husband became concerned and asked her about her lack of energy, she would say, "It's nothing. I just have a headache."

Strange Symptoms

Then one day, Kim noticed a strange metallic taste in her mouth. She also began smelling perfume, even though she did not usually wear it. Finally, Kim decided to go to see her doctor.

The doctor suggested that Kim undergo a few tests. One test was called an MRI, or Magnetic Resonance Imaging, which was able to take a "snapshot" of Kim's brain.

Test Results

Unfortunately, the results of Kim's MRI showed a small brain tumor. And although the tumor was not cancerous, Kim would probably need surgery to avoid further, more serious, complications. Specifically, the tumor might eventually lead to blindness if left untreated. Kim agreed to the operation.

Possible Side Effects

The night before Kim was to have surgery, her doctor visited her in her hospital room. Before proceeding with the operation, the doctor wanted to discuss all the possible side effects—which might include infection, paralysis, or loss of speech—so that Kim could make a final decision based on the best possible information. This is called informed consent.

One of the problems doctors often face is just how much (or how little) to tell a patient. On the one hand, patients like Kim need to know certain information before they can consent to surgery or other procedures that might have serious side effects. In fact, there are laws that make it mandatory for doctors to keep their patients informed of all possible outcomes. On the other hand, how much information is too much information, which might only cause more fear in the patient? How much knowledge does a patient need in order to give informed consent? There is a fine line between knowing enough and knowing too much.

An MRI scan of the back of the head showing a noncancerous tumor (green area)

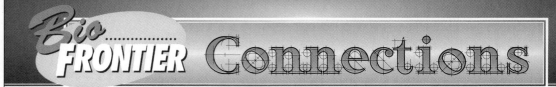

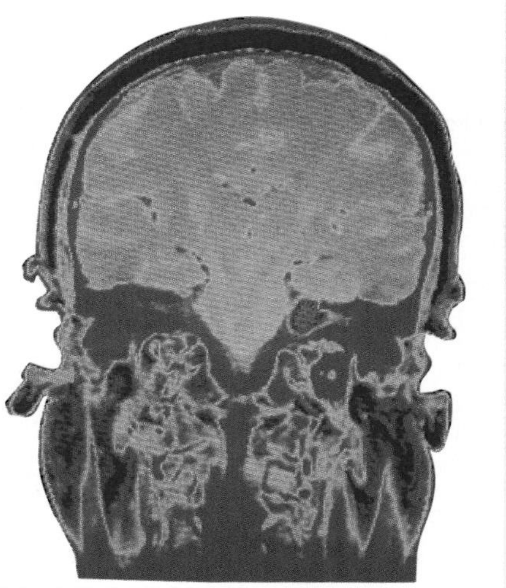

Making the Connection

If you were facing a serious operation, what kinds of questions would you ask your doctor? How would the answers to those questions help you to make an informed decision?

790 Chapter 35

Teacher Support: Managing Classroom Diversity

TECH PREP STUDENTS

Ask students interested in careers in the health-care field to investigate Magnetic Resonance Imaging, or MRI. If possible, have them interview a technician who administers the procedure. Students should ask questions such as: What is the role of the technician in diagnosing disease with an MRI? What skills and training are required to do the work? What, if any, health risks does the work entail?

GIFTED STUDENTS

Ask students to investigate what an MRI can reveal in tissues and organs that X-rays cannot. To find out the reason for the differences, they should also find out how the two methods work. What different scientific principles underlie each method? Ask students to explain what they find in a brief report to the class.

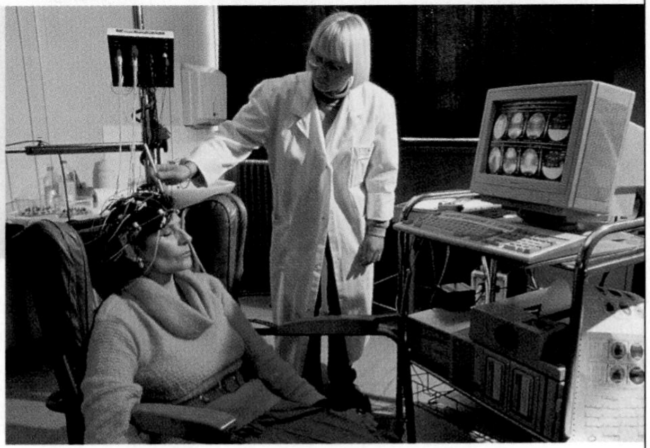

Figure 35–11
CAREER TRACK
An electroneurodiagnostic technologist is responsible for taking electroencephalogram (EEG) images of the brain. EEGs show the average electrical activity of the brain and are useful in studying the process of sleep and in diagnosing some brain abnormalities.

The Peripheral Nervous System

The peripheral nervous system includes all the nerves and associated cells that connect the brain and spinal cord to the rest of the body. The peripheral nervous system receives information from the environment and relays commands from the central nervous system to organs throughout the body.

There are two divisions in the peripheral nervous system—the sensory division and the motor division. The sensory division carries information from the sense organs to the central nervous system. The motor division transmits messages in the other direction—from the central nervous system to the rest of the body. The motor division is further divided into the **somatic nervous system** and the **autonomic nervous system.**

The Somatic Nervous System

The somatic nervous system controls voluntary movements. Every time you turn a page of this book, you are using the somatic nervous system to command the movements of your hand. Some somatic nerves are also part of reflexes and act with or without conscious control.

The Autonomic Nervous System

The autonomic nervous system regulates activities that are not under conscious control, including the beating of the heart and the contraction of muscles surrounding the digestive system. This system regulates the activities of many organs throughout the body. The autonomic nervous system consists of two distinct parts—the sympathetic nervous system and the parasympathetic nervous system. In nearly every case, nerves from both systems regulate each organ.

Why is each organ regulated by both nervous systems? The answer is that the effects of each system are different. For example, sympathetic nerves cause the heart rate to speed up, but parasympathetic nerves cause it to slow down—like the gas pedal and the brake of a car. Therefore, the autonomic nervous system can quickly speed up the activities of important organs or slam on the brakes—whichever is necessary.

Section Review 35–2

1. **Describe** the two major divisions of the nervous system.
2. **Critical Thinking—Making Inferences** Each hemisphere of the cerebrum receives sensory information and controls movement on the opposite side of the body. In a right-handed person, which hemisphere is dominant? In a left-handed person?

4 ASSESS

Quick Check

Give students copies of a drawing of a human figure that shows the major components of the nervous system. Ask students to label each component with its name and primary function.

Section Review 35–2

1. The central nervous system, which consists of the brain and spinal cord; the peripheral nervous system, which includes all the nerves and associated cells that connect the brain and spinal cord to the rest of the body.
2. In a right-handed person, the left hemisphere is dominant. In a left-handed person the right hemisphere is dominant.

Learning Modality

Auditory Learning Ask volunteers to describe and state the functions of each of the following nervous system components: cerebrum, cerebral cortex, cerebellum, brainstem, spinal cord, and peripheral nervous system. Correct any misconceptions.

TEACHER SUPPORT

Managing Classroom Diversity

AT-RISK STUDENTS
To help students keep track of the many divisions and subdivisions of the peripheral nervous system, ask them to make an outline showing how the following parts of the peripheral nervous system are related: sensory division, motor division, somatic nervous system, autonomic nervous system, sympathetic nervous system, and parasympathetic nervous system. Check students' understanding by asking them to give examples of behaviors controlled by each system. (For example, for the somatic nervous system, behaviors might include writing, eating, or running; for the autonomic nervous system, behaviors might include breathing, waking, or digesting food.)

Ancillary Support

The resource below can be used to support your teaching strategy for these two pages.

BL Inquiry Activity: Don't Forget to Breathe!

Section 35-3
The Senses

Performance Objective
- Name the five senses.

Mini Lab Skill: Experimenting

1 ENGAGE

Inquiry Activity
Observing

How Do I Know Thee?
Ask students how their nervous systems learn about the outside world. For example, how do they get the information they need to identify particular objects or substances? After students have had a chance to respond, do the following activity to help them appreciate the role played by each of the five senses in learning about the environment.

Ask students to identify several unknown objects, substances, or sounds using such procedures as the following.
- While wearing a blindfold, taste or smell various harmless substances, such as orange juice or ginger ale.
- Without looking, reach into a large paper bag and, by touch alone, identify several small objects, such as a coin, marble, or paper clip.
- While sitting back-to-back with another student, try to identify sounds the other student makes, such as clicking a retractable pen or turning the pages of a book.

2 EXPLORE

Discussion
Most information that reaches the brain from the sense organs is passed on to other parts of the body. Ask students to think of examples of observable behaviors that are responses to different types of sensory input. Which of the responses do they think are voluntary and which do they think are involuntary? Lead students in a discussion of which sense or senses they think have the greatest impact on their own behavior.

SECTION 35–3 The Senses

Guide for Reading
- **List** the five senses.

MINI LAB
- **Design an experiment** to determine your threshold for taste.

HOW DO YOU KNOW THAT there is a world around you? That might seem to be an obvious question, but philosophers have wondered about this for thousands of years. Many of them have come to an interesting conclusion—that what we know of the world depends entirely on our senses. In this very important way, we are at the mercy of our sensory systems.

The Five Senses

Our five senses—vision, hearing, smell, taste, and touch—each begins with specialized sense organs that respond to the environment. Sensory neurons carry impulses from these sense organs back to the central nervous system, where they form the basis for our understanding of the world.

Vision

Similar to other primates, humans have exceptionally good eyesight. In a world that is filled with sunlight, our vision, more than any other sense, shapes our understanding of everything around us.

Light enters the eye through the **cornea,** a tough transparent layer at the surface of the eye. The cornea focuses the entering light, which then passes through a fluid-filled chamber. At the back of this chamber is a disk of tissue called the **iris.** Tiny muscles adjust the size of the opening in the iris, called the **pupil,** to regulate the amount of light that enters the eye. Pigments in the iris give your eye its color, making it appear blue, brown, or green.

Just behind the pupil is the **lens,** a flexible structure filled with a transparent protein. Small muscles attached to the lens change its shape to help you adjust your eyes' focus to see near or distant objects. Behind the lens is a large chamber filled with a transparent fluid called the **vitreous** (VIH-tree-uhs) **humor.**

(a)

(b)

(c)

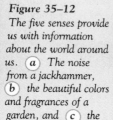

Figure 35–12 The five senses provide us with information about the world around us. (a) The noise from a jackhammer, (b) the beautiful colors and fragrances of a garden, and (c) the smell and taste of food would not be possible without input from the senses and interpretation by the central nervous system.

TEACHER SUPPORT

Background Information

Why do primates, including humans, have such good vision? Primates can see with great acuity, in three dimensions and in color, whereas most other vertebrates lack one or more of these visual features. Anthropologists attribute the evolution of primate vision to the arboreal, or tree-dwelling, habitat of primate ancestors. Visual acuity and depth perception, or the ability to see three-dimensionally, are especially important for moving in an arboreal environment. Misperceiving distance and falling short of the next branch could result in a long fall to the ground. Color vision is very useful for identifying objects in moderate-contrast environments, such as the dappled light among the branches of a tree.

Figure 35–13
The human eye is a complicated organ responsible for the sense of vision. The area on the retina that contains no rods or cones is called the blind spot.

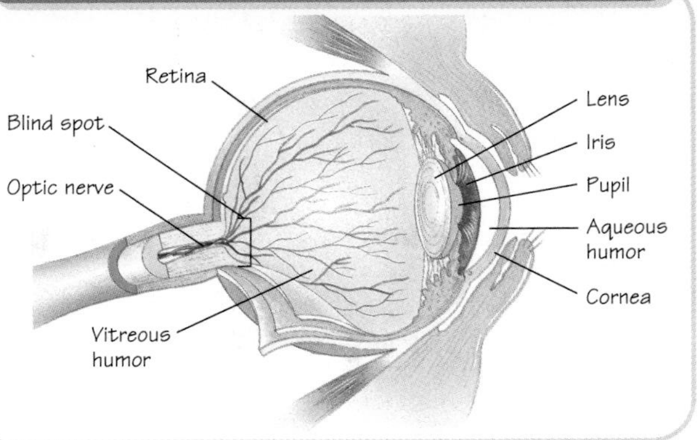

Similar to a miniature slide projector, the lens and cornea project an image of the scene in front of your eyes directly onto the **retina,** the layer of cells at the back of the eye. The light-sensitive photoreceptor cells in the retina come in two kinds—rods and cones. Rods are extremely sensitive to light, but they cannot detect color. Cones can detect color, but they need more light than rods to work properly.

Rods and cones are wired directly to a series of interneurons that are part of the retina itself. These cells help to analyze the pattern of cells stimulated by light and then relay that information to the brain through the optic nerve. A major portion of the human brain is devoted to receiving and analyzing signals from the optic nerve.

☑ *Checkpoint* What are rods and cones? ❶

Hearing and Balance

Sound is nothing more than vibrations in the air around us. Slow vibrations—those that shake the air 100 to 500 times a second—produce deep, low-pitched sounds. Higher pitches result from faster vibrations—1000 to 5000 times per second. Our ears allow us to sense the pitch and determine its loudness—how strong the vibration is.

Vibrations enter the ear through the **auditory canal,** causing the **tympanum,** the eardrum, to vibrate. The vibrations are picked up by three tiny bones, the

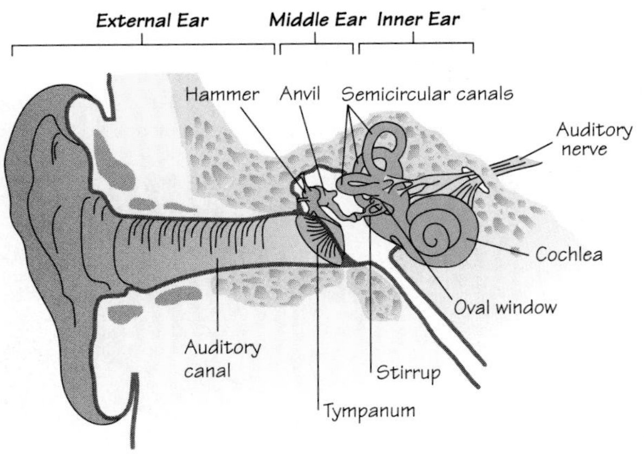

Figure 35–14
The human ear is divided into three parts—the outer ear, the middle ear, and the inner ear. Each of the structures within the ear is responsible for either hearing or maintaining balance.

3 TEACH

Investigate

Model Building Point out to students that sound travels in waves. Ask students what they think sound waves would look like if they could see them instead of hear them. Ask them to think about what else travels in waves that they could use as a model. Point out that water travels in waves when it is disturbed. Demonstrate by dropping a pebble into a large pan of water. Ask students to describe what they observe when the pebble hits the water. Help students relate this model to sound waves.

Inquiry Activity

Designing an Experiment

Comparing Sound and Light Although sound and light both are forms of energy, they differ in several important ways. Sound travels more slowly than light, but it can pass through most substances, whereas light travels only in straight lines and can pass only through transparent substances. Ask students how they could demonstrate one or more of these differences between sound and light, using their own ears and eyes as devices for the reception of sound and light.

Suggest that students work with a partner and use such procedures as the following.

- Standing at opposite ends of an athletic field, partners take turns simultaneously raising a hand and shouting, demonstrating that light travels faster than sound because they will see the motion before they hear the sound.
- While standing in adjacent rooms, partners tap on the wall between them, demonstrating that sound travels through substances whereas light does not.

☑ Checkpoint

❶ Light-sensitive photoreceptor cells in the retina; both rods and cones are light sensitive, and cones can also detect color.

TEACHER SUPPORT

Ecology Note

Noise pollution is a growing problem in the United States. Over half the population are exposed to harmful levels of noise. Excessive noise can have several different adverse effects on people. It can be stressful, contribute to high blood pressure and heart disease, lead to muscle tension and gastrointestinal problems, and disturb sleep. Excessive noise may even have an adverse effect on the developing fetus. What level of noise is considered excessive? Noises louder than the 80-decibel level—which is the loudness of a garbage disposal or dishwasher—lead to hearing loss on repeated exposure. Common sources of noise over 80 decibels include diesel trucks and busy city streets (90 decibels), outboard engines and blenders (100 decibels), auto horns and live rock bands (110 decibels), and thunderclaps (120 decibels). Noises louder than 180 decibels can result in death.

MINI LAB Experimenting

Teacher Notes

- For time required and materials needed, see page 782b.
- Solutions may be prepared one day ahead and dispensed shortly before class.
- For a 5 percent solution, add 5 g sucrose to 100 mL water; for a 0.5 percent solution, add 10 mL of the 5 percent solution to 90 mL water; for a 0.05 percent solution, add 10 mL of the 0.5 percent solution to 90 mL water.
- Caution students not to share cups of water nor to return used swabs to the cups of solution.

Answers to Analyze and Conclude

1. Students are likely to taste the 5 percent and 0.5 percent solutions; they are concentrated enough to stimulate taste receptors.
2. It refers to the concentration required to stimulate taste receptors.
3. Rinsing removes any trace of sucrose from the mouth, so one trial will not affect the results of the next.

Skills Trace
Experimenting

- Focus p. 794
- Practice p. 795
- Assess p. 805

Discussion

Although for humans and other primates vision is the most important of the five senses, the sense of smell can sometimes mean the difference between life and death. Ask the class to discuss ways the sense of smell can warn people of danger and help prevent harm. (Some ways include warning people of spoilage in food, fire in a building, or gas from a leak.)

Figure 35–15 *Nerve cells located in tissues lining the upper part of the nasal cavity are responsible for the sense of smell.*

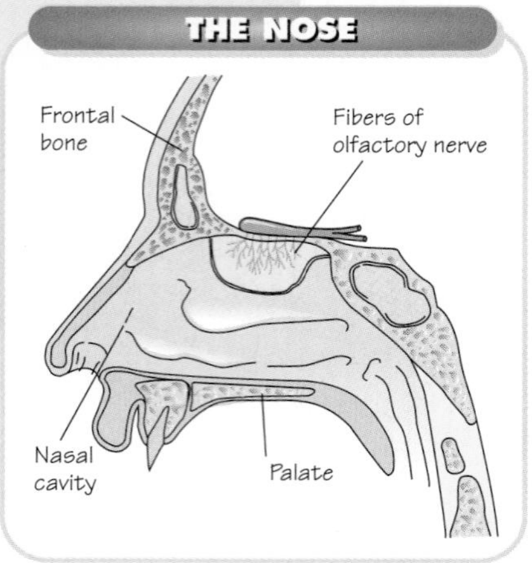

hammer, the anvil, and the stirrup. These bones transmit the vibrations to a thin membrane called the oval window. The oval window covers the opening for the inner ear. Vibrations of the oval window create pressure waves in the fluid-filled **cochlea** (KAHK-lee-uh) of the inner ear.

The cochlea is lined with tiny hair cells that are pushed back and forth by these pressure waves. In response to these movements, the hair cells produce nerve impulses that are sent to the brain through the auditory nerve.

The ear also contains a tiny organ that helps you to sense your position in space and maintain your balance. Three fluid-filled **semicircular canals** enable the nervous system to sense changes in the position of the head. When the head is moved quickly in any direction, pressure is developed in one or more of the canals, and tiny hairs near the ends of the canals sense these pressures.

Two tiny sacs located below the semicircular canals are embedded in a gelatinlike substance that contains tiny grains of calcium carbonate. The downward pressure produced by these tiny grains enables you to sense the pull of gravity. Together, the semicircular canals and these sacs enable you to sense your body's position and keep your balance steady.

Checkpoint What is the function of the semicircular canals? 1

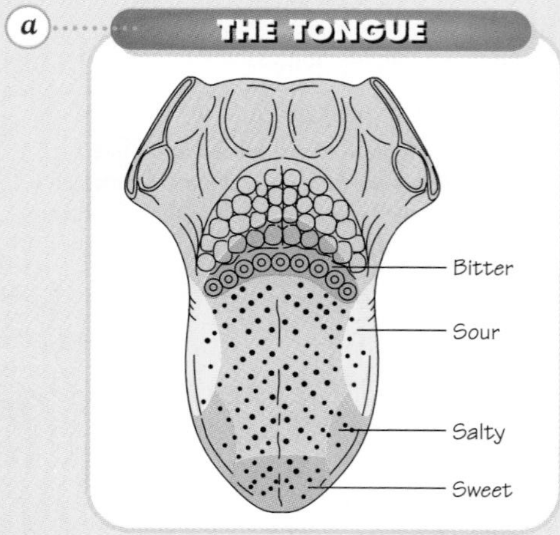

Figure 35–16 (a) *Although the tongue is covered with taste buds, the taste buds are grouped into four regions, depending on the "taste" they perceive.* (b) *This scanning electron micrograph shows what the surface of the tongue really looks like. The large disk-shaped objects are the taste buds (magnification: 240X).*

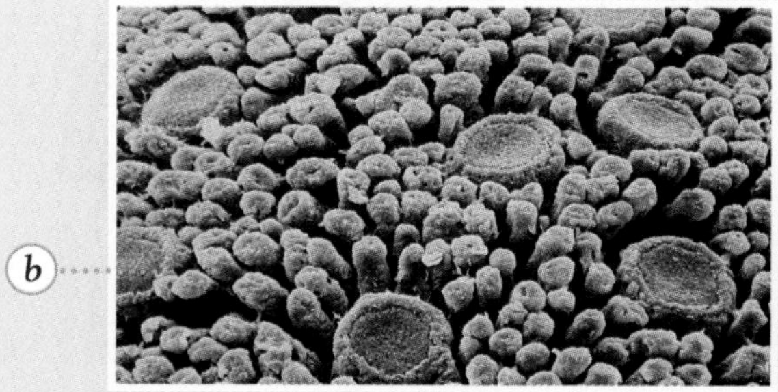

TEACHER SUPPORT Activity

MAPPING THE TONGUE

Taste buds for the four types of tastes that humans can perceive—sweet, sour, salty, and bitter—tend to be localized on the tongue, as shown in Figure 35–16a. Provide students with four harmless solutions, one for each type of taste, and ask them to observe where on their own tongues they can perceive each type of taste most strongly. They can apply the solutions with cotton swabs, using a mirror to help them guide the swabs to the correct region of the tongue. They should investigate how well they can taste each type of taste on different regions of the tongue. Tell students to rinse their mouths between each solution. Solutions should include sugar water (sweet), lemon juice (sour), salt water (salty), and tonic water (bitter). Provide a plastic trash bag for students to safely dispose of the cups and swabs after they have completed the activity.

Smell

You may never have thought of it this way, but your sense of smell is actually the ability to detect chemicals. Special cells in the upper part of the nasal passageway act as receptors for a variety of chemicals. When stimulated, these cells produce the nerve impulses that travel to the central nervous system.

Your sense of smell is capable of producing thousands of different sensations. In fact, much of what is commonly called the "taste" of food actually depends on your sense of smell. To prove this, eat a few bites of food while holding your nose. You'll discover that the food doesn't have much taste until you open your nose and breathe freely.

Taste

Your mouth contains chemical receptors called **taste buds,** which are located on the tongue. Although you are able to perceive hundreds of tastes, there are only four types of taste receptors—sweet, sour, salty, and bitter. Sensitivity to these different tastes varies on different parts of the tongue, as shown by the drawing in ***Figure 35–16.***

Touch and Related Senses

The largest sense organ in your body is the skin, which contains different receptors for touch, pain, heat, and cold. Each receptor responds to its particular stimulus and produces nerve impulses that signal the central nervous system.

Not all parts of the body are equally sensitive to touch, because not all parts have the same number of receptors. The greatest densities of touch receptors, for example, are found on your fingers, toes, and lips.

MINI LAB ····· Experimenting

How Tasty Is It?

PROBLEM *How can you determine your threshold for taste?* ***Design an experiment*** *to answer this question.*

SUGGESTED PROCEDURE

1. Rinse your mouth with water.
2. Using a clean cotton swab, place a drop of sugar solution on the tip of your tongue. Record your observations. Rinse your mouth with water.
3. Using a procedure similar to the one used in steps 1 and 2, design an experiment to determine the effects of two different concentrations of sugar solution on the tip of your tongue. Have your teacher check your procedure before carrying out your experiment.

ANALYZE AND CONCLUDE

1. Which sugar solutions were you able to taste? Explain why.
2. What do you think the word "threshold" means with regard to taste?
3. Why was it important for you to rinse your mouth between tastings?

Section Review 35-3

1. **List** the five senses.
2. **Critical Thinking—Drawing Conclusions** Why do you think you feel dizzy after spinning around for a few seconds?
3. **MINI LAB Design an experiment** to determine your threshold for taste.

4 ASSESS

Quick Check

Read the names of the structures of the eye and ear that are highlighted in this section. After each name, call on one student to describe the structure and another to identify its function.

Section Review 35-3

1. Vision, hearing, smell, taste, and touch.

2. The movement creates pressure in the semicircular canals inside the ear, which help to maintain balance.

3. Experimental designs should involve students' tasting increasingly concentrated solutions of a substance until the taste threshold is reached.

Skills Trace
Experimenting

- Focus p. 794
- Practice p. 795
- Assess p. 805

Checkpoint

1 They sense changes in the position of the head, which helps the body to sense position in space and maintain balance.

Learning Modality

Visual and Kinesthetic Learning On drawings of the eye and ear, have students trace the pathway of light or sound from the point at which it enters the eye or ear to the point at which the sensation is transmitted as a nervous impulse to the brain. As students move their fingers to each structure along the way, have them name the structure and explain its function.

Ancillary Support

The resources below can be used to support your teaching strategy for these two pages.

LM Investigating the Senses, #70
TR Writing in Biology: Thinking About Your Senses
Apply: Super Sensors
BL Inquiry Activity: Sense-Ability
TB The Eye and The Ear, #43

Section 35–4
Nerve Impulses and Drugs

Performance Objectives

• Explain how the sodium-potassium pump returns neurons to the resting state.

• Discuss the influence on the nervous system of stimulants, depressants, and opiates.

Mini Lab Skill: Predicting

1 ENGAGE

Inquiry Activity
Building a Model

Modeling the Sodium-Potassium Pump

Ask a few volunteers to use an air pump to add air to a partially inflated bicycle tire. Ask them how much effort it takes to pump air into the tire. Tell students that this effort is work and work requires energy. Ask students where the volunteers got the energy they needed to work the pump. (From their food.)

Explain how the air pump can be used as a model for the sodium-potassium pump they will read about in this section. Instead of a mechanical device, the sodium-potassium pump is a protein in the cell membrane. Instead of pumping air into a tire, it pumps positively charged sodium ions out of the cell. This work requires energy because the outside of the cell is already positively charged, just as the bicycle tire was already partially inflated with air. Ask students where the sodium-potassium pump gets the energy it needs to do its job. (ATP, which is the energy source for most cellular functions.)

SECTION 35–4 BRANCHING OUT In Depth

Nerve Impulses and Drugs

Guide for Reading

- **Describe** the function of the sodium-potassium pump.
- **Describe** the effects of drugs on the nervous system.

MINI LAB

- **Predict** how the nervous system will respond to a stimulus.

AS YOU HAVE READ, IN THE nervous system, neurons are similar to telephone wires carrying coded messages and passing important signals from one cell to the next. How, exactly, do neurons do this? What produces the electrical potential across the neuron cell membrane? What happens when an impulse moves along an axon? And what happens when chemical substances alter the nervous system? To answer these questions in depth, we have to look closely at the cell membrane and at the point of synapse between two nerves.

The Resting Potential

As you have learned, there is a difference in electrical charge in a neuron's membrane, called the resting potential. There are two forces that produce this potential, both of which depend upon the special properties of the neuron cell membrane.

The first force is an active-transport protein built into the membrane, the **sodium-potassium pump.** What does this pump do? **The sodium-potassium pump uses the energy from ATP to pump sodium ions (Na^+) out of the cell while at the same time pumping potassium ions (K^+) into the cell.**

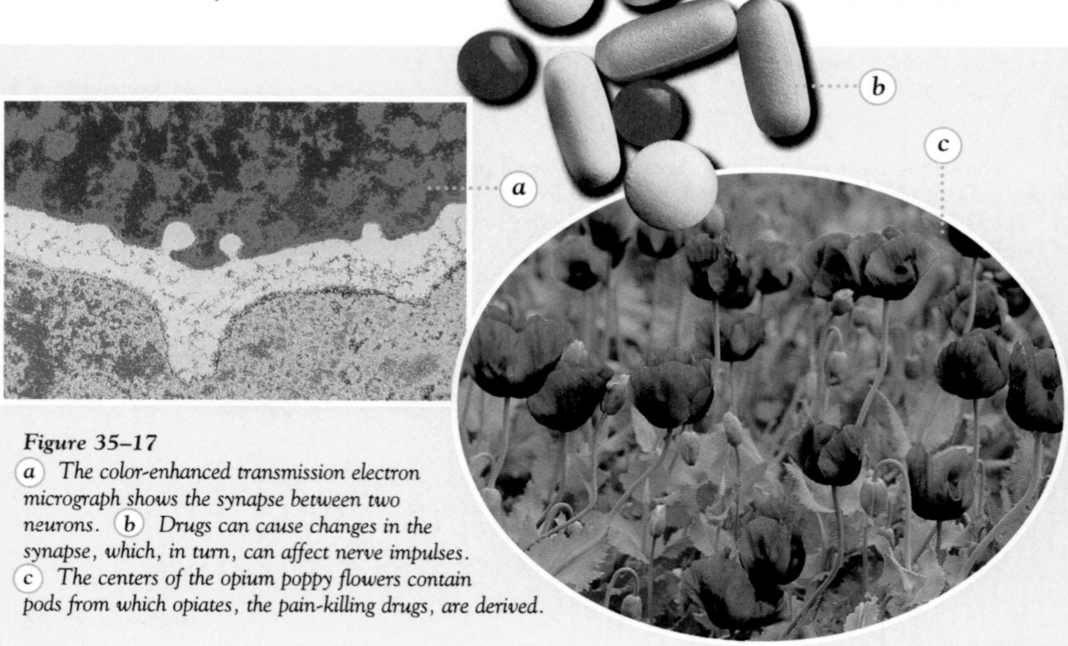

Figure 35–17
(a) The color-enhanced transmission electron micrograph shows the synapse between two neurons. (b) Drugs can cause changes in the synapse, which, in turn, can affect nerve impulses. (c) The centers of the opium poppy flowers contain pods from which opiates, the pain-killing drugs, are derived.

TEACHER SUPPORT

Ecology Note

Some drugs such as anesthetics and certain environmental toxins, including chlorinated hydrocarbons that are found in pesticides, can make neurons more or less likely to respond to electrical impulses. Often this is because the substance affects the permeability of membranes to calcium ions. When permeability is decreased so that there is a lower-than-normal concentration of calcium ions, sodium channels may not close completely between action potentials, allowing sodium ions to cross the membrane. This makes the neurons fire more readily, and muscle spasms may result. When membrane permeability is increased and the calcium ion concentration is higher than normal, the opposite result occurs; neurons become less excitable and more difficult to fire.

Figure 35–18
At resting potential, sodium ions (Na^+) are outside the cell membrane. As the action potential begins, the sodium gates open and Na^+ ions rush across the membrane. In a few milliseconds, the sodium gates close and the potassium gates open. This allows potassium ions (K^+) to cross the membrane. So many K^+ ions rush across the membrane that the outside of the membrane becomes more positive than the inside, thus restoring the resting potential.

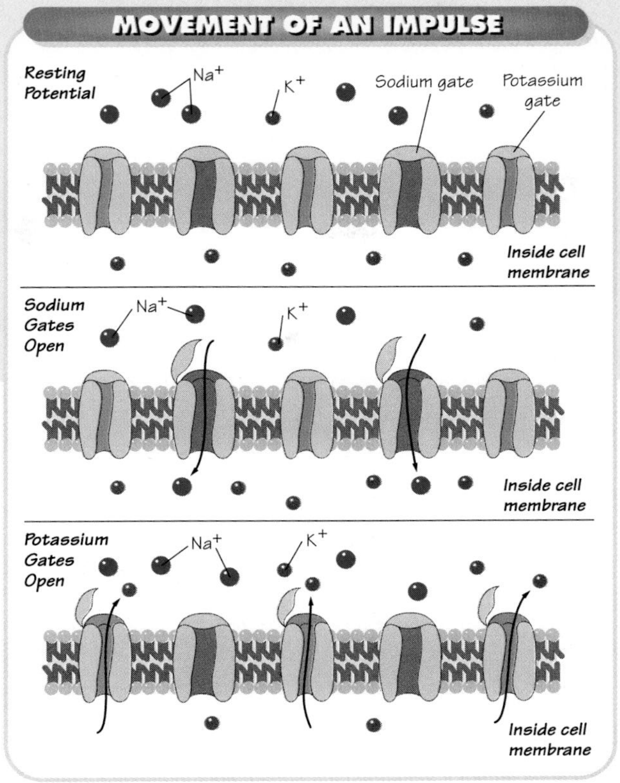

The difference in the concentrations of sodium and potassium ions on the two sides of the membrane is important because both of these ions are positive. Ions do not move across most cell membranes very easily, and once the sodium ions are pumped out of the cell, they tend to stay out. However, significant numbers of potassium ions do manage to leak across the membrane. Remember, potassium ions are located mostly inside the cell. This means that large numbers of positive ions leak out of the cell but few leak into it.

What is the result of positive charges leaking out of the cell? As you might expect, this leaves fewer positive ions inside the cell, meaning that it is negatively charged compared with the outside. The great difference in charges between the two sides of the membrane produces the resting potential.

The Action Potential

A nerve impulse consists of an action potential that rapidly moves down the axon. How does this happen? Remember that an impulse can be started by the environment, by another neuron, or by an electrical stimulus.

The cell membrane of a neuron contains thousands of tiny protein channels known as **voltage-sensitive gates,** which can allow either sodium or potassium to pass through. Generally, the gates are closed. However, when the voltage across the membrane changes—as it does when a stimulus is present—the sodium gates open, allowing Na^+ ions to rush across the membrane.

So many Na^+ ions rush across the membrane that for a few milliseconds, the inside of the membrane becomes more positive than the outside! As you might expect, the inward rush of positive charges in one region of the membrane causes the sodium gates just ahead of it to respond to the voltage change, and these gates open, too. Very quickly, the impulse spreads along the axon.

However, almost as rapidly as they open, the sodium gates close, and the

2 EXPLORE

Investigate

Long-Term Project Many people think of such drugs as alcohol or cocaine when they think of addictive drugs that affect the brain. They may be less likely to think of drugs such as caffeine, nicotine, or prescription pain killers. Ask students to take a simple survey of students in their school in which they ask respondents to:

1. Name drugs that affect the brain.
2. Name drugs that are addictive.

Ask students to summarize the results of their survey. Then have them make posters that alert teens to the dangers of addictive, mind-altering drugs that were not named by survey respondents.

3 TEACH

Ideas Through Images

Have students examine Figure 35–18, read the caption, and answer the following questions.

- **At resting potential, what charges do the inside and outside of the membrane have?** (The inside is negative; the outside is positive.)
- **How does a nerve impulse affect sodium gates in the membrane?** (A nerve impulse causes sodium gates to open and let sodium ions into the cell.)
- **How is the charge difference restored to that of the resting state?** (Potassium gates open and potassium rushes out of the cell, making the outside of the membrane more positive than the inside.)

TEACHER SUPPORT

Background Information

A nerve impulse usually is considered to be an all-or-nothing sort of phenomenon. This means that there is a threshold level below which a stimulus cannot trigger an action potential, whereas any stimulus at or above the threshold level triggers exactly the same response. However, if a neuron has just fired, this picture changes. There is a period of a few milliseconds, called the absolute refractory period, during which no stimulus can produce a response, even a stimulus above the threshold level. Then, for a slightly longer period, called the relative refractory period, an intense stimulus well above the threshold level is needed to provoke a response. The closer the neuron is to complete recovery, the less intense the stimulus must be to provoke a response. When the neuron is completely recovered, it responds in the all-or-nothing way once again.

Ancillary Support

The resource below can be used to support your teaching strategy for these two pages.

TR Explore: Measuring Your Potential

MINI LAB Predicting

Teacher Notes

- For time required and materials needed, see page 782b.
- The screening or plastic should be about 30–40 centimeters square.

Answers to Analyze and Conclude

1. The group member will blink when the paper is tossed.
2. Students may have predicted that the group member would be able to control his or her blinking. However, blinking in this way is an automatic response that the individual cannot control.
3. The advantage of having quick, automatic responses is that it allows us to act quickly without thinking. If we had to think before responding, we would be more likely to suffer injury.
4. The part of the central nervous system responsible for this response is the spinal cord. The response is called a reflex.

Skills Trace

Predicting

Focus p. 798
Practice p. 799
Assess p. 805

Discussion

Ask students to compare the effects of stimulants, depressants, and opiates on the nervous system. In this discussion, make sure students relate the effects of these drugs on neurotransmitters, synapses, and action potentials. Challenge students to think of specific examples of how the effects of these drugs are manifested in human behavior and how such behavior can lead to harm or injury.

MINI LAB Predicting

Face to Face

PROBLEM ***Predict*** *how the nervous system will respond to a stimulus.*

PROCEDURE

1. Have two members of your group stand a few meters away from each other. They should be facing each other.
2. Have one group member hold a piece of screening or a sheet of clear plastic in front of his or her face.
3. Have the second group member toss a crumpled piece of paper at the screening or plastic. Observe the eyes of the group member behind the screening.
4. Repeat steps 1 to 3, but this time have the group member behind the screening try not to respond to the tossed paper. Predict what will happen.

ANALYZE AND CONCLUDE

1. What response did the group member have when the paper was tossed?
2. Was your prediction correct about the group member being successful in stopping the response to the stimulus (tossed paper)? Why or why not?
3. What is the advantage of having this quick response?
4. Which part of the central nervous system is responsible for this response? What is this response called?

movement of sodium stops. A few milliseconds after the sodium gates open, the potassium gates open, allowing K^+ ions to rush out of the cell. Within a few milliseconds, the inside of the membrane is negative once again.

The rapid opening and closing of sodium and potassium gates makes the impulse possible. The small amounts of sodium and potassium that cross the cell membrane during an impulse are quickly pumped back by the sodium-potassium pump, and the neuron is ready for another impulse.

When an action potential reaches the synapse, it triggers the release of a neurotransmitter. The neurotransmitter molecules diffuse across the gap and bind to receptors in the dendrites of the next neuron. The receptors cause the ion gates to open, and the impulse continues.

☑ **Checkpoint** What are voltage-sensitive gates? ❶

Drugs and the Synapse

The nervous system depends on neurotransmitters to relay information about the world from cell to cell. This means that the synapse—the connection from one neuron to the next—is one of the body's most important relay stations.

What might happen if a chemical such as a **drug** that affected the synapse was introduced into the body? The nervous system could malfunction. A drug is any substance that causes a change in the body. **Drugs can affect the body in a variety of ways, causing changes in the brain, the nervous system, and the synapses between nerves.**

Stimulants

Some drugs, such as **stimulants,** increase the release of neurotransmitters at some synapses in the brain. This speeds up the nervous system, leading to a feeling of energy and well-being. When the effects of stimulants wear off, however, the brain's supply of neurotransmitters has been depleted. The user quickly falls into fatigue and depression. Long-term use causes hallucinations, circulatory problems, and psychological depression.

Even stronger effects are produced by drugs, such as **cocaine,** that act on neurons in what are known as the pleasure centers of the brain. The effects of cocaine are so strong that they produce **addiction**—an uncontrollable craving for more of the drug.

TEACHER SUPPORT — Managing Classroom Diversity

AT-RISK STUDENTS
Simplify, summarize, and give examples to reinforce the material on drugs and the nervous system. Tell students that most drugs that affect the nervous system do so in one of two ways, either by stimulating it or by depressing it. As the names suggest, stimulants speed up body processes whereas depressants slow them down. Stimulants include amphetamines ("speed"), caffeine (found in soft drinks, tea, chocolate, and coffee), cocaine, and nicotine. Depressants include alcohol, barbiturates ("sleeping pills"), and tranquilizers (also called sedatives). Point out that opiates are often included in the depressant category because they also slow down body processes. Opiates include opium and drugs derived from opium—heroin, morphine, and codeine.

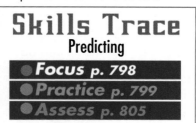

Cocaine causes the sudden release of a neurotransmitter called dopamine. Normally, dopamine is released when a basic need, such as hunger or thirst, is fulfilled. By fooling the brain into releasing dopamine, cocaine produces intense feelings of pleasure and satisfaction.

Cocaine is a powerful stimulant that increases the heart rate and blood pressure. For many first-time users, this stimulation is just too much—cocaine can damage the heart and has produced heart attacks, even in young people. In the United States, an inexpensive form of cocaine called crack has become one of the most dangerous drugs on the street. The intense high produced by crack wears off quickly and leaves the brain with too little dopamine. As a result, the user suddenly feels sad and depressed and quickly seeks another dose.

Depressants

Other drugs, called **depressants,** decrease the rate of brain activity. Some depressants, such as alcohol, enhance the effects of neurotransmitters that prevent some nerve cells from starting action potentials. This calms some parts of the brain that sense fear and relaxes the individual. However, long-term use of this type of drug can also cause problems. Depressant drugs reduce the effects of natural inhibitors of these neurons. As a result, the user comes to depend on the drug to relieve the anxieties of everyday life, which may seem unbearable without the drug.

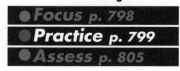

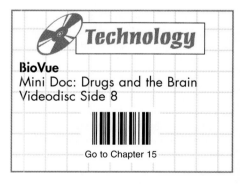

Figure 35–19 *Cocaine is made from the* Erythroxylum coca *plant, which grows mainly in South America.*

☑ Checkpoint What are depressants? ❷

Opiates

The opium poppy produces a powerful class of pain-killing drugs called **opiates.** These include chemical derivatives of opium, such as morphine and heroin. Opiates mimic natural chemicals in the brain known as endorphins, which normally help to overcome sensations of pain. The first few doses of these drugs produce strong feelings of pleasure and security, but the body quickly adjusts to the higher levels of endorphins. Once this happens, the body literally cannot do without them. If the user attempts to stop taking these drugs, the body cannot produce enough of the natural endorphins that are needed to prevent the user from the uncontrollable pain and sickness that accompany withdrawal from the drug.

Section Review 35–4

1. **Describe** the function of the sodium-potassium pump.
2. **Describe** the effects of drugs on the nervous system.
3. **MINI LAB** **Predict** how the nervous system will respond to a stimulus.
4. **BRANCHING OUT ACTIVITY** Use library references to make a chart of the following groups of drugs—stimulants, depressants, hallucinogens, opiates, cocaine, marijuana, alcohol, and tobacco. **Summarize** their long- and short-term effects on the nervous system.

4 ASSESS

Quick Check

Call on students to explain the structure and function of the sodium-potassium pump. Call on other students to name three types of drugs that affect the nervous system and give examples of each type.

Section Review 35–4

1. The sodium-potassium pump uses energy from ATP to pump sodium ions out of the cell and potassium ions into the cell.

2. Stimulants increase the release of neurotransmitters at synapses and speed up the nervous system. Depressants enhance the performance of neurotransmitters that prevent nerve impulses and slow down the nervous system. Opiates mimic endorphins and lead to feelings of pleasure.

3. Students may say that the nervous system responds automatically and almost instantaneously to some stimuli, such as the one described in the MINI LAB.

4. Students should summarize the direct effects of the drugs on the nervous system, as well as their effects on health and behavior.

☑ Checkpoints

❶ Voltage-sensitive gates are tiny protein channels in the cell membrane of a neuron that can allow either sodium or potassium to pass through.

❷ Drugs that decrease the rate of brain activity.

Skills Trace

Predicting

- Focus p. 798
- Practice p. 799
- Assess p. 805

Learning Modality

Visual Learning Ask students to create a schematic diagram that shows how the sodium-potassium pump works.

Technology

BioVue
Mini Doc: Drugs and the Brain
Videodisc Side 8

Go to Chapter 15

Ancillary Support

The resource below can be used to support your teaching strategy for these two pages.

BL Inquiry Activity: Get the Facts

Chapter 35

Laboratory Investigation

Observing the Structures of the Brain

Before the Lab

1. Sheep brains can be ordered from a butcher or biological supply company. Brains obtained from a biological supply company can be reused if they are stored in preservative between uses.
2. To save time, you may cut the brains in half prior to class.

Pre-Lab Discussion

Have students read the entire procedure for this investigation. Then ask students the following questions.

What is the purpose of this investigation? (To observe the structures of a sheep brain so as to better understand the anatomy of the human brain.)

What can you learn about the human brain by observing the brain of a sheep? (To recognize the major divisions of the brain, the lobes of the cerebrum, and gray and white matter.)

Why do you think a sheep brain is more useful for learning about the human brain than a frog brain would be? (Both sheep and humans are mammals, and all mammalian brains share many similarities.)

Skills Development

Students will use these skills while completing the laboratory investigation: observing, identifying, interpreting, comparing, and relating.

Teaching Strategies

1. Some students may be squeamish about handling the brain. Suggest that they work with a partner who does not mind handling the brain.
2. A three-dimensional model of the human brain, if available, may make it easier for students to compare the sheep brain with the human brain.

Laboratory Investigation

Observing the Structures of the Brain

In structure, the brain of a sheep is similar to the brain of a human. Most of the parts are located in identical areas. In this investigation, you will use the sheep brain to illustrate the anatomy of the human brain.

Problem

How can you **identify** the parts of the sheep brain?

Materials (per group)

- dissecting pan
- scalpel
- probe
- gloves
- sheep brain

Procedure

1. **Put on the pair of gloves provided. Place the sheep brain in a dissecting pan so that the raised side (dorsal) is up and the flat side (ventral) is resting on the pan.**
2. **Notice the large anterior section, the cerebrum. The cerebral cortex has many convolutions, or gyri (singular: gyrus), and grooves, called sulci (singular: sulcus). Each sulcus separates the cerebrum into lobes.**

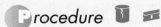

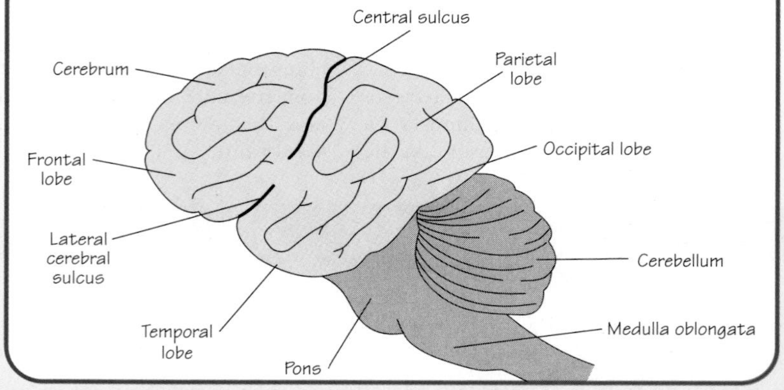

Safety Tips

- Warn students that unpreserved brains may be contaminated with virus or bacteria and that preserved brains are saturated with chemicals that may be toxic. Therefore, they should handle the brains carefully and only with gloves.
- Caution students to use care when handling and cutting with the scalpel.
- Remind students to wash their hands when they have finished the procedure.

3. **Locate the central sulcus that runs down from the top to the bottom of the cerebrum, midway between the front (anterior) and the back (posterior). In front of the central sulcus, you will find the frontal lobe. Behind the central sulcus is the parietal lobe.**
4. **Locate the lateral cerebral sulcus, a groove that runs horizontally along the cerebrum, separating the frontal lobe (above) from the temporal lobe (below).**
5. **Locate the occipital lobe, which is found posterior to the parietal lobe.**
6. **Posterior to the cerebrum is a smaller lobed structure called the cerebellum. Holding the brain in your hand, gently bend the cerebellum down. Although in the sheep the cerebellum is directly behind the cerebrum, in humans it is positioned similarly to where it is located when you bend the sheep's brain downward.**
7. **Posterior to the cerebellum, you will find the medulla oblongata, which forms a triangular shape. This part of the brain narrows into and becomes the spinal cord.**
8. **The midbrain section is more visible on the ventral (underneath) side. Locate the pons—a bridgelike, raised area in the cerebellum region. The pons is in front of the medulla oblongata.**
9. **With a scalpel, carefully cut the brain in half lengthwise. CAUTION: *Be very careful when using a sharp instrument.***
10. **Distinguish between the outer gray cortex area of the cerebellum and its inner white matter. The gray matter is slightly darker than the white and not really gray at all.**
11. **Dispose of the brain as directed by your teacher. Clean your dissecting pan and scalpel and probe. Remove your gloves and wash your hands thoroughly.**

Observations

1. Compare the sheep brain to the human brain.
2. Compare the size of the cerebrum with the other parts of the brain. What significance does the size of the cerebrum have?
3. Describe the location of the "gray" matter and the "white" matter in the brain. Other than by color, how do they differ?

Analysis and Conclusions

1. Were you able to identify the four lobes of the brain? Why or why not?
2. The hypothalamus is connected to the pituitary gland. What is the relationship between the hypothalamus and the pituitary gland?
3. What is the function of the medulla oblongata? Of the cerebellum?

More to Explore

Using reference materials, determine the areas of the cerebral cortex that have been successfully mapped by scientists according to their specific function.

Answers to Observations

1. Both brains have the same structures but with these differences: The sheep cerebellum is located behind the cerebrum, whereas the human cerebellum is located behind and under the cerebrum; there are separate olfactory lobes and two distinct lobes in the cerebellum in sheep brains but not in human brains; the fissures in the cerebellum differ between sheep and human brains.
2. The cerebrum is the largest of the major divisions of the brain. The larger the cerebrum, the more capable the animal is of functions such as learning, intelligence, and judgment.
3. The gray matter is located on the outside of the brain and the white matter is on the inside. The gray matter consists primarily of the cell bodies, the white matter of myelinated axons.

Answers to Analysis and Conclusions

1. Students should be able to identify the following parts of the brain: frontal lobe, temporal lobe, occipital lobe, and parietal lobe.
2. As students may recall from Chapter 34, when the hypothalamus detects certain body changes, it releases regulating hormones that either inhibit or stimulate the pituitary gland to release its hormones.
3. The medulla oblongata regulates the flow of information between the brain and the rest of the body; it also regulates heart rates, breathing, and blood pressure. The cerebellum coordinates muscle activities and balance.

More to Explore

Suggest that students compare a brain map of sensory functions with a brain map of motor functions and discuss how and why the two differ.

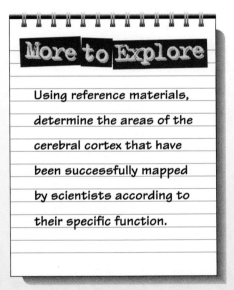

CHAPTER 35

Study Guide

Review Strategy

Divide the class into four groups and assign one section of the chapter to each group. Ask the groups to decide which information in their section is most important. Then have each group make a diagram or table to summarize the most important information. For example, for the first section, the group might draw a neuron with each of its parts labeled and use arrows to show how a nerve impulse passes through the neuron. For the last section, the group might draw a schematic of the sodium-potassium pump and make a table to compare and contrast the effects of different drugs on the nervous system. When the groups are finished, ask a spokesperson for each group to explain its work to the rest of the class. Do other class members agree with the selection of material and the way in which it is presented? Urge students to modify their work as necessary, then display their diagrams and tables in the classroom for use as study guides.

Recalling Main Ideas

1. a	4. c	7. b
2. c	5. d	8. c
3. d	6. a	9. b

Assessment

Reviewing What You Learned

1. The basic cellular unit of the nervous system.
2. Sensory neurons, motor neurons, and interneurons.
3. A resting potential is a difference in electrical charge between the positively charged outside of a membrane and the negatively charged inside of the membrane. An action potential is a rapid change in voltage on the inside of the axon, from negative to positive and back to negative.

Study Guide

Summarizing Key Concepts

The key concepts in each section of this chapter are listed below to help you review the chapter content. Make sure you understand each concept and its relationship to other concepts and to the theme of this chapter.

35–1 The Human Nervous System

- A neuron is made up of a cell body, dendrites, and an axon.
- An impulse begins when a neuron is stimulated by another neuron or by the environment. Once it begins, the impulse travels rapidly down the axon away from the cell body.

35–2 Organization of the Nervous System

- The central nervous system consists of the brain and the spinal cord.
- The peripheral nervous system includes all the nerves and associated cells that connect the brain and spinal cord to the rest of the body.

35–3 The Senses

- Our five senses—vision, hearing, smell, taste, and touch—each begins with specialized sense organs that respond to the environment.

35–4 Nerve Impulses and Drugs

- The sodium-potassium pump uses the energy from ATP to pump sodium ions out of the cell while at the same time pumping potassium ions into the cell.
- Drugs can affect the body in a variety of ways, causing changes in the brain, the nervous system, and the synapses between nerves.

Reviewing Key Terms

Review the following vocabulary terms and their meaning. Then use each term in a complete sentence.

35–1 The Human Nervous System

neuron	motor neuron
impulse	interneuron
cell body	resting potential
dendrite	action potential
axon	myelin
nerve	synapse
sensory neuron	neurotransmitter

35–2 Organization of the Nervous System

meninges	medulla oblongata
cerebrospinal fluid	pons
cerebrum	reflex
cerebral cortex	somatic nervous system
cerebellum	autonomic nervous system
brainstem	

35–3 The Senses

cornea	auditory canal
iris	tympanum
pupil	cochlea
lens	semicircular canal
vitreous humor	taste bud
retina	

35–4 Nerve Impulses and Drugs

sodium-potassium pump	stimulant
voltage-sensitive gate	cocaine
drug	addiction
	depressant
	opiate

Inquiry-Based Strategy

Have students look again at the gymnast on page 782. After reading the chapter, they know that the gymnast's ears are more important than her eyes in helping to maintain her balance. Ask students how they could show a connection between balance and the inner ear. Have them design their own experiment or follow a procedure such as the following.

Students should stand on one foot for as long as they can and record how long they hold their balance. Then they should turn around in a circle several times and immediately try to hold their balance on one foot again, and again they should record their time. Ask students to compare and explain the results.

Recalling Main Ideas

Choose the letter of the answer that best completes the statement or answers the question.

1. Axons connect with other nerve cells at
   a. synapses. c. the brainstem.
   b. nodes. d. Schwann cells.

2. Dendrites
   a. transmit impulses away from the cell body.
   b. contain nuclei.
   c. are specialized to receive impulses from other cells.
   d. are surrounded by Schwann cells.

3. Which type of neuron is responsible for transmitting impulses to a muscle?
   a. sensory c. interneuron
   b. myelinated d. motor

4. What is the space between two neurons called?
   a. dendrite c. synapse
   b. neurotransmitter d. axon

5. In which function is the cerebral cortex not involved?
   a. sensory c. associative
   b. motor d. involuntary

6. A loss of balance might result from a disease of the
   a. cerebellum. c. pons.
   b. cerebrum. d. cranium.

7. The brain and the spinal cord are cushioned by layers of tough, elastic tissue called
   a. myelins. c. corneas.
   b. meninges. d. synapses.

8. Which of these is an active-transport protein located in a neuron's membrane?
   a. neurotransmitter
   b. myelin
   c. sodium-potassium pump
   d. vitreous humor

9. Substances that cause a change in the body are known as
   a. myelins. c. neurotransmitters.
   b. drugs. d. meninges.

Putting It All Together

Using the information on pages xxx to xxxi, complete the following concept map.

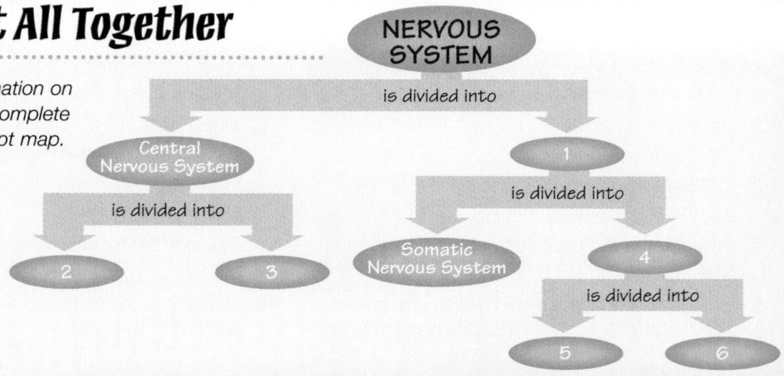

Putting It All Together

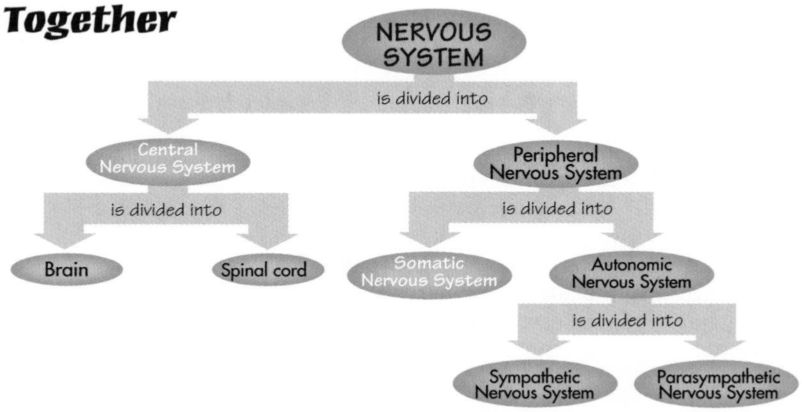

4. A material that wraps around axons and speeds the rate of transmission of nerve impulses.
5. A small space between the axon of one neuron and the dendrites of the next neuron, where impulses are transferred from neuron to neuron.
6. A sensory neuron carries impulses from a sense organ to the brain; a motor neuron carries impulses from the brain or spinal cord to muscles or other organs.
7. The central nervous system, which consists of the brain and spinal cord, and the peripheral nervous system, which includes all the nerves and associated cells that connect the brain and spinal cord to the rest of the body.
8. They cushion and protect the brain and spinal cord.
9. The functions of the cerebrum include learning, intelligence, and judgment; the function of the cerebellum is to coordinate and balance the actions of muscles; the function of the brainstem is to regulate the flow of information between the brain and the rest of the body.
10. The hypothalamus.
11. A quick, automatic response to a stimulus.
12. There are two divisions in the peripheral nervous system, the sensory division and the motor division.
13. The sympathetic and parasympathetic nervous systems regulate involuntary activities, like heart rate and digestion; the two systems have opposite effects on target organs.
14. Eyes (vision), ears (hearing), nose (smell), tongue (taste), and skin (touch).
15. An active-transport protein built into the membrane of a neuron to pump sodium ions out of the cell and potassium ions into the cell in order to return the cell to its resting potential.
16. Stimulants speed up the nervous system; depressants slow down the nervous system; opiates mimic brain chemicals that help overcome pain.

Expanding the Concepts

1. Myelin allows nerve impulses to travel down the axon much more rapidly than nonmyelinated axons.

Assessment

Reviewing What You Learned

Answer each of the following in a complete sentence.

1. What is a neuron?
2. List the three types of neurons.
3. What is a resting potential? An action potential?
4. What is myelin?
5. What is a synapse?
6. Explain the difference between a sensory neuron and a motor neuron.
7. Describe the two parts of the human nervous system.
8. Give the function of the meninges and the cerebrospinal fluid.
9. List the functions of the three parts of the brain.
10. Which area of the brain is linked to the pituitary gland?
11. What is a reflex?
12. How many divisions are there in the peripheral nervous system? Name them.
13. Describe the functions of the sympathetic and parasympathetic nervous systems.
14. Which organs are associated with the five senses?
15. What is the sodium-potassium pump?
16. List three types of drugs and their effects on the body.

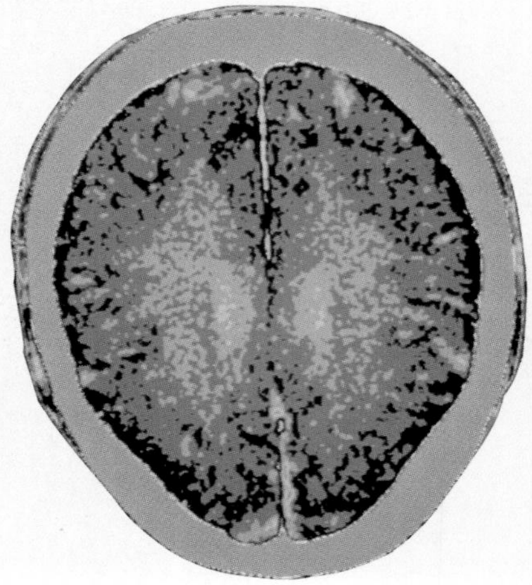

Expanding the Concepts

Discuss each of the following in a brief paragraph.

1. Describe the advantage of having an axon covered with myelin.
2. Describe how an action potential is carried from one neuron to the next.
3. Compare the central nervous system and the peripheral nervous system.
4. Describe the electrical state of the resting neuron.
5. Explain the sequences of changes associated with the passage of an impulse along the axon.
6. What are two factors that affect the rate at which impulses are transmitted along an axon?
7. Which parts of your nervous system are involved in reading and answering this question?
8. What changes in ion distribution occur in the area of an impulse?
9. Describe the function of the sodium-potassium pump.
10. How do the different types of drugs affect the nervous system?

Assessment (continued)

2. An action potential is carried from one neuron by neurotransmitters that diffuse across the synapse and attach to receptors on the next neuron. This causes positive ions to rush across the membrane and stimulate an action potential.
3. The central nervous system receives input from the body and sends out impulses to regulate body functions. The peripheral nervous system receives information from the environment and transmits it to the central nervous system. The peripheral nervous system also relays commands from the central nervous system to organs throughout the body.
4. The resting neuron has a negative charge on the inside of its membrane and a positive charge on the outside of the membrane.
5. As an impulse passes along the axon, positive ions rush across the cell membrane, reversing the charge difference so that the inside of the membrane is more positive than the outside. Then the potential reverses itself again, and the resting potential is restored.
6. The length of the axon and the presence or absence of a myelin sheath around the axon.
7. The eyes, sensory neurons, cerebral cortex, and motor neurons.
8. Positively charged sodium ions rush into the cell, changing the charge on the inside of the cell membrane from negative to positive. This is followed within milliseconds by an outward flow of potassium ions, which causes the inside of the membrane to become negatively charged once again.
9. To return the cell to its resting potential by using energy from ATP to pump sodium ions out of the cell and potassium ions into the cell.
10. Stimulants increase the release of neurotransmitters at some synapses in the brain, which speeds up the nervous system and leads to feelings of energy and well-being. Depressants enhance the effects of neurotransmitters that prevent some nerve cells from starting action potentials, thus decreasing the rate of brain activity and leading to feelings of calmness and relaxation. Opiates mimic natural endorphins, and thus help overcome sensations of pain and produce feelings of pleasure and security.

Extending Your Thinking

1. The two divisions of the autonomic nervous system have opposite effects on the organs they regulate. For example, sympathetic nerves speed up the heart and parasympathetic nerves slow it down. This is advantageous because, with two different sets of neurons, the autonomic nervous system can very quickly speed up or slow down the activities of important organs as needed.

2. Water refracts light in almost exactly the same way that the cornea of the eye does. As a result, the focusing action of the cornea is almost completely lost under water, producing a blurry image. Wearing goggles restores the air-cornea surface and also the focusing action of the cornea.

Extending Your Thinking

Use the skills you have developed in this chapter to answer the following.

1. **Relating concepts** The effects of the two divisions of the autonomic nervous system are said to be antagonistic. What does this mean? What is the advantage of this relationship?
2. **Applying concepts** When you go snorkeling with a face mask, you can see very clearly in the water. But if you remove the face mask, things become blurry. Why is this so?
3. **Predicting** Multiple sclerosis (MS) is characterized by the patchy destruction of myelin. Predict the symptoms that might be produced.
4. **Interpreting** Heat receptors of mammals are particularly concentrated on the tongue. These receptors keep humans from burning the mouth with hot food. What advantage is it for a wild mammal that doesn't cook its food to have so many heat receptors on its tongue?
5. **Designing an experiment** Design an experiment to determine the effects of fatigue on reaction time. Formulate a hypothesis and write up a procedure. Have your teacher check your experimental plan before you begin.

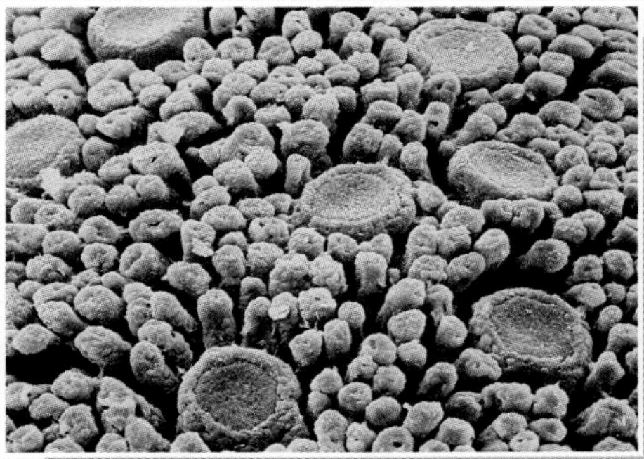

Applying Your Skills

Sensing Trouble

We respond to many stimuli in our environment every day. Through the use of our sense organs, we react to the stimuli, process the information, and respond very quickly. How does this happen?

1. Choose any two of the following situations:
   - **a.** Seeing an approaching ambulance in the rear-view mirror of a car, then pulling over to the side to get out of the way
   - **b.** Hearing a telephone ringing, then running to answer it
   - **c.** Eating a vegetable you don't like, then deciding to take a drink of water
   - **d.** Feeling chilly in a swimming pool, then deciding to get out of the water
2. Diagram the path taken when the sense organ first reacts to the stimulus in each situation to when the impulse is processed as a response.
3. Label the various neurons as well as the parts of one neuron.

• GOING FURTHER •

4. Determine the time it takes you to react to smelling a pizza burning and getting up to turn off the oven.

5. Experimental designs should include a way of measuring reaction time in participants when they are not fatigued and again when they are.

Skills Trace
Experimenting
- Focus p. 794
- Practice p. 795
- Assess p. 805

Applying Your Skills

Teacher Notes

- Each situation involves a different sense organ and a different type of response; however, the path of the nervous impulse—from sense organ to brain and then on to the muscles that control the response—should be represented in much the same way for each situation.
- Make sure students have properly labeled their diagrams and shown that nerve impulses travel from dendrites, to the cell body, and then on through the axon.

Answers

4. Answers will vary. Students may say that how quickly they react depends on how quickly they realize that the burned smell is coming from the pizza in the oven. Once the brain decides that action is called for, students should realize that it takes only milliseconds for the response to be initiated, in this case, getting up in order to turn off the oven.

Scoring Rubric

4 Response is thorough, accurate, and creative; shows an in-depth understanding of science skills, procedures, and concepts.

3 Response is complete, mostly accurate, and original; shows a satisfactory understanding of science skills, procedures, and concepts.

2 Response is mostly complete but includes some inaccuracies; shows an adequate understanding of science skills, procedures, and concepts.

1 Response is only partially complete and has many inaccuracies; shows an incomplete understanding of science skills, procedures, and concepts.

0 Response is mostly incomplete and/or inaccurate; shows a lack of understanding of science skills, procedures, and concepts.

3. With less myelin, nerve impulses in people with MS will travel more slowly. This will result in loss of control over motor functions, leading to paralysis, poor coordination, slurred speech, blurred vision, and tremor.

Skills Trace
Predicting
- Focus p. 798
- Practice p. 799
- Assess p. 805

4. The advantage relates to the thermoregulatory function of the tongue in some mammals. Mammals lose excess body heat by sweating, and for many mammals the primary organ for sweating is the tongue.

Chapter 36 Integumentary, Skeletal, and Muscular Systems

Content Management	Student Edition Activities
■ Section 36–1 The Integumentary System, pp. 807–808 Layers of Skin Hair and Nails	Laboratory Investigation: Mapping Your Sweat Glands, pp. 820–821
■ Section 36–2 The Skeletal System, pp. 809–812 Bones Joints	MINI LAB: All the Right Moves, p. 811
■ Section 36–3 The Muscular System, pp. 813–817 Muscle Tissue Muscle Structure Muscle Contraction Muscles and Movement	MINI LAB: Whose Side Are You On?, p. 817
◆ BRANCHING OUT • In Depth Section 36–4 The Biology of Exercise, pp. 818–819 Specialized Skeletal Muscle Fibers Exercise and Muscle Cells	

■ These sections cover all the necessary content and concepts for an enriched course in biology.
◆ This section covers content and concepts that are either applications or extensions of the enriched material.

Integration Strategies

SE Language Arts, p. 807

Assessment Strategies

SE Chapter Review, pp. 822–825
TR Section Reviews
Chapter Test
BL Chapter Review
Practice Test
CTB Chapter 36 Test

Tech Prep

Teaching strategies appropriate for students who are in technical/vocational programs or who are considering post-secondary technical education can be found on the following **TE** pages: 809, 811, 818.

Meeting the Standards

Sections 36–1 through 36–4 cover four of the six content standards under **The Cell,** two of the six content standards under **Matter, Energy, and Organization in Living Systems,** and one of the four content standards under **The Behavior of Organisms** as described on pages 184–187 of The National Science Education Standards.

Chapter Planning Guide

Teacher's Edition Activities	Other Activities	Media and Technology
Chapter Discovery Learning Activity, p. 806	**TR** Explore: Fingerprint Features **BL** Inquiry Activity: Holding It All Together	
Inquiry Activity: Learning From Broken Bones, p. 809 **Inquiry Activity:** Classifying Bones, p. 809 **Investigate:** Model Building, p. 810	**LM** Examining the Skeletal System, #71 **TR** **Explore:** What's in a Bone? **BL** **Inquiry Activity:** Getting a Feel For Your Skeleton	**BioVue Plus CD-ROMs:** The Body Shop: Dancing and Biomechanics **TB** Cross Section of Skin and the Structure of Bone, #44
Inquiry Activity: Controlling the Fingers, p. 813 **Activity:** Using Muscles to Communicate, p. 813 **Inquiry Activity:** Opposites Attract, p. 816 **Activity:** Classifying Muscle Pairs, p. 816	**LM** Observing the Muscular System, #72 **TR** **Enrich:** Hope for Jerry's Kids **BL** **Inquiry Activity:** Muscles in Motion	
Inquiry Activity: For Bigger Muscles, Which Is Better?, p. 818	**TR** **Writing in Biology:** Advice Columns **Apply:** Comparing Two Types of Muscles **BL** **Inquiry Activity:** Work It Out	

KEY: **SE** Student Edition **TE** Teacher's Edition **LM** Laboratory Manual **TR** Teaching Resources **BL** BioLog **TB** Transparency Box **CTB** Computer Test Bank

Materials List

TE **Chapter Discovery Learning Activity,** p. 806 (15–20 minutes); wrench and bolt, joy stick, hinge.
TE **Inquiry Activity:** Classifying Bones, p. 809 (15 minutes); model of human skeleton.
TE **Investigate:** Model Building, p. 810 (30 minutes); craft sticks, modeling clay, tacks.
SE **MINI LAB:** All the Right Moves, p. 811 (20–30 minutes); paper fan, backpack.
SE **MINI LAB:** Whose Side Are You On?, p. 817 (20 minutes); spring clothes pin, watch or clock with second hand.

CHAPTER 36

Integumentary, Skeletal, and Muscular Systems

Introducing the Chapter

. . . In Pictures

Have students examine the photograph, read the caption, and answer the following questions.

• **Which body system cools off the players by producing sweat?** (Integumentary system.)

• **Which body system protects the players' heads from the ball?** (Skeletal system.)

• **Which body system holds players' feet steady when they kick the ball?** (Muscular system.)

In this chapter, students will learn how the integumentary, skeletal, and muscular systems work together to control many other body activities.

Teaching Strategy

The first section of this chapter describes the structure and function of skin. The second section describes the features of bones and how bones move. The third section outlines the structure and function of muscles and explains how muscles control movement. The BRANCHING OUT section looks in depth at the effect of exercise on red and white muscle tissues.

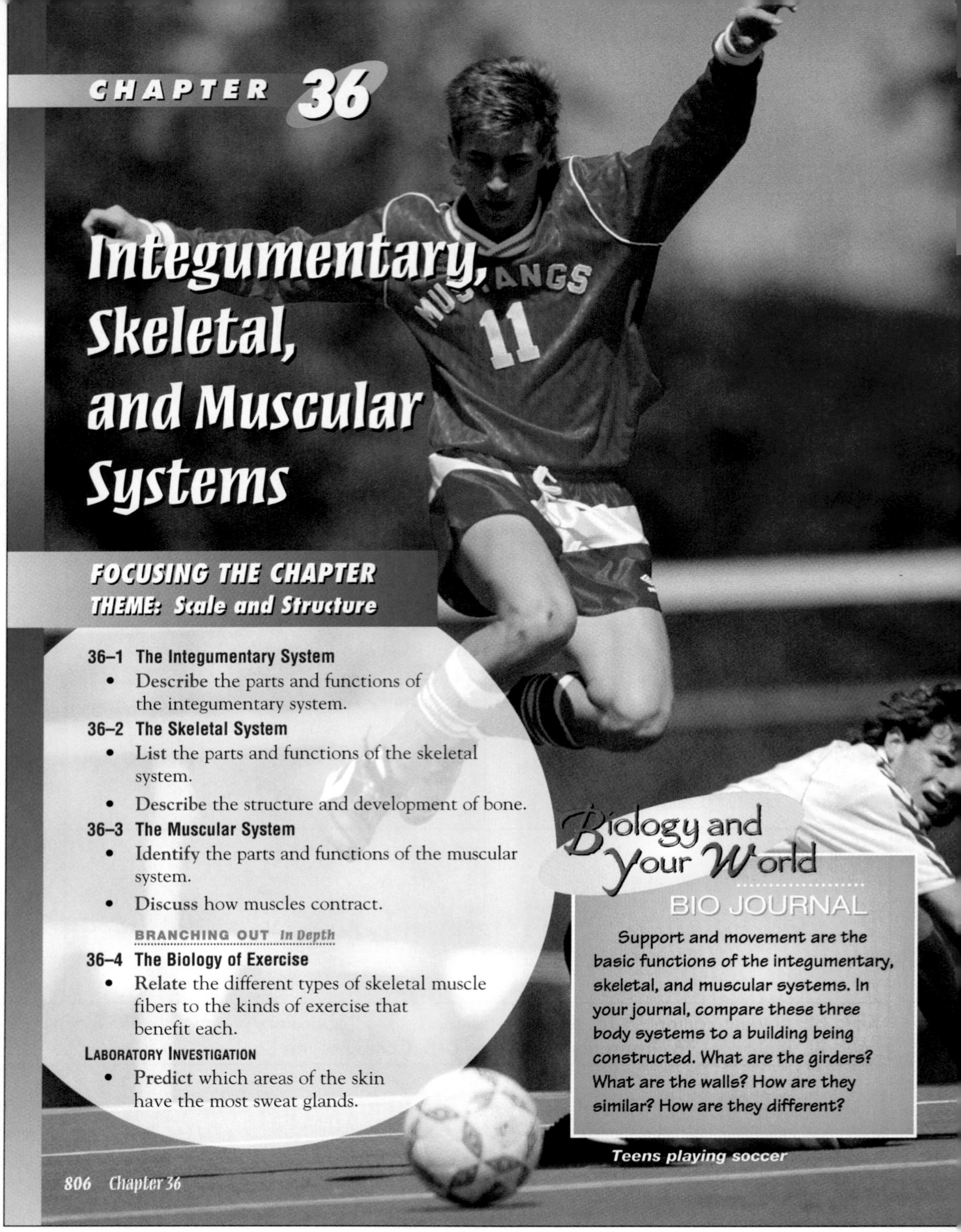

CHAPTER 36

Integumentary, Skeletal, and Muscular Systems

FOCUSING THE CHAPTER
THEME: Scale and Structure

36–1 The Integumentary System
- Describe the parts and functions of the integumentary system.

36–2 The Skeletal System
- List the parts and functions of the skeletal system.
- Describe the structure and development of bone.

36–3 The Muscular System
- Identify the parts and functions of the muscular system.
- Discuss how muscles contract.

BRANCHING OUT *In Depth*

36–4 The Biology of Exercise
- Relate the different types of skeletal muscle fibers to the kinds of exercise that benefit each.

LABORATORY INVESTIGATION
- Predict which areas of the skin have the most sweat glands.

Biology and Your World

BIO JOURNAL

Support and movement are the basic functions of the integumentary, skeletal, and muscular systems. In your journal, compare these three body systems to a building being constructed. What are the girders? What are the walls? How are they similar? How are they different?

Teens playing soccer

BIO JOURNAL

The skeletal system is the girders and the muscular system the walls. Ask students what part of the building the integumentary system is. (The siding or other exterior covering that protects the building from the environment.) Caution students that this comparison oversimplifies the functions of these body systems. Instruct students to keep their entries in their portfolios.

TEACHER SUPPORT

Chapter Discovery Learning Activity

JOINTS AND TOOLS

Some of the mechanical functions that bones and muscles perform when they work together can be observed in common tools and hardware items. Follow these steps to help students gain a working knowledge of the mechanics of body movement.

1. Pass around the following items and have students examine them to determine how each one moves: wrench and bolt; joy stick, hinge.

2. Ask students if they can identify joints in the body that move the same way as each of the items.

Results: The wrench and bolt move like the head (pivot joint), the joy stick moves like the shoulder (ball-and-socket joint), and the hinge moves like the knee (hinge joint). Ask students to name other common items that could be used to illustrate the movement of these joints.

The Integumentary System

SECTION 36–1

GUIDE FOR READING

- **Identify** the basic structures of the integumentary system.

WHEN YOU LOOK AT YOURSELF in the mirror, what do you notice first? Maybe you notice your hair or your skin—or another freckle. Did you know that one system of the body is responsible for the shade of your skin, your hair, and even your nails? This body system is the integumentary system. Your integumentary system acts like a protective covering for the rest of your body. In this section, we will examine the structures of the integumentary system.

Layers of Skin

The largest organ of the body—the **skin**—is part of the integumentary (ihn-tehg-yoo-MEHN-ter-ee) system. ● **The integumentary system includes your skin, hair, nails, and a number of important glands in the skin.** The skin itself is made up of two layers. The outer layer is called the **epidermis,** whereas the inner layer is called the **dermis.**

INTEGRATING LANGUAGE ARTS

The word integere *is a Latin verb meaning "to cover." How does this explain how the integumentary system got its name?*

Epidermis

The epidermis is made up of layers of epithelial cells. Deep in the epidermis, these cells grow and divide rapidly, producing new cells that are gradually pushed toward the surface of the skin. As they move upward, the cells begin making **keratin,** a tough, flexible protein. In humans, keratin is the major protein found in hair and fingernails.

Figure 36–1
The skin—the single largest organ of the body—is part of the integumentary system. (a) The small dark granules within this melanocyte are responsible for protecting the skin from the harmful ultraviolet rays of the sun. (b) Sweating is one way the body regulates temperature. (c) This sweat gland, which is one of about 3 million in the skin, helps to regulate body temperature. The green spheres inside the sweat gland are bacteria (magnification: 10,000X).

SECTION 36–1

The Integumentary System

Performance Objective

- List the skin's basic structures.

Laboratory Investigation Skill: Predicting

1 ENGAGE

Ideas Through Images

Have students examine Figure 36–1, read the caption, and answer the following questions.

- **Why do you think the skin is considered an organ?** (Like other organs, the skin is composed of tissues that work together to perform specific functions.)
- **What is the function of the skin cells called melanocytes?** (To protect the skin from ultraviolet radiation from the sun.)

2 EXPLORE

Discussion

Ask the class why sweat helps cool the body—at least when the humidity is low or a breeze is blowing. Guide students to conclude that sweat cools the body through the process of evaporation.

INTEGRATING LANGUAGE ARTS

The integumentary system provides the body with a protective covering.

TEACHER SUPPORT

Background Information

When the skin helps regulate body temperature through its vascular system, tiny capillaries in the dermis dilate so that more blood flows to the surface of the body. This helps the body lose heat, and it also explains why the skin may look flushed in hot weather or during exercise or a fever. When the capillaries constrict to retain heat and keep the body warm, less blood flows to the surface of the body. This explains why the skin may look pale in very cold weather.

Another response of the skin to cold is goose bumps. These are actually the erection of papillae, or vascular protuberances in the skin, that cause the hair to stand on end. In mammals with fur, goose bumps fluff up the fur and increase its insulating effect. In addition to cold, emotions such as fear and excitement can cause goose bumps.

Ancillary Support

The resources below can be used to support your teaching strategy for these two pages.

TR Explore: Fingerprint Features
BL Inquiry Activity: Holding It All Together

3 TEACH

Ideas Through Images

Have students examine Figure 36–2, read the caption, and answer the following questions.

- **If you were going to add melanocytes to this cross section of the skin, where would you place them?** (In the epidermis.)
- **What is the function of the sebaceous gland shown?** (The sebaceous gland produces oil that keeps the epidermis flexible and waterproof.)
- **How do you think oil from the sebaceous gland reaches the epidermis?** (The oil travels out the hair follicle to the surface of the skin.)
- **What is another gland found in the skin?** (Sweat gland.)
- **In addition to temperature control what other function do sweat glands perform?** (They help in the excretion of wastes—ammonia, salt, and other compounds.)
- **What do you think is the function of the layer of fat just under the dermis?** (Insulation; it helps the body retain heat.)

Laboratory Investigation

The Laboratory Investigation, Mapping Your Sweat Glands, on pages 820–821 is appropriate to use at this point in the chapter.

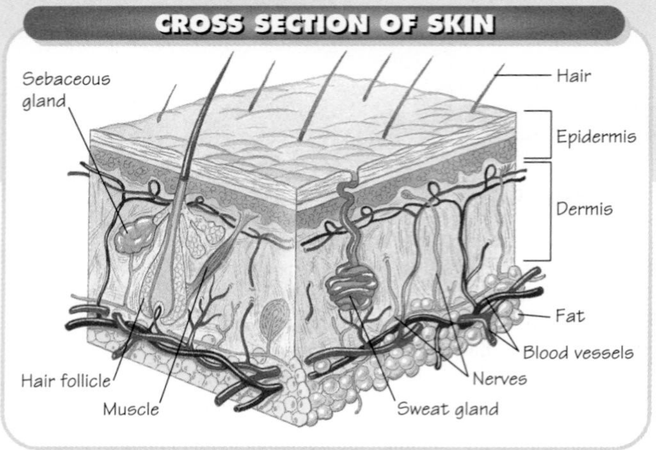

Figure 36–2
The skin consists of two layers—the epidermis and the dermis. The layer of fat in the dermis provides insulation.

As they near the surface, these cells die, but the keratin within remains, forming a tough, waterproof layer on the surface of the skin. As you walk, work, and bathe, you wash and scrape off millions of these dead cells every day. But don't worry, your skin produces more than enough new cells to take their place.

Cells that produce pigments, called melanocytes, are also found in the epidermis. They contain granules of **melanin,** a dark-brown pigment that gives skin its color. Most people have the same number of melanocytes in their skin, but dark-skinned people produce more melanin than people with light skin.

Dermis

The dermis supports the epidermis and contains cells such as nerve endings, blood vessels, and smooth muscles. When you feel something by touching it with your fingers, touch receptors in your dermis are picking up the sensation.

The dermis reacts to the body's needs in a number of ways. For example, on cold days—when you need to conserve heat—blood vessels in the dermis narrow, limiting the loss of heat. When the body is hot, the same vessels widen, bringing more blood to the skin. This warms the skin, causing the loss of heat.

The dermis also contains two types of glands—sweat glands and sebaceous (suh-BAY-shuhs), or oil, glands. Sweat glands produce a watery secretion that contains ammonia, salt, and other compounds. These glands are controlled by the nervous system, which activates them to cool the body when it gets too hot. Sebaceous glands produce an oily secretion that helps keep the epidermis flexible and waterproof.

Hair and Nails

Hair is produced from columns of cells that are filled with keratin and then die. Clusters of such cells make up **hair follicles,** which are anchored in the dermis. Cells multiply in the base of the follicle, causing the hair to grow longer.

Toenails and fingernails are formed in almost the same way, except that the keratin-forming cells in these tissues form a flattened plate. Nails cover and protect the tips of your fingers and toes.

Section Review 36–1

1. **Identify** the basic structures of the integumentary system.
2. **Critical Thinking—Inferring** Some scientists are concerned about the destruction of the ozone layer, which prevents the sun's ultraviolet radiation from reaching the Earth. Why might this be of concern for humans?

4 ASSESS

Quick Check

Write the term skin on the board and ask students to make a concept map below it. The concept map should incorporate the following terms: epidermis, dermis, keratin, melanocyte, sweat gland, and sebaceous gland. Ask each student you call on to add one of the terms to the concept map.

Section Review 36–1

1. The integumentary system includes skin, hair, nails, and a number of important glands in the skin. The skin is made up of the epidermis and the dermis.

2. Students should infer that the destruction of the ozone layer will lead to more ultraviolet radiation reaching Earth, potentially causing damage to people's skin.

Learning Modality

Auditory Learning Choose three students to be contestants on a quiz show. Call on other students to take turns describing features of the integumentary system. The first contestant to recognize a feature as it is being described raises his or her hand and tries to answer. If the first contestant answers incorrectly, the next contestant to raise a hand tries to answer. The contestant with the most correct answers wins.

SECTION 36–2

The Skeletal System

GUIDE FOR READING

- **List** the functions of an internal skeleton.
- **Compare** the three main kinds of joints.

MINI LAB

- **Classify** your joints based on the motions they make.

LIKE THE FRAMEWORK OF A tall building, the human skeleton contains important clues as to the kind of organisms we are. The shape of our hip bones shows that we walk on two legs. The structure of the bones in our hands, especially our thumbs, gives us the ability to hold and grasp objects. And the size and shape of our skull indicate that we have a well-developed nervous system.

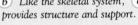

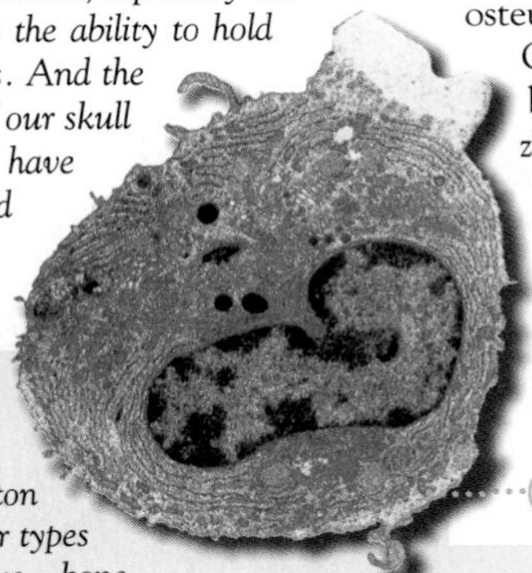

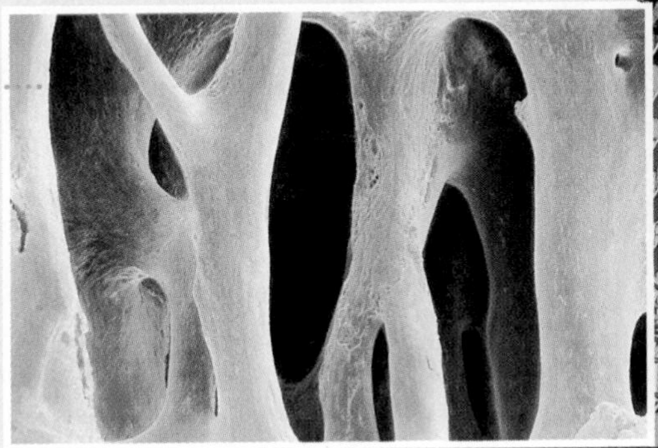

Figure 36–3 *The human skeleton is made up of four types of connective tissue—bone, cartilage, ligament, and tendon.* (a) *This electron micrograph shows a mature bone cell, or osteocyte, that makes up normal bone tissue.* (b) *Like the skeletal system,* (c) *the framework of this building provides structure and support.*

Bones

All vertebrates, humans included, have an internal skeletal system. **An internal skeleton provides support for the body, attachment sites for muscles, and protection for internal organs.** The skull protects the brain, and the ribs protect the heart and lungs. Bones store supplies of calcium and phosphorus that can be used by other tissues, and they also produce blood cells.

Bone Structure

Bones are surrounded by a tough membrane called the **periosteum** (per-ee-AHS-tee-uhm). Just inside the periosteum is a dense layer of **compact bone.** Compact bone appears to be solid, but a series of **Haversian** (huh-VER-zhuhn) **canals** containing nerves and blood vessels runs through it. A region of **spongy bone** is usually located just inside the compact bone. Although it is less dense than compact bone, spongy bone is strong and resilient.

TEACHER SUPPORT

Managing Classroom Diversity

GIFTED STUDENTS

Have students learn about the role of calcium in the body by finding answers to the following questions. Besides ossification, what functions does calcium serve? How is calcium stored in the body? What happens to the stored calcium when dietary calcium is too low for the body's needs? What conditions can result from calcium deficiency? Ask students to share their findings in an oral report.

TECH PREP STUDENTS

Chiropractic practice, which specializes in the skeletal system, offers several different technical careers including medical assisting, medical reception, and medical billing. Through interviews and library research, ask students to prepare a profile of three technical careers in chiropractic. Profiles should describe job duties, employment opportunities, educational requirements, and salary.

SECTION 36–2

The Skeletal System

Performance Objectives

- Identify the roles played by an internal skeleton.
- Distinguish among fixed, slightly movable, and freely movable joints.

Mini Lab Skill: Classifying

1 ENGAGE

Inquiry Activity

Observing

Learning From Broken Bones

Ask students if they or someone they know broke a bone. What symptoms did the injury cause? (Probably pain and swelling.) What limitations did the injury place on the person's activity? (The person may have had to wear a cast to restrict mobility and weight bearing.) Based on these responses, can students deduce which systems work closely together with the skeletal system? (The nervous system, the circulatory system, and the muscular system.)

2 EXPLORE

Inquiry Activity

Observing

Classifying Bones

Ask students to think of ways bones might be classified. After students respond, tell them that bones are classified by shape into four categories: long, short, flat, and irregular. Using a model of the human skeleton, point out examples of each type.

Ancillary Support

The resources below can be used to support your teaching strategy for these two pages.

TR Explore: What's in a Bone?
TB Cross Section of Skin and the Structure of Bone, #44

3 TEACH

Investigate

Model Building Ask students to construct a model of the bones of the leg using simple materials such as craft sticks, modeling clay, and tacks, or other materials of their choice. Require that the models have functioning joints and potential for growth in length of the long bones. (A functioning joint could be modeled by joining the ends of two craft sticks with a tack. Growth could be modeled by using broken segments of craft sticks joined with modeling clay for the long bones and replacing the segments with longer ones as the model bone grows.)

Ideas Through Images

Have students examine Figure 36–4, read the caption, and answer the following questions. Doing so will help familiarize them with the structure and function of the human skeletal system.

- **Which bones of the skeleton appear to protect the heart and lungs?** (Primarily the ribs.)
- **Which bones in the leg appear to be comparable to the radius and ulna in the arm?** (Tibia and fibula.)
- **Which bones are found in both the feet and the hands?** (Phalanges.)
- **Which bone do you think helps protect the knee from injury?** (Patella, or knee cap.)
- **What actions do you think the appendicular skeleton makes possible?** (Possible answers include walking, running, holding, grasping, and carrying.)

Figure 36–4
The human skeleton is made up of 206 bones. The axial skeleton, colored blue, includes the skull, the vertebral column, and the rib cage. The appendicular skeleton, colored beige, includes the bones of the arms, legs, hands, and feet.

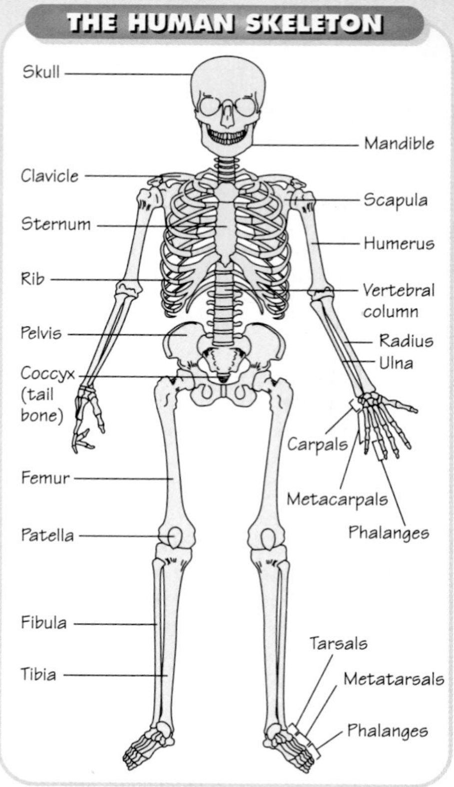

Embedded in both compact and spongy bone are cells called **osteocytes** (AHS-tee-oh-sights). Osteocytes help to build and maintain bones. They deposit the minerals that make up bone and can reabsorb them when the body needs them elsewhere.

As you can see in ***Figure 36–6***, inside many larger bones is a region of blood-forming tissue called **bone marrow.** White and red blood cells are produced in the bone marrow. The marrow also plays an important role in the immune response.

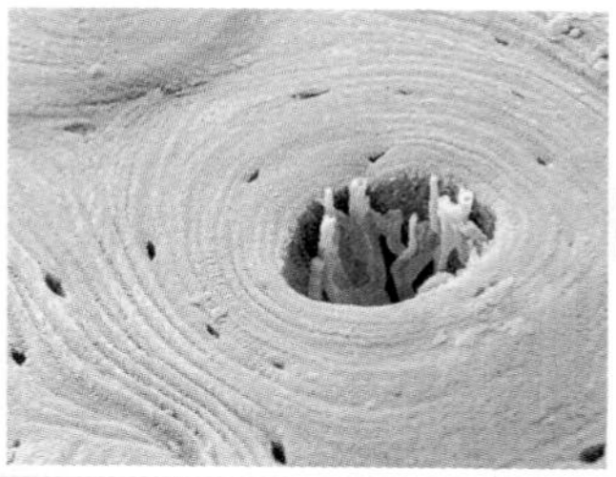

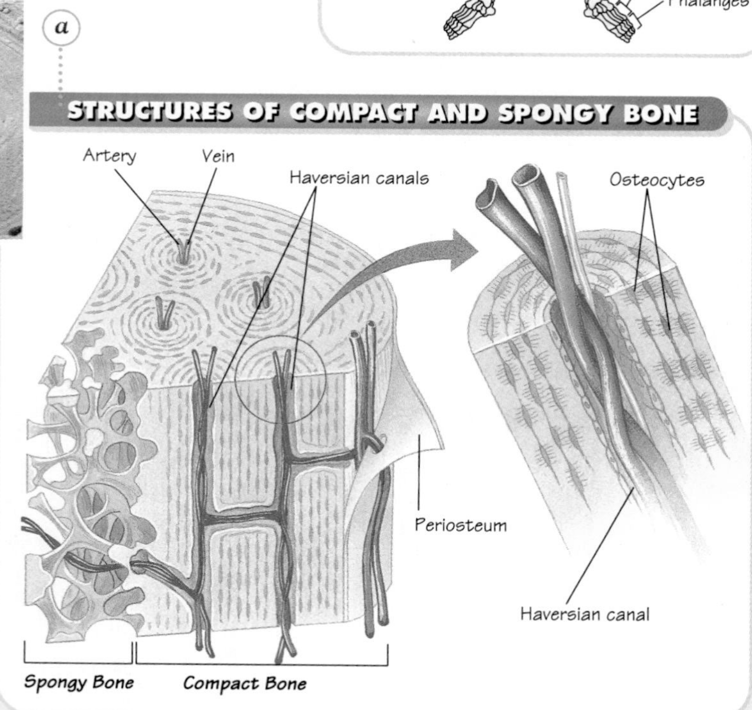

Figure 36–5
(a) This illustration shows the structures of compact and spongy bone. Running through compact bone is a network of tubes called Haversian canals, which contain blood vessels and nerves. (b) In this scanning electron micrograph of compact bone, some blood vessels can be seen in a Haversian canal (magnification: 315X).

TEACHER SUPPORT

Background Information

Contrary to popular belief, osteoporosis, or "brittle bone disease," is not due simply to a lack of calcium in the bones. In osteoporosis the protein framework of the bones becomes thinned so that less calcium can bind to the framework. This makes bones lighter, less dense, weaker, and thus more susceptible to fracture. The protein framework of bones is built up partly as a result of stimulation from male and female sex hormones, particularly during adolescence. Thus, bone density peaks at about age 20 and then decreases gradually after that age. Because women's sex hormones decline more dramatically during adulthood than men's, women are at greater risk of developing osteoporosis. Females who ingest plenty of calcium during their teenage years may have a lower risk of developing severe osteoporosis in old age because they have added to their mineral stores while their bones are still forming.

Bone Growth

Bones are produced from cartilage. During embryonic development, the human skeleton first appears almost as a cartilage "scale model." Gradually, this cartilage "model" is replaced by bone.

Osteocytes near the surface of the bone begin this process, gradually moving inward, depositing minerals that replace the cartilage with bone. The long bones of the arms and legs, for example, have growing points at either end called growth plates. Cartilage is produced at these plates and then is gradually replaced by bone as the skeleton enlarges. By the time you have stopped increasing in height—usually between the ages of 18 and 20—the growth plates have disappeared and the bone has reached its final size and shape.

Joints

Joints are the places where two bones meet. Your ability to move depends not only on your muscles, but also on the joints that must allow bones to move smoothly past each other. There are three kinds of joints—**fixed, slightly movable,** and **freely movable.**

Fixed joints allow little or no movement between bones. Some of the most important fixed joints are those located in the skull. Skull

MINI LAB ············ Classifying ····

All the Right Moves

PROBLEM *How can the motions you make be used to classify your joints?*

PROCEDURE

1. Try each of the actions listed below. Notice which freely movable joints are used and the kind of motion in each joint:
   - waving a paper fan
   - looking behind yourself
   - shrugging your shoulders
   - rotating your index finger
   - pushing open a door
   - lifting a backpack
2. Compare the motion in each joint with the illustration on page 812.

ANALYZE AND CONCLUDE

1. Which type of freely movable joint did you use in each action? Construct a table to record your answer.
2. Which joint was the easiest to classify? Which was the hardest? Why do you think this is so?

THE STRUCTURE OF BONE

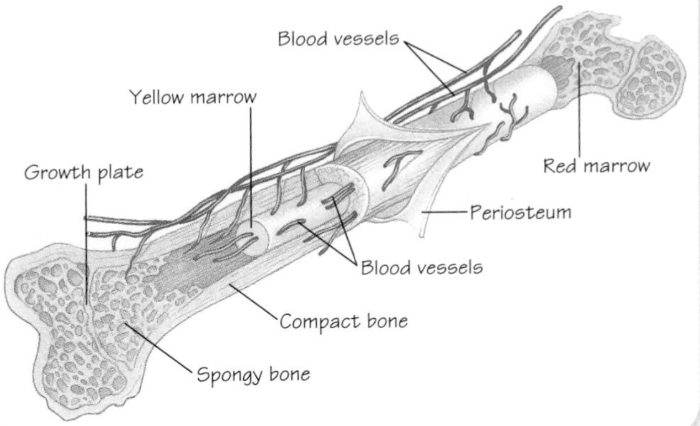

Figure 36–6
In a typical bone, such as the femur, blood vessels pass through the periosteum, carrying oxygen and nutrients to the bone. In addition to red marrow, most bones also contain yellow marrow, which is made up of blood vessels, nerve cells, and fat.

MINI LAB Classifying

Teacher Notes

- For time required and materials needed, see page 806b.
- If students are having difficulty deciding which joints are used in any of the actions, refer them to the illustration of the human skeleton in Figure 36–4.

Answers to Analyze and Conclude

1. Waving a fan uses a gliding joint; looking behind yourself uses a pivot joint; shrugging your shoulders uses a gliding joint; rotating your index finger uses an ellipsoid joint; pushing open a door uses a hinge joint; lifting a backpack uses a hinge joint.

2. Students may say that rotating a finger is easiest to classify because it obviously involves a ball-and-socket joint. They may also say that the hardest action to classify is the shoulder shrug. Shrugging the shoulders uses a joint between the clavicles (collarbones) and scapulas (shoulder blades).

Skills Trace
Classifying

- *Focus* p. 811
- *Practice* p. 812
- *Assess* p. 825

TEACHER SUPPORT

Managing Classroom Diversity

EDUCATIONAL EQUITY
Help students develop better spatial skills by showing them how to relate Figure 36–5 to Figure 36–6. Tell students to imagine cutting a thin slice from the center of the bone in Figure 36–6, standing the slice on one of its cut ends, and magnifying the slice. Point out that this is what they are seeing in Figure 36–5. Check students' understanding by asking them to identify the same structures in each drawing.

TECH PREP STUDENTS
Ask students interested in biotechnology to investigate the field of prosthetics. First have students find out how an artificial limb works. How does the patient control the artificial limb, how does it mimic the functions of the original limb, and what materials are used for bone, muscle, and skin? Then have students learn about careers in prosthetics. What do prosthetics technicians do on the job, and what training do they need?

Ancillary Support

The resources below can be used to support your teaching strategy for these two pages.

LM Examining the Skeletal System, #71
BL Inquiry Activity: Getting a Feel For Your Skeleton

4 ASSESS

Quick Check

Read each of the highlighted terms in this section. As you read, call on students to explain the terms without referring to their books.

Section Review 36-2

1. An internal skeleton provides support for the body, attachment sites for muscles, protection for internal organs, and a storage depot for calcium and phosphorus; some bones also produce blood cells.

2. Fixed joints allow little or no movement between bones, slightly movable joints allow a small amount of movement, and freely movable joints allow a wide range of movement.

3. Cartilage is gradually replaced by bone, starting before birth and continuing until adulthood.

4. By observing their own motions, as they did in the MINI LAB, students will see that the motions of many different joints fall into just a few different categories. For example, both the knee and the elbow move like a hinge, and both the hip and the shoulder turn like a ball in a socket.

Skills Trace

Classifying

- Focus p. 811
- Practice p. 812
- Assess p. 825

Learning Modality

Kinesthetic Learning Have students perform actions that illustrate each of the different types of freely movable joints described in this section. (For example, to illustrate a ball-and-socket joint, students might rotate their arms in a circle; to illustrate a gliding joint, they might wave their hands.)

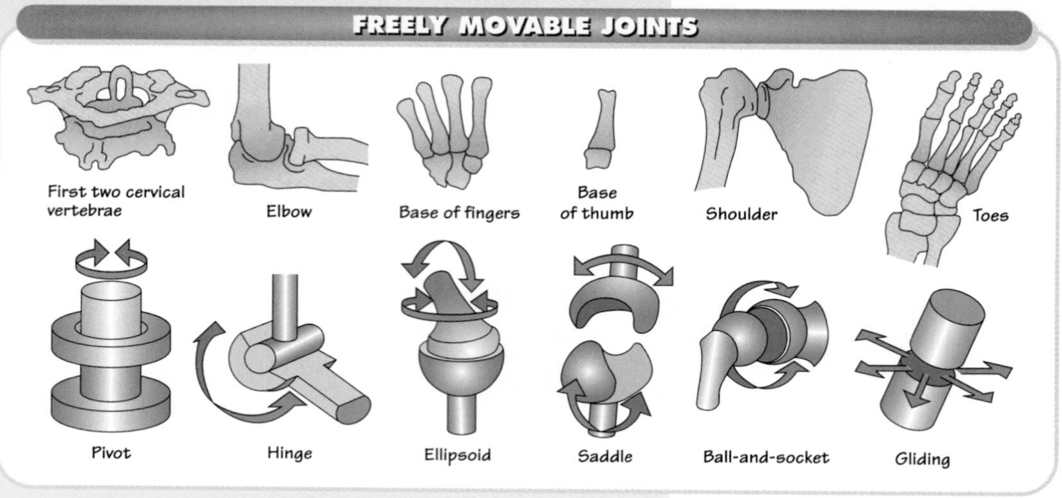

Figure 36–7
The six types of freely movable joints allow a wide range of motion. A pivot joint allows for rotation of one joint around another; a hinge joint permits back-and-forth motion; an ellipsoid joint allows for a hinge-type movement in two directions; a saddle joint allows for movement in two planes; a ball-and-socket joint permits circular movement; and a gliding joint permits a sliding motion of one bone over another.

bones do not move because their purpose is to protect the brain and sense organs in the head.

Slightly movable joints allow a small amount of movement. The bones of the spinal column as well as the ribs are slightly movable joints. The bones of the spinal column are separated from each other by pads of cartilage, called disks. Cartilage is extremely flexible and absorbs most of the shocks and strains of everyday activity.

Freely movable joints allow a wide range of movement. Ball-and-socket joints, located in the shoulders and hips, allow the widest range of movement. The other types of freely movable joints are shown in ***Figure 36–7.***

The ends of bones in freely movable joints are covered with layers of cartilage, providing a smooth surface at the point of contact. The joint itself is enclosed by a joint capsule. The capsule may include **ligaments**—tissues that connect the bones of the joint—and **tendons,** which connect muscles and bones. Inside the capsule is **synovial** (sih-NOH-vee-uhl) **fluid,** a natural lubricant that reduces friction and allows the cartilage-coated bones to slip past each other easily.

Section Review 36–2

1. **List** the functions of an internal skeleton.
2. **Compare** the three main kinds of joints.
3. **Critical Thinking—Inferring** Why do you think that the amount of cartilage as compared to bone decreases as a person develops?
4. **MINI LAB** How can your motions be used to **classify** your joints?

TEACHER SUPPORT

Background Information

Bones are crucial for learning about the evolution of humans and other vertebrates. This is because bones are made of hard, dense material that is more likely than softer tissues, such as muscle and skin, to be preserved and fossilized after an animal dies. Fossilization occurs as water gradually leaches away the organic material in the bones and replaces it with minerals. Paleontologists study fossils of extinct organisms to learn more about their anatomy and way of life. The task is difficult because it is unusual to find complete skeletons of extinct organisms. Instead, paleontologists must depend on the careful scrutiny of fragmentary and incomplete fossilized bones. By comparing the fossilized bones to the bones of living organisms, paleontologists try to draw inferences about how extinct organisms lived.

The Muscular System

GUIDE FOR READING

- **Compare** the three types of muscle tissue.
- **Describe** the process of muscle contraction.

MINI LAB
- **Compare** the actions of the muscles of your left hand with those of your right hand.

DESPITE THE FANTASIES OF Hollywood horror films, the skeleton cannot move by itself. Muscles provide the forces that put the body into motion. More than 40 percent of the mass of the human body is muscle—making it the most common tissue in the body. The muscular system includes the large muscles, which athletes proudly display as signs of physical development. But it also includes thousands of tiny muscles throughout the body that regulate blood pressure, move food through the digestive system, and power every movement of the body—from the blink of an eye to the hint of a smile.

Muscle Tissue

There are three types of muscle tissue—**skeletal, cardiac,** and **smooth**—that are specialized for a different job in the body. Each of these three types of muscle has a different cellular structure.

Skeletal Muscle Tissue

Skeletal muscle tissue is generally attached to the bones of the skeleton and is usually under voluntary control.

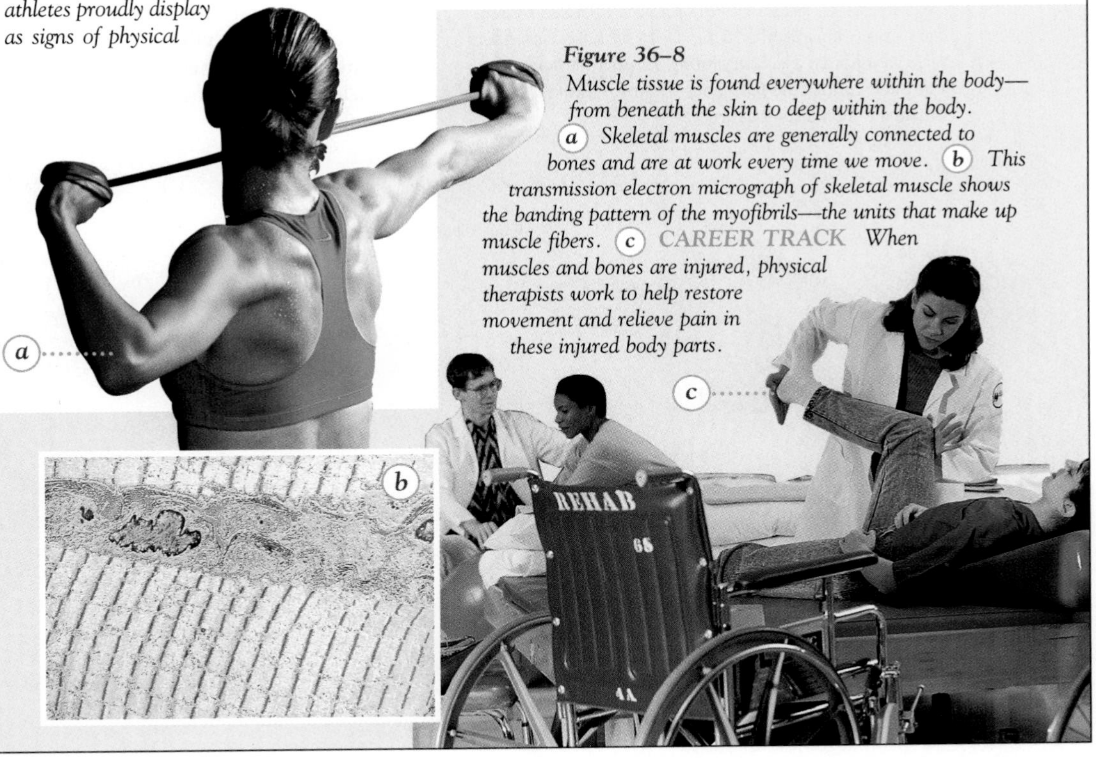

Figure 36–8 *Muscle tissue is found everywhere within the body—from beneath the skin to deep within the body.* (a) *Skeletal muscles are generally connected to bones and are at work every time we move.* (b) *This transmission electron micrograph of skeletal muscle shows the banding pattern of the myofibrils—the units that make up muscle fibers.* (c) CAREER TRACK *When muscles and bones are injured, physical therapists work to help restore movement and relieve pain in these injured body parts.*

TEACHER SUPPORT

Activity

USING MUSCLES TO COMMUNICATE

Ask students to name some of the roles that muscles play in the body. After they have had a chance to respond, point out that one important function of muscles is communication. Not only do we use muscles for speech, but we also use them to communicate nonverbally. To help students appreciate how important muscles are for effective communication, ask two volunteers to role-play a conversation that would elicit strong emotions such as anger, excitement, or happiness. Have the rest of the class observe the volunteers and make note of all the ways they use muscles to communicate. (Possible ways include various facial expressions, hand gestures, and body language.) Lead the class in a discussion of how much less effective the communication would have been if the role-players had not used their muscles in these ways.

SECTION 36–3

The Muscular System

Performance Objectives

- Distinguish among skeletal, cardiac, and smooth muscle tissue.
- Explain how muscles contract.

Mini Lab Skill: Comparing

1 ENGAGE

Inquiry Activity

Observing

Controlling the Fingers

Ask students to locate the muscles that control the fingers. Tell them they can observe the muscles that control their own fingers by following this procedure.

Have students place their hands, palm-side down, on top of their desks and drum their fingers. What do they observe in the backs of their hands? (Movement in the tendons.) Explain that the tendons they observe are attached to the phalanges in their fingers on one end and, on the other end, to the muscles that control the fingers. As students continue to drum their fingers, have them trace the movement of the tendons across their wrists. What do they observe in their lower arms? (Movement of the muscles that control the fingers.)

Ask students if they can think of a drawback in having the muscles that control the fingers located in the fingers themselves. (The muscles would be bulky and reduce flexibility.)

2 EXPLORE

Discussion

Tell students that the basic role of all muscles is to control movement. Ask them to describe examples of movements that muscles control, such as blinking the eyes or moving a pen. Guide the discussion to ways that muscles move air, blood, food, and water through the body.

3 TEACH

Ideas Through Images

Have students examine Figure 36–9, read the caption, and answer the following questions.

- **Where are each of these types of muscle tissue found in the body?** (Skeletal muscle is attached to bones; cardiac muscle is found in the heart; and smooth muscle is found in internal organs and blood vessels.)
- **Which of the three types of muscle tissue can be controlled voluntarily?** (Skeletal muscle tissue.)
- **Why do you think it is important for cardiac and smooth muscle tissues to perform involuntarily?** (Because the functions they perform are not conscious processes, but they are necessary for life.)
- **How could you demonstrate the action of a skeletal muscle?** (By moving an appendage, such as an arm or leg.)

Ideas Through Images

Have students examine Figure 36–10, read the caption, and answer the following questions.

- **How are the four different drawings related to one another?** (Each subsequent drawing shows an enlargement of a component part of the previous drawing.)
- **Which are smaller units, muscle fibers or myofibrils?** (Myofibrils.)
- **What are the components of myofibrils?** (Actin and myosin.)

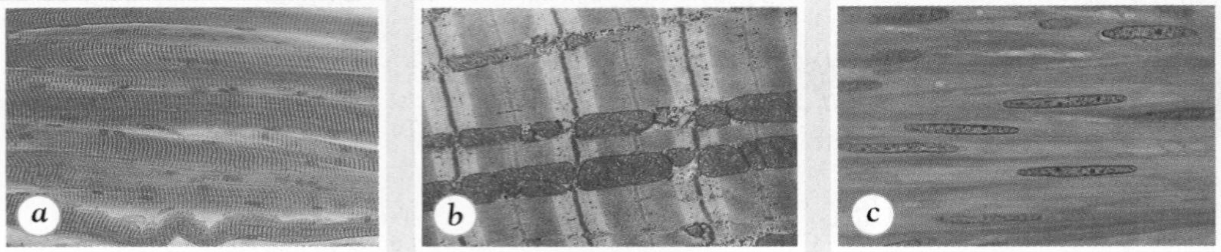

Figure 36–9
There are three types of muscle tissue—skeletal, cardiac, and smooth. (a) Because skeletal, or striated, muscle cells are long and slender, they are often called muscle fibers rather than muscle cells (magnification: 140X). (b) Unlike skeletal muscle tissue, cardiac muscle tissue contracts without direct stimulation by the nervous system (magnification: 200X). (c) Smooth muscle tissue is found in many internal organs and in the walls of many blood vessels. Their contractions move food through the digestive system and control the flow of blood through the circulatory system (magnification: 360X).

Skeletal muscle tissue is behind every conscious movement you make, whether you are lifting a weight or tying your shoelaces. This is because most skeletal muscle tissue is controlled directly by the nervous system. Skeletal muscle cells have many nuclei because they form during development from the fusion of scores of individual cells.

Skeletal muscle cells can be very large—as long as 60 centimeters in the cells in the large muscles of your arms and legs! Under the light microscope, skeletal muscle cells appear striated, or striped. For this reason, skeletal muscle tissue is often called striated muscle tissue.

Figure 36–10
Skeletal muscles are made up of densely packed muscle fibers. Each muscle fiber is made up of many thin fibers called myofibrils. Each myofibril, in turn, is made up of both thick contractile filaments—myosin—and thin contractile filaments—actin.

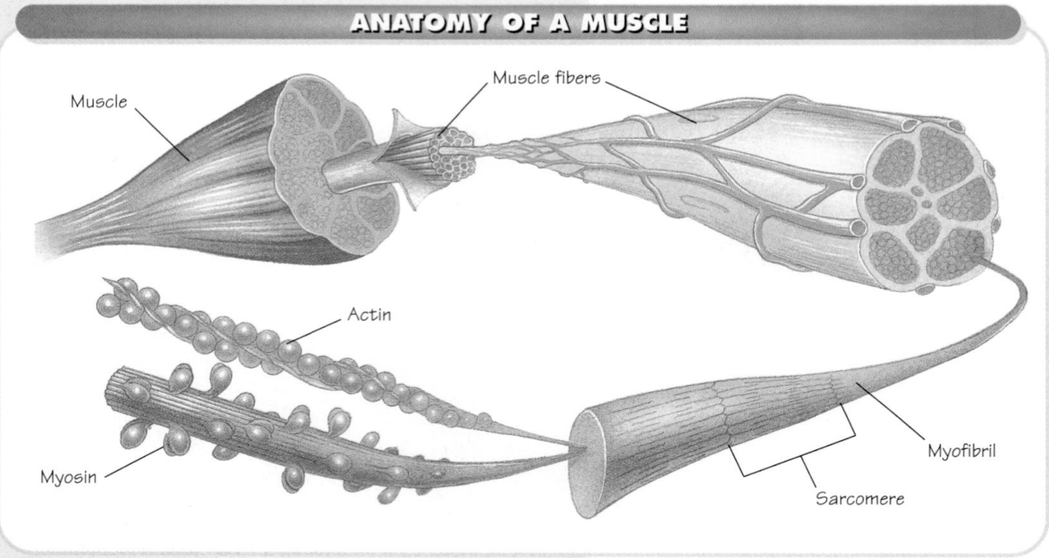

TEACHER SUPPORT

Historical Perspective

In the mid-nineteenth century, a scientist named Claude Bernard determined that skeletal muscles do not contract automatically as smooth and cardiac muscles do. Instead, skeletal muscles contract only when stimulated by nerve impulses. To isolate the role of nerves in muscle contraction, Bernard injected muscles with the drug curare, which is used by some Amazonian Native Americans for poisoning the tips of their hunting arrows. Curare blocks the transmission of nerve impulses to muscle, so Bernard was able to use it to observe skeletal muscle in the absence of nervous control. The result? Skeletal muscles treated with curare were paralyzed. Because smooth and cardiac muscles contract without nervous stimulation, curare does not affect them this way.

Problem Solving

INTERPRETING DATA

A Stimulating Situation

Your class is discussing the muscular system and muscular contraction. One of the students asks what causes a muscle twitch. The teacher responds by saying that a muscle twitch is a quick contraction of the muscle followed by immediate relaxation.

Another student wonders how you can maintain a muscle contraction over a length of time. The teacher explains that when there is a continuous stream of nerve impulses, the muscle fibers receive new stimulation before they are able to relax. The individual muscle twitches together form a smooth, continuous contraction called tetanization. If the muscle is continuously stimulated for a long period of time, however, it would be unable to respond to further stimulation and fatigue would set in.

The teacher shows the class the following graph to further explain muscular contraction. Look at the graph and answer the questions that follow.

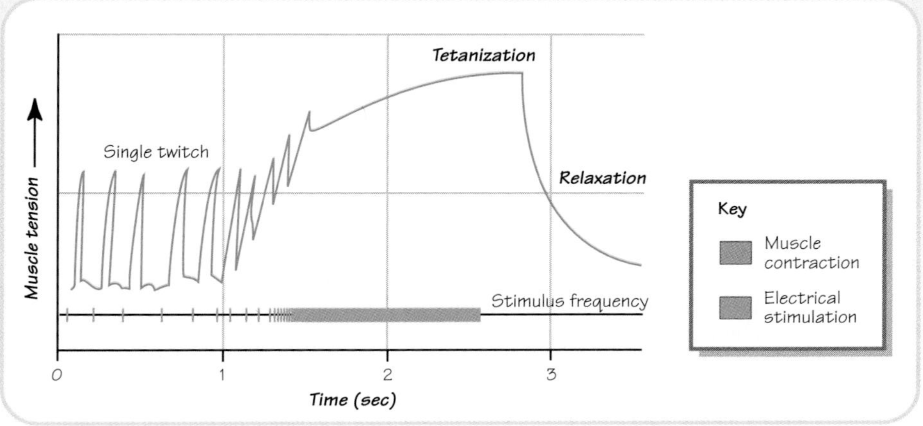

THINK ABOUT IT

1. Describe what happens when the stimulus frequency is slow.
2. Describe what happens when the stimulus frequency increases.
3. According to this graph, when does tetanization occur?
4. Fatigue can occur only in skeletal muscles. Can you explain why this is so?

Problem Solving

Interpreting Data

A Stimulating Situation

Students will use their knowledge of the nervous and muscular systems to interpret data on electrical stimulation and muscle contraction.

State Students are asked to determine the relationship between frequency of electrical stimulus and the contraction of muscle.
Solve Students can solve the problem by interpreting the data in the graph, which shows that, as the electrical stimulus increases in frequency, individual muscle twitches recur so often that the muscle does not have time to relax between contractions.
Test Students can test how well their interpretation of the data matches reality by observing how muscles actually work. Thus, the interpretation of the data appears to match reality.
Communicate Have volunteers summarize the relationship between electrical stimulation and tetanization. Then generate a discussion of how one would test the length of time it takes for muscle fatigue to set in.

Answers to THINK ABOUT IT

1. The muscle contracts in individual twitches.
2. The muscle does not have time to relax fully between twitches.
3. In about 3 seconds.
4. If cardiac or smooth muscle became fatigued, functions necessary for life would stop.

TEACHER SUPPORT

Facts and Figures

- There are approximately 600 different muscles in the human body and about 6 trillion individual muscle fibers.
- The largest muscle in the body is the gluteus maximus, which covers the buttock; the smallest muscle is the stapedius, which is located in the middle ear.
- Muscles are made up primarily of water (about 75 percent) and proteins (about 20 percent).
- Active muscles give off enough heat in one hour to boil almost a liter of water.
- Muscular strength usually peaks between the ages of 20 and 30.

Ancillary Support

The resources below can be used to support your teaching strategy for these two pages.

LM Observing the Muscular System, #72
TR Enrich: Hope for Jerry's Kids
BL Inquiry Activity: Muscles in Motion

MINI LAB

Comparing

Teacher Note

• For time required and materials needed, see page 806b.

Answers to Analyze and Conclude

1. In the second trial with either hand, students may score lower due to muscle fatigue.
2. In right-handed students, the score for the right hand is likely to be higher than the score for the left hand; in left-handed students, the score for the left hand is likely to be higher than the score for the right hand.
3. Students should conclude that muscles in the dominant hand tend to be better developed than muscles in the other hand.

Skills Trace
Comparing

Focus p. 817
Practice p. 817
Assess p. 824

Inquiry Activity

Observing

Opposites Attract

Point out to students that muscles can pull by contracting, but they cannot push. This is why most skeletal muscles are arranged in pairs that pull in opposite directions: One muscle in a pair bends a limb and the other muscle in the pair extends the limb. Ask students how they could observe muscle pairs working together to produce both types of movement. Suggest that they follow a procedure such as the following.

Working with a partner, students should observe the muscles in the upper arms as the partner curls the hand toward the shoulder while holding a heavy book. Where does the greatest amount of muscle contraction appear to be taking place? (In the front of the upper arm, or biceps muscle, in the curl.)

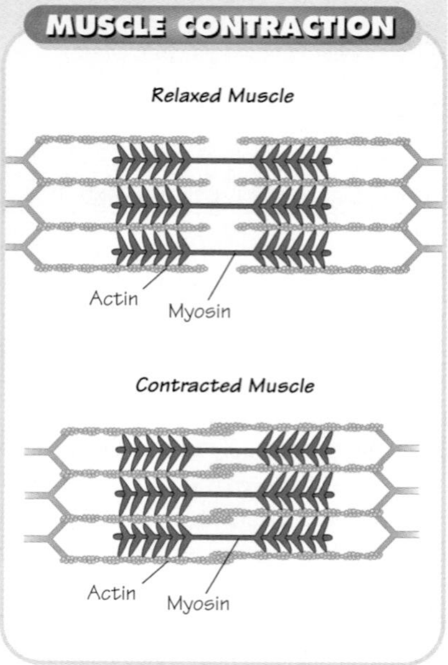

Figure 36–11 When a muscle is stimulated to contract, the myosin and actin filaments slide past each other, causing the muscle cells to shorten and the muscle to contract.

Cardiac Muscle Tissue

Cardiac muscle tissue is found in just one place in the body—the heart. **Cardiac muscle tissue is striated, but the smaller cardiac muscle cells have just one nucleus, and they are not under the direct control of the central nervous system.** Adjacent cardiac muscle cells form branching fibers that allow nerve impulses to move from cell to cell.

Smooth Muscle Tissue

The cells of smooth muscle tissue are spindle-shaped, have a single nucleus, and are not striated. Smooth muscle tissue is generally not under the conscious control of the nervous system. Smooth muscle tissue is found in the walls of many internal organs, except the heart. It is responsible for actions not under voluntary control, such as digestion. Although smooth muscle tissue contracts much more slowly than skeletal muscle tissue does, it can maintain its contraction for a much longer period of time.

Muscle Structure

To understand how a muscle works, we can look inside the kind of muscle cell that we understand best—the skeletal muscle cell. Scientists have learned a great deal about skeletal muscle, partly because the regular structure of these cells has made them easy to study.

Under the electron microscope, we can see that the striations in these cells are actually formed by an alternating pattern of thick and thin filaments. The thick filaments are made of a protein called **myosin.** Thin filaments contain another protein, called **actin.** These thick and thin filaments overlap in a regular pattern, producing the striations that appear under the light microscope.

These tiny actin and myosin filaments are the force-producing engines that cause a muscle to contract. One end of the myosin molecule sticks out just enough from the thick filament to form a cross-bridge that makes firm contact with the thin filament. Using the energy supplied by the splitting of ATP, the cross-bridge changes shape, pulling the thin filament along. The cross-bridge then releases the thin filament, snaps back to its original position, and "grabs" the thin filament again to start another cycle. The cross-bridges repeatedly bend, release, and reattach farther along the thin filament.

When hundreds of thousands of actin-myosin cross-bridges go through their cycle in a fraction of a second, the muscle cell contracts with considerable force. This process is known as the **sliding filament theory** of muscle contraction because the thick and thin filaments slide past each other as the muscle shortens. One molecule of ATP supplies the energy for each cycle.

☑ **Checkpoint** What is myosin? Actin? 1

TEACHER SUPPORT

Activity

CLASSIFYING MUSCLE PAIRS

Assign one type of muscle pair (flexors and extensors, adductors and abductors, levators and depressors, sphincters and dilators, or pronators and supinators) to each of five groups of students. Have each group investigate the type of action its muscle pair controls and find examples of that type of action. (For example, the muscles that bend and straighten the arm are flexors and extensors, the muscles that rotate the foot inward and outward are adductors and abductors, the muscles that raise and lower the mandible are levators and depressors, the muscles that contract and dilate the pupil are sphincters and dilators, and the muscles that turn the palm up and down are pronators and supinators.) Ask groups to explain and demonstrate their type of muscle pair to the class. Then have the groups pool their information in a table.

Muscle Contraction

To make well-coordinated movements, muscle contractions must be carefully controlled. In most skeletal muscles, this is the job of motor neurons.

A single motor neuron may form synapses to one or several muscle cells. An impulse in the motor neuron causes the release of a neurotransmitter, **acetylcholine** (as-ih-tihl-KOH-leen), which causes a new action potential. This, in turn, causes the release of calcium ions into the cytoplasm of muscle cells. When calcium flows into the cytoplasm, cross-bridges form, and the muscle contracts.

The contraction stops when enzymes break down the neurotransmitter. Calcium is then removed from the cytoplasm, and the contraction stops.

Muscles and Movement

Muscles produce force by contracting. Attached to bones by tendons, a muscle can pull two bones together, using the joint between them as a lever. When you lift a heavy object or pull something close to you, it's easy to see how muscle contraction produces the movement.

An individual muscle can pull by contracting, but it cannot push. If that is true, then how can you push a door open or do a pushup in gym class? The answer is that most skeletal muscles are arranged in pairs. These pairs oppose each other and produce forceful movements in either direction. Your upper arm, for example, contains one muscle—the biceps—that flexes, or bends, the arm. On the other side of the upper arm is another muscle—the triceps—that extends the arm. When you do a pushup, the triceps contracts, forcing the arm to extend and push down on the gym floor.

MINI LAB .... Comparing

Whose Side Are You On?

PROBLEM *How do the actions of the muscles of your left hand **compare** with those of your right hand?*

PROCEDURE

1. Count the number of times you can fully open a spring clothes pin with your right thumb and right index finger for 2 minutes. Have your partner time you. Record the results.
2. Rest for 1 minute and repeat step 1. Record the results.
3. Repeat steps 1 and 2 with your left hand. Record the results.

ANALYZE AND CONCLUDE

1. Compare the two performances of your right-hand muscles.
2. How did the performance of your right hand compare with that of your left hand?
3. What conclusions can you draw from these results?

Section Review 36-3

1. **Compare** the three types of muscle tissue.
2. **Describe** the process of muscle contraction.
3. **Critical Thinking—Relating Concepts** Why are skeletal muscles arranged in pairs?
4. **MINI LAB** How do the actions of the muscles of your left hand **compare** with those of your right hand?

4. Right-handed students are likely to score higher with the right hand, and left-handed students are likely to score higher with the left hand.

Skills Trace
Comparing

- Focus p. 817
- Practice p. 817
- Assess p. 824

Learning Modality

Visual Learning Have students make color-coded diagrams to illustrate the sliding filament theory. Ask volunteers to explain their diagrams to the rest of the class. Urge students to keep their diagrams for use as study guides.

Discussion

Ask students to discuss ways in which muscles and nerves are similar. Guide the discussion toward the following similarities.

- Both muscles and nerves show an all-or-nothing response; that is, individual muscle fibers, like neurons, either respond fully when stimulated or do not respond at all.
- Both muscle fibers and neurons have a short refractory period between twitches or impulses before they can be stimulated again.
- Muscles and nerves do not increase in number after birth but just grow larger in size.

4 ASSESS

Quick Check

Call on students to fill in the cells of a table that has the following columns and rows: (columns) Skeletal muscle, Cardiac muscle, Smooth muscle; (rows) Appearance, Location, Control. Correct any errors.

Section Review 36-3

1. Students should summarize the information on pages 813, 814, and 816.
2. Students should summarize the description given under Muscle Structure on page 816.
3. They are arranged in pairs because muscles can only pull by contracting. Pairs of muscle contract in opposite directions, allowing force to be exerted in either direction.

☑ Checkpoint

1 Myosin: protein that comprises the thick filaments in myofibrils. Actin: protein that comprises the thin filaments in myofibrils.

The Biology of Exercise

Performance Objectives
- Identify red muscle fibers and white muscle fibers.
- Distinguish between aerobic exercises and resistance exercises.

1 ENGAGE

Ideas Through Images

Have students examine Figure 36–12, read the caption, and answer the following questions.

- **Which activity shown in the figure is most likely to make you breathe hard?** (Bicycling, the aerobic exercise.)
- **Which activity is likely to build up your muscles the most?** (Weight lifting, the resistance exercise.)

2 EXPLORE

Inquiry Activity

Designing an Experiment

For Bigger Muscles, Which Is Better?

Ask students how they would design an experiment to compare the effects of aerobic exercise and resistance exercise on skeletal muscles. Suggest a design such as the following.

Select two subjects similar in strength. Have one subject perform an aerobic exercise such as running several times a week for a period of several weeks. Have the other subject follow the same schedule but perform a resistance exercise that strengthens the legs. Compare the strength or size of each subject's leg muscles before and after the exercise program.

What do students think the outcome of such an experiment would be? Why?

SECTION 36–4 BRANCHING OUT In Depth

The Biology of Exercise

GUIDE FOR READING

- **List** the two main types of muscle fibers in skeletal muscles.
- **Compare** aerobic exercises and resistance exercises.

AN ATHLETE MAY DEVOTE hours every day to developing and conditioning the muscular system. To a runner, a swimmer, or a weight lifter, the strength, flexibility, and endurance of the muscular system is the difference between winning and losing. But a well-conditioned muscular system is important even to those of us who are not competitive athletes. We depend on our skeletal muscles—whether walking, running, working, or playing—and we can make many of life's everyday challenges easier by keeping our muscles in good condition.

Specialized Skeletal Muscle Fibers

If you look at any large office that performs many different jobs, you will find specialists. One person might sell the product, another might handle the bookkeeping, and another the scheduling. What's the advantage of an arrangement like this? By allowing a few people to specialize at different tasks, the jobs get done more quickly and efficiently.

Even though the job description for a muscle is simple—contract on command—a large skeletal muscle contains specialists of its own. **Skeletal muscles contain two main types of muscle fibers—red and white—whose properties make them specialists at different kinds of exercise.**

Red muscle fibers contain large amounts of the reddish oxygen-storing protein **myoglobin.** Red fibers also have rich blood supplies and plenty of mitochondria to produce ATP through aerobic

Figure 36–12
Different types of exercise affect different types of skeletal muscle fibers. (a) Aerobic exercises, such as bicycling, affect red muscle fibers, whereas (b) resistance exercises, such as weight lifting, affect white muscle fibers. (c) When planning an exercise program, both aerobic and resistance-type exercises should be included.

TEACHER SUPPORT

Managing Classroom Diversity

TECH PREP STUDENTS
Many people with muscular problems benefit from physical therapy. Arrange to have students interested in health-care careers observe physical therapy technicians on the job. Ask the students to take notes on what they observe and summarize their observations in a short written report. Their reports should describe the types of patients the technician helps, specific activities the technician performs, and skills that seem to be most important for the job.

GIFTED STUDENTS
Ask students to learn how ATP is produced aerobically in red muscle cells and anaerobically in white muscle cells. Have them make flowcharts to show how the two processes differ. Ask them to explain their flowcharts to the rest of the class.

(oxygen-dependent) respiration. Red fibers are also called slow-twitch muscle fibers because they contract slowly after being stimulated by a motor neuron.

Red muscle fibers are usually able to meet their ATP needs from their own mitochondria. Red muscle fibers enable muscles to contract again and again, against slight resistance, without fatigue.

White muscle fibers contain little or no myoglobin, giving them a pale color. They have few mitochondria, but they store large reserves of **glycogen.** Glycogen is a compound that stores excess glucose in the body. When white muscle fibers need extra ATP, that glycogen is broken down to glucose, which is then used anaerobically (without oxygen) to generate ATP by fermentation.

White fibers are also called fast-twitch muscle fibers and can generate powerful contractions. Having few mitochondria, these fibers contain greater densities of contractile proteins than red fibers do. These powerful fibers fatigue easily, however, which means that they can produce maximum contractions for only a few seconds at a time.

Exercise and Muscle Cells

As you probably know, exercising a muscle causes it to get stronger. There are different kinds of exercise, of course, and each kind has different effects on each kind of skeletal muscle cell.

Aerobic exercises—such as running, swimming, and bicycling—cause your body systems to become more efficient. For example, your circulatory system benefits because the number of capillaries in the muscle increases, which increases its blood supply. More myoglobin is synthesized, especially in red fibers. Aerobic exercises also benefit the heart and lungs, helping to increase their capacity. All these effects increase physical endurance—the ability to perform an activity without fatigue. However, aerobic exercises do not result in large increases in muscle size.

Resistance exercises, such as weight lifting, increase muscle size. This effect is most pronounced in the white fibers, which grow in size and add more contractile proteins after such exercises.

Resistance exercises have little effect on red fibers, which means that they do not improve endurance. However, they do have a dramatic effect on maximum muscle strength. Because most skeletal muscles function in opposing pairs, weight training should include exercises that develop both muscles in each pair. This helps an individual to maintain coordination and flexibility.

Different forms of exercise develop different types of muscle fibers. This means that the best exercise programs should blend resistance and aerobic training, helping to develop muscles, heart, and lungs.

Section Review 36-4

1. **List** the two main types of muscle fibers found in skeletal muscles.
2. **Compare** aerobic exercises and resistance exercises.
3. **BRANCHING OUT ACTIVITY** Use a health book as a guide and **design** and **write** an exercise program for yourself that includes both aerobic and resistance exercises. Do not perform your exercise program unless it has been checked and approved by your doctor.

3 TEACH

Discussion

Have the class discuss no-cost ways teens might incorporate aerobic and resistance exercises into their daily routine. (Possible ways include walking or biking instead of riding on a bus or in a car, climbing stairs instead of taking elevators, and doing calisthenics such as push-ups while watching TV.)

4 ASSESS

Quick Check

Write the terms red muscle fibers and white muscle fibers on the chalkboard. Call on students to list each of the following words under the appropriate terms: glycogen, myoglobin, slow-twitch, fast-twitch, anaerobic, aerobic, endurance, and strength.

Section Review 36-4

1. Red muscle fibers and white muscle fibers.

2. Aerobic exercises such as running, swimming, and bicycling cause your body systems to become more efficient. Resistance exercises such as weight lifting produce an increase in muscle size.

3. Exercise programs should include both aerobic and resistance exercises, with resistance exercises for both of the muscles in opposing pairs of muscles. The programs should also include warm-up and cool-down periods.

Learning Modality

Auditory Learning Read the highlighted terms in this section, and after each term have a volunteer give a definition or example of the term. Ask other members of the class whether they agree with the definition or example given. If not, how would they change it? Conclude by having students explain how all of the highlighted terms are related.

Ancillary Support

The resources below can be used to support your teaching strategy for these two pages.

TR Writing in Biology: Advice Columns
Apply: Comparing Two Types of Muscles

BL Inquiry Activity: Work It Out

Chapter 36

Laboratory Investigation

Mapping Your Sweat Glands

Before the Lab

1. Gather the necessary materials, prepare the iodine solution, and precut the one-centimeter squares of blotting paper (two per student).
2. Have soap available so students can wash off the iodine after the lab.

Pre-Lab Discussion

Have students read the entire procedure for this investigation. Then ask students the following questions.

What is the purpose of this investigation? (To observe and map sweat glands in order to compare their distribution in different regions of the body.)

Why does a blue color on the blotting paper indicate the presence of sweat? (The blue color indicates that starch on the blotting paper has reacted with iodine in solution, and the iodine is in solution only if sweat is present on the skin.)

What are some factors that might affect the amount of sweat produced by the sweat glands during the investigation? (The temperature in the room, how students are dressed, what students were doing right before class, how nervous students are.)

How might these factors influence the results? (Being overheated or nervous may lead some students to sweat more than usual; being nervous is especially likely to lead to sweaty palms.)

Skills Development

Students will use these skills while completing the laboratory investigation: predicting, measuring, observing, comparing, interpreting data, evaluating, drawing conclusions, and communicating.

Laboratory Investigation

Mapping Your Sweat Glands

A solution of iodine reacts with starch by turning a blue-black color. When dried iodine comes in contact with the water given off by sweat glands, it becomes a solution again and will react with the starch in a piece of blotting paper, causing it to turn a blue-black color. In this investigation, you will take advantage of these changes to locate sweat glands in your skin.

Problem

Which areas of your skin have the most sweat glands? **Make a prediction** to answer this question.

Materials (per group)

- 4 squares of blotting paper, 1 cm × 1 cm
- medical adhesive tape
- iodine solution
- cotton swabs

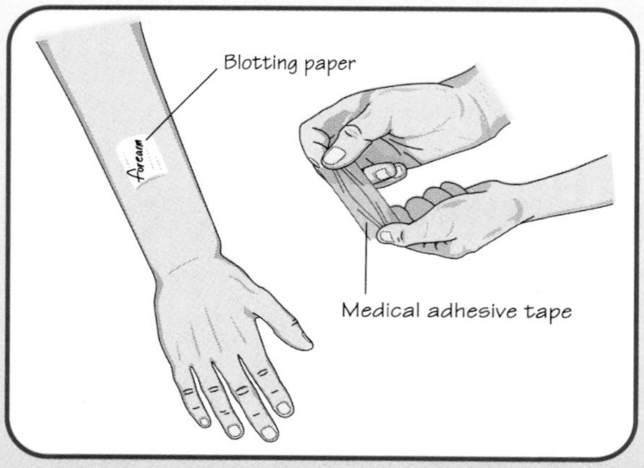

Procedure

1. **Wash and dry your hands and forearms thoroughly. Roll your sleeves up to above the elbow. Carefully dip the cotton swab into the iodine solution. CAUTION: *Be careful when using iodine because it stains clothing.***
2. **Find an area in the center of the palm of one of your hands that is free of creases. Using the iodine-soaked cotton swab, paint a 2-cm square on your palm and let it dry.**
3. **Repeat step 2 on the inside of one of your forearms.**
4. **Using a pencil, label one of the blotting-paper squares "Palm" and the other one "Forearm." Have your partner tape the blotting paper square labeled "Palm" over the iodine on your palm and the square labeled "Forearm" over the iodine on your forearm. Allow the blotting paper to remain in place for 20 minutes.**

Safety Tip

Warn students to avoid getting the iodine solution in their eyes, in open cuts, or on their clothing.

5. While you are waiting, write a prediction about whether the palm of your hand or your forearm has more sweat glands. Also predict whether all members of the class will have the same results.

6. After 20 minutes, have your lab partner remove the two paper squares. Count the number of blue-black dots on each one. Each dot indicates the presence of an active sweat gland.

7. Construct a data table similar to the one shown. Record the number of dots on the paper square for your palm. In the space marked "Distribution of Sweat Glands," draw or write a description of the pattern of dots.

Observations

1. What difference did you observe in the number of sweat glands per square centimeter on your palm and forearm?
2. What differences were there in the patterns of sweat glands?

DATA TABLE

Location of Sweat Glands	*Number of Active Sweat Glands*	*Distribution of Sweat Glands*
Middle surface of palm		
Inside of forearm		

Analysis and Conclusions

1. Which area tested—palm or forearm—had the greatest density of active sweat glands?
2. Were your predictions correct? Explain your answer.
3. How did the information in your data table compare with the information your classmates compiled?
4. What conclusion can you draw about the distribution of sweat glands on the skin?
5. Do all sweat glands produce the same amount of sweat? What evidence did you observe to support your answer?

More to Explore

Using the same materials, design an experiment to find out whether exercise affects the number of sweat glands that are active at any one time.

Answers to Observations

1. Students should observe more dots—and by inference more sweat glands—per square centimeter on the forearm than on the palm.
2. The pattern of dots (sweat glands) may differ for the forearm and palm.

Answers to Analysis and Conclusions

1. When the data are pooled for the entire class, it should be clear that the forearm tends to have a greater density of sweat glands than the palm.
2. Some students may have predicted that the palms have more sweat glands because people tend to be more aware of their hands.
3. There is likely to be variation in the density of sweat glands at the two sites when students compare data tables. However, students are likely to be similar to one another in having a greater density on the forearm than on the palm.
4. Students should conclude that sweat glands show a similar distribution from one individual to another, although the absolute numbers of sweat glands at each site may vary.
5. Answers will vary. Larger dots indicate a greater production of sweat by each sweat gland.

More to Explore

Experimental designs should measure sweat production in the same individuals both before and after exercise. Exercise leads to greater sweat production if it is vigorous enough. If greater sweat production is due to more sweat glands being active at one time, there will be a greater density of dots after exercise than before.

Teaching Strategies

1. Provide students with laboratory coats and goggles to protect their clothing and eyes from the iodine solution.
2. Distribute the iodine solution in small quantities to reduce the risk of spills.
3. While students wait the 20 minutes for the reaction to occur, have them discuss their predictions and construct data tables.
4. In addition to predicting which area, palm or forearm, has more sweat glands, encourage students to make other predictions that the data might be used to test, such as predictions about the relationship between sweating and gender or between sweating and body size.

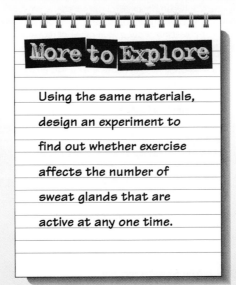

CHAPTER 36

Study Guide

Review Strategy

Divide the class into groups of three students each, and assign a different activity to each group. Activities might include swimming, running, playing a video game, or playing the piano. Have group members explain in detail the role played by tissues in each of the systems described in this chapter—the integumentary, skeletal, and muscular systems—when their activity is performed. Each member of the group should assume primary responsibility for one of the body systems. Have students illustrate their explanations with diagrams or drawings, and have them share their work with the rest of the class. Urge the class to come to a consensus, through discussion, on any points of disagreement.

Recalling Main Ideas

1. d
2. c
3. c
4. d
5. b
6. a
7. b
8. d
9. b
10. c

Assessment

Reviewing What You Learned

1. The integumentary system acts like a protective covering for the rest of the body. It includes skin, hair, nails, and a number of important glands in the skin.
2. Hair and nails.
3. Sweat glands and sebaceous glands.
4. Both hair and nails are formed from clusters of dead cells filled with keratin.
5. Bone, cartilage, ligament, and tendon tissues.
6. Compact bone is the dense outer layer of a bone, and spongy bone is less dense and usually located inside compact bone.

Study Guide

Summarizing Key Concepts

The key concepts in each section of this chapter are listed below to help you review the chapter content. Make sure you understand each concept and its relationship to other concepts and to the theme of this chapter.

36–1 The Integumentary System

- The integumentary system includes your skin, hair, nails, and a number of important glands in the skin.

36–2 The Skeletal System

- An internal skeleton provides support for the body, attachment sites for muscles, and protection for internal organs.
- There are three kinds of joints in the body. Fixed joints allow little or no movement between bones. Slightly movable joints allow a small amount of movement. Freely movable joints allow a wide range of movement.

36–3 The Muscular System

- Skeletal muscle tissue is generally attached to the bones of the skeleton and is usually under voluntary control. Cardiac muscle tissue is striated, but the smaller cardiac muscle cells have one nucleus and are not under the direct control of the central nervous system. Smooth muscle tissue is generally not under the conscious control of the nervous system.
- When hundreds of thousands of actin-myosin cross-bridges go through their cycle in a fraction of a second, the muscle cell contracts with considerable force.

36–4 The Biology of Exercise

- Skeletal muscles contain two main types of muscle fibers—red and white—whose properties make them specialists at different kinds of exercise.
- Aerobic exercises—such as running, swimming, and bicycling—cause your body systems to become more efficient. Resistance exercises, such as weight lifting, produce an increase in muscle size.

Reviewing Key Terms

Review the following vocabulary terms and their meaning. Then use each term in a complete sentence.

36–1 The Integumentary System

skin
epidermis
dermis
keratin
melanin
hair follicle

36–2 The Skeletal System

periosteum
compact bone
Haversian canal
spongy bone
osteocyte
bone marrow
fixed joint
slightly movable joint
freely movable joint
ligament
tendon
synovial fluid

36–3 The Muscular System

skeletal muscle tissue
cardiac muscle tissue
smooth muscle tissue
myosin
actin
sliding filament theory
acetylcholine

36–4 The Biology of Exercise

myoglobin
glycogen

Inquiry-Based Strategy

Ask students if they know how often, how fast, and for how long an aerobic exercise such as swimming, bicycling, or running should be performed to achieve and maintain a minimum level of cardiovascular fitness. Suggest that they first find out how a minimum fitness goal is defined and how progress toward that goal is measured. Suggest that students interview one or more fitness experts, such as an aerobics instructor or physical education teacher, as well as do library research to find answers to the questions. Have them apply what they learn by developing a fitness schedule of swimming, bicycling, or running four days a week. How fast and for how long would the average person have to do the chosen activity to maintain a minimum level of fitness? What role if any do age, gender, and initial level of fitness play in the equation?

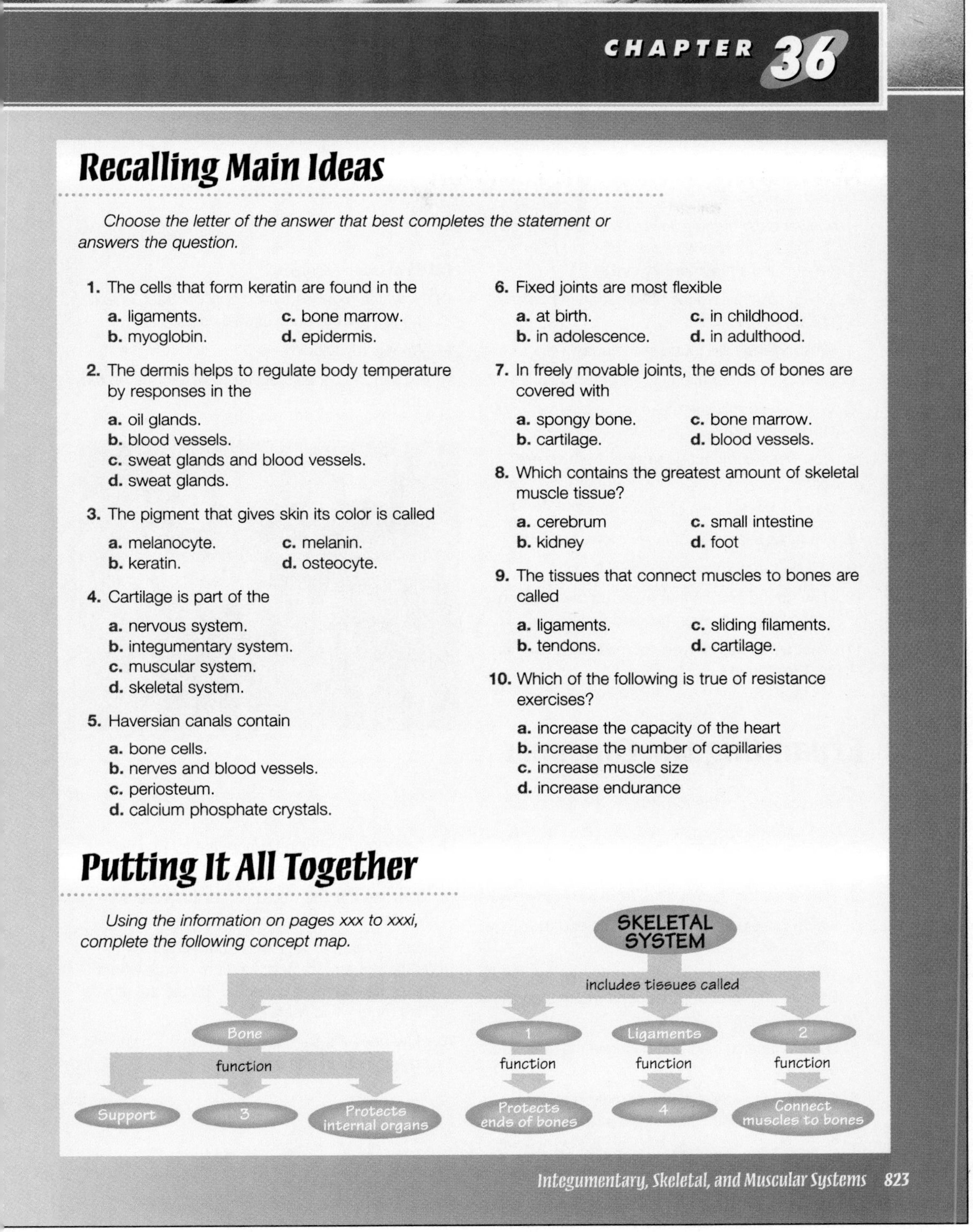

CHAPTER 36

Recalling Main Ideas

Choose the letter of the answer that best completes the statement or answers the question.

1. The cells that form keratin are found in the
   a. ligaments. c. bone marrow.
   b. myoglobin. d. epidermis.
2. The dermis helps to regulate body temperature by responses in the
   a. oil glands.
   b. blood vessels.
   c. sweat glands and blood vessels.
   d. sweat glands.
3. The pigment that gives skin its color is called
   a. melanocyte. c. melanin.
   b. keratin. d. osteocyte.
4. Cartilage is part of the
   a. nervous system.
   b. integumentary system.
   c. muscular system.
   d. skeletal system.
5. Haversian canals contain
   a. bone cells.
   b. nerves and blood vessels.
   c. periosteum.
   d. calcium phosphate crystals.
6. Fixed joints are most flexible
   a. at birth. c. in childhood.
   b. in adolescence. d. in adulthood.
7. In freely movable joints, the ends of bones are covered with
   a. spongy bone. c. bone marrow.
   b. cartilage. d. blood vessels.
8. Which contains the greatest amount of skeletal muscle tissue?
   a. cerebrum c. small intestine
   b. kidney d. foot
9. The tissues that connect muscles to bones are called
   a. ligaments. c. sliding filaments.
   b. tendons. d. cartilage.
10. Which of the following is true of resistance exercises?
    a. increase the capacity of the heart
    b. increase the number of capillaries
    c. increase muscle size
    d. increase endurance

Putting It All Together

Using the information on pages xxx to xxxi, complete the following concept map.

Putting It All Together

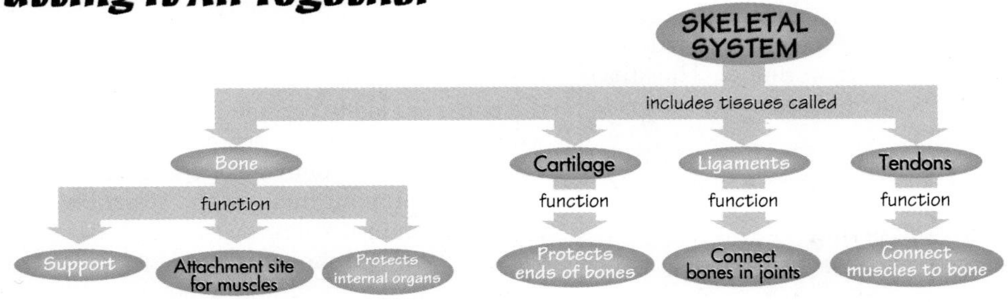

7. Osteocytes help to build and maintain bone by depositing minerals that make up bone and reabsorbing them when the body needs them elsewhere.
8. Students may identify any of the freely movable joints shown in Figure 36–7 on page 812.
9. It reduces friction and allows bones to slip past each other easily.
10. From the time of embryonic development until the ages of 18 to 20, the tissues that make up the skeleton change from consisting primarily of cartilage to consisting primarily of bone.
11. Skeletal, which is attached to bone; cardiac, which is found in the heart; and smooth, which is found in internal organs and blood vessels.
12. Acetylcholine is a neurotransmitter that carries an action potential from a neuron to a muscle cell.
13. Most skeletal muscles are arranged in opposing pairs that produce forceful movements in either direction.
14. A reddish oxygen-storing protein that is plentiful in red muscle fibers.
15. Aerobic exercises cause body systems to become more efficient by increasing the number of capillaries and the amount of myoglobin in the muscles and by increasing the capacity of the heart and lungs.

Expanding the Concepts

1. The expression means that the dead epidermal cells, which form a tough, waterproof covering for the body, serve the vital functions of protecting the body and keeping it dry.
2. The dermis is the lower layer of skin, whereas the epidermis is the upper layer. Also, the dermis contains blood vessels, smooth muscles, nerve endings, and glands, whereas the epidermis contains melanocytes and keratin.
3. Fixed, slightly movable, and freely movable. Fixed joints allow little or no movement between bones, slightly movable joints allow a small amount of movement, and freely movable joints allow a wide range of movement.
4. A tennis player develops tendinitis when the tendons on the outside of the elbows become torn, inflamed, and painful due to overexertion.

Assessment (continued)

5. Diagrams will depend on the type of joint shown, but they should show two bones connected at the joint, and they should also indicate the range of movement that the joint allows.

6. The function of skeletal muscle tissue is to move bones; its tissues are striated, or striped, and the cells contain many nuclei. The function of cardiac muscle tissue is to pump blood through the heart; its tissues are striated, and the small cells have just one nucleus. The function of smooth muscle tissue is to control movement in most internal organs and blood vessels; its tissues are not striated, and the spindle-shaped cells have a single nucleus.

Skills Trace
Comparing
- Focus p. 817
- Practice p. 817
- Assess p. 824

7. According to the theory, thick filaments of myosin form cross-bridges that attach to thin filaments of actin. Using energy supplied by ATP, the cross-bridges repeatedly bend, release, and reattach farther along the thin filaments. When hundreds of thousands of actin-myosin cross-bridges go through their cycle in a fraction of a second, the muscle cell contracts with considerable force.
8. Bones store supplies of calcium, which helps make them dense and hard. The stored calcium is also available for other tissues when needed.
9. An athlete with more red muscle fibers would be suited for endurance events, such as bicycling and swimming. An athlete with more white muscle fibers would be suited for strength events, such as weight lifting.
10. The skin helps maintain a balanced environment by producing sweat and dilating blood vessels to keep the body cool and by constricting blood vessels to keep the body warm. The skin also helps to keep the body from losing moisture and drying out.

Assessment

Reviewing What You Learned

Answer each of the following in a complete sentence.

1. What is the integumentary system?
2. Which structures does keratin form in humans and other animals?
3. Which glands are found in the dermis?
4. How are the formation of hair and nails related?
5. What kinds of tissue make up an internal skeletal system?
6. How does compact bone differ from spongy bone?
7. What is the function of osteocytes?
8. List three examples of freely movable joints.
9. Explain the purpose of synovial fluid.
10. How do the tissues that make up the skeleton change during human development?
11. What are the three types of muscles and where are they found?
12. What is acetylcholine?
13. How can muscles, which only contract, enable the skeleton to push as well as pull?
14. What is myoglobin?
15. Explain the benefits of aerobic exercises on the body.

Expanding the Concepts

Discuss each of the following in a brief paragraph.

1. What is meant when a biologist says that "we are alive because our surface is dead"?
2. How does the dermis differ from the epidermis?
3. Name three main classes of joints and their differences.
4. Tendinitis is an inflammation of the tendon. Explain what probably happens when a tennis player develops tendinitis.
5. Using a labeled diagram, describe the structure of a joint.
6. **Compare** the three types of muscle tissue by their function and cellular structure.
7. Describe the sliding filament theory of muscle contraction.
8. Describe the role of calcium in the skeletal system.
9. If an athlete has a greater number of red muscle fibers, for what kinds of events would he or she be more suited? Suppose the athlete had more white fibers?
10. How does the skin help to maintain a balanced environment in humans?

Extending Your Thinking

1. The athlete with 80 to 90 percent red muscle fibers is probably the marathon runner. The athlete with almost 70 percent white muscle fibers is probably the sprinter.

Skills Trace
Classifying
- Focus p. 811
- Practice p. 812
- Assess p. 825

2. When an infant is born, the relatively large head must squeeze through the birth canal. If the infant's skull bones were not flexible, the head might not fit through the birth canal. After birth the bones gradually become rigid and fixed to protect the brain and sense organs in the head.
3. Adverse effects of overexercising include too little body fat, joint injuries, and cessation of menstruation in females.
4. Models should show that students understand how the muscles attach to the bones and also how the triceps and biceps contract in opposite directions to allow the arm to both flex and extend.

Extending Your Thinking

Use the skills you have developed in this chapter to answer the following.

1. **Classifying** Two athletes have had their muscle tissue analyzed. One athlete's leg muscles contained between 80 and 90 percent red muscle fibers, while the other athlete's leg muscles had almost 70 percent white muscle fiber. Which athlete would you classify as a sprinter, and which one as a marathon runner?
2. **Using the writing process** At birth, the joints in an infant are flexible and not yet fixed. As the child develops, the bones become more rigid and grow together. Use reference materials to find out why the skull bones are flexible in a newborn, yet rigid as an adult. Then write a brief summary of your findings.
3. **Drawing conclusions** Although exercising can increase your strength and endurance, overexercising can have some adverse effects on the body. What are some adverse effects?
4. **Constructing a model** Using cardboard for bones and string for muscles, construct a working model of the biceps and triceps muscles of the upper arm. Be sure to show the relationship of these muscles to the humerus, ulna, and radius bones.
5. **Interpreting data** The line graph below plots the force of contraction of three different skeletal muscles. Using the data, describe the differences among the three muscles.

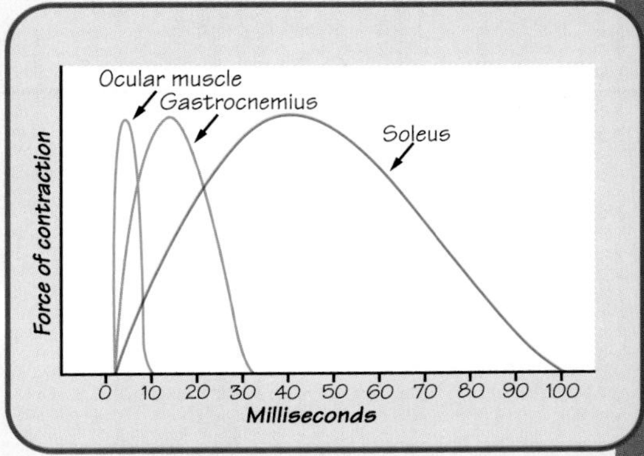

Applying Your Skills

Up Close

Biologists use a microscope to better understand the workings of the human body on a cellular level. In this activity, you'll use a microscope to differentiate among the following muscle tissue: smooth, skeletal, and cardiac.

1. Working with a partner, set up a compound microscope and obtain three "mystery slides," labeled A, B, and C, from your teacher.
2. Construct a data table to record the letter of each slide, the identity of the tissue, and characteristics that support your identification.
3. Place slide A on the stage of the microscope and examine it closely.
4. Discuss with your partner the identity of the cells or tissues. You may have to examine all the slides and identify some by a process of elimination.
5. Complete the data table for slide A and repeat the procedure using slides B and C.

• GOING FURTHER •

6. In your journal, think about the ease or difficulty of this activity. Which tissue was the easiest to identify? Which was the most difficult? Explain your answers.

Applying Your Skills

Teacher Notes

- To save class time, you may set up the microscopes and lay out the slides before class starts.
- If students are having difficulty distinguishing among the tissues on the three slides, suggest that they refer to the photographs of the three types of muscle tissue in Figure 36–9 on page 814. Also point out that, although skeletal and cardiac muscle tissues both appear striped under the microscope, skeletal muscle tissue has many more nuclei.

Answers

6. Answers may vary. Students may say that skeletal and cardiac muscle tissues are difficult to tell apart because both appear striated, or striped, under the microscope.

Scoring Rubric

4 Response is thorough, accurate, and creative; shows an in-depth understanding of science skills, procedures, and concepts.

3 Response is complete, mostly accurate, and original; shows a satisfactory understanding of science skills, procedures, and concepts.

2 Response is mostly complete but includes some inaccuracies; shows an adequate understanding of science skills, procedures, and concepts.

1 Response is only partially complete and has many inaccuracies; shows an incomplete understanding of science skills, procedures, and concepts.

0 Response is mostly incomplete and/or inaccurate; shows a lack of understanding of science skills, procedures, and concepts.

5. All three muscles show the same force of contraction, but the speed with which they attain this force and then relax again varies. The ocular muscle reaches the maximum force in fewer than 10 milliseconds and relaxes again just as quickly. It takes the gastrocnemius about twice as long as the ocular muscle to contract and relax, and it takes the soleus about twice as long as the gastrocnemius to contract and relax.

Chapter 37 Circulatory and Respiratory Systems

Content Management	Student Edition Activities
■ Section 37–1 The Circulatory System, pp. 827–834 Functions of the Circulatory System The Heart Blood Vessels Blood Pressure Blood Diseases of the Circulatory System The Lymphatic System	**MINI LAB:** Feel the Beat, p. 830
■ Section 37–2 The Respiratory System, pp. 835–840 What Is Respiration? The Human Respiratory System	**MINI LAB:** A Ballooning Effect, p. 838
◆ BRANCHING OUT • In Depth Section 37–3 The Hazards of Smoking, pp. 841–843 Tobacco Use Effects on the Respiratory System Effects on the Circulatory System Effects on Other Body Systems	**Laboratory Investigation:** Burning Tobacco, pp. 844–845

■ These sections cover all the necessary content and concepts for an enriched course in biology.
◆ This section covers content and concepts that are either applications or extensions of the enriched material.

Integration Strategies

SE Technology and Society, p. 830
Careers, p. 833
Careers, p. 842
Chemistry, p. 843

Assessment Strategies

SE Chapter Review, pp. 846–849
TR Section Reviews
Chapter Test
BL Chapter Review
Practice Test
CTB Chapter 37 Test

Tech Prep

Teaching strategies appropriate for students who are in technical/vocational programs or who are considering post-secondary technical education can be found on the following **TE** pages: 829 and 833.

Meeting the Standards

Sections 37–1 through 37–3 cover one of the six content standards under **The Cell,** three of the six content standards under **Matter, Energy, and Organization in Living Systems,** and one of the four content standards under **The Behavior of Organisms** as described on pages 184–187 of The National Science Education Standards.

Chapter Planning Guide

Teacher's Edition Activities	Other Activities	Media and Technology
Chapter Discovery Learning Activity, p. 826 **Inquiry Activity:** Modeling the Circulatory System, p. 828 **Investigate:** Model Building, p. 828 **Investigate:** Research, p. 831 **Activity:** Measuring Blood Pressure, p. 831 **Inquiry Activity:** What's Your Group?, p. 832	**LM** Simulating Blood Typing, #74 **TR** **Explore:** You Gotta Have Heart **BL** **Inquiry Activity:** You Gotta Have Heart	**CD-ROM:** The Total Heart **TB** Visualizing the Heart, #45
Inquiry Activity: How Does Activity Affect the Rate of Respiration?, p. 835 **Activity:** Modeling How We Breathe, p. 836 **Activity:** Relating Lung Capacity to Body Size, p. 838	**LM** Measuring Lung Capacity, #73 **TR** **Writing in Biology:** Fantastic Voyages **Apply:** Every Breath Counts **BL** **Inquiry Activity:** Every Breath You Take	**BioVue Animation:** See How They Run: Heart, Muscle, and Respiration, Videodisc Side 8 **BioVue Plus CD-ROMs:** See How They Run: Heart, Muscle, and Respiration **TB** Visualizing Human Respiration, #46
Inquiry Activity: Tobacco Toxicity, p. 841 **Investigate:** Long-Term Project, p. 842 **Activity:** The Cost of Smoking, p. 842	**TR** **Explore:** Danger: Hazardous to Your Life and Lifestyle **BL** **Inquiry Activity:** Smoke Gets in Your Lungs	

KEY: **SE** Student Edition **TE** Teacher's Edition **LM** Laboratory Manual **TR** Teaching Resources **BL** BioLog **TB** Transparency Box **CTB** Computer Test Bank

Materials List

TE Chapter Discovery Learning Activity, p. 826 (10 minutes); quart jar, cheesecloth, rubber band, large shallow pan.

SE MINI LAB: Feel the Beat, p. 830 (15–20 minutes); watch or clock with second hand.

TE Activity: Measuring Blood Pressure, p. 831 (15–20 minutes); sphygmomanometer, stethoscope.

TE Inquiry Activity: How Does Activity Affect the Rate of Respiration?, p. 835 (10–15 minutes); watch or clock with second hand.

TE Activity: Modeling How We Breathe, p. 836 (10–15 minutes to prepare model, 10 minutes for demonstration and discussion); bell jar, rubber sheet, two rubber bands, stopper, glass tube, small round balloon.

SE MINI LAB: A Ballooning Effect, p. 838 (20–30 minutes); round balloon, string, ruler.

TE Activity: Relating Lung Capacity to Body Size, p. 838 (10–15 minutes); calculator.

TE Inquiry Activity: Tobacco Toxicity, p. 841 (20 minutes to prepare solution, 10 minutes for demonstration and discussion); plant with aphids, tobacco, small pan, heat source, paper towel, spray bottle.

TE Activity: The Cost of Smoking, p. 842 (20 minutes); calculator, newspaper advertisements.

Chapter 37

Circulatory and Respiratory Systems

Introducing the Chapter

. . . In Pictures

Have students examine the photograph, read the caption, and answer the following questions.

• **Why is the swimmer's mouth wide open?** (So he can take in as much air as possible.)

• **Why does swimming require so much air?** (Because swimming is an aerobic exercise that uses up a great deal of oxygen.)

• **How does the oxygen that enters the swimmer's mouth get to the muscles that need it?** (The oxygen travels to the lungs, where it is picked up by the circulating blood and then transported to the muscles.)

In this chapter students will learn how the respiratory and circulatory systems supply muscles and the rest of the body with oxygen and other substances.

Teaching Strategy

The first section of this chapter describes the structures of the circulatory system and explains how they function. The second section explains the process of respiration and describes the human respiratory system. The BRANCHING OUT section looks in depth at the hazards of smoking tobacco.

BIO JOURNAL

Make sure students consider both positive and negative effects on their circulatory and respiratory systems. Some common harmful effects might include smoking cigarettes, not exercising, and eating a high-fat diet. Instruct students to keep their entries in their portfolios.

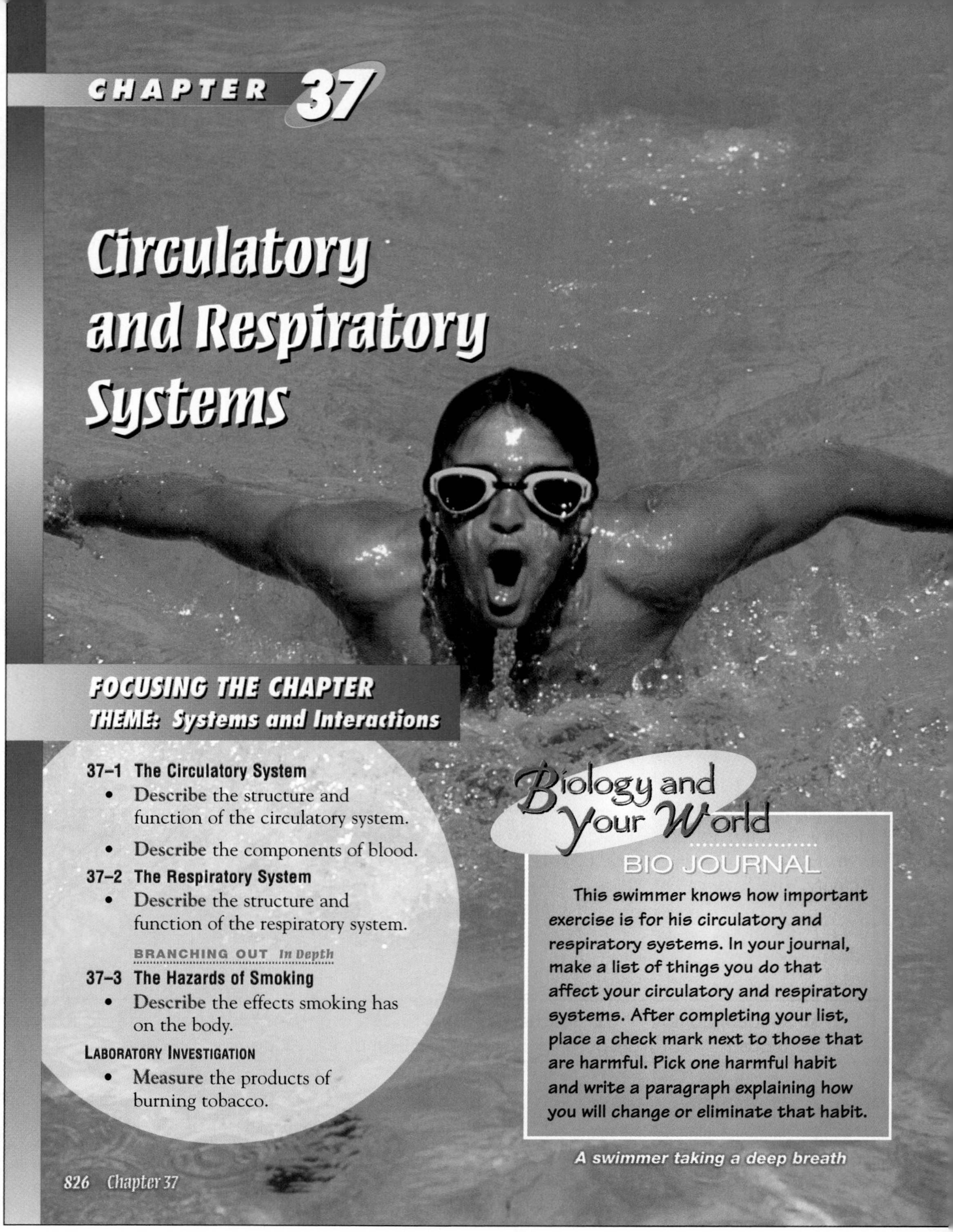

CHAPTER 37

Circulatory and Respiratory Systems

FOCUSING THE CHAPTER
THEME: Systems and Interactions

37–1 The Circulatory System
- **Describe** the structure and function of the circulatory system.
- **Describe** the components of blood.

37–2 The Respiratory System
- **Describe** the structure and function of the respiratory system.

BRANCHING OUT *In Depth*

37–3 The Hazards of Smoking
- **Describe** the effects smoking has on the body.

LABORATORY INVESTIGATION
- **Measure** the products of burning tobacco.

Biology and Your World

BIO JOURNAL

This swimmer knows how important exercise is for his circulatory and respiratory systems. In your journal, make a list of things you do that affect your circulatory and respiratory systems. After completing your list, place a check mark next to those that are harmful. Pick one harmful habit and write a paragraph explaining how you will change or eliminate that habit.

A swimmer taking a deep breath

TEACHER SUPPORT

Chapter Discovery Learning Activity

MOVEMENT OF MATERIALS

The exchange of oxygen and carbon dioxide across cell membranes in the alveoli of the lungs occurs by diffusion, a passive process that requires no input of energy. Follow these steps to help students understand how gas exchange occurs.

1. Fill a quart jar with water and cover the top of the jar with several layers of cheesecloth, held on tightly with a rubber band.

2. Lay the jar on its side in a large, shallow pan of water that is at least 5 cm deep, and have students observe what happens to the water in the jar and pan.

Results: The water diffuses across the cheesecloth "membrane" until the water in the jar and pan are at the same level, just as oxygen and carbon dioxide diffuse across a cell membrane until the concentration of each gas is the same on both sides of the membrane.

The Circulatory System

GUIDE FOR READING

- **List** the structures of the circulatory system.
- **Identify** the three types of blood vessels.
- **Compare** the functions of red blood cells, white blood cells, and platelets.

MINI LAB

- **Relate** your pulse rate to your activity level.

ONE OF THE SIGNS OF LIFE itself is your heartbeat. Even when you drift off to sleep, your heart beats out a steady rhythm. Why is this process so important that it must be kept going even while you sleep? Does it meet some great need of the trillions of cells that live inside you? It certainly does.

Each breath you take brings air into your body. Oxygen in that air is needed by every one of your cells. Not surprisingly, that oxygen needs to be delivered, and that's where the heart comes in. Its beating produces the force to move oxygen-carrying blood through the circulatory system to every part of your body. The circulatory system supplies cells throughout your body with substances they need to stay alive.

Functions of the Circulatory System

If an organism is composed of a small number of cells, it doesn't really need a circulatory system. Most cells in such organisms are in direct contact with the environment so that oxygen, nutrients, and wastes can easily diffuse across cell membranes from the outside.

Larger organisms, however, don't have this advantage. They need a circulatory system. Most of their cells are not in direct contact with the environment, and the substances made in one part of the organism may be needed in another part. In a way, this is the same problem faced by people who live in a large city. What is needed, of course, is a transportation system that moves people, goods, and waste materials from one place to another. The transportation

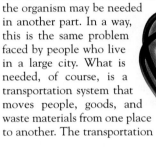

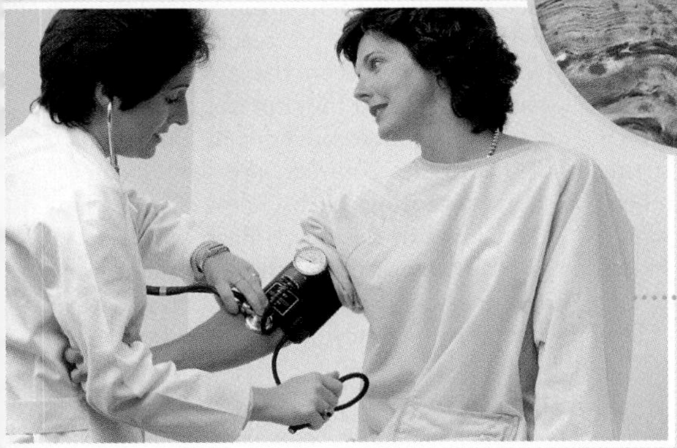

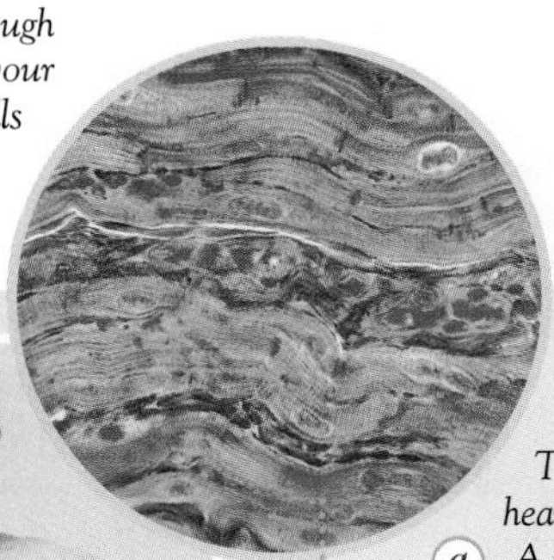

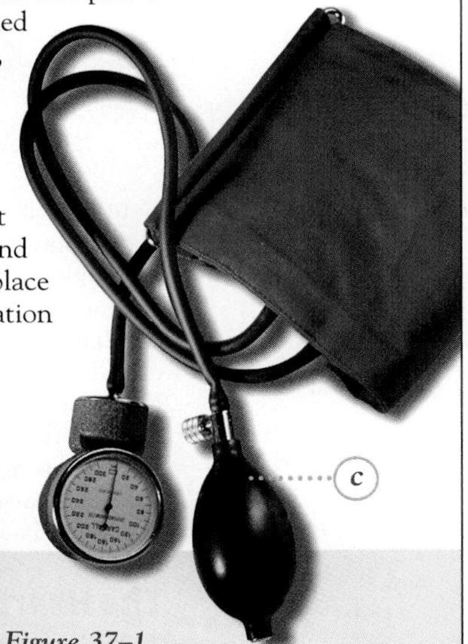

Figure 37–1
The circulatory system consists of the heart, the blood vessels, and the blood. (a) A measure of the pressure produced by the contractions of the heart and the muscles surrounding the heart is known as blood pressure. (b) The heart, which is made up almost entirely of cardiac muscle tissue, contracts at regular intervals, forcing blood through the circulatory system. (c) The instrument that measures blood pressure is called a sphygmomanometer.

SECTION 37–1
The Circulatory System

Performance Objectives

- Identify the components of the circulatory system.
- Distinguish among arteries, capillaries, and veins.
- Describe the roles of red blood cells, white blood cells, and platelets.

Mini Lab Skill: Relating

1 ENGAGE

Ideas Through Images

Have students examine Figure 37–1, read the caption, and answer the following questions.

- **Why is circulating blood under pressure?** (Contractions of the heart force it through the blood vessels.)
- **How does a sphygmomanometer assess the functioning of the heart?** (By measuring the pressure produced by the heart's contractions.)
- **Why do you think that high blood pressure can put a strain on the heart?** (The heart must work harder to pump the blood.)

TEACHER SUPPORT

Historical Perspective

In 1628, English physician William Harvey published a book on the circulatory system. It was a landmark publication because Harvey was the first to understand and write clearly about the circulation of the blood. Prior to that time, there were many misconceptions about the circulatory system—for example, that blood formed in the liver, that it moved only sluggishly and erratically if at all, and that pulmonary and systemic blood were different and not connected.

Through careful study of cadavers and living patients, Harvey proved all of these misconceptions wrong. He claimed that blood moves in a circle, that it is forced by the beating of the heart to all parts of the body in the arteries, and that it returns to the heart in the veins. Harvey also described the valves of the heart and veins and obviously understood how they help keep blood flowing in one direction through the circulatory system.

Ancillary Support

The resource below can be used to support your teaching strategy for these two pages.

TR Explore: You Gotta Have Heart

2 EXPLORE

Inquiry Activity

Building a Model

Modeling the Circulatory System

Ask students to use a building's ventilation system as a model for the circulatory system. Which structures are comparable to the blood vessels, heart, and lungs? (Air ducts that channel air throughout the building are comparable to the blood vessels; fans that force air through the ducts are comparable to the heart; and air vents that supply fresh air to the fans are comparable to the lungs.)

3 TEACH

Investigate

Model Building Have students investigate how heart valves work by using as a model of a heart valve an automatic door that opens in just one direction. Ask students to explain how the valve and door are similar in function. (Both allow only a one-way flow—of either blood or people—through an opening, and both open with pressure from just one side of the opening—either the force of blood pumped by the heart or the force of an electric current triggered by people standing in front of the door.) Ask students to explain why a revolving door would not be a good analogy for a heart valve. (Although a revolving door channels the flow of people, it allows movement both into and out of the building.)

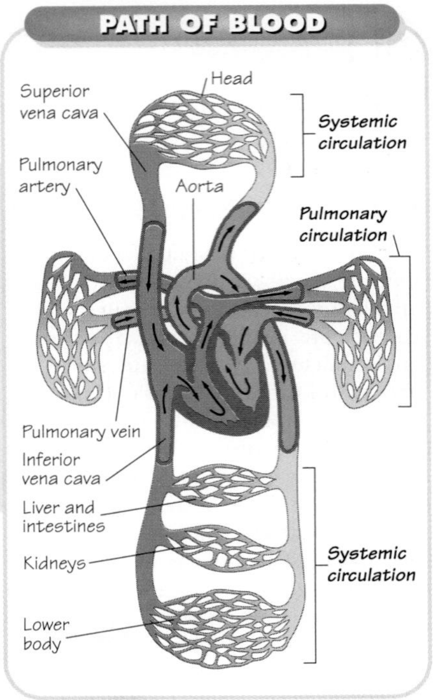

Figure 37–2 *In this diagram, the arrows show the path of blood through the body. The path of oxygen-poor blood is shown in blue. The path of oxygen-rich blood is shown in red.*

system of a city is its streets, highways, and rail lines. The transportation system of a living organism is its circulatory system.

Humans and other vertebrates have closed circulatory systems. This means that a circulating fluid—called **blood**—is pumped through a system of vessels. **The human circulatory system consists of the heart, a series of blood vessels, and the blood itself.**

The Heart

The heart is a hollow organ near the center of the chest composed almost entirely of muscle. The human heart is really like two separate pumps sitting side by side. Each side has two chambers: an **atrium** (AY-tree-uhm; plural: atria), the upper chamber that receives blood, and a **ventricle,** the lower chamber that pumps blood out of the heart. This means that the heart has a total of four chambers—two chambers on each side.

Each side of the heart pumps blood to a different part of the circulatory system. The right side of the heart pumps blood from the heart to the lungs. This pathway is called **pulmonary circulation.** Oxygen-poor blood is pumped by the right side of the heart through the lungs, where it gives off carbon dioxide and picks up oxygen. This oxygen-rich blood is then returned to the left side of the heart by the pulmonary veins.

The left side of the heart pumps blood to the rest of the body. This pathway is called **systemic circulation.** Oxygen-rich blood leaves the heart and supplies the body with oxygen-rich blood. By the time that blood returns from systemic circulation, cells throughout the body have picked up much of its oxygen and loaded it with carbon dioxide. In short, it is ready for another trip to the lungs. ***Figure 37–2*** shows the path of blood through the body.

Checkpoint What is pulmonary circulation? Systemic circulation? 1

Blood Flow Through the Heart

Blood enters the heart through the right and left atria. As the heart contracts, blood is forced first into the ventricles, then out from the ventricles into circulation. When it contracts, why doesn't some blood flow backward from the ventricles into the atria? Special flaps of tissue called **valves** reach across the passageways between the atria and the ventricles. Blood moving from the atria easily forces these valves open. But when the ventricles contract, the valves slam shut, preventing any backflow. There are four valves in the heart. Each valve ensures that blood moves through the heart in a one-way direction and increases the pumping efficiency of the heart.

TEACHER SUPPORT

Facts and Figures

- The average heart beats about 100,000 times a day and some 3 billion times in the average lifetime.
- The heart beats without external nervous regulation, except to control the speed and strength of its beat; it can even continue beating for several minutes after being removed from the body.
- At 140 beats per minute, the average heartbeat of a newborn is about twice as great as the average heartbeat of a teen.
- The heart typically moves about 9500 liters of blood each day and about 150 to 200 million liters of blood in an average lifetime.
- Cardiac muscle is supplied with more capillaries than any other tissue; it uses about 80 percent of the oxygen supplied by the blood compared with about 25 percent used by most other tissues.

Visualizing the Heart

The heart is a powerful muscle that continuously pumps blood throughout the body. It is about the size of a fist and is located near the center of the chest. It beats an average of 70 times per minute at rest.

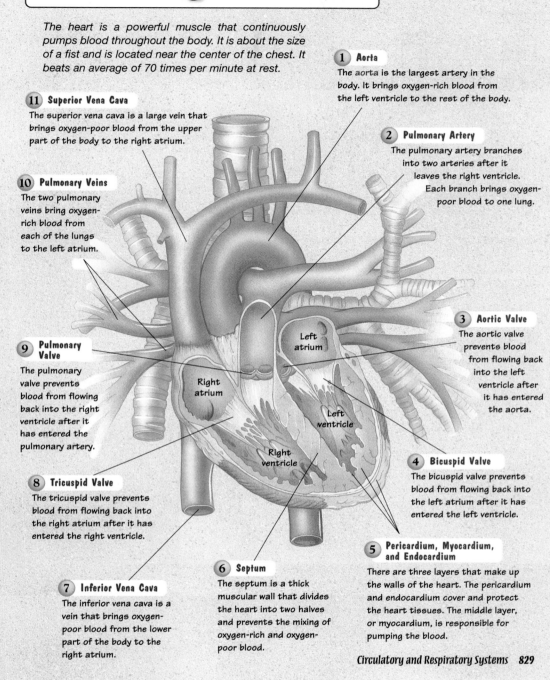

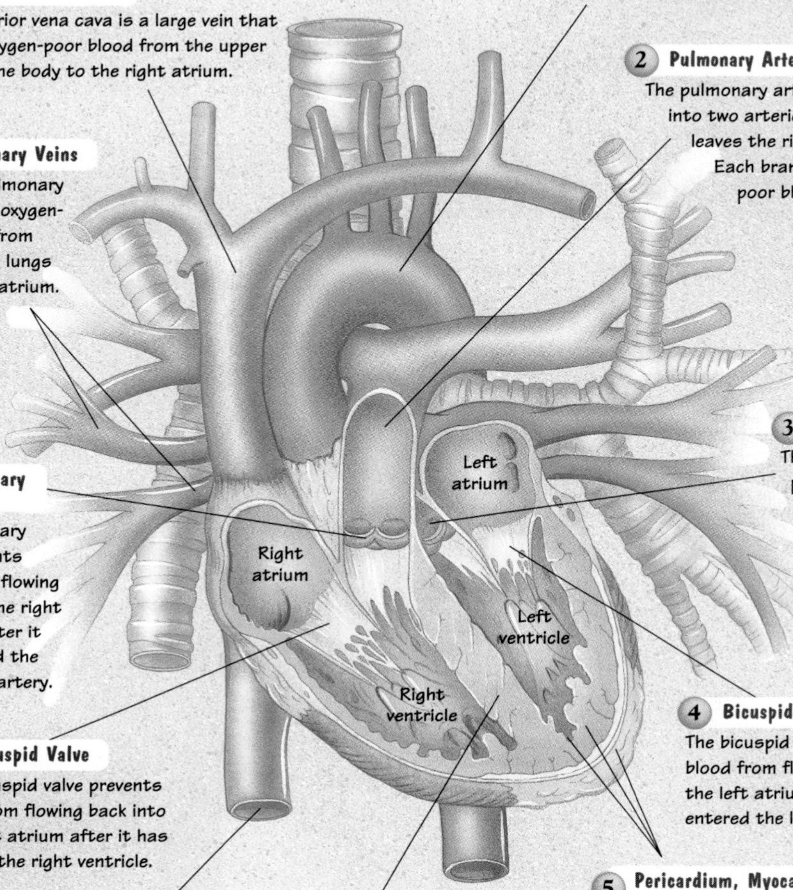

1 Aorta
The aorta is the largest artery in the body. It brings oxygen-rich blood from the left ventricle to the rest of the body.

2 Pulmonary Artery
The pulmonary artery branches into two arteries after it leaves the right ventricle. Each branch brings oxygen-poor blood to one lung.

3 Aortic Valve
The aortic valve prevents blood from flowing back into the left ventricle after it has entered the aorta.

4 Bicuspid Valve
The bicuspid valve prevents blood from flowing back into the left atrium after it has entered the left ventricle.

5 Pericardium, Myocardium, and Endocardium
There are three layers that make up the walls of the heart. The pericardium and endocardium cover and protect the heart tissues. The middle layer, or myocardium, is responsible for pumping the blood.

6 Septum
The septum is a thick muscular wall that divides the heart into two halves and prevents the mixing of oxygen-rich and oxygen-poor blood.

7 Inferior Vena Cava
The inferior vena cava is a vein that brings oxygen-poor blood from the lower part of the body to the right atrium.

8 Tricuspid Valve
The tricuspid valve prevents blood from flowing back into the right atrium after it has entered the right ventricle.

9 Pulmonary Valve
The pulmonary valve prevents blood from flowing back into the right ventricle after it has entered the pulmonary artery.

10 Pulmonary Veins
The two pulmonary veins bring oxygen-rich blood from each of the lungs to the left atrium.

11 Superior Vena Cava
The superior vena cava is a large vein that brings oxygen-poor blood from the upper part of the body to the right atrium.

Visualizing the Heart

To help students visualize how blood flows through the major vessels shown in the drawing, point out that arteries always carry blood away from the heart (either to the lungs or to the rest of the body) and that veins always carry blood toward the heart (either from the lungs or from the rest of the body).

Point out that the bicuspid valve is sometimes referred to as the mitral valve. Several heart disorders involve mitral valve defects.

Any of the valves of the heart may be defective in one of two basic ways: They may open inadequately, which is called stenosis, or close incompletely, which is called incompetence.

Ask students to examine the drawing to determine where the blood is pumped by the atria (to the ventricles) and by the ventricles (to the rest of the body). Then ask them why they think ventricles need thicker walls than atria. (Ventricles must be stronger to pump blood farther.)

Checkpoint

1 Pulmonary circulation is the pathway blood takes from the right side of the heart to the lungs. Systemic circulation is the pathway blood takes from the left side of the heart to the rest of the body.

TEACHER SUPPORT

Managing Classroom Diversity

AT-RISK STUDENTS
Help students who are having difficulty visualizing the working of the heart by tracing the path of blood flow into and out of the heart in the drawing. As you trace along each vein and artery, explain where the blood is coming from, where it is going, whether or not it is oxygenated, and what keeps it moving in the right direction. Check students' understanding by asking them to trace the path of blood flow through specific arteries or veins.

TECH PREP STUDENTS
Ask students interested in health-care careers to learn about the electrocardiograph, or ECG. Have them research what the test measures (changes in electrical activity of the heart) and how (with electrodes attached to the body). Have students obtain copies of normal and abnormal ECG printouts to share with the class and explain to the other students how the printouts are interpreted.

Technology

CD-ROM
The Total Heart

Ancillary Support

The resource below can be used to support your teaching strategy for these two pages.

TB Visualizing the Heart, #45

MINI LAB **Relating**

Teacher Notes

- For time required and materials needed, see page 826b.
- To save time, you may wish to have students omit step 1 or 2.
- Make sure that students have been inactive for several minutes before they take their resting pulse rate.
- You can extend the lab by having students count and record their pulse rate repeatedly every 30 to 60 seconds after exercising until the heart returns to its resting rate. Ask them how long it took for their heart to return to its resting rate.

Answers to Analyze and Conclude

1. The resting pulse rate in the wrist and neck should be about the same for each student.
2. Activity should increase each student's pulse rate.

Skills Trace
Relating
- Focus p. 830
- Practice p. 834
- Assess p. 848

INTEGRATING TECHNOLOGY AND SOCIETY

An artificial pacemaker is a small, battery-operated device that is surgically implanted near the heart when the heart's natural pacemaker cannot maintain a normal heart rhythm. It delivers regular electrical impulses through an electrode to the heart wall to make the heart beat steadily.

MINI LAB .... *Relating* ....

Feel the Beat

PROBLEM *How does your pulse rate **relate** to your activity level?*

PROCEDURE

CAUTION: *If you have any respiratory or circulatory conditions, do not perform this activity.*

1. Using the first two fingers of one hand, locate the pulse point on the inside of your wrist. It is next to the tendon near your thumb.
2. Lightly place the same two fingers against the same side of your neck near the corner of your jawbone.
3. At each location, count and record the number of pulses in 1 minute.
4. Repeat steps 1 to 3 after exercising in place for 1 minute.

ANALYZE AND CONCLUDE

1. How did your resting pulse rate compare in the wrist and the neck?
2. What effect did activity have on your pulse rate?

The Heartbeat

Although the heart is a single muscle, all of its cells do not all contract at the same time. Instead, cells of the atria contract first, and a wave of contraction spreads from the right atrium over the rest of the heart. This pattern of contraction makes the heart a more efficient pump, squeezing blood from one chamber to the next. How does this wavelike contraction happen?

Each contraction begins in a small group of cells in the right atrium. Because these cells "set the pace" for the heart as a whole, they are called the **pacemaker.** ● From the pacemaker, the contraction impulse is spread from cell to cell, producing a wave of contractions that reach all four chambers.

Blood Vessels

Blood leaving through the heart travels through a series of blood vessels that will carry it on its round trip through the body and back to the heart. **The three types of blood vessels that blood**

INTEGRATING TECHNOLOGY AND SOCIETY

Some people need an artificial pacemaker to help maintain a steady heart rate. Use reference materials to find out how an artificial pacemaker works.

HEARTBEAT CONTROL

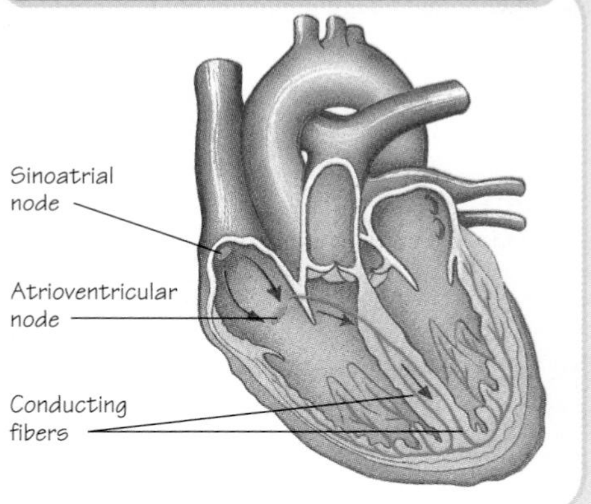

Figure 37–3 The rhythmic beating of the heart is maintained by the sinoatrial node—the pacemaker—located in the right atrium. The signal to contract spreads from the pacemaker through the cardiac muscle cells, causing the atria to contract. Then the impulse is picked up by the atrioventricular node, which is a bundle of fibers that carry the impulse to the ventricles, causing them to contract.

TEACHER SUPPORT

Background Information

Although the heart beats without outside nervous stimulation, changes in the rate at which the heart beats are under the control of the central nervous system. The sinoatrial node, or pacemaker, which controls the rate at which the heart beats, is itself controlled by the heart rate center, located in the medulla oblongata. Nerves of the autonomic nervous system leading from the medulla oblongata to the heart stimulate the heart muscle to beat either faster (nerves of the sympathetic division) or slower (nerves of the parasympathetic division). The heart rate center, in turn, is influenced by many factors, including pressure receptors in arteries and veins, emotions such as fear, hormones such as adrenaline, and environmental factors such as temperature.

moves through are the arteries, capillaries, and veins.**

Arteries—the superhighways of the circulatory system—are blood vessels that carry blood from the heart to the body. Except for the pulmonary arteries, all arteries carry oxygen-rich blood. Arteries have thick elastic walls that help them withstand the powerful spurts of blood produced when the heart contracts. The lining of an artery is surrounded by layers of elastic tissue and smooth muscle cells that allow an artery to expand under pressure.

Capillaries, the smallest of the blood vessels, are the side streets and alleys of the circulatory system. The exchange of nutrients and wastes takes place in the capillaries. Their walls are only one cell thick and may be so narrow that blood cells must pass through in single file.

Veins collect blood after it has passed through the capillary system. Like arteries, the walls of veins are lined with elastic tissue and smooth muscle. Veins, however, have thin walls and are less elastic than arteries. The largest veins contain one-way valves that keep blood flowing toward the heart. Many veins are located near skeletal muscles, and the contractions of those muscles help to push blood along to the heart. This is one reason why it is important to exercise regularly. Exercise helps to keep blood from accumulating in the limbs and from stretching the veins out of shape.

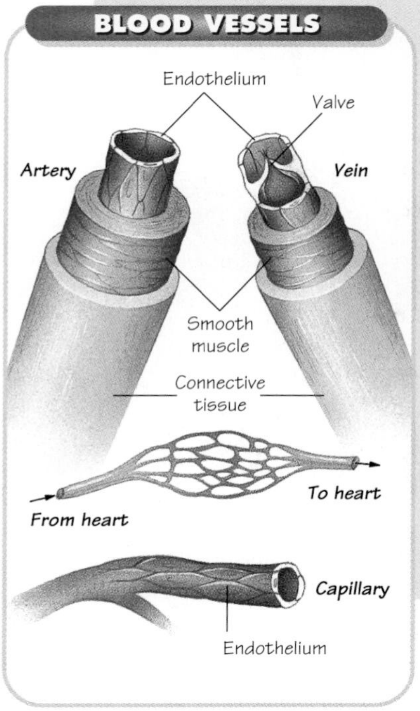

Figure 37–4
The layer of smooth muscle in arteries is much thicker than that of veins because the arteries have to withstand the high pressure of blood as it is pumped from the heart. Capillaries, on the other hand, contain only epithelial tissue and are only one cell thick.

Blood Pressure

Any pump produces pressure, and the heart is no exception. When the heart contracts, it produces a wave of fluid pressure in the arteries. Although the force of blood on the walls of the arteries, known as **blood pressure,** falls when the heart relaxes, the system still remains under pressure. This is good, too, because without that pressure, blood would not flow through the arteries and into the capillaries.

The body regulates blood pressure in two different ways. Sensory neurons at several places in the body detect the level of blood pressure and send impulses to the brainstem. When blood pressure is too high, the autonomic nervous system releases neurotransmitters that cause the smooth muscles around blood vessels to relax, lowering blood pressure. When blood pressure is too low, neurotransmitters are released that elevate blood pressure by causing these muscles to contract.

The kidneys also help to regulate blood pressure. Hormones produced by the heart and other organs cause the kidneys to remove more water from the

Ideas Through Images

Have students examine Figure 37–4, read the caption, and answer the following questions.

- **What role does smooth muscle play in arteries and veins?** (It allows the blood vessels to expand under pressure.)
- **Why do capillaries not have a layer of smooth muscle?** (Their walls must be very thin so the exchange of nutrients and wastes can take place.)
- **What function do the valves serve in veins, and why are they not found in arteries?** (The valves keep blood flowing toward the heart; they are not found in arteries, because arterial blood is pumped by the heart.)

Investigate

Research Have students investigate the two blood pressure measures, diastolic and systolic blood pressure. What does each actually measure? (Systolic pressure is the peak pressure at the moment the heart contracts and pumps blood into the arteries; diastolic pressure is the lowest pressure in the arteries just before the next contraction of the heart.) What values for each measure are considered normal? (Systolic pressure under 130 and diastolic pressure under 90.) Which is the greater cause for concern, high systolic or high diastolic blood pressure? (High diastolic blood pressure.)

TEACHER SUPPORT

Activity

MEASURING BLOOD PRESSURE
Bring a sphygmomanometer and stethoscope to class and, using a student volunteer, demonstrate how they are used to measure blood pressure. Place the arm cuff around the volunteer's upper arm and inflate it. Explain that this prevents the flow of arterial blood. Then, while listening with the stethoscope placed on the inside bend of the elbow, slowly release air from the cuff. Explain that the pressure when the sounds of the pulsing blood flow appear is the systolic pressure, and the pressure when the sounds disappear is the diastolic pressure. Encourage volunteers to try to take one another's blood pressure. Then lead the class in a discussion of how blood pressure varies from one part of the body to another. (Blood pressure is lower the farther it is taken from the heart—for example, it is lower in the legs than in the arms—because friction of the blood with the vessel walls reduces its pressure.)

Ancillary Support

The resource below can be used to support your teaching strategy for these two pages.

BL Inquiry Activity: You Gotta Have Heart

Discussion

Ask students to identify risk factors for high blood pressure. (Possible risk factors include a high-fat or high-sodium diet, obesity, stress, and lack of exercise.) Then lead students in a discussion of practical ways that teens could decrease their risk factors and lower their risk of high blood pressure. (Possible ways might include avoiding fast foods that are high in fat and salt and getting involved in sports or other physical activities to increase the amount of exercise.)

Inquiry Activity

Collecting and Organizing Data

What's Your Group?

Tell students that ABO blood groups refer to antigens on the surface of red blood cells. Receiving a transfusion of blood containing an antigen that one's own blood does not have causes the red blood cells to clump together, or agglutinate, a reaction that can be fatal. Ask students what blood group someone with group A blood could be given safely in a transfusion. How could they find out?

Suggest that students work in pairs to make a table showing compatible blood groups for each blood group in the ABO system. There should be a row and a column for each of the four blood groups—A, B, AB, and O—with rows representing recipient blood groups and columns representing donor blood groups. Cells should be filled in with yes or no to show which blood groups are compatible and which are not. Be sure students understand that people with group A blood have only the A antigen on their red blood cells, group B only the B antigen, group AB blood both A and B antigens, and group O neither antigen.

After students have completed the table, ask them why group O is called the "universal donor" and group AB the "universal recipient." (Group O blood can be given safely to people of any other blood group, and people with group AB blood can safely receive blood of any other group.)

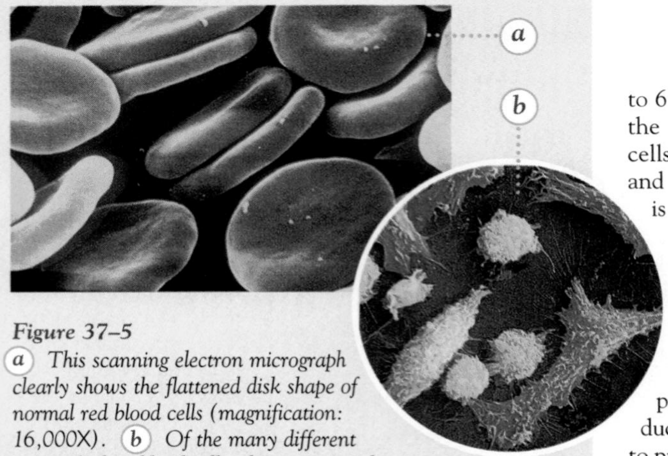

Figure 37–5
(a) This scanning electron micrograph clearly shows the flattened disk shape of normal red blood cells (magnification: 16,000X). (b) Of the many different types of white blood cells, this scanning electron micrograph shows two—macrophages and lymphocytes. The brown objects are the macrophages, which engulf bacteria. Lymphocytes, which produce antibodies to prevent disease, are the green spherical objects (magnification: 5000X).

blood when blood pressure is high. This reduces blood volume and lowers blood pressure.

Medical problems may result if blood pressure is either too high or too low. High blood pressure forces the heart to work harder, which may weaken or damage the heart muscle. People with high blood pressure are more likely to develop heart disease and to suffer from other diseases of the circulatory system.

The causes of high blood pressure are complex, but one of them is well understood—obesity. Although scientists have developed a number of drugs that can lower blood pressure, high blood pressure is easier to prevent than to cure. Exercise, weight control, and a sensible diet seem to be the keys to avoiding high blood pressure.

Blood

Roughly 8 percent of the mass of the human body is blood. For most of us, that means we contain anywhere from 4 to 6 liters of blood. About 45 percent of the volume of blood consists of living cells—**red blood cells, white blood cells,** and **platelets.** The remaining 55 percent is a fluid called **plasma.**

Plasma itself is 90 percent water. The remaining 10 percent consists of salts, sugars, and three groups of plasma proteins. The first, called serum albumin, helps to regulate osmotic pressure. Other plasma proteins, called globulins, are produced by the immune system and help to protect against infection. And the last of the plasma proteins is fibrinogen, which regulates blood clotting.

Red Blood Cells

Red blood cells are the most numerous cells in the blood—1 milliliter of blood contains nearly 5 million of them. Their scientific name—erythrocyte, means "red cell" and comes from the bright-red **hemoglobin** inside them. Hemoglobin is an iron-containing protein that dramatically increases the ability of blood to carry oxygen. **Red blood cells are oxygen carriers.** As red blood cells pass through the lungs, the hemoglobin within them quickly absorbs dissolved oxygen. When the same cells pass through capillaries in oxygen-poor regions of the body, oxygen is released into the surrounding tissues.

Red blood cells are produced in the bone marrow. As red blood cells develop, they lose their nuclei and their ability to divide. A typical red blood cell has a life span of roughly 120 days, which means that nearly 1 percent of your red blood cells must be replaced each day.

☑ **Checkpoint** What is hemoglobin? ①

White Blood Cells

White blood cells are blood cells that do not contain hemoglobin. White blood cells are also called leukocytes,

TEACHER SUPPORT

Background Information

There are five types of white blood cells in normal blood, three of which—the neutrophils, monocytes, and eosinophils—are phagocytic. Neutrophils migrate to infected areas, where they attack bacteria. Monocytes also move to sites of infection, where they mature into macrophages that engulf germs, destroy cancer-causing cells, and aid in antibody production. Eosinophils attack parasitic worms.

Lymphocytes, which make up about 30 percent of white blood cells, play a key role in the production of antibodies. (The main types of lymphocytes, B cells and T cells, are discussed in Chapter 40.) Basophils, which make up 0.4 percent of white blood cells, play a role in the body's response to tissue injury.

which means "white cells." They are much less common than red cells, which outnumber them almost 500 to 1. Like red blood cells, white blood cells are produced in the bone marrow and are released into the blood as cells with nuclei. Unlike red blood cells, white blood cells may live for many months and possibly even for years.

More than 20 different types of white blood cells are known. **White blood cells guard against infection, fight parasites, and attack bacteria.** Some actually engulf and digest these foreign cells. Others attack invading organisms in the tissues of the body. Still others produce chemical signals that activate the body's immune system to help fight infection.

Like an army with units in reserve, the body is able to increase the number of white blood cells dramatically when a "battle" is underway. In fact, a sudden increase in the number of white cells is one way in which physicians can tell that the body is fighting a serious infection.

Platelets and Blood Clotting

Try as we might to protect ourselves against injury, sooner or later just about everyone receives a cut or a scrape. Most of these injuries aren't serious. A minor cut or scrape may bleed for a few minutes, then stop. Have you ever wondered why bleeding stops so quickly?

The answer is that blood has the ability to form a clot, a tangle of microscopic fibers that block the flow of blood. **Blood clotting is made possible by cell fragments, called platelets, and a number of plasma proteins.**

When platelets come into contact with the broken edges of a blood vessel, their surfaces become sticky, and a cluster of platelets develops around the wound. These platelets then release a

Figure 37–6

(a) *In response to an injury to a blood vessel, proteins called fibrin form in the blood. Fibrin produces a netlike web that traps the red blood cells, thus forming a clot that constricts the wound and promotes healing.* (b) *Platelets, which are responsible for blood clotting, are actually fragments of larger cells. This color-enhanced scanning electron micrograph shows some inactive platelets (magnification: 9200X).*

series of chemicals that help to start a complicated clotting reaction. This reaction results in the formation of **fibrin,** which forms a netlike trap that covers the wound and traps the red blood cells. If the wound is small, a network of platelets and fibrin seals the leak within a few minutes, and bleeding stops.

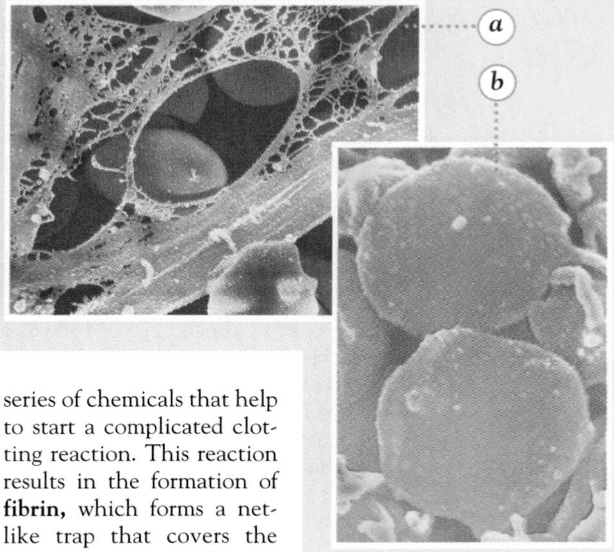

☑ *Checkpoint* What is fibrin? ②

Diseases of the Circulatory System

Unfortunately, diseases of the circulatory system are common. ● Many of them stem from a condition known as **atherosclerosis** (ath-er-oh-skluh-ROH-sihs), in which fatty deposits build up on the inner surfaces of arteries. If these deposits get too large, they obstruct the flow of blood.

Atherosclerosis is particularly dangerous in the coronary arteries, a set of small

INTEGRATING CAREERS

Use reference materials to find out the special training needed by a cardiologist, a doctor who treats heart disease.

Circulatory and Respiratory Systems **833**

Ideas Through Images

Have students examine Figure 37–6, read the caption, and answer the following questions.

• **Where does fibrin come from?** (Platelets release a series of chemicals that result in the formation of fibrin.)

• **What other role do platelets play in blood clotting?** (Platelets clump together to cover the wound and trap red blood cells.)

Discussion

Lead students in a discussion of why atherosclerosis is often the underlying cause of both heart attacks and strokes by asking the following questions.

• **What effect does lack of oxygen have on the heart and brain?** (Both heart and brain tissues need relatively great amounts of oxygen. When they do not get the oxygen they need, they die.)

• **How does lack of oxygen lead to heart attack or stroke?** (Heart attack occurs when heart tissue dies; stroke occurs when brain tissue dies.)

INTEGRATING CAREERS

After completing medical school, a doctor who wishes to become a cardiologist must take special training in the diagnosis and treatment of heart disease.

☑ Checkpoints

❶ An iron-containing protein that dramatically increases the ability of blood to carry oxygen.

❷ A protein that forms a netlike trap that covers a wound and traps the red blood cells.

Ancillary Support

The resource below can be used to support your teaching strategy for these two pages.

LM Simulating Blood Typing, #74

TEACHER SUPPORT

Managing Classroom Diversity

TECH PREP STUDENTS

Have students interested in health-care careers learn how and why blood counts are performed. They should also learn how important accuracy is in performing blood counts and what safety precautions must be taken when handling blood samples. Have students observe a laboratory technician performing blood counts on the job. Ask students to share what they learn with the class.

GIFTED STUDENTS

Have students find out the cause of hemophilia, how it is inherited, and why it occurs almost solely in males. Have students find a family tree for Queen Victoria of England (1819–1901), showing which of her descendants had the disease or carried the gene for it. Ask students to explain the inheritance of the disease to the class, using the family tree to illustrate their explanation.

4 ASSESS

Quick Check

Call on students to identify each of the following terms relating to the circulatory system: atrium, ventricle, pacemaker, arteries, veins, capillaries, hemoglobin, fibrin, and lymph. Review any terms they do not identify correctly.

Section Review 37–1

1. The heart, blood vessels, and blood.
2. Arteries, capillaries, and veins.
3. Red blood cells are oxygen carriers; white blood cells guard against infection, fight parasites, and attack bacteria; platelets are cell particles that make blood clotting possible.
4. Injections of normal clotting proteins would help a hemophiliac by replacing the products of the missing gene and initiating the complicated clotting reaction that results in the formation of fibrin.
5. In the MINI LAB students observed that as the activity level increases so does the pulse rate.

Skills Trace
Relating

- Focus p. 830
- Practice p. 834
- Assess p. 848

Learning Modality

Tactile Learning Ask students to turn to Figure 37–2 and, using their fingers, trace the path of blood through the circulatory system. Have students name and briefly state the function of each component of the system as their fingers trace over it.

Figure 37–7
The lymphatic system is made up of lymphatic vessels and lymph nodes. The lymphatic vessels collect lymph—fluid that leaves the circulatory system—and returns it to veins in the neck. The lymph nodes act as filters that prevent harmful materials from entering body cells.

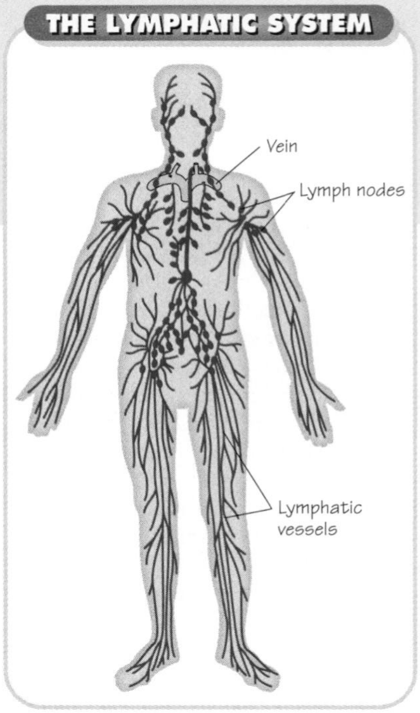

arteries that bring oxygen and nutrients to the heart muscle itself. If one of these becomes blocked, part of the heart muscle may begin to die from a lack of oxygen, a condition called a heart attack. The symptoms of a heart attack include nausea, shortness of breath, radiating pain down the left arm, and severe, crushing chest pain. People who show symptoms of a heart attack should be given medical attention immediately.

When one of the blood vessels leading to part of the brain is blocked, a stroke results. Brain cells served by that blood vessel gradually die from a lack of oxygen, and brain function in that region may be lost. Depending on the part of the brain that is affected, a stroke may cause paralysis, loss of the ability to speak, and even death.

The Lymphatic System

Fluid from the bloodstream is constantly leaking from the capillaries into the surrounding tissues. The leaking fluid helps to bring salts and nutrients into tissues where they are needed. More than 3 liters of fluid leak from the circulatory system into surrounding tissues every day.

What happens to all this fluid? A network of vessels called the **lymphatic** (lihm-FAT-ihk) **system** collects the fluid—**lymph** (LIHMF)—and returns it to the circulatory system. As ***Figure 37–7*** shows, these vessels empty the lymph back into general circulation through a vein under the left shoulder. Lymph vessels contain one-way valves, like veins, to keep lymph flowing in one direction.

Section Review 37–1

1. **List** the structures of the circulatory system.
2. **Identify** the three types of blood vessels.
3. **Compare** the functions of red blood cells, white blood cells, and platelets.
4. **Critical Thinking—Applying Concepts** Hemophilia is a genetic disorder in which the gene for normal blood clotting is missing. How would injections of normal clotting proteins help a hemophiliac?
5. **MINI LAB** How does your pulse rate **relate** to your activity level?

TEACHER SUPPORT

Background Information

Lymph nodes trap harmful substances such as bacteria, which are recognized as foreign by lymphocytes, a type of white blood cell that matures in the lymph nodes. This leads to an immune response. The lymph nodes often become swollen and painful when they react to infection in this way. Another component of the lymphatic system is the spleen, which is actually a large lymph node. Located in the upper left part of the abdomen behind the ribs, the spleen produces red blood cells in the fetus in addition to helping fight infection at all ages.

When the lymphatic system does not work properly or cannot keep up with the amount of fluid leaking into the tissues, the body or body part that is affected swells with the accumulating fluid. This is called edema. Many conditions are characterized by edema, including kidney failure, circulatory problems, heart disease, and some types of malnutrition.

The Respiratory System

SECTION 37–2

GUIDE FOR READING

- **Describe** the function of the respiratory system.

MINI LAB

- **Measure** your lung capacity.

WHEN PARAMEDICS RUSH TO the aid of an injured person, one of the first things they usually do is to check to see whether the victim is breathing. If the person is not breathing, paramedics will ignore other injuries—even broken bones and serious wounds—to get the person breathing again. There's no time to lose! If breathing stops for more than a few minutes, the person may die!

A well-trained paramedic understands how important the respiratory system is to life. This system provides nearly every cell in the body with oxygen—the same oxygen that is carried throughout the body by the circulatory system.

What Is Respiration?

In biology, the word respiration is used in two slightly different ways. At the cellular level, respiration is defined as the release of energy from the breakdown of food molecules in the presence of oxygen. Without oxygen, cells lose much of their ability to produce ATP, and that means that they cannot synthesize new molecules, pump ions, carry nerve impulses, or even move.

Because trillions of cells have a pressing need for oxygen, the human body must find a way to get that oxygen to them. It must also dispose of the carbon dioxide produced when food molecules are broken down. At the level of the organism, respiration is the exchange of gases—oxygen and carbon dioxide—between the organism and its environment.

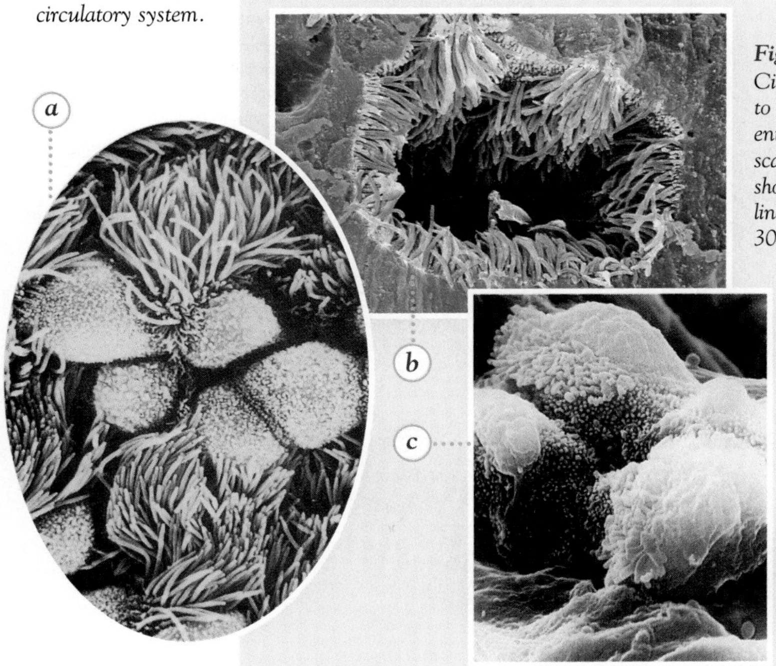

Figure 37–8
Cilia and goblet cells work together to prevent foreign particles from entering the lungs. (a) This scanning electron micrograph shows a close-up of the cilia that line the trachea (magnification: 3000X). (b) In this cross section of the trachea, the cilia have been colored green (magnification: 3570X). The yellow structures at the base of the cilia are goblet cells, which produce mucus. (c) Once the incoming air has been cleaned and filtered, it enters the alveoli of the lungs, where actual gas exchange takes place. (magnification: 5100X).

TEACHER SUPPORT

Facts and Figures

You may wish to share the following facts and figures about respiration with students to help them appreciate the significance of breathing, a vital function they may take for granted.

- We can go only a few minutes without breathing, as opposed to a few days without drinking and several days without eating.
- We take in over five times as much air daily (16 kilograms) as we do food and fluids combined (3 kilograms).
- During a normal resting breath, the average adult moves about half a liter of air into and out of the lungs, or a total of some 16,000 liters of air daily.
- About one-fourth of the body's blood supply is concentrated in the fine capillary net that surrounds the alveoli in the lungs.

SECTION 37–2

The Respiratory System

Performance Objective

- Explain how the respiratory system functions.

Mini Lab Skill: Measuring

1 ENGAGE

Ideas Through Images

Have students examine Figure 37–8, read the caption, and answer the following questions.

- **How do you think goblet cells help keep foreign particles out of the lungs?** (By producing mucus that traps them.)
- **How do you think the cilia function?** (They function like little fingers to move foreign particles out of the respiratory tract.)

2 EXPLORE

Inquiry Activity

Designing an Experiment

How Does Activity Affect the Rate of Respiration?

Remind students how the heart rate increased with activity in the MINI LAB in the last section. Then ask them how they think the rate of respiration, or breathing, would be affected by activity. How could they find out? Guide students in developing an experimental design such as the following.

Have students work with a partner. One student counts and records how many times the other student breathes per minute at rest and again following a brief activity. The two rates are then compared.

Ask students to perform the experiment or predict what would happen if they did.

3 TEACH

Visualizing Human Respiration

To help students visualize the way that air flows through the respiratory system, have them identify each of the structures through which the air passes, starting with the nose and mouth and ending with the alveoli. (Pharynx, larynx, bronchi, and bronchioles.) Point out that it is not until air reaches the alveoli that the exchange of oxygen and carbon dioxide takes place. The alveoli are surrounded by hundreds of millions of capillaries, which ensure that they are richly supplied with blood.

Lungs are elastic, but they are not composed of muscle tissue. They expand and contract in response only to changes in air pressure within the chest cavity. However, muscles do play a vital role in respiration. Have students discuss the role that muscles play by asking which muscles are involved and what their function is. (The muscles involved are the diaphragm and the intercostal muscles. When these muscles contract during respiration, the volume of the chest increases, causing the lungs to expand and air to be pulled into them. When the muscles relax, the chest volume decreases and the lungs contract, forcing the air out.)

Cardiopulmonary resuscitation, or CPR, involves one person breathing into the mouth of another person who is not breathing in order to provide the other person with oxygen. Ask students how CPR works when the exhaled air has already gone through the gas exchange process, giving up oxygen in exchange for carbon dioxide. How does the person receiving the "second-hand" air get enough oxygen to survive? (Exhaled air contains less oxygen than inhaled air; however, it still contains enough oxygen to keep a person alive who is not breathing on his or her own.)

Visualizing Human Respiration

The human respiratory system is responsible for bringing oxygen to the blood so that it can be distributed to the body cells. In addition, it removes carbon dioxide from the body.

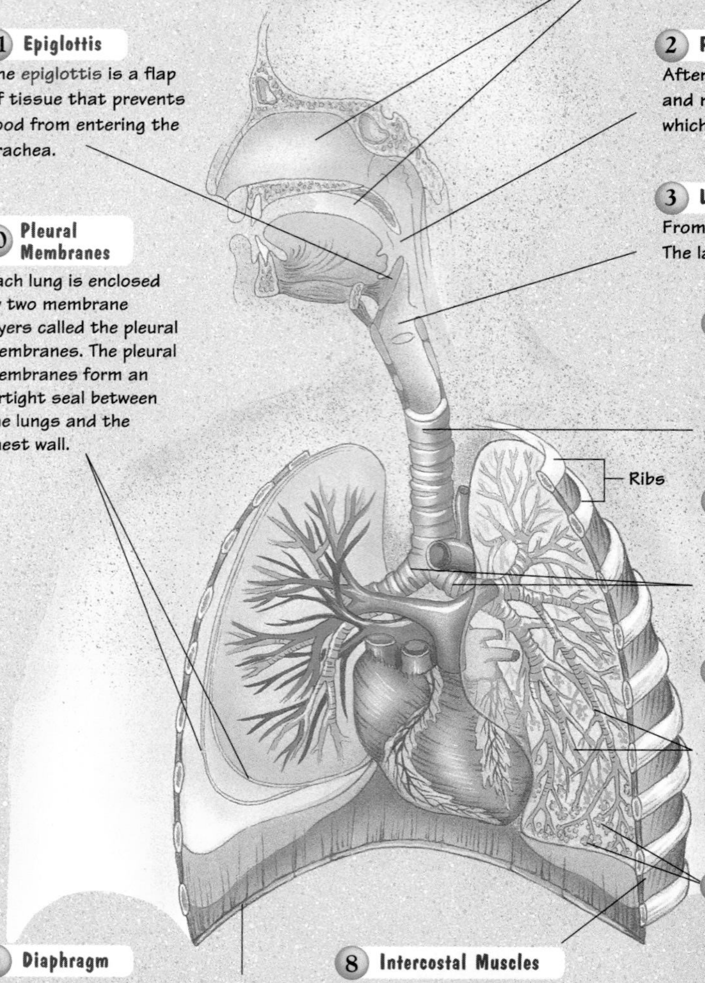

1 Nose and Mouth Air enters the body through the nose and mouth, where it is filtered, warmed, and moistened.

2 Pharynx After the air has been filtered, warmed, and moistened, it enters the pharynx, which is also a passageway for food.

3 Larynx From the pharynx, air enters the larynx. The larynx also contains the vocal cords.

4 Trachea (Windpipe) After the larynx, air enters the trachea—the main airway to the lungs. The trachea divides into two bronchi.

5 Bronchi The bronchi (singular: bronchus) are the tubes that bring air to the lungs from the trachea. Each bronchus leads to one lung.

6 Bronchioles Once inside the lungs, the bronchi branch into smaller and smaller air passageways called bronchioles. The bronchioles continue to divide until they finally end in clusters of tiny air sacs.

7 Alveoli The alveoli (singular: alveolus) are tiny air sacs that appear in grape-like clusters. Surrounding each alveolus is a network of capillaries, where gas exchange takes place.

8 Intercostal Muscles These muscles cause the chest cavity to expand when air is inhaled and get smaller when air is exhaled.

9 Diaphragm A dome-shaped muscle called the diaphragm separates the chest cavity from the abdominal cavity. Breathing is directed by contracting and relaxing the diaphragm.

10 Pleural Membranes Each lung is enclosed by two membrane layers called the pleural membranes. The pleural membranes form an airtight seal between the lungs and the chest wall.

11 Epiglottis The epiglottis is a flap of tissue that prevents food from entering the trachea.

TEACHER SUPPORT

Activity

MODELING HOW WE BREATHE

To help students understand how the diaphragm works, construct this simple model and demonstrate to the class how it works. Cover the bottom of a bell jar with a rubber sheet, and fit a stopper with a glass tube into the hole on top of the bell jar. Cover the end of the glass tube that extends into the jar with a small round balloon. Pull down on the rubber sheet and ask students to observe what happens to the balloon. (It should inflate slightly.) Push up on the rubber sheet and again ask students to observe what happens to the balloon. (It should deflate.) Ask students what parts of the respiratory system are modeled by the bell jar, balloon, and rubber sheet. (The bell jar models the chest cavity, the balloon the lungs, and the rubber sheet the diaphragm.) Why does pulling down on the rubber sheet cause air to move into the balloon? (Because it creates a partial vacuum in the bell jar.)

The Human Respiratory System

The function of the respiratory system is to bring about the exchange of oxygen and carbon dioxide. With each breath, air enters the body through the air passageways and fills the lungs, where gas exchange takes place.

As air moves through the respiratory system, it is warmed, moistened, and filtered. Many of the cells lining the respiratory system produce a thin layer of protective mucus. This layer also traps inhaled particles of dust or smoke. Cilia lining the passageways then sweep such materials away from the lungs, keeping them clean and open for the important work of gas exchange. The human respiratory system is illustrated on page 836.

☑ *Checkpoint* What do cilia do? ❶

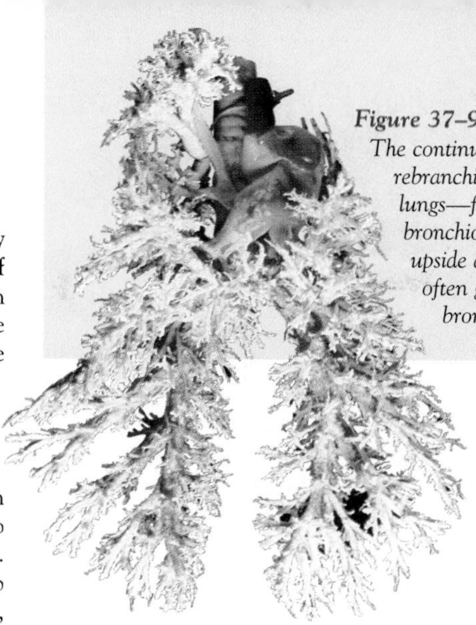

Figure 37–9
The continuous branching and rebranching of tubes in the lungs—from bronchi to bronchioles—resembles an upside down tree, so it is often given the name the bronchial tree.

Gas Exchange and Hemoglobin

There are nearly 300 million alveoli in a healthy lung, providing an enormous surface for gas exchange. Oxygen dissolves in the moisture on the inner surface of the alveoli and then diffuses across the thin capillary walls into the blood. Carbon dioxide in the bloodstream diffuses in the opposite direction—across the wall of the alveolus and into the air within it.

The process of gas exchange in the lungs is very efficient. The air that you

GAS EXCHANGE

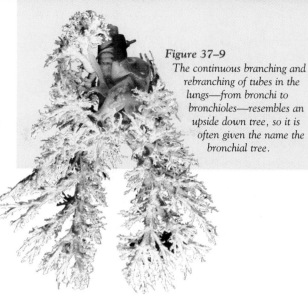

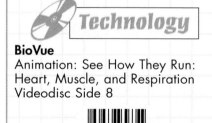

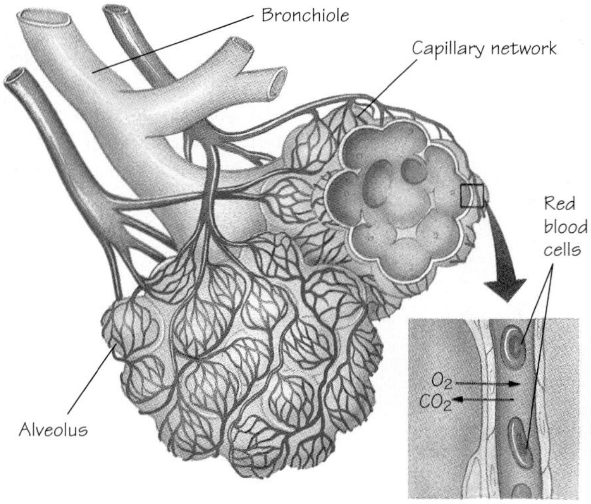

Figure 37–10
Gas exchange takes place in the alveoli of the lungs. Oxygen enters the blood by diffusing through the alveolus into the capillaries. Carbon dioxide, on the other hand, diffuses from the blood into the alveoli, where it will be exhaled out of the body.

Discussion

Lead students in a discussion of how the process of gas exchange occurs during respiration by asking the following questions.

- **What governs the diffusion of a gas across a membrane?** (Differences in concentration of the gas on either side of the membrane.)
- **Where is the oxygen concentration greater, in the moisture on the inner surfaces of the alveoli or in the capillary blood that is pumped to the lungs from the heart?** (In the moisture on the inner surfaces of the alveoli.)
- **In which direction will the oxygen diffuse because of the difference in concentration?** (From the lungs to the blood.)

☑ Checkpoint

❶ Cilia sweep inhaled particles of dust or smoke away from the lungs.

Technology

BioVue
Animation: See How They Run: Heart, Muscle, and Respiration
Videodisc Side 8

Go to Chapter 20

TEACHER SUPPORT — Ecology Note

Asthma, a potentially fatal respiratory disorder, is on the rise today among young people in the United States. Many experts believe that air pollution is one explanation for the increasing incidence of asthma. Although industrial air pollution has declined somewhat over the past few decades (due to laws regulating smokestack emissions and decreasing use of coal), there is more pollution than ever before from motor vehicle exhaust.

The exhaust from motor vehicles contains many substances that are harmful to the respiratory system, including carbon monoxide, carbon dioxide, nitrogen oxides, sulfur oxides, lead, and particulate hydrocarbons. Although new laws regulating vehicle emissions have reduced the amount of pollution released by automobiles, there are more and more automobiles in operation, especially in large cities, forcing pollution levels up.

Ancillary Support

The resources below can be used to support your teaching strategy for these two pages.

TR Writing in Biology: Fantastic Voyages
Apply: Every Breath Counts
BL Inquiry Activity: Every Breath You Take
TB Visualizing Human Respiration, #46

MINI LAB Measuring

Teacher Notes

• For time required and materials needed, see page 826b.
• Students should be allowed to participate in this investigation on a voluntary basis. You may wish to consult the school nurse to find out if there are any students who should be excused for health reasons.
• Pinching the nostrils shut while exhaling into the balloon will prevent air from escaping through the nose and give a more accurate estimate of lung capacity.
• Have students stretch out the balloon lengthwise several times before exhaling into it so that it will be easier to inflate.
• You may want to extend the MINI LAB by having students calculate the volume of air exhaled from the lungs, using the formula for the volume of a sphere: $V = 4/3\pi r^3$, where r is the radius of the expanded balloon. They can find r from the equation for the circumference, using the measured circumference of the inflated balloon for c: $c = 2\pi r$.

Answers to Analyze and Conclude

1. Each student's two measurements should be about the same; there may be considerable variation in measurements for different students.
2. Males are likely to have larger values than females because males tend to have a greater lung capacity.
3. People who exercise regularly are likely to have a larger lung capacity because exercise increases the body's demand for oxygen.

Skills Trace
Measuring

- Focus p. 838
- Practice p. 840
- Assess p. 849

MINI LAB Measuring

A Ballooning Effect

PROBLEM *How can you **measure** your lung capacity?*

PROCEDURE

CAUTION: *If you have any respiratory or circulatory conditions, do not perform this activity.*

1. Take two normal breaths. On the next breath, inhale as much air as you can. Then exhale into an empty round balloon, trying to empty your lungs as much as possible.
2. Hold the balloon closed while your partner uses a string to measure the circumference of the balloon at its widest part. Record the measurement.
3. Repeat steps 1 and 2.
4. Properly dispose of the balloons when you are finished.

ANALYZE AND CONCLUDE

1. How did your measurements compare? Compare them with those of other members of your class.
2. How did the measurements of males and females compare?
3. Do you think people who exercise regularly would have a larger lung capacity? Explain why or why not.

Figure 37–11 CAREER TRACK *Emergency Medical Technicians are trained to evaluate injuries and provide appropriate first-aid care. Certification in cardiopulmonary resuscitation (CPR) and advanced first aid is required for EMT certification.*

inhale contains 21 percent oxygen and 0.04 percent carbon dioxide. Exhaled air is usually less than 15 percent oxygen and 4 percent carbon dioxide. This means that the lungs remove about one third of the oxygen in the air that you inhale and increase the carbon dioxide content of that air by a factor of 100!

As you may recall, oxygen dissolves easily. You may therefore wonder why hemoglobin is needed at all. The reason is efficiency. Hemoglobin binds with so much oxygen that it increases the oxygen-carrying capacity of the blood more than 60 times.

Breathing

Breathing is the movement of air into and out of the lungs. Surprisingly, there are no muscles connected to the lungs. The force that drives air into the lungs comes from ordinary air pressure. The lungs are sealed in two sacs, called the pleural membranes, inside the chest cavity. At the bottom of the cavity is the diaphragm. When you inhale, or breathe in, the diaphragm contracts and expands the volume of the chest cavity. Because the chest cavity is tightly sealed, this creates a partial vacuum inside the cavity. Atmospheric pressure does the rest, filling the lungs as air rushes through the breathing passages.

Most of the time, exhaling is a passive event. When the diaphragm muscle relaxes, elastic tissues surrounding the chest cavity return to their original positions, placing pressure on the lungs. As a result of that pressure, air rushes back out of the lungs. As you know, sometimes you exhale with much greater force, as when you blow out a candle. Muscles surrounding the chest cavity provide that extra force, contracting vigorously just as the diaphragm relaxes.

☑ *Checkpoint* What is breathing? 1

TEACHER SUPPORT Activity

RELATING LUNG CAPACITY TO BODY SIZE

Researchers have determined that the capacity of the lungs is proportional to the surface area of the body, but the proportion differs for males and females. Give students the following values for surface area and lung capacity for a hypothetical male and female: For the male, surface area is 2.0 square meters and lung capacity is 5000 milliliters; for the female, surface area is 1.7 square meters and lung capacity is 3400 milliliters. Have students calculate the ratio of lung capacity to surface area for each individual. (For the male the ratio is 2500 milliliters per square meter; for the female the ratio is 2000 milliliters per square meter.) Why do males have a greater lung capacity than females? (Males have relatively more muscle tissue than females, and muscle tissue requires a relatively great amount of oxygen.)

Bio FRONTIER Connections

The Price of an Organ Donation

Heart and lung diseases strike millions of people each year. Those people whose organs cannot perform at a level that can keep them alive are candidates for heart or lung transplants. In order to receive a heart or lung transplant, these people must meet strict guidelines. After qualifying for a transplant, their names are placed on national waiting lists that match them with organs as they become available.

The Problems of Organ Donations

The problem with waiting for a heart or a lung is that there are not enough donors to keep up with the demand. In fact, twice as many people are on waiting lists as there are healthy organs available.

Unfortunately, organs of this type are donated only when other people die. That is, if they have given written permission or if their families give permission upon their death. Some states have a check-off box on driver's licenses that authorize organ donation in the event of death.

Although most people say they would be willing to donate their organs, few actually fill out a donor card. As a result, there are not enough available organs to meet the needs.

Organ donor registration card

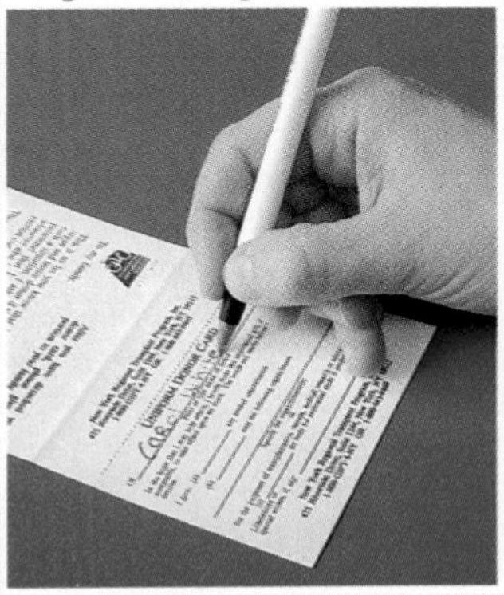

The Debate

Recently, someone suggested that families should be paid for the organs. This plan would require that a 1984 federal law making it illegal to receive payment for organs be changed. Some people believe that donating organs is a moral duty and that payment would merely encourage people to do the right thing.

Others believe that it is unethical to pay for organs. They fear that families might be too eager to receive payment and go against the wishes of the potential donor.

Critics also say that the idea of paying for organs would increase the costs of organ transplants. At present, the cost of obtaining an organ for transplant is nearly $50,000.

Heart specialist explaining procedure to a patient

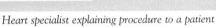

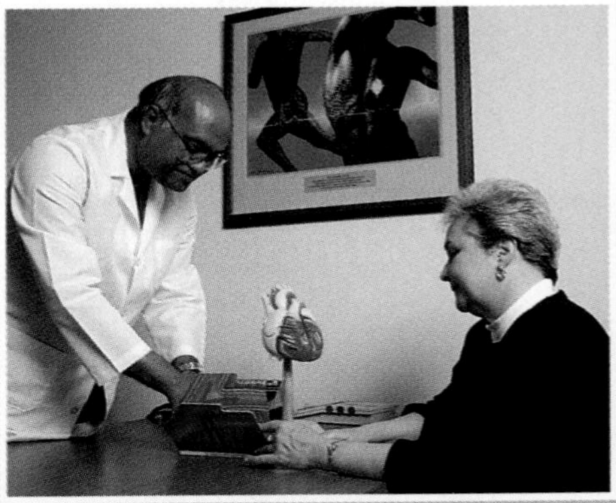

Making the Connection

There is also concern over who would be able to pay for the organs. Would only those patients who could afford them get organs because they could pay the price? Or would insurance companies be responsible for payment? What other reasons for or against this plan are there? Would you support this plan? Explain why or why not.

Connections

Single-lung transplants are performed on people with lung cancer or other diseases that affect primarily one lung or the other. Double-lung transplants are performed on people with serious chronic lung disorders such as cystic fibrosis. Heart and double-lung transplants are also performed, usually on people with advanced heart and lung disease.

The organs of people who die without leaving instructions regarding organ donation can be donated by a surviving spouse or next of kin. In some states, a surviving spouse or the next of kin can also override the deceased person's wishes to donate organs. Ask students to find out the laws regarding organ donation in their state.

In some states, organ donor status is shown on drivers' licenses. Ask students why they think organ donation is tied to drivers' licenses in this way. (Vehicular crashes kill many people and having the information on the driver's license makes it immediately accessible.)

Answers to Making the Connection

Some students may say they support the plan to allow payment for organs because it would increase the number of donor organs available. Other students may say they do not support the plan, because it would make organ transplants too expensive.

Checkpoint

1 The movement of air into and out of the lungs.

TEACHER SUPPORT Background Information

Lack of donor organs is the biggest problem associated with virtually every type of organ transplant. Another serious problem with organ transplants is rejection of the foreign tissue by the recipient's immune system. Even when tissue types are matched as closely as possible to minimize the risk of rejection, transplant patients must be given immunosuppressive drugs to prevent an immune response against the donated organ. Immunosuppressive drugs are risky because they leave the body open to infections that the suppressed immune system cannot fight.

Lung transplants present an additional challenge: Pulmonary changes and infections tend to occur very soon after death. Thus, the donor must be nearby when the lungs are removed so they can be transplanted into the recipient immediately. It is especially difficult to preserve the heart and lungs as a single unit for heart-lung transplants.

Ancillary Support

The resource below can be used to support your teaching strategy for these two pages.

LM Measuring Lung Capacity, #73

4 ASSESS

Quick Check

Name the major components of the respiratory system that are listed in Visualizing Human Respiration on page 836. Then call on students to summarize the function of each component without referring to the text. Call on other students to correct any misconceptions.

Section Review 37–2

1. The respiratory system brings about the exchange of oxygen and carbon dioxide.

2. People at high altitudes may have lower-than-normal levels of oxygen in their blood but normal levels of carbon dioxide. Because carbon dioxide, not oxygen, affects the breathing center in the brain, the breathing center would not trigger an increase in the rate of breathing, even if more oxygen was needed.

3. As students saw in the MINI LAB, they can measure their lung capacity by breathing into a balloon and measuring the circumference of the inflated balloon.

Skills Trace
Measuring
- Focus p. 838
- Practice p. 840
- Assess p. 849

Learning Modality

Visual Learning Have students make a schematic diagram of the respiratory system showing how air flows through it. Each of the following components should be included in the schematic: nose, mouth, pharynx, larynx, epiglottis, trachea, bronchi, bronchioles, alveoli, and diaphragm. Gas exchange in the alveoli should also be indicated with arrows showing which way oxygen and carbon dioxide move in the exchange.

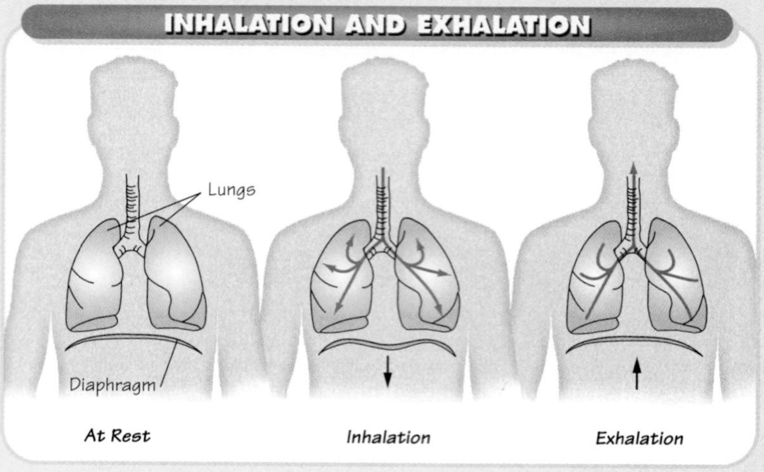

Figure 37–12 *At rest, the pressure inside the lungs is equal to the atmospheric pressure, or pressure outside the lungs. During inhalation, the diaphragm contracts, increasing the size of the chest cavity. This action causes the pressure inside the lungs to decrease and air to enter. As the diaphragm relaxes, the chest cavity gets smaller, which increases the pressure in the lungs. To equalize the pressure again, air is exhaled.*

How Breathing Is Controlled

As you know, you can control your breathing almost anytime you want—whether it's to blow up a balloon or to play a musical instrument. But this does not mean that breathing is purely voluntary. If you hold your breath for a minute or so, you'll see what we mean. Your chest begins to feel tight, your throat begins to burn, the muscles in your mouth and throat struggle to keep from breathing, and eventually your body takes over. It "forces" you to breathe!

Breathing is such an important function that your nervous system simply will not let you have complete control over it. The brain controls this process in a breathing center located in the medulla oblongata—part of the brain just above the spinal cord. Autonomic nerves from the medulla oblongata to the diaphragm and chest muscles produce the cycles of contraction that bring air into the lungs.

How does the medulla know when it's time to breathe? Cells in the breathing center monitor the amount of carbon dioxide in the blood. As the carbon dioxide level rises, nerve impulses from the center cause the diaphragm to contract, bringing air into the lungs. The higher the carbon dioxide level, the stronger these impulses. If the carbon dioxide level reaches a critical point, the impulses become so powerful that you cannot stop your breathing.

The breathing center responds to high carbon dioxide levels, and not to a lack of oxygen. As a result, when the air is thin, people sometimes do not sense a problem, and must be told to begin breathing pressurized air.

Section Review 37–2

1. **Describe** the function of the respiratory system.
2. **Critical Thinking—Inferring** As you have read, the breathing center in the brain responds to the level of carbon dioxide in the blood and not to the oxygen level. What consequences could this have on people at high altitudes?
3. **MINI LAB** How can you **measure** your lung capacity?

TEACHER SUPPORT

Background Information

There is the same percentage of oxygen in the air at all altitudes, but air pressure drops as altitude increases. Because differences in air pressure inside and outside the chest control how much the chest expands, the lower air pressure at high altitudes means that less air and oxygen are taken in with each breath. Above about 5500 meters, which is as high as humans live on a permanent basis, only about half as much oxygen is taken in with each breath as at sea level.

Hypoxia, or the relative lack of oxygen, produces mental confusion because the brain is especially sensitive to oxygen deprivation. Although people might get enough oxygen at high altitudes if they breathed deeply and rapidly, voluntary control over breathing is difficult to maintain when the mind is confused by lack of oxygen. In addition, breathing rapidly and deeply is tiring and puts a strain on the cardiovascular system.

The Hazards of Smoking

GUIDE FOR READING

- **List** the substances in cigarette smoke.
- **Describe** some health problems caused by smoking tobacco.

WHEN IT IS FUNCTIONING well, the respiratory system is simple and efficient. First, air enters through the breathing passages. Next, that air inflates the millions of alveoli in the lungs. And finally, oxygen from the air diffuses across thin membranes to enter the bloodstream, where it is quickly absorbed by hemoglobin. The circulatory system does the rest, taking this oxygen-rich blood to the rest of the body.

When people smoke, things can go wrong. The passageways can be blocked, the lungs themselves can be damaged, and other gases can interfere with hemoglobin. Understanding the biology behind the dangers of smoking is one of the best ways to avoid them.

Tobacco Use

Tobacco is a plant that was cultivated and smoked by Native Americans long before Europeans emigrated to the North American continent. The dried leaves of the plant are chewed or smoked in pipes, cigars, and cigarettes.

Tobacco contains many different chemical compounds. When it burns, many harmful compounds are produced. **Three of the most dangerous substances in tobacco are tar, carbon monoxide, and nicotine.** Tar is a brown sticky mixture of chemicals, nicotine is a stimulant drug, and carbon monoxide is a poisonous gas. When tobacco smoke is inhaled, these compounds quickly enter the airways and blood, affecting the body.

Figure 37–13 *Smoking causes many different disorders. Notice how (a) the lung of a nonsmoker differs from (b) that of a smoker. The holes in the smoker's lung are caused by ruptured alveoli. (c) Parts of this tobacco plant are used to make cigarettes, cigars, pipe tobacco, and chewing tobacco. Smoking any of these products has the greatest impact on the lungs.*

TEACHER SUPPORT

Facts and Figures

Sharing these facts and figures about the dangers of tobacco with students may help deter them from smoking.
- About 75 percent of deaths from lung cancer among women are caused by smoking.
- A cigarette smoker is 10 to 15 times more likely to get lung cancer than a nonsmoker.
- Someone who smokes two or more packs of cigarettes a day is 20 to 25 times more likely to die from lung cancer than a nonsmoker is.
- A male smoker aged 30 to 40 can expect to lose about eight years of life because of smoking.
- The risk of sudden death from heart attack is three times higher for a smoker than for a nonsmoker.
- For each death related to cocaine use and every 100 deaths related to alcohol use, there are an estimated 300 deaths related to nicotine use.

SECTION 37–3

The Hazards of Smoking

Performance Objectives
- Identify the compounds in cigarette smoke.
- Discuss health problems associated with smoking tobacco.

Laboratory Investigation Skill: Measuring

1 ENGAGE

Ideas Through Images

Have students examine Figure 37–13, read the caption, and answer the following questions.

- **How do you think the rupture of alveoli due to cigarette smoking affects gas exchange?** (There is less surface area for gas exchange, making it harder to take in oxygen and give off carbon dioxide.)
- **If smoking interferes with gas exchange in the lungs, how do you think smoking affects the circulatory system?** (It makes the circulatory system work harder.)

2 EXPLORE

Inquiry Activity

Observing

Tobacco Toxicity

Ask students what effect tobacco has on living things. Show them with the following activity.

Spray a tobacco solution—made by boiling tobacco for 15 minutes and then pouring the solution through a paper towel—on a plant infested with aphids. Ask students to observe what happens. (The aphids will die.) What conclusions about tobacco can they draw? (Tobacco is toxic to some living things.) Tell students that the nicotine in tobacco is so toxic that it is actually used as a pesticide.

3 TEACH

Ideas Through Images

Have students examine Figure 37–14, read the caption, and answer the following questions.

- **Why are smokers more likely than nonsmokers to be troubled by indigestion and heartburn?** (Because smoking inhibits the natural secretion of bicarbonate from the pancreas, which neutralizes stomach acid.)
- **Why might a smoker be more likely to lose blood than a nonsmoker?** (Because smoking decreases levels of a hormone involved in blood clotting.)
- **Why do you think smoking affects so many organ systems?** (Because its harmful components travel to all parts of the body through the circulatory system.)

INTEGRATING CAREERS

A respiratory therapist is responsible for administering respiratory care and life support to cardiopulmonary patients, either under the supervision of a physician or by prescription from a physician. For example, a respiratory therapist might educate patients on the proper use of an atomizer that delivers asthma medication.

Investigate

Long-Term Project Ask students to interview several people who either smoke or used to smoke. Have students find out why the people interviewed started to smoke, how smoking has affected their health and quality of life, and how difficult it is to quit smoking once one starts. If they had it to do over again, would the people interviewed ever start smoking? Why or why not? Ask students to share the results of their interviews with the rest of the class.

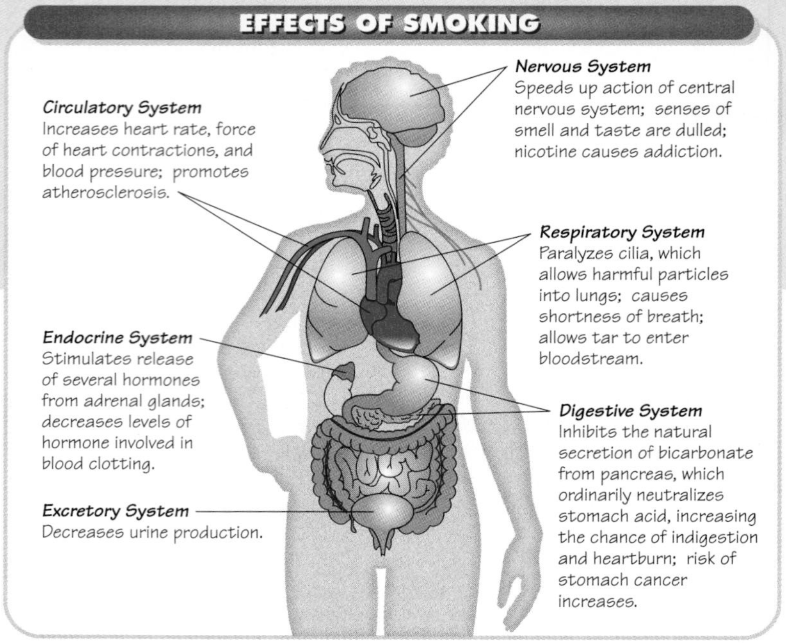

EFFECTS OF SMOKING
Circulatory System
Increases heart rate, force of heart contractions, and blood pressure; promotes atherosclerosis.
Nervous System
Speeds up action of central nervous system; senses of smell and taste are dulled; nicotine causes addiction.
Respiratory System
Paralyzes cilia, which allows harmful particles into lungs; causes shortness of breath; allows tar to enter bloodstream.
Endocrine System
Stimulates release of several hormones from adrenal glands; decreases levels of hormone involved in blood clotting.
Digestive System
Inhibits the natural secretion of bicarbonate from pancreas, which ordinarily neutralizes stomach acid, increasing the chance of indigestion and heartburn; risk of stomach cancer increases.
Excretory System
Decreases urine production.

Figure 37–14 *This illustration shows the effects of smoking on different systems of the body.*

Effects on the Respiratory System

As you have read earlier, the upper part of the respiratory system is generally able to filter out dust and foreign particles that might otherwise damage the lungs. ● Incredibly, millions of people engage in a habit—smoking tobacco—that damages and eventually destroys this protective system.

INTEGRATING CAREERS

A respiratory therapist works with people who have respiratory problems. What are some responsibilities of a respiratory therapist?

The respiratory system helps to protect the body from impurities and disease. Cilia and mucus keep dust and other foreign particles away from the lungs. Nicotine and carbon monoxide paralyze the cilia. With the cilia out of action, the inhaled particles stick to the walls of the respiratory tract or enter the lungs. The paralyzing effects of just one cigarette can last up to an hour!

In response to the irritation of cigarette smoke, the respiratory system increases mucus production. Without cilia to sweep it along, mucus builds up and obstructs the airways. This explains why smokers often cough—they have to clear their airways. Smoking also results in the swelling of the lining of the respiratory tract, which results in less air flow to the alveoli.

The tar in cigarettes affects the respiratory system, too. The tar accumulates in the lungs, where it can pass directly into the bloodstream. And a number of compounds in tar can cause cancer.

Checkpoint What happens to the cilia as a result of carbon monoxide and nicotine? 1

Respiratory Disorders Caused by Smoking

Smoking can cause such respiratory diseases as bronchitis, emphysema, and lung cancer. In **bronchitis,** the bronchi become swollen and clogged with mucus. Even smoking a moderate number of cigarettes can produce bronchitis. People with bronchitis often find simple activities, such as climbing stairs, difficult.

Long-term smoking can also cause **emphysema.** Emphysema is a loss of

TEACHER SUPPORT

Activity

THE COST OF SMOKING

Ask students to calculate the cost of smoking one, two, and three packs of cigarettes a day, from ages 15 through 65. Have students use the current price of cigarettes for the first five years and increase the price by 5 percent for each subsequent five-year period. After they have calculated the total cost, have students look through newspaper advertisements to find items that could have been purchased with the money spent on cigarettes, such as computers, stereo equipment, cars, even houses. What could a one-pack-a-day smoker afford to buy if he or she had not spent the money on cigarettes? A two-pack-a-day smoker? A three-pack-a-day smoker? Do students think that knowing how much they would end up spending on cigarettes in the course of a lifetime help deter most people from smoking? Why or why not?

elasticity in the tissue of the lungs. This makes breathing difficult. People with emphysema cannot get enough oxygen to the body tissues or rid the body of carbon dioxide.

The most serious consequence of smoking is **lung cancer.** Nearly 180,000 people in the United States develop lung cancer each year, and very few survive it. Lung cancer is particularly deadly because it spreads easily—small groups of cancer cells from the lungs break off and spread to other places in the body. This is called metastasis. By the time the cancer is detected, it usually has spread to dozens of other places in the body, causing a painful death. Lung cancer claims 87 percent of its victims in the first five years after it is detected.

Checkpoint What is bronchitis? ❷

Effects on the Circulatory System

Smoking affects the circulatory system, too. Every part of the circulatory system—the heart, the blood vessels, and the blood—is affected by smoking. **People who smoke have twice the rate of heart disease of nonsmokers. Besides an increased chance of a heart attack or stroke, smokers often have high blood pressure.** The circulatory system is most affected by the nicotine and carbon monoxide found in the smoke of tobacco products.

Carbon monoxide is an invisible, odorless, and highly poisonous gas. ● This gas can attach to the oxygen-binding site of hemoglobin. In fact, carbon monoxide binds more tightly than oxygen itself! Recall that hemoglobin is the oxygen-carrying agent in the blood. As more carbon monoxide combines with it, it has less room for oxygen. This continues until the oxygen-carrying ability of the blood is almost gone. As a result, the heart must work harder in order to deliver oxygen to the cells of the body.

The nicotine in cigarette smoke causes blood vessels to constrict, thus inhibiting blood flow. It also causes a rise in resting heart rate—an added burden for the heart. Nicotine also causes blood pressure to rise.

In addition, smoking tends to increase the buildup of fatty materials on the walls of blood vessels. This buildup leads to the development of atherosclerosis.

Effects on Other Body Systems

As you can see in ***Figure 37–14,*** smoking affects other body systems as well. Because nicotine is a stimulant drug, it has effects similar to those of other stimulant drugs, especially on the nervous system. In addition, smoking affects the digestive system, the endocrine system, and the excretory system.

INTEGRATING CHEMISTRY

What are some other sources of carbon monoxide?

Section Review 37–3

1. **List** the main components of cigarette smoke.
2. **Describe** some health problems caused by smoking tobacco.
3. **BRANCHING OUT ACTIVITY** **Design** and **construct** a poster for a middle school classroom that discourages students from smoking. Have your teacher approve your poster before it is displayed.

Laboratory Investigation

The Laboratory Investigation, Burning Tobacco, on pages 844–845 is appropriate to use at this point in the chapter.

INTEGRATING CHEMISTRY

Other sources of carbon monoxide include motor vehicle exhaust and faulty gas furnaces and water heaters.

4 ASSESS

Quick Check

Call on students to write on the chalkboard the names of all the body systems that are affected by smoking. Then call on other students to list under each body system some of the specific ways that smoking adversely affects it.

Section Review 37–3

1. Tar, carbon monoxide, and nicotine.

2. Smoking tobacco damages the cilia that protect the lungs, increases the production of mucus, and leads to respiratory diseases such as bronchitis, emphysema, and lung cancer. Smoking also increases heart rate and blood pressure and promotes atherosclerosis, heart disease, and stroke. In addition, smoking increases the amount of acid in the stomach and contributes to digestive problems and stomach cancer.

3. Posters should show that students understand the hazards of smoking, and they should present the material in a way that will get the attention of middle school students.

Checkpoints

❶ Cilia are paralyzed as a result of carbon monoxide and nicotine.

❷ A respiratory disease in which the bronchi become swollen and clogged with mucus.

Learning Modality

Auditory Learning Ask students to pretend that they are addressing a group of other teens about the hazards of smoking. In a three-minute presentation, have them summarize the most serious respiratory and cardiovascular effects of smoking. Ask other students to add any hazards that were omitted and to correct any errors.

Ancillary Support

The resources below can be used to support your teaching strategy for these two pages.

TR Explore: Danger: Hazardous to Your Life and Lifestyle

BL Inquiry Activity: Smoke Gets in Your Lungs

CHAPTER 37

Laboratory Investigation

Burning Tobacco

Before the Lab

1. Instead of tearing apart cigarettes to obtain tobacco, you may use loose cigarette tobacco that is sold to people who roll their own cigarettes.
2. Chop cigars into small enough pieces that the tobacco will burn evenly and completely.

Pre-Lab Discussion

Have students read the entire procedure for this investigation. Then ask students the following questions.

What is the purpose of this investigation? (To observe the tar that is produced when tobacco is burned and to compare the amount of tar produced by different types of tobacco.)

Which of the three most harmful substances in tobacco smoke do you think is visible? (Tar.)

What do you think tar looks like? (If students do not know what tar looks like, suggest that they think of the type of tar that is used to pave roads—a black, thick, sticky substance. Tell them that the tar in cigarette smoke resembles this, except that it is brown in color.)

What major health problem is caused by the tar in cigarette smoke? (Lung cancer.)

Skills Development

Students will use these skills while completing the laboratory investigation: interpreting diagrams, observing, measuring, recording and interpreting data, comparing, inferring, drawing conclusions, and communicating.

Laboratory Investigation

Burning Tobacco

Scientists have identified many harmful substances that are produced when tobacco is burned in a cigarette, pipe, or cigar. Of these, the most dangerous are nicotine, tar, and carbon monoxide. In this investigation, you will see how much tar is produced when different tobacco products are burned.

Problem

How can you **measure** the products of burning tobacco?

Materials (per group)

triple-beam balance
filter paper
tobacco from a cigarette, pipe, and cigar
cotton
test tube
test-tube holder
test-tube rack
Bunsen burner
matches

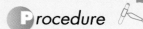

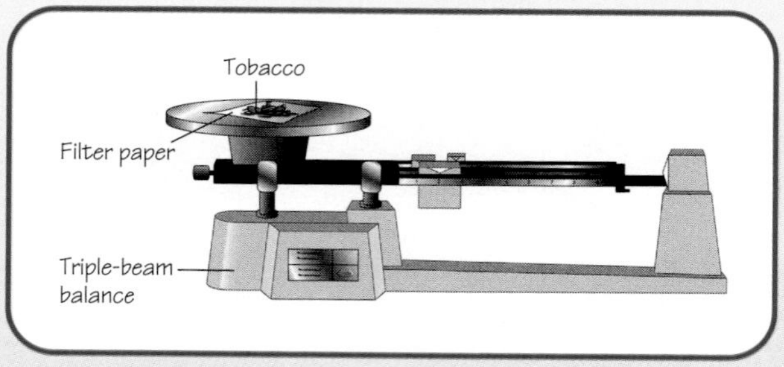

Procedure

1. **Place a piece of filter paper on a triple-beam balance. Using the balance, measure 2 g of cigarette tobacco. Place the tobacco in a test tube.**
2. **Copy the data table shown on a separate sheet of paper. Record your measurements in your data table.**
3. **Find the mass of a wad of cotton large enough to fill the opening of the test tube. Record its mass.**
4. **Put the cotton wad into the open end of the test tube.**
5. **Using a test-tube holder, heat the bottom of the test tube over a Bunsen burner flame.**
   CAUTION: ***Be careful with open flames. Keep the cotton pointed away from the flame, and keep the opening of the test tube away from others.***

Safety Tips

- Have students wear gloves, lab aprons, and safety goggles while they carry out the procedure.
- Instruct students to be careful of open flames, especially if they have long hair or loose clothing.
- Remind students to keep the cotton pointed away from the flame and to keep the open end of the test tube pointed away from themselves and others.
- Warn students to make sure the test tube is cool before they remove the cotton and weigh it.

DATA TABLE

Type of Tobacco	Mass of Cotton Before Heating	Mass of Cotton After Heating	Difference in Mass

6. After heating the tobacco for 3 minutes, turn off the Bunsen burner and place the test tube in a rack to cool.

7. Remove the cotton wad and measure and record its mass.

8. Follow the same procedure—steps 1 to 7—with the pipe tobacco and cigar tobacco.

Observations

1. What did you observe on the inside of the test tube while the tobacco was burning?
2. Did the appearance of the cotton change after it was heated?
3. Describe the appearance of tar.

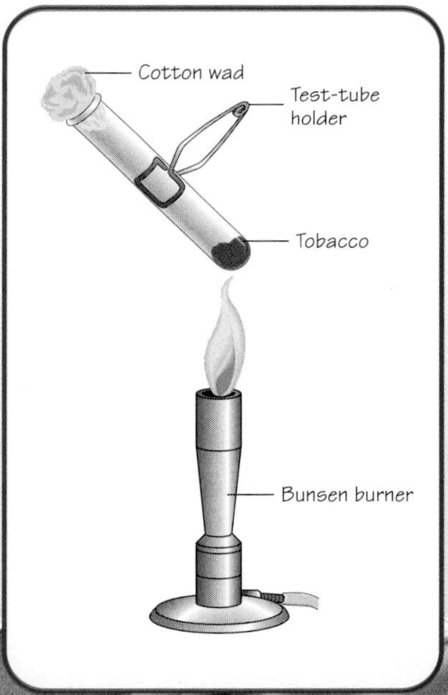

Analysis and Conclusions

1. Based on its appearance, what effect would tar have on the respiratory system?
2. Which of the three types of tobacco produced the most tar? How do you know?
3. Which type produced the least tar?
4. What could be done to make these measurements more precise?

More to Explore

Design an experiment to find out whether different cigarettes produce different amounts of tar.

Answers to
Observations

1. Students may observe condensed water vapor or tar.
2. The cotton changed from white to brown after the test tube was heated.
3. Tar appears to be a sticky, brown substance.

Answers to
Analysis and Conclusions

1. The sticky tar accumulates in the lungs, where it can cause cancer.
2. The type of tobacco that increased the mass of the cotton the most is the one that produced the most tar.
3. The type of tobacco that increased the mass of the cotton the least is the one that produced the least tar.
4. Having observed that some tar collected on the inside of the test tube, students may say that a more efficient means of collecting tar might be used so that all the tar that is produced with burning is collected and weighed.

More to Explore

The experimental design should compare the weight of cotton before and after burning tobacco taken from different brands of cigarettes. To get the clearest results, students could select brands that are labeled low tar and compare them with those that are not. Ask students to discuss the health risks of smoking low-tar cigarettes. (Although each cigarette may produce less tar, the smoker may smoke more of them and still be exposed to a high level of tar. Any level of tar can have adverse health effects.)

Teaching Strategies

1. Review the correct way to light and use a Bunsen burner.
2. Review the correct way to use a triple-beam balance.
3. Make sure that students heat the test tubes for a full 3 minutes so that the tobacco is completely burned. Ask students what effect incomplete burning of some of the tobacco would have on the results of the experiment. (The amount of tar in the incompletely burned samples might be underestimated.)
4. If there is not enough time to do the entire Laboratory Investigation, have students compare just two different types of tobacco.

Chapter 37

Study Guide

Review Strategy

Divide the class into groups of several students each, and have each group design a board game based on the circulatory system. Each game board should show the major components of the circulatory system, as well as the alveoli of the lungs, and have a pathway for players to follow that correctly reflects how blood components and other substances move through the circulatory system.

In each game, players may choose to be a blood component or a substance that the blood transports. Each player's moves should be governed by the real attributes of the blood component or substance represented. For example, a red blood cell would start at the bone marrow, move anywhere throughout the circulatory system, combine with oxygen at the lungs, and give up the oxygen at a tissue.

Each group should decide on an objective for its game and write a set of instructions for how the game is to be played. When the groups have finished preparing their board games, ask them to exchange and play the games. After students have had a chance to play, lead them in a discussion of how accurately each game models the ways in which blood components and other substances actually circulate throughout the body.

Recalling Main Ideas

1. a	4. d	7. a
2. a	5. c	8. c
3. d	6. c	9. b

Assessment

Reviewing What You Learned

1. To move throughout the body blood that carries oxygen and other substances that cells need and to remove waste.

Study Guide

Summarizing Key Concepts

The key concepts in each section of this chapter are listed below to help you review the chapter content. Make sure you understand each concept and its relationship to other concepts and to the theme of this chapter.

37–1 The Circulatory System

- The human circulatory system consists of the heart, a series of blood vessels, and the blood.
- The three kinds of blood vessels are arteries, capillaries, and veins.
- Red blood cells are oxygen carriers. White blood cells guard against infection, fight parasites, and attack bacteria. Platelets are responsible for blood clotting.

37–2 The Respiratory System

- The function of the respiratory system is to bring about the exchange of oxygen and carbon dioxide.

37–3 The Hazards of Smoking

- Three of the most dangerous substances in tobacco are tar, carbon monoxide, and nicotine.
- Smoking can cause such respiratory diseases as bronchitis, emphysema, and lung cancer.
- People who smoke have twice the rate of heart disease than nonsmokers. Besides an increased chance of a heart attack or stroke, smokers often have high blood pressure.

Reviewing Key Terms

Review the following vocabulary terms and their meaning. Then use each term in a complete sentence.

37–1 The Circulatory System

blood
atrium
ventricle
pulmonary circulation
systemic circulation
valve
aorta
pacemaker
artery
capillary
vein
blood pressure
red blood cell
white blood cell
platelet
plasma
hemoglobin
fibrin
atherosclerosis
lymphatic system
lymph

37–2 The Respiratory System

pharynx
larynx
trachea
bronchus
alveolus
diaphragm
epiglottis

37–3 The Hazards of Smoking

bronchitis
emphysema
lung cancer

Inquiry-Based Strategy

Lead students in a discussion of the following questions to increase their understanding of respiration. You may want to provide students with the questions and have them do some research before having the discussion.

What effect does very high barometric pressure have on respiration? (Very high barometric pressure forces the gases in air, especially nitrogen, into the blood in higher-than-normal concentrations, producing mental confusion and possibly convulsions or coma.)

Where is very high barometric pressure experienced? (Underwater, especially 60 meters or more below sea level.)

What dangers are posed by a rapid change from very high barometric pressure back to sea-level barometric pressure? (The nitrogen in the blood forms bubbles, which may block blood vessels.)

How can people prevent these effects? (By ascending from underwater slowly, which helps control pressure changes.)

Recalling Main Ideas

Choose the letter of the answer that best completes the statement or answers the question.

1. The upper chambers of the heart are called the
   a. atria. **c.** ventricles.
   b. myocardium. **d.** septum.
2. Oxygen-rich blood returns from the lungs to the heart's
   a. left atrium. **c.** left ventricle.
   b. right atrium. **d.** right ventricle.
3. Oxygen-poor blood enters the lungs from the
   a. left atrium. **c.** right atrium.
   b. left ventricle. **d.** right ventricle.
4. The largest vessel that transports oxygen-rich blood away from the heart is the
   a. pulmonary artery. **c.** vena cava.
   b. pulmonary vein. **d.** aorta.
5. Red blood cells contain an oxygen-absorbing protein called
   a. fibrinogen. **c.** hemoglobin.
   b. serum albumin. **d.** plasma.
6. Oxygen and carbon dioxide are exchanged with the circulatory system at the
   a. pharynx. **c.** alveoli.
   b. bronchi. **d.** bronchioles.
7. The medulla oblongata regulates breathing by monitoring the blood's level of
   a. carbon dioxide. **c.** hemoglobin.
   b. oxygen. **d.** carbon monoxide.
8. The condition that results from a loss of elasticity in the lungs is
   a. bronchitis. **c.** emphysema.
   b. lung cancer. **d.** stroke.
9. Which stimulant drug is found in cigarette smoke?
   a. globulin **c.** tar
   b. nicotine **d.** carbon dioxide

Putting It All Together

Using the information on pages xxx to xxxi, complete the following concept map.

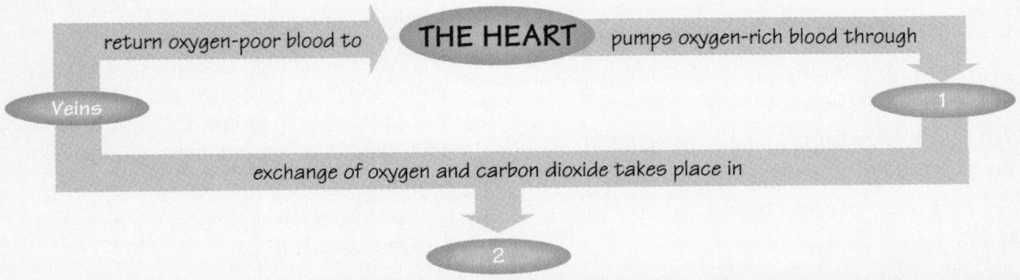

Putting It All Together

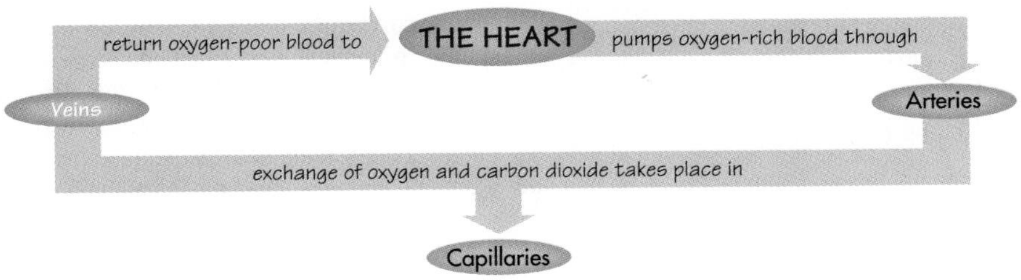

2. Pulmonary circulation moves blood from the heart to the lungs and back to the heart; systemic circulation moves blood from the heart to the rest of the body and back to the heart.
3. To prevent the backflow of blood and ensure that blood moves through the heart and veins in a one-way direction.
4. The pacemaker sets the pace for the heart as a whole by producing a wave of contractions that eventually reach all four chambers.
5. Red blood cells, white blood cells, platelets, and plasma.
6. Hemoglobin gives red blood cells their color; its function is to increase the ability of blood to carry oxygen.
7. Platelets cluster around a wound and release chemicals that lead to the formation of fibrin, which covers the wound and traps red blood cells.
8. To collect and return lymph to the circulatory system.
9. The nose or mouth, pharynx, larynx, trachea, bronchi, bronchioles, and alveoli.
10. Oxygen dissolves in the moisture on the inner surface of an alveolus and then diffuses across the thin capillary wall into the blood.
11. When the diaphragm muscle relaxes, elastic tissues surrounding the chest cavity return to their original positions, placing pressure on the lungs and causing air to rush out of the lungs.
12. Tar, carbon monoxide, and nicotine.

Expanding the Concepts

1. In a closed circulatory system, blood is pumped through a system of vessels. In an open circulatory system, blood works its way through body tissues in open spaces called sinuses that lead to vessels that carry blood back to the heart.
2. Diagrams should show blood flowing through veins from the "big" toe in the lower part of the body to the inferior vena cava, which carries the blood into the right atrium. From the right atrium, the blood should flow to the right ventricle and out the pulmonary artery to the lungs. It should return to the heart via the pulmonary vein to the left atrium, then go to the left ventricle and out of the aorta to the arteries of the arm, ending up in the fingers.

Assessment (continued)

3. Compared to white blood cells, red blood cells are smaller and much more numerous, consist of just one type instead of several, and have a relatively short life span. Like white blood cells, red blood cells are produced in bone marrow.

4. An elevated white blood cell count indicates the presence of infection. The role of white blood cells is to fight infection, and their numbers increase dramatically whenever the immune system is fighting an infection.

Skills Trace
Relating

- Focus p. 830
- Practice p. 834
- Assess p. 848

5. A condition in which fatty deposits build up on the inner surfaces of arteries, obstructing the flow of blood, leading to an increase in blood pressure.

6. A stroke and a heart attack are similar in their underlying causes; both are caused by atherosclerosis and obstructed blood flow. However, a stroke is due to obstructed blood flow to the brain, whereas a heart attack is due to obstructed blood flow to the heart muscle.

7. Respiration at the cellular level is the release of energy from the breakdown of food molecules in the presence of oxygen. At the level of the organism, respiration is the exchange of oxygen and carbon dioxide between the organism and its environment.

8. If your body did not contain hemoglobin, it might look very pale and have very little energy to carry out its various functions.

9. Having more alveoli and blood vessels in their lungs is advantageous to children born at high altitudes. This is because more of the limited supply of oxygen that enters the lungs can be picked up by the blood.

Assessment

Reviewing What You Learned

Answer each of the following in a complete sentence.

1. Explain the function of the circulatory system.
2. What is the difference between pulmonary circulation and systemic circulation?
3. What are the functions of the valves located in the heart and veins?
4. Explain the function of the pacemaker.
5. List the parts of the blood.
6. What is the name and function of the substance in red blood cells that gives them their red color?
7. How do platelets aid in blood clotting?
8. What is a function of the lymphatic system?
9. List, in order, the organs through which air passes on its way to the lungs.
10. Trace the path of oxygen as it moves from an alveolus to the capillaries.
11. Describe what happens when the diaphragm muscle relaxes.
12. What are three components of cigarette smoke?

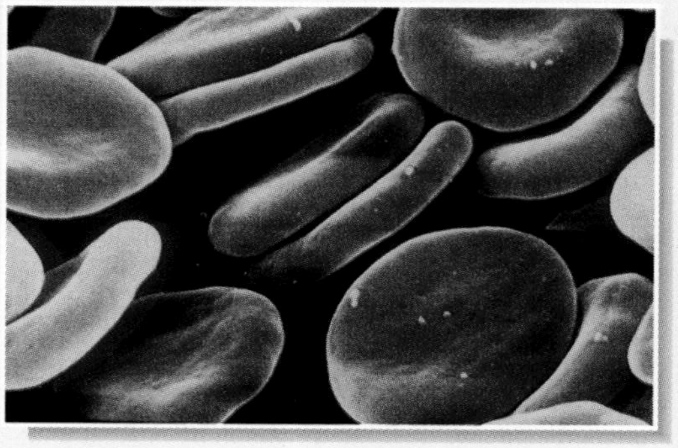

Expanding the Concepts

Discuss each of the following in a brief paragraph.

1. What is the difference between a closed circulatory system and an open circulatory system?
2. Draw a labeled diagram to trace the flow of blood from your "big" toe to your fingers.
3. Compare red blood cells and white blood cells.
4. How would you **relate** an elevated white blood cell count to the presence of an infection?
5. What is atherosclerosis? How does it affect blood pressure?
6. How are a stroke and a heart attack similar? How are they different?
7. How does respiration at the cellular level compare with respiration at the level of the organism?
8. If your body didn't contain hemoglobin, how might it look and work?
9. Children born at high altitudes develop more alveoli and more blood vessels in their lungs than children born at low altitudes. Is this an advantage or a disadvantage? Explain your answer.
10. Explain how smoking affects the circulatory system.

10. The carbon monoxide in tobacco smoke affects the circulatory system by reducing the oxygen-carrying capacity of the blood and forcing the heart to work harder. The nicotine in cigarette smoke causes blood vessels to constrict, inhibits blood flow, increases the resting heart rate, and increases blood pressure—again forcing the heart to work harder.

Extending Your Thinking

1. Because it exposes the person to carbon monoxide, passive smoking reduces the oxygen-carrying capacity of the blood. This, in turn, reduces the amount of oxygen that is available to tissues such as the muscles, thus adversely affecting the ability of the person to perform in sports.

2. Possible words include pneumatics (the study of gases), *Pneumococcus* (bacterium that causes pneumonia), pneumoconiosis (lung disease caused by inhaling dust), and pneumonectomy (surgical removal of a lung).

Extending Your Thinking

Use the skills you have developed in this chapter to answer the following.

1. **Applying concepts** Even if you don't smoke, you may be exposed to secondhand smoke. This "passive smoking" exposes you to carbon monoxide. What effect does passive smoking have on your ability to perform in sports?
2. **Giving examples** *Pneumo-* or *pneum-* are prefixes taken from Greek words meaning "related to air." For example, pneumonia is an inflammation of the lungs. Find other examples of words that have these prefixes and write their definitions.
3. **Designing an experiment** Design an experiment to find out how breathing rate varies in different age groups after short-term exercise. Exercise is considered short term if it is minimal and a person recovers in a brief amount of time.
4. **Using the writing process** Studies have shown that smoking tobacco harms the circulatory and respiratory systems of the body. As a result, many people believe that tobacco should be classified as an illegal drug. However, in some parts of the country, farmers depend upon their tobacco crops for their income and would face financial problems if tobacco use decreased. Choose one side of this issue and write a persuasive argument supporting your stand.
5. **Measuring** People who smoke often do not have the physical stamina that nonsmokers have. How could you measure the lung capacity of a smoker? Would you expect to find the same capacity as in a nonsmoker?

Applying Your Skills

Have a Heart

Place your right hand on your chest as if you were going to salute the flag. Can you feel the beating of your heart? Your heart is responsible for pumping blood to all parts of your body. Does your heart rate change if you are sitting, standing, or lying down? Try this activity to find out.

1. Sit down for 2 minutes. After 2 minutes, take your pulse for 1 minute. Record your pulse in your journal.
2. Stand for 2 minutes. Then take your pulse for 1 minute and record it in your journal.
3. Now lie down on the floor for 2 minutes. Then take your pulse for 1 minute and record it in your journal.

• GOING FURTHER •

4. Compare your standing, sitting, and lying-down pulse rates.
5. Did you observe any difference in the rates per minute? In your journal, explain your reasons for any differences.

3. The experiments should compare breathing rates in samples of people of different ages, both at rest and after short-term exercise. A good form of exercise to use would be stair climbing or running in place.
4. Some students may favor making tobacco an illegal drug in order to make it less available, and thus reduce its potential abuse. Students may also argue that making tobacco illegal would send a stronger antismoking message to young people and help discourage them from starting to smoke. Other students may favor keeping tobacco legal because farmers depend on the income from sales of tobacco. Students may also argue that keeping tobacco legal helps regulate its use, is less costly to enforce, and generates tax money that could be used for antismoking education.

5. You could measure the lung capacity of a smoker by having the smoker forcefully expel as much air as possible into a balloon and then measuring the circumference of the balloon. You would expect to find that the smoker has a smaller lung capacity than a nonsmoker.

Skills Trace

Measuring

Focus p. 838
Practice p. 840
Assess p. 849

Applying Your Skills

Teacher Notes

- Students who have circulatory or respiratory problems should not do this activity.
- If necessary, review the correct procedure for taking the pulse in the wrist or neck.

Answers

4. A student's standing, sitting, and lying-down pulse rates may vary slightly.
5. Students might explain a lower lying-down rate by saying that the heart does not have to work as hard. They might explain a higher sitting or standing rate by saying that upright posture requires a greater force to pump the blood "uphill" which would result in a faster heart rate.

Scoring Rubric

4 Response is thorough, accurate, and creative; shows an in-depth understanding of science skills, procedures, and concepts.

3 Response is complete, mostly accurate, and original; shows a satisfactory understanding of science skills, procedures, and concepts.

2 Response is mostly complete but includes some inaccuracies; shows an adequate understanding of science skills, procedures, and concepts.

1 Response is only partially complete and has many inaccuracies; shows an incomplete understanding of science skills, procedures, and concepts.

0 Response is mostly incomplete and/or inaccurate; shows a lack of understanding of science skills, procedures, and concepts.

Chapter 38 Digestive and Excretory Systems

Content Management	Student Edition Activities
■ Section 38–1 Nutrition, pp. 851–856 Energy and Materials Nutrients Balancing the Diet	MINI LAB: Magnetism in Your Cereal?, p. 852 Laboratory Investigation: Vitamin C in Fruit Juice, pp. 870–871
■ Section 38–2 The Digestive System, pp. 857–861 The Digestive Tract Regulating Nutrient Levels	
■ Section 38–3 The Excretory System, pp. 862–866 Chemical Wastes The Kidneys Control of Water Balance	MINI LAB: Examining a Kidney, p. 864
◆ BRANCHING OUT • In Action Section 38–4 A Cure for Ulcers?, pp. 867–869 Peptic Ulcers What Causes Ulcers?	

■ These sections cover all the necessary content and concepts for an enriched course in biology.
◆ This section covers content and concepts that are either applications or extensions of the enriched material.

Integration Strategies

SE Physics, p. 851
Chemistry, p. 859
Chemistry, p. 862

Assessment Strategies

SE Chapter Review, pp. 872–875
TR Section Reviews
Chapter Test
BL Chapter Review
Practice Test
CTB Chapter 38 Test

Tech Prep

Teaching strategies appropriate for students who are in technical/vocational programs or who are considering post-secondary technical education can be found on the following **TE** pages: 852, 858, 864, and 866.

Meeting the Standards

Sections 38–1 through 38–4 cover three of the six content standards under **The Cell** and three of the six content standards under **Matter, Energy, and Organization in Living Systems** as described on pages 184 and 186, respectively, of The National Science Education Standards.

Chapter Planning Guide

Teacher's Edition Activities	Other Activities	Media and Technology
Chapter Discovery Learning Activity, p. 850 **Inquiry Activity:** Does Fiber in the Diet Lower Cholesterol in the Blood?, p. 854 **Inquiry Activity:** How Much Fat Do You Eat?, p. 855 **Activity:** Combining Plant Proteins, p. 855	**LM** Measuring Food Energy, #75 **TR** **Writing in Biology:** Table for Two **Enrich:** The Cost of Hunger **BL** **Inquiry Activity:** Thought for Food	
Inquiry Activity: How Sweet It Is, p. 857 **Investigate:** Model Building, p. 857 **Activity:** Name That Organ, p. 857 **Investigate:** Model Building, p. 858	**TR** **Apply:** Food for Thought **BL** **Inquiry Activity:** The Human Food Processor	
Inquiry Activity: Filtering a Fluid, p. 862	**LM** Simulating Urinalysis, #76 **TR** **Explore:** Uses for Urinalysis **BL** **Inquiry Activity:** Cleaning Up	**TB** Visualizing Kidney Structure and Function, #47
Inquiry Activity: Proving Cause and Effect, p. 867 **Investigate:** Research, p. 867 **Investigate:** Long-Term Project, p. 868 **Activity:** Comparing Drugs, p. 869	**TR** **Explore:** Antacid Antics **BL** **Inquiry Activity:** A Pain in the Gut	

KEY: **SE** Student Edition **TE** Teacher's Edition **LM** Laboratory Manual **TR** Teaching Resources **BL** BioLog **TB** Transparency Box **CTB** Computer Test Bank

Materials List

SE MINI LAB: Magnetism in Your Cereal?, p. 852 (15–20 minutes); sealable plastic bag, 50 grams of dry breakfast cereal (containing 100 percent of the U.S. RDA for iron), magnet, balance scale.
TE Inquiry Activity: How Much Fat Do You Eat?, p. 855 (45–60 minutes over 3 days); table of food values, calculator.
TE Inquiry Activity: How Sweet It Is, p. 857 (10 minutes); unsalted soda cracker.
TE Activity: Name That Organ, p. 857 (20–30 minutes); model or diagram of human digestive system, pointer.
TE Investigate: Model Building, p. 858 (10–15 minutes); long balloon.
TE Inquiry Activity: Filtering a Fluid, p. 862 (10 minutes); water containing sand, funnel, beaker, paper coffee filter.
SE MINI LAB: Examining a Kidney, p. 864 (30 minutes); mammal kidney, lab tray, five different-colored pushpins, scalpel, file card, five different-colored pencils (the same colors as the pushpins).
TE Activity: Comparing Drugs, p. 869 (20 minutes); several different packages of over-the-counter drugs for acid indigestion and similar problems caused by stomach acid.

CHAPTER 38

Digestive and Excretory Systems

Introducing the Chapter

. . . In Pictures

This photograph shows an X-ray of a large intestine that has been infused with barium to make it opaque. This procedure is commonly done to aid doctors in diagnosing intestinal tract problems. Have students examine the photograph, read the caption, and answer the following questions.

- **Is the large intestine shown here larger or smaller than life-size?** (Somewhat smaller.)
- **Is the large intestine part of the digestive system or the excretory system?** (Digestive system.)
- **What do you think takes place inside the large intestine?** (Water is removed from undigested material to form feces.)

Teaching Strategy

The first section of the chapter explains why we need food and describes the six classes of nutrients. The way nutrients are extracted from food is described in the second section. The third section explains how wastes are filtered from the blood and excreted in urine. The BRANCHING OUT section describes the discovery of the cause of ulcers and how it led to a cure.

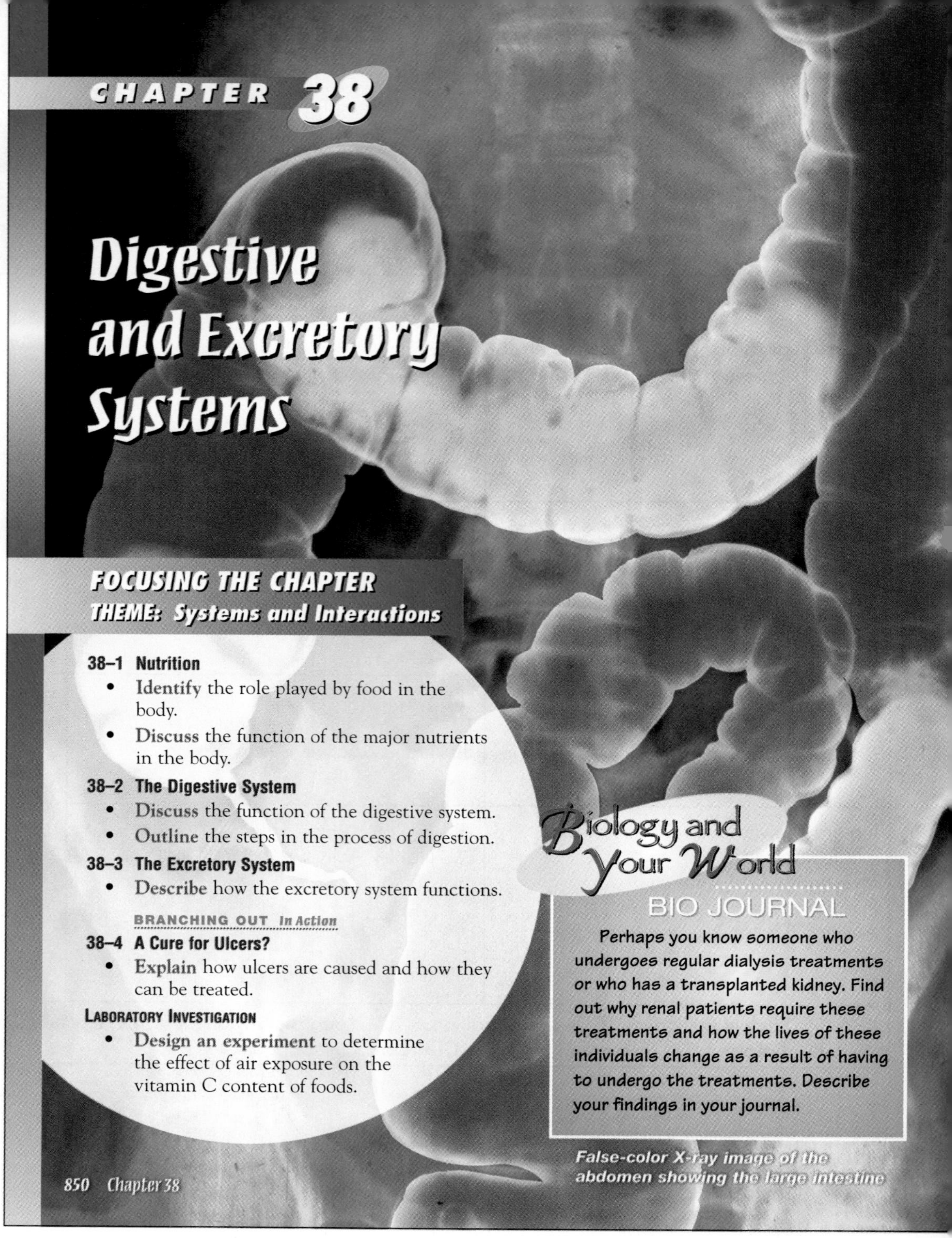

CHAPTER 38

Digestive and Excretory Systems

FOCUSING THE CHAPTER
THEME: Systems and Interactions

38–1 Nutrition
- **Identify** the role played by food in the body.
- **Discuss** the function of the major nutrients in the body.

38–2 The Digestive System
- **Discuss** the function of the digestive system.
- **Outline** the steps in the process of digestion.

38–3 The Excretory System
- **Describe** how the excretory system functions.

BRANCHING OUT *In Action*

38–4 A Cure for Ulcers?
- **Explain** how ulcers are caused and how they can be treated.

LABORATORY INVESTIGATION
- **Design an experiment** to determine the effect of air exposure on the vitamin C content of foods.

Biology and Your World

BIO JOURNAL

Perhaps you know someone who undergoes regular dialysis treatments or who has a transplanted kidney. Find out why renal patients require these treatments and how the lives of these individuals change as a result of having to undergo the treatments. Describe your findings in your journal.

False-color X-ray image of the abdomen showing the large intestine

BIO JOURNAL

If students do not know anyone who has undergone dialysis or had a kidney transplanted, have them contact a dialysis center to find out why the treatments are used and how they affect the people who have them. Instruct students to keep their entries in their portfolios.

TEACHER SUPPORT

Chapter Discovery Learning Activity

WISE FOOD CHOICES

Help students become more aware of the food choices they already make by taking a quick dietary survey.

1. Have students write down everything they can remember eating or drinking for the past 24 hours, and estimate about how much of each food or beverage they consumed.

2. Ask students to examine their 24-hour diet and identify which of the five food groups—breads, vegetables, fruits, meats, and dairy products—were represented in the foods they ate.

Results: Students' diets may vary greatly. Point out that a one-day diet may not accurately reflect what a person eats most of the time. A more accurate way of collecting information on diet is weighing and recording everything people eat over a period of several days. Have students review their diets at the end of Section 1.

Nutrition

GUIDE FOR READING

- **Explain** the function of food in the body.
- **List** the various classes of nutrients in the body.

MINI LAB

- **Observe** the presence of iron in cereal.

HOW IMPORTANT IS FOOD IN your life? Before you answer, think of some of the most important holidays or occasions you celebrate. What pictures come to mind? No matter where you live, chances are that a meal was the centerpiece of that special day. To most of us food is more than just nourishment—it is an important part of our culture. Human societies around the globe organize meetings and family gatherings around certain kinds of food.

The need to eat is one of your body's first priorities. In this section, you will see why your body needs food and what kinds of food are required to keep it healthy and strong.

Energy and Materials

Why do you need food? The most obvious answer is energy—the ability to do work. You need energy to climb stairs, lift books, run, and even to think. Like a car that needs gasoline, your body needs fuel for all that work, and food is your fuel.

But there is another reason that you need food. There's an old saying that "you are what you eat." And, like many sayings, it teaches us a valuable lesson. **The foods that we eat not only provide us with the energy to perform various types of actions, they also contain the materials from which our body cells and tissues are made.**

The energy available in food can be measured in a surprisingly simple way—by burning it! The amount of heat given off is measured and expressed in terms of calories. ● A calorie is the amount of heat energy needed to raise the temperature of 1 gram of water by 1 degree Celsius. On packaged foods, nutrition labels use the unit **Calorie,** which

INTEGRATING PHYSICS

What is energy? Work? How are they related? Measured?

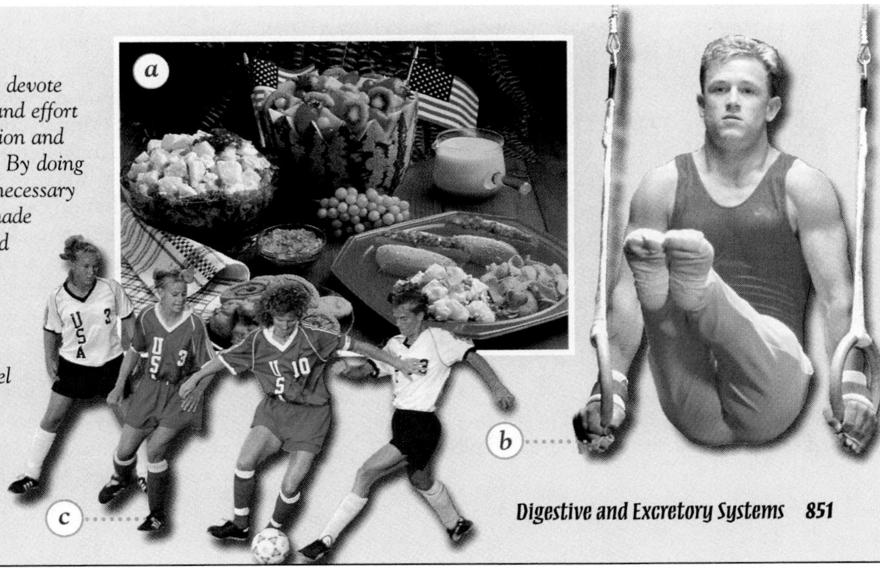

Figure 38–1 People of all cultures devote a great deal of time and effort to the (a) preparation and presentation of food. By doing so, eating, which is necessary to maintain life, is made more enjoyable. Food provides (b) this gymnast with the muscular strength he needs to support himself on the parallel bars and (c) these soccer players with the energy they need to run and kick.

TEACHER SUPPORT

Background Information

Cultures vary not only in which foods are eaten but also in which items are considered to be foods. The eating of insects, or entomophagy, illustrates this point well. Most people in the United States would be disgusted by the thought of eating insects, but insects have been considered a valuable nutritional resource, as well as a taste treat, for most of humankind from ancient times to the present. In Japan, for example, beetles are shelled, fried, and mixed with sugar, and grasshoppers are roasted with soy sauce. The complete absence of insects in North American diets is almost unique.

In addition to insects, there are many other nutritious items that are considered to be excellent foods in other cultures, yet for most people in the United States they are not eaten as foods. Examples include horses, dogs, salamanders, sea urchins, octopuses, seaweed, armadillos, and rattlesnakes.

SECTION 38–1

Nutrition

Performance Objectives

- Describe how the body uses food.
- Name the six classes of nutrients.

Mini Lab Skill: Observing
Laboratory Investigation Skill: Experimenting

1 ENGAGE

Ideas Through Images

Have students examine Figure 38–1, read the caption, and answer the following questions.

- **What are two things that food provides for the body?** (Energy and strength.)
- **What does the food shown in the photograph suggest about the non-nutritional role of food?** (That food is used to help celebrate traditions and holidays.)

2 EXPLORE

Discussion

Ask volunteers to describe foods they typically eat at each meal and any special foods they eat on holidays. Lead the class in a discussion of why people differ in the foods they eat. (For example, taste preferences, income, family and cultural backgrounds.)

INTEGRATING PHYSICS

Energy is the ability to do work, and work is done when a force moves an object through a distance. Thus, energy is defined in terms of work. Energy is measured in calories; work is measured in newton-meters, or joules.

3 TEACH

MINI LAB Observing

Teacher Notes

- For time required and materials needed, see page 850b.
- The more finely students crush the cereal, the more accurate their results will be.
- Guide students in identifying a method for testing whether the amount of iron they actually observe in the sample is consistent with the claim on the cereal box that each serving contains 100 percent of the U.S. Recommended Daily Allowance for iron. (The Recommended Daily Allowance for iron is 10 milligrams [mg] for adult males and 18 mg for adult females. Their samples of 50 mg should be almost the equivalent of one serving. Therefore, each sample should contain about 10–18 mg of iron.)

Answers to Analyze and Conclude

1. Students should compute the answer by dividing the mass of the magnetized cereal by the mass of the total sample, which is 50 g.
2. Evidence that iron was in the cereal is provided by the cereal's attraction to the magnet.
3. One way to compare the amount of iron at the top of the box with the amount at the bottom is to test two separate samples of cereal, one taken from the top of the box, the other taken from the bottom. The sample that has more magnetized cereal contains more iron.

Skills Trace
Observing
- Focus p. 852
- Practice p. 856
- Assess p. 875

MINI LAB .... Observing ....

Magnetism in Your Cereal?

PROBLEM *How can you **observe** the iron in your cereal?*

PROCEDURE

1. In a sealable plastic bag, crush 50 grams of a dry breakfast cereal that contains 100 percent of the U.S. Required Daily Allowance for iron.
2. Shake all the crushed cereal to one corner of the bag. Pass the magnet under the cereal and observe what happens. Use the magnet to drag any particles that are attracted to it to the empty part of the bag.
3. Remove the magnetized cereal and find its mass.

ANALYZE AND CONCLUDE

1. What percentage of the cereal was attracted by the magnet?
2. What evidence do you have that iron was in the cereal?
3. Describe a procedure you could use to compare the amount of iron in the cereal at the top of a cereal box and at the bottom.

Figure 38–2
CAREER TRACK
One of the jobs of a dietician is to help people choose a diet that will best meet that person's bodily needs.

represents 1000 calories, or 1 kilocalorie. Thus, a teaspoon of sugar contains 16 Calories, or 16,000 calories.

The basic energy needs of an average-sized teenager are between 1800 and 2800 kcal per day. If you engage in vigorous physical activity, however, your energy needs may be higher. What kinds of foods can meet those energy needs? Just about any kind. Chemical pathways in the body's cells can extract energy from almost any type of food.

☑ *Checkpoint* What is the function of food in the body? ❶

Nutrients

Although the body is able to manufacture many of the molecules it needs, it must still obtain the materials for this from the food it takes in. **The classes of nutrients that are part of any healthy diet are water, carbohydrates, fats, proteins, vitamins, and minerals.**

Water

Water is the most important of all nutrients. Water is needed by every cell in our body, and it makes up the bulk of blood, lymph, and other body fluids. Water dissolves food taken into the digestive system. Water in the form of sweat cools the body. Water is lost from the body as vapor in every breath we exhale and as the primary component of urine.

If enough water—at least a liter a day—is not taken in to replace what is lost, dehydration can result. This leads to problems with the circulatory, respiratory, and nervous systems. Drinking plenty of pure water is one of the best things you can do to help keep your body healthy.

Carbohydrates

Carbohydrates are major sources of food energy. Sugars—found in fruits, honey, sugar cane and sugar beets—are examples of simple carbohydrates.

TEACHER SUPPORT — Managing Classroom Diversity

MULTICULTURAL STRATEGY
Have students of different ethnic backgrounds bring in samples of foods or recipes for dishes that are part of their culture's cuisine. Ask students to explain when and how each food is eaten. If the class is not very ethnically diverse, you may wish to provide some samples or recipes yourself. Lead students in a discussion of the role that culture plays in what we eat. Emphasize that the cuisines of different cultures can provide equally nutritious meals.

TECH PREP STUDENTS
Have students interested in food service careers investigate the careers of dietetic technician and dietitian. Students should find out educational requirements for the job, necessary skills, usual job duties, the institutions or other settings where jobs are most often available, and typical salaries. Ask students to present what they learn in the form of a help-wanted advertisement.

Problem Solving
INTERPRETING DATA

It's All in the Analysis

You and a friend have just read an article in a sports magazine that says that diets high in fats increase an individual's chances of getting heart disease and certain cancers when the individual gets older. The article also points out that sufficient fiber—found in fruits, vegetables, beans, and whole grain breads—helps to lower the chance of getting these diseases.

Your friend wonders whether his diet is helping to prevent disease or causing it. He has decided to find out just how his diet compares with a balanced diet recommended by nutritionists. Using the list of all the foods he ate the day before, answer the questions that follow.

Breakfast 2 scrambled eggs 2 slices white bread 1 teaspoon butter orange juice ($\frac{3}{4}$ cup)	*Dinner* fried chicken (6 oz) roasted potatoes (1 cup) asparagus ($\frac{1}{2}$ cup) 1 slice white bread 1 glass soda
Lunch fast-food cheeseburger (bun, one-quarter pound beef, 1 slice cheese, mayonnaise, lettuce) French-fried potatoes (1 cup) milkshake (12 oz)	*Snacks* potato chips (one small bag) pretzels (1 cup)

Serving size One serving from the bread group is equal to 1 slice of bread or $\frac{1}{2}$ cup cooked cereal, rice, or pasta. One serving from the vegetable group is equal to $\frac{1}{2}$ cup cooked or raw vegetables, 1 cup leafy raw vegetables, or $\frac{1}{2}$ cup cooked beans. A serving of fruit is the size of a medium apple or banana, $\frac{1}{2}$ cup diced or cooked fruit, or $\frac{3}{4}$ cup juice. One cup of milk or yogurt or $1\frac{1}{2}$ ounces of cheese are equal to one serving from the milk group. One egg or 3 ounces of meat make up a serving from the meat group.

THINK ABOUT IT

1. Using the Food Guide Pyramid on page 856, classify the foods your friend ate by food group.
2. Determine how many servings of each food group your friend consumed.
3. Did your friend meet the minimum number of servings recommended in the guide? Explain your answer.
4. Based on the guide, what would you recommend to your friend regarding his diet?

Problem Solving
Interpreting Data
It's All in the Analysis

Students will draw on their knowledge of food groups to analyze a sample diet.

State Students are asked to evaluate a sample diet.
Solve Students can determine the number of servings of each type of food in the sample diet.
Test Students can compare the numbers of servings in the sample diet with the recommended number in the Food Guide Pyramid on page 856.
Communicate Have students make a food pyramid for the sample diet and compare it with the Food Guide Pyramid.

Answers to THINK ABOUT IT

1. Bread group: bread, bun, pretzels; vegetable group: lettuce, potatoes, asparagus; fruit group: orange juice; milk group: cheese, milkshake; meat group: eggs, hamburger, chicken; fats and sugars: butter, mayonnaise, French fries, milkshake, fried chicken, soda, potato chips.
2. Six servings from the bread group, five from the vegetable group, one from the fruit group, two from the milk group, and six from the meat group.
3. The friend had too few servings of some groups (bread, fruit, milk) and too many of others (meat, fats, and sugars).
4. To eat more bread, fruit, and low-fat milk products and to cut back on meat, fats, and sugars.

TEACHER SUPPORT

Facts and Figures

You may wish to share the following facts and figures about how Americans eat with your students. The information will help them understand why more than half of all Americans are overweight.

- Each day Americans eat a total of 4.5 million kilograms of butter and margarine, 170 million eggs, 1.4 million liters of ice cream and ice milk, 47 million hot dogs, and 4 hectares (75 acres) of pizza.
- The average American consumes 54 kilograms of sugar each year, of which 9 kilograms are in soft drinks.
- About 40 percent of calories in the average American's diet come from fat, compared with a recommended 30 percent or less.
- In a lifetime, the average American eats about 36 metric tons of food.

Checkpoint

1 To provide the body with energy and the materials to make tissues.

Inquiry Activity

Designing an Experiment

Does Fiber in the Diet Lower Cholesterol in the Blood?

Students may have heard that a high-fiber diet can help lower blood cholesterol levels by reducing the amount of time that cholesterol-containing foods stay in the digestive tract. However, recent evidence suggests that this is not the case. It is now believed that people who eat high-fiber diets tend to have low blood cholesterol levels because their diets are also low in fat. Ask students how the effect of fiber on blood cholesterol levels could be assessed independently of the effect of fat. (By comparing blood cholesterol levels in people who have low-fiber, low-fat diets with blood cholesterol levels in people who have high-fiber, low-fat diets.) Point out that even if fiber has no direct effect on blood cholesterol, high-fiber foods are good choices for weight-reduction diets because they fill you up without adding many calories.

Ideas Through Images

Have students examine Figure 38–3, read the caption, and answer the following questions.

- **Which foods are a good source of vitamin C?** (Citrus fruits, tomatoes, potatoes, leafy vegetables.)
- **Which vitamins are needed to prevent anemia?** (B_6, folic acid, B_{12}, and E.)
- **Which vitamins are found in foods at the base of the Food Guide Pyramid?** (The bread group foods at the base of pyramid contain vitamins B_1 and B_6, pantothenic acid, folic acid, and choline.)

Laboratory Investigation

The Laboratory Investigation, Vitamin C in Fruit Juice, on pages 870–871 is appropriate to use at this point in the chapter.

VITAMINS

VITAMIN	FOOD SOURCES	FUNCTION	RESULTS OF VITAMIN DEFICIENCY
Water-Soluble Vitamins			
B_1 (thiamine)	Yeast, liver, grains, legumes	Coenzyme for carboxylase	Beriberi, general sluggishness, heart damage
B_2 (riboflavin)	Milk products, eggs, vegetables	Coenzyme in electron transport (FAD)	Sores in mouth, sluggishness
Niacin	Red meat, poultry, liver	Coenzyme in electron transport (NAD)	Pellagra, skin and intestinal disorders, mental disorders
B_6 (pyridoxine)	Dairy products, liver, whole grains	Amino acid metabolism	Anemia, stunted growth, muscle twitches and spasms
Pantothenic acid	Liver, meats, eggs, whole grains, and other foods	Forms part of coenzyme A, needed in Krebs cycle	Reproductive problems, hormone insufficiencies
Folic acid	Whole grains and legumes, eggs, liver	Coenzyme in biosynthetic pathways	Anemia, stunted growth, inhibition of white cell formation
B_{12}	Meats, milk products, eggs	Required for enzymes in red cell formation	Pernicious anemia, nervous disorders
Biotin	Liver and yeast, vegetables, provided in small amounts by intestinal bacteria	Coenzyme in a variety of pathways	Skin and hair disorders, nervous problems, muscle pains
C (ascorbic acid)	Citrus fruits, tomatoes, potatoes, leafy vegetables	Required for collagen synthesis	Scurvy: lesions in skin and mouth, hemorrhaging near skin
Choline	Beans, grains, liver, egg yolks	Required for phospholipids and neurotransmitters	Not reported in humans
Fat-Soluble Vitamins			
A (retinol)	Fruits and vegetables, milk products, liver	Needed to produce visual pigment	Poor eyesight and night blindness
D (calciferol)	Dairy products, fish oils, eggs (also sunlight on skin)	Required for cellular absorption of calcium	Rickets: bone malformations
E (tocopherol)	Meats, leafy vegetables, seeds	Prevents oxidation of lipids in cell membranes	Slight anemia
K (phylloquinone)	Intestinal bacteria, leafy vegetables	Required for synthesis of blood-clotting factors	Problems with blood clotting, internal hemorrhaging

Figure 38–3
The table lists the food sources and the functions of the fourteen essential vitamins. Notice that the vitamins are categorized as water soluble or fat soluble. Because fat-soluble vitamins can be stored in the fatty tissues of the body, these vitamins should not be taken in excess of daily required amounts or they can become toxic.

Starches—found in grains, potatoes, and vegetables—are examples of complex carbohydrates. Starches are easily broken down by the digestive system into simple sugars and passed into the bloodstream, where they can provide energy to cells throughout the body.

Many carbohydrate-rich foods also contain cellulose, commonly referred to as "fiber." Unlike starch, the sugars in cellulose are linked together in such a way that humans and many other animals cannot break them apart. Even though we cannot digest cellulose, it is still important in the diet. Cellulose, or fiber, adds bulk to the material moving through the digestive system. This bulk helps the muscles of the digestive system to process foods more effectively. Foods such as lettuce, whole grain breads, and bran are rich in fiber.

TEACHER SUPPORT

Historical Perspective

When Vasco da Gama sailed around the Cape of Good Hope in 1497, many members of his crew died of scurvy, a disease that had plagued sea voyagers for centuries. Symptoms of scurvy include bleeding gums, loose teeth, joint pains, and weakness. By the 1700s, it was known that eating citrus fruit reduced the chances of getting scurvy, so sailors in the British navy were given limes to eat on long voyages. British sailors have been called "limeys" ever since.

In the 1800s, sailors in the Japanese navy suffered from beriberi, a serious disorder of the nervous, digestive, and circulatory systems. When vegetables, meat, and fish were added to their mostly white-rice diet, their symptoms improved.

It was not until the 1900s that scientists learned that both scurvy and beriberi are vitamin deficiency diseases. We now know that scurvy is due to a deficiency of vitamin C and beriberi to a deficiency of thiamine.

MINERALS

MINERAL	FOOD SOURCES	FUNCTION	RESULTS OF MINERAL DEFICIENCY
Calcium	Milk, cheese, legumes, dark-green vegetables	Bone formation, blood-clotting reactions, nerve and muscle function	Stunted growth, weakened bones, muscle spasms
Phosphorus	Milk products, eggs, meats	Bones and teeth, ATP and related nucleotides	Loss of bone minerals
Potassium	Most foods	Acid-base balance, nerve and muscle function	Muscular weakness, heart problems, death
Chlorine	Salt	Acid-base balance, nerve and muscle function, water balance	Intestinal problems, vomiting
Sodium	Salt	Acid-base balance, nerve and muscle function, water balance	Weakness, diarrhea, muscle spasms
Magnesium	Green vegetables	Enzyme cofactors, protein synthesis	Muscle spasms, stunted growth, irregular heartbeat
Iron	Eggs, leafy vegetables, meats, whole grains	Hemoglobin, electron-transport enzymes	Anemia, skin lesions
Fluorine	Drinking water, seafood	Structural maintenance of bones and teeth	Tooth decay, bone weakness
Iodine	Seafood, milk products, iodized salt	Thyroid hormone	Goiter (enlarged thyroid)

Figure 38–4
Nine of the body's important minerals are listed in this table, which also identifies some of the foods in which the mineral is found and the function the mineral has in the body.

Fats

Fats, or lipids, may have a bad reputation in today's society, but in proper amounts they are still an important part of a healthy diet. Your body needs certain essential fatty acids to manufacture the lipids in cell membranes and to produce certain hormones. Fats that can meet these requirements are found in most foods. In fact, only 60 grams of vegetable oil—about 2 tablespoons—meet the daily fatty acid needs of an average person.

Despite the fact that little fat is actually required in the diet, about 40 percent of the Calories in the diet of a typical American come from fat! Most nutritionists believe that this is far too much fat and may lead to serious health consequences, such as high blood pressure, heart disease, obesity, and diabetes.

Checkpoint What are fats? 1

Proteins

Proteins are important nutrients because of the amino acids they contain. The body uses the amino acids in proteins to build new cells and tissues. Rapidly growing tissues, including those in the skin and the lining of the digestive system, must constantly replace dead and dying cells with new ones. Of the 22 most common amino acids, your body is able to make 14—the other 8 must be obtained from food. Diets that are deficient in protein interfere with cell growth and can cause serious health problems.

Checkpoint What is the function of proteins in the body? 2

Vitamins and Minerals

If you think of proteins, fats, and carbohydrates as the building blocks of the body, you might think of vitamins as the tools that help to put them together. Vitamins are organic molecules that the body needs to help perform important chemical reactions.

Although vitamins are needed in very small amounts, vitamin deficiencies can have serious, even fatal, consequences.

Ideas Through Images

Have students examine Figure 38–4, read the caption, and answer the following questions.

- **Which minerals are needed for strong bones?** (Calcium, phosphorus, and fluorine.)
- **What minerals would you get from eating a cheese pizza with a whole-grain crust?** (The pizza contains calcium, phosphorus, potassium, chlorine, sodium, iron, and iodine.)
- **Why is seafood good for your teeth?** (Because it is a good source of fluorine, which helps prevent tooth decay.)

Inquiry Activity

Collecting and Organizing Data

How Much Fat Do You Eat?

Ask students how much fat they think they eat. Then have them find out by measuring every food they eat for three days, recording the percentage of calories from fat (from the label or a table of food values), and from the data, calculating their average daily percentage of calories from fat.

Checkpoints

1 Fats are nutrients that supply essential fatty acids that are used to manufacture lipids in cell membranes and to produce certain hormones.

2 Proteins provide the body with amino acids, which are used to build new cells and tissues.

TEACHER SUPPORT

Activity

COMBINING PLANT PROTEINS

Animal foods contain all eight essential amino acids that must come from the diet, but plant foods are deficient in one or more of the eight. In order to get all eight essential amino acids without eating meat, legumes must be combined with seeds, nuts, or grains. Alternatively, plant proteins can be combined with dairy products or eggs. Have students work in groups to develop one or more meatless dishes that contain all eight essential amino acids. (Possible dishes include peanuts and mixed nuts; beans and rice or tortilla; peanut butter, cheese, or egg salad sandwich; macaroni and cheese; rice pudding.) When they are finished, have the groups analyze one another's dishes and check to see whether they contain all eight essential amino acids. Which dishes are also low in fat? High in fiber?

Ancillary Support

The resources below can be used to support your teaching strategy for these two pages.

LM Measuring Food Energy, #75
TR Writing in Biology: Table for Two
Enrich: The Cost of Hunger
BL Inquiry Activity: Thought for Food

Ideas Through Images

Have students examine Figure 38–5, read the caption, and answer the following questions.

- **Why are there small circles and triangles scattered throughout each of the food groups?** (To show that they contribute fat and sugar to the diet.)
- **What is the significance of the pyramid shape of the Food Guide?** (It shows at a glance about how much of each type of food should be eaten each day.)

4 ASSESS

Quick Check

Call on students to name the six classes of nutrients. Call on other students to give examples of foods that are high in each nutrient.

Section Review 38–1

1. Food provides the energy needed for various types of actions and the materials needed to make body cells and tissues.

2. Water, carbohydrates, fats, proteins, vitamins, and minerals.

3. A balanced diet provides all the nutrients needed for good health.

4. You can observe the presence of iron in cereal by passing a magnet near crushed cereal.

Skills Trace
Observing
- Focus p. 852
- Practice p. 856
- Assess p. 875

Learning Modality

Visual Learning Have students make a concept map showing the six classes of nutrients and their major functions in the body.

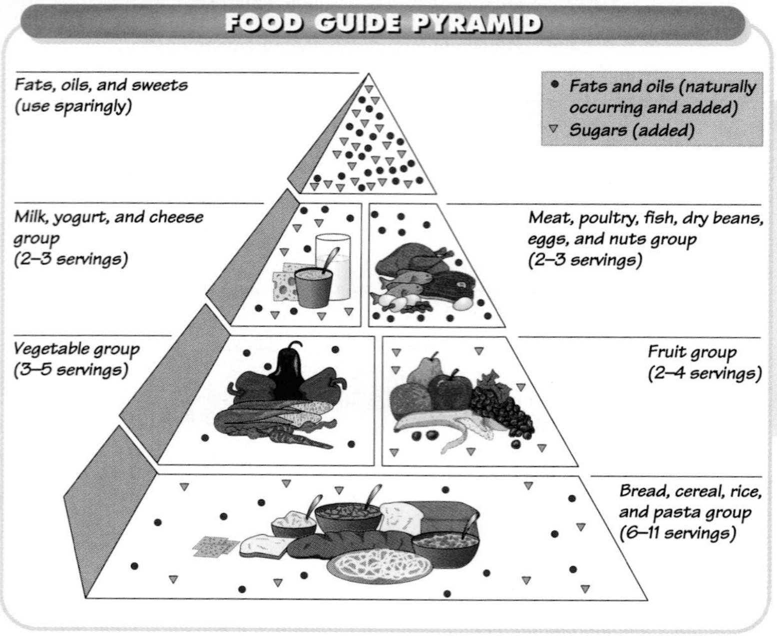

Figure 38–5 *The food guide pyramid illustrates the main characteristics of a balanced diet. Carbohydrate-rich foods should make up the major portion of the diet, while foods containing fats and sugars should be eaten sparingly.*

Fourteen vitamins, listed in ***Figure 38–3*** on page 854, are generally recognized as essential to human health—and there may be more. Eating a diet containing a variety of foods will supply the daily vitamin needs of nearly everyone.

As you know, food stores and pharmacies sell vitamin supplements containing the minimum daily requirement of each important vitamin. Unfortunately, taking extra-large doses of vitamins does not benefit the body and in some cases may cause it harm.

Minerals are inorganic substances that are needed in small amounts by the body. ***Figure 38–4*** on page 855 lists nine of the most important minerals. Calcium, for example, is required to produce the calcium phosphate that goes into bones and teeth. Iron is needed to make hemoglobin, the oxygen-carrying protein in red blood cells. And thyroxine, a hormone required for normal growth and development, cannot be synthesized without iodine.

☑ ***Checkpoint*** What roles do vitamins and minerals play in the body? ❶

Balancing the Diet

It's no easy matter to figure out the best balance of nutrients for the human diet, but nutritional scientists have done their best to do exactly that. The result is the food pyramid shown in ***Figure 38–5.*** The basic idea behind the pyramid is sound and simple—you should eat a variety of fresh foods each day, and you should limit your intake of fatty foods.

Section Review 38–1

1. **Explain** the function of food in the body.
2. **List** the various classes of nutrients in the body.
3. **Critical Thinking—Evaluating** Why should you eat a balanced diet?
4. **MINI LAB** How can you **observe** the presence of iron in cereal?

TEACHER SUPPORT

Ecology Note

Only about 10 percent of the energy incorporated into organisms at one trophic level is passed along to organisms at the next trophic level that consume them. Ecologists refer to this as the 10 percent principle. Most Americans eat high on food chains, eating animals that eat grain or other plant products. Eating high on the food chain is wasteful of energy. Eating a cow that ate grain yields only 10 percent of the energy one would get from the grain directly. Eating high on food chains is also expensive. Ten times as many people can be fed with the grain as with the cow. Eating low on food chains usually means eating low on the Food Guide Pyramid, so it is also good for your health.

The Digestive System

SECTION 38–2

Guide for Reading

- **Explain** the function of the digestive system in the body.
- **Describe** the action of insulin and glucagon.

FOOD PRESENTS EVERY ANIMAL with at least two challenges. The first, of course, is how to obtain it. Then, when an animal has caught, gathered, or engulfed its food, it faces a new challenge—how to break that food down into small molecules that can be passed to the cells that need them. In this section, we will focus our attention on this challenge.

To meet this challenge, the body is equipped with a remarkable organ system that begins to process food as soon as it is placed in the mouth. As the food passes through these organs, it gets disassembled, contributing its value to the body along the way.

The Digestive Tract

The human digestive system, like those of other vertebrates, is built around an alimentary canal—a one-way tube that passes through the body. **The function of the digestive system is to convert foods into simple molecules that can be absorbed and used by the cells of the body.**

The Mouth

Food enters the **mouth,** where the work of the digestive system begins. Chewing, which takes place in the mouth, seems simple enough—teeth tear and crush the moistened food to a fine paste until it is ready to be swallowed. But there is a great deal more to it than that.

Teeth are anchored in the bones of the jaw and are connected to the jaw by a network of blood vessels and nerves that enter through the roots of the teeth. The surfaces of the teeth, which are much tougher than ordinary bone, are protected by a coating of mineralized enamel. Teeth do much of the mechanical work

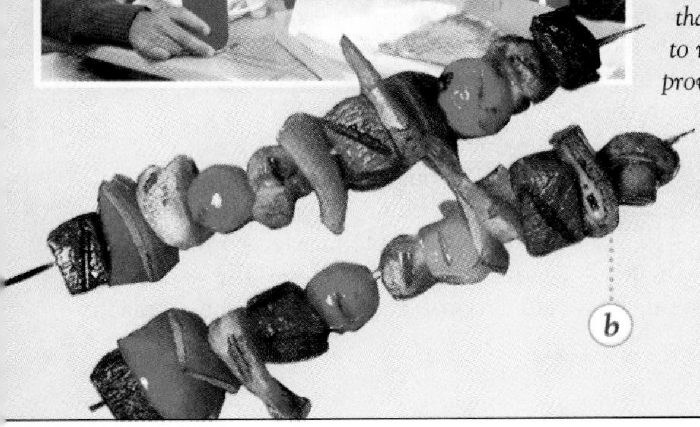

b

c

Figure 38–6 *The foods we eat—such as (a) pizza, (b) meats and vegetables, and (c) strawberries—must be broken down into molecules that are further broken down to release the energy and provide the nutrients they contain. The process by which foods are broken down is known as digestion.*

TEACHER SUPPORT

Activity

NAME THAT ORGAN

Using a model or diagram of the human digestive system, trace the path that food takes as it enters the body through the mouth, passes through the pharynx and esophagus to the stomach, empties into the small intestine, works its way through the large intestine, then exits the body through the anus. Identify and describe the function of each of these organs, as well as the teeth, tongue, salivary glands, pancreas, and liver. Then give students practice identifying the digestive organs by playing a quiz game. Describe the functions of the digestive organs, and have students who have volunteered to be contestants try to identify the organs you describe. The rest of the students act as judges, deciding whether the answers are correct and giving other contestants a chance to answer if they are not.

SECTION 38–2

The Digestive System

Performance Objectives

- Describe the role the digestive system plays in the body.
- Explain the functions of insulin and glucagon.

1 ENGAGE

Inquiry Activity

Observing

How Sweet It Is

Tell students that the foods we eat must be broken down chemically if the body is to extract nutrients from them. This process begins in the mouth; an enzyme in saliva breaks down starches into sugars. Ask students how they could observe this happening. After they have had a chance to respond, have students chew unsalted soda crackers for about five minutes. Then have them describe how the crackers taste and explain what has happened. (Slightly sweet, because some of the starches have been broken down into sugars.)

2 EXPLORE

Investigate

Model Building The teeth play an important role in digestion: Incisors cut food, canines tear it, and molars crush it. Ask students to think of a model for each of these mechanical actions that teeth perform. (Scissors and knives can cut like incisors, tweezers and pincers can be used to tear like canines, and mallets and vises can crush like molars.)

Checkpoint

1 They help the body perform important chemical reactions.

3 TEACH

Ideas Through Images

Have students examine Figure 38–7, read the caption, and answer the following questions.

- **Where is the sublingual salivary gland located? The parotid gland?** (Under the tongue and in front of the ear, respectively.)
- **What two roles does saliva play in digestion?** (It moistens food and starts breaking large complex starch molecules into simple glucose molecules.)

Investigate

Model Building Tell students that peristalsis, or the wavelike movement of muscles, is responsible for the relatively rapid movement of food through the digestive system, starting in the esophagus. Ask students how they could model peristalsis in order to observe this important body function. Suggest that they use a long balloon partially filled with water to model part of the alimentary canal, such as a segment of the small intestine. The water represents partially digested food. How would they manipulate the balloon to model peristalsis? (By squeezing the balloon and gradually moving the squeezed area from one end of the balloon to the other.) What happens to the water as the wave of peristalsis passes through the balloon? (The water is pushed from one end of the balloon to the other.)

Ideas Through Images

Have students examine Figure 38–8, read the caption, and answer the following questions.

- **How do muscle contractions move food through the alimentary canal?** (By narrowing one small section of the canal after another so that food is pushed along.)

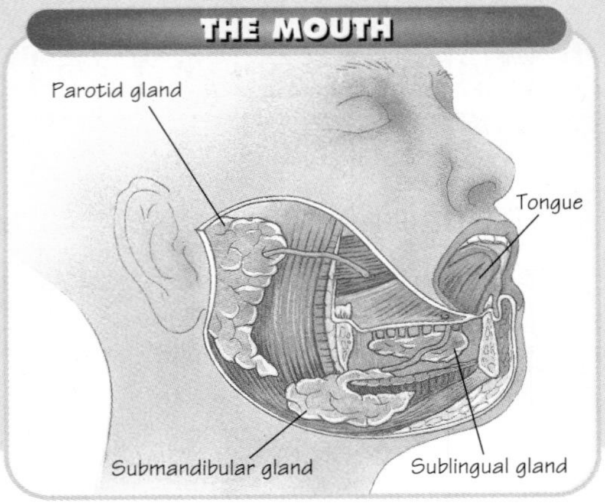

Figure 38–7
Digestion begins in the mouth, where teeth cut, grind, and crush food into a paste with the aid of saliva. Saliva, a fluid that is produced by salivary glands, not only moistens the food for easy swallowing, it also contains enzymes that begin to break large, complex starch molecules into simple glucose molecules.

of digestion by cutting, tearing, and crushing food into small fragments.

Human teeth include incisors, which are sharp enough to cut directly through meat; cuspids and bicuspids, which grasp and tear food; and molars, which have large, flat surfaces ideal for grinding food. Human tooth structure is intermediate between that of a plant-eating herbivore, in which molars are most common, and a carnivore, in which incisors are prominent. Our tooth structure reflects a mixed diet of meats and plants.

In the mouth, saliva, a fluid produced by the mouth's three pairs of **salivary glands,** helps to moisten the food and make it easier to chew. The release of saliva is under the control of the nervous system, and it can be triggered by the scent of food—especially when you are hungry!

Saliva not only helps to moisten food, it also helps to ease its passage through the digestive tract. Saliva also contains an enzyme called **amylase,** which breaks the chemical bonds in starches, releasing sugars. If you chew on starchy foods like crackers long enough, they will begin to taste sweet—a taste that comes from the chemical action of amylase on starch. Saliva also contains **lysozyme,** an enzyme that fights infection by digesting the cell walls of many bacteria.

Food is passed from the mouth into the rest of the digestive system by swallowing. Pushed by the tongue and muscles of the throat, the chewed clump of food, called a bolus, is forced down the throat. Just as this happens, a flap of tissue, known as the epiglottis (ehp-uh-GLAHT-ihs), is forced over the opening to the air passageways. This prevents food from clogging the air passageways—most of the time, anyway!

☑ **Checkpoint** What is amylase? 1

The Esophagus

After the bolus is swallowed, it passes through the **esophagus,** or food tube, into the stomach. Did you know that food can travel through the esophagus whether you're sitting up, lying down, or standing on your head? Even in astronauts, food passes through the esophagus in the weightlessness of space. The reason is that food is moved along by contractions of smooth muscle surrounding the esophagus. Known as **peristalsis** (per-uh-STAL-sihs), these contractions, which occur throughout the alimentary canal, squeeze the food through the 25 centimeters of the esophagus.

The Stomach

Food from the esophagus empties into a large muscular sac called the **stomach.** A thick ring of muscle, known as the cardiac sphincter, closes the esophagus after food has passed into the stomach,

TEACHER SUPPORT

Managing Classroom Diversity

TECH PREP STUDENTS
Have students interested in careers in dentistry investigate the careers of dental hygienist and dental assistant. For each career, they should learn what education and other training are required, what skills are necessary, what one does on the job, what the salary is, and what possibilities there are for advancement. If possible, students should interview both a dental hygienist and a dental assistant, as well as read occupational handbooks and similar sources in the library. Ask students to summarize their research in a table that facilitates a comparison of the two careers. Based on their table, which career, if either, do they think they would rather pursue? Why?

Figure 38–8
Once food is swallowed, it is forced through the alimentary canal—esophagus, stomach, small intestine, and large intestine—by the action of peristalsis, a series of periodic muscular contractions. Just below the entry to the large intestine is a small pouch known as the appendix. In humans the appendix is of little importance except when it becomes infected. This condition, which is known as appendicitis, usually requires the surgical removal of the appendix.

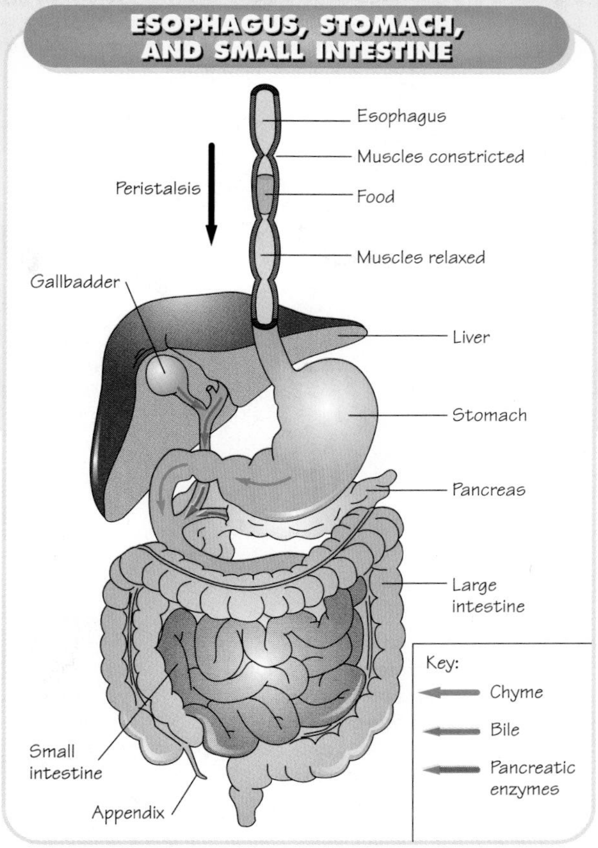

preventing the contents of the stomach from moving back into the esophagus. The size of the stomach enables you to eat a few large meals a day, rather than having to nibble all the time. Its walls produce a powerful combination of enzymes and strong acids, and contractions of its smooth muscles thoroughly mix the food you swallow.

The lining of the stomach contains millions of microscopic **gastric glands** that release a number of substances into the stomach. Some of these glands produce mucus, a fluid that lubricates and protects the stomach wall. Other glands produce hydrochloric acid, and still others produce **pepsin.** Pepsin, an enzyme that digests proteins, works best at low pH. Remember that low pH corresponds to high acidity. ● The combination of pepsin and hydrochloric acid in the stomach unfolds large proteins in foods and breaks them into smaller polypeptide fragments.

As digestion proceeds, stomach muscles contract to churn and mix stomach fluids and food, gradually producing a mixture known as chyme (KIGHM). After a few hours in the stomach, the pyloric valve—located at the junction of the stomach and small intestine—opens, and chyme is forced into the duodenum.

Checkpoint What is chyme? 2

The Small Intestine

The duodenum is the first of three parts of the **small intestine,** and it is the place where most of the chemical work of digestion takes place. As chyme enters from the stomach, it is mixed with enzymes and digestive fluids from the other accessory digestive organs and even from the lining of the duodenum itself.

Located just below the stomach is a gland called the **pancreas,** which serves two important functions. One function is to produce hormones that regulate blood sugar, which we will examine later. Within the digestive system, the pancreas plays the role of master chemist, producing enzymes that break down carbohydrates, proteins, lipids, and nucleic acids. The pancreas also produces sodium

INTEGRATING CHEMISTRY

What is pH? How does pH characterize acids? Bases?

• **How is chyme different from food?** (Chyme is a mixture of food and stomach fluids.)

• **Of which organ is the duodenum a part?** (The small intestine.)

• **What is peristalsis?** (A series of muscle contractions that move food through the alimentary canal.)

Discussion

Identify and locate on Figure 38–8 the sphincters that help regulate the movement of food through the digestive system: the cardiac sphincter (between the esophagus and stomach) and the pyloric sphincter (between the stomach and duodenum). Describe the specific role each sphincter plays. Then ask students to discuss how the sphincters of the digestive system are similar to the valves of the circulatory system. (Both prevent backflow in the system.)

INTEGRATING CHEMISTRY

The acidity or alkalinity of a substance is referred to as its pH, which is an abbreviation for hydrogen ion concentration. Acids have a pH below 7.0, bases a pH above 7.0.

Checkpoints

1 Amylase is an enzyme in saliva that breaks the chemical bonds in starches, releasing sugars.

2 Chyme is a mixture of stomach fluids and food.

TEACHER SUPPORT

Background Information

The gallbladder, which is shown in Figure 38–8, is located just beneath the liver. It is a pear-shaped bag about 9 centimeters long. Its function is to concentrate and store bile, which is produced by the liver and reaches the gallbladder through a network of tiny tubes. The gallbladder is capable of holding up to 50 milliliters of bile, which it expels through a duct to the small intestine when it is needed to help digest fats. Pancreatic digestive enzymes also reach the small intestine through the bile duct. Gallstones sometimes form in the bile, leading to pain, jaundice, and other symptoms if they block the bile duct. In some people, the stones can be pulverized with ultrasound. In other people, removal of the entire gallbladder may be necessary. Fortunately, it is possible to live a long, healthy life without a gallbladder.

Ancillary Support

The resources below can be used to support your teaching strategy for these two pages.

TR Apply: Food for Thought
BL Inquiry Activity: The Human Food Processor

Ideas Through Images

Have students examine Figure 38–9, read the caption, and answer the following questions.

- **How are the drawings in the figure related to one another?** (They show increasingly enlarged cross sections of the small intestine.)
- **Why are there so many capillaries inside each villus?** (Because that is where nutrients are absorbed into the blood.)
- **What are microvilli, and what is their role?** (Microvilli are tiny villi that project out from each villus; their role is to increase the surface area available for the absorption of nutrients.)

Discussion

Ask students why the small intestine is so long—about 7 meters in all—when the chemical breakdown of food is completed in the first 25 centimeters or so, in the first segment of the small intestine called the duodenum. (The rest of the small intestine—the jejunum and ileum—is where nutrients are absorbed into the blood. Because the nutrients must cross a membrane to get into the blood, the process requires a great deal of surface area. The length of the small intestine, along with the millions of villi and microvilli lining its surface, results in a huge surface area for the absorption of nutrients into the blood.)

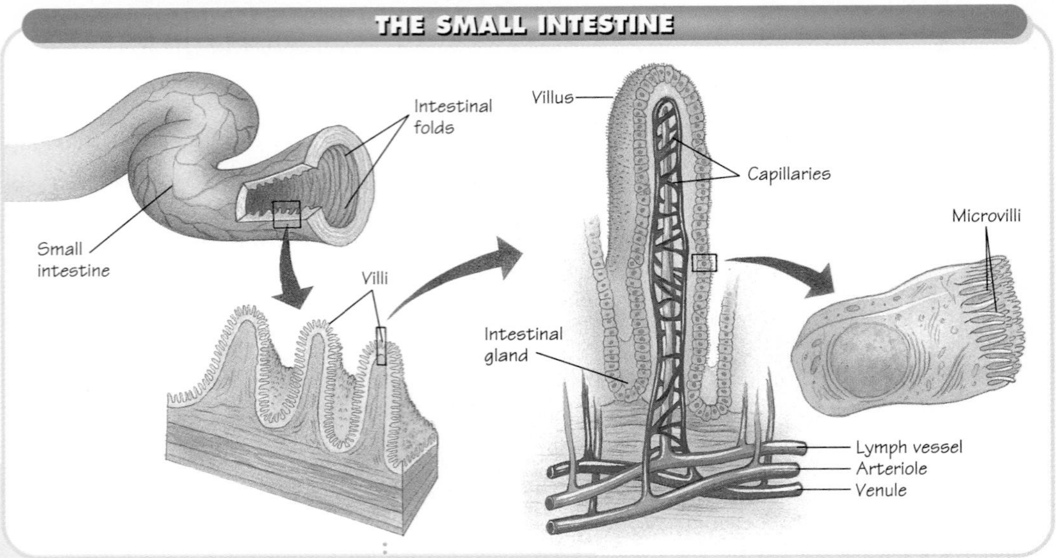

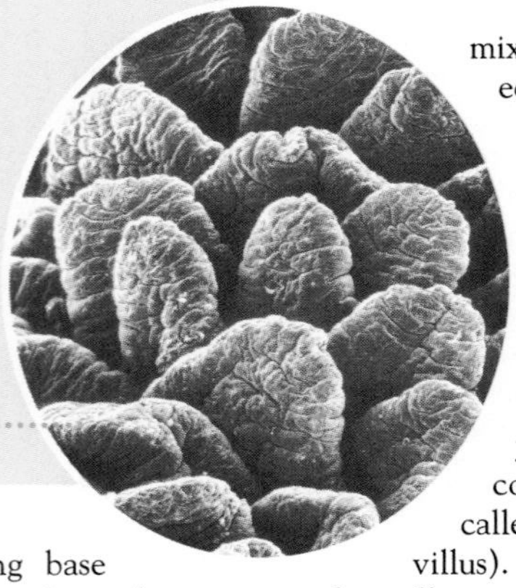

Figure 38–9
(a) The lining of the small intestine consists of folds that are covered with tiny projections called villi. Within each villus there is a network of blood capillaries and lymph vessels that absorb and carry away nutrients.
(b) This electron micrograph of villi shows how they greatly increase the surface area of the small intestine (magnification: 300X).

bicarbonate, a strong base that neutralizes stomach acid so that these enzymes can go to work.

To aid in this process, the **liver,** a large gland just above the stomach, produces **bile,** a fluid loaded with lipids and salts. Bile acts almost like a detergent, dissolving and dispersing the droplets of fat found in fatty foods. This makes it possible for enzymes to reach these fat molecules and break them down.

By the time chyme enters the remaining parts of the small intestine, nearly all the chemical work of digestion has been completed. The chyme is now a rich mixture of small nutrient molecules ready to be absorbed by the body. The remaining parts of the small intestine—the jejunum and the ileum—are specially adapted to absorb these nutrients. Nearly 7 meters in length, the folded surfaces of the jejunum and the ileum are covered with projections called **villi** (VIHL-igh; singular: villus). The surfaces of the cells of the villi are themselves covered with thousands of fingerlike projections known as microvilli. Slow, wavelike contractions of smooth muscles move the chyme along this absorptive surface.

Nutrient molecules are rapidly absorbed into the cells lining the small intestine. Sugars, amino acids, and other nutrients are then passed directly into the bloodstream. Fats take a different route. They are transported into tiny lymph vessels before being delivered to the bloodstream.

As you might expect, blood leaving the capillaries of the small intestine is

TEACHER SUPPORT

Background Information

Everyone knows what it feels like to be hungry. The sensations of hunger can be strong and unpleasant—in fact, they are commonly called hunger pangs. They occur when waves of muscle contractions travel over the entire stomach, which is already contracted because it is empty. Hunger pangs may last for several minutes and then disappear, only to return again at a later time.

Hunger pangs are under the direct control of the hunger center, which is located in the hypothalamus. The hunger center, in turn, is stimulated by the level of circulating nutrients, primarily glucose, although other nutrients also play a role, including fatty acids. When blood levels of the nutrients are low, the hunger center is stimulated to send out nerve impulses that lead to stomach contractions. When blood levels are high, another area of the hypothalamus is stimulated to stop the contractions.

nutrient-rich after a meal. Does this mean that levels of sugars and other nutrients in the blood rise and fall dramatically during the day? Not at all. All the blood leaving the small intestine passes through the liver before it flows to the rest of the body. This unusual arrangement places the liver in a position to monitor the blood before it enters the general circulation.

Not long after you eat something sweet, blood from the small intestine is loaded with energy-producing sugar. The liver efficiently removes most of the extra sugar from the blood and stores it in the form of glycogen, a polysaccharide. Liver cells keep this nutrient in reserve, and when blood sugar levels begin to fall, they release the stored sugars.

☑ *Checkpoint* What are villi? ❶

The Large Intestine

Nearly all the available nutrients have been removed from the chyme that enters the **large intestine,** or colon. The primary job of the colon is to remove water from the undigested material that is left, producing a concentrated waste material known as feces. This material passes through the rectum and is eliminated from the body.

Water is moved quickly across the colon wall while rich colonies of bacteria grow on the undigested material. These intestinal bacteria are helpful to the digestive process—some even produce compounds that the body is able to use, including vitamin K.

Regulating Nutrient Levels

Regulating the level of blood sugar is one of the body's most important jobs. If the blood has too little sugar, organs—including the brain—that depend upon it as a source of energy will begin to suffer. Two hormones produced by the pancreas help to regulate blood sugar. Inside the pancreas there are tiny "islands" of cells known as the **islets of Langerhans.** Some of these cells produce **insulin,** a polypeptide hormone.

When the blood sugar level rises, as it might after a meal, the islets of Langerhans in the pancreas detect this and release insulin into the bloodstream. **Insulin stimulates cells in the liver, muscles, and fatty tissues to remove sugar from the bloodstream and store it in the form of glycogen and fat.**

When blood sugar levels fall, as they might after several hours without eating, another hormone, called **glucagon,** is released by the islets of Langerhans. **Glucagon stimulates the liver, muscles, and fatty tissues to break down glycogen and fats and to release sugars into the blood.** This raises blood sugar back to a safe level.

When the body cannot produce enough insulin, blood sugar cannot be regulated and a disorder known as diabetes mellitus results. Most forms of juvenile-onset diabetes, a type of diabetes mellitus, can be treated with a carefuly controlled diet and daily injections of insulin.

Section Review 38-2

1. **Explain** the function of the digestive system in your body.
2. **Describe** the action of insulin and glucagon in your body.
3. **Critical Thinking—Relating** What functions do the enzymes amylase and pepsin serve in digestion?

TEACHER SUPPORT

Background Information

If diabetics have too much blood sugar, why are they sometimes advised to keep a candy bar handy? And why are diabetics often tired and weak if they have so much sugar in their blood? Doesn't sugar give us energy? Questions such as these reveal that diabetes can be a confusing disease. Help students understand this common disorder by explaining that sugar in the blood does not provide energy. To give us energy, sugar must enter the cells, and this requires insulin. Diabetics do not produce adequate insulin, so they may be given insulin injections or pills. However, it is difficult to give exactly the right amount of insulin, and too much insulin may sometimes be given, resulting in a dangerously low level of blood sugar. This is why diabetics may be advised to keep a quickly digested source of sugar handy.

4 ASSESS

Quick Check

Call on students to identify the organ that produces each of the following hormones and enzymes; call on other students to describe the role each hormone or enzyme plays in digestion: amylase, pepsin, bile, insulin, and glucagon. Point out any misconceptions.

Section Review 38-2

1. The digestive system converts food into simple molecules that can be absorbed and used by the cells of the body.

2. Insulin stimulates cells in the liver, muscles, and fatty tissues to remove sugar from the bloodstream and store it in the form of glycogen and fat. Glucagon stimulates the liver, muscles, and fatty tissues to break down glycogen and fats and to release sugars into the blood.

3. Amylase breaks the chemical bonds in starches, releasing sugars; pepsin unfolds large proteins and breaks them into smaller polypeptide fragments.

Learning Modality

Kinesthetic Learning Call on students to role-play the different organs of the digestive system. Have the students form a line with each organ in its correct position. Ask several other students to pretend to be food. As the "food" moves through the "digestive system," have the students playing organs move in a way that suggests how their organ contributes to the digestive process. Ask the rest of the class to volunteer brief descriptions of the role each organ plays to help digest the food.

☑ Checkpoint

❶ Villi are fingerlike projections that cover the surface of the jejunum and ileum and aid in the absorption of nutrients.

SECTION 38–3

The Excretory System

Performance Objectives

- Describe the role that the kidneys play in the body.
- Explain how filtration and reabsorption work.

Mini Lab Skill: Relating

1 ENGAGE

Inquiry Activity

Observing

Filtering a Fluid

Tell students that the main organs of the excretory system, the kidneys, filter wastes out of the blood and produce urine. Ask students to name as many other filters as they can. (Possible answers include the oil or fuel filter in a car, the air filter in a car or furnace, and the paper filter in a coffee maker.) What does each filter do? (Removes unwanted substances from a gas or fluid.) Have students observe how a filter works by watching as you pour water containing sand through a paper coffee filter.

2 EXPLORE

Discussion

Ask volunteers to estimate how much water and other fluids they consume each day. (Students may say they consume at least 1 or 2 liters of fluids each day.) Point out that this amount of water must also be excreted each day to maintain fluid balance in the body. Ask students how the body loses fluids. (Primarily in urine, unless one is sweating heavily.) How much sweat and urine must be produced each day to maintain fluid balance? (At least 1 or 2 liters.)

INTEGRATING CHEMISTRY

Protein metabolism converts ammonia to urea through the addition of carbon dioxide.

Guide for Reading

- **Explain** the function the kidneys perform in the body.
- **Describe** the processes of filtration and reabsorption.

MINI LAB

- **Relate** the structure of a kidney to its function.

INTEGRATING CHEMISTRY

How does protein metabolism produce urea?

THE CHEMISTRY OF THE human body is a marvelous thing. An intricate system of checks and balances controls everything from your blood pressure to your body temperature. Nutrients are absorbed, stored, and carefully released just as they are needed. But every living system, including the human body, produces chemical wastes—byproducts of chemical reactions that are no longer useful. Some are even toxic. Therefore, the body occasionally needs to throw things away. The body relies on a group of organs that work together to remove the unwanted, and often toxic, wastes.

Chemical Wastes

The elimination of chemical wastes from the body is known as excretion. The lungs, for example, excrete carbon dioxide, a chemical waste produced when energy is captured from food compounds. The skin excretes excess water and salt in sweat. This makes the lungs and the skin part of the excretory system, a system of organs that remove chemical wastes from the body. In this section, however, we will focus our attention on a pair of organs whose main function is excretion—the **kidneys.**

Why does the body need organs specialized for excretion? Part of the answer has to do with the chemistry of proteins. When the body uses the amino acids from proteins for food, it sometimes must remove their amino ($-NH_2$) groups.

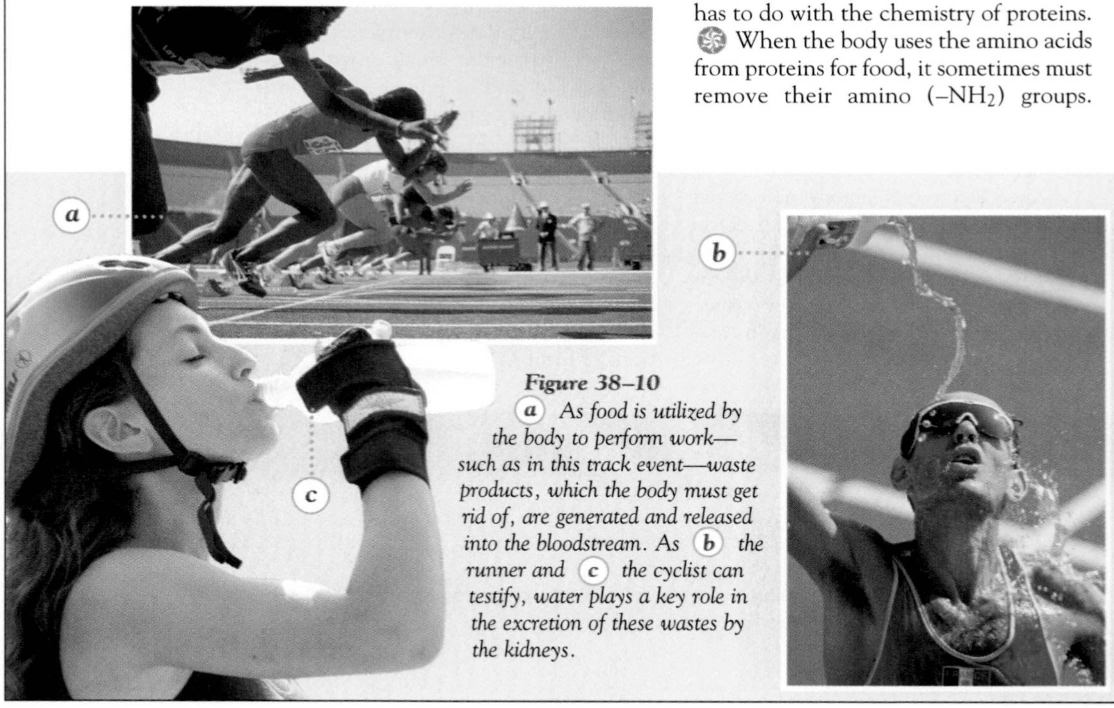

Figure 38–10 *(a) As food is utilized by the body to perform work—such as in this track event—waste products, which the body must get rid of, are generated and released into the bloodstream. As (b) the runner and (c) the cyclist can testify, water plays a key role in the excretion of these wastes by the kidneys.*

TEACHER SUPPORT

Facts and Figures

Share the following kidney facts and figures with students to help them appreciate the tremendous amount of work that is performed by this organ.

- The kidneys represent only 0.5 percent of body weight, on average, but they use up about 9 percent of the oxygen that the body takes in.
- Only a small portion of kidney tissue is used at any given time, so a person can live with just one kidney.
- Each kidney contains about 1,000,000 to 1,500,000 nephrons, each of which is about 3 centimeters long.
- If all the nephrons in a single kidney were stretched end to end, they would cover a distance of about 60 kilometers.
- The kidneys produce about 1 milliliter of urine per minute, and a daily total of about 1.5 liters.
- More than a liter of blood is filtered through each kidney every minute of the day.

PROTEIN METABOLISM

Figure 38–11

a *The breakdown of an amino acid such as alanine yields pyruvic acid and ammonia. The pyruvic acid is used for energy, while the ammonia is converted to urea by a complex series of reactions.*
b *The kidneys function in the removal of urea as well as the regulation of water in the bloodstream.*

$$H_2N - \overset{\overset{\displaystyle CH_3}{|}}{\underset{\underset{\displaystyle COOH}{|}}{C}} - H \; + \; \tfrac{1}{2}\,O_2 \; \longrightarrow \; \overset{\overset{\displaystyle CH_3}{|}}{\underset{\underset{\displaystyle COOH}{|}}{C}} = O \; + \; NH_3$$

Alanine　　　　　　　　　Pyruvic　　　Ammonia
　　　　　　　　　　　　　acid

$$2NH_3 \; + \; CO_2 \; \longrightarrow \; H_2N - \overset{\overset{\displaystyle }{|}}{\underset{\underset{\displaystyle O}{\|}}{C}} - NH_2 \; + \; H_2O$$

Ammonia　　Carbon　　　　　　Urea　　　　Water
　　　　　　dioxide

b

THE EXCRETORY SYSTEM

Vena cava — Aorta
— Renal artery
— Kidney
— Renal vein
— Ureter
— Urinary bladder
— Urethra

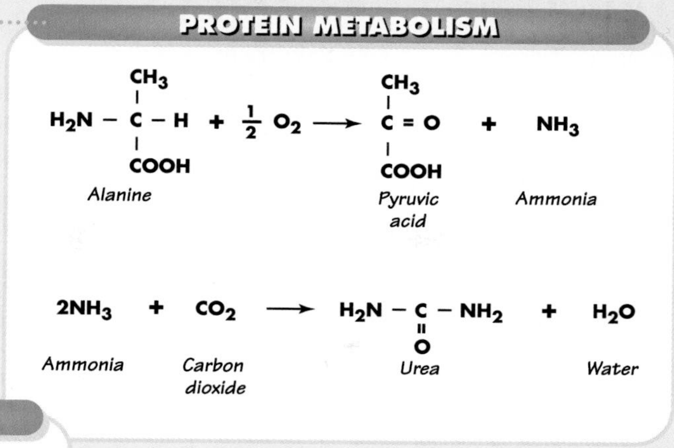

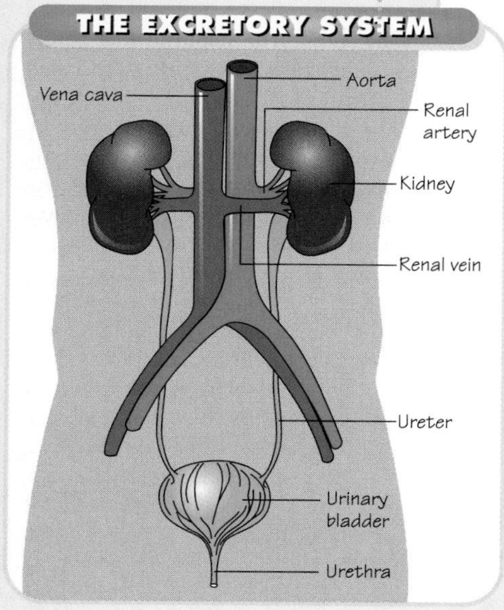

This produces ammonia, NH₃, a poisonous compound that the body quickly converts to urea. ● Urea is less toxic than ammonia and is very soluble in water, but it still must be removed from the bloodstream. **The removal of urea— a substance that is the result of the metabolism of proteins in body cells— along with the regulation of water in the bloodstream, is the principal job of the kidneys.**

☑ *Checkpoint* What is the function of the kidneys? ❶

The Kidneys

The kidneys, each about the size of a fist, are located on either side of the spinal column in the lower back. Blood flows into each kidney through a **renal artery** and leaves through a **renal vein.** A third vessel, called the **ureter,** leaves each kidney, carrying fluid to the **urinary bladder.**

Within each kidney is a complex filtration system that removes urea, excess water, and other wastes from the blood. As purified blood is returned to the body, these wastes are collected to form a fluid known as urine. Urine is stored in the bladder and then is eliminated from the body.

The Nephrons

Each kidney contains about a million tiny functional units known as **nephrons.** Refer to the illustration on page 865 as you read about the workings of a nephron. Blood enters each nephron through a single arteriole (small artery) and leaves through a venule (small vein). Each nephron also contains a collecting duct, which leads to the renal pelvis. Wastes and excess water are

Digestive and Excretory Systems **863**

3 TEACH

Ideas Through Images

Have students examine Figure 38–11, read the caption, and answer the following questions.

• **Once urea and other impurities have been removed from the blood, how does the blood leave the kidney?** (Through the renal vein.)

• **Where does the urea go after it is removed from the blood by the kidney?** (Into the urine, where it travels to the bladder through the ureter and then out of the body through the urethra.)

Discussion

Ask students to read the highlighted statement on this page that describes the functions of the kidney. Then ask students what they think would happen if the kidneys were not functioning well. What symptoms might this cause and how serious would it be? (Poisonous waste products would accumulate in the blood, leading to nausea, fatigue, and other symptoms, and ultimately to death if the condition went untreated. Poorly functioning kidneys also cause edema, or swelling of tissues due to the retention of excess fluids. Edema can place a strain on the cardiovascular system.)

☑ Checkpoint

❶ To remove urea that results from protein metabolism and regulate the water in the bloodstream.

TEACHER SUPPORT

Background Information

Among major diseases, kidney problems rank fifth in the United States, killing over 100,000 Americans each year. One of the most common kidney problems is kidney stones—insoluble crystals that form in the urine. These can be extremely painful as they pass through the kidney and ureter, and if stones block the flow of urine, an infection many result. Kidney stones can be disintegrated with ultrasound or removed surgically.

Nephritis, which is inflammation or infection of the nephrons, is a more serious condition. Symptoms include high blood pressure, weakness, fatigue, and edema. Repeated attacks of nephritis may lead to permanent kidney damage and kidney failure, in which the kidneys stop functioning altogether. Kidney failure requires dialysis or kidney transplant.

Ancillary Support

The resources below can be used to support your teaching strategy for these two pages.

LM Simulating Urinalysis, #76
BL Inquiry Activity: Cleaning Up

MINI LAB **Relating**

Teacher Notes

- For time required and materials needed, see page 850b.
- Remind students to use caution when handling the scalpel, to wear gloves during the procedure, and to wash their hands thoroughly when they are finished.
- Before students begin the MINI LAB, ask them how the mammal kidney they are about to examine might differ from a human kidney. (It might differ in size, depending on the animal it came from, but its structure and function should be similar to a human kidney.)
- Ask students either to point out on their specimen how blood flows through the kidney or to draw a schematic of blood flow through the kidney using their specimen as a model.

Answers to Analyze and Conclude

1. Answers will depend on the type of kidney students examine. Students may weigh the kidney and compare its weight to the average weight of 300 grams for a human kidney. Alternatively, students may compare the size of the kidney they examine with the size of their own fists because a human kidney is approximately fist-sized.

2. Cutting the organ open allows students to observe the inside of the kidney. This may help them appreciate how the renal artery and vein carry blood into and out of the kidney and how the nephrons filter wastes from the blood.

Skills Trace
Relating
- Focus p. 864
- Practice p. 866
- Assess p. 875

MINI LAB Relating

Examining a Kidney

PROBLEM *How does the structure of a kidney **relate** to its function?*

PROCEDURE

1. Obtain a mammal kidney and five different-colored pushpins.
2. Using reference materials, place a pin in or next to the renal artery, renal vein, and ureter. Slice the kidney lengthwise and identify as many structures as you can.
3. Use colored pencils and a file card to make a key to identify each part.

ANALYZE AND CONCLUDE

1. How does the size of the kidney you labeled compare with the size of a human kidney?
2. What structures and functions of the kidney are easier to understand when a real organ is examined?

removed from the bloodstream and gathered in the collecting duct. When blood enters the nephron, it flows into a spherical meshwork of thin-walled capillaries called a **glomerulus**—the filtering unit of the nephron. The blood is under such pressure in these small vessels that much of the blood plasma seeps out, almost like water from a leaky garden hose.

Filtration and Reabsorption

Blood cells, platelets, and plasma proteins are too large to leave the blood as it passes through the glomerulus. **In the glomerulus, blood plasma—containing water, salts, sugars, and nutrients—filters out of the bloodstream and is collected in Bowman's capsule.** This plasma, called the primary filtrate, is then passed from **Bowman's capsule** to the proximal tubule. It looks as though most of this plasma is about to be thrown away, but appearances can be deceiving.

More than 180 liters of blood plasma pass into the tubules of the kidneys each day. Needless to say, if you excreted this much fluid, life would be very difficult! Fortunately, this is not what happens. **As fluid moves through the proximal tubule, nearly all the material first removed from the blood is put back into the blood.** This process is called **reabsorption.**

Why should the nephron first throw nearly everything away, only to reabsorb most of the water and dissolved materials? This is a bit like cleaning a room by first carrying everything out into the hallway, then bringing back only the things you want to keep. The likely answer is that this is exactly what makes the kidney such an excellent filter.

By first removing nearly everything from the bloodstream, the kidneys ensure that drugs, poisons, and other dangerous compounds will be taken out of the bloodstream. As they then reabsorb most of what they have filtered out, these toxic compounds are left in the proximal tubule, where they will be eliminated in the urine.

Concentration and Water Balance

As the kidneys reabsorb material into the bloodstream, they draw back nearly 99 percent of the water that had first been filtered out. Urine, which now moves through the nephron toward the ureter, is further concentrated in a region of the nephron known as the **loop of Henle.** Depending on the demands of the body, the nephron can produce urine that is very concentrated, which conserves water, or very dilute, which eliminates water.

Checkpoint How do kidneys filter and reabsorb plasma? 1

TEACHER SUPPORT

Managing Classroom Diversity

TECH PREP STUDENTS

One of the most commonly performed medical laboratory procedures is urinalysis, or the examination of urine chemically, physically, and microscopically. Urinalysis is so commonly performed because the composition of urine reflects the status of many different body functions. Ask students interested in health care and laboratory technician careers to learn more about urinalysis by observing and interviewing a laboratory technician in a large medical practice or clinic. Students should find out some of the most common reasons that urinalysis is performed, what is measured in a routine urinalysis, what specific tools and techniques are used, how important accuracy is for a proper diagnosis, how urine specimens are collected, and what if any special precautions must be taken when handling them. Ask students to write up what they learn in the form of a mini–laboratory manual for urinalysis.

Visualizing Kidney Structure and Function

The most important organs of the excretory system are the kidneys, which consist of numerous tiny fluid-filtering structures called nephrons.

1 Renal Artery and Renal Vein
The renal artery brings blood to the kidney, while the renal vein carries the filtered blood away.

2 Renal Cortex and Renal Medulla
The human kidney consists of an outer renal cortex and an inner renal medulla, in which nephrons perform the task of filtration.

3 Renal Pelvis
The collecting ducts at the ends of nephrons merge and empty urine into the inner region of the kidney, called the renal pelvis, from which the urine is carried to the urinary bladder by way of the ureter.

4 Bowman's Capsule
Water, nutrients, and wastes are filtered from the blood that enters the glomerulus. This filtrate is collected in Bowman's capsule.

5 Proximal Tubule
Most of the water and nutrients are reabsorbed into the blood as the filtrate passes through the proximal tubule of the nephron.

6 Distal Tubule
Wastes that still remain in the blood are secreted into the distal tubule of the nephron and become part of the urine.

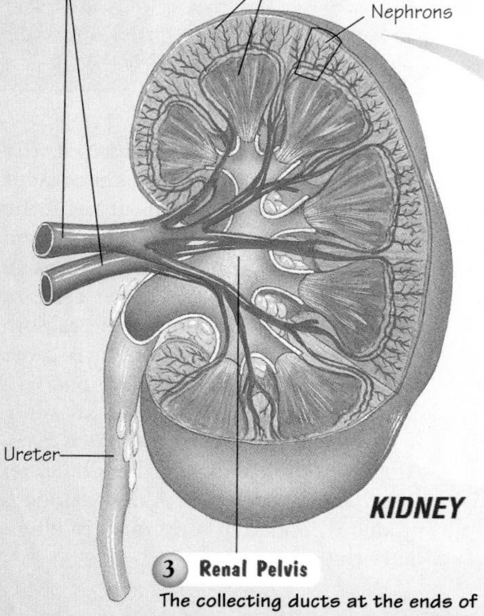

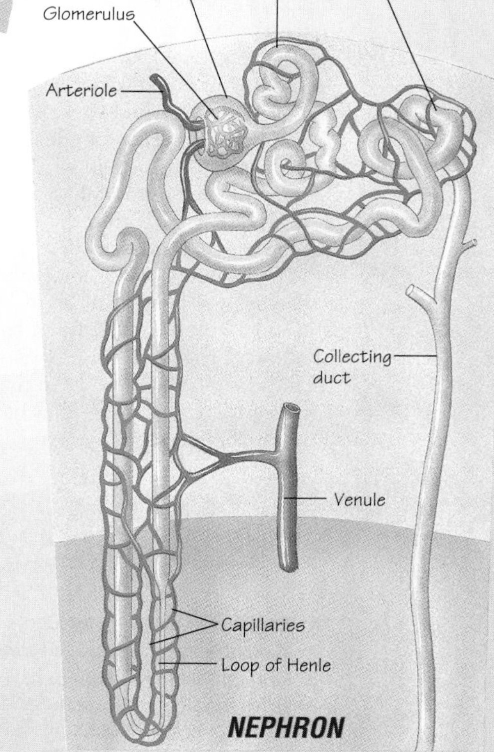

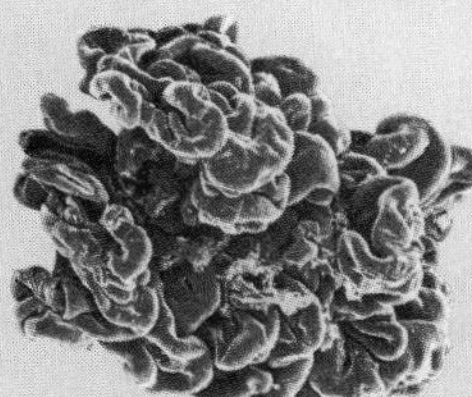

Scanning electron micrograph of a glomerulus (magnification: 400X)

Visualizing Kidney Structure and Function

Point out to students that each kidney has at least a million nephrons, each about 2 to 3 centimeters long. The kidney consists of two major parts: the outer cortex and medulla, which contain the nephrons; and the inner pelvis, which collects urine and passes it to the ureter.

About 180 liters of filtrate is produced each day, but most of it is reabsorbed, including 178 liters of water, 1200 grams of salt, and 250 grams of glucose and other useful substances. Some of the materials are reabsorbed by diffusion, others by active transport. Most reabsorption takes place in the proximal tubule.

Ask students to identify some substances that may be returned to the blood through reabsorption. (Glucose, amino acids, vitamins, and salts.) Then ask why the tubules are so long and so richly supplied with capillaries. (The length of the tubules increases the surface area available for reabsorption.)

Checkpoint

1 Capillaries reabsorb plasma and most of its components as the filtrate passes through the proximal tubule.

TEACHER SUPPORT

Historical Perspective

The English physician who was the first to use urinalysis to diagnose a patient's condition was Richard Bright. In 1829, Bright discovered that certain patients with edema (then called dropsy) had a substance in their urine that coagulated like egg white when the urine was boiled. We now know that substance is serum albumin, which does not normally appear in the urine. In patients with nephritis, serum albumin passes through the glomerular membranes and ends up in the urine. Because of Bright's work, nephritis is still sometimes referred to as Bright disease.

Other diseases that can be diagnosed from the characteristic way they change the urine include alkaptonuria, which turns the urine black when it is exposed to air, and maple syrup urine disease, which causes the urine to smell like maple syrup. Both of these diseases are disorders of protein metabolism, not the kidney.

Ancillary Support

The resources below can be used to support your teaching strategy for these two pages.

TR Explore: Uses for Urinalysis
TB Visualizing Kidney Structure and Function, #47

4 ASSESS

Quick Check

Ask students to make a concept map relating each of the following terms: kidney, glomerulus, proximal tubule, filtration, reabsorption, removal of wastes, regulation of water.

Section Review 38-3

1. The kidneys remove urea which results from protein metabolism, and regulate water in the bloodstream.

2. In filtration, blood plasma filters out of the bloodstream in the glomerulus and the filtrate is collected in Bowman's capsule. In reabsorption, nearly all the material first removed from the blood is put back into it as the filtrate moves through the proximal tubule.

3. Blood plasma, containing water, salts, sugars, and nutrients, filters into the glomerular capillaries. Primarily water filters out of the collecting tubule into the surrounding capillaries.

4. The million or more nephrons in the cortex and medulla of the kidney perform the function of purifying the blood and forming urine. The relatively large renal vein and artery carry blood to and from the kidney, and the rich capillary supply expedites filtration. The inner renal pelvis forms a cavity for the collection of urine, which then passes to the ureter.

Skills Trace
Relating
- Focus p. 864
- Practice p. 866
- Assess p. 875

Learning Modality

Tactile Learning Have students trace the movement of fluid through the kidney in the drawing on page 865. As their fingers trace over each structure, have them identify it and briefly describe the role it plays in filtration, reabsorption, or elimination of urine.

Figure 38–12
When disease or injury reduces kidney function, a kidney dialysis machine is used to filter the blood—much like the kidney itself. These young patients are undergoing kidney dialysis on a beach, using portable kidney dialysis machines. As their blood flows through porous tubes inside the machine, it is bathed in a solution whose composition is close to that of blood plasma. Waste products diffuse into this solution, returning purified blood to the patient. Kidney dialysis makes it possible for people to lead relatively normal lives while waiting for the transplant of a healthy kidney, which will set them free from dialysis machines.

Control of Water Balance

When you drink a glass of water, it is quickly absorbed by the digestive system and passed into the bloodstream. If that's all that happened, every time you took in fluids your blood would become more dilute. Osmosis would cause water to flow into the tissues of the body, and many of the tissues would swell. Needless to say, this doesn't usually happen. The reason, of course, is that the kidneys remove that excess water.

The kidneys don't accomplish this by removing any more water in filtration—they do it by putting less water back into the bloodstream during reabsorption. The kidneys, however, don't make this "decision" on their own—they have help from the brain.

The hypothalamus region of the brain closely monitors the water content of the blood. When it is about right, the hypothalamus signals the pituitary gland to release an **antidiuretic hormone** (ADH). ADH causes its target cells, in the tubules of the kidneys, to reabsorb more water. This action returns more water to the bloodstream and produces a concentrated urine that conserves water. If the water content of the blood rises, ADH is not released, and the tubules reabsorb much less water. A dilute urine is produced, and the body quickly eliminates the excess water.

Section Review 38-3

1. **Explain** the function the kidneys perform in your body.
2. **Describe** the processes of filtration and reabsorption.
3. **Critical Thinking—Comparing** How does the process that takes place within the glomerular capillaries differ from the one that occurs in the capillaries surrounding the collecting tubule?
4. **MINI LAB** How does the structure of a kidney **relate** to its function?

TEACHER SUPPORT

Managing Classroom Diversity

TECH PREP STUDENTS
Ask students who are interested in health-care careers to learn about a career as a dialysis technician. Suggest that they contact the nearest large hospital or dialysis center for information regarding specific job duties and the type of training that is required. Alternatively, students may learn more about the dialysis machine itself. How does it work, and what skills are required to operate and maintain it? Ask students to report their findings.

LEP STUDENTS
LEP students may have difficulty with some of the technical terminology in this section. Help them understand the terms by explaining that renal means "relating to, involving, or located in or near the kidneys." Thus, the renal artery and renal vein are the major vessels carrying blood to and from the kidney; the renal pelvis is the collection site for urine inside the kidney (a pelvis is a cavity); and renal failure means failure of the kidney.

BRANCHING OUT In Action

A Cure for Ulcers?

SECTION 38–4

Guide for Reading

- **Explain** how ulcers are caused and **describe** how they can be treated.

FOR MANY YEARS, DR. JOHN Warren, a pathologist at Royal Perth Hospital in Western Australia, had examined tissue taken from ulcer patients. In nearly all of them, he found a curious corkscrew-shaped bacterium. In 1982, he brought these bacteria to the attention of Barry Marshall, a 30-year-old physician at the hospital.

Marshall then examined his own ulcer patients and discovered that nearly all of them had this bacterium in their stomach linings. Could this bacterium be the cause of ulcers? And if so, what would be the implications of this discovery? Before we discuss the answer to these important questions, you need to learn what ulcers are and how they are treated today.

Peptic Ulcers

As you have read earlier, powerful acids and enzymes are released into the stomach during the process of digestion. They are capable of breaking down just about anything you eat—animal or vegetable. If that's the case, you might wonder why the stomach doesn't digest itself! Why don't these acids eat holes right through the lining of the stomach itself? The answer is that sometimes they do.

Normally, the lining of the stomach is protected by a thick layer of mucus. In addition, the cells lining the stomach are tightly connected to each other, which prevents acid from leaking between them. Finally, millions of damaged cells in the lining are discarded every day and replaced by new ones. Most of the time, these three mechanisms keep the lining strong and healthy.

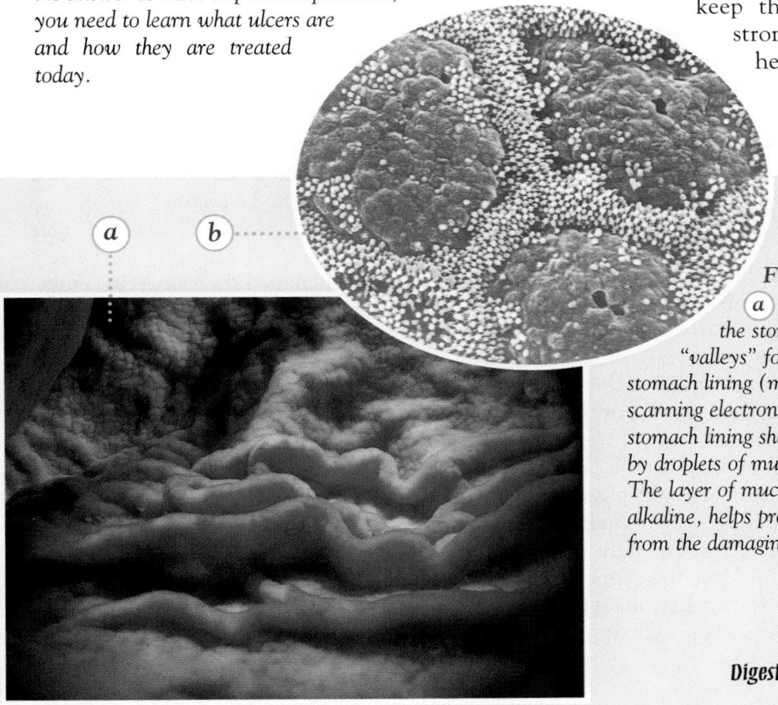

Figure 38–13 (a) *A view of the inner surface of the stomach shows the "hills" and "valleys" formed due to folds in the stomach lining (magnification: 15X).* (b) *A scanning electron micrograph of a portion of the stomach lining shows epithelial cells surrounded by droplets of mucus (magnification: 3550X). The layer of mucus, which is viscous and alkaline, helps protect the lining of the stomach from the damaging effects of acidic secretions.*

Section 38–4

A Cure for Ulcers?

Performance Objective

- Identify the cause of ulcers and explain how they are treated.

1 ENGAGE

Inquiry Activity

Designing an Experiment

Proving Cause and Effect Finding that a particular bacterium infects people with a certain disease does not prove that the bacterium causes the disease. Ask students to design an experiment to prove that a bacterium causes a disease. (The experiments should be designed to demonstrate that the disease occurs when the bacterium is introduced and is cured when the bacterium is destroyed. Healthy test subjects might be infected with the bacterium and observed to see whether they develop the disease. Then infected subjects might be treated with drugs known to kill the bacterium and observed to see whether they are cured.)

2 EXPLORE

Investigate

Research Ask students to research the bacterium that causes peptic ulcers, *Helicobacter pylori*. They should find out how *H. pylori* enters the digestive tract, how it causes ulcers, how common *H. pylori* infections are, and what percentage of infected people develop ulcers.

TEACHER SUPPORT

Historical Perspective

Clues that ulcers are caused by a contagious agent were apparent long before Dr. Barry Marshall's research with *H. pylori*. Sudden outbreaks of ulcers are well documented for recent times. For example, ulcers plagued the citizens of London during the air raids of World War II. But scientists blamed the outbreaks on stress and bad food. Since the 1950s, doctors have also known that family members of ulcer patients are three times more likely than the general population to develop ulcers themselves. Until recently, scientists called on heredity to explain this observation. In retrospect, an infectious agent is a more plausible explanation for both the family pattern and sudden outbreaks of ulcers. However, until Dr. Marshall's work, scientists believed that the stomach was too corrosive for any type of bacteria to survive in it for long. Thus, they repeatedly rejected a bacterial agent as the cause.

3 TEACH

Investigate

Long-Term Project Have students develop a questionnaire and take a survey to identify commonly held ideas about ulcers. In their questionnaires, students should ask people what they think causes ulcers, whether one gender or the other is more likely to get ulcers and why, what medications should be taken by people with ulcers, and what, if any, dietary restrictions people with ulcers should follow. Each student should administer the questionnaire to several different teens and adults. After they have shared the results of their surveys, lead students in a discussion of the accuracy of commonly held ideas about ulcers. How many, if any, of the people interviewed were aware that ulcers are now believed to be caused by bacteria and that antibiotics are prescribed to cure ulcers? Have students use the information from the surveys to make a brochure or poster that educates people about ulcers.

Discussion

Even after Dr. Barry Marshall cured seven out of ten of his ulcer patients with a drug that he found killed *H. pylori* in the test tube, the scientific community remained skeptical that *H. pylori* caused the ulcers. Ask students to discuss why the skepticism remained. Why were the cures insufficient to prove that *H. pylori* was the cause of the disease in the patients treated? What other explanations for the cures could be given? (The drugs killing *H. pylori* in the test tube does not necessarily mean that it worked the same way in the patients. The drug may have produced a cure in some other way—the placebo effect, for example—or the cure may have been unrelated to the drug, just occurring coincidentally. Thus, the results do not prove that *H. pylori* caused the disease.)

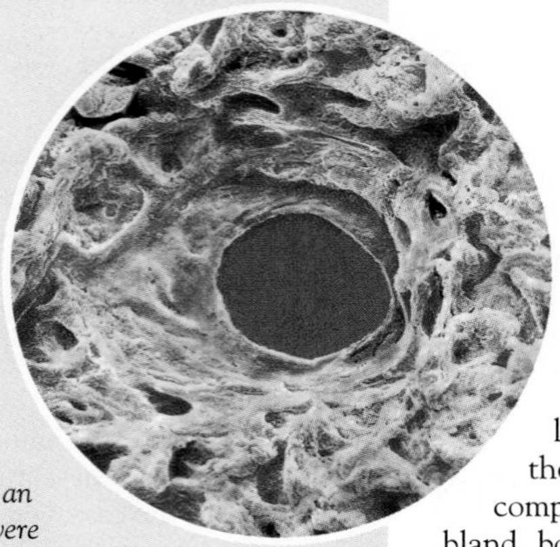

Figure 38–14
Because acid can damage the lining of the stomach, physicians assumed that a peptic ulcer, such as one shown in this scanning electron micrograph, was caused by the production of too much stomach acid. And because stress, overeating, and spicy foods stimulate acid production, each of these was assumed to play a role in causing an ulcer. As a result, ulcer victims were often told to relax, avoid certain foods, and take medication that suppressed the release of stomach acid.

Sometimes, however, stomach acids make direct contact with the cells of the stomach lining. This damages these cells in the same way that a strong acid would burn the skin of your hand. The pain and inflammation that results is known as **gastritis**—inflammation of the stomach.

If acid continues to attack these cells, it may literally eat its way through the stomach lining to produce a deep crater or even a hole in the stomach wall. This kind of damage is known as a **peptic ulcer.** Because the ulcer is actually an open wound, each release of acid into the stomach causes intense pain.

Peptic ulcers present serious medical problems for people around the world. As much as 10 percent of the adult population of the United States suffers from ulcers at some point in their lives. In some countries, the numbers are greater.

Because the release of stomach acid causes further damage to the ulcer, physicians have tried to prevent the release of stomach acid as a way of treating ulcers. A number of drugs can block the release of stomach acids, and physicians have prescribed these drugs to help ulcers heal themselves. Unfortunately, the success rate for this kind of treatment has been very low. Even when doctors were able to heal ulcers using such drugs, the ulcers usually reappeared when the drugs were stopped.

What was the result? There were millions of people taking expensive, ineffective drugs. To make matters worse, by blocking acid release, these drugs interfere with the normal digestive process. To compensate, ulcer patients must eat bland, boring foods that do not require stomach acid for their digestion.

Checkpoint What is a peptic ulcer? 1

What Causes Ulcers?

With so many treatments that didn't work and so much guesswork as to what caused ulcers, could it be that the real cause of this problem was something else? Something hidden in the bodies of ulcer patients? In the early 1980s, two young Australian medical scientists, Dr. John Warren and Dr. Barry Marshall, began to wonder. Could the bacterium—now known as *Helicobacter pylori*—that they both found in their ulcer patients be the cause of ulcers? After months of unsuccessful attempts, Marshall finally found the right conditions to grow this bacterium in the laboratory.

Before long, Marshall had found compounds that killed *H. pylori* in the test tube. He then used these drugs in combination with some antibiotics on his ulcer patients. Seven out of ten patients were completely cured of ulcers. He was sure that he had found the answer to this terrible affliction.

A Daring Experiment

You might think that the scientific community would have jumped at Marshall's exciting results. But his initial reports were met with skepticism. Most scientists believed that acid and stress caused ulcers, and they pointed out that

TEACHER SUPPORT

Background Information

A great deal has been learned about *H. pylori* since Dr. Barry Marshall's groundbreaking research. It is now known that *H. pylori* survives in the acid environment of the stomach by burrowing into the mucous lining. There, it damages the protective layer of mucus, leading in about 10 to 20 percent of infected people to serious gastritis, ulcers, or stomach cancer. Virtually all infected people develop at least mild inflammation of the stomach lining.

It is estimated that half the people in the world, including 40 million people in the United States, are infected with *H. pylori*. About one in ten people in the United States has an ulcer, and *H. pylori* is believed to be responsible 90 percent of the time. People who are infected with *H. pylori* can pass the infection on to others, explaining why ulcers often seem to run in families.

Marshall had never proved that this bacterium could actually cause an ulcer.

In June 1984, Marshall decided to try the ultimate experiment. He walked into his lab, mixed up a strong dose of *H. pylori* bacteria in a test tube, and swallowed it. Three days later, Marshall awoke with the excruciating pain of gastritis—the first sign that acid has attacked the wall of the stomach and an ulcer is developing. Vomiting and stomach pain kept on for days. He had proven—at least to his own satisfaction—that this bacterium was the cause of gastritis and ulcers.

Rigorous Testing

Marshall then conducted a full-scale experiment, with 100 ulcer patients, to test his ideas. He divided his patients into four groups. One of the groups received no medication, one received just antibiotics, one received the exact mixture of *H. pylori*-killing drugs and antibiotics that Marshall now thought best, and one just the *H. pylori*-killing drugs. After a year, the results were very clear.

Ulcers persisted in three of the groups. But in one group—the one receiving Marshall's combination of *H. pylori*-killing drugs and antibiotics—the *H. pylori* bacteria and the ulcers were gone in 70 percent of the patients. **Dr. Marshall had successfully shown that the *H. pylori* bacteria could cause ulcers and that ulcers could be cured by destroying the bacteria.** In the last few years, one medical panel after another has endorsed Marshall's work, and other scientists have duplicated his findings. By using newer, more powerful antibiotics, cure rates as high as 90 percent have now been reported. Doctors around the world are now getting used to a new bit of knowledge: Ulcers can be cured!

Barry Marshall's work is a perfect example of the scientific method in action. Part luck, part intuition, and part Marshall's hard work had produced the kind of overwhelming evidence that was needed to overcome the doubts of other scientists—and, ultimately, to save thousands of human lives.

Figure 38–15
Today, peptic ulcers are thought to be caused by a bacterium called Helicobacter pylori, *which means "screw-shaped bacterium from the stomach" (magnification: 5100X). Approximately 50 percent of Americans over the age of 50 are infected with* H. pylori. *In some developing countries, nearly all adults are infected with* H. pylori. *Infections by this bacterium seem to run in the family, which suggests that it is spread from person-to-person by contaminated drinking water, eating utensils, and food. Public health officials around the world are now devising ways to deal with this bacterium.*

Section Review 38-4

1. **Explain** how ulcers are caused and describe how they can be treated.
2. **BRANCHING OUT ACTIVITY** Many drugs originally marketed as anti-ulcer medications because they suppress acid release are now sold over the counter for antacid relief and the prevention of heartburn. **Formulate a hypothesis** to explain why this has happened.

4 ASSESS

Quick Check

Call on a student to define peptic ulcer. Call on another student to identify the cause of this disease. Call on a third student to name the types of drugs that are now used to cure a peptic ulcer.

Section Review 38-4

1. Ulcers are caused by the bacterium *H. pylori*; they can be cured with a combination of antibiotics and *H. pylori*–killing drugs.
2. Students may hypothesize that the drugs are useful in treating the painful symptoms of ulcers, heartburn, and related conditions even though the drugs do not cure these conditions.

Learning Modality

Auditory Learning Using the following straightforward statements, review how the research of Dr. Barry Marshall changed the way that ulcers are treated: Physicians used to believe that ulcers were caused by too much stomach acid. Marshall showed that ulcers are caused by bacteria. Thus, treatment shifted from drugs that reduce stomach acids to drugs that fight bacteria.

Checkpoint

1 A peptic ulcer is an open wound in the lining of the stomach.

TEACHER SUPPORT

Activity

COMPARING DRUGS
Have students examine the labels of several over-the-counter drugs for acid indigestion, heartburn, sour stomach, and similar problems caused by stomach acid to see which drugs neutralize the stomach from acid and which ones prevent the production of acid. How do the ingredients and side effects differ for the different types of drugs? Have students summarize their observations in a table. Then have students compare the drugs they examined with the drugs that are used to cure ulcers caused by *H. pylori*. Frequently the drugs cause side effects and young children may not be able to take some of them because they are too strong. On the positive side, anti–*H. pylori* drugs cure the ulcers rather than just temporarily alleviate the symptoms, as over-the-counter drugs do.

Ancillary Support

The resources below can be used to support your teaching strategy for these two pages.

TR Explore: Antacid Antics
BL Inquiry Activity: A Pain in the Gut

CHAPTER 38

Laboratory Investigation

Vitamin C in Fruit Juice

Before the Lab

1. Indophenol may be purchased from a biological supply company.
2. Purchase two or three different fruit juices in addition to orange juice for students to test.
3. Test the juices beforehand, and dilute them if necessary. If different juices are to be compared, dilute each of them equally. The juices should be dilute enough so that several drops will have to be added to the indophenol to change the color from blue to clear. If the ascorbic acid in the juice is too concentrated, only one drop will be needed to change the color, and this will make comparisons difficult.

Pre-Lab Discussion

Have students read the entire procedure for this investigation. Then ask students the following questions.

What is the purpose of this investigation? (To determine the effect of exposure to air on the vitamin C content of food.)

What causes the indophenol to turn from blue to clear? (The vitamin C, or ascorbic acid, in the juice.)

Why does this reaction occur? (Acids such as ascorbic acid are reducing agents; that is, they deoxidize other compounds by donating electrons. In indophenol, this leads to a change of color, from blue to clear.)

If just a few drops of one juice turn the indophenol blue but many drops of another juice are needed to bring about the same color change, which juice has more vitamin C? (The juice that required fewer drops to turn the indophenol from blue to clear has more vitamin C.)

Laboratory Investigation

DESIGNING AN EXPERIMENT

Vitamin C in Fruit Juice

Although many vertebrate animals can synthesize their own vitamin C, humans cannot. For this reason, you need to consume foods that will supply you with adequate amounts of this essential nutrient. Vitamin C is found in many vegetables, such as potatoes and broccoli, but orange juice is probably the best source for vitamin C. In this investigation, you will design an experiment to determine the effect exposure to air has on the vitamin C content of selected foods.

Problem

How does exposure to air affect the vitamin C content of certain foods? **Design an experiment** to answer the question.

Suggested Materials

- small beakers
- 100 percent orange juice, refrigerated
- water
- burette
- indophenol solution
- other kinds of fruit drinks
- glass stirring rod
- funnel

Suggested Procedure

1. **Set up your equipment as shown in the diagram.**
2. **While carefully standing on a chair, pour orange juice into the funnel at the top of the burette. Record the initial level of the juice in milliliters.**
3. **Pour 10 mL of indophenol indicator solution into a beaker. CAUTION:** ***Be careful using indophenol because it stains. Do not drink any of the substances used in the lab. Wash your hands thoroughly after cleaning up.***
4. **Place the beaker below the burette and turn the stop valve to the open position so that only one drop of orange juice falls into the indophenol.**
5. **As each drop of juice falls into the indophenol, stir the mixture and note the color.**
6. **Keep adding drops until the blue indicator color becomes colorless when you stir. Turn the burette valve off.**

Safety Tips

- Have students wear lab aprons and safety goggles while they carry out the procedure.
- Remind students to avoid splashing indophenol on their clothing in order to prevent stains.
- Emphasize that students should be careful when handling glass equipment. Ask them to notify you of any breakage.
- Make sure students are aware that the juices used in the investigation should not be consumed, because they may have become contaminated with bacteria after sitting outside the refrigerator.
- Instruct students to wash their hands when they have completed the procedure.

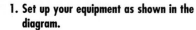

7. Read the level of the juice in the burette. Record this measurement.

8. Using the same technique as in steps 1 to 7, design an experiment to determine the effect that exposure to air has on the vitamin C content in orange juice. You may also wish to do a similar experiment with powdered drinks that are fortified with vitamin C.

9. Propose a hypothesis and write up your procedure. Make sure the procedure has only one variable and includes a control.

10. Obtain the approval of your teacher before carrying out your experiment.

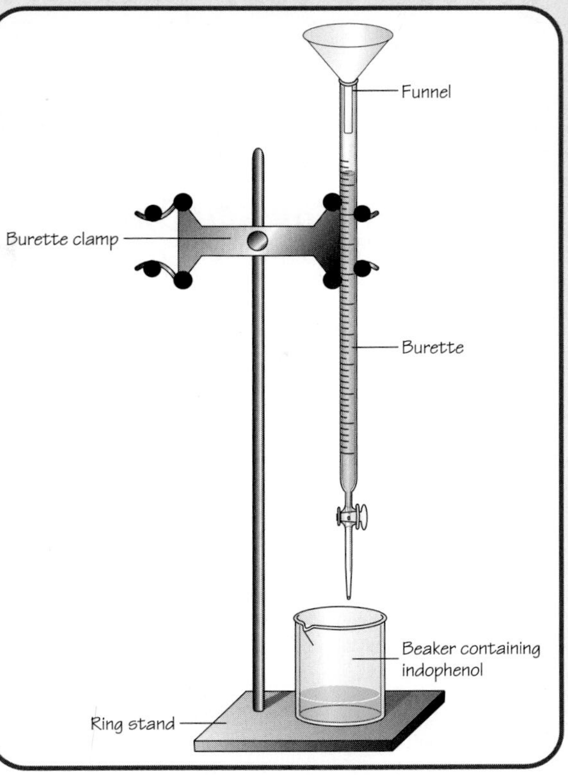

Observations

1. How many milliliters of the orange juice were needed to change the color of the indophenol?
2. Construct a bar graph to compare the number of milliliters of juice required in each trial of your experiment.
3. How did your data compare with that of other groups?

Analysis and Conclusions

1. What is the relationship between the volume of juice required to reach the end point of the titration and the vitamin C content of the juice?
2. Under what conditions did the orange juice have the highest vitamin C content? The lowest? Did your results support your hypothesis?
3. Do the results of your experiment suggest how to handle foods with vitamin C? Explain your answer.

More to Explore

What effect does temperature have on the vitamin C content in orange juice? Design an experiment to answer the question.

Skills Development
Students will use these skills while completing the laboratory investigation: hypothesizing, designing an experiment, measuring, observing, interpreting data, comparing, inferring, evaluating, drawing conclusions, and communicating.

Teaching Strategies
1. Students' hypotheses may vary. Make sure students understand that the less ascorbic acid there is in the juice, the more drops of juice they will need to change the indophenol from blue to clear.
2. Students may work in groups if there is not enough equipment for each student to work independently. Have members of each group take turns performing the different tasks so that all the students have an opportunity to practice each skill.
3. If the chairs in your classroom are not safe to stand on, provide a sturdy step stool for students to use in step 2.

Answers to
Observations

1. The number of drops needed to change the color of the indophenol will depend on the concentration of ascorbic acid in the juice samples tested.
2. The samples of juice that are low in ascorbic acid, including the samples that have been exposed to the air, will require more drops of juice to change the color of the indophenol. This should be reflected in students' bar graphs.
3. The data may vary somewhat from one group of students to another, but all the groups should find that the most dilute juices require the greatest number of milliliters to be added to the indophenol to produce the color change.

Answers to
Analysis and Conclusions

1. The volume of juice required to reach the end point of the titration is inversely related to the vitamin C content of the juice: The more vitamin C that is present, the fewer milliliters of juice that are required to turn the indophenol from blue to clear.
2. The freshest orange juice should have the highest vitamin C content. The longer the juice has been exposed to air, the lower the vitamin C content will be. These results support the hypothesis that exposure to air destroys vitamin C in foods.
3. The results suggest that foods containing vitamin C should be stored in sealed containers to reduce their exposure to air. This will help preserve their vitamin C content.

More to Explore

Students could investigate the effect of temperature on the amount of vitamin C in orange juice by heating juice samples to different temperatures, and then comparing the amounts of vitamin C they still contain. Students might hypothesize that the greater the temperature to which the juice is heated or the longer the juice is heated, the lower the vitamin C content of the juice will be.

Study Guide

Review Strategy

Divide the class into several small groups. Assign each group one food, such as cheese pizza, hamburger on a bun, garden salad, ice cream, or fresh fruit. Have the members of the group work together to identify the primary nutrients in the assigned food, and then write a concise description to illustrate how the nutrients in the food are digested and absorbed. Make sure students do not forget the fats or added sugars in the foods if these are significant. The descriptions should identify the path the foods take through the digestive system, the digestive organs and enzymes that are involved in breaking down the primary nutrients in the foods, and where and how absorption of the nutrients takes place. When the groups are finished, ask them to share their work. Have students compare different groups' analyses of the same nutrients—for example, the proteins in cheese pizza and a hamburger. Did the groups name the same organs and enzymes? Have groups work together to correct any discrepancies.

Recalling Main Ideas

1. b
2. c
3. a
4. d
5. d
6. c
7. a
8. c
9. b
10. d

Assessment

Reviewing What You Learned

1. Humans must consume nutrients for energy to perform various types of actions and for materials to make body cells and tissues.
2. The amount of heat energy needed to raise the temperature of 1 gram of water by 1 degree Celsius.
3. Water, carbohydrates, fats, proteins, vitamins, and minerals.

Study Guide

Summarizing Key Concepts

The key concepts in each section of this chapter are listed below to help you review the chapter content. Make sure you understand each concept and its relationship to other concepts and to the theme of this chapter.

38–1 Nutrition

- Foods provide energy to perform work and raw materials to build body tissues.
- Food energy is measured in units of the Calorie, which is equivalent to 1000 calories.
- A human body needs water, carbohydrates, fats, proteins, vitamins, and minerals.
- Carbohydrates, fats, and proteins provide energy and the material to build body tissues. Vitamins and minerals are needed in small amounts for the proper functioning of the body.

38–2 The Digestive System

- The digestive system converts food into simple molecules that the body can use.
- The process of digestion begins in the mouth by the action of enzymes such as amylase and pepsin. Food is digested in the stomach and is absorbed by the cells of the villi, which make up the lining of the small intestine.
- Insulin and glucagon help in regulating nutrient levels in the blood.

38–3 The Excretory System

- The kidneys remove wastes, such as urea, and regulate the water in the bloodstream.
- The kidneys, consisting of nephrons, carry out the filtration of blood plasma.
- The urine produced passes through the ureter to the bladder.

38–4 A Cure for Ulcers?

- Recent experiments indicate that the *H. pylori* bacterium can cause ulcers—craters in the stomach wall—by reducing the stomach's layer of protective mucus.

Reviewing Key Terms

Review the following vocabulary terms and their meaning. Then use each term in a complete sentence.

38–1 Nutrition

Calorie

38–2 The Digestive System

mouth
salivary gland
amylase
lysozyme
esophagus
peristalsis
stomach
gastric gland
pepsin
small intestine
pancreas
liver
bile
villus
large intestine
islet of Langerhans
insulin
glucagon

38–3 The Excretory System

kidney
renal artery
renal vein
ureter
urinary bladder
nephron
glomerulus
Bowman's capsule
reabsorption
loop of Henle
antidiuretic hormone

38–4 A Cure for Ulcers?

gastritis
peptic ulcer

Inquiry-Based Strategy

Ask students what meals and snacks would provide a balanced daily diet. Suggest that each student write a day's menus for breakfast, lunch, dinner, and two snacks that incorporate the correct number of servings of food from each of the five food groups, as shown in the Food Guide Pyramid on page 856. Be sure students indicate the serving size of each food. Ask volunteers to share their work with the rest of the class. If other class members do not like a particular food included in a menu, have them name another food from the same food group that they would substitute and identify how large one serving would be. Lead the class in a discussion of which menus are healthiest because they are also low in fat and salt and high in fiber. Which menus are most appealing?

CHAPTER 38

Recalling Main Ideas

Choose the letter of the answer that best completes the statement or answers the question.

1. The amount of heat energy given off by food is measured in

a. ATP. **c.** glucose molecules.
b. calories. **d.** carbohydrates.

2. Examples of carbohydrates include

a. vegetable oils. **c.** sugars and starches.
b. amino acids. **d.** lipids.

3. The foods at the top of the Food Guide Pyramid should be eaten

a. only sparingly.
b. at every meal.
c. four to six servings a day.
d. six to eleven servings a day.

4. The enzyme amylase breaks down the chemical bonds in

a. fats. **c.** sugars.
b. proteins. **d.** starches.

5. Food moves through the alimentary canal by

a. the cardiac sphincter. **c.** air pressure.
b. gravity. **d.** peristalsis.

6. Insulin is produced by the

a. stomach. **c.** pancreas.
b. duodenum. **d.** liver.

7. Where in the nephron is the blood plasma filtered out of the bloodstream?

a. glomerulus **c.** collecting tubule
b. Bowman's capsule **d.** loop of Henle

8. Which hormone returns more water to the bloodstream?

a. insulin **c.** ADH
b. glucagon **d.** pepsin

9. A peptic ulcer is an inflammation of the

a. gums. **c.** colon.
b. stomach wall. **d.** kidneys.

10. Dr. Barry Marshall's research showed that peptic ulcers are caused by

a. acid-blocking drugs. **c.** a virus.
b. stress and anxiety. **d.** a bacterium.

Putting It All Together

Using the information on pages xxx to xxxi, complete the following concept map.

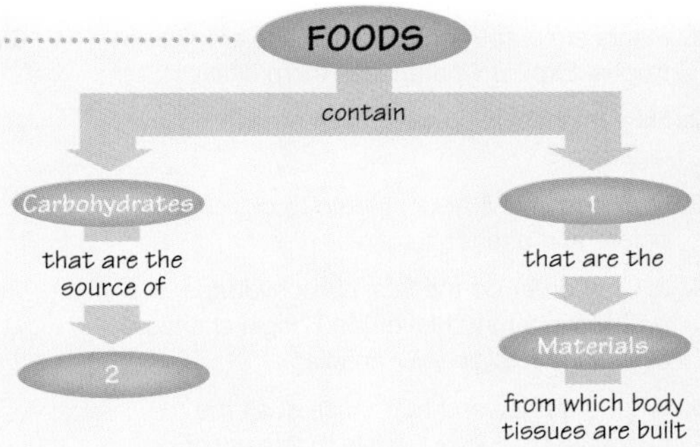

Putting It All Together

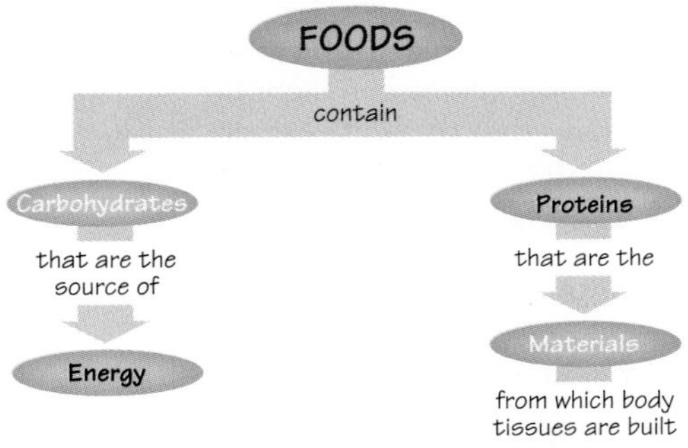

4. It adds bulk to the material moving through the digestive system, which helps the system process foods.
5. They are both needed for normal development and functioning of the body. Vitamins are organic whereas minerals are inorganic.
6. Leafy vegetables such as broccoli, lettuce, and spinach. It is needed to synthesize blood-clotting factors.
7. The Food Guide Pyramid shows how many servings of different types of foods should be eaten each day for a healthful diet. The foods at the base are needed in greater amounts than the foods at the apex.
8. Chewing food thoroughly helps break it down into small pieces so that more surface area is exposed to the action of digestive enzymes.
9. Peristalsis pushes food through the alimentary canal.
10. The kidneys, ureters, bladder, and urethra.
11. Proteins.
12. The fluid formed by the kidneys that contains waste products for excretion.
13. To remove waste products in people whose own kidneys do not function adequately.
14. Inflammation of the stomach.

Expanding the Concepts

1. A heterotroph is an organism that cannot make its own food from inorganic materials, and therefore must live on other organisms or their wastes. An autotroph is a self-nourishing organism that can synthesize organic molecules from simple inorganic materials.
2. It moistens the food, making it easier to chew and swallow.
3. The liver produces bile, which helps to dissolve and disperse the droplets of fat in fatty foods, making it possible for enzymes to reach the fat molecules and break them down. After absorption, some of the sugar from the bloodstream is stored in the liver as glycogen.

Assessment (continued)

4. Digestion of carbohydrates begins in the mouth as amylase in saliva starts to break down starches, releasing sugars. Digestion of proteins begins in the stomach as pepsin and hydrochloric acid break protein molecules into smaller polypeptide fragments. Digestion of fats begins in the duodenum as bile dissolves and disperses fat droplets.
5. It produces enzymes that help break down carbohydrates, proteins, lipids, and nucleic acids. It also produces insulin, which stimulates cells to remove sugar from the bloodstream and store it as glycogen and fat, and glucagon, which stimulates tissues to break down glycogen and fat and release sugars into the blood.
6. Kidneys remove wastes by forcing blood through a filtering system and then reabsorbing only the nonwaste blood components. The kidney is composed of over a million nephrons that purify the blood as it passes through. It also has an inner cavity, the renal pelvis, that collects the urine as it is formed, and passes it on to the ureters.
7. Insulin stimulates cells in the liver, muscles, and fatty tissues to remove sugar from the bloodstream. The cells then store the sugar in the form of glycogen and fat.
8. They might return more of the water to the purified blood as the filtrate passes through the tubules and collecting duct. With production of a more concentrated urine, less water is eliminated from the body.
9. When the water content is about right, the hypothalamus signals the pituitary gland to release antidiuretic hormone (ADH), which causes the tubules in the kidneys to reabsorb more water. If the water content of the blood rises, the hypothalamus does not release ADH, and the tubules reabsorb less water. This produces a less concentrated urine, which quickly eliminates the excess water from the body.
10. It reduces the risk of contaminating the food with bacteria. If hand washing reduces the risk of infection with *H. pylori*, then it may also reduce the incidence of stomach ulcers.

Assessment

Reviewing What You Learned

Answer each of the following in a complete sentence.

1. Why must humans consume nutrients?
2. How much energy does a calorie represent?
3. What are six categories of essential nutrients?
4. Why is cellulose an important part of the diet?
5. How are vitamins and minerals similar? How are they different?
6. What are some food sources of vitamin K? What is the function of this vitamin in the body?
7. What is the Food Guide Pyramid? Explain the significance of this shape.
8. Why is it important to chew food thoroughly before swallowing?
9. Explain the function of peristalsis.
10. List the organs that make up the excretory system.
11. What essential nutrients are the primary sources of wastes that the kidneys excrete?
12. What is urine?
13. Explain the function of a kidney dialysis machine.
14. What is gastritis?

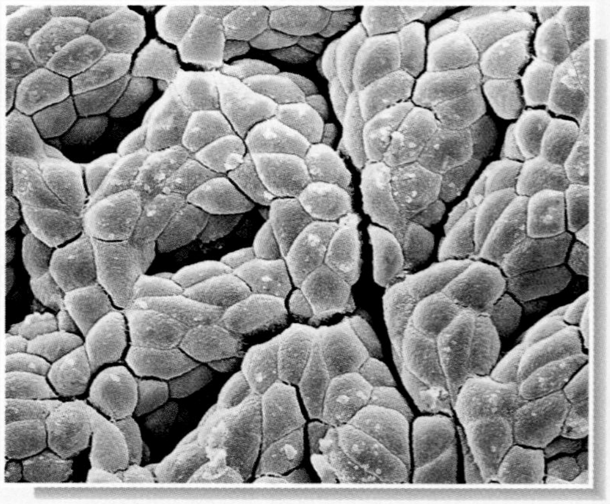

Expanding the Concepts

Discuss each of the following in a brief paragraph.

1. Plants are autotrophs and humans are heterotrophs. Explain what makes them different.
2. How might sipping water with a meal aid in digestion?
3. How does the liver contribute to digestion before and after absorption?
4. In what order do the fats, carbohydrates, and proteins in a mouthful of food begin chemical digestion? Explain your answer.
5. What enzymes and hormones does the pancreas produce? Explain their functions.
6. Explain how kidneys remove wastes. Relate the structure of a kidney to its function.
7. How does insulin affect the liver, muscles, and fatty tissues?
8. How might the kidneys respond to dehydration?
9. Describe the "feedback" mechanism that helps the kidneys maintain the body's water balance.
10. How could washing your hands before preparing a meal reduce the incidence of stomach ulcers?

Extending Your Thinking

1. The mirror clouds up when students breathe on it, due to the condensation of water vapor on the mirror. This illustrates that the lungs excrete water, as well as carbon dioxide.

Skills Trace
Observing
- Focus p. 852
- Practice p. 856
- Assess p. 875

2. Menus should include the correct number of servings of foods from each of the five food groups, as indicated in the Food Guide Pyramid. The correct serving size of each food should also be indicated.

Skills Trace
Relating
- Focus p. 864
- Practice p. 866
- Assess p. 875

Extending Your Thinking

Use the skills you have developed in this chapter to answer the following.

1. **Observing** Obtain a pocket-sized mirror. Hold it about 3 cm from your mouth and exhale onto it. What substance do you observe on the mirror? Explain how your observation illustrates a function of the excretory system.
2. **Relating** Create a poster describing a "Specials of the Day" menu. Include selections for a breakfast, lunch, and dinner that will appeal to your classmates and that also follow the dietary guidelines in the Food Guide Pyramid.
3. **Predicting** If you had your gallbladder removed, would you have to change your diet? Explain your answer.
4. **Applying concepts** Explain how the work of the Australian physicians John Warren and Barry Marshall on *Helicobacter pylori* involved each of the following parts of the scientific method:
   - Developing a question
   - Stating a problem
   - Gathering and interpreting data
   - Formulating a hypothesis
   - Experimenting
5. **Hypothesizing** Some scientists predict that more minerals than the ones already known will be discovered to be essential nutrients. For example, garlic may contain minerals that help fight infection. Formulate a hypothesis to explain how this may happen.

Applying Your Skills

A Recipe for Tenderness

The molecules in protein-rich foods—such as meats, eggs, and cheese—are often complex and enormous in size. Each protein molecule is coiled and folded so that the bonds between its atoms must be broken down bit by bit to reach its center. The stomach has seven different protein-digesting enzymes. In this activity, you will observe the effects of several enzymes.

1. Obtain four test tubes containing solidified gelatin.
2. Add 1 mL of each of the following three solutions to the top of the gelatin: fresh pineapple, canned pineapple, meat tenderizer, and water. Why is water a part of this investigation? Why is gelatin used?
3. Put the test tubes in a refrigerator for 24 hours. After 24 hours, measure the amount of gelatin that has dissolved in each of the test tubes. Record your results in a bar graph.
4. Was there any difference between the actions of the fresh and the canned pineapple? How can you explain your results?
5. Carefully clean out the test tubes using hot water and properly discard the contents.

• GOING FURTHER •

6. Design an experiment to compare the effects of two brands of meat tenderizers containing different enzymes.

3. People who have their gallbladders removed have more difficulty digesting fats. Therefore, they might have to eliminate some fatty foods from their diet to avoid gastrointestinal problems.
4. Development of a question: They wanted to know what causes stomach ulcers. Stating a problem: The control of stomach acids, the presumed cause, was not a very effective treatment. Gathering and interpreting data: They observed the bacterium *H. pylori* in many of their ulcer patients. Forming a hypothesis: They hypothesized that infection with *H. pylori* was the cause of stomach ulcers. Experimenting: Marshall infected himself with the bacterium to see if he would develop ulcers. He also treated his ulcer patients with drugs known to kill *H. pylori* in the test tube to see if they would be cured of ulcers once the bacterium was eliminated.
5. Hypotheses should reveal that students understand the role of white blood cells in fighting infections.

Applying Your Skills

Teacher Notes

- For best results, use unflavored gelatin, which does not contain sugar. Make sure each test tube has an equal amount of gelatin.
- Students are likely to observe that the greatest amount of gelatin was dissolved in the test tube to which meat tenderizer was added. This is because meat tenderizer contains enzymes that break down proteins.

Answers

2. The test tube to which water is added is used as a control. Gelatin is used because it consists primarily of protein. It is obtained from animal tissues by boiling them.
4. The fresh pineapple probably dissolved more of the gelatin than the canned pineapple did. Differences in the action of the fresh and canned pineapple might be due to substances added to or removed from the pineapple during the canning process.
6. To compare the effects of two brands of meat tenderizers, two test tubes of gelatin should be compared, one having one brand of meat tenderizer added, the other having the other brand of meat tenderizer added.

Scoring Rubric

4 Response is thorough, accurate, and creative; shows an in-depth understanding of science skills, procedures, and concepts.

3 Response is complete, mostly accurate, and original; shows a satisfactory understanding of science skills, procedures, and concepts.

2 Response is mostly complete but includes some inaccuracies; shows an adequate understanding of science skills, procedures, and concepts.

1 Response is only partially complete and has many inaccuracies; shows an incomplete understanding of science skills, procedures, and concepts.

0 Response is mostly incomplete and/or inaccurate; shows a lack of understanding of science skills, procedures, and concepts.

Chapter 39 Reproductive System

Content Management	Student Edition Activities
■ Section 39–1 The Human Reproductive System, pp. 877–881 Human Sexual Development The Male Reproductive System The Female Reproductive System The Menstrual Cycle	Laboratory Investigation: Reproductive Organs and Gametes, pp. 894–895
■ Section 39–2 Fertilization and Development, pp. 882–889 Fertilization The Developing Embryo The Placenta Fetal Development Labor and Birth	MINI LAB: Early Human Development, p. 888
◆ BRANCHING OUT • In Depth Section 39–3 Sexually Transmitted Diseases, pp. 890–893 STDs—A Growing Problem Bacterial Diseases Viral Diseases Avoiding STDs	MINI LAB: Number Sense, p. 892

■ These sections cover all the necessary content and concepts for an enriched course in biology.
◆ This section covers content and concepts that are either applications or extensions of the enriched material.

Integration Strategies

SE Health, p. 878
Health, p. 887
Health, p. 890

Assessment Strategies

SE Chapter Review, pp. 896–899
TR Section Reviews
Chapter Test
BL Chapter Review
Practice Test
CTB Chapter 39 Test

Tech Prep

Teaching strategies appropriate for students who are in technical/vocational programs or who are considering post-secondary technical education can be found on the following **TE** pages: 886 and 889.

Meeting the Standards

Sections 39–1 through 39–3 cover three of the six content standards under **The Cell,** one of the three content standards under **The Molecular Basis of Heredity,** and one of the five content standards under **The Interdependence of Organisms** as described on pages 184–186 of The National Science Education Standards.

Chapter Planning Guide

Teacher's Edition Activities	Other Activities	Media and Technology
Chapter Discovery Learning Activity, p. 876 **Investigate:** Model Building, p. 878 **Inquiry Activity:** Double Division, p. 879 **Investigate:** Research, p. 881	**LM** Comparing Ovaries and Testes, #77 Investigating the Menstrual Cycle, #78 **TR** **Writing in Biology:** Reporting on Reproduction **Enrich:** Sperm Warfare **BL** **Inquiry Activity:** Boy or Girl?	**TB** The Male and Female Reproductive Systems, #48 Menstrual Cycle, #49
Inquiry Activity: How Does a Baby Grow?, p. 882 **Investigate:** Research, p. 884 **Activity:** Who Is Responsible?, p. 885 **Investigate:** Cooperative Learning, p. 887 **Activity:** Uterine Expansion, p. 887	**TR** **Enrich:** Testing in Utero **BL** **Inquiry Activity:** Havin' My Baby	
Investigate: Long-Term Project, p. 890 **Inquiry Activity:** Infection Detection, p. 891 **Activity:** Spreading Disease, p. 892	**TR** **Explore:** A Little Goes a Long Way **BL** **Inquiry Activity:** STDs—No Laughing Matter	

KEY: **SE** Student Edition **TE** Teacher's Edition **LM** Laboratory Manual **TR** Teaching Resources **BL** BioLog **TB** Transparency Box **CTB** Computer Test Bank

Materials List

TE **Inquiry Activity: Double Division,** p. 879 (20 minutes); pieces of string, toothpicks.
TE **Activity: Uterine Expansion,** p. 887 (20 minutes); nine large, round balloons.

SE **MINI LAB: Early Human Development,** p. 888 (30–40 minutes); modeling clay.
SE **MINI LAB: Number Sense,** p. 892 (30 minutes); graph paper, calculator.

Chapter 39

Reproductive System

Introducing the Chapter

. . . In Pictures

The infants in this photograph may be only a few months old, but their development began at least a year before the picture was taken. Have students examine the photograph, read the caption, and answer the following questions.

- **What are some ways these infants will change between the age they are here and the age you are now?** (They will get bigger and stronger and develop many more cognitive and motor abilities.)
- **What are some ways the infants have already changed since they were conceived?** (They have developed all their organ systems and multiplied their size many times over.)

In this chapter students will learn about these and other ways that children develop from conception to birth.

Teaching Strategy

The first section of the chapter describes the male and female reproductive systems. The way a child is conceived and develops through birth is explained in the second section. The BRANCHING OUT section describes sexually transmitted diseases and ways to avoid them.

BIO JOURNAL

Stimulate students' thinking by pointing out that a caregiver must take responsibility for an infant's needs for food and water, safety, hygiene, cognitive stimulation, emotional warmth, and physical contact. Have students consider what would be involved in providing for each of these needs. Instruct students to keep their entries in their portfolios.

CHAPTER 39

Reproductive System

FOCUSING THE CHAPTER
THEME: Patterns of Change

Biology and Your World

BIO JOURNAL

The infants in this photograph may look contented and easy to care for; however, raising a child is harder than you may think. Have you ever baby-sat for a younger sibling or another person's child? Was this easier or harder than you expected? In your journal, describe your experience. If you have never cared for a younger child, describe what you think the experience would be.

A group of babies

TEACHER SUPPORT

Chapter Discovery Learning Activity

TRUE OR FALSE?

Students may be misinformed about the reproductive system because sex is a sensitive issue. Have students complete this activity to uncover their misconceptions.

1. Give students a list of statements such as the following: "Girls go through puberty earlier than boys."(True.) "The human gestation period is about ten calendar months." (False.) "You cannot get an STD from just one sexual contact." (False.)
2. Find out how many students think each statement is true and how many think each is false. Then work with the class to revise each false statement so that it is true.

Results: By reviewing basic facts about the reproductive system, students will have a better foundation for learning the material in the chapter. Urge students to keep the revised statements to review at the end of the chapter.

The Human Reproductive System

SECTION **39–1**

GUIDE FOR READING

- Describe the functions of the male and female reproductive systems.
- List the four phases of the menstrual cycle.

WHAT IS THE SINGLE MOST important day in your life? If you said "my birthday," you are not alone. Not only is your birthday important to you, it's also important to those closest to you. Think about how many things depend on your birthday. Your birthday determines when you are allowed to go to school, when you qualify for a driver's license, and when you may vote.

To the rest of society, your birthday may indeed be the day your life began. To a biologist, however, birth is as much the end of a process—the process of reproduction—as it is a beginning. The trillions of cells in a newborn baby all come from the fusion of two reproductive cells. Human reproduction is the story of how these cells are produced and come together to form a single cell, from which a new life develops.

Human Sexual Development

For the first six weeks of development, male and female human embryos are nearly identical. Then, in the seventh week, the primary reproductive organs, which will eventually produce reproductive cells, or **gametes** (GAM-eets), begin to develop into either **ovaries** in females or **testes** (TEHS-teez; singular: testis) in males.

The ovaries and testes are endocrine glands. The ovaries produce estrogens—a group of steroid hormones that cause development of the female reproductive organs. And the testes produce androgens—steroid hormones that cause the male reproductive organs to develop. Although the male and female reproductive organs develop from the same tissues in the embryo, these hormones determine whether they will develop in the male or female pattern.

Figure 39–1 *Many changes in your life—both social and physical—are dependent on your age, including (a) getting your driver's license, (b) graduating from high school, and (c) shaving.*

SECTION 39–1

The Human Reproductive System

Performance Objectives

- Explain how male and female reproductive systems function.
- Distinguish among follicle phase, ovulation, luteal phase, and menstruation.

Laboratory Investigation Skill: Observing

1 ENGAGE

Ideas Through Images

Have students examine Figure 39–1, read the caption, and answer the following questions.

- **What are some other changes in your life that are dependent on age?** (Possible changes include getting a job, being allowed to vote, getting vaccinated, joining the military, and starting to date.)
- **Why do you think so many changes in life are dependent on age?** (Because they require a certain level of physical, emotional, or intellectual maturity that usually comes with increasing age.)

TEACHER SUPPORT

Managing Classroom Diversity

MULTICULTURAL STRATEGY

Students from some cultural backgrounds may be more embarrassed than others by open discussions of topics pertaining to sex. These students may vary in how they express their feelings of discomfort, ranging from blushes and avoidance of eye contact to crude remarks. Throughout the chapter, give students options such as library research and written assignments that do not require open classroom discussion of sensitive topics.

EDUCATIONAL EQUITY

Call students' attention to the fact that many slang or uncouth expressions are commonly used to refer to the reproductive organs and their functions. Some of these expressions are derogatory, particularly to females. Raise students' awareness of the derogatory nature of the expressions and point out how their use can contribute to poor self-concept and low self-esteem.

Ancillary Support

The resource below can be used to support your teaching strategy for these two pages.

TR Writing in Biology: Reporting on Reproduction

2 EXPLORE

Discussion

Tell students that the ovaries in females and the testes in males produce sex hormones that control sexual development and reproduction. Have students discuss how sex hormones are regulated. (Like other endocrine hormones, levels of sex hormones are monitored by the hypothalamus, which stimulates the pituitary gland to produce hormones that regulate the ovaries and testes.)

3 TEACH

Investigate

Model Building Have students make a two-dimensional model showing the feedback system that regulates the production of sex hormones in males or females. Their models should include the hypothalamus and pituitary in addition to either the ovary or testis. Models should also show the hormones produced by each gland and the target organ of each hormone.

Ideas Through Images

Have students examine Figure 39–2, read the caption, and answer the following questions.

- **If sperm are produced in the testes, which reproductive organs and glands must they pass by or through to reach the urethra?** (The epididymis, vas deferens, seminal vesicle, prostate gland, and bulbourethral gland.)
- **Which vessel carries sperm from the testis to the urethra?** (The vas deferens.)

INTEGRATING HEALTH

Risks include increased blood pressure; liver and heart damage; infertility; and aggressive behavior. Females may develop facial hair and a low voice. Because steroids are injected, there is a risk of HIV infection and hepatitis B if needles have been shared.

During childhood, the reproductive glands, or gonads, continue to produce small amounts of estrogen and androgen, which help to shape development. However, the gonads are not capable of producing reproductive cells until puberty, a period of rapid sexual development that usually occurs in the early teenage years. During puberty, the gonads complete their development and the reproductive system becomes fully functional. Puberty may occur at any time between 9 and 15 years of age, and on average occurs about a year earlier in females than in males.

Puberty begins when hormone levels begin to increase. The hypothalamus releases substances that signal the pituitary gland to begin producing two hormones—**follicle-stimulating hormone** (FSH) and **luteinizing hormone** (LH).

In males, LH causes certain cells in the testes to produce **testosterone** (tehs-TAHS-ter-ohn), the principal androgen, or male hormone. FSH and testosterone are necessary for other cells in the testes to develop into **sperm,** the male gametes. These diploid (2n) cells undergo meiosis, which results in 4 haploid (n) cells, each of which contains 23 chromosomes. After the completion of meiosis, these cells develop into mature sperm cells with long flagella.

In addition to sperm development, testosterone is responsible for the development of a male's secondary sex characteristics. In puberty, the male's voice deepens, he begins to grow body hair, and he finds it easier to develop large muscles. ●

In females, FSH and LH stimulate the ovaries to produce the female sex hormones, **progesterone** and **estrogen,** responsible for the development of female secondary sex characteristics, such as breast development and widening of the hips. In addition, these hormones work with FSH and LH to produce female gametes called **ova** (singular: ovum), or eggs.

INTEGRATING HEALTH

Testosterone is a natural anabolic steroid. What are some of the risks involved in taking a synthetic anabolic steroid?

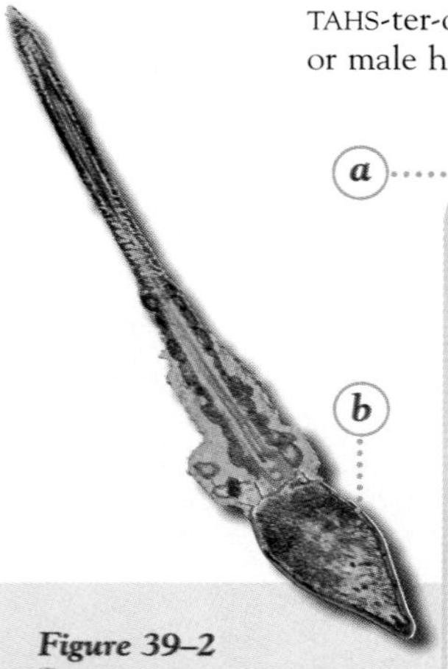

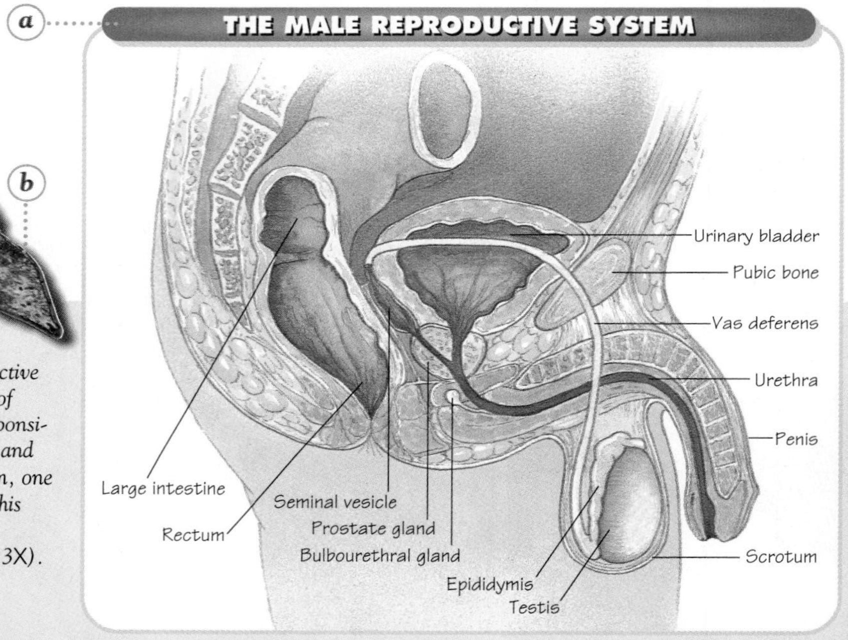

Figure 39–2 *(a) The male reproductive system is a collection of organs and glands responsible for the production and delivery of (b) sperm, one of which is shown in this electron micrograph (magnification: 87,413X).*

TEACHER SUPPORT

Background Information

During prenatal development, the testes form within the abdominal cavity and then move slowly downward, usually descending into the scrotum at about the time of birth. Sometimes the testes do not descend by birth, however, a condition that is called cryptorchidism. This condition can be corrected with hormones or surgery before puberty.

Although the external location of the testes may put them at greater risk of injury, it is necessary for the production of sperm. Sperm do not develop normally at internal body temperature, instead requiring the somewhat cooler temperature of the testes. If the testes are too warm, which sometimes happens from wearing tight clothing, sterility may result. Excessive cold may also inhibit sperm production. In cold weather, involuntary muscular actions move the testes closer to the body.

THE FEMALE REPRODUCTIVE SYSTEM

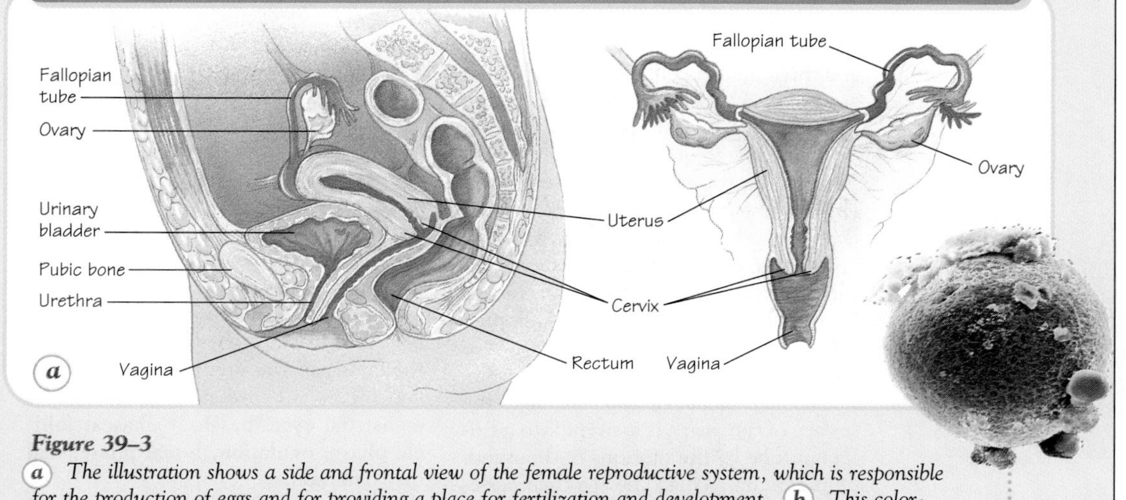

Figure 39–3
(a) The illustration shows a side and frontal view of the female reproductive system, which is responsible for the production of eggs and for providing a place for fertilization and development. (b) This color-enhanced electron micrograph of a single human egg shows its protective covering (colored red) as well as the remnants from the follicle (colored yellow) in which the egg developed (magnification: 470X).

The Male Reproductive System

The male reproductive system has the task of producing and delivering sperm. Sperm are produced in the testes, which descend from the abdominal cavity just before birth into a sac called the **scrotum,** located outside the body cavity. This location keeps the temperature of the testes about 2°C cooler than the rest of the body, for sperm development.

The testes are made up of tightly coiled tubules called **seminiferous** (sehm-uh-NIHF-er-uhs) **tubules.** More than 100 million sperm cells are produced in the seminiferous tubules every day. When mature, the sperm travel into the **epididymis** (ehp-uh-DIHD-ih-mihs), where they are stored. After a brief period, they are released into the **vas deferens** (VAS DEHF-uh-rehnz). The vas deferens extends upward from the scrotum into the abdominal cavity.

Glands lining the reproductive tract—including the seminal vesicle, the prostate, and the bulbourethral gland—release a nutrient-rich fluid called semen, in which sperm are suspended.

The Female Reproductive System

The female reproductive system produces gametes, too. However, the fact that fertilization and development of a baby both take place inside the female's body places special demands on the female reproductive system. In contrast to the millions of sperm produced each day, the ovaries produce, on average, just one egg every 28 days or so. Each time an egg is released from one of the ovaries, the rest of the reproductive tract must be prepared to nourish and support a developing embryo.

FSH stimulates the development of a **follicle**—a cluster of cells that contains a developing egg. As the follicle gets larger and larger, the egg passes through the early stages of meiosis. When meiosis is complete, a single large haploid (n) egg

Ideas Through Images

Have students examine Figure 39–3, read the caption, and answer the following questions.

- **How does an egg travel from the ovary to the uterus?** (Through the Fallopian tube.)
- **Why do you think that egg cells, such as the one shown here, are so much larger than sperm?** (Because they must provide nourishment for the earliest stages of the embryo's development.)

Inquiry Activity

Building a Model

Double Division

Ask students to build a model of meiosis, the type of cell division that leads to the production of haploid gametes. Suggest that they use materials such as pieces of string to represent cell membranes and small objects such as toothpicks to represent chromosomes. Models should show that the chromosomes divide once and the cell divides twice to produce four gametes, each with half the original number of chromosomes. Ask students why it is necessary for a sexually reproducing species to produce gametes with the haploid number of chromosomes. (So that the offspring will have the normal diploid number.)

Laboratory Investigation

The Laboratory Investigation, Reproductive Organs and Gametes, on pages 894–895 is appropriate to use at this point in the chapter.

TEACHER SUPPORT

Facts and Figures

Share the following facts and figures with students to help them appreciate the different roles that males and females play in the process of reproduction.

- Sperm have their greatest fertilizing ability during the first 36 hours after ejaculation.
- Sperm are among the smallest human cells; for a clump of sperm to be even barely visible to the naked eye, there must be about 100,000 of them in the clump.
- An egg cell is about 90,000 times larger than a sperm cell.
- Halfway through fetal development, a female has 6 to 7 million eggs; at birth only about 400,000 remain, and by puberty the number is down to 200,000 or fewer.
- Only about 400 of the remaining eggs actually mature during a woman's 30 to 40 years of potential reproduction.

Ancillary Support

The resources below can be used to support your teaching strategy for these two pages.

LM Comparing Ovaries and Testes, #77
TR Enrich: Sperm Warfare
BL Inquiry Activity: Boy or Girl?
TB The Male and Female Reproductive Systems, #48

Discussion

The production of eggs in females occurs cyclically—one egg matures and is ready to be fertilized about every 28 days. In males, sperm production occurs continuously. Ask students to discuss why the production of gametes is cyclical in females but not in males. (Females not only produce gametes; they also nourish the developing embryo. This requires gradual changes in the uterus in preparation for the fertilized egg. Males, in contrast, produce only gametes. As a result, their reproductive systems can work full time producing sperm.)

Ideas Through Images

Have students examine Figure 39–4, read the caption, and answer the following questions.

- **What are the four phases of the menstrual cycle?** (Follicle phase, ovulation, luteal phase, and menstruation.)
- **Which hormone appears to stimulate ovulation by surging to a dramatic peak just before ovulation occurs?** (LH, which is produced by the pituitary gland.)
- **What happens to the level of progesterone once ovulation has occurred?** (It gradually rises to a plateau.)
- **Why do changes in the lining of the uterus mirror changes taking place in the ovary during the menstrual cycle?** (The lining of the uterus is where a fertilized egg implants. It is shed during menstruation if an egg is not fertilized, and it builds up again as another follicle matures and ovulation occurs.)

and three smaller cells called polar bodies are produced. Because the polar bodies have little cytoplasm, they disintegrate.

While the follicle is developing, cells surrounding the egg produce larger and larger amounts of estrogen. When the level of these hormones reaches a critical point, hormones from the pituitary gland cause the follicle to rupture, and the egg is released into one of the two **Fallopian tubes.** The release of an egg is known as **ovulation.**

As the mature egg breaks through the surface of the ovary, it is swept into a Fallopian tube by the motions of thousands of microscopic cilia. The egg then passes into a muscular chamber called the **uterus.** The outer end of the uterus is called the cervix. Beyond the cervix is a canal known as the vagina, which is the passageway that leads to the outside of the body.

The Menstrual Cycle

Ovulation is just one of a series of events that occur in a pattern called the **menstrual cycle.** The menstrual cycle takes, on average, about 28 days. As an egg develops, the lining of the uterus is prepared to receive it. If the egg is fertilized after ovulation, it is implanted in the uterus and embryonic development begins. If it is not fertilized, the egg and the lining of the uterus pass out of the body. This is called menstruation. **The menstrual cycle has four phases: follicle phase, ovulation, luteal phase, and menstruation.**

Follicle Phase

The follicle phase begins when the level of estrogen in the bloodstream is low. The hypothalamus senses the low level of estrogen and causes the pituitary

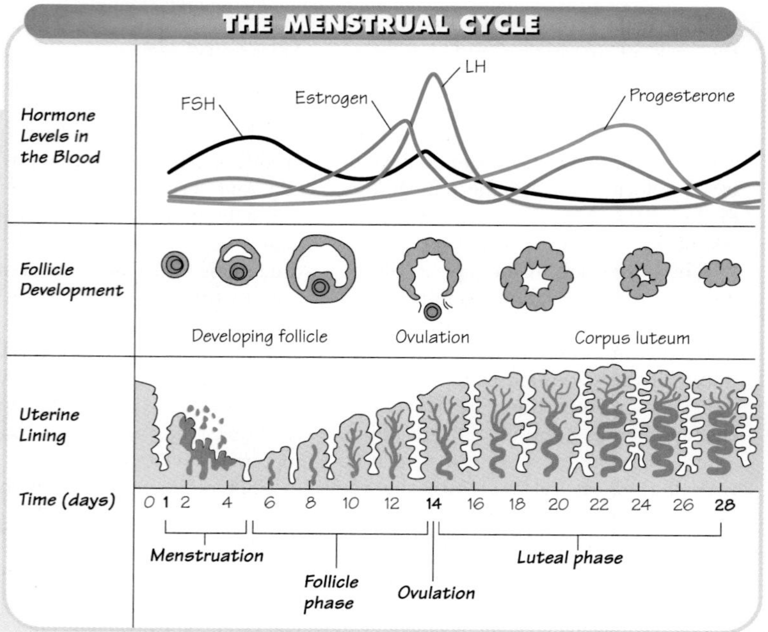

Figure 39–4
The menstrual cycle, which is controlled by hormones produced by the ovary (progesterone and estrogens) and the pituitary gland (FSH and LH), occurs on average about every 28 days. Notice the changes in hormone levels in the blood, the development of the follicle, and the changes in the uterine lining during the cycle, illustrated in the diagram.

TEACHER SUPPORT

Background Information

The first menstrual period is called menarche. It usually occurs around age 11 or 12 but may occur as early as age 9 or as late as age 18. Menstrual cycles then continue for some 30 to 40 years, usually interrupted only by pregnancies, until the time of menopause, which is defined as one full year without menstrual periods. This typically occurs at about age 47 to 49, but for some women it may occur as early as age 40 or as late as age 55. The length of a normal menstrual cycle typically ranges from 20 to 36 days, with an average of 28 days. The length of the menstrual period itself usually ranges from 3 to 6 days. There may be great variation in the menstrual cycle for a given female. Factors such as stress and weight loss can interfere with normal menstrual cycles, causing a female to have a late menstruation or to skip one or more menstrual periods altogether.

gland to release FSH and LH into the bloodstream. These hormones act on the ovary, stimulating a follicle to develop to maturity. As the egg develops, the cells of the follicle produce more and more estrogen. Estrogen causes the lining of the uterus to thicken in preparation for a fertilized egg.

Ovulation

Ovulation is the shortest phase of the cycle. When the egg is mature, the pituitary gland sends out a burst of LH. LH causes the wall of the follicle to break open and the egg is released into one of the Fallopian tubes.

Luteal Phase

The luteal phase of the cycle begins after the egg is released. As the egg moves through the Fallopian tube, the cells of the ruptured follicle undergo a transformation. The follicle turns yellow and is now known as the **corpus luteum** (KOR-puhs LOOT-ee-uhm), which means "yellow body" in Latin. The corpus luteum continues to produce estrogen, but now produces large amounts of progesterone too. Progesterone stimulates cell and tissue growth in the lining of the uterus, preparing it for pregnancy. Progesterone also inhibits the release of LH and FSH.

The chances of an egg being successfully fertilized are greatest around the time of ovulation. If the egg is not fertilized, the corpus luteum breaks down and estrogen levels decrease.

Menstruation

Menstruation begins when the level of estrogen in the blood becomes so low that the lining of the uterus cannot be maintained. Tissues detach from the uterine wall and are discharged through the vagina along with blood and the unfertilized egg. Menstruation usually lasts 3 to 7 days. When it ends, a new cycle begins.

What starts a new cycle? The drop in estrogen that causes menstruation is sensed by the hypothalamus. It signals the pituitary gland to release FSH, which starts the development of a new follicle—and the cycle begins all over again.

Figure 39–5
When hormone levels reach a certain point, an egg bursts from one of the ovaries into a Fallopian tube. The halo around the egg in this photograph is a protective layer of follicle cells called the corona radiata.

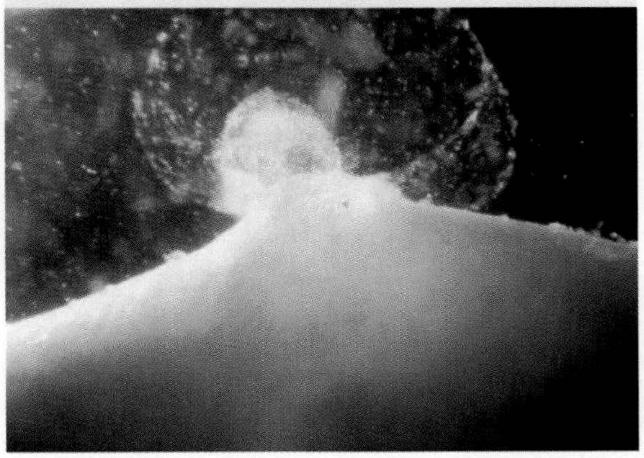

Section Review 39-1

1. **Describe** the functions of the male and female reproductive systems.
2. **List** the four phases of the menstrual cycle.
3. **Critical Thinking—Interpreting Diagrams** Which hormone is at its highest level during ovulation?

TEACHER SUPPORT

Background Information

To maintain good health of the reproductive system, males and females should not only have regular checkups with their doctors, they should also perform regular self-exams at home. For males, self-examination is used to detect cancer of the testes. While showering, they should feel each testis using a thumb and forefinger to detect hard lumps or swellings. This exam should be repeated monthly for life, starting in the teenage years.

For females, the purpose of self-examination is to detect breast cancer. While showering, they should raise the right arm and use the left hand to feel the right breast for hard lumps or swellings. Then they should repeat the exam with the right hand examining the left breast. Like testicular self-examination, breast self-examination should be repeated monthly for life, starting in the teenage years.

Investigate

Research The terms menarche and menopause refer, respectively, to the beginning and ending of menstrual cycles in females. Ask interested students to find out more about these two important landmarks in the female life cycle. For example, when does each one typically occur? What factors affect the timing of each event? How is fertility related to the events? What other physical changes are associated with menarche and menopause? Have students present a brief oral report to the class summarizing what they learn.

4 ASSESS

Quick Check

Call on students to identify the roles played by estrogen in females and testosterone in males.

Section Review 39-1

1. The male reproductive system produces and delivers sperm. The female reproductive system produces eggs and nourishes and supports a developing embryo and fetus.
2. Follicle phase, ovulation, luteal phase, and menstruation.
3. During ovulation, LH is at its highest level.

Learning Modality

Visual Learning On the chalkboard, write the following column and row headings for a table comparing male and female reproductive systems: (columns) Organs, Hormones, Gametes; (rows) Males, Females. Call on students to go to the chalkboard and fill in each cell of the table.

Ancillary Support

The resources below can be used to support your teaching strategy for these two pages.

LM Investigating the Menstrual Cycle, #78
TB Menstrual Cycle, #49

Section 39–2
Fertilization and Development

Performance Objectives

• Explain what happens when an egg is fertilized.

• Outline the functions of the placenta.

Mini Lab Skill: Modeling

1 ENGAGE

Ideas Through Images

Have students examine Figure 39–6, read the caption, and answer the following questions.

• **How do you think the sperm penetrates the egg?** (The sperm acts like a drill, with movements of the tail rotating the head like a bit.)

• **Why do you think the fertilized egg needs nourishment from the smaller cells that surround it?** (Because it is undergoing rapid growth.)

2 EXPLORE

Inquiry Activity

Collecting and Organizing Data

How Does a Baby Grow?

Point out to students that a baby starts out as a single fertilized egg. By birth, a baby typically weighs over 3 kilograms. What is the pattern of growth during the nine months from fertilization to birth? Direct students to answer this question by finding information on the size of the embryo and fetus at each month of development between fertilization and birth. Have students display the information in a series of drawings of embryos and fetuses that correctly show their relative size at each month. Post some of the drawings in the classroom for students to refer to while studying this section of the chapter.

SECTION 39–2

Fertilization and Development

GUIDE FOR READING

- **Describe** fertilization.
- **Describe** the importance of the placenta.

MINI LAB

- **Construct a model** of early human development.

A SINGLE CELL FORMED BY THE fusion of sperm and egg begins the process of development. To produce this cell, the reproductive system must bring these two gametes together. In humans and most other mammals, the fertilized egg develops within the body of its mother. This means that the human reproductive system must not only produce reproductive cells, it must also protect and nourish the developing embryo from fertilization to birth.

Fertilization

During sexual intercourse, the penis is inserted into the vagina to a point just below the cervix. Involuntary smooth muscle contractions of the penis cause an ejaculation, which is the release of several milliliters of semen into the vagina.

Semen contains as many as 100 million sperm per milliliter. Therefore, it's no exaggeration to say that after they are released, millions of sperm swim through the uterus toward the Fallopian tubes. Of the millions of sperm released, only a relatively small number will reach the upper region of the Fallopian tube. If an egg is present in one of the Fallopian tubes, its chances of being fertilized by one of these sperm are very good.

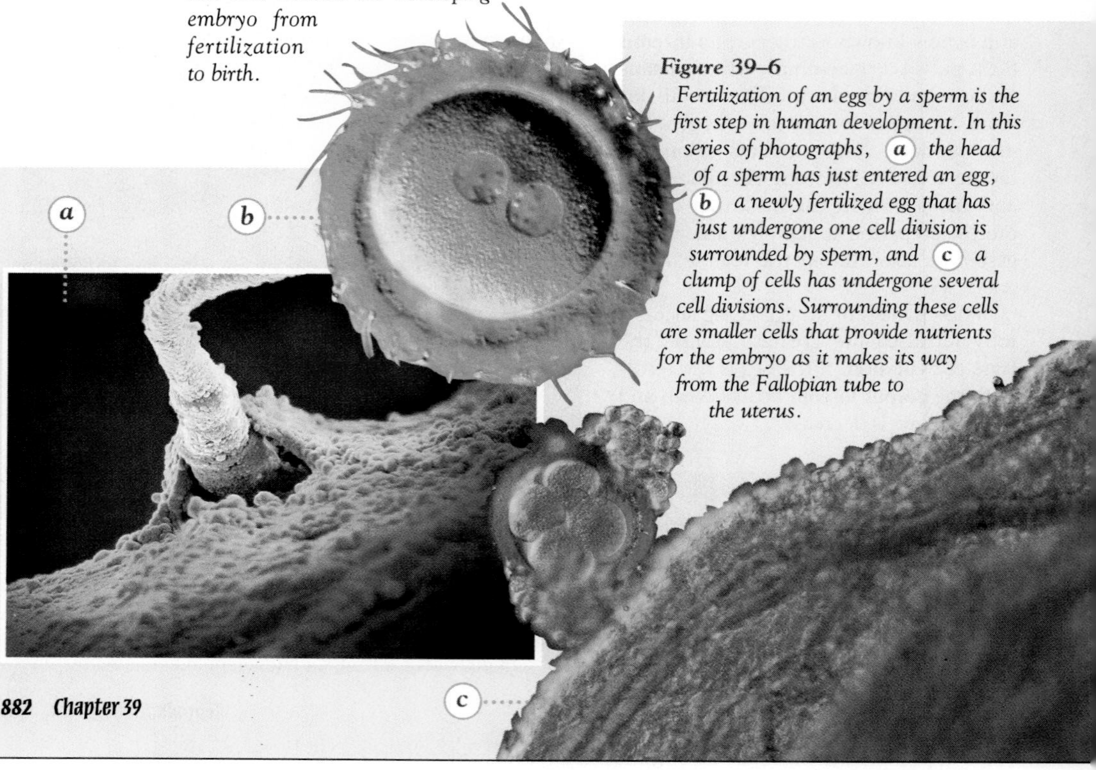

Figure 39–6 *Fertilization of an egg by a sperm is the first step in human development. In this series of photographs, (a) the head of a sperm has just entered an egg, (b) a newly fertilized egg that has just undergone one cell division is surrounded by sperm, and (c) a clump of cells has undergone several cell divisions. Surrounding these cells are smaller cells that provide nutrients for the embryo as it makes its way from the Fallopian tube to the uterus.*

TEACHER SUPPORT

Historical Perspective

Aristotle thought that semen was the seed that gave rise to a new individual and that the female body was simply the site where the seed was nourished. Some early microscopists even believed that they saw a miniature human, called a homunculus, crouched within each sperm. Although sperm were seen by early microscopists, human eggs were not observed until the 1900s. It was not until the 1940s that the fertilization of a human egg was seen. Thus, much of our knowledge about human reproduction is recent, and many unanswered questions remain.

The Fusion of Egg and Sperm

It might seem impossible for such a tiny sperm to fuse with the much larger egg. The egg is surrounded by a thick, protective layer that also includes cells from the follicle in which the egg developed. However, the outermost protective layer also contains binding sites to which sperm cells can attach. When a sperm attaches to these cells, a sac at the end of the sperm breaks open, releasing powerful enzymes that help to dissolve the protective layers around the egg.

Very often, more than one sperm attaches to the egg, and each begins to work its way through to the egg cell membrane. **As soon as one of the sperm makes direct contact with the egg cell membrane, the two cells fuse, the tail of the sperm breaks away, and the sperm nucleus enters the egg's cytoplasm. This process is known as fertilization.** Then, immediately following **fertilization,** rapid electrical and chemical changes take place in the egg cell membrane that prevent any other sperm cells from entering. A **zygote** (ZIGH-goht), or a fertilized egg, has been formed, and development begins.

MATURE SPERM

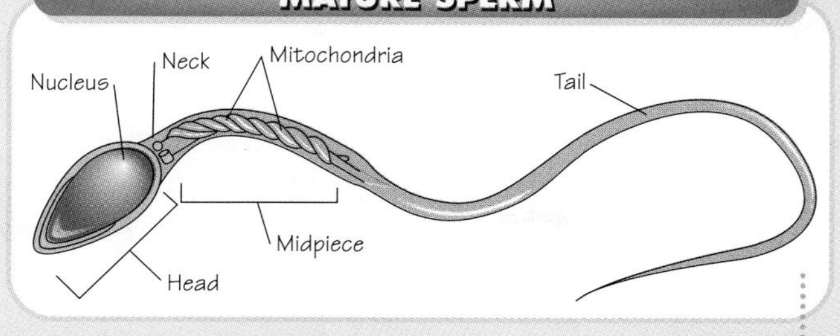

Figure 39–7
(a) A single human sperm consists of a head, a midpiece, and a tail. The head contains the nucleus, with its genetic material. The midpiece is packed with mitochondria that are needed for energy production. And the tail is used to propel the sperm forward. (b) Once inside a female's body, sperm are attracted by chemicals produced by an egg, causing all sperm to swim in the same direction toward the egg.

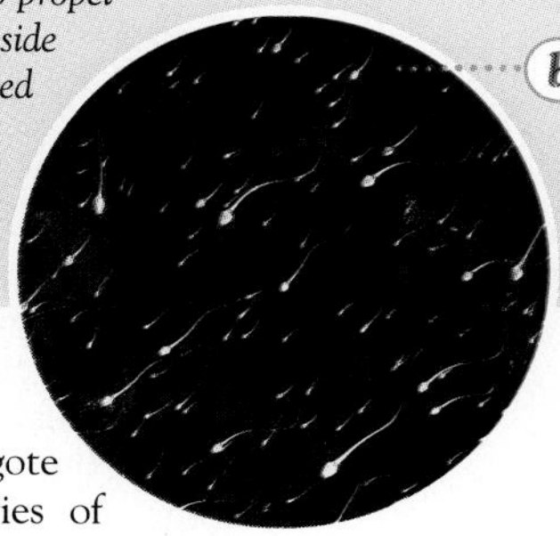

Cell Division

The newly formed zygote goes through a rapid series of cell divisions, gradually forming a solid ball of cells known as a **morula** (MOR-yoo-luh). As cell division in the zygote continues, it gradually develops a hollow cavity and becomes known as a blastocyst. Three to four days after ovulation, the blastocyst attaches itself to the wall of the uterus. The blastocyst may not look like much, but within a few months it will develop into the trillions of cells in a human baby. The precision and intricacy of this process is wonderful to behold—no builder ever executed a plan more exacting, yet the blueprints for this remarkable process are written on the smallest possible scale, the DNA sequence in the nucleus of a single human cell.

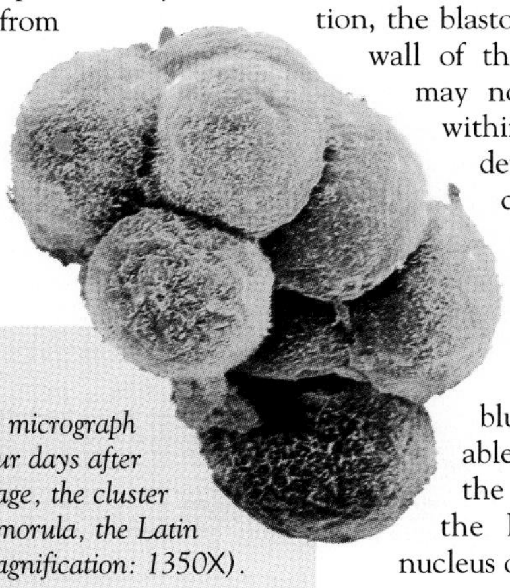

Figure 39–8
This scanning electron micrograph shows an egg about four days after fertilization. At this stage, the cluster of cells is known as a morula, the Latin word for mulberry (magnification: 1350X).

3 TEACH

Ideas Through Images

Have students examine Figure 39–7, read the caption, and answer the following questions.

- **Why does the sperm shown need so much energy from the mitochondria packed in its midpiece?** (To swim the relatively great distance through the uterus and Fallopian tube and to penetrate the protective layer of cells around the egg and the egg membrane.)
- **Which part of the sperm will become incorporated in the new person that develops after fertilization has occurred? What happens to the rest of the sperm?** (Only the nucleus will become part of the new person. The tail breaks away once fertilization occurs.)
- **Why do you think it is important for the egg to attract all the sperm when only one actually fertilizes the egg?** (Enzymes from many sperm help dissolve the protective layers around the egg so that one sperm can finally break through the membrane and fertilize the egg.)

Discussion

Only rarely does more than one sperm penetrate an egg. Ask students what prevents this from happening more often. (Penetration by one sperm leads to electrical and chemical changes that cause the egg membrane to become impermeable to other sperm.) Ask students to discuss what would happen if more than one sperm did penetrate an egg. (The extra set of chromosomes would lead to such abnormal embryonic development that the embryo would not survive.)

TEACHER SUPPORT

Background Information

There are a number of physiological factors helping to ensure that sperm successfully reach an egg in the Fallopian tube. Hormones in semen, called prostaglandins (because they were first discovered in the prostate gland), cause contractions in the uterus and Fallopian tubes. These contractions help propel the sperm toward the egg. There are also secretions of the uterus that aid in sperm transport. Sperm obtain energy for movement by metabolizing the sugar, fructose, that is found in seminal fluid. (Sperm are unusual in this regard because most other cells use glucose for energy.) Seminal fluid not only transports sperm and lubricates the urethra; its slight alkalinity also protects sperm from the typically acidic vaginal secretions. In addition, secretions from the prostate gland stimulate sperm to become motile as they are released during ejaculation.

Ideas Through Images

Have students examine Figure 39–9, read the caption, and answer the following questions.

- **How and why does the zygote shown in the figure differ from the newly released egg?** (It is a diploid cell due to fertilization by a sperm.)
- **How does the morula differ from the zygote?** (The morula consists of many more cells than the zygote.)
- **How does the blastocyst differ from the morula?** (The blastocyst contains a hollow cavity, whereas the morula is a solid mass of cells.)
- **What is HCG?** (HCG is human chorionic gonadotropin, a powerful chemical signal that keeps the corpus luteum alive and active.)
- **What is implantation?** (The process by which the cells of the zygote grow into the uterine walls.)

Investigate

Research Tell students that a blastocyst sometimes implants in the Fallopian tube or in the abdominal cavity instead of the uterus. This is referred to as ectopic pregnancy, and it occurs in about 1 percent of all pregnancies. Have students learn more about ectopic pregnancy through a combination of library research and interviews with relevant health-care professionals. Suggest that they find out what causes ectopic pregnancy, how it is diagnosed, what risks it poses for the embryo and the pregnant woman, and how it is treated. Ask students to share what they learn with the rest of the class.

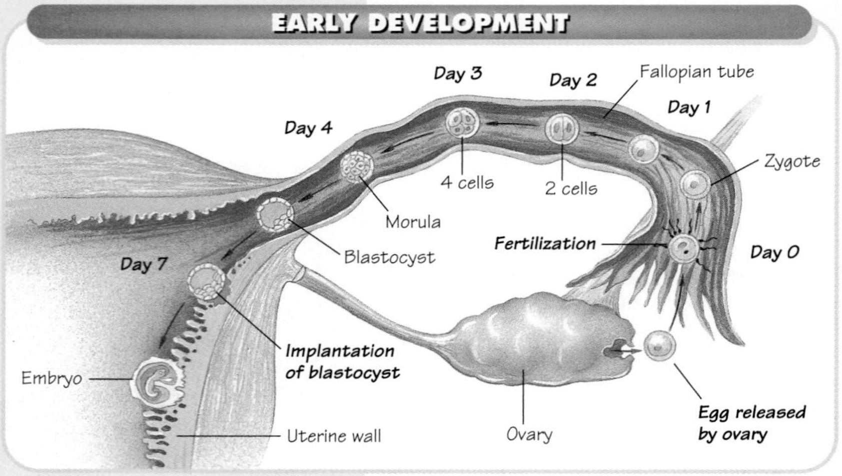

Figure 39–9
Once an egg is released from an ovary, it may become fertilized in a Fallopian tube. If fertilization occurs, the fertilized egg becomes known as a zygote. As the zygote continues its trip toward the uterus, it undergoes many cell divisions, becoming a morula and then a hollow ball of cells called a blastocyst. The blastocyst implants itself in the uterine wall and development begins.

Implantation

The cells of the zygote then grow into the uterine wall in a process known as **implantation.** Implantation is critical to the zygote for two reasons. First, the outermost cells of the zygote and the cells in the uterine wall will grow together to form structures that will nourish and support the developing **embryo.** Without that support, the zygote would not have enough stored food to develop on its own. Second, and most importantly, implantation produces chemical signals that preserve the uterine lining.

Here's how those chemical signals work. Recall that the corpus luteum, which produces progesterone, remains active for about two weeks after ovulation. Then it breaks down, progesterone synthesis stops, and the uterine wall is discarded in menstruation. However, as soon as they implant in the uterine wall, the outermost cells of the zygote produce a substance called **human chorionic gonadotropin** (HCG). HCG is a powerful chemical signal that keeps the corpus luteum alive and active. As a result, the uterine lining is preserved and the embryo can continue to develop.

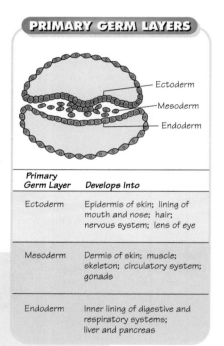

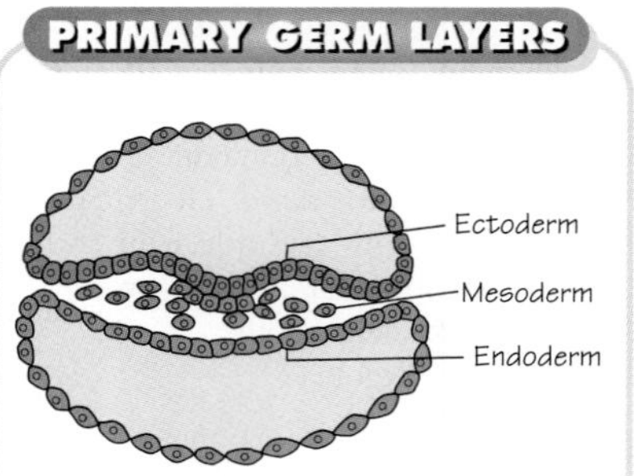

Primary Germ Layer	Develops Into
Ectoderm	Epidermis of skin; lining of mouth and nose; hair; nervous system; lens of eye
Mesoderm	Dermis of skin; muscle; skeleton; circulatory system; gonads
Endoderm	Inner lining of digestive and respiratory systems; liver and pancreas

Figure 39–10
During gastrulation, the three primary germ layers—ectoderm, mesoderm, and endoderm—are formed. All embryonic structures are derived from one of these three layers.

TEACHER SUPPORT

Background Information

Multiple births occur less often in humans than in some other species of mammals, but they still occur fairly often. Twins occur about once in every 90 births. About 70 percent of twins are fraternal, resulting when two different eggs are fertilized in the same menstrual cycle. Each fraternal twin develops a separate placenta. The remaining 30 percent of twins are identical, resulting when one egg splits into two separate embryos shortly after fertilization. Identical twins share the same placenta. Multiple births of three or more children are much less common. Triplets occur about once in every 8000 births, quadruplets about once in every 747,000 births, and quintuplets about once in every 41 million births. Women who take fertility drugs, such as clomiphene, which stimulate the ovaries to produce eggs, have a much higher rate of multiple births.

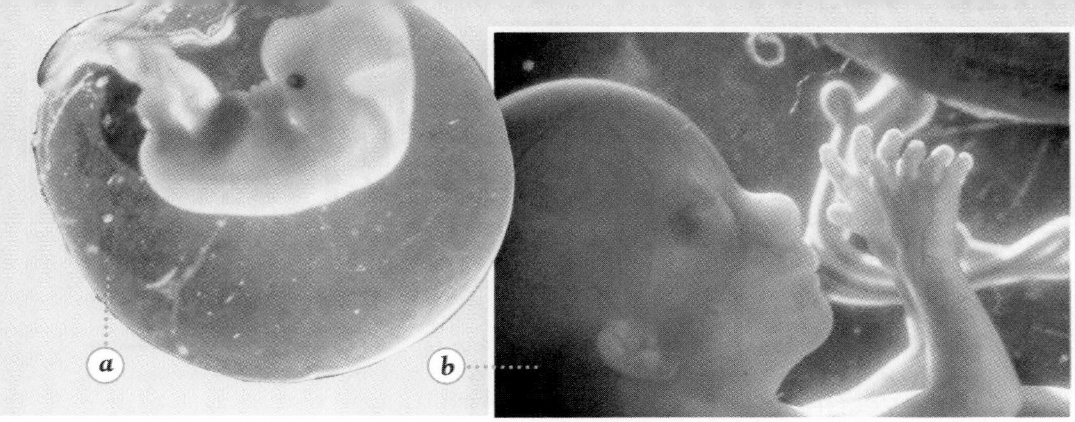

Figure 39–11
Up until the eighth week of development, a developing human is called an embryo. After this time, it is referred to as a fetus. (a) *At six to seven weeks after fertilization, the embryo is 13- to 18-mm long, has the beginnings of eyes, a beating heart, fingers, and a brain, which is nearly as large as the rest of the body.* (b) *By the fourth month, the ears, nose, and mouth have formed. Notice the umbilical cord, which connects the fetus to the placenta.*

The Developing Embryo

The early events of embryonic development are the same for humans as they are for most other mammals. The outer layer of the blastocyst grows into the uterus, surrounding the tissues of the developing embryo. A mass of cells that forms on one side of the blastocyst will become the embryo itself. In the first two weeks after fertilization, the cells in this mass sort themselves into two distinct layers.

Gastrulation

In a process known as **gastrulation** (gas-troo-LAY-shuhn), cells from the upper layer migrate inward to form a third layer between the first two. These three layers of cells—the ectoderm, mesoderm, and endoderm—are known as the primary germ layers of the embryo. In ***Figure 39–10,*** you can see that all the other organs and tissues of the embryo will be formed from these three primary germ layers.

The outer layers of the blastocyst form two important membranes that surround the embryo. These extra-embryonic membranes, located outside the embryo, are called the amnion and the chorion. Both of these membranes fill with fluid that helps to cushion the embryo and protect it from injury.

☑ Checkpoint What is gastrulation? ❶

Neurulation

Near the end of the third week of development, an especially critical event—neurulation—takes place. At about the seventeenth day after fertilization, the ectoderm begins to thicken into a line pointing to the head of the embryo. Gradually, this thickening produces a groove, and the raised edges of the groove move toward each other, forming a tube. By the end of the twenty-third day, the tube has sealed and then sunk beneath the ectoderm. What is this tube, and why is its formation so important? This neural tube, as it is called, becomes the nervous system. One end of the tube will eventually develop into the brain, and the remainder of the tube will become the spinal cord. The remaining ectoderm will then begin to form the skin of the embryo.

☑ Checkpoint What is neurulation? ❷

Ideas Through Images

Have students examine Figure 39–11, read the caption, and answer the following questions.

- **Why is the embryo surrounded by a fluid-filled membrane?** (To cushion it and protect it from injury.)
- **Which body systems have started to function by the time the embryo becomes a fetus?** (Circulatory, muscular, skeletal, integumentary, and nervous systems.)
- **Which body systems do not start to function until the baby is born?** (Digestive and respiratory systems.)

Discussion

Tell students that an embryo may develop abnormally, resulting in an infant with birth defects, which are also called congenital defects. Ask students to discuss the difference between congenital defects and hereditary defects, and to identify possible causes of birth defects besides heredity. (Congenital means present at birth. Some congenital defects are hereditary, that is, caused by genes inherited from the parents, but others are environmental, that is, caused by some type of trauma to the developing embryo or fetus, such as alcohol or nicotine exposure due to the mother's drinking or smoking.)

☑ Checkpoints

❶ Gastrulation is the process in which cells from the upper layer of the embryo migrate inward to form a third layer between the first two layers of cells.

❷ Neurulation is the formation of the neural tube, which will develop into the brain and spinal cord.

TEACHER SUPPORT

Activity

WHO IS RESPONSIBLE?
Ask two groups of volunteers to present a debate on the issue of responsibility for fetal exposure to drugs such as alcohol, nicotine, and cocaine. Assign one group the position that knowingly putting a fetus at risk should be illegal and punishable by law. Assign the other group the opposite position and have them try to convince the rest of the class of the correctness of their point of view. Both groups should research the issue so that they can base their arguments on facts and the opinions of experts. After the two groups have finished debating, ask the rest of the class to conclude which side was most convincing and to explain why.

Problem Solving
Interpreting Diagrams
Picturing Pregnancy

Students will draw on their knowledge of endocrine hormones to explain how birth is initiated.

State Students are asked to determine how hormones regulate the length of pregnancy.

Solve Students can solve the problem by interpreting diagrams that show changing hormone levels during pregnancy.

Test Students may test their analysis by researching the hormonal controls of pregnancy and childbirth.

Communicate Ask student volunteers to describe how levels of estrogen, progesterone, and HCG change throughout pregnancy. Have other students identify the role each hormone plays during pregnancy.

Answers to THINK ABOUT IT

1. At 30 days, the ovaries produce all of the estrogen and progesterone; at 120 days, the placenta also produces these two hormones; at full term, the placenta has taken over production of these hormones.

2. HCG is most abundant at 30 days, which is evident from the peak in the HCG curve at this time.

3. At 120 days, estrogen and progesterone are increasing and HCG is decreasing.

4. At the end of the pregnancy, the hormones drop to prepregnancy levels.

5. Estrogen promotes uterine contractions, and progesterone and HCG inhibit them. An increase in the ratio of estrogen to progesterone and HCG at full term is believed to be partly responsible for the uterine contractions of labor.

Problem Solving
INTERPRETING DIAGRAMS
Picturing Pregnancy

During a class discussion of human reproduction, one of your classmates says, "I have always wondered how the fetus 'knows' when it is time to be born. And how does it know to stay inside the uterus for nearly nine months?"

Your teacher shows the class an illustration that may help answer these questions. Look at the diagram and line graph below, then answer the questions that follow.

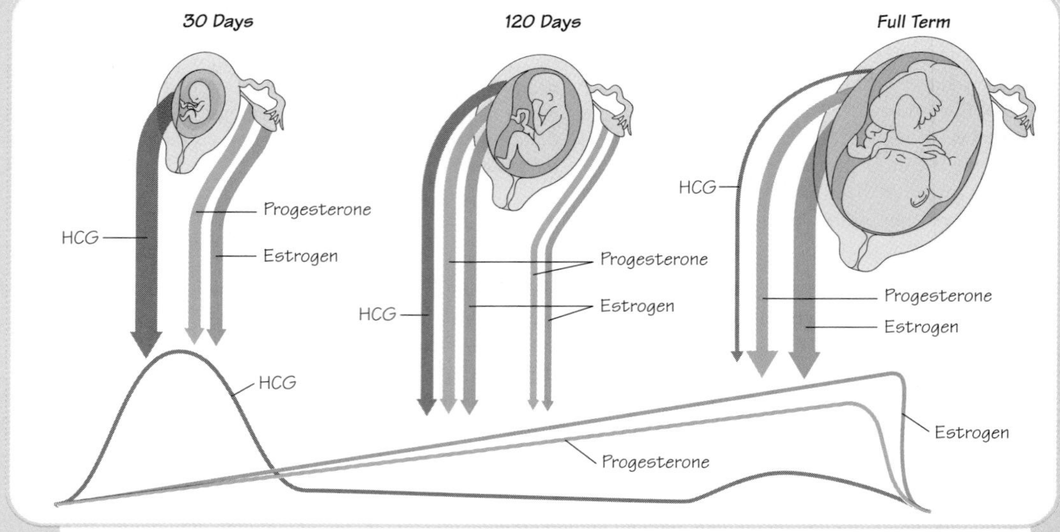

THINK ABOUT IT

1. What organs produce progesterone and estrogen at 30 days and 120 days in the pregnancy? How does this change at full term?
2. Which hormone is most abundant at 30 days? Give evidence to support your answer.
3. Which hormones are increasing at 120 days? Which hormone is decreasing?
4. Describe what happens to the levels of the hormones at the end of the pregnancy.
5. Based on what you know about the roles of these hormones, predict the "birth" day.

886 Chapter 39

TEACHER SUPPORT

Managing Classroom Diversity

TECH PREP STUDENTS
Ultrasound scanning was originally developed to examine the fetus before birth. Ask students interested in health-care careers to learn more about this widely used procedure. They should find out how and why ultrasound is used, as well as how it works. Ask students to share what they learn with the rest of the class. If possible, they should obtain copies of ultrasound images to illustrate their points.

GIFTED STUDENTS
Ask students to research other special medical procedures that are used in pregnancy, such as amniocentesis, chorionic villus sampling (CVS), fetoscopy, and fetal monitoring. When and why is each procedure performed, what information does it yield, and what scientific principles explain how it works? Ask students to summarize what they learn in a concisely written report.

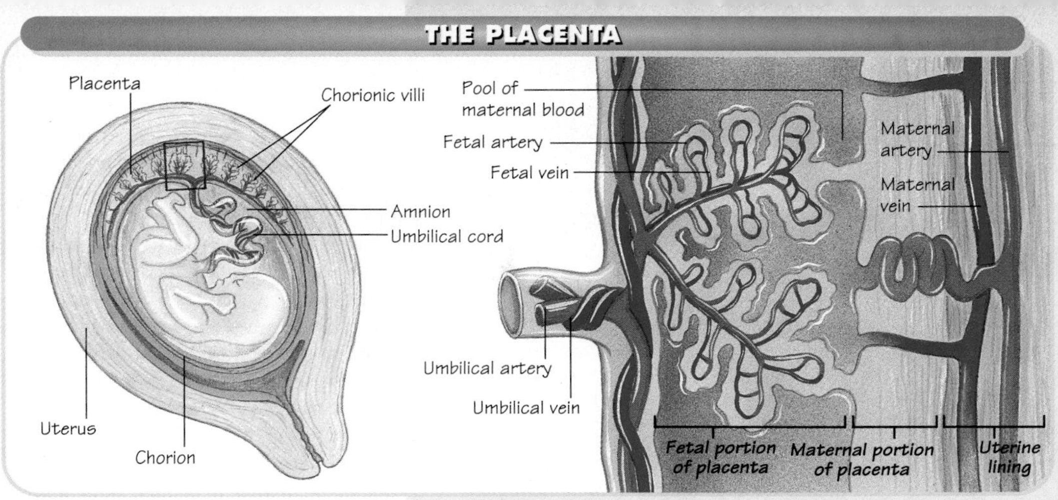

Figure 39–12
The placenta, formed from the chorion layer of the embryo and the uterine lining of the mother, is the connection between the mother and the developing embryo. Although fetal blood vessels branch extensively into pools of maternal blood, there is no mixing of blood. The placenta provides a large surface area for diffusion of oxygen, carbon dioxide, nutrients, and wastes between fetus and mother.

The Placenta

During the first few weeks of development, the cells of the embryo simply absorb nourishment from the surrounding cells of the mother. But within a few days, the embryo is too large for this to continue to meet its needs. Shortly after gastrulation is complete, the embryo forms an organ that will supply its needs for the rest of its development—the **placenta.**

In the fourth week of development, the amniotic sac expands to the point where it completely surrounds the embryo. This expansion squeezes the other extra-embryonic tissue into a thin stalk, connecting the embryo to the uterus. This stalk is the beginning of the **umbilical cord.**

You might think that the best way to bring food and oxygen to the embryo would be to link its blood directly to its mother through the umbilical cord. However, if this were the case, diseases could easily spread from mother to child. Serious problems could also result if the embryo and mother have different blood groups. ● So it should not be surprising that the blood supplies of mother and embryo do not mix directly.

Instead, they come into very close contact in the placenta. The placenta forms at the base of the umbilical cord, where it meets the uterine wall. Tiny blood vessels from the embryo pass through pools of maternal blood. Although the blood supplies do not mix, food, oxygen, carbon dioxide, and metabolic wastes pass back and forth between mother and embryo. **As the embryo grows, the placenta serves as its main organ of respiration, nourishment, and excretion.** Anything that the mother takes into her body, including drugs, passes through the placenta to the embryo.

Checkpoint What is the placenta? 1

INTEGRATING HEALTH

Use reference materials to find out what happens when an embryo and mother have different Rh factors in their blood.

Fetal Development

In the next few weeks, the skeletal system and the limbs of the embryo take shape. This is a particularly important time for the embryo because a number of

Ideas Through Images

Have students examine Figure 39–12, read the caption, and answer the following questions.

- **If maternal and fetal blood do not mix in the placenta, how do substances pass back and forth between mother and fetus?** (Substances cross the membranes of fetal blood vessels to and from the pool of maternal blood.)
- **What substances travel through the umbilical arteries? Through the umbilical vein?** (Oxygen and nutrients travel through the umbilical arteries, carbon dioxide and wastes through the umbilical vein.)

Investigate

Cooperative Learning Divide the class into six groups and assign each group one week of gestation from gestational weeks four through nine. Have each group investigate problems that may arise if the embryo is exposed to toxic substances during that week of development. (For example, infectious agents may lead to heart defects in week five and to blindness in week six.) Ask the groups to share what they learn with the rest of the class and discuss why each week of development is associated with particular abnormalities in this way.

Checkpoint

1 The organ that connects the mother and the fetus, providing a large surface area for the diffusion of oxygen, carbon dioxide, nutrients, and wastes between fetus and mother.

INTEGRATING HEALTH

For a first pregnancy, it would not matter. In subsequent pregnancies, however, the mother's immune system would attack the "foreign" blood of the fetus. To prevent this from happening, a pregnant woman with Rh^- blood is injected with an antibody that binds to the Rh antigen, preventing a reaction.

TEACHER SUPPORT

Activity

UTERINE EXPANSION

Use this activity to demonstrate how the uterus expands as pregnancy proceeds. Bring nine large, round balloons to class, and inflate each one to the approximate size of the uterus at each month of pregnancy. (The prepregnancy uterus is about the size of a fist.) Arrange the inflated balloons in the correct order on a table where students can see them. Have students identify the approximate size of the fetus at each month of development, and then compare the size of the fetus each month with the size of the balloon for that month. Ask students why the balloons are larger than the fetus. What else does the uterus contain that takes up so much space? (The placenta, amniotic sac, and amniotic fluid.) How does the ratio of the fetus to other uterine contents change as the pregnancy develops? (The fetus takes up more and more of the total intrauterine space.)

MINI LAB Modeling

Teacher Notes

• For time required and materials needed, see page 876b.

• Students will be unable to show many of the changes in the 5-week embryo and 11-week fetus because the changes are internal or difficult to represent (for example, the development of blood and blood vessels in the 5-week embryo and the development of functioning kidneys and bone marrow in the 11-week fetus). Students should learn, however, about these changes as well as the changes they can represent in their models.

Answers to Analyze and Conclude

1. By week 11, the fetus starts to look very human.

2. The zygote consists of a single cell—the fertilized egg. After the first cell division, the embryo consists of two cells. The morula is a solid mass of 16 cells, and the blastocyst is a hollow, fluid-filled ball of cells. All four of these early stages remain about the same size as the zygote. The 5-week embryo is about 2.5 centimeters long and has blood and blood vessels, a functioning heart, the beginnings of the nervous system and brain, eyes, facial features, and limb buds. The 11-week fetus is almost 8 centimeters long and has external genitalia, functioning bone marrow and kidneys, nails, hair, tooth buds, and a more upright posture.

Skills Trace
Modeling

Focus p. 888

Practice p. 889

Assess p. 899

MINI LAB Modeling

Early Human Development

PROBLEM *How can you* ***construct a model*** *of human development?*

PROCEDURE

1. Use modeling clay and reference materials to create a three-dimensional representation of each of the following stages in early human development: zygote, first cell division, morula, blastocyst, five-week embryo, and eleven-week fetus.
2. Label each model with its name and an estimation of its actual size.

ANALYZE AND CONCLUDE

1. At which stage can you begin to recognize human structures?
2. What changes have occurred at each stage of development?

external factors can disrupt development at this point. Although the placenta does act as a barrier to some disease-causing organisms, others—such as rubella (German measles) and most drugs, including alcohol, tobacco, and medications—can penetrate the placenta and prevent normal development.

By the end of eight weeks, the embryo is called a **fetus.** Its muscular system enables it to move around a bit, and its sexual organs have developed to the point where it is possible to tell a male from a female. Its heartbeat becomes loud enough to be heard through a stethoscope. It now begins to grow rapidly, and by the end of six months, it is nearly 35 centimeters long and has a mass of between 500 and 800 grams.

As the fetus enters its seventh month of growth, reflexes in its nervous system enable it to respond to sudden noises. Its lungs are enlarging rapidly, and its digestive system is almost ready to function. In many respects, after six months of growth, the fetus is almost ready to lead an independent existence.

Pregnancy usually continues for three more months, however, and there is good reason for that. A baby born early in the last three months of development may have serious problems adjusting to life outside. In particular, the respiratory system is not fully matured. Many babies born at this time are unable to regulate their body temperature. For this reason, premature babies are always at risk and must be given special care to increase their chances of survival.

☑ *Checkpoint* At what stage is an embryo called a fetus? 1

Figure 39–13
CAREER TRACK
A physician assistant performs routine medical care—physical examinations, administering injections and immunizations, administering or ordering certain medical procedures such as X-rays—and generally instructs and counsels patients.

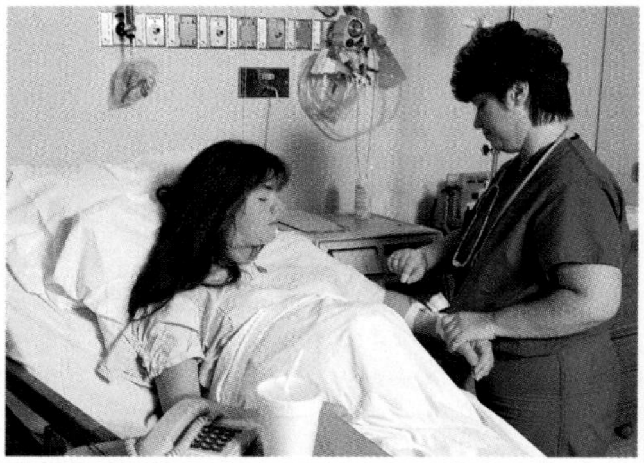

TEACHER SUPPORT Background Information

Students might wonder how and when an embryo starts developing into one gender or the other. When the gonads first appear in the embryo, they look the same in both genders. It is not until eight or nine weeks after fertilization that the gonads become recognizable as testes in male embryos and as ovaries in female embryos. The differentiation of the male embryo is believed to be due to the influence of one or more genes on the Y chromosome. For female embryos, the gonads develop into ovaries without any stimulation. Shortly after the male embryo's testes develop, they start secreting testosterone. This hormone, in turn, causes the previously undifferentiated external genitalia to form the penis and scrotum. In the absence of testosterone, the external genitalia develop into those of the female. Thus, the female appears to be the basic, or default, gender of the species.

Labor and Birth

Childbirth in humans takes place, on average, about nine months after fertilization. It is not known exactly how the body "decides" when it is time for a child to be born. The immediate signal is a pituitary hormone called **oxytocin.** This hormone stimulates contractions of the smooth muscles surrounding the uterus. Slowly at first, these muscles begin a series of contractions known as labor. As the contractions become more frequent and more powerful, the opening of the cervix expands until it reaches a diameter of nearly 10 centimeters—large enough for the head of the baby to pass through. At some point during this time, the amniotic sac bursts and the fluid in the sac passes out of the mother's body.

Childbirth

When the cervix has fully expanded and contractions come at intervals of 2 to 3 minutes, childbirth is about to begin. Contractions of the uterus force the baby, usually head first, out through the cervix, the vagina, and into the world.

As the baby leaves its mother's body, it may cough or cry to open up its fluid-filled lungs and take its first breath. Blood flow to the placenta dries up, and the placenta itself detaches from the wall of the uterus. It will follow the baby out through the birth canal. The umbilical cord is tied and cut, leaving only a small piece attached to the baby. The baby is now ready to begin life on its own.

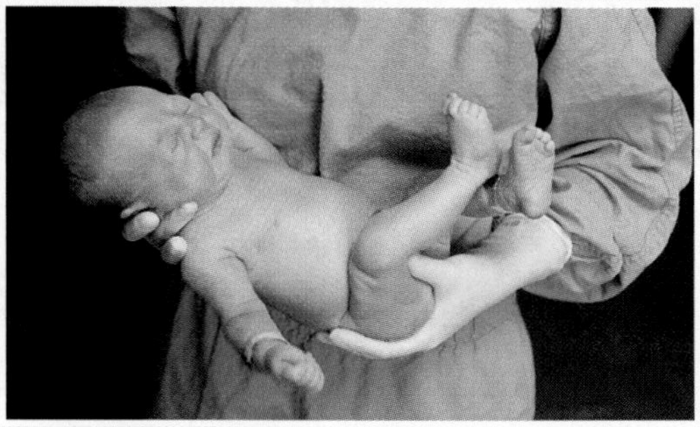

Figure 39–14
About nine months after fertilization, a baby is born. Identification bands, which match those of the mother, are placed around the baby's wrist and ankle.

After Childbirth

Just a few hours after childbirth, a pituitary hormone known as **prolactin** stimulates the production of milk in the breast tissues of the mother. By nursing her child soon after it is born, the mother stimulates the release of more oxytocin, which also helps to stop uterine bleeding. The mother also passes an important secretion to the baby in her first breast milk. This fluid, called colostrum, contains a remarkable mixture of special antibodies produced by the immune system. Colostrum helps to protect the baby from infections for many weeks. Colostrum is gradually replaced by mature milk. The milk that humans and other mammals produce for their offspring is a complete food. It contains all the vitamins, minerals, and other nutrients that the baby needs for the first few months of life.

Section Review 39–2

1. **Describe** fertilization.
2. **Describe** the importance of the placenta.
3. **Critical Thinking—Hypothesizing** What might happen to a fetus if the placenta became detached from the uterine wall?
4. **MINI LAB** How can you **construct a model** of early human development?

TEACHER SUPPORT

Managing Classroom Diversity

LEP STUDENTS

LEP students may have difficulty with the terminology in this section. Pair each LEP student with a student who is doing well in the course. Have the pairs work together to make flashcards, with a term from the section on one side of each card and a simple, concise definition on the other side. Then have the paired students quiz each other to reinforce and check their understanding of the terms.

TECH PREP STUDENTS

Obstetrical nurses and midwives often play crucial roles in labor and birth. Have students interested in health-care careers learn more about these two professions. Students should gather the information they need to compare and contrast required training, job responsibilities, and salaries. Ask students to summarize their findings in a brief report or table.

4 ASSESS

Quick Check

Call on students to name in sequence the stages of development of the embryo and fetus. Call on other students to identify the distinctive features that characterize the embryo or fetus at each stage.

Section Review 39-2

1. The fusion of the two cells.
2. It forms a protective barrier and serves as the main organ of respiration, nourishment, and excretion of the embryo/fetus.
3. The fetus might be cut off from the maternal blood supply and no longer be able to receive oxygen and nutrients or to excrete carbon dioxide and wastes.
4. A model of early human development can be constructed by molding clay to show the characteristics of the embryo and fetus at various stages of development.

Skills Trace
Modeling
- Focus p. 888
- Practice p. 889
- Assess p. 899

Learning Modality

Auditory Learning Read to the class the highlighted terms in this section. Call on students to define each of the terms.

Checkpoint

1 At the end of eight weeks of development.

Ancillary Support

The resources below can be used to support your teaching strategy for these two pages.

TR Enrich: Testing in Utero
BL Inquiry Activity: Havin' My Baby

Section 39–3

Sexually Transmitted Diseases

Performance Objectives

• Identify three bacterial diseases that are sexually transmitted.

• Identify three viral diseases that are sexually transmitted.

Mini Lab Skill: Interpreting

1 ENGAGE

Ideas Through Images

Have students examine Figure 39–15, read the caption, and answer the following questions.

• **What are some common diseases that are caused by bacteria and viruses?** (A common bacterial disease is strep throat; a common viral disease is influenza.)

• **How do bacterial and viral diseases differ in their treatment?** (Most bacterial diseases can be cured with antibiotics; viral diseases cannot.)

2 EXPLORE

Investigate

Long-Term Project Have students take a survey of other students in their school regarding knowledge of STDs and how to avoid them. Ask students to share the results of their surveys with the rest of the class. Lead the class in a discussion of misconceptions teens hold about STDs.

INTEGRATING HEALTH

Examples of STDs caused by organisms other than bacteria and viruses include trichomoniasis (protozoan), candidiasis (fungus), and pubic lice and scabies (arthropods).

SECTION 39–3 BRANCHING OUT In Depth

Sexually Transmitted Diseases

GUIDE FOR READING

- **List** three common sexually transmitted diseases caused by bacteria.
- **List** three common sexually transmitted diseases caused by viruses.

MINI LAB

- **Interpret data** from a graph to learn about an STD.

INTEGRATING HEALTH

Use reference materials to find out about STDs caused by protozoans, fungi, and arthropods.

IT IS A BIOLOGICAL FACT THAT human reproduction can take place only when living sperm cells come in contact with an egg. As you have read, these reproductive cells are sheltered from contact with the outside world, surrounded with nutrient-rich fluids to support their activities, and pass directly from the reproductive tract of the male into that of the female. Internal fertilization is an effective method of reproduction. However, it also creates a perfect opportunity for disease-causing organisms to exploit the reproductive system.

STDs—A Growing Problem

Diseases that are spread from one person to another by sexual contact are known as **sexually transmitted diseases,** or STDs. Sexually transmitted diseases are a serious health problem in the United States, infecting millions of people each year and accounting for thousands of deaths. Both bacteria and viruses can cause STDs. ● Because each sexual contact carries with it the risk of an STD, it is important to know and understand the most serious of these diseases.

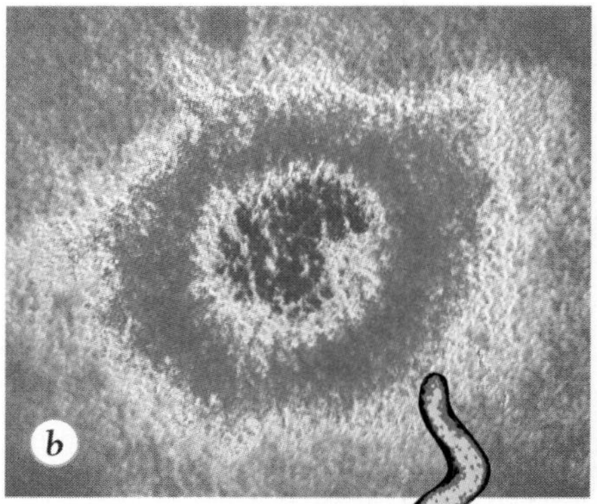

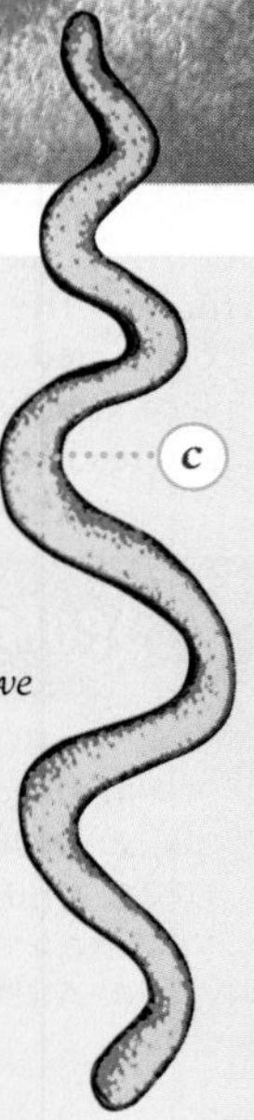

Figure 39–15 *Most sexually transmitted diseases are caused by bacteria and viruses.* (a) *Gonorrhea is caused by the bacterium called* Neisseria gonorrhoeae, *which is kidney-shaped and often found in pairs (magnification: 29,000X).* (b) *There are two forms of herpes virus, called Herpes simplex Type 1 and Type 2. Herpes simplex Type 1 causes sores around the mouth. Herpes simplex Type 2 causes sores on the reproductive organs and is sexually transmitted. Although the two forms are identical in appearance, they are different in their chemical makeup. This electron micrograph shows Herpes simplex Type 1 (magnification: 200,000X).* (c) *The bacterium that causes syphilis,* Treponema pallidum, *is a threadlike, spiral-shaped bacterium (magnification: 4000X).*

TEACHER SUPPORT

Historical Perspective

Syphilis has been known at least since the time of Columbus. Indeed, some historians believe that Columbus brought syphilis back to Europe from the Western Hemisphere. Other historians trace syphilis back even further, to biblical times. Whatever its origins, syphilis spread throughout the world during the age of exploration and discovery. The name syphilis was first used in the 1500s in a poem written by an Italian physician and poet named Fracastoro. The poem is about a Greek shepherd named Syphilis, who was punished by Apollo with the disease that was then known as the great pox, among many other names. Fracastoro not only gave syphilis its name; he also invented an early treatment for it, in which the patient was placed in a chamber above burning mercury ore. It was apparently a treatment of last resort because it caused the patient to lose teeth and suffer skeletal damage. Whether it cured the disease is unknown.

Bacterial Diseases

Although many of the most serious STDs are caused by bacteria, they can usually be treated and cured with antibiotics. Early detection and treatment are necessary to prevent any serious consequences of infection. **Three common STDs caused by bacteria are syphilis, gonorrhea, and chlamydia.**

Syphilis

One of the most serious and dangerous bacterial STDs is **syphilis.** This disease is caused by a corkscrew-shaped bacterium called a spirochete. The syphilis spirochete is a delicate organism that dies quickly when exposed to the air. However, sexual contact provides it with the perfect opportunity to pass from one person to another.

The first sign of this disease appears from 10 to 90 days after infection—a hard sore called a chancre (SHAN-ker) forms at the point where the organism passes through the skin. The sore disappears after a few weeks, but the infection does not. The spirochete spreads throughout the body, gradually infecting the circulatory and nervous systems.

In its early stages, syphilis can be cured with large doses of antibiotics. If left untreated, however, syphilis can cause serious physical damage and may even be fatal.

☑ *Checkpoint* What is syphilis? ❶

Gonorrhea

Another serious STD is **gonorrhea.** Gonorrhea infects the urinary and reproductive tracts, and it is easily passed from person to person through sexual contact. Males are usually aware of being infected because the bacterium causes pain during urination and may result in the discharge of blood and pus. In females, the symptoms are much milder. Many females do not even know they are infected. This is particularly dangerous, because gonorrhea can produce pelvic inflammatory disease (PID), which may make it impossible to ever have children.

☑ *Checkpoint* What is gonorrhea? ❷

Chlamydia

The single most common STD in the United States is one you may never have heard of—**chlamydia.** The bacterium that causes this disease thrives in the moist reproductive tracts of both males and females. It produces only a few symptoms, which may include a mild burning sensation during urination. Because of this, most people with chlamydia are unaware of the infection and continue to spread it to others without being treated. This is a cause for serious concern because long-term infection with this bacterium is now the leading cause of preventable infertility among women in their thirties.

☑ *Checkpoint* What is chlamydia? ❸

Figure 39–16
Chlamydia trachomatis, *the bacterium that causes chlamydia, is a viruslike bacterium. The two smaller spheres in this color-enhanced electron micrograph show two* Chlamydia *bacteria (magnification: 40,000X).*

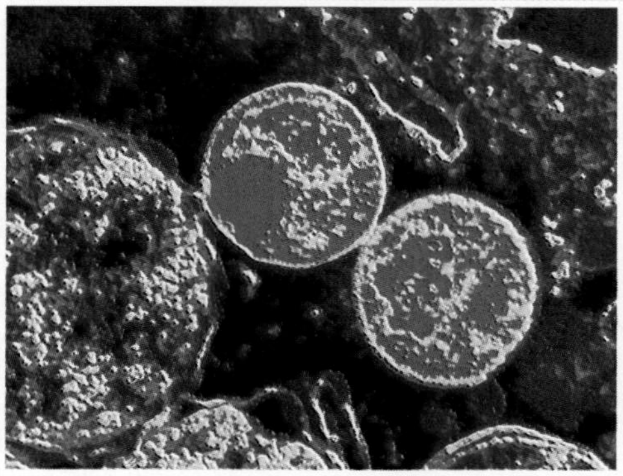

3 TEACH

Inquiry Activity

Designing an Experiment

Infection Detection

Ask students how they could tell if a newly discovered infectious disease was sexually transmitted. What data would help determine whether the disease was passed from person to person through sexual contact? (Data might include the symptoms of the disease, the age and previous sexual activity of infected individuals, and the needs and life cycle of the suspected pathogen.)

Discussion

Tell students that most STDs are caused by organisms that cannot live outside a warm, moist environment. Many other pathogens, in contrast, are much hardier. For example, the virus that causes chicken pox can live outside the body for several hours. Ask students to discuss why the organisms that cause STDs tend to be so fragile. (If the organisms were less fragile, they would spread nonsexually—for example, by direct, nonsexual contact, as the common cold is spread. Sexual transmission allows these fragile pathogens to remain in the warm, moist environment they require while still traveling from one host to another.)

☑ Checkpoints

❶ Syphilis is one of the most serious and dangerous bacterial STDs, caused by a corkscrew-shaped bacterium called a spirochete.

❷ Gonorrhea is a bacterial STD that infects the urinary and reproductive tracts and can lead to pelvic inflammatory disease in females if untreated.

❸ Chlamydia is the single most common STD, caused by a bacterium that produces few symptoms but leads to female infertility if untreated.

TEACHER SUPPORT

Background Information

Sexually transmitted diseases are the second most common communicable diseases in the United States, second only to the common cold. Most sexually transmitted diseases occur in teens and young adults up to about age 25, with 2.5 million teens—or about one out of every six—contracting an STD each year. The fastest-increasing STDs are genital warts, with an estimated 750,000 new cases each year, and chlamydia, with an estimated 4 million new cases each year. Even though most teens know that condoms can protect against STDs, including AIDS, only about 8 percent of sexually active teenage males and 2 percent of sexually active teenage females use condoms during sexual intercourse. To receive more information on STDs and how to avoid them, contact the Centers for Disease Control and Prevention National Sexually Transmitted Disease Hotline: 1-800-227-8922.

MINI LAB

Interpreting

Teacher Notes

- For time required and materials needed, see page 876b.
- Make sure that students correctly label the axes of their graphs.
- From the rates given in the table, ask students to estimate the number of cases of syphilis in the United States in 1990 and 1994, the years with the highest and lowest rates. (50,000 cases and 18,750 cases, respectively, based on a total population size of about 250 million people.)
- Ask students to discuss whether a line graph or bar graph is more useful for displaying the kind of data given here. (Both are equally useful for showing rates in a given year, but the line graph is better for showing trends in the data.)

Answers to Analyze and Conclude

1. The number of syphilis cases was highest in 1990 and lowest in 1994.
2. Between 1985 and 1994, the number of cases of syphilis increased steadily, reaching a peak in 1990; the number of cases then declined quickly, reaching a low point in 1994.
3. Students might predict that the number of cases of syphilis will continue to decline.

Skills Trace
Interpreting

- Focus p. 892
- Practice p. 893
- Assess p. 899

MINI LAB ········ *Interpreting* ····

Number Sense

PROBLEM *What can you learn about an STD by interpreting data on a graph?*

Year	Number of Cases of Syphilis (per 100,000 people)	Year	Number of Cases of Syphilis (per 100,000 people)
1985	11.5	1990	20.0
1986	11.5	1991	17.0
1987	14.5	1992	13.5
1988	17.0	1993	10.0
1989	19.0	1994	7.5

Source: Centers for Disease Control and Prevention, September 1995

PROCEDURE

1. Use the data in the table to construct a line graph.
2. List some generalizations you can make from the graph.

ANALYZE AND CONCLUDE

1. In which year was the number of reported cases of syphilis the highest? The lowest?
2. Based on the line graph you constructed, what can you say about the general trend in the number of cases between 1985 and 1994?
3. From this data, what trends could you predict for the next 10 years?

Viral Diseases

Unlike bacteria-caused STDs, which can usually be treated with antibiotics if discovered early enough, there are currently no drugs that will cure viral STD infections. Therefore, STDs caused by viruses are particularly serious. **Three common STDs caused by viruses are genital herpes, hepatitis B, and AIDS.**

Genital Herpes

One of the most common STDs is **genital herpes.** A virus known as Herpes Type II infects the genital areas of males and females, causing small reddish blisters. Visible evidence of the virus may disappear for weeks or months at a time, but the infection stays in the body. Visible herpes blisters may appear without warning, causing pain and shedding virus particles that may be passed on to sexual partners. There are some drugs available that can help to reduce the severity of genital herpes outbreaks, but none that can permanently cure the infection.

☑ *Checkpoint* What is genital herpes? 1

Hepatitis B

Hepatitis B is a virus that infects the liver and kills several thousand people each year. Unlike other STDs, the hepatitis B virus can survive on objects outside the body for a long period of time. Although there is now an effective vaccine, there is no cure for hepatitis B once an individual has been infected. Hepatitis B is particularly common among people with many sexual partners and presents a serious health risk.

☑ *Checkpoint* How does hepatitis B differ from other STDs? 2

AIDS

In many respects, the most dangerous STD of all is **AIDS** (acquired immune deficiency syndrome). The virus that causes AIDS attacks the immune system, leaving the person vulnerable to a variety of infections. Virus particles are present in the blood, semen, and vaginal fluids of people infected with AIDS. Therefore, sexual contact is one of the principal ways in which the disease is spread from person to person. Currently, there is no cure for AIDS.

TEACHER SUPPORT

Activity

SPREADING DISEASE

To help students appreciate how rapidly an STD can spread, have them perform this activity. Instruct each student to shake hands with six different classmates and to record the name of each person they shake hands with. Have one student refuse to shake hands to represent abstinence, and have two students shake hands only with each other to represent a monogamous relationship. After students have shaken hands, select one student at random to represent the original carrier of an STD. Have students examine the list of names of the people they shook hands with. How many shook hands directly with the carrier of the disease? How many shook hands with someone else who shook hands with the carrier? What percentage of the class had contact, either directly or indirectly, with the carrier? Have volunteers summarize what the results of the activity imply for the spread of STDs.

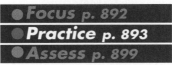

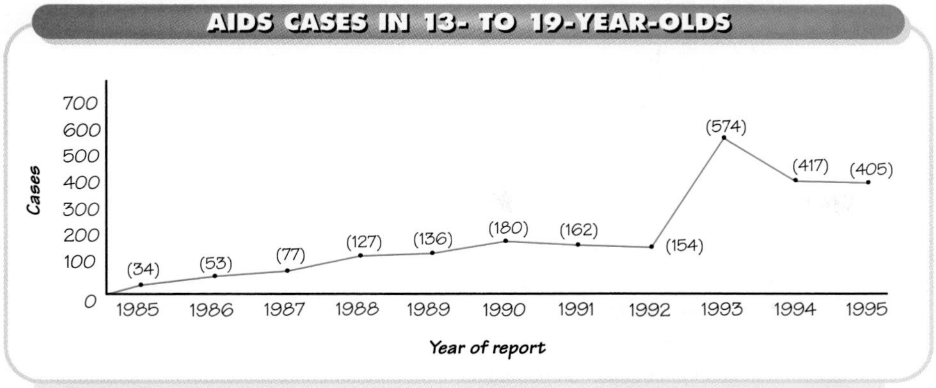

Figure 39–17
This graph shows the number of AIDS cases in 13- to 19-year-olds in the United States from 1985 through 1995. Notice the sharp increase in 1993, followed by a gradual decline.

Avoiding STDs

As you have seen, STDs are serious diseases that are spread by sexual contact. Are there any ways to avoid these diseases, which can ruin your health and even threaten your life? Yes, there are. The great irony of STDs is that although many of them cannot be cured, all of them can be prevented by understanding what conditions they require to spread from person to person.

Nearly all STDs infect the reproductive tracts of males and females. This usually means that bacteria or infectious virus particles are present in semen or vaginal fluids of infected individuals. Because these fluids are exchanged during intercourse, infectious particles from one person can easily be transmitted to another.

STDs require intimate contact between people for infections to be transmitted. Therefore, individuals who engage in sexual intercourse risk not only an unintended pregnancy but serious diseases as well. In contrast, abstaining from sexual contact provides complete protection against all STDs and pregnancy as well.

Section Review 39–3

1. **List** three common sexually transmitted bacterial diseases.
2. **List** three common sexually transmitted viral diseases.
3. **MINI LAB** What can you learn about an STD by **interpreting data** from a graph?
4. **BRANCHING OUT ACTIVITY** Choose one of the sexually transmitted diseases discussed in this chapter and research the effects it would have on a pregnant woman or her developing fetus. **Summarize** your findings in a brief report.

4 ASSESS

Quick Check

Call on students to compare and contrast chlamydia and genital herpes. (Both are among the most common STDs, but chlamydia is bacterial and curable with antibiotics, whereas herpes is viral and incurable.)

Section Review 39-3

1. Syphilis, gonorrhea, and chlamydia.
2. Genital herpes, hepatitis B, and AIDS.
3. You can learn how the rate of an STD changes through time.

Skills Trace
Interpreting
- Focus p. 892
- Practice p. 893
- Assess p. 899

4. Reports will depend on the diseases that students choose to research. Ask volunteers to share their findings with the rest of the class.

Checkpoints

1. Genital herpes is a common viral STD that causes small reddish blisters in genital areas.
2. Unlike other STDs, hepatitis B virus can survive on objects outside the body for a long period of time.

Learning Modality

Visual Learning Have students make a concept map on the chalkboard that incorporates each of the following terms: bacterial STDs, viral STDs, syphilis, gonorrhea, chlamydia, genital herpes, hepatitis B, and AIDS.

Ancillary Support

The resources below can be used to support your teaching strategy for these two pages.

TR Explore: A Little Goes a Long Way
BL Inquiry Activity: STDs—No Laughing Matter

Chapter 39

Laboratory Investigation

Reproductive Organs and Gametes

Before the Lab

1. Prepared slides of human reproductive organs and gametes can be purchased from a biological supply company.
2. If prepared slides are not available, distribute drawings or photographs of gonads and gametes for students to examine and compare. Textbooks on human anatomy and physiology are good sources of these illustrations.

Pre-Lab Discussion

Have students read the entire procedure for this investigation. Then ask students the following questions.

What is the purpose of this investigation? (To observe the microscopic structure of human gonads and gametes.)

What does it mean to take a cross section of an organ such as the testis or ovary? (To take an ultrathin slice of the organ by cutting at right angles to the axis of the organ.)

How do you think a seminiferous tubule would appear in a cross section of the testis and a follicle in a cross section of the ovary? (Both structures would appear circular in cross section.)

Skills Development

Students will use these skills while completing the laboratory investigation: observing, comparing, inferring, communicating, and drawing conclusions.

Laboratory Investigation

Reproductive Organs and Gametes

The egg and sperm are microscopic structures that can best be observed in slides that have been professionally sectioned, stained, and preserved. In this investigation, you will examine some prepared slides and use the knowledge you have gained from this chapter to interpret what you see.

Problem

What can you **observe** in the microscopic structure of reproductive organs and gametes?

Materials (per group)

compound microscope
prepared slides of the following:
- human testis
- ovary
- sperm

Procedure

1. **Obtain a prepared slide of the cross section of a human testis. Using the low-power objective of the microscope, examine the slide and draw what you see. Find an area that has well-defined circular structures. These are the seminiferous tubules.**
2. **Switch to the high-power objective on the microscope. Select one seminiferous tubule and draw the structures inside it.**

Cross section of a human testis (magnification: 250X)

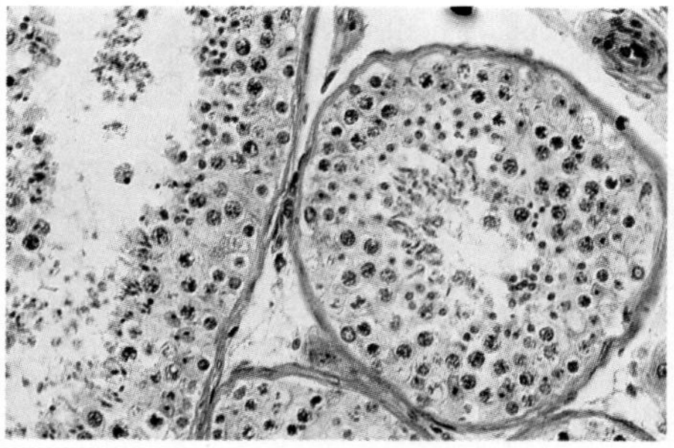

Safety Tip

Caution students to handle the prepared microscope slides with care and to notify you of any breakage.

3. Locate and identify the cells at various stages of development. The cells located just inside the walls of the tubule are the cells in which meiosis begins. The cells closest to the center of the tubule are at later stages of meiosis, and the cells closest to the center of the tubule are the sperm.

4. Obtain a prepared slide of human sperm. Using the low-power objective of the microscope, examine the slide. Locate one sperm and then switch the microscope to high power. Draw what you observe.

5. Obtain a prepared slide of a human ovary and observe it under the low-power objective of the microscope. Locate a large cell that has a distinct nucleus surrounded by a lightly stained area of cytoplasm. This is an egg.

Cross section of a human ovary and egg (magnification: 250X)

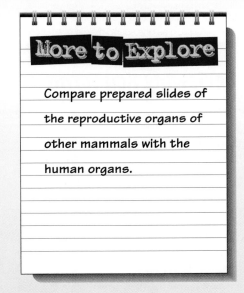

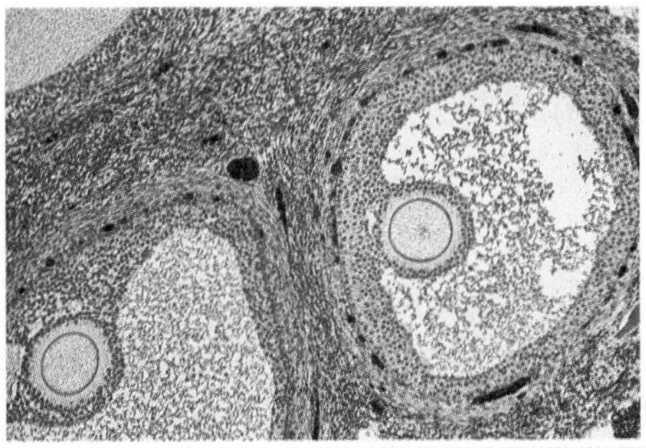

6. Find the largest follicle, a fluid-filled cavity that surrounds an egg. Switch the microscope to high power and draw what you observe. Try to locate the fluid-filled space, the egg itself, the egg's nucleus, and the layers of follicle cells surrounding the egg.

Observations

1. How many enlarged follicles with mature eggs did you observe in the cross section of the ovary?
2. How many mature sperm did you observe in the seminiferous tubule?

Analysis and Conclusions

1. How much of the testis did you see?
2. Explain how a human testis is able to produce millions of sperm each day.
3. How does the volume of cytoplasm in the egg compare with the volume of cytoplasm in the sperm?
4. Which structures were easiest to identify? Which were the hardest?

More to Explore

Compare prepared slides of the reproductive organs of other mammals with the human organs.

Answers to Observations

1. The number of enlarged follicles will vary. Within an ovary, only one follicle is usually developing at any one time to produce a single mature egg cell.
2. The number of mature sperm will vary, though it may be more than students can easily count.

Answers to Analysis and Conclusions

1. On high power, students might examine only part of one seminiferous tubule.
2. Although the testis is relatively small, it contains hundreds of highly coiled seminiferous tubules that together can produce millions of sperm each day.
3. The volume of cytoplasm is much larger in the egg than in the sperm.
4. Students might say that the mature follicles were easiest to identify because they are so large and that the immature sperm were hardest to identify because they are so small.

More to Explore

Students should be urged to identify similarities and differences in the reproductive organs of humans and other mammals. Overall, the gonads and gametes of mammals are more similar than different.

Teaching Strategies

1. If necessary, review with students the proper method of changing from low to high power with the microscope. Remind students to center the image before changing objectives and to use only the fine adjustment knob with the high-power objective.

2. You may wish to show and discuss drawings or photographs of testes and ovaries before the lab to familiarize students with what they will observe.

CHAPTER 39

Study Guide

Review Strategy

Have students write two concise, informative paragraphs that correctly incorporate all of the following terms: testis, ovary, pituitary, LH, FSH, estrogen, testosterone, ovum, sperm, seminiferous tubule, follicle.

After students have finished writing, have them exchange their paragraphs with a partner and then evaluate what the partner wrote. Are all of the statements accurate? Have partners consult the text to resolve any differences of opinion.

Recalling Main Ideas

1. a
2. b
3. d
4. c
5. a
6. d
7. c
8. b

Assessment

Reviewing What You Learned

1. Sperm and ovum (eggs).
2. A period of rapid sexual development that usually occurs in the early teenage years.
3. Deep voice and body hair.
4. Progesterone is produced in the ovary; its function is to stimulate cell and tissue growth in the lining of the uterus and to inhibit the release of LH and FSH.
5. When an egg is mature, the pituitary gland sends out a burst of LH, which causes the wall of the follicle to break open and the egg to be released into one of the Fallopian tubes.
6. Menstruation is triggered when the level of estrogen in the blood becomes too low to maintain the lining of the uterus.
7. Fertilization usually takes place in the upper region of the Fallopian tube; the fertilized egg then travels to the uterus.
8. A zygote forms when an egg is fertilized by a sperm.

Study Guide

Summarizing Key Concepts

The key concepts in each section of this chapter are listed below to help you review the chapter content. Make sure you understand each concept and its relationship to other concepts and to the theme of this chapter.

39–1 The Human Reproductive System

- The male reproductive system has the task of producing and delivering sperm. The female reproductive system produces gametes, too. Because fertilization and the development of a baby both take place inside the female's body, this puts special demands on the female reproductive system.
- The menstrual cycle has four phases: follicle phase, ovulation, luteal phase, and menstruation.

39–2 Fertilization and Development

- As soon as one sperm makes direct contact with the egg cell membrane, the two cells fuse, the tail of the sperm breaks away, and the sperm nucleus enters the egg's cytoplasm. This process is called fertilization.
- As the embryo grows, the placenta serves as its main organ of respiration, nourishment, and excretion.

39–3 Sexually Transmitted Diseases

- Three common STDs caused by bacteria are syphilis, gonorrhea, and chlamydia.
- Three common STDs caused by viruses are genital herpes, hepatitis B, and AIDS.

Reviewing Key Terms

Review the following vocabulary terms and their meaning. Then use each term in a complete sentence.

39–1 The Human Reproductive System

gamete
ovary
testis
follicle-stimulating hormone
luteinizing hormone
testosterone
sperm
progesterone
estrogen
ovum
scrotum
seminiferous tubule
epididymis
vas deferens
follicle
Fallopian tube
ovulation
uterus
menstrual cycle
corpus luteum

39–2 Fertilization and Development

fertilization
zygote
morula
implantation
embryo
human chorionic gonadotropin
gastrulation
placenta
umbilical cord
fetus
oxytocin
prolactin

39–3 Sexually Transmitted Diseases

sexually transmitted disease
syphilis
gonorrhea
chlamydia
genital herpes
hepatitis B
AIDS

Inquiry-Based Strategy

Ask students to discuss how twins occur. Guide the discussion toward the conclusion that there are two different ways that twins can come about: Two eggs may be produced by the ovary and fertilized by different sperm, producing two different zygotes; or a single zygote can divide and develop into two identical embryos. Check students' understanding by asking them to explain the difference between identical and fraternal twins. (Students should realize that identical twins, also called monozygotic twins, have exactly the same chromosomes because they develop from a single zygote. In contrast, fraternal twins, also called dizygotic twins, are no more alike genetically than other siblings, because they develop from two different zygotes.)

Recalling Main Ideas

Choose the letter of the answer that best completes the statement or answers the question.

1. Among other changes, human gonads begin to produce reproductive cells during
   a. puberty.
   b. the first six weeks of development.
   c. formation of the zygote.
   d. childhood.

2. Testosterone controls the development of
   a. secondary sex characteristics.
   b. secondary sex characteristics and sperm.
   c. sperm.
   d. eggs.

3. Fertilization generally takes place in the
   a. ovary.
   b. uterus.
   c. vagina.
   d. Fallopian tube.

4. During the follicle phase, cell and tissue growth in the uterus is stimulated by
   a. progesterone.
   b. FSH.
   c. estrogen.
   d. LH.

5. In the developing embryo, the neural tube forms from the
   a. ectoderm.
   b. endoderm.
   c. mesoderm.
   d. amnion.

6. As the embryo develops, the placenta supplies it with
   a. metabolic wastes.
   b. blood and oxygen.
   c. food and blood.
   d. food and oxygen.

7. Childbirth is initiated by
   a. the cervix.
   b. prolactin.
   c. oxytocin.
   d. colostrum.

8. Genital herpes is caused by a
   a. bacterium.
   b. virus.
   c. protozoan.
   d. fungus.

Putting It All Together

Using the information on pages xxx to xxxi, complete the following concept map.

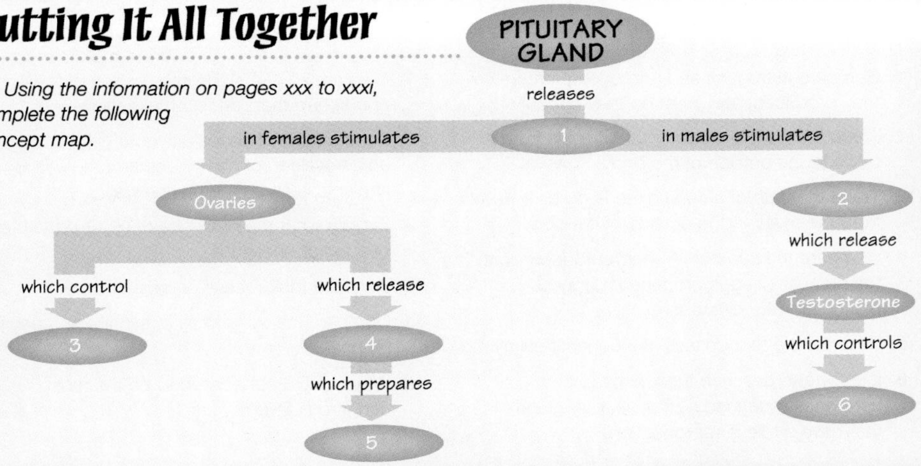

Putting It All Together

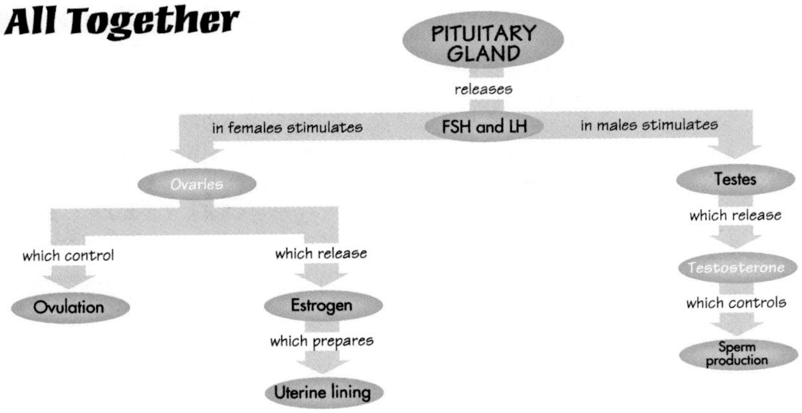

9. A hollow ball of cells that a zygote forms as it grows through cell division.
10. The process in which cells from the upper layer of the blastocyst migrate inward to form a third layer between the first two cell layers.
11. A thin stalk of extra-embryonic tissue that connects the embryo to the uterus.
12. At the end of eight weeks.
13. Oxytocin.
14. A hard sore called a chancre that forms at the point where the organism passed through the skin.
15. Genital herpes, hepatitis B, and AIDS.

Expanding the Concepts

1. Estrogens are female sex hormones produced by the ovaries; they control ovulation and the development of secondary sex characteristics in females. Androgens are male sex hormones produced by the testes; they control sperm production and the development of secondary sex characteristics in males.
2. Sperm are produced in the seminiferous tubules of the testis. When mature, they travel into the epididymis. After a brief storage period, they are released into the vas deferens, which extends upward from the scrotum into the abdominal cavity. From there, they leave the body through the urethra.
3. After the egg is released from the ovary, it is swept into a Fallopian tube. The egg then passes into the uterus. Next it travels through the outer end of the uterus, called the cervix, and into the vagina, the passageway that leads the egg outside the body.
4. In contrast to the millions of sperm produced each day, the ovaries produce just one egg every 28 days or so. Usually, only one egg is fertilized at a time, so producing more than one egg a month would waste energy that is needed to prepare the uterus for pregnancy. Sperm are tiny and many sperm are needed to fertilize one egg. The production of sperm is also the only biological contribution to reproduction that a male makes. For these reasons it is a good investment of energy for a male to produce a large quantity of sperm.

Assessment (continued)

5. During the follicle phase, FSH and LH stimulate a follicle in the ovary to develop to maturity, and estrogen produced by the developing follicle causes the lining of the uterus to thicken. During ovulation, a burst of LH causes the wall of the follicle to break open, and the egg is released and swept into the Fallopian tube. During the luteal phase, the egg moves through the Fallopian tube and the follicle develops into the corpus luteum, which starts producing progesterone. Menstruation begins when the lining of the uterus cannot be maintained due to declining levels of estrogen.
6. In males, LH stimulates the testes to produce testosterone. LH and FSH are necessary for the testes to produce sperm. In females, LH and FSH stimulate the ovaries to produce progesterone and estrogen. LH and FSH are also necessary for the ovaries to produce eggs.
7. Diagrams should show the nuclei of the two cells fusing to form a zygote with the diploid number of chromosomes.
8. As a zygote travels through a Fallopian tube, it undergoes several cell divisions to become a cluster of cells known as a morula. The morula gradually develops a hollow cavity and becomes known as a blastocyst, which implants itself on the uterine wall.
9. HCG in the blood of a female indicates pregnancy.
10. Near the end of the third week of embryonic development, the ectoderm begins to thicken into a line pointing to the head of the embryo. Gradually, this thickening produces a groove, and the raised edges of the groove move toward each other to form the neural tube, which becomes the nervous system.
11. The initial sore of syphilis is followed by a lack of symptoms as the bacterium gradually infects the circulatory and nervous systems, eventually causing serious damage, even death. In contrast, genital herpes causes a painful rash that recurs without warning but no other symptoms.

Assessment

Reviewing What You Learned

Answer each of the following in a complete sentence.

1. What are the two human gametes called?
2. What is puberty?
3. Identify two secondary sex characteristics of human males.
4. Where is progesterone produced, and what is its function?
5. Explain ovulation.
6. What change in the blood triggers menstruation?
7. Where does fertilization usually take place? Where does the fertilized egg go next?
8. How does a zygote form?
9. Describe a blastocyst.
10. What is gastrulation?
11. From what tissue does the umbilical cord form?
12. When does an embryo become a fetus?
13. What hormone stimulates contractions of the uterus?
14. What is the first symptom of a syphilis infection?
15. Name three sexually transmitted diseases caused by a virus.

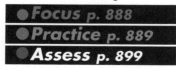

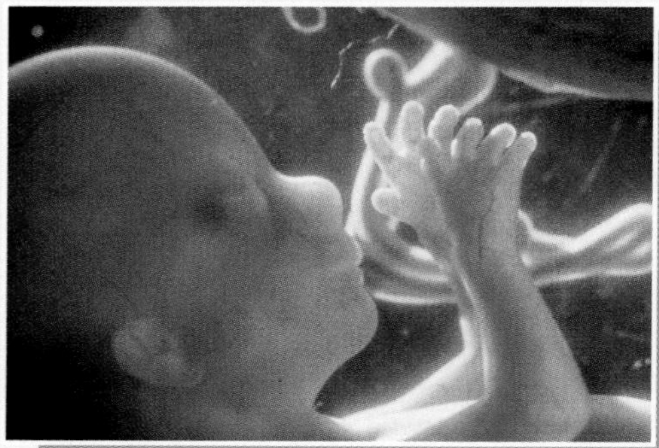

Expanding the Concepts

Discuss each of the following in a brief paragraph.

1. Compare estrogens and androgens. Where are they produced, and what do they control?
2. Trace the path of a sperm as it travels from a testis to the outside of the body.
3. Trace the path of an unfertilized egg as it travels from the ovary to the outside of the body.
4. Compare the number of sperm produced with the number of eggs produced. Suggest reasons for the difference.
5. Describe the four phases of the menstrual cycle.
6. Identify and describe the function of the hormones produced by the pituitary gland that have a role in reproduction.
7. Diagram and label the interactions of the egg and sperm that result in fertilization.
8. Describe the changes a zygote goes through as it travels through a Fallopian tube until it implants itself on the uterine wall.
9. Explain what the presence of HCG in the blood of a female indicates.
10. Describe the process of neurulation.
11. Compare the symptoms of syphilis and genital herpes.
12. Why is AIDS considered to be the most dangerous STD?

12. AIDS is considered the most dangerous STD because the virus that causes it attacks the immune system. This leaves the infected person vulnerable to a variety of other infections.

Extending Your Thinking

1. Accept any reasonable model that correctly represents the role of the placenta as a protective barrier, as well as the site of diffusion of substances between mother and child.

Skills Trace
Modeling
- Focus p. 888
- Practice p. 889
- Assess p. 899

Extending Your Thinking

Use the skills you have developed in this chapter to answer the following.

1. **Modeling** Construct a model placenta. Explain how it acts as a lifeline between mother and baby.
2. **Developing hypotheses** The World Health Organization (WHO) states that the percentage of adults in the United States who are reported to have at least one STD is much higher than the percentage in other countries. Develop a hypothesis to account for this difference.
3. **Making judgments** You have learned that drugs can be passed from the mother to the embryo or fetus through the placenta. Drinking alcohol during pregnancy can cause irreversible problems for a baby, including slowed growth, later behavioral problems, and mental retardation. Should drinking alcohol during pregnancy be made illegal? Why or why not?
4. **Interpreting data** Examine the graph showing the reported rates of gonorrhea. In what year was the rate of gonorrhea highest in the United States? Lowest? What changes have taken place between 1970 and 1994? Predict how many people might contract gonorrhea in a city of one million.

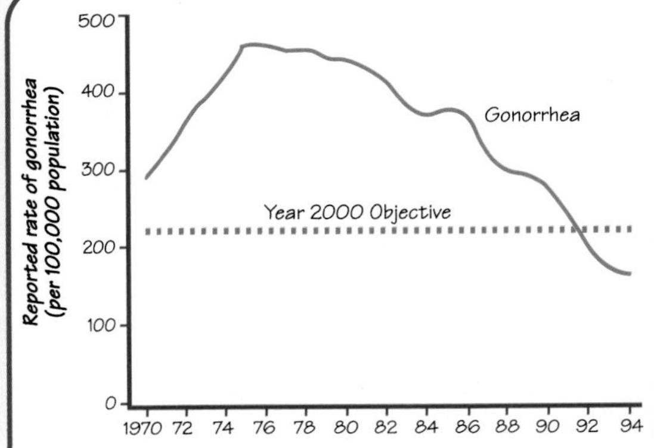

Source: Centers for Disease Control and Prevention, 1995

Applying Your Skills

In Vitro Fertilization

Since the birth of Louise Brown in 1979, in vitro *fertilization has enabled some couples with reproductive problems to conceive a child from their own egg and sperm. In this research project, you'll apply the information in this chapter to explain how* in vitro *fertilization works.*

1. Obtain reference materials on *in vitro* fertilization from an encyclopedia, library book, magazine articles, or other sources.
2. Describe the reproductive problems that *in vitro* fertilization can overcome.
3. List the steps in the *in vitro* fertilization process.
4. Explain each step, comparing it with the process of fertilization described in this chapter.

• GOING FURTHER •

5. In your journal, discuss reasons for and against this means of reproduction.

2. One hypothesis is that American adults are more sexually active than adults in other countries. Another is that sexually transmitted diseases are underreported in other countries.
3. Some students may argue that drinking alcohol during pregnancy should be made illegal in order to help prevent damage to fetuses. Other students may argue that drinking alcohol during pregnancy should not be made illegal, because such a law would be difficult to enforce or because it discriminates against women.

4. The rate of gonorrhea was highest in 1975 and lowest in 1994. Between 1970 and 1994, there was a net decrease of 47 percent. At the 1994 rate, 1600 people might contract gonorrhea in a city of 1 million.

Skills Trace

Interpreting

- Focus p. 892
- Practice p. 893
- Assess p. 899

Applying Your Skills

Teacher Note

- You may wish to have students research other forms of treatment for infertile couples, such as GIFT, ZIFT, or artificial insemination.

Answers

2. *In vitro* fertilization was originally developed to help couples with infertility caused by damaged Fallopian tubes, but it is now used to help other types of infertility.
3. During *in vitro* fertilization, the ovaries are stimulated to produce eggs, which are then removed from the ovaries and fertilized in the laboratory by semen from the male partner or from a donor if the partner is infertile. Several embryos at early stages of cell division are then introduced into the uterus.
4. Ovaries are stimulated to produce eggs, which is similar to ovulation except that more than one egg is released; ovaries and semen are combined to bring about fertilization, which is the same except that it occurs outside the female's body; embryos are introduced into the uterus, which is similar to implantation, except that the eggs did not come through the Fallopian tubes.
5. Students may favor *in vitro* fertilization because it allows couples to have children who otherwise could not. Students may oppose *in vitro* fertilization on religious grounds.

Scoring Rubric

4 Response is thorough, accurate, and creative; shows an in-depth understanding of science skills, procedures, and concepts.

3 Response is complete, mostly accurate, and original; shows a satisfactory understanding of science skills, procedures, and concepts.

2 Response is mostly complete but includes some inaccuracies; shows an adequate understanding of science skills, procedures, and concepts.

1 Response is only partially complete and has many inaccuracies; shows an incomplete understanding of science skills, procedures, and concepts.

0 Response is mostly incomplete and/or inaccurate; shows a lack of understanding of science skills, procedures, and concepts.

Chapter 40 Immune System

Content Management	Student Edition Activities
■ Section 40–1 Disease, pp. 901–904 Defining Disease The Germ Theory of Disease Pathogens Fighting Disease	**MINI LAB:** Another Generation, p. 902 **Laboratory Investigation:** Inhibiting Bacterial Growth, pp. 916–917
■ Section 40–2 The Body's Defense System, pp. 905–911 Nonspecific Defenses Specific Defenses Antibody Immunity Cell-Mediated Immunity Immune Disorders	
◆ BRANCHING OUT • In Depth Section 40–3 Cancer, pp. 912–915 A Cellular Disease Causes of Cancer Treating Cancer	**MINI LAB:** Going by the Numbers, p. 914

■ These sections cover all the necessary content and concepts for an enriched course in biology.
◆ This section covers content and concepts that are either applications or extensions of the enriched material.

Integration Strategies

SE Social Studies, p. 904
Health, p. 909
Biology and Society, p. 915

Assessment Strategies

SE Chapter Review, pp. 918–921
TR Section Reviews
Chapter Test
BL Chapter Review
Practice Test
CTB Chapter 40 Test

Tech Prep

Teaching strategies appropriate for students who are in technical/vocational programs or who are considering post-secondary technical education can be found on the following **TE** pages: 901 and 913.

Meeting the Standards

Sections 40–1 through 40–3 cover three of the six content standards under **The Cell,** two of the three content standards under **The Molecular Basis of Heredity,** and two of the five content standards under **The Interdependence of Organisms** as described on pages 184–186 of The National Science Education Standards.

Chapter Planning Guide

Teacher's Edition Activities	Other Activities	Media and Technology
Chapter Discovery Learning Activity, p. 900 **Investigate:** Research, p. 903	**LM** Modeling Disease Transmission, #79 Comparing the Effectiveness of Antiseptics, #80 **TR** **Writing in Biology:** Reflections and Directions **Apply:** Antibiotics vs. Bacteria **BL** **Inquiry Activity:** I Don't Feel Well	
Inquiry Activity: The One and Only Cause, p. 905 **Inquiry Activity:** Keeping Diseases at Bay, p. 906 **Investigate:** Role-Playing, p. 907	**TR** **Explore:** Hot 'n Cold **BL** **Inquiry Activity:** In Defense of Good Health	**BioVue Mini Doc:** AIDS and the Immune System, Videodisc Side 8 **TB** The Immune Response, #50
Inquiry Activity: A Campaign Against Death, p. 912 **Investigate:** Research, p. 913	**TR** **Enrich:** With Every Breath You Take **BL** **Inquiry Activity:** It's a Killer	

KEY: SE Student Edition **TE** Teacher's Edition **LM** Laboratory Manual **TR** Teaching Resources **BL** BioLog **TB** Transparency Box **CTB** Computer Test Bank

Materials List

TE **Chapter Discovery Learning Activity,** p. 900 (20 minutes); photographs of people from around the world with diseases not common in the United States.
SE **MINI LAB: Another Generation,** p. 902 (20 minutes); 128 kidney beans or other small objects.

TE **Inquiry Activity: A Campaign Against Death,** p. 912 (1–2 hours); poster board, colored pencils or markers.
SE **MINI LAB: Going by the Numbers,** p. 914 (30 minutes); graph paper, calculator.

Chapter 40

Immune System

Introducing the Chapter

. . . In Pictures

A macrophage is a type of phagocyte that engulfs and destroys invading pathogens as part of the body's nonspecific defenses. The *E. coli* being consumed in this photograph may be the strain of that bacterium that causes one kind of food poisoning. After students have examined the photograph, ask them the following questions.

- **How do macrophages protect the body from harmful bacteria?** (By attacking and consuming the bacteria.)
- **If macrophages consume enough bacteria, what might they be preventing?** (They might be preventing a disease caused by the bacteria.)

Tell students that in this chapter they will learn about both diseases and the body's response to infection by disease-causing organisms.

Teaching Strategy

In the first section of this chapter, students will learn about infectious diseases and the pathogens that cause them. In the second section, they will learn about the function of the body's immune system. The BRANCHING OUT section provides students with an in-depth understanding of cancer, including its causes and treatments.

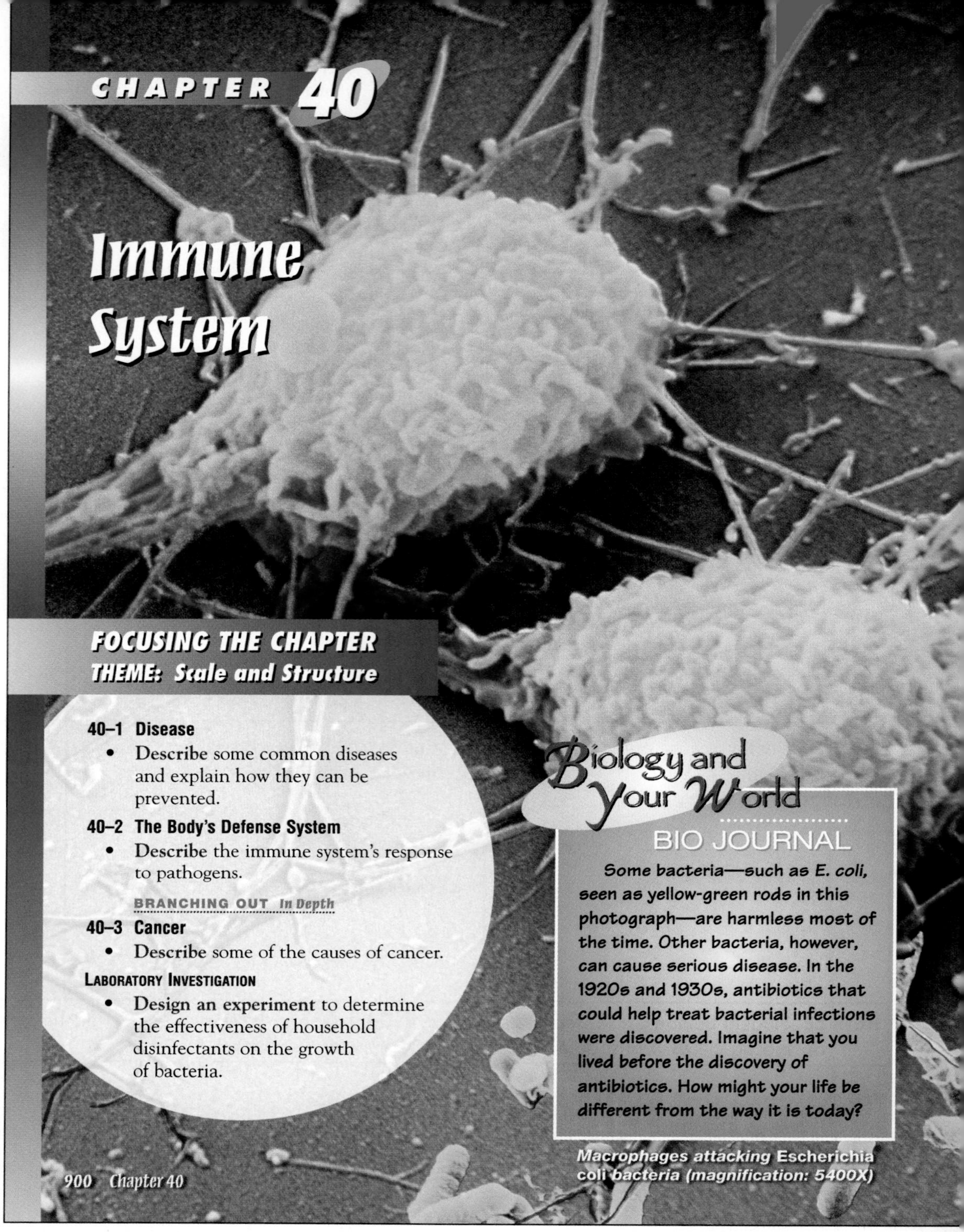

CHAPTER 40

Immune System

FOCUSING THE CHAPTER
THEME: Scale and Structure

40–1 Disease
- **Describe** some common diseases and explain how they can be prevented.

40–2 The Body's Defense System
- **Describe** the immune system's response to pathogens.

BRANCHING OUT *In Depth*

40–3 Cancer
- **Describe** some of the causes of cancer.

LABORATORY INVESTIGATION
- **Design an experiment** to determine the effectiveness of household disinfectants on the growth of bacteria.

Biology and Your World

BIO JOURNAL

Some bacteria—such as *E. coli*, seen as yellow-green rods in this photograph—are harmless most of the time. Other bacteria, however, can cause serious disease. In the 1920s and 1930s, antibiotics that could help treat bacterial infections were discovered. Imagine that you lived before the discovery of antibiotics. How might your life be different from the way it is today?

Macrophages attacking Escherichia coli bacteria (magnification: 5400X)

BIO JOURNAL

The Bio Journal topic can be used to stimulate classroom discussion about the cause of infectious diseases. Begin by asking students how they think diseases can be passed from one person to another. Then ask what the droplets of moisture released in the sneeze or cough have in them that causes diseases. Instruct students to keep their entries in their portfolios.

TEACHER SUPPORT

Chapter Discovery Learning Activity

WORLDWIDE DISEASES

Display a variety of photographs of people suffering from various diseases that are not commonly found in the United States. These might include people with leprosy, smallpox, polio, and bubonic plague. (Such photographs can be found in health or microbiology texts.) Point out that these diseases can occur in the United States, but they are not common. Then ask students why diseases common in other parts of the world are rarely seen here. Have groups discuss this question and brainstorm for a list of ways that such diseases can be prevented.

Disease

SECTION 40–1

Guide for Reading

- **Define** disease.
- **State** the germ theory of disease.
- **List** Koch's postulates.

MINI LAB
- **Predict** the growth of bacteria by using a model.

"IF YOU'VE GOT YOUR HEALTH, you've got everything." There's a lot of truth to this old saying. Good health makes it possible for you to work, study, and play. Unfortunately, most of us take our health for granted—until we catch a cold or develop a disease, something that interferes with the body's normal activities. When that happens, the value of good health becomes all too obvious. Why do we get sick? What is the best way to avoid disease? In this section, we will try to answer these questions.

Defining Disease

A disease is any change that disrupts the normal functions of the body. Some diseases, such as Huntington disease or cystic fibrosis, are genetic. Others, such as brown lung, a disease of coal miners, are produced by materials in the environment. But many diseases are produced by other organisms, including bacteria, fungi, protozoans, and viruses. A disease-causing organism is called a **pathogen**—literally, a "sickness-maker." The diseases caused by pathogens are generally known as **infectious diseases** because the organisms that cause them usually enter, or infect, the body of the person they make ill.

☑ **Checkpoint** What is an infectious disease? ❶

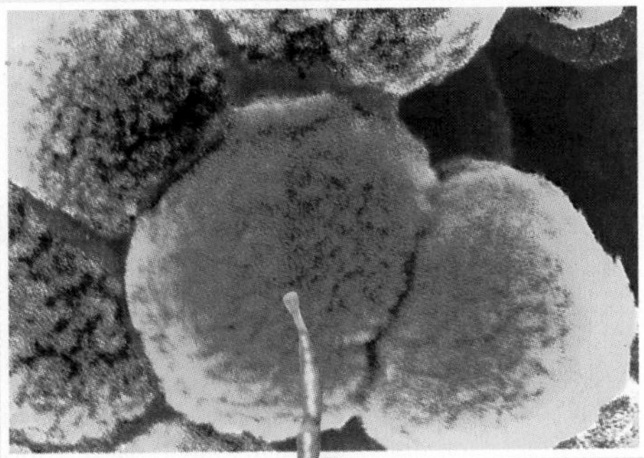

Figure 40–1
Diseases are caused by a variety of pathogens, including (a) Neisseria meningitis, *the bacterium that causes meningitis (magnification: 20,580X),* (b) Mycobacterium tuberculosis, *the bacterium that causes tuberculosis (magnification: 30,000X), and* (c) Borrelia burgdorferi, *the bacterium that causes Lyme disease, which is carried by the deer tick shown here (magnification: 12X).*

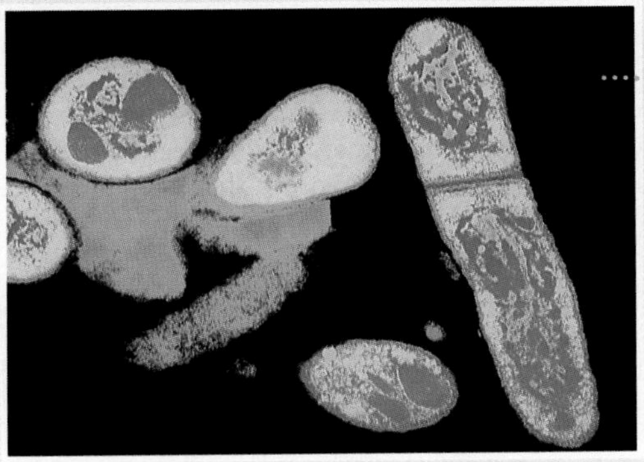

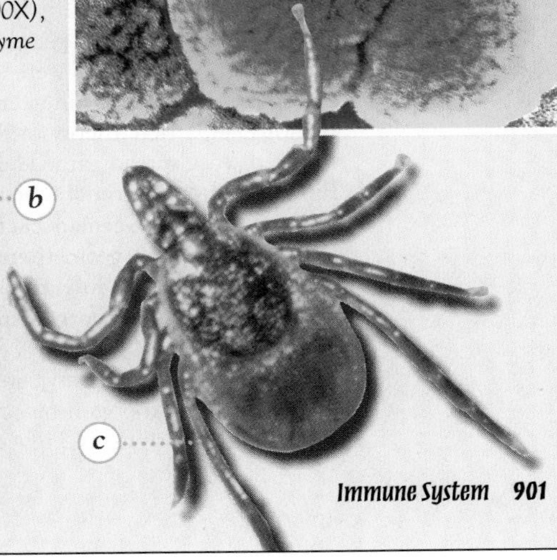

Section 40–1
Disease

Performance Objectives
- State the meaning of the word disease.
- Explain what the germ theory of disease is.
- Identify Koch's postulates.

Mini Lab Skill: Predicting
Laboratory Investigation Skill: Designing an experiment

1 ENGAGE

Ideas Through Images

Have students examine Figure 40–1, read the caption, and answer the following questions.

- **How would you define an infection?** (Some students might say that an infection is another name for a sickness. Others might suggest that an infection is the contamination of the body by bacteria or some other disease-causing microorganism.)
- **What are some ways that the human body can become infected?** (A typical response might mention breathing in microorganisms from the air or eating them with food.)

☑ **Checkpoint**

❶ A disease caused by a pathogen.

TEACHER SUPPORT

Managing Classroom Diversity

TECH PREP STUDENTS
Many students will enter careers in which sanitary procedures are essential to prevent the spread of pathogens, including those in food service, health care, and biotechnology. Ask these students to interview someone in a field of their choice to find out about such procedures and then write a set of instructions that could be used by someone new to the job.

MULTICULTURAL STRATEGY
Students from other parts of the world might have family members with firsthand knowledge of some infectious diseases, such as malaria, plague, and yellow fever, that are not common in the United States. Ask these students to interview members of their families, gather accounts of the effects of these diseases, and prepare a presentation to the class.

Ancillary Support

The resources below can be used to support your teaching strategy for these two pages.

LM Modeling Disease Transmission, #79
Comparing the Effectiveness of Antiseptics, #80
TR Writing in Biology: Reflections and Directions

2 EXPLORE

MINI LAB Predicting

Teacher Note
• For time required and materials needed, see page 900b.

Answers to Analyze and Conclude
1. To produce 128 bacteria takes 7 generations, or 210 seconds. In actual time, that would be 210 minutes, or 3.5 hours.
2. Since bacteria double every 30 minutes, in 24 hours there would be 2^{48} bacteria, or over 140 trillion.
3. Students should infer that it is necessary to treat wounds quickly because the population of bacteria that infects a wound could grow tremendously in only a short time.

Skills Trace
Predicting
- Focus p. 902
- Practice p. 904
- Assess p. 921

3 TEACH

Correcting Misconceptions

Ask students whether they think that going outside without a coat on a cold day is one sure way to get a cold. Many students will agree to that proposition. Point out that according to the germ theory of disease, infectious diseases are caused by microorganisms. Since a cold can be caught from another person, it must be an infectious disease caused by a microorganism. Thus, not wearing a coat probably has little to do with contracting that disease. Ask students for other common notions of how one becomes sick with an infectious disease.

MINI LAB Predicting

Another Generation

PROBLEM *How can you use a model to **predict** the growth of bacteria?*

PROCEDURE

1. Place a kidney bean (or other small object), representing a bacterium, on the table. Wait 30 seconds—which represents the actual 30 minutes that it takes a bacterium to divide—and then put another kidney bean down next to the first.
2. After another 30 seconds, add one kidney bean for each kidney bean that is already on the table.
3. Repeat step 2 until there are 128 kidney beans on the table. Construct a data table to record each generation and the number of bacteria produced.

ANALYZE AND CONCLUDE

1. How much time does it take to produce 128 bacteria?
2. Predict how many bacteria would be produced in 24 hours.
3. What can you infer from this activity about why it is necessary to treat wounds quickly?

The Germ Theory of Disease

At one time, many people believed that infectious diseases were caused by evil spirits. In the mid-nineteenth century, however, a new theory of the way in which disease spread gained acceptance. **Pioneered by the French chemist Louis Pasteur and the German bacteriologist Robert Koch, the germ theory of disease suggested that infectious diseases were caused by microorganisms, which many people call "germs."**

As you know, the world around us is filled with microorganisms of various shapes and descriptions. How can we be sure which of these scores of possible organisms actually causes a particular disease? Koch provided the answer in a series of rules, called **Koch's postulates,** that are used to identify the microorganism that causes a specific disease. **Koch's postulates include the following:**

- **The pathogen should always be found in the body of a sick organism (the host) and should not be found in a healthy organism.**
- **The pathogen must be isolated and grown in a pure culture.**
- **When purified pathogens are injected into a new host, they cause the disease.**
- **The same pathogen should be reisolated from the second host and grown in a pure culture. The pathogen should still be the same as the original pathogen.**

By focusing attention on the biological causes of disease, Pasteur, Koch, and many other scientists produced a revolution in human thinking. For the first time, disease did not seem to be an unavoidable consequence of being alive. And, if a particular pathogen could be identified, there was hope that the disease it caused could be prevented or cured.

Pathogens

Many of the microorganisms that fill the world around also live in and around the human body. The large intestine, for example, harbors dense colonies of bacteria. Bacteria and yeast are found in the mouth, throat, and excretory system. Fortunately, most of these organisms are harmless, and a few of them are actually beneficial.

This being the case, why are some organisms considered pathogens? In some cases, the pathogens actually destroy

TEACHER SUPPORT — Historical Perspective

Robert Koch (1843–1910) was a German surgeon who, along with Louis Pasteur, became a founder of modern bacteriology. In 1876, he was working as a country doctor near Breslau when an anthrax epidemic struck the area's cattle. Lending his expertise, Koch was able to obtain the pathogen, *Bacillus anthracis*, from infected cattle, transfer it to mice, and recover the same pathogen in the end. From this and later work, Koch established his rules, or postulates, for identifying the causative agent for a disease. His most famous discovery came in 1882, when he identified the bacterium that causes tuberculosis, *Mycobacterium tuberculosis*. Koch was one of the first to use a solid medium to grow bacteria, originally on glass slides. In 1887 his assistant, Julius Petri, devised a shallow dish with a cover for the purpose, and Petri dishes have been used around the world ever since.

cells as they grow. Many pathogens, including viruses and many bacteria, grow directly inside cells of the human body, eating their food and ultimately destroying the cell. Other pathogens, including many bacteria, produce **toxins,** or poisons that disrupt bodily functions and produce illness. Finally, many pathogens, especially parasitic worms, produce sickness when they block the flow of blood, remove nutrients from the digestive system, and disrupt other bodily functions. ***Figure 40–2*** lists some of the most common pathogens, including viruses and bacteria, and the diseases they cause.

Viruses are tiny particles that invade and replicate within living cells. Viruses attach to the surface of a cell, insert their genetic material in the form of RNA or DNA, and take over many of the functions of the host cell. Nearly all living organisms—including plants, insects, mammals, and even bacteria—can be infected by viruses.

Although bacteria are often helpful, certain bacteria cause some of the most serious diseases of all. Bacteria are one of the main reasons why it is important to handle food carefully. Bacteria grow quickly in warm, partially-cooked food

Figure 40–2 *This chart lists some of the viruses, bacteria, protozoans, worms, and fungi that cause disease. Notice how each disease is spread.*

PATHOGENS AND DISEASE

TYPE OF PATHOGEN	DISEASE	ORGANISM THAT CAUSES THE DISEASE	METHODS OF SPREADING THE DISEASE
Viruses	Smallpox	Variola	Airborne; personal contact
	Common cold	Rhinovirus	Airborne; direct contact with infected person
	Influenza	Two types (A, B), plus many subtypes	Airborne; droplet infection; direct contact with infected person
	Measles	Measles	Droplets in air; direct contact with secretions of infected person
	AIDS	HIV	Sexual contact; contaminated blood products or hypodermic needles
	Chickenpox	Varicella	Airborne; direct contact with infected person
Bacteria	Tuberculosis	*Mycobacterium tuberculosis*	Droplets in air; contaminated milk and dairy products
	Meningitis	*Neisseria meningitis*	Direct exposure to organism
	Diphtheria	*Corynebacterium diphtheriae*	Contact with infected person or carrier; contaminated raw milk
	Rocky Mountain spotted fever	*Rickettsia rickettsii*	Bite of infected tick
	Lyme disease	*Borrelia burgdorferi*	Bite of infected tick
	Cholera	*Vibrio cholerae*	Contaminated drinking water
	Tetanus	*Clostridium tetani*	Dirty wound; usually a puncture wound
Protozoans	African sleeping sickness	*Trypanosoma*	Spread by tsetse fly
	Malaria	*Plasmodium*	Spread by mosquitoes
Worms	Schistosomiasis	*Schistosoma mansoni*	Freshwater streams and rice paddies
	Beef tapeworm	*Taenia saginata*	Contaminated meat
Fungi	Athlete's foot	Imperfect fungi	Contact with infected person; shower stalls
	Ringworm	Imperfect fungi	Exchange of hats, combs, and athletic headgear with infected person

Ideas Through Images

Have students examine Figure 40–2, read the caption, and answer the following questions.

- **What is a pathogen?** (A disease-causing organism.)
- **What are the different types of pathogens?** (Viruses, bacteria, protozoans, worms, and fungi.)
- **Are all bacteria pathogens?** (No. Most bacteria are harmless, and some are even beneficial.)
- **What are some methods by which diseases are spread?** (Through the air, by personal contact, through droplets in the air, through contact with secretions, through contaminated blood, through contaminated foods, through bites of flies and ticks, by the exchange of headgear, and so on.)
- **Can HIV be spread by the exchange of athletic headgear or the bite of a tsetse fly?** (No. HIV can be spread only by sexual contact, contaminated blood products, or hypodermic needles.)

Investigate

Research Ask each student to choose one of the infectious diseases in the chart in Figure 40–2, or some other infectious disease of which they are aware, and write a report on the disease. In this report, students should include information on the disease pathogen, method by which it is spread, symptoms, treatment, and prevention.

TEACHER SUPPORT

Ecology Note

The ability to eliminate or control a disease depends greatly on the life cycle of the pathogen that causes it. Tetanus, for example, is hard to control because the soil is the reservoir of its pathogen, *Clostridium tetani*. A reservoir is any place a population of a microorganism is maintained. Easier to control is a pathogen whose reservoir is primarily the human body, such as the measles virus, which can be held in check through immunizations. Much more difficult to control is a pathogen whose reservoir is an infected animal, or vector. Since the 1920s, public health authorities have been trying to control the bacterium that causes Rocky Mountain spotted fever. But controlling that pathogen means controlling the population of the wood tick that serves as its vector, a task that has proven difficult.

Ancillary Support

The resource below can be used to support your teaching strategy for these two pages.

BL Inquiry Activity: I Don't Feel Well

Discussion

Begin a discussion of methods for fighting disease by asking students why they have been told so often to wash their hands before eating. Most will know that washing eliminates germs. In this discussion, emphasize the following points.

- Good personal hygiene is the most important way to eliminate contact with pathogens.
- Antibiotics are useful against living things only. Viral diseases, such as the common cold, cannot be fought with such drugs.

INTEGRATING SOCIAL STUDIES

An epidemic of bubonic plague, later called the Black Death, swept through Western Europe in the fourteenth century with devastating effects. Historians estimate that one-third to one-half of the population were killed.

Laboratory Investigation

The Laboratory Investigation, Inhibiting Bacterial Growth, on pages 916–917 is appropriate to use at this point in the chapter.

4 ASSESS

Quick Check

Have students classify the diseases listed in Figure 40–2 according to the methods by which they are spread.

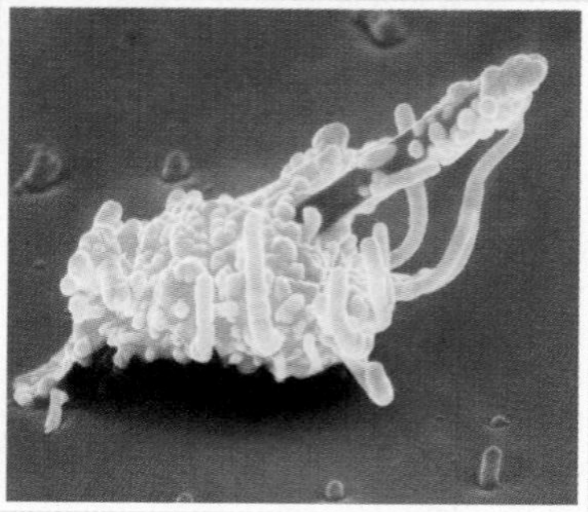

Figure 40–3 *Although white blood cells normally trap and digest pathogens, this white blood cell is engulfing a cancer-causing asbestos fiber. Unfortunately, it cannot be digested.*

INTEGRATING SOCIAL STUDIES

What effect did the bubonic plague have on the populations of Europe in the Middle Ages?

and are always present in uncooked meat. Many types of bacteria, especially the species known as *Salmonella*, can grow quickly enough to produce high levels of the toxins that produce food poisoning. The only way to make food completely safe is to cook it completely.

Although many pathogens are either viruses or bacteria, there are other pathogens as well. Fungi, protozoans, insects, and parasitic worms also cause disease.

Fighting Disease

Once a pathogen has been identified, biologists search for clues as to how it is passed from person to person. If a disease is thoroughly understood, preventing it usually becomes clear. Then, the best way to fight the disease is to avoid it.

Many diseases are spread by animals. The **vectors**—animals that carry disease-causing organisms from host to host—are the key to stopping such diseases. Malaria and yellow fever are fought by controlling the mosquito population. Lyme disease can be prevented by avoiding deer ticks, which carry it. Bubonic plague, the "black death" that killed millions in Europe in the Middle Ages, is spread by fleas that live on rats and mice. ● Aggressive measures to control these rodents have made serious outbreaks of the plague rare.

Diseases that are spread from one person to another can be controlled by simple habits of personal hygiene. Washing one's hands thoroughly helps to prevent the spread of many pathogens. The common cold is spread by coughing, sneezing, and hand-to-hand contact. Such measures as covering your mouth with a tissue can limit infection.

If prevention fails, drugs have been developed for use against all sorts of pathogens. Perhaps the most useful single class of infection-fighting drugs are **antibiotics**—compounds that kill bacteria without harming cells of humans or animals. Many of these compounds are produced naturally. Antibiotics work by interfering with the cellular processes of microorganisms. For example, penicillin, the first antibiotic to be discovered, interferes with cell wall synthesis, disabling and killing bacteria. Streptomycin and tetracycline interfere with protein synthesis on bacterial ribosomes. Because viruses use the ribosomes of the infected cell to make their proteins, antibiotics are not effective against viruses.

Section Review 40–1

1. **Define** disease.
2. **State** the germ theory of disease.
3. **List** Koch's postulates.
4. **Critical Thinking—Drawing Conclusions** Why might Koch's postulates be difficult to apply to a viral infection?
5. **MINI LAB** How can you **predict** the growth of bacteria by using a model?

Section Review 40–1

1. Any change that disrupts the normal functions of the body.
2. Infectious diseases are caused by microorganisms.
3. Students should list the four postulates given on page 902.
4. Koch's second postulate states that the pathogen must be isolated and grown in pure culture. Because viruses are not living, they could not be grown in pure culture in the same way that living organisms can.
5. If the rate of growth of the bacteria is known, then a model can be used to simulate bacterial growth without actually growing the bacteria.

Skills Trace

Predicting

- Focus p. 902
- Practice p. 904
- Assess p. 921

Learning Modality

Visual Learning Ask each student to make a cartoon panel of four drawings that represent Koch's four postulates about how to identify the pathogen of a particular disease.

GUIDE FOR READING

- Describe the function of the immune system.
- Define immunity.

SOMETIMES IT MAY SEEM THAT we are surrounded by a world of pathogens that threaten our existence every moment of the day. In such a hostile environment, how does the body cope with the threat of infection? The answer is that the body has a protective system, a series of defenses that guard against disease.

The body's defense against infection is provided by the immune system. Unlike many of the body's other systems, the work of the immune system goes on behind the scenes. In fact, if it is working properly, you may never notice it. But when something does go wrong with the immune system, life itself is threatened by the pathogens it normally holds at bay.

Nonspecific Defenses

The immune system is the body's primary defense against pathogens. It consists of nonspecific and specific defenses against infection. The skin is the body's most important nonspecific defense. Few pathogens can penetrate the tough layers of keratin protein at the skin's outer surface. The importance of these layers becomes obvious as soon as the skin is broken. As you know, even a small cut or scrape quickly becomes infected if it is not taken care of. Why does this happen? Because even the smallest cut breaks the protective barrier, giving microorganisms

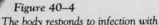

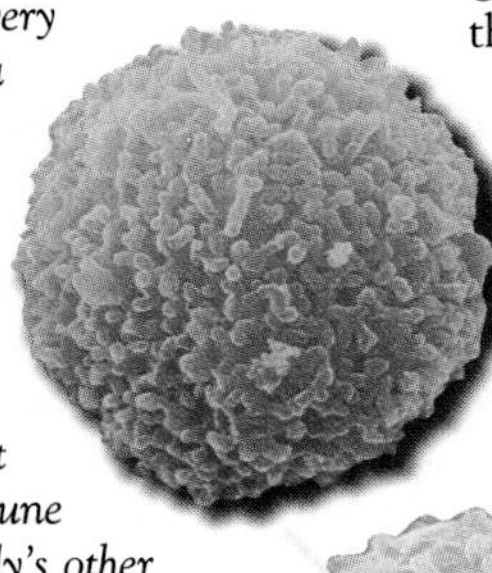

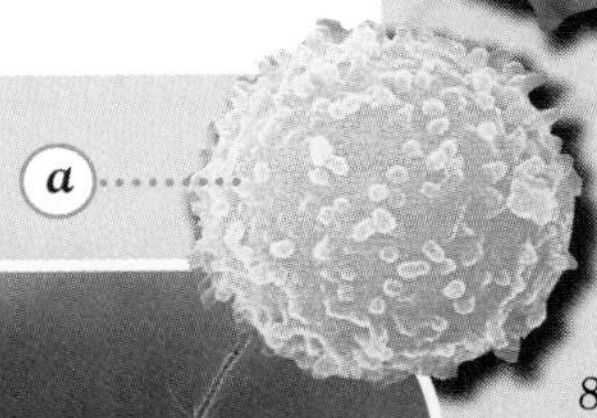

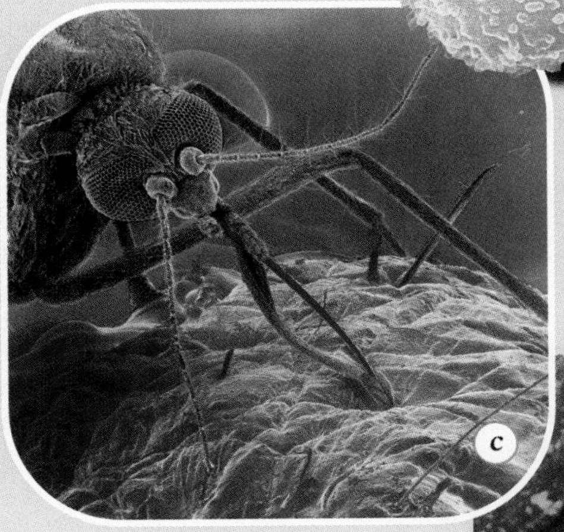

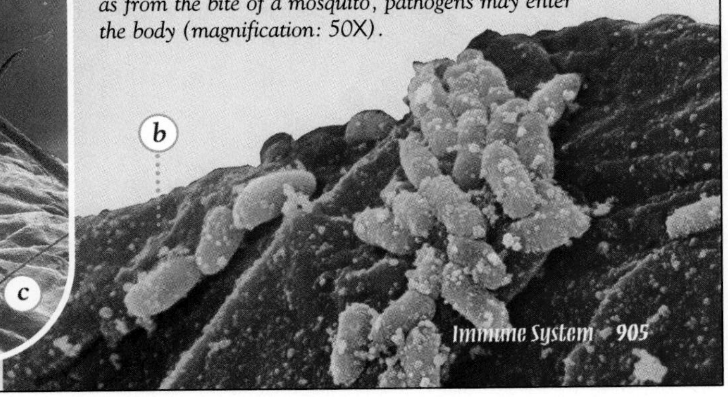

Figure 40–4 The body responds to infection with specific defenses and nonspecific defenses. (a) Specialized white blood cells such as lymphocytes are the body's main specific defense (magnification: 1500X). (b) The skin provides the body with its most important nonspecific defense. It keeps bacteria, seen as green rods in this electron micrograph, from breaking through (magnification: 8000X). (c) When there is a break in the skin, such as from the bite of a mosquito, pathogens may enter the body (magnification: 50X).

TEACHER SUPPORT

Historical Perspective

A significant step in understanding the immune system came in 1883 through the work of the Russian biologist Elie Metchnikoff (1845–1916). His interest at the time was in discovering the cause of inflammation in animal tissue. His subject of study was starfish larvae, used because their transparent bodies allowed for clear observation of internal processes. Wondering how the organism's cells would react to a foreign body, Metchnikoff plucked a thorn from one of the roses in his rose garden and plunged it into a larva. A day later, he noticed the thorn was surrounded by a swarm of cells. Through further study, he identified similar cells in humans, specifically the white blood cells in pus. He recognized that these cells are able to digest foreign particles, and he named the cells phagocytes, from the Greek words meaning "to eat cells."

SECTION 40–2

The Body's Defense System

Performance Objectives

- Explain how the immune system works.
- Define the term immunity.

1 ENGAGE

Inquiry Activity

Designing an Experiment

The One and Only Cause

Ask students how scientists could prove that a virus called HIV is the cause of AIDS. Have students work in pairs or small groups to design an experiment that would prove that hypothesis. Remind them that Koch's postulates provide a model of how to identify the pathogen that causes a specific disease. Then tell students that their experiments can be as creative as possible, except that they cannot propose to inject HIV into a living person. Discuss their results, as well as the difficulties inherent in this task, when all groups have finished.

Ideas Through Images

Have students examine Figure 40–4, read the caption, and answer the following questions.

- **How does the skin protect the body from disease?** (It provides a barrier that prevents pathogens from infecting the organs inside the body.)
- **What is the danger when the skin is broken, such as from a cut or puncture?** (The danger is that pathogens will move through the skin and infect the body.)

Ancillary Support

The resource below can be used to support your teaching strategy for these two pages.

TR Apply: Antibiotics vs. Bacteria

2 EXPLORE

Inquiry Activity
Hypothesizing

Keeping Diseases at Bay
Some students may remember the immunizations they have had, either the injections they had when they were younger or a booster shot for tetanus recently. Point out that the physician injects a small amount of a substance into their bodies to help prevent a disease. Ask students how they think the substance accomplishes that goal. Have small groups meet to formulate a hypothesis about how a vaccine prevents disease.

3 TEACH

Ideas Through Images

Have students examine Figure 40–5, read the caption, and answer the following questions.

- **Which white blood cells are involved in the inflammatory response?** (Phagocytes.)
- **Why does an inflamed area on the skin become red?** (Because the blood vessels near the wound expand.)
- **How does expansion of blood vessels contribute to the healing of the wound?** (The expansion of blood vessels allows phagocytes to leak out and attack the invading pathogens.)
- **What does an increased number of white blood cells in the blood signal?** (That the body is fighting an infection.)

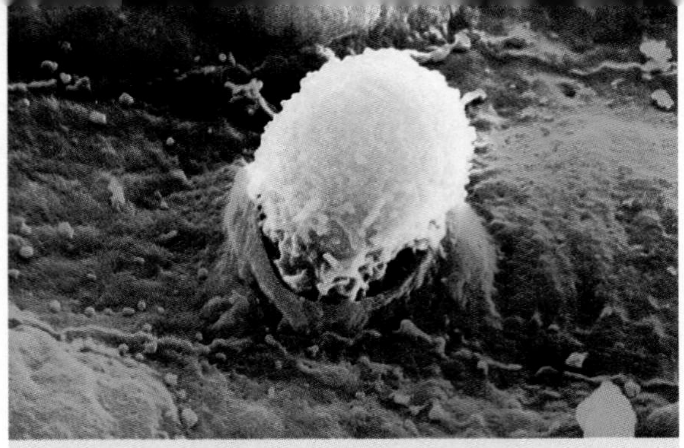

Figure 40–5
During the inflammatory response, white blood cells leak out of the blood vessels to attack a pathogen. In this scanning electron micrograph, a white blood cell is squeezing through the endothelium of a vein to join the attack (magnification: 3450X).

on the skin's surface a chance to enter the body.

The skin is considered a nonspecific defense because it is not directed against any one pathogen. Instead, a nonspecific defense guards against all infections, regardless of their cause. Other nonspecific defenses are found in the mouth and respiratory passages, where millions of microorganisms enter every day. Passages leading to the lungs are coated with mucus that traps airborne pathogens. Cells lining these passages sweep these trapped cells into the digestive system, where they are destroyed by digestive enzymes. Other pathogens that enter the mouth, eyes, and excretory system may be destroyed by lysozyme, an enzyme that breaks down cell walls of some bacteria.

☑ *Checkpoint* What is a nonspecific defense? ❶

Inflammation

If pathogens do enter the body through a cut, they grow quickly, spreading and releasing toxins into the tissues. When this happens, a second nonspecific defense is activated. This is called the **inflammatory response** because it can cause the skin to turn a "flaming" red color. Blood vessels near the wound expand, and white blood cells leak from the vessels to invade the infected tissues. Many of these white cells, which are called **phagocytes,** engulf and destroy bacteria. The infected tissue may become swollen and painful as the battle between the pathogens and white blood cells rages.

☑ *Checkpoint* What is the inflammatory response? ❷

Fever

When a serious infection causes pathogens to spread, the body responds in two ways. First, the immune system releases chemicals that increase the body's temperature. You have probably experienced this elevated body temperature, called a fever. Second, the immune system produces millions of white blood cells to fight the infection. An increased number of white cells in the blood is a sign that the body is dealing with a serious infection.

Specific Defenses

The immune system is also capable of powerful specific defenses that produce **immunity** against particular diseases. **Immunity is the ability of the body to resist a specific pathogen.** There are two kinds of immunity—antibody immunity and cell-mediated immunity.

Ever since ancient times, people have observed that individuals who recover from certain diseases, such as mumps and measles, never again become sick with the same disease. In other words, most people who recover from the mumps or measles are permanently immune—they will never get the mumps or measles again.

TEACHER SUPPORT

Managing Classroom Diversity

GIFTED STUDENTS
Ask students to investigate the spread of HIV/AIDS around the world. They could use library books and periodicals to find out where the disease originated and where it has spread. You could ask them to prepare a presentation for the class that would include a world map showing where AIDS has been the greatest problem so far and where it is expected to become a problem in the near future.

LEP STUDENTS/AT-RISK STUDENTS
Have students who are unfamiliar with the terminology used in this section look up the following words in a dictionary and write out a definition for each: allergy, antibody, antigen, asthma, autoimmune, bind, immunity, infection, inflammation, mediate, nonspecific, pathogen, site, specific, suppress, and vaccine.

Antibody Immunity

Exposure to certain diseases produces permanent immunity because it stimulates cells in the immune system to make proteins called **antibodies.** The molecules that stimulate the production of antibodies are known as **antigens.** An antigen is any substance that triggers the specific defense of the immune system. The antibody is the basic functional unit of the specific immune response.

As ***Figure 40–6*** shows, an antibody is shaped like the letter Y and has two identical antigen-binding sites. This means that an antibody can attach to two antigens. Why is this good? If the antigen is on the surface of a virus particle, it means that antibodies can link the virus particles into a clump, preventing them from entering a cell. The clump of viruses and antibodies attract phagocytes, which engulf and destroy the whole mass. If the immune system produces enough antibodies to a particular virus, it can prevent that virus from causing disease.

Antibodies can prevent bacterial infections, too. When antibodies bind to the surfaces of bacteria, they mark the cells for destruction by phagocytes and other white blood cells.

Lymphocytes

The immune system also includes a special class of white blood cells called **lymphocytes.** One group of lymphocytes, the B lymphocytes, or **B cells,** matures in bone marrow. These cells produce antibodies.

How do B cells produce antibody proteins that fit their antigens so precisely? In a sense, they are custom-made. As B cells develop, the antibody genes within each of them rearrange themselves in a slightly different way. When their development is complete, the immune system contains literally millions of B cells—each capable of producing a slightly different antibody.

When a pathogen enters the body, molecules on its surface act as antigens to stimulate the immune system. This is helped along by **T cells,** lymphocytes that have matured in the thymus gland. In a few days, B cells whose antibodies closely match the shape of the antigen have started to grow and divide rapidly. This produces a large number of specialized B cells called **plasma cells,** which release antibodies into the bloodstream to fight the infection. Millions of plasma cells may be produced from a handful of B cells stimulated by antigen.

Although it may take many days for enough plasma cells to form and help to overcome an infection, these cells have another important function—they produce permanent immunity. When a person contracts measles, for example, antigens on the surface of the virus stimulate the production of millions of

ANTIBODY STRUCTURE

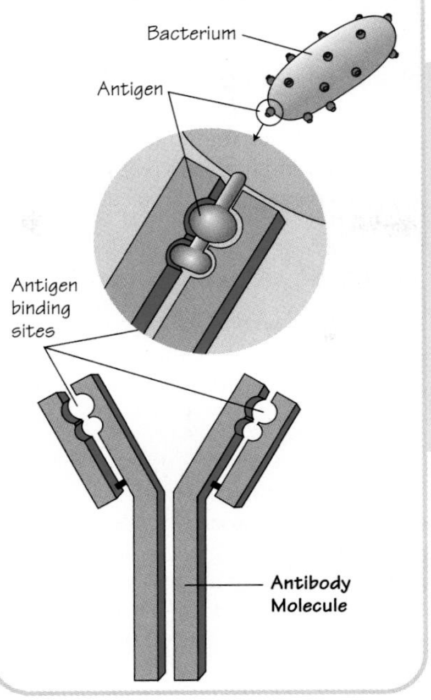

Figure 40–6 The antibody molecule is the basic functional unit of an immune response. Each antibody molecule has two antigen-binding sites, which are specific for a particular antigen.

Ideas Through Images

Have students examine Figure 40–6, read the caption, and answer the following questions.

- **What is an antigen?** (An antigen is any substance that triggers the specific defense of the immune system.)
- **What cells produce antibodies, and how do antibodies prevent infection?** (B cells produce antibodies, which prevent infection by binding with antigens.)
- **How is an antibody a specific defense against disease?** (As B cells develop, the antibodies within each of them rearrange themselves in a slightly different way so that they fit different antigens precisely.)
- **What happens to viruses and bacteria that bind to antibodies?** (They are engulfed and destroyed by phagocytes.)

Investigate

Role-Playing Divide the class into groups, and ask each group to write a one-act play that would represent one of the defenses of the body against disease. Groups might focus on nonspecific defenses, the inflammatory response, antibody immunity, or cell-mediated immunity. Tell students their plays may be humorous but should also be informative.

Checkpoints

1. A defense against infection that is not directed against any one pathogen.
2. A nonspecific defense that involves a battle between white blood cells and pathogens at the site where pathogens have entered the body through a cut.

TEACHER SUPPORT

Background Information

The key to the ability of antibodies to bind with a seemingly unlimited variety of antigens is in the structure of these proteins: two long chains of amino acids and two short chains. The regions at the end of each of these four chains—two on each branch of the Y—can be varied by the B cell that secretes the antibody, and a slight variance in the amino acids in those regions can create a binding site that fits exactly with the antigen encountered.

Different types of antibodies work in different ways. Some can neutralize an antigen, as in the case of a diphtheria toxin, by binding to the toxin's side groups. Some can bind to viruses, making them harmless. Some can attach to bacterial cells and destroy them by releasing a chemical. When antibodies attach to bacterial cells, it also makes phagocytosis easy and efficient.

Ancillary Support

The resources below can be used to support your teaching strategy for these two pages.

TR Explore: Hot 'n Cold
BL Inquiry Activity: In Defense of Good Health

Ideas Through Images

Have students examine Figure 40–7, read the caption, and answer the following questions.

• **What are the two kinds of immunity?** (Antibody immunity and cell-mediated immunity.)

• **What kinds of cells are involved in each?** (B cells, T cells, and phagocytes are involved in antibody immunity; killer T cells and memory T cells are involved in cell-mediated immunity.)

• **Where are B cells and T cells produced?** (B cells are produced in bone marrow; T cells are produced in the thymus gland.)

• **What is the function of plasma cells?** (The B cells called plasma cells secrete antibodies, which bind with antigens and prepare them to be destroyed by phagocytes.)

• **How does the immune system recognize the same pathogens if they enter the body in the future?** (Memory B cells store information about the pathogen for any future attacks.)

• **How do killer T cells destroy pathogens?** (Killer T cells attack antigen-bearing cells and disrupt their cell membranes.)

Discussion

Initiate a discussion of vaccines by asking students what vaccinations, or immunizations, they have had in their lives. Point out that vaccines are mild, weakened, or killed forms of pathogens that are purposely introduced into the body to provoke an immune response. Emphasize that the specific defense that protects the body from future infection by the pathogen is antibody immunity. The vaccine allows the body to make antibodies against a harmless antigen that may someday be needed against a dangerous invading pathogen.

plasma cells to fight the infection. As a result, if the person survives the infection, his or her immune system retains those cells and is always ready to respond with a massive supply of the measles antibody.

Vaccines

Vaccines take advantage of this fact. A **vaccine** is a weakened or mild form of a pathogen that causes permanent immunity when injected into the body. For example, when you were vaccinated against polio, weakened polio viruses were used to stimulate the B cells in your body that are capable of making antipolio antibodies. As a result, if you are ever exposed to the polio virus, your body is prepared to fight this virus with millions of plasma cells ready to make polio antibodies.

☑ *Checkpoint* What is a vaccine? 1

Figure 40–7
If an infection occurs, the body responds by either of two immune responses—the production of antibodies or the production of killer T cells. In antibody immunity, antigens cause B cells to multiply. Some B cells develop into plasma cells that secrete antibodies. Other B cells develop into memory B cells, which store information about the pathogen in order to provide future immunity. In cell-mediated immunity, T cells multiply, producing three types of T cells—killer T cells, helper T cells, and suppressor T cells.

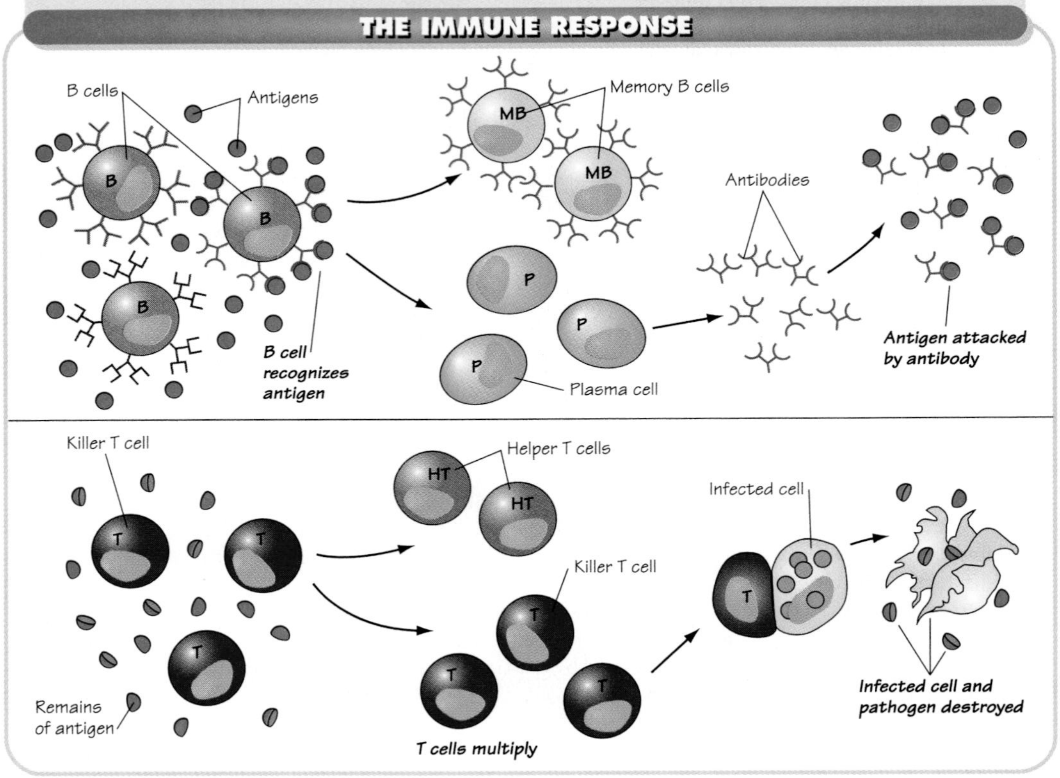

TEACHER SUPPORT — Background Information

The American Academy of Pediatrics recommends the following immunization schedule for children.
• 0–1 month—Hepatitis B
• 2 months—DTP (diphtheria/tetanus/pertussis); OPV (oral polio vaccine); Hib (*Haemophilus influenzae* B)
• 2–4 months—Hepatitis B
• 4 months—DTP, OPV, Hib
• 6 months—DTP, OPV, Hib
• 6–18 months—Hepatitis B
• 12–15 months—MMR (measles/mumps/rubella); Hib
• 12–18 months—DTP; varicella
• 4–6 years—DTP, OPV, MMR (before entering school)
• 14–16 years—Td (tetanus booster every 10 years)

Except for the polio vaccine, all these immunizations are administered by injection. This schedule is revised periodically as vaccines are improved or new ones are developed.

Cell-Mediated Immunity

Antibodies alone are not enough to protect the body against some pathogens. In these cases, the immune system has a powerful weapon—the **killer T cell.** Killer T cells make direct contact with antigen-bearing cells, disrupting their cell membranes and destroying them. This process is known as **cell-mediated immunity.** The actions of killer T cells are extremely important in fighting certain types of infections. Killer T cells attack and destroy virus-infected cells, and they are also important in fighting protozoans and multicellular parasites.

Unfortunately, killer T cells are also responsible for the rejection of tissue transplants. The cells of your body have a special set of protein markers on their surfaces that enable the immune system to recognize them as your own. If tissues from another person are transplanted into the body, the immune system checks these markers, recognizes them as foreign, and attacks them. To prevent tissue rejection, physicians search for an organ donor whose cell markers are nearly identical to those of the recipient. They may also use drugs, such as cyclosporine, that suppress the cell-mediated immune response.

In addition to killer T cells, there are other types of T cells that are involved in the immune response. **Helper T cells** are the first cells to identify the specific pathogen in the body. The helper T cells then send a message to the B cells "telling" them to produce antibodies for that particular pathogen.

A third kind of T cell is a **suppressor T cell.** After an infection has been fought off successfully, suppressor T cells shut off the immune response in both B cells and killer T cells.

Checkpoint What is the function of helper T cells? 2

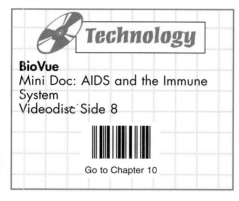

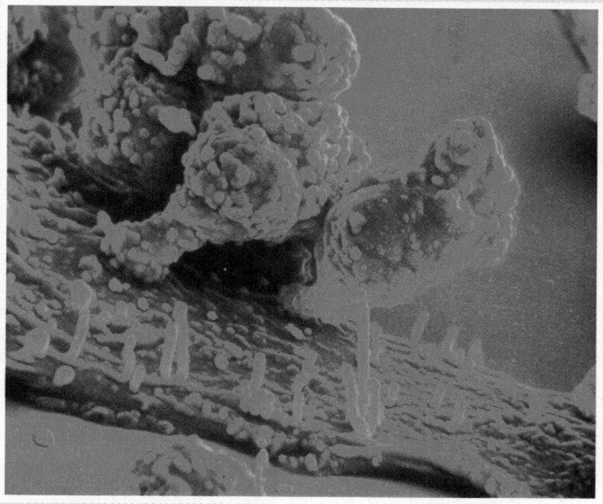

Figure 40–8
In this photograph, the killer T cells, which become elongated when active, are attacking a cancer cell's membrane (magnification: 6000X).

Immune Disorders

Although the immune system protects the body against many pathogens, sometimes disorders occur. There are two main types of disorders. In the first type, the body overreacts to harmless substances. Allergies and autoimmune diseases are examples of this type of disorder. In the second type, the immune system becomes too weak to fight infection. AIDS is an example of this type of disorder.

Allergies

When the immune system overreacts to an antigen in the environment, an **allergy** results. An allergic reaction occurs when antigens trigger a type of immune cell, called a mast cell, to release chemicals called **histamines.** Histamines produce an inflammatory response that includes sneezing, runny nose, and itchy eyes, which allergy sufferers know all too well. ● The offending antigens may be part of a pollen grain, a mold spore, the toxin from a bee sting, or even household dust.

INTEGRATING HEALTH

What are antihistamines? How do they help allergy sufferers?

Ideas Through Images

Have students examine Figure 40-8, read the caption, and answer the following questions.

- **What kind of immunity are killer T cells involved in?** (Cell-mediated immunity.)
- **How do killer T cells destroy invading pathogens?** (By attacking antigen-bearing cells, disrupting their cell membranes and destroying them. Killer T cells also attack virus-infected cells, protozoans, and multicellular parasites.)

INTEGRATING HEALTH

Antihistamines are drugs that counteract the effects of the body's release of histamines. Since histamines are what produce such irritations as sneezing, runny nose, and itching eyes, taking an antihistamine reduces some of these symptoms.

Checkpoints

1. A weakened or mild form of a pathogen that causes permanent immunity when injected into the body.
2. Helper T cells identify the specific pathogen in the body and then send a message to the B cells, "telling" them to produce antibodies for that particular pathogen.

Technology

BioVue
Mini Doc: AIDS and the Immune System
Videodisc Side 8

Go to Chapter 10

TEACHER SUPPORT

Facts and Figures

- HIV is classified as a human retrovirus, which is a group of single-stranded RNA viruses. Other retroviruses are thought to be the cause of certain cancers, including rare forms of leukemia.
- A normal number of helper T cells in a healthy person is about 1200 per mm^2 of blood. A person infected with HIV experiences a decline in that number. When the number falls below 200 per mm^2 of blood, the person is classified as having AIDS.
- Illnesses that typically afflict someone with AIDS include *Pneumocystis carinii* pneumonia, a cancer called Kaposi's sarcoma, yeast infections of the lungs, and tuberculosis.
- The Global AIDS Policy Coalition estimates that by the year 2000 between 40 and 110 million people will have contracted HIV worldwide.
- The countries of the developing world account for over 90 percent of AIDS cases.

Ancillary Support

The resource below can be used to support your teaching strategy for these two pages.

TB The Immune Response, #50

Connections

No one knows the source of AIDS, or why it appeared suddenly in the late 1970s. Most scientists believe it originated in Africa. It could have been a virus in monkeys that mutated and somehow infected humans. The problem with that hypothesis is that HIV has never been isolated from any animal source.

In the United States, AIDS is often associated with homosexual men, the group in which the virus first spread, and is sometimes thought of as a "homosexual disease" by the general public. That misconception is easily corrected by reference to the spread of HIV in other parts of the world, especially Africa, Southeast Asia, and India, where it is associated primarily with heterosexual sex. In fact, the AIDS epidemic is much more widespread in those regions than it is in the United States.

Answers to Making the Connection

A typical response might suggest that information about AIDS transmission would influence a decision to be sexually active. Some might suggest that knowing that HIV is not easily spread might help alleviate any fear about being around someone who has AIDS. Many students might suggest that people have a right to privacy, and thus an employer has no right to require AIDS testing of employees. Some might argue that the seriousness of the AIDS epidemic outweighs any right to privacy Americans have.

Biology and You .... Connections

AIDS

Each square of this quilt is dedicated to a person who has died of AIDS.

Although scientists do not have enough information to cure AIDS, they do know more than enough to prevent it. HIV, the virus that causes AIDS, is not easily spread. People who live with, care for, work with, or go to school with people with HIV are not at risk of contracting the virus by casual contact. The virus that causes AIDS can be spread only by coming into direct contact with an infected person's body fluids, such as blood, semen, and vaginal secretions.

Blood Transfusions

Prior to 1985, donated blood used for transfusions and other medical procedures, such as treatments for hemophilia, was not tested for the presence of HIV. As a result, several thousand people became infected with HIV and eventually died of AIDS. Today, blood supplies are carefully screened for HIV and other viruses.

Injected Drug Use

HIV infection among users of illegal drugs, on the other hand, has skyrocketed. Sharing needles to inject drugs may pass on HIV-laden blood directly from one person's bloodstream into the bloodstream of another. This action is one of the most dangerous and irresponsible things a person can do. Not only are drugs such as heroin and cocaine dangerous in their own right, but the injection of these drugs also carries with them the added risk of contracting AIDS.

A Sexually Transmitted Disease

AIDS can also be spread by sexual contact. The presence of the virus in the semen and vaginal fluids of an infected person means that every sexual contact that person has carries with it the risk of passing on AIDS. The most effective way to protect yourself from HIV infection is to abstain from sexual intercourse. By doing so, you help to prevent the spread of this deadly disease.

Making the Connection

How does information about AIDS transmission help you to make decisions about your behavior? How does it help you when you encounter someone who has HIV? Do you think employers should have the right to require all their employees to be tested for HIV? Why or why not?

Teacher Support — Background Information

Information about the transmission of HIV and the treatment of AIDS continually changes as research improves our understanding of the disease. For that reason, up-to-date material is essential. Many state and local governments have agencies that disseminate information about AIDS. Numerous private organizations also provide information. The *Encyclopedia of Associations*, a multivolume reference updated annually, contains a list of such groups under the heading *AIDS*. The Centers for Disease Control and Prevention (CDC), a federal agency, disseminates information about HIV/AIDS to health-care professionals and educators through the following service:

CDC National AIDS Clearinghouse (NAC)
P.O. BOX 6003
Rockville, MD 20849-6003
Phone: (800) 458-5231
Fax: (301) 738-6616
Website: http://cdcnac.aspensys.com:86

Allergic reactions can create a dangerous condition called **asthma,** in which smooth muscle contractions reduce the size of air passageways in the lungs, making breathing difficult. Asthma attacks are usually triggered by a particular antigen, and so the best response to the condition is to avoid that antigen. New drugs make it possible to provide immediate relief from asthma attacks, relaxing the smooth muscles to make breathing easier.

Autoimmune Diseases

Sometimes the immune system makes mistakes and attacks its own cells, producing what is called an **autoimmune disease.** Myasthenia gravis and multiple sclerosis are two autoimmune diseases. In myasthenia gravis, antibodies attack the nerve receptors of the muscles. In multiple sclerosis, the immune system attacks the myelin sheath that surrounds nerve fibers. Multiple sclerosis, which may be triggered by a viral infection, usually strikes people between the ages of 20 and 40.

AIDS

The importance of a healthy, functioning immune system has been underscored by a disease that was first recognized in the early 1980s. At that time, physicians began to see an increase in the number of unusual infections. Some of these infections included protozoans in the lungs, severe fungal infections in the mouth and throat, and a rare form of skin cancer. Normally, such infections are prevented by the immune system, so doctors immediately realized that the immune systems of their patients had been weakened. They called the disease **AIDS** (acquired immune deficiency syndrome).

The spread of the disease made scientists suspect that it was caused by a virus. In 1984, that virus—now known as **HIV** (human immunodeficiency virus)—was discovered. HIV infects, weakens, and gradually destroys the helper T cells. As the disease progresses, which may take many years, HIV-infected individuals suffer one infection after another from organisms that the immune system normally controls with ease.

To date, there is no cure for AIDS, although some progress has been made in developing drugs that make it difficult for HIV to infect cells and to reproduce. Fortunately, HIV does not spread easily from person to person, and the way in which the virus is transmitted—in blood and other body fluids—is now well understood. The best way to stop this dangerous disease is to avoid contact with the virus.

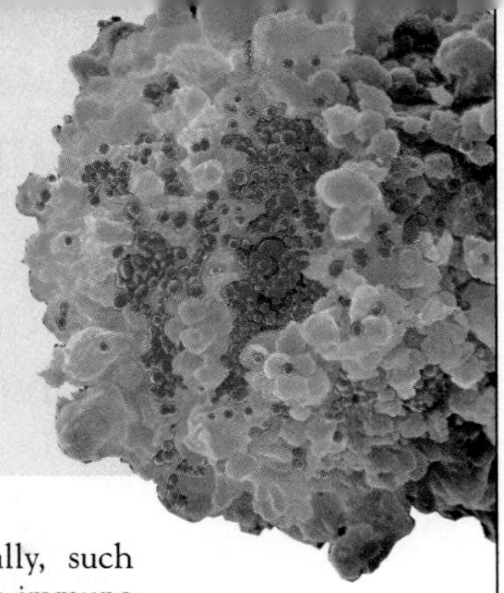

Figure 40–9
The helper T cell, colored green in this scanning electron micrograph, has been infected with HIV. The red objects are HIV, the virus responsible for causing AIDS (magnification: 6000X).

Section Review 40–2

1. **Describe** the function of the immune system.
2. **Define** immunity.
3. **Critical Thinking—Comparing** Compare the role of B cells and T cells in the immune response.

Ideas Through Images

Have students examine Figure 40–9, read the caption, and answer the following questions.

- **What is the function of helper T cells in the immune response?** (Helper T cells identify the specific pathogen in the body and send a message to the B cells "telling" them to produce antibodies for that particular pathogen.)
- **How would the immune system be harmed if HIV infected and destroyed most of a person's helper T cells?** (The B cells would have no way of "knowing" when to produce antibodies for particular pathogens.)
- **What would you predict might happen to a person infected with HIV?** (Various pathogens could infect that person without being attacked by the immune system.)

4 ASSESS

Quick Check

Ask students to make flowcharts that show the processes involved in the inflammatory response, antibody immunity, and cell-mediated immunity.

Section Review 40–2

1. The immune system is the body's primary defense against pathogens. It consists of nonspecific defenses, including the skin, inflammation, and fever, as well as specific defenses, including antibody immunity and cell-mediated immunity.

2. Immunity is the ability of the body to resist a specific pathogen.

3. Both B cells and T cells are involved in antibody immunity. B cells are lymphocytes that produce antibodies. Helper T cells help stimulate the production of B cells by identifying the specific pathogen in the body. T cells are also involved in cell-mediated immunity. Killer T cells attack and destroy invading cells and viruses. After an infection has been fought off, suppressor T cells shut off the immune response in both B cells and killer T cells.

Learning Modality

Visual Learning Have students make their own drawings of the two types of immunity, incorporating both the information shown in Figure 40–7 and the information given in the text on pages 907–909.

Section 40–3
Cancer

Performance Objectives
- Explain what cancer is.
- Identify some of the causes of cancer.

Mini Lab Skill: Interpreting

1 ENGAGE

Ideas Through Images
Have students examine Figure 40–10, read the caption, and answer the following questions.

- **What control over cells has the body lost when cancer occurs?** (The ability to control how cells multiply.)
- **What happens when cancer cells invade an area of healthy cells?** (The cancer cells crowd out and destroy the healthy cells.)
- **Does the immune system respond to the multiplication of cancer cells?** (Yes. Killer T cells attack cancer cells.)

Inquiry Activity
Communicating

A Campaign Against Death
Ask students what kind of public relations campaign could work to persuade teenagers not to smoke cigarettes. Every student most likely knows about the connection between smoking and lung cancer. Point out that although many adults have quit smoking in recent years, young people continue to begin the habit. Have small groups of students work together to design a poster or write a radio transcript that would influence the decisions of their peers not to smoke.

SECTION 40–3 BRANCHING OUT *In Depth*

Cancer

Guide for Reading
- **Define** cancer.
- **Describe** some of the causes of cancer.

MINI LAB
- **Interpret** data regarding cancer.

CANCER! FEW WORDS IN THE English language conjure up the dread and fear that this word does. Cancers are the second leading cause of death in the United States, claiming more than half a million lives each year. And cancers are a worldwide threat, affecting people of every nationality and culture.

What is this disease that takes such a toll on human life? Where does it come from, and why is it so difficult to treat? As you will see, one of the things that makes cancer so different from other diseases is that the cells that cause it are not invading pathogens—they are the body's own cells, which have, in a sense, turned against it.

A Cellular Disease

The growth of the many trillions of cells throughout the body is closely regulated. Controls on cell growth are necessary in a complex organism to keep tissues and organs together. **Cancer begins when a cell or a group of cells escapes the body's normal growth controls.** When this happens, the cells grow into a **tumor,** a mass of growing, unregulated cells.

If a tumor forms in a sensitive area of the body, such as the brain or spinal cord, its very presence can be dangerous.

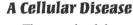

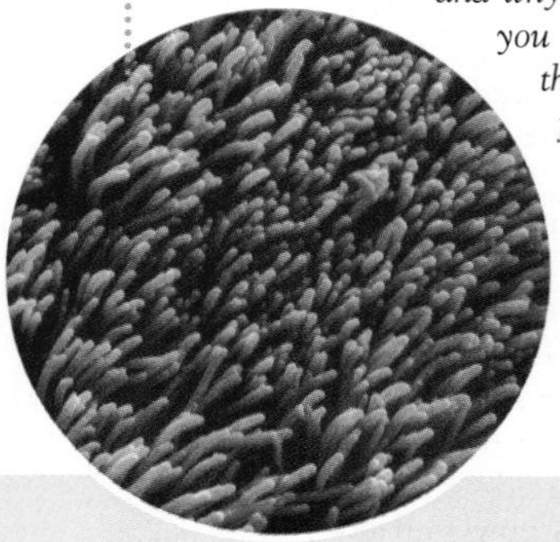

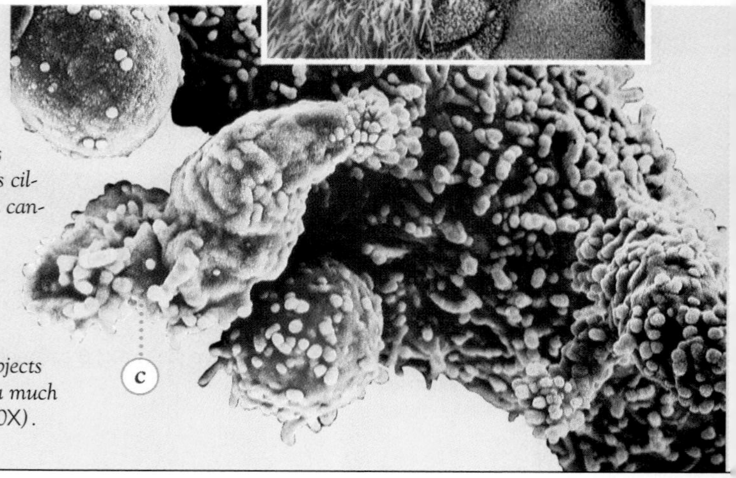

Figure 40–10 *Cancer occurs when cells multiply uncontrollably and destroy healthy tissue. (a) In a healthy lung, the walls of the bronchi are covered with countless cilia (magnification: 4000X). (b) When cancer cells, the gray objects, invade the bronchi, they crowd out and destroy the healthy tissue (magnification: 3000X). (c) The invasion of cancer cells stimulates the production of T cells. In this electron micrograph, the smaller beige objects are T cells, which are trying to destroy a much larger cancer cell (magnification: 10,000X).*

TEACHER SUPPORT

Facts and Figures

- The risk of contracting some kind of cancer is very low in a person's 20s. That risk doubles in the person's 30s, and doubles again in each succeeding decade of life.
- If current trends continue, about 30 percent of Americans alive today will develop some form of cancer.
- In the 1930s, only 1 of 5 people diagnosed with cancer lived 5 years or more; now more than half do.
- Smoking is associated not only with lung cancer but also with cancer of the pancreas, bladder cancer, mouth cancer, cancer of the esophagus, and cervical cancer.
- In 1992, the deaths of 520,578 Americans were attributed to cancer, more than a quarter of which were caused by lung cancer.
- In the United States, 1 of every 9 women will develop breast cancer.

However, the most dangerous tumors are those that are capable of spreading from their places of origin to invade other parts of the body.

Physicians classify tumors according to their ability to spread. A tumor that does not spread to surrounding tissue is called a benign tumor. A tumor that spreads and destroys healthy tissue is called a malignant tumor.

It is often said that cancer is not one disease but many. Cancers differ from each other according to the tissues in which they originate. Lung cancers originate in the tissues of the lung, skin cancers are produced when cells in the skin begin to grow out of control, and breast cancers begin in the tissues of the breast. Each type of cancer has its own pattern of growth and invasion, and each presents unique problems.

☑ Checkpoint What is a tumor? ❶

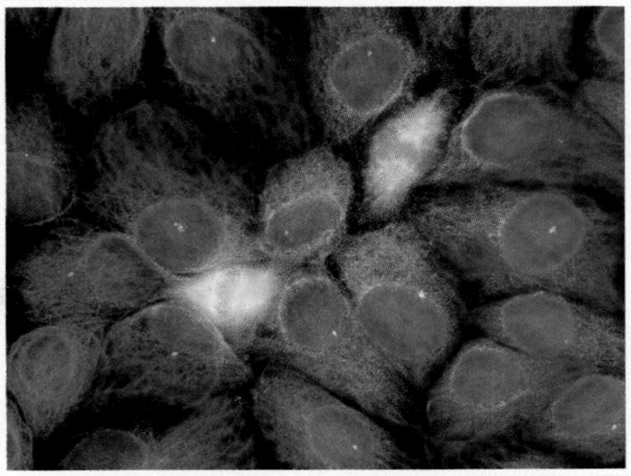

Figure 40–11
Immunofluorescence is a technique that uses antibodies to attach fluorescent dyes to specific structures within the cell. This immunofluorescent light micrograph shows a malignant form of skin cancer (magnification: 320X).

Causes of Cancer

One of the most baffling elements of the cancer puzzle has been the many different causes of cancer. **Some cancers are caused by biological agents, such as viruses. Others are caused by chemicals in the environment or in the foods we eat. And others have a physical cause—radiation.**

Viruses

Cancer-causing viruses were first discovered in animals. In the early 1900s, Peyton Rous discovered that a type of cancer in chickens could be caused by viruses passed from one animal to the next. Although many similar viruses have been discovered in animals, only a few human cancers seem to be caused by viruses. One of these is the human papilloma virus (HPV), which is sexually transmitted. Chronic HPV infections can lead to cancer of the reproductive organs. Hepatitis, which infects the liver, may lead to liver cancer. And the Epstein-Barr virus, in very rare instances, can produce a cancer known as Burkitt's lymphoma.

Radiation

Radiation has been recognized as a cause of cancer ever since the first experiments with radioactive substances. Exposures to high levels of radioactivity can cause leukemia, a cancer of the blood, and several other cancers. However, the most common and most dangerous form of cancer-causing radiation is all around us—sunlight. Exposure to the ultraviolet radiation in sunlight brings with it a risk of skin cancer. Although most forms of skin cancer can be successfully treated with surgery, one often fatal form of skin cancer—malignant melanoma—is increasing in frequency at an alarming rate.

Chemicals

Chemicals can also cause cancer. A cancer-causing chemical is known as a **carcinogen,** and scientists have identified hundreds of them. Carcinogens

2 EXPLORE

Investigate

Research Have students research and write a report about one type of cancer. Allow students to choose the type they want to research, but make sure the major cancers are covered, including lung cancer, breast cancer, skin cancer, and prostate cancer. Require that each report include information on the probable cause, major symptoms, preventative measures, and treatments associated with the cancer, as well as some data about how common it is in the United States.

3 TEACH

Ideas Through Images

Have students examine Figure 40–11, read the caption, and answer the following questions.

- **What are three types of causes of cancers?** (Biological agents, chemicals, and radiation.)
- **Which of those types is responsible for skin cancer?** (Radiation from the sun.)
- **How can you prevent skin cancer?** (By avoiding exposure to sunlight. Ways to avoid sunlight include wearing hats, staying out of the direct sun, and using sunscreens.)

☑ Checkpoint

❶ A mass of cells that results when a cell or group of cells somehow escapes the body's normal regulatory controls and grows uncontrollably.

TEACHER SUPPORT

Managing Classroom Diversity

TECH PREP STUDENTS
Many students who plan careers in technical fields will work with carcinogens, including those in agriculture, food service, health care, natural resources, energy technology, and industrial technology. Ask such students to research what kind of carcinogens are associated with their fields and what procedures are in place to avoid them or avoid releasing them into the environment.

EDUCATIONAL EQUITY
Breast cancer is one of the leading killers of women, and yet it is often not discussed with teenage girls. Have interested students collaborate on a report about breast cancer, both by doing research and by contacting local organizations that focus on the disease. Make sure students find out about the risk factors, causes, symptoms, and treatments of this cancer, including recommendations about mammograms.

Ancillary Support

The resources below can be used to support your teaching strategy for these two pages.

TR Enrich: With Every Breath You Take
BL Inquiry Activity: It's a Killer

MINI LAB Interpreting

Teacher Notes
- For time required and materials needed, see page 900b.
- Divide students into pairs for this activity.
- You may want to review with the class how to construct a bar graph using data from a table.

Answers to Analyze and Conclude
1. In males, the death rate from lung cancer has risen 85 percent; in females, the rate has risen 438 percent.
2. A typical response will suggest that the use of tobacco has risen somewhat in men over the past 30 years but has risen tremendously in women over the same period.

Skills Trace
Interpeting
Focus p. 914
Practice p. 915
Assess p. 921

Discussion
Begin a discussion of the causes of cancer by reviewing the three types of causes: viruses, radiation, and chemicals. Ask students to name various carcinogens, including chemicals in some foods and industrial pollution. Then direct the discussion to the effect that viruses, radiation, and chemicals might have on a person's genes. Emphasize that all three causes could produce changes in the genes that would allow cells to multiply uncontrollably.

MINI LAB Interpreting

Going by the Numbers

PROBLEM *How can you **interpret** data regarding cancer?*

PROCEDURE

LUNG CANCER DEATH RATES *

Gender	1960–1962	1990–1992
Male	40.2	74.4
Female	6.0	32.2

* per 100,000 U.S. population

1. Based on the data table, construct a bar graph.
2. After examining the data table and bar graph with your partner, discuss some reasons to explain the changes that occurred in lung cancer death rates over the 30-year span.
3. Discuss some reasons to explain why there are differences in lung cancer death rates between males and females.

ANALYZE AND CONCLUDE

1. Determine the percentage change in lung cancer death rates in males and females during the 30-year period.
2. Because 80 percent of lung cancers are caused by smoking tobacco, what can you infer about the use of tobacco in men over the past 30 years? In women?

cause cells to lose control of their normal functions, thus causing cancer. Some carcinogens are naturally occurring compounds, such as aflatoxin, a compound produced by fungi. Others, such as benzene, are synthetic compounds. Health researchers have worked hard to identify the most dangerous carcinogens so they can be removed from the workplace and the food supply.

Ironically, the single most damaging source of carcinogens in most countries is not a contaminant of food, water, or air. Some of the most powerful carcinogens are found in tobacco smoke. Smoking tobacco or inhaling tobacco smoke causes lung cancer, which is responsible for more than 30 percent of all cancer deaths in the United States.

Cancer Genes

For many years, researchers were puzzled as to how causes as different as sunlight, chemicals, and viruses could produce cancer. However, all the causes of cancer have one thing in common—they all produce mutations, or changes in DNA. Carcinogenic chemicals cause errors in DNA replication; sunlight and other forms of radiation damage nucleic acids directly; and cancer-causing viruses introduce new genes into the cells they infect.

Why should mutations be so important? In recent years, biologists have discovered that a series of important proteins regulate the rate at which cells pass through the phases of the cell cycle. These proteins, and the genes that encode them, are responsible for the controlled cell growth that occurs normally in the body. If one of these key genes is damaged or mutated, controls over cell growth would be lost. And a group of cells would begin to grow out of control, just like a tumor.

One of these key genes is a protein called p53. Although p53 has many functions, its most important function is to check the condition of a cell's genetic information before it is allowed to divide. If damage to DNA is detected, p53 prevents the cell from entering mitosis. In that way, it ensures that DNA damage is repaired before the cell is allowed to divide. How important is p53 in avoiding cancer? More than half of all human

TEACHER SUPPORT Background Information

The treatment of cancer often proceeds in order through the three established therapies: first surgery, then radiation, and finally chemotherapy. Researchers have recently been developing new therapies that utilize the immune system. For example, in one technique cancer cells are injected into mice, whose immune systems produce antibodies that bind to the cancer cells. Researchers then extract those antibodies and duplicate them with human proteins, thus creating antibodies in the lab that are both safe to inject into the human body and specific to the cancer antigens. Then, those antibodies are combined with either a chemical toxin or a radioactive molecule. Injected into the body, the antibodies head for the cancer antigens, carrying with them a substance that will destroy the cancer. At this point, such therapy remains in the experimental stage.

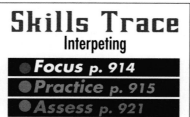

Figure 40–12
CAREER TRACK
An immunologist studies how organisms defend themselves against infection by pathogens. Here, an immunologist is using a technique that analyzes and measures the concentration of antibodies in order to test for a parasitic disease.

tumors have a damaged or inactive p53 gene! Damage to p53 or the many other genes that help to regulate cell growth seems to be the source of nearly all human cancers.

Treating Cancer

In their early stages, most cancers produce few symptoms. This is unfortunate, because cancers are easier to treat if they are found early. Once a tumor is discovered, it should receive immediate medical attention. In some cases, surgery is the best treatment. In their early stages, all the skin cancers, as well as cancers of the breast, the intestine, and the bladder, can be completely removed by surgery. This often results in a complete cure.

If the cancer has spread or if the tumor cannot be completely removed, a different approach is needed. Some cancers can be treated with radiation, to which fast-growing cells are especially sensitive. Radiation is used for localized tumors. Other types of cancers are treated with **chemotherapy**—mixtures of drugs that interfere with important processes such as DNA replication and cell division.

Chemotherapy has proven especially useful against certain forms of childhood leukemia, a cancer of the white blood cells. However, the powerful drugs used in chemotherapy to kill cancer cells have serious side effects—they kill many normal cells as well, causing nausea, headaches, and sometimes a temporary loss of hair.

Because no drug has proven completely effective against all cancers, the search goes on for compounds that will do a better job of killing tumor cells with fewer side effects. Medical science is closer than ever before in pinpointing the exact genetic causes of cancer, and there is good reason to hope that new technologies may conquer this disease. ●

INTEGRATING BIOLOGY AND SOCIETY

Find out from the American Cancer Society the seven warning signs of cancer.

Section Review 40-3

1. **Define** cancer.
2. **Describe** some of the causes of cancer.
3. **MINI LAB** How can you **interpret** data regarding cancer?
4. **BRANCHING OUT ACTIVITY** Using reference materials, find out the ten leading causes of death from cancer in 1960 to 1962 for both men and women. Then find out the ten leading causes of death from cancer in 1990 to 1992 for both men and women. **Compare** the lists and try to explain any differences you see.

INTEGRATING BIOLOGY AND SOCIETY

According to the American Cancer Society, following are the seven warning signs of cancer:
- A change in bowel or bladder habits.
- A sore that does not heal.
- Any unusual bleeding or discharge.
- A thickening or lump in a breast or elsewhere on the body.
- Indigestion or difficulty in swallowing.
- An obvious change in a wart or mole.
- A nagging cough or hoarseness.

4 ASSESS

Quick Check

Have students outline the section, using the heads and subheads as primary and secondary heads in their outlines.

Section Review 40-3

1. When a cell or a group of cells somehow escapes the body's normal regulatory controls and grows uncontrollably.
2. Among the causes of cancer are viruses, radiation, and chemicals.
3. Interpreting data regarding cancer involves comparing rates in different years, noting any changes, and inferring reasons for those changes by drawing upon knowledge about the causes of specific cancers.

Skills Trace
Interpreting

Focus p. 914
Practice p. 915
Assess p. 921

4. The ten leading causes of death for 1960–62, in order: Men—lung, colon and rectum, prostate, colon, stomach, pancreas, leukemia, rectum, bladder, liver; Women—breast, colon and rectum, colon, cervix uteri, ovary, stomach, pancreas, other uterus, lung, liver. For 1990–92, in order: Men—lung, prostate, colon and rectum, colon, pancreas, leukemia, non-Hodgkin's lymphoma, stomach, esophagus, bladder; Women—lung, breast, colon and rectum, colon, ovary, pancreas, non-Hodgkin's lymphoma, leukemia, brain, other uterus. Students should note the difference in the rank of lung cancer in women, from eighth place in 1960–62 to first in 1990–92. That difference can be explained only by an increase in smoking among women.

Learning Modality

Auditory Learning Orally ask questions about the causes and treatments of cancer and call on students to respond.

Chapter 40

Laboratory Investigation

Inhibiting Bacterial Growth

Before the Lab

1. Purchase the Petri dishes with sterile nutrient agar from a biological supply company. If preparing your own is preferable, mix 3 g beef extract, 5 g peptone, 15 g agar, and 1 L distilled water, and then heat until the agar is dissolved. Pour the mixture into Petri dishes and sterilize.

2. Collect several household disinfectants for students to use in their experiments, including bleach and various popular commercial bathroom and kitchen disinfectants.

Pre-Lab Discussion

Have students read the entire procedure for this investigation. Then ask students the following questions.

What is the purpose of this investigation? (To design an experiment to find out which household disinfectant is most effective in preventing the growth of bacteria.)

What is the purpose of rubbing your fingers over the surface of the sterile agar? (To contaminate the sterile agar with bacteria on the fingers.)

What do you predict will occur in the location where you place 2 drops of hydrogen peroxide? (No bacteria will grow in that location.)

What is the purpose of a household disinfectant? (To prevent the growth of microorganisms in the bathroom, kitchen, and other places around the house.)

Skills Development

Students will use these skills while completing the laboratory investigation: observing, communicating, comparing, designing an experiment, interpreting data, and drawing conclusions.

CHAPTER 40

Laboratory Investigation

DESIGNING AN EXPERIMENT

Inhibiting Bacterial Growth

Disinfectants are products used to destroy bacteria and viruses. How do you know which type of disinfectant is effective against which type of bacteria? In this investigation, you will compare the bacteria-inhibiting powers of several kinds of disinfectants.

Problem

Which household disinfectant is the most effective in preventing the growth of bacteria? **Design an experiment** to find the answer.

Suggested Materials

- 2 Petri dishes containing sterile nutrient agar
- glass-marking pencil
- sterile medicine dropper
- transparent tape
- hydrogen peroxide
- metric ruler
- 2 other types of household disinfectants

Suggested Procedure

1. Obtain 2 Petri dishes. Open each Petri dish and have your partner rub his or her fingers over the entire surface of the sterile agar. Replace the covers.

2. Open the cover of one Petri dish and, using the medicine dropper, place 2 drops of hydrogen peroxide in the middle of the dish.

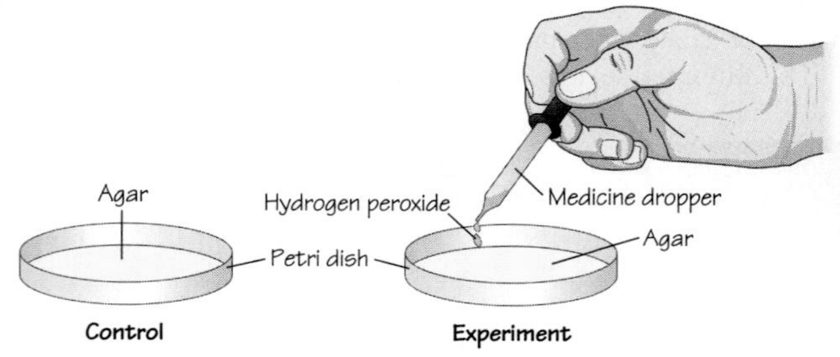

Safety Tips

- Caution students that they will be working with cultures of bacteria. They should never open the Petri dishes once the dishes have been covered, and they should always wash their hands after handling the dishes.
- Remind students to handle glass items carefully and to notify you of any breakage.

3. **Turn the dish over and, with the glass-marking pencil, label it Hydrogen Peroxide. Using transparent tape, tape the cover closed.**

4. **Turn over the other dish and label it Control.**

5. **Place the Petri dishes in an area where they will remain undisturbed and at room temperature for 24 hours. CAUTION:** ***Do not open the Petri dishes again.***

6. **After 24 hours, without opening the Petri dishes, observe the surfaces of the nutrient agar in each dish. Record your observations in a data table similar to the one shown.**

7. **Return the Petri dishes to their storage place and observe them after 48 hours and after 72 hours. Record your observations.**

8. **Return the unopened Petri dishes to your teacher for sterilization and proper disposal. CAUTION:** ***Always wash your hands after handling a used Petri dish.***

9. **Using a procedure similar to the one given in steps 1 to 8, design an experiment to determine the effectiveness of various disinfectants on the prevention of the growth of bacteria.**

10. **Be sure to include a control. Obtain the approval of your teacher before beginning your procedure.**

Observations

1. What effect did hydrogen peroxide have on the growth of bacteria after 24, 48, and 72 hours?
2. What effect did each of the other disinfectants have on the growth of bacteria after 24, 48, and 72 hours?

DATA TABLE

Disinfectant	After 24 Hours	After 48 Hours	After 72 Hours
Hydrogen peroxide			

Analysis and Conclusions

1. Which disinfectant was the most effective against the growth of bacteria? Give evidence to support your answer.
2. Did every group in the class reach the same conclusion? How can you account for any differences?
3. What conclusion can you draw from your experiment about choosing disinfectants for your home?

More to Explore

Design an experiment to compare the effectiveness of disinfectants on bacteria samples from the soil.

Teaching Strategies

1. Demonstrate how to contaminate the sterile agar with the fingers and where to place the drops of hydrogen peroxide.
2. Discuss with groups the disinfectants they plan to use in their experiments. All groups could use the same two disinfectants, or groups could vary disinfectants and compare effectiveness at the conclusion of the lab.
3. Review and approve students' experimental designs before they proceed.

Answers to
Observations

1. In every case after 24 hours, the drops of hydrogen peroxide will have prevented the growth of bacteria in the areas where the drops were placed. Students may observe a larger area of no growth due to the diffusion of hydrogen peroxide through the sterile agar. There may be little or no change in this growth pattern after 48 or 72 hours, but some students may observe that the hydrogen peroxide will lose its effectiveness over time. Conversely, the bacteria could exhaust the supply of nutrients in the agar and begin to die off.
2. Students' responses will depend on the disinfectants they test. They may observe the same pattern of growth as they did with the hydrogen peroxide. Some disinfectants, though, may not be as effective in inhibiting bacterial growth. In such cases, the bacteria's area of growth may significantly increase over time.

Answers to
Analysis and Conclusions

1. Students might discover that some commercial products are ineffective in stopping bacterial growth, or they might observe that some products will eliminate bacteria completely from the agar. In any case, students should support their conclusions with observations from their experiments.
2. Every group probably did not reach the same conclusion, especially if groups tested different products in their experiments.
3. A typical response might suggest that some commercial products are more effective than others, and the ones that work well should be chosen for use in the home.

More to Explore

A typical experiment will be quite similar to this lab, with the difference being that the sterile agar in all but the control dish will be contaminated with different soil samples.

CHAPTER 40

Study Guide

Review Strategy

Divide students into groups, and ask each group to develop a board game that utilizes the information presented in this chapter. A typical game might focus on how pathogens could make it through the body's nonspecific and specific defenses. Students might use dice to move pieces around the board or create cards to be drawn by players. Encourage groups to be creative in their designs but also inclusive in their use of the chapter's material. Point out that the purpose of their games is to help students learn the information.

Recalling Main Ideas

1. c
2. a
3. b
4. b
5. d
6. a
7. d
8. c
9. a
10. b

Assessment

Reviewing What You Learned

1. A disease-causing organism.
2. According to the germ theory of disease, infectious diseases are caused by microorganisms.
3. Malaria and African sleeping sickness.
4. A type of bacterum, *Mycobacterium tuberculosis*.
5. The skin, the mucus and cells of the mouth and respiratory passages, lysozyme, the inflammatory response, and fever.
6. Through the white blood cells called phagocytes that engulf and destroy invading pathogens.
7. The ability of the body to resist a specific pathogen.
8. B cells are lymphocytes that mature in bone marrow and produce antibodies; T cells are lymphocytes that mature in the thymus gland and are involved in many aspects of immunity.

Study Guide

Summarizing Key Concepts

The key concepts in each section of this chapter are listed below to help you review the chapter content. Make sure you understand each concept and its relationship to other concepts and to the theme of this chapter.

40–1 Disease

- A disease is any change that disrupts the normal functions of the body.
- Pioneered by the French chemist Louis Pasteur and the German bacteriologist Robert Koch, the germ theory of disease suggested that infectious diseases were caused by microorganisms, which many people call germs.
- Koch's postulates include the following: The pathogen should always be found in the body of a sick organism and should not be found in a healthy organism. The pathogen must be isolated and grown in a pure culture. When purified pathogens are injected into a new host, they cause the disease. The same pathogen should be re-isolated from the second host and grown in a pure culture. The pathogen should still be the same as the original pathogen.

40–2 The Body's Defense System

- The immune system is the body's primary defense against pathogens. It consists of nonspecific and specific defenses against infection.
- Immunity is the ability of the body to resist a specific pathogen.

40–3 Cancer

- Cancer begins when a cell or a group of cells somehow escapes the body's normal growth controls.
- Some cancers are caused by biological agents such as viruses. Others are caused by chemicals in the environment or in the food we eat. And others have a physical cause—radiation.

Reviewing Key Terms

Review the following vocabulary terms and their meaning. Then use each term in a complete sentence.

40–1 Disease

pathogen
infectious disease
Koch's postulates
toxin
vector
antibiotic

40–2 The Body's Defense System

inflammatory response
phagocyte
immunity
antibody
antigen
lymphocyte
B cell
T cell
plasma cell
vaccine
killer T cell
cell-mediated immunity
helper T cell
suppressor T cell
allergy
histamine
asthma
autoimmune disease
AIDS
HIV

40–3 Cancer

tumor
carcinogen
chemotherapy

Inquiry-Based Strategy

Ask students what would happen if the body's immune system malfunctioned and began to attack its own tissues. Tell them that this does occur in a significant portion of the population, some estimates being as high as 5–7 percent. Have students investigate these autoimmune diseases. Allow them to find out for themselves what illnesses are classified as autoimmune. (Major autoimmune diseases include rheumatoid arthritis, multiple sclerosis, juvenile diabetes, and lupus.) Instruct students to write a report that includes a general definition and survey of these diseases, as well as specific information about one autoimmune disease of their choice.

Recalling Main Ideas

Choose the letter of the answer that best completes the statement or answers the question.

1. Disease-causing organisms are called
   a. toxins. c. pathogens.
   b. bacteria. d. antigens.
2. Measles, smallpox, the common cold, and AIDS are caused by
   a. viruses. c. fungi.
   b. bacteria. d. parasitic worms.
3. Cholera, a disease caused by a bacterium, is spread by
   a. mosquitoes.
   b. contaminated water.
   c. fleas on rats and mice.
   d. hand-to-hand contact.
4. Antibiotics are drugs used against
   a. viruses. c. fungi.
   b. bacteria. d. AIDS.
5. Nonspecific defense mechanisms of the immune system include
   a. B lymphocytes. c. vaccination.
   b. antibodies. d. the skin and lysozymes.
6. Antibody production is stimulated by the presence of
   a. antigens. c. killer T cells.
   b. inflammation. d. phagocytes.
7. When antigens trigger mast cells,
   a. histamines are released.
   b. an allergic reaction occurs.
   c. the immune system overreacts.
   d. all of the above.
8. HIV weakens and gradually destroys
   a. mast cells. c. helper T cells.
   b. B cells. d. plasma cells.
9. Tumors capable of spreading from one part of the body to another are said to be
   a. malignant. c. benign.
   b. cellular. d. lung cancer.
10. All cancers seem to be caused by
    a. chemicals. c. radiation.
    b. mutations. d. viruses.

Putting It All Together

Using the information on pages xxx to xxxi, complete the following concept map.

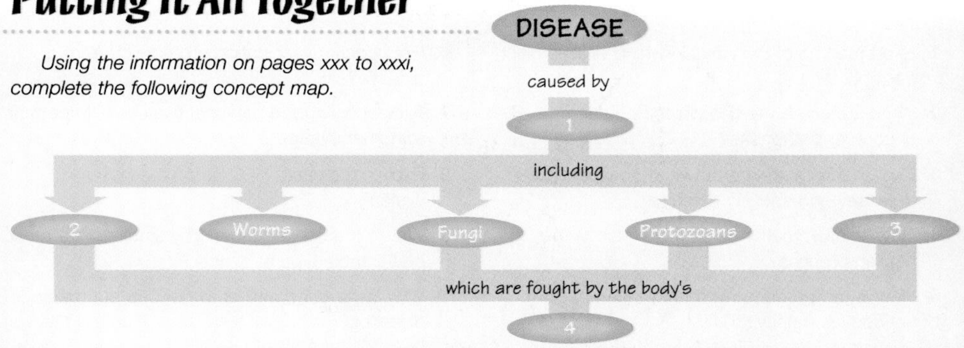

Putting It All Together

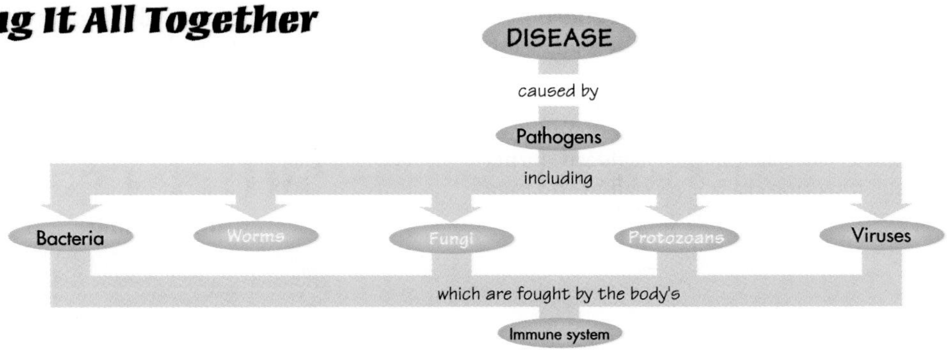

9. Antibody immunity and cell-mediated immunity.
10. Killer T cells make direct contact with antigen-bearing cells, disrupting their cell membranes and destroying them.
11. Diseases in which the immune system makes mistakes and attacks its own cells.
12. HIV, or human immunodeficiency virus, is the pathogen that causes AIDS.
13. A benign tumor is a tumor that does not spread to surrounding tissue; a malignant tumor is a tumor that spreads and destroys healthy tissue.
14. Three ways cancer can be treated is through surgery, radiation, and chemotherapy.
15. A cancer-causing chemical.

Expanding the Concepts

1. All responses should mention that viruses are tiny, nonliving, particles that invade and replicate within living cells, whereas bacteria are living, unicellular organisms.
2. In the air, in droplets in the air, through insect bites, through direct contact with infected persons and objects, and through contaminated water or food.
3. Nonspecific defenses are not directed against any one pathogen. By contrast, specific defenses produce immunity against specific diseases.
4. During the inflammation response, blood vessels expand, and white blood cells called phagocytes leak from the vessels to invade the infected tissues. The phagocytes engulf and destroy pathogens, and thus help heal the injury.
5. Antibody immunity is a specific defense against a pathogen that involves the production of proteins called antibodies, which attach to the pathogens and mark them for destruction. By contrast, cell-mediated immunity involves the attack and destruction of antigen-bearing cells by killer T cells.
6. When a vaccine is injected into the body, it produces antibodies against the specific pathogen in the vaccine. The result is permanent immunity.

Assessment (continued)

7. Many diseases are spread from one person to another by sneezing, coughing, and hand-to-hand contact. Washing the hands thoroughly and other such measures of personal hygiene can prevent the spread of pathogens, and thus enhance health.
8. HIV weakens and destroys helper T cells, and in that way weakens the immune system. Without a strong immune system, the HIV-infected person has difficulty fighting off pathogens that invade the body.
9. Powerful carcinogens are found in tobacco smoke. If people would simply avoid exposure to tobacco smoke, the cancer that results would be prevented.
10. Cancers differ from one another according to the tissues in which they originate. In addition, each type of cancer has its own pattern of growth and invasion, and each presents unique problems.

Extending Your Thinking

1. Assuming that only one bacterium entered the body, then it would double during the next 15 minutes and every 15 minutes thereafter, or 4 times every hour. Thus, in 4 hours the population would double 160 times, for a total of 65,536 bacterial cells.

Skills Trace
Predicting

- Focus p. 902
- Practice p. 904
- Assess p. 921

2. Some students may suggest that at the time Jenner had no choice but to test the vaccine on the boy. Others might assert that using a living person in such a test is irresponsible.
3. A typical response might consider the four postulates in turn: HIV may not always be found in the body of someone with AIDS, or it may be found in a healthy person without AIDS. HIV may not be able to be isolated and grown in a pure culture. When HIV is injected into a new host, maybe it does not always cause the disease. And HIV isolated from a second host may not be exactly the same as the original pathogen.
4. A typical response might suggest that the virus that causes influenza must change enough from year to year that the antibodies produced during the previous infection do not recognize the invading virus particles as the same pathogen.

5. A typical response might suggest that since the death rates for both males and females decreased dramatically, some change has occurred to lessen every American's chances of dying of stomach cancer.

Skills Trace
Interpreting

- Focus p. 914
- Practice p. 915
- Assess p. 921

Assessment

Reviewing What You Learned

Answer each of the following in a complete sentence.

1. What is a pathogen?
2. Explain the germ theory of disease.
3. List two diseases caused by protozoans.
4. What kind of pathogen causes tuberculosis?
5. Give some examples of the body's nonspecific defense against pathogens.
6. How does the inflammatory response fight infection?
7. What is immunity?
8. What are B cells? T cells?
9. Name the two types of immunity.
10. Describe the function of killer T cells.
11. What are autoimmune diseases?
12. What is HIV?
13. What is a benign tumor? A malignant tumor?
14. Name three ways in which cancer can be treated.
15. What is a carcinogen?

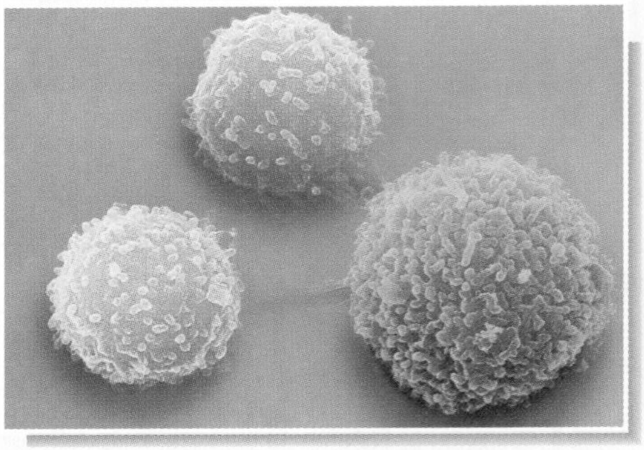

Expanding the Concepts

Discuss each of the following in a brief paragraph.

1. Explain some of the ways in which viruses differ from bacteria.
2. What are some ways in which humans encounter pathogens?
3. Explain the difference between nonspecific defenses and specific defenses.
4. How is inflammation of an injury part of the healing process?
5. How is cell-mediated immunity different from antibody immunity?
6. How does a vaccination protect you from a disease?
7. Explain why good personal hygiene is important to human health.
8. Explain the effect HIV has on the immune system.
9. Why is the cancer caused by smoking the most preventable type of cancer?
10. Why is cancer considered not one but many diseases?

Extending Your Thinking

Use the skills you have developed in this chapter to answer the following.

1. **Predicting** *E. coli* bacteria, which normally live in your large intestine, sometimes contaminate meat and cause food poisoning. Under ideal conditions, these bacteria can divide every 15 minutes. Starting with one bacterium, predict how many bacteria would be produced in 4 hours.
2. **Making judgments** The first vaccine was developed by Edward Jenner to fight smallpox. Jenner tested his theory of immunity on an eight-year-old boy. Do you think Jenner was right in doing so? Defend your answer.
3. **Applying concepts** Some scientists say that HIV has not been proven to cause AIDS. By referring to Koch's postulates, explain what they mean.
4. **Inferring** Because the immune system generally protects you with active immunity after an infection, why is it possible to get "the flu" year after year?
5. **Interpreting data** Examine the statistics for stomach cancer in the data table. How would you interpret the information found there?

STOMACH CANCER DEATH RATES*

Gender	1960–1962	1990–1992	Change
Male	16.2	6.7	– 59%
Female	8.2	3.0	– 63%

*per 100,000 U.S. population

Applying Your Skills

"This Will Only Hurt a Little"

When vaccinations are involved, a visit to the doctor's office is not always pleasant for a child. However, vaccinations are necessary in preventing many diseases.

1. Using library references, find out what vaccinations for children are recommended by the American Academy of Pediatrics.
2. Describe the pathogen and symptoms that each vaccine prevents.
3. Describe how each vaccine is made.
4. List any side effects associated with the vaccine.
5. Organize your data into a table.

• GOING FURTHER •

6. In your journal, discuss whether parents should be required to have their children vaccinated and who should pay for the vaccinations if the parents are unable to pay.

Applying Your Skills

Teacher Notes

• To find the information to complete this activity, students might consult encyclopedias, microbiology textbooks, or standard medical and health references found in a typical public library, such as *The American Medical Association Family Medical Guide* and *Mayo Clinic Family Health Book*.

• Advise students that in their research they might discover that the term immunization is commonly used as a synonym for vaccination.

Answers

1. The recommended schedule of vaccinations is given in the Teacher Support box on TE page 908.
2. Students should describe the pathogens and symptoms of hepatitis B, diphtheria, tetanus, pertussis, polio, influenza, measles, mumps, and rubella.
3. Vaccines are made in various ways, and students may not be able to find information about each one. Bacterial vaccines are usually prepared by growing the bacteria in culture, killing the organisms with heat or chemicals, and then suspending the killed bacteria in a salt solution. Viral vaccines normally use living viruses that have been weakened, or attenuated, in some way, such as by cultivating them at temperatures above normal for the virus.
4. Side effects vary with the vaccine and with the individual.
5. A typical table might include the following column heads: Disease, Pathogen, Symptoms, Vaccine, Vaccine Schedule, and Vaccine Side Effects.

Scoring Rubric

4 Response is thorough, accurate, and creative; shows an in-depth understanding of science skills, procedures, and concepts.

3 Response is complete, mostly accurate, and original; shows a satisfactory understanding of science skills, procedures, and concepts.

2 Response is mostly complete but includes some inaccuracies; shows an adequate understanding of science skills, procedures, and concepts.

1 Response is only partially complete and has many inaccuracies; shows an incomplete understanding of science skills, procedures, and concepts.

0 Response is mostly incomplete and/or inaccurate; shows a lack of understanding of science skills, procedures, and concepts.

Periodic Table of the Elements

Key

6	Atomic number
C	Element symbol
Carbon	Element name
12.011	Atomic mass

	1 1A	2 2A	3 3B	4 4B	5 5B	6 6B	7 7B	8 8B	9 8B
1	1 **H** Hydrogen 1.00794								
2	3 **Li** Lithium 6.941	4 **Be** Beryllium 9.0122							
3	11 **Na** Sodium 22.990	12 **Mg** Magnesium 24.305							
4	19 **K** Potassium 39.098	20 **Ca** Calcium 40.08	21 **Sc** Scandium 44.956	22 **Ti** Titanium 47.88	23 **V** Vanadium 50.94	24 **Cr** Chromium 51.996	25 **Mn** Manganese 54.938	26 **Fe** Iron 55.847	27 **Co** Cobalt 58.9332
5	37 **Rb** Rubidium 85.468	38 **Sr** Strontium 87.62	39 **Y** Yttrium 88.9059	40 **Zr** Zirconium 91.224	41 **Nb** Niobium 92.91	42 **Mo** Molybdenum 95.94	43 **Tc** Technetium (98)	44 **Ru** Ruthenium 101.07	45 **Rh** Rhodium 102.906
6	55 **Cs** Cesium 132.91	56 **Ba** Barium 137.33	**57 to 71**	72 **Hf** Hafnium 178.49	73 **Ta** Tantalum 180.95	74 **W** Tungsten 183.85	75 **Re** Rhenium 186.207	76 **Os** Osmium 190.2	77 **Ir** Iridium 192.22
7	87 **Fr** Francium (223)	88 **Ra** Radium 226.025	**89 to 103**	104 **Rf** Rutherfordium (261)	105 **Db** Dubnium (262)	106 **Sg** Seaborgium (263)	107 **Bh** Bohrium (262)	108 **Hs** Hassium (265)	109 **Mt** Meitnerium (266)

57 **La** Lanthanum 138.906	58 **Ce** Cerium 140.12	59 **Pr** Praseodymium 140.908	60 **Nd** Neodymium 144.24	61 **Pm** Promethium (145)	62 **Sm** Samarium 150.36
89 **Ac** Actinium 227.028	90 **Th** Thorium 232.038	91 **Pa** Protactinium 231.036	92 **U** Uranium 238.029	93 **Np** Neptunium 237.048	94 **Pu** Plutonium (244)

Phase at 20°C

- C Solid
- Br Liquid
- H Gas

Metallic Properties

- Li Metal
- B Semimetal
- C Nonmetal

10	11 1B	12 2B	13 3A	14 4A	15 5A	16 6A	17 7A	18 8A
								2 **He** Helium 4.003
			5 **B** Boron 10.81	6 **C** Carbon 12.011	7 **N** Nitrogen 14.007	8 **O** Oxygen 15.999	9 **F** Fluorine 18.998	10 **Ne** Neon 20.179
			13 **Al** Aluminum 26.98	14 **Si** Silicon 28.086	15 **P** Phosphorus 30.974	16 **S** Sulfur 32.06	17 **Cl** Chlorine 35.453	18 **Ar** Argon 39.948
28 **Ni** Nickel 58.69	29 **Cu** Copper 63.546	30 **Zn** Zinc 65.39	31 **Ga** Gallium 69.72	32 **Ge** Germanium 72.59	33 **As** Arsenic 74.922	34 **Se** Selenium 78.96	35 **Br** Bromine 79.904	36 **Kr** Krypton 83.80
46 **Pd** Palladium 106.42	47 **Ag** Silver 107.868	48 **Cd** Cadmium 112.41	49 **In** Indium 114.82	50 **Sn** Tin 118.71	51 **Sb** Antimony 121.75	52 **Te** Tellurium 127.60	53 **I** Iodine 126.905	54 **Xe** Xenon 131.29
78 **Pt** Platinum 195.08	79 **Au** Gold 196.967	80 **Hg** Mercury 200.59	81 **Tl** Thallium 204.383	82 **Pb** Lead 207.2	83 **Bi** Bismuth 208.98	84 **Po** Polonium (209)	85 **At** Astatine (210)	86 **Rn** Radon (222)
110 **Uun** Ununnilium (269)	111 **Uuu** Unununium (272)	112 **Uub** Ununbium (277)						

The names of elements 104-108 are under dispute. This table provides proposed names from the International Union of Pure and Applied Chemistry (IUPAC).

Mass numbers in parentheses are those of the most stable or common isotope.

63 **Eu** Europium 151.96	64 **Gd** Gadolinium 157.25	65 **Tb** Terbium 158.925	66 **Dy** Dysprosium 162.50	67 **Ho** Holmium 164.93	68 **Er** Erbium 167.26	69 **Tm** Thulium 168.934	70 **Yb** Ytterbium 173.04	71 **Lu** Lutetium 174.967
95 **Am** Americium (243)	96 **Cm** Curium (247)	97 **Bk** Berkelium (247)	98 **Cf** Californium (251)	99 **Es** Einsteinium (252)	100 **Fm** Fermium (257)	101 **Md** Mendelevium (258)	102 **No** Nobelium (259)	103 **Lr** Lawrencium (260)

APPENDIX B

Care and Use of the Microscope

THE COMPOUND MICROSCOPE

One of the most essential tools in the study of biology is the microscope. With the help of different types of microscopes, biologists have developed detailed concepts of cell structure and function. The type of microscope used in most biology classes is the compound microscope. It contains a combination of lenses and can magnify objects normally unseen with the unaided eye.

The eyepiece lens is located in the top portion of the microscope. This lens usually has a magnification of 10×. A compound microscope usually has two other interchangeable lenses. These lenses, called objective lenses, are at the bottom of the body tube on the revolving nosepiece. By revolving the nosepiece, either of the objectives can be brought into direct line with the body of the tube.

The shorter objective is of low power in its magnification, usually 10×. The longer one is of high power, usually 40× or 43×. The magnification is always marked on the objective. To determine the total magnification of a microscope, multiply the magnifying power of the eyepiece by the magnifying power of the objective being used. For example, the eyepiece magnifying power, 10×, multiplied by the low-power objective, 10×, equals 100×. The total magnification is 100×.

A microscope also produces clear contrasts to enable the viewer to distinguish between objects that lie very close together. Under a microscope the detail of objects is very sharp. The ability of a microscope to produce contrast and detail is called resolution, or resolving power. Although microscopes can have the same magnifying power, they can differ in resolving power.

Learning the name, function, and location of each of the microscope's parts is necessary for proper use. Use the following procedures when working the microscope:

1. Remove the microscope from its storage area by placing one hand beneath the base and grasping the arm of the microscope with the other hand.
2. Gently place the microscope on the lab table with the arm facing you. The microscope's base should be resting evenly on the table, approximately 10 centimeters from the table's edge.
3. Raise the body tube by turning the coarse adjustment knob until the objective lens is about 2 centimeters above the opening of the stage.
4. Revolve the nosepiece so that the low-power objective (10×) is directly in line with the body tube. A click indicates that the lens is in line with the opening of the stage.
5. Look through the eyepiece and switch on the lamp or adjust the mirror so that a circle of light can be seen. This is the field of view. Moving the lever of the diaphragm permits a greater or smaller amount of light to come through the opening of the stage.
6. Place a prepared slide on the stage. Place the specimen over the center of the opening of the stage. Fasten the stage clip to hold the slide in position.
7. Look at the microscope from the side. Carefully turn the coarse adjustment knob to lower the body tube until the low-power objective almost touches

MICROSCOPE PARTS AND THEIR FUNCTION

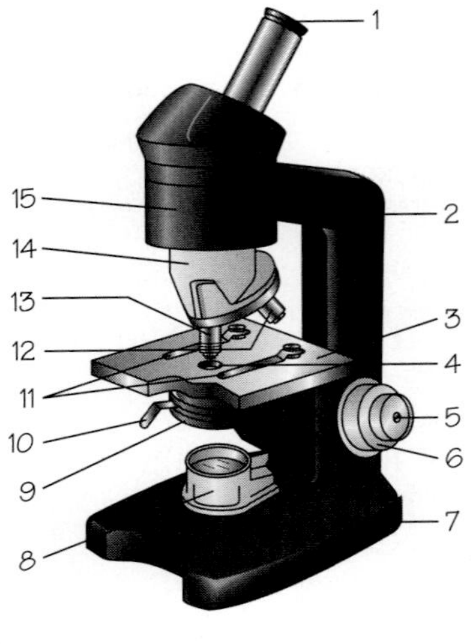

1. ***Eyepiece*** Contains a magnifying lens
2. ***Arm*** Supports the body tube
3. ***Stage*** Supports the slide being observed
4. ***Opening of the stage*** Permits light to travel up to the eyepiece
5. ***Fine adjustment*** Moves the body tube slightly to sharpen the focus
6. ***Coarse adjustment*** Moves the body tube up and down for focusing
7. ***Base*** Supports the microscope
8. ***Illuminator*** Produces light or reflects light up through the body tube
9. ***Diaphragm*** Regulates the amount of light entering the body tube
10. ***Diaphragm lever*** Opens and closes the diaphragm
11. ***Stage clips*** Hold the slide in position
12. ***Low-power objective*** Provides a magnification of 10× and is the shorter of the objectives
13. ***High-power objective*** Provides a magnification of 43× and is the longer of the objectives
14. ***Revolving nosepiece*** Contains the low- and high-power objectives and can be rotated to change magnification
15. ***Body tube*** Maintains a proper distance between the eyepiece and the objective lenses

the slide or until the body tube can no longer be moved. Do not allow the objective to touch the slide.

8. Look through the eyepiece and observe the specimen. If the field of view is out of focus, use the coarse adjustment knob to raise the body tube while looking through the eyepiece. When the specimen comes into view, use the fine adjustment knob to focus the specimen. Be sure to keep both eyes open when viewing a specimen. This helps prevent eyestrain.
9. Adjust the lever of the diaphragm to allow the right amount of light to enter.
10. To view the specimen under high power (43×), revolve the nosepiece until the high-power objective is in line with the body tube and clicks into place.
11. Look through the eyepiece and use the fine adjustment knob to bring the specimen into focus.
12. After every use remove the slide. Clean the stage of the microscope and the lenses with lens paper. Do not use other types of paper to clean the lenses, as they may scratch the lenses.

PREPARING A WET-MOUNT SLIDE

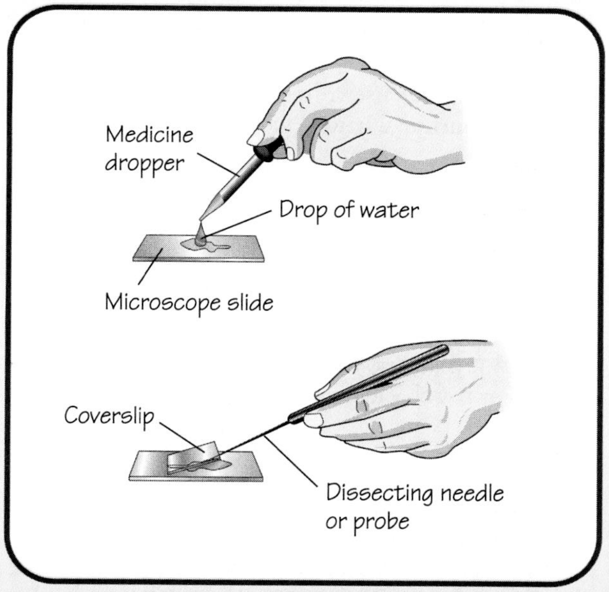

1. Obtain a clean microscope slide and a coverslip. A coverslip is very thin, permitting the objective lens to be lowered close to the specimen.
2. Place the specimen in the middle of the microscope slide. The specimen must be thin enough for light to pass through it.
3. Using a medicine dropper, place a drop of water on the specimen.
4. Lower one edge of the coverslip so that it touches the side of the drop of water at a 45-degree angle. The water will spread evenly along the edge of the coverslip. Using a dissecting needle or probe, slowly lower the coverslip over the specimen and water. Try not to trap any air bubbles under the coverslip because they will interfere with the view of the specimen. If air bubbles are present, gently tap the surface of the coverslip over the air bubble with a pencil eraser.
5. Remove any excess water at the edge of the coverslip with a paper towel. If the specimen begins to dry out, add a drop of water at the edge of the coverslip.

STAINING TECHNIQUES

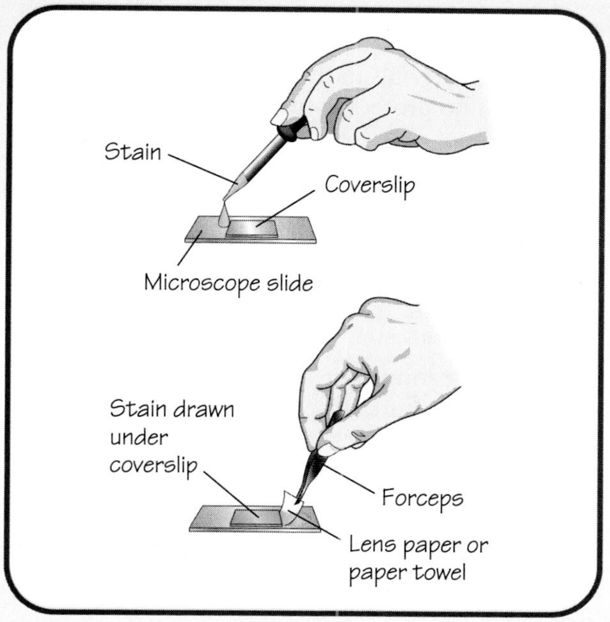

1. Obtain a clean microscope slide and coverslip.
2. Place the specimen in the middle of the microscope slide.
3. Using a medicine dropper, place a drop of water on the specimen.
4. Place one edge of the coverslip so that it touches the side of the drop of water at a 45-degree angle. After the water spreads along the edge of the coverslip, use a dissecting needle or probe to lower the coverslip over the specimen.
5. Add a drop of stain at the edge of the coverslip. Using forceps, touch a small piece of lens paper or paper towel to the opposite edge of the coverslip. The paper causes the stain to be drawn under the coverslip and stain the cells. Some common stains are methylene blue, iodine, fuchsin, and Wright's.

APPENDIX C Science Safety Rules

ONE OF THE FIRST THINGS A SCIENTIST *learns is that working in the laboratory can be an exciting experience. But the laboratory can also be quite dangerous if proper safety rules are not followed at all times. To prepare yourself for a safe year in the laboratory, read over the following safety rules. Then read them a second time. Make sure you understand each rule. Ask your teacher to explain any rules you don't understand.*

DRESS CODE

1. Many materials in the laboratory can cause eye injury. To protect yourself from possible injury, wear safety goggles whenever you are working with chemicals, burners, or any substance that might get into your eyes. Never wear contact lenses in the laboratory.
2. Wear a laboratory apron or coat whenever you are working with any chemicals or heated substances.
3. Tie back long hair to keep it away from any chemicals, burners, candles, or any other laboratory equipment.
4. Before working in the laboratory, remove or tie back any article of clothing or jewelry that could hang down and touch chemicals and flames.

GENERAL SAFETY RULES

5. Read all directions for an experiment several times. Then follow the directions exactly as they are written. If you are in doubt about any part of the experiment, ask your teacher for assistance.
6. Never perform investigations that are not authorized by your teacher. Obtain permission before "experimenting" on your own.
7. Never handle any equipment unless you have specific permission.
8. Take extreme care not to spill any material in the laboratory. If spills occur, ask your teacher immediately about the proper cleanup procedure. Never simply pour chemicals or other substances into the sink or trash container.
9. Never eat in the laboratory.

FIRST AID

10. Report all accidents, no matter how minor, to your teacher immediately.
11. Learn what to do in case of specific accidents, such as getting acid in your eyes or on your skin. (Rinse any acids that may splash on your body with lots of water.)
12. Know the location of the first-aid kit. Your teacher should administer any required first aid due to injury. Or your teacher may send you to the school nurse or call a physician.
13. Know where and how to report an accident or fire. Find out the location of the fire extinguisher, phone, and fire alarm. Keep a list of important phone numbers, such as those for the fire department and school nurse, near the phone. Report any fires to your teacher at once.

HEATING AND FIRE SAFETY

14. Again, never use a heat source such as a candle or burner without wearing safety goggles.
15. Never heat a chemical you are not instructed to heat. A chemical that is harmless when cool can be dangerous when heated.
16. Maintain a clean work area and keep all materials away from flames.
17. Do not plug too many devices into one socket. Never touch electrical devices with wet hands.
18. Make sure you know how to light a Bunsen burner. (Your teacher will demonstrate the proper procedure for lighting a burner.) If the flame leaps out of a burner toward you, turn the gas off immediately. Do not touch the burner. It may be hot. And never leave a lighted burner unattended!
19. When heating a test tube or bottle, point it away from yourself and others. Chemicals can splash or boil out of a heated test tube.
20. Never heat a liquid in a closed container. The expanding gases produced may blow the container apart, causing injury to yourself or others. Never reach across a flame.

21. Never pick up a container that has been heated without first holding the back of your hand near it. If you can feel the heat on the back of your hand, the container may be too hot to handle. Use tongs or heat-proof gloves when handling hot containers.

USING CHEMICALS SAFELY

22. Never mix chemicals "for the fun of it." You might produce a dangerous, possibly explosive substance.

23. Never touch, taste, or smell any chemicals in the laboratory. Many chemicals are poisonous. If you are instructed to note the fumes in an experiment, gently wave your hand over the opening of a container and direct the fumes toward your nose. Do not inhale the fumes directly from the container.

24. Use only those chemicals needed in the investigation. Keep all lids closed when a chemical is not being used. Notify your teacher whenever chemicals are spilled.

25. Dispose of all chemicals as instructed by your teacher. To avoid contamination, never return chemicals to their original containers.

26. Be extra careful when working with acids or bases. Pour such chemicals over the sink, not over your workbench.

27. When diluting an acid, pour the acid into water. Never pour water into the acid.

28. If any acids get on your skin or clothing, rinse them off with water. Immediately notify your teacher of any acid spill.

USING GLASSWARE SAFELY

29. Never force glass tubing into a rubber stopper. A turning motion and lubricant will be helpful when inserting glass tubing into rubber stoppers or rubber tubing. Your teacher will demonstrate the proper way to insert glass tubing.

30. Never heat glassware that is not thoroughly dry. Use a wire screen to protect glassware from any flame.

31. Keep in mind that hot glassware will not appear hot. Never pick up glassware that is not thoroughly cooled.

32. If you are instructed to cut glass tubing, fire-polish the ends immediately to remove sharp edges.

33. Never use broken or chipped glassware. If any glassware breaks, notify your teacher and dispose of the glassware in the proper trash container.

34. Never eat or drink from laboratory glassware. Thoroughly clean glassware before putting it away.

USING SHARP INSTRUMENTS

35. Handle scalpels or razor blades with extreme care. Never cut material toward you; cut away from you.

36. Notify your teacher immediately if you cut yourself when in the laboratory.

ANIMAL SAFETY

37. No experiments that will cause pain, discomfort, or harm to mammals, birds, reptiles, fishes, and amphibians should be done in the classroom or at home.

38. Animals should be handled only if necessary. If an animal is excited or frightened, pregnant, feeding, or with its young, special handling is required.

39. Your teacher will instruct you as to how to handle each animal species that may be brought into the classroom.

40. Clean your hands thoroughly after handling animals or the cage containing animals.

END-OF-EXPERIMENT RULES

41. When an experiment is completed, clean up your work area and return all equipment to its proper place.

42. Wash your hands before and after you perform every experiment.

43. Turn off all burners before leaving the laboratory. Check that the gas line leading to the burner is off as well.

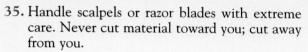

APPENDIX D Metric System

THE METRIC SYSTEM OF MEASUREMENT is used by scientists throughout the world. It is based on units of ten. Each unit is ten times larger or ten times smaller than the next unit. The most commonly used units of the metric system are given below. After you have finished reading about the metric system, try to put it to use. How tall are you in meters? What is your mass? What is your normal body temperature in degrees Celsius?

COMMONLY USED METRIC UNITS

Length The distance from one point to another

meter (m)	A meter is slightly longer than a yard. 1 meter = 1000 millimeters (mm) 1 meter = 100 centimeters (cm) 1000 meters = 1 kilometer (km)

Volume The amount of space an object takes up

liter (L)	A liter is slightly more than a quart. 1 liter = 1000 milliliters (mL)

Mass The amount of matter in an object

gram (g)	A gram has a mass equal to about one paper clip. 1000 grams = 1 kilogram (kg)

Temperature The measure of hotness or coldness

degrees Celsius (°C)	0°C = freezing point of water 100°C = boiling point of water

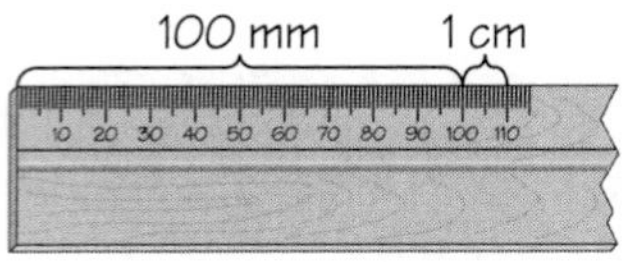

METRIC RULER

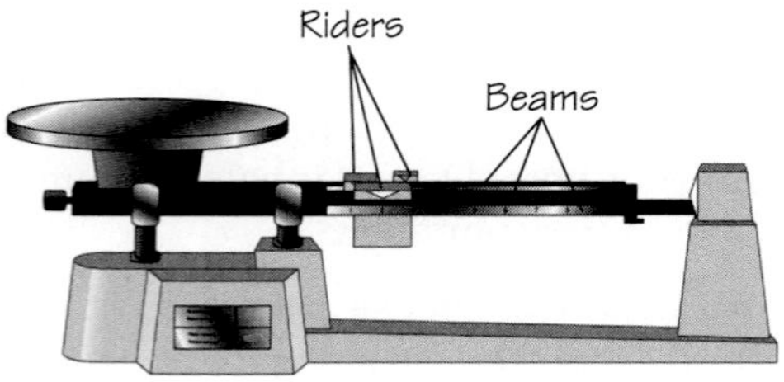

TRIPLE-BEAM BALANCE

GRADUATED CYLINDER

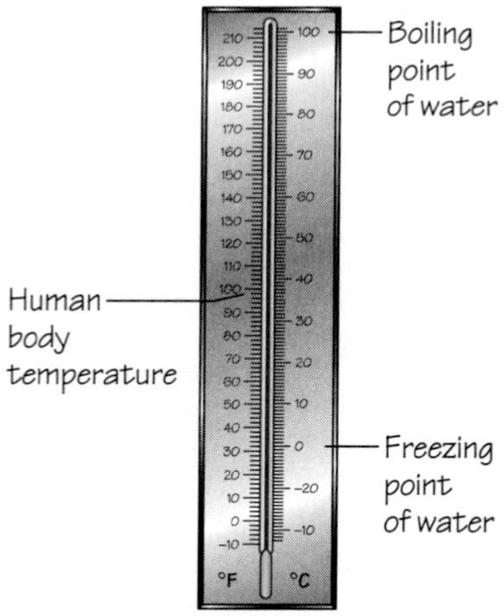

THERMOMETER

METRIC—ENGLISH SYSTEM EQUIVALENTS

2.54 centimeters (cm) = 1 inch (in.)
1 meter (m) = 39.37 inches (in.)
1 kilometer (km) = 0.62 miles (mi)
1 liter (L) = 1.06 quarts (qt)
250 milliliters (mL) = 1 cup (c)
1 kilogram (kg) = 2.2 pounds (lb)
28.3 grams (g) = 1 ounce (oz)
$°C = 5/9 \times (°F - 32)$

Six-Kingdom Classification System

Kingdom Eubacteria

Outer cell wall contains complex carbohydrates; all species have at least one inner cell membrane; live in diverse environments.

PHYLUM CYANOBACTERIA (blue-green bacteria)
Photosynthetic autotrophs, once called blue-green algae; contain pigments phycocyanin and chlorophyll *a*; some fix atmospheric nitrogen. Examples: *Anabaena, Nostoc*.

PHYLUM PROCHLOROBACTERIA
Photosynthetic autotrophs containing chlorophylls *a* and *b*; strikingly similar to chloroplasts; few species identified to date. Example: *Prochloron*.

Kingdom Archaebacteria

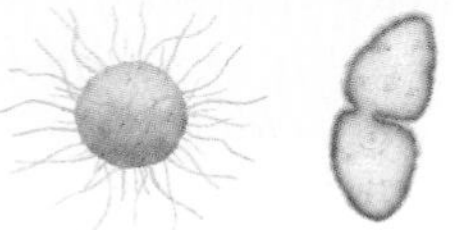

Single-celled prokaryotic organism; cell membrane contains lipids not found in any other organism; many survive in absence of oxygen; known as methanogens and produce methane gas; live in harsh environments. Examples: *Thermoplasma, Sulfolobus*.

Kingdom Protista

Eukaryotic; usually unicellular; some multicellular or colonial; heterotrophic or autotrophic organisms.

ANIMALLIKE PROTISTS Unicellular; heterotrophic; usually motile; also known as protozoa.

PHYLUM CILIOPHORA (ciliates)
All have cilia at some point in development; almost all use cilia to move; characterized by two types of nuclei: macronuclei and micronuclei; most have a sexual process known as conjugation. Examples: *Paramecium, Didinium, Stentor*.

PHYLUM ZOOMASTIGINA (animallike flagellates)
Possess one or more flagella (some have thousands); some are internal symbionts of wood-eating animals. Examples: *Trypanosoma, Trichonympha*.

PHYLUM SPOROZOA
Nonmotile parasites; produce small infective cells called spores; life cycles usually complex, involving more than one host species; cause a number of diseases, including malaria. Example: *Plasmodium*.

PHYLUM SARCODINA
Use pseudopods for feeding and movement; some produce elaborate shells that contain silica or calcium carbonate; most free-living; a few parasitic. Examples: *Ameba, foraminifers*.

PLANTLIKE PROTISTS Mostly unicellular photosynthetic autotrophs that have characteristics similar to green plants or fungi. A few species are multicellular or heterotrophic.

PHYLUM EUGLENOPHYTA (plantlike flagellates)
Primarily photosynthetic; most live in fresh water; possess two unequal flagella; lack a cell wall. Example: *Euglena*.

PHYLUM PYRROPHYTA (fire algae)
Two flagella; most live in salt water, are photosynthetic, and have a rigid cell wall that contains cellulose; some are luminescent; many are symbiotic. Examples: *Gonyaulax, Noctiluca*.

PHYLUM CHRYSOPHYTA (golden algae)
Photosynthetic; aquatic; mostly unicellular; contain yellow-brown pigments; most are diatoms, which build a two-part cell covering that contains silica. Examples: *Thallasiosira, Orchromonas, Navicula*.

PHYLUM CHLOROPHYTA (green algae)
Live in fresh and salt water; unicellular or multicellular; chlorophylls and accessory pigments similar to those in vascular plants; food stored as starch. Examples: *Ulva* (sea lettuce), *Chlamydomonas, Spirogyra, Acetabularia*.

PHYLUM PHAEOPHYTA (brown algae)

Live almost entirely in salt water; multicellular; contain brown pigment fucoxanthin; food stored as oils and carbohydrates. Examples: *Fucus* (rockweed), kelps, *Sargassum*.

PHYLUM RHODOPHYTA (red algae)

Live almost entirely in salt water; multicellular; contain red pigment phycoerythrin; food stored as carbohydrates. Examples: *Chondrus* (Irish moss), coralline algae.

FUNGUSLIKE PROTISTS Lack chlorophyll and absorb food through cell walls. Unlike true fungi, the funguslike protists contain centrioles and lack chitin in their cell walls.

PHYLUM ACRASIOMYCOTA (cellular slime molds)

Spores develop into independent, free-living amebalike cells that may come together to form a multicellular structure; this structure, which behaves much like a single organism, forms a fruiting body that produces spores. Example: *Dictyostelium*.

PHYLUM MYXOMYCOTA (acellular slime molds)

Spores develop into haploid cells that can switch between flagellated and amebalike forms; these haploid cells fuse to form a zygote that grows into a plasmodium, which ultimately forms spore-producing fruiting bodies. Example: *Physarum*.

PHYLUM OOMYCOTA (water molds)

Unicellular or multicellular; mostly aquatic; cell walls contain cellulose or a polysaccharide similar to cellulose; form zoospores asexually and eggs and sperms sexually. Example: *Saprolegnia* (freshwater molds).

KINGDOM FUNGI

Eukaryotic; unicellular or multicellular; cell walls typically contain chitin; mostly decomposers; some parasites; some commensal or mutualistic symbionts; asexual reproduction by spore formation, budding, or fragmentation; sexual reproduction involving mating types; classified according to type of fruiting body and style of spore formation; heterotrophic.

PHYLUM ZYGOMYCOTA (conjugation fungi)

Cell walls of chitin; hyphae lack cross walls; sexual reproduction by conjugation produces diploid zygospores; asexual reproduction produces haploid spores; most parasites; some decomposers. Example: *Rhizopus stolonifer* (black bread mold).

PHYLUM ASCOMYCOTA (sac fungi)

Cell walls of chitin; hyphae have perforated cross walls; most multicellular; yeasts unicellular; sexual reproduction produces ascospores; asexual reproduction by spore formation or budding; some cause plant diseases such as chestnut blight and Dutch elm disease. Examples: *Neurospora* (red bread mold), baker's yeast, morels, truffles.

PHYLUM BASIDIOMYCOTA (club fungi)

Cell walls of chitin; hyphae have cross walls; sexual reproduction involves basidiospores, which are borne on club-shaped basidia; asexual reproduction by spore formation. Examples: most mushrooms, puffballs, shelf fungi, rusts.

PHYLUM DEUTEROMYCOTA (imperfect fungi)

Cell walls of chitin; sexual reproduction never observed; members resemble ascomycetes, basidiomycetes, or zygomycetes; most are thought to be ascomycetes that have lost the ability to form asci. Examples: *Penicillium*, athlete's foot fungus.

KINGDOM PLANTAE

Eukaryotic; overwhelmingly multicellular and nonmotile; photosynthetic autotrophs; possess chlorophylls *a* and *b* and other pigments in organelles called chloroplasts; cell walls contain cellulose; food stored as starch; reproduce sexually; alternate haploid (gametophyte) and diploid (sporophyte) generations; botanists typically use the term division rather than phylum.

DIVISION BRYOPHYTA (bryophytes)

Generally small, multicellular green plants; live on land in moist habitats; lack vascular tissue; lack true roots, leaves, and stems; gametophyte dominant; water required for reproduction. Examples: mosses, liverworts, hornworts.

DIVISION PSILOPHYTA (whisk ferns)

Primitive vascular plants; no differentiation between root and shoot; produce only one kind of spore; motile sperm must swim in water.

DIVISION LYCOPHYTA (lycopods)

Primitive vascular plants; usually small; sporophyte dominant; possess roots, stems, and leaves; water required for reproduction. Examples: club mosses, quillworts.

DIVISION SPHENOPHYTA (horsetails)

Primitive vascular plants; stem comprises most of mature plant and contains silica; produce only one kind of spore; motile sperm must swim in water. Only one living genus: *Equisetum*.

DIVISION PTEROPHYTA (ferns)

Vascular plants well-adapted to live in predominantly damp or seasonally wet environments; sporophyte dominant and well-adapted to terrestrial life; gametophyte inconspicuous; reproduction still dependent on water for free-swimming gametes. Examples: cinnamon ferns, Boston ferns, tree ferns, maidenhair ferns.

GYMNOSPERMS Four divisions of seed plants—Cycadophyta, Ginkgophyta, Coniferophyta, and Gnetophyta. Gymnosperms are characterized by seeds that develop exposed, or "naked," on fertile leaves—there is no ovary wall (fruit) surrounding the seeds. Gymnosperms lack flowers.

DIVISION CYCADOPHYTA (cycads)

Evergreen, slow-growing, tropical and subtropical shrubs; many resemble small palm trees; palmlike or fernlike compound leaves; possess symbiotic cyanobacteria in special roots; sexes are separate—individuals have either male pollen-producing cones or female seed-producing cones.

DIVISION GINKGOPHYTA

Deciduous trees with fan-shaped leaves; sexes separate; outer skin of ovule develops into a fleshy, fruitlike covering. Only one living species: *Ginkgo biloba* (ginkgo).

DIVISION GNETOPHYTA

Few species; live mostly in deserts; functional xylem cells are alive; sexes are separate. Examples: *Welwitschia*, *Ephedra* (joint fir).

DIVISION CONIFEROPHYTA (conifers)

Cones predominantly wind-pollinated; most are evergreen; most temperate and subarctic shrubs and trees; many have needlelike leaves; in most species, sexes are not separate. Examples: pines, spruces, cedars, firs.

DIVISION ANTHOPHYTA

Members of this division are commonly called angiosperms, or flowering plants. Nearly all familiar trees, shrubs, and garden plants are angiosperms. Seeds develop enclosed within ovaries; fertile leaves modified into flowers; flowers pollinated by wind or by animals, including insects, birds, and bats; occur in many different forms; found in most land and freshwater habitats; a few species found in shallow saltwater and estuarine areas.

Class Monocotyledonae (monocots) Embryo with a single cotyledon; leaves with predominantly parallel venation; flower parts in threes or multiples of three; vascular bundles scattered throughout stem. Examples: lilies, corns, grasses, irises, palms, tulips.

Class Dicotyledonae (dicots) Embryo with two cotyledons; leaves with variation in netlike patterns; flower parts in fours or fives (or multiples thereof); vascular bundles arranged in rings in stem. Examples: roses, maples, oaks, daisies, apples.

KINGDOM ANIMALIA

Multicellular; eukaryotic; typical heterotrophs that ingest their food; lack cell walls; approximately 35 phyla; in most phyla, cells are organized into tissues that make up organs; most reproduce sexually; motile sperm have flagella; nonmotile egg is much larger than sperm; development involves formation of a hollow ball of cells called a blastula.

SUBKINGDOM PARAZOA

Animals that possess neither tissues nor organs; most asymmetrical.

PHYLUM PORIFERA (sponges)

Aquatic; lack true tissues and organs; motile larvae and sessile adults; filter feeders; internal skeleton made up of spongin and/or spicules of calcium carbonate or silica. Examples: Venus' flower baskets, bath sponges, tube sponges.

SUBKINGDOM METAZOA

Animals with definite symmetry; definite tissues; most possess organs.

PHYLUM CNIDARIA

Previously known as coelenterates; aquatic; mostly carnivorous; two layers of true tissue; radial symmetry; tentacles bear stinging nematocysts; many alternate between polyp and medusa body forms; gastrovascular cavity.

Class Hydrozoa Polyp form dominant; colonial or solitary; life cycle typically includes a medusa generation that reproduces sexually and a polyp generation that reproduces asexually. Examples: hydras, Portuguese man-of-wars.

Class Scyphozoa Medusa form dominant; some species bypass polyp stage. Examples: lion's mane jellyfishes, moon jellies, sea wasps.

Class Anthozoa Colonial or solitary polyps; no medusa stage. Examples: reef corals, sea anemones, sea pens, sea fans.

PHYLUM PLATYHELMINTHES (flatworms)

Three layers of tissue (endoderm, mesoderm, ectoderm); bilateral symmetry; some cephalization; acoelomate; free-living or parasitic.

Class Turbellaria Free-living carnivores and scavengers, live in fresh water, in salt water, or on land; move with cilia. Example: planarians.

Class Trematoda (flukes) Parasites; life cycle typically involves more than one host. Examples: *Schistosoma,* liver flukes.

Class Cestoda (tapeworms) Internal parasites; lack digestive tract; body composed of many repeating sections (proglottids).

PHYLUM NEMATODA (roundworms)

Digestive system has two openings—a mouth and an anus; pseudocoelomates. Examples: *Ascaris lumbricoides* (human ascarid), hookworms, *Trichinella.*

PHYLUM MOLLUSCA (mollusks)

Soft-bodied; usually (but not always) possess a hard, calcified shell secreted by a mantle; most adults have bilateral symmetry; muscular foot; divided into seven classes; digestive system with two openings; coelomates.

Class Pelecypoda (bivalves) Two-part hinged shell; wedge-shaped foot; typically sessile as adults; primarily aquatic; some burrow in mud or sand. Examples: clams, oysters, scallops, mussels.

Class Gastropoda (gastropods) Use broad, muscular foot in movement; most have spiral, chambered shell; some lack shell; distinct head; some terrestrial, others aquatic; many are cross-fertilizing hermaphrodites. Examples: snails, slugs, nudibranchs, sea hares, sea butterflies.

Class Cephalopoda (cephalopods) Foot divided into tentacles; live in salt water; closed circulatory system; sexes separate. Examples: octopuses, squids, nautiluses, cuttlefishes.

PHYLUM ANNELIDA (segmented worms)

Body composed of segments separated by internal partitions; digestive system has two openings; coelomate; closed circulatory system.

Class Polychaeta (polychaetes) Live in salt water; pair of bristly, fleshy appendages on each segment; some live in tubes. Examples: sandworms, bloodworms, fanworms, feather-duster worms, plume worms.

Class Oligochaeta (oligochaetes) Lack appendages; few bristles; terrestrial or aquatic. Examples: *Tubifex,* earthworms.

Class Hirudinea (leeches) Lack appendages; carnivores or blood-sucking external parasites; most live in fresh water. Example: *Hirudo medicinalis* (medicinal leech).

PHYLUM ARTHROPODA (arthropods)

Exoskeleton of chitin; jointed appendages; segmented body; many undergo metamorphosis during development; open circulatory system; ventral nerve cord; largest animal phylum.

Subphylum Trilobita (trilobites) Two furrows running from head to tail divide body into three lobes; one pair of unspecialized appendages on each body segment; each appendage divided into two branches—a gill and a walking leg; all extinct.

Subphylum Chelicerata (chelicerates) First pair of appendages specialized as feeding structures called chelicerae; body composed of two parts—cephalothorax and abdomen; lack antennae; most terrestrial. Examples: horseshoe crabs, ticks, mites, spiders, scorpions.

Subphylum Crustacea (crustaceans) Most aquatic; most live in salt water; two pairs of antennae; mouthparts called mandibles; appendages consist of two branches; many have a carapace that covers part or all of the body. Examples: crabs, crayfishes, pill bugs, water fleas, barnacles.

Subphylum Uniramia Almost all terrestrial; one pair of antennae; mandibles; unbranched appendages; generally divided into five classes.

Class Chilopoda (centipedes) Long body consisting of many segments; one pair of legs per segment; poison claws for feeding; carnivorous.

Class Diplopoda (millipedes) Long body consisting of many segments; two pairs of legs per segment; mostly herbivorous.

Class Insecta (insects) Body divided into three parts—head, thorax, and abdomen; three pairs of legs and usually two pairs of wings attached to thorax; some undergo complete metamorphosis; approximately 25 orders. Examples: termites, ants, beetles, flies, moths, grasshoppers.

PHYLUM ECHINODERMATA (echinoderms)

Live in salt water; larvae have bilateral symmetry; adults typically have five-part radial symmetry; endoskeleton; tube feet; water vascular system used in respiration, excretion, feeding, and locomotion.

Class Crinoidea (crinoids) Filter feeders; feathery arms; mouth and anus on upper surface of body disk; some sessile. Examples: sea lilies, feather stars.

Class Asteroidea (starfishes) Star-shaped; carnivorous; bottom dwellers; mouth on lower surface. Examples: crown-of-thorns starfishes, sunstars.

Class Ophiuroidea Small body disk; long armored arms; most have only five arms; lack an anus; most are filter feeders or detritus feeders. Examples: brittle stars, basket stars.

Class Echinoidea Lack arms; body encased in rigid, boxlike covering; covered with spines; most grazing herbivores or detritus feeders. Examples: sea urchins, sand dollars.

Class Holothuroidea (sea cucumbers) Cylindrical body with feeding tentacles on one end; lie on their side; mostly detritus or filter feeders; endoskeleton greatly reduced.

PHYLUM CHORDATA (chordates)

Notochord and pharyngeal gill slits during at least part of development; hollow dorsal nerve cord.

Subphylum Urochordata (tunicates) Live in salt water; tough outer covering (tunic); display chordate features during larval stages; many adults sessile, some free-swimming. Examples: sea squirts, sea peaches.

Subphylum Cephalochordata (lancelets) Fishlike; live in salt water; filter feeders; no internal skeleton. Example: *Branchiostoma*.

Subphylum Vertebrata Most possess a vertebral column (backbone) that supports and protects dorsal nerve cord; endoskeleton; distinct head with a skull and brain.

Jawless Fishes Characterized by long eellike body and a circular mouth; two-chambered heart; lack scales, paired fins, jaws, and bones; ectothermic; possess a notochord as adults. Once considered a single class—Agnatha—jawless fishes are now divided into two classes: Myxini and Cephalaspidomorphi. Although the term agnatha no longer refers to a true taxonomic group, it is still used informally.

Class Myxini (hagfishes) Mostly scavengers; live in salt water; short tentacles around mouth; rasping tongue; extremely slimy; open circulatory system.

Class Cephalaspidomorphi (lampreys) Larvae filter feeders; adults are parasites whose circular mouth is lined with rasping, toothlike structures; many live in both salt water and fresh water during the course of their lives.

Class Chondrichthyes (cartilaginous fishes) Jaw; fins; endoskeleton of cartilage; most live in salt water; typically several gill slits; tough small scales with spines; ectothermic; two-chambered heart; males possess structures for internal fertilization. Examples: sharks, rays, skates, sawfishes.

Class Osteichthyes (bony fishes) Bony endoskeleton; aquatic; ectothermic; well-developed respiratory system, usually involving gills; possess swim bladder; paired fins; divided into two groups—ray-finned fishes (Actinopterygii), which include most living species, and fleshy-finned fishes (Sarcopterygii), which include lungfishes and the coelacanth. Examples: salmons, perches, sturgeons, tunas, goldfishes, eels.

Class Amphibia (amphibians) Adapted primarily to life in wet places; ectothermic; most carnivorous; smooth, moist skin; typically lay eggs that develop in water; usually have gilled larvae; most have three-chambered heart; adults either aquatic or terrestrial; terrestrial forms respire using lungs, skin, and/or lining of the mouth.

ORDER URODELA (newts and salamanders) Possess tail as adults; carnivorous; usually have four legs; usually aquatic as larvae and terrestrial as adults.

ORDER ANURA (frogs and toads) Adults in almost all species lack tail; aquatic larvae called tadpoles; well-developed hind legs adapted for jumping.

ORDER APODA (legless amphibians) Wormlike; lack legs; carnivorous; terrestrial burrowers; some undergo direct development; some are viviparous.

Class Reptilia (reptiles) As a group, adapted to fully terrestrial life, although some live in water; dry, scale-covered skin; ectothermic; most have three-chambered heart; internal fertilization; amniotic eggs typically laid on land; extinct forms include dinosaurs and flying reptiles.

ORDER RHYNCHOCEPHALIA (tuatara) "Teeth" formed by serrations of jawbone; found only in New Zealand; carnivorous. One species: *Sphenodon punctatus*.

ORDER SQUAMATA (lizards and snakes) Most carnivorous; majority terrestrial; lizards typically have legs; snakes lack legs. Examples: iguanas, geckos, skinks, cobras, pythons, boas.

ORDER CROCODILIA (crocodilians) Carnivorous; aquatic or semiaquatic; four-chambered heart. Examples: alligators, crocodiles, caimans, gharials.

ORDER CHELONIA (turtles) Bony shell; ribs and vertebrae fused to upper part of shell; some terrestrial, others semiaquatic or aquatic; all lay eggs on land. Examples: snapping turtles, tortoises, hawksbill turtles, box turtles.

Class Aves (birds) Endothermic; feathered over much of body surface; scales on legs and feet; bones hollow and lightweight in flying species; four-chambered heart; well-developed lungs and air sacs for efficient air exchange; about 27 orders. Examples: owls, eagles, ducks, chickens, pigeons, penguins, sparrows, storks.

Class Mammalia (mammals) Endothermic; subcutaneous fat; hair; most viviparous; suckle young with milk produced in mammary glands; four-chambered heart; four legs; use lungs for respiration.

Monotremes (egg-laying mammals)

ORDER MONOTREMATA (monotremes) Exhibit features of both mammals and reptiles; possess a cloaca; lay eggs that hatch externally; produce milk from primitive nipplelike structures. Examples: duck-billed platypuses, spiny anteaters, short-beaked echidnas.

Marsupials (pouched mammals)

ORDER MARSUPIALIA (marsupials) Young develop in the female's uterus but emerge at very early stage of development; development completed in mother's pouch. Examples: opossums, kangaroos, koalas.

Placentals Young develop to term in uterus; nourished through placenta; some born helpless, others able to walk within hours of birth; about 16 orders.

ORDER INSECTIVORA (insectivores) Among the most primitive of living placental mammals; feed primarily on small arthropods. Examples: shrews, moles, hedgehogs.

ORDER CHIROPTERA (bats) Flying mammals, with forelimbs adapted for flight; most nocturnal; most navigate by echolocation; most species feed on insects, nectar, or fruits; some species feed on blood. Examples: fruit bats, flying foxes, vampire bats.

ORDER PRIMATES (primates) Highly developed brain and complex social behavior; excellent binocular vision; quadrupedal or bipedal locomotion; five digits on hands and feet. Examples: lemurs, monkeys, chimpanzees, humans.

ORDER EDENTATA (edentates) Teeth reduced or absent; feed primarily on social insects such as termites and ants. Examples: anteaters, armadillos.

ORDER LAGOMORPHA (lagomorphs) Small herbivores with chisel-shaped front teeth; generally adapted to running and jumping. Examples: rabbits, pikas, hares.

ORDER RODENTIA (rodents) Mammalian order with largest number of species; mostly herbivorous, but some omnivorous; sharp front teeth. Examples: rats, beavers, guinea pigs, hamsters, gerbils, squirrels.

ORDER CETACEA (cetaceans) Fully adapted to aquatic existence; feed, breed, and give birth in water; forelimbs specialized as flippers; external hindlimbs absent; many species capable of long, deep dives; some use echolocation to navigate; communicate using complex auditory signals. Examples: whales, porpoises, dolphins.

ORDER CARNIVORA (carnivores) Mostly carnivorous; live in salt water or on land; aquatic species must return to land to breed. Examples: dogs, seals, cats, bears, raccoons, weasels, skunks, pandas.

ORDER PROBOSCIDEA (elephants) Herbivorous; largest land animal; long, flexible trunk.

ORDER SIRENIA (sirenians) Aquatic herbivores; slow-moving; forelimbs modified as flippers; hindlimbs absent; little body hair. Examples: manatees, sea cows.

ORDER PERISSODACTYLA (odd-toed ungulates) Hooved herbivores; odd number of hooves; one hoof generally derived from middle digit on each foot; teeth, jaw, and digestive system adapted to plant material. Examples: horses, donkeys, rhinoceroses, tapirs.

ORDER ARTIODACTYLA (even-toed ungulates) Hooved herbivores; hooves derived from two digits on each foot; digestive system adapted to thoroughly process tough plant material. Examples: sheep, cows, hippopotamuses, antelopes, camels, giraffes, pigs.

Glossary

Pronunciation Key

When difficult names or terms first appear in the text, a pronunciation key follows in parentheses. A syllable in small capital letters receives the most stress. The key below lists the letters used in the pronunciations. It includes examples of words using each sound and shows how those words would be written.

Symbol	Example	Respelling
a	hat	(HAT)
ay	pay; late	(PAY); (LAYT)
ah	star; hot	(STAHR); (HAHT)
ai	air; dare	(AIR); (DAIR)
aw	law; all	(LAW); (AWL)
eh	met	(MEHT)
ee	bee; eat	(BEE); (EET)
er	learn; sir; fur	(LERN); (SER); (FER)
ih	fit	(FIHT)
igh	mile; sigh	(MIGHL); (SIGH)
oh	no	(NOH)
oi	soil; boy	(SOIL); (BOI)
oo	root; rule	(ROOT); (ROOL)
or	born; door	(BORN); (DOR)
ow	plow; out	(PLOW); (OWT)

Symbol	Example	Respelling
u	put; book	(PUT); (BUK)
uh	fun	(FUHN)
yoo	few; use	(FYOO); (YOOZ)
ch	chill; reach	(CHIHL); (REECH)
g	go; dig	(GOH); (DIHG)
j	jet; gently; bridge	(JEHT); (JEHNT-lee); (BRIHJ)
k	kite; cup	(KIGHT); (KUHP)
ks	mix	(MIHKS)
kw	quick	(KWIHK)
ng	bring	(BRIHNG)
s	say; cent	(SAY); (SEHNT)
sh	she; crash	(SHEE); (KRASH)
th	three	(THREE)
y	yet; onion	(YEHT); (UHN-yuhn)
z	zip; always	(ZIHP); (AWL-wayz)
zh	treasure	(TREH-zher)

A

abdomen: in arthropods, the body segment containing most of the internal organs, including the reproductive organs; in mammals, the cavity region between the diaphragm and the pelvis; in vertebrates, the part of the body cavity containing the digestive and reproductive organs

abiotic factor: physical environmental factor, such as climate, type of soil and its acidity, or availability of nutrients

acid: compound that donates H^+ ions

actin: protein found in the thin filaments of muscle fiber

action potential: rapid change in voltage on the inside of the axon from negative to positive and then back to negative

active site: region of an enzyme where a substrate binds

active transport: movement of a substance against a concentration difference; a process that requires energy

adaptation: evolution of physical and behavioral traits that make organisms better suited to survive in their environment

adaptive radiation: pattern of evolution in which selection and adaptation lead to the formation of a new species in a relatively short period of time

addiction: uncontrollable craving for a substance

age-structure diagram: diagram that illustrates the percentages of individuals within different age groups

AIDS (acquired immune deficiency syndrome): fatal disease of the immune system caused by HIV infection

air sac: in birds, an extension of the respiratory system where air collects

alcoholic fermentation: in yeasts, the process by which pyruvic acid is converted to alcohol and carbon dioxide

alga; pl. **algae**: single-celled photosynthetic organism classified as a protist

alimentary canal: one-way digestive track that begins at the mouth; includes the esophagus, stomach, small intestine, and large intestine; ends at the anus

allele (uh-LEEL): different form of a gene for a specific trait

allergy: overreaction of the immune system to an antigen in the environment

alternation of generations: variation in a life cycle that switches back and forth between the production of diploid (2n) and haploid (n) cells; in plants, pattern of reproduction in which the organism alternates between sporophyte and gametophyte phases

alveolus (al-VEE-uh-lus; pl. **alveoli**, al-VEE-uh-ligh): tiny air sac in the lungs appearing in a grapelike cluster surrounding a network of capillaries where gas exchange takes place

amebocyte (uh-MEE-boh-sight): wandering cell in sponges

amino acid: molecule of which proteins are made, containing a central carbon bonded to an amino group, a carboxyl group, a hydrogen atom, and another group called R group

amniocentesis (am-nee-oh-sehn-TEE-sihs): prenatal technique that involves withdrawing a small amount of fluid from the sac surrounding the fetus

amnion: membrane of the sac that envelops the embryo

amniotic (am-nee-AHT-ik) **egg**: self-sufficient developing egg encased in a shell that allows for gas exchange but keeps liquid inside

amylase: enzyme in saliva that breaks down the chemical bonds in starches, releasing sugars

anal pore: waste-discharging region on a paramecium

analogous structure: similar in appearance and function but dissimilar in anatomical development and origin

anaphase: third phase of mitosis during which duplicated chromosomes separate from each other

angiosperm: flowering plant whose seeds develop within a matured ovary (fruit)

animal society: any group of animals living together

annual: plant that completes its life cycle (from seed to maturity, flower, and seed production) within a single growing season

annual tree ring: layer of xylem cells produced in a tree stem in one year, with growth affected by seasonal variation; in cross section, seen as a concentric circle

anther: sac at the tip of a filament where pollen is produced and released

anthropoid (AN-thruh-poid): any of a higher order of primates; includes humans, apes, and monkeys

antibiotic: drug or compound that can destroy bacteria

antibody: large protein that is the basic functional unit of a specific immune response

anticodon: three nucleotides in transfer RNA that bind to a codon in mRNA

antidiuretic hormone (ADH): hormone that helps to regulate the fluid balance of the body

antigen: molecule that stimulates the production of an antibody

aorta: largest artery in the human body

artery: blood vessel that carries blood from the heart to the body

artificial selection: method of selective breeding of organisms to produce offspring with desirable characteristics

ascus: tough sac of an ascomycete that contains the spores produced by sexual reproduction

asthma: condition in which smooth muscle contractions reduce the size of air passageways in the lungs, making breathing difficult

atherosclerosis (ath-er-oh-skluh-ROH-sihs): condition in which fatty deposits build up on the inner surfaces of arteries, obstructing the flow of blood

atom: smallest unit of a chemical element

ATP (adenosine triphosphate): energy-storage compound in cells

atrium (AY-tree-uhm; pl. **atria**, AY-tree-ah): upper chamber of the heart that receives the blood

auditory canal: region where vibrations enter the ear

autoimmune disease: condition that results when the immune system attacks its own cells

autonomic nervous system: part of the motor division of the peripheral nervous system that regulates activities not under conscious control

autosome: any chromosome other than a sex chromosome

autotroph: organism that uses energy from the sun to change simple nonliving chemical nutrients in its environment into living tissue

auxin: plant hormone that produces phototropism, stimulating cell growth near the tip of a root or stem

axon: single long, branched extension of the cell body of a neuron that carries impulses away from the cell body

B

B cell: lymphocyte that matures in bone marrow and produces antibodies

bacillus (buh-SIHL-uhs; pl. **bacilli**, buh-SIHL-igh): rod-shaped bacteria

bacteriophage: any virus that infects bacteria

bacterium; pl. **bacteria**: prokaryote with a cell membrane and genetic material not surrounded by a nuclear envelope

base: compound that donates OH^- ions or accepts H^+ ions

behavior: animal's response to its environment

berry: soft ovary wall that encloses many seeds

biennial: plant that flowers and produces seeds in the second year of its life cycle

bilateral symmetry: body form of an organism that has identical left and right sides, specialized front and back ends, and upper and lower sides

bile: lipid and salt fluid produced by the liver to aid digestion

binary fission: asexual form of reproduction in which a cell divides in half to produce two identical daughter cells

binocular vision: ability to perceive depth using both eyes at the same time

biodegradable: capable of being broken down into unharmful products by the life processes of living things

biodiversity: variety of organisms, their genetic information, and biological communities in which they live

biological magnification: process whereby substances such as toxic metals and chemicals are passed up the trophic levels of the food web at increasing concentrations

biology: science of life

biome: ecosystem identified by its climax community

biotic factor: biological environmental factor, such as the living things with which an organism might interact

blood: fluid medium of transport of the circulatory system in vertebrates

blood pressure: measure of the force exerted by blood against the walls of arteries

bone marrow: blood-forming tissue that produces white and red blood cells

book gill: respiratory organ of some marine arthropods

book lung: respiratory organ of most spiders made of numerous layers of tissue that resemble the pages of a book

brain: bundle of nerves and neural connections that controls the nervous system

brainstem: structure that connects the brain to the spinal cord; includes the medulla oblongata and the pons

bronchitis: respiratory disease caused by the bronchi becoming swollen and clogged with mucus

bronchus (BRAHN-kus; pl. **bronchi**, BRAHN-kigh): one of many air tubes that enter the lungs and branch off, for gas exchange

budding: type of asexual reproduction in which an outgrowth of an organism breaks away and develops into a new organism

C

calorie: amount of heat energy needed to raise the temperature of 1 gram of water by 1°C

Calvin cycle: chemical pathway used to convert energy from ATP and $NADP^+$ into sugars; also called the light-independent reactions

capillary: small blood vessel in which the exchange of nutrients and wastes takes place

carbohydrate: class of macromolecules that includes sugars and starches; source of chemical energy

carcinogen: cancer-causing chemical

cardiac muscle tissue: muscle tissue found in the heart; not under direct control of the central nervous system

carpel: female leaf of a flower

carrying capacity: largest number of individuals of a particular species that can survive over long periods of time in a given environment

cartilage: strong, resilient connective tissue

catalyst: substance that speeds up a chemical reaction without itself being used up in the reaction

cell: smallest working unit of living things

cell body: largest part of the neuron in which metabolic activity takes place

cell cycle: period of time from the beginning of one cell division to the beginning of the next

cell division: process in which a cell divides into two independent daughter cells

cell-mediated immunity: immune response in which foreign cells are destroyed by contact with T cells

cell membrane: part of the cell's outer boundary; contains a lipid bilayer

cell theory: principle stating that all living things are composed of cells, cells are the smallest working units of living things, and all cells come from preexisting cells by cell division

cell transformation: the changing of a cell's genetic makeup by the insertion of DNA

cell wall: tough, porous boundary that lies outside the cell membrane; found in plant cells and in some bacteria but not in animal cells

centralization: concentration of nerve cells that form nerve cords or nerve rings around the mouth of most primitive invertebrates

centriole: small structure in animal cells that helps to organize microtubules

centromere: the part of a chromosome in which the chromatids are attached

cephalization (sehf-uh-lih-ZAY-shun): concentration of nerve cells and sensory cells in the head of an organism

cephalothorax: in chelicerates, body segment formed from fused head and thorax; carries the legs

cerebellum (ser-uh-BEHL-uhm): second-largest part of the brain; coordinates movement

cerebral cortex: deeply creased surface of the cerebrum

cerebrospinal (ser-uh-broh-SPIGH-nuhl) **fluid**: fluid that fills the space between the meninges to cushion the brain and spinal cord

cerebrum (SER-uh-bruhm): largest and most complex structure of the nervous system; consists of two lobes or hemispheres; controls voluntary activities

chelicera (kuh-LIHS-er-uh; pl. **chelicerae**, kuh-LIHS-er-ee): unique, specialized mouthpart of chelicerates used for grasping and crushing

chemical compound: substance formed by the bonding of atoms of different elements in definite proportions

chemical reaction: process that changes one set of substances into a new set of substances

chemiosmosis: process of ATP formation in chloroplasts and mitochondria

chemotherapy: mixture of drugs that interfere with important cell processes; used for treating cancer

chitin (KIGH-tihn): structural carbohydrate that is the main component of arthropod exoskeletons; reinforces the cell walls of fungi; also found in insect skeletons

chlamydia: sexually transmitted disease caused by a bacterium that can bring about infertility in females

chlorophyll: principal pigment of green plants

chloroplast: organelle found in plants and certain types of algae; harvests the energy of sunlight

chorionic villus (kor-ee-AHN-ihk VIHL-uhs) **sampling**: technique that involves the removal and examination of tissue surrounding the fetus

chromatid: strand of a chromosome that occurs in identical pairs; combined with its sister chromatid, constitutes a chromosome

chromatin: material of chromosomes that consists of DNA and proteins

chromatophore: specialized cell capable of changing color

chromosomal mutation: change in the number or structure of a cell's chromosomes; a mutation that affects the entire chromosome

chromosome: structure in the nucleus of a cell that contains DNA bound to proteins

chromosome deletion: phenomenon in which a broken-off piece of chromosome is left out during meiosis, which usually results in a genetic disorder

chromosome translocation: phenomenon in which a broken-off piece of chromosome becomes reattached to another chromosome

cilium; pl. **cilia**: short, hairlike projection of some cells; in ciliates, used to pull the organism through water with a coordinated rowing movement

circular muscle: in annelids, a muscle that surrounds the longitudinal muscle, lengthening the segment as it contracts

class: classification category of related orders

classical conditioning: associative learning; learning to associate a stimulus with either a reward or a punishment

climate: temperature range, average annual precipitation, humidity, and amount of sunshine that a region typically experiences

climax community: collection of plants and animals that results when an ecosystem reaches a relatively stable state in the interaction between organisms and their environment

clitellum: in an annelid, the structure that secretes a ring of mucus into which eggs and sperm are released

cloaca: body cavity into which the intestinal and genitourinary tracts empty

clone: group of genetically identical organisms produced by the division of a single cell

closed circulatory system: system in which blood moves only through blood vessels

cocaine: addictive stimulant drug that causes the brain to release dopamine and acts on the neurons of the brain

coccus (KAHK-uhs; pl. **cocci**, KAHK-sigh): spherical bacterium

cochlea (KAHK-lee-uh): fluid-filled portion of the inner ear that creates pressure waves

codominance: genetic condition in which both dominant and recessive alleles are expressed

codon: group of three nucleotides in mRNA that specifies an amino acid

coelom (SEE-lohm): mesoderm-lined cavity that provides an open space inside the body within which organs can grow and function

coevolution: simultaneous, progressive change of structures and behaviors in two different organisms in response to changes in each organism over time

collar cell: sponge cell made of fused cilia surrounding a whiplike flagella; used for beating water and filtering food

common descent: principle that species have descended from common ancestors

communication: passing information from one organism to another

compact bone: dense layer of hard bone with minuscule spaces for Haversian canals

compound light microscope: microscope that uses lenses and light to magnify an image

cone: reproductive structure of a conifer; male cone produces pollen and female cone produces ovules

conjugation: form of sexual reproduction that results in new combinations of genes

conservation: managing of natural resources in a way that maintains biodiversity

consumer: organism that eats other organisms to obtain energy and nutrients

continental drift: geological theory suggesting that continents move slowly over hundreds of millions of years

contour feather: strong, lightweight feather that provides a large surface area for a bird's flight

contractile vacuole: specialized structure in some protists; used to collect and expel water

control: in an experiment, the test group in which the variable is not altered; used as a benchmark to measure the variable's effect

convergent evolution: process by which unrelated species independently evolve superficial similarities when adapting to similar environments

cornea: tough transparent layer at the surface of the eye through which light enters

corpus luteum (KOR-puhs LOOT-ee-uhm): name given to the follicle after ovulation because of its yellow color

cortex: layer of spongy cells beneath the epidermis of a plant

cotyledon (kaht-uh-LEED-uhn): tiny seed leaf found in a plant embryo inside a seed

covalent bond: attraction between two atoms in which electrons are shared between two atoms

crop: widening in the digestive tract for the temporary storage of food

crossing-over: exchange between homologous chromosomes

cyclin: protein that regulates the timing of the cell cycle

cytokinesis: division of the cytoplasm that takes place during the anaphase and telophase phases of mitosis in most cells

cytoplasm: portion of the cell outside the nucleus

cytoskeleton: supporting framework of a eukaryotic cell

D

decomposer: organism that feeds on the dead bodies of animals and plants or on their waste products

demographic transition: change in growth rate resulting from changes in birth rate

dendrite: any of many small branched extensions of the cell body of a neuron that carry impulses toward the cell body

density-dependent limiting factor: population-limiting factor that operates more strongly on large, dense populations than on small, less crowded ones

density-independent limiting factor: population-limiting factor that acts on organisms regardless of the size of the population

depressant: one of a group of drugs that decreases the rate of brain activity and slows down the actions of the nervous system

dermis: inner layer of skin; supports the epidermis and contains nerve endings, blood vessels, smooth muscle, and glands

diaphragm: dome-shaped muscle that pulls the bottom of the chest cavity downward, increasing its volume; separates the chest cavity from the abdominal cavity

dicot: angiosperm that produces seeds with two cotyledons

diffusion: process by which substances spread through a liquid or gas from regions of high concentration to regions of low concentration

diploid: description of a cell that contains a double set of chromosomes; represented by the term 2n

DNA (deoxyribonucleic acid): nucleic acid that transmits genetic information from one generation to the next and codes for the production of proteins

DNA fingerprinting: technique used to identify an individual from the unique pattern of DNA

DNA replication: process in which DNA is copied

domesticate: to tame, raise, and breed animals for human purposes

dominant: form of gene that is expressed when present and excludes the recessive form; represented with a capital letter

dorsal hollow nerve cord: develops into the main nerve pathway from the body to the brain; characteristic of chordates

double fertilization: process of two fertilization events taking place inside an embryo sac

down feather: soft, fluffy feather that insulates the skin of a bird

drug: substance that causes a change in the body

drug-resistant bacteria: bacteria not susceptible to one or more antibodies

drupe: soft, fleshy ovary wall that encloses a single tough, stony seed of a fruit

E

ecological pyramid: diagram showing the decreasing amounts of energy, living tissue, or number of organisms at successive trophic levels

ecological succession: process by which an existing ecosystem is gradually and progressively replaced by another ecosystem

ecology: scientific study of interactions between different kinds of living things and the environments in which they live

ecosystem: collection of organisms—producers, consumers, and decomposers—interacting with each other and with their physical environment

ecosystem diversity: variety of habitats, living communities, and ecological processes in the living world

ectoderm: outer embryonic cell layer from which the nervous system, the skin, and other associated body coverings are derived in animal development

ectotherm: organism—such as a fish, amphibian, or reptile—that relies on interactions with the environment to control body temperature; cold-blooded organism

egg: female reproductive cell

electron: subatomic particle that carries a negative charge

electron microscope: microscope that uses a beam of electrons to examine a sample

electron transport chain: series of molecules located in the inner membrane of the mitochondrion that receive high-energy electrons from electron carriers

embryo: early stage of development of an organism resulting from fertilization

emphysema: respiratory disease in which the alveoli lose their elasticity and breathing becomes difficult

endocrine system: body system made up of a series of glands that produce and release chemicals into the bloodstream

endoderm: inner embryonic cell layer from which the tissues and organs of the digestive tract and other internal organs are developed

endodermis: layer of cells forming the inner boundary of the cortex of most roots and controlling entry into the vascular cylinder

endoplasmic reticulum: network of membranes within a cell that process and transport proteins and other macromolecules

endoskeleton: skeletal system located within the body

endosperm: food-rich tissue that surrounds the embryo of a plant

endospore: type of asexual spore formed inside a bacterial cell that develops a thick wall enclosing part of the cytoplasm and DNA, enabling the bacteria to survive for years

endosymbiont hypothesis: hypothesis that billions of years ago, eukaryotic cells arose as a combination of different prokaryotic cells

endotherm: organism, such as a mammal or a bird, that generates and maintains body heat through chemical reactions in the body; warmblooded organism

enhanced greenhouse effect: increased retention of heat in the Earth's atmosphere as a result of increased levels of carbon dioxide and other greenhouse gases to the atmosphere

environment: combination of physical and biological factors that influence life

enzyme: molecule that serves as a catalyst in organic reactions

epidemic: uncontrolled spread of disease

epidermis: outer layer of skin made up of layers of epithelial cells

epididymis (ehp-uh-DIHD-ih-mihs): tube in males that stores sperm

epiglottis: flap of tissue that prevents food from entering the trachea

esophagus: tube through which food passes from the pharynx to the stomach

estrogen: hormone in females involved in the development of the reproductive organs

eukaryote: organism made of cells that contain nuclei

evolution: process of change over a period of time

exon: expressed sequence of mRNA; a region that remains in mRNA after the introns are removed

exoskeleton: external skeletal system

experiment: controlled test to determine the validity of a hypothesis

exponential growth: rapid growth of a population whose living conditions are ideal

external fertilization: method of fertilization in which eggs and sperm meet outside the organism's body

extracellular digestion: process in which food is digested outside the cells

F

Fallopian tube: one of the two tubes in a female's reproductive system that receives the ovum from the ovary and passes it to the uterus

family: classification of a group of closely related genera

family group: group of related animals living together

feather: lightweight covering of a bird's body

fermentation: regeneration of NAD^+ to keep glycolysis running in the absence of oxygen

fertilization: fusion of egg and sperm to form a zygote

fetus: name given to an embryo after eight weeks of development

fibrin: netlike trap of plasma protein that forms a blood clot

filament: stamen that emerges from a flower

filtration: transport process that removes urea, excess water, and other wastes from the blood

fin: winglike structure on a fish used in swimming

fitness: an organism's ability to successfully pass on its genes to its offspring

fixed joint: joining place of two bones where there is little or no movement, such as in the skull

flagellum; pl. **flagella**: whiplike projection found on some cells; typically used for movement

flame cell: specialized cell with a tuft of cilia that conducts water and wastes through the branching tubes that serve as an excretory system in flatworms

flower: reproductive structure of an angiosperm

follicle: cluster of cells that contains a developing egg

follicle-stimulating hormone (FSH): hormone secreted by the pituitary gland that stimulates the development of sperm in males and the follicle in females

food chain: sequence of organisms related to one another as food and consumer

food web: interconnecting food chains in an ecological community

foot: in a mollusk, the muscular structure that usually contains the mouth

fossil: preserved bone or other trace of an ancient organism

frameshift mutation: gene mutation that involves the insertion or deletion of a nucleotide, thus changing the grouping of codons

freely movable joint: joining place of two bones where there is a wide range of movements, such as in the shoulders, hips, elbows, and knees

frond: large leaf of a fern

fruit: ripened ovary that contains angiosperm seeds

fruiting body: reproductive structure that produces spores

G

gamete (GAM-eet): haploid reproductive cell that can unite with another haploid cell to form a new individual

gametophyte: in plants, the haploid gamete-bearing generation that reproduces by fertilization

gastric gland: microscopic gland that appears in great numbers in the lining of the stomach and produces mucus, acid, and pepsin to aid digestion

gastritis: inflammation of the stomach caused by stomach acids making direct contact with the cells of the stomach lining

gastrovascular cavity: digestive sac with a single opening to the outside from which food enters and wastes leave

gastrulation (gas-troo-LAY-shuhn): process of cell migration during which the primary germ layers of the embryo are formed

gemmule (JEHM-yool): in sponges, a cluster of ball-shaped amebocytes that can grow into a new individual

gene: segment of DNA that codes for a specific protein; the unit by which hereditary characteristics are transmitted

gene mutation: mutation that involves only a single gene

gene pool: all the alleles of all the genes of the members of a population that interbreed

genetic code: language of the instructions in DNA and RNA that code for the amino acid sequence of a polypeptide

genetic diversity: genetic material in the gene pool of a species; variety of different forms of genes present in a population

genetic drift: random change in allele frequency, often producing offspring that will be different from the original population by chance

genetic engineering: manipulation and insertion of genes and DNA from different sources into an organism

genetics: study of heredity

genital herpes: sexually transmitted disease caused by a virus that affects the genital areas of males and females

genotype: genetic composition of an organism

genus; pl. **genera**: classification of a major group of closely related organisms

geologic time scale: unit of time—such as eons, eras, periods, and epochs—based on information contained in rocks

geotropism: response of an organism to the force of gravity, usually by turning downward or upward

gill: featherlike respiratory organ of many aquatic species; used to obtain oxygen from the water

gizzard: portion of digestive tract where food is ground into small, absorbable particles

global warming: prediction that the enhanced greenhouse effect will cause a significant rise in Earth's average temperature

glomerulus: ball of capillaries in a nephron that filters blood

glucagon: hormone that breaks down glycogen and fats and releases sugars into the blood

glycogen: compound that stores excess glucose in the body

glycolysis: series of reactions in which a molecule of glucose is broken down

Golgi apparatus: network of membranes within a cell that, in conjunction with the endoplasmic reticulum, processes and transports proteins and other macromolecules; contains special enzymes that attach carbohydrates or lipids to a protein

gonorrhea: sexually transmitted disease caused by a bacterium that infects the urinary and reproductive tracts

gradualism: theory that evolutionary change occurs slowly and steadily over long periods of time

grafting: artificial method of propagation

greenhouse effect: retention of heat in the Earth's atmosphere due to the presence of greenhouse gases

green revolution: substantial increase in crop yields that resulted from the introduction of modern agricultural practices

growth rate: change in the size of a population

gullet: depression on a paramecium used for the intake of food particles

gut: digestive tract

gymnosperm: seed plant in which the seeds are exposed to the air, usually in a cone-shaped structure

H

habitat: surroundings in which a species lives and thrives; defined in terms of the plant community and the abiotic factors

habituation: decreased response to a repeated stimulus

hair follicle: clusters of columns of epidermal cells anchored in the dermis; produce hair

half-life: length of time required for half of a radioactive element to decay to its more stable form

haploid: description of a cell that contains a single set of chromosomes; often represented by the letter n

Haversian (huh-VER-zhuhn) **canal**: small channel in compact bone through which nerve and blood vessels run

helper T cell: type of lymphocyte in the immune system that identifies a specific pathogen in the body

hemoglobin: iron-containing protein found in red blood cells that helps to transport oxygen

hepatitis B: disease caused by a virus that can cause inflammation of the liver; can be transmitted sexually

heredity: biological inheritance of traits from parent to offspring

hermaphrodite (her-MAF-ruh-dight): organism that has both male and female reproductive organs and produces both sperm and eggs

heterotroph: organism that cannot manufacture its own food

heterozygous (heht-er-oh-ZIGH-guhs): description of an organism that has a mixed pair of alleles for a trait

histamine: chemical released by a mast cell to produce an inflammatory response to an allergy

HIV (human immunodeficiency virus): virus that infects cells in the immune system and destroys helper T cells

hominid: any of a family of two-legged primates; includes humans and closely related primates but not apes

hominoid: any of a superfamily of primates; includes humans and apes

homologous structures: structures that have a common origin but not necessarily a common function

homozygous (hoh-moh-ZIGH-guhs): description of an organism that has an identical pair of alleles for a trait

hormone: chemical that travels throughout the bloodstream and affects the behavior of other cells

human chorionic gonadotropin (HCG): hormone produced by the cells' zygote that keeps the corpus luteum alive and preserves the uterine lining

Human Genome Project: worldwide scientific undertaking to identify the complete nucleotide sequence in human DNA

hybrid: offspring of parents with different characteristics

hybridization: mating of two organisms with dissimilar genetic characteristics

hydrostatic (high-droh-STAT-ihk) **skeleton**: skeletal system in which the muscles surround and are supported by a water-filled body cavity

hypha (HIGH-fuh; pl. **hyphae**, HIGH-fee): threadlike, branching filament that is the most basic structure in a fungus

hypothalamus (high-poh-THAL-uh-muhs): region of the brain that directly or indirectly controls the release of hormones from the pituitary gland

hypothesis; pl. **hypotheses**: possible explanation of, preliminary conclusion about, or guess at the solution to a problem

I

immunity: ability of the body to resist a specific pathogen

implantation: process during which the cells of a zygote grow into the uterine wall

imprinting: learning mechanism in the early life of an animal in which a stimulus establishes a characteristic behavior

impulse: electrical signal carried by neurons in the nervous system

inbreeding: mating of organisms with similar genetic characteristics

incomplete dominance: genetic condition in which neither allele is completely dominant or recessive

independent assortment: process by which different genes do not influence each other's segregation into gametes

infectious disease: disease caused by a pathogen

inflammatory response: activation of a nonspecific defense to a pathogen

inorganic compound: very generally, a compound that does not contain carbon chains

insight learning: application of past experience to a new situation

instinct: genetically programmed, innate behavior

insulin: polypeptide hormone that removes sugar from the bloodstream

internal fertilization: method of fertilization in which the eggs and sperm meet inside the body of the egg-producing individual

interneuron: neuron that connects the sensory and motor neurons and carries impulses between them

interphase: G_1, S, and G_2 phases; occurs between cell divisions

intracellular digestion: process by which food is digested inside the internal cells of a simple multicellular animal

intron: intervening sequence that is removed from mRNA and thus not expressed

ion: charged particle formed by an atom that has gained or lost one or more of its electrons

ionic bond: attraction between oppositely charged ions

iris: disk of tissue located at the back of the cornea

islets of Langerhans: clusters of endocrine cells in the pancreas

K

karyotype (KAR-ee-uh-tighp): diagrammatic representation of individual chromosomes cut out from a photograph and grouped together

keratin: tough, flexible structural protein found in hair, fingernails, and epidermis

kidney: one of a pair of specialized excretion organs that removes nitrogen and other nonsolid wastes from the body and regulates water in the bloodstream

killer T cell: type of lymphocyte in the immune system that attacks and destroys a virus-infected cell

kingdom: highest ranking classification of living organisms that falls into one of the six major groups

Koch's postulates: series of rules used to identify the microorganism that causes a specific disease

Krebs cycle: series of reactions in which the chemical bonds in pyruvic acid are broken apart; also called citric acid cycle

L

lactic acid fermentation: in animals, the conversion of pyruvic acid to lactic acid

large intestine: colon; part of the digestive system that produces a waste material known as feces

larynx: structure in which air enters the respiratory system and the vocal cords are located
lateral line: collection of skin pores that connect to a system of tubes that help a fish detect patterns of movement in the surrounding water
leaf: specific outgrowth of a vascular plant that captures sunlight for photosynthesis
learning: ability to change behavior as a result of experience; acquisition of knowledge or a skill
legume: fruit with a pod that splits open on two sides
lens: flexible structure behind the pupil filled with a transparent protein that helps adjust eyes to focus to see near or far objects
ligament: band of tissue that connects the bones of a joint
light-dependent reaction: response that requires the direct involvement of light; produces NADPH
light-independent reaction: response that does not directly involve light; *see also* Calvin cycle
lipid: waxy, fatty, or oily compound used to store and release energy; one of the classes of macromolecules
lipid bilayer: double-layered pattern formed by phospholipids in water; the principal component of cell membranes
liver: large gland situated above the stomach that produces bile to aid digestion
longitudinal muscle: in annelids, a muscle that runs along the length of the body, shortening the segments as it contracts
loop of Henle: region of the nephron of the kidney where concentrated urine is produced
lung: respiratory organ in which gas exchange takes place
lung cancer: disease caused by small groups of cancer in the lungs; usually the consequence of smoking
luteinizing hormone (LH): hormone secreted by the pituitary gland that stimulates testosterone production in males and the development of the follicle, ovulation, and production of the corpus luteum in females
lymph (LIHMF): fluid found in intracellular spaces and in the lymphatic vessels of vertebrates
lymphatic (lihm-FAT-ihk) **system**: network of vessels that collects fluid that leaks from the capillaries and returns it to the circulatory system
lymphocyte: white blood cell that produces antibodies to assist the immune system
lysogenic infection: process in which viral genes combine with the host cell's DNA, produce viral mRNA, and gradually make new viruses
lysosome: saclike membrane filled with chemicals and enzymes that can break down almost any substance within a cell
lysozyme: enzyme in saliva that fights infection by digesting the cell walls of bacteria
lytic infection: process in which viral enzymes destroy a host cell's DNA, ribosomes, and resources to reproduce

M

macromolecule: large organic polymer, such as a carbohydrate, lipid, protein, or nucleic acid
macronucleus: the larger of the two nuclei of a ciliate; stores multiple copies of commonly used genes
Malpighian (mal-PIHG-ee-uhn) **tubule**: structure that excretes nitrogenous wastes; found in many arthropods
mammary gland: gland that enables a female to nourish her young with milk
mandible: in arthropods, specialized mouthpart used for biting
mantle: thin, delicate layer of tissue that covers the internal organs of a mollusk
mated pair: male and female living together
medulla oblongata (mih-DUHL-uh ahb-lahn-GAHT-uh): part of the brainstem that regulates the flow of information between the brain and the rest of the body; controls involuntary functions
medusa: free-swimming stage in the life cycle of a cnidarian
meiosis (migh-OH-sihs): process of cell division that reduces the number of chromosomes in the cell by half, from diploid to haploid; creates gametes used for sexual reproduction
melanin: dark-brown pigment that gives skin its color
meninges (muh-NIHN-jeez): three layers of tough, elastic tissues that cushion the brain and spinal cord
menstrual cycle: pattern of events in females that involves the development and release of an egg

for fertilization and the preparation of the uterus to receive a fertilized egg

mesoderm: middle embryonic cell layer from which the skeletal, muscular, and other tissues are developed

mesoglea (mehs-oh-GLEE-uh): in cnidarians, the jellylike layer between the endoderm and ectoderm

messenger RNA (mRNA): form of RNA that carries genetic information from the DNA in the nucleus to the ribosomes in the cytoplasm

metamorphosis: process of changing form and shape

metaphase: second phase of mitosis during which the chromosomes complete their attachment to the spindle and line up across the center of the cell

microclimate: climate conditions of a particular area that vary over small distances

micronucleus: the smaller of the two nuclei of a ciliate; stores copies of all the cell's genes

mitochondrion; pl. **mitochondria**: an organelle found in the cells of most plants and animals; produces energy from a chemical fuel and oxygen

mitosis: process of cell division in eukaryotic cells

molar: tooth in the rear of the mouth adapted for grinding

molecular clock: theory that mutations in DNA occur at a constant rate; used to estimate time frames of departure from common ancestry

molecule: group of atoms united by covalent bonds

molting: process of shedding an exterior layer or exoskeleton to allow for renewal or growth

monocot: angiosperm that produces seeds with one cotyledon

monoculture: farming strategy whereby a single highly productive crop is planted in a large field

monomer: small, individual molecule that forms a polymer

morula (MOR-yoo-luh): solid ball of cells produced by cell division of a zygote

motor neuron: specialized neuron that carries impulses from the brain or spinal cord to muscles or other organs

mouth: opening through which food is taken in for digestion

multiple allele: type of gene that is determined by more than two alleles for a single trait

mutation: abrupt alteration in the genetic information of a cell

mutualism: reciprocal relationship in which two organisms benefit each other

mycelium (migh-SEE-lee-uhm): mass of hyphae that grows into the food source and forms the body of the fungus

myelin (MIGH-uh-lihn): material that forms a protective sheath around an axon; white fatty substance that surrounds many vertebrate nerve cells

myoglobin: reddish oxygen-storing protein found in skeletal muscles

myosin: protein that makes up the thick filaments of muscle fiber

N

natural selection: process in nature that over time results in the survival of the fittest

negative feedback: regulatory system that enables conditions within the body to remain constant

nematocyst: poisonous stinger used in cnidarians for defense and catching prey

nephridium (nee-FRIHD-ee-uhm; pl. **nephridia**, nee-FRIHD-ee-uh): excretory organ that removes nitrogen-containing wastes from the blood; found in many invertebrates

nephron: any of the numerous blood-filtering units of a kidney

nerve: bundle of nerve fibers

nerve cord: group of nerve cells that extend along the length of the body

nervous system: network of nerve cells and nervous tissue that receives and relays information about activities within the body and monitors and responds to internal and external changes

neuron: cell that carries impulses throughout the nervous system; consists of a cell body, dendrites, and an axon

neurotransmitter (NOO-roh-trans-miht-er): a chemical used by one neuron to signal another cell

neutron: subatomic particle that carries no charge

niche: full range of physical and biological conditions in which the organisms in a species can live and the way in which the organisms use those conditions

nictitating membrane: transparent eyelid that protects the eye underwater and keeps it moist in air

nonbiodegradable: incapable of being broken down into unharmful products by the life processes of living things

nondisjunction: failure of chromosome pair to separate correctly during meiosis

notochord: flexible, rodlike structure that provides body support; unique to chordates

nucleic acid: DNA or RNA that consists of nucleotides and genetic information

nucleotide: compound made of a phosphate group, a nitrogenous base, and a 5-carbon sugar; forms the basic structural unit of DNA

nucleus; pl. **nuclei**: in an atom, the compact core that contains the neutron and protons; in a cell, the structure that contains nearly all of the cell's DNA

nut: fruit with a hard ovary wall forming a protective shell around the seed

nutrient cycle: path along which nutrients that are available in fixed quantities on Earth are passed from one organism to another and from one part of the biosphere to another

O

ocellus (oh-SEHL-uhs; pl. **ocelli**, oh-SEHL-igh): simple eyespot that detects the presence or absence of light

olfactory bulb: part of the brain specialized for the sense of smell

open circulatory system: system in which blood is pumped from the heart through vessels and open spaces

operant conditioning: trial-and-error learning

operator: special region of DNA to which the repressor binds

operculum: bony structure that protects the gills; found in bony fishes

opiate: one of a group of drugs derived from the opium poppy; plant that mimics endorphins in the brain; often used as a pain-killing drug

optic lobe: structure in the brain that processes visual information

order: classification of several families of similar organisms

organ: group of tissues that work together to perform a specific function

organelle: small structure that performs a specialized function within a cell

organic compound: very generally, a substance that contains a chain of a least two carbon atoms

organism: individual living thing

organ system: group of organs that perform several closely related functions

osmosis: diffusion of water through a selectively permeable membrane

osteocyte (AHS-tee-oh-sight): cell embedded in both compact and spongy bone that helps build and maintain bones

ovary: in animals, the female reproductive gland that produces eggs and female hormones; in flowering plants, the structure that contains the egg cells of a flower

oviparous (oh-VIHP-uh-ruhs): producing eggs that develop and hatch outside the female's body

ovoviviparous (oh-voh-vigh-VIHP-uh-ruhs): producing eggs that develop and hatch within the female's body and are born alive

ovulation: process in which an egg is released from the ovary

ovule: in a seed plant, the place where female gametophytes are produced

ovum; pl. **ova**: female gamete or egg

oxytocin: pituitary hormone that stimulates contractions of the smooth muscles surrounding the uterus

P

pacemaker: area of the heart that regulates the heartbeat; the sinoatrial node

pancreas: gland situated below the stomach that produces digestive enzymes and regulates blood sugar

parasite: organism that takes nourishment from and lives at the expense of its host

passive transport: movement of substances across the cell membrane from regions of high concentration to regions of low concentration; occurs without the cell expending energy

pathogen: disease-causing organism

pedigree: diagram that tracks the inheritance of a single gene through several generations of a family

pedipalp: specialized leglike appendage of chelicerates that are used for grasping, sensing, and fertilizing

pepsin: protein-digesting enzyme produced by gastric glands in the stomach

peptic ulcer: lesion in the stomach wall caused by stomach acid

perennial: plant that lives for more than two years

periosteum (per-ee-AHS-tee-uhm): tough membrane that covers the bones

peristalsis: muscular contractions that pass food through the alimentary canal or digestive tract

petal: one of the white or colorful leaflike parts of a flower

phagocyte: white blood cell that engulfs and destroys bacteria

pharyngeal (fuh-RIHN-jee-uhl) **slit**: a narrow opening in the throat region of chordates

pharynx: muscular structure in the back of the mouth; connects the mouth with the rest of the digestive tract

phenotype: form of a genetic trait displayed by an organism

pheromone (FAIR-uh-mohn): chemical signal produced by an organism to influence the behavior or development of another organism of the same species

phloem (FLOH-ehm): vascular tissue that transports products of photosynthesis and substances from one part of the plant to another

photosynthesis: process by which green plants use the energy of sunlight to produce carbohydrates

phototropism: growth response of a plant to light, usually by turning toward or away from light

pH scale: measurement system that indicates the acidity or basicity of a solution

phylum (FIGH-luhm; pl. **phyla**, FIGH-luh): category made up of several classes of different organisms that share important characteristics

phytochrome: red-light-sensitive pigment that enables plants to sense day and night, changing seasons, and developmental processes

pigment: colored substances that reflect or absorb light

pistil: female reproductive organ of a flowering plant, composed of ovary, style, and stigma

pith: in dicots, the ground tissue inside the ring of a vascular bundle

pituitary gland: tiny endocrine gland at the base of the brain that secretes hormones that regulate the activity of other endocrine glands

placenta: organ that connects a mother with her developing embryo and provides a place for the exchange of nutrients, oxygen, wastes, and carbon dioxide

plasma: fluid part of the blood; constitutes about 55 percent of the total volume of blood

plasma cell: specialized B cell that releases antibodies into the bloodstream to fight infection

plasmid: small, circular DNA molecule in some bacteria that can be used for cell transformation

platelet: cell fragments in the blood that aid in blood clotting

point mutation: gene mutation that involves a single nucleotide

pollen: tiny spore that contains the male reproductive cells of a plant

pollination: transfer of pollen that precedes fertilization

polygenic trait: inherited characteristic controlled by more than one gene

polymer: large molecule assembled from small, individual molecules

polyp: sessile stage in the life cycle of a cnidarian

pons: region of connecting tissue at the base of the brainstem

population: group of organisms of a single species that live in a given area

powder feather: feather in aquatic birds that releases a water-repelling powder

premolar: teeth directly in front of the molar teeth

primary producer: organism that uses energy from the sun to change simple nonliving chemical nutrients in its environment into living tissue

progesterone: female hormone that promotes development of the uterine wall

proglottid (proh-GLAHT-ihd): segment of a tapeworm's body that contains reproductive structures

prokaryote: organism that does not contain nuclei; typically is small and single celled

prolactin: pituitary hormone that stimulates the production of milk in the breast tissue of the mother

promoter: special region of DNA to which RNA polymerase binds at the beginning of the process of transcription

prophase: first phase of mitosis during which each chromosome consists of two chromatids

prosimian (proh-SIHM-ee-uhn): any of a suborder of primates

protein: polymer of amino acids used for building cells, catalyzing reactions, and other purposes

protist: eukaryotic organism that does not share a unique set of characteristics

proton: subatomic particle that carries a positive charge

protonema (proht-oh-NEE-muh): tangle of thin filaments germinating from a moss spore and developing into a leafy moss plant

provirus: viral DNA that has become part of the host cell's DNA

pseudopod (SOO-doh-pahd): temporary projection from an ameboid cell used for movement and feeding; cytoplasm streams into the pseudopod and the rest of the cell follows

pulmonary circulation: pathway of blood vessels on the right side of the heart that carries blood between the heart and lungs

punctuated equilibrium: pattern of long periods of stability that are interrupted by episodes of rapid change

pupil: opening in the iris that regulates the amount of light that enters the eye

R

radial symmetry: arrangement of body parts that repeat around an imaginary line drawn through the center of an organism; shown in cnidarians and some adult echinoderms

radula (RAJ-oo-luh): the feeding structure in the mouth of many mollusks

reabsorption: process by which the material that was removed from the blood is put back into the blood without the toxic compounds

receptor: specific chemical binding site for a particular hormone

recessive: form of gene that is not expressed in the presence of the dominant form; represented with a lowercase letter

recombinant DNA: pieces of DNA from two or more sources that are reassembled to act as a single DNA molecule

red blood cell: blood cell that contains hemoglobin and constitutes almost half the total volume of blood; also called an erythrocyte

reflex: quick, automatic response to a stimulus

renal artery: artery through which blood flows into the kidney

renal vein: vein through which blood leaves the kidney

repressor: protein that blocks a gene's transcription by binding to the operator

reproductive isolation: separation of different species that cannot interbreed

respiration: release of energy from the breakdown of food molecules in the presence of oxygen

resting potential: product of a net excess of negative charges on the inside of the membrane

restriction enzyme: protein that cuts DNA at a specific sequence of nucleotides

retina: layer of cells at the back of the eye

retrovirus: virus containing an enzyme that copies its genetic information from RNA to DNA

RFLP (RIHF-lihp) **(restriction fragment length polymorphism)**: dark band revealed when pieces of DNA are probed; can be used to identify and classify an individual's unique DNA pattern

rhizoid (RIGH-zoid): rootlike anchoring structure of moss plants that absorbs water and nutrients from the soil

rhizome: underground stem of a vascular plant

ribosomal RNA (rRNA): form of RNA that is an important component of ribosomes

ribosome: small particles in a cell that are made of RNA and protein; sites of protein assembly

ring vessel: in an anneid, structure that pumps blood, thus functioning as a miniature heart

RNA (ribonucleic acid): principal molecule that carries out the instructions coded in DNA

root: descending structure of a plant that branches into the soil, anchors the plant, and absorbs water and nutrients

S

salivary gland: gland in the mouth that produces saliva, a fluid that moistens food and makes food easier to chew

scale: in fish, one of many overlapping rigid plates that form a protective covering; in seed-bearing plants, the surface of a reproductive structure on which the seeds are exposed

scanning probe microscope: microscope that traces the surface of a sample with a small tip called a probe

science: process of thinking and learning about the world

scientific method: system of asking questions, developing explanations, and testing those explanations against the reality of the natural world

scolex (SKOH-lehks): front end of a tapeworm; contains suckers and hooks

scrotum: sac located outside a male's body cavity that contains the testes

sedimentary rock: kind of rock formed when silt, sand, or clay builds up on the bottom of a river, lake, or ocean

seed: reproductive structure that includes a developing plant and a food reserve enclosed in a resistant outer covering

seed cone: female cone that contains mature seeds

segment: one of several body compartments that allows an animal to increase in body size with minimal new genetic material

segregation: process that separates the two alleles of a gene during gamete formation

selective breeding: producing a new generation by mating individuals with desired characteristics

semicircular canal: one of three fluid-filled organs that help sense position in space and maintain balance

seminiferous (sehm-uh-NIHF-er-uhs) **tubule**: tightly coiled tubules in males in which sperm cells are produced

sensory neuron: specialized neuron that carries impulses from the sense organs to the brain and the spinal cord

sepal: structure that encloses and protects the developing flower bud and opens as the flower blooms

septum; pl. **septa**: dividing wall or membrane

seta; pl. **setae**: external bristles

sex chromosome: X and Y chromosomes that determine the sex of an individual

sex-linked gene: gene located on the sex chromosome

sexually transmitted disease (STD): disease spread from one person to another by sexual contact

shell: in mollusks, protective structure formed by glands in the mantle

siphon: tube through which water is forced out

skeletal muscle tissue: muscle tissue generally attached to bones; can be contracted voluntarily

skin: outer protective covering of the body; largest organ of the body

sliding filament theory: concept that thick and thin filaments slide past each other and cause the muscle to contract

slightly movable joint: joining place of two bones where there is a small amount of movement and flexibility, such as in the spinal column or ribs

small intestine: portion of the digestive tract in which most of the chemical work of digestion takes place

smooth muscle tissue: spindle-shaped, unstriated muscle tissue found in internal organs and blood vessels; not under conscious control of the nervous system

social insect colony: highly structured living group performing tasks that no single insect could accomplish

sodium-potassium pump: protein in nerve cell that moves sodium ions out of the cell and potassium ions into the cell

solution: uniform mixture of substances

somatic nervous system: part of the motor division of the peripheral nervous system that controls voluntary movements

speciation: formation of a new species brought about by genetic changes that prevent breeding between the new, genetically different groups

species: smallest group in the classification system of organisms that share similar characteristics and interbreed in nature

species diversity: number and variety of different life forms

sperm: male gamete

spicule: one of many small, spikelike structures that form the skeleton of a sponge

spinal cord: collection of nerve fibers that extends from the brain; part of the central nervous system of a vertebrate

spindle: cluster of microtubules that span the cell nucleus

spirillum (spigh-RIHL-uhm; pl. **spirilla**, spigh-RIHL-uh): spiral-shaped bacteria

spongin: protein that makes up the tough but flexible skeleton of some sponges

spongy bone: region of resilient, supportive bone tissue within the compact bone with an interlaced pattern that withstands stress

spore: small, typically single-celled structure capable of producing a new individual, either immediately or after a period of dormancy

sporophyte: in plants, the diploid spore-bearing generation that reproduces by spores

stamen: male leaf that produces pollen

statocyst: organ of balance found in many invertebrates

stem: main, upward-growing part of a vascular plant that provides support and conducts water and nutrients

stereoisomer: molecule that has the same atoms and bonds of another molecule but has atoms oriented differently in space

stigma: sticky tip of the style of a plant

stimulant: any one of a group of drugs that increase the release of neurotransmitters at some synapses in the brain to speed up the nervous system

stoma (STOH-muh; pl. **stomata**, STOH-muh-tuh): in the epidermis of a plant, one of many small openings that can open and close to allow gas exchange and to prevent water loss

stomach: large muscular sac where contractions mix food and enzymes and acids digest food

style: in a flower plant, the stemlike narrow part of the carpel

substrate: in a chemical reaction, the component that binds to an enzyme

superorganism: colony of interdependent organisms that act as a unit, able to achieve far more than individuals acting separately

suppressor T cell: type of lymphocyte in the immune system that shuts off the immune response in killer T cells and in B cells

sustainability: degree to which a human activity is in harmony with the biosphere and does not deteriorate the biosphere's living and nonliving parts

swim bladder: expandable structure that holds gas to change a fish's internal density and depth in the water

symbiosis (sihm-bigh-OH-sihs): beneficial relationship between two organisms that live together

synapse (SIHN-aps): place where a neuron can transfer an impulse to another cell

synovial (sih-NOH-vee-uhl) **fluid**: lubricant found in a joint that reduces friction and allows bones to slip past each other easily

syphilis: sexually transmitted disease caused by a bacterium that can result in death

systemic circulation: pathway of blood vessels on the left side of the heart that supplies the body with oxygen-rich blood and returns oxygen-poor blood to the heart

T

target cell: cell that has a receptor for a particular hormone

taste bud: one of many chemical receptors located on the tongue

taxonomy: science of naming organisms and assigning them to groups

T cell: white blood cell that matures in the thymus gland and regulates other cells of the immune system

telophase: fourth and final phase of mitosis during which two distinct nuclei form within the cell

tendon: cord of tissue that connects muscles and bones

testis (TEHS-tihs; pl. **testes**, TEHS-teez): male reproductive gland that produces sperm and male hormones

testosterone (tehs-TAHS-ter-ohn): male hormone produced in the testes that stimulates sperm production and the development of male sex organs and secondary sex characteristics

tetrapod: body plan that includes four limbs or legs

theory: logical explanation for a broad range of observations

thigmotropism (thihg-MAH-truh-pihz-uhm): response to touch

thyroid gland: an endocrine gland that produces the hormone thyroxine

tissue: mass of similar cells that performs a specific function

toxin: poisonous substance

trachea: tube that carries air from the larynx to the lungs; also called the windpipe

tracheal (TRAY-kee-uhl) **tube**: air-conducting passage for the diffusion of oxygen

tracheid (TRAY-kee-ihd): specialized water-conducting thick-walled tubelike cell of a vascular plant

trait: inherited characteristic that distinguishes one organism from another

transcription: process in which the nucleotide sequence of a DNA molecule is copied into RNA

transfer RNA (tRNA): form of RNA that carries an amino acid to the ribosome during the assembly of a protein

transformation: process of reproduction in which genetic material is added to or replaces portions of a bacteria's DNA

transgenic: description of an organism that has been transformed or altered with genes from another organism

translation: process by which the nucleotides in mRNA are decoded into a sequence of amino acids in a polypeptide

transpiration: loss of water vapor though the stomata of a vascular plant

trichocyst: tiny bottle-shaped structure embedded in the pellicle of a paramecium and discharged for purposes of defense

trisomy: condition caused by cells that contain three copies of a chromosome rather than two

trochophore (TRAHK-oh-for): free-swimming larva stage of a mollusk

trophic level: feeding level in the flow of food energy and nutrients from primary producers to highest level consumers

tropism: response of an organism to an environmental stimulus

tube foot: suction-cuplike structure connected to the water vascular system of an echinoderm

tumor: mass of cells

tympanic membrane: portion of the ear that vibrates in response to sound; eardrum

tympanum: eardrum

U

umbilical cord: thin tube of embryonic tissue that connects the embryo to the uterus

ureter: vessel that carries urine from the kidney to the urinary bladder

urinary bladder: sac that stores urine before it is eliminated from the body

uterus: muscular chamber in a female's reproductive system in which a fertilized egg can develop

V

vaccine: weakened or mild form of a pathogen that causes permanent immunity when injected into the body

vacuole: saclike structure in a cell that stores materials—such as proteins, fats, and carbohydrates—in animal cells, and water and dissolved salts in plant cells

valve: specialized flap of tissue that prevents a backflow of blood

variable: factor that differs among test groups in an experiment and is measured against a control

vascular cylinder: central region of xylem and phloem cells carrying water and nutrients between the roots and the rest of the plant

vascular plant: plant with tracheids that draw water upward

vascular tissue: specialized tissue that transports water and nutrients throughout a land plant

vas deferens (VAS DEHF-uh-rehnz): duct that extends from the scrotum to the ejaculatory duct

vector: animal that carries a disease-causing organism from host to host

vector pollination: spread of pollen from one plant to another by an insect or animal

vegetative reproduction: process of asexual reproduction in which offspring are produced from the division of cells of the parent plant

vein: blood vessel that returns blood to the heart

ventricle: lower chamber of the heart that pumps the blood out of the heart

vertebra; pl. **vertebrae:** any of the individual segments of bone that make up the backbone, or vertebral column

vertebral column: backbone that encloses and protects the spinal cord

vestigial organ: structure in an organism that seems to have little or no obvious purpose

villus; pl., **villi:** any of the numerous projections on the folded surfaces of the small intestine that increase the surface area for the absorption of food molecules

virus: nonliving particle that contains DNA or RNA and that can infect a living cell

vitreous (VIH-tree-uhs) **humor:** transparent fluid that fills the large chamber behind the lens of the eye

viviparous (vigh-VIHP-er-uhs): retaining the developing embryo inside the female's body and bearing offspring alive

vocal cord: elastic fold of tissue that vibrates and produces sound when exhaled air is passed by it

voltage-sensitive gate: one of thousands of tiny protein channels in the cell membrane of a neuron through which sodium or potassium passes

W

water vascular system: in echinoderms, a network of fluid-filled tubes and appendages, used for many purposes

white blood cell: blood cell that fights infection, parasites, and bacterial disease; also called a leukocyte

X

xylem (ZIGH-luhm): vascular tissue that carries water and nutrients from the roots to the branches and leaves of a plant

Z

zero population growth: lack of population growth due to equality of a population's birth rate and death rate

zoospore (ZOH-oh-spor): reproductive cell that produces a new individual by cell division

zygote (ZIGH-goht): fertilized egg

Index

A

B

C

D

E

F

G

H

I

J

K

L

M

N

O

P

Q

R

S

T

U

Credits

Photo Research: Natalie Goldstein

Photo Credits

Cover Frans Lanting/Minden Pictures, Inc.; Borders Corel Professional Photos CD-ROM™; **iv** t; Patricia Agre/Photo Researchers, Inc.; **iv** c; David Scharf/Peter Arnold, Inc.; **iv** bl; ©Philippe Plailly/Science Photo Library/Photo Researchers, Inc.; **iv** br; Leonard Lessin/Peter Arnold, Inc.; **v** t; Corel Professional Photos CD-ROM™; **v** bl; ©Alfred Pasieka/Scince Photo Library/Photo Researchers, Inc.; **v** br; Rich Cane/Sports Chrome East/West ; **vi** tl; Corel Professional Photos CD-ROM™; **vi** t;r; Corel Professional Photos CD-ROM™; **vi** bl; Corbis-Bettmann; **vi** br; Corel Professional Photos CD-ROM™; **vii** t; ©Biophoto Associates/Photo Researchers, Inc.; **vii** c; Dr. Dennis Kenkel/Phototake; **vii** b; Gopal Morti/CNRI/Phototake; **viii** tr; K. G. Murti/Visuals Unlimited; **viii** cl; ©Oliver Meckes/Photo Researchers, Inc.; **viii** cr; ©Michael Fairchild/Peter Arnold, Inc.; **viii** b; Corel Professional Photos CD-ROM™; **ix** tl; Tui De Roy/Bruce Coleman, Inc.; **ix** tr; Frans Lanting/Minden Pictures, Inc.; **ix** bl; Gerard Lacz/Peter Arnold, Inc.; **ix** br; Corel Professional Photos CD-ROM™; **x** t; Corel Professional Photos CD-ROM™; **x** bl; Dan Budnik/Woodfin Camp & Associates; **x** br; Michael Fogden/DRK Photo; **xi** tl; Art Wolfe Incorporated; **xi** tr; Lionel Isy Schwart/The Image Bank; **xi** c; D. Cavagnaro/DRK Photo; **xi** b; Bullaty/Lomeo/The Image Bank; **xii** tl; ©Holt Studios International (Miss P. Peackock)/Photo Researchers, Inc.; **xii** tr; T.E. Adams/Visuals Unlimited; **xii** bl; David M. Phillips/Visuals Unlimited; **xii** b; r; ©Phil A. Dotson/Photo Researchers, Inc.; **xiii** tl; Visuals Unlimited; **xiii** tr; Larry Lipsky/DRK Photo; **xiii** c; Corel Professional Photos CD-ROM™; **xiii** b; Frans Lanting/Minden Pictures, Inc.; **xiv** tl; ©David Scharf/Peter Arnold, Inc.; **xiv** tr; Arthur J. Olson, The Scripps Research Institute, La Jolla, California, Copyr; 1988; **xiv** c; David Phillips/Visuals Unlimited; **xiv** b; ©Roger HartRainbow; **xv** t; Jeff Foot/DRK Photo; **xv** c; Robert & Linda Mitchell Photography; **xv** b; D. Cavagnaro/DRK Photo; **xvi** tl; Jeffrey L. Rotman; **xvi** tr; ©Jackie Lewin, EM Unit Royal Free Hospital/Science Photo Library/Photo Researchers, Inc.; **xvi** bl; Larry Lipsky/DRK Photo; **xvi** br; ©Photo Researchers, Inc.; **xvii** tl; photographer/DRK Photo; **xvii** tr; Art Wolfe Incorporated; **xvii** bl; ©Andrew Syred/Science Photo Library/Photo Researchers, Inc.; **xvii** br; S. Nielsen/DRK Photo; **xviii** t; ©Sophie de Wilde Jacana/Jacana Scientific Control/Photo Researchers, Inc.; **xviii** c; Runk/Schoenberger/Grant Heilman Photography; **xviii** bl; Martim Harvey/The Wildlife Collection; **xix** t; John Callanan/The Image Bank; **xix** c; Johnny Johnson/DRK Photo; **xix** bl; Mark Moffett/Minden Pictures, Inc.; **xix** br; Art Wolfe Incorporated; **xx** tl; ©Professors P.M. Motta and S. Correr/Science Photo Library/Photo Researchers, Inc.; **xx** tr; Rob Tringali, Jr./Sports Chrome East/West ; **xx** c; GJLP/CNRI/Phototake; **xx** b; ©Dr. Morley Read/Science Photo Library/Photo Researchers, Inc.; **xxi** tl; Paul J. Sutton/Duomo Photography, Inc.; **xxi** tr; ©Prof. P. Motta/Dept. of Anatomy/ University "La Sapienza", Rome/Science Photo Library/Photo Researchers, Inc.; **xxi** c; ©Prof. Arnold Brody/Science Photo Library/Photo Researchers, Inc.; **xxi** b; David Phillips/Visuals Unlimited; **xxii** tl; William Sallaz/The Image Bank; **xxii** tr; Lennart Nilsson ©Boehringer Ingelheim International GmbH; **xxii** c; ©Professors P.M. Motta and J. Van Blerkom/Science Photo Library/Photo Researchers, Inc.; **xxii** b; Electra/Phototake; **xxiii** t; ©Don Fawcett/Photo Researchers, Inc.; **xxiii** cr; ©Lennart Nilsson, THE INCREDIBLE MACHINE; **xxiii** cl; ©Boehringer Ingelheim International GmbH, Photo by Lennart Nilsson, THE INCREDIBLE MACHINE; **xxiii** b; ©Boehringer Ingelheim International GmbH, Photo by Lennart Nilsson; **1** Stephen Wilkes/The Image Bank; **2** Thomas D. Mangelsen/Peter Arnold, Inc.; **3** t; Jeff Hunter/The Image Bank; c; Johnny Johnson/Animals Animals/Earth Scenes; b; C & M Denis-Huot/C & M Denis-Huot; **4** l; David Scharf/Peter Arnold, Inc.; r; Jim Brandenburg/Minden Pictures, Inc.; **5** tl; Robert & Linda Mitchell Photography; tc; Dwight Kuhn Photography; tr; Luiz C. Marigo/Peter Arnold, Inc.; c; Frans Lanting/Minden Pictures, Inc.; bl; Tom and Pat Leeson/DRK Photo; br; A. Cosmos Blank/Photo Researchers, Inc.; **6** t; Vic Verlinder/The Image Bank; b; ©Norbert Wu; **7** Corel Professional Photos CD-ROM™; **8** MC. Chamberlain/DRK Photo; **9** t; David Scharf/Peter Arnold, Inc.; c; Corel Professional Photos CD-ROM™; b; David Scharf/Peter Arnold, Inc.; **10** NASA; **11** l; Photo Researchers, Inc.; r; Frans Lanting/Minden Pictures, Inc.; **13** l; Patricia Agre/Photo Researchers, Inc.; r; F. Ruggeri/The Image Bank; **15** l; Coco McCoy/Rainbow; c; Penny Tweedie/Woodfin Camp & Associates; r; Bios (Klein-Hubert)/Peter Arnold, Inc.; **16** l; D. Cornwell/The Granger Collection Ltd.; r; Courtesy National Archives; **19** l; Robert Frerck/Woodfin Camp & Associates; r; USDA/Science Source/Photo Researchers, Inc.; **24** Thomas D. Mangelsen/Peter Arnold, Inc.; **26** ©Philippe Plailly/Science Photo Library/Photo Researchers, Inc.; **27** t; Corel Professional Photos CD-ROM™; b; Harald Sund/The Image Bank; **30** t; ©Hermann Eisenbeiss/Photo Researchers, Inc.; b; ©Jerry Mason/Science Photo Library/Photo Researchers, Inc.; **31** ©Will and Deni McIntyre/Photo Researchers, Inc.; **33** Michael Fogden/DRK Photo; inset; Joe Van Os/The Image Bank; **35** David Young-Wolff/PhotoEdit; **36** Leonard Lessin/Peter Arnold, Inc.; **37** t; Peter L. Chapman/Stock, Boston ; b; ICM Production/The Image Bank; **38** ©Bachmann/Photo Researchers, Inc.; **39** ©Leonard Lessin/Peter Arnold, Inc.; **40** © Tom & Pat Leeson; **46** Joe Van Os/The Image Bank; **48** ©Cecil Fox/Science SourcePhoto Researchers, Inc.; **49** l; The Bettmann Archive; c; ©Leonard Lessin/Peter Arnold, Inc.; r; Corbis-Bettmann; **50** tl; Corel Professional Photos CD-ROM™; b; ©Mark Burnett/Photo Researchers, Inc.; b inset; George J. Wilder/Visuals Unlimited; tr; Joe Devenney/The Image Bank; **52** tl; ©CNRI/Science Photo Library/Photo Researchers, Inc.; tr; ©Manfred Kage/Peter Arnold, Inc.; b; ©Philippe Plailly/Science Photo LibraryPhoto Researchers, Inc.; **53** l; ©Manfred Kage/Peter Arnold, Inc.; r; ©Manfred Kage/Peter Arnold, Inc.; **54** Antonio M. Rosario/The Image Bank; **55** t; ©Dan McCoy/Rainbow; b; Paul Silverman/Fundamental Photographs; **57** t; Dr. Dennis Kunkel/Phototake; c; Dr. Dennis Kunkel/Phototake; b; Dr. Dennis Kenkel/Phototake; **58** t; Visuals Unlimited/David M. Phillips; b; ©Andrew McClenaghan/Science Photo Library/Photo Researchers, Inc.; **59** ©Dr. Arnold Brody/Science Photo Library/Photo Researchers, Inc.; **60** t; M. Eichelberger/Visuals Unlimited; b; Michael Abramson/Woodfin Camp & Associates; **61** ©Ed Reschke/Peter Arnold, Inc.; **63** tl; ©Don Fawcett/Science Source/Photo Researchers, Inc.; tr; ©Biophoto Assoc./Science SourcePhoto Researchers, Inc.; b; Don W. Fawcett/Visuals Unlimited; **64** ©Dr. Gopal Hurti/Science Photo Library/Photo Researchers, Inc.; **65** t; K.R. Porter/Photo Researchers, Inc.; b; ©Biophoto Association/Science SourcePhoto Researchers, Inc.; **66** l; ©Dan McCoy/Rainbow; c; James Dennis/CNRI/Phototake; r; ©Don W. Fawcett/Rainbow; **72** Dr. Gopal Hurti/Science Photo Library/Photo Researchers, Inc.; **73** David M. Phillips/Visuals Unlimited; **74** Lindsay Hebberd/Woodfin Camp & Associates; **75** t; F. M. Whitney/The Image Bank; b; Corel Professional Photos CD-ROM™; **77** l; Runk/Scoenberger/Grant Heilman Photography; r; ©Alfred Pasieka/Science Photo Library/Photo Researchers, Inc.; **78** The Image Bank; inset; Ross M. Horowitz/The Image Bank; **79** t; Rich Cane/Sports Chrome East/West; b; Alan PitcairnGrant Heilman Photography; **81** l; Richard Jackson/RO-MA Stock©; r; Flip Nicklin/Minden Pictures, Inc.; **85** t; Kuhn, Inc./The Image Bank; b; Martin Rogers/Stock, Boston; **86** l; ©Biophoto Assoc./Photo Researchers, Inc.; r; C. Bradley Simmons/Bruce Coleman, Inc.; **92** ©Photo Researchers, Inc.; **94** t; Alan Pitcairn/Grant Heilman Photography; b; David M. Phillips/Visuals Unlimited; **98** Runk/Scoenberger/Grant Heilman Photography; **99** Corel Professional Photos CD-ROM™; **100** K.G. Murti/Visuals Unlimited; **101** t; ©Clay Myers/Photo Researchers, Inc.; c; ©Tim Davis/Photo Researchers, Inc.; b; ©Photo Researchers, Inc.; **105** l; David M. Phillips/Visuals Unlimited; r; R. Celentine/Visuals Unlimited; **106** Lennart Nilsson/Bonnier Alba; **108** t; ©Dr. Gopal Murti/Photo Researchers, Inc.; b; R. Calentine/Visuals Unlimited; **109** l; ©CNRI/Science Phtoto Library/Photo Researchers, Inc.; r; Lennart Nilsson/Bonnier Alba; **111** ©Dr. Brain Eyden/Science Photo LibraryPhoto Researchers, Inc.; **112** t; Corel Professional Photos CD-ROM™; bl; ©Hans Pfletschinger/Peter Arnold, Inc.; br; ©Hans Pfletschinger/Peter Arnold, Inc.; **113** ©Will and Deni McIntyre/Science Source/Photo Researchers, Inc.; **114** Corel Professional Photos CD-ROM™; **117** ©Dr. Gopal Murti/Photo Researchers, Inc.; **118** David M. Phillips/Visuals Unlimited; **119** Corel Professional Photos CD-ROM™; **121** ©The Stock Market/William Roy; **122** ©Archive Photos/Lambert Photography, 1993/PNI; **123** l; John Eastcott/Yva Momatiuk/DRK Photo; c; Johnny Johnson/DRK Photo; r; ©Bill BacHman/Photo Researchers, Inc.; **124** t; ©Tom and Pat Leeson/Photo Researchers, Inc.; b; Corbis-Bettmann; b inset; Larry Lefever/Grant Heilman Photography; **125** ©Philippe Plailly/Science Photo LibraryPhoto Researchers, Inc.; **131** l; Corel Professional Photos CD-ROM™; r; ©David M. Phillips/Photo Researchers, Inc.; **135** l; Cliff Riedinger/Natural Selection Stock Photography, Inc.; r; Al Hamdan/The Image Bank; **138** l; ©IFA/Peter Arnold, Inc.; r; Corel Professional Photos CD-ROM™; **139** bl; Hans Reinhard/Bruce Coleman, Inc.; br; Larry Lefever/Grant Heilman Photography; **144** ©Jerome Wexler/Photo Researchers, Inc.; **146** Chip Henderson/Tony Stone Images; **147** l; Runk/Schoenberger/Grant Heilman Photography; r; ©Oliver Meckes/Photo Researchers, Inc.; **148** l; ©Martin Cooper/Peter Arnold, Inc.; r; ©CNRI/Science Photo Library/Photo Researchers, Inc.; **150** ©Ed Reschke/Peter Arnold, Inc.; **151** l; Carnegie Institution of Washington; r; ©Stephen Collins/National Audobon Society/Photo Researchers, Inc.; **153** ©Biophoto Associates/Photo Researchers, Inc.; **154** ©Gunn & Stewart/Mary EvansPhoto Researchers, Inc.; **155** l; Dr. Dennis Kunkel/Phototake; r; Stanley Flegler/Visuals Unlimited; **156** ©Reinhard Kunkel/Peter Arnold, Inc.; **158** l; Kunkel/Phototake; r; A. Berliner/Liaison International; **160** t; Cabisco/Visuals Unlimited; b; ©Robert Maier/Animals Animals; **161** ©Will & Deni McIntyre/Photo Researchers, Inc.; **162** ©Applied Biosystems/Peter Arnold, Inc.; **165** FBI; **168** ©Biophoto Associates/Photo Researchers, Inc.; **170** ©Kenneth Eward/BioGrafx—Science SourcePhoto Researchers, Inc.; **171** tl; Ian Yedmans/Woodfin Camp & Associates; tr; ©Dr. Gopal Murti/Science Photo LibraryPhoto Researchers, Inc.; b; Lynn Saville; **173** Cold Spring Harbor Laboratory; **175** ©R. Langridge/D. McCoy/Rainbow; **176** l; Cold Spring Harbor Laboratory; r; ©Science SourcePhoto Researchers, Inc.; **177** The Hulton-Deutsch Collection/Woodfin Camp & Associates; **178** t; ©James Holmes/Cellmark Diagnostic/Science Photo Library/Photo Researchers, Inc.; b; Superstock; **181** l; National Museum of American History, Smithsonian Institution; c; Professor Oscar Miller/Science Photo Library/Photo Researchers, Inc.; r; ©Ken Eward/Biografx/Photo Researchers, Inc.; **187** l; Larry Lefever/Grant Heilman Photography; r; Gopal Morti/CNRI/Phototake; **194** Claude Revy, Jean/Phototake; **196** ©Mitsuaki Iwago/Photo Researchers, Inc.; **197** t; Photograph courtesy of Appaloosa Museum & Heritage C, Moscow, ID; b; ©Fritz Prenzel/Peter Arnold, Inc.; **198** Corbis-Bettman; **201** l; ©Philippe Plailly/Science Photo Library/Photo Researchers, Inc.; **201** r; ©Matt Meadows/Peter Arnold, Inc.; **203** K. G. Murti/Visuals Unlimited; **204** ©Leonard Lessin/Peter Arnold, Inc.; **205** l; Wackson Lab/Visuals Unlimited; r; Museum of Israel/Jerusalem/Giraudon, Paris, Superstock; **206** Keith Wood/Visuals Unlimited; **207** l; Gerard R. Lazo; r; Stewart Cohen/Tony Stone Images; **208** Grant Heilman Photography; **209** ©Philippe Plailly/Science Photo Library/Photo Researchers, Inc.; **214** Wackson Lab/Visuals Unlimited; **215** ©Fritz Prenzel/Peter Arnold, Inc.; **217** Henry Holdsworth/Minden Pictures, Inc.; **218** Frans Lanting/Minden Pictures, Inc.; **219** l; N. H. (Dan) Cheatham/DRK Photo; rt; Clyde H. Smith/Peter Arnold, Inc.; rb; ©Oliver Meckes/Photo Researchers, Inc.; **220** Charles Darwin Museum, Down

House & The Royal College of Surgeons; **221** tl; Syndics of Cambridge University Library; tr; Joe McDonald/Bruce Coleman, Inc./PNI; b; ©Fritz Polking/Peter Arnold, Inc.; **222** Barbara Gerlach/DRK Photo; **224** t; ©Jeffrey L. Rotman/Peter Arnold, Inc.; bl; ©Soames Summerhays/Photo Researchers, Inc.; br; Carr Clifton/Minden Pictures, Inc.; **225** l; Stanley Breeden/DRK Photo; r; T. Wiewandt /DRK Photo; **226** l; Frans Lanting/Minden Pictures, Inc.; r; Frans Lanting/Minden Pictures, Inc.; inset; David Cavagnaro/DRK Photo; **227** Derek Witty; **228** l; Lewis Kemper/DRK Photo; r; Frans Lanting/Minden Pictures, Inc.; **230** l; Runk/Schoenberger/Grant Heilman Photography; r; ©M.E. Warren/Photo Researchers, Inc.; **231** l; ©Biophoto Associates/Photo Researchers, Inc.; r; ©David M. Phillips/Science Source/Photo Researchers, Inc.; **232** t; Robert & Linda Mitchell Photography; c; ©Michael Fairchild/Peter Arnold, Inc.; b; Mitsuaki Iwago/Minden Pictures, Inc.; **233** Breck P. Kent; **234** Robert & Linda Mitchell Photography; **235** t; Runk/Schoenberger/Grant Heilman Photography; b; Breck P. Kent; **236** Corel Professional Photos CD-ROM™; **238** Corel Professional Photos CD-ROM™; **239** Robert & Linda Mitchell Photography; **240** Mark Moffett/Minden Pictures, Inc.; **241** t; Jeremy Woodhouse/DRK Photo; bl; Benn Mitchell/The Image Bank; br; S. Nielsen/DRK Photo; **242** l; Frans Lanting/Minden Pictures, Inc.; rt; Perry Conway/Corbis; rb; Ron Kimball Studios; **246** tr; Darell Gulin/DRK Photo; tl; Tom Bean/DRK Photo; b; Dietrich Gehring/DRK Photo; **249** ©Hank Morgan/Rainbow; **253** tl; Tui De Roy/Bruce Coleman, Inc.; tr; Tui De Roy/Bruce Coleman, Inc.; bl; Tui De Roy/Bruce Coleman, Inc.; br; Norman Owen Tomalin/Bruce Coleman, Inc.; **260** Darell Gulin/DRK Photo; **261** Corel Professional Photos CD-ROM™; **262** ©The Stock Market/ZEFA Germany; **263** tl; Corel Professional Photos CD-ROM™; tr; Corel Professional Photos CD-ROM™; b; Corel Professional Photos CD-ROM™; **265** l; Corel Professional Photos CD-ROM™; c; ©Stephen Dalton/Photo Researchers, Inc.; r; Robert & Linda Mitchell Photography; **268** l; Corel Professional Photos CD-ROM™; c; Art Wolfe Incorporated; r; ©M.I. Waler/Science SourcePhoto Researchers, Inc.; **269** Wolfgang Kaehler; **271** l; D. Cavagnaro/DRK Photo; c; G. Prance/Visuals Unlimited; r; Robert Burke; **272** t; ©Ken Edward/Science Source/Photo Researchers, Inc.; b; Jeff Spielman/The Image Bank; **274** ©Ken Edward/Science SourcePhoto Researchers, Inc.; **278** Frans Lanting/Minden Pictures, Inc.; **279** Tim Laman/The Wildlife Collection; **281** Charles Gurche/The Wildlife Collection; **282** Holt Studios International (Nigel Cattlin)/Photo Researchers, Inc.; **283** t; Art Wolfe/Art Wolfe Incorporated; bl; New England Aquarium/Paul Erickson/Animals Animals/Earth Scenes; br; Breck P. Kent; **286** l; Earth Satellite Corporation/Science Photo Library/Photo Researchers, Inc.; r; ©Mark Burnett/Photo Researchers, Inc.; **287** tl; Wolfgang Kaehler; tr; ©Johnny Johnson/Animals Animals; b; Robert Frerck/Odyssey Productions; **288** Robert Frerck/Odyssey Productions; l inset; Peter Miller/The Image Bank; r inset; Tom Brakefield/DRK Photo; **291** t; Gary Gray/DRK Photo; bl; Kennan Ward /DRK Photo; br; Tom Bean /DRK Photo; **297** t; John Gerlach/DRK Photo; b; Doug Milner Photography/DRK Photo; **300** t; Marty Cordano/DRK Photo; bl; Stephen J. Krasemann/DRK Photo; br; Frans Lanting/Minden Pictures, Inc.; **304** Robert & Linda Mitchell Photography; **308** Art Wolfe Incorporated; **309** Charlie Palek/Animals Animals; **310** ©Clyde H. Smith/Peter Arnold, Inc.; **311** l; Photograph courtesy of Dr. George Bowes, Department of Botany and the C for Aquatic Plants, University of Florida, Gainesville, Florida; r; Momatiuk/Eastcott/Woodfin Camp & Associates; **315** l; ©Tui De Roy/Oxford Scientific Films/Animals Animals; c; Dan Budnik/Woodfin Camp & Associates; r; Dan Budnik/Woodfin Camp & Associates; **318** Jeffrey L. Rotman; **319** l; ©1994, Art Montes De Oca/FPG International Corp.; r; Michael Quackenbush/The Image Bank; **320** ©Norbert Wu; **322** l; Corel Professional Photos CD-ROM™; r; Guido Alberto Rossi/The Image Bank; **326** David M. Phillips/Visuals Unlimited; **330** Dan Budnik/Woodfin Camp & Associates; **332** Kevin Schafer/Tom Stack & Associates; **333** t; Bullaty/Lomeo/The Image Bank; b; Steve Krongard/The Image Bank; **336** l; ©Michael Sewell/Peter Arnold, Inc.; r; ©Allan Morgan/Peter Arnold, Inc.; **337** t; Lionel Isy Schwart/The Image Bank; bl; Anthony Johnson/The Image Bank; **337** br; John Banagan/The Image Bank; **340** tl; Wolfgang Kaehler; tr; Frans Lanting/Minden Pictures, Inc.; b; ©Francois Gohier/Photo Researchers, Inc.; **341** The Image Bank; **342** t; Lynn M. Stone/DRK Photo; b; Carr Clifton/Minden Pictures, Inc.; **343** t; Tom Bean/DRK Photo; c; Frans Lanting/Minden Pictures, Inc.; b; Art Wolfe Incorporated; **342-343** Background; Rand McNally; **344** tl; Jeffrey L. Rotman; tr; Carr Clifton/Minden Pictures, Inc.; bl; ©Norbert Wu; br; C.C. Lockwood/DRK Photo; Background; Rand McNally; **346** Jim Brandenburg/Minden Pictures, Inc.; r inset; Frank S. Balthis/Natural Selection Stock Photography, Inc.; l inset; Bullaty/Lomeo/The Image Bank; **348** l; Charles Mauzy/Natural Selection Stock Photography, Inc.; r; Geoffrey Clifford/Woodfin Camp & Associates; **350** l; ©NASA/Science Photo Library/Photo Researchers, Inc.; r; Ira Block/The Image Bank; **356** Tom Bean/DRK Photo; **357** Frans Lanting/Minden Pictures, Inc.; **358** Andre Gallant/The Image Bank; **359** l; American Museum of Natural History, Photo by P. Hollembeak/J. Beckett; c; Bill Ross/Woodfin Camp & Associates; r; Corel Professional Photos CD-ROM™; **360** Bob Harrington/Michigan Department of Natural Resources; **363** l inset; Giraudon/Art Resource, NY; r inset; Grant V. Faint/The Image Bank; A. Baccaccio/The Image Bank; **364** l; Miao Wang/The Image Bank; r; A. Upitis/The Image Bank; **365** Photo provided by the National Cattlemen's Association; **367** Jim Brandenburg/Minden Pictures, Inc.; **368** t; Guido A. Rossi/The Image Bank; c; Guido Rossi/The Image Bank; bl; ©Uniphoto, Inc.; br; ©Lowell Georgia/Photo Researchers, Inc.; Background; Corel Professional Photos CD-ROM™; **370** Paul McCormick/The Image Bank; **371** t; A. Ramey/Woodfin Camp & Associates; inset; ©Photo Researchers, Inc.; b; Jeffrey D. Smith/Woodfin Camp & Associates; **372** l; Robert Phillips/The Image Bank; r; ©John Mead/Photo Researchers, Inc.; **373** t; Kevon Schafer/Natural Selection Stock Photography, Inc.; c; G. Brimacombe/The Image Bank; b; Mark Moffett/Minden Pictures, Inc.; **374** ©E.R. Degginger/Animals Animals; **375** ©Bernard Giani/Photo Researchers, Inc.; inset; Robert Cameron/Cameron & Company; **377** Jeff Foott Productions; **382** Wolfgang Kaehler; **383** D. Cavagnaro/DRK Photo; **385** John Trager/Tom Stack & Associates; **386** ©Francois GohierPhoto Researchers, Inc.; **387** t; Corel Professional Photos CD-ROM™; b; NASA; **388** l; Tom Bean/DRK Photo; r; David M. Dennis /Tom Stack & Associates; **391** Jonathan Blair/Woodfin Camp & Associates; **392** Joe Englander/Natural Selection Stock Photography, Inc.; **393** t; Corel Professional Photos CD-ROM™; bl; Steve Proehl/The Image Bank; br; Corel Professional Photos CD-ROM™; **398** t; T.E. Adams/Visuals Unlimited; bl; ©CNRI/Science Photo Library/Photo Researchers, Inc.; br; ©Dr. L. Caro/Science Photo Library/Photo Researchers, Inc.; **399** l; Corel Professional Photos CD-ROM™; r; ©Bonnie Sue Rauch/Photo Researchers, Inc.; **401** l; ©Holt Studios International (Miss P. Peackock)/Photo Researchers, Inc.; r; ©NIBSC/Science Phot Library/Photo Researchers, Inc.; **402** ©CNRI/Science Photo Library/Photo Researchers, Inc.; **403** ©NIBSC/Science Phot LibraryPhoto Researchers, Inc.; **404** t; ©Soames Summerhays/Photo Researchers, Inc.; b; T.A. Wiewandt/DRK Photo; **405** Roger Ressmeyer/Corbis; **406** Sidney Fox/Visuals Unlimited; **408** Don & Pat Valenti/DRK Photo; **412** ©Karen Tweedy-Holmes Animals Animals; **413** ©Lee D. Simon/Science Source/Photo Researchers, Inc.; **414** Chuck Place/The Image Bank; **415** t; David M. Phillips/Visuals Unlimited; bl; A.M. Siegelman/Visuals Unlimited; br; ©Alfred Pasieka/Peter Arnold, Inc.; **418** l; John D. Cunningham/Visuals Unlimited; r; ©Norbert Wu; **419** l; William E. Ferguson; r; Mike Abbey/Visuals Unlimited; **420** l; ©Phil A. Dotson/Photo Researchers, Inc.; c; Tom Bean/DRK Photo; r; Corel Professional Photos CD-ROM™; **422** l; ©Noble Proctor/Science Source/Photo Researchers, Inc.; r; John D. Cunningham/Visuals Unlimited; **423** tl; Jack M. Bostrack/Visuals Unlimited; bl; ©Viard/Jacana/Photo Researchers, Inc.; r; S. Nielsen/DRK Photo; **424** Michael Fogden/DRK Photo; **425** tl; Corel Professional Photos CD-ROM™; tr; Corel Professional Photos CD-ROM™; b; ©Ed Reschke/Peter Arnold, Inc.; **427** r; Walt Anderson/Visuals Unlimited; l; William E. Ferguson; inset; Jeff Foott/DRK Photo; **428** Anne Rippy/The Image Bank; **429** Antonio M. Rosario/The Image Bank; **431** Gary Braasch/Woodfin Camp & Associates; **432** l; Wayne Lankinen/DRK Photo; r; ©Hans Pfletschinger/Peter Arnold, Inc.; **433** ©Merlin D. Tuttle/Bat Conservation Photo Researchers, Inc.; **434** Carolina Biological Supply Company / Phototake NYC; **435** t; William E. Ferguson; b; ©Jeff Lepore/Photo Researchers, Inc.; **438** ©Phil A. Dotson/Photo Researchers, Inc.; **440** John Eastcott/Yva Momatiuk/DRK Photo; **441** ©Merlin D. Tuttle/Bat Conservation International/Photo Researchers, Inc.; **442** Stephen Frink/Water House Stock Photography; **443** l; O. Louis Mazzatenta/National Geographic Image Collection; c; K. Push/Visuals Unlimited; r; ©Kevin Schafer/Peter Arnold, Inc.; **444** Ken Lucas/Visuals Unlimited; **446** t; Jeffrey L. Rotman; bl; Doug Sokell/Visuals Unlimited; br; Robert Parks/The Wildlife Collection; **447** Dave B. Fleetham/Visuals Unlimited; **448** Daniel W. Gotshall/Visuals Unlimited; **449** t; ©Zig Leszczynski/Animals Animals; bl; Visuals Unlimited; br; ©CNRI/Science Photo Library/Photo Researchers, Inc.; **450** t; ©Robert Dunne/Photo Researchers, Inc.; b; A. Kerstitch/Visuals Unlimited; **451** tl; Henry Holdsworth/The Wildlife Collection; tr; Mark W. Moffett/Minden Pictures, Inc.; b; Hal Beral/Visuals Unlimited; **452** t; ©Norbert Wu; b; Hal Beral/Visuals Unlimited; **457** Jeffrey L. Rotman; **459** Flip Nicklin/Minden Pictures, Inc.; **460** l; ©Bruce Watkins/Animals Animals; r; Carolina Biological Supply/Phototake; **461** ©Kevin Aitke/Peter Arnold, Inc.; **462** Carolina Biological Supply/Phototake; **466** Hal Beral/Visuals Unlimited; **468** Stuart Westmorland/Tony Stone Images; **469** t; Corel Professional Photos CD-ROM™; bl; Corel Professional Photos CD-ROM™; br; Art Wolfe/Tony Stone Images; **470** From WONDERFUL LIFE: The Burgess Shale and the Nature of History by Stephen Jay Gould. Copyr ©1989 by Stephen Jay Gould. Reprinted by permission of W.W. Norton & Company, Inc.; **471** t; ©Steinhart Aquarium/Tom McHughPhoto Researchers, Inc.; b; ©Estate of Dr. J. Metzner/Peter Arnold, Inc.; **473** Davd M. Dennis/Tom Stack & Associates; **475** tl; ©BIOS (Pu Tao)/Peter Arnold, Inc.; tr; Corel Professional Photos CD-ROM™; b; Superstock ; **476** tl; Corel Professional Photos CD-ROM™; tr; Corel Professional Photos CD-ROM™; bl; Art Wolfe/Tony Stone Images; br; Larry LipskyDRK Photo; **477** Art Wolfe/Tony Stone Images; **478** tl; Frans Lanting/Minden Pictures, Inc.; tr; Hans Reinhard/Bruce Coleman, Inc.; b; ©Gerard Lacz/Peter Arnold, Inc.; **479** t; ©The Stock Market/ZEFA Germany; c; ©The Stock Market/ZEFA Germany; b; ©The Stock Market/ZEFA Germany; **480** Peter Arnold, Inc.; **484** l; John Cancalosi/DRK Photo; r; Kim Heacox/DRK Photo; **486** t; ©Michael Fogden/Animals Animals; bl; Visuals Unlimited; br; Corel Professional Photos CD-ROM™; **492** Larry Lipsky/DRK Photo; **493** ©Phil A. DotsonPhoto Researchers, Inc.; **494** Norman Owen Tomalin/Bruce Coleman, Inc.; **495** t; Douglas Mazonowicz/Bruce Coleman, Inc.; bl; ©De Sazo/Photo Researchers, Inc.; br; Michael Holford Photographs; **496** tl; Rod Williams/Bruce Coleman, Inc.; tr; Frans Lanting/Minden Pictures, Inc.; bl; Chamberlain, M.C./DRK Photo; br; ©BIOS (Compost/Visage)/Peter Arnold, Inc.; **498** l; Cleveland Museum of Natural History, c; Phil Schermeister, 1989/All Stock/PNI, rt, rb; David L. Brill Photograph; **501** ©Jean-Loup Charmet/Science Photo Library/Photo Researchers, Inc.; **502** l; The Metropolitan Museum of Art, Bashford Dean Memorial Collection, Purchase, 1929.(29.158.142); c; The Metropolitan Museum of Art, Gift of Jean Jacques Reubell, in memory of his mother, Julia C. Coster, and of his wife, Adeline E. Post, both of New York City, 1926. (26.145.104); r; Museo America, Madrid/Bridgeman Art Library, London/Superstock; **505** ©Hank Morgan/Photo Researchers, Inc.; **508** ©BIOS (Compost/Visage)/Peter Arnold, Inc.; **510** ©John Reader/Science Photo Library/Photo Researchers, Inc.; **511** ©Photo Researchers, Inc.; **513** Tammy Peluso/Tom Stack & Associates; **514** ©Manfred Kage/Peter Arnold, Inc.; **515** t; ©NIBSC/Science Photo Library/Photo Researchers, Inc.; bl; ©CNRI/Science Photo

LibraryPhoto Researchers, Inc.; br; David M. Phillips/ Visuals Unlimited; **516** l; CNRI/Phototake; r; Martin Rotker/Phototake; **517** tl; David Phillips/Visuals Unlimited; tc; David M. Phillips/Visuals Unlimited; tr; Mike Gabridge/Visuals Unlimited; b; Richard Nowitz/ Phototake; **519** l; David M. Phillips/Visuals Unlimited; c; ©David Scharf/Peter Arnold, Inc.; r; Cabisco/Visuals Unlimited; **520** l; ©Dr. Jeremy Burgess/Science Photo Labrary/Photo Researchers, Inc.; r; ©R. Knanft/Photo Researchers, Inc.; **521** ©Philippe Plailly/Eurelios/ Science Photo Library/Photo Researchers, Inc.; **522** Hans Gelderblom/Visuals Unlimited; **524** Arthur J. Olson, The Scripps Research Institute, La Jolla, California, Copyr 1988; **525** l; Corel Professional Photos CD-ROM™; rt; Corel Professional Photos CD-ROM™; rb; Corel Professional Photos CD-ROM™; **527** l; John Edwards/Tony Stone Images; r; John Colwell/Grant Heilman Photography; **528** Jeffrey Hutcherson/DRK Photo; **532** ©Oliver Meckes/Photo Researchers, Inc.; **533** CDC/Phototake; **534** Frans Lanting/Minden Pictures, Inc.; **535** tl; Philip Sze/ Visuals Unlimited; tr; Cabisco/Visuals Unlimited; b; Stanley Flegler/Visuals Unlimited; **536** ©Scott Camazine/Photo Researchers, Inc.; inset; ©Eric Grave/ Science SourcePhoto Researchers, Inc.; **537** t; A.M Siegelman/Visuals Unlimited; c; A.M. Siegelman/ Visuals Unlimited; b; A.M. Siegelman/Visuals Unlimited; **538** t; M. Abbey/Visuals Unlimited; c; A.M. Siegelman/Visuals Unlimited; b; Ken Wagner/ Visuals Unlimited; **539** ©Tom E. Adams/Peter Arnold, Inc.; **540** l; ©Cabisco/Peter Arnold, Inc.; r; David Phillips/Visuals Unlimited; **542** l; ©Ed Reschke/Peter Arnold, Inc.; r; ©Stanley Flegler/Peter Arnold, Inc.; inset; ©James W. Richardson/Peter Arnold, Inc.; **543** l; ©Ralph Lee Hopkins/Peter Arnold, Inc.; r; ©Ed Reschke/Peter Arnold, Inc.; inset; ©Stanley Flegler/ Photo Researchers, Inc.; **544** Don & Pat Valenti/DRK Photo; **545** t; D. Cavagnaro/DRK Photo; b; ©Ed Reschke/Peter Arnold, Inc.; **546** ©CNRI/Science Photo LibraryPhoto Researchers, Inc.; **547** t; John D. Cunningham/Visuals Unlimited; bl; Mitch Kezar/ Phototake; br; ©Nigel Cattlin/Holt Studios Int. Photo Researchers, Inc.; **548** t; W.E. Ferry/Visuals Unlimited; b; ©Breck Kent/Animals Animals; **549** ©Rod Planck/ Photo Researchers, Inc.; **550** M. Abbey/Visuals Unlimited; **554** Michael Melford/The Image Bank; **556** D. Cavagnaro/DRK Photo; **557** t; ©Michel Viard/ Peter Arnold, Inc.; bl; ©Linda Sims/Photo Researchers, Inc.; br; ©Manfred Kage/Peter Arnold, Inc.; **558** ©Bud Lehnhausen/Photo Researchers, Inc.; inset; ©Nancy Sefton/Photo Researchers, Inc.; **560** ©Philip Szer/ Photo Researchers, Inc.; **561** ©Daniel W. Gotshall/ Photo Researchers, Inc.; **562** l; Ken Wagner/Phototake; c; ©E.R. Degginger/Photo Researchers, Inc.; r; John D. Cunningham/Phototake; **565** t; ©Scott Camazine/ Photo Researchers, Inc.; bl; ©Walter H. Hodge/Peter Arnold, Inc.; bc; ©Henry Holdsworth/Peter Arnold, Inc.; br; ©Roger HartRainbow; **566** ©Ed Reschke/Peter Arnold, Inc.; **568** t; Jeff Foot/DRK Photo; bl; Garry Gay/The Image Bank; br; Michael Newman/PhotoEdit; **569** t; Bob Elsdale/The Image Bank; b; Michal Heron/ Woodfin Camp & Associates; **570** ©John D. Cunningham/Photo Researchers, Inc.; **572** ©Stephen Dalton/Photo Researchers, Inc.; **574** Frans Lanting/ Minden Pictures, Inc.; **575** ©Ed Reschke/Peter Arnold, Inc.; **576** ©Riccardo Marcialis/Photo Researchers, Inc.; **577** t; Alan Pitcairn/Grant Heilman Photography; bl; Corel Professional Photos CD-ROM™; br; Corel Professional Photos CD-ROM™; **578** Runk/ Schoenberger/Grant Heilman Photography; **580** l; Robert & Linda Mitchell Photography; c; Holt Confer/ Grant Heilman Photography; r; E.F. Anderson/Visuals Unlimited; **581** l; Robert & Linda Mitchell Photography; r; ©Larry Brownstein/Rainbow; **583** S. Nielsen/DRK Photo; **584** l; Michael Fogden/DRK Photo; c; Dwight Kuhn/DRK Photo; r; Pascal Perret/ The Image Bank; **585** Thomas Hovland/Grant Heilman Photography; **588** l; Robert & Linda Mitchell Photography; c; Runk/Schoenberger/Grant Heilman Photography; r; Paul E. Loven/The Image Bank; **589** l; ©Ed Reschke/Peter Arnold, Inc.; r; ©Ed Reschke/Peter Arnold, Inc.; **590** l; Christi Carter/Grant Heilman Photography; c; Alan Pitcairn/Grant Heilman Photography; r; Alan Pitcairn/Grant Heilman Photography; **591** t; ©Herminia Dosal/Photo Researchers, Inc.; c; ©G. Buttner/Naturbild/Okapia/ Photo Researchers, Inc.; b; Steve Kaufman/DRK Photo; **593** D. Cavagnaro/DRK Photo; **594** ©Adam Hart-Davis/Science Photo Library/Photo Researchers, Inc.; **598** Jim Brandenburg/ Minden Pictures, Inc.; **599** John Eastcott/Yva Momatiuk/DRK Photo; **600** Larry Lefever/Grant Heilman Photography; **601** t; Carr Clifton/Minden Pictures, Inc.; b; Joseph Van Os/The Image Bank; b inset; ©S.E. Cornelius /Photo Researchers, Inc.; **603** l; Dwight R. Kuhn/DRK Photo; r; Robert & Linda Mitchell Photography; **606** Stephen J. Krasemann/ DRK Photo; **607** t; ©Dr. Jeremy Burgess/Science Photo Library/Photo Researchers, Inc.; b; ©Dr. Jeremy Burgess/Science Photo Library/Photo Researchers, Inc.; **609** t; John W. Banagan/The Image Bank; c-1; Robert & Linda Mitchell Photography; c-2; ©Jim Steinberg/ Photo Researchers, Inc.; b l; Robert & Linda Mitchell Photography; b r; Robert & Linda Mitchell Photography; **611** l; Carr Clifton/Minden Pictures, Inc.; c; John D. Cunningham/Visuals Unlimited; rt; Corel Professional Photos CD-ROM™; rb; Tim Laman/Minden Pictures, Inc.; **612** tl; Robert & Linda Mitchell Photography; tr; Robert & Linda Mitchell Photography; b; ©Jerome Wexler/Photo Researchers, Inc.; **615** t; Ken Wagner/Phototake; b; Ken Wagner/ Phototake; **616** l; ©Coco McCoy/ Rainbow; c; ©Kevin Schafer/Peter Arnold, Inc.; r; D. Cavagnaro/DRK Photo; **617** tl; ©Ed Reschke/Peter Arnold, Inc.; tr; Alan & Linda Detrich/Photo Researchers, Inc.; bl; ©Holt Studios Int./Photo Researchers, Inc.; br; Brownie Harris/Tony Stone Images; **618** Patricia Agre/Photo Researchers, Inc.; **624** Robert & Linda Mitchell Photography; **625** ©Jerome Wexler /Photo Researchers, Inc.; **627** ©Terry Qing/ FPG International Corp.; **628** Hall Baral/Visuals Unlimited; **629** t; ©Norbert Wu; bl; ©Stephen Frink/ Photo Researchers, Inc.; br; Jeffrey L. Rotman; **630** ©Louisa PrestonPhoto Researchers, Inc.; **631** ©Dr. E.R. Degginger/Photo Researchers, Inc.; **633** ©M.I. Walker/Science Source/ Photo Researchers, Inc.; **634** tl; ©Oxford Scientific Films/Animals Animals; tr; ©Norbert Wu; b; John D. Cunningham/Visuals Unlimited; **635** ©Norbert Wu; **636** t; ©Dr. Jeremy Burgess/Science Photo Library/ Photo Researchers, Inc.; c; ©Jackie Lewin, EM Unit Royal Free Hospital/ Science Photo Library/Photo Researchers, Inc.; b; ©Milton Love/Peter Arnold, Inc.; **637** ©M.I. Walker/Science Sourcer/Photo Researchers, Inc.; **638** Dwight Kuhn Photography; **639** ©CNRI/ Science Photo Library/Photo Researchers, Inc.; **640** t; Sinclair Stammers/Science Photo Library/Photo Researchers, Inc.; c; ©L. Jensen/Photo Researchers, Inc.; b; Photo courtesy of USDA Nematology Laboratory, Beltsville, Maryland; **642** ©M.I. Walker/Science Sourcer/Photo Researchers, Inc.; **644** Cabisco/Visuals Unlimited; **646** ©Norbert Wu; **647** Arthur M. Siegelman/Visuals Unlimited; **648** ©Steve Krasemann/Peter Arnold, Inc.; **649** t; Jeff Foott Productions; bl; ©M.H. Sharp/Photo Researchers, Inc.; br; ©Tom McHugh/Photo Researchers, Inc.; **651** tl; ©Lynn Funkhouser/Peter Arnold, Inc.; tr; ©Norbert Wu/DRK Photo; b; ©Peter Parks/Mo Young Productions; **652** ©Ed Reschke/Peter Arnold, Inc.; **654** t; Larry Lipsky/DRK Photo; c; ©B.B. Cadbury/Photo Researchers, Inc.; b; ©Norbert Wu/ DRK Photo; **656** l; ©David Thompson/Oxford Scientific Films/Animals Animals; c; ©Oxford Scientific Films/Animals Animals; r; Richard Nowitz/ PNI; **657** t; ©Kjell B. Sandved/Photo Researchers, Inc.; c; ©Norbert Wu/DRK Photo; b; ©Fred Winner/Jacana/ Photo Researchers, Inc.; **658** t; ©Fred McConnaughey/ Photo Researchers, Inc.; bl; ©Fred Bavendam/Peter Arnold, Inc.; br; ©Norbert Wu; **660** t; ©Norbert Wu; c; ©Dan McCoy/Rainbow; b; ©Fred Bavendam/Peter Arnold, Inc.; **661** F. Stuart Westmorland/Mo Young Productions; **663** ©Jeanne White/Photo Researchers, Inc.; **666** ©Seitre/Peter Arnold, Inc.; **668** Marty Snyderman; **669** t; Art Wolfe Incorporated; b; Robert & Linda Mitchell Photography; **670** l; ©Holt Studios International (Nigel Cattlin)/Photo Researchers, Inc.; r; ©J H Robinson/Photo Researchers, Inc.; **672** ©Andrew Syred/Science Photo Library/Photo Researchers, Inc.; **673** ©Hans Pfletschinger/Peter Arnold, Inc.; **674** t; Robert & Linda Mitchell Photography; bl; ©Mark Burnett/Photo Researchers, Inc.; br; ©Manfred Kage/Peter Arnold, Inc.; **675** t; ©Michael Lustbader/Photo Researchers, Inc.; b; ©Tom McHugh/Photo Researchers, Inc.; **676** lt; Robert & Linda Mitchell Photography; lb; ©John R. McGregor/ Peter Arnold, Inc.; r; ©Stephen Dalton/Oxford Scientific Films/Animals Animals; **677** tl; Larry Lipsky/ DRK Photo; tr; Robert & Linda Mitchell Photography; b; Dwight R. Kuhn/DRK Photo; **679** Robert F. Sisson, ©National Geographic Society; **680** ©Dr. Jeremy Burgess/Science Photo Library/Photo Researchers, Inc.; **681** ©Oxford Scientific Films/Animals Animals; **684** S. Nielsen/DRK Photo; **685** Robert & Linda Mitchell Photography; **686** ©Norbert Wu; **687** l; Stephen Frink/Water House Stock Photography; rt; Stephen Frink/Water House Stock Photography; rb; ©Gerard Lacz/Peter Arnold, Inc.; **688** t; ©Kelvin Aitken/Peter Arnold, Inc.; b; ©A. W. Ambler/Photo Researchers, Inc.; **690** Jeffrey L. Rotman; **691** t; ©Norbert Wu; c; ©Steinhart Aquarium/Tom McHugh/Photo Researchers, Inc.; b; ©Nicole Duplaix/Peter Arnold, Inc.; **692** t; ©Sophie de Wilde Jacana/Jacana Scientific Control/Photo Researchers, Inc.; b inset; Runk/ Schoenberger/Grant Heilman Photography; b; Tom Stack/Tom Stack & Associates; **693** t; Jeffrey L. Rotman; bl; ©Stephen Dalton/Photo Researchers, Inc.; br; ©J. W. Mowbray/Photo Researchers, Inc.; **695** t; ©Dr. Paul A. Zahl/Photo Researchers, Inc.; bl; ©Tom McHugh/Steinhart Aquarium/Photo Researchers, Inc.; br; James H. Carmichael Jr./The Image Bank; **697** ©Nuridsany et Perennou/Photo Researchers, Inc.; **698** l; ©J. L. Lepore /Photo Researchers, Inc.; r; ©Hans Pfletschinger/Peter Arnold, Inc.; **699** l; ©Gregory Ochocki/Photo Researchers, Inc.; c; ©Steinhart Aquarium/Tom McHugh/Photo Researchers, Inc.; r; ©Jeffrey Rotman/Peter Arnold, Inc.; **700** t; ©Peter Skinner/Photo Researchers, Inc.; b; Robert Frerck/ Woodfin Camp & Associates; **701** Corel Professional Photos CD-ROM™; **702** ©Oxford Scientific Films/ Animals Animals; ©Oxford Scientific Films/Animals Animals; **706** ©Norbert Wu; **707** ©Francois Gohier/ Photo Researchers, Inc.; **708** Art Wolfe Incorporated; **709** t; Michael Fogden/DRK Photo; c; Frans Lanting/ Minden Pictures, Inc.; b; Frans Lanting/Minden Pictures, Inc.; **711** l; Martim Harvey/The Wildlife Collection; r; ©Ed Reschke/Peter Arnold, Inc.; **712** t; ©Stephen Dalton/Photo Researchers, Inc.; b; Martin Harvey/The Wildlife Collection; **713** lt; Robert Lankinen/The Wildlife Collection; lb; Mark Moffett/ Minden Pictures, Inc.; r; ©Martha Cooper/Peter Arnold, Inc.; **714** l; John Giustina/The Wildlife Collection; c; ©Jim Zipp /Photo Researchers, Inc.; r; ©Adam Jones/Photo Researchers, Inc.; **715** l; Frans Lanting/Minden Pictures, Inc.; c; Frans Lanting/ Minden Pictures, Inc.; r; ©C. K. Lorenz/Photo Researchers, Inc.; **718** l; ©Breck P. Kent/Animals Animals; r; ©Robert Holmgren/Peter Arnold, Inc.; **719** t; Art Wolfe Incorporated; b; Penny Tweedie/Woodfin Camp & Associates; **720** t; Martyn Cowley; bl; Martyn Cowley; br; Frans Lanting/Minden Pictures, Inc.; **722** David Norhcott/DRK Photo; **726** Frans Lanting/ Minden Pictures, Inc.; **727** ©Stephen Dalton/Photo Researchers, Inc.; **728** David Fritts/Tony Stone Images; **729** l; ©Stephen J. Krasemann/Peter Arnold, Inc.; r; Thomas Kitchin/Tom Stack & Associates; inset; Frans Lanting/Minden Pictures, Inc.; **730** tl; Corel Professional Photos CD-ROM™; tr; Gerard Lacz/Peter Arnold, Inc.; b; John Callanan/The Image Bank; **732** tl; ©Michael P. Gadomski /Photo Researchers, Inc.; tr; ©Martin Dohrn/Photo Researchers, Inc.; b; Chris Huss/ The Wildlife Collection; **733** Frans Lanting/Minden Pictures, Inc.; **734** tl; Martin Harvey/The Wildlife Collection; tr; ©The Stock Market/ZEFA Germany; cl; Michael Fogden/DRK Photo; cc; Ivan Polunin/Bruce Coleman, Inc; cr; Corel Professional Photos CD-ROM™; bl; Robert & Linda Mitchell Photography; br; ©Jim Sipp/Photo Researchers, Inc.; **735** tl; Johnny Johnson/DRK Photo; tr; Corel Professional Photos CD-ROM™; cl; Corel Professional Photos CD-ROM™; cr; Doug Perrine/DRK Photo; bl; Corel Professional Photos CD-ROM™; bc; Doug Perrine/DRK Photo; br; Stephen KrasemannDRK Photo; **737** t; Kevin R. Morris/Corbis; bl; ©C. Prescott-Allen/Animals Animals; br; Bates Littlehales/National Geographic Image Collection; **738** t; Johnny Johnson/DRK Photo; b; Corel Professional Photos CD-ROM™; **739** t; ©Tim Davis/Photo Researchers, Inc.; b; Superstock; **740**

Darrel Gulin/PNI; **741** David Smart/DRK Photo; **744** Gerard Lacz/Peter Arnold, Inc.; **745** Corel Professional Photos CD-ROM™; **746** ©David McDonald/Oxford Scientific Films/Animals Animals; **747** t; Michael Fogden/DRK Photo; bl; Frans Lanting/Minden Pictures, Inc.; br; ©Manfred Kage/Peter Arnold, Inc.; **748** l; Robert & Linda Mitchell Photography; r; Laura Dwight/PhotoEdit; **750** tl; Sovfoto/Eastfoto/PNI; tr; ©John Mitchell/Photo Researchers, Inc.; b; ©Susan Kuklin/Photo Researchers, Inc.; **751** John Eastcott/Yva Momatiuk/DRK Photo; **752** l; Otis Imboden/National Geographic Image Collection; r; ©Francois Gohier/ Photo Researchers, Inc.; **753** lt; Stanley Breeden/DRK Photo; lb; Fred Bavendam ; r; ©Scott Camazine/Photo Researchers, Inc.; **754** t; Mark Moffett/Minden Pictures, Inc.; bl; ©Gary Retherford/Photo Researchers, Inc.; br; Mark Moffett/Minden Pictures, Inc.; **755** l; Manoh Shah/DRK Photo; r; Art Wolfe Incorporated; **756** ©M.I. Walker/Science Sourcer/Photo Researchers, Inc.; **760** Laura Dwight/PhotoEdit; **761** Mark Moffett/ Minden Pictures, Inc.; **763** Photo © Lois Greenfield, 1996; **764** Leo Mason/The Image Bank; **765** l; Mel Di Giacomo/The Image Bank; c; Rob Tringali, Jr./Sports Chrome East/West; r; Silver Burdett Ginn; **768** t; Kagen/Monkmeyer; bl; Bill Truslow/Tony Stone Images; br; Kopstein/Monkmeyer; **769** ©Professors P.M. Motta and S. Correr/Science Photo Library/Photo Researchers, Inc.; **771** ©Geoff Tompkinson/Science Photo Library/Photo Researchers, Inc.; **772** Ken Karp Photography; **774** t; David Wagner/Phototake; bl; Mark C. Burnett/Stock, Boston/PNI; br; Stock, Boston/ PNI; **778** David Wagner/Phototake; **779** Kagen/ Monkmeyer; **780** ©Professors P.M. Motta and S. Correr/Science Photo Library/Photo Researchers, Inc.; **782** Robert Tringali/Sports Chrome East/West; **783** l; Ken Karp Photography; c; Dr. David Scott/CNRI/ Phototake; r; Jeff Spielman/The Image Bank; **785** David M. Phillips/Visuals Unlimited; **787** l; Gary Cralle/The Image Bank; c; ©Prof. P. Motta/Dept. of Anatomy/ University of " LaSapienza", Rome/Science Photo Library./Photo Researchers, Inc.; r; ©Allsport/ Simon Bruty; **788** GJLP/CNRI/Phototake; **790** ©Mehau Kulyk/Science Photo Library/Photo Researchers, Inc.; **791** ©Catherine Poudras/Science Photo Library/Photo Researchers, Inc.; **792** l; Robert Brenner/PhotoEdit; c; Val Corbett/Tony Stone Images; r; Phillip Kretchmar/The Image Bank; **794** ©Omikron/ Science Source/Photo Researchers, Inc.; **796** t; John Ramey/The Image Bank; bl; ©Don Fawcett/Heuser, Reese/Science Source/Photo Researchers, Inc.; br; Robert Freck/Woodfin Camp & Associates; **799** ©Dr. Morley Read/Science Photo Library/Photo Researchers, Inc.; **804** GJLP/CNRI /Phototake; **805** ©Omikron/ Science Source/Photo Researchers, Inc.; **806** ©Bob Daemmrich; **807** c; Paul J. Sutton/Duomo Photography, Inc.; r; © Lennart Nilsson, Behold Man, Little Brown and Company; **809** t; Dr. Gobal Murti/ Phototake; bl; ©Prof. P. Motta/Dept. of Anatomy/ University "La Sapienza", Rome/Science Photo Library/ Photo Researchers, Inc.; br; Brett Froomer/The Image Bank; **810** ©Andrew Syred/Science Photo Library/ Photo Researchers, Inc.; **813** bl; ©CNRI/Science Photo Library/Photo Researchers, Inc.; br; Ydav Levy/ Phototake; t; William R. Sallaz/Duomo Photography, Inc.; **814** l; John D. Cunningham/Visuals Unlimited; c; Don W. Fawcett/Visuals Unlimited; r; Carolina Biological Supply Company/Phototake; **818** t; William R. Sallaz/Duomo Photography, Inc.; bl; ©Allsport/Gary Newkirk, 1993); br; William R. Sallaz/Duomo Photography, Inc.; **824** ©Allsport/Gary Newkirk; **826** Zao-Grimberg/The Image Bank; **827** t; ©Will and Deni McIntyre/Photo Researchers, Inc.; c; ©Eric Grave/ Science Source/Photo Researchers, Inc.; b; T. Rosenthal/Superstock; **832** l; Visuals Unlimited; r; Microworks/Phototake; **833** l; Lennart Nilsson, THE INCREDIBLE MACHINE, National Geographic Society, @ Boehringer Ingelheim International GmbH; r; ©Biophoto Assoc. Science Source/Photo Researchers, Inc.; **835** t; ©Proff. Motta, Correr & Nottola/University "LaSapienza", Rome/Science Photo Library/Photo Researchers, Inc.; bl; Michael Gabridge/ Visuals Unlimited; br; ©Prof. Arnold Brody/Science Photo Library/Photo Researchers, Inc.; **837** Art Siegel; **838** ©Will & Deni McIntyrePhoto Researchers, Inc.; **839** t; Ydav Levy/Phototake; b; David M. Grossman/ Phototake; **841** l; ©A. Glauberman/Photo Researchers, Inc.; r; Peter Holden/Visuals Unlimited; **848** David Phillips/Visuals Unlimited; **850** ©CNRI/Science Photo Library/Photo Researchers, Inc.; **851** lt; Phillip Kretchmar/The Image Bank; lb; ©Bob Daemmrich; r; William Sallaz/The Image Bank; **852** Nathan Benn/ Stock, Boston/PNI; **853** l; Corel Professional Photos CD-ROM™; rb; Corel Professional Photos CD-ROM™; rt; Corel Professional Photos CD-ROM™; **857** lt; R. Hutchings/PhotoEdit; lb; Corel Professional Photos CD-ROM™; r; Mary Kate Denny/PhotoEdit; **860** Lennart Nilsson ©Boehringer Ingelheim International GmbH; **862** t; Walter Iooss, Jr./The Image Bank; bl; ©Allsport/Al Bello; br; ©Allsport/Billy Strickland; **865** Lennart Nilsson ©Boehringer Ingelheim International GmbH; **866** ©Dan McCoy/ Rainbow; **867** t; ©CNRI/Science Photo Library/Photo Researchers, Inc.; b; Lennart Nilsson ©Boehringer Ingelheim International GmbH; **868** ©Prof. J. James/ Science Photo Library/Photo Researchers, Inc.; **869** ©Prof. R. Motta/Dept. of Anatomy/University "La Sapienza", Rome/Science Photo Library/Photo Researchers, Inc.; **874** ©Prof. P. Motta/Dept. of Anatomy/University "La Sapienza", Rome/Science Photo Library/Photo Researchers, Inc.; **876** Penny Gentieu/Tony Stone Images; **877** t; ©Mr. Richard Hutchings/Photo Researchers, Inc.; bl; P. Rivera/ Superstock ; br; ©Arthur Tilley/FPG International Corp.; **878** Electra/Phototake; **879** ©Motta & Familiari/Anatomy Dept./Univerisity "La Sapienza", Rome/Science Photo Library/Photo Researchers, Inc.; **881** ©C. Edelmann/La Villette/Photo Researchers, Inc.; **882** t; Tony Stone Images; bl; ©Lennart Nilsson, A CHILD IS BORN; br; ©Lennart Nilsson, A CHILD IS BORN; **883** t; Douglas Struthers/Tony Stone Images; b; ©Professors P.M. Motta and J. Van Blerkom/ Science Photo Library/Photo Researchers, Inc.; **885** l; ©Petit Format/Nestle/Science SourcePhoto Researchers, Inc.; r; ©Petit Format/Nestle/Photo Researchers, Inc.; **888** T. Rosenthal/Superstock ; **889** ©Suzanne Szasz/ Photo Researchers, Inc.; **890** t; ©Dr. Kar Lounatmaa/ Science Photo Libray/Photo Researchers, Inc.; bl; ©A.B. Dowsett/Science Photo Library/Photo Researchers, Inc.; br; ©Alfred Pasieka/Science Photo Library/Photo Researchers, Inc.; **891** ©Alfred Pasieka/ Science Photo Library/Photo Researchers, Inc.; **894** ©Manfred Kage/Peter Arnold, Inc.; **895** ©Manfred Kage/Peter Arnold, Inc.; **898** ©Petit Format/Nestle/ Photo Researchers, Inc.; **900** ©Manfred Kage/Peter Arnold, Inc.; **901** rt; ©Tektoff-Merieux, CNRI/Science Photo Library/Photo Researchers, Inc.; rb; National Institutes of Health, Rocky Mountain Lab; l; ©Dr. Kari Lounatmaa/Science Photo Library/Photo Researchers, Inc.; **904** ©Boehringer Ingelheim International GmbH, Photo by Lennart Nilsson, THE INCREDIBLE MACHINE; **905** t; ©Don Fawcett/Photo Researchers, Inc.; bl; ©Lennart Nilsson, THE INCREDIBLE MACHINE; br; ©Lennart Nilsson, THE INCREDIBLE MACHINE, National Geographic Society; **906** ©NIBSC/Science Photo Library/Photo Researchers, Inc.; **909** Science VU/©Boehringer-Ingelheim/Visuals Unlimited; **910** ©R. Ellis/Sygma; **911** ©NIBSC/ Science Photo Library/Photo Researchers, Inc.; **912** tl; ©Boehringer Ingelheim International GmbH, Photo by Lennart Nilsson, THE INCREDIBLE MACHINE, National Geographic Society; tr; ©Boehringer Ingelheim International GmbH, Photo by Lennart Nilsson, THE INCREDIBLE MACHINE; b; ©Boehringer Ingelheim International GmbH, Photo by Lennart Nilsson; **913** ©Nancy Kedersha/Science Photo Library/Photo Researchers, Inc.; **915** ©Sinclair Stammers/Science Photo Library/Photo Researchers, Inc.

Illustration

Academy Artworks Inc. **90**; **95**; **139** top; **159**; **257**; **353**; **436** right; **437** top; **463** top; **488**; **489**; **500**; **550**; **571** top; **595** top; **621** top; **643** top left; **662**; **667**; **719** top left; **723** top left; **749**; **773**; **776**; **820**; **844**; **845** bottom left; **856**; **871** top; **916**; **922 - 923**; **924**; **925** left, right; **928**. Ernest Albanese **35** top, bottom; **79** top; **82**; **83** top; **88**; **91**; **816**; **863** top. Glory Bechtold **125**; **126** spot art; **127**; **128**; **129** spot art; **137** spot art; **421** top; **426**; **429** spot art; **430**; **560**; **561**; **564**; **567**; **579** spot art; **586**; **602**; **604**; **605**; **607** top left; **610**; **612** bottom left; **613**. Scott Bodell **108** top, middle. Dartmouth Publishing, Inc. **27** inset; **39**; **172**; **189**; **190**; **199**; **203** bottom; **210**; **220** top; **223**; **254**; **323**; **388** bottom; **389** top, bottom. Electra-Graphics, Inc. **36** top left; **40** bottom; **367** bottom; **379**; **405**; **529** top. Carlyn Iverson **14** top left; **106** top left; **134**; **152** spot art; **174**; **175** bottom left; **177** bottom; **179**; **182**; **183**; **188**; **191**; **203** top; **285**; **288**; **290**; **292**; **298**; **316** spot art; **317**; **348** bottom; **349**; **630**; **632**; **634** bottom right; **637**; **639**; **641**; **690** bottom; **697** top right; **929** spot art; **930** spot art; **931** spot art; **302**; **362**; **371**. Thomas LaPadula for S.I. International **18**. Laura Maggio **8** top; **28**; **29**; **30** top inset, bottom; **33** inset. Elizabeth Morales **54** top, bottom; **56** top, bottom; **59** top; **61**; **62**; **63** insets; **65** insets; **67**; **92**; **93**; **470** bottom; **472** top, bottom; **474**; **481**; **482**; **483**; **485**; **487**; **497**; **516** top; **522** top right; **769** top; **784**; **785** bottom right; **786**; **788** top, bottom; **789** top, bottom; **793** top, bottom; **794** top, bottom; **797**; **800**; **808**; **810** top, bottom; **811**; **812**; **814** bottom; **828**; **830**; **831**; **834**; **837** bottom; **840**; **842**; **858**; **859**; **860**; **863** middle; **878**; **879**; **880**; **883** top right; **884** top, bottom; **886**; **887**; **907**; **908**. Hilda Muinos **68**; **69**; **115**; **270**. Laurie O'Keefe **111**insets; **228** top; **245** top; **264**; **299**; **301**; **334**; **335** top; **338** top, bottom; **394**; **417**; **445**; **447** top; **448** bottom; **453**; **454** top, bottom; **455**; **456**; **458**; **462** bottom right; **537** top right; **538** top right; **539** top right; **544**; **545** top, bottom; **549**; **650**; **658** top right; **673**; **711** top; **721**; **731**. Rose Sievers **36** top right; **47**; **76**.

Charts and Graphs

Ernest Albanese **341**; **504**; **505**; **507** top; **579**; **592**; **652**; **678**; **770**; **777** top; **785** top; **815**; **825**; **845** top; **853**; **855**; **893**. Dartmouth Publishing, Inc. **312**; **314**; **320**; **321**; **324** top; **361** bottom. ElectraGraphics, Inc. **347**. Joe Galka **390-391**; **396-397**. Marnie Ingman **10** top right; **14** top right; **21** bottom left; **102** bottom; **113**; **284**; **303**; **305**. Michelle LoGerfo **821** left; **854**; **903**; **914**; **917** left; **921**. Laura Maggio **899**. Hilda Muinos **102** top. Evelyn O'Shea **152**; **395**; **555**. Rose Sievers **32**; **42**; **43**; **83** bottom; **87**; **103**; **126**; **128** top, bottom; **136**; **137**; **141** top; **149** top, bottom; **150**; **184**; **195**; **211** top; **230**; **243**; **245** middle; **248**; **250**; **267**; **275**; **313**; **316**; **327**; **335**; **351**; **372** top; **376**; **377**; **407**; **409** top; **416**; **418** top; **421** bottom; **429**; **436** left; **559**; **633**.

Visual Essays

Glory Bechtold **582**; **587**. Scott Bodell **107**. Andy Graziano **251**. Carlyn Iverson **84**; **89**; **133**; **185**; **523**; **689**; **696**. Elizabeth Morales **499**; **766**; **829**; **836**; **865**. J/B Woolsey Associates **293**; **294**; **295**. Laurie O'Keefe **368** spot art; **655**; **671**; **716**.

Editorial Support

Lillian Duggan, Holly Gordon, Mary Hicks, Kim Merlino, Allan Sison